TEACHER EDITION

INDIANA

ALGEBRA 1

McGraw Hill Education

About the Cover

The cover image illustrates a Helicoid-punctured-warped-large.

Meet the Artist

The cover art was generated by Paul Nylander, a mechanical engineer with strong programming and mathematical skills that he uses to design complex engineering systems. Nylander says that he always enjoyed science and art as a hobby. When he was in high school, he had some aptitude for math, but programming was difficult for him. However, he became much more interested in programming when he began studying computer graphics. Most of Nylander's artwork is created in Mathematica, POV-Ray, and C++.

You can find a short bio and description of his work at:
http://virtualmathmuseum.org/mathart/ArtGalleryNylander/Nylanderindex.html.

connectED.mcgraw-hill.com

McGraw Hill Education

Send all inquiries to:
McGraw-Hill Education
8787 Orion Place
Columbus, OH 43240

ISBN: 978-0-07-673270-8 *(Teacher Edition)*
MHID: 0-07-673270-3 *(Teacher Edition)*
ISBN: 978-0-07-673268-5 *(Student Edition)*
MHID: 0-07-673268-1 *(Student Edition)*

Printed in the United States of America.

1 2 3 4 5 6 7 8 9 DOW 23 22 21 20 19 18 17 16 15

STEM

McGraw-Hill is committed to providing instructional materials in Science, Technology, Engineering, and Mathematics (STEM) that give all students a solid foundation, one that prepares them for college and careers in the 21st century.

Contents in Brief

Authors

Our lead authors ensure that the Macmillan/McGraw-Hill and Glencoe/McGraw-Hill mathematics programs are truly vertically aligned by beginning with the end in mind–success in Algebra 1 and beyond. By "backmapping" the content from the high school programs, all of our mathematics programs are well articulated in their scope and sequence.

Lead Authors

John A. Carter, Ph.D.

Principal
Westlake High School
Austin, Texas

Areas of Expertise: Using technology and manipulatives to visualize concepts; mathematics achievement of English-language learners

Gilbert J. Cuevas, Ph.D.

Professor of Mathematics Education
Texas State University—San Marcos
San Marcos, Texas

Areas of Expertise: Applying concepts and skills in mathematically rich contexts; mathematical representations; use of technology in the development of geometric thinking

Roger Day, Ph.D., NBCT

Mathematics Department Chairperson
Pontiac Township High School
Pontiac, Illinois

Areas of Expertise: Understanding and applying probability and statistics; mathematics teacher education

Carol Malloy, Ph.D.: In Memoriam

Associate Professor Emerita
University of North Carolina at Chapel Hill
Chapel Hill, North Carolina

Areas of Expertise: Representations and critical thinking; student success in Algebra 1

Program Author

Jerry Cummins
Mathematics Consultant
Former President, National Council of Supervisors of Mathematics
Hinsdale, Illinois

Areas of Expertise: Graphing Technology and Mathematics

Contributing Authors

Dinah Zike FOLDABLES
Educational Consultant
Dinah-Might Activities, Inc.
San Antonio, Texas

Jay McTighe
Educational Author and Consultant
Columbia, Maryland

Consultants and Reviewers

These professionals were instrumental in providing valuable input and suggestions for improving the effectiveness of the mathematics instruction.

Lead Consultant

Viken Hovsepian
Professor of Mathematics
Rio Hondo College
Whittier, California

Consultants

Mathematical Content

Lead Consultant
Viken Hovsepian
Professor of Mathematics
Rio Hondo College
Whittier, California

Grant A. Fraser, Ph.D.
Professor of Mathematics
California State University, Los Angeles
Los Angeles, California

Arthur K. Wayman, Ph.D.
Professor of Mathematics Emeritus
California State University, Long Beach
Long Beach, California

Gifted and Talented

Shelbi K. Cole
Research Assistant
University of Connecticut
Storrs, Connecticut

College Readiness

Robert Lee Kimball, Jr.
Department Head, Math and Physics
Wake Technical Community College
Raleigh, North Carolina

Differentiation for English-Language Learners

Susana Davidenko
State University of New York
Cortland, New York

Alfredo Gómez
Mathematics/ESL Teacher
George W. Fowler High School
Syracuse, New York

Graphing Calculator

Ruth M. Casey
T^3 National Instructor
Frankfort, Kentucky

Mathematical Fluency

Robert M. Capraro
Associate Professor
Texas A&M University
College Station, Texas

Pre-AP

Dixie Ross
Lead Teacher for Advanced Placement Mathematics
Pflugerville High School
Pflugerville, Texas

Reading and Writing

ReLeah Cossett Lent
Author and Educational Consultant
Morganton, Georgia

Lynn T. Havens
Director of Project CRISS
Kalispell, Montana

Reviewers

Corey Andreasen
Mathematics Teacher
North High School
Sheboygan, Michigan

Mark B. Baetz
Mathematics Coordinating Teacher
Salem City Schools
Salem, Virginia

Kathryn Ballin
Mathematics Supervisor
Newark Public Schools
Newark, New Jersey

Kevin C. Barhorst
Mathematics Department Chair
Independence High School
Columbus, Ohio

Brenda S. Berg
Mathematics Teacher
Carbondale Community High School
Carbondale, Illinois

Sheryl Pernell Clayton
Mathematics Teacher
Hume Fogg Magnet School
Nashville, Tennessee

Bob Coleman
Mathematics Teacher
Cobb Middle School
Tallahassee, Florida

Jane E. Cotts
Mathematics Teacher
O'Fallon Township High School
O'Fallon, Illinois

Michael D. Cuddy
Mathematics Instructor
Zypherhills High School
Zypherhills, Florida

Melissa M. Dalton, NBCT
Mathematics Instructor
Rural Retreat High School
Rural Retreat, Virginia

Trina Louise Davis
Teacher
Fort Mill High School
Fort Mill, South Carolina

Tina S. Dohm
Mathematics Teacher
Naperville Central High School
Naperville, Illinois

Laurie L.E. Ferrari
Teacher
L'Anse Creuse High School—North
Macomb, Michigan

Patricia R. Frazier
Mathematics Department Chair/Instructor
Celina High School
Celina, Ohio

Steve Freshour
Mathematics Teacher
Parkersburg South High School
Parkersburg, West Virginia

Shirley D. Glover
Mathematics Teacher
TC Roberson High School
Asheville, North Carolina

Caroline W. Greenough
Mathematics Teacher
Cape Fear Academy
Wilmington, North Carolina

Michelle Hanneman
Mathematics Teacher
Moore High School
Moore, Oklahoma

Marcia Hausman
Mathematics Teacher
Sunman Dearborn Middle School
Brookville, Indiana

Theresalynn Haynes
Mathematics Teacher
Glenbard East High School
Lombard, Illinois

Sandra Hester
Mathematics Teacher/AIG Specialist
North Henderson High School
Hendersonville, North Carolina

Jacob K. Holloway
Mathematics Teacher
Capitol Heights Junior High School
Montgomery, Alabama

Robert Hopp
Mathematics Teacher
Harrison High School
Harrison, Michigan

Eileen Howanitz
Mathematics Teacher/Department Chairperson
Valley View High School
Archbald, Pennsylvania

Charles R. Howard, NBCT
Mathematics Teacher
Tuscola High School
Waynesville, North Carolina

Sue Hvizdos
Mathematics Department Chairperson
Wheeling Park High School
Wheeling, West Virginia

Elaine Keller
Mathematics Teacher
Mathematics Curriculum Director K–12
Northwest Local Schools
Canal Fulton, Ohio

Tim Kern
Mathematics Teacher
Tri West High School
Lizton, Indiana

Sheila A. Kotter
Mathematics Educator
River Ridge High School
New Port Richey, Florida

Frank Lear
Mathematics Department Chair
Cleveland High School
Cleveland, Tennessee

Jennifer Lewis
Mathematics Teacher
Triad High School
Troy, Illinois

Catherine McCarthy
Mathematics Teacher
Glen Ridge High School
Glen Ridge, New Jersey

Jacqueline Palmquist
Mathematics Department Chair
Waubonsie Valley High School
Aurora, Illinois

Thom Schacher
Mathematics Teacher
Otsego High School
Otsego, Michigan

Laurie Shappee
Teacher/Mathematics Coordinator
Larson Middle School
Troy, Michigan

Jennifer J. Southers
Mathematics Teacher
Hillcrest High School
Simpsonville, South Carolina

Sue Steinbeck
Mathematics Department Chair
Parkersburg High School
Parkersburg, West Virginia

Kathleen D. Van Sise
Mathematics Teacher
Mandarin High School
Jacksonville, Florida

Karen Wiedman
Mathematics Teacher
Taylorville High School
Taylorville, Illinois

Digital Light Source, Richard Hutchings/McGraw-Hill Education

Digital Light Source

The *Indiana Glencoe High School Math Series* is about connecting math content, rigor, and adaptive instruction for student success.

When students arrive in class for a new school year, you can be assured that **Indiana Glencoe Algebra 1** provides the flexibility to meet your classroom needs. As you build teacher-student relationships and a classroom environment that encourages learning, **Indiana Glencoe Algebra 1** provides a flexible print and digital solution that allows you to:

- Focus on personalized learning for all students with differentiated instruction and math content that meets rigorous standards.
- Engage students in a variety of ways with projects, activities and resources that make math come to life and enable students to connect math to their world.
- Drive success on state assessments with dynamic digital tools that support and inform instructional decisions.

Curriculum focused on Understanding By Design

The ***Indiana Glencoe High School Math Series*** is designed so that students remain challenged, interested, and on-track for success in the classroom.

The **Understanding By Design** framework guided the development of the ***Indiana Glencoe High School Math Series*** to create a coherent curriculum. The backward design evaluates the desired results first to lead to effectively planned instruction.

Identifying Desired Results-**Indiana Glencoe Algebra 1** addresses the big ideas in math and focuses students on Essential Questions in each chapter. Follow-up Essential Questions embedded throughout the chapter to ensure students apply newly acquired knowledge.

Determine Acceptable Evidence-Students have multiple opportunities to demonstrate their understanding by explaining, interpreting, critiquing and applying mathematical concepts throughout.

- **Practice & Problem Solving Problems**
- **Indiana Interactive Student Guide Problems**
- **HOT Problems**

Plan Learning Experiences and Instruction-Activities to engage students in hands-on learning are available throughout the program including:

- **Algebra Labs**
- **Chapter Projects**
- **Graphing Technology Labs**

"In mathematics, essential questions are used to develop students' understanding of key concepts as well as core processes."

— Jay McTighe,
co-author of Understanding by Design

Achievement for all Learners

The *Indiana Glencoe High School Math Series* recognizes that no classroom and no student is alike. **Indiana Glencoe Algebra 1** fully supports the 3-Tier RtI model with print and digital resources that consider the needs of all students. Every lesson provides easy-to-use resources that provide additional support and resources online and offline.

TIER 1 Daily Intervention

OL On grade level
Core instruction targets on-level students. Comprehensive instructional materials help you personalize instruction for every student.

- Diagnostic Teaching
- Options for Differentiated Instruction
- Leveled Exercise Sets, Resources, and Technology
- Data-Driven Decision Making

ELL English Language Learners
Comprehensive resources are found throughout the program.

- Teacher Edition with strategies to modify activities and lesson content
- Multilingual eGlossary with definitions for each vocabulary word in 13 languages

BL Beyond grade level
At every step, resources and assignments are available for advanced learners.

- Higher-Order Thinking Questions
- Differentiated Homework Options
- Enrichment Masters
- Differentiated Instruction: Extension

TIER 2 Strategic Intervention

AL Approaching grade level
You can choose from a myriad of intervention tips and ancillary materials to support struggling learners.

- Using Manipulatives
- Alternate Teaching Strategies
- Online resources, including animations, examples, and Personal Tutors

AL Significantly below grade level
For students who are far below grade level, ***Math Triumphs*** provides step-by-step instruction, vocabulary support, and meaningful practice.

Digital Tools to Enhance Learning Opportunities

Engaging Your Students in New Ways

The ***Indiana Glencoe High School Math Series*** provides tools that support classroom learning, pique students' curiosity and engage them in activities to help them master math content and retain knowledge of key concepts and skills—all at your fingertips.

The Geometer's Sketchpad is proven to increase engagement, understanding and achievement. This premier digital learning tool makes math come alive by giving students a tangible, visual way to see the math in action through dynamic model manipulation of lines, shapes and functions.

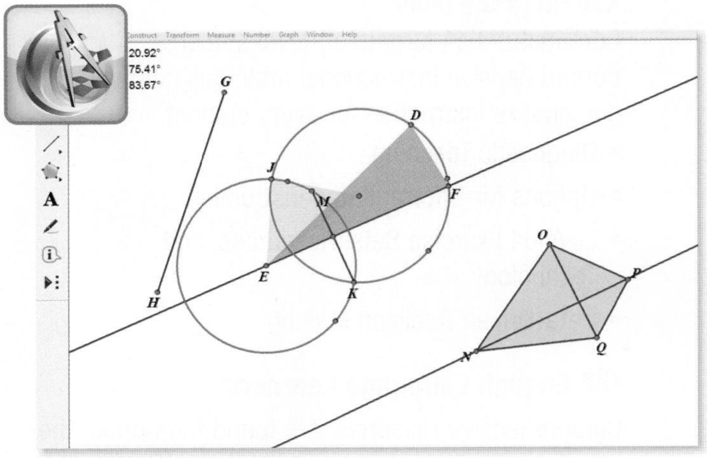

BrainPOP® animations can be used in a variety of ways such as key concept introduction, reinforcement or as an illustration of abstract concepts. Students can't help but to be engaged with these colorful animations.

Professional Development

McGraw-Hill Education recognizes that learning is a lifelong endeavor. To ensure student and teacher success, we have built-in resources to the *Indiana Glencoe High School Math Series* featuring best-practices, implementation support, alternative teaching practices and much more.

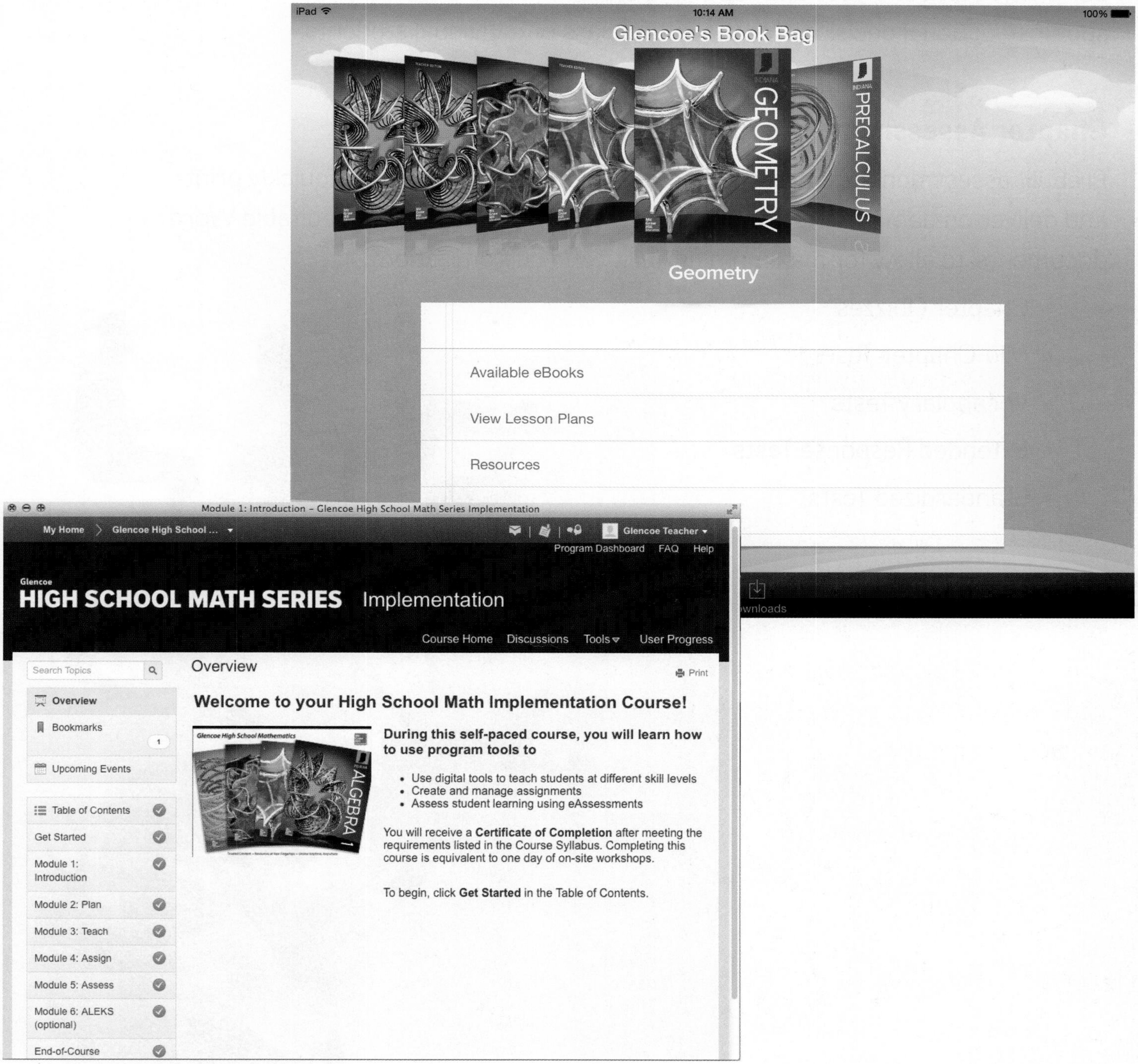

Assessment Tools that Inform Instruction

A comprehensive variety of print and online assessment options are built into the **Indiana Glencoe Algebra 1** program. Using traditional assessment combined with our online test generator and reporting system, you can use data to make on-the-spot instructional decisions for the entire class or individual students.

Chapter Assessment Resources

Prebuilt assessment resources are provided with every chapter to quickly print and deliver on demand. As an added feature, most are available in editable Word documents, to allow for maximum flexibility and customization:

- Chapter Quizzes
- Mid-Chapter Tests
- Vocabulary Tests
- Extended Response Tests
- Standardized Tests

Caia Image/Glow Images

eAssessment

Validate student learning and practice for the ISTEP+ with our secure online test center, eAssessment. Manage your content, create and assign quizzes and tests that can be assigned online or in traditional format. The reporting system enables you to see performance at both a class and a student level which allows you to modify instruction or provide targeted support to improve student achievement.

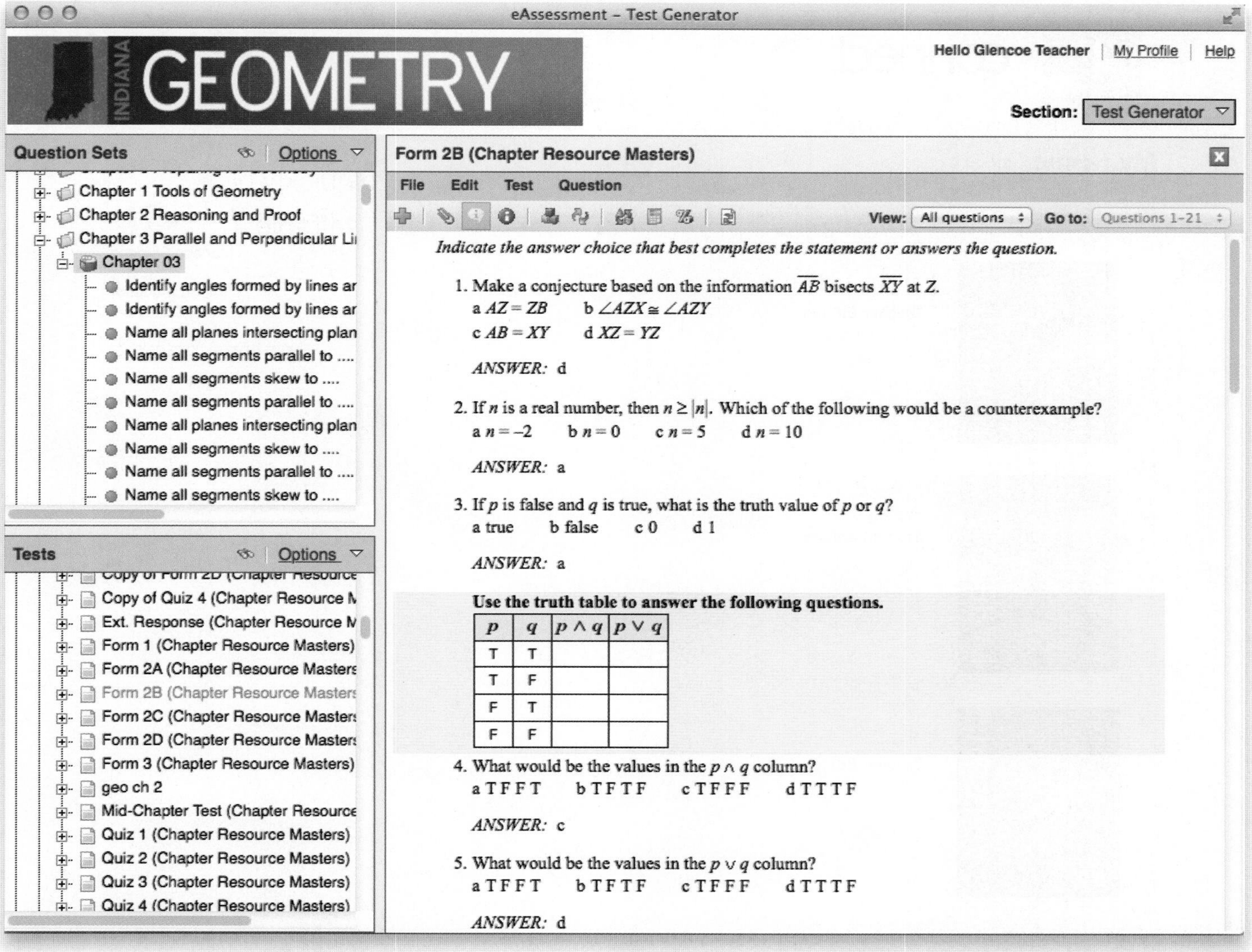

ConnectED-Your Online Dashboard

In the age of digital transition, ConnectED is a time-saving one-stop-shop that has all of your digital classroom resources in one place. Through this portal, you can access the complete Indiana eStudent Edition and eTeacher Edition, Indiana Interactive Student Guide, Interactive Teacher Guide, digital resources, videos and animations, assessment tools and planning tools.

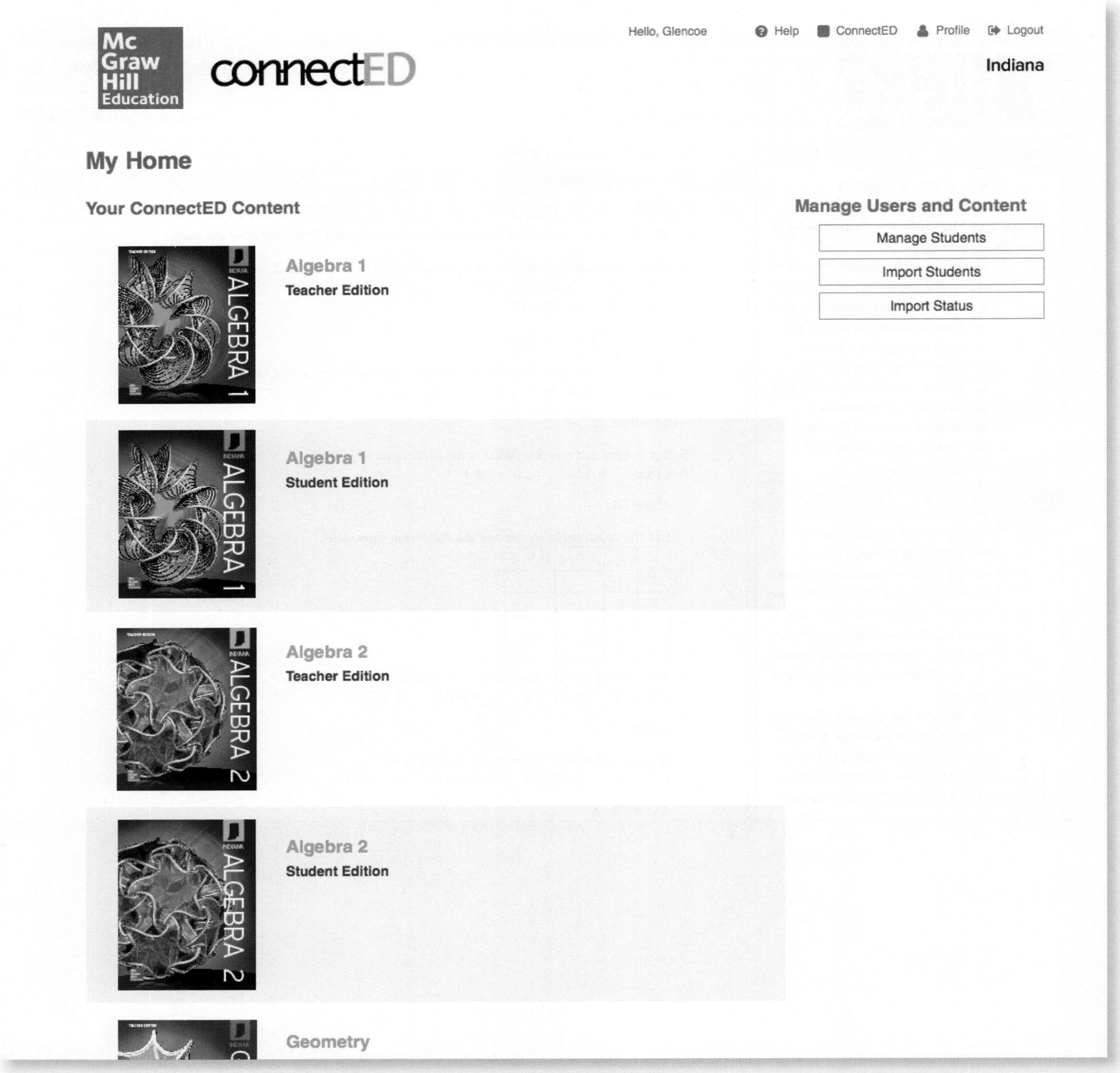

ConnectED allows you to plan your class, anytime, anywhere in order to enable you to:

- Build lesson plans with easy to find resources
- Search for activities to meet a variety of learning modalities
- Teach with technology by providing virtual manipulatives, lesson animations, whole-class presentations and more
- Provide students with access from any computer or iOS and Android tablets to student eBooks, tutorials, graphing tools, virtual manipulatives and the eGlossary.
- Access eAssessment to assign online assessments, track student progress, provide practice for online testing, generate reports and differentiate instruction.

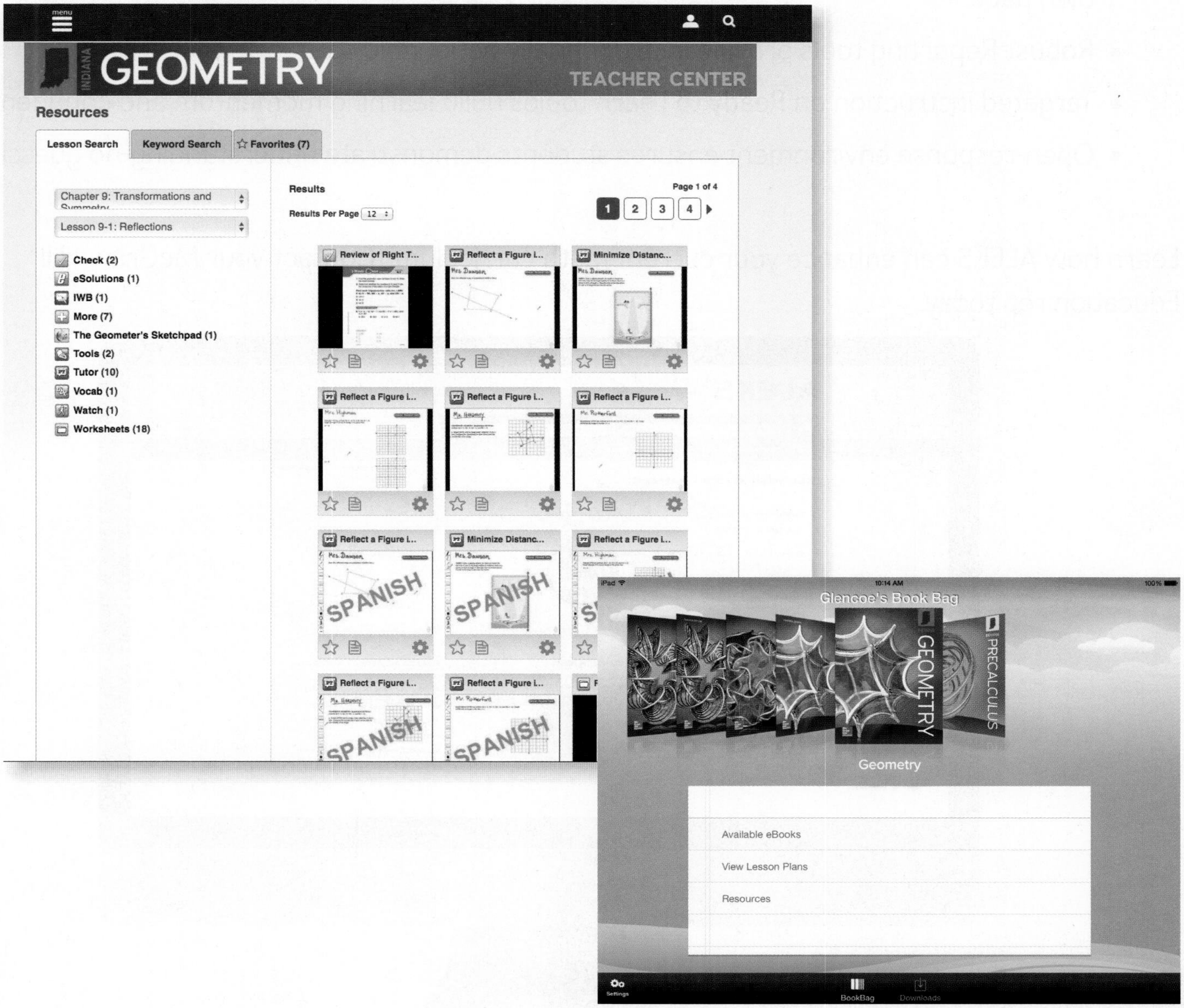

ALEKS

Using Technology to Simplify Differentiated Instruction

Differentiating instruction can be a challenge. It's ALEKS to the rescue! This online resource uses adaptive questioning to provide each student with a personalized learning path.

Support each student's unique needs

- Knowledge checks identify what a student knows and where there are gaps
- Personalized instruction allows students to progress at their own pace
- Robust Reporting tools provide instructionally-actionable data
- Targeted instruction on Ready to Learn topics build learning momentum and confidence
- Open-response environment ensures students demonstrate understanding-no guessing!

Learn how ALEKS can enhance your current math curriculum. Contact your McGraw-Hill Education rep today.

Professional Development

McGraw-Hill Education recognizes that learning is a lifelong endeavor. To ensure student and teacher success, we have built-in resources to the ***Indiana Glencoe High School Math Series*** featuring best-practices, implementation support, alternative teaching practices and much more.

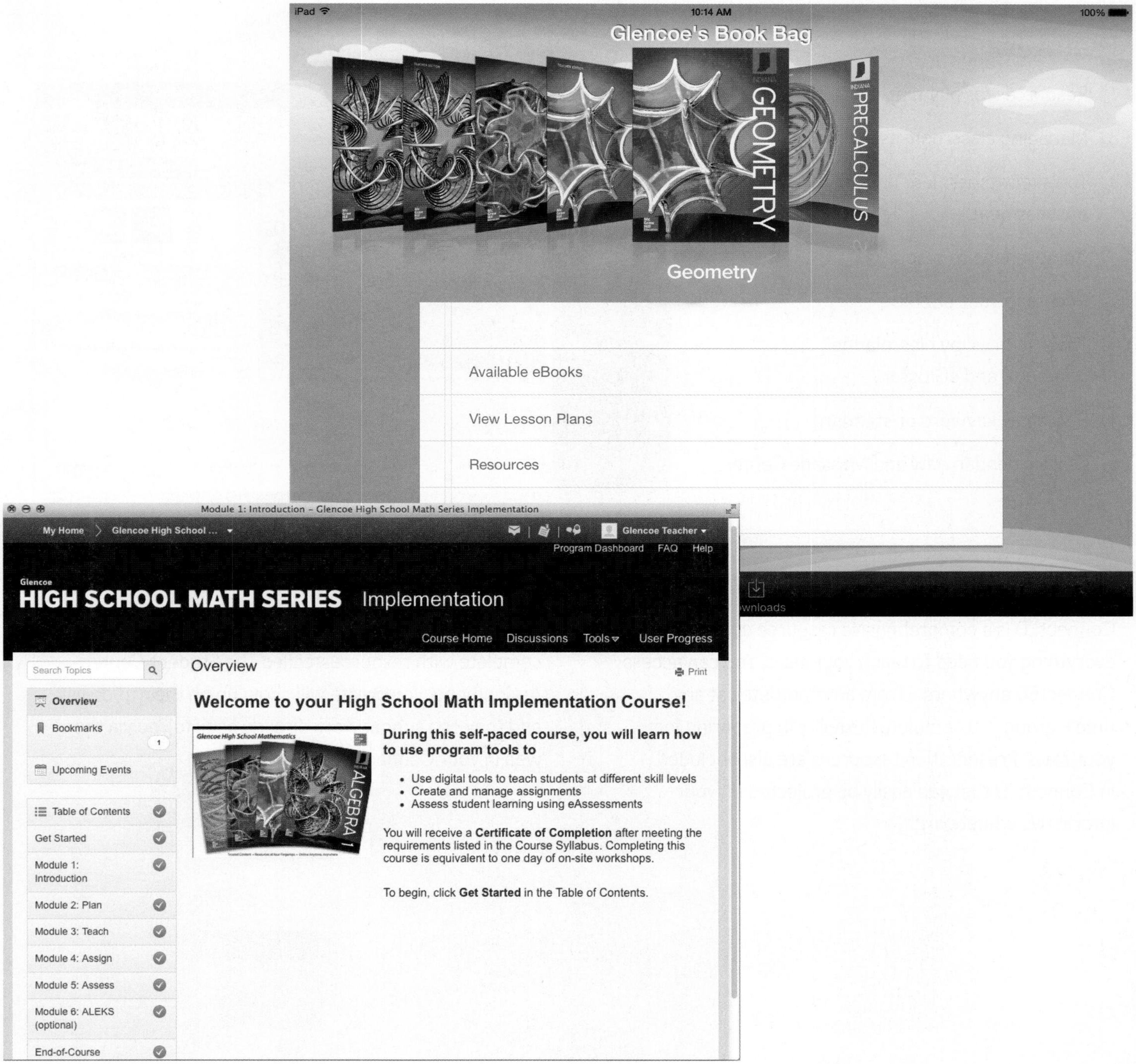

Getting Started with *ConnectED*

ConnectED is the digital platform for your program

ConnectED is a one-stop shop for you to access the eBook, digital resources, videos, assessment tools, and planning tools. It allows you to send work electronically to your students via their own ConnectED accounts.

Features

1. Resources for planning
2. Managing classroom assignments
3. Tools for assessment (including eAssessment)
4. Comprehensive resources
5. Access to your eBook
6. Tools such as my files, planner, notebook, and eGlossary
7. Search by keyword or standard
8. Quick calendar view and Message Center

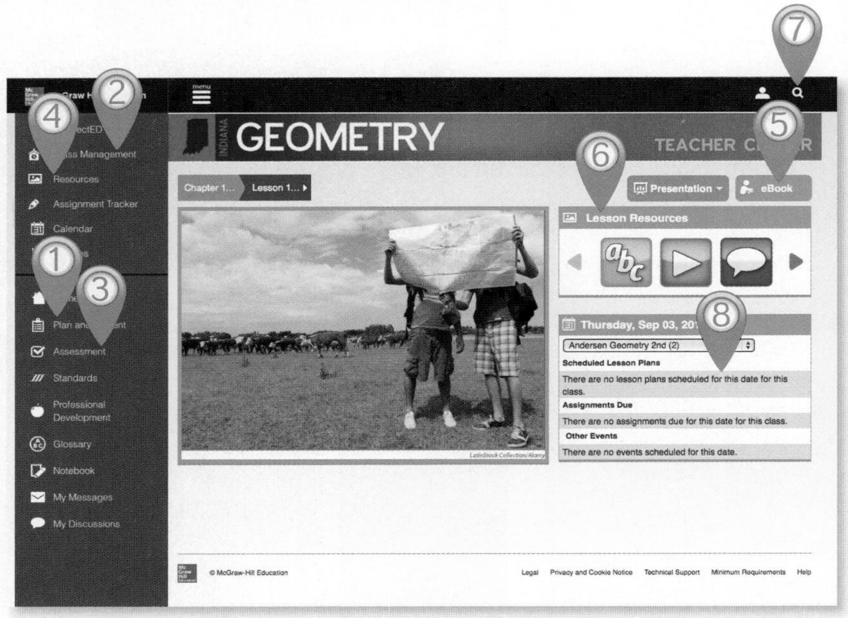

For You

ConnectED is a comprehensive resource containing everything you need to teach your class. You can access ConnectED anywhere – from any computer, at any time – giving you complete flexibility in preparing for your class. Presentation resources are also included in ConnectED that can easily be projected on your interactive whiteboard.

For Your Students

Students have their own version of ConnectED, complete with resources, called The Student Center. Assignments you create will show up on their to-do list, and they can submit work directly back to you via the web in your ConnectED account.

Getting Started with *ConnectED Mobile*

ConnectED Mobile is the app interface for ConnectED

The ConnectED Mobile app works on select iOS and Android devices. It allows complete access to your eBook, along with your planning tools and resources.

Available on the App Store

GET IT ON Google play

Features

1. Your courses in ConnectED
2. Download your eBook for use offline
3. Lesson plans from your Plan and Present tab
4. Comprehensive list of resources from the Resource tab and access to those for mobile devices
5. Management of your content downloaded in the app

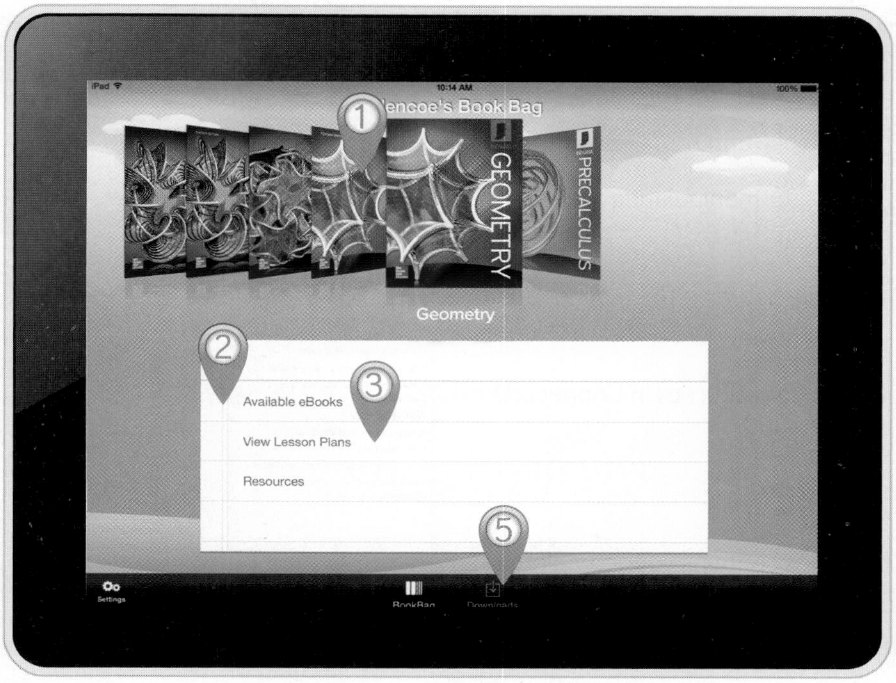

For You

ConnectED Mobile gives you another way to plan for class. You can use it to access lesson plans, preview resources, and see the complete book. In addition, you can view notes students have made in their own books to see their thoughts on a topic.

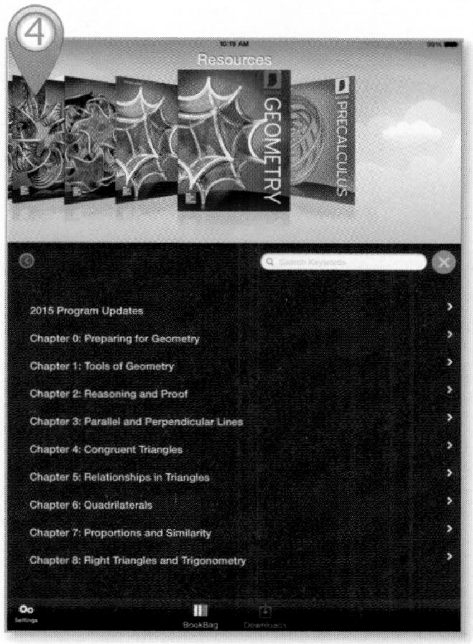

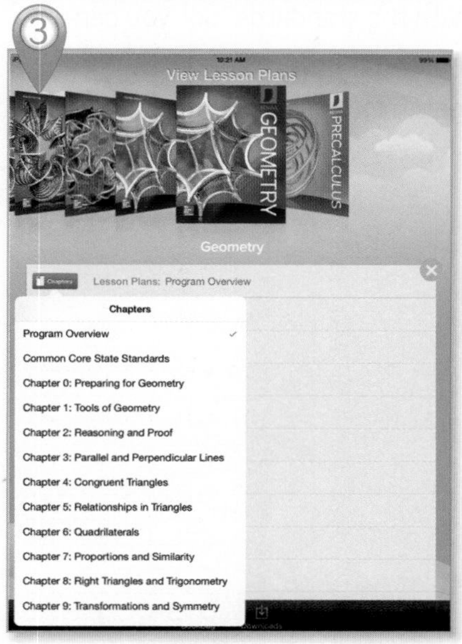

For Your Students

Students can use the eBook in ConnectED Mobile to replace the print book.

Expanded features such as Personal Tutors and other resources go beyond the limitations of the printed page to bring math into your students' lives.

Getting Started with Your *Teacher eBook*

Preparing for Your Digital Transition

The Teacher eBook makes it easy for you to plan wherever you are. You can access it using the Open eBook icon in your Teacher Edition of ConnectED.

Features

1. Standards Correlation
2. Table of Contents
3. Tools for manipulating the content
4. Toggle between the teacher and student view
5. Links to resources in ConnectED

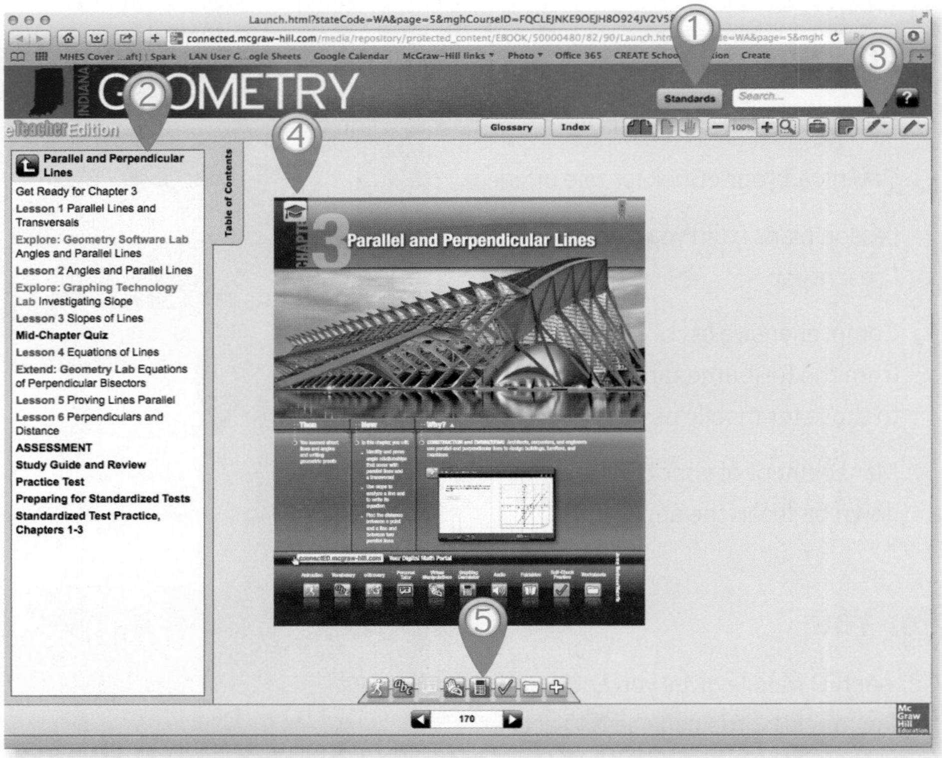

For You

The eBook contains your complete teacher tools with links to resources in ConnectED.

With the standards tool, you can track your progress digitally or search for specific content.

Getting Started with Your *Student eBook*

Meeting Students Anywhere

The Student eBook makes it easy for your students to access their program anywhere. They can access it using the Open eBook icon.

Features

1. Standards Correlation
2. Table of Contents
3. Tools for manipulating the content
4. Links to resources in ConnectED

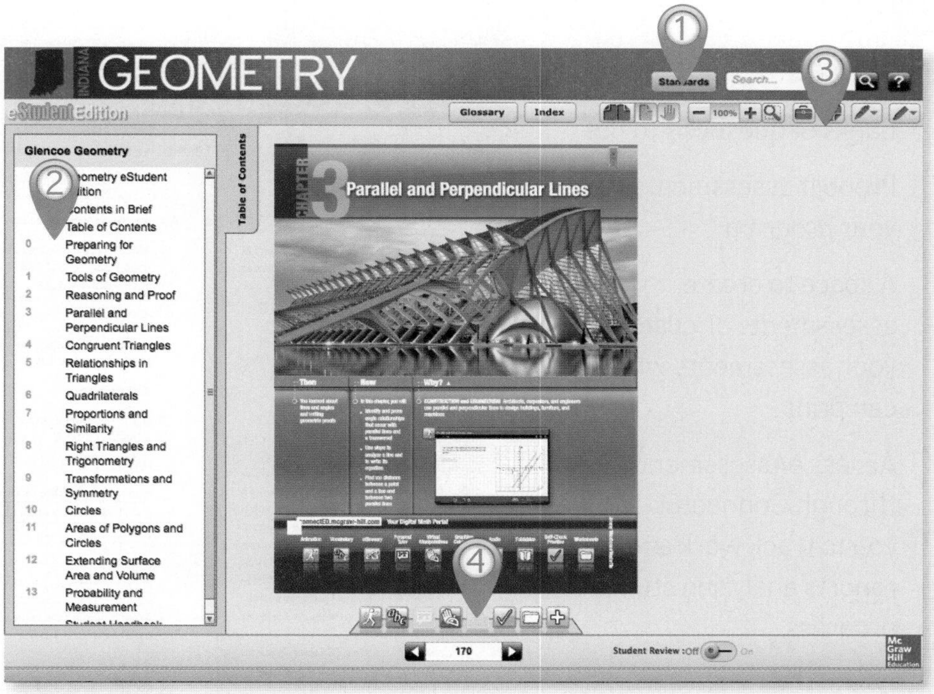

For You

You can project the eBook using a projector or interactive whiteboard to share with the class.

For Your Students

The eBook contains the complete student tools with links to resources in ConnectED.

The eBook in ConnectED Mobile is available offline for home use if students do not have access to the Web.

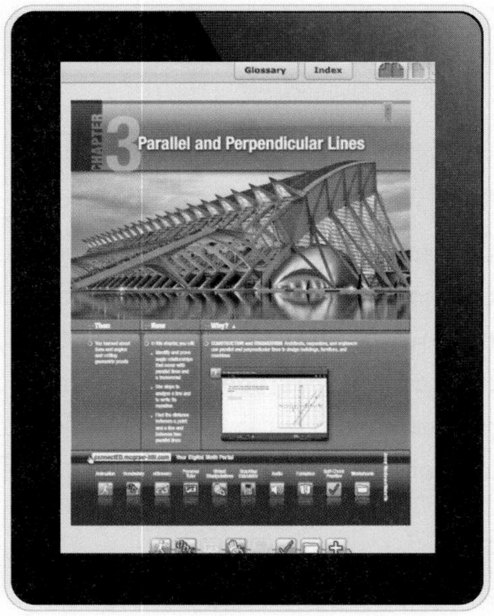

Getting Started with *eAssessment*

Simplify the Process for Data-Driven Decision Making

eAssessment is a tool within ConnectED that allows teachers to create tests and other assignments. eAssessment allows these assignments to be delivered online or offline.

Features

① Banks of questions to use

② Prebuilt assessments for your program

③ A space to create assessments or customize your assessments which you can print

④ Access eAssessment through ConnectED to allow you to track work and create reports analyzing student progress.

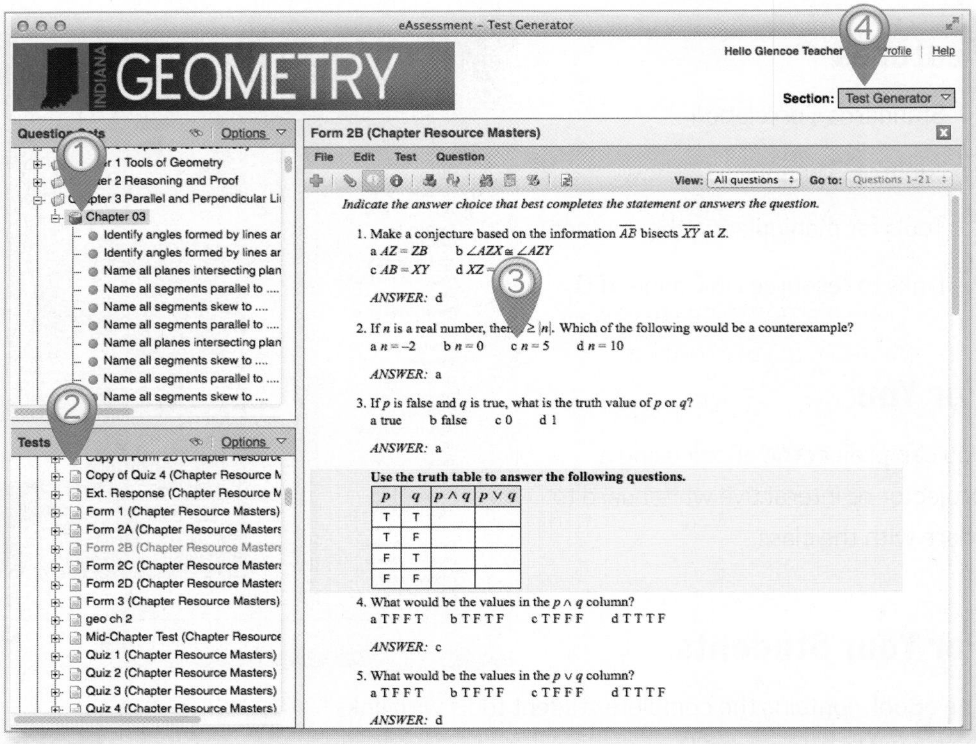

For You

You can build a wide variety of assignments in eAssessment.

With a series of clicks, teachers can select questions by subject, standard, lesson, or a host of other factors. **If you assign the work to be completed online, the system will collect data for every student and the class.** Reports on proficiency and accuracy can help make data-driven decisions for instruction.

For Your Students

The online assignments are not limited to assessments. You can allow your students to practice by giving them multiple attempts at the assignment. You can also choose to allow students to see the right answer to or receive feedback from each question. The system can also lock down the assignment with time restrictions, offering the assessment only when the teacher prefers.

Getting Started with *eSolutions Manual*

All Answers, Always Up to Date

eSolutions Manual replaces the traditional solutions manual with a digital version that you can access 24/7 and use to create custom reports.

Features

1. Each lesson is available.
2. You have the choice to show answers, solutions, both or neither.
3. Decide which questions to use: evens, odds, or your own list.
4. The report can be delivered online or in print.

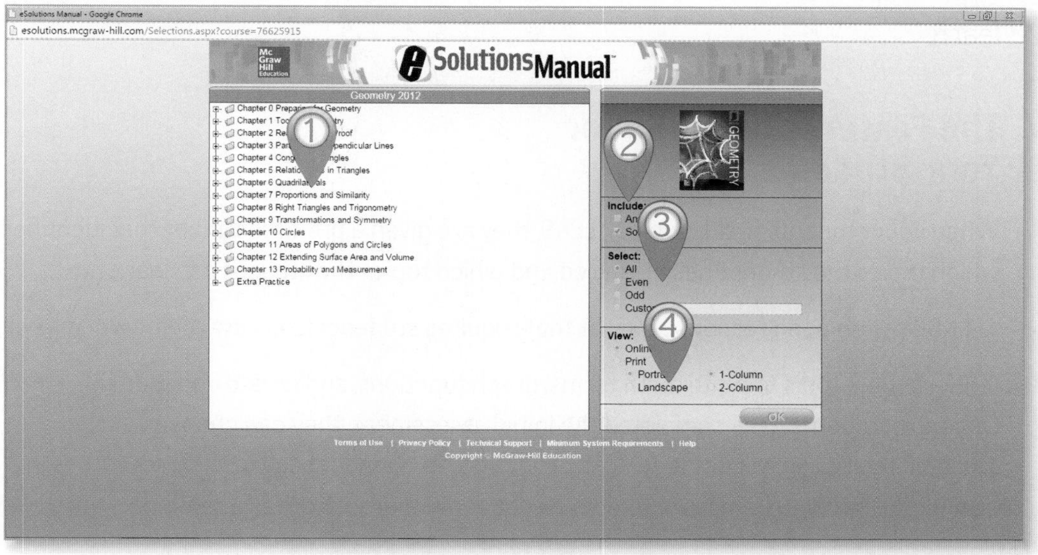

For You

eSolutions Manual allows for significantly more flexibility than the traditional solutions manual.

You can create sets of answers or solutions for your own use or to help students assess their own work.

For Your Students

Using the "view online" feature in class allows you to project on a screen or interactive whiteboard in a presentation style. The questions are displayed one at a time and can be shown in steps to help students work the question as you project it.

Getting Started with *ALEKS*

Personalized Learning for Individual Success

Artificial intelligence and open-response questioning help to identify precisely what each student knows and doesn't know. Through *truly* individualized learning and assessment, ALEKS delivers a personalized learning path that includes the exact topics each student is most ready to learn.

The Features of ALEKS for Your Students

When your students first log in to ALEKS, they are given a pre-assessment that identifies which topics the student has mastered and which topics the student can learn next.

ALEKS uses an open response format that requires students to create their own answer.

It offers them tools to write math terms, graph functions, and create equations. Once the students have completed the initial assessment, they can choose which available topic they will practice next. Students can connect back to their resources in ConnectED to help them learn a topic, or get additional support as a reminder.

The Features of ALEKS for You

You have a complete dashboard of reports that allow you to understand what students have learned and what they are ready to learn. Standards reports help address what topics students have mastered and can make suggestions on what students are ready to learn. You can also use the program to help drive in-class instruction with data-based decisions.

For You

As a formative assessment tool, ALEKS provides detailed information about students and the class. You can create small groups for students who need practice on the same topic or identify students who may have fallen behind or are progressing ahead of the class. The artificial intelligence in ALEKS can help you provide automatic differentiated content for your students to ensure that every student is able to master the content they are ready to learn.

For Your Students

The personal instruction in ALEKS has a variety of classroom models. Many teachers assign students to complete a set amount of time on ALEKS or to master a set number of topics. The ALEKS system can allow you to quickly see how much work students have done online. You may use a flipped model of instruction with ALEKS or have a weekly day for practice in which all students use ALEKS in a computer lab. The variety of ways to use ALEKS is limited only by your resources and imagination.

Getting Started with *The Geometer's Sketchpad*

Make Math More Dynamic for Your Students

The Geometer's Sketchpad™ is the world's leading software for teaching mathematics. Sketchpad™ gives students at all levels a tangible, visual way to learn mathematics that increases their engagement, understanding, and achievement.

Sketchpad is software-based and can be used with or without Internet access. Activities can be found under the Plan and Present and Resource tabs in your program in ConnectED.

Features

① Tools to create geometric figures such as points, lines, circles, and polygons.

② Menus that can be used to create specific constructions such as perpendicular lines and midpoints.

③ Algebra tools such as graphs and number lines are also available to use.

④ The system will help you automatically label your work.

Getting Started with Professional Development

Ongoing Program Support and Research-based Professional Development

With access to your professional learning environment via ConnectED, you will receive practical, content-specific, professional development that supports you every step of the way.

Quick-Start

Videos, how-to guides, and discussion boards help you get started immediately.

Implementation Course

This deeper dive into all program features includes planning tools, data collection, and reporting as well as pedagogy and standards.

Administrator Support

Step-by-step guides, teacher checklists, and space to collaborate with other *Indiana Glencoe High School Math Series* users.

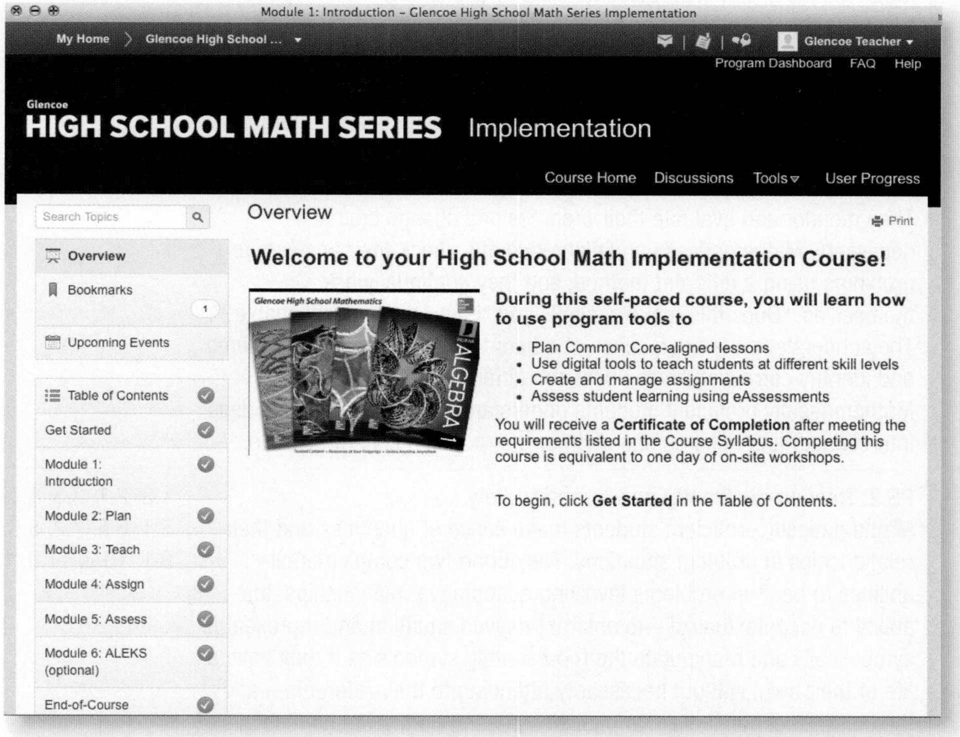

Indiana Process Standards for Mathematics: Algebra I

The Process Standards demonstrate the ways in which students should develop conceptual understanding of mathematical content, and the ways in which students should synthesize and apply mathematical skills.

Standards	Student Edition Lesson(s)	Student Edition Page(s)
Algebra 1		
PS.1: Make sense of problems and persevere in solving them. Mathematically proficient students start by explaining to themselves the meaning of a problem and looking for entry points to its solution. They analyze givens, constraints, relationships, and goals. They make conjectures about the form and meaning of the solution and plan a solution pathway, rather than simply jumping into a solution attempt. They consider analogous problems and try special cases and simpler forms of the original problem in order to gain insight into its solution. They monitor and evaluate their progress and change course if necessary. Mathematically proficient students check their answers to problems using a different method, and they continually ask themselves, "Does this make sense?" and "Is my answer reasonable?" They understand the approaches of others to solving complex problems and identify correspondences between different approaches. Mathematically proficient students understand how mathematical ideas interconnect and build on one another to produce a coherent whole.	0.1, 1.8, 2.4, 3.4, 4.5, 5.4, 6.4, 7.5, 8.8, 9.3, 10.5, 11.1, 12.4	P005–P006, 56–61, 97–102, 182–188, 247–253, 306–311, 357–362, 424–429, 516–521, 564–571, 648–653, 676–682, 771–778
PS.2: Reason abstractly and quantitatively. Mathematically proficient students make sense of quantities and their relationships in problem situations. They bring two complementary abilities to bear on problems involving quantitative relationships: the ability to decontextualize—to abstract a given situation and represent it symbolically and manipulate the representing symbols as if they have a life of their own, without necessarily attending to their referents—and the ability to contextualize, to pause as needed during the manipulation process in order to probe into the referents for the symbols involved. Quantitative reasoning entails habits of creating a coherent representation of the problem at hand; considering the units involved; attending to the meaning of quantities, not just how to compute them; and knowing and flexibly using different properties of operations and objects.	1.3, 2.1, 3.3, 4.1, 5.1, 6.5, 7.2, 8.5, 9.1, 10.3, 11.8, 12.2	16–21, 75–79, 172–179, 216–222, 285–289, 364–368, 398–404, 494–499, 635–638, 726–731, 757–762, 543–552

Standards	Student Edition Lesson(s)	Student Edition Page(s)
PS.3: Construct viable arguments and critique the reasoning of others. Mathematically proficient students understand and use stated assumptions, definitions, and previously established results in constructing arguments. They make conjectures and build a logical progression of statements to explore the truth of their conjectures. They analyze situations by breaking them into cases and recognize and use counterexamples. They organize their mathematical thinking, justify their conclusions and communicate them to others, and respond to the arguments of others. They reason inductively about data, making plausible arguments that take into account the context from which the data arose. Mathematically proficient students are also able to compare the effectiveness of two plausible arguments, distinguish correct logic or reasoning from that which is flawed, and—if there is a flaw in an argument—explain what it is. They justify whether a given statement is true always, sometimes, or never. Mathematically proficient students participate and collaborate in a mathematics community. They listen to or read the arguments of others, decide whether they make sense, and ask useful questions to clarify or improve the arguments.	1.3, 2.5, Extend 3.5, 4.2, 5.5, 6.1, 7.4, 8.1, 9.2, 10.4, 11.2, Extend 12.1	16–21, 103–108, 196, 226–231, 312–315, 335–340, 414–419, 465–470, 555–559, 642–645, 684–688, 755–756
PS.4: Model with mathematics. Mathematically proficient students apply the mathematics they know to solve problems arising in everyday life, society, and the workplace using a variety of appropriate strategies. They create and use a variety of representations to solve problems and to organize and communicate mathematical ideas. Mathematically proficient students apply what they know and are comfortable making assumptions and approximations to simplify a complicated situation, realizing that these may need revision later. They are able to identify important quantities in a practical situation and map their relationships using such tools as diagrams, two-way tables, graphs, flowcharts and formulas. They analyze those relationships mathematically to draw conclusions. They routinely interpret their mathematical results in the context of the situation and reflect on whether the results make sense, possibly improving the model if it has not served its purpose.	1.1, 2.9, 3.2, 4.5, 5.1, 6.5, 7.6, 8.7, 9.7, 10.4, 11.7, 12.5	5–9, 132–138, 163–168, 247–253, 285–290, 364–369, 432–436, 510–515, 598–605, 642–646, 720–725, 780–785
PS.5: Use appropriate tools strategically. Mathematically proficient students consider the available tools when solving a mathematical problem. These tools might include pencil and paper, models, a ruler, a protractor, a calculator, a spreadsheet, a computer algebra system, a statistical package, or dynamic geometry software. Mathematically proficient students are sufficiently familiar with tools appropriate for their grade or course to make sound decisions about when each of these tools might be helpful, recognizing both the insight to be gained and their limitations. Mathematically proficient students identify relevant external mathematical resources, such as digital content, and use them to pose or solve problems. They use technological tools to explore and deepen their understanding of concepts and to support the development of learning mathematics. They use technology to contribute to concept development, simulation, representation, reasoning, communication and problem solving.	Extend 1.7, 2.4, Extend 3.2, 4.4, Extend 5.6, Extend 6.1, Extend 7.5, 8.2, Extend 9.6, 10.6, Extend 11.8, 12.3	55, 97–101, 169–170, 239–244, 323, 342–343, 430–431, 472–476, 596–597, 656–661, 733–734, 764–769

Standards	Student Edition Lesson(s)	Student Edition Page(s)
PS.6: Attend to precision. Mathematically proficient students communicate precisely to others. They use clear definitions, including correct mathematical language, in discussion with others and in their own reasoning. They state the meaning of the symbols they choose, including using the equal sign consistently and appropriately. They express solutions clearly and logically by using the appropriate mathematical terms and notation. They specify units of measure and label axes to clarify the correspondence with quantities in a problem. They calculate accurately and efficiently and check the validity of their results in the context of the problem. They express numerical answers with a degree of precision appropriate for the problem context.	Extend 1.3, 2.8, 3.4, 4.2, 5.2, 6.6, 7.4, 8.9, 9.5, 10.1, 11.6, 12.2	23–24, 126–131, 182–188, 226–232, 292–297, 372–376, 414–420, 522–529, 583–589, 621–626, 712–719, 757–763
PS.7: Look for and make use of structure. Mathematically proficient students look closely to discern a pattern or structure. They step back for an overview and shift perspective. They recognize and use properties of operations and equality. They organize and classify geometric shapes based on their attributes. They see expressions, equations, and geometric figures as single objects or as being composed of several objects.	1.2, 2.5, 3.6, Extend 4.1, 5.5, 6.3, 7.7, 8.6, 9.6, 10.2, 11.2, 12.8	10–14, 103–108, 197–201, 224–225, 312–315, 350–355, 438–442, 503–508, 590–594, 628–632, 684–688, 803–808
PS.8: Look for and express regularity in repeated reasoning. Mathematically proficient students notice if calculations are repeated and look for general methods and shortcuts. They notice regularity in mathematical problems and their work to create a rule or formula. Mathematically proficient students maintain oversight of the process, while attending to the details as they solve a problem. They continually evaluate the reasonableness of their intermediate results.	1.4, 2.7, 3.1, 4.1, 5.4, 6.1, 7.1, 8.4, 9.3, 10.2, 11.5, 12.6	25–31, 119–124, 155–162, 216–223, 306–311, 335–341, 391–397, 486–491, 564–571, 628–633, 706–711, 786–792

Indiana Academic Standards for Mathematics: Algebra I

The Mathematics standards for Algebra I are supplemented by the Process Standards for Mathematics.
The Mathematics standards for Algebra I are made up of 6 strands: Real Numbers and Expressions; Functions; Linear Equations, Inequalities, and Functions; Systems of Equations and Inequalities; Quadratic and Exponential Equations and Functions; and Data Analysis and Statistics. The skills listed in each strand indicate what students should know and be able to do in Algebra I.

Standards	Student Edition Lesson(s)	Student Edition Page(s)
Algebra 1		
Real Numbers and Expressions		
AI.RNE.1: Understand the hierarchy and relationships of numbers and sets of numbers within the real number system.	0.2	P7, P10
AI.RNE.2: Explain why the sum or product of two rational numbers is rational; that the sum of a rational number and an irrational number is irrational; and that the product of a nonzero rational number and an irrational number is irrational.	Extend 10.2	634
AI.RNE.3: Rewrite and evaluate numeric expressions with positive rational exponents using the properties of exponents.	7.1, 7.2, 7.3	391–396, 398–404, 406–412
AI.RNE.4: Simplify square roots of non-perfect square integers and algebraic monomials.	10.2, 10.3	628–632, 635–638
AI.RNE.5: Simplify algebraic rational expressions, with numerators and denominators containing monomial bases with integer exponents, to equivalent forms.	11.3, Extend 11.3, 11.4, 11.5, 11.6, 11.7	690–695, 697, 698–703, 706–710, 712–718, 720–724
AI.RNE.6: Factor common terms from polynomials and factor polynomials completely. Factor the difference of two squares, perfect square trinomials, and other quadratic expressions.	1.4, 8.5, Explore 8.6, 8.6, 8.7, 8.8, 8.9	27–30, 494–499, 501–502, 503–508, 510–514, 516–520, 522–528
AI.RNE.7: Understand polynomials are closed under the operations of addition, subtraction, and multiplication with integers; add, subtract, and multiply polynomials and divide polynomials by monomials.	Explore 8–1, 8–1, 8–2, Explore 8–3, 8–3, 8–4	463–464, 465–471, 472–477, 478–479, 480–485, 486–491

Standards	Student Edition Lesson(s)	Student Edition Page(s)
Functions		
AI.F.1: Understand that a function from one set (called the domain) to another set (called the range) assigns to each element of the domain exactly one element of the range. Understand that if f is a function and *x* is an element of its domain, then *f(x)* denotes the output of f corresponding to the input x. Understand the graph of f is the graph of the equation $y = f(x)$.	1.6, 1.7	40–46, 47–54
AI.F.2: Describe qualitatively the functional relationship between two quantities by analyzing a graph (e.g., where the function is increasing or decreasing, linear or nonlinear, has a maximum or minimum value). Sketch a graph that exhibits the qualitative features of a function that has been verbally described. Identify independent and dependent variables and make predictions about the relationship.	1.6, 1.7, 1.8	42–45, 47–53, 56–60
AI.F.3: Identify the domain and range of relations represented in tables, graphs, verbal descriptions, and equations.	1.6, 1.7	40–45, 47–53
AI.F.4: Understand and interpret statements that use function notation in terms of a context; relate the domain of the function to its graph and to the quantitative relationship it describes.	1.6, 1.7, 1.8, 3.3, 3.6, 7.5, 9.1	40–45, 47–53, 56–60, 176, 197–201, 424–428, 543
Linear Equations, Inequalities, and Functions		
AI.L.1: Understand that the steps taken when solving linear equations create new equations that have the same solution as the original. Solve fluently linear equations and inequalities in one variable with integers, fractions, and decimals as coefficients. Explain and justify each step in solving an equation, starting from the assumption that the original equation has a solution. Justify the choice of a solution method.	Explore 2.2, 2.2, Explore 2.3, 2.3, 2.4, 2.7, 3.4, 5.1, Explore 5.2, 5.2, 5.3	81–82, 83–88, 90, 91–95, 97–101, 119–123, 182–187, 285–289, 291, 292–296, 298–302
AI.L.2: Represent real-world problems using linear equations and inequalities in one variable and solve such problems. Interpret the solution and determine whether it is reasonable.	2.1, 2.2, 2.3, 2.4, 2.7, 3.4, 5.1, 5.2, 5.3	75–80, 85–88, 92–95, 101, 119–123, 184–187, 287–289, 293–296, 229–302
AI.L.3: Represent real-world and other mathematical problems using an algebraic proportion that leads to a linear equation and solve such problems.	2.6, 3.6	111–116, 197–201
AI.L.4: Represent linear functions as graphs from equations (with and without technology), equations from graphs, and equations from tables and other given information (e.g., from a given point on a line and the slope of the line).	Explore 4.1, 4.1, 4.2, 4.3, 4.5, 4.6	215, 216–222, 226–231, 233–237, 247–252, 255–261

Standards	Student Edition Lesson(s)	Student Edition Page(s)
AI.L.5: Represent real-world problems that can be modeled with a linear function using equations, graphs, and tables; translate fluently among these representations, and interpret the slope and intercepts.	3.3, 4.1, 4.2, 4.3, 4.5, 4.6	172–179, 219–222, 228–231, 236–237, 247–252, 255–261
AI.L.6: Translate among equivalent forms of equations for linear functions, including slope-intercept, point-slope, and standard. Recognize that different forms reveal more or less information about a given situation.	4.1, 4.2, 4.3	216–222, 226–231, 233–237
AI.L.7: Represent real-world problems using linear inequalities in two variables and solve such problems; interpret the solution set and determine whether it is reasonable. Solve other linear inequalities in two variables by graphing.	5.6, Extend 5.6	317–321, 323
AI.L.8: Solve compound linear inequalities in one variable, and represent and interpret the solution on a number line. Write a compound linear inequality given its number line representation.	Explore 5.4, 5.4	305, 310
AI.L.9: Solve absolute value linear equations in one variable.	2.5	103–108
AI.L.10: Graph absolute value linear equations in two variables.	9.7	599–604
AI.L.11: Solve equations and formulas for a specified variable, including equations with coefficients represented by variables.	2.8	126–130
Systems of Equations and Inequalities		
AI.SEI.1: Understand the relationship between a solution of a pair of linear equations in two variables and the graphs of the corresponding lines. Solve pairs of linear equations in two variables by graphing; approximate solutions when the coordinates of the solution are non-integer numbers.	6.1, Extend 6.1	335–340, 342–323
AI.SEI.2: Understand that, given a system of two equations in two variables, replacing one equation by the sum of that equation and a multiple of the other produces a system with the same solutions. Solve pairs of linear equations in two variables using substitution and elimination.	6.2, 6.3, 6.4	344–348, 350–355, 357–361
AI.SEI.3: Write a system of two linear equations in two variables that represents a real-world problem and solve the problem with and without technology. Interpret the solution and determine whether the solution is reasonable.	6.1, 6.2, 6.3, 6.4, 6.5	335–340, 346–348, 352–355, 359–361, 364–368
AI.SEI.4: Represent real-world problems using a system of two linear inequalities in two variables and solve such problems; interpret the solution set and determine whether it is reasonable. Solve other pairs of linear inequalities by graphing with and without technology.	6.6, Extend 6.6	372–375, 377

Standards	Student Edition Lesson(s)	Student Edition Page(s)
Quadratic and Exponential Equations and Functions		
AI.QE.1: Distinguish between situations that can be modeled with linear functions and with exponential functions. Understand that linear functions grow by equal differences over equal intervals, and that exponential functions grow by equal factors over equal intervals. Compare linear functions and exponential functions that model real-world situations using tables, graphs, and equations.	7.5, Extend 7.7, 9.6, Extend 9.6	426–428, 444, 590–594, 596–597
AI.QE.2: Represent real-world and other mathematical problems that can be modeled with exponential functions using tables, graphs, and equations of the form $y = ab^x$ (for integer values of $x > 1$, rational values of $b > 0$ and $b \neq 1$); translate fluently among these representations and interpret the values of a and b.	Explore 7.5, 7.5, 7.6	422–423, 424–428, 432–435
AI.QE.3: Graph exponential and quadratic equations in two variables with and without technology.	Explore 7.5, 7.5, 9.1, 9.2	422–423, 424–428, 543–552, 555–559
AI.QE.4: Solve quadratic equations in one variable by inspection (e.g., for $x^2 = 49$), finding square roots, using the quadratic formula, and factoring, as appropriate to the initial form of the equation.	8.5, 8.6, 8.7, 8.8, 8.9, 9.2, 9.4, 9.5	496–499, 503–508, 510–514, 518–520, 524–528, 555–559, 574–578, 583–588
AI.QE.5: Represent real-world problems using quadratic equations in one or two variables and solve such problems with and without technology. Interpret the solution and determine whether it is reasonable.	8.5, 8.6, 8.7, 8.8, 8.9, 9.1, 9.2, 9.4, 9.5	497–499, 506–508, 512–514, 518–520, 526–528, 548–552, 557–559, 576–578, 587–588
AI.QE.6: Use the process of factoring to determine zeros, lines of symmetry, and extreme values in real-world and other mathematical problems involving quadratic functions; interpret the results in the real-world contexts.	9.2, 9.3, 9.4, Extend 9.4	555–559, 564–570, 574–558, 580–581
AI.QE.7: Describe the relationships among the solutions of a quadratic equation, the zeros of the function, the *x*-intercepts of the graph, and the factors of the expression.	9.2, 9.3, 9.4, Extend 9.4	555–560, 564–571, 574–579, 580–581

Standards	Student Edition Lesson(s)	Student Edition Page(s)
Data Analysis and Statistics		
AI.DS.1: Distinguish between random and non-random sampling methods, identify possible sources of bias in sampling, describe how such bias can be controlled and reduced, evaluate the characteristics of a good survey and well-designed experiment, design simple experiments or investigations to collect data to answer questions of interest, and make inferences from sample results.	12.1, Extend 12.1, 12.2	747–753, 755–756, 757–762
AI.DS.2: Graph bivariate data on a scatter plot and describe the relationship between the variables.	4.5, Extend 4.5	247–252, 254
AI.DS.3: Use technology to find a linear function that models a relationship for a bivariate data set to make predictions; interpret the slope and y-intercept, and compute (using technology) and interpret the correlation coefficient.	4.5, Extend 4.5, 4.6, Extend 9.6	247–252, 254, 255–261, 596–597
AI.DS.4: Distinguish between correlation and causation.	Extend 4.5	254
AI.DS.5: Understand that patterns of association can also be seen in bivariate categorical data by displaying frequencies and relative frequencies in a two-way table. Construct and interpret a two-way table summarizing data on two categorical variables collected from the same subjects. Use relative frequencies calculated for rows or columns (including joint, marginal, and conditional relative frequencies) to describe possible associations and trends in the data.	Extend 12.7	801–802
AI.DS.6: Understand that statistics and data are non-neutral and designed to serve a particular interest. Analyze the possibilities for whose interest might be served and how the representations might be misleading.	Extend 4.5, 12.1, Extend 12.1, 12.2	254, 747–753, 755–756, 757–762

Notes

CHAPTER 0

Preparing For Algebra

Jack Hollingsworth/Photodisc/Getty Images

connectED.mcgraw-hill.com **Your Digital Math Portal**

Vocabulary p. P2

Multilingual eGlossary p. P2

Personal Tutor p. P18

Foldables p. P2

CHAPTER 1

Expressions, Equations, and Functions

connectED.mcgraw-hill.com **Your Digital Math Portal**

Animation pp. 18, 90

Vocabulary pp. 4, 139

Multilingual eGlossary pp. 4, 74

Personal Tutor pp. 6, 99

CHAPTER 2 Linear Equations

Mathematical Content

Virtual Manipulatives pp. 27, 90

Graphing Calculator pp. 55, 118

Foldables pp. 4, 74

Self-Check Practice pp. 3, 100

CHAPTER 3 Linear Functions

Mathematical Content

Flame/Alamy

connectED.mcgraw-hill.com **Your Digital Math Portal**

Animation pp. 150, 248

Vocabulary pp. 152, 272

Multilingual eGlossary pp. 152, 214

Personal Tutor pp. 158, 248

CHAPTER 4

Equations of Linear Functions

Oleg Kozlov/Alamy

Virtual Manipulatives pp. 158, 248

Graphing Calculator pp. 169, 215

Foldables pp. 152, 214

Self-Check Practice pp. 207, 213

CHAPTER 5 Linear Inequalities

connectED.mcgraw-hill.com Your Digital Math Portal

Animation pp. 291, 332

Vocabulary pp. 284, 378

Multilingual eGlossary pp. 284 334

Personal Tutor pp. 293, 342

CHAPTER 6 Systems of Linear Equations and Inequalities

Virtual Manipulatives pp. 291, 336

Graphing Calculator pp. 323, 342

Foldables pp. 284, 334

Self-Check Practice pp. 300, 383

CHAPTER 7 Exponents and Exponential Functions

connectED.mcgraw-hill.com Your Digital Math Portal

Animation pp. 398, 481

Vocabulary pp. 390, 530

Multilingual eGlossary pp. 390, 462

Personal Tutor pp. 406,473

CHAPTER 8 Quadratic Expressions and Equations

Virtual Manipulatives pp. 424, 480

Foldables pp. 390, 462

Self-Check Practice pp. 389, 518

CHAPTER 9 Quadratic Functions and Equations

connectED.mcgraw-hill.com **Your Digital Math Portal**

Animation pp. 574, 655

Vocabulary pp. 524, 663

Multilingual eGlossary pp. 524, 618

Personal Tutor pp. 572, 627

CHAPTER 10

Radical Functions and Geometry

CHAPTER 11 Rational Functions and Equations

connectED.mcgraw-hill.com **Your Digital Math Portal**

Animation pp. 672, 793

Vocabulary pp. 674, 746

Multilingual eGlossary pp. 674, 746

Personal Tutor pp. 697, 748

CHAPTER 12 Statistics and Probability

Virtual Manipulatives pp. 686, 764

Graphing Calculator pp. 697, 810

Foldables pp. 674, 746

Self-Check Practice pp. 679, 751

Student Handbook

Built-In Workbooks

Reference

CHAPTER 0 Preparing for Algebra

Jack Hollingsworth/Getty Images

Now

Chapter 0 contains lessons on topics from previous courses. You can use this chapter in various ways.

- Begin the school year by taking the Pretest. If you need additional review, complete the lessons in this chapter. To verify that you have successfully reviewed the topics, take the Posttest.
- As you work through the text, you may find that there are topics you need to review. When this happens, complete the individual lessons that you need.
- Use this chapter for reference. When you have questions about any of these topics, flip back to this chapter to review definitions or key concepts.

connectED.mcgraw-hill.com **Your Digital Math Portal**

Animation | Vocabulary | eGlossary | Personal Tutor | Virtual Manipulatives | Graphing Calculator | Audio | Foldables | Self-Check Practice | Worksheets

Using Chapter 0

The concepts presented in Chapter 0 are review from previous courses. You may wish to use all or some of the chapter at the beginning of the school year to refresh students' skills. Or you may wish to begin with Chapter 1 and use the Chapter 0 lessons as needed to reinforce prerequisite skills as you progress through the program.

FOLDABLES® StudyOrganizer

Dinah Zike's Foldables®

Each chapter of *Glencoe Algebra 1* features a Foldable Study Organizer students can make to organize their notes. Encourage students to use these tools to make their study time more productive.

Content Standards
AI.RNE.1

Process Standards
PS.1

Get Started on the Chapter

You will review several concepts, skills, and vocabulary terms as you study Chapter 0. To get ready, identify important terms and organize your resources.

FOLDABLES StudyOrganizer

Throughout this text, you will be invited to use Foldables to organize your notes.

Why should you use them?

- They help you organize, display, and arrange information.
- They make great study guides, specifically designed for you.
- You can use them as your math journal for recording main ideas, problem-solving strategies, examples, or questions you may have.
- They give you a chance to improve your math vocabulary.

How should you use them?

- Write general information — titles, vocabulary terms, concepts, questions, and main ideas – on the front tabs of your Foldable.
- Write specific information — ideas, your thoughts, answers to questions, steps, notes, and definitions — under the tabs.
- Use the tabs for:
  - math concepts in parts, like types of triangles,
  - steps to follow, or
  - parts of a problem, like *compare* and *contrast* (2 parts) or *what*, *where*, *when*, *why*, and *how* (5 parts).
- You may want to store your Foldables in a plastic zipper bag that you have three-hole punched to fit in your notebook.

When should you use them?

- Set up your Foldable as you begin a chapter, or when you start learning a new concept.
- Write in your Foldable every day.
- Use your Foldable to review for homework, quizzes, and tests.

ReviewVocabulary

English		Español
integer	p. P7	entero
absolute value	p. P11	valor absolute
opposites	p. P11	opuestos
reciprocal	p. P18	recíproco
perimeter	p. P23	perímetro
circle	p. P24	círculo
diameter	p. P24	diámetro
center	p. P24	centro
circumference	p. P24	circunferencia
radius	p. P24	radio
area	p. P26	area
volume	p. P29	volumen
surface area	p. P31	area de superficie
probability	p. P33	probabilidad
sample space	p. P33	espacio muestral
complements	p. P33	complementos
tree diagram	p. P34	diagrama de árbol
odds	p. P35	probabilidades
mean	p. P37	media
median	p. P37	mediana
mode	p. P37	moda
range	p. P38	rango
quartile	p. P38	cuartil
interquartile range	p. P38	amplitud intercuartílica
outliers	p. P39	valores atípicos
bar graph	p. P41	gráfica de barras
histogram	p. P41	histograma
line graph	p. P42	gráfica lineal
circle graph	p. P42	gráfica circular
box-and-whisker plot	p. P43	diagrama de caja y patillas

CHAPTER 0 Pretest

Determine whether you need an estimate or an exact answer. Then solve.

1. **SHOPPING** Addison paid \$1.29 for gum and \$0.89 for a package of notebook paper. She gave the cashier a \$5 bill. If the tax was \$0.14, how much change should Addison receive? **exact; \$2.68**

2. **DISTANCE** Luis rode his bike 1.2 miles to his friend's house, then 0.7 mile to the video store, then 1.9 miles to the library. If he rode the same route back home, about how far did he travel in all? **estimate; about 8 mi**

Find each sum or difference.

3. $20 + (-7)$ **13**
4. $-15 + 6$ **−9**
5. $-9 - 22$ **−31**
6. $18.4 - (-3.2)$ **21.6**
7. $23.1 + (-9.81)$ **13.29**
8. $-5.6 + (-30.7)$ **−36.3**

Find each product or quotient.

9. $11(-8)$ **−88**
10. $-15(-2)$ **30**
11. $63 \div (-9)$ **−7**
12. $-22 \div 11$ **−2**

Replace each ● with <, >, or = to make a true sentence.

13. $\frac{7}{20}$ ● $\frac{2}{5}$ **<**
14. 0.15 ● $\frac{1}{8}$ **>**
15. Order $0.5, -\frac{1}{7}, -0.2$, and $\frac{1}{3}$ from least to greatest. **$-0.2, -\frac{1}{7}, \frac{1}{3}, 0.5$**

Find each sum or difference. Write in simplest form.

16. $\frac{5}{6} + \frac{2}{3}$ **$1\frac{1}{2}$**
17. $\frac{11}{12} - \frac{3}{4}$ **$\frac{1}{6}$**
18. $\frac{1}{2} + \frac{4}{9}$ **$\frac{17}{18}$**
19. $-\frac{3}{5} + \left(-\frac{1}{5}\right)$ **$-\frac{4}{5}$**

Find each product or quotient.

20. $2.4(-0.7)$ **−1.68**
21. $-40.5 \div (-8.1)$ **5**

Name the reciprocal of each number.

22. $\frac{4}{11}$ **$\frac{11}{4}$**
23. $-\frac{3}{7}$ **$-\frac{7}{3}$**

Find each product or quotient. Write in simplest form.

24. $\frac{2}{21} \div \frac{1}{3}$ **$\frac{2}{7}$**
25. $\frac{1}{5} \cdot \frac{3}{20}$ **$\frac{3}{100}$**
26. $\frac{6}{25} \div \left(-\frac{3}{5}\right)$ **$-\frac{2}{5}$**
27. $\frac{1}{9} \cdot \frac{3}{4}$ **$\frac{1}{12}$**
28. $-\frac{2}{21} \div \left(-\frac{2}{15}\right)$ **$\frac{5}{7}$**
29. $2\frac{1}{2} \cdot \frac{2}{15}$ **$\frac{1}{3}$**

Express each percent as a fraction in simplest form.

30. 20% **$\frac{1}{5}$**
31. 7.5% **$\frac{3}{40}$**

Use the percent proportion to find each number.

32. 18 is what percent of 72? **25%**
33. 35 is what percent of 200? **17.5%**
34. 24 is 60% of what number? **40**

35. **TEST SCORES** James answered 14 items correctly on a 16-item quiz. What percent did he answer correctly? **87.5%**

36. **BASKETBALL** Emily made 75% of the baskets that she attempted. If she made 9 baskets, how many attempts did she make? **12**

Find the perimeter and area of each figure.

37.
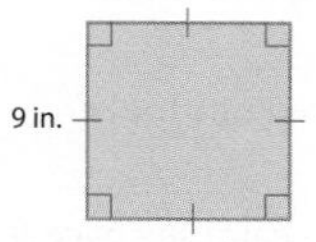

36 in.; 81 in²

38.
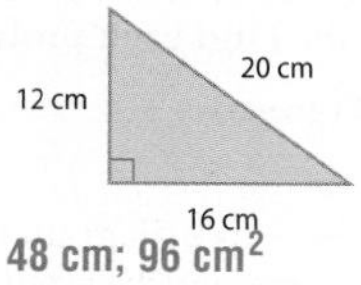

48 cm; 96 cm²

39. A parallelogram has side lengths of 7 inches and 11 inches. Find the perimeter. **36 in.**

40. **GARDENS** Find the perimeter of the garden. **23 m**

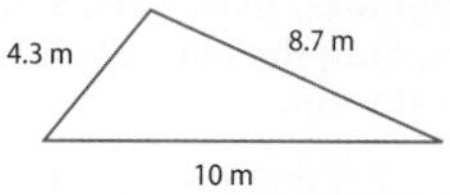

Using the Pretest

The Chapter 0 Pretest assesses students' understanding of the concepts presented in Chapter 0. You may use the pretest to determine whether students need to complete each lesson in Chapter 0 before beginning the content in Chapter 1.

connectED.mcgraw-hill.com P3

Additional Answers

57.

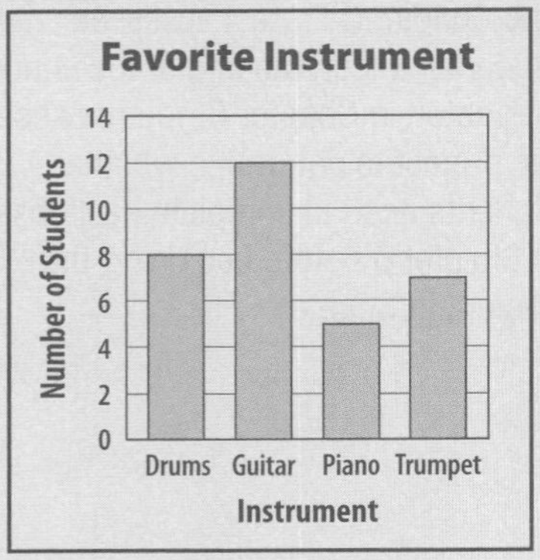

58.

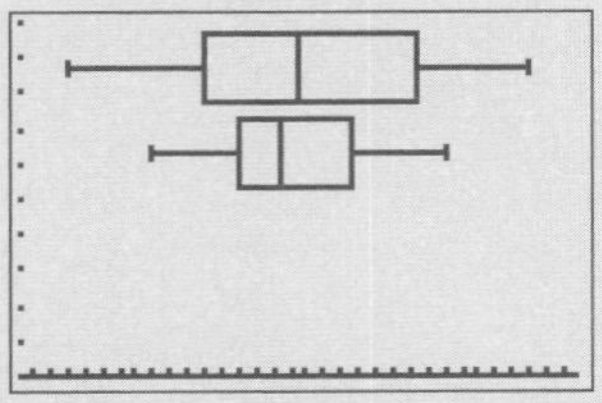

[32.3, 64.7] scl: 1

59. **Money Spent at the Fair**

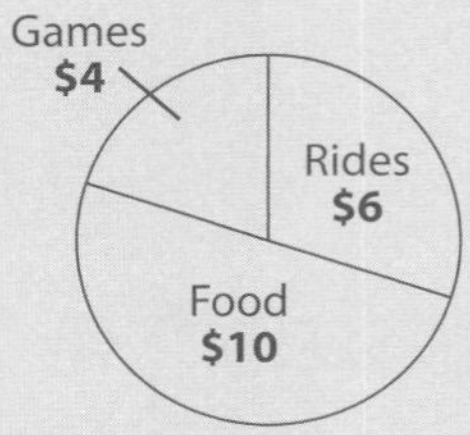

Sample answer: a circle graph would show how each category compares to the total amount spent.

Pretest *Continued*

Find the circumference and area of each circle. Round to the nearest tenth.

41.

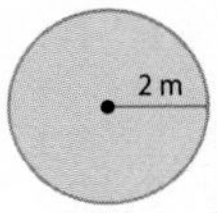

12.6 m; 12.6 m^2

42.

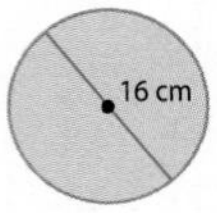

50.3 cm; 201.1 cm^2

43. **BIRDS** The floor of a birdcage is a circle with a circumference of about 47.1 inches. What is the diameter of the birdcage floor? Round to the nearest inch. 15 in.

Find the volume and surface area of each rectangular prism given the measurements below.

44. $\ell = 3$ cm, $w = 1$ cm, $h = 3$ cm 9 cm^3; 30 cm^2

45. $\ell = 6$ ft, $w = 2$ ft, $h = 5$ ft 60 ft^3; 104 ft^2

46. Find the volume and surface area of the rectangular prism. 30 cm^3; 62 cm^2

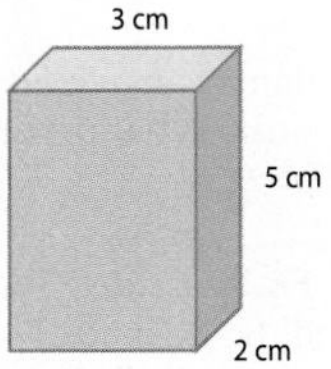

One pencil is randomly selected from a case containing 3 red, 4 green, 2 black, and 6 blue pencils. Find each probability.

47. P(green) $\frac{4}{15}$

48. P(red or blue) $\frac{3}{5}$

49. Use a tree diagram to find the sample space for the event *a die is rolled, and a coin is tossed*. State the number of possible outcomes. 12

One coin is randomly selected from a jar containing 20 pennies, 15 nickels, 3 dimes, and 12 quarters. Find the odds of each outcome. Write in simplest form.

50. a penny 2:3

51. a penny or nickel 7:3

52. A coin is tossed 50 times. The results are shown in the table. Find the experimental probability of heads. Write as a fraction in simplest form. $\frac{11}{25}$

Lands Face-Up	Number of Times
heads	22
tails	28

Find the mean, median, and mode for each set of data.

53. {10, 11, 18, 24, 30} 18.6; 18; no mode

54. {4, 8, 9, 9, 10, 14, 16} 10; 9; 9

55. Find the range, median, lower quartile, and upper quartile for {16, 19, 21, 24, 25, 31, 35}. 19; 24; 19; 31

56. **SCHOOL** Devonte's scores on his first four Spanish tests are 92, 85, 90, and 92. What test score must Devonte earn on the fifth test so that the mean will be exactly 90? 91

57. **MUSIC** The table shows the results of a survey in which students were asked to choose which of four instruments they would like to learn. Make a bar graph of the data. See margin.

Favorite Instrument	
Instrument	**Number of Students**
drums	8
guitar	12
piano	5
trumpet	7

58. Make a double box-and-whisker plot of the data.
A: 42, 50, 38, 59, 50, 44, 46, 62, 47, 35, 55, 56
B: 47, 49, 48, 49, 40, 54, 56, 42, 57, 45, 45, 46
See margin.

59. **EXPENSES** The table shows how Dylan spent his money at the fair. What type of graph is the best way to display these data? Explain your reasoning and make a graph of the data. See margin.

Money Spent at the Fair	
How Spent	**Amount ($)**
rides	6
food	10
games	4

LESSON 0-1 Plan for Problem Solving

Objective

- Use the four-step problem-solving plan.

NewVocabulary
four-step problem-solving plan
defining a variable

Process Standards
PS.1

Using the **four-step problem-solving plan** can help you solve any word problem.

KeyConcept Four-Step Problem Solving Plan

Step 1 Understand the Problem.
Step 2 Plan the Solution.
Step 3 Solve the Problem.
Step 4 Check the Solution.

Each step of the plan is important.

Step 1 Understand the Problem

To solve a verbal problem, first read the problem carefully and explore what the problem is about.

- Identify what information is given.
- Identify what you need to find.

Step 2 Plan the Solution

One strategy you can use is to write an equation. Choose a variable to represent one of the unspecified numbers in the problem. This is called **defining a variable**. Then use the variable to write expressions for the other unspecified numbers in the problem.

Step 3 Solve the Problem

Use the strategy you chose in Step 2 to solve the problem.

Step 4 Check the Solution

Check your answer in the context of the original problem.

- Does your answer make sense?
- Does it fit the information in the problem?

Example 1 Use the Four-Step Plan

PT

FLOORS Ling's hallway is 10 feet long and 4 feet wide. He paid $200 to tile his hallway floor. How much did Ling pay per square foot for the tile?

Understand We are given the measurements of the hallway and the total cost of the tile. We are asked to find the cost of each square foot of tile.

Plan Write an equation. Let f represent the cost of each square foot of tile. The area of the hallway is 10×4 or 40 ft^2.

40	times	the cost per square foot	equals	200.
40	•	f	=	200

Solve $40 \cdot f = 200$. Find f mentally by asking, "What number times 40 is 200?"
$f = 5$
The tile cost $5 per square foot.

Check If the tile costs $5 per square foot, then 40 square feet of tile costs $5 \cdot 40$ or $200. The answer makes sense.

1 Focus

VerticalAlignment

Lesson 0-1 Use the four-step problem-solving plan.

After Lesson 0-1 Use the four-step plan to analyze and solve real-world problems.

2 Teach

Examples 1 and 2 show how to use the four-step plan to solve real-world problems.

Additional Example

1 **LAWNS** Mr. Nunez's lawn is 50 feet long and 35 feet wide. He paid a lawn service $350 to aerate and reseed his lawn. What did the lawn service charge per square foot? $0.20 per square foot

Teach with Tech

Interactive Whiteboard Use the board as you step through an example. Use a new page on the whiteboard to organize notes for each of the 4 steps. Save and post on your class Web site.

Additional Example

2 **BOOKS** A used book store had a sale on all paperbacks for $0.45 each. The store had $72.45 in sales. How many books did the store sell? 161 books

Tips for New Teachers

Estimation Point out to students that if a problem involves having enough money to purchase items, it is a good idea to round up at least one of the items to ensure that there is enough money for the purchases.

3 Assess

Formative Assessment

Use Exercises 1–6 to assess whether students understand how to use the four-step problem-solving plan.

Name the Math

Ask students to describe the four steps they would use to solve a problem.

When an exact value is needed, you can use estimation to check your answer.

PT

Example 2 Use the Four-Step Plan

TRAVEL Emily's family drove 254.6 miles. Their car used 19 gallons of gasoline. Describe the car's gas mileage.

Understand We are given the total miles driven and how much gasoline was used. We are asked to find the gas mileage of the car.

Plan Write an equation. Let G represent the car's gas mileage.

gas mileage = number of miles ÷ number of gallons used

$G = 254.6 \div 19$

Solve $G = 254.6 \div 19$

$= 13.4$ mi/gal

The car's gas mileage is 13.4 miles per gallon.

Check Use estimation to check your solution.

260 mi ÷ 20 gal = 13 mi/gal

Since the solution 13.4 is close to the estimate, the answer is reasonable.

Exercises

Determine whether you need an estimate or an exact answer. Then use the four step problem-solving plan to solve.

1. **DRIVING** While on vacation, the Jacobson family drove 312.8 miles the first day, 177.2 miles the second day, and 209 miles the third day. About how many miles did they travel in all? **estimate; about 700 mi**

2. **PETS** Ms. Hernandez boarded her dog at a kennel for 4 days. It cost $18.90 per day, and she had a coupon for $5 off. What was the final cost for boarding her dog? **exact; $70.60**

3. **MEASUREMENT** William is using a 1.75-liter container to fill a 14-liter container of water. About how many times will he need to fill the smaller container? **estimate; about 7 times**

4. **SEWING** Fabric costs $5.15 per yard. The drama department needs 18 yards of the fabric for their new play. About how much should they expect to pay? **estimate; about $100**

5. **FINANCIAL LITERACY** The table shows donations to help purchase a new tree for the school. How much money did the students donate in all? **exact; $98.75**

Number of Students	Amount of Each Donation
20	$2.50
15	$3.25

6. **SHOPPING** Is $12 enough to buy a half gallon of milk for $2.30, a bag of apples for $3.99, and four cups of yogurt that cost $0.79 each? Explain. **Estimate; yes, the total cost is about $2 + $4 + $4, or $10.**

P6 | Lesson 0-1 | Plan for Problem Solving

LESSON 0-2 Real Numbers

Objective

- Classify and use real numbers.

NewVocabulary
positive number
negative number
natural number
whole number
integer
rational number
square root
principal square root
perfect square
irrational number
real number
graph
coordinate

Content Standards
AI.RNE.1

A number line can be used to show the sets of natural numbers, whole numbers, integers, and rational numbers. Values greater than 0, or **positive numbers**, are listed to the right of 0, and values less than 0, or **negative numbers**, are listed to the left of 0.

natural numbers: 1, 2, 3, …

whole numbers: 0, 1, 2, 3, …

integers: …, −3, −2, −1, 0, 1, 2, 3, …

rational numbers: numbers that can be expressed in the form $\frac{a}{b}$, where a and b are integers and $b \neq 0$

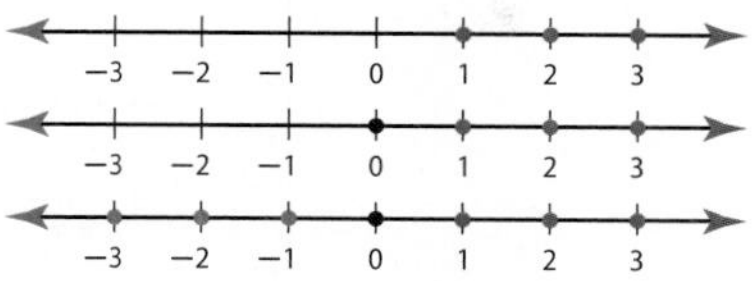

A **square root** is one of two equal factors of a number. For example, one square root of 64, written as $\sqrt{64}$, is 8 since $8 \cdot 8$ or 8^2 is 64. The nonnegative square root of a number is the **principal square root**. Another square root of 64 is −8 since $(-8) \cdot (-8)$ or $(-8)^2$ is also 64. A number like 64, with a square root that is a rational number, is called a **perfect square**. The square roots of a perfect square are rational numbers.

A number such as $\sqrt{3}$ is the square root of a number that is not a perfect square. It cannot be expressed as a terminating or repeating decimal; $\sqrt{3} \approx 1.73205\ldots$. Numbers that cannot be expressed as terminating or repeating decimals, or in the form $\frac{a}{b}$, where a and b are integers and $b \neq 0$, are called **irrational numbers**. Irrational numbers and rational numbers together form the set of **real numbers**.

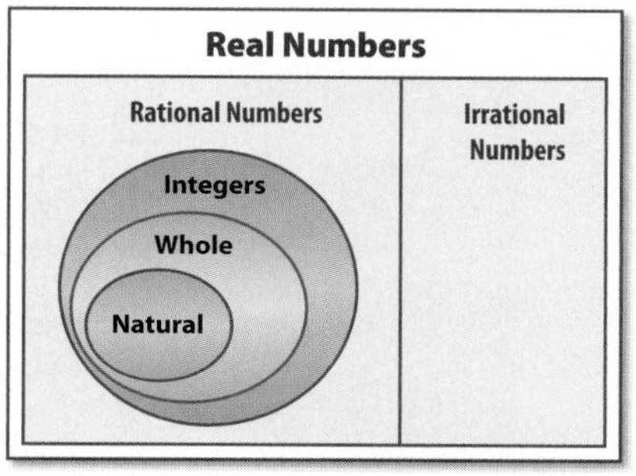

Example 1 Classify Real Numbers

Name the set or sets of numbers to which each real number belongs.

a. $\frac{5}{22}$

Because 5 and 22 are integers and $5 \div 22 = 0.2272727\ldots$ or $0.2\overline{27}$, which is a repeating decimal, this number is a rational number.

b. $\sqrt{81}$

Because $\sqrt{81} = 9$, this number is a natural number, a whole number, an integer, and a rational number.

c. $\sqrt{56}$

Because $\sqrt{56} = 7.48331477\ldots$, which is not a repeating or terminating decimal, this number is irrational.

1 Focus

VerticalAlignment

Lesson 0-2 Classify and use real numbers.

After Lesson 0-2 Graph real numbers as solutions to equations and inequalities.
Find square roots as solutions to quadratic equations.

2 Teach

Example 1 shows how to classify real numbers. **Example 2** shows how to graph real numbers on a number line. **Example 3** shows how to write repeating decimals as fractions. **Example 4** shows how to simplify expressions involving square roots. **Example 5** shows how to estimate square roots to the nearest whole number.

Additional Example

1 Name the set or sets of numbers to which each real number belongs.

a. $\frac{9}{10}$ rational number

b. $\sqrt{121}$ natural number, whole number, integer, rational number

c. $\sqrt{18}$ irrational number

Teach with Tech

Interactive Whiteboard Draw a set diagram on the board showing how the set of real numbers is seperated into rational and irrational numbers, integers, whole numbers, etc. Create a list of 12 real numbers, and have students come to the board to drag them into the correct set in the diagram.

Additional Examples

2 Graph each set of numbers on a number line.

a. $\left\{\frac{3}{4}, -\frac{1}{4}, \frac{7}{4}, -1\frac{1}{2}\right\}$

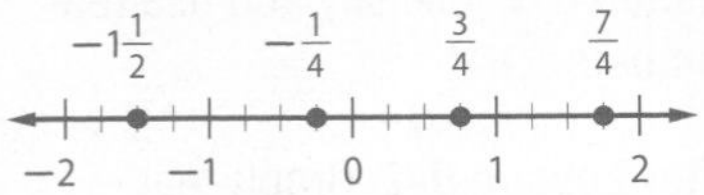

From least to greatest, the order is $-1\frac{1}{2}, -\frac{1}{4}, \frac{3}{4}, \frac{7}{4}$.

b. $\left\{\sqrt{25}, 4.\overline{6}, \sqrt{15}, 4\frac{3}{8}\right\}$

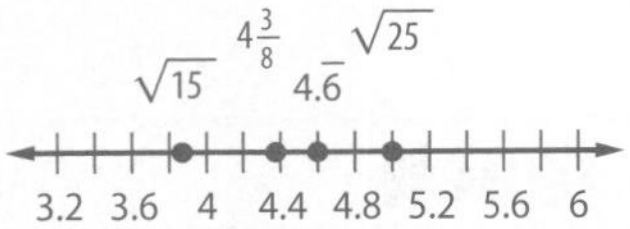

From least to greatest, the order is $\sqrt{15}, 4\frac{3}{8}, 4.\overline{6}, \sqrt{25}$.

c. $\left\{-\frac{9}{4}, -2\frac{7}{10}, -2.1, -\sqrt{8}\right\}$

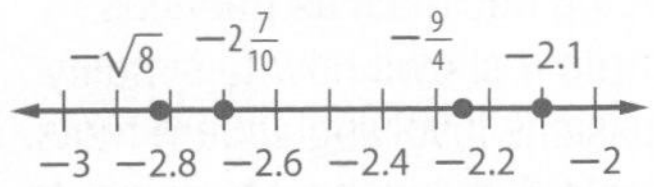

From least to greatest, the order is $-\sqrt{8}, -2\frac{7}{10}, -\frac{9}{4}, -2.1$

3 Write $0.\overline{23}$ as a fraction in simplest form. $\frac{23}{99}$

Tips for New Teachers

Number Lines Instruct students to be consistent in the scales on their number lines. Remind them to show tick marks at equal intervals.

To **graph** a set of numbers means to draw, or plot, the points named by those numbers on a number line. The number that corresponds to a point on a number line is called the **coordinate** of that point. The rational numbers and the irrational numbers complete the number line.

PT

Example 2 Graph and Order Real Numbers

Graph each set of numbers on a number line. Then order the numbers from least to greatest.

a. $\left\{\frac{5}{3}, -\frac{4}{3}, \frac{2}{3}, -\frac{1}{3}\right\}$

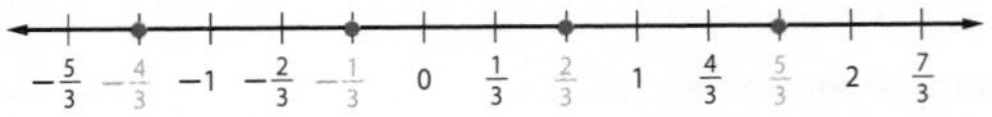

From least to greatest, the order is $-\frac{4}{3}, -\frac{1}{2}, \frac{2}{3}$, and $\frac{5}{3}$.

b. $\left\{6\frac{4}{5}, \sqrt{49}, 6.\overline{3}, \sqrt{57}\right\}$

Express each number as a decimal. Then order the decimals.

$6\frac{4}{5} = 6.8$ $\quad \sqrt{49} = 7$ $\quad 6.\overline{3} = 6.33333333\ldots$ $\quad \sqrt{57} = 7.5468344\ldots$

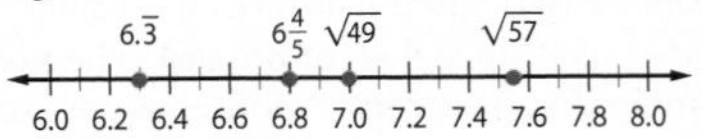

From least to greatest, the order is $6.\overline{3}, 6\frac{4}{5}, \sqrt{49}$, and $\sqrt{57}$.

c. $\left\{\sqrt{20}, 4.7, \frac{12}{3}, 4\frac{1}{3}\right\}$

$\sqrt{20} = 4.47213595\ldots$ $\quad 4.7 = 4.7$ $\quad \frac{12}{3} = 4.0$ $\quad 4\frac{1}{3} = 4.33333333\ldots$

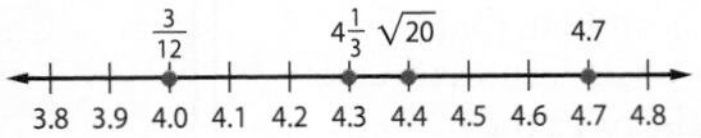

From least to greatest, the order is $\frac{12}{3}, 4\frac{1}{3}, \sqrt{20}$, and 4.7.

Any repeating decimal can be written as a fraction.

PT

Example 3 Write Repeating Decimals as Fractions

Write $0.\overline{7}$ as a fraction in simplest form.

Step 1

$N = 0.777\ldots$	Let N represent the repeating decimal.
$10N = 10(0.777\ldots)$	Since only one digit repeats, multiply each side by 10.
$10N = 7.777\ldots$	Simplify.

Step 2 Subtract N from $10N$ to eliminate the part of the number that repeats.

$10N = 7.777\ldots$

$\underline{-(N = 0.777\ldots)}$

$9N = 7$	Subtract.
$\frac{9N}{9} = \frac{7}{9}$	Divide each side by 9.
$N = \frac{7}{9}$	Simplify.

P8 | Lesson 0-2 | Real Numbers

StudyTip

Perfect Squares Keep a list of perfect squares in your notebook. Refer to it when you need to simplify a square root.

Perfect squares can be used to simplify square roots of rational numbers.

KeyConcept Perfect Square

Words Rational numbers with square roots that are rational numbers.

Examples 25 is a perfect square since $\sqrt{25} = 5$.

144 is a perfect square since $\sqrt{144} = 12$.

Example 4 Simplify Roots

Simplify each square root.

a. $\sqrt{\frac{4}{121}}$

$\sqrt{\frac{4}{121}} = \sqrt{\left(\frac{2}{11}\right)^2}$ — $2^2 = 4$ and $11^2 = 121$

$= \frac{2}{11}$ — Simplify.

b. $-\sqrt{\frac{49}{256}}$

$-\sqrt{\frac{49}{256}} = -\sqrt{\left(\frac{7}{16}\right)^2}$ — $7^2 = 49$ and $16^2 = 256$

$= -\frac{7}{16}$

You can estimate roots that are not perfect squares.

Example 5 Estimate Roots

Estimate each square root to the nearest whole number.

a. $\sqrt{15}$

Find the two perfect squares closest to 15. List some perfect squares.

1, 4, 9, 16, 25, 36, …

15 is between 9 and 16.

$9 < 15 < 16$ — Write an inequality.

$\sqrt{9} < \sqrt{15} < \sqrt{16}$ — Take the square root of each number.

$3 < \sqrt{15} < 4$ — Simplify.

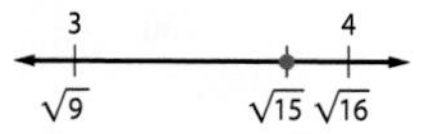

Since 15 is closer to 16 than 9, the best whole-number estimate for $\sqrt{15}$ is 4.

Additional Examples

4 Simplify each square root.

a. $\sqrt{\frac{64}{16}}$ 2

b. $-\sqrt{\frac{25}{144}}$ $-\frac{5}{12}$

5 Estimate each square root to the nearest whole number.

a. $\sqrt{34}$ 6

b. $\sqrt{97}$ 10

3 Assess

Formative Assessment

Use Exercises 1–35 to assess whether students understand real numbers.

Ticket Out the Door

Ask students to write one rational number and one irrational number on a sheet of paper. Have them label each as rational or irrational.

Additional Answers

13. $-\frac{6}{5}, -\frac{3}{5}, \frac{3}{4}$, and $\frac{7}{5}$

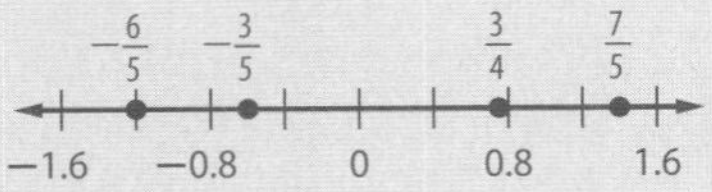

14. $-\frac{7}{9}, -\frac{4}{9}, \frac{1}{9}$, and $\frac{1}{2}$

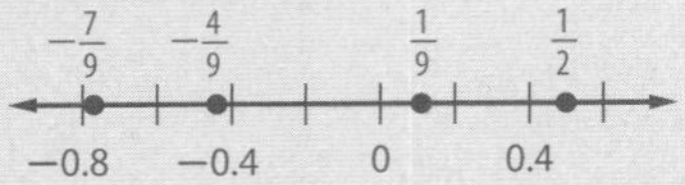

15. $2\frac{1}{4}, 2.\overline{3}, \sqrt{7}$, and $\sqrt{8}$

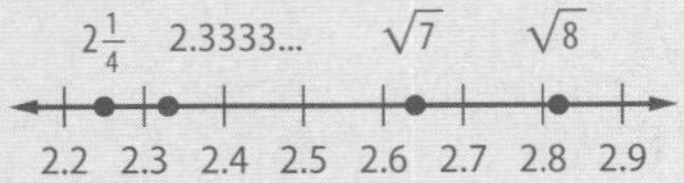

16. $0.\overline{1}, \frac{4}{5}, \sqrt{2}$, and $\sqrt{3}$

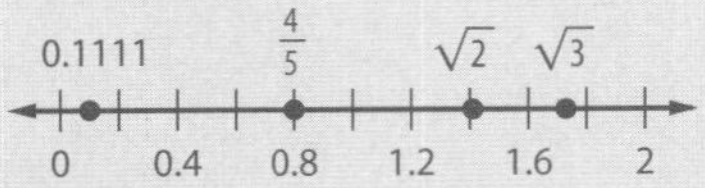

17. $-3\frac{3}{4}, -3.5, -\sqrt{10}$, and $-\frac{15}{5}$

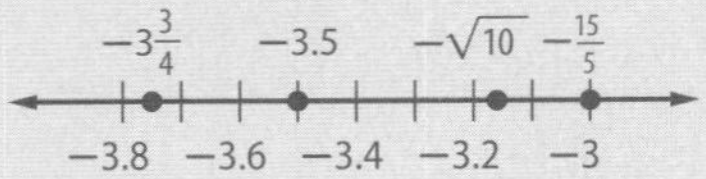

18. $\sqrt{64}, 8\frac{2}{7}, \frac{26}{3}$, and 8.8

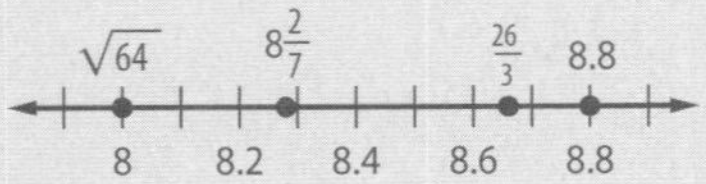

b. $\sqrt{130}$

Find the two perfect squares closest to 130. List some perfect squares.

81, 100, 121, 144

130 is between 121 and 144.

$121 < 130 < 144$ Write an inequality.

$\sqrt{121} < \sqrt{130} < \sqrt{144}$ Take the square root of each number.

$11 < \sqrt{130} < 12$ Simplify.

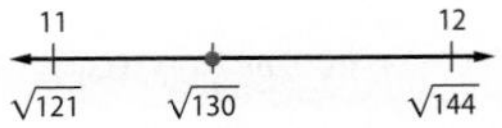

Since 130 is closer to 121 than to 144, the best whole number estimate for $\sqrt{130}$ is 11.

CHECK $\sqrt{130} \approx 11.4018$ Use a calculator.

Rounded to the nearest whole number, $\sqrt{130}$ is 11. So the estimate is valid.

StudyTip

Draw a Diagram
Graphing points on a number line can help you analyze your estimate for accuracy.

1. integers, rationals **4.** naturals, wholes, integers, rationals **6.** naturals, wholes, integers, rationals **8.** naturals, wholes, integers, rationals

Exercises

Name the set or sets of numbers to which each real number belongs.

1. $-\sqrt{64}$
2. $\frac{8}{3}$ rationals
3. $\sqrt{28}$ irrationals
4. $\frac{56}{7}$
5. $-\sqrt{22}$ irrationals
6. $\frac{36}{6}$
7. $-\frac{5}{12}$ rationals
8. $\frac{18}{3}$
9. $\sqrt{10.24}$ rationals
10. $\frac{-54}{19}$ rationals
11. $\sqrt{\frac{82}{20}}$ irrationals
12. $-\frac{72}{8}$ integers, rationals

Graph each set of numbers on a number line. Then order the numbers from least to greatest. 13–18. See margin.

13. $\left\{\frac{7}{5}, -\frac{3}{5}, \frac{3}{4}, -\frac{6}{5}\right\}$
14. $\left\{\frac{1}{2}, -\frac{7}{9}, \frac{1}{9}, -\frac{4}{9}\right\}$
15. $\left\{2\frac{1}{4}, \sqrt{7}, 2.\overline{3}, \sqrt{8}\right\}$
16. $\left\{\frac{4}{5}, \sqrt{2}, 0.\overline{1}, \sqrt{3}\right\}$
17. $\left\{-3.5, -\frac{15}{5}, -\sqrt{10}, -3\frac{3}{4}\right\}$
18. $\left\{\sqrt{64}, 8.8, \frac{26}{3}, 8\frac{2}{7}\right\}$

Write each repeating decimal as a fraction in simplest form.

19. $0.\overline{5}$ $\frac{5}{9}$
20. $0.\overline{4}$ $\frac{4}{9}$
21. $0.\overline{13}$ $\frac{13}{99}$
22. $0.\overline{21}$ $\frac{7}{33}$

Simplify each square root.

23. $-\sqrt{25}$ −5
24. $\sqrt{361}$ 19
25. $\pm\sqrt{36}$ ±6
26. $\sqrt{0.64}$ 0.8
27. $\pm\sqrt{1.44}$ ±1.2
28. $-\sqrt{6.25}$ −2.5
29. $\sqrt{\frac{16}{49}}$ $\frac{4}{7}$
30. $\sqrt{\frac{169}{196}}$ $\frac{13}{14}$
31. $\sqrt{\frac{25}{324}}$ $\frac{5}{18}$

Estimate each root to the nearest whole number.

32. $\sqrt{112}$ 11
33. $\sqrt{252}$ 16
34. $\sqrt{415}$ 20
35. $\sqrt{670}$ 26

P10 | Lesson 0-2 | Real Numbers

LESSON 0-3 Operations with Integers

Objective

- Add, subtract, multiply, and divide integers.

NewVocabulary

absolute value
opposites
additive inverses

An integer is any number from the set {…, −3, −2, −1, 0, 1, 2, 3, …}. You can use a number line to add integers.

Example 1 Add Integers with the Same Sign

Use a number line to find −3 + (−4).

Step 1 Draw an arrow from 0 to −3.

Step 2 Draw a second arrow 4 units to the left to represent adding −4.

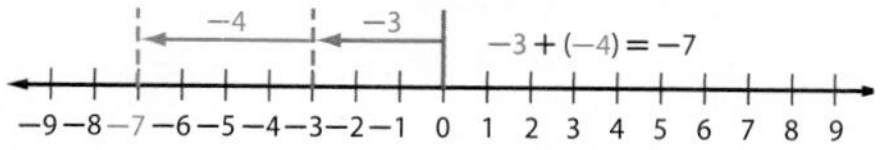

The second arrow ends at −7. So, −3 + (−4) = −7.

You can also use absolute value to add integers. The **absolute value** of a number is its distance from 0 on the number line.

Same Signs (+ + or − −)		Different Signs (+ − or − +)	
3 + 5 = 8	3 and 5 are positive. Their sum is positive.	3 + (−5) = −2	−5 has the greater absolute value. Their sum is negative.
−3 + (−5) = −8	−3 and −5 are negative. Their sum is negative.	−3 + 5 = 2	5 has the greater absolute value. Their sum is positive.

Example 2 Add Integers Using Absolute Value

Find −11 + (−7).

$-11 + (-7) = -(|-11| + |-7|)$ Add the absolute values. Both numbers are negative, so the sum is negative.

$= -(11 + 7)$ Absolute values of nonzero numbers are always positive.

$= -18$ Simplify.

Every positive integer can be paired with a negative integer. These pairs are called **opposites**. A number and its opposite are **additive inverses**. Additive inverses can be used when you subtract integers.

Example 3 Subtract Positive Integers

Find 18 − 23.

$18 - 23 = 18 + (-23)$ To subtract 23, add its inverse.

$= -(|-23| - |18|)$ Subtract the absolute values. Because $|-23|$ is greater than $|18|$, the result is negative.

$= -(23 - 18)$ Absolute values of nonzero numbers are always positive.

$= -5$ Simplify.

1 Focus

VerticalAlignment

Lesson 0-3 Add, subtract, multiply, and divide integers.

After Lesson 0-3 Evaluate expressions and solve equations that involve operations with integers.

2 Teach

Example 1 shows how to use a number line to add integers. **Example 2** shows how to use absolute values to add integers. **Example 3** shows how to subtract integers. **Example 4** shows how to multiply and divide integers.

Additional Examples

1. Use a number line to find −2 + 3. 1

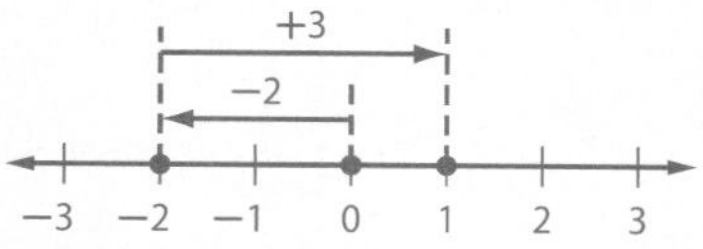

2. Find −15 + (−4). −19

3. Find 11 − 15. −4

WatchOut!

Preventing Errors Remind students to subtract the lesser absolute value from the greater absolute value when adding integers with different signs. The sum will have the sign of the number with the greater absolute value.

Teach with Tech

Wiki On your secure classroom wiki have all students contribute to the notes on this chapter and save as a reference.

Additional Example

4 Find each product or quotient.

a. −9(4) −36

b. −112 ÷ (−8) 14

c. −11(−11) 121

d. 96 ÷ (−6) −16

3 Assess

Formative Assessment

Use Exercises 1–23 to assess whether students understand how to add, subtract, multiply, and divide integers.

Crystal Ball

Ask students how they think today's lesson on adding and subtracting integers will help with tomorrow's lesson on adding and subtracting rational numbers.

StudyTip

Products and Quotients The product or quotient of two numbers having the *same sign* is positive. The product or quotient of two numbers having *different signs* is negative.

Same Signs (+ + or − −)		Different Signs (+ − or − +)	
3(5) = 15	3 and 5 are positive. Their product is positive.	3(−5) = −15	3 and −5 have different signs. Their product is negative.
−3(−5) = 15	−3 and −5 are negative. Their product is positive.	−3(5) = −15	−3 and 5 have different signs. Their product is negative.

PT

Example 4 Multiply and Divide Integers

Find each product or quotient.

a. 4(−5)

4(−5) = −20 different signs ⟶ negative product

b. −51 ÷ (−3)

−51 ÷ (−3) = 17 same sign ⟶ positive quotient

c. −12(−14)

−12(−14) = 168 same sign ⟶ positive product

d. −63 ÷ 7

−63 ÷ 7 = −9 different signs ⟶ negative quotient

Exercises

Find each sum or difference.

1. −8 + 13 **5** **2.** 11 + (−19) **−8** **3.** −19 − 8 **−27**

4. −77 + (−46) **−123** **5.** 12 − 34 **−22** **6.** 41 + (−56) **−15**

7. 50 − 82 **−32** **8.** −47 − 13 **−60** **9.** −80 + 102 **22**

Find each product or quotient.

10. 5(18) **90** **11.** 60 ÷ 12 **5** **12.** −12(15) **−180**

13. −64 ÷ (−8) **8** **14.** 8(−22) **−176** **15.** 54 ÷ (−6) **−9**

16. 30(14) **420** **17.** −23(5) **−115** **18.** −200 ÷ 2 **−100**

19. **WEATHER** The outside temperature was −4°F in the morning and 13°F in the afternoon. By how much did the temperature increase? **17°**

20. **DOLPHINS** A dolphin swimming 24 feet below the ocean's surface dives 18 feet straight down. How many feet below the ocean's surface is the dolphin now? **42 ft**

21. **MOVIES** A movie theater gave out 50 coupons for $3 off each movie. What is the total amount of discounts provided by the theater? **$150**

22. **WAGES** Emilio earns $11 per hour. He works 14 hours a week. His employer withholds $32 from each paycheck for taxes. If he is paid weekly, what is the amount of his paycheck? **$122**

23. **FINANCIAL LITERACY** Talia is working on a monthly budget. Her monthly income is $500. She has allocated $200 for savings, $100 for vehicle expenses, and $75 for clothing. How much is available to spend on entertainment? **$125**

LESSON 0-4 Adding and Subtracting Rational Numbers

Objective

- Compare and order; add and subtract rational numbers.

You can use different methods to compare rational numbers. One way is to compare two fractions with common denominators. Another way is to compare decimals.

Example 1 Compare Rational Numbers

Replace ● with <, >, or = to make $\frac{2}{3}$ ● $\frac{5}{6}$ a true sentence.

Method 1 Write the fractions with the same denominator.

The least common denominator of $\frac{2}{3}$ and $\frac{5}{6}$ is 6.

$\frac{2}{3} = \frac{4}{6}$

$\frac{5}{6} = \frac{5}{6}$

Since $\frac{4}{6} < \frac{5}{6}$, $\frac{2}{3} < \frac{5}{6}$.

Method 2 Write as decimals.

Write $\frac{2}{3}$ and $\frac{5}{6}$ as decimals. You may want to use a calculator.

2 [÷] 3 [ENTER] .6666666667

So, $\frac{2}{3} = 0.\overline{6}$.

5 [÷] 6 [ENTER] .8333333333

So, $\frac{5}{6} = 0.8\overline{3}$.

Since $0.\overline{6} < 0.8\overline{3}$, $\frac{2}{3} < \frac{5}{6}$.

You can order rational numbers by writing all of the fractions as decimals.

Example 2 Order Rational Numbers

Order $5\frac{2}{9}$, $5\frac{3}{8}$, 4.9, and $-5\frac{3}{5}$ from least to greatest.

$5\frac{2}{9} = 5.\overline{2}$ $\quad$ $5\frac{3}{8} = 5.375$

$4.9 = 4.9$ $\quad$ $-5\frac{3}{5} = -5.6$

$-5.6 < 4.9 < 5.\overline{2} < 5.375$. So, from least to greatest, the numbers are $-5\frac{3}{5}$, 4.9, $5\frac{2}{9}$, and $5\frac{3}{8}$.

To add or subtract fractions with the same denominator, add or subtract the numerators and write the sum or difference over the denominator.

1 Focus

Vertical Alignment

Lesson 0-4 Compare and order rational numbers.
Add and subtract rational numbers.

After Lesson 0-4 Solve equations that involve adding and subtracting rational numbers.

2 Teach

Example 1 shows how to compare rational numbers. **Example 2** shows how to order rational numbers. **Example 3** shows how to find the sum and difference of fractions with like denominators. **Example 4** shows how to find the sum and difference of fractions with unlike denominators. **Example 5** shows how to use a number line to add rational numbers. **Example 6** shows how to find the sum of rational numbers. **Example 7** shows how to subtract rational numbers.

Additional Examples

1. Replace ● with <, >, or = to make $\frac{4}{5}$ ● $\frac{5}{8}$ a true statement. >
2. Order $3\frac{3}{8}$, $-3\frac{3}{7}$, $3.\overline{45}$, and $-3\frac{2}{5}$ from least to greatest. $-3\frac{3}{7}$, $-3\frac{2}{5}$, $3\frac{3}{8}$, $3.\overline{45}$

Additional Examples

3 Find each sum or difference. Write in simplest form.

a. $\frac{5}{11}+\frac{3}{11}$ $\frac{8}{11}$

b. $\frac{11}{18}-\frac{7}{18}$ $\frac{2}{9}$

c. $\frac{3}{8}-\frac{5}{8}$ $-\frac{1}{4}$

4 Find each sum or difference. Write in simplest form.

a. $\frac{4}{5}+\frac{7}{10}$ $1\frac{1}{2}$

b. $\frac{5}{6}-\frac{5}{18}$ $\frac{5}{9}$

c. $\frac{3}{10}-\frac{3}{4}$ $-\frac{9}{20}$

Teach with Tech

Interactive Whiteboard Create a template that you can use to show addition of fractions, such as:

$$\frac{\square}{\square}+\frac{\square}{\square}=\frac{\square+\square}{\square}=\frac{\square}{\square}$$

Display the template on the board and use it as you work through examples.

StudyTip

Mental Math If the denominators of the fractions are the same, you can use mental math to determine the sum or difference.

PT

Example 3 Add and Subtract Like Fractions

Find each sum or difference. Write in simplest form.

a. $\frac{3}{5}+\frac{1}{5}$

$\frac{3}{5}+\frac{1}{5}=\frac{3+1}{5}$ The denominators are the same. Add the numerators.

$=\frac{4}{5}$ Simplify.

b. $\frac{7}{16}-\frac{1}{16}$

$\frac{7}{16}-\frac{1}{16}=\frac{7-1}{16}$ The denominators are the same. Subtract the numerators.

$=\frac{6}{16}$ Simplify.

$=\frac{3}{8}$ Rename the fraction.

c. $\frac{4}{9}-\frac{7}{9}$

$\frac{4}{9}-\frac{7}{9}=\frac{4-7}{9}$ The denominators are the same. Subtract the numerators.

$=-\frac{3}{9}$ Simplify.

$=-\frac{1}{3}$ Rename the fraction.

To add or subtract fractions with unlike denominators, first find the least common denominator (LCD). Rename each fraction with the LCD, and then add or subtract. Simplify if possible.

PT

Example 4 Add and Subtract Unlike Fractions

Find each sum or difference. Write in simplest form.

a. $\frac{1}{2}+\frac{2}{3}$

$\frac{1}{2}+\frac{2}{3}=\frac{3}{6}+\frac{4}{6}$ The LCD for 2 and 3 is 6. Rename $\frac{1}{2}$ as $\frac{3}{6}$ and $\frac{2}{3}$ as $\frac{4}{6}$.

$=\frac{3+4}{6}$ Add the numerators.

$=\frac{7}{6}$ or $1\frac{1}{6}$ Simplify.

b. $\frac{3}{8}-\frac{1}{3}$

$\frac{3}{8}-\frac{1}{3}=\frac{9}{24}-\frac{8}{24}$ The LCD for 8 and 3 is 24. Rename $\frac{3}{8}$ as $\frac{9}{24}$ and $\frac{1}{3}$ as $\frac{8}{24}$.

$=\frac{9-8}{24}$ Subtract the numerators.

$=\frac{1}{24}$ Simplify.

c. $\frac{2}{5}-\frac{3}{4}$

$\frac{2}{5}-\frac{3}{4}=\frac{8}{20}-\frac{15}{20}$ The LCD for 5 and 4 is 20. Rename $\frac{2}{5}$ as $\frac{8}{20}$ and $\frac{3}{4}$ as $\frac{15}{20}$.

$=\frac{8-15}{20}$ Subtract the numerators.

$=-\frac{7}{20}$ Simplify.

P14 | Lesson 0-4 | Adding and Subtracting Rational Numbers

> **StudyTip**
> **Number Line** To use a number line, put your pencil at the first number. If you are adding or subtracting a positive number, then move left to find the difference. To find the sum, move your pencil to the right.

You can use a number line to add rational numbers.

Example 5 Add Decimals

Use a number line to find 2.5 + (−3.5).

Step 1 Draw an arrow from 0 to 2.5.

Step 2 Draw a second arrow 3.5 units to the left.

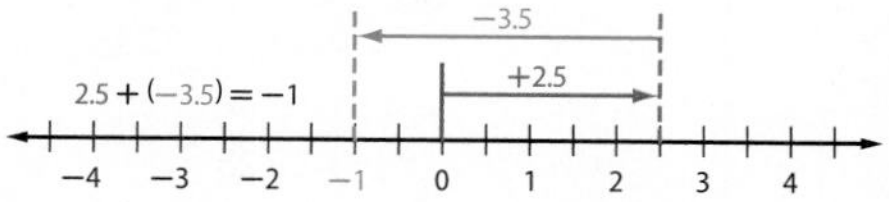

The second arrow ends at −1.

So, 2.5 + (−3.5) = −1.

You can also use absolute value to add rational numbers.

Same Signs (+ + or − −)		Different Signs (+ − or − +)	
3.1 + 2.5 = 5.6	3.1 and 2.5 are positive, so the sum is positive.	3.1 + (−2.5) = 0.6	3.1 has the greater absolute value, so the sum is positive.
−3.1 + (−2.5) = −5.6	−3.1 and −2.5 are negative, so the sum is negative.	−3.1 + 2.5 = −0.6	−3.1 has the greater absolute value, so the sum is negative.

Example 6 Use Absolute Value to Add Rational Numbers

Find each sum.

a. −13.12 + (−8.6)

$-13.12 + (-8.6) = -(|-13.12| + |-8.6|)$ — Both numbers are negative, so the sum is negative.

$= -(13.12 + 8.6)$ — Absolute values of nonzero numbers are always positive.

$= -21.72$ — Simplify.

b. $\frac{7}{16} + \left(-\frac{3}{8}\right)$

$\frac{7}{16} + \left(-\frac{3}{8}\right) = \frac{7}{16} + \left(-\frac{6}{16}\right)$ — The LCD is 16. Replace $-\frac{3}{8}$ with $-\frac{6}{16}$.

$= \left(\left|\frac{7}{16}\right| - \left|-\frac{6}{16}\right|\right)$ — Subtract the absolute values. Because $\left|\frac{7}{16}\right|$ is greater than $\left|-\frac{6}{16}\right|$, the result is positive.

$= \frac{7}{16} - \frac{6}{16}$ — Absolute values of nonzero numbers are always positive.

$= \frac{1}{16}$ — Simplify.

Additional Examples

5 Use a number line to find −1.25 + 1.5. 0.25;

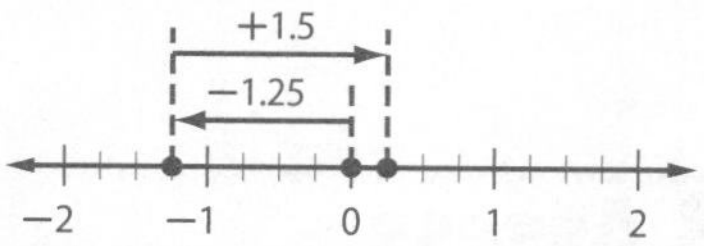

6 Find each sum.

a. −12.6 + (−3.9) −16.5

b. $-\frac{2}{3} + \frac{5}{9}$ $-\frac{1}{9}$

> **WatchOut!**
> **Preventing Errors** Calculation errors are common when adding rational numbers with decimals. Encourage students to align decimals and to annex zeros as placeholders when the decimals have different place values.

connectED.mcgraw-hill.com P15

Additional Example

7 Find $-17.55 - (-24.5)$. 6.95

3 Assess

Formative Assessment

Use Exercises 1–41 to assess whether students understand how to compare and order rational numbers, and add and subtract rational numbers.

Yesterday's News

Ask students to describe how yesterday's lesson on operations with integers helped with today's lesson on adding and subtracting rational numbers.

To subtract a negative rational number, add its inverse.

Example 7 Subtract Decimals

Find $-32.25 - (-42.5)$.

$-32.25 - (-42.5) = -32.25 + 42.5$ — To subtract -42.5, add its inverse.

$= |42.5| - |-32.25|$ — Subtract the absolute values. Because $|42.5|$ is greater than $|-32.25|$, the result is positive.

$= 42.5 - 32.25$ — Absolute values of nonzero numbers are always positive.

$= 10.25$ — Simplify.

Exercises

Replace each ● with <, >, or = to make a true sentence.

1. $-\frac{5}{8} \bullet \frac{3}{8}$ **<**
2. $\frac{4}{5} \bullet 0.71$ **>**
3. $\frac{5}{6} \bullet 0.875$ **<**
4. $1.2 \bullet 1\frac{2}{9}$ **<**
5. $\frac{8}{15} \bullet 0.5\overline{3}$ **=**
6. $-\frac{7}{11} \bullet -\frac{2}{3}$ **>**

Order each set of rational numbers from least to greatest.

7. $3.8, 3.06, 3\frac{1}{6}, 3\frac{3}{4}$ **$3.06, 3\frac{1}{6}, 3\frac{3}{4}, 3.8$**
8. $2\frac{1}{4}, 1\frac{7}{8}, 1.75, 2.4$ **$1.75, 1\frac{7}{8}, 2\frac{1}{4}, 2.4$**
9. $0.11, -\frac{1}{9}, -0.5, \frac{1}{10}$ **$-0.5, -\frac{1}{9}, \frac{1}{10}, 0.11$**
10. $-4\frac{3}{5}, -3\frac{2}{5}, -4.65, -4.09$ **$-4.65, -4\frac{3}{5}, -4.09, -3\frac{2}{5}$**

Find each sum or difference. Write in simplest form.

11. $\frac{2}{5} + \frac{1}{5}$ **$\frac{3}{5}$**
12. $\frac{3}{9} + \frac{4}{9}$ **$\frac{7}{9}$**
13. $\frac{5}{16} - \frac{4}{16}$ **$\frac{1}{16}$**
14. $\frac{6}{7} - \frac{3}{7}$ **$\frac{3}{7}$**
15. $\frac{2}{3} + \frac{1}{3}$ **1**
16. $\frac{5}{8} + \frac{7}{8}$ **$1\frac{1}{2}$**
17. $\frac{4}{3} + \frac{4}{3}$ **$2\frac{2}{3}$**
18. $\frac{7}{15} - \frac{2}{15}$ **$\frac{1}{3}$**
19. $\frac{1}{3} - \frac{2}{9}$ **$\frac{1}{9}$**
20. $\frac{1}{2} + \frac{1}{4}$ **$\frac{3}{4}$**
21. $\frac{1}{2} - \frac{1}{3}$ **$\frac{1}{6}$**
22. $\frac{3}{7} + \frac{5}{14}$ **$\frac{11}{14}$**
23. $\frac{7}{10} - \frac{2}{15}$ **$\frac{17}{30}$**
24. $\frac{3}{8} + \frac{1}{6}$ **$\frac{13}{24}$**
25. $\frac{13}{20} - \frac{2}{5}$ **$\frac{1}{4}$**

Find each sum or difference. Write in simplest form if necessary.

26. $-1.6 + (-3.8)$ **-5.4**
27. $-32.4 + (-4.5)$ **-36.9**
28. $-38.9 + 24.2$ **-14.7**
29. $-9.16 - 10.17$ **-19.33**
30. $26.37 + (-61.1)$ **-34.73**
31. $72.5 - (-81.3)$ **153.8**
32. $43.2 + (-27.9)$ **15.3**
33. $79.3 - (-14)$ **93.3**
34. $1.34 - (-0.458)$ **1.798**
35. $-\frac{1}{6} - \frac{2}{3}$ **$-\frac{5}{6}$**
36. $\frac{1}{2} - \frac{4}{5}$ **$-\frac{3}{10}$**
37. $-\frac{2}{5} + \frac{17}{20}$ **$\frac{9}{20}$**
38. $-\frac{4}{5} + \left(-\frac{1}{3}\right)$ **$-1\frac{2}{15}$**
39. $-\frac{1}{12} - \left(-\frac{3}{4}\right)$ **$\frac{2}{3}$**
40. $-\frac{7}{8} - \left(-\frac{3}{16}\right)$ **$-\frac{11}{16}$**

41. **GEOGRAPHY** About $\frac{7}{10}$ of the surface of Earth is covered by water. The rest of the surface is covered by land. How much of Earth's surface is covered by land? **$\frac{3}{10}$**

LESSON 0-5 Multiplying and Dividing Rational Numbers

Objective

- Multiply and divide rational numbers.

NewVocabulary

multiplicative inverses
reciprocals

The product or quotient of two rational numbers having the *same sign* is positive. The product or quotient of two rational numbers having *different signs* is negative.

Example 1 Multiply and Divide Decimals

Find each product or quotient.

a. 7.2(−0.2)

different signs → negative product

$7.2(-0.2) = -1.44$

b. −23.94 ÷ (−10.5)

same sign → positive quotient

$-23.94 \div (-10.5) = 2.28$

To multiply fractions, multiply the numerators and multiply the denominators. If the numerators and denominators have common factors, you can simplify before you multiply by canceling.

Example 2 Multiply Fractions

Find each product.

a. $\frac{2}{5} \cdot \frac{1}{3}$

$\frac{2}{5} \cdot \frac{1}{3} = \frac{2 \cdot 1}{5 \cdot 3}$ Multiply the numerators. Multiply the denominators.

$= \frac{2}{15}$ Simplify.

b. $\frac{3}{5} \cdot 1\frac{1}{2}$

$\frac{3}{5} \cdot 1\frac{1}{2} = \frac{3}{5} \cdot \frac{3}{2}$ Write $1\frac{1}{2}$ as an improper fraction.

$= \frac{3 \cdot 3}{5 \cdot 2}$ Multiply the numerators. Multiply the denominators.

$= \frac{9}{10}$ Simplify.

c. $\frac{1}{4} \cdot \frac{2}{9}$

$\frac{1}{4} \cdot \frac{2}{9} = \frac{1}{\cancel{4}_2} \cdot \frac{\cancel{2}^1}{9}$ Divide by the GCF, 2.

$= \frac{1 \cdot 1}{2 \cdot 9}$ or $\frac{1}{18}$ Multiply the numerators. Multiply the denominators and simplify.

Example 3 Multiply Fractions with Different Signs

Find $\left(-\frac{3}{4}\right)\left(\frac{3}{8}\right)$.

$\left(-\frac{3}{4}\right)\left(\frac{3}{8}\right) = -\left(\frac{3}{4} \cdot \frac{3}{8}\right)$ different signs → negative product

$= -\left(\frac{3 \cdot 3}{4 \cdot 8}\right)$ or $\frac{9}{32}$ Multiply the numerators. Multiply the denominators and simplify.

1 Focus

VerticalAlignment

Lesson 0-5 Multiply and divide rational numbers.

After Lesson 0-5 Evaluate expressions and solve equations that involve multiplying and dividing rational numbers.

2 Teach

Example 1 shows how to find the product or quotient of decimals with the same signs or different signs. **Example 2** shows how to find the product of fractions. **Example 3** shows how to find the product of fractions with different signs. **Example 4** shows how to find the reciprocal of a number. **Example 5** shows how to divide fractions.

Additional Examples

1 Find each product or quotient.

a. −5.4(0.05) −0.27

b. −6.84 ÷ (−2.4) 2.85

2 Find each product.

a. $\frac{4}{7} \cdot \frac{4}{5}$ $\frac{16}{35}$

b. $\frac{1}{4} \cdot 3\frac{5}{6}$ $\frac{23}{24}$

c. $\frac{3}{8} \cdot \frac{2}{3}$ $\frac{1}{4}$

3 Find $\left(\frac{7}{10}\right)\left(-\frac{2}{3}\right)$. $-\frac{7}{15}$

Teach with Tech

Interactive Whiteboard Find a Web site with an applet that gives an area model of multiplying fractions. Demonstrate the model with several examples and explain how it shows multiplying the numerators and multiplying the denominators.

Additional Examples

4 Name the reciprocal of each number.

a. $\frac{4}{9}$ $\frac{9}{4}$

b. $2\frac{7}{8}$ $\frac{8}{23}$

5 Find each quotient.

a. $\frac{3}{5} \div \frac{1}{4}$ $2\frac{2}{5}$

b. $\frac{3}{10} \div \frac{2}{9}$ $1\frac{7}{20}$

c. $\frac{7}{8} \div 2\frac{1}{3}$ $\frac{3}{8}$

d. $-\frac{2}{3} \div \frac{4}{5}$ $-\frac{5}{6}$

WatchOut!

Preventing Errors Remind students that they must rewrite division by a fraction as multiplication by the reciprocal *before* they can divide by the common factors in the numerators and denominators.

Two numbers whose product is 1 are called **multiplicative inverses** or **reciprocals**.

Example 4 Find the Reciprocal

Name the reciprocal of each number.

a. $\frac{3}{8}$

$\frac{3}{8} \cdot \frac{8}{3} = 1$ The product is 1.

The reciprocal of $\frac{3}{8}$ is $\frac{8}{3}$.

b. $2\frac{4}{5}$

$2\frac{4}{5} = \frac{14}{5}$ Write $2\frac{4}{5}$ as $\frac{14}{5}$.

$\frac{14}{5} \cdot \frac{5}{14} = 1$ The product is 1.

The reciprocal of $2\frac{4}{5}$ is $\frac{5}{14}$.

To divide one fraction by another fraction, multiply the dividend by the reciprocal of the divisor.

Example 5 Divide Fractions

Find each quotient.

a. $\frac{1}{3} \div \frac{1}{2}$

$\frac{1}{3} \div \frac{1}{2} = \frac{1}{3} \cdot \frac{2}{1}$ Multiply $\frac{1}{3}$ by $\frac{2}{1}$, the reciprocal of $\frac{1}{2}$.

$= \frac{2}{3}$ Simplify.

b. $\frac{3}{8} \div \frac{2}{3}$

$\frac{3}{8} \div \frac{2}{3} = \frac{3}{8} \cdot \frac{3}{2}$ Multiply $\frac{3}{8}$ by $\frac{3}{2}$, the reciprocal of $\frac{2}{3}$.

$= \frac{9}{16}$ Simplify.

StudyTip

Use Estimation You can justify your answer by using estimation. $\frac{3}{8}$ is close to $\frac{1}{2}$ and $\frac{2}{3}$ is close to 1. So, the quotient is close to $\frac{1}{2}$ divided by 1 or $\frac{1}{2}$.

c. $\frac{3}{4} \div 2\frac{1}{2}$

$\frac{3}{4} \div 2\frac{1}{2} = \frac{3}{4} \div \frac{5}{2}$ Write $2\frac{1}{2}$ as an improper fraction

$= \frac{3}{4} \cdot \frac{2}{5}$ Multiply $\frac{3}{4}$ by $\frac{2}{5}$, the reciprocal of $2\frac{1}{2}$.

$= \frac{6}{20}$ or $\frac{3}{10}$ Simplify.

d. $-\frac{1}{5} \div \left(-\frac{3}{10}\right)$

$-\frac{1}{5} \div \left(-\frac{3}{10}\right) = -\frac{1}{5} \cdot \left(-\frac{10}{3}\right)$ Multiply $-\frac{1}{5}$ by $-\frac{10}{3}$, the reciprocal of $-\frac{3}{10}$.

$= \frac{10}{15}$ or $\frac{2}{3}$ Same sign ⟶ positive quotient; simplify.

Exercises

Find each product or quotient. Round to the nearest hundredth if necessary.

1. 6.5(0.13) **0.85**
2. −5.8(2.3) **−13.34**
3. 42.3 ÷ (−6) **−7.05**
4. −14.1(−2.9) **40.89**
5. −78 ÷ (−1.3) **60**
6. 108 ÷ (−0.9) **−120**
7. 0.75(−6.4) **−4.8**
8. −23.94 ÷ 10.5 **−2.28**
9. −32.4 ÷ 21.3 **−1.52**

Find each product. Simplify before multiplying if possible.

10. $\frac{3}{4} \cdot \frac{1}{5}$ **$\frac{3}{20}$**
11. $\frac{2}{5} \cdot \frac{3}{7}$ **$\frac{6}{35}$**
12. $-\frac{1}{3} \cdot \frac{2}{5}$ **$-\frac{2}{15}$**
13. $-\frac{2}{3} \cdot \left(-\frac{1}{11}\right)$ **$\frac{2}{33}$**
14. $2\frac{1}{2} \cdot \left(-\frac{1}{4}\right)$ **$-\frac{5}{8}$**
15. $3\frac{1}{2} \cdot 1\frac{1}{2}$ **$\frac{21}{4}$ or $5\frac{1}{4}$**
16. $\frac{2}{9} \cdot \frac{1}{2}$ **$\frac{1}{9}$**
17. $\frac{3}{2} \cdot \left(-\frac{1}{3}\right)$ **$-\frac{1}{2}$**
18. $\frac{1}{3} \cdot \frac{6}{5}$ **$\frac{2}{5}$**
19. $-\frac{9}{4} \cdot \frac{1}{18}$ **$-\frac{1}{8}$**
20. $\frac{11}{3} \cdot \frac{9}{44}$ **$\frac{3}{4}$**
21. $\left(-\frac{30}{11}\right) \cdot \left(-\frac{1}{3}\right)$ **$\frac{10}{11}$**
22. $-\frac{3}{5} \cdot \frac{5}{6}$ **$-\frac{1}{2}$**
23. $\left(-\frac{1}{3}\right)\left(-7\frac{1}{2}\right)$ **$\frac{5}{2}$ or $2\frac{1}{2}$**
24. $\frac{2}{7} \cdot 4\frac{2}{3}$ **$\frac{4}{3}$ or $1\frac{1}{3}$**

Name the reciprocal of each number.

25. $\frac{6}{7}$ **$\frac{7}{6}$ or $1\frac{1}{6}$**
26. $\frac{1}{22}$ **22**
27. $-\frac{14}{23}$ **$-\frac{23}{14}$ or $-1\frac{9}{14}$**
28. $2\frac{3}{4}$ **$\frac{4}{11}$**
29. $-5\frac{1}{3}$ **$-\frac{3}{16}$**
30. $3\frac{3}{4}$ **$\frac{4}{15}$**

Find each quotient.

31. $\frac{2}{3} \div \frac{1}{3}$ **2**
32. $\frac{16}{9} \div \frac{4}{9}$ **4**
33. $\frac{3}{2} \div \frac{1}{2}$ **3**
34. $\frac{3}{7} \div \left(-\frac{1}{5}\right)$ **$-\frac{15}{7}$ or $-2\frac{1}{7}$**
35. $-\frac{9}{10} \div 3$ **$-\frac{3}{10}$**
36. $\frac{1}{2} \div \frac{3}{5}$ **$\frac{5}{6}$**
37. $2\frac{1}{4} \div \frac{1}{2}$ **$\frac{9}{2}$ or $4\frac{1}{2}$**
38. $-1\frac{1}{3} \div \frac{2}{3}$ **−2**
39. $\frac{11}{12} \div 1\frac{2}{3}$ **$\frac{11}{20}$**
40. $4 \div \left(-\frac{2}{7}\right)$ **−14**
41. $-\frac{1}{3} \div \left(-1\frac{1}{5}\right)$ **$\frac{5}{18}$**
42. $\frac{3}{25} \div \frac{2}{15}$ **$\frac{9}{10}$**

43. **PIZZA** A large pizza at Pizza Shack has 12 slices. If Bobby ate $\frac{1}{4}$ of the pizza, how many slices of pizza did he eat? **3 slices**

44. **MUSIC** Samantha practices the flute for $4\frac{1}{2}$ hours each week. How many hours does she practice in a month? **18 hours**

45. **BAND** How many band uniforms can be made with $131\frac{3}{4}$ yards of fabric if each uniform requires $3\frac{7}{8}$ yards? **34 uniforms**

46. **CARPENTRY** How many boards, each 2 feet 8 inches long, can be cut from a board 16 feet long if there is no waste? **6 boards**

47. **SEWING** How many 9-inch ribbons can be cut from $1\frac{1}{2}$ yards of ribbon? **6 ribbons**

3 Assess

Formative Assessment

Use Exercises 1–47 to assess whether students understand how to multiply and divide rational numbers.

Ticket Out the Door

Ask students to write a problem in which the product or quotient of two rational numbers is negative.

Tips for New Teachers

Negative Fractions Remind students that a negative fraction can be written as $-\frac{1}{2}$ or $\frac{-1}{2}$.

1 Focus

VerticalAlignment

Before Lesson 0-6 Use and apply the percent proportion.

Lesson 0-6 Use proportions to solve problems involving percent of change.

2 Teach

Example 1 shows how to express a percent as a fraction. **Example 2** shows how to use the percent proportion to find the part. **Example 3** shows how to use the percent proportion to find the percent in a real-world problem. **Example 4** shows how to use the percent proportion to find the whole.

Additional Examples

1 Express each percent as a fraction.

a. 43% $\frac{43}{100}$

b. 130% $\frac{13}{10}$

c. 0.2% $\frac{1}{500}$

2 24% of 25 is what number? 6

LESSON 0-6 The Percent Proportion

Objective

- Use and apply the percent proportion.

NewVocabulary
percent
percent proportion

A **percent** is a ratio that compares a number to 100. To write a percent as a fraction, express the ratio as a fraction with a denominator of 100. Fractions should be expressed in simplest form.

Example 1 Percents as Fractions

Express each percent as a fraction or mixed number.

a. 79%

$79\% = \frac{79}{100}$ Definition of percent

b. 107%

$107\% = \frac{107}{100}$ Definition of percent

$= 1\frac{7}{100}$ Simplify.

c. 0.5%

$0.5\% = \frac{0.5}{100}$ Definition of percent

$= \frac{5}{1000}$ Multiply the numerator and denominator by 10 to eliminate the decimal.

$= \frac{1}{200}$ Simplify.

In the **percent proportion**, the ratio of a part of something to the whole (base) is equal to the percent written as a fraction.

part → $\frac{a}{b} = \frac{p}{100}$ ← percent
whole →

Example: 25% (percent) of 40 (whole) is 10 (part).

You can use the percent proportion to find the part.

Example 2 Find the Part

40% of 30 is what number?

$\frac{a}{b} = \frac{p}{100}$ The percent is 40, and the base is 30. Let *a* represent the part.

$\frac{a}{30} = \frac{40}{100}$ Replace *b* with 30 and *p* with 40.

$100a = 30(40)$ Find the cross products.

$100a = 1200$ Simplify.

$\frac{100a}{100} = \frac{1200}{100}$ Divide each side by 100.

$a = 12$ Simplify.

The part is 12. So, 40% of 30 is 12.

P20 | Lesson 0-6

Teach with Tech

Interactive Whiteboard Create a template that you can use to show the percent proportion, such as $\frac{\square}{\square} = \frac{\square}{100}$. Write an example of a percent application. Have students select the values to be entered in each square of the template.

You can also use the percent proportion to find the percent of the base.

Example 3 Find the Percent

SURVEYS Kelsey took a survey of students in her lunch period. 42 out of the 70 students Kelsey surveyed said their family had a pet. What percent of the students had pets?

$\frac{a}{b} = \frac{p}{100}$ The part is 42, and the base is 70. Let p represent the percent.

$\frac{42}{70} = \frac{p}{100}$ Replace a with 42 and b with 70.

$4200 = 70p$ Find the cross products.

$\frac{4200}{70} = \frac{70p}{70}$ Divide each side by 70.

$60 = p$ Simplify.

The percent is 60, so $\frac{60}{100}$ or 60% of the students had pets.

StudyTip

Percent Proportion In percent problems, the whole, or base usually follows the word *of*.

Example 4 Find the Whole

67.5 is 75% of what number?

$\frac{a}{b} = \frac{p}{100}$ The percent is 75, and the part is 67.5. Let b represent the base.

$\frac{67.5}{b} = \frac{75}{100}$ Replace a with 67.5 and p with 75.

$6750 = 75b$ Find the cross products.

$\frac{6750}{75} = \frac{75b}{75}$ Divide each side by 75.

$90 = b$ Simplify.

The base is 90, so 67.5 is 75% of 90.

Exercises

Express each percent as a fraction or mixed number in simplest form.

1. 5% $\frac{1}{20}$
2. 60% $\frac{3}{5}$
3. 11% $\frac{11}{100}$
4. 120% $1\frac{1}{5}$
5. 78% $\frac{39}{50}$
6. 2.5% $\frac{1}{40}$
7. 0.6% $\frac{3}{500}$
8. 0.4% $\frac{1}{250}$
9. 1400% **14**

Use the percent proportion to find each number.

10. 25 is what percent of 125? **20%**
11. 16 is what percent of 40? **40%**
12. 14 is 20% of what number? **70**
13. 50% of what number is 80? **160**
14. What number is 25% of 18? **4.5**
15. Find 10% of 95. **9.5**
16. What percent of 48 is 30? **62.5%**
17. What number is 150% of 32? **48**
18. 5% of what number is 3.5? **70**
19. 1 is what percent of 400? **0.25%**
20. Find 0.5% of 250. **1.25**
21. 49 is 200% of what number? **24.5**
22. 15 is what percent of 12? **125%**
23. 36 is what percent of 24? **150%**

Additional Examples

3 **PARTY FAVORS** In a bag of party favors, 39 out of 60 are whistles. What percent of the party favors are whistles? 65%

4 38.25 is 45% of what number? 85

Tips for New Teachers

Reasoning Encourage students to check that their answers are reasonable. For example, have them identify the part and the whole in each problem. Then have them reason: If the percent is less than 100%, the part should be less than the whole; if the percent is greater than 100%, the part should be greater than the whole.

3 Assess

Formative Assessment

Use Exercises 1–31 to assess whether students understand how to use the percent proportion to solve problems involving percents.

Name the Math

Ask students to explain how they would use the percent proportion to find what percent of 40 is 14.

Tips for New Teachers

Word Problems Remind students that they should work backward when a problem starts with the result and asks for something that happened earlier.

24. BASKETBALL Madeline usually makes 85% of her shots in basketball. If she attempts 20, how many will she likely make? **17 shots**

25. TEST SCORES Brian answered 36 items correctly on a 40-item test. What percent did he answer correctly? **90%**

26. CARD GAMES Juanita told her dad that she won 80% of the card games she played yesterday. If she won 4 games, how many games did she play? **5 games**

27. SOLUTIONS A glucose solution is prepared by dissolving 6 milliliters of glucose in 120 milliliters of pure solution. What is the percent of glucose in the resulting solution? **5%**

28. DRIVER'S ED Kara needs to get a 75% on her driving education test in order to get her license. If there are 35 questions on the test, how many does she need to answer correctly? **27 questions**

29. HEALTH The U.S. Food and Drug Administration requires food manufacturers to label their products with a nutritional label. The label shows the information from a package of macaroni and cheese.

a. The label states that a serving contains 3 grams of saturated fat, which is 15% of the daily value recommended for a 2000-Calorie diet. How many grams of saturated fat are recommended for a 2000-Calorie diet? **20 g**

b. The 470 milligrams of sodium (salt) in the macaroni and cheese is 20% of the recommended daily value. What is the recommended daily value of sodium? **2350 mg**

c. For a healthy diet, the National Research Council recommends that no more than 30 percent of the total Calories come from fat. What percent of the Calories in a serving of this macaroni and cheese come from fat? **44%**

Nutrition Facts

Serving Size 1 cup (228g)
Servings per container 2

Amount per serving	
Calories 250	Calories from Fat 110
	%Daily value*
Total Fat 12g	18%
Saturated Fat 3g	15%
Cholesterol 30mg	10%
Sodium 470mg	20%
Total Carbohydrate 31g	10%
Dietary Fiber 0g	0%
Sugars 5g	
Protein 5g	
Vitamin A 4% • Vitamin C 2%	
Calcium 20% • Iron 4%	

30. TEST SCORES The table shows the number of points each student in Will's study group earned on a recent math test. There were 88 points possible on the test. Express all answers to the nearest tenth of a percent.

Name	Will	Penny	Cheng	Minowa	Rob
Score	72	68	81	87	75

a. Find Will's percent correct on the test. **81.8%**

b. Find Cheng's percent correct on the test. **92.0%**

c. Find Rob's percent correct on the test. **85.2%**

d. What was the highest percentage? The lowest? **Minowa 98.9%; Penny 77.3%**

31. PET STORE In a pet store, 15% of the animals are hamsters. If the store has 40 animals, how many of them are hamsters? **6 animals**

P22 | Lesson 0-6 | The Percent Proportion

LESSON 0-7 Perimeter

Objective

- Find the perimeter of two-dimensional figures.

NewVocabulary
perimeter
circle
diameter
circumference
center
radius

Perimeter is the distance around a figure. Perimeter is measured in linear units.

Rectangle

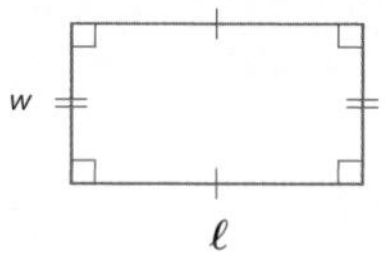

$P = 2(\ell + w)$ or
$P = 2\ell + 2w$

Parallelogram

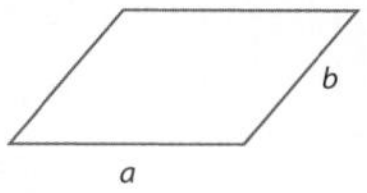

$P = 2(a + b)$ or
$P = 2a + 2b$

Square

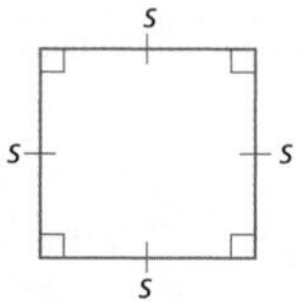

$P = 4s$

Triangle

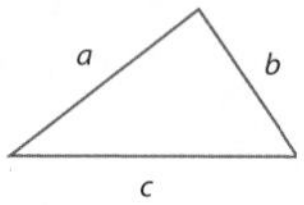

$P = a + b + c$

Example 1 Perimeters of Rectangles and Squares

Find the perimeter of each figure.

a. a rectangle with a length of 5 inches and a width of 1 inch

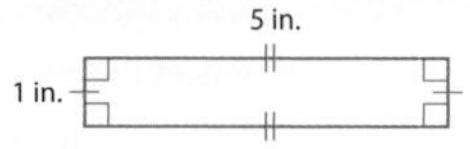

$P = 2(\ell + w)$ Perimeter formula
$= 2(5 + 1)$ $\ell = 5, w = 1$
$= 2(6)$ Add.
$= 12$ The perimeter is 12 inches.

b. a square with a side length of 7 centimeters

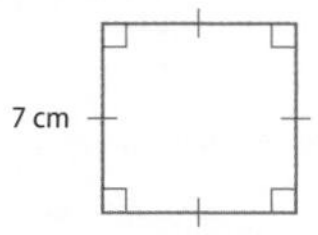

$P = 4s$ Perimeter formula
$= 4(7)$ Replace s with 7.
$= 28$ The perimeter is 28 centimeters.

1 Focus

VerticalAlignment

Lesson 0-7 Find the perimeter of two-dimensional figures.

After Lesson 0-7 Represent and find perimeter using polynomials.

2 Teach

Example 1 shows how to find the perimeter of a rectangle and a square. **Example 2** shows how to find the perimeter of a parallelogram and a triangle. **Example 3** shows how to find the circumference of a circle.

Additional Example

1 Find the perimeter of each figure.

a. a rectangle with a width of 3 feet and a length of 13 feet

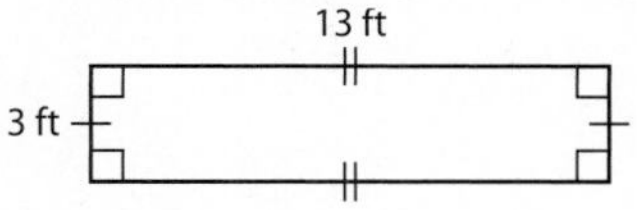

32 feet

b. a square with a side length of 11 millimeters

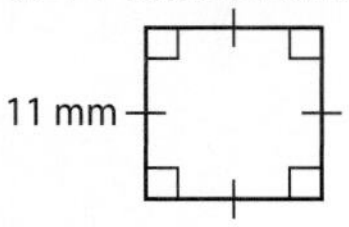

44 millimeters

Teach with Tech

Blog On your secure classroom blog, have students create a blog entry to list and describe real-world applications of perimeter.

Additional Examples

2 Find the perimeter of each figure.

a.

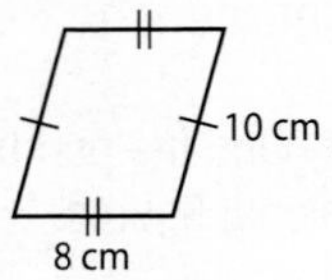

36 centimeters

b.

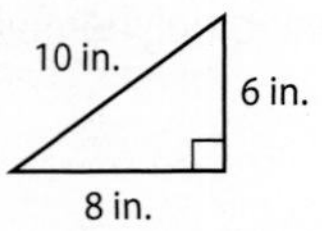

24 inches

3 Find the circumference of each circle to the nearest tenth.

a. The radius is 9 inches. about 56.5 inches

b. The diameter is 12 millimeters. about 37.7 millimeters

c.

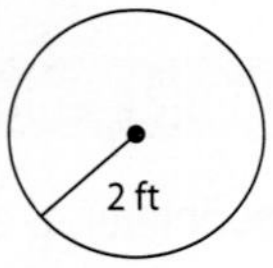

about 12.6 ft

StudyTip

Congruent Marks The hash marks on the figures indicate sides that have the same length.

Example 2 Perimeters of Parallelograms and Triangles

Find the perimeter of each figure.

a.

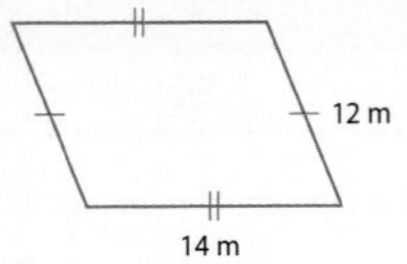

$P = 2(a + b)$ Perimeter formula

$= 2(14 + 12)$ $a = 14, b = 12$

$= 2(26)$ Add.

$= 52$ Multiply.

The perimeter of the parallelogram is 52 meters.

b.

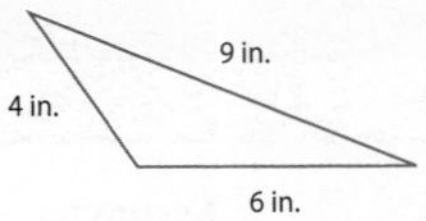

$P = a + b + c$ Perimeter formula

$= 4 + 6 + 9$ $a = 4, b = 6, c = 9$

$= 19$ Add.

The perimeter of the triangle is 19 inches.

A **circle** is the set of all points in a plane that are the same distance from a given point.

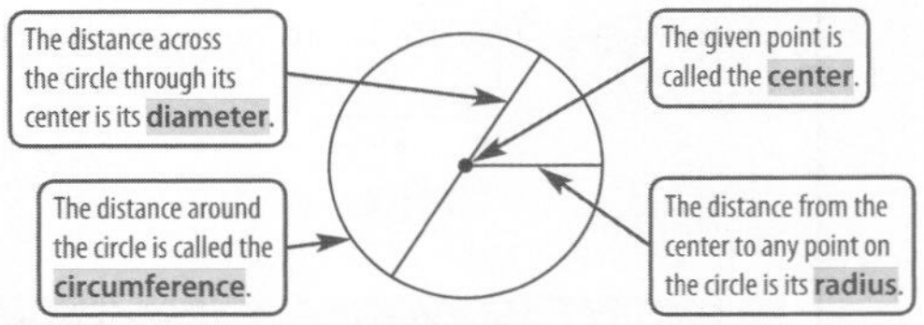

The formula for the circumference of a circle is $C = \pi d$ or $C = 2\pi r$.

StudyTip

Pi To perform a calculation that involves π, use a calculator.

Example 3 Circumference

Find each circumference to the nearest tenth.

a. The radius is 4 feet.

$C = 2\pi r$ Circumference formula

$= 2\pi(4)$ Replace r with 4.

$= 8\pi$ Simplify.

The exact circumference is 8π feet.

8 [π] [ENTER] **25.13274123**

The circumference is about 25.1 feet.

b. The diameter is 15 centimeters.

$C = \pi d$ Circumference formula

$= \pi(15)$ Replace d with 15.

$= 15\pi$ Simplify.

≈ 47.1 Use a calculator to evaluate 15π.

The circumference is about 47.1 centimeters.

c.

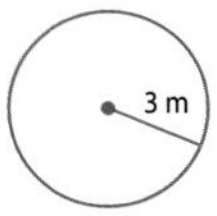

$C = 2\pi r$ Circumference formula

$= 2\pi(3)$ Replace r with 3.

$= 6\pi$ Simplify.

≈ 18.8 Use a calculator to evaluate 6π.

The circumference is about 18.8 meters.

Exercises

Find the perimeter of each figure.

1. 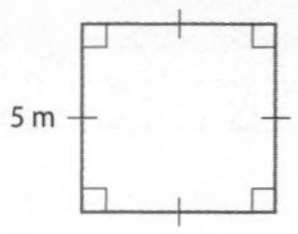

20 m

2. 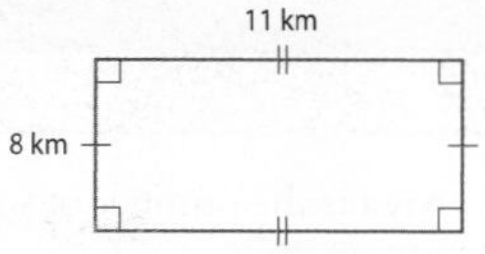

38 km

3. 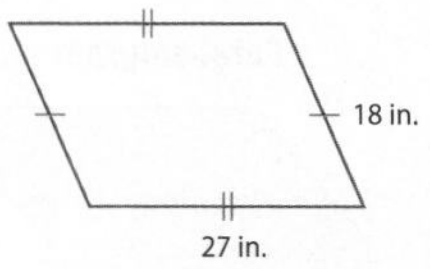

90 in.

4. 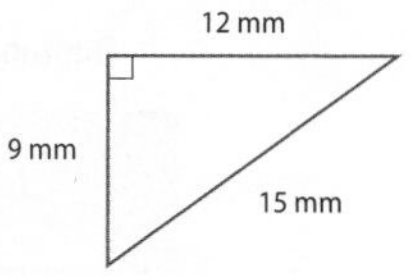

36 mm

5. a square with side length 8 inches **32 in.**

6. a rectangle with length 9 centimeters and width 3 centimeters **24 cm**

7. a triangle with sides 4 feet, 13 feet, and 12 feet **29 ft**

8. a parallelogram with side lengths $6\frac{1}{4}$ inches and 5 inches **$22\frac{1}{2}$ in.**

9. a quarter-circle with a radius of 7 inches **25.0 in.**

Find the circumference of each circle. Round to the nearest tenth.

10. 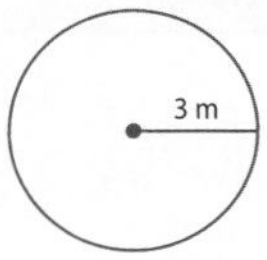

18.8 m

11. 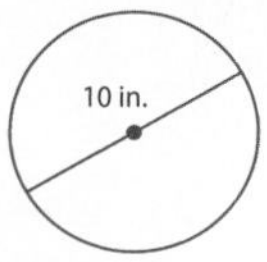

31.4 in.

12. 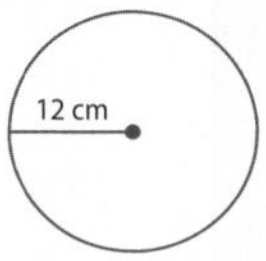

75.4 cm

13. GARDENS A square garden has a side length of 5.8 meters. What is the perimeter of the garden? **23.2 m**

14. ROOMS A rectangular room is $12\frac{1}{2}$ feet wide and 14 feet long. What is the perimeter of the room? **53 ft**

15. CYCLING The tire for a 10-speed bicycle has a diameter of 27 inches. Find the distance traveled in 10 rotations of the tire. Round to the nearest tenth. **848.2 in.**

16. GEOGRAPHY Earth's circumference is approximately 25,000 miles. If you could dig a tunnel to the center of the Earth, how long would the tunnel be? Round to the nearest tenth mile. **3978.9 mi**

Find the perimeter of each figure. Round to the nearest tenth.

17. 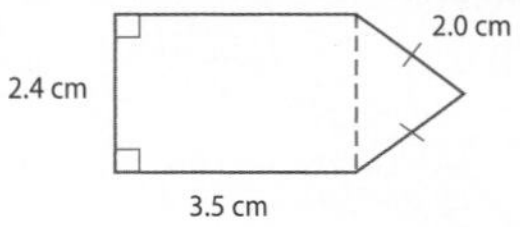

13.4 cm

18. 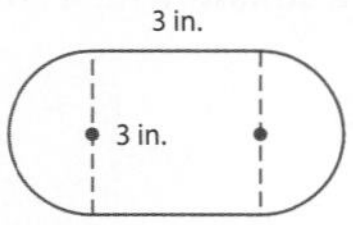

15.4 in.

19. 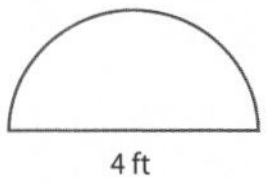

10.3 ft

20. 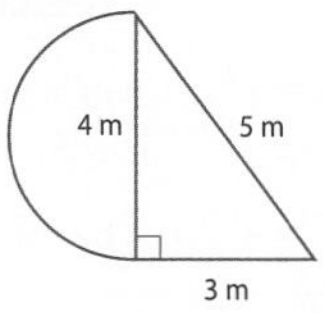

14.3 m

WatchOut!

Student Misconceptions Radius and diameter are often confused when using the formulas for circumference. Remind students to check that they used radius and diameter appropriately.

3 Assess

Formative Assessment

Use Exercises 1–20 to assess whether students understand how to find perimeter and circumference.

Ticket Out the Door

Ask students to write a sentence that compares finding the perimeter of a square to finding the circumference of a circle.

connectED.mcgraw-hill.com P25

1 Focus

VerticalAlignment

Before Lesson 0-8 Find the area of two-dimensional figures.

Lesson 0-8 Represent and find area using polynomials.

2 Teach

Example 1 shows how to find the area of a rectangle and a square. **Example 2** shows how to find the area of a parallelogram and a triangle. **Example 3** shows how to find the area of a circle when given the radius or diameter. **Example 4** shows how to estimate the area of an irregular figure.

Additional Example

1 Find the area of each figure.

a. a rectangle that has a length of 14 inches and a width of 5 inches

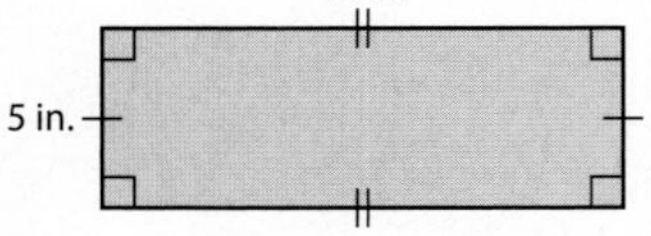

70 square inches

b. a square that has a side length of 6 meters

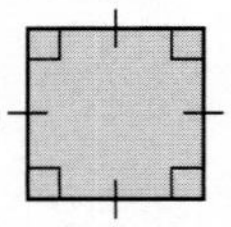

36 square meters

LESSON 0-8 Area

Objective

- Find the area of two-dimensional figures.

NewVocabulary

area

Area is the number of square units needed to cover a surface. Area is measured in square units.

Rectangle

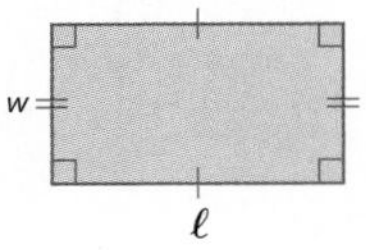

$A = \ell w$

Parallelogram

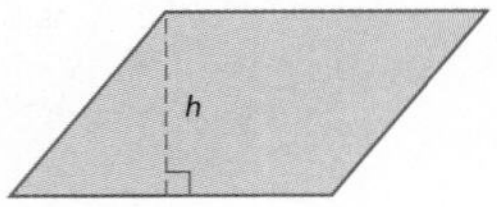

$A = bh$

Square

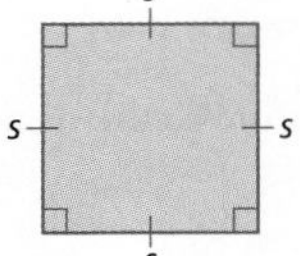

$A = s^2$

Triangle

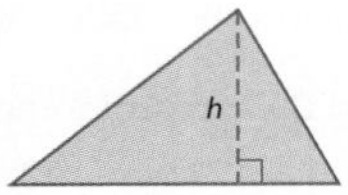

$A = \frac{1}{2}bh$

Example 1 Areas of Rectangles and Squares

Find the area of each figure.

a. a rectangle with a length of 7 yards and a width of 1 yard

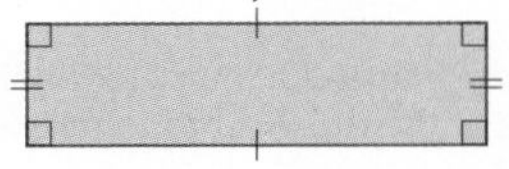

$A = \ell w$ Area formula

$= 7(1)$ $\ell = 7, w = 1$

$= 7$ The area of the rectangle is 7 square yards.

b. a square with a side length of 2 meters

$A = s^2$ Area formula

$= 2^2$ $s = 2$

$= 4$ The area is 4 square meters.

Teach with Tech

Interactive Whiteboard Display a parallelogram on the board and an altitude. Trace over the triangle formed by the altitude, one side of the parallelogram, and a portion of the base. Then trace over the quadrilateral formed by the altitude, the remaining portion of the base, and the other two sides. Drag the triangle and the quadrilateral to show students that the pieces form a rectangle. Thus, area of the parallelogram is the same as the area of the rectangle with the same base and height.

Example 2 Areas of Parallelograms and Triangles

Find the area of each figure.

a. **a parallelogram with a base of 11 feet and a height of 9 feet**

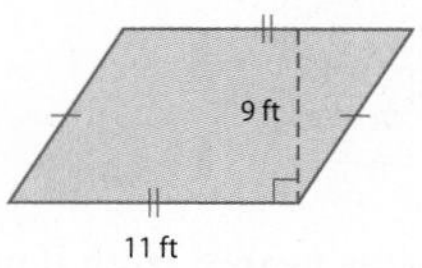

$A = bh$ — Area formula

$= 11(9)$ — $b = 11, h = 9$

$= 99$ — Multiply.

The area is 99 square feet.

b. **a triangle with a base of 12 millimeters and a height of 5 millimeters**

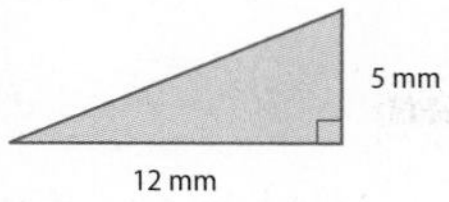

$A = \frac{1}{2}bh$ — Area formula

$= \frac{1}{2}(12)(5)$ — $b = 12, h = 5$

$= 30$ — Multiply.

The area is 30 square millimeters.

The formula for the area of a circle is $A = \pi r^2$.

Example 3 Areas of Circles

Find the area of each circle to the nearest tenth.

a. **a radius of 3 centimeters**

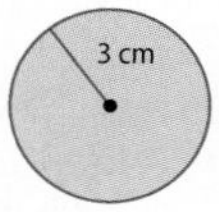

$A = \pi r^2$ — Area formula

$= \pi(3)^2$ — Replace r with 3.

$= 9\pi$ — Simplify.

≈ 28.3 — Use a calculator to evaluate 9π.

The area is about 28.3 square centimeters.

b. **a diameter of 21 meters**

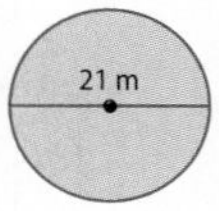

$A = \pi r^2$ — Area formula

$= \pi(10.5)^2$ — Replace r with 10.5.

$= 110.25\pi$ — Simplify.

≈ 346.4 — Use a calculator to evaluate 110.25π.

The area is about 346.4 square meters.

StudyTip

Mental Math You can use mental math to check your solutions. Square the radius and then multiply by 3.

Example 4 Estimate Area

Estimate the area of the polygon if each square represents 1 square mile.

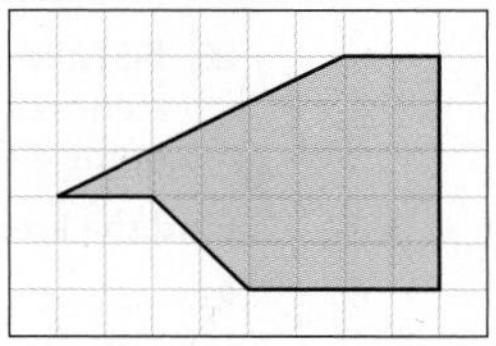

One way to estimate the area is to count each square as one unit and each partial square as a half unit, no matter how large or small.

$A \approx$ squares + partial squares

$\approx 21(1) + 8(0.5)$ — 21 whole squares and 8 partial squares

$\approx 21 + 4$ or 25

The area of the polygon is about 25 square miles.

Additional Examples

2 Find the area of each figure.

a. a parallelogram with a base of 9 yards and a height of 7 yards

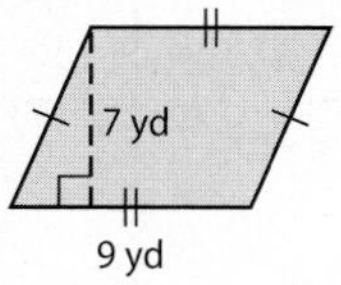

63 square yards

b. a triangle with a base of 13 centimeters and a height of 8 centimeters

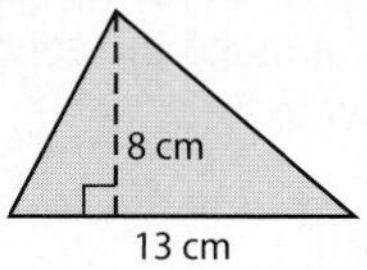

52 square centimeters

3 Find the area of each circle to the nearest tenth.

a. a radius of 4 kilometers.

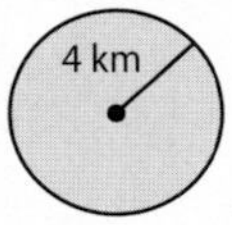

about 50.3 square kilometers

b. a diameter of 15 feet.

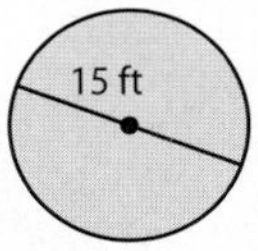

about 176.7 square feet

4 Estimate the area of the polygon if each square represents 1 square mile. 46

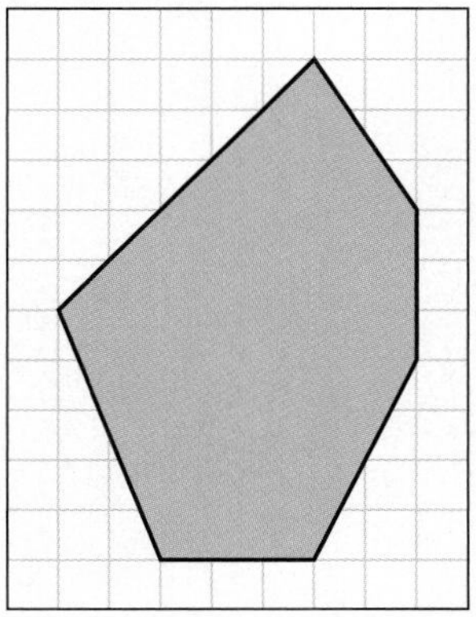

WatchOut!

Preventing Errors For Exercise 17, remind students that the inverse of squaring a number is taking the square root of the number.

3 Assess

Formative Assessment

Use Exercises 1–23 to assess whether students understand the concept of area and how to find it.

Crystal Ball

Ask students to write how they think today's lesson on area will relate to a future lesson on surface area.

Exercises

Find the area of each figure.

1. 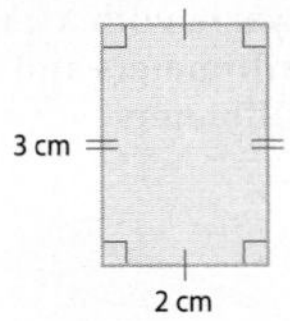

6 cm^2

2. 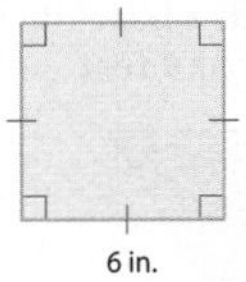

36 in^2

3. 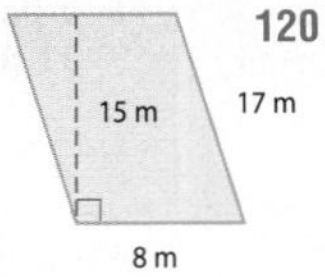

120 m^2

Find the area of each figure. Round to the nearest tenth if necessary.

4. a triangle with a base 12 millimeters and height 11 millimeters 66 mm^2
5. a square with side length 9 feet 81 ft^2
6. a rectangle with length 8 centimeters and width 2 centimeters 16 cm^2
7. a triangle with a base 6 feet and height 3 feet 9 ft^2
8. a quarter-circle with a diameter of 4 meters 3.1 m^2
9. a semi-circle with a radius of 3 inches 14.1 in^2

Find the area of each circle. Round to the nearest tenth.

10. 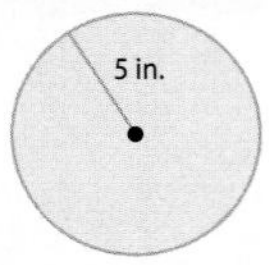

78.5 in^2

11. 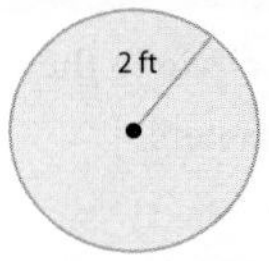

12.6 ft^2

12. 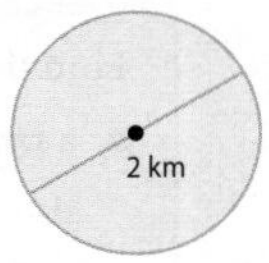

3.1 km^2

13. The radius is 4 centimeters. 50.3 cm^2
14. The radius is 7.2 millimeters. 162.9 mm^2
15. The diameter is 16 inches. 201.1 in^2
16. The diameter is 25 feet. 490.9 ft^2
17. **CAMPING** The square floor of a tent has an area of 49 square feet. What is the side length of the tent? 7 ft

Estimate the area of each polygon in square units.

18. 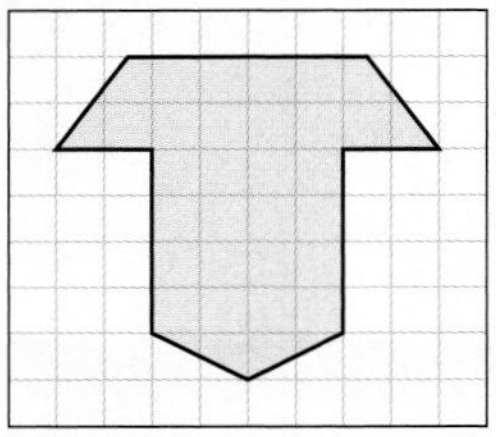
Sample answer: 31 units²

19. 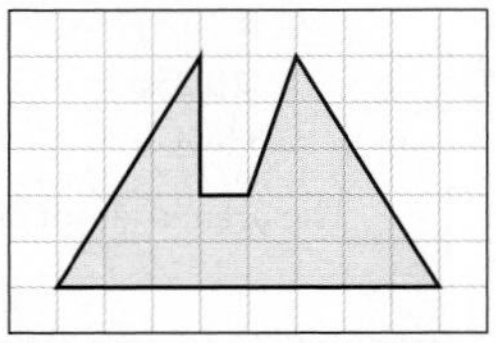
Sample answer: 20.5 units²

20. **HISTORY** Stonehenge is an ancient monument in Wiltshire, England. The giant stones of Stonehenge are arranged in a circle 30 meters in diameter. Find the area of the circle. Round to the nearest tenth square meter. 706.9 m^2

Find the area of each figure. Round to the nearest tenth.

21. 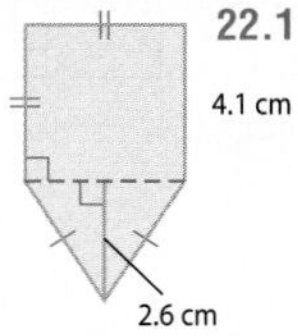

22.1 cm^2

22. 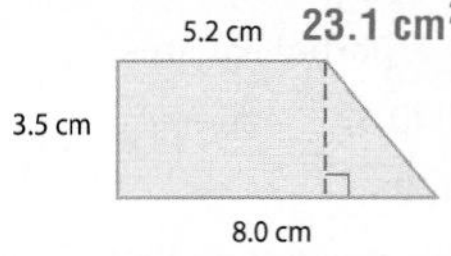

23.1 cm^2

23. 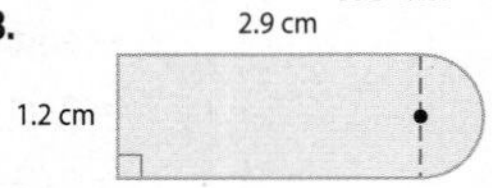

4.0 cm^2

P28 | Lesson 0-8 | Area

LESSON 0-9 Volume

Objective

- Find the volumes of rectangular prisms and cylinders.

NewVocabulary

volume

Volume is the measure of space occupied by a solid. Volume is measured in cubic units.

To find the volume of a rectangular prism, multiply the length times the width times the height. The formula for the volume of a rectangular prism is shown below.

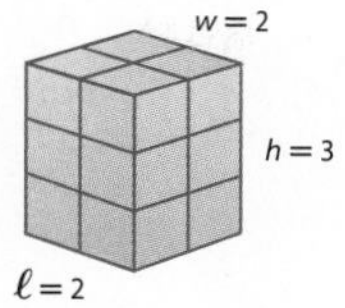

$$V = \ell \cdot w \cdot h$$

The prism at the right has a volume of $2 \cdot 2 \cdot 3$ or 12 cubic units.

Example 1 Volumes of Rectangular Prisms

Find the volume of each rectangular prism.

a. The length is 8 centimeters, the width is 1 centimeter, and the height is 5 centimeters.

$V = \ell \cdot w \cdot h$ — Volume formula
$= 8 \cdot 1 \cdot 5$ — Replace ℓ with 8, w with 1, and h with 5.
$= 40$ — Simplify.

The volume is 40 cubic centimeters.

b.

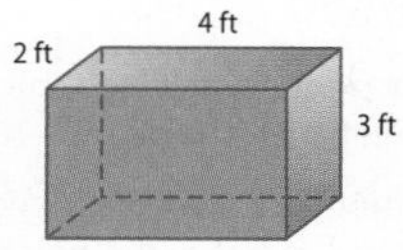

The prism has a length of 4 feet, width of 2 feet, and height of 3 feet.

$V = \ell \cdot w \cdot h$ — Volume formula
$= 4 \cdot 2 \cdot 3$ — Replace ℓ with 4, w with 2, and h with 3.
$= 24$ — Simplify.

The volume is 24 cubic feet.

The volume of a solid is the product of the area of the base and the height of the solid. For a cylinder, the area of the base is πr^2. So the volume is $V = \pi r^2 h$.

Example 2 Volume of a Cylinder

Find the volume of the cylinder.

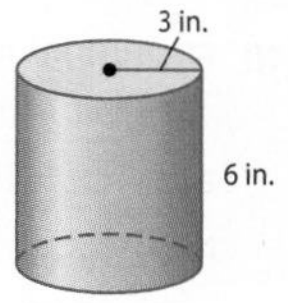

$V = \pi r^2 h$ — Volume of a cylinder
$= \pi(3^2)6$ — $r = 3, h = 6$
$= 54\pi$ — Simplify.
≈ 169.6 — Use a calculator.

The volume is about 169.6 cubic inches.

1 Focus

VerticalAlignment

Lesson 0-9 Find the volumes of rectangular prisms and cylinders.

After Lesson 0-9 Represent and find volume using polynomials.

2 Teach

Example 1 shows how to find the volume of a rectangular prism. **Example 2** shows how to find the volume of a cylinder.

Additional Examples

1 Find the volume of each rectangular prism.

a. The length is 12 meters, the width is 9 meters, and the height is 4 meters. 432 cubic meters

b.

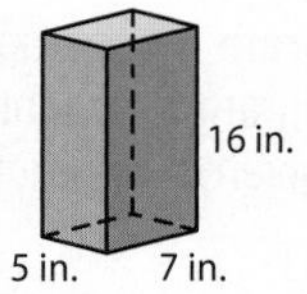

560 cubic inches

2 Find the volume of the cylinder.

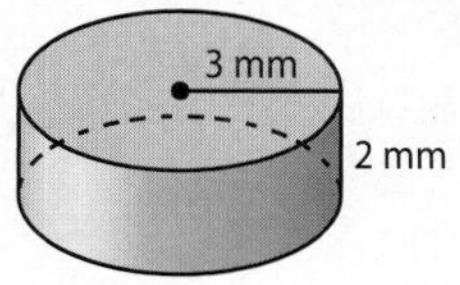

about 56.5 cubic millimeters

Teach with Tech

Web Page Add information about volumes of three-dimensional figures to your class Web page.

WatchOut!

Common Error Students may use square units rather than cubic units for volume. Remind them that they multiply three dimensions in a rectangular prism, and the square of the radius times height in a cylinder, so the result for both is cubic units.

3 Assess

Formative Assessment

Use Exercises 1–19 to assess whether students understand volume and how to find the volume of rectangular prisms and cylinders.

Name the Math

Ask students to explain the procedure for finding the volume of a rectangular prism or a cylinder.

Tips for New Teachers

Draw a Diagram Encourage students to draw a diagram to organize the information given in the problem.

Exercises

Find the volume of each rectangular prism given the length, width, and height.

1. $\ell = 5$ cm, $w = 3$ cm, $h = 2$ cm **30 cm³**
2. $\ell = 10$ m, $w = 10$ m, $h = 1$ m **100 m³**
3. $\ell = 6$ yd, $w = 2$ yd, $h = 4$ yd **48 yd³**
4. $\ell = 2$ in., $w = 5$ in., $h = 12$ in. **120 in³**
5. $\ell = 13$ ft, $w = 9$ ft, $h = 12$ ft **1404 ft³**
6. $\ell = 7.8$ mm, $w = 0.6$ mm, $h = 8$ mm **37.44 mm³**

Find the volume of each rectangular prism.

7. **20 m³**

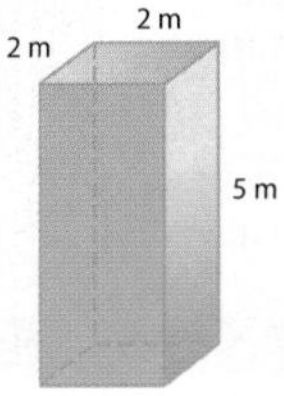

8. **144 in³**

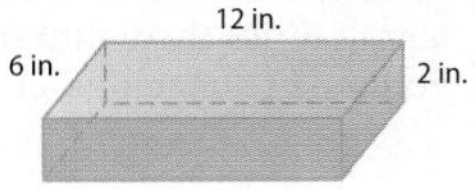

9. **GEOMETRY** A cube measures 3 meters on a side. What is its volume? **27 m³**
10. **AQUARIUMS** An aquarium is 8 feet long, 5 feet wide, and 5.5 feet deep. What is the volume of the aquarium? **220 ft³**
11. **COOKING** What is the volume of a microwave oven that is 18 inches wide by 10 inches long with a depth of $11\frac{1}{2}$ inches? **2070 in³**
12. **BOXES** A cardboard box is 32 inches long, 22 inches wide, and 16 inches tall. What is the volume of the box? **11,264 in³**
13. **SWIMMING POOLS** A children's rectangular pool holds 480 cubic feet of water. What is the depth of the pool if its length is 30 feet and its width is 16 feet? **1 ft**
14. **BAKING** A rectangular cake pan has a volume of 234 cubic inches. If the length of the pan is 9 inches and the width is 13 inches, what is the height of the pan? **2 in.**
15. **GEOMETRY** The volume of the rectangular prism at the right is 440 cubic centimeters. What is the width? **4 cm**

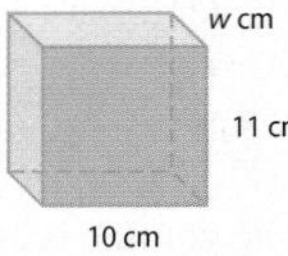

Find the volume of each cylinder. Round to the nearest tenth.

16.

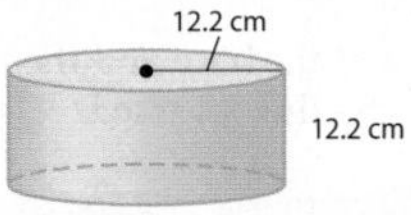

5704.7 cm³

17. **2770.9 in³**

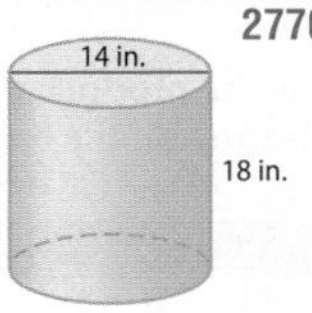

18.

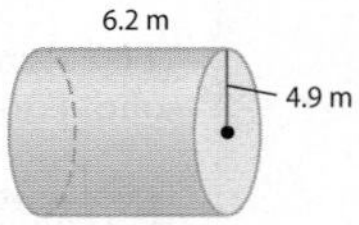

467.7 m³

19. **FIREWOOD** Firewood is usually sold by a measure known as a *cord*. A full cord may be a stack 8 × 4 × 4 feet or a stack 8 × 8 × 2 feet.
   a. What is the volume of a full cord of firewood? **128 ft³**
   b. A "short cord" of wood is 8 × 4 × the length of the logs. What is the volume of a short cord of $2\frac{1}{2}$-foot logs? **80 ft³**
   c. If you have an area that is 12 feet long and 2 feet wide in which to store your firewood, how high will the stack be if it is a full cord of wood? **5 ft 4 in.**

LESSON 0-10 Surface Area

Objective

- Find the surface areas of rectangular prisms and cylinders.

NewVocabulary

surface area

Surface area is the sum of the areas of all the surfaces, or faces, of a solid. Surface area is measured in square units.

KeyConcept Surface Area

Prism

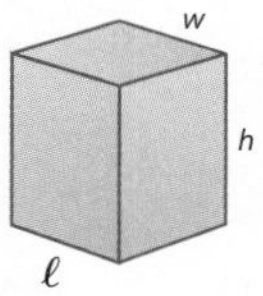

$S = 2\ell w + 2\ell h + 2wh$

Cylinder

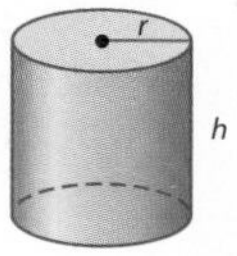

$S = 2\pi rh + 2\pi r^2$

Example 1 Find Surface Areas

Find the surface area of each solid. Round to the nearest tenth if necessary.

a.

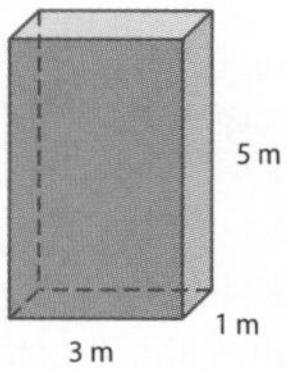

The prism has a length of 3 meters, width of 1 meter, and height of 5 meters.

$S = 2\ell w + 2\ell h + 2wh$	Surface area formula
$= 2(3)(1) + 2(3)(5) + 2(1)(5)$	$\ell = 3$, $w = 1$, $h = 5$
$= 6 + 30 + 10$	Multiply.
$= 46$	Add.

The surface area is 46 square meters.

b.

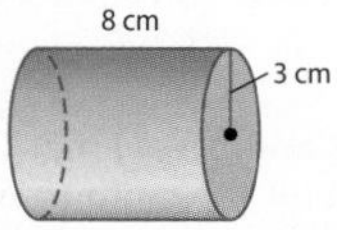

The height is 8 centimeters and the radius of the base is 3 centimeters. The surface area is the sum of the area of each base, $2\pi r^2$, and the area of the side, given by the circumference of the base times the height or $2\pi rh$.

$S = 2\pi rh + 2\pi r^2$	Formula for surface area of a cylinder.
$= 2\pi(3)(8) + 2\pi(3^2)$	$r = 3$, $h = 8$
$= 48\pi + 18\pi$	Simplify.
$\approx 207.3 \text{ cm}^2$	Use a calculator.

1 Focus

VerticalAlignment

Lesson 0-10 Find the surface areas of rectangular prisms and cylinders.

After Lesson 0-10 Represent and find surface areas using polynomials.

2 Teach

Example 1 shows how to use a formula to find the surface area of a rectangular prism and a cylinder.

Additional Example

1 Find the surface area of each solid. Round to the nearest tenth if necessary.

a.

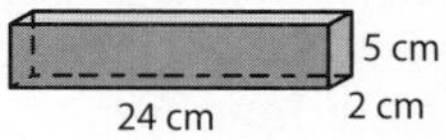

356 square centimeters

b.

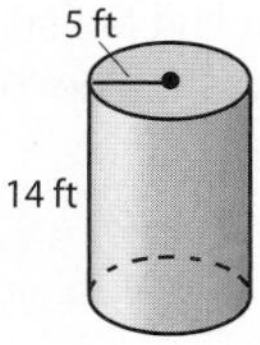

about 596.9 square feet

Teach with Tech

Video Recording Separate students into 4 groups. Have each group record themselves teaching how to find the surface area of a prism or a cylinder. Share the videos with the entire class.

WatchOut!

Preventing Errors It is easy for some students to overlook sides when finding the surface area of a rectangular prism. Suggest that they systematically list the sides of the prism to avoid this error.

3 Assess

Formative Assessment

Use Exercises 1–18 to assess whether students understand and can find the surface area of rectangular prisms and cylinders.

Yesterday's News

Have students explain how the lesson on the area of two-dimensional figures helped them with today's lesson on the surface area of rectangular prisms.

Tips for New Teachers

Alternate Method Point out that another way to find the surface area of a solid is to draw the net of the solid on grid paper.

Exercises

Find the surface area of each rectangular prism given the measurements below.

1. $\ell = 6$ in., $w = 1$ in., $h = 4$ in **68 in²**
2. $\ell = 8$ m, $w = 2$ m, $h = 2$ m **72 m²**
3. $\ell = 10$ mm, $w = 4$ mm, $h = 5$ mm **220 mm²**
4. $\ell = 6.2$ cm, $w = 1$ cm, $h = 3$ cm **55.6 cm²**
5. $\ell = 7$ ft, $w = 2$ ft, $h = \frac{1}{2}$ ft **37 ft²**
6. $\ell = 7.8$ m, $w = 3.4$ m, $h = 9$ m **254.64 m²**

Find the surface area of each solid.

7. **48 m²**

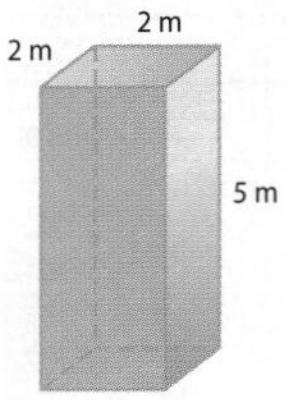

8. **52 ft²**

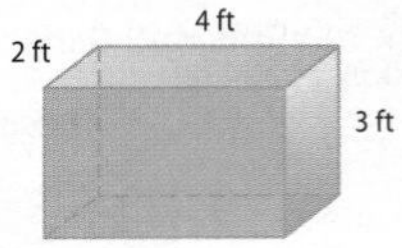

9. **216 in²**

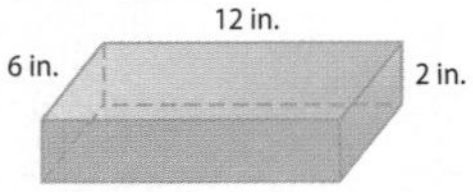

10. **111.2 mm²**

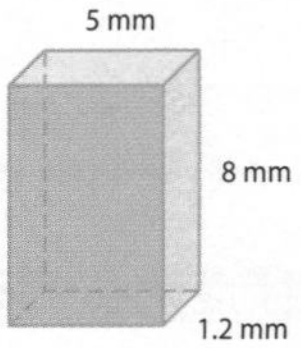

11. **480.7 in²**

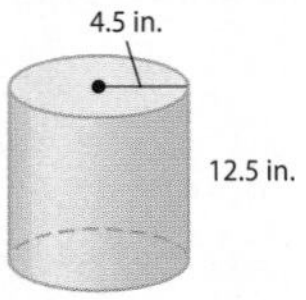

12. **362.1 cm²**

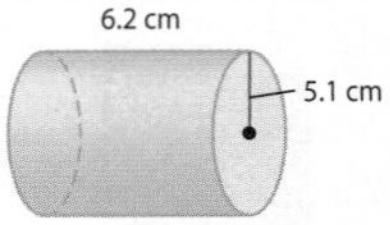

13. **GEOMETRY** What is the surface area of a cube with a side length of 2 meters? **24 m²**

14. **GIFTS** A gift box is a rectangular prism 14 inches long, 5 inches wide, and 4 inches high. If the box is to be covered in fabric, how much fabric is needed if there is no overlap? **292 in²**

15. **BOXES** A new refrigerator is shipped in a box 34 inches deep, 66 inches high, and $33\frac{1}{4}$ inches wide. What is the surface area of the box in square feet? Round to the nearest square foot. (*Hint:* 1 ft² = 144 in²) **77 ft²**

16. **PAINTING** A cabinet is 6 feet high, 3 feet wide, and 2 feet long. The entire outside surface of the cabinet is being painted except for the bottom. What is the surface area of the cabinet that is being painted? **66 ft²**

17. **SOUP** A soup can is 4 inches tall and has a diameter of $3\frac{1}{4}$ inches. How much paper is needed for the label on the can? Round your answer to the nearest tenth. **40.8 in²**

18. **CRAFTS** For a craft project, Sarah is covering all the sides of a box with stickers. The length of the box is 8 inches, the width is 6 inches, and the height is 4 inches. If each sticker has a length of 2 inches and a width of 4 inches, how many stickers does she need to cover the box? **26 stickers**

P32 | Lesson 0-10 | Surface Area

LESSON 0-11 Simple Probability and Odds

Objective

- Find the probability and odds of simple events.

NewVocabulary
probability
sample space
equally likely
complements
tree diagram
odds

The **probability** of an event is the ratio of the number of favorable outcomes for the event to the total number of possible outcomes. When you roll a die, there are six possible outcomes: 1, 2, 3, 4, 5, or 6. This list of all possible outcomes is called the **sample space**.

When there are n outcomes and the probability of each one is $\frac{1}{n}$, we say that the outcomes are **equally likely**. For example, when you roll a die, the 6 possible outcomes are equally likely because each outcome has a probability of $\frac{1}{6}$. The probability of an event is always between 0 and 1, inclusive. The closer a probability is to 1, the more likely it is to occur.

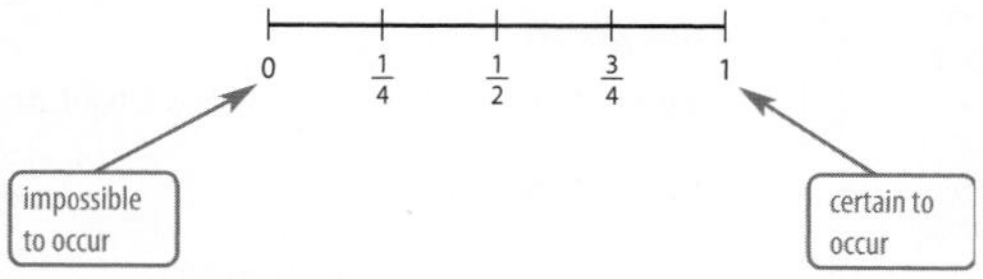

Example 1 Find Probabilities

A die is rolled. Find each probability.

a. rolling a 1 or 5

There are six possible outcomes. There are two favorable outcomes, 1 and 5.

$$\text{probability} = \frac{\text{number of favorable outcomes}}{\text{total number of possible outcomes}} = \frac{2}{6}$$

So, $P(1 \text{ or } 5) = \frac{2}{6}$ or $\frac{1}{3}$.

b. rolling an even number

Three of the six outcomes are even numbers. So, there are three favorable outcomes.

3 even numbers

Sample space: 1, 2, 3, 4, 5, 6 $\quad \frac{3}{6}$

6 total possible outcomes

So, $P(\text{even number}) = \frac{3}{6}$ or $\frac{1}{2}$.

The events for rolling a 1 and for *not* rolling a 1 are called **complements**.

$P(1)$ $\quad P(\text{not } 1)$ $\quad P(\text{sum of probabilities})$

$$\frac{1}{6} + \frac{5}{6} = \frac{6}{6} \text{ or } 1$$

The sum of the probabilities for any two complementary events is always 1.

Eyewire/Getty Images

1 Focus

VerticalAlignment

Lesson 0-11 Find the probability and odds of simple events.

After Lesson 0-11 Find the probability of compound events. Use permutations and combinations to find probabilities.

2 Teach

Example 1 shows how to find probability when rolling a die. **Example 2** shows how to find the probability that an event occurs or does not occur. **Example 3** shows how to use a tree diagram to count outcomes. **Example 4** shows how to use the Fundamental Counting Principle to find the number of possible choices. **Example 5** shows how to find the odds of an event.

Additional Example

1 A die is rolled. Find each probability.

a. rolling a 3 or an even number $\frac{2}{3}$

b. rolling at least a 2 $\frac{5}{6}$

Additional Examples

2 A bag contains 12 tiles with the letter A, 6 tiles with the letter S, 9 tiles with the letter P, and 5 tiles with the letter E. One tile is randomly drawn. Find each probability.

a. A $\frac{3}{8}$, 0.375, 37.5%

b. P or S $\frac{15}{32}$, about 0.47, or about 47%

c. not E $\frac{27}{32}$, about 0.84, or about 84%

3 A travel agency is offering specialty trips to Australia, Brazil, and India. The agency offers the trips in budget, luxury, and adventure. Use a tree diagram to determine the number of different trips possible.
9 possible trips

Place	Type	Outcomes
Australia	Adventure	A, A
	Budget	A, B
	Luxury	A, L
Brazil	Adventure	B, A
	Budget	B, B
	Luxury	B, L
India	Adventure	I, A
	Budget	I, B
	Luxury	I, L

Teach with Tech

Portable Media Player Have students find the total number of songs on their portable media player and the number of songs for each genre of music. Ask students to find the probability that a randomly chosen song will be from that genre.

PT

Example 2 Find Probabilities

A bowl contains 5 red chips, 7 blue chips, 6 yellow chips, and 10 green chips. One chip is randomly drawn. Find each probability.

a. blue

There are 7 blue chips and 28 total chips.

$P(\text{blue chip}) = \frac{7}{28}$ ← number of favorable outcomes / ← number of possible outcomes

$= \frac{1}{4}$

The probability can be stated as $\frac{1}{4}$, 0.25, or 25%.

b. red or yellow

There are 5 + 6 or 11 chips that are red or yellow.

$P(\text{red or yellow}) = \frac{11}{28}$ ← number of favorable outcomes / ← number of possible outcomes

≈ 0.39

The probability can be stated as $\frac{11}{28}$, about 0.39, or about 39%.

c. not green

There are 5 + 7 + 6 or 18 chips that are not green.

$P(\text{not green}) = \frac{18}{28}$ ← number of favorable outcomes / ← number of possible outcomes

$= \frac{9}{14}$ or about 0.64

The probability can be stated as $\frac{9}{14}$, about 0.64, or about 64%.

StudyTip
Alternate Method A chip drawn will either be green or not green. So, another method for finding *P*(not green) is to find *P*(green) and subtract that probability from 1.

One method used for counting the number of possible outcomes is to draw a **tree diagram**. The last column of a tree diagram shows all of the possible outcomes.

PT

Example 3 Use a Tree Diagram to Count Outcomes

School baseball caps come in blue, yellow, or white. The caps have either the school mascot or the school's initials. Use a tree diagram to determine the number of different caps possible.

Color	Design	Outcomes
blue	mascot	blue, mascot
	initials	blue, initials
yellow	mascot	yellow, mascot
	initials	yellow, initials
white	mascot	white, mascot
	initials	white, initials

The tree diagram shows that there are 6 different caps possible.

StudyTip
Counting Outcomes When counting possible outcomes, make a column in your tree diagram for each part of the event.

This example is an illustration of the **Fundamental Counting Principle**, which relates the number of outcomes to the number of choices.

KeyConcept Fundamental Counting Principle

Words	If event *M* can occur in *m* ways and is followed by event *N* that can occur in *n* ways, then the event *M* followed by *N* can occur in $m \cdot n$ ways.
Example	If there are 4 possible sizes for fish tanks and 3 possible shapes, then there are $4 \cdot 3$ or 12 possible fish tanks.

Example 4 Use the Fundamental Counting Principle

a. An ice cream shop offers one, two, or three scoops of ice cream from among 12 different flavors. The ice cream can be served in a wafer cone, a sugar cone, or in a cup. Use the Fundamental Counting Principle to determine the number of choices possible.

There are 3 ways the ice cream is served, 3 different servings, and there are 12 different flavors of ice cream.

Use the Fundamental Counting Principle to find the number of possible choices.

number of scoops		number of flavors		number of serving options		number of choices of ordering ice cream
3	·	12	·	3	=	108

So, there are 108 different ways to order ice cream.

b. Jimmy needs to make a 3-digit password for his log-on name on a Web site. The password can include any digit from 0-9, but the digits may not repeat. How many possible 3-digit passwords are there?

If the first digit is a 4, then the next digit cannot be a 4.

We can use the Fundamental Counting Principle to find the number of possible passwords.

1st digit		2nd digit		3rd digit		number of passwords
10	·	9	·	8	=	720

So, there are 720 possible 3-digit passwords.

StudyTip

Odds The sum of the number of successes and the number of failures equals the size of the sample space, or the number of possible outcomes.

The **odds** of an event occurring is the ratio that compares the number of ways an event can occur (successes) to the number of ways it cannot occur (failures).

Example 5 Find the Odds

Find the odds of rolling a number less than 3.

There are six possible outcomes; 2 are successes and 4 are failures.

So, the odds of rolling a number less than 3 are $\frac{1}{2}$ or 1:2.

Additional Examples

4 **a.** A printing shop is offering a special on business cards in white or off-white from among 18 different fonts. The ink on the cards can be raised or flat. Use the Fundamental Counting Principle to determine the number of choices possible. 72 choices

b. Kara needs to make a password consisting of 3 numbers followed by two letters. The numbers can be any digit 0–9 and the digits can repeat. The letters can be any letter, lowercase, and they cannot repeat. How many possible passwords are there? 650,000 passwords

5 Find the odds of rolling a number on a die that is greater than 2. 2:1

Tips for New Teachers

Probability and Odds Make sure that students do not confuse the fraction representation of odds with the fraction representation of probability. In Example 5, the *odds* of rolling a number less than 3 is $\frac{1}{2}$, while the *probability* is $\frac{1}{3}$.

WatchOut!

Common Misconception The terms *odds* and *probability* are often confused and used interchangeably. Suggest that students read problems carefully for the use of these terms, and check that they applied the correct concept in solving the problems. Remind them that probabilities are never greater than 1, but that odds can be greater than 1.

3 Assess

Formative Assessment

Use Exercises 1–22 to assess whether students understand simple probability and odds.

Ticket Out the Door

Ask students to find the probability and odds of randomly drawing a yellow marker out of a bag that contains 3 yellow markers, 2 blue markers, and 4 red markers. $\frac{1}{3}$; 1:2

Exercises

One coin is randomly selected from a jar containing 70 nickels, 100 dimes, 80 quarters, and 50 one-dollar coins. Find each probability.

1. P(quarter) $\frac{4}{15}$

2. P(dime) $\frac{1}{3}$

3. P(quarter or nickel) $\frac{1}{2}$

4. P(value greater than \$0.10) $\frac{13}{30}$

5. P(value less than \$1) $\frac{5}{6}$

6. P(value at most \$1) 1

One of the polygons below is chosen at random. Find each probability.

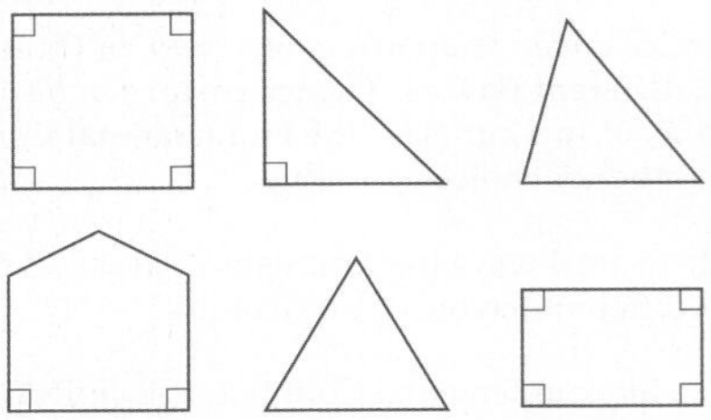

7. P(triangle) $\frac{1}{2}$

8. P(pentagon) $\frac{1}{6}$

9. P(not a quadrilateral) $\frac{2}{3}$

10. P(more than 2 right angles) $\frac{1}{3}$

Use a tree diagram to find the sample space for each event. State the number of possible outcomes.

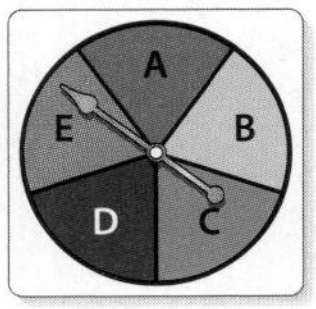

11. The spinner at the right is spun and two coins are tossed. **20**

12. At a restaurant, you choose two sides to have with breakfast. You can choose white or whole wheat toast. You can choose sausage links, sausage patties, or bacon. **6**

13. How many different 3-character codes are there using A, B, or C for the first character, 8 or 9 for the second character, and 0 or 1 for the third character? **12 codes**

A bag is full of different colored marbles. The probability of randomly selecting a red marble from the bag is $\frac{1}{8}$. The probability of selecting a blue marble is $\frac{13}{24}$. Find each probability.

14. P(not red) $\frac{7}{8}$

15. P(not blue) $\frac{11}{24}$

Find the odds of each outcome if a computer randomly picks a letter in the name THE UNITED STATES OF AMERICA.

16. the letter A **1:7** **17.** the letter T **1:5** **18.** a vowel **11:13** **19.** a consonant **13:11**

Margaret wants to order a sub at the local deli.

Subs	
ham, salami, roast beef, turkey, bologna, pepperoni	
Dressing	**Toppings**
mayonnaise, mustard, vinegar, oil	lettuce, onions, peppers, olives

20. Find the number of possible orders of a sub with one topping and one dressing option. **96 orders**

21. Find the number of possible ham subs with mayonnaise, any combination of toppings or no toppings at all. **16 orders**

22. Find the number of possible orders of a sub with any combination of dressing and/or toppings. **6 • 16 • 16 or 1536 orders**

P36 | Lesson 0-11 | Simple Probability and Odds

LESSON 0-12 Measures of Center, Variation, and Position

Objective

- Find measures of central tendency, variation, and position.

NewVocabulary

variable
data
measurement or quantitative data
categorical or qualitative data
univariate data
measures of center or central tendency
mean
median
mode
measures of spread or variation
range
quartile
measures of position
lower quartile
upper quartile
five-number summary
interquartile range
outlier

A **variable** is a characteristic of a group of people or objects that can assume different values called **data**. Data that have units and can be measured are called **measurement** or **quantitative data**. Data that can be organized into different categories are called **categorical** or **qualitative data**. Some examples of both types of data are listed below.

Measurement Data	Categorical Data
Times: 15 s, 20 s, 45 s, 19 s	**Favorite color:** blue, red, purple, green
Ages: 10 yr, 15 yr, 14 yr, 16 yr	**Hair color:** black, blonde, brown
Distance: 5 mi, 30 mi, 18 mi	**Phone Numbers:** 555-1234, 555-5678

Measurement data in one variable, called **univariate data**, are often summarized using a single number to represent what is average or typical. Measures of what is average are also called **measures of center** or **central tendency**. The most common measures of center are mean, median, and mode.

KeyConcept Measures of Center

- The **mean** is the sum of the values in a data set divided by the total number of values in the set.
- The **median** is the middle value or the mean of the two middle values in a set of data when the data are arranged in numerical order.
- The **mode** is the value or values that appear most often in a set of data. A set of data can have no mode, one mode, or more than one mode.

Example 1 Measures of Center

PT

BASEBALL The table shows the number of hits Marcus made for his team. Find the mean, median, and mode.

Team Played	Hits
Badgers	3
Hornets	6
Bulldogs	5
Vikings	2
Rangers	3
Panthers	7

Mean: To find the mean, find the sum of all the hits and divide by the number of games in which he made these hits.

$$\text{mean} = \frac{3+6+5+2+3+7}{6} = \frac{26}{6} \text{ or about 4 hits}$$

Median: To find the median, order the numbers from least to greatest and find the middle value or values.

2, 3, 3, 5, 6, 7

$\frac{3+5}{2}$ or 4 hits — Since there is an even number of values, find the mean of the middle two.

Mode: From the arrangement of the data values, we can see that the value that occurs most often in the set is 3, so the mode of the data set is 3 hits.

Marcus's mean and median number of hits for these games was 4, and his mode was 3 hits.

1 Focus

VerticalAlignment

Lesson 0-12 Find measures of central tendency, variation, and position.

After Lesson 0-12 Identify and use sample statistics and population parameters.

2 Teach

Example 1 shows how to find the mean, median, and mode of a set of data. **Example 2** shows how to find the range of a set of data. **Example 3** shows how to find the quartiles, maximum and minimum values, and any outliers of a set of data. **Example 4** shows how outliers affect the measures of central tendency and variation.

Additional Example

1 **SWIMMING** The table shows the number of laps Ekta swam each day. Find the mean, median, and mode.

Day	Number of Laps
Saturday	6
Sunday	8
Monday	8
Tuesday	6
Wednesday	4
Thursday	9
Friday	5

≈6.6 laps; 6 laps; 56 and 8 laps

Teach with Tech

Interactive Whiteboard Write a set of data on the board. Have a student arrange the data from least to greatest. Then separate the data into two groups to find the median. After discussing Example 6, use the data to find the quartiles.

Additional Examples

2 **CELL PHONES** The number of minutes Sara talked on her phone each day this week is 63, 21, 24, 52, 74, 56, and 38. Find the range of the minutes.
53 minutes

3 Find the minimum, lower quartile, median, upper quartile, and maximum of the data shown below.
27, 25, 44, 13, 29, 44, 52, 28, 41
13; 27.5; 35; 44; 52

Two very different data sets can have the same mean, so statisticians also use **measures of spread** or **variation** to describe how widely the data values vary. One such measure is the **range**, which is the difference between the greatest and least values in a set of data.

PT

Example 2 Range

WALKING The times in minutes it took Olivia to walk to school each day this week are 18, 15, 15, 12, and 14. Find the range.

range = greatest value − least value — Definition of range

= 18 − 12 or 6 — The greatest value is 18, and the least value is 12.

The range of the times is 6 minutes.

Statisticians often talk about the position of a value relative to other values in a set. **Quartiles** are common **measures of position** that divide a data set arranged in ascending order into four groups, each containing about one fourth or 25% of the data. The median marks the second quartile Q_2 and separates the data into upper and lower halves. The first or **lower quartile** Q_1 is the median of the lower half, while the third or **upper quartile** Q_3 is the median of the upper half.

StudyTip
Calculating Quartiles
When the number of values in a set of data is odd, the median is not included in either half of the data when calculating Q_1 or Q_3.

25 31 36 39 40 41 44 45 49 50 54

25 ↑ minimum; 36 ↑ Q_1 lower quartile; 41 ↑ Q_2 median; 49 ↑ Q_3 upper quartile; 54 ↑ maximum

|← 25% →|← 25% →|← 25% →|← 25% →|

The three quartiles, along with the minimum and maximum values, are called a **five- number summary** of a data set.

PT

Example 3 Five-Number Summary

FUNDRAISER The number of boxes of donuts Aang sold for a fundraiser each day for the last 11 days were 22, 16, 35, 26, 14, 17, 28, 29, 21, 17, and 20. Find the minimum, lower quartile, median, upper quartile, and maximum of the data set. Then interpret this five-number summary.

Order the data from least to greatest. Use the list to determine the quartiles.

14, 16, 17, 17, 20, 21, 22, 26, 28, 29, 35

14 ↑ Min.; 17 ↑ Q_1; 21 ↑ Q_2; 28 ↑ Q_3; 35 ↑ Max.

The minimum is 14, the lower quartile is 17, the median is 21, the upper quartile is 28, and the maximum is 35. Over the last 11 days, Aang sold a minimum of 14 boxes and a maximum of 35 boxes. He sold fewer than 17 boxes 25% of the time, fewer than 21 boxes 50% of the time, and fewer than 28 boxes 75% of the time.

The difference between the upper and lower quartiles is called the **interquartile range**. The interquartile range, or IQR, contains about 50% of the values.

14, 16, 17, 17, 20, 21, 22, 26, 28, 29, 35

17 ↑ Q_1; 28 ↑ Q_3

|← IQR = $Q_1 - Q_3$ or 11 →|

P38 | Lesson 0-12 | Measures of Center, Variation, and Position

Before deciding on which measure of center best describes a data set, check for outliers. An **outlier** is an extremely high or extremely low value when compared with the rest of the values in the set. To check for outliers, look for data values that are beyond the upper or lower quartiles by more than 1.5 times the interquartile range.

Example 4 Effect of Outliers

TEST SCORES **Students taking a make-up test received the following scores: 88, 79, 94, 90, 45, 71, 82, and 88.**

a. Identify any outliers in the data.

First determine the median and upper and lower quartiles of the data.

45, 71, 79, 82, 88, 88, 90, 94

$Q_1 = \frac{71 + 79}{2}$ or 75 $\quad Q_2 = \frac{82 + 88}{2}$ or 85 $\quad Q_3 = \frac{88 + 90}{2}$ or 89

Find the interquartile range.

$IQR = Q_3 - Q_1 = 89 - 75$ or 14

Use the interquartile range to find the values beyond which any outliers would lie.

$Q_1 - 1.5(IQR)$	and	$Q_3 + 1.5(IQR)$	Values beyond which outliers lie
$75 - 1.5(14)$		$89 + 1.5(14)$	$Q_1 = 75$, $Q_3 = 89$, and IQR = 14
54		110	Simplify.

There are no scores greater than 110, but there is one score less than 54. The score of 45 can be considered an outlier for this data set.

b. Find the mean and median of the data set with and without the outlier. Describe what happens.

Data Set	Mean	Median
with outlier	$\frac{88 + 79 + 94 + 90 + 45 + 71 + 82 + 88}{8}$ or about 79.6	85
without outlier	$\frac{88 + 79 + 94 + 90 + 71 + 82 + 88}{7}$ or about 84.6	88

Removal of the outlier causes the mean and median to increase, but notice that the mean is affected more by the removal of the outlier than the median.

StudyTip

Interquartile Range When the interquartile range is a small value, the data in the set are close together. A large interquartile range means that the data are spread out.

Exercises

Find the mean, median, mode, and range for each data set.

1. number of students helping at the cookie booth each hour: 3, 5, 8, 1, 4, 11, 3
2. weight in pounds of boxes loaded onto a semi truck: 201, 201, 200, 199, 199
3. car speeds in miles per hour observed by a highway patrol officer: 60, 53, 53, 52, 53, 55, 55, 57 **54.75 mph; 54 mph; 53 mph; 8 mph**
4. number of songs downloaded by students last week in Ms. Turner's class: 3, 7, 21, 23, 63, 27, 29, 95, 23 **≈32 songs; 23 songs; 23 songs; 92 songs**
5. ratings of an online video: 2, 5, 3.5, 4, 4.5, 1, 1, 4, 2, 1.5, 2.5, 2, 3, 3.5 **≈2.8; 2.75; 2; 4**

1. 5 students; 4 students; 3 students; 10 students
2. 200 lb; 200 lb; 201 lb and 199 lb; 2 lb

Additional Example

4 TEXT MESSAGES The table shows the number of text messages Tumu received.

Text Messages					
15	28	20	17	24	14
11	24	15	16	19	40
24	11	21	18	10	15

a. Identify any outliers in the data. 40

b. Find the mean and median of the data set with and without the outlier. Describe the effect.

Data Set	Mean	Median
with outlier	19	17.5
without outlier	≈17.8	17

Removal of the outlier causes the mean and median to decrease, but the mean is affected more.

Tips for New Teachers

Sense-Making Advise students that the median is not included in the lower half or upper half of data when they are finding quartiles. If there is an odd number of values in the data set, the median is the middle number, and it is not included in either half. If there is an even number of values of the data set, the median is the mean of the two middle numbers.

3 Assess

Formative Assessment

Use Exercises 1–18 to assess whether students understand measures of center, spread, and position and how to calculate them.

Name the Math

Ask students to explain how they would find the mean, median, mode, and range of the following data: 18, 10, 23, 11, 18.

Tips for New Teachers

Calculating Median Remind students to order the data from least to greatest before finding the median of the data.

Additional Answers

8a. Brand A: 15 washes, 3 washes; Brand B: 15 washes, 7 washes

8b. Brand A; sample answer: Brand A has a smaller measure of spread, so all the results are closer to the mean.

10. 62 people; 66 people; 73 people; 82 people; 99 people

11. 2 books; 5 books; 10 books; 17 books; 18 books

14. 3, 3, 5, 7, 8; Cole had a minimum of 3 servings and a maximum of 8 servings of fruits and vegetables, ate 7 or more servings at least 25% of the time, ate 5 or more servings at least 50% of the time, and ate 3 or more servings at least 75% of the time.

15. ≈138.3 mi, 101.5 mi; no outliers

16. ≈59.71 min, 45 min; 190 min; ≈51.6 min, 42.5 min; mean

18c. ≈$20.15; $19.12; $14.99; $18.75

18d. If n is added to each value in the data set, then n is added to the mean, median, and mode. The range will remain the same. If each value in the data set is multiplied by n, the mean, median, mode, and range will be multiplied by n.

---

6. **SCHOOL SUPPLIES** The table shows the cost of school supplies. Find the mean, median, mode and range of the costs. **$2.50; $2.25; $2.00; $4.75**

Cost of School Supplies	
Supply	**Cost**
pencils	$0.50
pens	$2.00
paper	$2.00
pocket folder	$1.25
calculator	$5.25
notebook	$3.00
erasers	$2.50
markers	$3.50

7. **BOWLING** Sue's average for 9 games of bowling is 108. What is the lowest score she can receive for the tenth game to have an mean of 110? **128**

8. **LAUNDRY** Two brands of laundry detergents were tested to determine how many times a shirt could be washed before it faded. The results for 6 shirts in number of washes follow.

Brand A: 16, 15, 13, 14, 16, 16

Brand B: 11, 16, 18, 12, 15, 18

a. Find the mean and range for each brand. **a–b. See margin.**

b. Which brand performed more consistently? Explain.

Find the minimum, lower quartile, median, upper quartile, and maximum values for each data set. **10–11. See margin.**

9. prices in dollars of smartphones: 311, 309, 312, 314, 399, 312 **$309; $311; $312; $314; $399**

10. attendance at an event for the last nine years: 68, 99, 73, 65, 67, 62, 80, 81, 83

11. books a student checks out of the library: 17, 9, 10, 17, 18, 5, 2

12. ounces of soda dispensed into 36-ounce cups: 36.1, 35.8, 35.2, 36.5, 36.0, 36.2, 35.7, 35.8, 35.9, 36.4, 35.6 **35.2 oz; 35.7 oz; 35.9 oz; 36.2 oz; 36.5 oz**

13. ages of riders on a roller coaster: 45, 17, 16, 22, 25, 19, 20, 21, 32, 37, 19, 21, 24, 20, 18, 22, 23, 19 **16 years old; 19 years old; 21 years old; 24 years old; 45 years old**

14. **NUTRITION** The table shows the number of servings of fruit and vegetables that Cole eats one week. Find the minimum, median, lower quartile, upper quartile, and maximum number of servings. Then interpret this five-number summary. **See margin.**

Fruits and Vegetables	
Day	**Number of Servings**
Monday	5
Tuesday	7
Wednesday	5
Thursday	4
Friday	3
Saturday	3
Sunday	8

Find the mean and median of the data set, and then identify any outliers. If the set has an outlier, find the mean and median without the outlier, and state which measure is affected more by the removal of this value. **15–16. See margin.**

15. distance traveled in miles to visit relatives during winter break: 210, 45, 10, 108, 452, 225, 35, 95, 140, 25, 65, 250

16. time spent on social networking Web sites in minutes per day: 25, 35, 45, 30, 65, 50, 25, 100, 45, 35, 5, 105, 110, 190, 40, 30, 80

17. batting averages for the last 10 seasons: 0.267, 0.305, 0.304, 0.201, 0.284, 0.302, 0.311, 0.289, 0.300, 0.292 **≈0.286, 0.296; 0.201; ≈0.295, 0.300; mean**

18. **CHALLENGE** The cost of 8 different pairs of pants at a department store are $39.99, $31.99, $19.99, $14.99, $19.99, $23.99, $36.99, and $26.99.

a. Find the mean, median, mode, and range of the pants prices. **≈$26.87; $25.49; $19.99; $25**

b. Suppose each pair of pants needs to be hemmed at an additional cost of $8 per pair. Including these alteration costs, what are the mean, median, mode, and range of the pant prices? **≈$34.87; $33.49; $27.99; $25**

c. Suppose the original price of each pair of pants is discounted by 25%. Find the mean, median, mode, and range of the discounted pant prices. **c–d. See margin.**

d. Make a conjecture as to the effect on the mean, median, mode, and range of a data set if the same value n is added to each value in the data set. What is the effect on these same measures if each item in a data set is multiplied by the same value n?

LESSON 0-13 Representing Data

Objective

- Represent sets of data using different visual displays.

NewVocabulary

frequency table
bar graph
cumulative frequency
histogram
line graph
stem-and-leaf plot
circle graph
box-and-whisker plot

A **frequency table** uses tally marks to record and display frequencies of events. A **bar graph** compares categories of data with bars representing the frequencies.

Example 1 Make a Bar Graph

Make a bar graph to display the data.

Sport	Tally	Frequency
basketball	𝍸𝍸𝍸	15
football	𝍸𝍸𝍸𝍸𝍸	25
soccer	𝍸𝍸𝍸 III	18
baseball	𝍸𝍸𝍸𝍸 I	21

Step 1 Draw a horizontal axis and a vertical axis. Label the axes as shown. Add a title.

Step 2 Draw a bar to represent each sport. The vertical scale is the number of students who chose each sport. The horizontal scale identifies the sport.

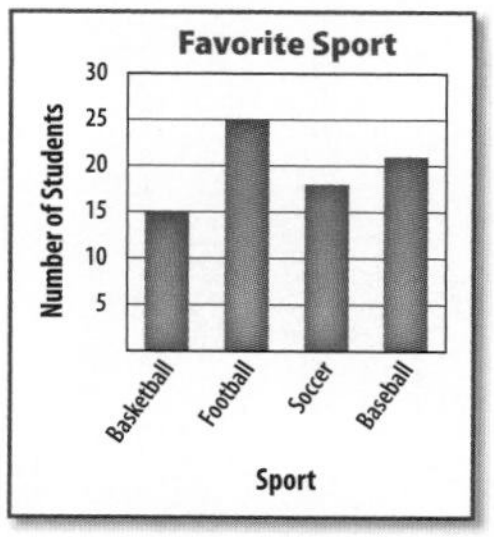

The **cumulative frequency** for each event is the sum of its frequency and the frequencies of all preceding events. A **histogram** is a type of bar graph used to display numerical data that have been organized into equal intervals.

Example 2 Make a Histogram and a Cumulative Frequency Histogram

Make histograms of the frequency and the cumulative frequency.

Age at Inauguration	40–44	45–49	50–54	55–59	60–64	65–69
U.S. Presidents	2	7	13	12	7	3

Find the cumulative frequency for each interval.

Age	< 45	< 50	< 55	< 60	< 65	< 70
Presidents	2	2 + 7 = 9	9 + 13 = 22	22 + 12 = 34	34 + 7 = 41	41 + 3 = 44

Make each histogram like a bar graph but with no space between the bars.

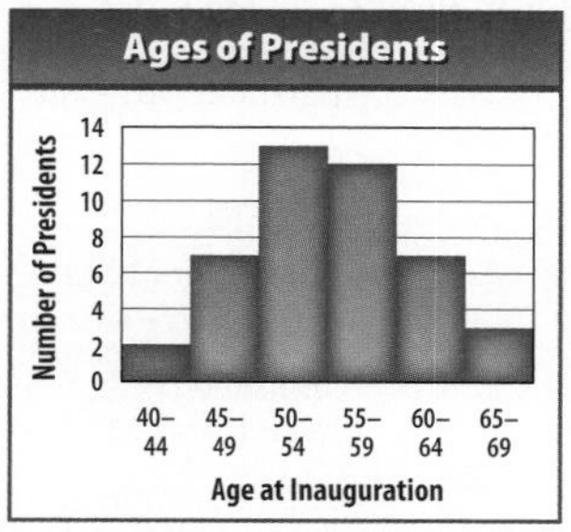

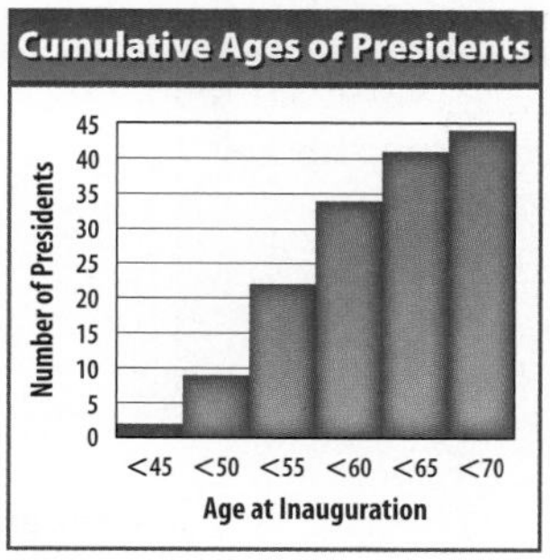

1 Focus

VerticalAlignment

Lesson 0-13 Represent sets of data using different visual displays.

After Lesson 0-13 Analyze data in visual displays. Recognize misleading graphs.

2 Teach

Example 1 shows how to make a bar graph. **Example 2** shows how to make a histogram and a cumulative frequency histogram. **Example 3** shows how to make a line graph. **Example 4** shows how to make a stem-and-leaf plot. **Example 5** shows how to make a circle graph. **Example 6** shows how to make a box-and-whisker plot. **Example 7** shows how to compare two sets of data using a double box-and-whisker plot. **Example 8** shows how to choose an appropriate display for a set of data.

Additional Example

1 MUSIC The table shows the results of a student survey on favorite music. Make a bar graph to display the data.

Music	Frequency
Country	13
Hip-Hop	35
Metal	20
Rock	32

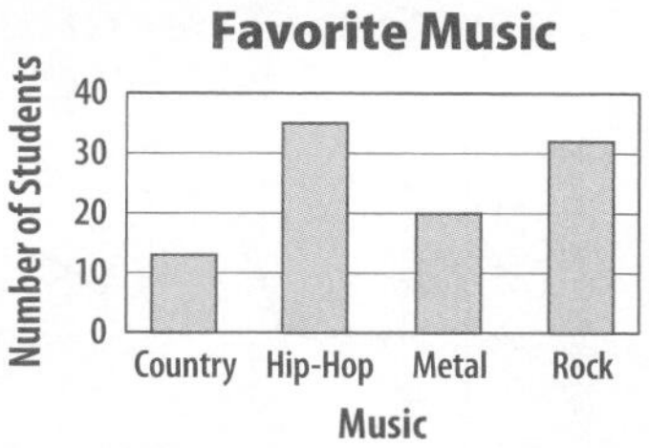

Additional Examples

2 VOLUNTEERS The table shows the ages of the volunteers at an animal shelter. Make histograms of the frequencies and the cumulative frequencies.

Ages	Frequency
16–25	6
26–35	4
36–45	9
46–55	12
56–65	8

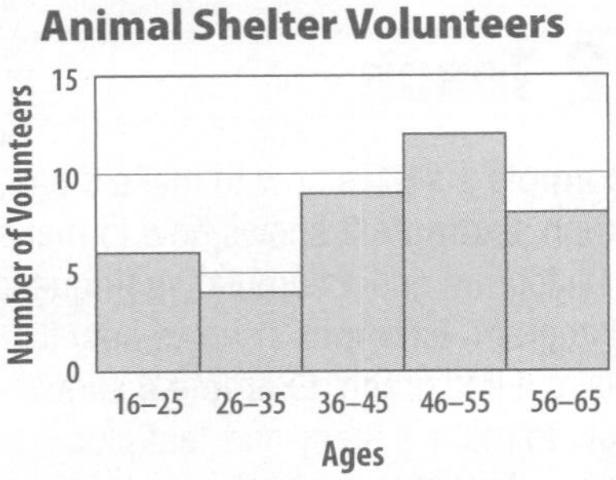

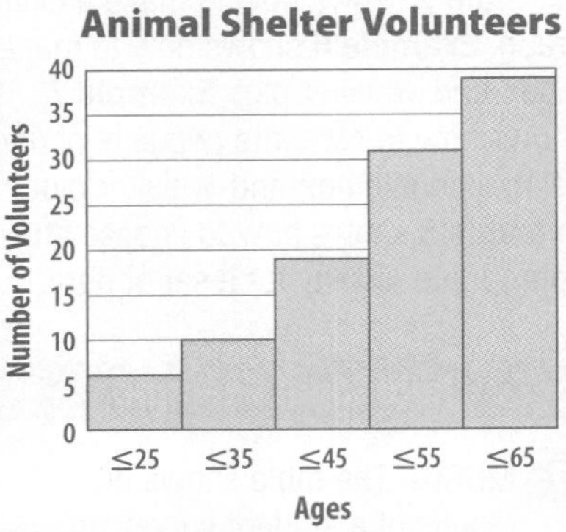

3 WIND Make a line graph of the wind speed forecast data.

Wind Speed Forecast (mph)			
Midnight	4	Noon	21
3:00 A.M.	5	3:00 P.M.	24
6:00 A.M.	8	6:00 P.M.	14
9:00 A.M.	11	9:00 P.M.	17

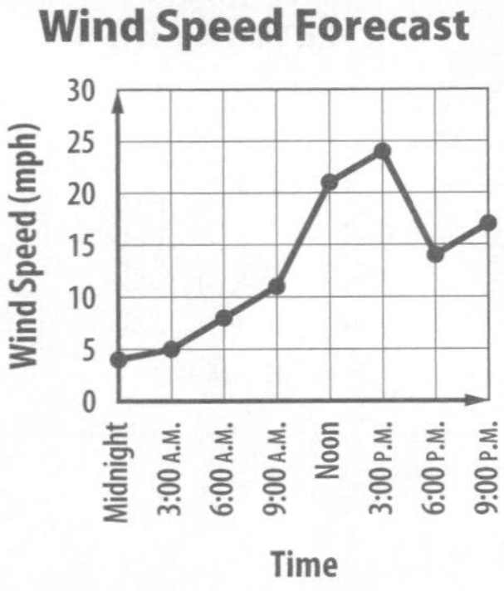

Another way to represent data is by using a line graph. A **line graph** usually shows how data change over a period of time.

Example 3 Make a Line Graph

Sales at the Marshall High School Store are shown in the table. Make a line graph of the data.

School Store Sales Amounts					
September	$670	December	$168	March	$412
October	$229	January	$290	April	$309
November	$300	February	$388	May	$198

Step 1 Draw a horizontal axis and a vertical axis and label them as shown. Include a title.

Step 2 Plot the points.

Step 3 Draw a line connecting each pair of consecutive points.

Data can also be organized and displayed by using a stem-and-leaf plot. In a **stem-and-leaf plot**, the digits of the least place value usually form the *leaves*, and the rest of the digits form the *stems*.

Real-World Example 4 Make a Stem-and-Leaf Plot

ANIMALS The speeds (mph) of 20 of the fastest land animals are listed at the right. Use the data to make a stem-and-leaf plot.

42	40	40	35	50
32	50	36	50	40
45	70	43	45	32
40	35	61	48	35

Source: *The World Almanac*

The least place value is ones. So, 32 miles per hour would have a stem of 3 and a leaf of 2.

Stem	Leaf
3	2 2 5 5 5 6
4	0 0 0 0 2 3 5 5 8
5	0 0 0
6	1
7	0

Key: 3|2 = 32

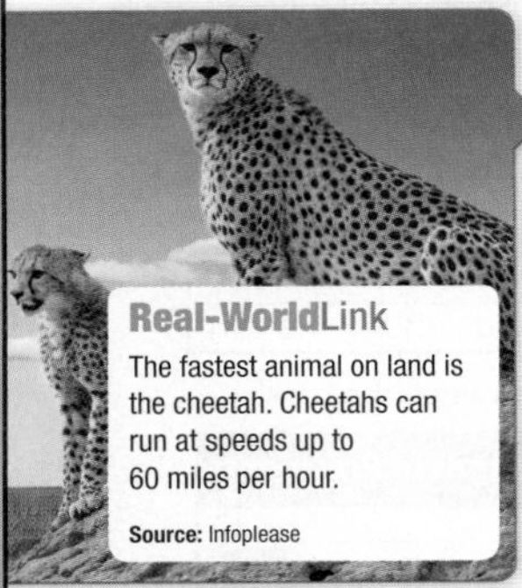

Real-WorldLink

The fastest animal on land is the cheetah. Cheetahs can run at speeds up to 60 miles per hour.

Source: Infoplease

A **circle graph** is a graph that shows the relationship between parts of the data and the whole. The circle represents all of the data.

Example 5 Make a Circle Graph

The table shows how Lily spent 8 hours of one day at summer camp. Make a circle graph of the data.

Summer Camp	
Activity	**Hours**
canoeing	3
crafts	1
eating	2
hiking	2

First, find the ratio that compares the number of hours for each activity to 8. Then multiply each ratio by 360° to find the number of degrees for each section of the graph.

Canoeing: $\frac{3}{8} \cdot 360° = 135°$

Crafts: $\frac{1}{8} \cdot 360° = 45°$

Eating: $\frac{2}{8} \cdot 360° = 90°$

Hiking: $\frac{2}{8} \cdot 360° = 90°$

Summer Camp

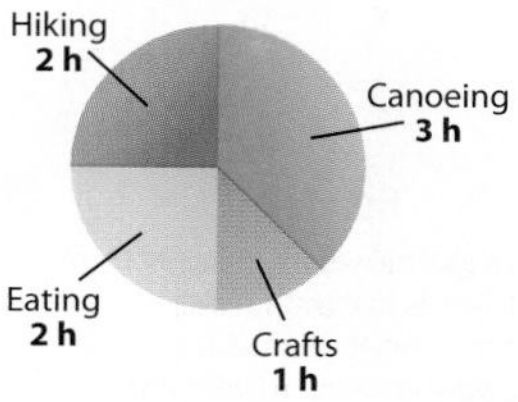

WatchOut!

Circle Graphs The sum of the measures of each section of a circle graph should be 360°.

A **box-and-whisker plot** is a graphical representation of the five-number summary of a data set. The box in a box-and-whisker plot represents the interquartile range.

Example 6 Make a Box-and-Whisker Plot

Draw a box-and-whisker plot for these data. Describe how the outlier affects the quartile points.

14, 30, 16, 20, 18, 16, 20, 18, 22, 13, 8

Step 1 Order the data from least to greatest. Then determine the maximum, minimum and the quartiles.

8, 13, **14**, 16, 16, **18**, 18, 20, **20**, 22, 30

min. (8), Q_1 (14), Q_2 (18), Q_3 (20), max. (30)

Determine the interquartile range.

$IQR = Q_3 - Q_1$

$= 20 - 14$ or 6

Check to see if there are any outliers.

$14 - 1.5(6) = 5$ $\quad$ $20 + 1.5(6) = 29$

Numbers less than 5 or greater than 29 are outliers.

The only outlier is 30.

Step 2 Draw a number line that includes the minimum and maximum values in the data. Place dots above the number line to represent the three quartile points, any outliers, the minimum value that is not an outlier, and the maximum value that is not an outlier.

Teach with Tech

Blog On your secure classroom blog, have students write a blog entry explaining when they would use different types of data displays. Be sure students describe data sets that would best be shown using line graphs, bar graphs, and circle graphs.

Additional Examples

4 **SHIPPING** The weights in pounds of 25 packages shipped from a mailing center are listed below. Use the data to make a stem-and-leaf plot.

3	18	35	20	5
9	4	2	10	12
15	15	22	5	17
16	9	2	38	2
3	11	23	41	3

Weights of Packages

Stem	Leaf
0	2 2 2 3 3 3 4 5 5 9 9
1	0 1 2 5 5 6 7 8
2	0 2 3
3	5 8
4	1

Key: *3|8 = 38 pounds*

5 The table shows how the Astronomy Club raised $500. Make a circle graph of the data.

Astronomy Club Fundraising	
Source	**Amount ($)**
Car Washes	125
Fish Fry	150
Game-a-thon	75
Poster Sales	150

Astronomy Club Fundraising

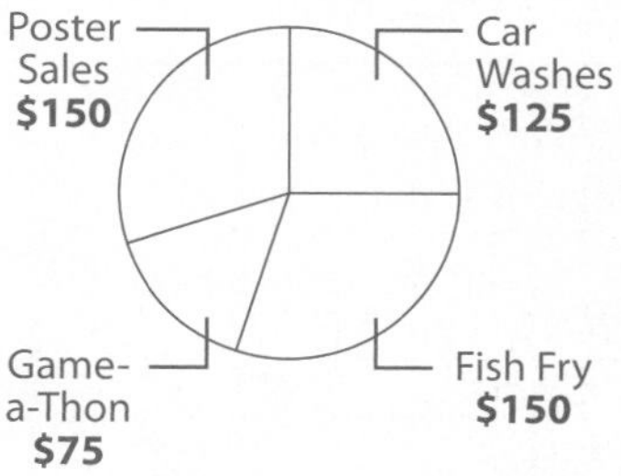

6 Draw a box-and-whisker plot for these data.
20, 17, 23, 26, 19, 28, 4, 20, 24

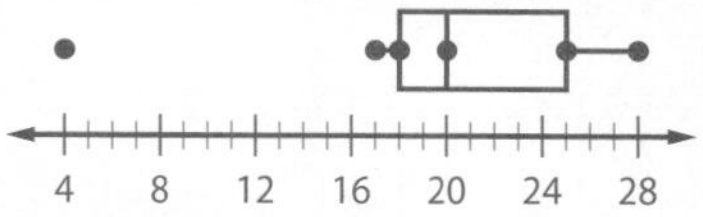

Additional Example

7 Mrs. Heflin is comparing the performances of her class on the past two chapter tests.

Chapter 5: 76, 81, 72, 83, 88, 79, 77, 84, 86, 79, 79, 81, 83, 85

Chapter 6: 91, 88, 77, 69, 93, 86, 88, 94, 65, 70, 63, 72, 91, 68

a. Draw a double box-and-whisker plot for the data.

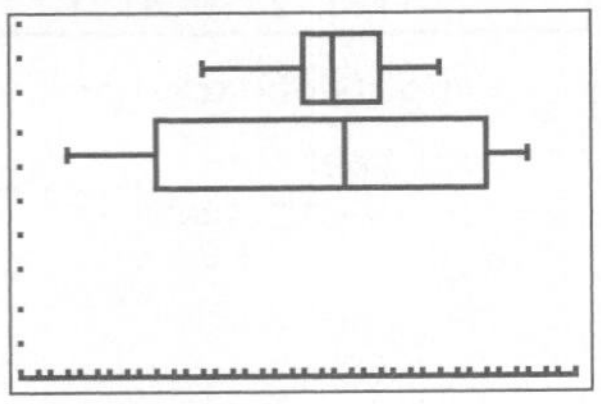

[60, 97] scl: 1

b. Use the box-and-whisker plot to compare the data. The data have significantly different interquartile ranges. While the median scores are about the same, the scores for Chapter 6 varied much more than the scores for Chapter 5.

c. Would it be appropriate to say students did much better on the Chapter 6 test? Explain. No, some scores were better and some were not as good.

Step 3 Draw the box and the whiskers. The vertical rules go through the quartiles. The outliers are not connected to the whiskers.

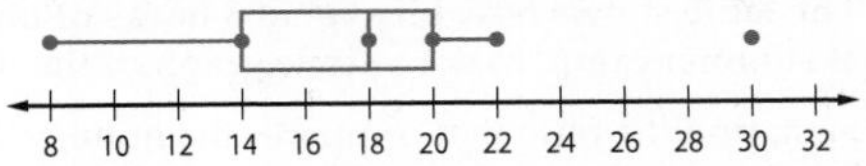

Step 4 Omit 30 from the data. Repeat Step 1 to determine Q_1, Q_2, and Q_3.

8, 13, **14,** 16, **16, 18,** 18, **20,** 20, 22

Q_1 (14), $Q_2 = 17$, Q_3 (20)

Removing the outlier does not affect Q_1 or Q_2 and thus does not affect the interquartile range. The value of Q_2 changes from 18 to 17.

StudyTip

Parallel Box-and-Whisker Plot A double box-and-whisker plot is sometimes called a *parallel box-and-whisker plot.*

Example 7 Compare Data

CLIMATE Lucas is going to go to college in either Dallas or Nashville. He wants to live in a place that does not get too cold. So he decides to compare the average monthly low temperatures of each city.

Average Monthly Low Temperatures (°F)

Month	Dallas	Nashville
Jan.	36	28
Feb.	41	31
Mar.	49	39
Apr.	56	47
May	65	57
June	73	65
July	77	70
Aug.	76	68
Sept.	69	61
Oct.	58	49
Nov.	47	40
Dec.	39	32

Source: weather.com

a. Draw a double box-and-whisker plot for the data.

Determine the quartiles and outliers for each city.

Dallas

36, 39, 41, 47, 49, 56, 58, 65, 69, 73, 76, 77

$Q_1 = 44$ $Q_2 = 57$ $Q_3 = 71$

Nashville

28, 31, 32, 39, 40, 47, 49, 57, 61, 65, 68, 70

$Q_1 = 35.5$ $Q_2 = 48$ $Q_3 = 63$

There are no outliers. Draw the plots using the same number line.

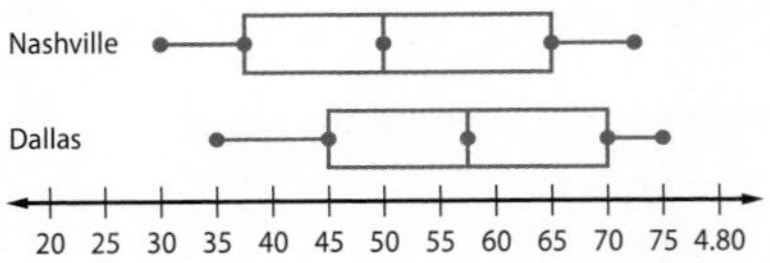

b. Use the double box-and-whisker plot to compare the data.

The interquartile range of temperatures for both cities is about the same. However, all quartiles of the Dallas temperatures are shifted to the right of those of Nashville, meaning Dallas has higher average low temperatures.

c. One night in August, a weather reporter stated the low for Nashville as being "only 65." Is it appropriate for the weather reporter to use the word only in the statement? Is 65 an unusually low temperature for Nashville in August? Explain your answer.

No, 65 is not an unusually low temperature for August in Nashville. It is lower than the average, but not by much.

Additional Answers

1.

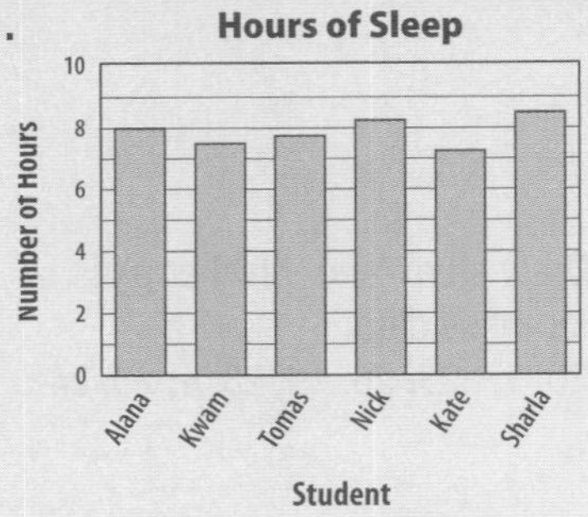

2a.

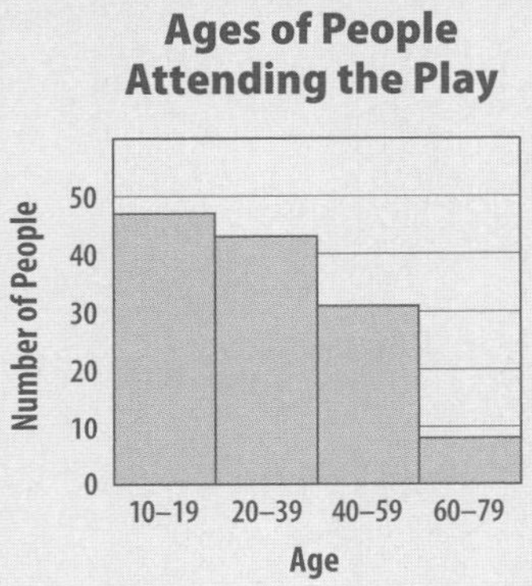

2b.

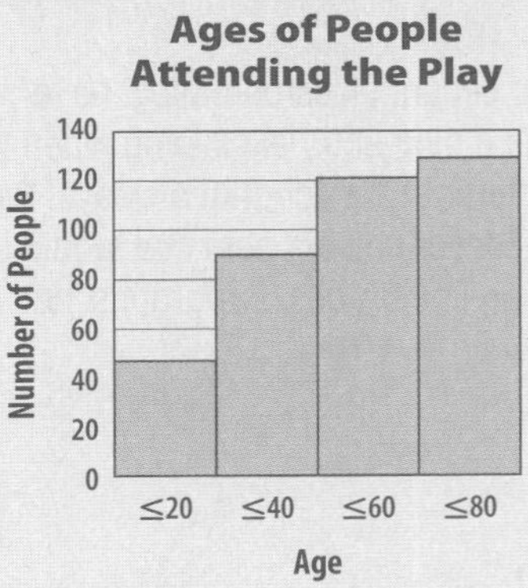

When displaying data, some graphs are better choices than others.

Example 8 Select a Display

Which type of graph is the best way to display each set of data? Explain.

a. the results of the women's Olympic High Jump event from 1972 to 2008

Since the data would show change over time, a line graph would give the reader a clear picture of changes in height.

b. the percent of students in class who have 0, 1, 2, 3, or more than 3 pets

Since the data would show how parts are related to the whole, a circle graph would give the reader a clear picture of how different segments of the class relate to the whole class.

Exercises

1. **SURVEYS** Alana surveyed several students to find the number of hours of sleep they typically get each night. The results are shown in the table. Make a bar graph of the data. **See margin.**

Hours of Sleep					
Alana	8	Kwam	7.5	Tomas	7.75
Nick	8.25	Kate	7.25	Sharla	8.5

2. **PLAYS** The frequency table at the right shows the ages of people attending a high school play.
   a. Make a histogram to display the data.
   b. Make a cumulative frequency histogram showing the number of people attending who were less than 20, 40, 60, or 80 years old. **a, b. See margin.**

Age	Tally	Frequency
0–19	卌 卌 卌 卌 卌 卌 卌 卌 卌 II	47
20–39	卌 卌 卌 卌 卌 卌 卌 卌 III	43
40–59	卌 卌 卌 卌 卌 卌 I	31
60–79	卌 III	8

3. **LAWN CARE** Marcus started a lawn care service. The chart shows how much money he made over summer break. Make a line graph of the data. **See margin.**

Lawn Care Profits ($)								
Week	1	2	3	4	5	6	7	8
Profit	25	40	45	50	75	85	95	95

Use each set of data to make a stem-and-leaf plot and a box-and-whisker plot. Describe how the outliers affect the quartile points.

4. {65, 63, 69, 71, 73, 59, 60, 70, 72, 66, 71, 58} **4, 5. See margin.**
5. {31, 30, 28, 26, 22, 34, 26, 31, 47, 32, 18, 33, 26, 23, 18}
6. **FINANCIAL LITERACY** The table shows how Ping spent his allowance of $40. Make a circle graph of the data. **See margin.**

Allowance	
How Spent	Amount ($)
savings	15
downloaded music	8
snacks	5
T-shirt	12

7. **JOGGING** The table shows the number of miles Hannah jogged each day for 10 days. Make a line graph of the data. **See margin.**

Day	1	2	3	4	5	6	7	8	9	10
Miles Jogged	2	2	3	3.5	4	4.5	2.5	3	4	5

Additional Example

8 Determine which graph is the best way to display each set of data. Explain.

a. the amount of sales for each novel an author writes Since the data will change from novel to novel, a line graph will provide a clear picture of the difference in sales from novel to novel.

b. a person's monthly budget Since the data will show how parts are related to a whole, a circle graph will provide a clear distribution of the different parts of a budget.

3 Assess

Formative Assessment

Use Exercises 1–14 to assess whether students understand how to make visual displays including bar graphs, histograms, line graphs, stem-and-leaf plots, circle graphs, and box-and-whisker plots.

Yesterday's News

Ask students to explain how yesterday's lesson on measures of variation and central tendency helped with today's lesson on representing data in stem-and-leaf plots and box-and-whisker plots.

Additional Answers

4.

Stem	Leaf
5	8 9
6	0 3 5 6 9
7	0 1 1 2 3

Key: $5|8 = 58$

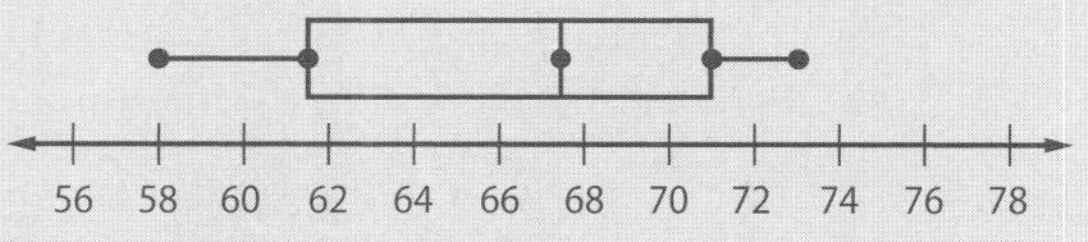

There are no outliers.

5–7. See p. P46.

3. **Lawn Care Profits**

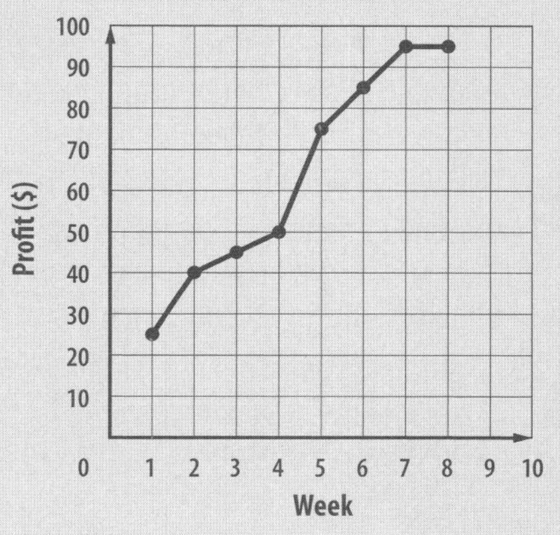

WatchOut!

Preventing Errors In the Exercises, remind students that outliers do not form part of the whiskers of a box-and-whisker plot. Whiskers extend to the greatest value and the least value that are not outliers. Encourage students to carefully distinguish minimum and maximum values from outliers so they do not make outliers part of the whisker.

8b. The interquartile range for both teams is about the same. However, all quartiles of the Lions scores are shifted to the right of those of the Eagles, meaning the Lions have a higher average score.

8c. No, 60 is not an unusually high score for the Lions. It is higher than the average, but not by much.

9b. Most of the data for third period are spread fairly evenly from about 80 to 89, with the lowest score being 67 and the highest score being 99. Most of the data for sixth period are between 79 and 91, with the lowest score for the class being 70 and the highest score being 94.

9c. The sixth period class has a smaller range, a higher median, and a larger interquartile range than the third period class.

14b. 2-liters: \$0.01, \$0.03, \$0.03, \$0.03, \$0.02, \$0.02, \$0.02 12-packs: \$0.02, \$0.03, \$0.02, \$0.02, \$0.02, \$0.03, \$0.02

8. BASKETBALL Two basketball teams are analyzing the number of points they scored in each game this season.

Lions: 48, 52, 55, 49, 53, 55, 51, 50, 46, 53, 47, 55, 50, 51, 60, 52, 57, 56, 58, 55
Eagles: 35, 39, 37, 40, 44, 42, 53, 42, 40, 44, 48, 46, 43, 47, 45, 41, 45, 43, 47, 48

a. Make a double box-and-whisker plot to display the data. **See margin.**

b. How does the number of points scored by the Lions compare to the number of points scored by the Eagles?

c. In the first game of the post season, a sports announcer reported the Lions scored a whopping 60 points. Is it appropriate for the announcer to use the word whopping in the statement? Is 60 an unusually high number of points for the Lions to score? Explain your answer.

9. TESTS Mr. O'Neil teaches two algebra classes. The test scores for the two classes are shown.

Third Period											
77	98	85	79	76	86	84	91	67	88	93	87
99	78	81	80	82	84	83	85	84	95	90	88
Sixth Period											
91	93	88	75	80	78	81	90	82	95	76	88
89	79	93	88	85	94	83	88	91	72	88	70

a. Make a double box-and-whisker plot to display the data. **See margin.**

b. Write a brief description of each data distribution.

c. How do the scores from the third period class compare to the scores from the sixth period class?

Which type of graph is the best way to display each set of data? Explain.

10. an organization's dollar contributions to 4 different charities **10–12. See margin.**

11. the prices of a college football ticket from 1990 to the present

12. the percent of glass, plastic, paper, steel, and aluminum in a recycling center

13. DISCUS The winning distances for the girls' discus throw at an annual track meet are shown below. **13a–b, d. See margin.**

Year	1999	2000	2001	2002	2003	2004	2005	2006	2007	2008	2009	2010
Distance (m)	119	124	126	129	130	130	133	135	136	137	138	140

13c. Sample answer: The histogram shows frequencies, while the stem and leaf shows all data points.

a. Make a stem-and-leaf plot to display the winning distances.

b. Make a histogram to display the winning distances.

c. What does the stem-and-leaf plot show you that the histogram does not?

d. If this trend continues, what would you expect the winning distance to be in 2030? Is your answer reasonable? Explain.

14. DRINKS Tate is buying drinks for a party. He is comparing 2-liter bottles to 12-packs of 12-ounce cans. The prices of 2-liter bottles are \$0.99, \$1.99, \$1.87, \$1.79, \$1.29, \$1.43, and \$1.15. The prices of 12-packs are \$2.50, \$4.25, \$3.34, \$2.65, \$3.19, \$3.89, and 2.99.

a. Make a double box-and-whisker plot to display the data. **14a, c, d. See margin.**

b. Notice that instead of comparing price per item it would be more beneficial to compare price per ounce. What is the price per ounce of each item if a 2-liter is approximately 67 ounces and a 12-pack is 144 ounces? Round to the nearest cent.

c. Make a new double box-and-whisker plot from the data obtained in part **b**.

d. Which is the better deal, the 12-packs of cans or the 2-liter bottles? Explain.

Additional Answers

7. **Miles Jogged**

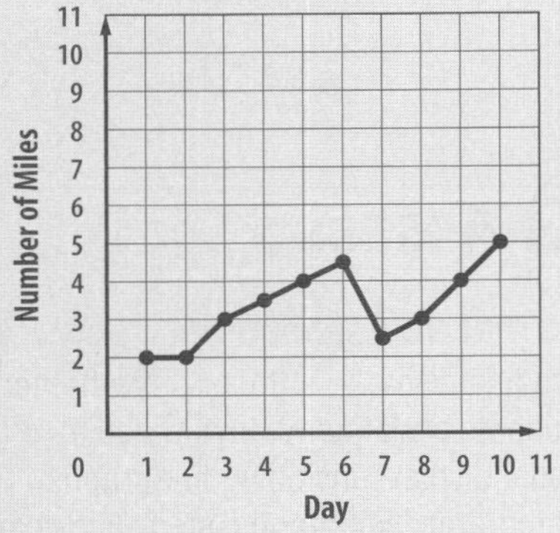

8a.

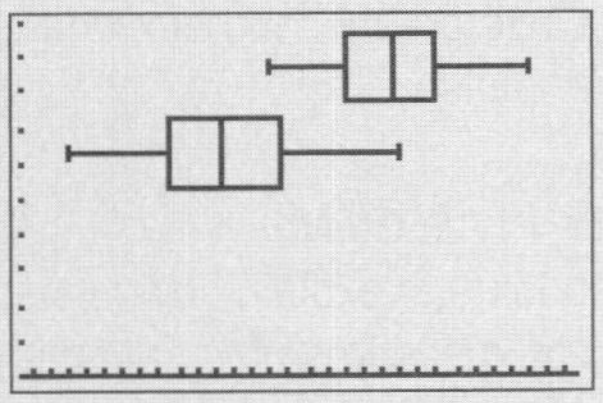

[32.5, 62.5] scl: 1

9a.

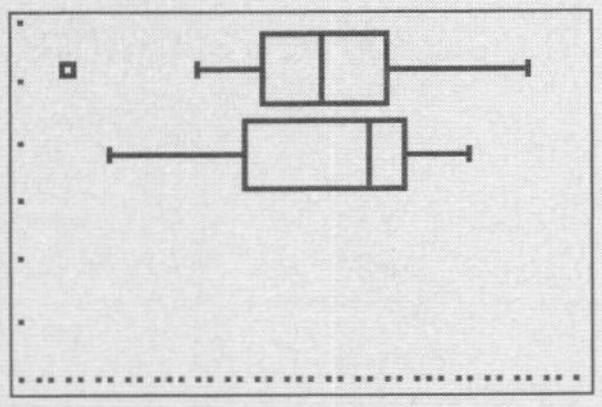

[63.8, 102.2] scl: 1

10. Sample answer: a bar graph would show the contribution amounts for all four charities.

11. Sample answer: a line graph would show how the cost of a seat changes during those years.

12. Sample answer: a circle graph would show how each category compares to the whole recycling center.

5.

Stem	Leaf
1	8 8
2	1 3 6 6 6 8
3	0 1 1 2 3 4
4	7

Key: 1|8 = 18

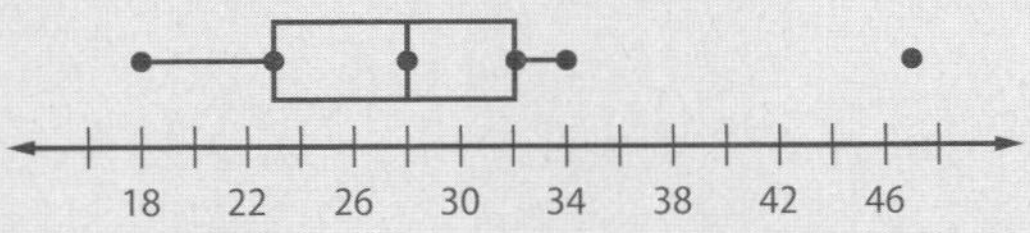

Removing 47 leaves Q_1 the same, changes Q_2 to 27 and Q_3 to 31.

6. **Allowance**

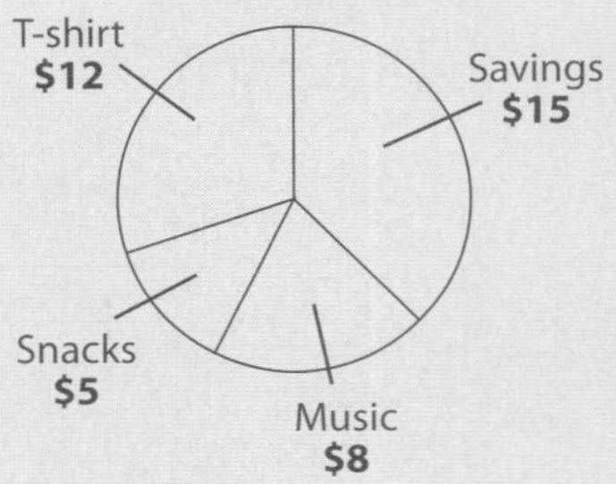

CHAPTER 0 Posttest

Determine whether you need an estimate or an exact answer. Then use the four-step problem-solving plan to solve.

1. **DISTANCE** Fabio rode his scooter 2.3 miles to his friend's house, then 0.7 mile to the grocery store, then 2.1 miles to the library. If he rode the same route back home, about how far did he travel in all? **estimate; about 10 mi**

2. **SHOPPING** The regular price of a T-shirt is \$9.99. It is on sale for 15% off. Sales tax is 6%. If you give the cashier a \$10 bill, how much change will you receive? **exact; \$1**

Find each sum or difference.

3. $-31 + (-4)$ **−35**
4. $48 - 55$ **−7**
5. $-71 - (-10)$ **−61**
6. $31 - 42.9$ **−11.9**
7. $-11.5 + 8.1$ **−3.4**
8. $-0.38 - (-1.06)$ **0.68**

Find each product or quotient.

9. $-21(-5)$ **105**
10. $-81 \div (-3)$ **27**
11. $-120 \div 8$ **−15**
12. $-39 \div -3$ **13**

Replace each ● with <, >, or = to make a true sentence.

13. -0.62 ● $-\frac{6}{7}$ **>**
14. $\frac{12}{44}$ ● $\frac{8}{11}$ **<**
15. Order $4\frac{4}{5}$, 4.85, $2\frac{5}{8}$, and 2.6 from least to greatest. **2.6, $2\frac{5}{8}$, $4\frac{4}{5}$, 4.85**

Find each sum or difference. Write in simplest form.

16. $\frac{1}{7} + \frac{5}{7}$ $\frac{6}{7}$
17. $\frac{7}{8} - \frac{1}{8}$ $\frac{3}{4}$
18. $\frac{1}{6} + \left(-\frac{1}{2}\right)$ $-\frac{1}{3}$
19. $-\frac{1}{12} - \left(-\frac{3}{4}\right)$ $\frac{2}{3}$

Find each product or quotient.

20. $-1.2(9.3)$ **−11.16**
21. $-20.93 \div (-2.3)$ **9.1**
22. $10.5 \div (-1.2)$ **−8.75**
23. $(-3.4)(-2.8)$ **9.52**

Name the reciprocal of each number.

24. 6 $\frac{1}{6}$
25. $1\frac{2}{5}$ $\frac{5}{7}$
26. $-2\frac{3}{7}$ $-\frac{7}{17}$
27. $-\frac{1}{2}$ -2
28. $\frac{4}{3}$ $\frac{3}{4}$
29. $5\frac{1}{3}$ $\frac{3}{16}$

Find each product or quotient. Write in simplest form.

30. $\frac{2}{5} \cdot \frac{5}{9}$ $\frac{2}{9}$
31. $\frac{4}{5} \div \frac{1}{5}$ 4
32. $-\frac{7}{8} \cdot 2$ $-1\frac{3}{4}$
33. $\frac{1}{3} \div 2\frac{1}{4}$ $\frac{4}{27}$
34. $-6 \cdot \left(-\frac{3}{4}\right)$ $4\frac{1}{2}$
35. $\frac{7}{18} \div \left(-\frac{14}{15}\right)$ $-\frac{5}{12}$

36. **PICNIC** Joseph is mixing $5\frac{1}{2}$ gallons of orange drink for his class picnic. Every $\frac{1}{2}$ gallon requires 1 packet of orange drink mix. How many packets of orange drink mix does Joseph need? **11 packets**

Express each percent as a fraction in simplest form.

37. 6% $\frac{3}{50}$
38. 140% $\frac{7}{5}$

Use the percent proportion to find each number.

39. 50% of what number is 31? **62**
40. What number is 110% of 51? **56.1**
41. Find 8% of 95. **7.6**

42. **SOLUTIONS** A solution is prepared by dissolving 24 milliliters of saline in 150 milliliters of pure solution. What is the percent of saline in the pure solution? **16%**

43. **SHOPPING** Marta got 60% off a pair of shoes. If the shoes cost \$9.75 (before sales tax), what was the original price of the shoes? **\$24.38**

Find the perimeter and area of each figure.

44.
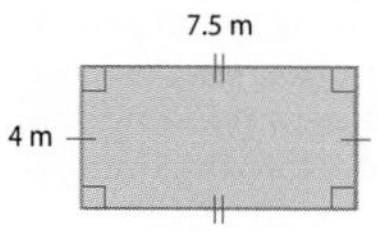

23 m; 30 m²

45.
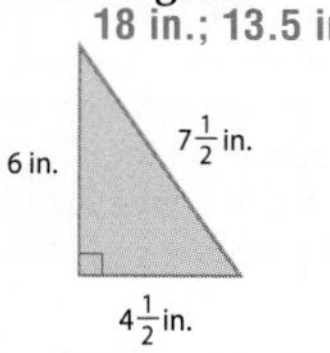

18 in.; 13.5 in²

46. A parallelogram has a base of 20 millimeters and a height of 6 millimeters. Find the area. **120 mm²**

47. **GARDENS** Find the perimeter of the garden. **13.5 m**

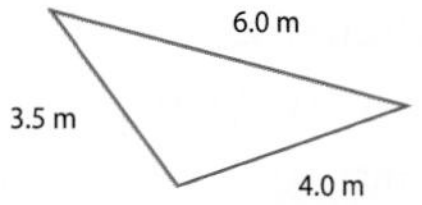

Using the Posttest

Use the Chapter 0 Posttest to assess students' understanding of the concepts after you have presented the lessons in Chapter 0. If students are still having difficulty with one or more concepts, refer to *Math Triumphs 8/9* for strategies for reteaching.

Additional Answers

13a.

Stem	Leaf
11	9
12	4 6 9
13	0 0 3 5 6 7 8
14	0
	Key: *11 | 9 = 119*

13b.

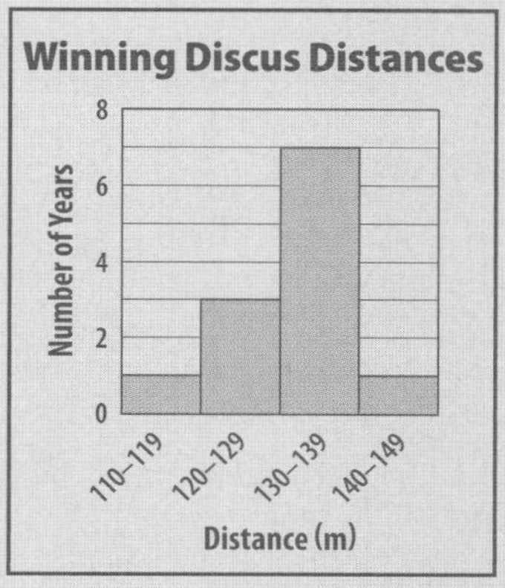

13d. Sample answer: The winning distance increased by 16 meters from 2000 to 2010. If this continues, in 2030 the winning distance will be 32 meters more than in 2010, or 172 meters. It is unreasonable to expect that every year girls will be able to throw farther and farther, at some time the distance will level off.

14a.

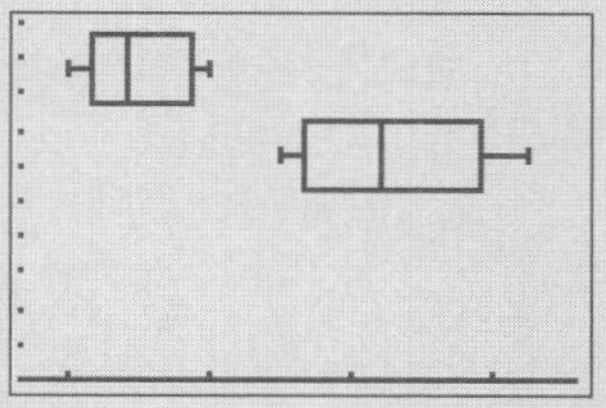

[0.664, 4.576] scl: 1

14c.

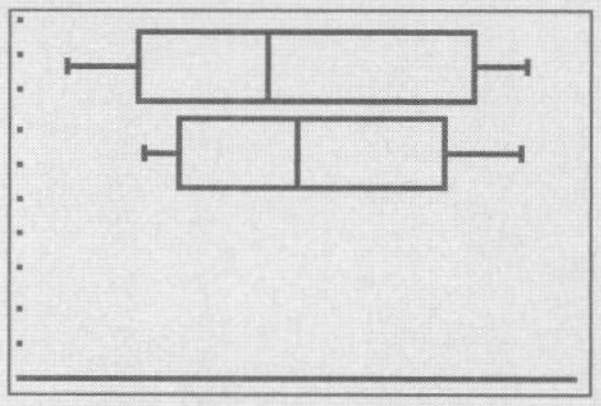

[0.01, 0.03] scl: 1

14d. Sample answer: There is not a significant difference in price per ounce. The 2-liters are between \$0.01 and \$0.03 per ounce and the 12-packs are between \$0.02 and \$0.03 per ounce.

Additional Answers

69.

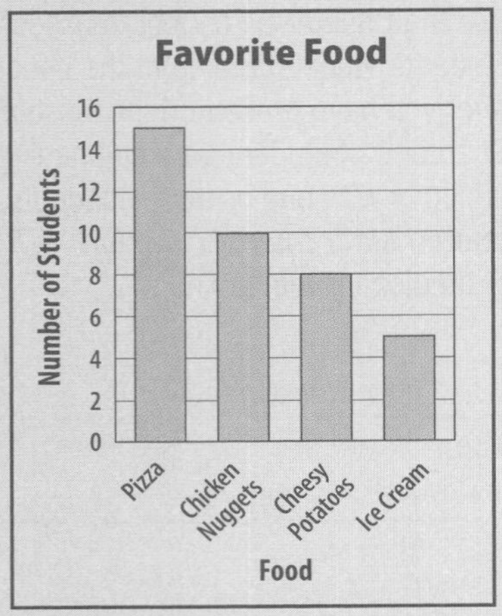

70.

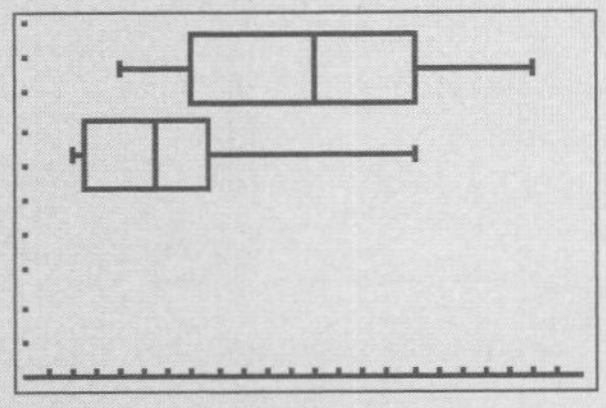

[14, 37] scl: 1

71.

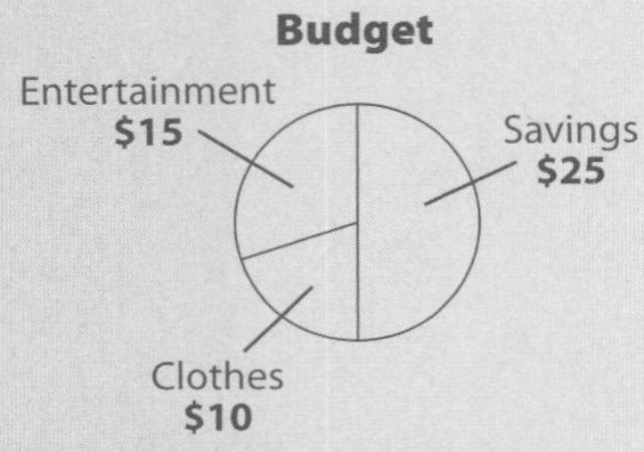

Sample answer: a circle graph would show how each category compares to the total allowance.

Posttest *Continued*

Find the circumference and area of each circle. Round to the nearest tenth.

48.

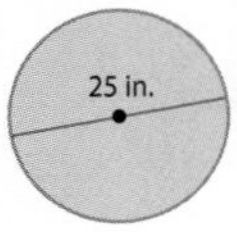

78.5 in.; 490.9 in^2

49.

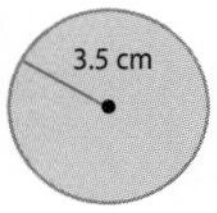

22.0 cm; 38.5 cm^2

50. **PARKS** A park has a circular area for a fountain that has a circumference of about 16 feet. What is the radius of the circular area? Round to the nearest tenth. 2.5 ft

Find the volume and surface area of each rectangular prism given the measurements below.

51. $\ell = 1.5$ m, $w = 3$ m, $h = 2$ m 9 m^3; 27 m^2

52. $\ell = 4$ in., $w = 1$ in., $h = \frac{1}{2}$ in. 2 in^3; 13 in^2

53. Find the volume and surface area of the rectangular prism. 7.8 m^3; 30.2 m^2

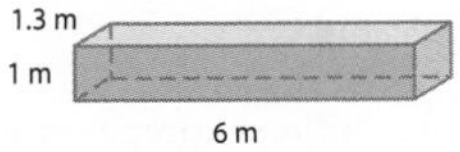

One marble is randomly selected from a jar containing 3 red, 4 green, 2 black, and 6 blue marbles. Find each probability.

54. P(red or blue) $\frac{3}{5}$

55. P(green or red) $\frac{7}{15}$

56. P(not black) $\frac{13}{15}$

57. P(not blue) $\frac{3}{5}$

58. A movie theater is offering snack specials. You can choose a small, medium, large, or jumbo popcorn with or without butter, and soda or bottled water. Use a tree diagram to find the sample space for the event. State the number of possible outcomes. 16 outcomes

One coin is randomly selected from a jar containing 20 pennies, 15 nickels, 3 dimes, and 12 quarters. Find the odds of each outcome. Write in simplest form.

59. a dime 3:47

60. a value less than \$0.25 19:6

61. a value greater than \$0.10 6:19

62. a value less than \$0.05 2:3

63. **SCHOOL** In a science class, each student must choose a lab project from a list of 15, write a paper on one of 6 topics, and give a presentation about one of 8 subjects. How many ways can students choose to do their assignments? 720 ways

64. **GAMES** Marcos has been dealt seven different cards. How many different ways can he play his cards if he is required to play one card at a time? 5040 ways

Find the mean, median, and mode for each set of data.

65. {99, 88, 88, 92, 100} 93.4; 92; 88

66. {30, 22, 38, 41, 33, 41, 30, 24} 32.375; 31.5; 30 and 41

67. Find the range, median, lower quartile, and upper quartile for {77, 75, 72, 70, 79, 77, 70, 76}. 9; 75.5; 71; 77

68. **TESTS** Kevin's scores on the first four science tests are 88, 92, 82, and 94. What score must he earn on the fifth test so that the mean will be 90? 94

69. **FOOD** The table shows the results of a survey in which students were asked to choose their favorite food. Make a bar graph of the data. See margin.

Favorite Foods	
Food	**Number of Students**
pizza	15
chicken nuggets	10
cheesy potatoes	8
ice cream	5

70. Make a double box-and-whisker plot of the data.
A: 26, 18, 26, 29, 18, 20, 35, 32, 31, 24, 26, 22
B: 16, 20, 16, 19, 21, 30, 25, 22, 21, 19, 16, 17
See margin.

71. **BUDGET** The table shows how Kat spends her allowance. Which graph is the best way to display these data? Explain your reasoning and make a graph of the data. See margin.

Category	Amount (\$)
Savings	25
Clothes	10
Entertainment	15

Chapter Planner

	Diagnostic Assessment Quick Check		
	LESSON 1-1 45 min: 1 day; 90 min: 0.75 day	**LESSON 1-2** 45 min: 1.5 days; 90 min: 0.75 day	**LESSON 1-3** 45 min: 1 day; 90 min: 0.5 day
Title	**Variables and Expressions**	**Order of Operations**	**Properties of Numbers**
Objectives	▪ Write verbal expressions for algebraic expressions. ▪ Write algebraic expressions for verbal expressions.	▪ Evaluate numerical expressions by using the order of operations. ▪ Evaluate algebraic expressions by using the order of operations.	▪ Recognize the properties of equality and identity. ▪ Recognize the Commutative and Associative Properties.
Key Vocabulary	algebraic expressions variable term factor product power exponent base	evaluate order of operations	equivalent expressions additive identity multiplicative identity multiplicative inverse reciprocal
Content Standards	PS.4	PS.7	PS.2, PS.3
Multiple Representations	✓		✓
Lesson Resources	connectED.mcgraw-hill.com Leveled Worksheets Vocabulary Personal Tutor Self-Check Quiz ▪ *5-Minute Check* ▪ *Study Notebook*	connectED.mcgraw-hill.com Leveled Worksheets Quiz 1 Vocabulary Personal Tutor Self-Check Quiz ▪ *5-Minute Check* ▪ *Study Notebook* ▪ *Teaching Algebra with Manipulatives*	connectED.mcgraw-hill.com Leveled Worksheets Vocabulary Animations Personal Tutor Self-Check Quiz ▪ *5-Minute Check* ▪ *Study Notebook*
Resources for Every Lesson	IWB eStudent Edition IWB Interactive Classroom	▪ eTeacher Edition ▪ eSolutions Manual ▪ McGraw-Hill eAssessment	
Differentiated Instruction	pp. 6, 9	pp. 11, 15	pp. 18, 22

IWB All digital assets are Interactive Whiteboard ready.

Suggested Pacing			
Time Periods	Instruction	Review & Assess	Total
45-minute	12 days	2 days	14 days
90-minute	6 days	1 day	7 days

EXTEND 1-3 **45 min:** 0.5 day **90 min:** 0.25 day	LESSON 1-4 **45 min:** 1 day **90 min:** 0.5 day	LESSON 1-5 **45 min:** 2 days **90 min:** 0.5 day	LESSON 1-6 **45 min:** 1.5 days **90 min:** 0.5 day
Algebra Lab: Accuracy	**The Distributive Property**	**Equations**	**Relations**
▪ Choose a level of accuracy appropriate to limitations on measurement when reporting quantities.	▪ Use the Distributive Property to evaluate expressions. ▪ Use the Distributive Property to simplify expressions.	▪ Solve equations with one variable. ▪ Solve equations with two variables.	▪ Represent relations. ▪ Interpret graphs of relations.
accuracy	like terms simplest form coefficient	open sentence equation solving solution replacement set set element solution set identify	coordinate system coordinate plane *x*- and *y*-axes origin ordered pair *x*- and *y*-coordinates relation mapping domain range independent variable dependent variable
PS.6	PS.8, AI.RNE.6		AI.F.1, AI.F.2, AI.F.3, AI.F.4
connectED.mcgraw-hill.com Virtual Manipulatives Vocabulary **Materials:** ▪ rulers that measure in centimeters, millimeters, and meters ▪ calculators	connectED.mcgraw-hill.com Leveled Worksheets Quiz 2 Vocabulary Animations Personal Tutor Virtual Manipulatives Self-Check Quiz ▪ *5-Minute Check* ▪ *Study Notebook* ▪ *Teaching Algebra with Manipulatives*	connectED.mcgraw-hill.com Leveled Worksheets Vocabulary Animations Personal Tutor Self-Check Quiz ▪ *5-Minute Check* ▪ *Study Notebook*	connectED.mcgraw-hill.com Leveled Worksheets Quiz 3 Vocabulary Animations Personal Tutor Virtual Manipulatives Self-Check Quiz ▪ *5-Minute Check* ▪ *Study Notebook* ▪ *Teaching Algebra with Manipulatives*
IWB eStudent Edition IWB Interactive Classroom	▪ eTeacher Edition ▪ eSolutions Manual ▪ McGraw-Hill eAssessment		
	pp. 27, 31	pp. 35, 39	pp. 45, 46
	Formative Assessment Mid-Chapter Quiz		

Chapter Planner

	LESSON 1-7 (45 min: 1.5 days; 90 min: 0.75 day)	EXTEND 1-7 (45 min: 0.5 day; 90 min: 0.5 day)	LESSON 1-8 (45 min: 1.5 days; 90 min: 1 day)
Title	**Functions**	**Graphing Technology Lab: Representing Functions**	**Interpreting Graphs of Functions**
Objectives	▪ Determine whether a relation is a function. ▪ Find function values.	▪ Use technology to represent a function as a graph and as a table.	▪ Interpret intercepts, and symmetry of graphs of functions. ▪ Interpret positive, negative, increasing, and decreasing behavior, extrema, and end behavior of graphs of functions.
Key Vocabulary	function discrete function continuous function vertical line test function notation nonlinear function		intercept *x*-intercept *y*-intercept symmetry positive negative increasing decreasing extrema relative maximum relative minimum end behavior
Content Standards	AI.F.1, AI.F.2, AI.F.3, AI.F.4	PS.5	AI.F.2, AI.F.4, PS.1
Multiple Representations			
Lesson Resources	connectED.mcgraw-hill.com Leveled Worksheets Vocabulary Animations Personal Tutor Virtual Manipulatives Self-Check Quiz ▪ *5-Minute Check* ▪ *Study Notebook* ▪ *Teaching Algebra with Manipulatives*	connectED.mcgraw-hill.com Animations Personal Tutor **Materials:** ▪ TI-Nspire Technology	connectED.mcgraw-hill.com Leveled Worksheets Quiz 4 Vocabulary Animations Personal Tutor Self-Check Quiz ▪ *5-Minute Check* ▪ *Study Notebook*
Resources for Every Lesson	IWB eStudent Edition IWB Interactive Classroom	▪ eTeacher Edition ▪ eSolutions Manual ▪ McGraw-Hill eAssessment	
Differentiated Instruction	pp. 50, 54		pp. 57, 61

Summative Assessment
Study Guide and Review
Practice Test

IWB All digital assets are Interactive Whiteboard ready.

Quick Review Math Handbook*

is Glencoe's mathematical handbook for students and parents.

HotWords includes a glossary of terms.

HotTopics consists of two parts:

- explanations of key mathematical concepts
- exercises to check students' understanding.

Lesson	Hot Topics Section	Lesson	Hot Topics Section
1-1	6.1	1-5	6.4
1-2	1.1, 1.3, 6.3	1-6	6.7
1-3	6.2	1-7	6.7
1-4	6.2	1-8	6.7

**Also available in Spanish*

Teacher to Teacher

Larry Hummel
Central City High School
Central City, NE

Use Before Lesson 1-6

"I like to introduce the CBL or CBR with a graphing calculator with Example 3. I give students a graph and see if they can duplicate it by moving back and forth in front of the range finder. It really makes them think about what the graph represents."

Project CRISS℠

STUDY SKILL

Encourage students to write process notes as they study new concepts and algorithms.

Process notes help students work through the steps of problem solving by writing the steps in the left column and the sample steps for an example in the right column.

These process notes describe how to use the order of operations to evaluate an expression, which students study in Lesson 1-2.

Topic:	Notes
Step 1 Evaluate expressions inside grouping symbols.	$14 - 30 \div 5 + (6 - 2)^2$
Step 2 Evaluate all powers.	$= 14 - 30 \div 5 + (4)^2$
Step 3 Do all multiplications and/or divisions from left to right.	$= 14 - 30 \div 5 + (16)$
Step 4 Do all additions and subtractions from left to right.	$= 14 - 6 + 16$ $= 8 + 16$ $= 24$

Creating Independence through Student-owned Strategies

CHAPTER 1

Expressions, Equations, and Functions

Assessment and Intervention

SE = Student Edition, **TE** = Teacher Edition, **CRM** = Chapter Resource Masters

DIAGNOSTIC ASSESSMENT

Diagnosis	Prescription
Beginning Chapter 1	
Get Ready for Chapter 1 **SE**	Response to Intervention **TE**
Beginning Every Lesson	
Then, Now, Why? **SE** 5-Minute Check	Chapter 0 **SE** *Quick Review Math Handbook*

FORMATIVE ASSESSMENT

Diagnosis	Prescription
During/After Every Lesson	
Guided Practice **SE**, every example Check Your Understanding **SE** H.O.T. Problems **SE** Spiral Review **SE** Additional Examples **TE** Watch Out! **TE** Step 4, Assess **TE** Chapter 1 Quizzes **CRM**, pp. 57–58 Self-Check Quizzes connectED.mcgraw-hill.com	TIER 1 Intervention Skills Practice **CRM**, Ch. 1 connectED.mcgraw-hill.com TIER 2 Intervention Differentiated Instruction **TE** Differentiated Homework Options **TE** Study Guide and Intervention **CRM**, Ch. 1 *Quick Review Math Handbook* TIER 3 Intervention *Math Triumphs, Alg. 1,* Ch. 1, 2, 3, 5, and 6
Mid-Chapter	
Mid-Chapter Quiz **SE** Mid-Chapter Test **CRM**, p. 59 McGraw-Hill eAssessment	TIER 1 Intervention Skills Practice **CRM**, Ch. 1 connectED.mcgraw-hill.com TIER 2 Intervention Study Guide and Intervention **CRM**, Ch. 1; *Quick Review Math Handbook* TIER 3 Intervention *Math Triumphs, Alg. 1,* Ch. 1, 2, 3, 5, and 6
Before Chapter Test	
Chapter Study Guide and Review **SE** Practice Test **SE** Standardized Test Practice **SE** Chapter Test connectED.mcgraw-hill.com Standardized Test Practice connectED.mcgraw-hill.com Vocabulary Review connectED.mcgraw-hill.com McGraw-Hill eAssessment	TIER 1 Intervention Skills Practice **CRM**, Ch. 1 connectED.mcgraw-hill.com TIER 2 Intervention Study Guide and Intervention **CRM**, Ch. 1; *Quick Review Math Handbook* TIER 3 Intervention *Math Triumphs, Alg. 1,* Ch. 1, 2, 3, 5, and 6

SUMMATIVE ASSESSMENT

Diagnosis	Prescription
After Chapter 1	
Multiple-Choice Tests, Forms 1, 2A, 2B **CRM**, pp. 61–66 Free-Response Tests, Forms 2C, 2D, 3 **CRM**, pp. 67–72 Vocabulary Test **CRM**, p. 60 Extended Response Test **CRM**, p. 73 Standardized Test Practice **CRM**, pp. 74–76 McGraw-Hill eAssessment	Study Guide and Intervention **CRM**, Ch. 1 *Quick Review Math Handbook* connectED.mcgraw-hill.com

Differentiated Instruction

Option 1 Reaching All Learners AL OL BL ELL

Naturalist Challenge students to write open sentences about a plant or animal they are interested in. For example, the gestation period of armadillos can be described using the sentence 60 days $\leq$ gestation period $\leq$ 120 days.

Auditory/Musical If students have difficulty with the concept of mapping, have those who are familiar with reading music make a mapping of the relation between different notes and the number of beats the notes contain. For example, a whole note is held for 4 beats, and a half note for 2 beats. In this case, the domain is the set that contains all of the types of notes and the range is the set that contains the number of beats the notes are held.

Option 2 Approaching Level AL

Play a song with a fast tempo (measured in beats per minute) for 10 seconds and then for 20 seconds. Ask students to count the number of beats each time. Help students understand that the number of beats played is the dependent variable because it is affected by the length of time the song is played. The length of time the song is played is the independent variable because it is unaffected by the number of beats played.

Option 3 English Learners ELL

Write the name and an example of each property of numbers studied in Lesson 1-3 on the board. Have students who are fluent in other languages tell the class how to express the names of these properties and their meanings in those languages.

Option 4 Beyond Level BL

On each of six cards write an equation that represents a function. For each of these six equations, write a table, graph, or mapping that is also a representation of the function on another card. Make a set of cards for each pair of students. Have partners play a matching game with the cards, taking turns turning two cards over until the same function is represented in both cards turned over.

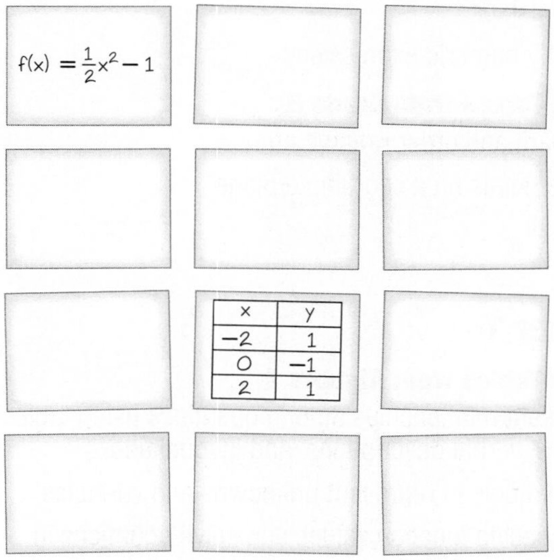

Professional Development

McGraw Hill

Targeted professional development has been articulated throughout Algebra 1. More quality, customized professional development is available from McGraw-Hill Professional Development. Visit connectED.mcgraw-hill.com for details on each product.

- Online Lessons emphasize the strategies and techniques used to teach Algebra 1. Includes streaming video, interactive pages, and online tools.
- Video Workshops allow mentors, coaches, or leadership personnel to facilitate on-site workshops on educational strategies in mathematics and mathematical concepts.
- MHPD Online (www.mhpdonline.com) offers online professional development with video clips of instructional strategies, links, student activities, and news and issues in education.
- Teaching Today (teachingtoday.glencoe.com) gives secondary teachers practical strategies and materials that inspire excellence and innovation in teaching.

Focus on Mathematical Content

VerticalAlignment

Before Chapter 1

Related Topics before Grade 8
- perform operations on integers
- simplify integer expressions
- use concrete models to solve equations
- validate conclusions from mathematical properties and relationships
- simplify numeric expressions

Related Topics from Grade 8
- compare and order rational numbers
- locate points on a coordinate plane

Chapter 1

Related Topics from Algebra 1
- represent relationships among quantities using tables, graphs, verbal descriptions, and inequalities
- use symbols to represent unknowns and variables
- find specific function values and solve equations in problem situations
- use the Commutative, Associative, and Distributive Properties to simplify algebraic expressions
- interpret and make critical predictions from functional relationships
- describe independent and dependent quantities in functional relationships
- identify mathematical domains and ranges and determine reasonable domain and range values for given situations, both continuous and discrete
- connect equation notation with function notation

After Chapter 1

Preparation for Algebra 2
- use the necessary algebraic skills required to simplify algebraic expressions and inequalities in problem situations
- use properties and attributes of functions, and apply functions to problem situations

Lesson-by-Lesson Preview

1-1 Variables and Expressions

Algebraic expressions contain one or more numbers and variables along with arithmetic operations. They can be written as mathematical expressions or verbal expressions. They do not contain an equals sign.

- A variable is a symbol used to represent an unknown number or value. Though any letter can be used as a variable, many letters used as variables are chosen because they are the first letter of the quantity they represent, such as *t* for *time*.
- Algebraic expressions may contain powers. When evaluating a power, the exponent tells you how many times the base is used as a factor.

1-2 Order of Operations

When evaluating an expression, the set of rules that specifies which operation to do first is the order of operations.

- First, perform operations inside grouping symbols. Grouping symbols include parentheses, brackets, braces, and fraction bars. Perform operations inside the innermost grouping symbol first.
- Then, evaluate all powers.
- Next, perform all multiplications and/or divisions from left to right. Finally, perform all additions and/or subtractions from left to right.

1-3 Properties of Numbers

Identity and Equality Properties can be used to justify each step when evaluating expressions and solving equations.

- The Properties of Equality are often used to solve equations. These properties include the Reflexive, Symmetric, Transitive, and Substitution Properties.
- The Commutative Property states that the order in which numbers are added or multiplied does not change their sum or product.
- The Associative Property states that the way three or more numbers are grouped when adding or multiplying does not affect their sum or product.
- The Commutative and Associative Properties do not apply to either subtraction or division because order and grouping affect differences and quotients.

Using these properties can often help make mental calculations easier.

Get educator support from the Math Forum's T2T. You may want to search for or ask about teaching strategies on the difference between a relation and a function. Start your search at connectED.mcgraw-hill.com.

1-4 The Distributive Property

The Distributive Property can be used to evaluate numerical expressions and simplify algebraic expressions.

- The Distributive Property permits a factor outside the parentheses to be distributed to each term of an addition or subtraction expression inside the parentheses. So, $25(8 + 4)$ can be rewritten as $25(8) + 25(4)$, making it easier to evaluate the expression.
- When applying the Distributive Property to algebraic expressions, the coefficients of like terms can be combined and the expressions simplified. For example, the expression $13a + 29a$ can be rewritten as $(13 + 29)a$, which can be simplified as $42a$.

1-5 Equations

An equation is an algebraic statement that contains an equals sign.

- An open sentence is neither true nor false until the variables have been replaced with specific values.
- The process of finding a value for each variable that makes an equation true is called *solving the equation.* A solution set is a set of numbers that makes an equation true.

1-6 Relations

A relation can be represented as a set of ordered pairs, (x, y), as an equation, a table, a mapping, or a graph.

- A mapping lists the x-values in the domain and the y-values in the range. An arrow is drawn from each x-value in the domain to its corresponding y-value in the range.
- The domain contains values of the independent variable and the range contains values of the dependent variable.

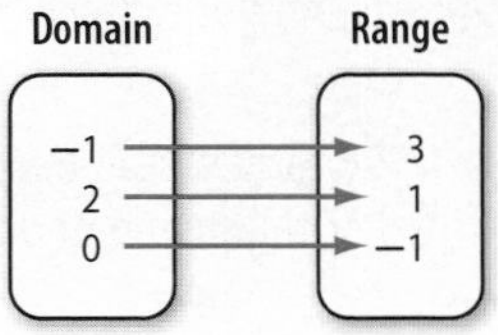

- A table lists the set of x-coordinates in the first column and their corresponding y-coordinates in the second column.
- A coordinate plane consists of a horizontal axis (the x-axis) and a vertical axis (the y-axis) and the intersection of the axes (the origin).

1-7 Functions

A function is a relationship between input and output in which each input value has exactly one output.

- The set of input values is the *domain* of the function, and the set of output values is the *range.*
- A vertical line test can be used to check if a graph is a function. If the graph does not touch any drawn vertical line more than once, it is a function.
- A discrete function's graph consists of points that are not connected. A continuous function's graph forms a line or smooth curve.
- In a function, if x represents the independent quantity (elements of the domain), $f(x)$ represents the dependent quantity (elements of the range).

1-8 Interpreting Graphs of Functions

To interpret a graph, estimate and interpret key features.

- intercepts: points where the graph intersects the x-axis or the y-axis
- intervals where the function is increasing, decreasing:
  - A function is increasing if the graph goes up and decreasing if the graph goes down when viewed from left to right.
- intervals where the function is positive, or negative:
  - A function is positive where its graph lies above the x-axis, and negative where its graph lies below the x-axis.
- extrema (relative maxima and minuma):
  - Point A is a relative maximum if no other nearby points have a greater y-coordinate. Point A is a relative minimum if no other nearby points have a lesser y-coordinate.
- symmetry: A graph has line symmetry in the y-axis or some other vertical line if each half of the graph on either side of the line matches exactly.
- end behavior: the behavior of the values of a function at the positive and negative extremes in its domain

Chapter Project

Want to be Your Own Boss?

Students use what they have learned about expressions to complete a project.

This chapter project entrepreneurial literacy as well as several specific skills identified as being essential to student success by the Framework for 21st Century Learning.

Visit connectED.mcgraw-hill.com for student and teacher handouts.

KeyVocabulary Introduce the key vocabulary in the chapter using the routine below.

Define: An algebraic expression is an expression consisting of one or more numbers and variables along with one or more arithmetic operations.

Example: $x - 7$

Ask: What is the variable? x What is the operation? subtraction What is 7? a number

CHAPTER 1 Expressions, Equations, and Functions

Then

You have learned how to perform operations on whole numbers.

Now

In this chapter, you will:

- Write algebraic expressions.
- Use the order of operations.
- Solve equations.
- Represent and interpret relations and functions.
- Use function notation.
- Interpret the graphs of functions.

Why? ▲

SCUBA DIVING A scuba diving store rents air tanks and wet suits. An algebraic expression can be written to represent the total cost to rent this equipment. This expression can be evaluated to determine the total cost for a group of people to rent the equipment.

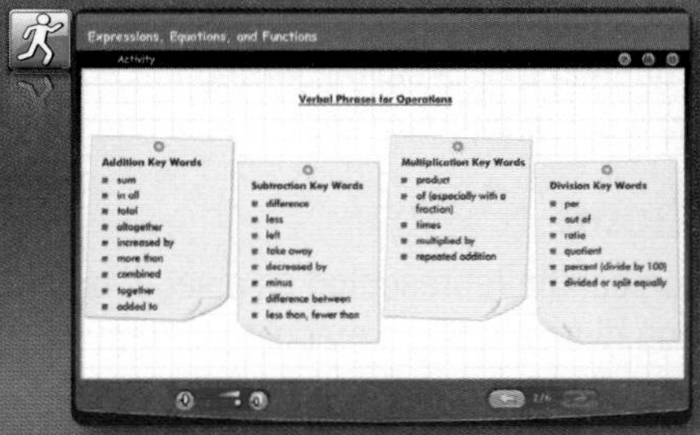

connectED.mcgraw-hill.com Your Digital Math Portal

Animation | Vocabulary | eGlossary | Personal Tutor | Virtual Manipulatives | Graphing Calculator | Audio | Foldables | Self-Check Practice | Worksheets

Content Standards
AI.RNE.6, AI.F.1, AI.F.2, AI.F.3, AI.F.4

Process Standards
PS.1, PS.2, PS.3, PS.4, PS.5, PS.6, PS.7, PS.8

Get Ready for the Chapter

Diagnose Readiness | You have two options for checking prerequisite skills.

1 Textbook Option Take the Quick Check below. Refer to the Quick Review for help.

QuickCheck

Write each fraction in simplest form. If the fraction is already in simplest form, write *simplest form.*

1. $\frac{24}{36}$ $\frac{2}{3}$
2. $\frac{34}{85}$ $\frac{2}{5}$
3. $\frac{36}{12}$ 3
4. $\frac{27}{45}$ $\frac{3}{5}$
5. $\frac{11}{18}$ simplest form
6. $\frac{5}{65}$ $\frac{1}{13}$
7. $\frac{19}{1}$ 19
8. $\frac{16}{44}$ $\frac{4}{11}$
9. $\frac{64}{88}$ $\frac{8}{11}$
10. **ICE CREAM** Fifty-four out of 180 customers said that cookie dough ice cream was their favorite flavor. What fraction of customers was this? $\frac{3}{10}$

Find the perimeter of each figure.

11. 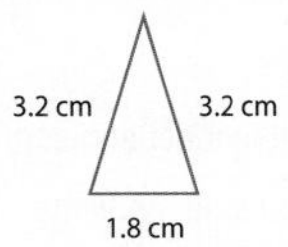

8.2 cm

12. 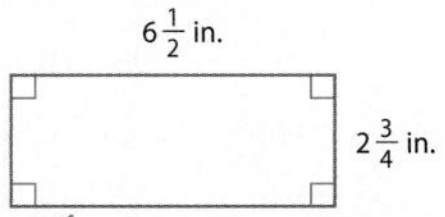

$18\frac{1}{2}$ in.

13. **FENCING** Jolon needs to fence a rectangular garden. The dimensions of the garden are 6 meters by 4 meters. How much fencing does Jolon need to purchase? **20 m**

Evaluate.

14. $6 \cdot \frac{2}{3}$ 4
15. $4.2 \cdot 8.1$ 34.02
16. $\frac{3}{8} \div \frac{1}{4}$ $\frac{3}{2}$ or $1\frac{1}{2}$
17. $5.13 \div 2.7$ 1.9
18. $3\frac{1}{5} \cdot \frac{3}{4}$
19. $2.8 \cdot 0.2$ 0.56
20. **CONSTRUCTION** A board measuring 7.2 feet must be cut into three equal pieces. Find the length of each piece. **2.4 ft**

18. $\frac{12}{5}$ or $2\frac{2}{5}$

QuickReview

Example 1 (Used in Lessons 1-2 and 1-5)

Write $\frac{24}{40}$ in simplest form.

Find the greatest common factor (GCF) of 24 and 40.

factors of 24: 1, 2, 3, 4, 6, 8, 12, 24
factors of 40: 1, 2, 4, 5, 8, 10, 20, 40

The GCF of 24 and 40 is 8.

$\frac{24 \div 8}{40 \div 8} = \frac{3}{5}$ Divide the numerator and denominator by their GCF, 8.

Example 2 (Used in Lessons 1-1 through 1-6)

Find the perimeter.

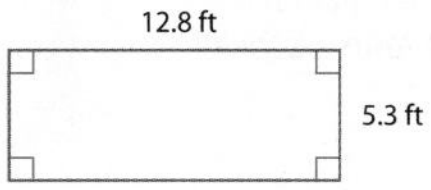

$P = 2\ell + 2w$

$= 2(12.8) + 2(5.3)$ $\ell = 12.8$ and $w = 5.3$

$= 25.6 + 10.6$ or 36.2 Simplify.

The perimeter is 36.2 feet.

Example 3 (Used in Lessons 1-1 through 1-6)

Find $2\frac{1}{4} \div 1\frac{1}{2}$.

$2\frac{1}{4} \div 1\frac{1}{2} = \frac{9}{4} \div \frac{3}{2}$ Write mixed numbers as improper fractions.

$= \frac{9}{4}\left(\frac{2}{3}\right)$ Multiply by the reciprocal.

$= \frac{18}{12}$ or $1\frac{1}{2}$ Simplify.

2 Online Option Take an online self-check Chapter Readiness Quiz at connectED.mcgraw-hill.com.

Essential Question

- How can mathematical ideas be represented?

Sample answer: You can represent mathematical ideas verbally, algebraically, numerically, and graphically. For example, an equation can be described in words or could be represented by a table of values or a graph.

Essential Questions frame each chapter. These open-ended questions guide student inquiry into the "big ideas" central to each chapter. Throughout the Student Edition, Exercises that refer to the chapter or follow up Essential Questions are indicated by the icon.

Get Ready for the Chapter

Response to Intervention (RtI)

Use the *Quick Check* results and the Intervention Planner chart to help you determine your Response to Intervention. The If-Then statements in the chart below help you decide the appropriate tier of RtI and suggest intervention resources for each tier.

InterventionPlanner

TIER 1 On Level OL

If students miss about 25% of the exercises or less,

Then choose a resource:

SE Lessons 0-4, 0-5, and 0-7

connectED.mcgraw-hill.com Self-Check Quiz

TIER 2 Strategic Intervention AL approaching grade level

If students miss about 50% of the exercises,

Then choose a resource:

Quick Review Math Handbook

connectED.mcgraw-hill.com Extra Examples, Personal Tutor, Homework Help

TIER 3 Intensive Intervention 2 or more grades below level

If students miss about 75% of the exercises,

Then use *Math Triumphs, Alg. 1,* Ch. 1, 2, 3, 5 and 6

connectED.mcgraw-hill.com Extra Examples, Personal Tutor, Homework Help, Review Vocabulary

Diagnose students' readiness for each chapter by using either the intext **Quick Check** or the online **Chapter Readiness Quiz**. Then use the **Intervention Planner** to choose the correct program resource to reinforce each student's prerequisite skills.

FOLDABLES® StudyOrganizer

Dinah Zike's Foldables®

Focus Students write notes about expressions, equations, and functions as they are presented in each lesson of this chapter.

Teach Have students make and label their Foldables as illustrated. Have students write a summary of each lesson on its corresponding sheet. Under the summaries, they should include an example of the lesson's main concept. Point out that the ninth tab should be used to list the properties described in the chapter, and the last tab should be used to list the chapter's vocabulary.

When to Use It Encourage students to add to their Foldables as they work through the chapter and to use them to review for the chapter test.

Differentiated Instruction

Student-Built Glossary, pp. 1–2

Students should complete the chart by providing the definition of each term and an example as they progress through Chapter 1. This study tool can also be used to review for the chapter test.

Foldables® are a unique way to enhance students' study skills. Encourage students to add to their Foldable as they work through the chapter and to use it for review for the chapter test.

Get Started on the Chapter

You will learn several new concepts, skills, and vocabulary terms as you study Chapter 1. To get ready, identify important terms and organize your resources. You may wish to refer to Chapter 0 to review prerequisite skills.

FOLDABLES StudyOrganizer

Expressions, Equations, and Functions Make this Foldable to help you organize your Chapter 1 notes about expressions, equations, and functions. Begin with five sheets of plain paper.

1 **Fold** the sheets of paper in half along the width. Then cut along the crease.

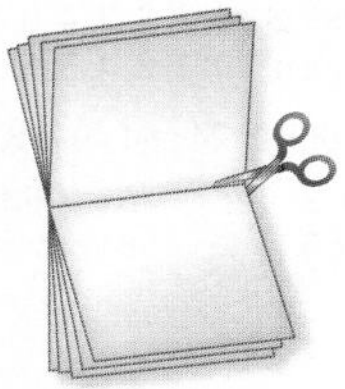

2 **Staple** the ten half-sheets together to form a booklet.

3 **Cut** nine centimeters from the bottom of the top sheet, eight centimeters from the second sheet, and so on.

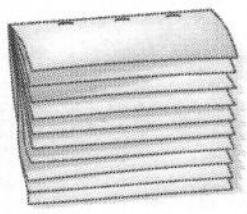

4 **Label** each of the tabs with a lesson number. The ninth tab is for Properties and the last tab is for Vocabulary.

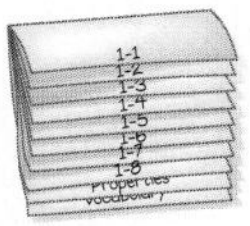

NewVocabulary

English		Español
algebraic expression	p. 5	expression algebraica
variable	p. 5	variable
term	p. 5	término
power	p. 5	potencia
coefficient	p. 28	coeficiente
equation	p. 33	ecuación
solution	p. 33	solución
identity	p. 35	identidad
relation	p. 40	relacíon
domain	p. 40	domino
range	p. 40	rango
independent variable	p. 42	variable independiente
dependent variable	p. 42	variable dependiente
function	p. 47	función
intercept	p. 56	intersección
line symmetry	p. 57	simetría
end behavior	p. 57	comportamiento final

ReviewVocabulary

additive inverse inverso aditivo a number and its opposite

multiplicative inverse inverso multiplicativo two numbers with a product of 1

perimeter perímetro the distance around a geometric figure

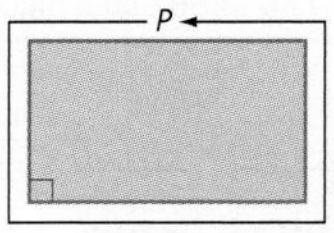

LESSON 1-1 Variables and Expressions

Then
- You performed operations on integers.

Now
1. Write verbal expressions for algebraic expressions.
2. Write algebraic expressions for verbal expressions.

Why?
- Cassie and her friends are at a baseball game. The stadium is running a promotion where hot dogs are $0.10 each. Suppose *d* represents the number of hot dogs Cassie and her friends eat. Then 0.10*d* represents the cost of the hot dogs they eat.

NewVocabulary
algebraic expression
variable
term
factor
product
power
exponent
base

Process Standards
PS.4

1 Write Verbal Expressions

An **algebraic expression** consists of sums and/or products of numbers and variables. In the algebraic expression $0.10d$, the letter d is called a variable. In algebra, **variables** are symbols used to represent unspecified numbers or values. Any letter may be used as a variable.

$$0.10d \qquad 2x + 4 \qquad 3 + \frac{z}{6} \qquad p \cdot q \qquad 4cd \div 3mn$$

A **term** of an expression may be a number, a variable, or a product or quotient of numbers and variables. For example, $0.10d$, $2x$ and 4 are each terms.

The term that contains *x* or other letters is sometimes referred to as the *variable term*. → $2x + 4$ ← A term that does not have a variable is a *constant term*.

In a multiplication expression, the quantities being multiplied are **factors**, and the result is the **product**. A raised dot or set of parentheses are often used to indicate a product. Here are several ways to represent the product of *x* and *y*.

$$xy \qquad x \cdot y \qquad x(y) \qquad (x)y \qquad (x)(y)$$

An expression like x^n is called a **power**. The word *power* can also refer to the exponent. The **exponent** indicates the number of times the base is used as a factor. In an expression of the form x^n, the **base** is x. The expression x^n is read "x to the nth power." When no exponent is shown, it is understood to be 1. For example, $a = a^1$.

x^n: base (x), exponent (n)

Example 1 Write Verbal Expressions

PT

Write a verbal expression for each algebraic expression.

a. $3x^4$

three times x to the fourth power

b. $5z^2 + 16$

5 times z to the second power plus sixteen

GuidedPractice

1A. $16u^2 - 3$ **16 times *u* to the second power minus 3**

1B. $\frac{1}{2}a + \frac{6b}{7}$ **one half of *a* plus the quotient of 6 times *b* and 7**

1 Focus

VerticalAlignment

Before Lesson 1-1 Perform operations on integers.

Lesson 1-1 Write verbal expressions for algebraic expressions.
Write algebraic expressions for verbal expressions.

After Lesson 1-1 Evaluate algebraic expressions.

2 Teach

Scaffolding Questions

Have students read the **Why?** section of the lesson.

Ask:
- How do you find the cost of the hot dogs that Cassie and her friends eat? Multiply the number of hot dogs by $0.10.
- What does the expression 0.10*d* stand for? 0.10 times *d*, the number of hot dogs
- What other variable could you use to represent the number of hot dogs? Sample answer: *h*

1 Write Verbal Expressions

Example 1 shows how to translate an algebraic expression into a verbal expression.

Lesson 1-1 Resources

Resource	Approaching Level AL	On Level OL	Beyond Level BL	English Learners ELL
Teacher Edition	▪ Differentiated Instruction, p. 6	▪ Differentiated Instruction, pp. 6, 9	▪ Differentiated Instruction, p. 9	▪ Differentiated Instruction, p. 6
Chapter Resource Masters	▪ Study Guide and Intervention, pp. 5–6 ▪ Skills Practice, p. 7 ▪ Practice, p. 8 ▪ Word Problem Practice, p. 9	▪ Study Guide and Intervention, pp. 5–6 ▪ Skills Practice, p. 7 ▪ Practice, p. 8 ▪ Word Problem Practice, p. 9 ▪ Enrichment, p. 10	▪ Practice, p. 8 ▪ Word Problem Practice, p. 9 ▪ Enrichment, p. 10	▪ Study Guide and Intervention, pp. 5–6 ▪ Skills Practice, p. 7 ▪ Practice, p. 8 ▪ Word Problem Practice, p. 9
Other	▪ 5-Minute Check 1-1 ▪ Study Notebook	▪ 5-Minute Check 1-1 ▪ Study Notebook	▪ 5-Minute Check 1-1 ▪ Study Notebook	▪ 5-Minute Check 1-1 ▪ Study Notebook

Study Tips offer students helpful information about the topics they are studying.

Formative Assessment

Use the Guided Practice exercises after each Example to determine students' understanding of concepts.

Additional Example

1 Write a verbal expression for each algebraic expression.

a. $8x^2$ eight times x squared

b. $y^5 - 16y$ the difference of y to the fifth power and 16 times y

2 Write Algebraic Expressions

Examples 2 and 3 show how to translate a verbal expression into an algebraic expression.

Additional Examples

2 Write an algebraic expression for each verbal expression.

a. 5 less than a number c $c - 5$

b. 9 plus the product of 2 and d $9 + 2d$

c. two fifths of the area a $\frac{2}{5}a$ or $\frac{2a}{5}$

3 **ENTERTAINMENT** Mr. Nehru bought two adult tickets and three student tickets for the planetarium show. Write an algebraic expression that represents the cost of the tickets. Let a be the cost of adult tickets and c be the cost of student tickets. The cost of the tickets is represented by $2a + 3c$.

Additional Examples also in Interactive Classroom PowerPoint® Presentations

IWB Interactive White Board READY

StudyTip

Modeling When writing an expression to model a situation, begin by identifying the important quantities and their relationships.

2 Write Algebraic Expressions

Another important skill is translating verbal expressions into algebraic expressions.

KeyConcept Translating Verbal to Algebraic Expressions

Operation	Verbal Phrases
Addition	more than, sum, plus, increased by, added to
Subtraction	less than, subtracted from, difference, decreased by, minus
Multiplication	product of, multiplied by, times, of
Division	quotient of, divided by

Example 2 Write Algebraic Expressions

Write an algebraic expression for each verbal expression.

a. a number t more than 6

The words *more than* suggest addition.
Thus, the algebraic expression is $6 + t$ or $t + 6$.

b. 10 less than the product of 7 and f

Less than implies subtraction, and *product* suggests multiplication.
So the expression is written as $7f - 10$.

c. two thirds of the volume v

The word *of* with a fraction implies that you should multiply.
The expression could be written as $\frac{2}{3}v$ or $\frac{2v}{3}$.

GuidedPractice

2A. the product of p and 6 $6p$

2B. one third of the area a $\frac{1}{3}a$

Real-WorldCareer

Sports Marketing Sports marketers promote and manage athletes, teams, facilities and sports-related businesses and organizations. A minimum of a bachelor's degree in sports management or business administration is preferred.

Variables can represent quantities that are known and quantities that are unknown. They are also used in formulas, expressions, and equations.

Real-World Example 3 Write an Expression

SPORTS MARKETING **Mr. Martinez orders 250 key chains printed with his athletic team's logo and 500 pencils printed with their Web address. Write an algebraic expression that represents the cost of the order.**

Let k be the cost of each key chain and p be the cost of each pencil. Then the cost of the key chains is $250k$ and the cost of the pencils is $500p$. The cost of the order is represented by $250k + 500p$.

GuidedPractice $40p + 200c$

3. **COFFEE SHOP** Katie bakes 40 pastries and makes coffee for 200 people. Write an algebraic expression to represent this situation.

Image Source/Getty Images

DifferentiatedInstruction AL OL ELL

If you identify students who have trouble writing mathematical or verbal expressions,

Then pair them with other students as mentors for practicing these skills. The transition from verbal expressions to algebraic expressions is easier for some students than others.

Check Your Understanding

= Step-by-Step Solutions begin on page R13.

Example 1 Write a verbal expression for each algebraic expression. 1–3. Sample answers given.

1. $2m$ the product of 2 and m
2. $\frac{2}{3}r^4$ two thirds times r raised to the fourth power
3. $a^2 - 18b$ a squared minus 18 times b

Example 2 Write an algebraic expression for each verbal expression.

4. the sum of a number and 14 $n + 14$
5. 6 less a number t $6 - t$
6. 7 more than 11 times a number $11n + 7$
7. 1 minus the quotient of r and 7 $1 - \frac{r}{7}$
8. two fifths of the square of a number j $\frac{2}{5}j^2$
9. n cubed increased by 5 $n^3 + 5$

Example 3

10. **GROCERIES** Mr. Bailey purchased some groceries that cost d dollars. He paid with a \$50 bill. Write an expression for the amount of change he will receive. $50 - d$

Practice and Problem Solving

Extra Practice is on page R1.

Example 1 Write a verbal expression for each algebraic expression. 11–18. Sample answers given.

11. $4q$ four times a number q
12. $\frac{1}{8}y$ one eighth of y
13. $15 + r$ 15 plus r
14. $w - 24$
15. $3x^2$
16. $\frac{r^4}{9}$
17. $2a + 6$
18. $r^4 \cdot t^3$

14. w minus 24 15. 3 times x squared 16. r to the fourth power divided by 9
17. 6 more than the product 2 times a
18. the product of a number r raised to the fourth power and a number t cubed

Example 2 Write an algebraic expression for each verbal expression.

19. x more than 7 $7 + x$
20. a number less 35 $n - 35$
21. 5 times a number $5n$
22. one third of a number $\frac{1}{3}n$
23. f divided by 10 $\frac{f}{10}$
24. the quotient of 45 and r $\frac{45}{r}$
25. three times a number plus 16 $3n + 16$
26. 18 decreased by 3 times d $18 - 3d$
27. k squared minus 11 $k^2 - 11$
28. 20 divided by t to the fifth power $\frac{20}{t^5}$

Example 3

29. **GEOMETRY** The volume of a cylinder is π times the radius r squared multiplied by the height h. Write an expression for the volume. $\pi r^2 h$

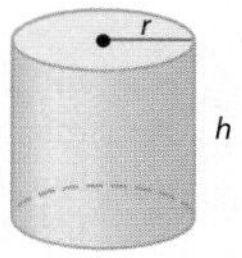

30. **FINANCIAL LITERACY** Jocelyn makes x dollars per hour working at the grocery store and n dollars per hour babysitting. Write an expression that describes her earnings if she babysat for 25 hours and worked at the grocery store for 15 hours. $25n + 15x$

Write a verbal expression for each algebraic expression. 31–33. Sample answers given.

31. $25 + 6x^2$
32. $6f^2 + 5f$
33. $\frac{3a^5}{2}$

31. twenty-five plus six times a number squared
32. six times a number squared plus five times the number
33. three times a number raised to the fifth power divided by two

B

34. **SENSE-MAKING** A certain smartphone family plan costs \$55 per month plus additional usage costs. If x is the number of cell phone minutes used above the plan amount and y is the number of megabytes of data used above the plan amount, interpret the following expressions.
    a. $0.25x$ cost of extra minutes at \$0.25 per minute
    b. $2y$ cost of extra data used at \$2 per megabyte
    c. $0.25x + 2y + 55$ total monthly cost

Differentiated Homework Options

Level	Assignment	Two-Day Option	
AL Basic	11–33, 38–40, 42–61	11–33 odd, 43–46	12–32 even, 38–40, 42, 47–61
OL Core	11–33 odd, 34–40, 42–61	11–33, 43–46	34–40, 42, 47–61
BL Advanced	34–55, (optional: 56–61)		

Teaching the Process Standards

Modeling Mathematically proficient students are able to identify important quantities in a practical situation and map their relationships using such tools algebraic expressions and equations. Encourage students to interpret the expressions they write to ensure that they have represented the situation accurately.

Focus on Mathematical Content

Writing Algebraic Expressions When writing algebraic expressions that involve multiplication, the multiplication symbol × should not be used, since it is easily confused with the variable x.

Teach with Tech features throughout the Teacher Edition offer tips on using various types of technology such as interactive whiteboards, document cameras, blogs, and more, to enhance your teaching.

Teach with Tech

Interactive Whiteboard Write an algebraic expression on the board. Have students come to the board and use the highlighter tool to identify the variable. Copy the expression and have students replace the highlight with the value.

3 Practice

Formative Assessment

Use Exercises 1–10 to check for understanding.

Use the chart at the bottom of this page to customize assignments for your students.

Teaching the Process Standards

Sense-Making Mathematically proficient students consider simpler forms of the original problem in order to gain insight into its solution. In Exercise 34, point out to students that complex expressions are made up of simpler expressions. When writing a verbal expression for an algebraic expression, they need to make sure that each of the simple expressions is represented.

Study Guide and Intervention

AL OL ELL

NAME ______ DATE ______ PERIOD ______

1-1 Study Guide and Intervention

Variables and Expressions

Write Verbal Expressions An **algebraic expression** consists of one or more numbers and variables along with one or more arithmetic operations. In algebra, **variables** are symbols used to represent unspecified numbers or values. Any letter may be used as a variable.

Example Write a verbal expression for each algebraic expression.

a. $6n^2$
the product of 6 and n squared

b. $n^3 - 12m$
the difference of n cubed and twelve times m

Exercises

Write a verbal expression for each algebraic expression.

1. $w - 1$
2. $\frac{1}{3}a^3$
3. $81 + 2x$
4. $12d$
5. 8^4
6. 6^2
7. $2n^2 + 4$
8. $a^3 \cdot b^3$
9. $2x^3 - 3$
10. $\frac{6k^3}{5}$
11. $\frac{1}{4}b^2$
12. $7n^3$
13. $3x + 4$
14. $\frac{2}{3}k^5$
15. $3b^2 + 2a^3$
16. $4(n^2 + 1)$

Lesson 1-1

Practice

AL OL BL ELL

NAME ______ DATE ______ PERIOD ______

1-1 Practice

Variables and Expressions

Write a verbal expression for each algebraic expression.

1. $23f$
2. 7^5
3. $5m^2 + 2$
4. $4d^3 - 10$
5. $x^3 \cdot y^4$
6. $b^2 - 3c^3$
7. $\frac{k^5}{6}$
8. $\frac{4n^2}{7}$

Write an algebraic expression for each verbal expression.

9. the difference of 10 and u
10. the sum of 18 and a number
11. the product of 33 and j
12. 74 increased by 3 times y
13. 15 decreased by twice a number
14. 91 more than the square of a number
15. three fourths the square of b
16. two fifths the cube of a number
17. **BOOKS** A used bookstore sells paperback fiction books in excellent condition for \$2.50 and in fair condition for \$0.50. Write an expression for the cost of buying x excellent-condition paperbacks and f fair-condition paperbacks.
18. **GEOMETRY** The surface area of the side of a right cylinder can be found by multiplying twice the number π by the radius times the height. If a circular cylinder has radius r and height h, write an expression that represents the surface area of its side.

Word Problem Practice

AL OL BL ELL

NAME ______ DATE ______ PERIOD ______

1-1 Word Problem Practice

Variables and Expressions

1. **SOLAR SYSTEM** It takes Earth about 365 days to orbit the Sun. It takes Uranus about 85 times as long. Write a numerical expression to describe the number of days it takes Uranus to orbit the Sun.

2. **TECHNOLOGY** There are 1024 bytes in a kilobyte. Write an expression that describes the number of bytes in a computer chip with n kilobytes.

3. **THEATER** H. Howard Hughes, Professor Emeritus of Texas Wesleyan College and his wife Erin Connor Hughes attended a record 6136 theatrical shows. Write an expression for the average number of shows they attended per year if they accumulated the record over y years.

4. **TIDES** The difference between high and low tides along the Maine coast in November is 19 feet on Monday and x feet on Tuesday. Write an expression to show the average rise and fall of the tide for Monday and Tuesday.

5. **BLOCKS** A toy manufacturer produces a set of blocks that can be used by children to build play structures. The product packaging team is analyzing different arrangements for packaging their blocks. One idea they have is to arrange the blocks in the shape of a cube, with b blocks along one edge.

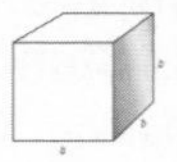

a. Write an expression representing the total number of blocks packaged in a cube measuring b blocks on one edge.

b. The packaging team decides to take one layer of blocks off the top of this package. Write an expression representing the number of blocks in the top layer of the package.

c. The team finally decides that their favorite package arrangement is to take 2 layers of blocks off the top of a cube measuring b blocks along one edge. Write an expression representing the number of blocks left behind after the top two layers are removed.

Lesson 1-1

35 **DREAMS** It is believed that about $\frac{3}{4}$ of our dreams involve people that we know.

a. Write an expression to describe the number of dreams that feature people you know if you have d dreams. **$\frac{3}{4}d$**

b. Use the expression you wrote to predict the number of dreams that include people you know out of 28 dreams. **21**

C **36.** **SPORTS** In football, a touchdown is awarded 6 points and the team can then try for a point after a touchdown.

a. Write an expression that describes the number of points scored on touchdowns T and points after touchdowns p by one team in a game. **$6T + p$**

b. If a team wins a football game 27-0, write an equation to represent the possible number of touchdowns and points after touchdowns by the winning team. **$6T + p = 27$**

c. If a team wins a football game 21-7, how many possible number of touchdowns and points after touchdowns were scored during the game by both teams? **Sample answer: 4 touchdowns and 4 points after touchdowns**

37. **MULTIPLE REPRESENTATIONS** In this problem, you will explore the multiplication of powers with like bases.

a. **Tabular** Copy and complete the table.

10^2	×	10^1	=	10 × 10 × 10	=	10^3
10^2	×	10^2	=	10 × 10 × 10 × 10	=	10^4
10^2	×	10^3	=	10 × 10 × 10 × 10 × 10	=	? **10^5**
10^2	×	10^4	=	? **10 × 10 × 10 × 10 × 10 × 10**	=	? **10^6**

b. **Algebraic** Write an equation for the pattern in the table. **$10^2 \times 10^x = 10^{(2 + x)}$**

c. **Verbal** Make a conjecture about the exponent of the product of two powers with like bases. **The exponent of the product of two powers is the sum of the exponents of the powers with the same base.**

H.O.T. Problems Use Higher-Order Thinking Skills

38. **REASONING** Explain the differences between an algebraic expression and a verbal expression. **Algebraic expressions include variables, numbers, and symbols. Verbal expressions contain words.**

39. **OPEN ENDED** Define a variable to represent a real-life quantity, such as time in minutes or distance in feet. Then use the variable to write an algebraic expression to represent one of your daily activities. Describe in words what your expression represents, and explain your reasoning. **See margin.**

40. **CRITIQUE** Consuelo and James are writing an algebraic expression for *three times the sum of n squared and 3.* Is either of them correct? Explain your reasoning.

Consuelo	James
$3(n^2 + 3)$	$3n^2 + 3$

Consuelo; James left out the parentheses around $n^2 + 3$.

41. **CHALLENGE** For the cube, x represents a positive whole number. Find the value of x such that the volume of the cube and 6 times the area of one of its faces have the same value. **6**

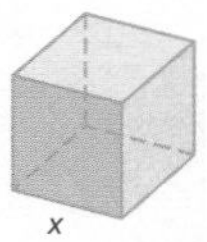

42. **WRITING IN MATH** Describe how to write an algebraic expression from a real-world situation. Include a definition of algebraic expression in your own words.

42. Sample answer: An algebraic expression is a math phrase that contains one or more numbers or variables. To write an algebraic expression from real-world situation, first assign variables. Then determine the arithmetic operations done on the variables. Finally, put the terms in order.

Enrichment

OL BL

NAME ______ DATE ______ PERIOD ______

1-1 Enrichment

Toothpick Triangles

Variable expressions can be used to represent patterns and help solve problems. Consider the problem of creating triangles out of toothpicks shown below.

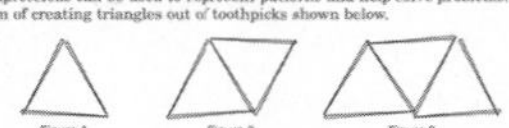

Figure 1 Figure 2 Figure 3

1. How many toothpicks does it take to create each figure?

2. How many toothpicks does it take to make up the perimeter of each image?

3. Sketch the next three figures in the pattern.

H.O.T. Problems require students to use Higher Order Thinking to solve problems.

Multiple Representations

In Exercise 37, students use a table and algebraic expressions to explore the multiplication of powers with like bases.

Standardized Test Practice

43. Which expression best represents the volume of the cube? **D**

A the product of three and five
B three to the fifth power
C three squared
D three cubed

44. Which expression best represents the perimeter of the rectangle? **H**

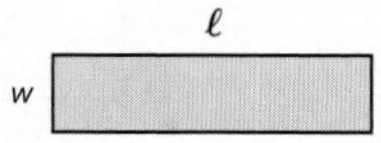

F $2\ell w$
G $\ell + w$
H $2\ell + 2w$
J $4(\ell + w)$

45. SHORT RESPONSE The yards of fabric needed to make curtains is 3 times the length of a window in inches, divided by 36. Write an expression that represents the yards of fabric needed in terms of the length of the window ℓ. $\frac{3\ell}{36}$

46. GEOMETRY Find the area of the rectangle. **B**

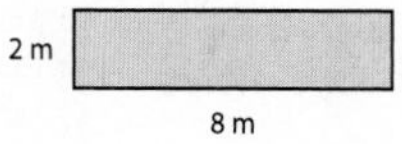

A 14 square meters
B 16 square meters
C 50 square meters
D 60 square meters

Spiral Review

47. AMUSEMENT PARKS A roller coaster enthusiast club took a poll to see what each member's favorite ride was. Make a bar graph of the results. (Lesson 0-13) **See Ch. 1 Answer Appendix.**

Our Favorite Rides							
Ride	Big Plunge	Twisting Time	The Shiner	Raging Bull	The Bat	Teaser	The Adventure
Number of Votes	5	22	16	9	25	6	12

48. SPORTS The results for an annual 5K race are shown at the right. Make a box-and-whisker plot for the data. Write a sentence describing what the length of the box-and-whisker plot tells about the times for the race. (Lesson 0–13) **See margin.**

Annual 5K Race Results			
Joe	14:48	Carissa	19:58
Jessica	19:27	Jordan	14:58
Lupe	15:06	Taylor	20:47
Dante	20:39	Mi-Ling	15:48
Tia	15:54	Winona	21:35
Amber	20:49	Angel	16:10
Amanda	16:30	Catalina	20:21

49. 5.6; 6.5; 7 **50. 0.4; 0; 0 and −1**

Find the mean, median, and mode for each set of data. (Lesson 0–12)

49. {7, 6, 5, 7, 4, 8, 2, 2, 7, 8}

50. {−1, 0, 5, 2, −2, 0 ,−1, 2, −1, 0}

51. {17, 24, 16, 3, 12, 11, 24, 15} **15.25; 15.5; 24**

52. SPORTS Lisa has a rectangular trampoline that is 6 feet long and 12 feet wide. What is the area of her trampoline in square feet? (Lesson 0–8) **72 ft²**

Find each product or quotient. (Lesson 0–5)

53. $\frac{3}{5} \cdot \frac{7}{11}$ $\frac{21}{55}$

54. $\frac{4}{3} \div \frac{7}{6}$ $\frac{8}{7}$

55. $\frac{5}{6} \cdot \frac{8}{3}$ $\frac{20}{9}$

Skills Review

Evaluate each expression.

56. $\frac{3}{5} + \frac{4}{9}$ $\frac{47}{45}$

57. 5.67 − 4.21 **1.46**

58. $\frac{5}{6} - \frac{8}{3}$ $-1\frac{5}{6}$

59. 10.34 + 14.27 **24.61**

60. $\frac{11}{12} + \frac{5}{36}$ $\frac{19}{18}$

61. 37.02 − 15.86 **21.16**

Teaching the Process Standards

Critique Mathematically proficient students have learned to examine claims. In Exercise 40, students should see that the flaw in James's solution is the missing grouping symbols. If students have trouble, suggest that they write a verbal expression for each algebraic expression and then compare these to the original verbal expression.

WatchOut!

Preventing Errors Students often ignore the order of operations and read, write, and evaluate expressions from left to right. Remind students to always follow the order of operations.

4 Assess

Ticket Out the Door Give each student a slip of paper on which is written an algebraic expression. As they leave the room, ask each student to translate the algebraic expression into a verbal expression.

Additional Answers

39. Sample answer: x is the number of minutes it takes to walk between my house and school. $2x + 15$ represents the amount of time in minutes I spend walking each day since I walk to and from school and I take my dog on a 15 minute walk.

48.

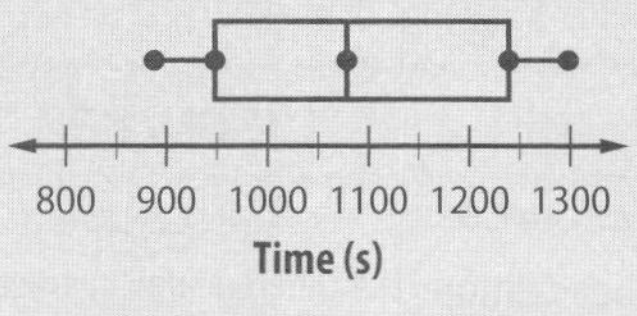

The length of the box-and-whisker plot shows how spread out the runners were.

DifferentiatedInstruction OL BL

Extension Suggest that students write an expression that represents their allowance. Ask them to write a verbal expression to represent their allowance and then an algebraic expression. Have them use their expressions to explain the difference between a verbal expression and an algebraic expression.

1 Focus

VerticalAlignment

Before Lesson 1-2 Express algebraic expressions verbally.

Lesson 1-2 Evaluate numerical expressions by using the order of operations. Evaluate algebraic expressions by using the order of operations.

After Lesson 1-2 Evaluate expressions using properties of numbers.

2 Teach

Scaffolding Questions

Have students read the **Why?** section of the lesson.

Ask:

- How would you translate $4(78.95) + 3(68.95)$? Multiply 4 times 78.95 and then add the product of 3 and 68.95.
- What are the operations in the expression? multiplication and addition
- What does $4(78.95)$ represent? cost of four adult tickets

All of the **Lesson Resources** are leveled for students who are **approaching grade level**, **on grade level**, and **beyond grade level**, and for students who are **English language learners**.

LESSON 1-2 Order of Operations

Then

- You expressed algebraic expressions verbally.

Now

- 1 Evaluate numerical expressions by using the order of operations.
- 2 Evaluate algebraic expressions by using the order of operations.

Why?

- The admission prices for SeaWorld Adventure Park in Orlando, Florida, are shown in the table. If four adults and three children go to the park, the expression below represents the cost of admission for the group.

$4(78.95) + 3(68.95)$

Ticket	Price ($)
Adult	78.95
Child	68.95

Ken Biggs/The Image Bank/Getty Images

New Vocabulary is listed at the beginning of every lesson.

NewVocabulary
evaluate
order of operations

Process Standards
PS.7

1 Evaluate Numerical Expressions

To find the cost of admission, the expression $4(78.95) + 3(68.95)$ must be evaluated. To **evaluate** an expression means to find its value.

PT

Example 1 Evaluate Expressions

Evaluate 3^5.

$3^5 = 3 \cdot 3 \cdot 3 \cdot 3 \cdot 3$ Use 3 as a factor 5 times.

$= 243$ Multiply.

GuidedPractice

1A. 2^4 16 **1B.** 4^5 1024 **1C.** 7^3 343

The numerical expression that represents the cost of admission contains more than one operation. The rule that lets you know which operation to perform first is called the **order of operations**.

KeyConcept Order of Operations

Step 1 Evaluate expressions inside grouping symbols.

Step 2 Evaluate all powers.

Step 3 Multiply and/or divide from left to right.

Step 4 Add and/or subtract from left to right.

PT

Example 2 Order of Operations

Evaluate $16 - 8 \div 2^2 + 14$.

$16 - 8 \div 2^2 + 14 = 16 - 8 \div 4 + 14$ Evaluate powers.

$= 16 - 2 + 14$ Divide 8 by 4.

$= 14 + 14$ Subtract 2 from 16.

$= 28$ Add 14 and 14.

GuidedPractice

2A. $3 + 42 \cdot 2 - 5$ 82 **2B.** $20 - 7 + 8^2 - 7 \cdot 11$ 0

Lesson 1-2 Resources

Resource	Approaching Level AL	On Level OL	Beyond Level BL	English Learners ELL
Teacher Edition	▪ Differentiated Instruction, p. 11	▪ Differentiated Instruction, pp. 11, 15	▪ Differentiated Instruction, p. 15	
Chapter Resource Masters	▪ Study Guide and Intervention, pp. 11–12 ▪ Skills Practice, p. 13 ▪ Practice, p. 14 ▪ Word Problem Practice, p. 15 ▪ Graphing Calculator Activity, p. 17	▪ Study Guide and Intervention, pp. 11–12 ▪ Skills Practice, p. 13 ▪ Practice, p. 14 ▪ Word Problem Practice, p. 15 ▪ Enrichment, p. 16 ▪ Graphing Calculator Activity, p. 17	▪ Practice, p. 14 ▪ Word Problem Practice, p. 15 ▪ Enrichment, p. 16 ▪ Graphing Calculator Activity, p. 17	▪ Study Guide and Intervention, pp. 11–12 ▪ Skills Practice, p. 13 ▪ Practice, p. 14 ▪ Word Problem Practice, p. 15 ▪ Graphing Calculator Activity, p. 17
Other	▪ 5-Minute Check 1-2 ▪ Study Notebook ▪ Teaching Algebra with Manipulatives	▪ 5-Minute Check 1-2 ▪ Study Notebook ▪ Teaching Algebra with Manipulatives	▪ 5-Minute Check 1-2 ▪ Study Notebook	▪ 5-Minute Check 1-2 ▪ Study Notebook ▪ Teaching Algebra with Manipulatives

StudyTip

Grouping Symbols Grouping symbols such as parentheses ( ), brackets [ ], and braces { } are used to clarify or change the order of operations.

When one or more grouping symbols are used, evaluate within the innermost grouping symbols first.

Example 3 Expressions with Grouping Symbols

Evaluate each expression.

a. $4 \div 2 + 5(10 - 6)$

$4 \div 2 + 5(10 - 6) = 4 \div 2 + 5(4)$ — Evaluate inside parentheses.
$= 2 + 5(4)$ — Divide 4 by 2.
$= 2 + 20$ — Multiply 5 by 4.
$= 22$ — Add 2 to 20.

b. $6[32 - (2 + 3)^2]$

$6[32 - (2 + 3)^2] = 6[32 - (5)^2]$ — Evaluate innermost expression first.
$= 6[32 - 25]$ — Evaluate power.
$= 6[7]$ — Subtract 25 from 32.
$= 42$ — Multiply.

StudyTip

Grouping Symbols A fraction bar is considered a grouping symbol. So, evaluate expressions in the numerator and denominator before completing the division.

c. $\frac{2^3 - 5}{15 + 9}$

$\frac{2^3 - 5}{15 + 9} = \frac{8 - 5}{15 + 9}$ — Evaluate the power in the numerator.
$= \frac{3}{15 + 9}$ — Subtract 5 from 8 in the numerator.
$= \frac{3}{24}$ or $\frac{1}{8}$ — Add 15 and 9 in denominator, and simplify.

GuidedPractice

3A. $5 \cdot 4(10 - 8) + 20$ **60** **3B.** $15 - [10 + (3 - 2)^2] + 6$ **10** **3C.** $\frac{(4 + 5)^2}{3(7 - 4)}$ **9**

2 Evaluate Algebraic Expressions

To evaluate an algebraic expression, replace the variables with their values. Then find the value of the numerical expression using the order of operations.

Example 4 Evaluate an Algebraic Expression

Evaluate $3x^2 + (2y + z^3)$ if $x = 4$, $y = 5$, $z = 3$.

$3x^2 + (2y + z^3)$
$= 3(4)^2 + (2 \cdot 5 + 3^3)$ — Replace x with 4, y with 5, and z with 3.
$= 3(4)^2 + (2 \cdot 5 + 27)$ — Evaluate 3^3.
$= 3(4)^2 + (10 + 27)$ — Multiply 2 by 5.
$= 3(4)^2 + (37)$ — Add 10 to 27.
$= 3(16) + 37$ — Evaluate 4^2.
$= 48 + 37$ — Multiply 3 by 16.
$= 85$ — Add 48 to 37.

GuidedPractice

Evaluate each expression.

4A. $a^2(3b + 5) \div c$ if $a = 2, b = 6, c = 4$ **23** **4B.** $5d + (6f - g)$ if $d = 4, f = 3, g = 12$ **26**

DifferentiatedInstruction AL OL

If students have difficulty evaluating complex algebraic expressions,

Then pair these students with advanced students and suggest that they work through the exercises step-by-step.

1 Evaluate Numerical Expressions

Example 1 shows how to evaluate numerical expressions with one term. **Examples 2 and 3** show how to use the order of operations to evaluate expressions with more than one operation or grouping symbol.

Formative Assessment

Use the Guided Practice exercises after each Example to determine students' understanding of concepts.

Additional Examples

1. Evaluate 2^6. 64
2. Evaluate $48 \div 2^3 \cdot 3 + 5$. 23
3. Evaluate each expression.
   a. $(8 - 3) \cdot 3(3 + 2)$ 75
   b. $4[12 \div (6 - 2)]^2$ 36
   c. $\frac{2^5 - 6 \cdot 2}{3^3 - 5 \cdot 3 - 2}$ 2

Focus on Mathematical Content

Grouping Symbols Grouping symbols include parentheses, ( ), brackets, [ ], braces, { }, and fraction bars, as in $\frac{5 + 7}{2}$. Evaluate expressions inside grouping symbols first when using the order of operations.

2 Evaluate Algebraic Expressions

Example 4 shows how to evaluate an algebraic expression by replacing the variables with their values and using the order of operations. **Example 5** shows how to find the value of a variable in a formula when the values of all the other variables are known.

Additional Example

4. Evaluate $2(x^2 - y) + z^2$ if $x = 4$, $y = 3$, and $z = 2$. 30

Additional Example

5 ARCHITECTURE Each side of the Great Pyramid of Giza, Egypt, is a triangle. The base of each triangle once measured 230 meters. The height of each triangle once measured 187 meters. The area of a triangle is one-half the product of the base b and its height h.

a. Write an expression that represents the area of one side of the Great Pyramid. $\frac{1}{2}(bh)$

b. Find the area of one side of the Great Pyramid. 21,505 m^2

Additional Examples also in Interactive Classroom PowerPoint® Presentations

IWB Interactive White Board READY

Teach with Tech

Document Camera Use numbers and operation tiles to create a numeric expression such as $6 \div (3^2 - 2 \cdot 3) + 3$. Have students remove the operation performed in each step and replace them with the number tiles that are equivalent (like removing the $2 \cdot 3$ tiles and replacing them with 6).

Check Your Understanding exercises are intended to be completed in class. **Example references** show students where to look back for review.

3 Practice

Formative Assessment

Use Exercises 1–14 to check for understanding.

Use the chart at the bottom of the next page to customize assignments for your students.

Real-WorldLink

The National Oceanic & Atmospheric Administration (NOAA) developed the Science on a Sphere system to educate people about Earth's processes. There are five computers and four video projectors that power the sphere.

Source: NOAA

Real-World Example 5 Write and Evaluate an Expression

ENVIRONMENTAL STUDIES Science on a Sphere (SOS)® demonstrates the effects of atmospheric storms, climate changes, and ocean temperature on the environment. The volume of a sphere is four thirds of π multiplied by the radius r to the third power.

a. Write an expression that represents the volume of a sphere.

Words	four thirds	of	π multiplied by radius to the third power
Variable	Let r = radius.		
Equation	$\frac{4}{3}$	$\times$	πr^3 or $\frac{4}{3}\pi r^3$

b. Find the volume of the 3-foot radius sphere used for SOS.

$V = \frac{4}{3}\pi r^3$	Volume of a sphere
$= \frac{4}{3}\pi(3)^3$	Replace r with 3.
$= \left(\frac{4}{3}\right)\pi(27)$	Evaluate $3^3 = 27$.
$= 36\pi$	Multiply $\frac{4}{3}$ by 27.

The volume of the sphere is 36π cubic feet.

GuidedPractice

5. FOREST FIRES According to the California Department of Forestry, an average of 539.2 fires each year are started by burning debris, while campfires are responsible for an average of 129.1 each year.

A. Write an algebraic expression that represents the number of fires, on average, in d years of debris burning and c years of campfires. **$539.2d + 129.1c$**

B. How many fires would there be in 5 years? **3342 fires**

Check Your Understanding

● = Step-by-Step Solutions begin on page R13.

Examples 1–3 Evaluate each expression.

1. 9^2 **81**
2. 4^4 **256**
3. 3^5 **243**
4. $30 - 14 \div 2$ **23**
5. (●) $5 \cdot 5 - 1 \cdot 3$ **22**
6. $(2 + 5)4$ **28**
7. $[8(2) - 4^2] + 7(4)$ **28**
8. $\frac{11 - 8}{1 + 7 \cdot 2}$ **$\frac{3}{15}$ or $\frac{1}{5}$**
9. $\frac{(4 \cdot 3)^2}{9 + 3}$ **12**

Example 4 Evaluate each expression if $a = 4$, $b = 6$, and $c = 8$.

10. $8b - a$ **44**
11. $2a + (b^2 \div 3)$ **20**
12. $\frac{b(9 - c)}{a^2}$ **$\frac{6}{16}$ or $\frac{3}{8}$**

Example 5

13. **BOOKS** Akira bought one new book for \$20 and three used books for \$4.95 each. Write and evaluate an expression to find how much money the books cost. **$20 + 3 \times 4.95$; \$34.85**

14. **REASONING** Koto purchased food for herself and her friends. She bought 4 cheeseburgers for \$2.25 each, 3 French fries for \$1.25 each, and 4 drinks for \$4.00. Write and evaluate an expression to find how much the food cost. **$4 \times 2.25 + 3 \times 1.25 + 4.00$; \$16.75**

NOAA Photo by Will von Dauster

WatchOut!

Student Misconceptions Caution that not all calculators follow the order of operations when evaluating expressions. Nonscientific calculators evaluate expressions in the order they are entered. All scientific calculators (including graphing calculators) follow the order of operations. However, for longer expressions, you may have to use grouping symbols or be creative when entering the expression in order to get the correct answer.

Practice and Problem Solving

Extra Practice is on page R1.

Examples 1–3 Evaluate each expression.

15. 7^2 **49**
16. 14^3 **2744**
17. 2^6 **64**
18. $35 - 3 \cdot 8$ **11**
19. $18 \div 9 + 2 \cdot 6$ **14**
20. $10 + 8^3 \div 16$ **42**
21. $24 \div 6 + 2^3 \cdot 4$ **36**
22. $(11 \cdot 7) - 9 \cdot 8$ **5**
23. $29 - 3(9 - 4)$ **14**
24. $(12 - 6) \cdot 5^2$ **150**
25. $3^5 - (1 + 10^2)$ **142**
26. $108 \div [3(9 + 3^2)]$ **2**
27. $[(6^3 - 9) \div 23]4$ **36**
28. $\frac{8 + 3^3}{12 - 7}$ **7**
29. $\frac{(1 + 6)9}{5^2 - 4}$ **3**

Example 4 Evaluate each expression if $g = 2$, $r = 3$, and $t = 11$.

30. $g + 6t$ **68**
31. $7 - gr$ **1**
32. $r^2 + (g^3 - 8)^5$ **9**
33. $(2t + 3g) \div 4$ **7**
34. $t^2 + 8rt + r^2$ **394**
35. $3g(g + r)^2 - 1$ **149**

Example 5

36. **GEOMETRY** Write an algebraic expression to represent the area of the triangle. Then evaluate it to find the area when $h = 12$ inches. **$\frac{1}{2}h(h + 6)$; 108 in²**

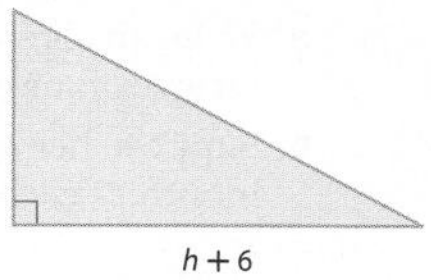

37. **AMUSEMENT PARKS** In 2004, there were 3344 amusement parks and arcades. This decreased by 148 by 2009. Write and evaluate an expression to find the number of amusement parks and arcades in 2009. **3344 − 148 = 3196**

B 38. **STRUCTURE** Kamilah sells tickets at Duke University's athletic ticket office. If p represents a preferred season ticket, b represents a blue zone ticket, and g represents a general admission ticket, interpret and then evaluate the following expressions. **a–c. See margin.**

a. $45b$ b. $15p + 35g$ c. $6p + 11b + 22g$

Duke University Football Ticket Prices	
Preferred Season Ticket	$100
Blue Zone	$80
General Admission	$70

Source: Duke University

Evaluate each expression.

39. 4^2 **16**
40. 12^3 **1728**
41. 3^6 **729**
42. 11^5 **161,051**
43. $(3 - 4^2)^2 + 8$ **177**
44. $23 - 2(17 + 3^3)$ **−65**
45. $3[4 - 8 + 4^2(2 + 5)]$ **324**
46. $\frac{2 \cdot 8^2 - 2^2 \cdot 8}{2 \cdot 8}$ **6**
47. $25 + \left[(16 - 3 \cdot 5) + \frac{12 + 3}{5}\right]$ **29**
48. $7^3 - \frac{2}{3}(13 \cdot 6 + 9)4$ **111**

Evaluate each expression if $a = 8$, $b = 4$, and $c = 16$.

49. $a^2bc - b^2$ **4080**
50. $\frac{c^2}{b^2} + \frac{b^2}{a^2}$ **$\frac{65}{4}$**
51. $\frac{2b + 3c^2}{4a^2 - 2b}$ **$\frac{97}{31}$**
52. $\frac{3ab + c^2}{a}$ **44**
53. $\left(\frac{a}{b}\right)^2 - \frac{c}{a - b}$ **0**
54. $\frac{2a - b^2}{ab} + \frac{c - a}{b^2}$ **$\frac{1}{2}$**

55. **SALES** One day, 28 small and 12 large merchant spaces were rented. Another day, 30 small and 15 large spaces were rented. Write and evaluate an expression to show the total rent collected. **28(7) + 12(9.75) + 30(7) + 15(9.75); $669.25**

Differentiated Homework Options

Level	Assignment	Two-Day Option	
AL Basic	15–35, 59, 60, 62–82	15–35 odd, 65–68	16–34 even, 59, 60, 62–64, 69–82
OL Core	15–35 odd, 36–38, 39–53 odd, 55–60, 62–82	15–35, 65–68	39–60, 62–64, 69–82
BL Advanced	36–76, (optional: 77–82)		

Teaching the Process Standards

Reasoning Mathematically proficient students decontextualize information to represent it symbolically, manipulate the symbols, and then contextualize to interpret the solution. To help in these processes, encourage students to write each variable they define and its meaning.

Structure Mathematically proficient students can see complicated things, such as some algebraic expressions, as single objects or as being composed of several objects. Encourage students to analyze an expression by examining each part of the expression. For example in Exercise 38, $15p + 35g$ consists of the sum of two products.

WatchOut!

Preventing Errors Students may be reluctant to take time to show all the steps they use when evaluating an expression. Help them to see that these steps enable them to diagnose errors and to prevent calculation errors that may keep them from getting correct values.

Additional Answers

38a. the cost of 45 blue zone tickets; 45(80) = $3600

38b. the cost of 15 preferred and 35 general tickets; 15(100) + 35(70) = $3950

38c. the total cost of 6 preferred, 11 blue zone, and 22 general admission tickets; 6(100) + 11(80) + 22(70) = $3020

The Differentiated Homework Options provide leveled assignments. Many of the homework exercises are paired, so that the students can do the odds one day and the evens on the next day.

C **56. SHOPPING** Evelina is shopping for back-to-school clothes. She bought 3 skirts, 2 pairs of jeans, and 4 sweaters. Write and evaluate an expression to find how much she spent, without including sales tax. **3(25.99) + 2(39.99) + 4(22.99); $249.91**

Clothing	
skirt	$25.99
jeans	$39.99
sweater	$22.99

57 PYRAMIDS The pyramid at the Louvre has a square base with a side of 35.42 meters and a height of 21.64 meters. The Great Pyramid in Egypt has a square base with a side of 230 meters and a height of 146.5 meters. The expression for the volume of a pyramid is $\frac{1}{3}Bh$, where B is the area of the base and h is the height.

a. Draw both pyramids and label the dimensions. **See margin.**

b. Write a verbal expression for the difference in volume of the two pyramids.

c. Write an algebraic expression for the difference in volume of the two pyramids. Find the difference in volume.

57b. one third times 230 squared times 146.5 minus one third times 35.42 squared times 21.64

58. FINANCIAL LITERACY A sales representative receives an annual salary s, an average commission each month c, and a bonus b for each sales goal that she reaches.

a. Write an algebraic expression to represent her total earnings in one year if she receives four equal bonuses. $s + 12c + 4b$

b. Suppose her annual salary is $52,000 and her average commission is $1225 per month. If each of the four bonuses equals $1150, what does she earn annually? **$71,300**

57c. $\frac{1}{3}(230)^2(146.5) - \frac{1}{3}(35.42)^2(21.64)$**; 2,574,233.656 m³**

H.O.T. Problems Use Higher-Order Thinking Skills

59. ERROR ANALYSIS Tara and Curtis are simplifying $[4(10) - 3^2] + 6(4)$. Is either of them correct? Explain your reasoning.

Tara	Curtis
$[4(10) - 3^2] + 6(4)$	$[4(10) - 3^2] + 6(4)$
$= [4(10) - 9] + 6(4)$	$= [4(10) - 9] + 6(4)$
$= 4(1) + 6(4)$	$= (40 - 9) + 6(4)$
$= 4 + 6(4)$	$= 31 + 6(4)$
$= 4 + 24$	$= 31 + 24$
$= 28$	$= 55$

Curtis; Tara subtracted 10 − 9 before multiplying 4 by 10.

63. Sample answer: Area of a trapezoid $\frac{1}{2}h(b_1 + b_2)$**; according to the order of operations you have to add the lengths of the bases together first and then multiply by the height and by** $\frac{1}{2}$**.**

60. REASONING Explain how to evaluate $a[(b - c) \div d] - f$ if you were given values for a, b, c, d, and f. How would you evaluate the expression differently if the expression was $a \cdot b - c \div d - f$? **See margin.**

61. PERSEVERANCE Write an expression using the whole numbers 1 to 5 using all five digits and addition and/or subtraction to create a numeric expression with a value of 3. **Sample answer: 5 + 4 − 3 − 2 − 1**

62. OPEN ENDED Write an expression that uses exponents, at least three different operations, and two sets of parentheses. Explain the steps you would take to evaluate the expression. **See students' work.**

63. WRITING IN MATH Choose a geometric formula and explain how the order of operations applies when using the formula.

64. WRITING IN MATH Equivalent expressions have the same value. Are the expressions $(30 + 17) \times 10$ and $10 \times 30 + 10 \times 17$ equivalent? Explain why or why not. **See margin.**

Study Guide and Intervention
AL OL ELL

NAME ______ DATE ______ PERIOD ______

1-2 Study Guide and Intervention
Order of Operations

Evaluate Numerical Expressions Numerical expressions often contain more than one operation. To evaluate them, use the rules for order of operations shown below.

Order of Operations	
	Step 1 Evaluate expressions inside grouping symbols.
	Step 2 Evaluate all powers.
	Step 3 Do all multiplication and/or division from left to right.
	Step 4 Do all addition and/or subtraction from left to right.

Example 1 Evaluate each expression.

a. 3^4
$3^4 = 3 \cdot 3 \cdot 3 \cdot 3$ Use 3 as a factor 4 times.
$= 81$ Multiply.

b. 6^3
$6^3 = 6 \cdot 6 \cdot 6$ Use 6 as a factor 3 times.
$= 216$ Multiply.

Example 2 Evaluate each expression.

a. $3[2 + (12 \div 3)^2]$
$3[2 + (12 \div 3)^2] = 3(2 + 4^2)$ Divide 12 by 3.
$= 3(2 + 16)$ Find 4 squared.
$= 3(18)$ Add 2 and 16.
$= 54$ Multiply 3 and 18.

b. $\frac{3 + 2^3}{4^2 \cdot 3}$
$\frac{3 + 2^3}{4^2 \cdot 3} = \frac{3 + 8}{4^2 \cdot 3}$ Evaluate power in numerator.
$= \frac{11}{4^2 \cdot 3}$ Add 3 and 8 in the numerator.
$= \frac{11}{16 \cdot 3}$ Evaluate power in denominator.
$= \frac{11}{48}$ Multiply.

Lesson 1-2

Exercises
Evaluate each expression.

1. 5^2 2. 3^3 3. 10^4
4. 12^2 5. 8^3 6. 2^8
7. $(8 - 4) \cdot 2$ 8. $(12 + 4) \cdot 6$ 9. $10 + 8 \cdot 1$
10. $15 - 12 \div 4$ 11. $12(20 - 17) - 3 \cdot 6$ 12. $24 \div 3 \cdot 2 - 3^2$
13. $3^2 \div 3 + 2^2 \cdot 7 - 20 \div 5$ 14. $\frac{4 + 3^2}{12 + 1}$ 15. $250 \div [5(3 \cdot 7 + 4)]$
16. $\frac{2 \cdot 4^2 - 8 \div 2}{(5 + 2) \cdot 2}$ 17. $\frac{4(5^2) - 4 \cdot 3}{4(4 \cdot 5 + 2)}$ 18. $\frac{5^2 - 3}{20(3) + 2(3)}$

Practice
AL OL BL ELL

NAME ______ DATE ______ PERIOD ______

1-2 Practice
Order of Operations

Evaluate each expression.

1. 11^2 2. 8^3 3. 5^4
4. $(15 - 5) \cdot 2$ 5. $9 \cdot (3 + 4)$ 6. $5 + 7 \cdot 4$
7. $4(3 + 5) - 5 \cdot 4$ 8. $22 \div 11 \cdot 9 - 3^2$ 9. $6^2 + 3 \cdot 7 - 9$
10. $3[10 - (27 \div 9)]$ 11. $2[5^2 + (36 \div 6)]$ 12. $162 \div [6(7 - 4)^2]$
13. $\frac{5^2 \cdot 4 - 5 \cdot 4^2}{5(4)}$ 14. $\frac{(2 \cdot 5)^2 + 4}{3^2 - 5}$ 15. $\frac{7 + 3^2}{4^2 \cdot 2}$

Evaluate each expression if $a = 12$, $b = 9$, and $c = 4$.

16. $a^2 + b - c^2$ 17. $b^2 + 2a - c^2$
18. $2c(a + b)$ 19. $4a + 2b - c^2$
20. $(a^2 \div 4b) + c$ 21. $c^2 \cdot (2b - a)$
22. $\frac{bc^2 + a}{c}$ 23. $\frac{2c^3 - ab}{4}$
24. $2(a - b)^2 - 5c$ 25. $\frac{b^2 - 2c^2}{a + c - b}$

26. **CAR RENTAL** Ann Carlyle is planning a business trip for which she needs to rent a car. The car rental company charges $36 per day plus $0.50 per mile over 100 miles. Suppose Ms. Carlyle rents the car for 5 days and drives 180 miles.

a. Write an expression for how much it will cost Ms. Carlyle to rent the car.

b. Evaluate the expression to determine how much Ms. Carlyle must pay the car rental company.

27. **GEOMETRY** The length of a rectangle is $3n + 2$ and its width is $n - 1$. The perimeter of the rectangle is twice the sum of its length and its width.

a. Write an expression that represents the perimeter of the rectangle.

b. Find the perimeter of the rectangle when $n = 4$ inches.

Word Problem Practice
AL OL BL ELL

NAME ______ DATE ______ PERIOD ______

1-2 Word Problem Practice
Order of Operations

1. **SCHOOLS** Jefferson High School has 100 less than 5 times as many students as Taft High School. Write and evaluate an expression to find the number of students at Jefferson High School if Taft High School has 300 students.

2. **GEOGRAPHY** Guadalupe Peak in Texas has an altitude that is 671 feet more than double the altitude of Mount Sunflower in Kansas. Write and evaluate an expression for the altitude of Guadalupe Peak if Mount Sunflower has an altitude of 4039 feet.

3. **TRANSPORTATION** The Plaid Taxi Cab Company charges $1.75 per passenger plus $3.45 per mile for trips less than 10 miles. Write and evaluate an expression to find the cost for Max to take a Plaid taxi 8 miles to the airport.

4. **GEOMETRY** The area of a circle is related to the radius of the circle such that the product of the square of the radius and a number π gives the area. Write and evaluate an expression for the area of a circular pizza below. Approximate π as 3.14.

5. **BIOLOGY** Lavania is studying the growth of a population of fruit flies in her laboratory. She notices that the number of fruit flies in her experiment is five times as large after any six-day period. She observes 20 fruit flies on October 1. Write and evaluate an expression to predict the population of fruit flies Lavania will observe on October 31.

6. **CONSUMER SPENDING** During a long weekend, Devon paid a total of x dollars for a rental car so he could visit his family. He rented the car for 4 days at a rate of $36 per day. There was an additional charge of $0.20 per mile after the first 200 miles driven.

a. Write an algebraic expression to represent the amount Devon paid for additional mileage only.

b. Write an algebraic expression to represent the number of miles over 200 miles that Devon drove the rented car.

c. How many miles did Devon drive overall if he paid a total of $174 for the car rental?

Lesson 1-2

Enrichment
OL BL

NAME ______ DATE ______ PERIOD ______

1-2 Enrichment

The Four Digits Problem

One well-known mathematics problem is to write expressions for consecutive numbers beginning with 1. On this page, you will use the digits 1, 2, 3, and 4. Each digit is used only once. You may use addition, subtraction, multiplication (not division), exponents, and parentheses in any way you wish. Also, you can use two digits to make one number, such as 12 or 34.

Express each number as a combination of the digits 1, 2, 3, and 4.

$1 = (3 \times 1) - (4 - 2)$	18 = ______	$35 = 2^{(4+1)} + 3$
2 = ______	$19 = 3(2 + 4) + 1$	36 = ______
3 = ______	20 = ______	37 = ______
4 = ______	21 = ______	38 = ______
5 = ______	22 = ______	39 = ______
6 = ______	$23 = 31 - (4 \times 2)$	40 = ______

WatchOut!

Error Analysis For Exercise 59, students should see that Tara and Curtis have done something different in the second step. Explain to students that once they have identified a difference, they do not need to look at subsequent steps.

Standardized Test Practice

65. Let m represent the number of miles. Which algebraic expression represents the number of feet in m miles? **A**

A $5280m$

B $\frac{5280}{m}$

C $m + 5280$

D $5280 - m$

66. SHORT RESPONSE

Simplify: $[10 + 15(2^3)] \div [7(2^2) - 2]$

Step 1 $[10 + 15(8)] \div [7(4) - 2]$

Step 2 $[10 + 120] \div [28 - 2]$

Step 3 $130 \div 26$

Step 4 $\frac{1}{5}$

Which is the first *incorrect* step? Explain the error. **Step 4; the answer is 5.**

67. EXTENDED RESPONSE Consider the rectangle below.

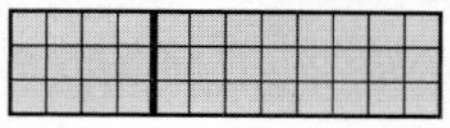

Part A Which expression models the area of the rectangle? **G**

F $4 + 3 \times 8$ H $3 \times 4 + 8$

G $3 \times (4 + 8)$ J $3^2 + 8^2$

Part B Draw one or more rectangles to model each other expression.

See Ch. 1 Answer Appendix.

68. GEOMETRY What is the perimeter of the triangle if $a = 9$ and $b = 10$? **B**

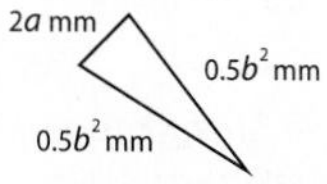

A 164 mm C 28 mm

B 118 mm D 4 mm

Spiral Review

Write a verbal expression for each algebraic expression. (Lesson 1-1)

69. $14 - 9c$ **14 minus 9 times *c***

70. $k^3 + 13$ ***k* cubed plus 13**

71. $\frac{4 - v}{w}$ **the difference of 4 and *v* divided by *w***

72. MONEY Destiny earns $8 per hour babysitting and $15 for each lawn she mows. Write an expression to show the amount of money she earns babysitting h hours and mowing m lawns. (Lesson 1-1) **$8h + 15m$**

Find the area of each figure. (Lesson 0-8)

73. 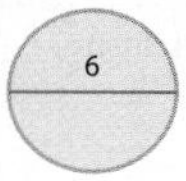

9π units^2

74. 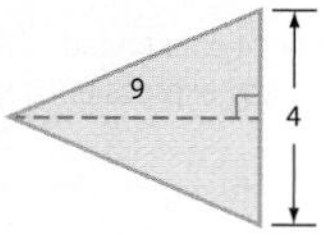

18 units^2

75. 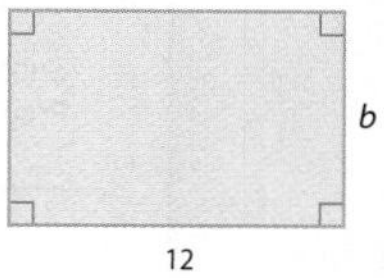

$12b$ units^2

76. SCHOOL Aaron correctly answered 27 out of 30 questions on his last biology test. What percent of the questions did he answer correctly? (Lesson 0-6) **90%**

Skills Review

Find the value of each expression.

77. $5.65 - 3.08$ **2.57**

78. $6 \div \frac{4}{5}$ **$\frac{15}{2}$**

79. $4.85(2.72)$ **13.192**

80. $1\frac{1}{12} + 3\frac{2}{3}$ **$4\frac{3}{4}$**

81. $\frac{4}{9} \cdot \frac{3}{2}$ **$\frac{2}{3}$**

82. $7\frac{3}{4} - 4\frac{7}{10}$ **$3\frac{1}{20}$**

Differentiated Instruction OL BL

Extension Write the numbers 2, 3, 4, and 8 on the board. Tell students to make the number 8 by using each of the four numbers exactly once along with any operation and grouping symbols. Sample answers: $(4 + 8) \div 3 \cdot 2$; $8 \div 4 \cdot 3 + 2$

Every effort is made to show **answers** on the reduced Student Edition page or in the margin of the Teacher Edition.

Teaching the Process Standards

Perseverance Mathematically proficient students try simpler forms of the original problem in order to gain insight. In Exercise 61, suggest that students start by combining pairs of numbers.

4 Assess

Name the Math Write a numerical and an algebraic expression on the board. Have students work with a partner and take turns explaining how to evaluate one of the expressions using the order of operations.

Formative Assessment

Check for student understanding of Lessons 1-1 and 1-2.

Quiz 1, p. 57

Additional Answers

57a.

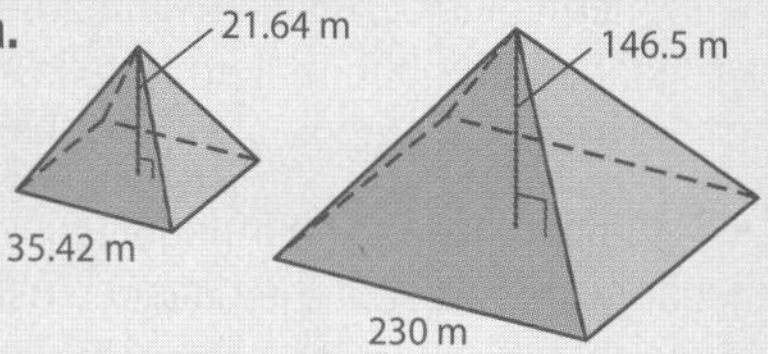

60. Sample answer: First I would subtract c from b and then divide by d. Then I would multiply that by a and then subtract f. Without grouping symbols, first a and b would be multiplied together, then c would be divided by d, and then c divided by d would be subtracted from a multiplied by b. Then f would be subtracted from the result.

64. The expressions are equivalent. To simplify the first expression, simplify the expression in the parentheses first to get 47. Then multiply by 10 to get 470. The order of operations states to multiply before adding. So, perform the multiplication first in the second expression. The result is 300 + 170. Then add to get 470.

1 Focus

VerticalAlignment

Before Lesson 1-3 Use the order of operations to simplify expressions.

Lesson 1-3 Recognize the properties of equality and identity. Recognize the Commutative and Associative Properties.

After Lesson 1-3 Represent relationships among quantities using equations and inequalities.

2 Teach

Scaffolding Questions

Have students read the **Why?** section of the lesson.

Ask:

- If the distance from Natalie's house to the mall is 32 miles, what is the distance from the mall to Natalie's house? 32 miles
- If the two distances are equal, how can you represent the distance using numbers? $32 = 32$
- What do you think the Reflexive Property means? A quantity is equal to itself.

Scaffolding Questions give direction and momentum to the lesson, clarify its purpose, and keep students on task.

LESSON 1-3 Properties of Numbers

Then

- You used the order of operations to simplify expressions.

Now

1. Recognize the properties of equality and identity.
2. Recognize the Commutative and Associative Properties.

Why?

- Natalie lives 32 miles away from the mall. The distance from her house to the mall is the same as the distance from the mall to her house. This is an example of the Reflexive Property.

NewVocabulary
equivalent expressions
additive identity
multiplicative identity
multiplicative inverse
reciprocal

Process Standards
PS.2, PS.3

1 Properties of Equality and Identity

The expressions $4k + 8k$ and $12k$ are called **equivalent expressions** because they represent the same number. The properties below allow you to write an equivalent expression for a given expression.

KeyConcept Properties of Equality

Property	Words	Symbols	Examples
Reflexive Property	Any quantity is equal to itself.	For any number a, $a = a$.	$5 = 5$ $4 + 7 = 4 + 7$
Symmetric Property	If one quantity equals a second quantity, then the second quantity equals the first.	For any numbers a and b, if $a = b$, then $b = a$.	If $8 = 2 + 6$, then $2 + 6 = 8$.
Transitive Property	If one quantity equals a second quantity and the second quantity equals a third quantity, then the first quantity equals the third quantity.	For any numbers a, b, and c, if $a = b$ and $b = c$, then $a = c$.	If $6 + 9 = 3 + 12$ and $3 + 12 = 15$, then $6 + 9 = 15$.
Substitution Property	A quantity may be substituted for its equal in any expression.	If $a = b$, then a may be replaced by b in any expression.	If $n = 11$, then $4n = 4 \cdot 11$

The sum of any number and 0 is equal to the number. Thus, 0 is called the **additive identity**.

KeyConcept Addition Properties

Property	Words	Symbols	Examples
Additive Identity	For any number a, the sum of a and 0 is a.	$a + 0 = 0 + a = a$	$2 + 0 = 2$ $0 + 2 = 2$
Additive Inverse	A number and its opposite are additive inverses of each other.	$a + (-a) = 0$	$3 + (-3) = 0$ $4 - 4 = 0$

Lesson 1-3 Resources

Resource	Approaching Level AL	On Level OL	Beyond Level BL	English Learners ELL
Teacher Edition	▪ Differentiated Instruction, p. 18	▪ Differentiated Instruction, p. 22	▪ Differentiated Instruction, p. 22	
Chapter Resource Masters	▪ Study Guide and Intervention, pp. 18–19 ▪ Skills Practice, p. 20 ▪ Practice, p. 21 ▪ Word Problem Practice, p. 22	▪ Study Guide and Intervention, pp. 18–19 ▪ Skills Practice, p. 20 ▪ Practice, p. 21 ▪ Word Problem Practice, p. 22 ▪ Enrichment, p. 23	▪ Practice, p. 21 ▪ Word Problem Practice, p. 22 ▪ Enrichment, p. 23	▪ Study Guide and Intervention, pp. 18–19 ▪ Skills Practice, p. 20 ▪ Practice, p. 21 ▪ Word Problem Practice, p. 22
Other	▪ 5-Minute Check 1-3 ▪ Study Notebook	▪ 5-Minute Check 1-3 ▪ Study Notebook	▪ 5-Minute Check 1-3 ▪ Study Notebook	▪ 5-Minute Check 1-3 ▪ Study Notebook

There are also special properties associated with multiplication. Consider the following equations.

$4 \cdot n = 4$	$6 \cdot m = 0$
The solution of the equation is 1. Since the product of any number and 1 is equal to the number, 1 is called the **multiplicative identity**.	The solution of the equation is 0. The product of any number and 0 is equal to 0. This is called the **Multiplicative Property of Zero**.

Two numbers whose product is 1 are called **multiplicative inverses** or **reciprocals**. Zero has no reciprocal because any number times 0 is 0.

KeyConcept Multiplication Properties

Property	Words	Symbols	Examples
Multiplicative Identity	For any number *a*, the product of *a* and 1 is *a*.	$a \cdot 1 = a$ $1 \cdot a = a$	$14 \cdot 1 = 14$ $1 \cdot 14 = 14$
Multiplicative Property of Zero	For any number *a*, the product of *a* and 0 is 0.	$a \cdot 0 = 0$ $0 \cdot a = 0$	$9 \cdot 0 = 0$ $0 \cdot 9 = 0$
Multiplicative Inverse	For every number $\frac{a}{b}$, where $a, b \neq 0$, there is exactly one number $\frac{b}{a}$ such that the product of $\frac{a}{b}$ and $\frac{b}{a}$ is 1.	$\frac{a}{b} \cdot \frac{b}{a} = 1$ $\frac{b}{a} \cdot \frac{a}{b} = 1$	$\frac{4}{5} \cdot \frac{5}{4} = \frac{20}{20}$ or 1 $\frac{5}{4} \cdot \frac{4}{5} = \frac{20}{20}$ or 1

PT

Example 1 Evaluate Using Properties

Evaluate $7(4 - 3) - 1 + 5 \cdot \frac{1}{5}$. Name the property used in each step.

$7(4 - 3) - 1 + 5 \cdot \frac{1}{5} = 7(1) - 1 + 5 \cdot \frac{1}{5}$ — Substitution: $4 - 3 = 1$

$= 7 - 1 + 5 \cdot \frac{1}{5}$ — Multiplicative Identity: $7 \cdot 1 = 7$

$= 7 - 1 + 1$ — Multiplicative Inverse: $5 \cdot \frac{1}{5} = 1$

$= 6 + 1$ — Substitution: $7 - 1 = 6$

$= 7$ — Substitution: $6 + 1 = 7$

StudyTip

Arguments As you evaluate an expression, you are constructing an argument using stated assumptions, definitions, and previously established results. The properties of numbers are valid reasons for steps in the argument.

GuidedPractice

Name the property used in each step.

1A. $2 \cdot 3 + (4 \cdot 2 - 8)$

$= 2 \cdot 3 + (8 - 8)$ __?__ Substitution

$= 2 \cdot 3 + (0)$ __?__ Additive Inverse

$= 6 + 0$ __?__ Substitution

$= 6$ __?__ Additive Identity

1B. $7 \cdot \frac{1}{7} + 6(15 \div 3 - 5)$

$= 7 \cdot \frac{1}{7} + 6(5 - 5)$ __?__

$= 7 \cdot \frac{1}{7} + 6(0)$ __?__

$= 1 + 6(0)$ __?__

$= 1 + 0$ __?__

$= 1$ __?__

1B. Substitution; Additive Inverse; Multiplicative Inverse; Multiplicative Property of Zero; Additive Identity

2 Properties of Equality and Identity

Example 1 shows how to use the identity and equality properties to justify each step when evaluating expressions.

Formative Assessment

Use the Guided Practice exercises after each Example to determine students' understanding of concepts.

Additional Example

1 Evaluate $\frac{1}{4}(12 - 8) + 3(15 \div 5 - 2)$. Name the property used in each step.

$\frac{1}{4}(12 - 8) + 3(15 \div 5 - 2)$

$= \frac{1}{4}(4) + 3(15 \div 5 - 2)$
Substitution: $12 - 8 = 4$

$= \frac{1}{4}(4) + 3(3 - 2)$
Substitution: $15 \div 5 = 3$

$= \frac{1}{4}(4) + 3(1)$
Substitution: $3 - 2 = 1$

$= \frac{1}{4}(4) + 3$
Multiplicative Identity: $3(1) = 3$

$= 1 + 3$
Multiplicative Inverse: $\frac{1}{4}(4) = 1$

$= 4$
Substitution: $1 + 3 = 4$

Additional Examples also in Interactive Classroom PowerPoint® Presentations

IWB Interactive White Board READY

Teaching the Process Standards

Arguments Mathematically proficient students understand and use stated assumptions, definitions, and previously established results in constructing arguments. Encouraging them to think of each problem solution as a logical progression of statements establishes good habits for this course and advanced courses.

Focus on Mathematical Content

Properties of Multiplication Some of the properties of multiplication include the Multiplicative Identity Property, the Multiplicative Property of Zero, and the Multiplicative Inverse Property. The Multiplicative Identity Property states that the product of any number and 1 is that number; the Multiplicative Property of Zero states that the product of any number and zero is 0; and the Multiplicative Inverse Property states that the product of a number and its reciprocal is 1.

Teach with Tech

Audio Recording Have students work in pairs to record descriptions of the properties in their own words. Then have them listen to the recordings of other pairs.

2 Use Commutative and Associative Properties

Example 2 shows how to use the Commutative and Associative Properties for Addition to solve a real-world problem. **Example 3** shows how to use the Commutative and Associative Properties for Multiplication to evaluate a numerical expression.

Additional Example

2 HORSEBACK RIDING Migina made a list of trail lengths to find the total miles she rode. Find the total miles Migina rode her horse.

Trails	
Name	**Miles**
Bent Tree	4.25
Knob Hill	6.50
Meadowrun	9.00
Pinehurst	7.75

27.5 miles

Focus on Mathematical Content

Commutative and Associative Properties The Commutative Property states that the order in which you add or multiply numbers does not change their sum or product. The Associative Property states that the way you group 3 or more numbers when you add or multiply them does not change their sum or product.

Additional Answer (Guided Practice)

2. $300 + 30.50 + 25.50 + 50$

$= 300 + 50 + 30.50 + 25.50$ Commutative (+)

$= (300 + 50) + (30.50 + 25.50)$ Associative (+)

$= 350 + 56$ Substitution

$= 406$ Substitution

The cost is $406.

2 Use Commutative and Associative Properties

Nikki walks 2 blocks to her friend Sierra's house. They walk another 4 blocks to school. At the end of the day, Nikki and Sierra walk back to Sierra's house, and then Nikki walks home.

The distance from Nikki's house to school	equals	the distance from the school to Nikki's house.
$2 + 4$	$=$	$4 + 2$

This is an example of the **Commutative Property** for addition.

Key Concept boxes highlight definitions, formulas, and other important ideas. Multiple representations—words, symbols, examples, models—aid students' understanding.

KeyConcept Commutative Property

Words	The order in which you add or multiply numbers does not change their sum or product.
Symbols	For any numbers a and b, $a + b = b + a$ and $a \cdot b = b \cdot a$.
Examples	$4 + 8 = 8 + 4$ $\quad 7 \cdot 11 = 11 \cdot 7$

An easy way to find the sum or product of numbers is to group, or associate, the numbers using the **Associative Property**.

KeyConcept Associative Property

Words	The way you group three or more numbers when adding or multiplying does not change their sum or product.
Symbols	For any numbers a, b, and c, $(a + b) + c = a + (b + c)$ and $(ab)c = a(bc)$.
Examples	$(3 + 5) + 7 = 3 + (5 + 7)$ $\quad (2 \cdot 6) \cdot 9 = 2 \cdot (6 \cdot 9)$

Get Animated activities are online illustrations of key concepts through animations, Interactive Labs, and BrainPOPs®.

Real-WorldLink

A child's birthday party may cost about $200 depending on the number of children invited.

Source: Family Corner

Digital Vision/Getty Images

Real-World Example 2 Apply Properties of Numbers

PARTY PLANNING Eric makes a list of items that he needs to buy for a party and their costs. Find the total cost of these items.

Party Supplies	
Item	**Cost ($)**
balloons	6.75
decorations	14.00
food	23.25
beverages	20.50

Balloons		Decorations		Food		Beverages
6.75	+	14.00	+	23.25	+	20.50

$= 6.75 + 23.25 + 14.00 + 20.50$ Commutative (+)

$= (6.75 + 23.25) + (14.00 + 20.50)$ Associative (+)

$= 30.00 + 34.50$ Substitution

$= 64.50$ Substitution

The total cost is $64.50.

GuidedPractice

2. **FURNITURE** Rafael is buying furnishings for his first apartment. He buys a couch for $300, lamps for $30.50, a rug for $25.50, and a table for $50. Find the total cost of these items. **See margin.**

DifferentiatedInstruction AL

If students have difficulty with the concepts of the Commutative and Associative Properties,

Then consider using manipulatives that will visually verify the properties for the Commutative Property. For example, show students that a big bucket of water and a small bucket of water equals a small bucket of water and a big bucket of water.

18 | Lesson 1-3 | Properties of Numbers

Example 3 Use Multiplication Properties

Evaluate 5 • 7 • 4 • 2 using the properties of numbers. Name the property used in each step.

5 • 7 • 4 • 2 = 5 • 2 • 7 • 4	Commutative (×)
= (5 • 2) • (7 • 4)	Associative (×)
= 10 • 28	Substitution
= 280	Substitution

Guided Practice

Evaluate each expression using the properties of numbers. Name the property used in each step. **3A, 3B. See margin.**

3A. 2.9 • 4 • 10

3B. $\frac{5}{3}$ • 25 • 3 • 2

Check Your Understanding

◯ = Step-by-Step Solutions begin on page R13.

Example 1 **Evaluate each expression. Name the property used in each step.** **1–4. See Ch. 1 Answer Appendix for steps.**

1. (1 ÷ 5)5 • 14 **14**
2. 6 + 4(19 − 15) **22**
3. 5(14 − 5) + 6(3 + 7) **105**
4. **FINANCIAL LITERACY** Carolyn has 9 quarters, 4 dimes, 7 nickels, and 2 pennies, which can be represented as 9(25) + 4(10) + 7(5) + 2. Evaluate the expression to find how much money she has. Name the property used in each step. **302¢ or $3.02**

Examples 2–3 **Evaluate each expression using the properties of numbers. Name the property used in each step.** **5–8. See Ch. 1 Answer Appendix for steps.**

5. 23 + 42 + 37 **102**
6. 2.75 + 3.5 + 4.25 + 1.5 **12**
7. 3 • 7 • 10 • 2 **420**
8. $\frac{1}{4}$ • 24 • $\frac{2}{3}$ **4**

Practice and Problem Solving

Extra Practice is on page R1.

Example 1 **Evaluate each expression. Name the property used in each step.** **9–14. See Ch. 1 Answer Appendix for steps.**

9. 3(22 − 3 • 7) **3**
10. 7 + (9 − 3^2) **7**
11. $\frac{3}{4}$[4 ÷ (7 − 4)] **1**
12. [3 ÷ (2 • 1)]$\frac{2}{3}$ **1**
13. 2(3 • 2 − 5) + 3 • $\frac{1}{3}$ **3**
14. 6 • $\frac{1}{6}$ + 5(12 ÷ 4 − 3) **1**

Example 2

15. **GEOMETRY** The expression 2 • $\frac{22}{7}$ • 14^2 + 2 • $\frac{22}{7}$ • 14 • 7 represents the approximate surface area of the cylinder at the right. Evaluate this expression to find the approximate surface area. Name the property used in each step. **1848 in^2; See Ch. 1 Answer Appendix for steps.**

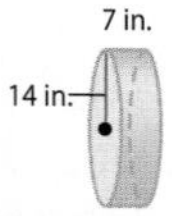

16. **REASONING** A traveler checks into a hotel on Friday and checks out the following Tuesday morning. Use the table to find the total cost of the room including tax. **$291**

Hotel Rates Per Day		
Day	**Room Charge**	**Sales Tax**
Monday–Friday	$72	$5.40
Saturday–Sunday	$63	$5.10

Differentiated Homework Options

Level	Assignment	Two-Day Option	
AL Basic	9–28, 54–56, 58–80	9–27 odd, 61–64	10–28 even, 54–56, 58–60, 65–80
OL Core	9–29 odd, 30, 31–47 odd, 48–56, 58–80	9–28, 61–64	29–56, 58–60, 65–80
BL Advanced	29–74, (optional: 75–80)		

Additional Example

3 Evaluate 2 • 8 • 5 • 7 using the properties of numbers. Name the property used in each step.

2 • 8 • 5 • 7	
= 2 • 5 • 8 • 7	Commutative (×)
= (2 • 5) • (8 • 7)	Associative (×)
= 10 • 56	Substitution
= 560	Substitution

Additional Examples exactly parallel the examples in the text. Step-by-step solutions for these examples are included in **Interactive Classroom**.

3 Practice

Formative Assessment

Use Exercises 1–8 to check for understanding.

Use the chart at the bottom of this page to customize assignments for your students.

Teaching the Process Standards

Reasoning Mathematically proficient students create a coherent representation of the problem at hand and flexibly use different properties of operations. Encourage students to represent problems in multiple ways and compare the results.

Additional Answers (Guided Practice)

3A. 2.9 • 4 • 10

= 2.9 • 10 • 4	Comm. (×)
= (2.9 • 10) • 4	Assoc. (×)
= 29 • 4	Substitution
= 116	Substitution

3B. $\frac{5}{3}$ • 25 • 3 • 2

= $\frac{5}{3}$ • 3 • 25 • 2	Comm. (×)
= $\left(\frac{5}{3} \cdot 3\right)$ • (25 • 2)	Assoc. (×)
= 5 • 50	Substitution
= 250	Substitution

Study Guide and Intervention

AL OL ELL

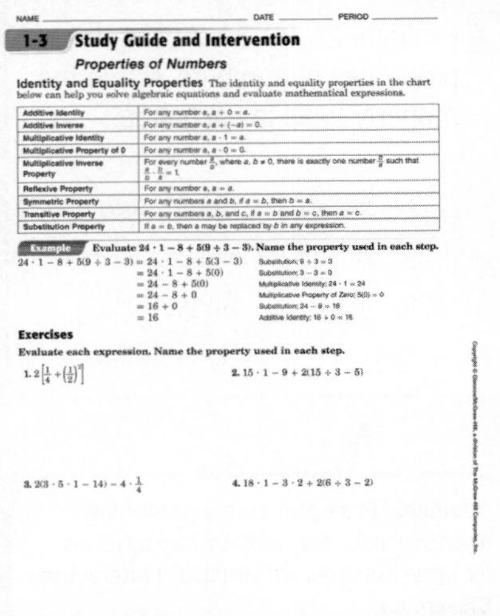
NAME ______ DATE ______ PERIOD ______

1-3 Study Guide and Intervention

Properties of Numbers

Identity and Equality Properties The identity and equality properties in the chart below can help you solve algebraic equations and evaluate mathematical expressions.

Additive Identity	For any number a, a + 0 = a.
Additive Inverse	For any number a, a + (−a) = 0.
Multiplicative Identity	For any number a, a · 1 = a.
Multiplicative Property of 0	For any number a, a · 0 = 0.
Multiplicative Inverse Property	For every number a/b, where a, b ≠ 0, there is exactly one number b/a such that a/b · b/a = 1.
Reflexive Property	For any number a, a = a.
Symmetric Property	For any numbers a and b, if a = b, then b = a.
Transitive Property	For any numbers a, b, and c, if a = b and b = c, then a = c.
Substitution Property	If a = b, then a may be replaced by b in any expression.

Example Evaluate 24 · 1 − 8 + 5(9 ÷ 3 − 3). Name the property used in each step.

Exercises

Evaluate each expression. Name the property used in each step.

Practice

AL OL BL ELL

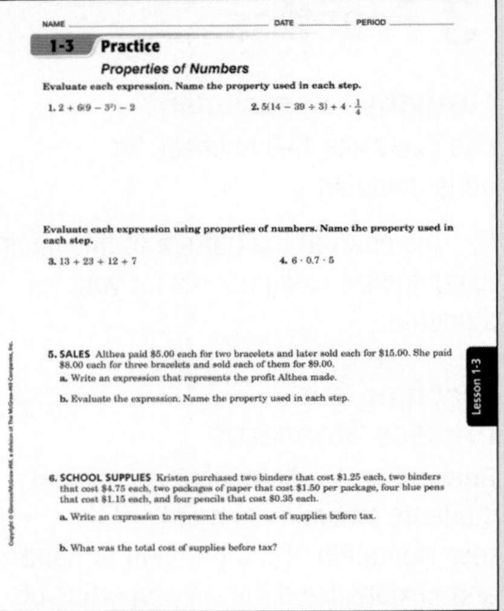
NAME ______ DATE ______ PERIOD ______

1-3 Practice

Properties of Numbers

Evaluate each expression. Name the property used in each step.

Evaluate each expression using properties of numbers. Name the property used in each step.

5. SALES Althea paid $5.00 each for two bracelets and later sold each for $15.00. She paid $8.00 each for three bracelets and sold each of them for $9.00.

a. Write an expression that represents the profit Althea made.

b. Evaluate the expression. Name the property used in each step.

6. SCHOOL SUPPLIES Kristen purchased two binders that cost $1.25 each, two binders that cost $4.75 each, two packages of paper that cost $1.50 per package, four blue pens that cost $1.15 each, and four pencils that cost $0.35 each.

a. Write an expression to represent the total cost of supplies before tax.

b. What was the total cost of supplies before tax?

Word Problem Practice

AL OL BL ELL

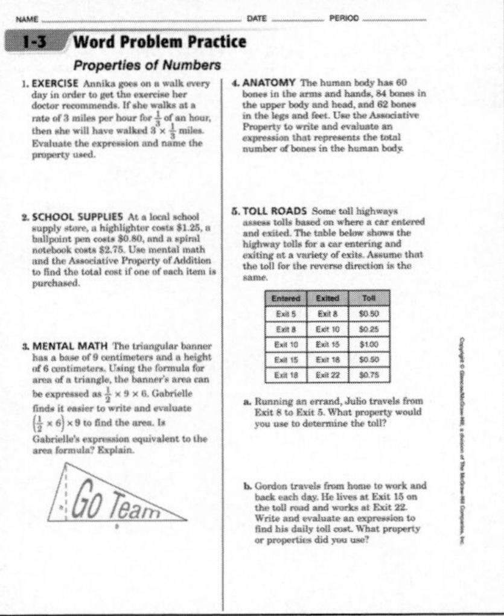
NAME ______ DATE ______ PERIOD ______

1-3 Word Problem Practice

Properties of Numbers

Enrichment

OL BL

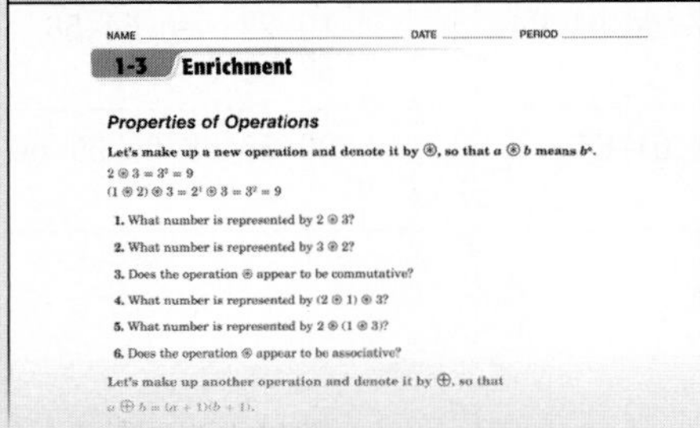
NAME ______ DATE ______ PERIOD ______

1-3 Enrichment

Properties of Operations

Examples 2–3 **Evaluate each expression using properties of numbers. Name the property used in each step.** 17–28. See Ch. 1 Answer Appendix for steps.

17. $25 + 14 + 15 + 36$ 90

18. $11 + 7 + 5 + 13$ 36

19. $3\frac{2}{3} + 4 + 5\frac{1}{3}$ 13

20. $4\frac{4}{9} + 7\frac{2}{9}$ $11\frac{2}{3}$

21. $4.3 + 2.4 + 3.6 + 9.7$ 20

22. $3.25 + 2.2 + 5.4 + 10.75$ 21.6

23. $12 \cdot 2 \cdot 6 \cdot 5$ 720

24. $2 \cdot 8 \cdot 10 \cdot 2$ 320

25. $0.2 \cdot 4.6 \cdot 5$ 4.6

26. $3.5 \cdot 3 \cdot 6$ 63

27. $1\frac{5}{6} \cdot 24 \cdot 3\frac{1}{11}$ 136

28. $2\frac{3}{4} \cdot 1\frac{1}{8} \cdot 32$ 99

B **29. SCUBA DIVING** The sign shows the equipment rented or sold by a scuba diving store.

a. Write two expressions to represent the total sales to rent 2 wet suits, 3 air tanks, 2 dive flags, and selling 5 underwater cameras. See margin.

b. What are the total sales? $149.35

30. COOKIES Bobby baked 2 dozen chocolate chip cookies, 3 dozen sugar cookies, and a dozen oatmeal raisin cookies. How many total cookies did he bake? 72

Evaluate each expression if $a = -1$, $b = 4$, and $c = 6$.

31. $4a + 9b - 2c$ 20

32. $-10c + 3a + a$ −64

33. $a - b + 5a - 2b$ −18

34. $8a + 5b - 11a - 7b$ −5

35. $3c^2 + 2c + 2c^2$ 192

36. $3a - 4a^2 + 2a$ −9

37. FOOTBALL A football team is on the 35-yard line. The quarterback is sacked at the line of scrimmage. The team gains 0 yards, so they are still at the 35-yard line. Which identity or property does this represent? Explain. Additive Identity; $35 + 0 = 35$

Find the value of x. Then name the property used.

38. $8 = 8 + x$ 0; Additive Identity

39. $3.2 + x = 3.2$ 0; Additive Identity

40. $10x = 10$ 1; Multiplicative Identity

41. $\frac{1}{2} \cdot x = \frac{1}{2} \cdot 7$ 7; Reflexive Property

42. $x + 0 = 5$ 5; Additive Identity

43. $1 \cdot x = 3$ 3; Multiplicative Identity

44. $5 \cdot \frac{1}{5} = x$ 1; Multiplicative Inverse

45. $2 + 8 = 8 + x$ 2; Commutative Property

46. $x + \frac{3}{4} = 3 + \frac{3}{4}$ 3; Reflexive Property

47. $\frac{1}{3} \cdot x = 1$ 3; Multiplicative Inverse

48. GEOMETRY Write an expression to represent the perimeter of the triangle. Then find the perimeter if $x = 2$ and $y = 7$. $4 + 5x + 4 + 5x + 3y$; 49

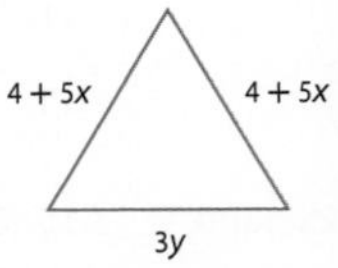

49. SPORTS Tickets to a baseball game cost $25 each plus a $4.50 handling charge per ticket. If Sharon has a coupon for $10 off and orders 4 tickets, how much will she be charged? $108

50. PRECISION The table shows prices on children's clothing.

Shorts	Shirts	Tank Tops
$7.99	$8.99	$6.99
$5.99	$4.99	$2.99

a. Interpret the expression $5(8.99) + 2(2.99) + 7(5.99)$.

b. Write and evaluate three different expressions that represent 8 pairs of shorts and 8 tops. See margin.

c. If you buy 8 shorts and 8 tops, you receive a discount of 15%. Find the greatest and least amount of money you can spend on the 16 items at the sale. $101.86; $61.06

50a. the total cost for 5 shirts, 2 tank tops, and 7 shorts

Additional Answers

29a. Sample answer: $2(10.95) + 3(7.5) + 2(5) + 5(18.99)$; $2(10.95 + 5) + 3(7.5) + 5(18.99)$

50b. Sample answer: $8(7.99) + 4(4.99) + 4(6.99) = \$111.84$; $8(5.99) + 4(8.99) + 4(2.99) = \$95.84$; $4(7.99) + 4(5.99) + 4(4.99) + 4(2.99) = \$87.84$

51. **GEOMETRY** A regular octagon measures $(3x + 5)$ units on each side. What is the perimeter if $x = 2$? **88 units**

52. **MULTIPLE REPRESENTATIONS** You can use *algebra tiles* to model and explore algebraic expressions. The rectangular tile has an area of x, with dimensions 1 by x. The small square tile has an area of 1, with dimensions 1 by 1.

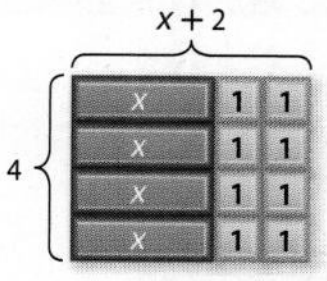

a. **Concrete** Make a rectangle with algebra tiles to model the expression $4(x + 2)$ as shown above. What are the dimensions of this rectangle? What is its area? **length: $x + 2$, width: 4; $4(x + 2)$**

b. **Analytical** What are the areas of the green region and of the yellow region? **$4x$; 8**

c. **Verbal** Complete this statement: $4(x + 2) = \underline{?}$. Write a convincing argument to justify your statement. **See margin.**

53. **GEOMETRY** A **proof** is a logical argument in which each statement you make is supported by a statement that is accepted as true. It is given that $\overline{AB} \cong \overline{CD}$, $\overline{AB} \cong \overline{BD}$, and $\overline{AB} \cong \overline{AC}$. Pedro wants to prove $\triangle ADB \cong \triangle ADC$. To do this, he must show that $\overline{AD} \cong \overline{AD}$, $\overline{AB} \cong \overline{DC}$ and $\overline{BD} \cong \overline{AC}$.

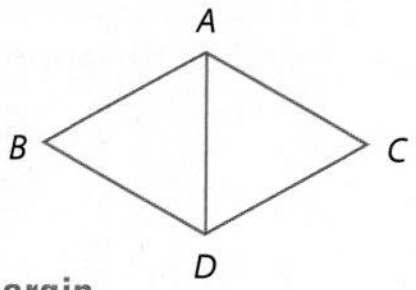

a. Copy the figure and label $\overline{AB} \cong \overline{CD}$, $\overline{AB} \cong \overline{BD}$, and $\overline{AB} \cong \overline{AC}$. **See margin.**

b. Explain how he can use the Reflexive and Transitive Properties to prove $\triangle ADB \cong \triangle ADC$. **See margin.**

c. If AC is x centimeters, write an equation for the perimeter of $ACDB$. **$P = x + x + x + x$**

H.O.T. Problems Use Higher-Order Thinking Skills

54. **OPEN ENDED** Write two equations showing the Transitive Property of Equality. Justify your reasoning. **See margin.**

55. **ARGUMENTS** Explain why 0 has no multiplicative inverse. **Sample answer: You cannot divide by 0.**

56. **REASONING** The sum of any two whole numbers is always a whole number. So, the set of whole numbers {0, 1, 2, 3, 4, … } is said to be closed under addition. This is an example of the **Closure Property**. State whether each statement is *true* or *false*. If false, justify your reasoning.

a. The set of whole numbers is closed under subtraction. **False; $3 - 4 = -1$, which is not a whole number.**

b. The set of whole numbers is closed under multiplication. **true**

c. The set of whole numbers is closed under division. **False; $2 \div 3 = \frac{2}{3}$, which is not a whole number.**

57. **CHALLENGE** Does the Commutative Property *sometimes*, *always* or *never* hold for subtraction? Explain your reasoning. **See margin.**

58. **REASONING** Explain whether 1 can be an additive identity. Give an example to justify your answer. **No; $3 + 1 \neq 3$**

59. **WHICH ONE DOESN'T BELONG?** Identify the equation that does not belong with the other three. Explain your reasoning. **See margin.**

$x + 12 = 12 + x$	$7h = h \cdot 7$	$1 + a = a + 1$	$(2j)k = 2(jk)$

60. **WRITING IN MATH** Determine whether the Commutative Property applies to division. Justify your answer. **See margin.**

WatchOut!

Preventing Errors Some students may have difficulty remembering the names of the properties in this lesson. Remind these students that they already know how to use the properties. Encourage them to think of word associations that will help them relate what they know to the correct names of the properties.

Teaching the Process Standards

Precision Mathematically proficient students express numerical answers with a degree of precision appropriate for the problem context. In Exercise 50, remind students that money problems should be answered to the nearest cent, fractions of cents are not reasonable.

Arguments Mathematically proficient students make conjectures and build a logical progression of statements to explore the truth of their conjectures. In Exercises 53 and 55, point out to students that as they are building their skills in writing arguments that will be useful in later courses.

Exercise Alert

Manipulatives Exercise 52 requires the use of algebra tiles.

Multiple Representations

In Exercise 52, students use algebra tiles and algebraic expressions to discover how the Distributive Property applies to algebraic expressions.

Additional Answers

52c. The area of the rectangle is $x + 1 + 1 + x + 1 + 1 + x + 1 + 1 + x + 1 + 1$ or $4x + 8$. Therefore, $4(x + 2) = 4x + 8$.

53a.

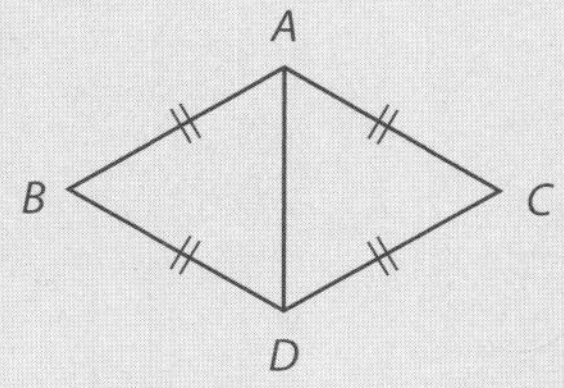

53b. $\overline{AD} \cong \overline{AD}$ by the Reflexive Property. The Transitive Property shows that if $\overline{AB} \cong \overline{AC}$ and $\overline{AC} \cong \overline{DC}$, then $\overline{AB} \cong \overline{DC}$, and if $\overline{AB} \cong \overline{BD}$ and $\overline{AB} \cong \overline{AC}$, then $\overline{BD} \cong \overline{AC}$.

54. Sample answer: $5 = 3 + 2$ and $3 + 2 = 4 + 1$ so $5 = 4 + 1$; $5 + 7 = 8 + 4$, and $8 + 4 = 12$, so $5 + 7 = 12$.

57. Sometimes; when a number is subtracted by itself then it holds, but otherwise it does not.

59. $(2j)k = 2(jk)$; The other three equations illustrate the Commutative Property of Addition or Multiplication. This equation represents the Associative Property of Multiplication.

60. The Commutative Property does not apply to division. For $a \div b = b \div a$ to be true, a and b must be nonzero and equal or opposites.

Standardized Test Practice exercises help students solidify their knowledge using exercises in a testing format.

4 Assess

Crystal Ball Ask students to write a brief statement on how they think the properties of identity and equality connect to the next lesson on the Distributive Property.

The **Four-Step Teaching Plan** shows you how to **Focus**, **Teach**, **Practice**, and **Assess** each lesson. Each lesson ends with a creative strategy for closing the lesson.

Standardized Test Practice

61. A deck is shaped like a rectangle with a width of 12 feet and a length of 15 feet. What is the area of the deck? **D**

A 3 ft^2
B 27 ft^2
C 108 ft^2
D 180 ft^2

62. GEOMETRY A box in the shape of a rectangular prism has a volume of 56 cubic inches. If the length of each side is multiplied by 2, what will be the approximate volume of the box? **J**

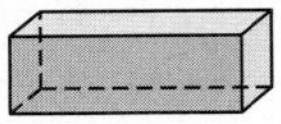

F 112 in^3 H 336 in^3
G 224 in^3 J 448 in^3

63. $27 \div 3 + (12 - 4) =$ **C**

A $\frac{-11}{5}$ C 17
B $\frac{27}{11}$ D 25

64. GRIDDED RESPONSE Ms. Beal had 1 bran muffin, 16 ounces of orange juice, 3 ounces of sunflower seeds, 2 slices of turkey, and half a cup of spinach. Find the total number of grams of protein she consumed. **39.5**

Protein Content	
Food	**Protein (g)**
bran muffin (1)	3
orange juice (8 oz)	2
sunflower seeds (1 oz)	2
turkey (1 slice)	12
spinach (1 c)	5

Spiral Review

Evaluate each expression. (Lesson 1-2)

65. $3 \cdot 5 + 1 - 2$ **14**
66. $14 \div 2 \cdot 6 - 5^2$ **17**
67. $\frac{3 \cdot 9^2 - 3^2 \cdot 9}{3 \cdot 9}$ **6**

68. GEOMETRY Write an expression for the perimeter of the figure. (Lesson 1-1) **$10 + z$**

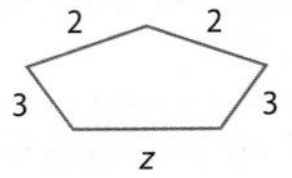

Find the perimeter and area of each figure. (Lessons 0-7 and 0-8)

69. a rectangle with length 5 feet and width 8 feet **26 ft; 40 ft^2**

70. a square with length 4.5 inches **18 in.; 20.25 in^2**

71. SURVEY Andrew took a survey of his friends to find out their favorite type of music. Of the 34 friends surveyed, 22 said they liked rock music the best. What percent like rock music the best? (Lesson 0-6) **about 64.7%**

Name the reciprocal of each number. (Lesson 0-5)

72. $\frac{6}{17}$ **$\frac{17}{6}$**
73. $\frac{2}{23}$ **$\frac{23}{2}$**
74. $3\frac{4}{5}$ **$\frac{5}{19}$**

Skills Review

Find each product. Express in simplest form.

75. $\frac{12}{15} \cdot \frac{3}{14}$ **$\frac{6}{35}$**
76. $\frac{5}{7} \cdot \left(-\frac{4}{5}\right)$ **$-\frac{4}{7}$**
77. $\frac{10}{11} \cdot \frac{21}{35}$ **$\frac{6}{11}$**
78. $\frac{63}{65} \cdot \frac{120}{126}$ **$\frac{12}{13}$**
79. $-\frac{4}{3} \cdot \left(-\frac{9}{2}\right)$ **6**
80. $\frac{1}{3} \cdot \frac{2}{5}$ **$\frac{2}{15}$**

Differentiated Instruction OL BL

Extension Activities help you cultivate skills that students will need to have success in higher mathematics.

Extension Have students use a real-world situation to explain and demonstrate one of the properties of numbers. For example, Lee Ann pays \$8 + \$3 for a notebook and paper, and Rick pays \$9 + \$2 for a notebook and paper. If Lee Ann's total is equal to Rick's total and Rick paid \$11, then Lee Ann paid \$11 too. This illustrates the Transitive Property of Equality, which states that if $a = b$ and $b = c$, then $a = c$. In this case, $a = 8 + 3$, $b = 9 + 2$, and $c = 11$.

EXTEND 1-3 Algebra Lab
Accuracy

All measurements taken in the real world are approximations. The greater the care with which a measurement is taken, the more accurate it will be. **Accuracy** refers to how close a measured value comes to the actual or desired value. For example, a fraction is more accurate than a rounded decimal.

Process Standards
PS.6

Activity 1 When Is Close Good Enough?

Measure the length of your desktop. Record your results in centimeters, in meters, and in millimeters.

Analyze the Results

2. Sample answer: Yes; in centimeters, the measurement was rounded to the half; in meters, the measurement was rounded to the tenth.

1. Did you round to the nearest whole measure? If so, when? **Sample answer: yes; in millimeters**
2. Did you round to the nearest half, tenth, or smaller? If so, when?
3. Which unit of measure was the most appropriate for this task? **centimeters**
4. Which unit of measure was the most accurate? **millimeters**

Deciding where to round a measurement depends on how the measurement will be used. But calculations should not be carried out to greater accuracy than that of the original data.

Activity 2 Decide Where to Round

a. **Elan has \$13 that he wants to divide among his 6 nephews. When he types $13 \div 6$ into his calculator, the number that appears is 2.166666667. Where should Elan round?**

Since Elan is rounding money, the smallest increment is a penny, so round to the hundredths place. This will give him 2.17, and $\$2.17 \times 6 = \$13.02$. Elan will be two pennies short, so round to \$2.16. Since $\$2.16 \times 6 = \$12.96$, Elan can give each of his nephews \$2.16.

b. **Dante's mother brings him a dozen cookies, but before she leaves she eats one and tells Dante he has to share with his two sisters. Dante types $11 \div 3$ into his calculator and gets 3.666666667. Where should Dante round?**

After each sibling receives 3 cookies, there are two cookies left. In this case, it is more accurate to convert the decimal portion to a fraction and give each sibling $\frac{2}{3}$ of a cookie.

c. **Eva measures the dimensions of a box as 8.7, 9.52, and 3.16 inches. She multiplies these three numbers to find the measure of the volume. The result shown on her calculator is 261.72384. Where should Eva round?**

Eva should round to the tenths place, 261.7, because she was only accurate to the tenths place with one of her measures.

Exercises

5. Jessica wants to divide \$23 six ways. Her calculator shows 3.833333333. Where should she round? **the hundredths place; \$3.83**
6. Ms. Harris wants to share 2 pizzas among 6 people. Her calculator shows 0.3333333333. Where should she round? **She should convert to a fraction and give each person $\frac{1}{3}$.**
7. The measurements of an aquarium are 12.9, 7.67, and 4.11 inches. The measure of the volume is given by the product 406.65573. Where should the number be rounded? **the tenths place; 406.7**

1 Focus

Objective Choose a level of accuracy appropriate to limitations on measurement when reporting quantities.

Materials for Each Student

- rulers that measure in centimeters, millimeters, and meters
- calculators

2 Teach

Working in Cooperative Groups

Have students work in groups of three or four, mixing abilities, to complete Activities 1–3, Analyze the Results 1–4, and Exercises 5–7.

Teaching Tip
It is important that students understand that a solution to a problem cannot be more accurate then the level of accuracy in the given measurements, or values.

3 Assess

Formative Assessment
Use Exercises 8–15 to assess whether students understand how to choose a level of accuracy appropriate to limitations on measurement when reporting quantities.

Algebra Lab
Accuracy *Continued*

For most real-world measurements, a decision must be made on the level of accuracy needed or desired.

Activity 3 Find an Appropriate Level of Accuracy

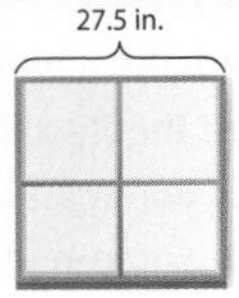

a. Jon needs to buy a shade for the window opening shown, but the shades are only available in whole inch increments. What size shade should he buy?

He should buy the 27-inch shade because it will be enough to cover the glass.

b. Tom is buying flea medicine for his dog. The amount of medicine depends on the dog's weight. The medicine is available in packages that vary by 10 dog pounds. How accurate does Tom need to be to buy the correct medicine?

He needs to be accurate to within 10 pounds.

c. Tyrone is building a jet engine. How accurate do you think he needs to be with his measurements?

He needs to be very accurate, perhaps to the thousandth of an inch.

Exercises

8. Matt's table is missing a leg. He wants to cut a piece of wood to replace the leg. How accurate do you think he needs to be with his measurements? **Accurate to the nearest millimeter, or the table will wobble.**

For each situation, determine where the rounding should occur and give the rounded answer.

9. Sam wants to divide \$111 seven ways. His calculator shows 15.85714286. **the hundredths place; \$15.85**

10. Kiri wants to share 3 pies among 11 people. Her calculator shows 0.2727272727. **She should convert to a fraction and give each person about a quarter of a pie.**

11. Evan's calculator gives him the volume of his soccer ball as 137.2582774. Evan measured the radius of the ball to be 3.2 inches. **the tenths place; 137.3**

For each situation, determine the level of accuracy needed. Explain.

12. You are estimating the length of your school's basketball court. Which unit of measure should you use: 1 foot, 1 inch, or $\frac{1}{16}$ inch?

12. 1 ft; this is a large surface, using the inch measure or smaller would most likely be more precise than necessary, so it stands to use the largest measure available.

13. You are estimating the height of a small child. Which unit of measure should you use: 1 foot, 1 inch, or $\frac{1}{16}$ inch?

13. 1 in.; this is a small height, if a foot measure was used it would not be very accurate, so using an inch would be the most acceptable measure.

14. TRAVEL Curt is measuring the driving distance from one city to another. How accurate do you think he needs to be with his measurement? **Sample answer: He needs to be accurate to within a few miles.**

15. MEDICINE A nurse is administering medicine to a patient based on his weight. How accurate do you think she needs to be with her measurements? **Sample answer: She needs to be very accurate, perhaps to the thousandths of a milliliter.**

24 | Extend 1-3 | Algebra Lab: Accuracy

LESSON 1-4 The Distributive Property

Then

- You explored Associative and Commutative Properties.

Now

1. Use the Distributive Property to evaluate expressions.
2. Use the Distributive Property to simplify expressions.

Why?

- John burns approximately 420 Calories per hour by inline skating. The chart below shows the time he spent inline skating in one week.

Day	Mon	Tue	Wed	Thu	Fri	Sat	Sun
Time (h)	1	$\frac{1}{2}$	0	1	0	2	$2\frac{1}{2}$

To determine the total number of Calories that he burned inline skating that week, you can use the Distributive Property.

NewVocabulary
like terms
simplest form
coefficient

Content Standards
AI.RNE.6

Process Standards
PS.8

1 Evaluate Expressions

There are two methods you could use to calculate the number of Calories John burned inline skating. You could find the total time spent inline skating and then multiply by the Calories burned per hour. Or you could find the number of Calories burned each day and then add to find the total.

Method 1 Rate Times Total Time

$$420\left(1 + \frac{1}{2} + 1 + 2 + 2\frac{1}{2}\right)$$
$$= 420(7)$$
$$= 2940$$

Method 2 Sum of Daily Calories Burned

$$420(1) + 420\left(\frac{1}{2}\right) + 420(1) + 420(2) + 420\left(2\frac{1}{2}\right)$$
$$= 420 + 210 + 420 + 840 + 1050$$
$$= 2940$$

Either method gives the same total of 2940 Calories burned. This is an example of the **Distributive Property**.

KeyConcept Distributive Property

Symbol For any numbers a, b, and c,
$a(b + c) = ab + ac$ and $(b + c)a = ba + ca$ and
$a(b - c) = ab - ac$ and $(b - c)a = ba - ca$.

Examples

$3(2 + 5) = 3 \cdot 2 + 3 \cdot 5$
$3(7) = 6 + 15$
$21 = 21$

$4(9 - 7) = 4 \cdot 9 - 4 \cdot 7$
$4(2) = 36 - 28$
$8 = 8$

The Symmetric Property of Equality allows the Distributive Property to be written as follows.

If $a(b + c) = ab + ac$, then $ab + ac = a(b + c)$.

connectED.mcgraw-hill.com 25

1 Focus

VerticalAlignment

Before Lesson 1-4 Explore Associative and Commutative Properties.

Lesson 1-4 Use the Distributive Property to evaluate expressions. Use the Distributive Property to simplify expressions.

After Lesson 1-4 Transform and solve equations.

2 Teach

Scaffolding Questions

Have students read the **Why?** section of the lesson.

Ask:

- How can you represent the time John spent inline skating that week? $1 + \frac{1}{2} + 0 + 1 + 0 + 2 + 2\frac{1}{2}$
- By what would you multiply the quantity to find the total number of Calories burned? 420
- How can you represent the total number of Calories burned as one quantity? $420\left(1 + \frac{1}{2} + 0 + 1 + 0 + 2 + 2\frac{1}{2}\right)$

Lesson 1-4 Resources

Resource	Approaching Level AL	On Level OL	Beyond Level BL	English Learners ELL
Teacher Edition	• Differentiated Instruction, p. 27	• Differentiated Instruction, p. 27	• Differentiated Instruction, p. 31	
Chapter Resource Masters	• Study Guide and Intervention, pp. 24–25 • Skills Practice, p. 26 • Practice, p. 27 • Word Problem Practice, p. 28	• Study Guide and Intervention, pp. 24–25 • Skills Practice, p. 26 • Practice, p. 27 • Word Problem Practice, p. 28 • Enrichment, p. 29	• Practice, p. 27 • Word Problem Practice, p. 28 • Enrichment, p. 29	• Study Guide and Intervention, pp. 24–25 • Skills Practice, p. 26 • Practice, p. 27 • Word Problem Practice, p. 28
Other	• 5-Minute Check 1-4 • Study Notebook • Teaching Algebra with Manipulatives	• 5-Minute Check 1-4 • Study Notebook • Teaching Algebra with Manipulatives	• 5-Minute Check 1-4 • Study Notebook	• 5-Minute Check 1-4 • Study Notebook • Teaching Algebra with Manipulatives

1 Evaluate Expressions

Examples 1 and 2 show how to use the Distributive Property to rewrite and evaluate expressions.

Formative Assessment

Use the Guided Practice exercises after each Example to determine students' understanding of concepts.

Additional Examples

1 **FITNESS** Julio walks 5 days a week. He walks at a fast rate for 7 minutes and cools down for 2 minutes. Use the Distributive Property to write and evaluate an expression that determines the total number of minutes Julio walks.

$5(7 + 2)$
$= 5(7) + 5(2)$ Distributive Prop.
$= 35 + 10$ Multiply.
$= 45$ Add.

2 Use the Distributive Property to rewrite $12 \cdot 82$. Then evaluate. $(10 + 2)82 = 820 + 164$ or 984

Additional Examples also in Interactive Classroom PowerPoint® Presentations

IWB Interactive White Board READY

Tips for New Teachers

Mental Math Mental calculations with the Distributive Property prepare students for multiplying algebraic expressions in later chapters of this text. Consider having students complete additional practice with this skill.

Teaching the Process Standards

Sense-Making and Perseverance Mathematically proficient students start by explaining the meaning of a problem to themselves and looking for entry points. Encourage students to discuss problems with peers as they grow and apply their skills.

Gail Mooney/Masterfile

Real-WorldLink

The record attendance for a single baseball game was set in 1959. There were 92,706 spectators at a game between the Los Angeles Dodgers and the Chicago White Sox.

Source: Baseball Almanac

StudyTip

Sense-Making and Perseverance The four-step problem solving plan is a tool for making sense of any problem. When making and executing your plan, continually ask yourself, "Does this make sense?" Monitor and evaluate your progress and change course if necessary.

Real-World Example 1 Distribute Over Addition

SPORTS A group of 7 adults and 6 children are going to a University of South Florida Bulls baseball game. Use the Distributive Property to write and evaluate an expression for the total ticket cost.

USF Bulls Baseball Tickets	
Ticket	**Cost ($)**
Adult Single Game	5
Children Single Game (12 and under)	3
Groups of 10 or more Single Game	2
Senior Single Game (65 and over)	3

Source: USF

Understand You need to find the cost of each ticket and then find the total cost.

Plan $7 + 6$ or 13 people are going to the game, so the tickets are $2 each.

Solve Write an expression that shows the product of the cost of each ticket and the sum of adult tickets and children's tickets.

$2(7 + 6) = 2(7) + 2(6)$ Distributive Property
$= 14 + 12$ Multiply.
$= 26$ Add.

The total cost is $26.

Check The total number of tickets needed is 13 and they cost $2 each. Multiply 13 by 2 to get 26. Therefore, the total cost of tickets is $26.

GuidedPractice

1. **SPORTS** A group of 3 adults, an 11-year old, and 2 children under 10 years old are going to a baseball game. Write and evaluate an expression to determine the cost of tickets for the group. **$5(3) + 3(2 + 1) = 15 + 9$ or $24**

You can use the Distributive Property to make mental math easier.

Example 2 Mental Math

Use the Distributive Property to rewrite $7 \cdot 49$. Then evaluate.

$7 \cdot 49 = 7(50 - 1)$ Think: $49 = 50 - 1$
$= 7(50) - 7(1)$ Distributive Property
$= 350 - 7$ Multiply.
$= 343$ Subtract.

GuidedPractice

Use the Distributive Property to rewrite each expression. Then evaluate.

2A. 304(15) **$(300 + 4)(15)$; 4560**

2B. $44 \cdot 2\frac{1}{2}$ **$(44)\left(2 + \frac{1}{2}\right)$; 110**

2C. 210(5) **$(200 + 10)5$; 1050**

2D. 52(17) **$(50 + 2)17$; 884**

2 Simplify Expressions

You can use algebra tiles to investigate how the Distributive Property relates to algebraic expressions.

Focus on Mathematical Content

Distributive Property Multiplication can be distributed over addition or subtraction. If *a*, *b*, and *c* are any numbers, then $a(b \pm c) = a(b) \pm a(c)$. The variable *a* on the left side of the equation is distributed over the addition or subtraction of *b* and *c*.

Teach with Tech

Interactive Whiteboard On the board, work through several examples using the Distributive Property. Save the examples and the work to a file, and send it to your students so that they can use it for reference outside of class.

Problem-Solving Tip

Make a Model It can be helpful to visualize a problem using algebra tiles or folded paper.

The rectangle at the right has 3 x-tiles and 6 1-tiles. The area of the rectangle is $x + 1 + 1 + x + 1 + 1 + x + 1 + 1$ or $3x + 6$. Therefore, $3(x + 2) = 3x + 6$.

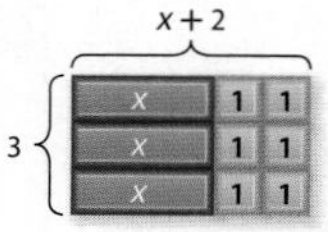

Example 3 Algebraic Expressions

Rewrite each expression using the Distributive Property. Then simplify.

a. $\mathbf{7(3w - 5)}$

$7(3w - 5) = 7 \cdot 3w - 7 \cdot 5$ — Distributive Property

$= 21w - 35$ — Multiply.

b. $\mathbf{(6v^2 + v - 3)4}$

$(6v^2 + v - 3)4 = 6v^2(4) + v(4) - 3(4)$ — Distributive Property

$= 24v^2 + 4v - 12$ — Multiply.

Guided Practice

3A. $(8 + 4n)2$ **$8(2) + 4n(2)$; $16 + 8n$**

3B. $-6(r + 3g - t)$

3C. $(2 - 5q)(-3)$

3D. $-4(-8 - 3m)$

3B. $-6(r) + (-6)(3g) + (-6)(-t)$; $-6r - 18g + 6t$
3C. $2(-3) + (-5q)(-3)$; $-6 + 15q$
3D. $(-4)(-8) + (-4)(-3m)$; $32 + 12m$

Review Vocabulary

term a number, a variable, or a product or quotient of numbers and variables

Like terms are terms that contain the same variables, with corresponding variables having the same power.

$5x^2 + 2x - 4$ — three terms

$6a^2 + a^2 + 2a$ — like terms ($6a^2$, a^2); unlike terms (a^2, $2a$)

The Distributive Property and the properties of equality can be used to show that $4k + 8k = 12k$. In this expression, $4k$ and $8k$ are like terms.

$4k + 8k = (4 + 8)k$ — Distributive Property

$= 12k$ — Substitution

An expression is in **simplest form** when it contains no like terms or parentheses.

Example 4 Combine Like Terms

a. Simplify $\mathbf{17u + 25u}$.

$17u + 25u = (17 + 25)u$ — Distributive Property

$= 42u$ — Substitution

b. Simplify $\mathbf{6t^2 + 3t - t}$.

$6t^2 + 3t - t = 6t^2 + (3 - 1)t$ — Distributive Property

$= 6t^2 + 2t$ — Substitution

Guided Practice

Simplify each expression. If not possible, write *simplified*.

4A. $6n - 4n$ **$2n$**

4B. $b^2 + 13b + 13$ **simplified**

4C. $4y^3 + 2y - 8y + 5$ **$4y^3 - 6y + 5$**

4D. $7a + 4 - 6a^2 - 2a$ **$-6a^2 + 5a + 4$**

2 Simplify Expressions

Example 3 shows how to use the Distributive Property to rewrite expressions and then simplify the expressions. **Example 4** shows how to use the Distributive Property to combine like terms and then simplify the expressions. **Example 5** shows how to write and simplify an expression using properties.

Additional Examples

3 Rewrite each expression using the Distributive Property. Then simplify.

a. $12(y + 3)$

$12(y + 3)$

$= 12 \cdot y + 12 \cdot 3$ Distributive Prop.

$= 12y + 36$ Multiply.

b. $4(y^2 + 8y + 2)$

$4(y^2 + 8y + 2)$

$= 4(y^2) + 4(8y) + 4(2)$ Distributive Prop.

$= 4y^2 + 32y + 8$ Multiply.

4 **a.** Simplify $17a + 21a$. $38a$

b. Simplify $12b^2 - 8b^2 + 6b$. $4b^2 + 6b$

Examples illustrate lesson concepts and closely mirror the exercises. **Guided Practice** exercises give students an opportunity to try a similar problem on their own.

Tips for New Teachers

Like Terms Point out that *like terms* could be defined as terms with the same variable, but different coefficients.

Checking Answers When simplifying expressions, students may wish to check their answers by choosing nonzero values for the variables and evaluating the original and simplified expressions. If the results are the same, the expressions are likely to be equivalent.

New teachers, or teachers new to teaching mathematics, may especially appreciate the **Tips for New Teachers.**

Differentiated Instruction AL OL

If students have difficulty using the Distributive Property,

Then have them use algebra tiles to find products for problems such as $2(x + 1)$ or $5(x + 2)$. Have students work in pairs. Point out that one of the quantities being multiplied goes on the left side of the mat, and the other goes on the top. Using algebra tiles will help students visualize the Distributive Property.

Additional Example

5 Use the expression *six times the sum of x and y increased by four times the difference of 5x and y.*

a. Write an algebraic expression for the verbal expression.
$6(x + y) + 4(5x - y)$

b. Simplify the expression and indicate the properties used.

$= 6(x) + 6(y) + 4(5x) - 4(y)$ Distributive Property

$= 6x + 6y + 20x - 4y$ Multiply.

$= 6x + 20x + 6y - 4y$ Commutative (+)

$= (6 + 20)x + (6 - 4)y$ Distributive Property

$= 26x + 2y$ Substitution

WatchOut!

Preventing Errors To make it easier for students to identify the coefficient of expressions such as $\frac{x^2}{3}$, remind them that since x^2 is in the numerator, they can rewrite the expression as $\frac{1}{3}x^2$. Write the following on the board for clarification.

$$\frac{1}{3} \cdot x^2 = \frac{1}{3} \cdot \frac{x^2}{1} = \frac{x^2}{3}$$

Additional Answers (Guided Practice)

5A. $5(q^2 - r) + 8(3q + 2r)$

5B. $= 5(q^2) + 5(-r) + 8(3q) + 8(2r)$ Distributive Property

$= 5q^2 + (-5r) + 24q + 16r$ Multiply.

$= 5q^2 + 24q + 16r + (-5r)$ Commutative (+)

$= 5q^2 + 24q + [16 + (-5)]r$ Distributive Property

$= 5q^2 + 24q + 11r$ Substitution

Math HistoryLink

Kambei Mori (c. 1600–1628)
Kambei Mori was a Japanese scholar who popularized the abacus. He changed the focus of mathematics from philosophy to computation.

Example 5 Write and Simplify Expressions

Use the expression *twice the difference of 3x and y increased by five times the sum of x and 2y.*

a. Write an algebraic expression for the verbal expression.

Words	twice the difference of $3x$ and y	increased by	five times the sum of x and $2y$
Variables	Let x and y represent the numbers.		
Expression	$2(3x - y)$	$+$	$5(x + 2y)$

b. Simplify the expression, and indicate the properties used.

$2(3x - y) + 5(x + 2y) = 2(3x) - 2(y) + 5(x) + 5(2y)$ Distributive Property

$= 6x - 2y + 5x + 10y$ Multiply.

$= 6x + 5x - 2y + 10y$ Commutative (+)

$= (6 + 5)x + (-2 + 10)y$ Distributive Property

$= 11x + 8y$ Substitution

GuidedPractice 5A, 5B. See margin.

5. Use the expression *5 times the difference of q squared and r plus 8 times the sum of 3q and 2r.*

A. Write an algebraic expression for the verbal expression.

B. Simplify the expression, and indicate the properties used.

The **coefficient** of a term is the numerical factor. For example, in $6ab$, the coefficient is 6, and in $\frac{x^2}{3}$, the coefficient is $\frac{1}{3}$. In the term y, the coefficient is 1 since $1 \cdot y = y$ by the Multiplicative Identity Property.

ConceptSummary Properties of Numbers

The following properties are true for any numbers a, b, and c.

Properties	Addition	Multiplication
Commutative	$a + b = b + a$	$ab = ba$
Associative	$(a + b) + c = a + (b + c)$	$(ab)c = a(bc)$
Identity	0 is the identity. $a + 0 = 0 + a = a$	1 is the identity. $a \cdot 1 = 1 \cdot a = a$
Zero	—	$a \cdot 0 = 0 \cdot a = 0$
Distributive	$a(b + c) = ab + ac$ and $(b + c)a = ba + ca$	
Substitution	If $a = b$, then a may be substituted for b.	

28 | Lesson 1-4 | The Distributive Property

Check Your Understanding

● = Step-by-Step Solutions begin on page R13.

Example 1

1. **PILOT** A pilot at an air show charges \$25 per passenger for rides. If 12 adults and 15 children ride in one day, write and evaluate an expression to describe the situation. **25(12 + 15); \$675**

Example 2 **Use the Distributive Property to rewrite each expression. Then evaluate.**

2. 14(51) **14(50 + 1); 714**
3. $6\frac{1}{9}(9)$ $\left(6+\frac{1}{9}\right)9$; **55**

Example 3 **Use the Distributive Property to rewrite each expression. Then simplify.**

4. $2(4 + t)$ **$2(4) + 2(t)$; $8 + 2t$**
5. $(g - 9)5$ **$g(5) + (-9)(5)$; $5g - 45$**

Example 4 **Simplify each expression. If not possible, write *simplified*.**

6. $15m + m$ **$16m$**
7. $3x^3 + 5y^3 + 14$ **simplified**
8. $(5m + 2m)10$ **$70m$**

Example 5 **Write an algebraic expression for each verbal expression. Then simplify, indicating the properties used.**

9. 4 times the sum of 2 times x and six
10. one half of 4 times y plus the quantity of y and 3

9. $4(2x + 6)$
$= 4(2x) + 4(6)$ Distributive Property
$= 8x + 24$ Multiply.

10. $\frac{1}{2}(4y) + (y + 3)$
$= 2y + y + 3$ Multiply.
$= 3y + 3$ Simplify.

Practice and Problem Solving

Extra Practice is on page R1.

Example 1

11. **TIME MANAGEMENT** Margo uses dots to track her activities on a calendar. Red dots represent homework, yellow dots represent work, and green dots represent track practice. In a typical week, she uses 5 red dots, 3 yellow dots, and 4 green dots. How many activities does Margo do in 4 weeks? **48 activities**

12. **REASONING** The Red Cross is holding blood drives in two locations. In one day, Center 1 collected 715 pints and Center 2 collected 1035 pints. Write and evaluate an expression to estimate the total number of pints of blood donated over a 3-day period. **3(715 + 1035); 5250 pt**

14. 7(13) + 7(12); 175 **16.** 3(15) + 8(15); 165 **17.** 14(8) − 14(5); 42

Example 2 **Use the Distributive Property to rewrite each expression. Then evaluate.**

13. (4 + 5)6 **6(4) + 6(5); 54**
14. 7(13 + 12)
15. 6(6 − 1) **6(6) − 6(1); 30**
16. (3 + 8)15
17. 14(8 − 5)
18. (9 − 4)19 **19(9) − 19(4); 95**
19. 4(7 − 2) **4(7) − 4(2); 20**
20. 7(2 + 1) **7(2) + 7(1); 21**
21. 7 • 497 **7(500 − 3); 3479**
22. 6(525) **6(500 + 25); 3150**
23. $36 \cdot 3\frac{1}{4}$ $36\left(3+\frac{1}{4}\right)$; **117**
24. $\left(4\frac{2}{7}\right)21$ $\left(4+\frac{2}{7}\right)21$; **90**

Example 3 **Use the Distributive Property to rewrite each expression. Then simplify.**

25. $2(x + 4)$ **$2(x) + 2(4)$; $2x + 8$**
26. $(5 + n)3$ **$5(3) + n(3)$; $15 + 3n$**
27. $(4 - 3m)8$ **$4(8) + (-3m)(8)$; $32 - 24m$**
28. $-3(2x - 6)$ **$-3(2x) + (-3)(-6)$; $-6x + 18$**

Example 4 **Simplify each expression. If not possible, write *simplified*.**

29. $13r + 5r$ **$18r$**
30. $3x^3 - 2x^2$ **simplified**
31. $7m + 7 - 5m$ **$2m + 7$**
32. $5z^2 + 3z + 8z^2$
33. $(2 - 4n)17$ **$34 - 68n$**
34. $11(4d + 6)$ **$44d + 66$**
35. $7m + 2m + 5p + 4m$
36. $3x + 7(3x + 4)$ **$24x + 28$**
37. $4(fg + 3g) + 5g$

32. $13z^2 + 3z$
35. $13m + 5p$
37. $4fg + 17g$

Example 5 **Write an algebraic expression for each verbal expression. Then simplify, indicating the properties used.** **38–39. See margin.**

38. the product of 5 and m squared, increased by the sum of the square of m and 5
39. 7 times the sum of a squared and b minus 4 times the sum of a squared and b

Differentiated Homework Options

Level	Assignment	Two-Day Option	
AL Basic	11–47, 57–77	11–47 odd, 60–63, 72–77	12–46 even, 57–59, 64–71
OL Core	11–47 odd, 48, 49–55 odd, 57–77	11–47, 60–63	48–55, 57–59, 64–77
BL Advanced	48–71, (optional: 72–77)		

3 Practice

Formative Assessment

Use Exercises 1–10 to check for understanding.

Use the chart at the bottom of this page to customize assignments for your students.

Tips for New Teachers

Common Misconceptions Some students are confused when an expression is presented with the parentheses first, such as (4 − 3)6. Suggest that students use the Commutative Property of Multiplication to rewrite the expression as 6(4 − 3) to avoid confusion.

Exercise Alert

Manipulatives Exercise 55 requires students to use algebra tiles.

Teaching the Process Standards

Reasoning Mathematically proficient students make sense of quantities and their relationships in problem situations. To help in these processes, encourage students to use the 4-step problem solving plan Understand-Plan-Solve-Check.

Additional Answers

38. $5m^2 + (m^2 + 5)$
$= (5m^2 + m^2) + 5$ Associative (+)
$= 6m^2 + 5$ Substitution

39. $7(a^2 + b) - 4(a^2 + b)$
$= 7a^2 + 7b - 4a^2 - 4b$ Substitution
$= 7a^2 - 4a^2 + 7b - 4b$ Commutative (+)
$= (7 - 4)a^2 + (7 - 4)b$ Distributive Property
$= 3a^2 + 3b$ Substitution

Study Guide and Intervention

AL OL ELL

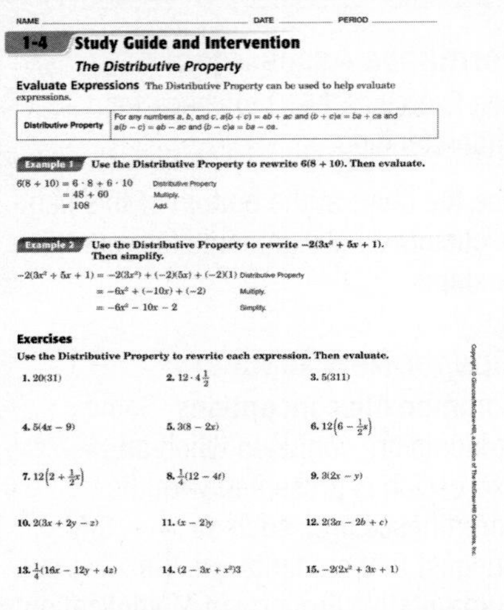
NAME ______ DATE ______ PERIOD ______

1-4 Study Guide and Intervention

The Distributive Property

Evaluate Expressions The Distributive Property can be used to help evaluate expressions.

Distributive Property: For any numbers a, b, and c, a(b + c) = ab + ac and (b + c)a = ba + ca and a(b − c) = ab − ac and (b − c)a = ba − ca.

Example 1 Use the Distributive Property to rewrite 6(8 + 10). Then evaluate.

6(8 + 10) = 6 · 8 + 6 · 10 Distributive Property
= 48 + 60 Multiply.
= 108 Add.

Example 2 Use the Distributive Property to rewrite −2(3x² + 5x + 1). Then simplify.

−2(3x² + 5x + 1) = −2(3x²) + (−2)(5x) + (−2)(1) Distributive Property
= −6x² + (−10x) + (−2) Multiply.
= −6x² − 10x − 2 Simplify.

Exercises

Use the Distributive Property to rewrite each expression. Then evaluate.

1. 20(31) 2. 12 · 4½ 3. 5(311)
4. 5(4x − 9) 5. 3(8 − 2x) 6. 12(6 − ½x)
7. 12(2 + ½x) 8. ¼(12 − 4t) 9. 3(2x − y)
10. 2(3x + 2y − z) 11. (x − 2)y 12. 2(3a − 2b + c)
13. ¼(16x − 12y + 4z) 14. (2 − 3x + x²)3 15. −2(2x² + 3x + 1)

Practice

AL OL BL ELL

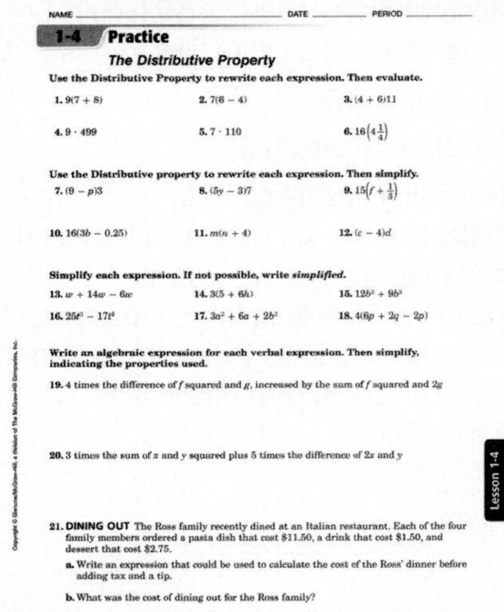
NAME ______ DATE ______ PERIOD ______

1-4 Practice

The Distributive Property

Use the Distributive Property to rewrite each expression. Then evaluate.

1. 9(7 + 8) 2. 7(6 − 4) 3. (4 + 6)11
4. 9 · 499 5. 7 · 110 6. 16(4¼)

Use the Distributive property to rewrite each expression. Then simplify.

7. (9 − p)3 8. (5y − 3)7 9. 15(f + ⅓)
10. 16(3b − 0.25) 11. m(n + 4) 12. (c − 4)d

Simplify each expression. If not possible, write *simplified*.

13. w + 14w − 6w 14. 3(5 + 6h) 15. 12b² + 9b²
16. 25t³ − 17t³ 17. 3a² + 6a + 2b² 18. 4(6p + 2q − 2p)

Write an algebraic expression for each verbal expression. Then simplify, indicating the properties used.

19. 4 times the difference of f squared and g, increased by the sum of f squared and 2g

20. 3 times the sum of x and y squared plus 5 times the difference of 2x and y

21. DINING OUT The Ross family recently dined at an Italian restaurant. Each of the four family members ordered a pasta dish that cost $11.50, a drink that cost $1.50, and dessert that cost $2.75.

a. Write an expression that could be used to calculate the cost of the Ross' dinner before adding tax and a tip.

b. What was the cost of dining out for the Ross family?

Lesson 1-4

Word Problem Practice

AL OL BL ELL

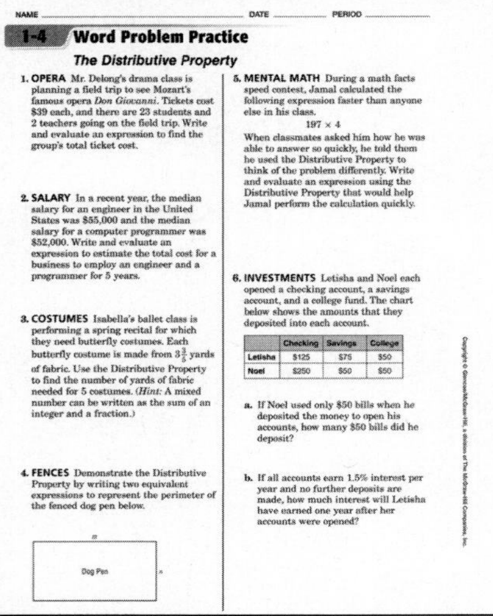
NAME ______ DATE ______ PERIOD ______

1-4 Word Problem Practice

The Distributive Property

1. OPERA Mr. Delong's drama class is planning a field trip to see Mozart's famous opera *Don Giovanni*. Tickets cost $39 each, and there are 23 students and 2 teachers going on the field trip. Write and evaluate an expression to find the group's total ticket cost.

2. SALARY In a recent year, the median salary for an engineer in the United States was $55,000 and the median salary for a computer programmer was $52,000. Write and evaluate an expression to estimate the total cost for a business to employ an engineer and a programmer for 5 years.

3. COSTUMES Isabella's ballet class is performing a spring recital for which they need butterfly costumes. Each butterfly costume is made from 3½ yards of fabric. Use the Distributive Property to find the number of yards of fabric needed for 5 costumes. (*Hint:* A mixed number can be written as the sum of an integer and a fraction.)

4. FENCES Demonstrate the Distributive Property by writing two equivalent expressions to represent the perimeter of the fenced dog pen below.

5. MENTAL MATH During a math facts speed contest, Jamal calculated the following expression faster than anyone else in the class.

197 × 4

When classmates asked him how he was able to answer so quickly, he told them he used the Distributive Property to think of the problem differently. Write and evaluate an expression using the Distributive Property that would help Jamal perform the calculation quickly.

6. INVESTMENTS Letisha and Noel each opened a checking account, a savings account, and a college fund. The chart below shows the amounts that they deposited into each account.

	Checking	Savings	College
Letisha	$125	$75	$50
Noel	$250	$50	$50

a. If Noel used only $50 bills when he deposited the money to open his accounts, how many $50 bills did he deposit?

b. If all accounts earn 1.5% interest per year and no further deposits are made, how much interest will Letisha have earned one year after her accounts were opened?

40. **GEOMETRY** Find the perimeter of an isosceles triangle with side lengths of $5 + x$, $5 + x$, and xy. Write in simplest form. **$xy + 10 + 2x$ units**

41. **GEOMETRY** A regular hexagon measures $3x + 5$ units on each side. What is the perimeter in simplest form? **$18x + 30$ units**

Simplify each expression. **43. $14m + 11g$ 44. $8a^2 + 4a$ 45. $12k^3 + 12k$**

42. $6x + 4y + 5x$ **$11x + 4y$**
43. $3m + 5g + 6g + 11m$
44. $4a + 5a^2 + 2a^2 + a^2$
45. $5k + 3k^3 + 7k + 9k^3$
46. $6d + 4(3d + 5)$ **$18d + 20$**
47. $2(6x + 4) + 7x$ **$19x + 8$**

B 48. **FOOD** Kenji is picking up take-out food for his study group.

a. Interpret the expression $4(2.49) + 3(1.29) + 3(0.99) + 5(1.49)$.

48a. the cost of four sandwiches, three soups, three salads, and five drinks

b. How much would it cost if Kenji bought four of each item on the menu? **$25.04**

Menu	
Item	**Cost ($)**
sandwich	2.49
cup of soup	1.29
side salad	0.99
drink	1.49

Use the Distributive Property to rewrite each expression. Then simplify.

49. $\left(\frac{1}{3} - 2b\right)27$ **$9 - 54b$**
50. $4(8p + 4q - 7r)$ **$32p + 16q - 28r$**
51. $6(2c - cd^2 + d)$ **$12c - 6cd^2 + 6d$**

Simplify each expression. If not possible, write *simplified*.

52. $6x^2 + 14x - 9x$ **$6x^2 + 5x$**
53. $4y^3 + 3y^3 + y^4$ **$7y^3 + y^4$**
54. $a + \frac{a}{5} + \frac{2}{5}a$ **$\frac{8}{5}a$**

C 55. **MULTIPLE REPRESENTATIONS** The area of the model is $2(x - 4)$ or $2x - 8$. The expression $2(x - 4)$ is in *factored form*.

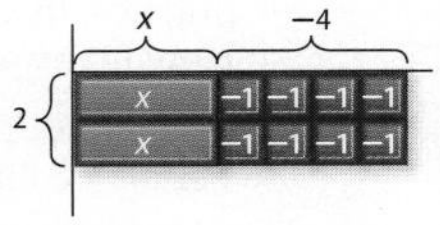

a. **Geometric** Use algebra tiles to form a rectangle with area $2x + 6$. Use the result to write $2x + 6$ in factored form. **$2(x + 3)$**

b. **Tabular** Use algebra tiles to form rectangles to represent each area in the table. Record the factored form of each expression.

Area	Factored Form
$2x + 6$	**$2(x + 3)$**
$3x + 3$	**$3(x + 1)$**
$3x - 12$	**$3(x - 4)$**
$5x + 10$	**$5(x + 2)$**

c. **Verbal** Explain how you could find the factored form of an expression. **Divide each term of the expression by the same number. Then write the expression as a product.**

H.O.T. Problems Use Higher-Order Thinking Skills

56. **PERSEVERANCE** Use the Distributive Property to simplify $6x^2[(3x - 4) + (4x + 2)]$. **$42x^3 - 12x^2$**

57. **REASONING** Should the Distributive Property be a property of multiplication, addition, or both? Explain your answer. **Both; It should be considered a property of both. Both operations are used in $a(b + c) = ab + ac$.**

58. **WRITING IN MATH** Why is it helpful to represent verbal expressions algebraically? **See margin.**

59. **WRITING IN MATH** Use the data about skating on page 25 to explain how the Distributive Property can be used to calculate quickly. Also, compare the two methods of finding the total Calories burned. **See margin.**

Enrichment

OL BL

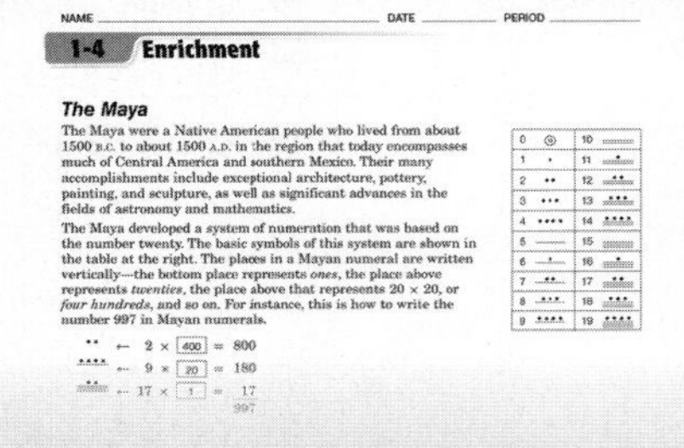
NAME ______ DATE ______ PERIOD ______

1-4 Enrichment

The Maya

The Maya were a Native American people who lived from about 1500 B.C. to about 1500 A.D. in the region that today encompasses much of Central America and southern Mexico. Their many accomplishments include exceptional architecture, pottery, painting, and sculpture, as well as significant advances in the fields of astronomy and mathematics.

The Maya developed a system of numeration that was based on the number twenty. The basic symbols of this system are shown in the table at the right. The places in a Mayan numeral are written vertically—the bottom place represents *ones*, the place above represents *twenties*, the place above that represents 20 × 20, or *four hundreds*, and so on. For instance, this is how to write the number 997 in Mayan numerals.

← 2 × 400 = 800
← 9 × 20 = 180
← 17 × 1 = 17
997

Multiple Representations

In Exercise 55, students use models and a table to investigate factoring using the Distributive Property.

A **Study Guide and Intervention**, **Practice**, **Word Problem Practice**, and **Enrichment Master** are shown for every lesson. These masters can be found in the Chapter Resource Masters.

Standardized Test Practice

60. Which illustrates the Symmetric Property of Equality? **A**

A If $a = b$, then $b = a$.

B If $a = b$, and $b = c$, then $a = c$.

C If $a = b$, then $b = c$.

D If $a = a$, then $a + 0 = a$.

61. Anna is three years younger than her sister Emily. Which expression represents Anna's age if we express Emily's age as y years? **G**

F $y + 3$ H $3y$

G $y - 3$ J $\frac{3}{y}$

62. Which property is used below?
If $4xy^2 = 8y^2$ and $8y^2 = 72$, then $4xy^2 = 72$. **D**

A Reflexive Property

B Substitution Property

C Symmetric Property

D Transitive Property

63. SHORT RESPONSE A drawer contains the socks in the chart. What is the probability that a randomly chosen sock is blue? **$\frac{1}{3}$ or about 33.3%**

Color	Number
white	16
blue	12
black	8

Spiral Review

Evaluate each expression. Name the property used in each step. (Lesson 1-3) **64–66. See margin.**

64. $14 + 23 + 8 + 15$

65. $0.24 \cdot 8 \cdot 7.05$

66. $1\frac{1}{4} \cdot 9 \cdot \frac{5}{6}$

67. SPORTS Braden runs 6 times a week for 30 minutes and lifts weights 3 times a week for 20 minutes. Write and evaluate an expression for the number of hours Braden works out in 4 weeks. (Lesson 1-2) **$\frac{4[6(30) + 3(20)]}{60}$; 16 hours**

SPORTS Refer to the table showing Blanca's cross-country times for the first 8 meets of the season. Round answers to the nearest second. (Lesson 0-12)

Cross Country	
Meet	**Time**
1	22:31
2	22:21
3	21:48
4	22:01
5	21:48
6	20:56
7	20:34
8	20:15

68. Find the mean of the data. **21:32**

69. Find the median of the data. **21:48**

70. Find the mode of the data. **21:48**

71. SURFACE AREA What is the surface area of the cube? (Lesson 0-10)
384 in^2

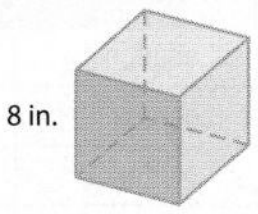

Skills Review

Evaluate each expression.

72. $12(7 + 2)$ **108**

73. $11(5) - 8(5)$ **15**

74. $(13 - 9) \cdot 4$ **16**

75. $3(6) + 7(6)$ **60**

76. $(1 + 19) \cdot 8$ **160**

77. $16(5 + 7)$ **192**

Differentiated Instruction BL

Extension Ask students to demonstrate whether they can distribute division over addition in the same way that they distribute multiplication over addition. Sample answer: It depends on how the division is written.

$$24 \div (2 + 6) \stackrel{?}{=} 24 \div 2 + 24 \div 6$$
$$24 \div 8 \stackrel{?}{=} 12 + 4$$
$$3 \neq 16$$

$$(2 + 6) \div 24 \stackrel{?}{=} \frac{2}{24} + \frac{6}{24}$$
$$8 \div 24 \stackrel{?}{=} \frac{1}{12} + \frac{3}{12}$$
$$\frac{1}{3} = \frac{4}{12}$$

Teaching the Process Standards

Perseverance Mathematically proficient students try simpler forms of the original problem to gain insight. In Exercise 56, encourage students to use what they have learned from simpler Distributive property problems to simplify complex expressions.

4 Assess

Name the Math Write $6(m + 8)$ on the board. Have students tell how they would simplify the expression.

Formative Assessment

Check for student understanding of Lessons 1-3 and 1-4.

Quiz 2, p. 57

Additional Answers

58. Sample answer: Algebraic expressions are helpful because they are easier to interpret and apply than verbal expressions. They can also be rewritten in a more simplified form.

59. Sample answer: You can use the Distributive Property to calculate quickly by expressing any number as a sum or difference of two more convenient numbers. Answers should include the following: Both methods result in the correct answer. In one method you multiply then add, and in the other you add then multiply.

64. $14 + 23 + 8 + 15$

$= (14 + 23) + (8 + 15)$	Associative (+)
$= 37 + 23$	Substitution
$= 60$	Substitution

65. $0.24 \cdot 8 \cdot 7.05$

$= (0.24 \cdot 8) \cdot 7.05$	Associative (×)
$= 1.92 \cdot 7.05$	Substitution
$= 13.536$	Substitution

66. $1\frac{1}{4} \cdot 9 \cdot \frac{5}{6}$

$= \left(1\frac{1}{4} \cdot 9\right)\frac{5}{6}$	Associative (×)
$= 11\frac{1}{4} \cdot \frac{5}{6}$	Substitution
$= 9\frac{3}{8}$	Substitution

Formative Assessment

Use the Mid-Chapter Quiz to assess students' progress in the first half of the chapter.

For problems answered incorrectly, have students review the lessons indicated in parentheses.

Summative Assessment

Mid-Chapter Test, p. 59

McGraw-Hill eAssessment Customize and create multiple versions of your Mid-Chapter Quiz and their answer keys.

FOLDABLES® StudyOrganizer

Before students complete the Mid-Chapter Quiz, encourage them to review the information for Lessons 1-1 through 1-4 in their Foldables.

The **Mid-Chapter Quiz** reviews skills and concepts presented in previous lessons.

CHAPTER 1 Mid-Chapter Quiz

Lessons 1-1 through 1-4

Write a verbal expression for each algebraic expression. (Lesson 1-1) **1. twenty-one minus x to the third power**

1. $21 - x^3$
2. $3m^5 + 9$

2. the sum of three times m to the fifth power and nine

Write an algebraic expression for each verbal expression. (Lesson 1-1)

3. five more than s squared **$s^2 + 5$**
4. four times y to the fourth power **$4y^4$**

5. **CAR RENTAL** The XYZ Car Rental Agency charges a flat rate of $29 per day plus $0.32 per mile driven. Write an algebraic expression for the rental cost of a car for x days that is driven y miles. (Lesson 1-1) **$29x + 0.32y$**

Evaluate each expression. (Lesson 1-2)

6. $24 \div 3 - 2 \cdot 3$ **2**
7. $5 + 2^2$ **9**
8. $4(3 + 9)$ **48**
9. $36 - 2(1 + 3)^2$ **4**
10. $\dfrac{40 - 2^3}{4 + 3(2^2)}$ **2**

11. **AMUSEMENT PARK** The costs of tickets to a local amusement park are shown. Write and evaluate an expression to find the total cost for 5 adults and 8 children. (Lesson 1-2) **5(45) + 8(25) = 425**

12. **MULTIPLE CHOICE** Write an algebraic expression to represent the perimeter of the rectangle shown below. Then evaluate it to find the perimeter when $w = 8$ cm. (Lesson 1-2) **C**

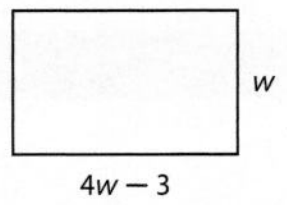

A 37 cm
B 232 cm
C 74 cm
D 45 cm

Evaluate each expression. Name the property used in each step. (Lesson 1-3) **13–17. See Ch.1 Answer Appendix for steps.**

13. $(8 - 2^3) + 21$ **21**
14. $3(1 \div 3) \cdot 9$ **9**
15. $[5 \div (3 \cdot 1)]\frac{3}{5}$ **1**
16. $18 + 35 + 32 + 15$ **100**
17. $0.25 \cdot 7 \cdot 4$ **7**

Use the Distributive Property to rewrite each expression. Then evaluate. (Lesson 1-4)

18. $3(5 + 2)$ **$3(5) + 3(2)$; 21**
19. $(9 - 6)12$ **$9(12) - 6(12)$; 36**
20. $8(7 - 4)$ **$8(7) - 8(4)$; 24**

Use the Distributive Property to rewrite each expression. Then simplify. (Lesson 1-4)

21. $4(x + 3)$ **$4(x) + 4(3)$; $4x + 12$**
22. $(6 - 2y)7$ **$6(7) - 2y(7)$; $42 - 14y$**
23. $-5(3m - 2)$ **$-5(3m) - 5(-2)$; $-15m + 10$**

24. **DVD SALES** A video store chain has three locations. Use the information in the table below to write and evaluate an expression to estimate the total number of DVDs sold over a 4-day period. (Lesson 1-4)

Location	Daily Sales Numbers
Location 1	145
Location 2	211
Location 3	184

4(145 + 211 + 184); 2160

25. **MULTIPLE CHOICE** Rewrite the expression $(8 - 3p)(-2)$ using the Distributive Property. (Lesson 1-4) **H**

F $16 - 6p$
G $-10p$
H $-16 + 6p$
J $10p$

32 | Chapter 1 | Mid-Chapter Quiz

InterventionPlanner

TIER 1 On Level OL	TIER 2 Strategic Intervention AL approaching grade level	TIER 3 Intensive Intervention 2 or more grades below level
If students miss about 25% of the exercises or less,	**If** students miss about 50% of the exercises,	**If** students miss about 75% of the exercises,
Then choose a resource: **SE** Lessons 1-1, 1-2, 1-3, and 1-4 Skills Practice, pp. 7, 13, 20, and 26 **TE** Chapter Project connectED.mcgraw-hill.com Self-Check Quiz	**Then** choose a resource: Study Guide and Intervention, Chapter 1, pp. 5, 11, 18, and 24 *Quick Review Math Handbook* connectED.mcgraw-hill.com Extra Examples, Personal Tutor, Homework Help	**Then** use *Math Triumphs, Alg. 1,* Ch. 1, 2, 3, and 5 connectED.mcgraw-hill.com Extra Examples, Personal Tutor, Homework Help, Review Vocabulary

LESSON 1-5 Equations

Then
- You simplified expressions.

Now
1. Solve equations with one variable.
2. Solve equations with two variables.

Why?
- Mark's baseball team scored 3 runs in the first inning. At the top of the third inning, their score was 4. The open sentence below represents the change in their score.

$$3 + r = 4$$

The solution is 1. The team got 1 run in the second inning.

Paul Rees/ImageState

New Vocabulary
open sentence
equation
solving
solution
replacement set
set
element
solution set
identity

1 Solve Equations

A mathematical statement that contains algebraic expressions and symbols is an **open sentence**. A sentence that contains an equals sign, =, is an **equation**.

expression → $3x + 7$ $3x + 7 = 13$ ← equation

Finding a value for a variable that makes a sentence true is called **solving** the open sentence. This replacement value is a **solution**.

A set of numbers from which replacements for a variable may be chosen is called a **replacement set**. A **set** is a collection of objects or numbers that is often shown using braces. Each object or number in the set is called an **element**, or member. A **solution set** is the set of elements from the replacement set that make an open sentence true.

Example 1 Use a Replacement Set

PT

Find the solution set of the equation $2q + 5 = 13$ if the replacement set is {2, 3, 4, 5, 6}.

Use a table to solve. Replace q in $2q + 5 = 13$ with each value in the replacement set.

q	$2q + 5 = 13$	True or False?
2	$2(2) + 5 = 13$	false
3	$2(3) + 5 = 13$	false
4	$2(4) + 5 = 13$	true
5	$2(5) + 5 = 13$	false
6	$2(6) + 5 = 13$	false

Since the equation is true when $q = 4$, the solution of $2q + 5 = 13$ is $q = 4$.

The solution set is {4}.

Guided Practice

Find the solution set for each equation if the replacement set is {0, 1, 2, 3}.

1A. $8m - 7 = 17$ {3} **1B.** $28 = 4(1 + 3d)$ {2}

1 Focus

Vertical Alignment

Before Lesson 1-5 Simplify expressions.

Lesson 1-5 Solve equations with one variable. Solve equations with two variables.

After Lesson 1-5 Explore different representations of relations.

2 Teach

Scaffolding Questions

Have students read the **Why?** section of the lesson.

Ask:
- How would you translate the sentence $3 + r = 4$? Three plus r is equal to four.
- What does the variable r represent in the sentence? the number of runs in the second inning
- How do you know that the solution is 1? 3 + 1 is equal to 4.

Lesson 1-5 Resources

Resource	Approaching Level AL	On Level OL	Beyond Level BL	English Learners ELL
Teacher Edition		▪ Differentiated Instruction, pp. 35, 39	▪ Differentiated Instruction, pp. 35, 39	
Chapter Resource Masters	▪ Study Guide and Intervention, pp. 30–31 ▪ Skills Practice, p. 32 ▪ Practice, p. 33 ▪ Word Problem Practice, p. 34 ▪ Spreadsheet Activity, p. 36	▪ Study Guide and Intervention, pp. 30–31 ▪ Skills Practice, p. 32 ▪ Practice, p. 33 ▪ Word Problem Practice, p. 34 ▪ Enrichment, p. 35 ▪ Spreadsheet Activity, p. 36	▪ Practice, p. 33 ▪ Word Problem Practice, p. 34 ▪ Enrichment, p. 35 ▪ Spreadsheet Activity, p. 36	▪ Study Guide and Intervention, pp. 30–31 ▪ Skills Practice, p. 32 ▪ Practice, p. 33 ▪ Spreadsheet Activity, p. 36
Other	▪ 5-Minute Check 1-5 ▪ Study Notebook	▪ 5-Minute Check 1-5 ▪ Study Notebook	▪ 5-Minute Check 1-5 ▪ Study Notebook	▪ 5-Minute Check 1-5 ▪ Study Notebook

Every chapter includes a worked-out **Standardized Test Example** that is similar to problems found on the state assessments.

1 Solve Equations

Example 1 shows how to use a replacement set to solve equations. **Example 2** shows how to use the order of operations to solve an equation in a standardized test. **Example 3** shows that some equations have a unique solution and some have no solution. **Example 4** shows how to recognize an equation that is an identity.

Formative Assessment

Use the Guided Practice exercises after each Example to determine students' understanding of concepts.

Additional Examples

1. Find the solution set of the equation $4a + 7 = 23$ if the replacement set is {2, 3, 4, 5, 6}. {4}
2. **STANDARDIZED TEST PRACTICE** Solve $3 + 4(2^3 - 2) = b$. B
   A 19 **B** 27 **C** 33 **D** 42
3. Solve each equation.
   a. $4 + (3^2 + 7) \div n = 8$ 4
   b. $4n - (12 + 2) = n(6 - 2) - 9$ no solution

Additional Examples also in Interactive Classroom PowerPoint® Presentations

IWB Interactive White Board READY

Tips for New Teachers

No Solution Versus Zero Solution Make sure students understand that having no solution is not the same as having a solution of 0. No solution means the equation is never true, while a solution of 0 means the equation is true when the variable equals 0.

Testing Values For Examples 3b and 4, have students test many values for x to help them understand and identify when there are no solutions or infinite solutions to an equation.

You can often solve an equation by applying the order of operations.

Standardized Test Example 2 Apply the Order of Operations

Solve $6 + (5^2 - 5) \div 2 = p$.

A 3 **B** 6 **C** 13 **D** 16

Read the Test Item

You need to apply the order of operations to the expression in order to solve for p.

Solve the Test Item

$6 + (5^2 - 5) \div 2 = p$	Original equation
$6 + (25 - 5) \div 2 = p$	Evaluate powers.
$6 + 20 \div 2 = p$	Subtract 5 from 25.
$6 + 10 = p$	Divide 20 by 2.
$16 = p$	Add.

The correct answer is D.

Test-Taking Tip

Rewrite the Equation If you are allowed to write in your testing booklet, it can be helpful to rewrite the equation with simplified terms.

Guided Practice

2. Solve $t = 9^2 \div (5 - 2)$. J

F 3 **G** 6 **H** 14.2 **J** 27

Some equations have a unique solution. Other equations do not have a solution.

Example 3 Solutions of Equations

Solve each equation.

a. $7 - (4^2 - 10) + n = 10$

Simplify the equation first and then look for a solution.

$7 - (4^2 - 10) + n = 10$	Original equation
$7 - (16 - 10) + n = 10$	Evaluate powers.
$7 - 6 + n = 10$	Subtract 10 from 16.
$1 + n = 10$	Subtract 6 from 7.

The only value for n that makes the equation true is 9. Therefore, this equation has a unique solution of 9.

b. $n(3 + 2) + 6 = 5n + (10 - 3)$

$n(3 + 2) + 6 = 5n + (10 - 3)$	Original equation
$n(5) + 6 = 5n + (10 - 3)$	Add 3 + 2.
$n(5) + 6 = 5n + 7$	Subtract 3 from 10.
$5n + 6 = 5n + 7$	Commutative (×)

No matter what real value is substituted for n, the left side of the equation will always be one less than the right side. So, the equation will never be true. Therefore, there is no solution of this equation.

Study Tip

Guess and Check When the solution to an equation is not easy to see, substitute values for x and test the equation. Continue to test values until you get a true statement. For example, if $3x + 16 = 73$, test values for x.

$3(10) + 16 = 48$ too low
$3(20) + 16 = 76$ too high
$3(19) + 16 = 73$ ✓

Guided Practice

3A. $(18 + 4) + m = (5 - 3)m$ 22

3B. $8 \cdot 4 \cdot k + 9 \cdot 5 = (36 - 4)k - (2 \cdot 5)$ no solution

Focus on Mathematical Content

Open Sentences An open sentence is a mathematical statement that contains two algebraic expressions and a symbol to compare them. An open sentence with an equals sign, =, is an equation.

ReadingMath

Identities An identity is an equation that shows that a number or expression is equivalent to itself.

An equation that is true for every value of the variable is called an **identity**.

Example 4 Identities

Solve $(2 \cdot 5 - 8)(3h + 6) = [(2h + h) + 6]2$.

$(2 \cdot 5 - 8)(3h + 6) = [(2h + h) + 6]2$	Original Equation
$(10 - 8)(3h + 6) = [(2h + h) + 6]2$	Multiply $2 \cdot 5$.
$2(3h + 6) = [(2h + h) + 6]2$	Subtract 8 from 10.
$6h + 12 = [(2h + h) + 6]2$	Distributive Property
$6h + 12 = [3h + 6]2$	Add $2h + h$.
$6h + 12 = 6h + 12$	Distributive Property

No matter what value is substituted for h, the left side of the equation will always be equal to the right side. So, the equation will always be true. Therefore, the solution of this equation could be any real number.

GuidedPractice

Solve each equation.

4A. $12(10 - 7) + 9g = g(2^2 + 5) + 36$ **all real numbers**

4B. $2d + (2^3 - 5) = 10(5 - 2) + d(12 \div 6)$ **no solution**

4C. $3(b + 1) - 5 = 3b - 2$ **all real numbers**

4D. $5 - \frac{1}{2}(c - 6) = 4$ **8**

2 Solve Equations with Two Variables

Some equations contain two variables. It is often useful to make a table of values and use substitution to find the corresponding values of the second variable.

Example 5 Equations Involving Two Variables

MOVIE RENTALS **Mr. Hernandez pays $10 each month for movies delivered by mail. He can also rent movies in the store for $1.50 per title. Write and solve an equation to find the total amount Mr. Hernandez spends this month if he rents 3 movies from the store.**

The cost of the movie plan is a flat rate. The variable is the number of movies he rents from the store. The total cost is the price of the plan plus $1.50 times the number of movies from the store. Let C be the total cost and m be the number of movies.

$C = 1.50m + 10$	Original equation
$= 1.50(3) + 10$	Substitute 3 for m.
$= 4.50 + 10$	Multiply.
$= 14.50$	

Mr. Hernandez spends $14.50 on movie rentals in one month.

GuidedPractice

5. TRAVEL Amelia drives an average of 65 miles per hour. Write and solve an equation to find the time it will take her to drive 36 miles. **$d = 65t$; $t \approx 33$ min or 0.55 h**

DifferentiatedInstruction OL BL

If students have strong verbal skills,

Then challenge them to write and solve real-world equations involving one variable and two variables. Suggest that students write equations about a plant or animal in which they are interested.

Additional Example

4 Solve $(5 + 8 \div 4) + 3k = 3(k + 32) - 89$. The solution could be any real number.

2 Solve Equations with Two Variables

Example 5 shows how to write and solve an equation with two variables to solve a real-world problem.

Additional Example

5 **GYM MEMBERSHIP** Dalila pays $16 per month for a gym membership. In addition, she pays $2 per Pilates class. Write and solve an equation to find the total amount Dalila spent this month if she took 12 Pilates classes. $c = 2p + 16$; $40

Teach with Tech

Student Response System Give students an equation and a set of four numbers. Ask students to check each of these numbers to see which is a solution of the equation. Give students a key, and have them respond with the choice that is a solution to the equation.

3 Practice

Formative Assessment

Use Exercises 1–10 to check for understanding.

Use the chart at the bottom of the next page to customize assignments for your students.

Teaching the Process Standards

Modeling Mathematically proficient students are able to identify important quantities in a practical situation and map their relationships using such tools as diagrams. In Exercise 34, ask students to recall the definition of a regular octagon. A diagram can help as they model the situation mathematically.

Sense-Making Mathematically proficient students transform algebraic expressions to get the information they need. In Exercise 47, point out to students that the same formula is used to find each value when given different information.

Additional Answers

57.

x	$3x+5$	y
−2	3(−2) + 5	−1
−1	3(−1) + 5	2
0	3(0) + 5	5
1	3(1) + 5	8
2	3(2) + 5	11

58.

x	$-2x-3$	y
−2	−2(−2) − 3	1
−1	−2(−1) − 3	−1
0	−2(0) − 3	−3
1	−2(1) − 3	−5
2	−2(2) − 3	−7

59.

x	$\frac{1}{2}x+2$	y
−2	$\frac{1}{2}(-2)+2$	1
−1	$\frac{1}{2}(-1)+2$	1.5
0	$\frac{1}{2}(0)+2$	2
1	$\frac{1}{2}(1)+2$	2.5
2	$\frac{1}{2}(2)+2$	3

60.

x	$4.2x-1.6$	y
−2	4.2(−2) − 1.6	−10
−1	4.2(−1) − 1.6	−5.8
0	4.2(0) − 1.6	−1.6
1	4.2(1) − 1.6	2.6
2	4.2(2) − 1.6	6.8

Check Your Understanding

● = Step-by-Step Solutions begin on page R13.

Example 1 Find the solution set of each equation if the replacement set is {11, 12, 13, 14, 15}.

1. $n + 10 = 23$ {13}
2. $7 = \frac{c}{2}$ {14}
3. $29 = 3x - 7$ {12}
4. $(k - 8)12 = 84$ {15}

Example 2

5. **MULTIPLE CHOICE** Solve $\frac{d+5}{10} = 2$. **B**

   A 10 B 15 C 20 D 25

Examples 3–4 Solve each equation.

6. $x = 4(6) + 3$ 27
7. $14 - 82 = w$ −68
8. $5 + 22a = 2 + 10 \div 2$ $\frac{1}{11}$
9. $(2 \cdot 5) + \frac{c^3}{3} = c^3 \div (1^5 + 2) + 10$ all real numbers

Example 5

10. **RECYCLING** San Francisco has a recycling facility that accepts unused paint. Volunteers blend and mix the paint and give it away in 5-gallon buckets. Write and solve an equation to find the number of buckets of paint given away from the 30,000 gallons that are donated. $b = \frac{g}{5}$; 6000 buckets

Practice and Problem Solving

Extra Practice is on page R1.

Example 1 Find the solution set of each equation if the replacement sets are y: {1, 3, 5, 7, 9} and z: {10, 12, 14, 16, 18}.

11. $z + 10 = 22$ {12}
12. $52 = 4z$ no solution
13. $\frac{15}{y} = 3$ {5}
14. $17 = 24 - y$ {7}
15. $2z - 5 = 27$ {16}
16. $4(y + 1) = 40$ {9}
17. $22 = \frac{60}{y} + 2$ {3}
18. $111 = z^2 + 11$ {10}

Examples 2–4 Solve each equation.

19. $a = 32 - 9(2)$ 14
20. $w = 56 \div (2^2 + 3)$ 8
21. $\frac{27+5}{16} = g$ 2
22. $\frac{12 \cdot 5}{15 - 3} = y$ 5
23. $r = \frac{9(6)}{(8+1)3}$ 2
24. $a = \frac{4(14-1)}{3(6)-5} + 7$ 11
25. $(4 - 2^2 + 5)w = 25$ 5
26. $7 + x - (3 + 32 \div 8) = 3$ 3
27. $3^2 - 2 \cdot 3 + u = (3^3 - 3 \cdot 8)(2) + u$ no solution
28. $(3 \cdot 6 \div 2)v + 10 = 3^2v + 9$ no solution
29. $6k + (3 \cdot 10 - 8) = (2 \cdot 3)k + 22$ all real numbers
30. $(3 \cdot 5)t + (21 - 12) = 15t + 3^2$ all real numbers
31. $(2^4 - 3 \cdot 5)q + 13 = (2 \cdot 9 - 4^2)q + \left(\frac{3 \cdot 4}{12} - 1\right)$ 13
32. $\frac{3 \cdot 22}{18+4}r - \left(\frac{4^2}{9+7} - 1\right) = r + \left(\frac{8 \cdot 9}{3} \div 3\right)$ 4
33. **SCHOOL** A conference room can seat a maximum of 85 people. The principal and two counselors need to meet with the school's juniors to discuss college admissions. If each student must bring a parent with them, how many students can attend each meeting? Assume that each student has a unique set of parents. 41 students
34. **MODELING** The perimeter of a regular octagon is 128 inches. Find the length of each side. 16 in.

Differentiated Homework Options

Level	Assignment	Two-Day Option	
AL Basic	11–36, 64–67, 69–90	11–35 odd, 71–74	12–36 even, 64–67, 69, 70, 75–90
OL Core	11–61 odd, 62–67, 69–90	11–36, 71–74	37–67, 69, 70, 75–90
BL Advanced	37–84, (optional: 85–90)		

Example 5

35. **SPORTS** A 200-pound athlete who trains for four hours per day requires 2836 Calories for basic energy requirements. During training, the same athlete requires an additional 3091 Calories for extra energy requirements. Write an equation to find C, the total daily Calorie requirement for this athlete. Then solve the equation.

35. $C = 2836 + 3091$; 5927 Calories/day

36. **ENERGY** An electric generator can power 3550 watts of electricity. Write and solve an equation to find how many 75-watt light bulbs a generator could power. $3550 = 75x$; about 47 light bulbs

B **Make a table of values for each equation if the replacement set is {−2, −1, 0, 1, 2}.**

37. $y = 3x - 2$

38. $3.25x + 0.75 = y$

37, 38. See Ch.1 Answer Appendix.

Solve each equation using the given replacement set.

39. $t - 13 = 7$; {10, 13, 17, 20} 20

40. $14(x + 5) = 126$; {3, 4, 5, 6, 7} 4

41. $22 = \frac{n}{3}$; {62, 64, 66, 68, 70} 66

42. $35 = \frac{g - 8}{2}$; {78, 79, 80, 81} 78

Solve each equation.

43. $\frac{3(9) - 2}{1 + 4} = d$ 5

44. $j = 15 \div 3 \cdot 5 - 4^2$ 9

45. $c + (3^2 - 3) = 21$ $c = 15$

46. $(3^3 - 3 \cdot 9) + (7 - 2^2)b = 24b$ $b = 0$

47. **SENSE-MAKING** Blood flow rate can be expressed as $F = \frac{p_1 - p_2}{r}$, where F is the flow rate, p_1 and p_2 are the initial and final pressure exerted against the blood vessel's walls, respectively, and r is the resistance created by the size of the vessel.

a. Write and solve an equation to determine the resistance of the blood vessel for an initial pressure of 100 millimeters of mercury, a final pressure of 0 millimeters of mercury, and a flow rate of 5 liters per minute. $5 = \frac{100 - 0}{r}$; 20

b. Use the equation to complete the table below.

Initial Pressure p_1 (mm Hg)	Final Pressure p_2 (mm Hg)	Resistance r (mm Hg/L/min)	Blood Flow Rate F (L/min)
100	0	20	5
100	0	30	≈3.33
165	5	40	4
90	30	10	6

Determine whether the given number is a solution of the equation.

48. $x + 6 = 15$; 9 yes

49. $12 + y = 26$; 14 yes

50. $2t - 10 = 4$; 3 no

51. $3r + 7 = -5$; 2 no

52. $6 + 4m = 18$; 3 yes

53. $-5 + 2p = -11$; −3 yes

54. $\frac{q}{2} = 20$; 10 no

55. $\frac{w - 4}{5} = -3$; −11 yes

56. $\frac{g}{3} - 4 = 12$; 48 yes

57–60. See margin.

C **Make a table of values for each equation if the replacement set is {−2, −1, 0, 1, 2}.**

57. $y = 3x + 5$

58. $-2x - 3 = y$

59. $y = \frac{1}{2}x + 2$

60. $4.2x - 1.6 = y$

61. **GEOMETRY** The length of a rectangle is 2 inches greater than the width. The length of the base of an isosceles triangle is 12 inches, and the lengths of the other two sides are 1 inch greater than the width of the rectangle.

a. Draw a picture of each figure and label the dimensions. See margin.

b. Write two expressions to find the perimeters of the rectangle and triangle. See margin.

c. Find the width of the rectangle if the perimeters of the figures are equal. $4 + 4w = 2w + 14$, $w = 5$ in.

Additional Answers

61a.

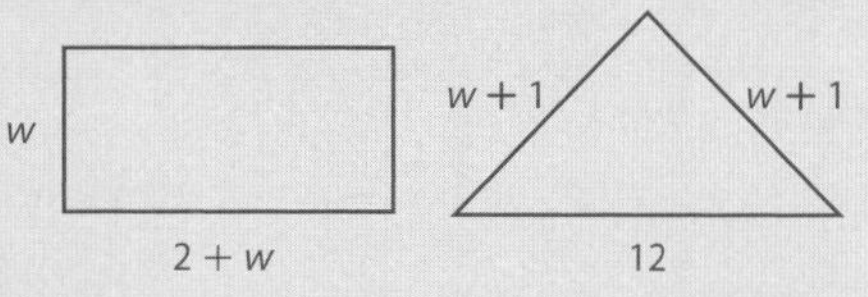

61b. perimeter of rectangle $= 2(2 + w) + 2w = 4 + 4w$;
perimeter of triangle $= 2(w + 1) + 12 = 2w + 14$

Enrichment

OL BL

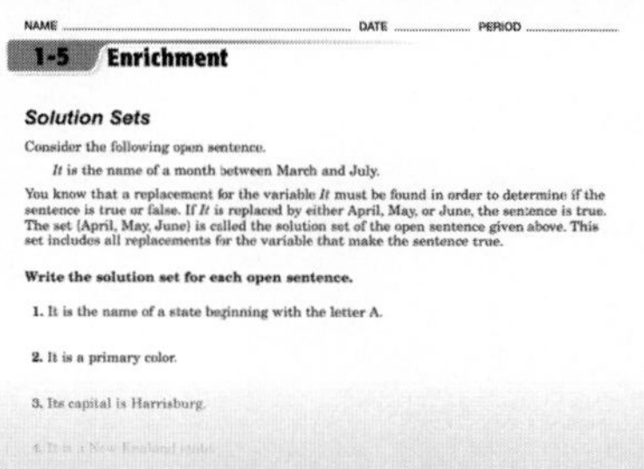
1-5 Enrichment

Solution Sets

Consider the following open sentence.

It is the name of a month between March and July.

Write the solution set for each open sentence.

1. It is the name of a state beginning with the letter A.
2. It is a primary color.
3. Its capital is Harrisburg.

Study Guide and Intervention

AL OL ELL

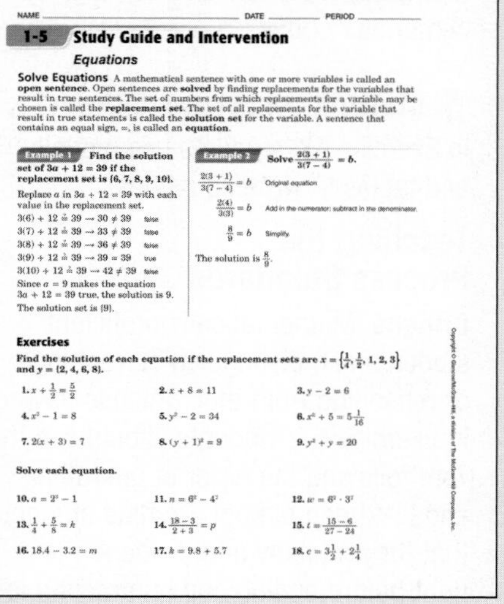
1-5 Study Guide and Intervention

Equations

Exercises

Practice

AL OL BL ELL

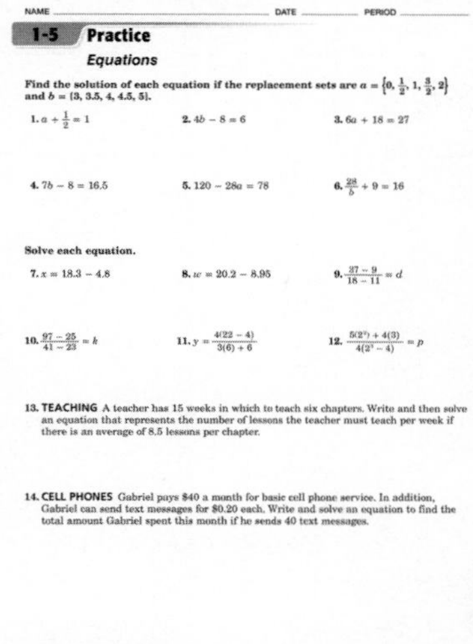
1-5 Practice

Equations

Solve each equation.

13. TEACHING A teacher has 15 weeks in which to teach six chapters. Write and then solve an equation that represents the number of lessons the teacher must teach per week if there is an average of 8.5 lessons per chapter.

14. CELL PHONES Gabriel pays $40 a month for basic cell phone service. In addition, Gabriel can send text messages for $0.20 each. Write and solve an equation to find the total amount Gabriel spent this month if he sends 40 text messages.

Lesson 1-5

Word Problem Practice

AL OL BL ELL

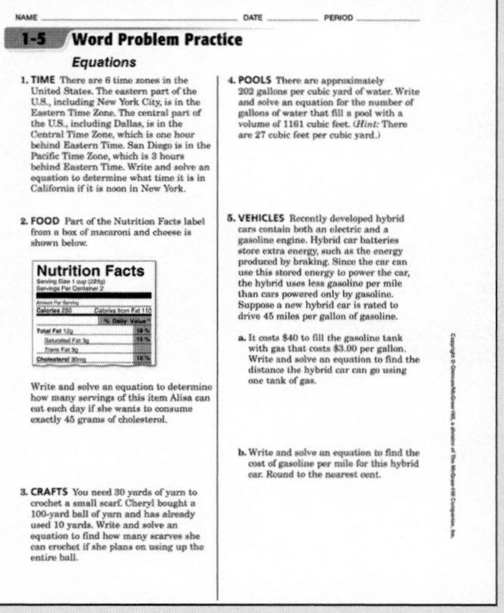
1-5 Word Problem Practice

Equations

1. TIME
2. FOOD
3. CRAFTS
4. POOLS
5. VEHICLES

Exercise Alert

Manipulatives Exercise 63 requires centimeter cubes.

Multiple Representations

In Exercise 63, students use models and tables to write equations.

Teaching the Process Standards

Critique Mathematically proficient students can distinguish correct logic or reasoning from that which is flawed. In Exercise 67, students should see that Tom followed the order of operations and Li-Cheng did not. Remind students that they multiply and divide left to right before adding and subtracting left to right.

Additional Answers

63b.

Layers	1	2	3	4	5	6	7
Cubes	4	8	12	16	20	24	28

64. Sample answer: An equation contains an equals sign and an expression does not. An equation is made up of 2 expressions and an equals sign.

70. Sample answer: Equations with no real numbers for solutions may have the same variables on each side of the equation, but are different by some number or operation. Equations that have all of the real numbers as solutions are equations with the same variables and same numbers and operations on both sides of the equation.

62. CONSTRUCTION The construction of a building requires 10 tons of steel per story.

a. Define a variable and write an equation for the number of tons of steel required if the building has 15 stories. **Sample answer: t = tons of steel; $t = 10(15)$**

b. How many tons of steel are needed? **150 tons of steel**

63. MULTIPLE REPRESENTATIONS In this problem, you will further explore writing equations.

a. Concrete Use centimeter cubes to build a tower similar to the one shown at the right. **See students' work.**

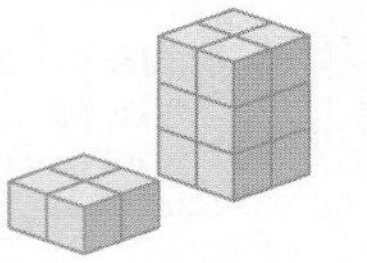

b. Tabular Copy and complete the table shown below. Record the number of layers in the tower and the number of cubes used in the table. **See margin.**

Layers	1	2	3	4	5	6	7
Cubes	?	?	?	?	?	?	?

c. Analytical As the number of layers in the tower increases, how does the number of cubes in the tower change? **Each layer adds 4 more cubes to the tower.**

d. Algebraic Write a rule that gives the number of cubes in terms of the number of layers in the tower. **The number of cubes = $4L$, where L is the number of layers in the tower.**

H.O.T. Problems Use Higher-Order Thinking Skills

64. REASONING Compare and contrast an expression and an equation. **See margin.**

65. OPEN ENDED Write an equation that is an identity. **Sample answer: $3x + 12 = 3(x + 4)$**

66. REASONING Explain why an open sentence always has at least one variable.

67. CRITIQUE Tom and Li-Cheng are solving the equation $x = 4(3 - 2) + 6 \div 8$. Is either of them correct? Explain your reasoning.

66. Sample answer: A sentence that contains no variable will be true or false, which means it cannot be an open sentence.

67. Tom; Li-Cheng added 6 + 4 instead of dividing 6 by 8. She did not follow the order of operations.

Tom

$x = 4(3 - 2) + 6 \div 8$
$= 4(1) + 6 \div 8$
$= 4 + 6 \div 8$
$= 4 + \frac{6}{8}$
$= 4\frac{3}{4}$

Li-Cheng

$x = 4(3 - 2) + 6 \div 8$
$= 4(1) + 6 \div 8$
$= 4 + 6 \div 8$
$= 10 \div 8$
$= \frac{5}{4}$

68. CHALLENGE Find all of the solutions of $x^2 + 5 = 30$. **5, −5**

69. OPEN ENDED Write an equation that involves two or more operations with a solution of −7. **Sample answer: $3x - 2 = -23$**

70. WRITING IN MATH Explain how you can determine that an equation has no real numbers as a solution. How can you determine that an equation has all real numbers as solutions? **See margin.**

Standardized Test Practice

71. Which of the following is *not* an equation? **C**

A $y = 6x - 4$

B $\frac{a+4}{2} = \frac{1}{4}$

C $(4 \cdot 3b) + (8 \div 2c)$

D $55 = 6 + d^2$

72. SHORT RESPONSE The expected attendance for the Drama Club production is 65% of the student body. If the student body consists of 300 students, how many students are expected to attend? **195 students**

73. GEOMETRY A speedboat and a sailboat take off from the same port. The diagram shows their travel. What is the distance between the boats? **G**

F 12 mi

G 15 mi

H 18 mi

J 24 mi

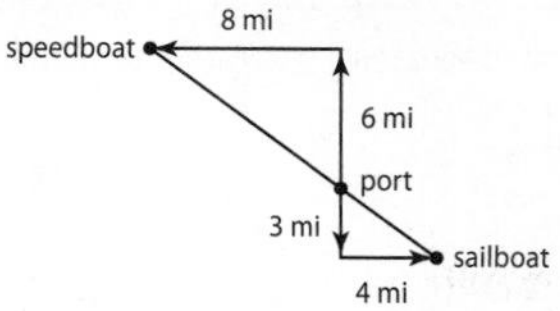

74. Michelle can read 1.5 pages per minute. How many pages can she read in two hours? **D**

A 90 pages

B 120 pages

C 150 pages

D 180 pages

Spiral Review

75. ZOO A zoo has about 500 children and 750 adults visit each day. Write an expression to represent about how many visitors the zoo will have over a month. (Lesson 1-4) **30(500 + 750)**

Find the value of *p* in each equation. Then name the property that is used. (Lesson 1-3)

76. $7.3 + p = 7.3$ **$p = 0$; Additive Identity**

77. $12p = 1$ **$p = \frac{1}{12}$; Multiplicative Inverse**

78. $1p = 4$ **$p = 4$; Multiplicative Identity**

79. MOVING BOXES The figure shows the dimensions of the boxes Steve uses to pack. How many cubic inches can each box hold? (Lesson 0-9) **1040 in^3**

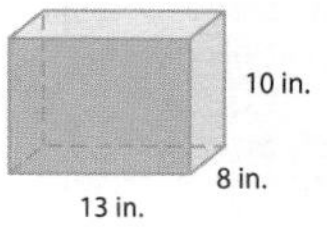

Express each percent as a fraction. (Lesson 0-6)

80. 35% $\frac{7}{20}$

81. 15% $\frac{3}{20}$

82. 28% $\frac{7}{25}$

For each problem, determine whether you need an estimate or an exact answer. Then solve. (Lessons 0-6 and 0-1)

83. TRAVEL The distance from Raleigh, North Carolina, to Philadelphia, Pennsylvania, is approximately 428 miles. The average gas mileage of José's car is 45 miles per gallon. About how many gallons of gas will be needed to make the trip? **estimate; 10 gal**

84. PART-TIME JOB An employer pays \$8.50 per hour. If 20% of pay is withheld for taxes, what are the take-home earnings from 28 hours of work? **exact; \$190.40**

Skills Review

Find each sum or difference.

85. $1.14 + 5.6$ **6.74**

86. $4.28 - 2.4$ **1.88**

87. $8 - 6.35$ **1.65**

88. $\frac{4}{5} + \frac{1}{6}$ $\frac{29}{30}$

89. $\frac{2}{7} + \frac{3}{4}$ $\frac{29}{28}$

90. $\frac{6}{8} - \frac{1}{2}$ $\frac{1}{4}$

DifferentiatedInstruction OL BL

Extension Write the solution set {15} on the board. Have students write two equations, based on real-world situations, that match the solution set. For example, students could write, "Bryce scored 86 on a science test with *p* points for extra credit." $p + 71 = 86$; $86 - p = 71$

4 Assess

Yesterday's News Ask students to write a brief statement on how yesterday's lesson on evaluating expressions helped them with today's lesson on finding solutions for open sentences.

1 Focus

VerticalAlignment

Before Lesson 1-6 Solve equations with one or two variables.

Lesson 1-6 Represent relations. Interpret graphs as relations.

After Lesson 1-6 Use algebraic, tabular, graphical, and verbal descriptions of linear functions.

2 Teach

Scaffolding Questions

Have students read the **Why?** section of the lesson.

Ask:

- What happens to the pressure on your body as you dive deeper into the ocean? It increases.
- Does the pressure depend on the depth or does the depth depend on the pressure? Pressure depends on depth.
- Which variable do you think is the dependent variable? P, the pressure independent variable? h, the depth

LESSON 1-6 Relations

Then

- You solved equations with one or two variables.

Now

1. Represent relations.
2. Interpret graphs of relations.

Why?

- The deeper in the ocean you are, the greater pressure is on your body. This is because there is more water over you. The force of gravity pulls the water weight down, creating a greater pressure.

The equation that relates the total pressure of the water to the depth is $P = rgh$, where

$P =$ the pressure,
$r =$ the density of water,
$g =$ the acceleration due to gravity, and
$h =$ the height of water above you.

Jeff Hunter/Photographer's Choice RF/Getty Images

NewVocabulary
coordinate system
coordinate plane
x- and y-axes
origin
ordered pair
x- and y-coordinates
relation
mapping
domain
range
independent variable
dependent variable

Content Standards
AI.F.1, AI.F.2, AI.F.3, AI.F.4

1 Represent a Relation

This relationship between the depth and the pressure exerted can be represented by a line on a coordinate grid.

A **coordinate system** is formed by the intersection of two number lines, the *horizontal axis* and the *vertical axis*.

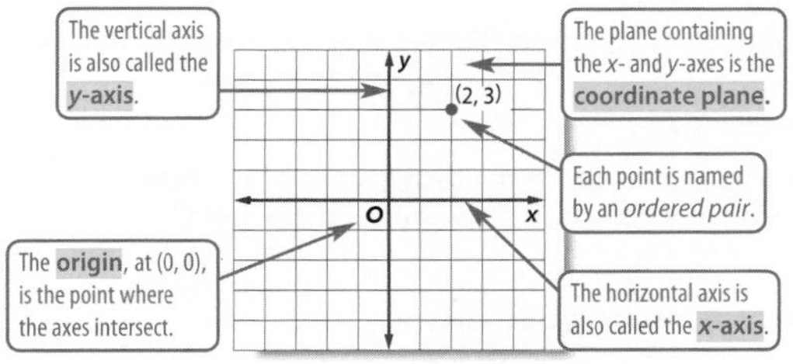

A point is represented on a graph using ordered pairs.

- An **ordered pair** is a set of numbers, or *coordinates*, written in the form (x, y).
- The x-value, called the **x-coordinate**, represents the horizontal placement of the point.
- The y-value, or **y-coordinate**, represents the vertical placement of the point.

A set of ordered pairs is called a **relation**. A relation can be represented in several different ways: as an equation, in a graph, with a table, or with a mapping.

A **mapping** illustrates how each element of the *domain* is paired with an element in the *range*. The set of the first numbers of the ordered pairs is the **domain**. The set of second numbers of the ordered pairs is the **range** of the relation. This mapping represents the ordered pairs $(-2, 4)$, $(-1, 4)$, $(0, 6)$ $(1, 8)$, and $(2, 8)$.

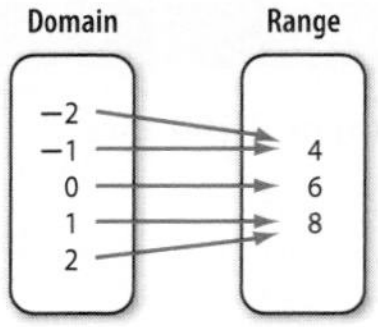

40 | Lesson 1-6

Lesson 1-6 Resources

Resource	Approaching Level AL	On Level OL	Beyond Level BL	English Learners ELL
Teacher Edition		▪ Differentiated Instruction, p. 45	▪ Differentiated Instruction, pp. 45, 46	
Chapter Resource Masters	▪ Study Guide and Intervention, pp. 37–38 ▪ Skills Practice, p. 39 ▪ Practice, p. 40 ▪ Word Problem Practice, p. 41	▪ Study Guide and Intervention, pp. 37–38 ▪ Skills Practice, p. 39 ▪ Practice, p. 40 ▪ Word Problem Practice, p. 41 ▪ Enrichment, p. 42	▪ Practice, p. 40 ▪ Word Problem Practice, p. 41 ▪ Enrichment, p. 42	▪ Study Guide and Intervention, pp. 37–38 ▪ Skills Practice, p. 39 ▪ Practice, p. 40 ▪ Word Problem Practice, p. 41
Other	▪ 5-Minute Check 1-6 ▪ Study Notebook ▪ Teaching Algebra with Manipulatives	▪ 5-Minute Check 1-6 ▪ Study Notebook ▪ Teaching Algebra with Manipulatives	▪ 5-Minute Check 1-6 ▪ Study Notebook	▪ 5-Minute Check 1-6 ▪ Study Notebook ▪ Teaching Algebra with Manipulatives

StudyTip

Sense-Making Each representation of the same relation serves a different purpose. Graphing the points can show the pattern between the points. A mapping shows you at a glance if elements are paired with the same element.

Study the different representations of the same relation below.

Ordered Pairs

(1, 2)
(−2, 4)
(0, −3)

Table

x	y
1	2
−2	4
0	−3

Graph

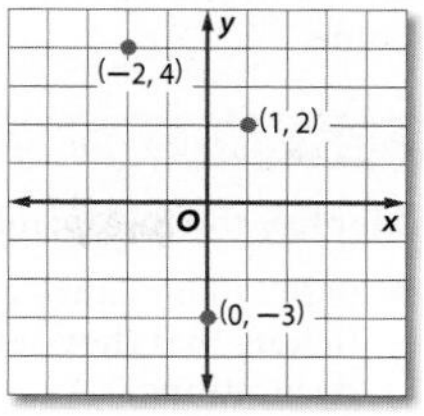

Mapping

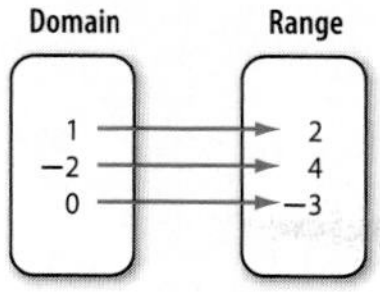

The x-values of a relation are members of the domain and the y-values of a relation are members of the range. In the relation above, the domain is {−2, 1, 0} and the range is {−3, 2, 4}.

Example 1 Representations of a Relation

a. Express {(2, 5), (−2, 3), (5, −2), (−1, −2)} as a table, a graph, and a mapping.

Table
Place the x-coordinates into the first column of the table. Place the corresponding y-coordinates in the second column of the table.

x	y
2	5
−2	3
5	−2
−1	−2

Graph
Graph each ordered pair on a coordinate plane.

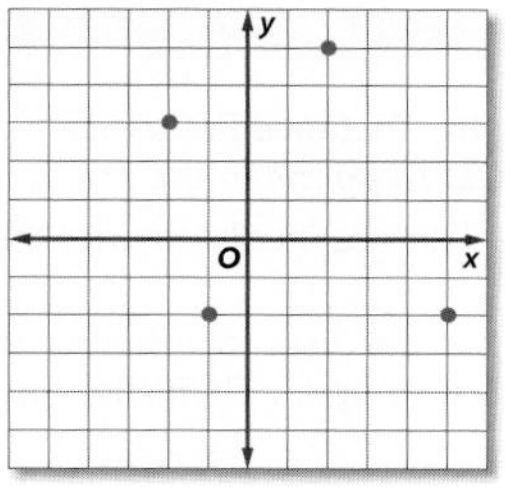

Mapping
List the x-values in the domain and the y-values in the range. Draw arrows from the x-values in the domain to the corresponding y-values in the range.

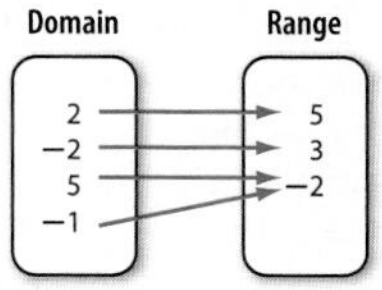

b. Determine the domain and the range of the relation.

The domain of the relation is {2, −2, 5, −1}. The range of the relation is {5, 3, −2}.

GuidedPractice

1A. Express {(4, −3), (3, 2), (−4, 1), (0, −3)} as a table, graph, and mapping. **See margin.**

1B. Determine the domain and range. **D = {4, 3, −4, 0}; R = {−3, 2, 1}**

1 Represent a Relation

Example 1 shows how to represent a relation as a table, a graph, and a mapping. **Example 2** shows how to identify the independent and dependent variables in a relation.

Formative Assessment

Use the Guided Practice exercises after each Example to determine students' understanding of concepts.

Additional Example

1 a. Express {(4, 3), (−2, −1), (2, −4), (0, −4)} as a table, a graph, and a mapping.

x	y
4	3
−2	−1
2	−4
0	−4

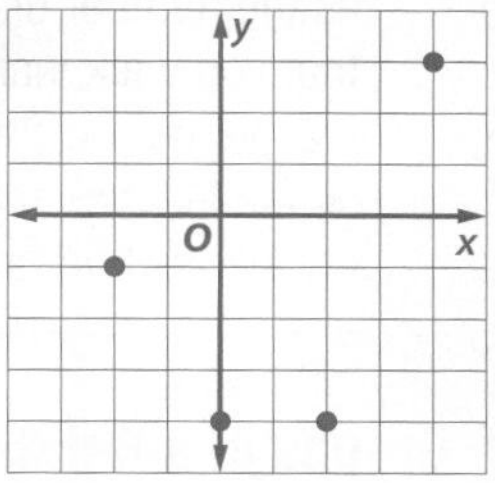

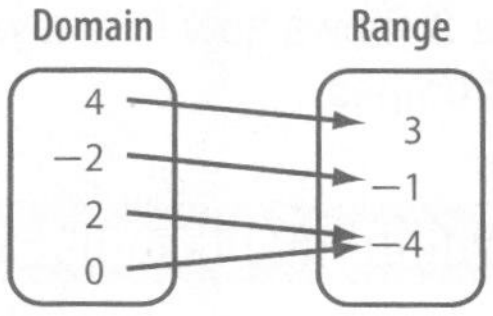

b. Determine the domain and range of the relation. D = {4, −2, 2, 0}; R = {3, −1, −4}

Additional Examples also in Interactive Classroom PowerPoint® Presentations

IWB Interactive White Board READY

Teaching the Process Standards

Sense-Making Mathematically proficient students can explain correspondences between equations, verbal descriptions, tables, and graphs and search for regularity or trends. Encourage students to become familiar with and use multiple representations for relations.

Additional Answer (Guided Practice)

1A.

x	y
4	−3
3	2
−4	1
0	−3

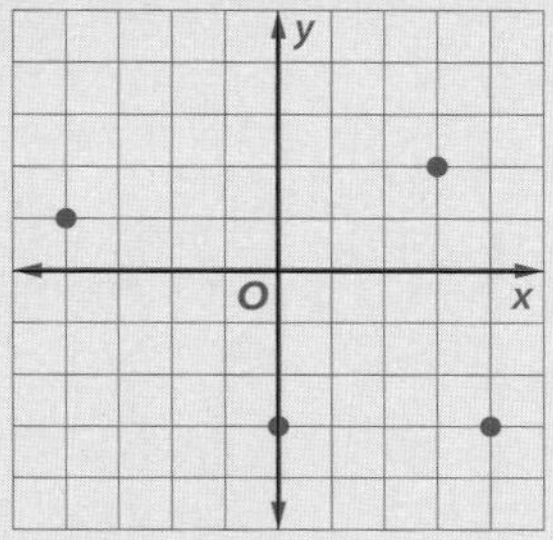

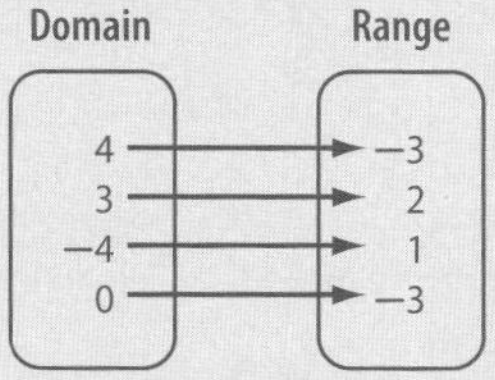

Additional Example

2 Identify the independent and the dependent variables for each relation.

a. **CLIMATE** In warm climates, the average amount of electricity used rises as the daily average temperature increases and falls as the daily average temperature decreases. independent variable: temperature; dependent variable: amount of electricity used

b. **CALORIES** The number of calories you burn increases as the number of minutes that you walk increases. independent variable: time; dependent variable: number of calories burned

2 Graphs of a Relation

Example 3 shows how to analyze and interpret graphs.

Additional Example

3 The graph represents the temperature in Ms. Ling's classroom on a winter day. Describe what happens in the graph.

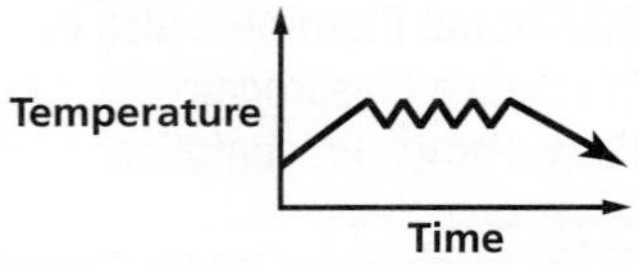

Sample answer: The temperature increases after the heat is turned on. Then the temperature fluctuates up and down because of the thermostat. Finally, the temperature drops when the heat is turned off.

Focus on Mathematical Content

Domain and Range Domain refers to the x-coordinates, or inputs of a relation, and range refers to the y-coordinates or outputs. Repeated values for the domain and range should be listed only once.

In a relation, the value of the variable that determines the output is called the **independent variable**. The variable with a value that is dependent on the value of the independent variable is called the **dependent variable**. The domain contains values of the independent variable. The range contains the values of the dependent variable.

Real-World Example 2 Independent and Dependent Variables

Identify the independent and dependent variables for each relation.

a. DANCE **The dance committee is selling tickets to the Fall Ball. The more tickets that they sell, the greater the amount of money they can spend for decorations.**

The number of tickets sold is the independent variable because it is unaffected by the money spent on decorations. The money spent on decorations is the dependent variable because it depends on the number of tickets sold.

b. MOVIES **Generally, the average price of going to the movies has steadily increased over time.**

Time is the independent variable because it is unaffected by the cost of attending the movies. The price of going to the movies is the dependent variable because it is affected by time.

Real-WorldLink

In 1948, a movie ticket cost $0.36. In 2008, the average ticket price in the United States was $7.18.

Source: National Association of Theatre Owners

Erik Dreyer/The Image Bank/Getty Images

GuidedPractice

Identify the independent and dependent variables for each relation.

2A. The air pressure inside a tire increases with the temperature.

2B. As the amount of rain decreases, so does the water level of the river.

2A. I: the temperature; D: the air pressure.
2B. I: the amount of rain; D: the water level.
3A. The graph indicates two periods where the car was stopped. The rate of the car is relatively fast in the first section and then slows down.
3B. As time increases, the income increases overall, although not at a constant rate.

2 Graphs of a Relation

A relation can be graphed without a scale on either axis. These graphs can be interpreted by analyzing their shape.

Example 3 Analyze Graphs

The graph represents the distance Francesca has ridden on her bike. Describe what happens in the graph.

Bike Ride

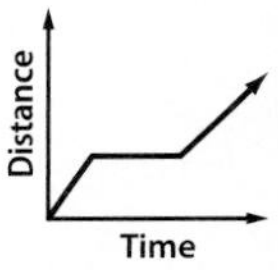

As time increases, the distance increases until the graph becomes a horizontal line.

So, time is increasing but the distance remains constant. At this section Francesca stopped. Then she continued to ride her bike.

GuidedPractice

Describe what is happening in each graph.

3A. **Driving to School**

3B. **Change in Income**

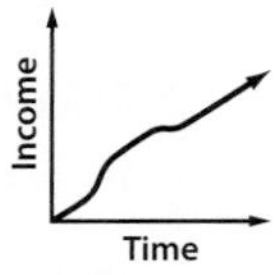

Additional Answer

1.

x	y
4	3
−2	2
5	−6

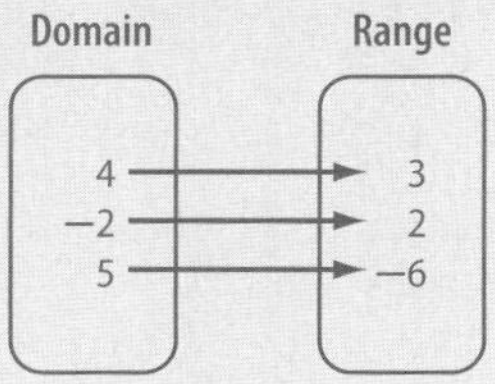

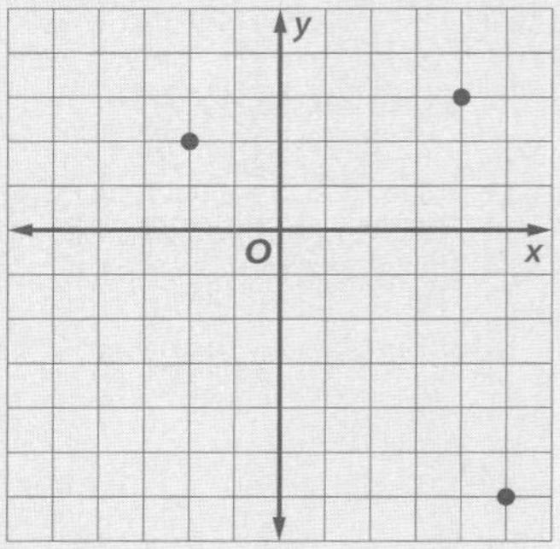

D = {−2, 4, 5};
R = {−6, 2, 3}

Check Your Understanding

◯ = Step-by-Step Solutions begin on page R13.

Example 1 **Express each relation as a table, a graph, and a mapping. Then determine the domain and range.** **1–2. See margin.**

1. {(4, 3), (−2, 2), (5, −6)}

2. {(5, −7), (−1, 4), (0, −5), (−2, 3)}

Example 2 **Identify the independent and dependent variables for each relation.**

3. Increasing the temperature of a compound inside a sealed container increases the pressure inside a sealed container. **3–6. See margin.**

4. Mike's cell phone is part of a family plan. If he uses more minutes than his share, then there are fewer minutes available for the rest of his family.

5. Julian is buying concert tickets for himself and his friends. The more concert tickets he buys the greater the cost.

6. A store is having a sale over Labor Day weekend. The more purchases, the greater the profits.

Example 3 **MODELING** **Describe what is happening in each graph.** **7. See margin.**

7. The graph represents the distance the track team runs during a practice.

8. The graph represents revenues generated through an online store.

Overall, the sales increase steadily but there are two sections where the sales decrease or remain constant.

Practice and Problem Solving

Extra Practice is on page R1.

Example 1 **Express each relation as a table, a graph, and a mapping. Then determine the domain and range.** **9–14. See Ch. 1 Answer Appendix.**

9. {(0, 0), (−3, 2), (6, 4), (−1, 1)}

10. {(5, 2), (5, 6), (3, −2), (0, −2)}

11. {(6, 1), (4, −3), (3, 2), (−1, −3)}

12. {(−1, 3), (3, −6), (−1, −8), (−3, −7)}

13. {(6, 7), (3, −2), (8, 8), (−6, 2), (2, −6)}

14. {(4, −3), (1, 3), (7, −2), (2, −2), (1, 5)}

Example 2 **Identify the independent and dependent variables for each relation.**

15 The Spanish classes are having a fiesta lunch. Each student that attends is to bring a Spanish side dish or dessert. The more students that attend, the more food there will be. **15–16. See Ch. 1 Answer Appendix.**

16. The faster you drive your car, the longer it will take to come to a complete stop.

Example 3 **MODELING** **Describe what is happening in each graph.** **17–18. See Ch. 1 Answer Appendix.**

17. The graph represents the height of a bungee jumper.

18. The graph represents the sales of lawn mowers.

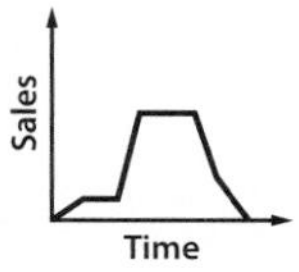

Differentiated Homework Options

Level	Assignment	Two-Day Option	
AL Basic	9–20, 38, 40, 42–60	9–19 odd, 43–46	10–20 even, 38, 40, 42, 47–60
OL Core	9–31 odd, 32–38, 40, 42–60	9–20, 43–46	21–38, 40, 42, 47–60
BL Advanced	21–54, (optional: 55–60)		

3 Practice

Formative Assessment

Use Exercises 1–8 to check for understanding.

Use the chart at the bottom of this page to customize assignments for your students.

Teaching the Process Standards

Modeling Mathematically proficient students can analyze relationships between quantities mathematically to draw conclusions. Encourage students to think about the numerical relationship that is represented by each portion of a graph.

Additional Answers

2.

x	y
5	−7
−1	4
0	−5
−2	3

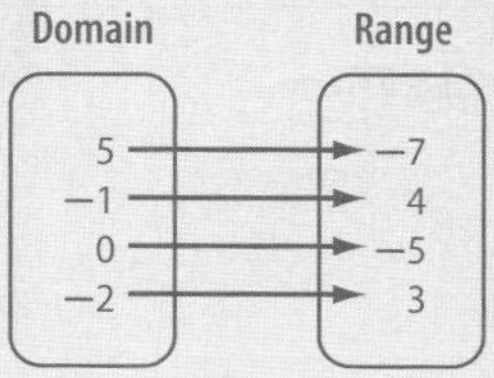

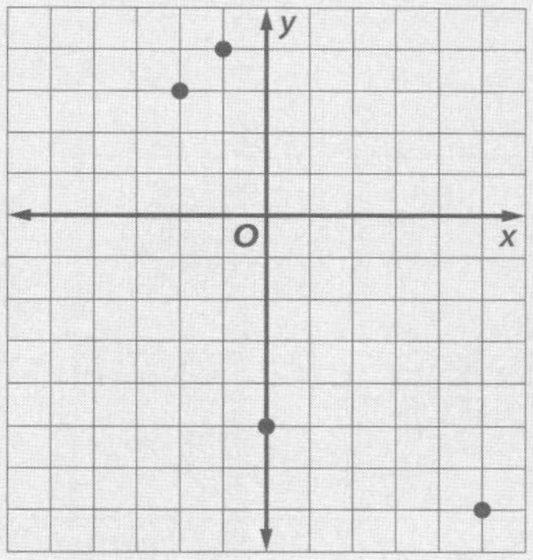

D = {−2, −1, 0, 5};
R = {−7, −5, 3, 4}

3. I: the temperature of the compound; D: the pressure of the compound

4. I: the number of minutes Mike uses on his cell phone; D: the number of minutes that are left

5. I: number of concert tickets; D: cost of tickets

6. I: number of customers who purchase something; D: the profits

7. The track team starts by running or walking, and then stops for a short period of time, then continues at the same pace. Finally, they run or walk at a slower pace.

Study Guide and Intervention

AL OL ELL

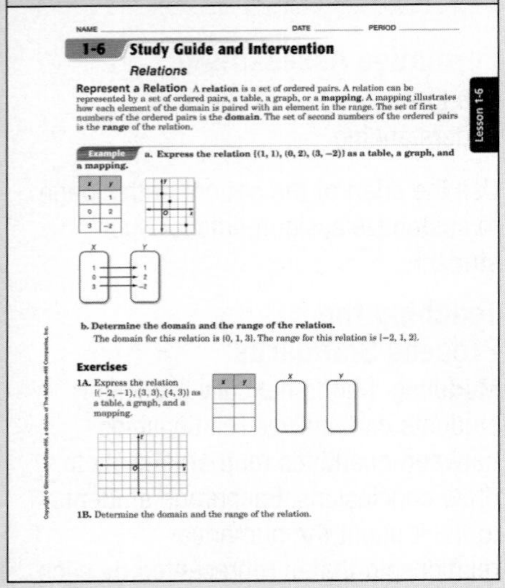
NAME ____ DATE ____ PERIOD ____

1-6 Study Guide and Intervention

Relations

Represent a Relation A **relation** is a set of ordered pairs. A relation can be represented by a set of ordered pairs, a table, a graph, or a **mapping**. A mapping illustrates how each element of the domain is paired with an element in the range. The set of first numbers of the ordered pairs is the **domain**. The set of second numbers of the ordered pairs is the **range** of the relation.

Example a. Express the relation {(1, 1), (0, 2), (3, −2)} as a table, a graph, and a mapping.

b. Determine the domain and the range of the relation.

The domain for this relation is {0, 1, 3}. The range for this relation is {−2, 1, 2}.

Exercises

1A. Express the relation {(−2, −1), (3, 3), (4, 3)} as a table, a graph, and a mapping.

1B. Determine the domain and the range of the relation.

Practice

AL OL BL ELL

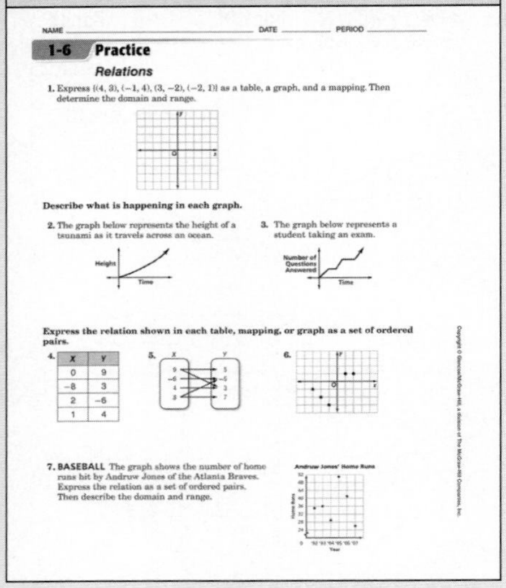
NAME ____ DATE ____ PERIOD ____

1-6 Practice

Relations

1. Express {(4, 3), (−1, 4), (3, −2), (−2, 1)} as a table, a graph, and a mapping. Then determine the domain and range.

Describe what is happening in each graph.

2. The graph below represents the height of a tsunami as it travels across an ocean.

3. The graph below represents a student taking an exam.

Express the relation shown in each table, mapping, or graph as a set of ordered pairs.

7. BASEBALL The graph shows the number of home runs hit by Andruw Jones of the Atlanta Braves. Express the relation as a set of ordered pairs. Then describe the domain and range.

Word Problem Practice

AL OL BL ELL

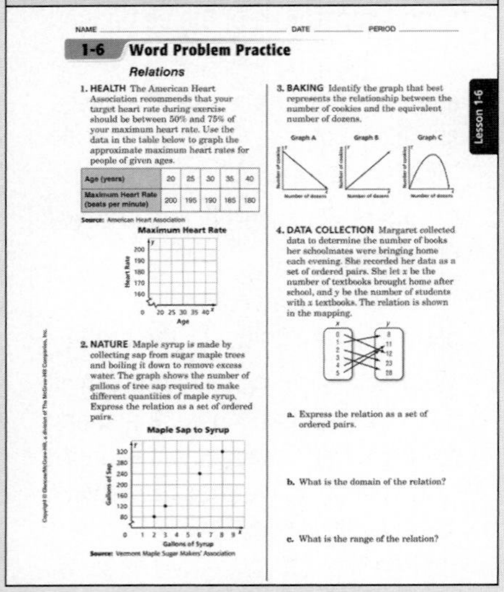
NAME ____ DATE ____ PERIOD ____

1-6 Word Problem Practice

Relations

1. HEALTH The American Heart Association recommends that your target heart rate during exercise should be between 50% and 75% of your maximum heart rate. Use the data in the table below to graph the approximate maximum heart rates for people of given ages.

Age (years)	20	25	30	35	40
Maximum Heart Rate (beats per minute)	200	195	190	185	180

2. NATURE Maple syrup is made by collecting sap from sugar maple trees and boiling it down to remove excess water. The graph shows the number of gallons of tree sap required to make different quantities of maple syrup. Express the relation as a set of ordered pairs.

3. BAKING Identify the graph that best represents the relationship between the number of cookies and the equivalent number of dozens.

4. DATA COLLECTION Margaret collected data to determine the number of books her schoolmates were bringing home each evening. She recorded her data as a set of ordered pairs. She let x be the number of textbooks brought home after school, and y be the number of students with x textbooks. The relation is shown in the mapping.

a. Express the relation as a set of ordered pairs.

b. What is the domain of the relation?

c. What is the range of the relation?

MODELING **Describe what is happening in each graph.**

19. The graph represents the value of a rare baseball card.

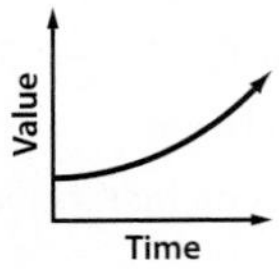

See Ch. 1 Answer Appendix.

20. The graph represents the distance covered on an extended car ride.

See Ch. 1 Answer Appendix.

For Exercises 21–23, use the graph at the right.

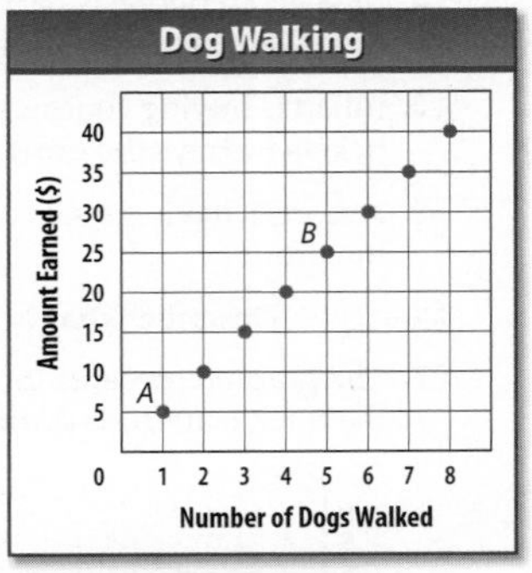

B 21. Name the ordered pair at point *A* and explain what it represents.

22. Name the ordered pair at point *B* and explain what it represents.

23. Identify the independent and dependent variables for the relation. **I: number of dogs walked; D: amount earned**

21. (1, 5); The dog walker earns $5 for walking 1 dog.

22. (5, 25); The dog walker earns $25 for walking 5 dogs.

For Exercises 24–26, use the graph at the right.

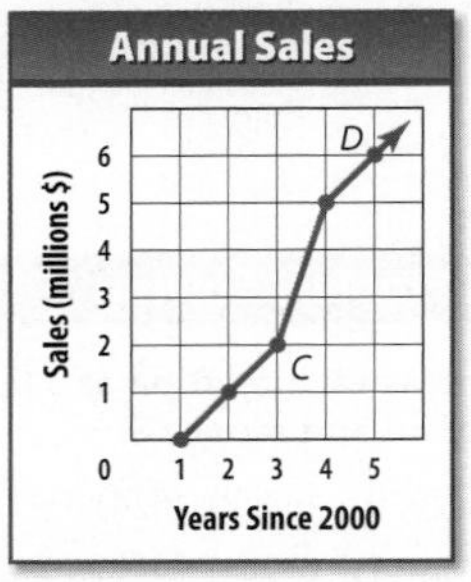

24. Name the ordered pair at point *C* and explain what it represents.

25. Name the ordered pair at point *D* and explain what it represents.

26. Identify the independent and dependent variables. **I: year; D: sales**

24. (3, 2); In the year 2003, sales were about $2 million.

25. (5, 6); In the year 2005, sales were about $6 million.

Express each relation as a set of ordered pairs. Describe the domain and range.

27.

Buying Aquarium Fish	
Number of Fish	Total Cost
1	$2.50
2	$4.50
5	$10.50
8	$16.50

{(1, 2.50), (2, 4.50), (5, 10.50), (8, 16.50)}; D = {1, 2, 5, 8}; R = {2.50, 4.50, 10.50, 16.50}

28.

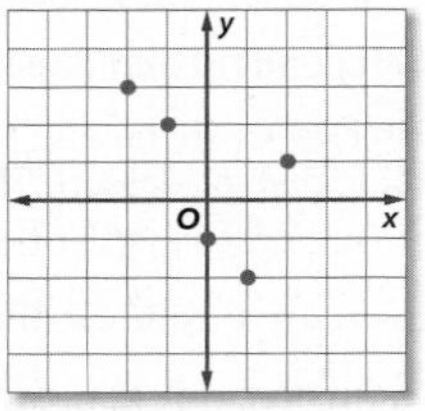

{(−2, 3), (−1, 2), (0, −1), (1, −2), (2, 1)}; D = {−2, −1, 0, 1, 2}; R = {3, 2, −1, −2, 1}

Express the relation in each table, mapping, or graph as a set of ordered pairs.

29.

x	y
4	−1
8	9
−2	−6
7	−3

30.

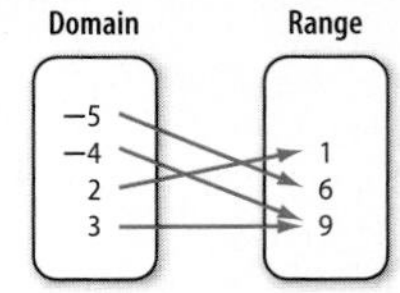

31.

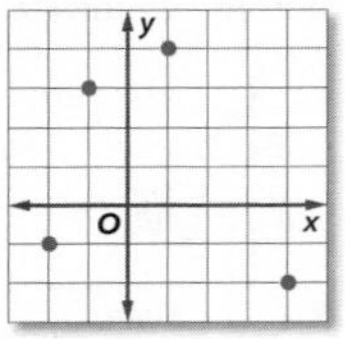

29. {(4, −1), (8, 9), (−2, −6), (7, −3)}

30. {(−5, 6), (−4, 9), (2, 1), (3, 9)}

31. {(4, −2), (−1, 3), (−2, −1), (1, 4)}

Enrichment

OL BL

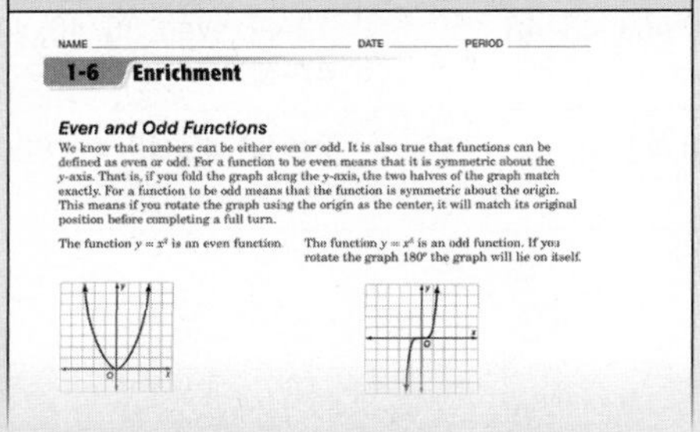
NAME ____ DATE ____ PERIOD ____

1-6 Enrichment

Even and Odd Functions

We know that numbers can be either even or odd. It is also true that functions can be defined as even or odd. For a function to be even means that it is symmetric about the y-axis. That is, if you fold the graph along the y-axis, the two halves of the graph match exactly. For a function to be odd means that it is symmetric about the origin. This means if you rotate the graph using the origin as the center, it will match its original position before completing a full turn.

The function $y = x^2$ is an even function.

The function $y = x^3$ is an odd function. If you rotate the graph 180° the graph will lie on itself.

Additional Answers

32. Graph B; the graph indicates 2 stopping periods where the athlete prepared for the next event.

33. Sample answer:

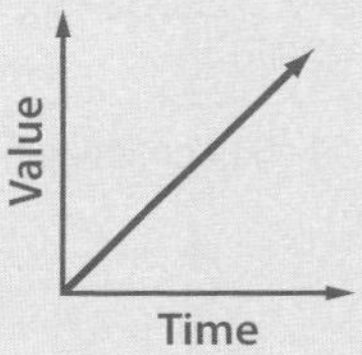

32. SPORTS In a triathlon, athletes swim 2.4 miles, bicycle 112 miles, and run 26.2 miles. Their total time includes transition time from one activity to the next. Which graph best represents a participant in a triathlon? Explain. **See margin.**

Graph A | Graph B | Graph C

Draw a graph to represent each situation. 33–36. See margin.

33. ANTIQUES A grandfather clock that is over 100 years old has increased in value from when it was first purchased.

34. CAR A car depreciates in value. The value decreases quickly in the first few years.

35. REAL ESTATE A house typically increases in value over time.

36. EXERCISE An athlete alternates between running and walking during a workout.

37 PHYSIOLOGY A typical adult has about 2 pounds of water for every 3 pounds of body weight. This can be represented by the equation $w = 2\left(\frac{b}{3}\right)$, where w is the weight of water in pounds and b is the body weight in pounds. **a–d. See Ch. 1 Answer Appendix.**

a. Make a table to show the relation between body and water weight for people weighing 100, 105, 110, 115, 120, 125, and 130 pounds. Round to the nearest tenth if necessary.

b. What are the independent and dependent variables?

c. State the domain and range, and then graph the relation.

d. Reverse the independent and dependent variables. Graph this relation. Explain what the graph indicates in this circumstance.

H.O.T. Problems Use Higher-Order Thinking Skills

38. OPEN ENDED Describe a real-life situation that can be represented using a relation and discuss how one of the quantities in the relation depends on the other. Then represent the relation in three different ways. **See Ch. 1 Answer Appendix.**

39. CHALLENGE Describe a real-world situation where it is reasonable to have a negative number included in the domain or range. **See students' work.**

40. PRECISION Compare and contrast dependent and independent variables.

40, 42. See margin.

41. CHALLENGE The table presents a relation. Graph the ordered pairs. Then reverse the y-coordinate and the x-coordinate in each ordered pair. Graph these ordered pairs on the same coordinate plane. Graph the line $y = x$. Describe the relationship between the two sets of ordered pairs. **See Ch. 1 Answer Appendix.**

x	y
0	1
1	3
2	5
3	7

42. WRITING IN MATH Use the data about the pressure of water on page 40 to explain the difference between dependent and independent variables.

Differentiated Instruction OL BL

Social You may want to spend extra time on independent and dependent variables, since an understanding of these concepts provides the foundation for later work with functions. For Exercise 38, have students generate several real-world scenarios with independent and dependent variables. Then have students work in small groups to compare and contrast variables.

Teaching the Process Standards

Precision Mathematically proficient students use clear definitions in discussion with others and in their own reasoning. In Exercise 40, explain to students that to compare and contrast two things requires identifying similarities and differences.

Tips for New Teachers

Sense-Making For Exercise 41, explain to students that reversing the x- and y-coordinates results in the inverse of a relation. Point out that the inverse of a relation has the same number of ordered pairs as the relation.

Additional Answers

34. Sample answer:

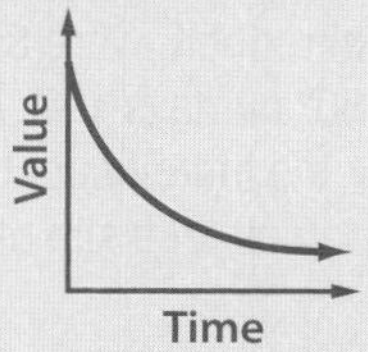

35. Sample answer:

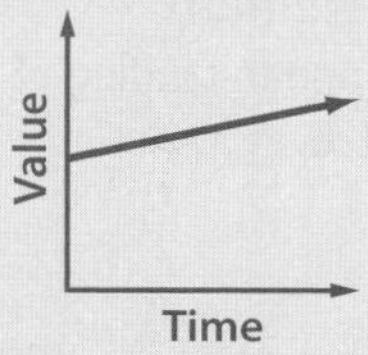

36. Sample answer:

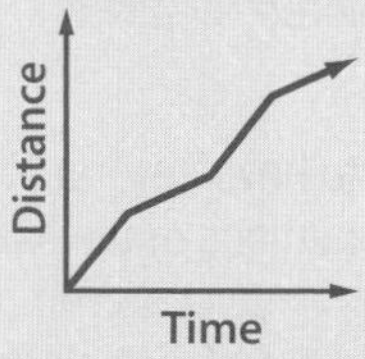

40. Sample answer: A dependent variable is determined by the independent variable for a given relation.

42. Sample answer: Real-world data can be recorded and visualized in a graph and by expressing an event in terms of another event. Graphs and mappings give you a visual representation of the situation which is easier to analyze and evaluate. The value of a dependent variable is dependent on the value of the independent variable. The independent variable is the depth of water. The pressure exerted under the water depends on the height or depth of the water.

Teach with Tech

Interactive Whiteboard Create a short quiz of several expressions (such as $6 \cdot 5 - 4 \div 1$) to determine if students understand the order of operations. You can do this at the board or use your SRS software. Ask students to perform the first, second, etc… operations. You can develop a key (such as A for add, B for subtract, C for multiply, and D for divide) for responses. You will be able to track how many students understand the order of operations.

4 Assess

Ticket out the Door Tell students that temperatures, in Fahrenheit, were 81°, 84°, 85°, 86°, and 88° on days 1–5. Ask students to identify the independent and dependent variables on a slip of paper.

Formative Assessment

Check for student understanding of Lessons 1-5 and 1-6.

Quiz 3, p. 58

Follow-up

Students have explored relations.

Ask:

- Why is it helpful to have several different representations of the same relation? Sample answer: Different representations of the same relation can show different aspects of the relationship. For example, a mapping is helpful because it allows you to quickly visualize how many times an element in the domain is paired with an element in the range, or vice versa.

Standardized Test Practice

43. A school's cafeteria employees surveyed 250 students asking what beverage they drank with lunch. They used the data to create the table below.

Beverage	Number of Students
milk	38
chocolate milk	112
juice	75
water	25

What percent of the students surveyed preferred drinking juice with lunch? **B**

A 25% C 35%

B 30% D 40%

44. Which of the following is equivalent to $6(3 - g) + 2(11 - g)$? **H**

F $2(20 - g)$ H $8(5 - g)$

G $8(14 - g)$ J $40 - g$

45. SHORT RESPONSE Grant and Hector want to build a clubhouse at the midpoint between their houses. If Grant's house is at point G and Hector's house is at point H, what will be the coordinates of the clubhouse? **(−1, −3)**

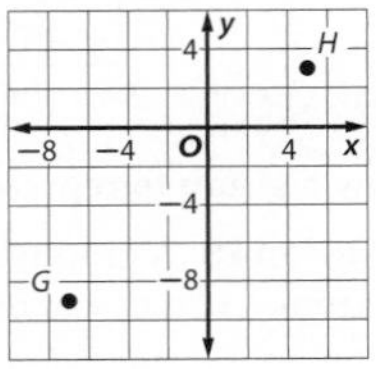

46. If $3b = 2b$, which of the following is true? **A**

A $b = 0$

B $b = \frac{2}{3}$

C $b = 1$

D $b = \frac{3}{2}$

Spiral Review

Solve each equation. (Lesson 1-5)

47. $6(a + 5) = 42$ **2**

48. $92 = k + 11$ **81**

49. $17 = \frac{45}{w} + 2$ **3**

50. HOT-AIR BALLOON A hot-air balloon owner charges \$150 for a one-hour ride. If he gave 6 rides on Saturday and 5 rides on Sunday, write and evaluate an expression to describe his total income for the weekend. (Lesson 1-4) **150(6 + 5); \$1650**

51. LOLLIPOPS A bag of lollipops contains 19 cherry, 13 grape, 8 sour apple, 15 strawberry, and 9 orange flavored lollipops. What is the probability of drawing a sour apple flavored lollipop? (Lesson 0-11) $\frac{1}{8}$

Find the perimeter of each figure. (Lesson 0-7)

52.

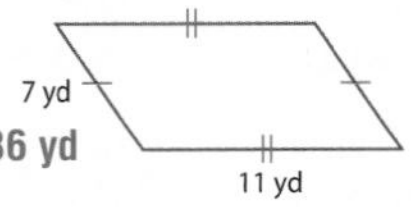

36 yd

53.

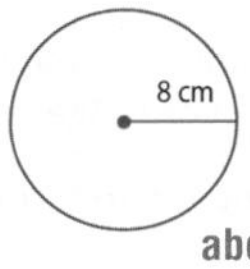

about 50.27 cm

54.

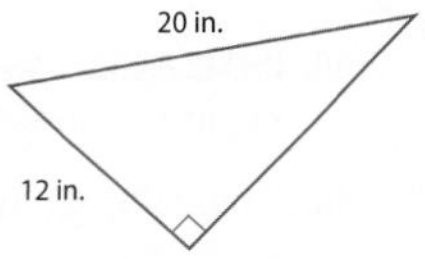

48 in.

Skills Review

Evaluate each expression.

55. 8^2 **64**

56. $(-6)^2$ **36**

57. $(2.5)^2$ **6.25**

58. $(-1.8)^2$ **3.24**

59. $(3 + 4)^2$ **49**

60. $(1 - 4)^2$ **9**

Differentiated Instruction BL

Extension Have students draw a graph that shows the height of water in a tub as it is filling, when the water is turned off, when a person gets into the water, then out, and as it is draining. Remind students to label the axes of their graphs. Have students exchange and discuss their graphs. See students' graphs.

LESSON 1-7 Functions

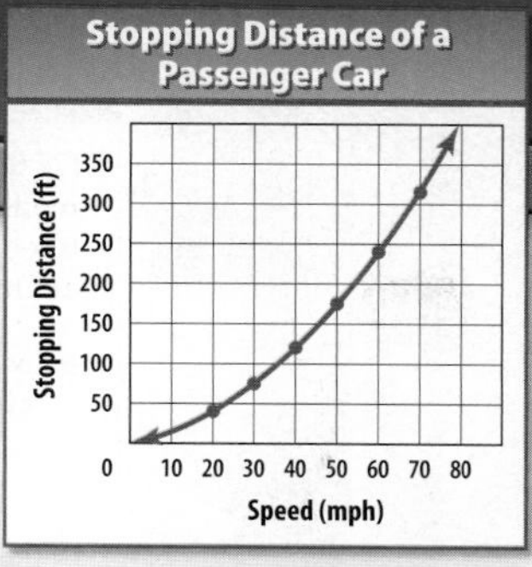

Then
- You solved equations with elements from a replacement set.

Now
1. Determine whether a relation is a function.
2. Find function values.

Why?
- The distance a car travels from when the brakes are applied to the car's complete stop is the stopping distance. This includes time for the driver to react. The faster a car is traveling, the longer the stopping distance. The stopping distance is a function of the speed of the car.

NewVocabulary
function
discrete function
continuous function
vertical line test
function notation
nonlinear function

Content Standards
AI.F.1, AI.F.2, AI.F.3, AI.F.4

1 Identify Functions

A **function** is a relationship between input and output. In a function, there is exactly one output for each input.

KeyConcept Function

Words A function is a relation in which each element of the domain is paired with *exactly* one element of the range.

Examples

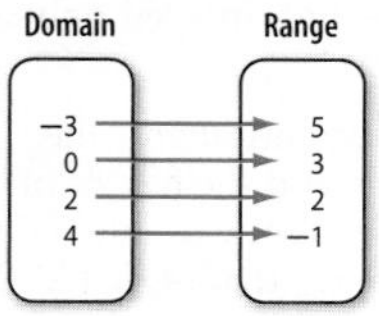

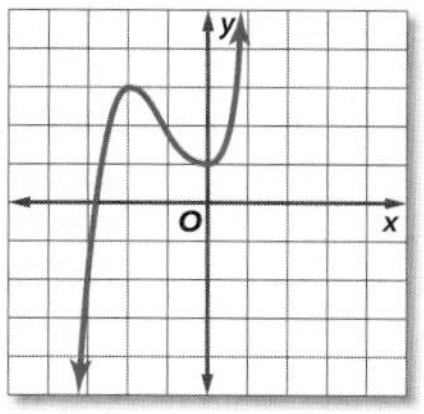

Example 1 Identify Functions

Determine whether each relation is a function. Explain.

a.

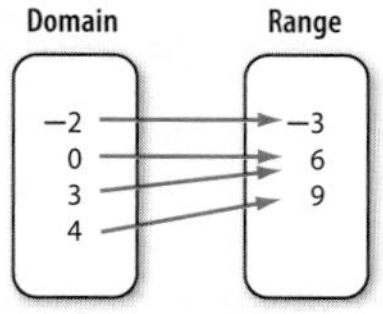

For each member of the domain, there is only one member of the range. So this mapping represents a function. It does not matter if more than one element of the domain is paired with one element of the range.

b.

Domain	1	3	5	1
Range	4	2	4	−4

The element 1 in the domain is paired with both 4 and −4 in the range. So, when x equals 1 there is more than one possible value for y. This relation is not a function.

GuidedPractice

1. $\{(2, 1), (3, -2), (3, 1), (2, -2)\}$ Not a function; sample answer: The value 2 in the domain is paired with 1 and −2.

1 Focus

VerticalAlignment

Before Lesson 1-7 Solve equations with elements from a replacement set.

Lesson 1-7 Determine whether a relation is a function. Find function values.

After Lesson 1-7 Use algebraic, tabular, graphical, and verbal descriptions of linear functions.

2 Teach

Scaffolding Questions

Have students read the **Why?** section of the lesson.

Ask:
- What does the ordered pair (30, 75) on the graph represent? the stopping distance of a car traveling at 30 mph
- About how many feet does it take to stop traveling at 60 mph? about 240 ft
- On what does the stopping distance depend? the speed of the car

Lesson 1-7 Resources

Resource	Approaching Level AL	On Level OL	Beyond Level BL	English Learners ELL
Teacher Edition	▪ Differentiated Instruction, p. 50	▪ Differentiated Instruction, p. 50	▪ Differentiated Instruction, pp. 50, 54	▪ Differentiated Instruction, p. 50
Chapter Resource Masters	▪ Study Guide and Intervention, pp. 43–44 ▪ Skills Practice, p. 45 ▪ Practice, p. 46 ▪ Word Problem Practice, p. 47	▪ Study Guide and Intervention, pp. 43–44 ▪ Skills Practice, p. 45 ▪ Practice, p. 46 ▪ Word Problem Practice, p. 47 ▪ Enrichment, p. 48	▪ Practice, p. 46 ▪ Word Problem Practice, p. 47 ▪ Enrichment, p. 48	▪ Study Guide and Intervention, pp. 43–44 ▪ Skills Practice, p. 45 ▪ Practice, p. 46 ▪ Word Problem Practice, p. 47
Other	▪ 5-Minute Check 1-7 ▪ Study Notebook ▪ Teaching Algebra with Manipulatives	▪ 5-Minute Check 1-7 ▪ Study Notebook ▪ Teaching Algebra with Manipulatives	▪ 5-Minute Check 1-7 ▪ Study Notebook	▪ 5-Minute Check 1-7 ▪ Study Notebook ▪ Teaching Algebra with Manipulatives

1 Identify Functions

Example 1 shows how to determine if a relation is a function. **Example 2** shows how to draw a graph of a real-world situation and how to determine whether the function is discrete or continuous. **Example 3** shows how to determine if an equation is a function by graphing and using the vertical line test.

Formative Assessment

Use the Guided Practice exercises after each Example to determine students' understanding of concepts.

Additional Example

1 Determine whether each relation is a function. Explain.

a.

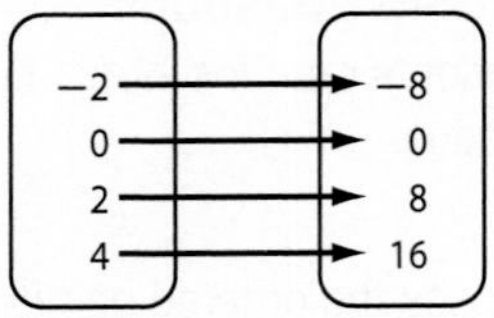

Function; each element of the domain is paired with exactly one member of the range.

b.

Domain	Range
−7	−12
−4	−9
2	3
5	0

Function; each element of the domain is paired with exactly one member of the range.

Additional Examples also in Interactive Classroom PowerPoint® Presentations

IWB Interactive White Board READY

A graph that consists of points that are not connected is a **discrete function**. A function graphed with a line or smooth curve is a **continuous function**.

Real-WorldLink

The Icehotel, located in the Arctic Circle in Sweden, is a hotel made out of ice. The ice insulates the igloo-like hotel so the temperature is at least −8°C.

Source: Icehotel

Lars Thulin/Johner Images/age fotostock

Real-World Example 2 Draw Graphs

ICE SCULPTING At an ice sculpting competition, each sculpture's height was measured to make sure that it was within the regulated height range of 0 to 6 feet. The measurements were as follows: Team 1, 4 feet; Team 2, 4.5 feet; Team 3, 3.2 feet; Team 4, 5.1 feet; Team 5, 4.8 feet.

a. Make a table of values showing the relation between the ice sculpting team and the height of their sculpture.

Team Number	1	2	3	4	5
Height (ft)	4	4.5	3.2	5.1	4.8

b. Determine the domain and range of the function.

The domain of the function is {1, 2, 3, 4, 5} because this set represents values of the independent variable. It is unaffected by the heights.

The range of the function is {4, 4.5, 3.2, 5.1, 4.8} because this set represents values of the dependent variable. This value depends on the team number.

c. Write the data as a set of ordered pairs. Then graph the data.

Use the table. The team number is the independent variable and the height of the sculpture is the dependent variable. Therefore, the ordered pairs are (1, 4), (2, 4.5), (3, 3.2), (4, 5.1), and (5, 4.8).

Because the team numbers and their corresponding heights cannot be between the points given, the points should not be connected.

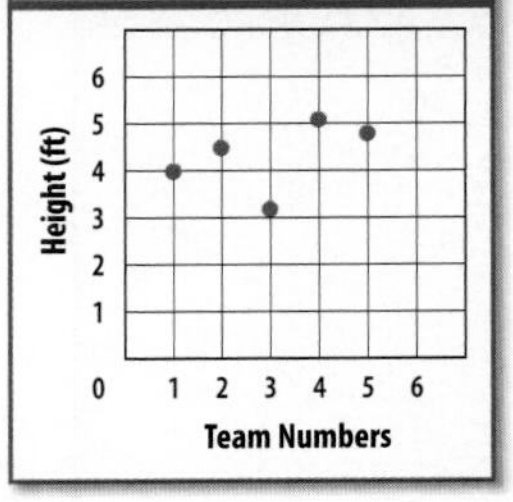

d. State whether the function is *discrete* or *continuous*. Explain your reasoning.

Because the points are not connected, the function is discrete.

GuidedPractice

2. A bird feeder will hold up to 3 quarts of seed. The feeder weighs 2.3 pounds when empty and 13.4 pounds when full. **2A–2D. See Ch. 1 Answer Appendix.**

A. Make a table that shows the bird feeder with 0, 1, 2, and 3 quarts of seed in it weighing 2.3, 6, 9.7, 13.4 pounds respectively.

B. Determine the domain and range of the function.

C. Write the data as a set of ordered pairs. Then graph the data.

D. State whether the function is *discrete* or *continuous*. Explain your reasoning.

Focus on Mathematical Content

Functions The set of x-values is the domain, and the corresponding set of y-values is the range. A function is a relation in which each element of the domain is paired with exactly one element of the range.

48 | Lesson 1-7 | Functions

StudyTip

Vertical Line Test One way to perform the vertical line test is to use a pencil. Place your pencil vertically on the graph and move from left to right. If the pencil passes over the graph in only one place, then the graph represents a function.

You can use the **vertical line test** to see if a graph represents a function. If a vertical line intersects the graph more than once, then the graph is not a function. Otherwise, the relation is a function.

Function

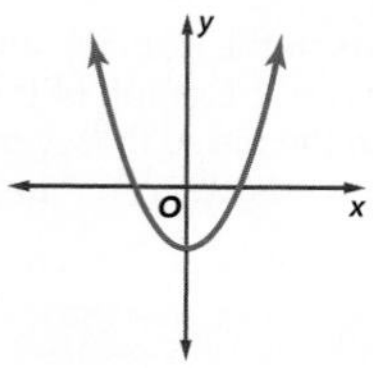

Not a Function

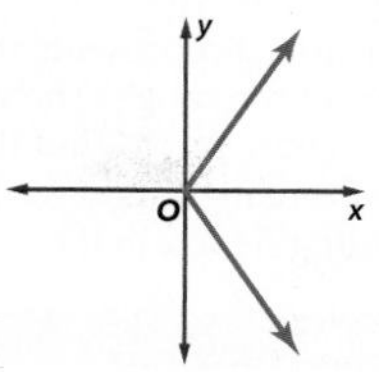

Function

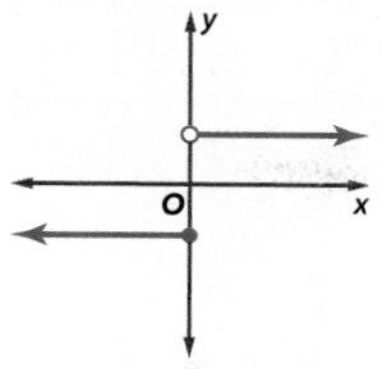

Recall that an equation is a representation of a relation. Equations can also represent functions. Every solution of the equation is represented by a point on a graph. The graph of an equation is the set of all its solutions, which often forms a curve or a line.

Example 3 Equations as Functions

Determine whether $-3x + y = 8$ is a function.

First make a table of values. Then graph the equation.

x	−1	0	1	2
y	5	4.5	11	14

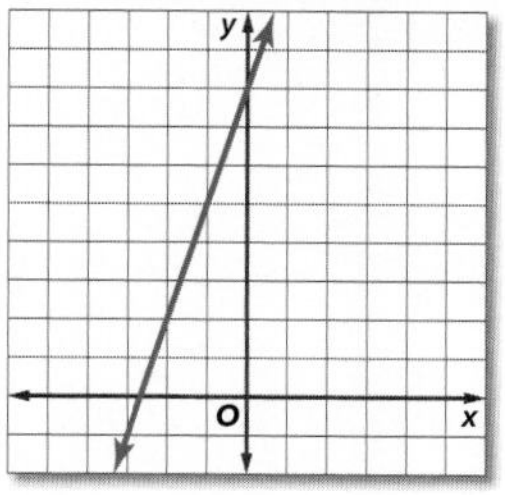

Connect the points with a smooth graph to represent all of the solutions of the equation. The graph is a line. To use the vertical line test, place a pencil at the left of the graph to represent a vertical line. Slowly move the pencil across the graph.

For any value of x, the vertical line passes through no more than one point on the graph. So, the graph and the equation represent a function.

GuidedPractice **Determine whether each relation is a function.**

3A. $4x = 8$ no

3B. $4x = y + 8$ yes

A function can be represented in different ways.

ConceptSummary Representations of a Function

Table

x	y
−2	1
0	−1
2	1

Mapping

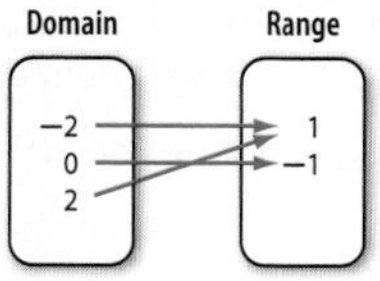

Equation

$f(x) = \frac{1}{2}x^2 - 1$

Graph

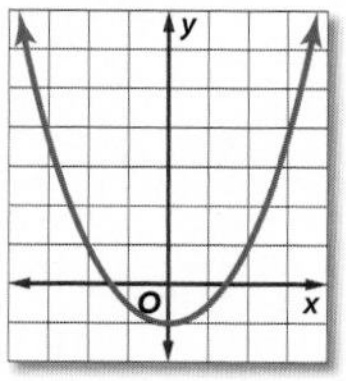

Teach with Tech

Interactive Whiteboard Display a graph on the board and demonstrate the vertical line test. Draw a vertical line and drag it from left to right across the graph. Show students that if there is any place where a vertical line intersects the graph at more than one point, the graph is not a function.

Additional Examples

2 **SCHOOL CAFETERIA** There are three lunch periods at a school. During the first period, 352 students eat. During the second period, 304 students eat. During the third period, 391 students eat.

a. Make a table showing the number of students for each of the three lunch periods.

Period	1	2	3
Number of Students	352	304	391

b. Determine the domain and range of the function.
D = {1, 2, 3}; R = {352, 304, 391}

c. Write the data as a set of ordered pairs. Then graph the data. {(1, 352), (2, 304), (3, 391)}

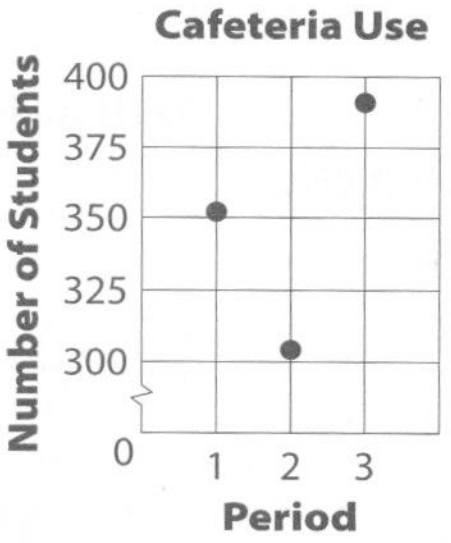

d. State whether the function is *discrete* or *continuous*. Explain your reasoning. Because the points are not connected, the function is discrete.

3 Determine whether $x = -2$ represents a function. not a function

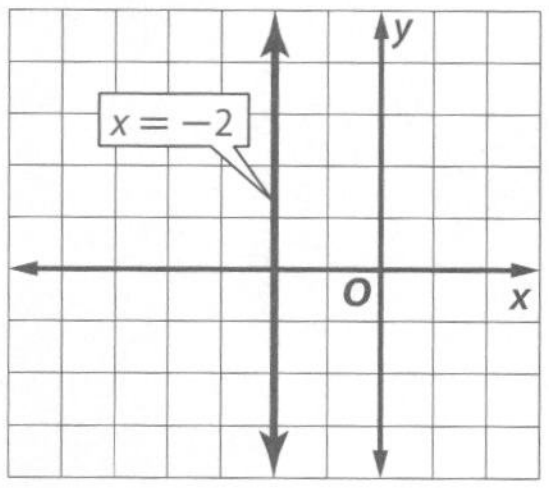

2 Find Function Values

Example 4 shows how to find the element in the range that corresponds to a given element in the domain of a linear function. **Example 5** shows how to find the element in the range that corresponds to a given element in the domain of a nonlinear function.

WatchOut!

Preventing Errors Function notation is sometimes difficult for students to comprehend. Stress that $f(x)$ does not mean "f times x."

Additional Examples

4 For $f(x) = 3x - 4$, find each value.

a. $f(4)$ 8

b. $f(-5)$ -19

5 If $h(t) = 1248 - 160t + 16t^2$, find each value.

a. $h(3)$ 912

b. $h(2z)$ $1248 - 320z + 64z^2$

StudyTip

Function Notation Functions are indicated by the symbol $f(x)$. This is read *f of x*. Other letters, such as g or h, can be used to represent functions.

2 Find Function Values

Equations that are functions can be written in a form called **function notation**. For example, consider $y = 3x - 8$.

Equation	Function Notation
$y = 3x - 8$	$f(x) = 3x - 8$

In a function, x represents the elements of the domain, and $f(x)$ represents the elements of the range. The graph of $f(x)$ is the graph of the equation $y = f(x)$. Suppose you want to find the value in the range that corresponds to the element 5 in the domain. This is written $f(5)$ and is read *f of 5*. The value $f(5)$ is found by substituting 5 for x in the equation.

PT

Example 4 Function Values

For $f(x) = -4x + 7$, find each value.

a. $f(2)$

$f(2) = -4(2) + 7$ — $x = 2$

$= -8 + 7$ — Multiply.

$= -1$ — Add.

b. $f(-3) + 1$

$f(-3) + 1 = [-4(-3) + 7] + 1$ — $x = -3$

$= 19 + 1$ — Simplify.

$= 20$ — Add.

GuidedPractice

For $f(x) = 2x - 3$, find each value.

4A. $f(1)$ **-1**

4B. $6 - f(5)$ **-1**

4C. $f(-2)$ **-7**

4D. $f(-1) + f(2)$ **-4**

A function with a graph that is not a straight line is a **nonlinear function**.

PT

Example 5 Nonlinear Function Values

If $h(t) = -16t^2 + 68t + 2$, find each value.

a. $h(4)$

$h(4) = -16(4)^2 + 68(4) + 2$ — Replace t with 4.

$= -256 + 272 + 2$ — Multiply.

$= 18$ — Add.

b. $2[h(g)]$

$2[h(g)] = 2[-16(g)^2 + 68(g) + 2]$ — Replace t with g.

$= 2(-16g^2 + 68g + 2)$ — Simplify.

$= -32g^2 + 136g + 4$ — Distributive Property

GuidedPractice

If $f(t) = 2t^3$, find each value.

5A. $f(4)$ **128**

5B. $3[f(t)] + 2$ **$6t^3 + 2$**

5C. $f(-5)$ **-250**

5D. $f(-3) - f(1)$ **-56**

DifferentiatedInstruction AL OL BL ELL

If students are visual learners,

Then as a preview of later chapters, have students represent several nonlinear functions graphically to share with the class. Nonlinear functions could include quadratic, absolute value, and exponential functions, with a variety of examples for each. The emphasis should be on the shape of the graphs.

Check Your Understanding

● = Step-by-Step Solutions begin on page R13.

Examples 1, 3 **Determine whether each relation is a function. Explain.**

1.

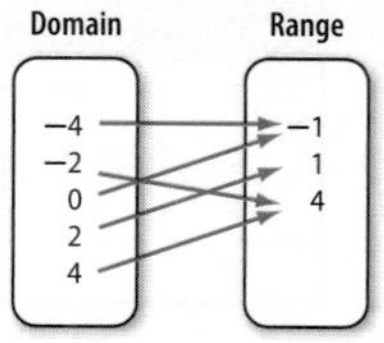

Yes; for each input there is exactly one output.

2.

Domain	Range
2	6
5	7
6	9
6	10

No; the domain value 6 is paired with both 9 and 10.

3. {(2, 2), (−1, 5), (5, 2), (2, −4)}

4. $y = \frac{1}{2}x - 6$

3. No; the domain value 2 is paired with 2 and −4.

4. Yes; the graph passes the vertical line test.

5.

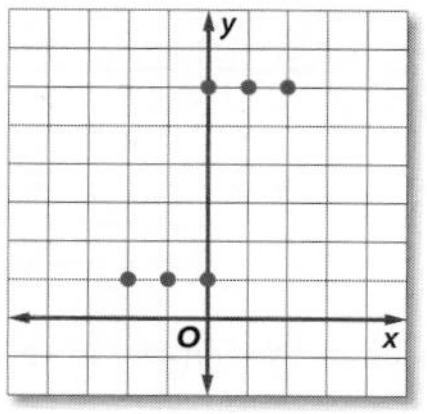

No; when $x = 0$, $y = 1$ and $y = 6$.

6.

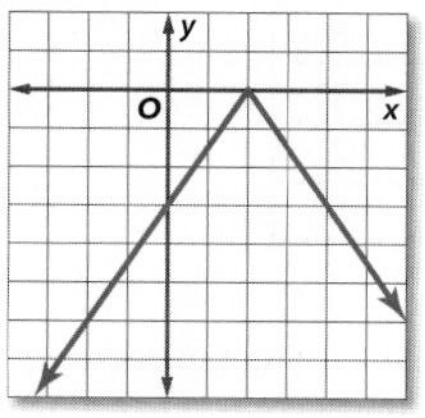

Yes; the graph passes the vertical line test.

7.

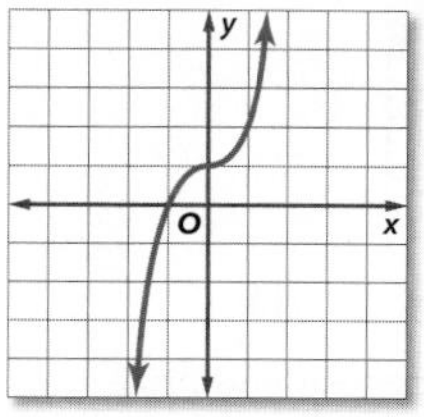

Yes; the graph passes the vertical line test.

8.

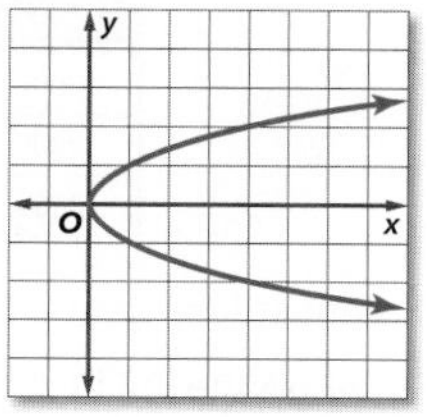

No; the graph does not pass the vertical line test.

Example 2

9. SCHOOL ENROLLMENT The table shows the total enrollment in U.S. public schools.

School Year	2004–05	2005–06	2006–07	2007–08
Enrollment (in thousands)	48,560	48,710	48,948	49,091

Source: *The World Almanac*

9a. {(0, 48,560), (1, 48,710), (2, 48,948), (3, 49,091)}

a. Write a set of ordered pairs representing the data in the table if x is the number of school years since 2004–2005.

b. Draw a graph showing the relationship between the year and enrollment. **9b. See margin.**

c. Describe the domain and range of the data. The domain is the school year and the range is the enrollment.

10. REASONING The cost of sending cell phone pictures is given by $y = 0.25x$, where x is the number of pictures that you send and y is the cost in dollars. **a–c. See margin.**

a. Write the equation in function notation. Interpret the function in terms of the context.

b. Find $f(5)$ and $f(12)$. What do these values represent?

c. Determine the domain and range of this function.

Examples 4–5 **If $f(x) = 6x + 7$ and $g(x) = x^2 - 4$, find each value.**

11. $f(-3)$ -11

12. $f(m)$ $6m + 7$

13. $f(r - 2)$ $6r - 5$

14. $g(5)$ 21

15. $g(a) + 9$ $a^2 + 5$

16. $g(-4t)$ $16t^2 - 4$

17. $f(q + 1)$ $6q + 13$

18. $f(2) + g(2)$ 19

19. $g(-b)$ $b^2 - 4$

connectED.mcgraw-hill.com

Students can access online resources such as **Personal Tutor**, **Extra Examples**, and **Self-Check Quizzes** at connectED.mcgraw.hill.com

3 Practice

Formative Assessment

Use Exercises 1–19 to check for understanding.

Use the chart at the bottom of the next page to customize assignments for your students.

Teaching the Process Standards

Reasoning Mathematically proficient students make sense of quantities and their relationships in problem situations. In Exercise 10, students interpret the function and function values. Encourage students to interpret each function that they use to represent a real-world situation.

Additional Answers

9b.

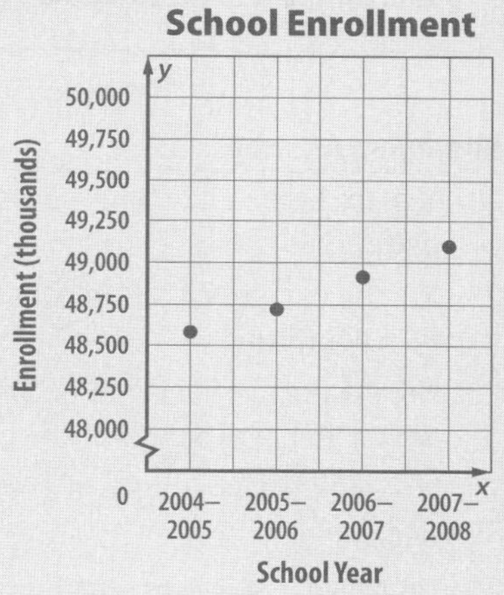

10a. If x represents the school year and $f(x)$ is the enrollment, then $f(x) = 0.25x$; \$1.25, \$3.00.

10b. $f(5) = 1.25$, $f(12) = 3$; It costs \$1.25 to send 5 photos and \$3.00 to send 12 photos.

10c. The domain is the number of pictures sent and the range is the cost.

connectED.mcgraw-hill.com

Teaching the Process Standards

Sense-Making Mathematically proficient students can explain correspondences between equations, verbal descriptions, tables, and graphs.

Perseverance Mathematically proficient students consider analogous problems, and try special cases and simpler forms of the original problem in order to gain insight. In Exercise 53, students may wish to evaluate the function for several values of b to look for a pattern.

WatchOut!

Error Analysis For Exercise 54, Corazon forgot that each point in the table would have to correspond to a point on the graph for them to be the same.

Additional Answers

20. Yes; for each input there is exactly one output.
21. No; the domain value 4 is paired with both 5 and 6.
22. No; the domain value −5 is paired with both 3 and 5.
23. Yes; for each input there is exactly one output.
24. No; when $x = 4$, $y = 4$ and $y = 6$.
25. Yes; the graph passes the vertical line test.

26b. **Home Value**

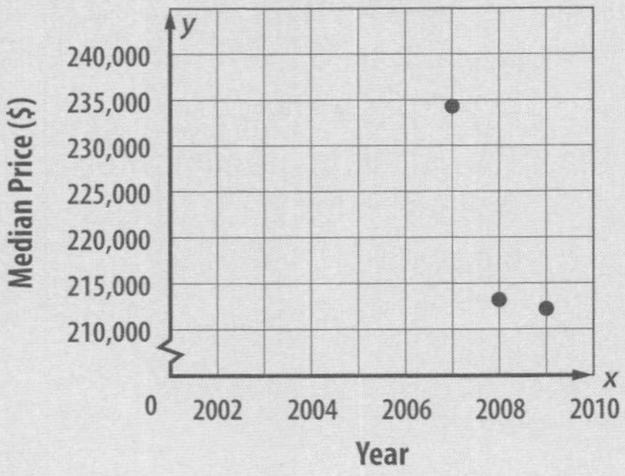

Practice and Problem Solving

Extra Practice is on page R1.

Example 1 **Determine whether each relation is a function. Explain.** **20–25. See margin.**

20.

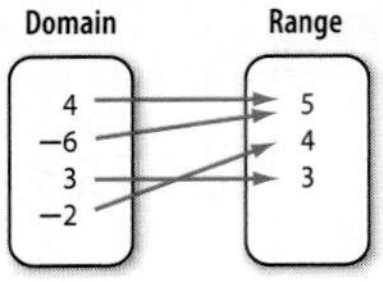

21.

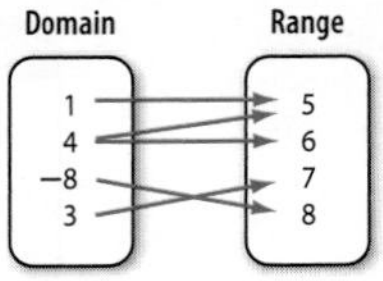

22.

Domain	Range
4	6
−5	3
6	−3
−5	5

23.

Domain	Range
−4	2
3	−5
4	2
9	−7
−3	−5

24.

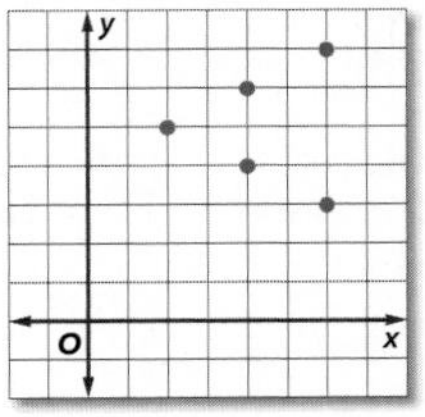

25.

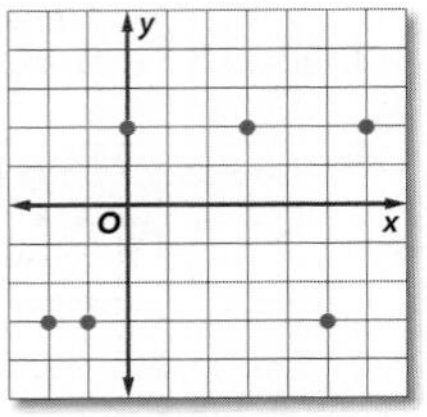

Example 2 **26.** **SENSE-MAKING** The table shows the median home prices in the United States, from 2007 to 2009.

Year	Median Home Price ($)
2007	234,300
2008	213,200
2009	212,200

a. Write a set of ordered pairs representing the data in the table. **a. {(2007, 234,300), (2008, 213,200), (2009, 212,200)}**

b. Draw a graph showing the relationship between the year and price. **See margin.**

c. What is the domain and range for this data? **The domain is the year. The range is the median home price.**

Example 3 **Determine whether each relation is a function.**

27. $\{(5, -7), (6, -7), (-8, -1), (0, -1)\}$ **yes**

28. $\{(4, 5), (3, -2), (-2, 5), (4, 7)\}$ **no**

29. $y = -8$ **yes**

30. $x = 15$ **no**

31. $y = 3x - 2$ **yes**

32. $y = 3x + 2y$ **yes**

Examples 4–5 **If $f(x) = -2x - 3$ and $g(x) = x^2 + 5x$, find each value.**

33. $f(-1)$ **−1**

34. $f(6)$ **−15**

35. $g(2)$ **14**

36. $g(-3)$ **−6**

37. $g(-2) + 2$ **−4**

38. $f(0) - 7$ **−10**

39. $f(4y)$ $-8y - 3$

40. $g(-6m)$ $36m^2 - 30m$

41. $f(c - 5)$ $-2c + 7$

42. $f(r + 2)$ $-2r - 7$

43. $5[f(d)]$ $-10d - 15$

44. $3[g(n)]$ $3n^2 + 15n$

B **45.** **EDUCATION** The average national math test scores $f(t)$ for 17-year-olds can be represented as a function of the national science scores t by $f(t) = 0.8t + 72$.

a. Graph this function. Interpret the function in terms of the context. **See Ch. 1 Answer Appendix.**

b. What is the science score that corresponds to a math score of 308? **295**

c. What is the domain and range of this function? **The domain is the set of science scores. The range is the set of math scores.**

Differentiated Homework Options

Level	Assignment	Two-Day Option	
AL Basic	20–44, 49, 50, 52, 54–75	21–43 odd, 54–59	20–44 even, 49, 50, 52, 60–75
OL Core	21–47 odd, 48–50, 52, 54–75	20–44, 56–59	45–50, 52, 54, 55, 60–75
BL Advanced	45–69, (optional: 70–75)		

Determine whether each relation is a function.

46.

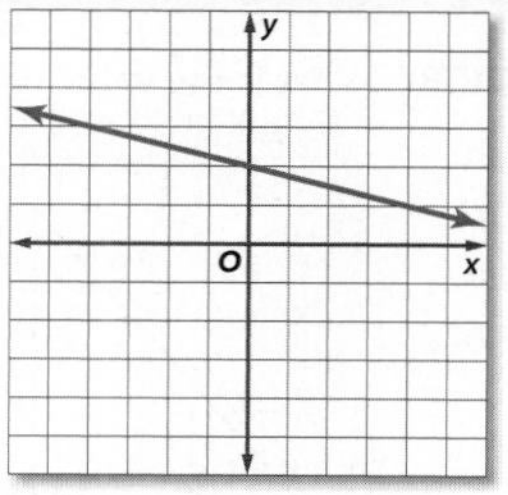

yes

47.

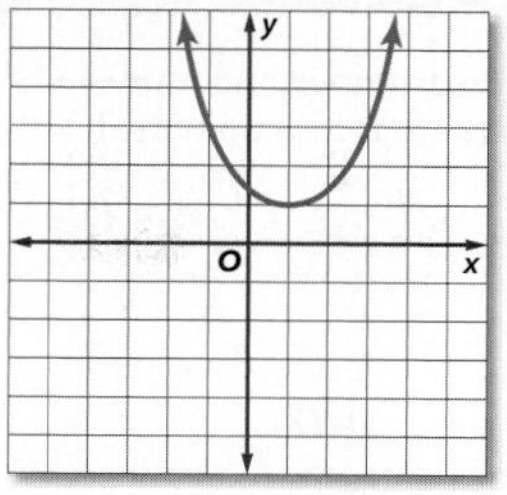

yes

48b. Sample answer:

h	7.50h$
3	$22.50
5	$37.50
2	$15
4	$30
6	$45

48. BABYSITTING Christina earns $7.50 an hour babysitting.

a. Write an algebraic expression to represent the money Christina will earn if she works h hours. **7.50h$**

b. Choose five values for the number of hours Christina can babysit. Create a table with h and the amount of money she will make during that time.

c. Use the values in your table to create a graph. **See Ch. 1 Answer Appendix.**

d. Does it make sense to connect the points in your graph with a line? Why or why not? **Yes, because they could pay Christina for partial hours that she worked.**

H.O.T. Problems Use Higher-Order Thinking Skills

49. OPEN ENDED Write a set of three ordered pairs that represent a function. Choose another display that represents this function. **See Ch. 1 Answer Appendix.**

C **50. REASONING** The set of ordered pairs {(0, 1), (3, 2), (3, −5), (5, 4)} represents a relation between x and y. Graph the set of ordered pairs. Determine whether the relation is a function. Explain. **See Ch. 1 Answer Appendix.**

51. CHALLENGE Consider $f(x) = -4.3x - 2$. Write $f(g + 3.5)$ and simplify by combining like terms. **$f(g + 3.5) = -4.3g - 17.05$**

52. WRITE A QUESTION A classmate graphed a set of ordered pairs and used the vertical line test to determine whether it was a function. Write a question to help her decide if the same strategy can be applied to a mapping.
Sample answer: Isn't a mapping another representation of a set of ordered pairs?

53. PERSEVERANCE If $f(3b - 1) = 9b - 1$, find one possible expression for $f(x)$.
Sample answer: $f(x) = 3x + 2$

54. ERROR ANALYSIS Corazon thinks $f(x)$ and $g(x)$ are representations of the same function. Maggie disagrees. Who is correct? Explain your reasoning.
Maggie; the graph represents $f(x) = -2x + 1$ and the table represents $g(x) = -2x - 1$.

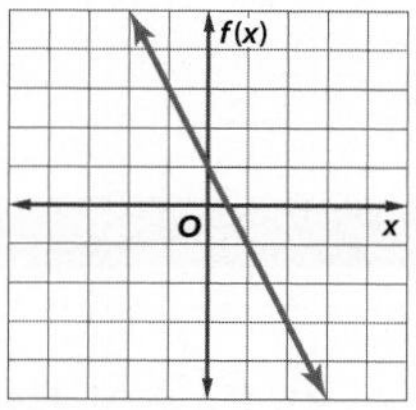

x	$g(x)$
−1	1
0	−1
1	−3
2	−5
3	−7

55. **WRITING IN MATH** How can you determine whether a relation represents a function? **See margin.**

Additional Answer

55. Sample answer: You can determine whether each element of the domain is paired with exactly one element of the range. For example, if given a graph, you could use the vertical line test; if a vertical line intersects the graph more than once, then the relation that the graph represents is not a function.

Study Guide and Intervention

AL OL ELL

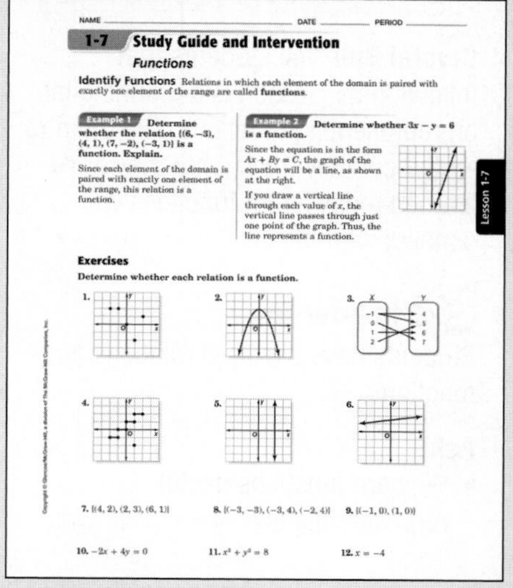

1-7 Study Guide and Intervention

Functions

Identify Functions Relations in which each element of the domain is paired with exactly one element of the range are called **functions**.

Exercises

Determine whether each relation is a function.

Practice

AL OL BL ELL

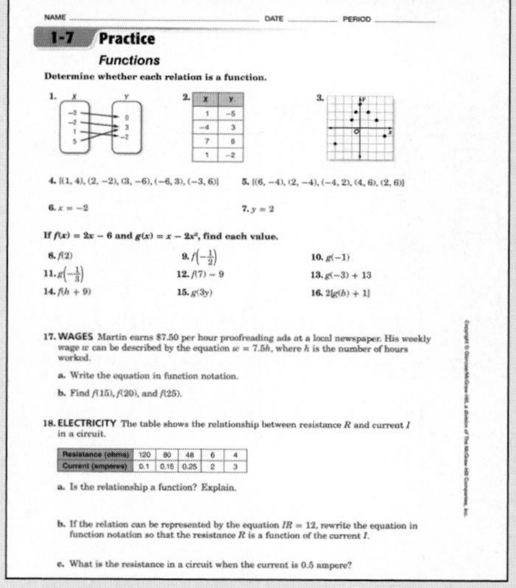

1-7 Practice

Functions

Determine whether each relation is a function.

Word Problem Practice

AL OL BL ELL

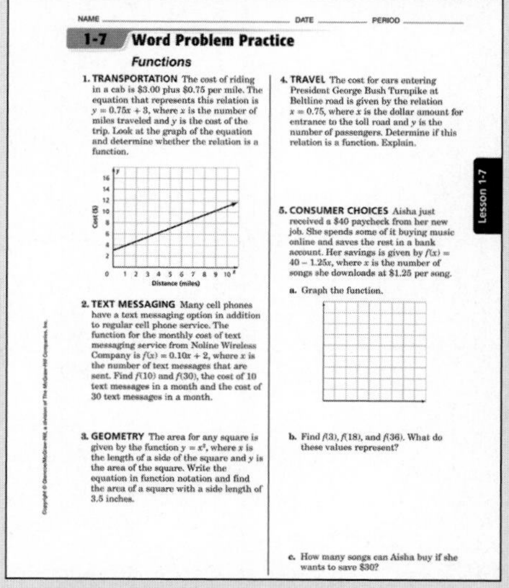

1-7 Word Problem Practice

Functions

Enrichment

OL BL

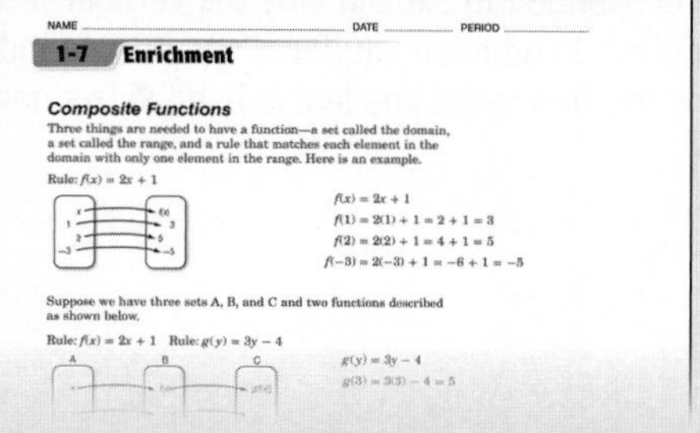

1-7 Enrichment

Composite Functions

4 Assess

Crystal Ball Tell students that following this lesson is a graphing lab on representing functions. Ask them to write how they think what they have learned today about functions will connect with the lab.

Follow-up

Students have explored relations and functions.

Ask:

- Why are functions useful representations? Sample answer: They pair exactly one element of the domain with exactly one element of the range. So, for every input, you get exactly one output. This is useful when representing certain relationships.

Additional Answers

63. $4(1.99) + 10(0.25) + 4(1.85) = 17.86$, so the cost is $17.86.

64. Sample answer: four times *y* plus two

65. Sample answer: two thirds times *x*

66. Sample answer: *a* squared times *b* plus 5

Standardized Test Practice

56. Which point on the number line represents a number whose square is less than itself? **B**

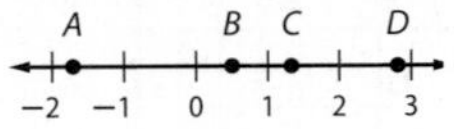

A *A* **C** *C*
B *B* **D** *D*

57. Determine which of the following relations is a function. **J**

F $\{(-3, 2), (4, 1), (-3, 5)\}$
G $\{(2, -1), (4, -1), (2, 6)\}$
H $\{(-3, -4), (-3, 6), (8, -2)\}$
J $\{(5, -1), (3, -2), (-2, -2)\}$

58. GEOMETRY What is the value of x? **A**

A 3 in.
B 4 in.
C 5 in.
D 6 in.

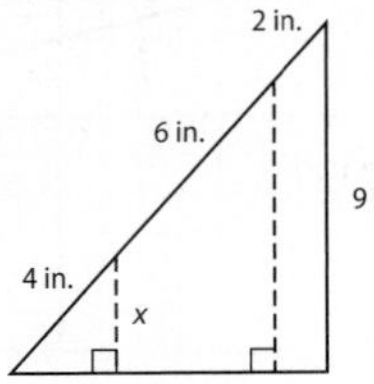

59. SHORT RESPONSE Camille made 16 out of 19 of her serves during her first volleyball game. She made 13 out of 16 of her serves during her second game. During which game did she make a greater percent of her serves? **her first game**

Spiral Review

Solve each equation. (Lesson 1-5)

60. $x = \frac{27 + 3}{10}$ **3**

61. $m = \frac{3^2 + 4}{7 - 5}$ $\frac{13}{2}$

62. $z = 32 + 4(-3)$ **20**

63. SCHOOL SUPPLIES The table shows the prices of some items Tom needs. If he needs 4 glue sticks, 10 pencils, and 4 notebooks, write and evaluate an expression to determine Tom's cost. (Lesson 1-4) **See margin.**

School Supplies Prices	
glue stick	$1.99
pencil	$0.25
notebook	$1.85

Write a verbal expression for each algebraic expression. (Lesson 1-1)

64. $4y + 2$

65. $\frac{2}{3}x$

66. $a^2b + 5$ **64–66. See margin.**

Find the volume of each rectangular prism. (Lesson 0-9)

67.

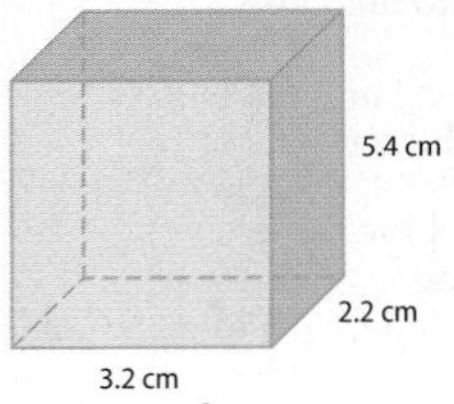

38.016 cm³

68.

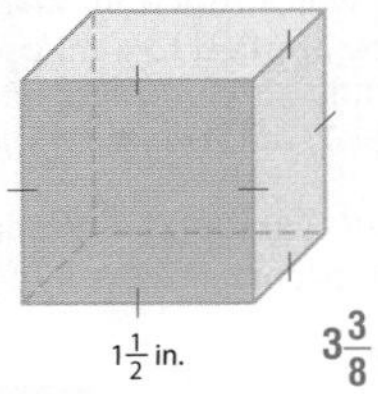

$3\frac{3}{8}$ **in³**

69.

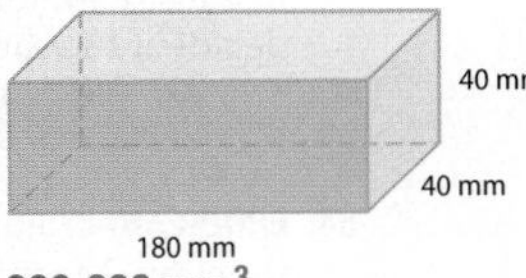

288,000 mm³

Skills Review

Evaluate each expression.

70. If $x = 3$, then $6x - 5 = \underline{?}$. **13**

71. If $n = -1$, then $2n + 1 = \underline{?}$. **−1**

72. If $p = 4$, then $3p + 4 = \underline{?}$. **16**

73. If $q = 7$, then $7q - 9 = \underline{?}$ **40**

74. If $k = -11$, then $4k + 6 = \underline{?}$ **−38**

75. If $y = 10$, then $8y - 15 = \underline{?}$ **65**

Differentiated Instruction BL

Extension Beyond-level students benefit from opportunities to learn independently. Students should be challenged to explain why the vertical line test can be used to tell whether a graph represents a function. In addition, students can pursue independent work to develop an understanding of how and why the *horizontal line* test is used in mathematics.

EXTEND 1-7

Graphing Technology Lab
Representing Functions

You can use TI-Nspire Technology to explore the different ways to represent a function.

Process Standards
PS.5

Activity

Graph $f(x) = 2x + 3$ on the TI-Nspire graphing calculator.

Step 1 Add a new **Graphs** page.

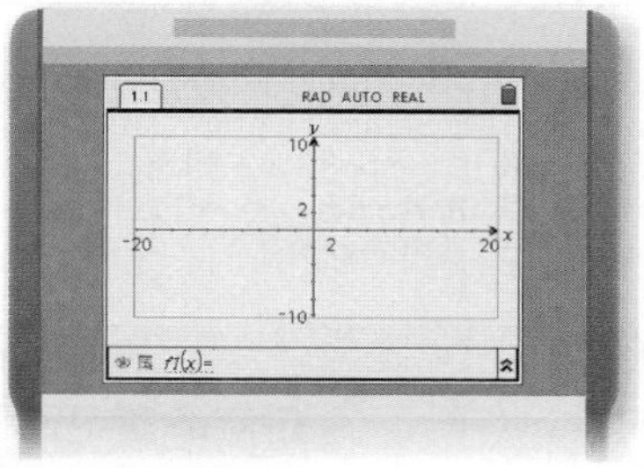

Step 2 Enter $2x + 3$ in the entry line.

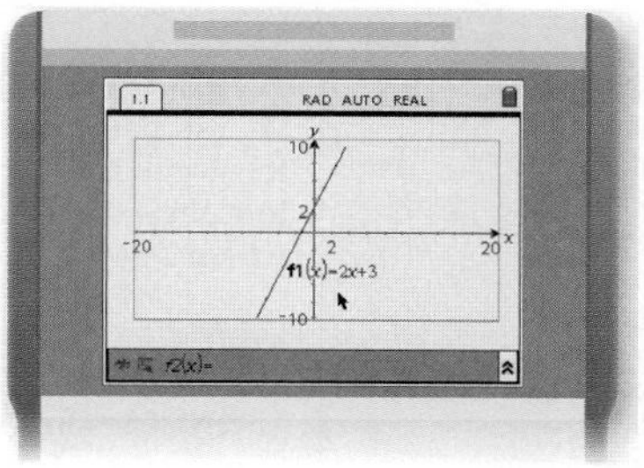

Represent the function as a table.

Step 3 Select the **Show Table** option from the **View** menu to add a table of values on the same display.

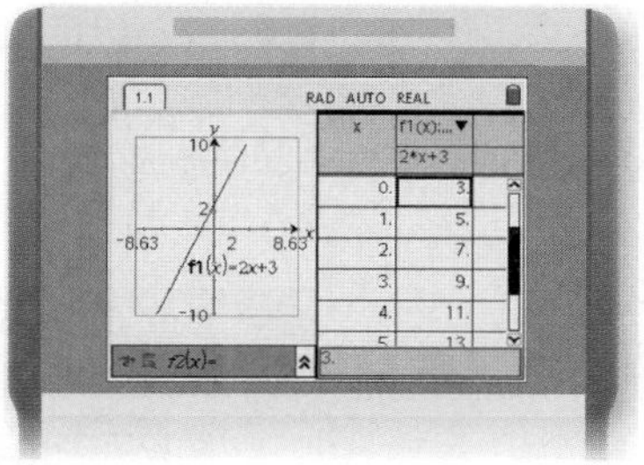

Step 4 Press **ctrl** and **tab** to toggle from the table to the graph. On the graph side, select the line and move it. Notice how the values in the table change.

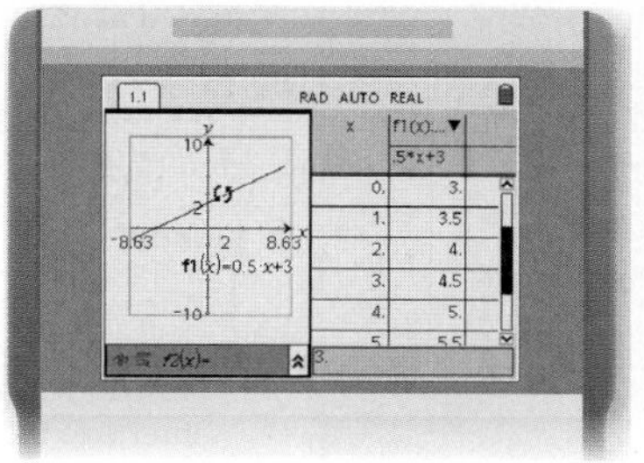

Analyze the Results

1–6. See Ch. 1 Answer Appendix.

TOOLS **Graph each function. Make a table of five ordered pairs that also represents the function.**

1. $g(x) = -x - 3$

2. $h(x) = \frac{1}{3}x + 3$

3. $f(x) = -\frac{1}{2}x - 5$

4. $f(x) = 3x - \frac{1}{2}$

5. $g(x) = -2x + 5$

6. $h(x) = \frac{1}{5}x + 4$

1 Focus

Objective Use technology to represent a function as a graph and as a table.

Materials for Each Group

- TI-Nspire Technology

Teaching Tip

The graphing calculator opens on the same screen as when it was turned off. Have students press the **home** button to begin the lab.

2 Teach

Working in Cooperative Groups

Have students of mixed abilities work in groups of two or three to complete the Activity and Exercises 1–2.

- For Step 3, students can also press **Ctrl** T to add a function table.
- For Step 4, students may need to follow these steps to grab the line and move it. After toggling to the graph, press **tab** until the pointer appears on the screen. Move the pointer to the line until an icon appears. Use the click button to grab the line. Use the navigating arrows to move it. Note: If students grab the line near an end, rotating circles will appear, and they can rotate the line. If they grab the line near the middle, a cross with arrows will appear, and they can translate the line.
- For Exercises 1–6, students can add pages to the open document. Press **Ctrl** I. Page 1.2 and so on will appear on the screen.

Practice Have students complete Exercises 3–6.

3 Assess

Formative Assessment

Use Exercise 5 to assess whether students know how to represent a function as a graph and as a table.

From Concrete to Abstract

Ask:

- How is the graph of a function related to the table of the function? Sample answer: The graph shows the direction and steepness of the line, while the table shows the coordinates of the points on the line for x and $f(x)$.

Teaching the Process Standards

Tools Mathematically proficient students consider the available tools when solving a mathematical problem. Developing a familiarity with technology will give students flexibility.

1 Focus

VerticalAlignment

Before Lesson 1-8 Represent relations. Interpret graphs as relations.

Lesson 1-8 Interpret key features of graphs of functions.

After Lesson 1-8 Interpret key features of graphs of quadratic, exponential, radical, and rational functions.

2 Teach

Scaffolding Questions

Have students read the **Why?** section of the lesson.

Ask:

- Why would a linear function not model the sale of video games well? Linear functions can only increase over time or decrease over time. Linear functions cannot increase and then decrease, or vice versa.
- Describe some points or areas on a graph of video game sales that might be of more interest to someone in the video game industry than other points. The high and low points on the graph and the far right side of the graph.

LESSON 1-8 Interpreting Graphs of Functions

Then

- You identified functions and found function values.

Now

1. Interpret intercepts, and symmetry of graphs of functions.
2. Interpret positive, negative, increasing, and decreasing behavior, extrema, and end behavior of graphs of functions.

Why?

- Sales of video games, including hardware, software, and accessories, have increased at times and decreased at other times over the years. Annual retail video game sales in the U.S. from 2000 to 2009 can be modeled by the graph of a nonlinear function.

NewVocabulary
intercept
x-intercept
y-intercept
line symmetry
positive
negative
increasing
decreasing
extrema
relative maximum
relative minimum
end behavior

Content Standards
AI.F.2, AI.F.4

Process Standards
PS.1

1 Interpret Intercepts and Symmetry

To interpret the graph of a function, estimate and interpret key features. The **intercepts** of a graph are points where the graph intersects an axis. The y-coordinate of the point at which the graph intersects the y-axis is called a **y-intercept**. Similarly, the x-coordinate of the point at which a graph intersects the x-axis is called an **x-intercept**.

PT

Real-World Example 1 Interpret Intercepts

PHYSICS **The graph shows the height y of an object as a function of time x. Identify the function as *linear* or *nonlinear*. Then estimate and interpret the intercepts.**

Height of Launched Object

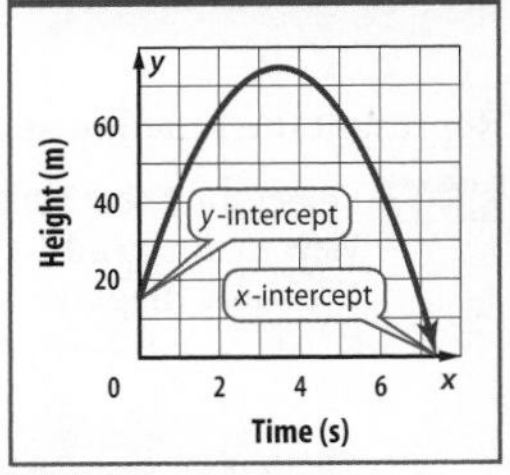

Linear or Nonlinear: Since the graph is a curve and not a line, the graph is nonlinear.

y-Intercept: The graph intersects the y-axis at about (0, 15), so the y-intercept of the graph is about 15. This means that the object started at an initial height of about 15 meters above the ground.

x-Intercept(s): The graph intersects the x-axis at about (7.4, 0), so the x-intercept is about 7.4. This means that the object struck the ground after about 7.4 seconds.

GuidedPractice

1. The graph shows the temperature y of a medical sample thawed at a controlled rate. Identify the function as *linear* or *nonlinear*. Then estimate and interpret the intercepts.
   See Ch. 1 Answer Appendix.

Controlled Thaw of Sample

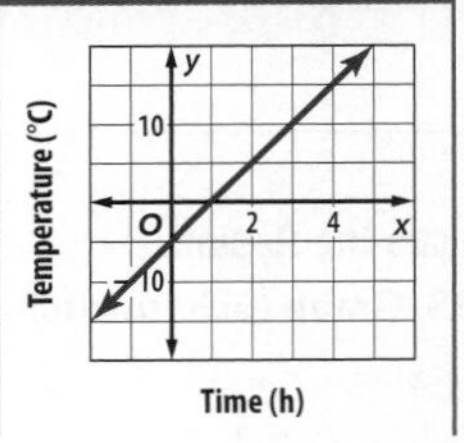

56 | Lesson 1-8

Lesson 1-8 Resources

Resource	Approaching Level AL	On Level OL	Beyond Level BL	English Learners ELL
Teacher Edition	▪ Differentiated Instruction, p. 57	▪ Differentiated Instruction, p. 57	▪ Differentiated Instruction, p. 61	▪ Differentiated Instruction, p. 57
Chapter Resource Masters	▪ Study Guide and Intervention, pp. 49–50 ▪ Skills Practice, p. 51 ▪ Practice, p. 52 ▪ Word Problem Practice, p. 53	▪ Study Guide and Intervention, pp. 49–50 ▪ Skills Practice, p. 51 ▪ Practice, p. 52 ▪ Word Problem Practice, p. 53 ▪ Enrichment, p. 54	▪ Practice, p. 52 ▪ Word Problem Practice, p. 53 ▪ Enrichment, p. 54	▪ Study Guide and Intervention, pp. 49–50 ▪ Skills Practice, p. 51 ▪ Practice, p. 52 ▪ Word Problem Practice, p. 53
Other	▪ 5-Minute Check 1-8 ▪ Study Notebook	▪ 5-Minute Check 1-8 ▪ Study Notebook	▪ 5-Minute Check 1-8 ▪ Study Notebook	▪ 5-Minute Check 1-8 ▪ Study Notebook

The graphs of some functions exhibit another key feature: symmetry. A graph possesses **line symmetry** in the y-axis or some other vertical line if each half of the graph on either side of the line matches exactly.

Real-World Example 2 Interpret Symmetry

PHYSICS An object is launched. The graph shows the height y of the object as a function of time x. Describe and interpret any symmetry.

The right half of the graph is the mirror image of the left half in approximately the line $x = 3.5$ between approximately $x = 0$ and $x = 7$.

In the context of the situation, the symmetry of the graph tells you that the time it took the object to go up is equal to the time it took to come down.

Height of Launched Object

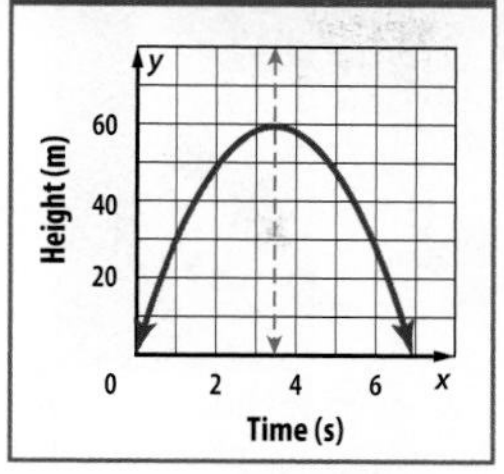

StudyTip

Symmetry The graphs of most real-world functions do not exhibit symmetry over the entire domain. However, many have symmetry over smaller portions of the domain that are worth analyzing.

GuidedPractice

2. Describe and interpret any symmetry exhibited by the graph in Guided Practice 1. **There is no vertical line symmetry.**

2 Interpret Extrema and End Behavior

Interpreting a graph also involves estimating and interpreting where the function is increasing, decreasing, positive, or negative, and where the function has any extreme values, either high or low.

KeyConcepts Positive, Negative, Increasing, Decreasing, Extrema, and End Behavior

A function is **positive** where its graph lies *above* the x-axis, and **negative** where its graph lies *below* the x-axis.

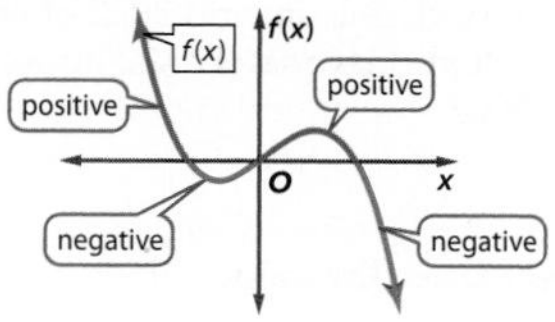

A function is **increasing** where the graph goes *up* and **decreasing** where the graph goes *down* when viewed from left to right.

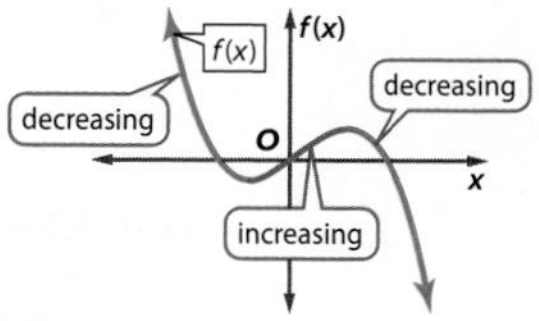

The points shown are the locations of relatively high or low function values called **extrema**. Point A is a **relative minimum**, since no other nearby points have a lesser y-coordinate. Point B is a **relative maximum**, since no other nearby points have a greater y-coordinate.

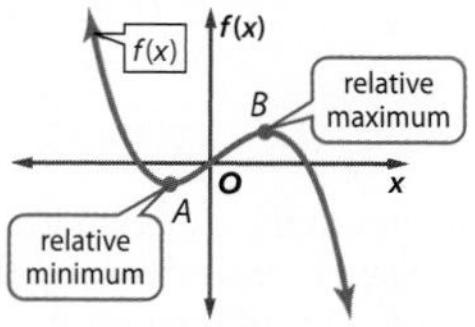

End behavior describes the values of a function at the positive and negative extremes in its domain.

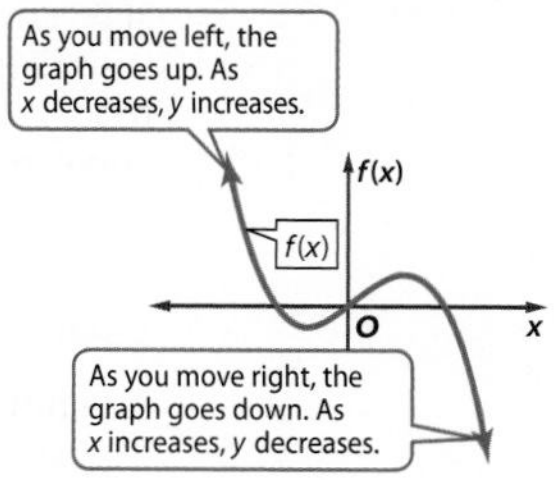

StudyTip

End Behavior The end behavior of some graphs can be described as approaching a specific y-value. In this case, a portion of the graph looks like a horizontal line.

DifferentiatedInstruction AL OL ELL

If students are having trouble interpreting key features of graphs,

Then have students work together discussing examples in this lesson. You may also want them to complete some exercises cooperatively.

1 Interpret Intercepts and Symmetry

Example 1 shows how to identify the graph of a function as linear or nonlinear and interpret the intercepts. **Example 2** shows how to identify and interpret any symmetry exhibited by the graph of a function.

Formative Assessment

Use the Guided Practice exercises after each Example to determine students' understanding of concepts.

Additional Example

1 **COLLEGE** The graph shows the cost at a community college y as a function of the number of credit hours taken x. Identify the function as *linear* or *nonlinear.* Then estimate and interpret the intercepts of the graph of the function

College Costs

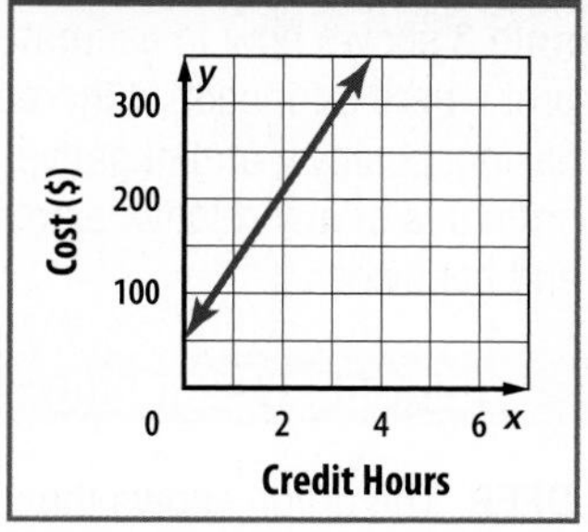

Linear; no x-intercept, the cost of college is never 0; y-intercept ≈ 50, there is an additional fee of $50 added to the cost charged per credit hour taken.

Additional Examples also in Interactive Classroom PowerPoint® Presentations

IWB Interactive White Board READY

Additional Example

2 **MANUFACTURING** The graph shows the cost y to manufacture x units of a product. Describe and interpret any symmetry.

Manufacturing Costs

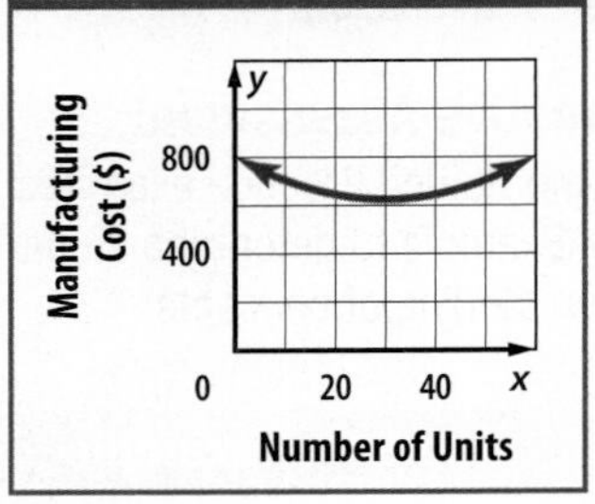

The right half of the graph is the mirror image of the left half in approximately the line $x = 30$. The symmetry of the graph tells you that the cost to produce n more or n less than 30 units will be the same.

2 Interpret Extrema and End Behavior

Example 3 shows how to estimate and interpret where a function is increasing, decreasing, positive, and negative, the x-coordinates of any relative extrema, and end behavior.

Additional Example

3 **DEER** The graph shows the population y of deer x years after the animals are introduced on an island. Estimate and interpret where the function is positive, negative, increasing, and decreasing, the x-coordinates of any relative extrema, and the end behavior of the graph.

Deer Population

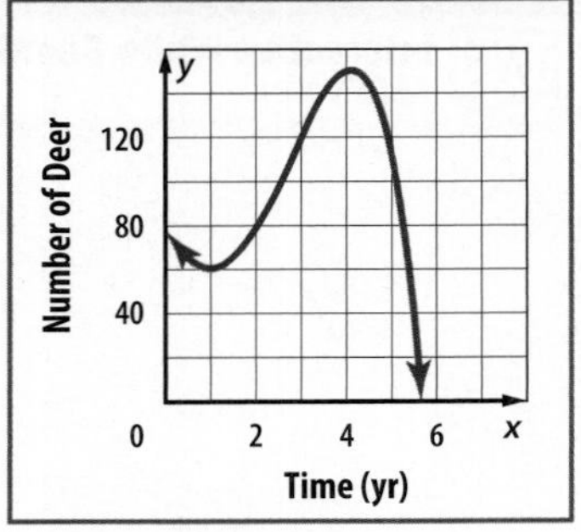

See bottom margin.

Real-WorldLink

The first successful commercially sold portable video game system was released in 1989 and sold for $120.

Source: *PCWorld*

StudyTip

Constant A function is *constant* where the graph does not go up or down as the graph is viewed from left to right.

Real-World Example 3 Interpret Extrema and End Behavior

VIDEO GAMES **U.S. retail sales of video games from 2000 to 2009 can be modeled by the function graphed at the right. Estimate and interpret where the function is positive, negative, increasing, and decreasing, the x-coordinates of any relative extrema, and the end behavior of the graph.**

U.S. Video Games Sales

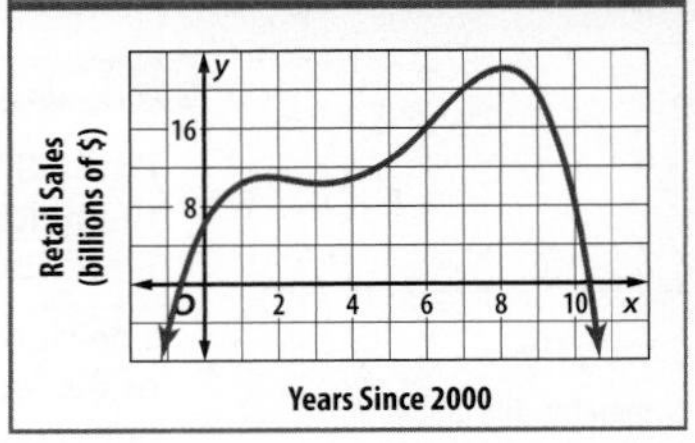

Positive: between about $x = -0.6$ and $x = 10.4$

Negative: for about $x < -0.6$ and $x > 10.4$

This means that there were positive sales between about 2000 and 2010, but the model predicts negative sales after about 2010, indicating the unlikely collapse of the industry.

Increasing: for about $x < 1.5$ and between about $x = 3$ and $x = 8$

Decreasing: between about $x = 2$ and $x = 3$ and for about $x > 8$

This means that sales increased from about 2000 to 2002, decreased from 2002 to 2003, increased from 2003 to 2008, and have been decreasing since 2008.

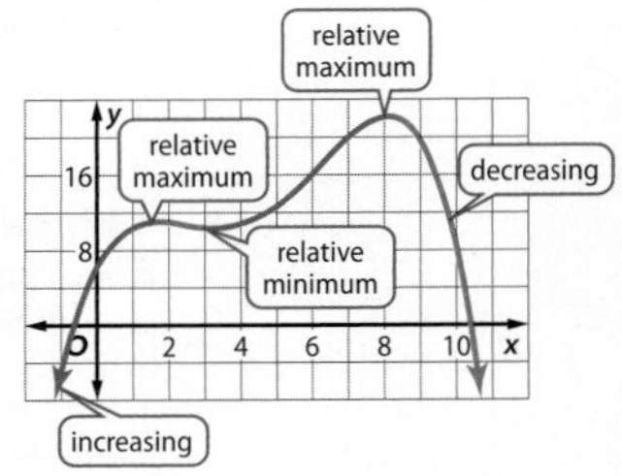

Relative Maximums: at about $x = 1.5$ and $x = 8$

Relative Minimum: at about $x = 3$

The extrema of the graph indicate that the industry experienced two relative peaks in sales during this period: one around 2002 of approximately $10.5 billion and another around 2008 of approximately $22 billion. A relative low of $10 billion in sales came in about 2003.

End Behavior:
As x increases or decreases, the value of y decreases.

The end behavior of the graph indicates negative sales several years prior to 2000 and several years after 2009, which is unlikely. This graph appears to only model sales well between 2000 and 2009 and can only be used to predict sales in 2010.

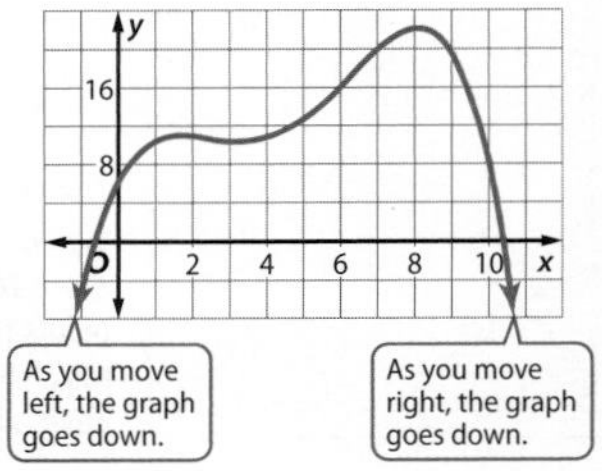

GuidedPractice

3. Estimate and interpret where the function graphed in Guided Practice 1 is positive, negative, increasing, or decreasing, the x-coordinate of any relative extrema, and the end behavior of the graph. **See Ch. 1 Answer Appendix.**

Additional Answer (Additional Example)

3. Nonlinear; the y-intercept is about 75, indicating an initial population of 75 deer. The x-intercept of about 5.6 indicates that the population died out about 5.6 years after the deer were introduced to the island. The graph has no line symmetry. The population decreased the first year, increased between year 1 and year 4, and then decreased to 0 after year 4. The population experienced a relative low at the end of year 1 and a relative high at then end of year 4. As the years passed, the population decreased to 0.

Check Your Understanding

◯ = Step-by-Step Solutions begin on page R13.

Examples 1–3 **SENSE-MAKING** Identify the function graphed as *linear* or *nonlinear*. Then estimate and interpret the intercepts of the graph, any symmetry, where the function is positive, negative, increasing, and decreasing, the x-coordinate of any relative extrema, and the end behavior of the graph. **1–3. See Ch. 1 Answer Appendix.**

1.

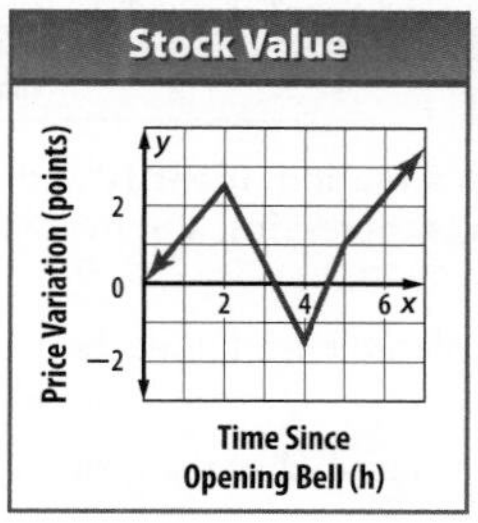

2.

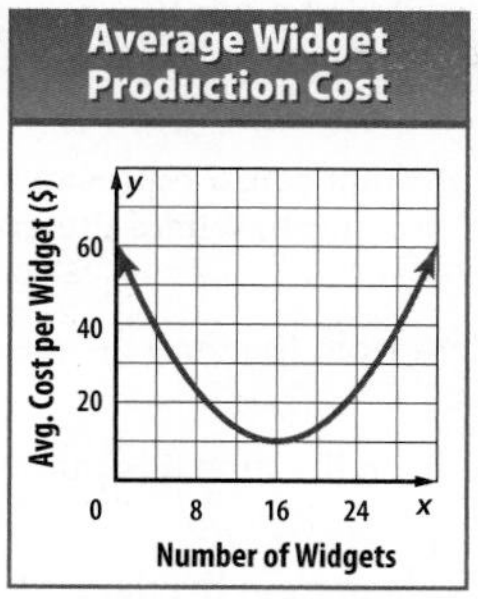

3.

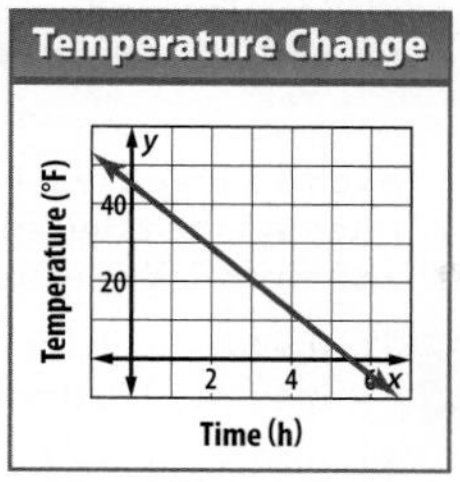

Practice and Problem Solving

Extra Practice is on page R1.

Examples 1–3 **SENSE-MAKING** Identify the function graphed as *linear* or *nonlinear*. Then estimate and interpret the intercepts of the graph, any symmetry, where the function is positive, negative, increasing, and decreasing, the x-coordinate of any relative extrema, and the end behavior of the graph. **4–9. See Ch. 1 Answer Appendix.**

4.

5.

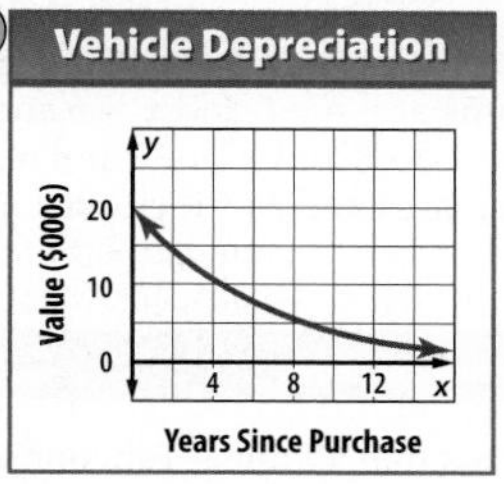

6.

7.

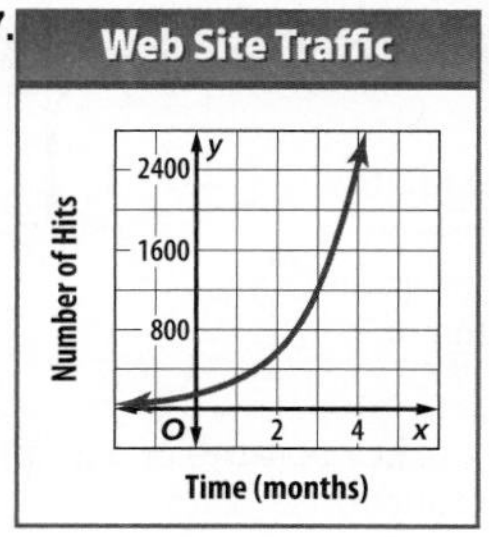

8.

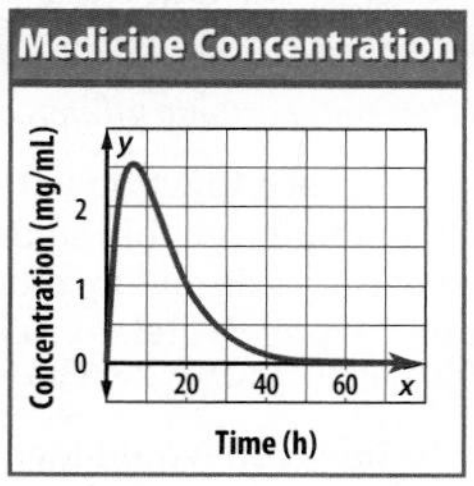

9.

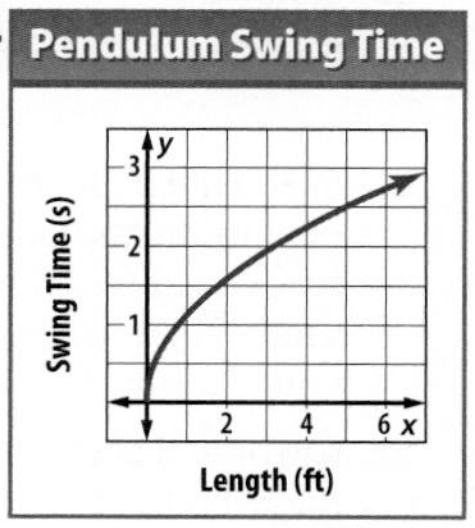

Differentiated Homework Options

Level	Assignment	Two-Day Option	
AL Basic	4–9, 18, 20–38	5–9 odd, 23–26	4–8 even, 18, 20–24, 27–38
OL Core	5–9 odd, 10–14, 18, 23–38	4–9, 23–26	10–14, 18, 27–38
BL Advanced	4–34, (optional 35–38)		

3 Practice

Formative Assessment

Use Exercises 1–3 to check for understanding.

Use the chart at the bottom of this page to customize assignments for your students.

Teach with Tech

Interactive Whiteboard Display graphs of linear, quadratic, and polynomial functions on the board. Use the highlighter tool to show intercepts, symmetry, where the graph is positive, negative, increasing, and decreasing, and end behavior.

Teaching the Process Standards

Sense-Making Mathematically proficient students start by explaining to themselves the meaning of a problem. Encourage students to develop a habit of asking themselves about each key feature of the graph of a function.

Study Guide and Intervention

AL OL ELL

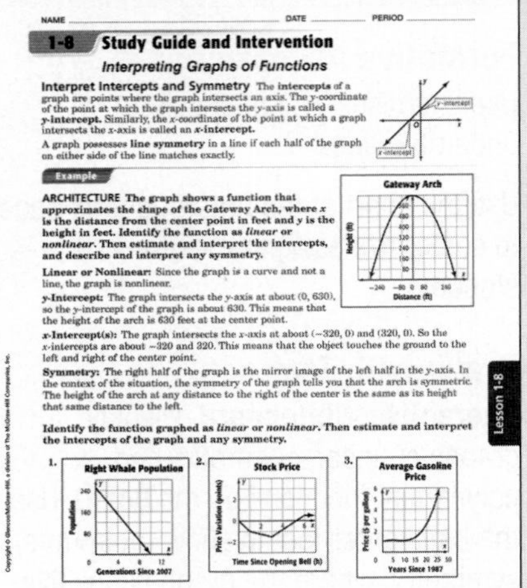
NAME ______ DATE ______ PERIOD ______

1-8 Study Guide and Intervention

Interpreting Graphs of Functions

Interpret Intercepts and Symmetry The intercepts of a graph are points where the graph intersects an axis. The y-coordinate of the point at which the graph intersects the y-axis is called a **y-intercept.** Similarly, the x-coordinate of the point at which a graph intersects the x-axis is called an **x-intercept.**

A graph possesses **line symmetry** in a line if each half of the graph on either side of the line matches exactly.

Example

ARCHITECTURE The graph shows a function that approximates the shape of the Gateway Arch, where x is the distance from the center point in feet and y is the height in feet. Identify the function as *linear* or *nonlinear*. Then estimate and interpret the intercepts, and describe and interpret any symmetry.

Linear or Nonlinear: Since the graph is a curve and not a line, the graph is nonlinear.

y-Intercept: The graph intersects the y-axis at about (0, 630), so the y-intercept of the graph is about 630. This means that the height of the arch is 630 feet at the center point.

x-Intercept(s): The graph intersects the x-axis at about (−320, 0) and (320, 0). So the x-intercepts are about −320 and 320. This means that the object touches the ground to the left and right of the center point.

Symmetry: The right half of the graph is the mirror image of the left half in the y-axis. In the context of the situation, the symmetry of the graph tells you that the arch is symmetric. The height of the arch at any distance to the right of the center is the same as its height that same distance to the left.

Identify the function graphed as *linear* or *nonlinear*. Then estimate and interpret the intercepts of the graph and any symmetry.

1. Right Whale Population 2. Stock Price 3. Average Gasoline Price

Practice

AL OL BL ELL

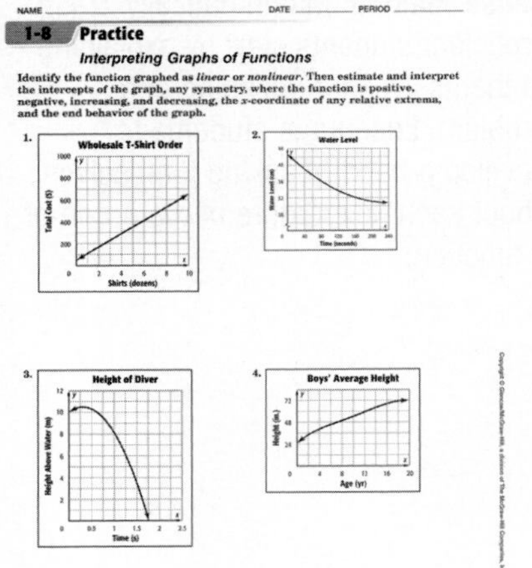
NAME ______ DATE ______ PERIOD ______

1-8 Practice

Interpreting Graphs of Functions

Identify the function graphed as *linear* or *nonlinear*. Then estimate and interpret the intercepts of the graph, any symmetry, where the function is positive, negative, increasing, and decreasing, the x-coordinate of any relative extrema, and the end behavior of the graph.

1. Wholesale T-Shirt Order 2. Water Level

3. Height of Diver 4. Boys' Average Height

Word Problem Practice

AL OL BL ELL

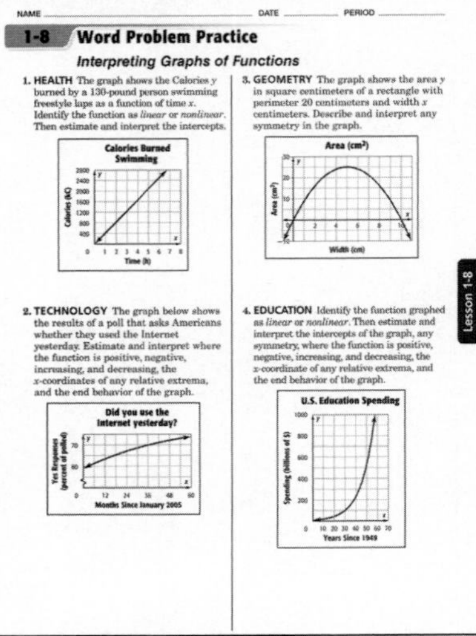
NAME ______ DATE ______ PERIOD ______

1-8 Word Problem Practice

Interpreting Graphs of Functions

1. HEALTH The graph shows the Calories y burned by a 130-pound person swimming freestyle laps as a function of time x. Identify the function as *linear* or *nonlinear*. Then estimate and interpret the intercepts.

2. TECHNOLOGY The graph below shows the results of a poll that asks Americans whether they used the Internet yesterday. Estimate and interpret where the function is positive, negative, increasing, and decreasing, the x-coordinates of any relative extrema, and the end behavior of the graph.

3. GEOMETRY The graph shows the area y in square centimeters of a rectangle with perimeter 20 centimeters and width x centimeters. Describe and interpret any symmetry in the graph.

4. EDUCATION Identify the function graphed as *linear* or *nonlinear*. Then estimate and interpret the intercepts of the graph, any symmetry, where the function is positive, negative, increasing, and decreasing, the x-coordinate of any relative extrema, and the end behavior of the graph.

B 10. **FERRIS WHEEL** At the beginning of a Ferris wheel ride, a passenger cart is located at the same height as the center of the wheel. The position y in feet of this cart relative to the center t seconds after the ride starts is given by the function graphed at the right. Identify and interpret the key features of the graph. (*Hint:* Look for a pattern in the graph to help you describe its end behavior.) **See Ch. 1 Answer Appendix.**

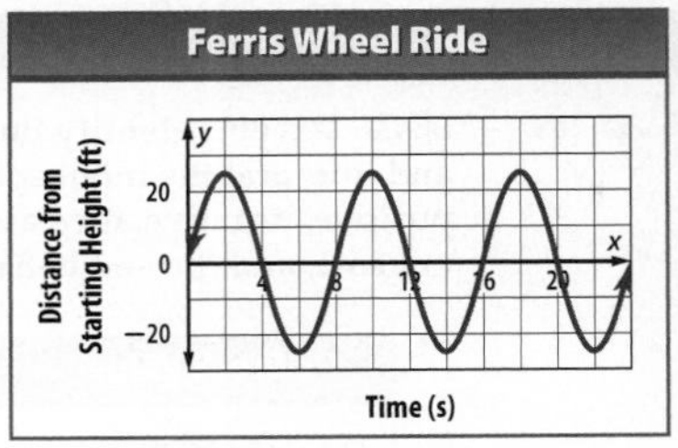

Sketch a graph of a function that could represent each situation. Identify and interpret the intercepts of the graph, where the graph is increasing and decreasing, and any relative extrema. 11–13. See Ch. 1 Answer Appendix.

11. the height of a corn plant from the time the seed is planted until it reaches maturity 120 days later

12. the height of a football from the time it is punted until it reaches the ground 2.8 seconds later

13. the balance due on a car loan from the date the car was purchased until it was sold 4 years later

Sketch graphs of functions with the following characteristics. 14–17. See Ch. 1 Answer Appendix.

14. The graph is linear with an x-intercept at -2. The graph is positive for $x < -2$, and negative for $x > -2$.

C 15. A nonlinear graph has x-intercepts at -2 and 2 and a y-intercept at -4. The graph has a relative minimum of -4 at $x = 0$. The graph is decreasing for $x < 0$ and increasing for $x > 0$.

16. A nonlinear graph has a y-intercept at 2, but no x-intercepts. The graph is positive and increasing for all values of x.

17. A nonlinear graph has x-intercepts at -8 and -2 and a y-intercept at 3. The graph has relative minimums at $x = -6$ and $x = 6$ and a relative maximum at $x = 2$. The graph is positive for $x < -8$ and $x > -2$ and negative between $x = -8$ and $x = -2$. As x decreases, y increases and as x increases, y increases.

20. True; a function can have no more than one y-intercept. If a graph has more than one y-intercept, then it is not the graph of a function. A function can also have no y-intercept if it is not defined for $x = 0$.

H.O.T. Problems Use Higher-Order Thinking Skills

18. **CRITIQUE** Katara thinks that all linear functions have exactly one x-intercept. Desmond thinks that a linear function can have at most one x-intercept. Is either of them correct? Explain your reasoning. **See margin.**

19. As x increases or decreases, y approaches 0.

19. **CHALLENGE** Describe the end behavior of the graph shown.

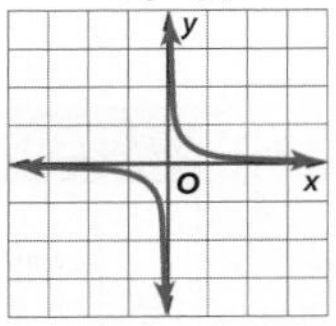

20. **REASONING** Determine whether the following statement is *true* or *false*. Explain.

Functions have at most one y-intercept.

21. **OPEN ENDED** Sketch the graph of a function with one relative maximum and one relative minimum that could represent a real-world function. Label each axis and include appropriate units. Then identify and interpret the relative extrema of your graph. **21, 22. See Ch. 1 Answer Appendix.**

22. **WRITING IN MATH** Describe how you would identify the key features of a graph described in this lesson using a table of values for a function.

Enrichment

OL BL

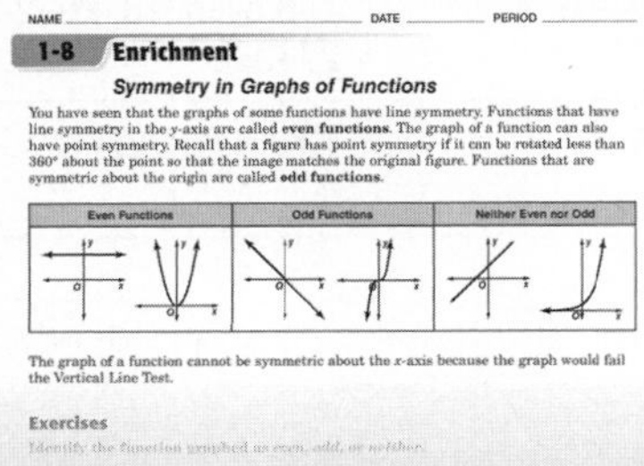
NAME ______ DATE ______ PERIOD ______

1-8 Enrichment

Symmetry in Graphs of Functions

You have seen that the graphs of some functions have line symmetry. Functions that have line symmetry in the y-axis are called **even functions.** The graph of a function can also have point symmetry. Recall that a figure has point symmetry if it can be rotated less than 360° about the point so that the image matches the original figure. Functions that are symmetric about the origin are called **odd functions.**

Even Functions	Odd Functions	Neither Even nor Odd

The graph of a function cannot be symmetric about the x-axis because the graph would fail the Vertical Line Test.

Exercises

Standardized Test Practice

23. Which sentence best describes the end behavior of the function shown? C

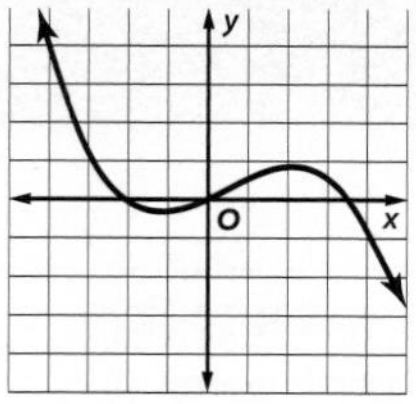

A As x increases, y increases, and as x decreases, y increases.

B As x increases, y increases, and as x decreases, y decreases.

C As x increases, y decreases, and as x decreases, y increases.

D As x increases, y decreases, and as x decreases, y decreases.

24. Which illustrates the Transitive Property of Equality? G

F If $c = 1$, then $c \cdot \frac{1}{c} = 1$.

G If $c = d$ and $d = f$, then $c = f$.

H If $c = d$, then $d = c$.

J If $c = d$ and $d = c$, then $c = 1$.

25. Simplify the expression $5d(7 - 3) - 16d + 3 \cdot 2d$. A

A $10d$ C $21d$

B $14d$ D $25d$

26. What is the probability of selecting a red card or an ace from a standard deck of cards? H

F $\frac{1}{26}$ G $\frac{1}{2}$ H $\frac{7}{13}$ J $\frac{15}{26}$

Spiral Review

Determine whether each relation is a function. (Lesson 1-7)

27. yes

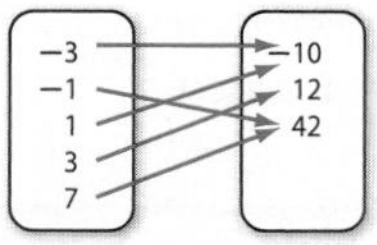

28. $\{(0, 2), (3, 5), (0, -1), (-2, 4)\}$ no

29. yes

x	y
17	6
18	6
19	5
20	4

30. GEOMETRY Express the relation in the graph at the right as a set of ordered pairs. Describe the domain and range. (Lesson 1-6)

30. $\{(1, 3), (2, 6), (3, 9), (4, 12), (5, 15), (6, 18), (7, 21)\}$, Domain: $\{1, 2, 3, 4, 5, 6, 7\}$ Range: $\{3, 6, 9, 12, 15, 18, 21\}$

Equilateral Triangles

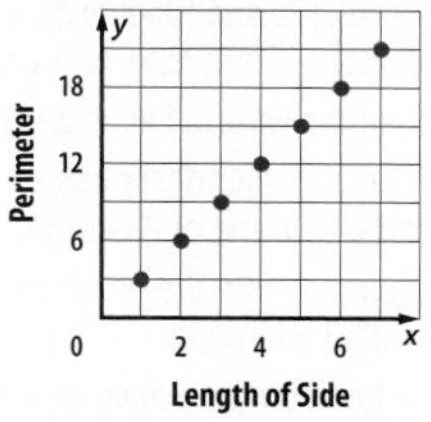

Use the Distributive Property to rewrite each expression. (Lesson 1-4)

31. $\frac{1}{2}d(2d + 6)$ $d^2 + 3d$

32. $-h(6h - 1)$ $-6h^2 + h$

33. $3z - 6x$ $3(z - 2x)$

34. CLOTHING Robert has 30 socks in his sock drawer. 16 of the socks are white, 6 are black, 2 are red, and 6 are yellow. What is the probability that he randomly pulls out a black sock? (Lesson 0-11) $\frac{1}{5}$

Skills Review

Evaluate each expression.

35. $(-7)^2$ 49

36. 3.2^2 10.24

37. $(-4.2)^2$ 17.64

38. $\left(\frac{1}{4}\right)^2$ $\frac{1}{16}$

DifferentiatedInstruction OL BL

Extension Have pairs of students challenge each other to draw graphs with given key features. One student draws a graph without showing it to the other and describes its key features. The second student should draw a graph that fits the description. Discuss similarities and differences in the graphs and whether both graphs fit the description. Then switch roles and repeat.

Teaching the Process Standards

Critique Mathematically proficient students understand and use definitions in constructing arguments. In Exercise 18, neither person is correct. Linear functions can have 0, 1, or infinitely many x-intercepts. Remind students that the graph of a linear function may be a horizontal line. These functions are called constant functions. The function $f(x) = 0$, called the zero function, lies entirely on the x-axis. Therefore, it has infinitely many x-intercepts. All other constant functions lie entirely above or below the x-axis and parallel to it. These functions have no x-intercepts.

4 Assess

Ticket Out the Door Make several copies each of graphs for five real-world functions. Give one graph to each student. As the students leave the room, ask them to describe and interpret one or more of the following characteristics of the graph: intercepts, its symmetry, where the function is positive, negative, increasing, or decreasing, the location of any relative extrema, or end behavior.

Formative Assessment

Check for student understanding of Lessons 1-7 and 1-8.

Quiz 4, p. 58

Additional Answers

18. Neither; the line $y = 2$ has no x-intercept while the line $y = 0$ has infinitely many x-intercepts.

Formative Assessment

KeyVocabulary The page reference after each word denotes where that term was first introduced. If students have difficulty answering questions 1–7, remind them that they can use these page references to refresh their memories about the vocabulary terms.

Summative Assessment

Vocabulary Test, p. 60

Vocabulary Review

Vocabulary Review provides students the opportunity to check their understanding of important concepts and terminology in an online game format.

Students can use the **Vocabulary Check** in the Study Guide and Review and the **Vocabulary Review** to review the vocabulary of the chapter.

FOLDABLES StudyOrganizer

Dinah Zike's Foldables®

Have students look through the chapter to make sure they have included examples in their Foldables for each lesson of the chapter. Suggest that students keep their Foldables handy while completing the Study Guide and Review pages. Point out that their Foldables can serve as a quick review when studying for the chapter test.

CHAPTER 1 Study Guide and Review

Study Guide

KeyConcepts

Order of Operations (Lesson 1-2)

- Evalute expressions inside grouping symbols.
- Evaluate all powers.
- Multiply and/or divide in order from left to right.
- Add or subtract in order from left to right.

Properties of Equality (Lessons 1-3 and 1-4)

- For any numbers a, b, and c:

Reflexive: $a = a$

Symmetric: If $a = b$, then $b = a$.

Transitive: If $a = b$ and $b = c$, then $a = c$.

Substitution: If $a = b$, then a may be replaced by b in any expression.

Distributive: $a(b + c) = ab + ac$ and $a(b - c) = ab - ac$

Commutative: $a + b = b + a$ and $ab = ba$

Associative: $(a + b) + c = a + (b + c)$ and $(ab)c = a(bc)$

Solving Equations (Lesson 1-5)

- Apply order of operations and the properties of real numbers to solve equations.

Relations, Functions, and Interpreting Graphs of Functions (Lessons 1-6 through 1-8)

- Relations and functions can be represented by ordered pairs, a table, a mapping, or a graph.
- Use the vertical line test to determine if a relation is a function.
- End behavior describes the long-term behavior of a function on either end of its graph.
- Points where the graph of a function crosses an axis are called intercepts.
- A function is positive on a portion of its domain where its graph lies above the x-axis, and negative on a portion where its graph lies below the x-axis.

FOLDABLES StudyOrganizer

Be sure the Key Concepts are noted in your Foldable.

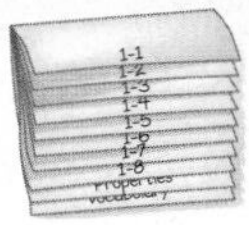

KeyVocabulary

algebraic expression (p. 5)	ordered pair (p. 40)
base (p. 5)	order of operations (p. 10)
coefficient (p. 28)	origin (p. 40)
coordinate system (p. 40)	power (p. 5)
dependent variable (p. 42)	range (p. 40)
domain (p. 40)	reciprocal (p. 17)
end behavior (p. 57)	relation (p. 40)
equation (p. 33)	relative maximum (p. 57)
exponent (p. 5)	relative minimum (p. 57)
function (p. 47)	replacement set (p. 33)
independent variable (p. 42)	simplest form (p. 27)
intercept (p. 56)	solution (p. 33)
like terms (p. 27)	term (p. 5)
line symmetry (p. 57)	variables (p. 5)
mapping (p. 40)	vertical line test (p. 49)

VocabularyCheck

State whether each sentence is *true* or *false*. If *false*, replace the underlined term to make a true sentence.

1. A coordinate system is formed by two intersecting number lines. **true**
2. An exponent indicates the number of times the base is to be used as a factor. **true**
3. An expression is in simplest form when it contains like terms and parentheses. **false; not in simplest form**
4. In an expression involving multiplication, the quantities being multiplied are called factors. **true**
5. In a function, there is exactly one output for each input. **true**
6. Order of operations tells us to perform multiplication before subtraction. **true**
7. Since the product of any number and 1 is equal to the number, 1 is called the multiplicative inverse. **false; multiplicative identity**

Lesson-by-Lesson Review

1-1 Variables and Expressions

Write a verbal expression for each algebraic expression.

8. $h - 7$ **9.** $3x^2$ **10.** $5 + 6m^3$

8–10. See margin.

Write an algebraic expression for each verbal expression.

11. a number increased by 9 $x + 9$

12. two thirds of a number d to the third power $\frac{2}{3}d^3$

13. 5 less than four times a number $4x - 5$

Evaluate each expression.

14. 2^5 32 **15.** 6^3 216 **16.** 4^4 256

17. **BOWLING** Fantastic Pins Bowling Alley charges $2.50 for shoe rental plus $3.25 for each game. Write an expression representing the cost to rent shoes and bowl g games. $2.50 + 3.25g$

Example 1

Write a verbal expression for $4x + 9$.

nine more than four times a number x

Example 2

Write an algebraic expression for *the difference of twelve and two times a number cubed.*

Variable Let x represent the number.

Expression $12 - 2x^3$

Example 3

Evaluate 3^4.

The base is 3 and the exponent is 4.

$3^4 = 3 \cdot 3 \cdot 3 \cdot 3$ Use 3 as a factor 4 times.

$= 81$ Multiply.

1-2 Order of Operations

Evaluate each expression.

18. $24 - 4 \cdot 5$ 4 **19.** $15 + 3^2 - 6$ 18

20. $7 + 2(9 - 3)$ 19 **21.** $8 \cdot 4 - 6 \cdot 5$ 2

22. $[(2^5 - 5) \div 9]11$ 33 **23.** $\frac{11 + 4^2}{5^2 - 4^2}$ 3

Evaluate each expression if $a = 4$, $b = 3$, and $c = 9$.

24. $c + 3a$ 21

25. $5b^2 \div c$ 5

26. $(a^2 + 2bc) \div 7$ 10

27. **ICE CREAM** The cost of a one-scoop sundae is $2.75, and the cost of a two-scoop sundae is $4.25. Write and evaluate an expression to find the total cost of 3 one-scoop sundaes and 2 two-scoop sundaes. $2.75(3) + 4.25(2)$; $16.75

Example 4

Evaluate the expression $3(9 - 5)^2 \div 8$.

$3(9 - 5)^2 \div 8 = 3(4)^2 \div 8$ Work inside parentheses.

$= 3(16) \div 8$ Evaluate 4^2.

$= 48 \div 8$ Multiply.

$= 6$ Divide.

Example 5

Evaluate the expression $(5m - 2n) \div p^2$ if $m = 8$, $n = 4$, $p = 2$.

$(5m - 2n) \div p^2$

$= (5 \cdot 8 - 2 \cdot 4) \div 2^2$ Replace m with 8, n with 4, and p with 2.

$= (40 - 8) \div 2^2$ Multiply.

$= 32 \div 2^2$ Subtract.

$= 32 \div 4$ Evaluate 2^2.

$= 8$ Divide.

Students can complete the exercises in the **Lesson-by-Lesson Review** as they prepare for the chapter test. If they need extra help, examples are provided.

Lesson-by-Lesson Review

Intervention If the given examples are not sufficient to review the topics covered by the questions, remind students that the lesson references tell them where to review that topic in their textbooks.

Two-Day Option Have students complete the Lesson-by-Lesson Review. Then you can use McGraw-Hill eAssessment to customize another review worksheet that practices all the objectives of this chapter or only the objectives on which your students need more help.

Additional Answers

8. the difference between h and 7

9. the product of 3 and x squared

10. five more than the product of six and m cubed

Additional Answers

28. $18 \cdot 3(1 \div 3)$
$= 18 \cdot (3)\frac{1}{3}$ Substitution
$= 18 \cdot 1$ Multiplicative Inverse
$= 18$ Multiplicative Identity

29. $[5 \div (8 - 6)]\frac{2}{5}$
$= [5 \div 2]\frac{2}{5}$ Substitution
$= \frac{5}{2} \cdot \frac{2}{5}$ Substitution
$= 1$ Multiplicative Inverse

30. $(16 - 4^2) + 9$
$= 16 - 16 + 9$ Substitution
$= 0 + 9$ Additive Inverse
$= 9$ Additive Identity

31. $2 \cdot \frac{1}{2} + 4(4 \cdot 2 - 7)$
$= 2 \cdot \frac{1}{2} + 4(8 - 7)$ Substitution
$= 2 \cdot \frac{1}{2} + 4(1)$ Substitution
$= 1 + 4(1)$ Multiplicative Inverse
$= 1 + 4$ Multiplicative Identity
$= 5$ Substitution

32. $18 + 41 + 32 + 9$
$= 18 + 32 + 41 + 9$ Commutative (+)
$= (18 + 32) + (41 + 9)$ Associative (+)
$= 50 + 50$ Substitution
$= 100$ Substitution

33. $7\frac{2}{5} + 5 + 2\frac{3}{5}$
$= 7\frac{2}{5} + 2\frac{3}{5} + 5$ Commutative (+)
$= \left(7\frac{2}{5} + 2\frac{3}{5}\right) + 5$ Associative (+)
$= 10 + 5$ Substitution
$= 15$ Substitution

34. $8 \cdot 0.5 \cdot 5$
$= 8 \cdot 5 \cdot 0.5$ Commutative (×)
$= (8 \cdot 5) \cdot 0.5$ Associative (×)
$= 40 \cdot 0.5$ Substitution
$= 20$ Substitution

35. $5.3 + 2.8 + 3.7 + 6.2$
$= 5.3 + 3.7 + 2.8 + 6.2$ Commutative (+)
$= (5.3 + 3.7) + (2.8 + 6.2)$ Associative (+)
$= 9 + 9$ Substitution
$= 18$ Substitution

CHAPTER 1 Study Guide and Review *Continued*

1-3 Properties of Numbers

Evaluate each expression using properties of numbers. Name the property used in each step. **28–35. See margin.**

28. $18 \cdot 3(1 \div 3)$
29. $[5 \div (8 - 6)]\frac{2}{5}$
30. $(16 - 4^2) + 9$
31. $2 \cdot \frac{1}{2} + 4(4 \cdot 2 - 7)$
32. $18 + 41 + 32 + 9$
33. $7\frac{2}{5} + 5 + 2\frac{3}{5}$
34. $8 \cdot 0.5 \cdot 5$
35. $5.3 + 2.8 + 3.7 + 6.2$

36. **SCHOOL SUPPLIES** Monica needs to purchase a binder, a textbook, a calculator, and a workbook for her algebra class. The binder costs \$9.25, the textbook \$32.50, the calculator \$18.75, and the workbook \$15.00. Find the total cost for Monica's algebra supplies. **\$75.50**

Example 6

Evaluate $6(4 \cdot 2 - 7) + 5 \cdot \frac{1}{5}$. Name the property used in each step.

$6(4 \cdot 2 - 7) + 5 \cdot \frac{1}{5}$
$= 6(8 - 7) + 5 \cdot \frac{1}{5}$ Substitution
$= 6(1) + 5 \cdot \frac{1}{5}$ Substitution
$= 6 + 5 \cdot \frac{1}{5}$ Multiplicative Identity
$= 6 + 1$ Multiplicative Inverse
$= 7$ Substitution

1-4 The Distributive Property

Use the Distributive Property to rewrite each expression. Then evaluate. **37–42. See margin.**

37. $(2 + 3)6$
38. $5(18 + 12)$
39. $8(6 - 2)$
40. $(11 - 4)3$
41. $-2(5 - 3)$
42. $(8 - 3)4$

Rewrite each expression using the Distributive Property. Then simplify. **43–48. See margin.**

43. $3(x + 2)$
44. $(m + 8)4$
45. $6(d - 3)$
46. $-4(5 - 2t)$
47. $(9y - 6)(-3)$
48. $-6(4z + 3)$

49. **TUTORING** Write and evaluate an expression for the number of tutoring lessons Mrs. Green gives in 4 weeks. **4(3 + 5 + 4); 48**

Tutoring Schedule	
Day	**Students**
Monday	3
Tuesday	5
Wednesday	4

Example 7

Use the Distributive Property to rewrite the expression 5(3 + 8). Then evaluate.

$5(3 + 8) = 5(3) + 5(8)$ Distributive Property
$= 15 + 40$ Multiply.
$= 55$ Simplify.

Example 8

Rewrite the expression $6(x + 4)$ using the Distributive Property. Then simplify.

$6(x + 4) = 6 \cdot x + 6 \cdot 4$ Distributive Property
$= 6x + 24$ Simplify.

Example 9

Rewrite the expression $(3x - 2)(-5)$ using the Distributive Property. Then simplify.

$(3x - 2)(-5)$
$= (3x)(-5) - (2)(-5)$ Distributive Property
$= -15x + 10$ Simplify.

37. $2(6) + 3(6)$; 30
38. $5(18) + 5(12)$; 150
39. $8(6) - 8(2)$; 32
40. $11(3) - 4(3)$; 21
41. $-2(5) - (-2)(3)$; -4
42. $8(4) - 3(4)$; 20
43. $3(x) + 3(2)$; $3x + 6$
44. $m(4) + 8(4)$; $4m + 32$
45. $6(d) - 6(3)$; $6d - 18$
46. $-4(5) - (-4)(2t)$; $-20 + 8t$
47. $(9y)(-3) - (6)(-3)$; $-27y + 18$
48. $-6(4z) + (-6)(3)$; $-24z - 18$

1-5 Equations

Find the solution set of each equation if the replacement sets are *x*: {1, 3, 5, 7, 9} and *y*: {6, 8, 10, 12, 14}.

50. $y - 9 = 3$ {12}

51. $14 + x = 21$ {7}

52. $4y = 32$ {8}

53. $3x - 11 = 16$ {9}

54. $\frac{42}{y} = 7$ {6}

55. $2(x - 1) = 8$ {5}

Solve each equation.

56. $a = 24 - 7(3)$ 3

57. $z = 63 \div (3^2 - 2)$ 9

58. **AGE** Shandra's age is four more than three times Sherita's age. Write an equation for Shandra's age. Solve if Sherita is 3 years old $3K + 4 = E$; 13

Example 10

Solve the equation $5w - 19 = 11$ if the replacement set is *w*: {2, 4, 6, 8, 10}.

Replace *w* in $5w - 19 = 11$ with each value in the replacement set.

w	$5w - 19 = 11$	True or False?
2	$5(2) - 19 = 11$	false
4	$5(4) - 19 = 11$	false
6	$5(6) - 19 = 11$	true
8	$5(8) - 19 = 11$	false
10	$5(10) - 19 = 11$	false

Since the equation is true when $w = 6$, the solution of $5w - 19 = 11$ is $w = 6$.

1-6 Relations

Express each relation as a table, a graph, and a mapping. Then determine the domain and range.

59. {(1, 3), (2, 4), (3, 5), (4, 6)}

60. {(−1, 1), (0, −2), (3, 1), (4, −1)}

61. {(−2, 4), (−1, 3), (0, 2), (−1, 2)}

59–61. See Ch. 1 Answer Appendix.

Express the relation shown in each table, mapping, or graph as a set of ordered pairs.

62.

x	*y*
5	3
3	−1
1	2
−1	0

{(5, 3), (3, −1), (1, 2), (−1, 0)}

63.

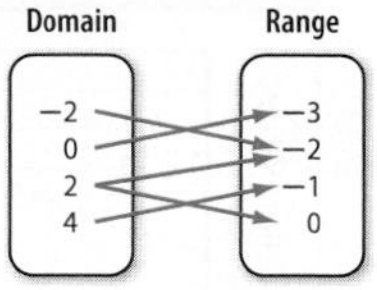

64. **GARDENING** On average, 7 plants grow for every 10 seeds of a certain type planted. Make a table to show the relation between seeds planted and plants growing for 50, 100, 150, and 200 seeds. Then state the domain and range and graph the relation. See margin.

63. {(−2, −2), (0, −3), (2, −2), (2, 0), (4, −1)}

Example 11

Express the relation {(−3, 4), (1, −2), (0, 1), (3, −1)} as a table, a graph, and a mapping.

Table

Place the *x*-coordinates into the first column. Place the corresponding *y*-coordinates in the second column.

x	*y*
−3	4
1	−2
0	1
3	−1

Graph

Graph each ordered pair on a coordinate plane.

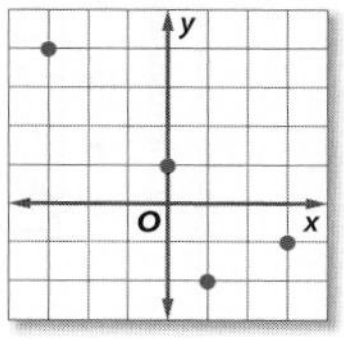

Mapping

List the *x*-values in the domain and the *y*-values in the range. Draw arrows from the *x*-values in set *X* to the corresponding *y*-values in set *Y*.

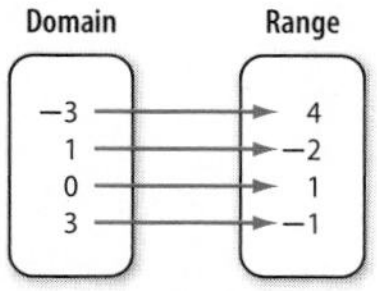

Additional Answer

64.

Planted	Growing
50	35
100	70
150	105
200	140

D = {50, 100, 150, 200}
R = {35, 70, 105, 140}

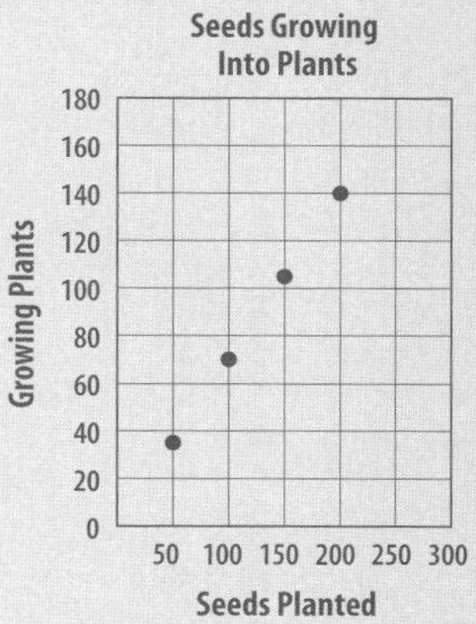

connectED.mcgraw-hill.com 65

Anticipation Guide

Have students complete the Chapter 1 Anticipation Guide and discuss how their responses have changed now that they have completed Chapter 1.

Additional Answers

74. **Studying**

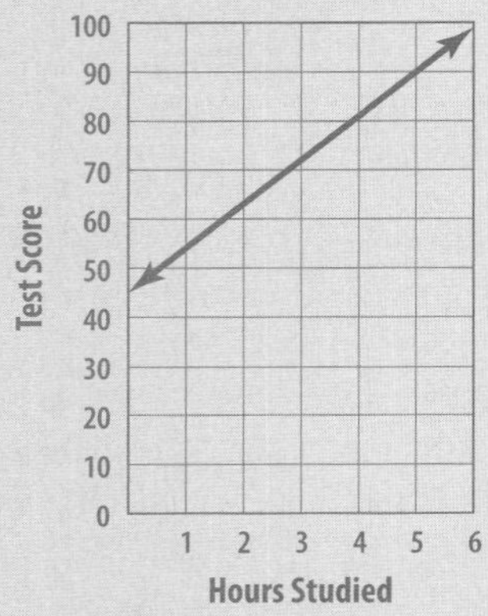

75. Nonlinear; the graph intersects the y-axis at about (0, 56), so the y-intercept is about 56. This means that about 56,000 U.S. patents were granted in 1980. The graph has no symmetry. The graph does not intersect the x-axis, so there is no x-intercept. This means that in no year were 0 patents granted. The function is positive for all values of x, so the number of patents will always have a positive value. The function is increasing for all values of x. The y-intercept is a relative minimum, so the number of patents granted was at its lowest in 1980. As x increases, y increases. As x decreases, y decreases.

CHAPTER 1

Study Guide and Review *Continued*

1-7 Functions

Determine whether each relation is a function.

65.

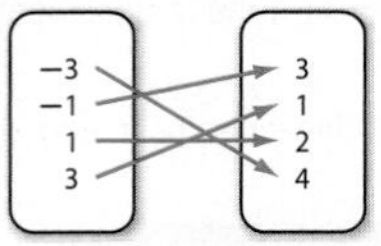

function

66.

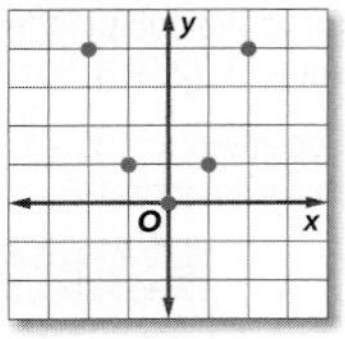

function

67. {(8, 4), (6, 3), (4, 2), (2, 1), (6, 0)} **not a function**

If $f(x) = 2x + 4$ and $g(x) = x^2 - 3$, find each value.

68. $f(-3)$ **−2** 69. $g(2)$ **1** 70. $f(0)$ **4**

71. $g(-4)$ **13** 72. $f(m + 2)$ **$2m + 8$** 73. $g(3p)$ **$9p^2 - 3$**

74. **GRADES** A teacher claims that the relationship between number of hours studied for a test and test score can be described by $g(x) = 45 + 9x$, where x represents the number of hours studied. Graph this function. **See margin.**

Example 12

Determine whether $2x - y = 1$ represents a function.

First make a table of values. Then graph the equation.

x	y
−1	−3
0	−1
1	1
2	3
3	5

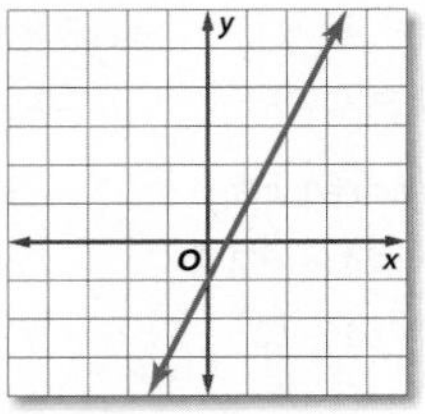

Using the vertical line test, it can be shown that $2x - y = 1$ does represent a function.

1-8 Interpreting Graphs of Functions

75. Identify the function graphed as *linear* or *nonlinear*. Then estimate and interpret the intercepts of the graph, any symmetry, where the function is positive, negative, increasing, and decreasing, the x-coordinate of any relative extrema, and the end behavior of the graph. **See margin.**

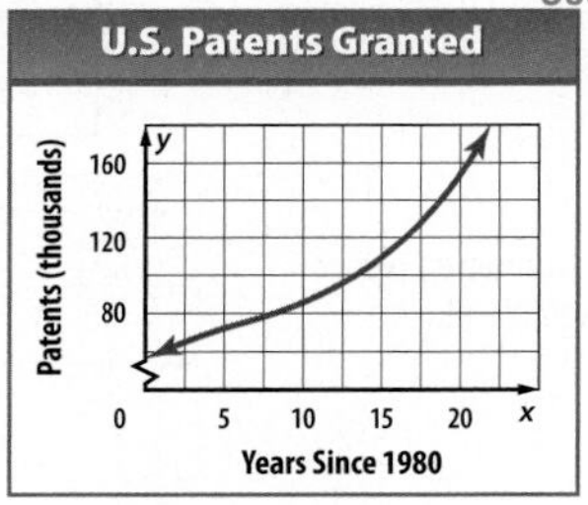

Example 13

POPULATION The population of Haiti from 1994 to 2010 can be modeled by the function graphed below. Estimate and interpret where the function is increasing, and decreasing, the x-coordinates of any relative extrema, and the end behavior of the graph.

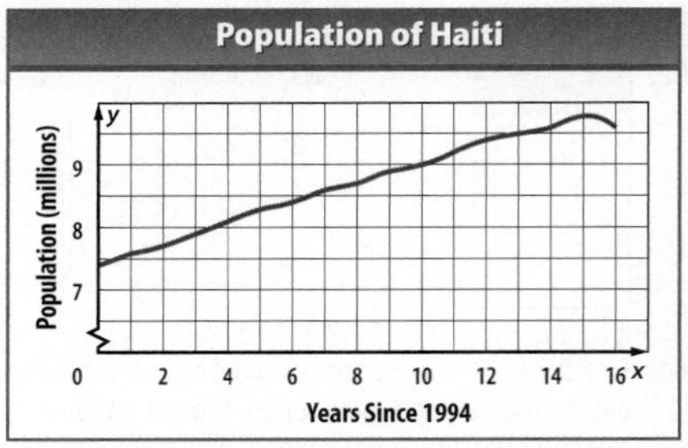

The population increased from 1994 to 2009 and decreased from 2009 to 2010. The relative maximum of the graph indicates that the population peaked in 2009.

As x increases or decreases, y decreases. The end behavior indicates a decline in population from 2009 to 2010.

Additional Answers (Practice Test)

7. $13 + (16 - 4^2)$
$= 13 + (16 - 16)$ Substitution
$= 13 + 0$ Additive Inverse
$= 13$ Additive Identity

8. $\frac{2}{9}[9 \div (7 - 5)]$
$= \frac{2}{9}[9 \div 2]$ Substitution
$= \frac{2}{9} \cdot \frac{9}{2}$ Substitution
$= 1$ Multiplicative Inverse

9. $37 + 29 + 13 + 21$
$= 37 + 13 + 29 + 21$ Commutative Property (+)
$= (37 + 13) + (29 + 21)$ Associative Property (+)
$= 50 + 50$ Substitution
$= 100$ Simplify.

10. $4(x + 3)$
$= 4(x) + 4(3)$
$= 4x + 12$

11. $(5p - 2)(-3)$
$= (5p)(-3) - (2)(-3)$
$= -15p + 6$

CHAPTER 1 Practice Test

Write an algebraic expression for each verbal expression.

1. six more than a number $n + 6$
2. twelve less than the product of three and a number $3n - 12$
3. four divided by the difference between a number and seven $\frac{4}{n-7}$

Evaluate each expression.

4. $32 \div 4 + 2^3 - 3$ 13
5. $\frac{(2 \cdot 4)^2}{7 + 3^2}$ 4

6. **MULTIPLE CHOICE** Find the value of the expression $a^2 + 2ab + b^2$ if $a = 6$ and $b = 4$. C

   A 68

   B 92

   C 100

   D 121

Evaluate each expression. Name the property used in each step. 7–9. See margin.

7. $13 + (16 - 4^2)$
8. $\frac{2}{9}[9 \div (7 - 5)]$
9. $37 + 29 + 13 + 21$

Rewrite each expression using the Distributive Property. Then simplify. 10–11. See margin.

10. $4(x + 3)$
11. $(5p - 2)(-3)$

12. **MOVIE TICKETS** A company operates three movie theaters. The chart shows the typical number of tickets sold each week at the three locations. Write and evaluate an expression for the total typical number of tickets sold by all three locations in four weeks.
   $4(438 + 374 + 512)$; 5296

Location	Tickets Sold
A	438
B	374
C	512

Find the solution of each equation if the replacement sets are x: {1, 3, 5, 7, 9} and y: {2, 4, 6, 8, 10}.

13. $3x - 9 = 12$ 7
14. $y^2 - 5y - 11 = 13$ 8

15. **CELL PHONES** The ABC Cell Phone Company offers a plan that includes a flat fee of \$29 per month plus a \$0.12 charge per minute. Write an equation to find C, the total monthly cost for m minutes. Then solve the equation for $m = 50$.
   $C = 29 + 0.12m$; \$35

Express the relation shown in each table, mapping, or graph as a set of ordered pairs.

16.

x	y
−2	4
1	2
3	0
4	−2

{(−2, 4), (1, 2), (3, 0), (4, −2)}

17.

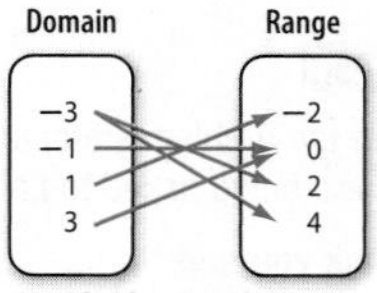

{(−3, 2), (−3, 4), (−1, 0), (1, −2), (3, 0)}

18. **MULTIPLE CHOICE** Determine the domain and range for the relation {(2, 5), (−1, 3), (0, −1), (3, 3), (−4, −2)}. F

   F D: {2, −1, 0, 3, −4}, R: {5, 3, −1, 3, −2}

   G D: {5, 3, −1, 3, −2}, R: {2, −1, 0, 3, 4}

   H D: {0, 1, 2, 3, 4}, R: {−4, −3, −2, −1, 0}

   J D: {2, −1, 0, 3, −4}, R: {2, −1, 0, 3, 4}

19. Determine whether the relation {(2, 3), (−1, 3), (0, 4), (3, 2), (−2, 3)} is a function. yes

If $f(x) = 5 - 2x$ and $g(x) = x^2 + 7x$, find each value.

20. $g(3)$ 30
21. $f(-6y)$ $5 + 12y$

22. See Ch. 1 Answer Appendix.

22. Identify the function graphed as *linear* or *nonlinear*. Then estimate and interpret the intercepts of the graph, any symmetry, where the function is positive, negative, increasing, and decreasing, the x-coordinate of any relative extrema, and the end behavior of the graph.

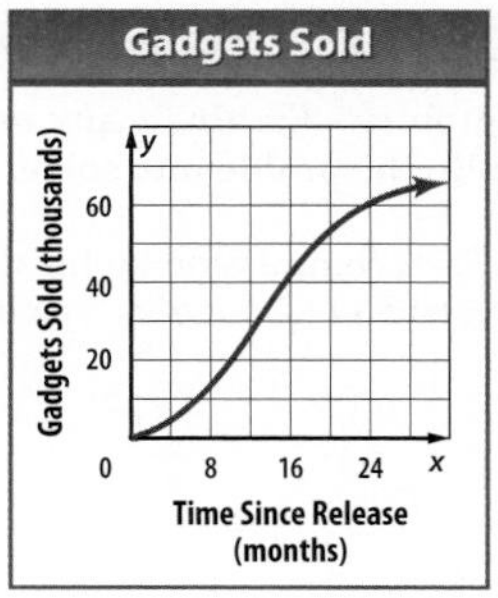

Summative Assessment

Use these alternate leveled chapter tests to differentiate assessment for your students.

Leveled Chapter 1 Tests

Form	Type	Level	Page(s)
1	MC	AL	61–62
2A	MC	OL	63–64
2B	MC	OL	65–66
2C	FR	OL	67–68
2D	FR	OL	69–70
3	FR	BL	71–72
Vocabulary Test			60
Extended-Response Test			73

MC = multiple-choice questions
FR = free-response questions

Six forms of **chapter tests,** a **Vocabulary Test,** and an **Extended-Response Test** are provided for each chapter. These are available in the Chapter Resource Masters.

McGraw-Hill eAssessment Customize and create multiple versions of your chapter tests and their answer keys. All of the questions from the leveled chapter tests in the *Chapter 1 Resource Masters* are also available on McGraw-Hill eAssessment.

Intervention Planner

TIER 1 On Level OL	TIER 2 Strategic Intervention AL approaching grade level	TIER 3 Intensive Intervention 2 or more grades below level
If students miss about 25% of the exercises or less,	**If** students miss about 50% of the exercises,	**If** students miss about 75% of the exercises,
Then choose a resource:	**Then** choose a resource:	**Then** use *Math Triumphs Alg. 1*, Ch. 1, 2, 3, 5, and 6
SE Lessons 1-1, 1-2, 1-3, 1-4, 1-5, 1-6, 1-7, and 1-8	Study Guide and Intervention, Chapter 1 pp. 5, 11, 18, 24, 30, 37, 43, and 49	connectED.mcgraw-hill.com Extra Examples, Personal Tutor, Homework Help, Review Vocabulary
Skills Practice, pp. 7, 13, 20, 26, 32, 39, 45, and 51	*Quick Review Math Handbook*	
TE Chapter Project	connectED.mcgraw-hill.com Extra Examples, Personal Tutor, Homework Help	
connectED.mcgraw-hill.com Self-Check Quiz		

1 Focus

Objective Use the strategy of eliminating unreasonable answers to solve standardized test problems.

2 Teach

Scaffolding Questions

Ask:

- Have you ever thought that someone gave an unreasonable explanation for something that occurred? In general, what made you think the explanation was unreasonable? Sample answer: The explanation did not fit the circumstances or was unusual.
- In general, how would a reasonable explanation differ from an unreasonable explanation? Sample answer: A reasonable explanation would fit the facts or details of the situation, whereas the unreasonable explanation would not.

CHAPTER 1

Preparing for Standardized Tests

Eliminate Unreasonable Answers

You can eliminate unreasonable answers to help you find the correct one when solving multiple choice test items. Doing so will save you time by narrowing down the list of possible correct answers.

Strategies for Eliminating Unreasonable Answers

iStop/Alamy

Step 1

Read the problem statement carefully to determine exactly what you are being asked to find.

Ask yourself:

- What am I being asked to solve?
- What format (i.e., fraction, number, decimal, percent, type of graph) will the correct answer be?
- What units (if any) will the correct answer have?

Step 2

Carefully look over each possible answer choice and evaluate for reasonableness.

- Identify any answer choices that are clearly incorrect and eliminate them.
- Eliminate any answer choices that are not in the proper format.
- Eliminate any answer choices that do not have the correct units.

Step 3

Solve the problem and choose the correct answer from those remaining. Check your answer.

Standardized Test Example

Read each problem. Eliminate any unreasonable answers. Then use the information in the problem to solve.

Jason earns 8.5% commission on his weekly sales at an electronics retail store. Last week he had $4200 in sales. What was his commission for the week?

A $332 **C** $425

B $357 **D** $441

Using mental math, you know that 10% of $4200 is $420. Since 8.5% is less than 10%, you know that Jason earned less than $420 in commission for his weekly sales. So, answer choices C and D can be eliminated because they are greater than $420. The correct answer is either A or B.

$4200 × 0.085 = $357

So, the correct answer is B.

Exercises

Read each problem. Eliminate any unreasonable answers. Then use the information in the problem to solve.

1. Coach Roberts expects 35% of the student body to turn out for a pep rally. If there are 560 students, how many does Coach Roberts expect to attend the pep rally? B

A 184

B 196

C 214

D 390

2. Jorge and Sally leave school at the same time. Jorge walks 300 yards north and then 400 yards east. Sally rides her bike 600 yards south and then 800 yards west. What is the distance between the two students? J

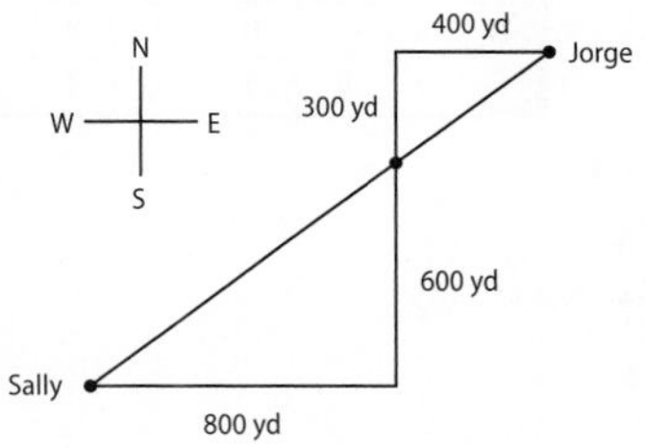

F 500 yd

G 750 yd

H 1,200 yd

J 1,500 yd

3. What is the range of the relation below? C

{(1, 2), (3, 4), (5, 6), (7, 8)}

A all real numbers

B all even numbers

C {2, 4, 6, 8}

D {1, 3, 5, 7}

4. The expression $3n + 1$ gives the total number of squares needed to make each figure of the pattern where n is the figure number. How many squares will be needed to make Figure 9? F

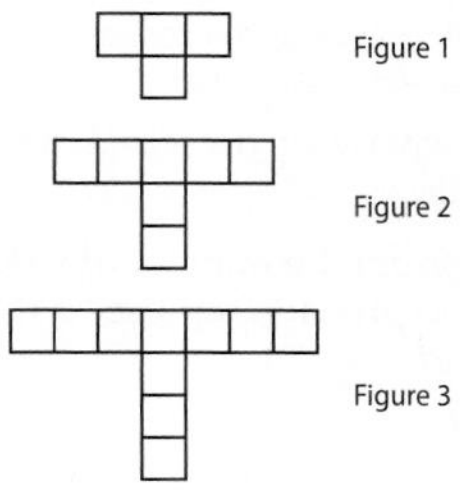

F 28 squares

G 32.5 squares

H 56 squares

J 88.5 squares

5. The expression $3x - (2x + 4x - 6)$ is equivalent to B

A $-3x - 6$

B $-3x + 6$

C $3x + 6$

D $3x - 6$

Additional Example

In a poll on favorite exercise activities, 22.5% of the students in the survey voted for weight lifting. If 1200 students participated in the poll, how many voted for weight lifting? B

A 246

B 270

C 318

D 390

3 Assess

Use Exercises 1–5 to assess students' understanding.

Diagnose Student Errors

Survey student responses for each item. Class trends may indicate common errors and misconceptions.

1. A multiplied exponent times base
B found 2^5 instead of 2^6
C correct
D found 2^7 instead of 2^6

2. F end behavior on left correct, end behavior on right incorrect
G end behavior on both left and right incorrect
H correct
J end behavior on right correct, end behavior on left incorrect

3. A misunderstood relationship between feet and yards
B misunderstood relationship between feet and yards
C correct
D misunderstood relationship between feet and yards

4. F confused domain and range
G correct
H does not understand difference between domain and range
J guess

5. A underestimate
B correct
C overestimate
D overestimate

6. F guess
G guess
H guess
J correct

7. A does not understand concept of function
B correct
C does not understand concept of function
D does not understand concept of function

CHAPTER 1

Standardized Test Practice

Chapter 1

Multiple Choice

Read each question. Then fill in the correct answer on the answer document provided by your teacher or on a sheet of paper.

1. Evaluate the expression 2^6. **C**

A 12
B 32
C 64
D 128

2. Which sentence best describes the end behavior of the function shown? **H**

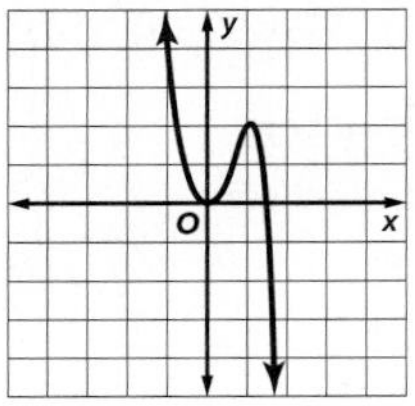

F As x increases, y increases, and as x decreases, y increases.
G As x increases, y increases, and as x decreases, y decreases.
H As x increases, y decreases, and as x decreases, y increases.
J As x increases, y decreases, and as x decreases, y decreases.

3. Let y represent the number of yards. Which algebraic expression represents the number of feet in y? **C**

A $y - 3$
B $y + 3$
C $3y$
D $\frac{3}{y}$

4. What is the domain of the following relation? **G**

$$\{(1, 3), (-6, 4), (8, 5)\}$$

F $\{3, 4, 5\}$
G $\{-6, 1, 8\}$
H $\{-6, 1, 3, 4, 5, 8\}$
J $\{1, 3, 4, 5, 8\}$

5. The table shows the number of some of the items sold at the concession stand at the first day of a soccer tournament. Estimate how many items were sold from the concession stand throughout the four days of the tournament. **B**

Concession Sales Day 1 Results	
Item	Number Sold
Popcorn	78
Hot Dogs	80
Chip	48
Sodas	51
Bottled Water	92

A 1350 items
B 1400 items
C 1450 items
D 1500 items

6. There are 24 more cars than twice the number of trucks for sale at a dealership. If there are 100 cars for sale, how many trucks are there for sale at the dealership? **J**

F 28
G 32
H 34
J 38

7. Refer to the relation in the table below. Which of the following values would result in the relation *not* being a function? **B**

x	−6	−2	0	?	3	5
y	−1	8	3	−3	4	0

A −1
B 3
C 7
D 8

Test-Taking Tip

Question 7 A function is a relation in which each element of the domain is paired with *exactly* one element of the range.

Additional Answers

9a. Sample answer: $3(3.80) + 2(5.25) + 2(12.95) + 42.50$; $3(3.80) + 2(5.25 + 12.95) + 42.50$

11b. See students' graphs. Sample answer: The points lie in a straight line.

11c. Sample answer: When x increases by 1, y increases by 2.

12b. 288π cm^3; Sample answer: Substitute 6 for r in the expression. Take 6 to the third power. Multiply by 4, then divide by 3. Pi is irrational so it appears in the answer.

70 | Chapter 1 | Standardized Test Practice

Short Response/Gridded Response

Record your answers on the answer sheet provided by your teacher or on a sheet of paper.

8. The edge of each box below is 1 unit long.

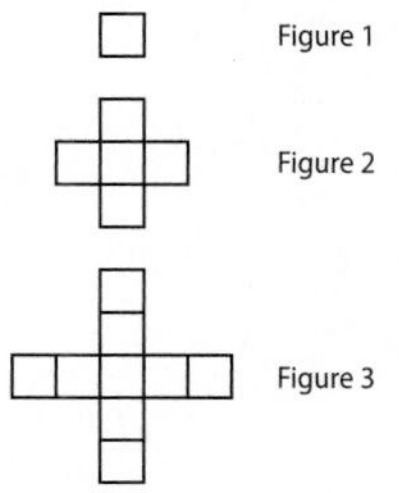

a. Make a table showing the perimeters of the first 3 figures in the pattern. **4 units, 12 units, 20 units**

b. Look for a pattern in the perimeters of the shapes. Write an algebraic expression for the perimeter of Figure n. **$4 + 8(n - 1)$ or $8n - 4$**

c. What would be the perimeter of Figure 10 in the pattern? **76 units**

9. The table shows the costs of certain items at a corner hardware store.

Item	Cost
box of nails	\$3.80
box of screws	\$5.25
claw hammer	\$12.95
electric drill	\$42.50

a. Write two expressions to represent the total cost of 3 boxes of nails, 2 boxes of screws, 2 hammers, and 1 electric drill. **See margin.**

b. What is the total cost of the items purchased? **\$90.30**

10. GRIDDED RESPONSE Evaluate the expression below. **20**

$$\frac{5^3 \cdot 4^2 - 5^2 \cdot 4^3}{5 \cdot 4}$$

11. Use the equation $y = 2(4 + x)$ to answer each question. **b–c. See margin.**

a. Complete the table for each value of x.

x	y
1	**10**
2	**12**
3	**14**
4	**16**
5	**18**
6	**20**

b. Plot the points from the table on a coordinate grid. What do you notice about the points?

c. Make a conjecture about the relationship between the change in x and the change in y.

Extended Response

Record your answers on a sheet of paper. Show your work.

12. The volume of a sphere is four-thirds the product of π and the radius cubed.

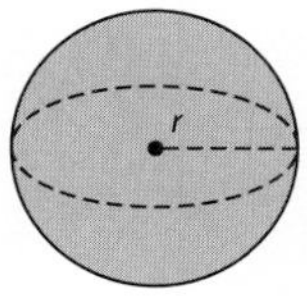

a. Write an expression for the volume of a sphere with radius r. **$\left(\frac{4}{3}\right)\pi r^3$**

b. Find the volume of a sphere with a radius of 6 centimeters. Describe how you found your answer. **See margin.**

Need ExtraHelp?

If you missed Question...	1	2	3	4	5	6	7	8	9	10	11	12
Go to Lesson...	1-2	1-8	1-1	1-6	1-4	1-5	1-7	1-5	1-3	1-2	1-4	1-1

The items in the **Standardized Test Practice** help students practice the kinds of questions found on state assessments. The **Need Extra Help?** box allows students to diagnose and address weaknesses.

Formative Assessment

You can use these pages to benchmark student progress.

Standardized Test Practice, pp. 74–76

Answer Sheet Practice

Have students simulate taking a standardized test by recording their answers on a practice recording sheet.

Student Recording Sheet

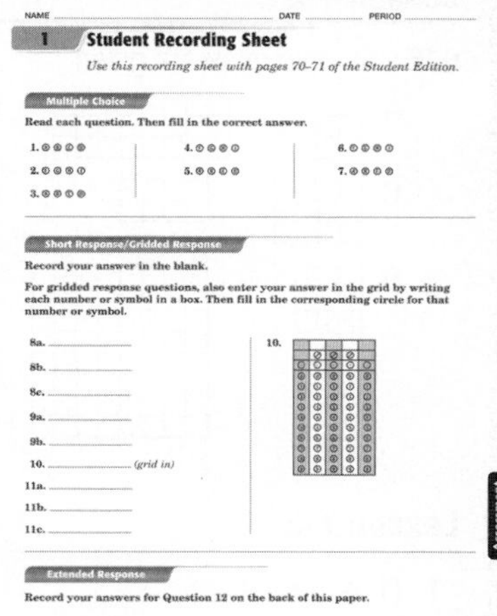

McGraw-Hill eAssessment Create practice tests that align to your state standards, the Common Core State Standards, and other national standards such as TIMSS and NAEP.

Homework Option

Get Ready for Chapter 2 Assign students the exercises on p. 73 as homework to assess whether they possess the prerequisite skills needed for the next chapter.

Lesson 1-1

47.

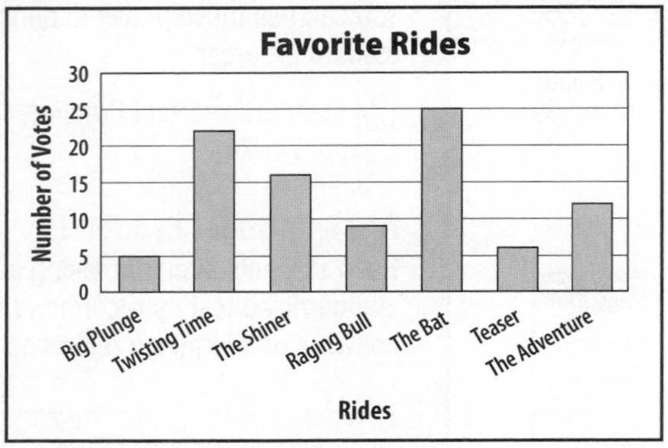

Lesson 1-2

67B. Sample answers given.

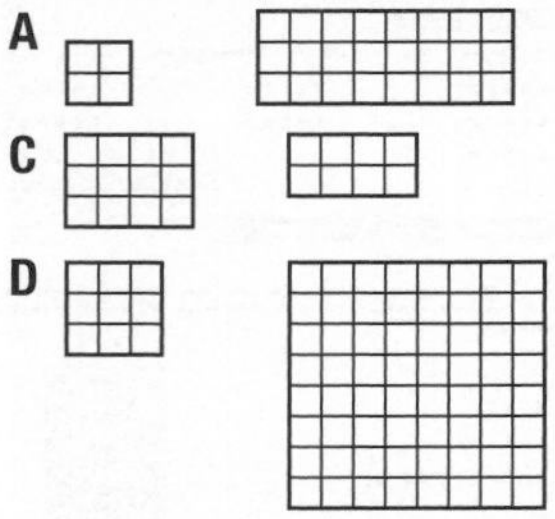

Lesson 1-3

1. $(1 \div 5)5 \cdot 14$
$= \frac{1}{5} \cdot 5 \cdot 14$ Substitution
$= (1) \cdot 14$ Multiplicative Inverse
$= 14$ Multiplicative Identity

2. $6 + 4(19 - 15)$
$= 6 + 4(4)$ Substitution
$= 6 + 16$ Substitution
$= 22$ Substitution

3. $5(14 - 5) + 6(3 + 7)$
$= 5(9) + 6(10)$ Substitution
$= 45 + 60$ Substitution
$= 105$ Substitution

4. $9(25) + 4(10) + 7(5) + 2$
$= 225 + 40 + 35 + 2$ Substitution
$= 302$ Substitution
Carolyn has 302¢ or \$3.02.

5. $23 + 42 + 37$
$= 23 + 37 + 42$ Commutative (+)
$= (23 + 37) + 42$ Associative (+)
$= 60 + 42$ Substitution
$= 102$ Substitution

6. $2.75 + 3.5 + 4.25 + 1.5$
$= 2.75 + 4.25 + 3.5 + 1.5$ Commutative (+)
$= (2.75 + 4.25) + (3.5 + 1.5)$ Associative (+)
$= 7 + 5$ Substitution
$= 12$ Substitution

7. $3 \cdot 7 \cdot 10 \cdot 2$
$= 3 \cdot 2 \cdot 7 \cdot 10$ Commutative (×)
$= (3 \cdot 2) \cdot (7 \cdot 10)$ Associative (×)
$= 6 \cdot 70$ Substitution
$= 420$ Substitution

8. $\frac{1}{4} \cdot 24 \cdot \frac{2}{3}$
$= \frac{1}{4} \cdot \left(24 \cdot \frac{2}{3}\right)$ Associative (×)
$= \frac{1}{4} \cdot 16$ Substitution
$= 4$ Substitution

9. $3(22 - 3 \cdot 7)$
$= 3(22 - 21)$ Substitution
$= 3(1)$ Substitution
$= 3$ Multiplicative Identity

10. $7 + (9 - 3^2)$
$= 7 + (9 - 9)$ Substitution
$= 7 + 0$ Additive Inverse
$= 7$ Additive Identity

11. $\frac{3}{4}[4 \div (7 - 4)]$
$= \frac{3}{4}[4 \div 3]$ Substitution
$= \frac{3}{4} \cdot \frac{4}{3}$ Substitution
$= 1$ Multiplicative Inverse

12. $[3 \div (2 \cdot 1)]\frac{2}{3}$
$= [3 \div 2]\frac{2}{3}$ Multiplicative Identity
$= \frac{3}{2} \cdot \frac{2}{3}$ Substitution
$= 1$ Multiplicative Inverse

13. $2(3 \cdot 2 - 5) + 3 \cdot \frac{1}{3}$
$= 2(6 - 5) + 3 \cdot \frac{1}{3}$ Substitution
$= 2(1) + 3 \cdot \frac{1}{3}$ Substitution
$= 2 + 3 \cdot \frac{1}{3}$ Multiplicative Identity
$= 2 + 1$ Multiplicative Inverse
$= 3$ Substitution

14. $6 \cdot \frac{1}{6} + 5(12 \div 4 - 3)$
$= 6 \cdot \frac{1}{6} + 5(3 - 3)$ Substitution
$= 6 \cdot \frac{1}{6} + 5(0)$ Additive Inverse
$= 6 \cdot \frac{1}{6} + 0$ Multiplicative Property of Zero
$= 1 + 0$ Multiplicative Inverse
$= 1$ Additive Identity

15. $2 \cdot \frac{22}{7} \cdot 14^2 + 2 \cdot \frac{22}{7} \cdot 14 \cdot 7$
$= 2 \cdot \frac{22}{7} \cdot 196 + 2 \cdot \frac{22}{7} \cdot 14 \cdot 7$ Substitution
$= \frac{44}{7} \cdot 196 + \frac{44}{7} \cdot 14 \cdot 7$ Substitution
$= 1232 + 616$ Substitution
$= 1848$ Substitution
The surface area is 1848 in^2.

17. $25 + 14 + 15 + 36 = 25 + 15 + 14 + 36$ Commutative (+)
$= (25 + 15) + (14 + 36)$ Associative (+)
$= 40 + 50$ Substitution
$= 90$ Substitution

18. $11 + 7 + 5 + 13 = 11 + 5 + 7 + 13$ Commutative(+)
$= (11 + 5) + (7 + 13)$ Associative (+)
$= 16 + 20$ Substitution
$= 36$ Substitution

19. $3\frac{2}{3} + 4 + 5\frac{1}{3} = 3\frac{2}{3} + 5\frac{1}{3} + 4$ Commutative (+)
$= \left(3\frac{2}{3} + 5\frac{1}{3}\right) + 4$ Associative (+)
$= 9 + 4$ Substitution
$= 13$ Substitution

20. $4\frac{4}{9} + 7\frac{2}{9} = 4 + \frac{4}{9} + 7 + \frac{2}{9}$ Substitution
$= 4 + 7 + \frac{4}{9} + \frac{2}{9}$ Commutative (+)
$= (4 + 7) + \left(\frac{4}{9} + \frac{2}{9}\right)$ Associative (+)
$= 11 + \frac{6}{9}$ Substitution
$= 11\frac{2}{3}$ Substitution

21. $4.3 + 2.4 + 3.6 + 9.7$
$= 4.3 + 9.7 + 2.4 + 3.6$ Commutative (+)
$= (4.3 + 9.7) + (2.4 + 3.6)$ Associative (+)
$= 14 + 6$ Substitution
$= 20$ Substitution

22. $3.25 + 2.2 + 5.4 + 10.75$
$= 3.25 + 10.75 + 2.2 + 5.4$ Commutative (+)
$= (3.25 + 10.75) + (2.2 + 5.4)$ Associative (+)
$= 14 + 7.6$ Substitution
$= 21.6$ Substitution

23. $12 \cdot 2 \cdot 6 \cdot 5 = 12 \cdot 6 \cdot 2 \cdot 5$ Commutative (×)
$= (12 \cdot 6) \cdot (2 \cdot 5)$ Associative (×)
$= 72 \cdot 10$ Substitution
$= 720$ Substitution

24. $2 \cdot 8 \cdot 10 \cdot 2 = (2 \cdot 8) \cdot (10 \cdot 2)$ Associative (×)
$= 16 \cdot 20$ Substitution
$= 320$ Substitution

25. $0.2 \cdot 4.6 \cdot 5 = (0.2 \cdot 4.6) \cdot 5$ Associative (×)
$= 0.92 \cdot 5$ Substitution
$= 4.6$ Substitution

26. $3.5 \cdot 3 \cdot 6 = 3.5 \cdot (3 \cdot 6)$ Associative (×)
$= 3.5 \cdot 18$ Substitution
$= 63$ Substitution

27. $1\frac{5}{6} \cdot 24 \cdot 3\frac{1}{11}$
$= 1\frac{5}{6}\left(24 \cdot 3\frac{1}{11}\right)$ Associative (×)
$= 1\frac{5}{6}\left(24 \cdot \frac{34}{11}\right)$ Substitution
$= 1\frac{5}{6} \cdot \frac{816}{11}$ Substitution
$= \frac{8976}{66}$ Substitution
$= 136$ Substitution

28. $2\frac{3}{4} \cdot 1\frac{1}{8} \cdot 32$
$= \left(2\frac{3}{4} \cdot 1\frac{1}{8}\right) \cdot 32$ Associative (×)
$= \left(\frac{11}{4} \cdot \frac{9}{8}\right) \cdot 32$ Substitution
$= \frac{99}{32} \cdot 32$ Substitution
$= 99$ Substitution

Mid-Chapter Quiz

13. $(8 - 2^3) + 21$
$= (8 - 8) + 21$ Substitution
$= 0 + 21$ Additive Inverse
$= 21$ Additive Identity

14. $3(1 \div 3) \cdot 9$
$= 3 \cdot \frac{1}{3} \cdot 9$ Substitution
$= 1 \cdot 9$ Multiplicative Inverse
$= 9$ Multiplicative Identity

15. $[5 \div (3 \cdot 1)]\frac{3}{5}$
$= [5 \div 3]\frac{3}{5}$ Multiplicative Identity
$= \frac{5}{3} \times \frac{3}{5}$ Substitution
$= 1$ Multiplicative Inverse

16. $18 + 35 + 32 + 15$
$= 18 + 32 + 35 + 15$ Commutative Property (+)
$= (18 + 32) + (35 + 15)$ Associative Property (+)
$= 50 + 50$ Substitution
$= 100$ Substitution

17. $0.25 \cdot 7 \cdot 4$
$= 0.25 \cdot (7 \cdot 4)$ Associative Property (×)
$= 0.25 \cdot 28$ Substitution
$= 7$ Substitution

Lesson 1-5

37.

x	$3x - 2$	y
−2	3(−2) − 2	−8
−1	3(−1) − 2	−5
0	3(0) − 2	−2
1	3(1) − 2	1
2	3(2) − 2	4

38.

x	$3.25x + 0.75$	y
−2	3.25(−2) + 0.75	−5.75
−1	3.25(−1) + 0.75	−2.55
0	3.25(0) + 0.75	0.75
1	3.25(1) + 0.75	4
2	3.25(2) + 0.75	7.25

Lesson 1-6

9.

x	y
0	0
−3	2
6	4
−1	1

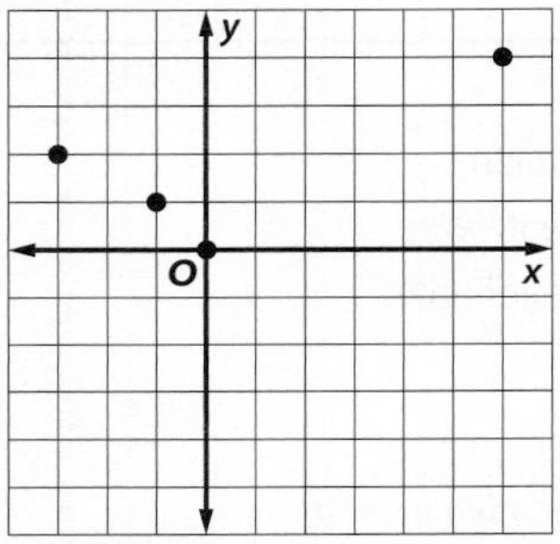

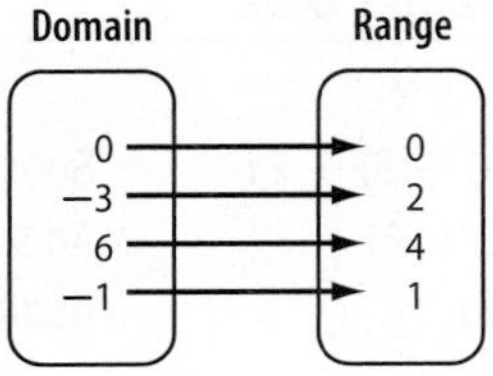

D = {0, −3, 6, −1};
R = {0, 2, 4, 1}

10.

x	y
5	2
5	6
3	−2
0	−2

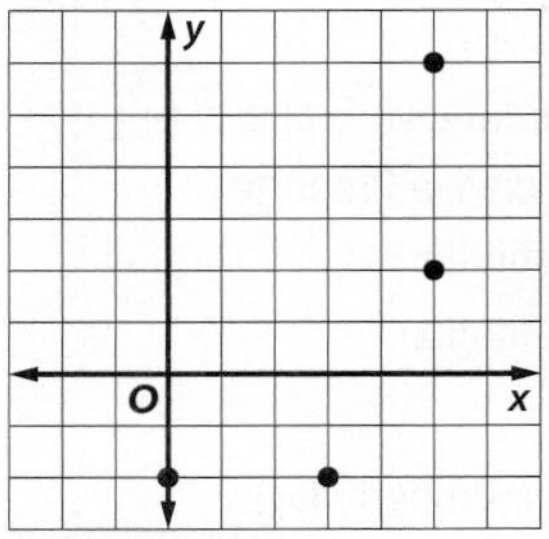

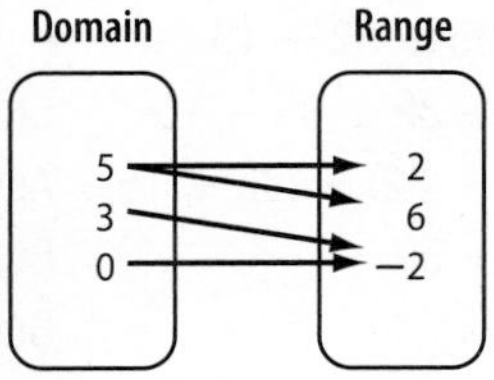

D = {0, 3, 5};
R = {−2, 2, 6}

11.

x	y
6	1
4	−3
3	2
−1	−3

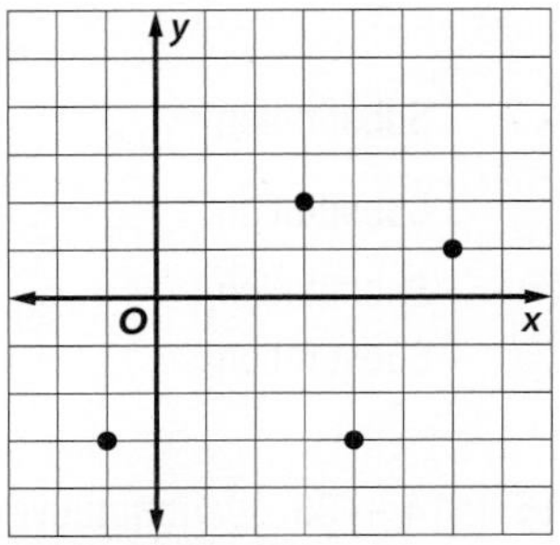

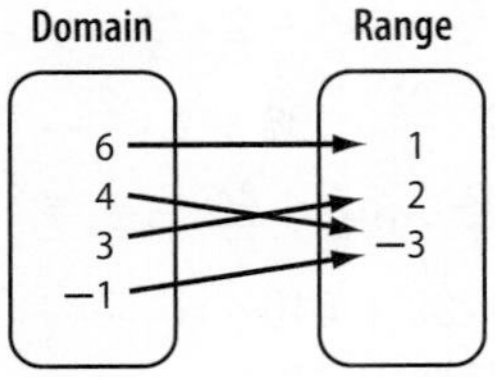

D = {6, 4, 3, −1};
R = {1, −3, 2}

12.

x	y
−1	3
3	−6
−1	−8
−3	−7

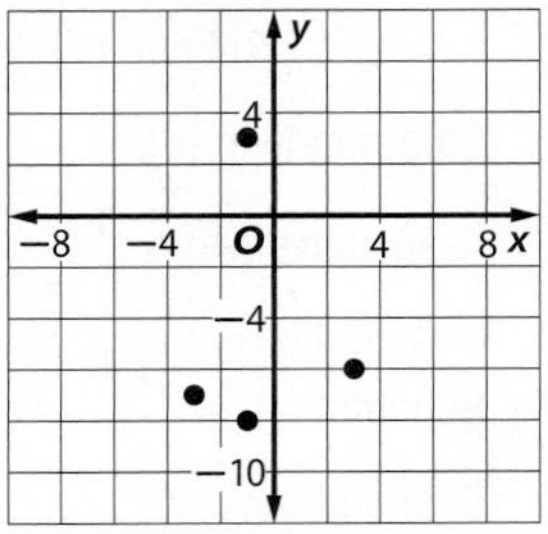

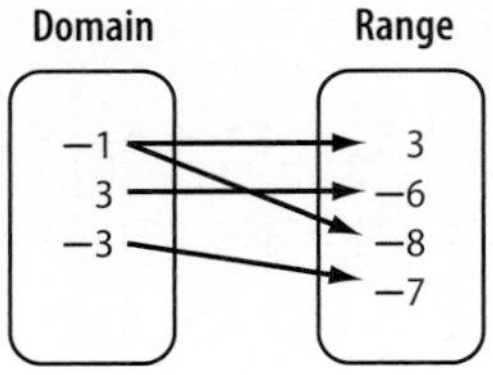

D = {−3, −1, 3};
R = {−8, −7, −6, 3}

13.

x	y
6	7
3	−2
8	8
−6	2
2	−6

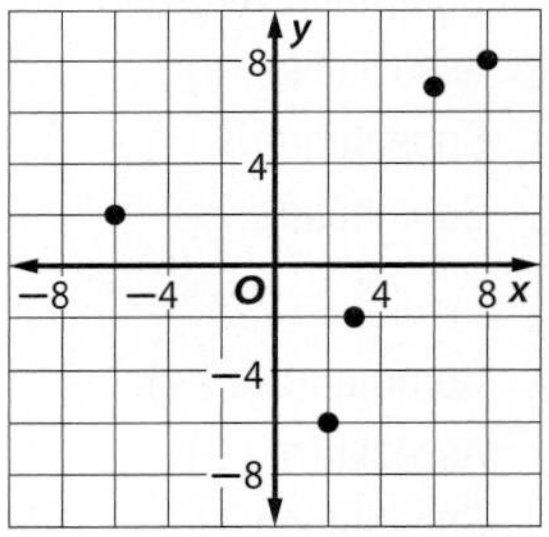

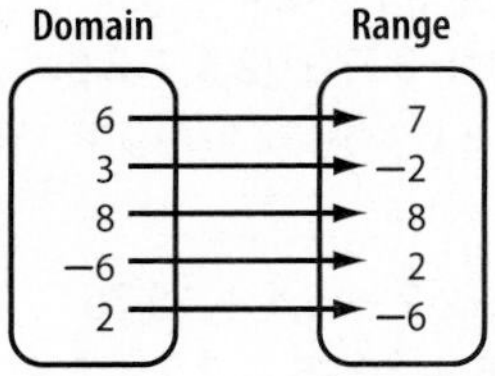

D = {−6, 2, 3, 6, 8}; R = {−6, −2, 2, 7, 8}

14.

x	y
4	−3
1	3
7	−2
2	−2
1	5

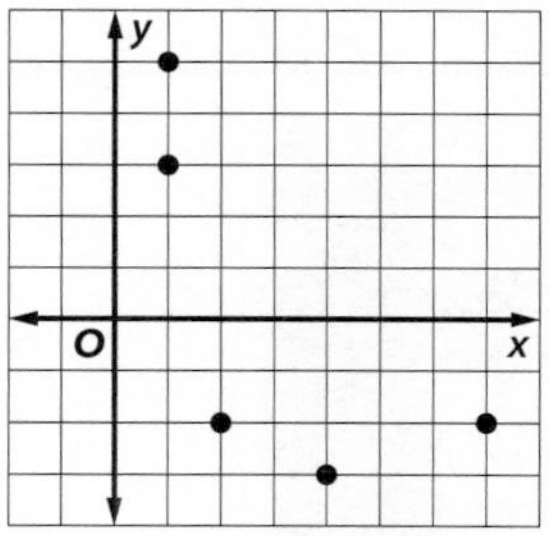

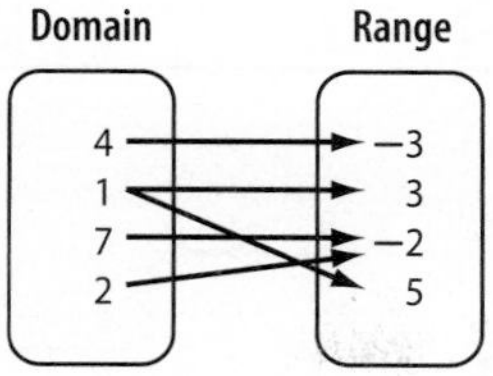

D = {1, 2, 4, 7}; R = {−3, −2, 3, 5}

15. I: the number of students who attend the fiesta; D: the amount of food that there will be at the fiesta

16. I: the speed of the car; D: the length of time it takes to stop the car

17. The bungee jumper starts at the maximum height then jumps. After the initial jump, the jumper bounces up and down until coming to a rest.

18. The sales of lawn mowers are high for part of the year, but low or decreasing for the rest of the time.

19. The baseball card increases in value quickly.

20. The graph shows the car moving, and then stopping, and then moving at a faster pace. The car stops a second time, then continues moving.

37a.

Body Weight (lb)	100	105	110	115	120	125	130
Water Weight (lb)	66.7	70	73.3	76.7	80	83.3	86.7

37b. The independent variable is *b*, the dependent variable is *w*.

37c. D = {100, 105, 110, 115, 120, 125, 130};
R = {66.7, 70, 73.3, 76.7, 80, 83.3, 86.7}

Water Weight Per Body Weight

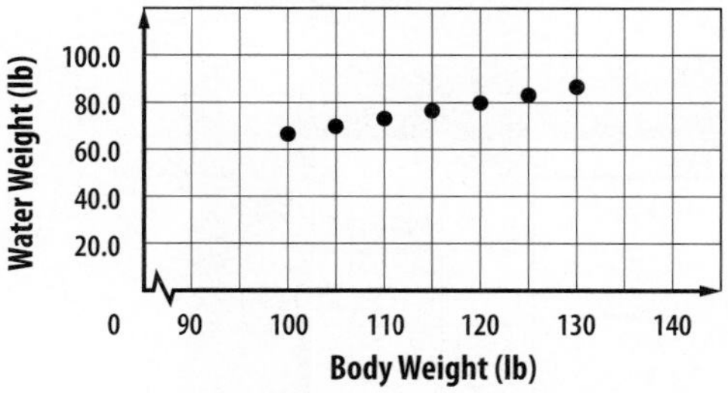

37d.

Body Weight Per Water Weight

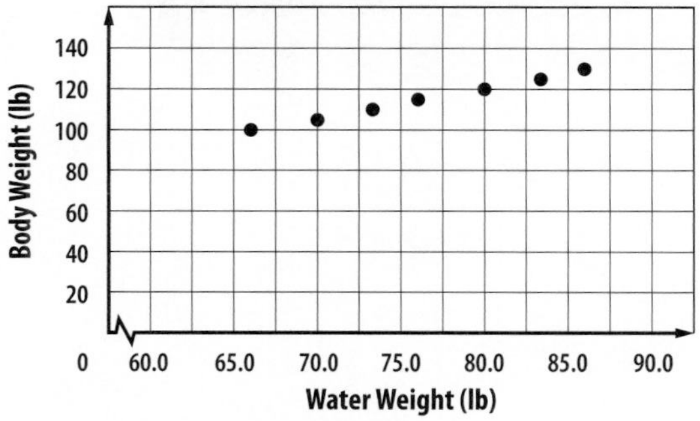

The body weight is dependent on the water weight. As the water weight increases, the body weight also increases.

38. Sample answer: The number of movie tickets bought and the total cost of the tickets can be represented using a relation. The total cost depends on the number of tickets bought.
{(0, 0), (1, 9), (2, 18), (3, 27)}

Number of Tickets	Total Cost
0	$0.00
1	$9.00
2	$18.00
3	$27.00

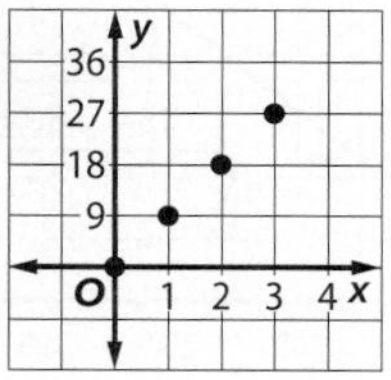

41. Reversing the coordinates gives (1, 0), (3, 1), (5, 2), and (7, 3).

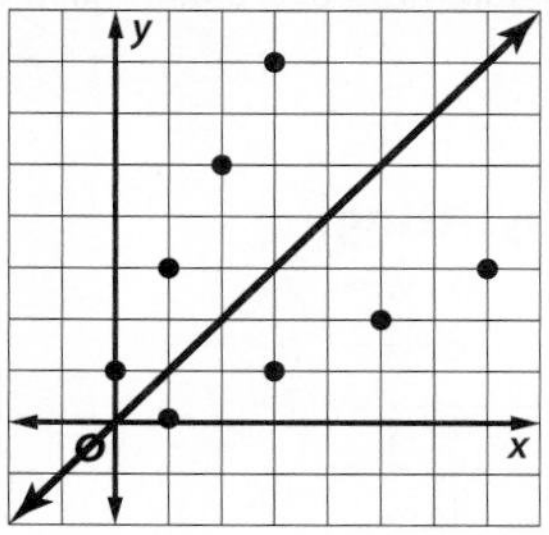

Each point in the original relation is the same distance from the line as the corresponding point of the reverse relation. The graphs are symmetric about the line $y = x$.

Lesson 1-7 (Guided Practice)

2A.

Amount of Seed (qt)	0	1	2	3
Weight (lb)	2.3	6	9.7	13.4

2B. The domain is the set of possible amounts of seed (0 to 3 quarts), and the range is the set of total weights possible (2.3 to 13.4 pounds).

2C. {(0, 2.3), (1, 6), (2, 9.7), (3, 13.4)};

Weight of Seed

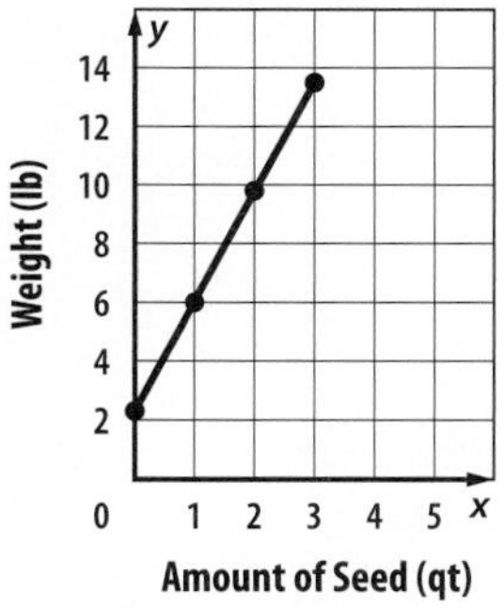

2D. Continuous; sample answer: Because the amount of both variables can be any amount up until the feeder is full, we can connect the points on the graph.

Lesson 1-7

45a.

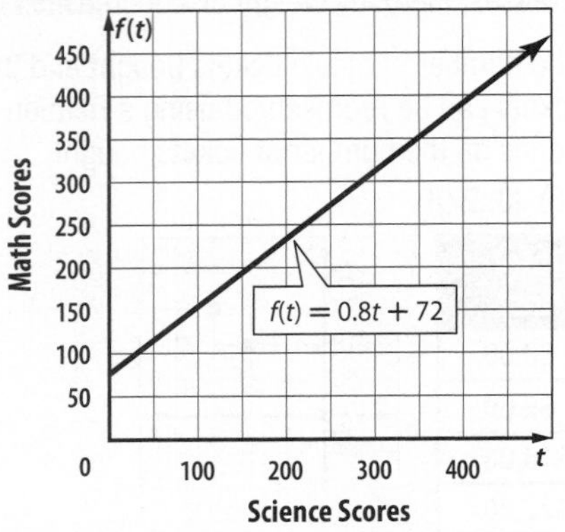

When the science score is 0, the math score is 72. For each point the science score increases, the math score increases by 0.8 point.

48c. Sample answer:

Amount Earned Babysitting

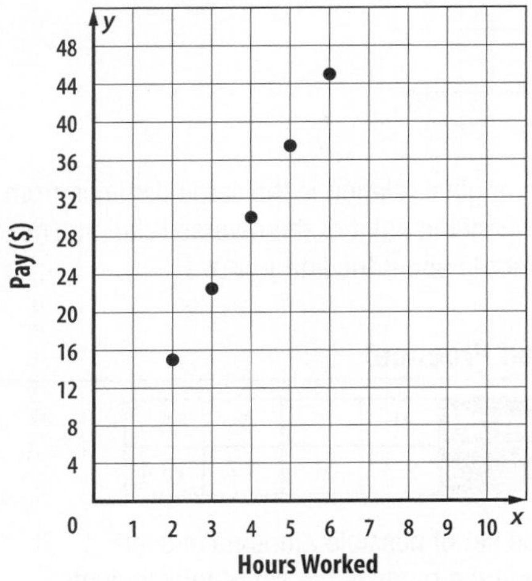

49. Sample answer: {(−2, 3), (0, 3), (2, 5)}

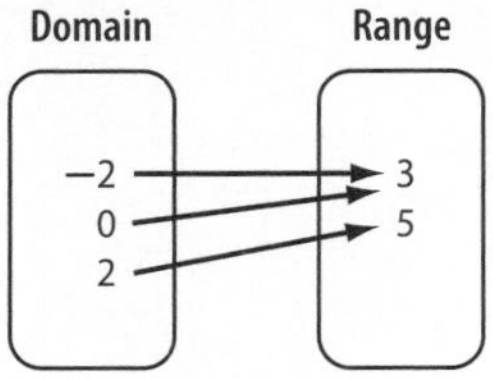

50.

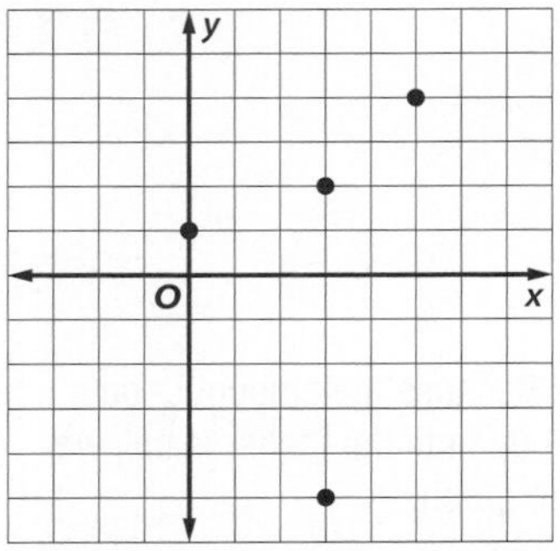

Not a function; one member of the domain, 3, is paired with two different members of the range, −5 and 2.

Extend 1-7

1.

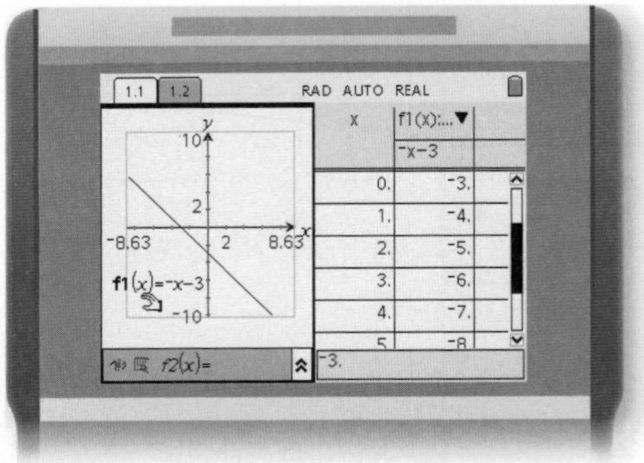

2.

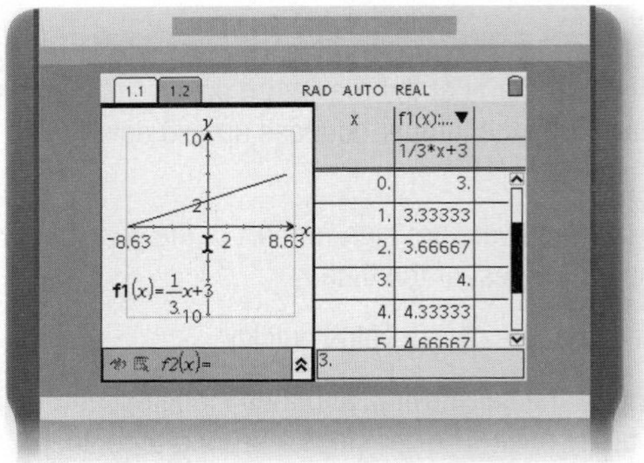

3.

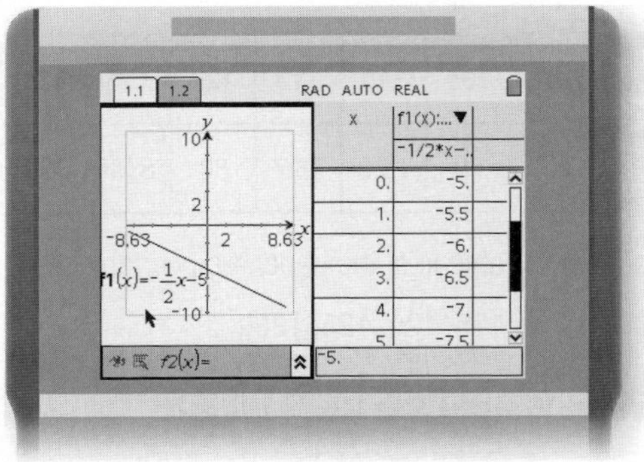

4.

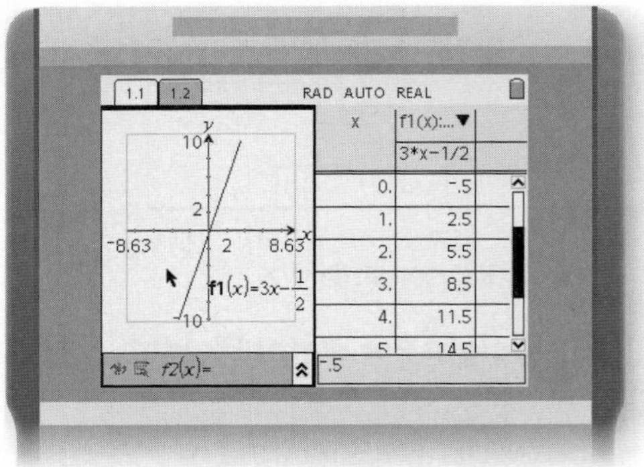

5.

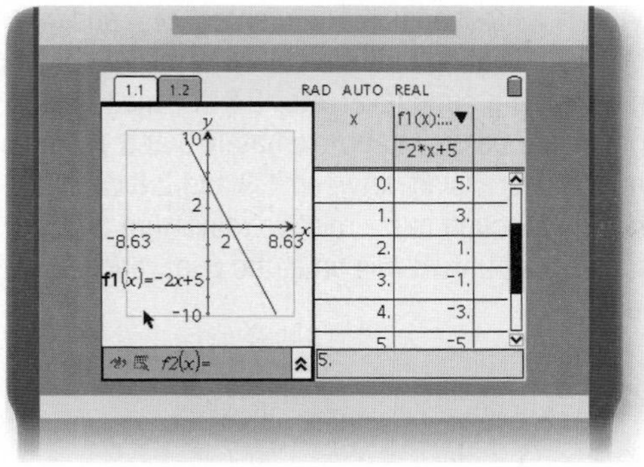

6.

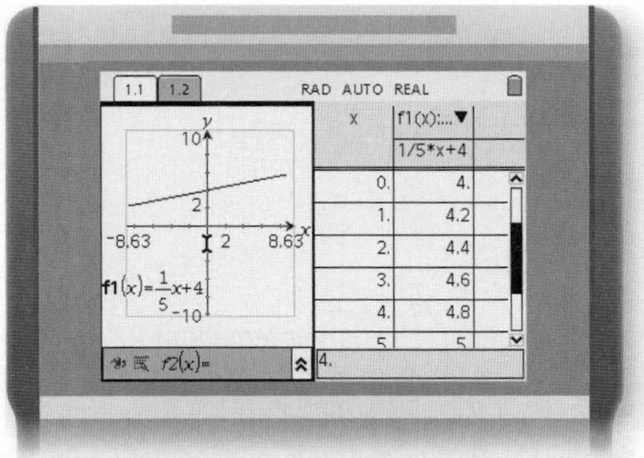

Lesson 1-8 (Guided Practice)

1. Linear; a y-intercept of about -5 means that the temperature was about $-5°$ at the beginning of the sample time. An x-int. of about 1 means that after about 1 hour, the temperature was 0°.

3. The function is positive for $x > 1$ and negative for $x < 1$. This means that the temperatures were below zero before 1 hour of elapsed time, but after 1 hour had passed, all the temperatures were above zero. The function is increasing for all values of x, which means that the day gets warmer as time elapses. There are no relative maxima or minima since the function continues to increase for all values of x as the temperatures continue to increase over time. As x increases, the value of y increases. As x decreases, the value of y decreases. The end behavior of the graph indicates that as the day goes on, the temperatures increase.

Lesson 1-8

1. Nonlinear; the y-intercept is 0, so there is no change in the stock value at the opening bell. The x-intercepts are 0, about 3.2, and about 4.5, so there is no change in the stock value after 0 hours, after about 3.2 hours, and after about 4.5 hours after the opening bell. The graph has no line symmetry. The stock went up in value for the first 3.2 hours, then dropped below the starting value from about 3.2 hours until 4.5 hours, and finally went up again after 4.5 hours. The stock value starts the day increasing in value for the first 2 hours, then it goes down in value from 2 hours until 4 hours, and after 4 hours it goes up in value for the remainder of the day. The stock had a relative high value after 2 hours and then a relative low value after 4 hours. As the day goes on, the stock increases in value.

2. Nonlinear; the y-intercept is about 60, so there is an initial production cost of about \$60. There are no x-intercepts, so the cost per widget will never be \$0. The cost of producing 0 to 16 widgets is the same as the cost of producing 16 to 32 widgets. There is always a cost for producing any number of widgets. The average production cost decreases for making 0 to 16 widgets and then goes up for producing 16 to 32 widgets. The lowest production cost occurs when 16 widgets are produced. As greater numbers of widgets are produced, the average cost per widget will continue to increase.

3. Linear; the y-intercept is about 45, so the temperature was about 45°F when the measurement started. The x-intercept is about 5.5, so after about 5.5 hours, the temperature was 0°F. The graph has no line symmetry. The temperature is above zero for the first 5.5 hours, and then below zero after 5.5 hours. The temperature is going down for the entire time. There are no extrema. As the time increases, the temperature will continue to drop, which is not very likely.

4. Linear; the y-intercept is about -400, so the mowing service has a start-up cost of about \$400. The x-intercept is about 4, so after about 4 weeks, the profit will be \$0. The graph has no line symmetry. The profits will be in the negative until after about 4 weeks, and then will be positive for all time afterwards. The profits are constantly increasing. There are no extrema. As the number of weeks increases, the profits will increase.

5. Nonlinear; the y-intercept is about 20, so the purchase price of the vehicle was about \$20,000. There is no x-intercept, so the value of the vehicle will never equal 0. The graph has no line symmetry. The value of the vehicle is always positive.The value of the vehicle is always decreasing. There are no extrema. As the number of years increase, the value of the vehicle decreases.

6. Nonlinear; the y-intercept is about 5, so the company has a profit of about \$5000 without spending any money on advertising. The x-intercepts are about -1 and about 21, so the company will make a profit of \$0 if they spend \$21,000 on advertising. Spending between \$0 to \$10,000 on advertising will produce the same profits as spending between \$10,000 to \$20,000. The company will make a profit if they spend between \$0 and \$210,000. If they spend more than \$210,000 on advertising, they will lose money. The profits will increase until the company spends about \$100,000, and then the profits will decrease for any amount greater than \$100,000. Spending about \$100,000 will produce the greatest profit. As more money is spent on advertising, the profits will decrease so that the company is losing money.

7. Nonlinear; the y-intercept is about 100. This means that the web site had 100 hits before the time began. There is no x-intercept. The function is positive for all values of x. This means that the web site has never experienced a time of inactivity. The function is increasing for all values of x, with no relative maxima or minima. As x increases, y increases, which means that the upward trend in the number of hits is expected to continue.

8. Nonlinear; the y-intercept is 0, which means that at the start, there was no medicine in the bloodstream. There appears to be no x-intercept, which means that the medicine does not ever fully leave the bloodstream for the time shown. The function is positive for all values of x, which means that after the medicine is taken, there is always some amount in the bloodstream. The function is increasing between about $x = 0$ and $x = 8$ and decreasing for $x > 8$, with a maximum value of about 1.5 at about $x = 8$. This means that the concentration of medicine increased over the first 8 hours to a maximum concentration of about 2.5 mg/mL, and then decreased. As x increases, the value of y decreases towards 0, which means that the concentration of medicine in the bloodstream becomes less and less, until there is practically none left.

9. Nonlinear; the x- and y-intercept is 0, which means that a pendulum with no length cannot complete a swing. The function is positive and increasing for all values of x. Also, as x increases, y increases. The function has no relative minima or maxima. This means that as the pendulum gets longer, the time it takes for it to complete one full swing increases.

10. The graph is nonlinear with a y-intercept of 0, indicating that the cart started at the same height as the center of the wheel. The x-intercepts are 4, 8, 12, 16, 20, and 24, indicating that the ride returned to this same height 4, 8, 12, 16, and 20 seconds after the ride started. The function is positive between times 0 and 4, 8 and 12, and 16 and 20 seconds. During these times, the cart was higher than the center of the wheel. The function is negative between times 4 and 8, 12 and 16, and 20 and 24 seconds. During these times, the car was lower than the center of the wheel. The function is increasing between times 0 and 2, 6 and 10, 14 and 18, and 22 and 24 seconds. During these times, the wheel was rotating such that the cart was ascending. The function is decreasing between times 2 and 6, 10 and 14, 18 and 22 seconds. During these times, the wheel was rotating such that the cart was descending. The cart reached a maximum height of about 25 feet above the center of the wheel 2, 10, and 18 seconds after the ride started and a minimum height of about 25 feet below the center of the wheel 6, 14, and 22 seconds after the ride started. The up and down pattern in the graph suggests that if the ride continues for more than 24 seconds, the cart will continue to move back and forth between 25 feet above and 25 feet below the center of the wheel.

11. Sample answer: The function has a y-intercept of 0 and an x-intercept of 0, indicating that the plant started with no height as a seed in the ground. The function is increasing over its domain, so that plant was always getting taller. The function has no relative extrema.

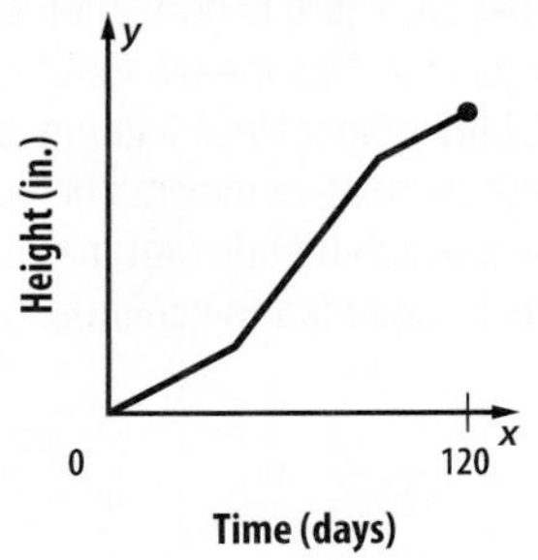

12. Sample answer: The function has a y-intercept of 4 and an x-intercept of 2.8, indicating that the ball started at a height of 4 feet and returned to ground level after 2.8 seconds. The function is increasing between approximately 0 and 1.5 seconds after the punt and decreasing between 1.5 and 2.8 seconds after the punt. The function has a relative maximum at about 1.5 seconds after the punt. At this time, the punt reached its maximum height.

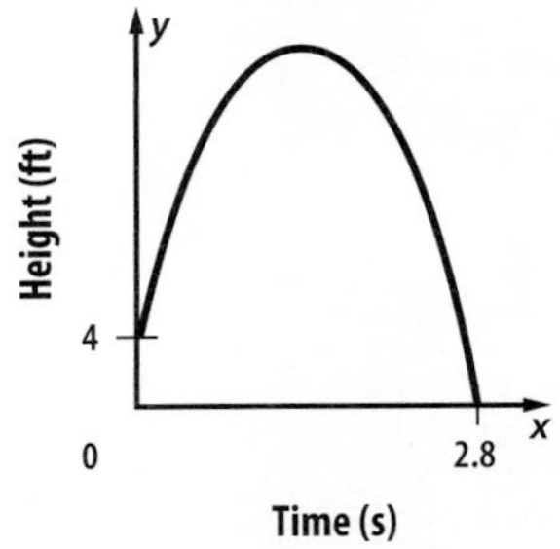

13. Sample answer: The function has a y-intercept of 27, indicating that the initial balance of the loan was $27,000. The x-intercept of 4 indicates that the loan was paid off after 4 years. The function is decreasing over its entire domain, indicting that the amount owed on the loan was always decreasing. The function has no relative extrema.

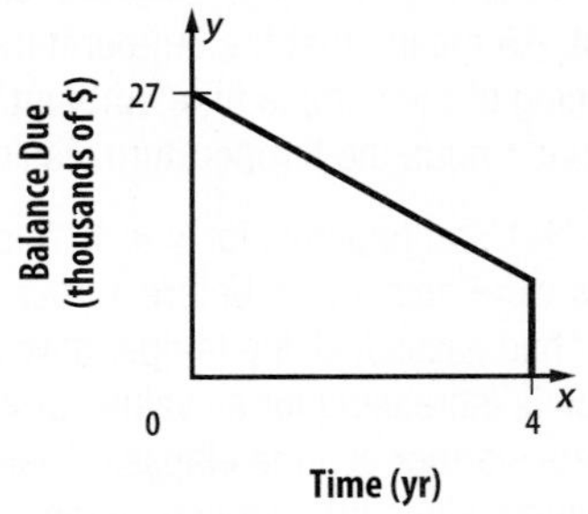

14. Sample graph:

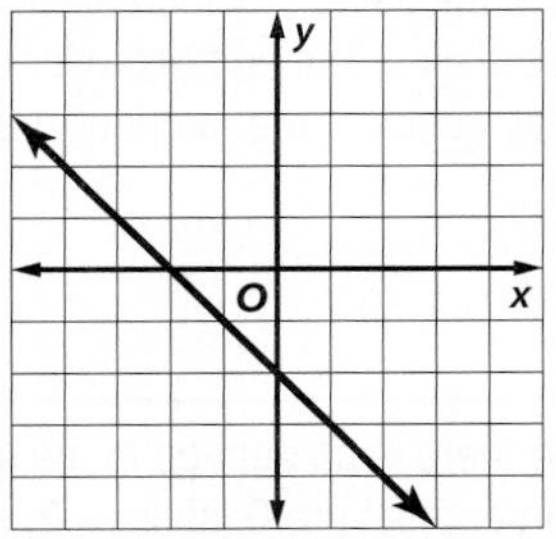

15. Sample graph:

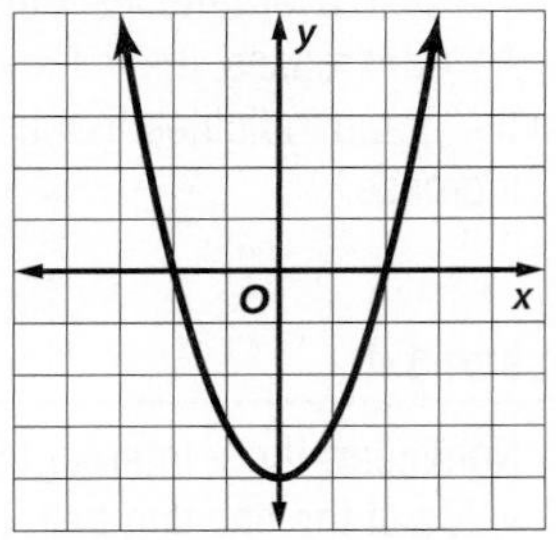

16. Sample graph:

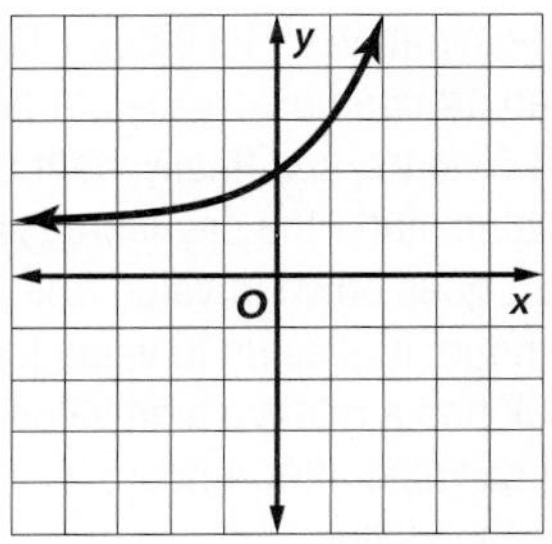

17. Sample graph:

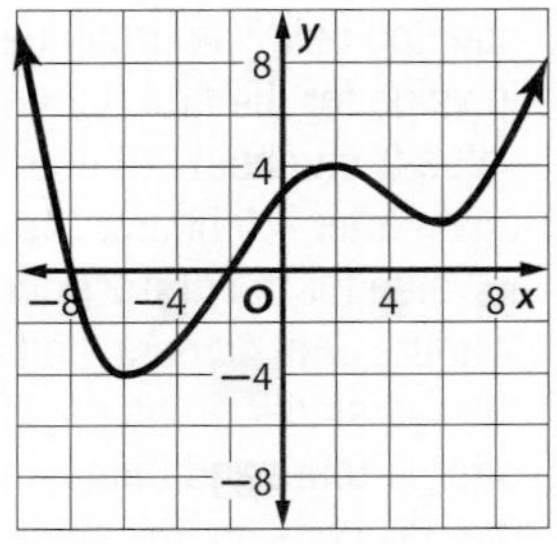

21. The graph has a relative maximum at about $x = 2$ and a relative minimum at about $x = 4.5$. This means that the weekly gasoline price spiked around week 2 at a high of about \$3.50/gal and dipped around week 5 to a low of about \$1.50/gal.

Average Weekly Gasoline Price

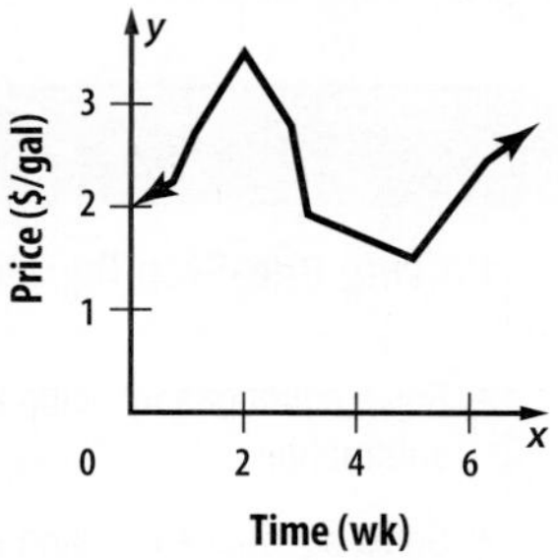

22. Sample answer: You could observe what the value of y is when x is zero to determine the y-intercept, and look for x-values that have a corresponding y-value of zero to determine the x-intercepts of the graph. The function is positive for x-values that have positive corresponding y-values and negative for x-values that have negative corresponding y-values. The function is increasing where as the x-values increase, the corresponding y-values increase and decreasing where as the x-values decrease, the corresponding y-values decrease. A relative maximum is located where the y-values change from increasing to decreasing. A relative minimum is located where the y-values change from decreasing to increasing. To describe the end behavior of the function, observe the value of y as x decreases and the value of y as x-increases, noticing whether it continues to increase, decrease, or approach a specific value.

Study Guide and Review

59.

x	y
1	3
2	4
3	5
4	6

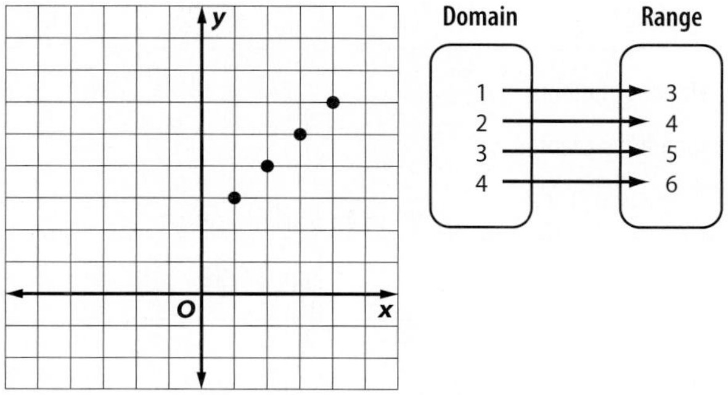

D = {1, 2, 3, 4}; R = {3, 4, 5, 6}

60.

x	y
−1	1
0	−2
3	1
4	−1

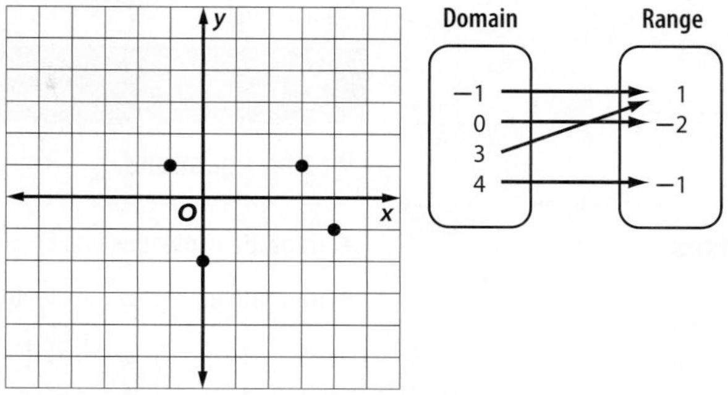

D = {−1, 0, 3, 4}; R = {−2, −1, 1}

61.

x	y
−2	4
−1	3
0	2
−1	2

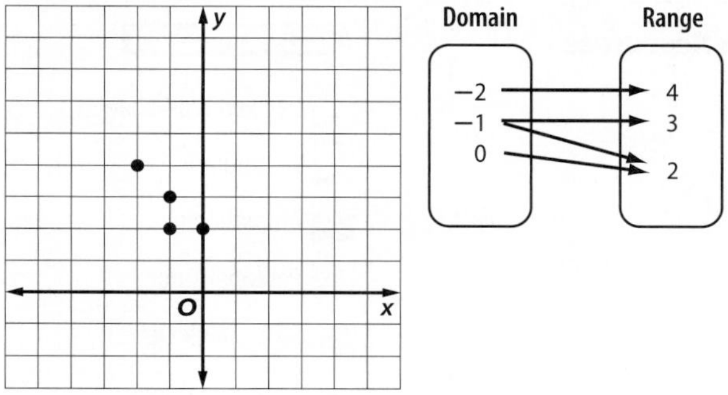

D = {−2, −1, 0}; R = {2, 3, 4}

Practice Test

22. Nonlinear; the x- and y-intercepts are 0. This means that no gadgets have been sold prior to being released. The graph has no symmetry. The total number of gadgets sold is always positive, and is always increasing. There are no extrema. As time increases, the total number of gadgets sold continues to increase, but at a much slower rate than during months 0 to 24.

Chapter Planner

	Diagnostic Assessment Quick Check		
	LESSON 2-1 45 min: 1 day / 90 min: 1 day	**EXPLORE 2-2** 45 min: 0.5 day / 90 min: 0.25 day	**LESSON 2-2** 45 min: 1 day / 90 min: 0.75 day
Title	**Writing Equations**	**Algebra Lab: Solving Equations**	**Solving One-Step Equations**
Objectives	▪ Translate sentences into equations. ▪ Translate equations into sentences.	▪ Use algebra tiles to solve addition, subtraction, and multiplication equations.	▪ Solve equations by using addition or subtraction. ▪ Solve equations by using multiplication and division.
Key Vocabulary	formula	algebra tiles solve an equation	solve an equation equivalent equations
Content Standards	PS.2, AI.L.2	AI.L.1	AI.L.1, AI.L.2
Multiple Representations			
Lesson Resources	connectED.mcgraw-hill.com Leveled Worksheets Vocabulary Animations Personal Tutor Self-Check Quiz ▪ *5-Minute Check* ▪ *Study Notebook*	connectED.mcgraw-hill.com Vocabulary Animations Virtual Manipulatives ▪ *Teaching Algebra with Manipulatives* **Materials:** ▪ algebra tiles ▪ equation mat	connectED.mcgraw-hill.com Leveled Worksheets Vocabulary Animations Personal Tutor Virtual Manipulatives Self-Check Quiz ▪ *5-Minute Check* ▪ *Study Notebook* ▪ *Teaching Algebra with Manipulatives*
Resources for Every Lesson	IWB eStudent Edition IWB Interactive Classroom	▪ eTeacher Edition ▪ eSolutions Manual ▪ McGraw-Hill eAssessment	
Differentiated Instruction	pp. 77, 80		pp. 87, 89

IWB All digital assets are Interactive Whiteboard ready.

Suggested Pacing			
Time Periods	Instruction	Review & Assess	Total
45-minute	11 days	2 days	13 days
90-minute	9 days	1 day	10 days

EXPLORE 2-3 (45 min: 0.5 day; 90 min: 0.25 day)	LESSON 2-3 (45 min: 1 day; 90 min: 0.75 day)	LESSON 2-4 (45 min: 1 day; 90 min: 1 day)	LESSON 2-5 (45 min: 1 day; 90 min: 1 day)
Algebra Lab: Solving Multi-Step Equations	**Solving Multi-Step Equations**	**Solving Equations with the Variable on Each Side**	**Solving Equations Involving Absolute Value**
■ Use algebra tiles to solve multi-step equations.	■ Solve equations involving more than one operation. ■ Solve equations involving consecutive integers.	■ Solve equations with the variable on each side. ■ Solve equations involving grouping symbols.	■ Evaluate absolute value expressions. ■ Solve absolute value equations.
	multi-step equation consecutive integers number theory	identity	
AI.L.1	AI.L.1, AI.L.2	PS.1, PS.5, AI.L.1, AI.L.2	PS.3, PS.7, AI.L.9
connectED.mcgraw-hill.com Animations Virtual Manipulatives ■ *Teaching Algebra with Manipulatives* **Materials:** ■ algebra tiles ■ equation mat	connectED.mcgraw-hill.com Leveled Worksheets Quiz 1 Vocabulary Animations Personal Tutor Virtual Manipulatives Self-Check Quiz ■ *5-Minute Check* ■ *Study Notebook* ■ *Teaching Algebra with Manipulatives*	connectED.mcgraw-hill.com Leveled Worksheets Vocabulary Animations Personal Tutor Virtual Manipulatives Self-Check Quiz ■ *5-Minute Check* ■ *Study Notebook* ■ *Teaching Algebra with Manipulatives*	connectED.mcgraw-hill.com Leveled Worksheets Quiz 2 Animations Personal Tutor Virtual Manipulatives Self-Check Quiz ■ *5-Minute Check* ■ *Study Notebook*
IWB eStudent Edition IWB Interactive Classroom	■ eTeacher Edition ■ eSolutions Manual ■ McGraw-Hill eAssessment		
	pp. 92, 93, 96	pp. 98, 102	pp. 104, 109
			Formative Assessment Mid-Chapter Quiz

Chapter Planner

	LESSON 2-6 (45 min: 1 day; 90 min: 0.75 day)	EXTEND 2-6 (45 min: 0.5 day; 90 min: 0.25 day)	LESSON 2-7 (45 min: 1 day; 90 min: 0.75 day)
Title	**Ratios and Proportions**	**Spreadsheet Lab: Descriptive Modeling**	**Percent of Change**
Objectives	▪ Compare ratios. ▪ Solve proportions.	▪ Use a spreadsheet to investigate different metrics	▪ Find the percent of change. ▪ Solve problems involving percent of change.
Key Vocabulary	ratio proportion means extremes rate unit rate scale scale model	metric debt-to-income ratio	percent of change percent of increase percent of decrease
Content Standards	AI.L.3		PS.8, AI.L.1, AI.L.2
Multiple Representations	✓		✓
Lesson Resources	connectED.mcgraw-hill.com Leveled Worksheets Vocabulary Animations Personal Tutor Self-Check Quiz ▪ *5-Minute Check* ▪ *Study Notebook* ▪ *Teaching Algebra with Manipulatives*	connectED.mcgraw-hill.com Vocabulary Animations Personal Tutor ▪ *Teaching Algebra with Manipulatives* **Materials:** ▪ computer with spreadsheet software	connectED.mcgraw-hill.com Leveled Worksheets Quiz 3 Vocabulary Animations Personal Tutor Virtual Manipulatives Self-Check Quiz ▪ *5-Minute Check* ▪ *Study Notebook* ▪ *Teaching Algebra with Manipulatives*
Resources for Every Lesson	IWB eStudent Edition IWB Interactive Classroom	▪ eTeacher Edition ▪ eSolutions Manual ▪ McGraw-Hill eAssessment	
Differentiated Instruction	pp. 113, 114, 117		pp. 121, 124

IWB All digital assets are Interactive Whiteboard ready.

EXTEND 2-7 (45 min: 0.5 day; 90 min: 0.25 day)	LESSON 2-8 (45 min: 1 day; 90 min: 1 day)	LESSON 2-9 (45 min: 1 day; 90 min: 1 day)
Algebra Lab: Percentiles	**Literal Equations and Dimensional Analysis**	**Weighted Averages**
▪ Find the percentile rank of a data item in a set of scores.	▪ Solve equations for given variables. ▪ Use formulas to solve real-world problems.	▪ Solve mixture problems. ▪ Solve uniform motion problems.
percentile decile	literal equation dimensional analysis unit analysis	weighted average mixture problem uniform motion problem rate problem
	PS.6, A.CED.4, A.REI.3	PS.4, A.REI.1, A.REI.3
connectED.mcgraw-hill.com Vocabulary Animations ▪ *Teaching Algebra with Manipulatives* **Materials:** ▪ paper ▪ scissors	connectED.mcgraw-hill.com Leveled Worksheets Vocabulary Animations Personal Tutor Virtual Manipulatives Self-Check Quiz ▪ *5-Minute Check* ▪ *Study Notebook* ▪ *Teaching Algebra with Manipulatives*	connectED.mcgraw-hill.com Leveled Worksheets Quiz 4 Vocabulary Animations Personal Tutor Self-Check Quiz ▪ *5-Minute Check* ▪ *Study Notebook* ▪ *Teaching Algebra with Manipulatives*
IWB eStudent Edition IWB Interactive Classroom	▪ eTeacher Edition ▪ eSolutions Manual ▪ McGraw-Hill eAssessment	
	pp. 127, 131	pp. 134, 138

Summative Assessment
Study Guide and Review
Practice Test

Assessment and Intervention

SE = Student Edition, **TE** = Teacher Edition, **CRM** = Chapter Resource Masters

	Diagnosis	Prescription
DIAGNOSTIC ASSESSMENT	**Beginning Chapter 2**	
	Get Ready for Chapter 2 **SE**	Intervention **TE**
	Beginning Every Lesson	
	Then, Now, Why? **SE** 5-Minute Check	Chapter 0 **SE** *Quick Review Math Handbook*
FORMATIVE ASSESSMENT	**During/After Every Lesson**	
	Guided Practice **SE**, every example Check Your Understanding **SE** H.O.T. Problems **SE** Spiral Review **SE** Additional Examples **TE** Watch Out! **TE** Step 4, Assess **TE** Chapter 2 Quizzes **CRM**, pp. 63–64 Self-Check Quizzes connectED.mcgraw-hill.com	TIER 1 Intervention Skills Practice **CRM**, Ch. 1–2 connectED.mcgraw-hill.com TIER 2 Intervention Differentiated Instruction **TE** Differentiated Homework Options **TE** Study Guide and Intervention **CRM**, Ch. 1–2 *Quick Review Math Handbook* TIER 3 Intervention *Math Triumphs, Alg. 1,* Ch. 1–5
	Mid-Chapter	
	Mid-Chapter Quiz **SE** Mid-Chapter Test **CRM**, p. 65 McGraw-Hill eAssessment	TIER 1 Intervention Skills Practice **CRM**, Ch. 1–2 connectED.mcgraw-hill.com TIER 2 Intervention Study Guide and Intervention **CRM**, Ch. 1–2; *Quick Review Math Handbook* TIER 3 Intervention *Math Triumphs, Alg. 1,* Ch. 1–5
	Before Chapter Test	
	Chapter Study Guide and Review **SE** Practice Test **SE** Standardized Test Practice **SE** Chapter Test connectED.mcgraw-hill.com Standardized Test Practice connectED.mcgraw-hill.com Vocabulary Review connectED.mcgraw-hill.com McGraw-Hill eAssessment	TIER 1 Intervention Skills Practice **CRM**, Ch. 1–2 connectED.mcgraw-hill.com TIER 2 Intervention Study Guide and Intervention **CRM**, Ch. 1–2; *Quick Review Math Handbook* TIER 3 Intervention *Math Triumphs, Alg. 1,* Ch. 1–5
SUMMATIVE ASSESSMENT	**After Chapter 2**	
	Multiple-Choice Tests, Forms 1, 2A, 2B **CRM**, pp. 67–72 Free-Response Tests, Forms 2C, 2D, 3 **CRM**, pp. 73–78 Vocabulary Test **CRM**, p. 66 Extended Response Test **CRM**, p. 79 Standardized Test Practice **CRM**, pp. 80–82 McGraw-Hill eAssessment	Study Guide and Intervention **CRM**, Ch. 1–2 *Quick Review Math Handbook* connectED.mcgraw-hill.com

Differentiated Instruction

Option 1 Reaching All Learners AL OL BL ELL

Auditory/Musical Have students clap twice each second for 5 seconds. Then have students clap twice each second for 10 seconds. Write the following on the board, leaving space between the equations:

5 seconds = 10 claps

10 seconds = 20 claps

Point out that each value in the second equation is double the first, but the equation is still true. Write $\times$ 2 under each side of the first equation.

5 seconds = 10 claps
× 2 × 2
10 seconds = 20 claps

Explain that when you perform the same operation on each side of a true equation, the result is a true equation.

Intrapersonal Have students make a list of four items and their prices. The items can be in the price range of their choosing. Then have students calculate the price of each item after a discount of 15%.

Option 2 Approaching Level AL

Explain to students that often class scores do not all carry the same weight toward the final grade. Tell students that homework counts 10%, quizzes count 30%, tests count 40%, and the final exam counts 20%. Have students compute the final grade for a homework average of 86%, quiz average of 89%, test average of 95%, and final exam of 98%. 0.929 or 92.9% Ask students to determine if this weighted average is greater than or less than the non-weighted average? greater than

Option 3 English Learners ELL

Have students make study cards for the key concepts in this chapter. On one side of the card, students write the name of the concept. On the flip side, students give an example of how the concept is used.

Option 4 Beyond Level BL

The study of number theory can be quite interesting for students. Ask pairs of students to write and solve their own consecutive integer problems, using Example 3 in Lesson 2-3 as a guide. Then have pairs "teach" the class how to solve their problem.

CHAPTER 2

Linear Equations

Focus on Mathematical Content

Vertical Alignment

Before Chapter 2

Related Topics before Grade 8

- simplify numerical expressions involving order of operations
- find solutions to application problems involving percent

Related Topics from Grade 8

- make connections among various representations of a numerical relationship
- validate conclusions using mathematical properties
- use proportional relationships in similar figures to find missing measurements

Previous Topics from Algebra 1

- use the Distributive Property to simplify algebraic expressions

Chapter 2

Related Topics from Algebra 1

- describe functional relationships for given problem situations and write equations to answer questions arising from the situations
- represent relationships among quantities using diagrams, verbal descriptions, and equations
- find specific function values, and transform and solve equations in problem situations
- solve problems involving proportional change
- use the Commutative, Associative, and Distributive Properties to simplify expressions

After Chapter 2

Preparation for Algebra 2

- use the necessary algebraic skills required to simplify algebraic expressions and inequalities in problem situations
- use tools to simplify expressions and to transform and solve equations

Lesson-by-Lesson Preview

2-1 Writing Equations

Variables can be used to represent an unknown amount when writing equations from a verbal sentence.

- The ability to write an equation from a verbal sentence is needed when solving word problems.
- Following the four-step problem-solving plan can help solve any word problem.

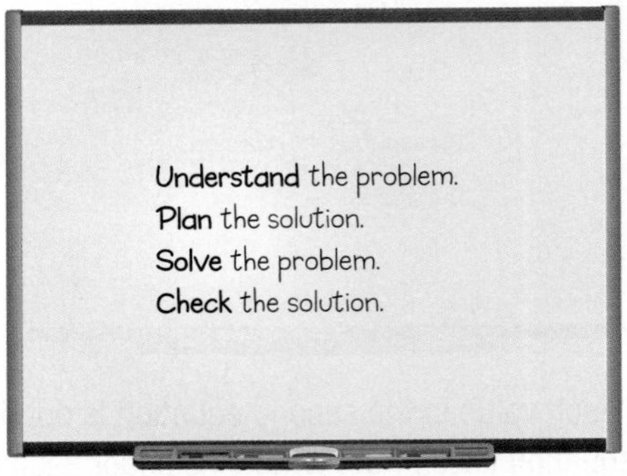

- When a verbal sentence can be translated into an equation that states a rule for the relationship between certain quantities, the equation is called a formula. It can be used to solve problems about those quantities.

2-2 Solving One-Step Equations

Solving an equation means finding the value of the variable in the equation that makes the equation true.

- To solve an equation, isolate the variable (with a coefficient of 1) on one side of the equation.
- Use the Properties of Equality to maintain equivalent equations in each step in this process.
- The Addition/Subtraction Property of Equality permits the same number to be added/subtracted to each side of an equation.
- The Multiplication/Division Property of Equality permits each side of an equation to be multiplied/divided by the same nonzero number.

2-3 Solving Multi-Step Equations

Multi-step equations involve more than one operation. These equations can be solved using the Properties of Equality and the strategy of undoing each operation by working backward.

In *number theory*, multi-step equations are written and solved to understand the relationship between numbers, such as consecutive integers.

2-4 Solving Equations with the Variable on Each Side

To solve equations with variables on each side:

- Simplify. Use the Distributive Property to remove any grouping symbols. Simplify again using the properties of equality.
- If all the variable terms are eliminated and the result, such as $3 = 5$, is not a true equation, there is no solution.
- If both sides of the equation are identical, the equation is an *identity*. All values are solutions for this equation.

2-5 Solving Equations Involving Absolute Value

The *absolute value* of a number is the distance the number is from zero on a number line. Open sentences involving an absolute value expression can be either an equation or an inequality.

- To solve an equation involving an absolute value, first isolate the absolute value on one side of the equation.
- Then, rewrite the equation as a compound sentence using the word *or*.
- The solution set of an absolute value equation can be graphed on a number line or written in set notation.

2-6 Ratios and Proportions

A ratio is a comparison of two numbers by division. A ratio is called a rate if the two numbers of a ratio represent measurements with different units, such as miles and hours.

A *proportion* is an equation stating that two ratios are equal.

2-7 Percent of Change

A *percent* is a ratio that compares a number to 100. The ratio of the change of an amount to the original amount is called a *percent of change*.

- If the new number is greater than the original number, the percent of change is a *percent of increase*.
- If the new number is less than the original number, the percent of change is a *percent of decrease*.

Percent of change can be found by solving for r in $\frac{\text{amount of change}}{\text{original number}} = \frac{r}{100}$. Finding sales tax and discounts are applications of percent of change.

2-8 Literal Equations and Dimensional Analysis

Some equations contain more than one variable. The processes for solving one-step or multi-step equations are used to solve these equations for one variable in terms of the other variable(s). A formula or equation with multiple variables is called a *literal equation*. Many formulas require using *dimensional analysis*, the process of carrying units of measure throughout a computation.

2-9 Weighted Averages

A *weighted average* is the sum of the product of the number of units in a set of data and the value per unit divided by the sum of the number of units. Mixture and uniform motion (rate) problems are applications of weighted averages.

Professional Development

Targeted professional development has been articulated throughout Algebra 1. More quality, customized professional development is available from McGraw-Hill Professional Development. Visit connectED.mcgraw-hill.com for details on each product.

- Online Lessons emphasize the strategies and techniques used to teach Algebra 1. Includes streaming video, interactive pages, and online tools.
- Video Workshops allow mentors, coaches, or leadership personnel to facilitate on-site workshops on educational strategies in mathematics and mathematical concepts.
- MHPD Online (www.mhpdonline.com) offers online professional development with video clips of instructional strategies, links, student activities, and news and issues in education.
- Teaching Today (teachingtoday.glencoe.com) gives secondary teachers practical strategies and materials that inspire excellence and innovation in teaching.

Chapter Project

UPC ABCs

Students use what they have learned about expressions to complete a project.

This chapter project addresses business literacy, as well as several specific skills identified as being essential to student success by the Framework for 21st Century Learning.

Visit connectED.mcgraw-hill.com for student and teacher handouts.

KeyVocabulary Introduce the key vocabulary in the chapter using the routine below.

Define: A formula is an equation that states a rule for the relationship between certain quantities.

Example: The formula for the perimeter of a rectangle is $P = 2\ell + 2w$.

Ask: If $\ell = 4$ and $w = 7$, what does P equal? 22

CHAPTER 2 Linear Equations

Then

You learned to simplify algebraic expressions.

Now

In this chapter, you will:

- Create equations that describe relationships.
- Solve linear equations in one variable.
- Solve proportions.
- Use formulas to solve real-world problems.

Why?

SHOPPING In recent years, the percent of change in sales per year at shopping malls in the U.S. averaged 5%. A store manager can use this data to set a sales goal for the upcoming year.

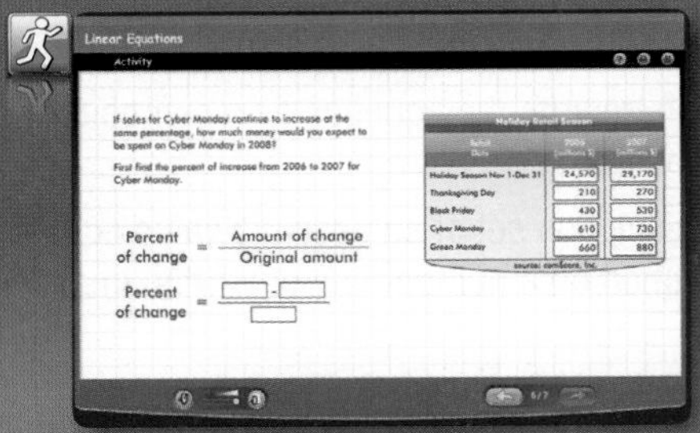

connectED.mcgraw-hill.com Your Digital Math Portal

Animation | Vocabulary | eGlossary | Personal Tutor | Virtual Manipulatives | Graphing Calculator | Audio | Foldables | Self-Check Practice | Worksheets

Content Standards
AI.L.1, AI.L.2, AI.L.3, AI.L.9, AI.L.11

Process Standards
PS.1, PS.2, PS.3, PS.4, PS.5, PS.6, PS.7, PS.8

Get Ready for the Chapter

Diagnose Readiness | You have two options for checking prerequisite skills.

1 Textbook Option Take the Quick Check below. Refer to the Quick Review for help.

QuickCheck

Write an algebraic expression for each verbal expression.

1. four less than three times a number n $3n - 4$
2. a number d cubed less seven $d^3 - 7$
3. the difference between two times b and eleven $2b - 11a$

Evaluate each expression.

4. $(9 - 4)^2 + 3$ 28
5. $\frac{3 \cdot 8 - 12 \div 2}{3^2}$ 2
6. $5(8 - 2) \div 3$ 10
7. $\frac{1}{3}(21) + \frac{1}{8}(32)$ 11
8. $72 \div 9 + 3 \cdot 2^3$ 32
9. $\frac{11 - 3}{2} + 7$ 11
10. $2[(5 - 3)^2 + 8] + (3 - 1) \div 2$ 25
11. **BAKERY** Sue buys 1 carrot cake for $14, 6 large chocolate chip cookies for $1.50 each, and a dozen doughnuts for $0.45 each. How much money did Sue spend at the bakery? $28.40

Find each percent.

12. What percent of 400 is 260? 65%
13. Twelve is what percent of 60? 20%
14. What percent of 25 is 75? 300%
15. **ICE CREAM** What percent of the people surveyed prefer strawberry ice cream? 21%

Favorite Flavor	Number of Responses
vanilla	82
chocolate	76
strawberry	42

QuickReview

Example 1 (Used in Lessons 2-1 through 2-9)

Write an algebraic expression for the phrase *the product of eight and w increased by nine.*

the product of eight and w increased by nine

8 · w + 9

The expression is $8w + 9$.

Example 2 (Used in Lessons 2-1 through 2-4)

Evaluate $9 - \left[\frac{8 + 2^2}{2} - 2(5 \times 2 - 8)\right]$.

$9 - \left[\frac{8 + 2^2}{2} - 2(5 \times 2 - 8)\right]$ Original expression

$= 9 - \left[\frac{8 + 2^2}{2} - 2(2)\right]$ Evaluate inside the parentheses.

$= 9 - \left(\frac{8 + 2^2}{2} - 4\right)$ Multiply.

$= 9 - \left(\frac{8 + 4}{2} - 4\right)$ Evaluate the power.

$= 9 - (6 - 4)$ Add and then divide.

$= 7$ Simplify.

Example 3 (Used in Lesson 2-7)

32 is what percent of 40?

$\frac{a}{b} = \frac{p}{100}$ Use the percent proportion.

$\frac{32}{40} = \frac{p}{100}$ Replace a with 32 and b with 40.

$32(100) = 40p$ Find the cross products.

$3200 = 40p$ Multiply.

$80 = p$ Divide each side by 40.

32 is 80% of 40.

2 Online Option Take an online self-check Chapter Readiness Quiz at connectED.mcgraw-hill.com.

Essential Question

- Why is it helpful to represent the same mathematical idea in different ways? Sample answer: Depending on the situation, one representation may be more helpful than another. For example, if you want to look for trends or patterns, a graph may be most helpful. If you want to find specific values, a function may be most helpful.

Get Ready for the Chapter

Response to Intervention (RtI)

Use the *Quick Check* results and the Intervention Planner chart to help you determine your Response to Intervention. The If-Then statements in the chart below help you decide the appropriate tier of RtI and suggest intervention resources for each tier.

InterventionPlanner

TIER 1 On Level OL

If students miss about 25% of the exercises or less,

Then choose a resource:

SE Lessons 1-1, 1-2, and 0-6

Skills Practice, Chapter 1, pp. 7, 39

connectED.mcgraw-hill.com Self-Check Quiz

TIER 2 Strategic Intervention AL approaching grade level

If students miss about 50% of the exercises,

Then choose a resource:

Study Guide and Intervention, Chapter 1, pp. 5, 37

Quick Review Math Handbook

connectED.mcgraw-hill.com Extra Examples, Personal Tutor, Homework Help

TIER 3 Intensive Intervention 2 or more grades below level

If students miss about 75% of the exercises,

Then use *Math Triumphs, Alg. 1,* Ch. 1–5

connectED.mcgraw-hill.com Extra Examples, Personal Tutor, Homework Help, Review Vocabulary

FOLDABLES StudyOrganizer

Dinah Zike's Foldables®

Focus As students read and study this chapter, they should show examples and write notes about linear equations in their study booklets.

Teach Have students make and label their Foldables as illustrated. Have students fill in the appropriate pages of their booklets with study notes as they cover each lesson in this chapter. At the end of each lesson, ask students to use the booklets to take notes, write and solve equations, solve real-world problems, or to record and define vocabulary words and concepts.

When to Use It Encourage students to add to their Foldables as they work through the chapter and to use them to review for the chapter test.

Differentiated Instruction

Student-Built Glossary, pp. 1–2

Students should complete the chart by providing the definition of each term and an example as they progress through Chapter 2. This study tool can also be used to review for the chapter test.

Get Started on the Chapter

You will learn several new concepts, skills, and vocabulary terms as you study Chapter 2. To get ready, identify important terms and organize your resources. You may wish to refer to Chapter 0 to review prerequisite skills.

FOLDABLES StudyOrganizer

Linear Equations Make this Foldable to help you organize your Chapter 2 notes about linear equations. Begin with 5 sheets of grid paper.

1 **Fold** each sheet in half along the width.

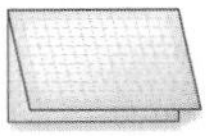

2 **Unfold** each sheet and tape to form one long piece.

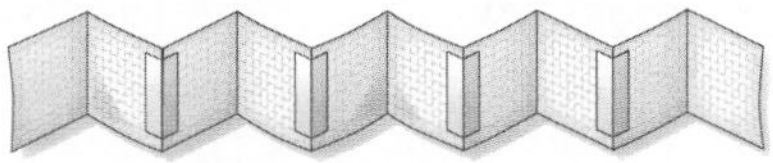

3 **Label** each page with the lesson number as shown. Refold to form a booklet.

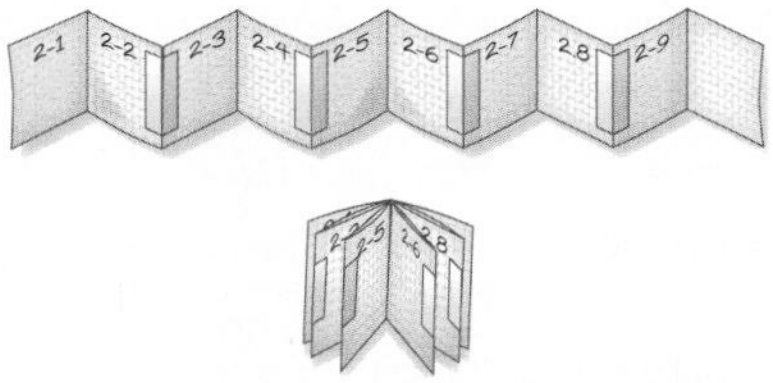

NewVocabulary

English		Español
formula	p. 76	fórmula
solve an equation	p. 83	resolver una ecuación
equivalent equations	p. 83	ecuaciones equivalentes
multi-step equation	p. 91	ecuación de varios pasos
identity	p. 98	identidad
ratio	p. 111	razón
proportion	p. 111	proporción
rate	p. 113	tasa
unit rate	p. 113	tasa unitaria
scale model	p. 114	modelo de escala
percent of change	p. 119	porcentaje de cambio
literal equation	p. 127	ecuación literal
dimensional analysis	p. 128	análisis dimensional
weighted average	p. 132	promedio ponderado

ReviewVocabulary

algebraic expression expresion algebraica an expression consisting of one or more numbers and variables along with one or more arithmetic operations

coordinate system sistema de coordenedas the grid formed by the intersection of two number lines, the horizontal axis and the vertical axis

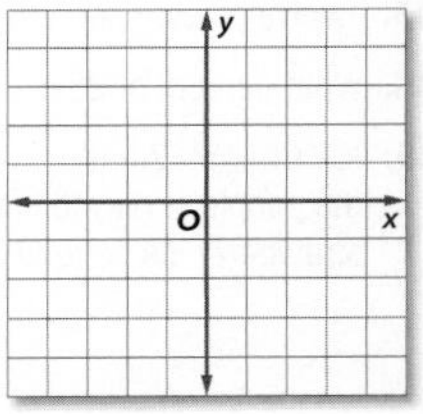

function función a relation in which each element of the domain is paired with exactly one element of the range

LESSON 2-1 Writing Equations

Then

- You evaluated and simplified algebraic expressions.

Now

1. Translate sentences into equations.
2. Translate equations into sentences.

Why?

- The Daytona 500 is widely considered to be the most important event of the NASCAR circuit. The distance around the track is 2.5 miles, and the race is a total of 500 miles. We can write an equation to determine how many laps it takes to finish the race.

NewVocabulary
formula

Content Standards
AI.L.2

Process Standards
PS.2

1 Write Verbal Expressions To write an equation, identify the unknown for which you are looking and assign a variable to it. Then, write the sentence as an equation. Look for key words such as *is, is as much as, is the same as,* or *is identical to* that indicate where you should place the equals sign.

Consider the Daytona 500 example above.

Words	The length of each lap	times the	number of laps	is	the length of the race.
Variable	Let ℓ represent the number of laps in the race.				
Equation	2.5	$\times$	ℓ	$=$	500

Example 1 Translate Sentences into Equations

Translate each sentence into an equation.

a. Seven times a number squared is five times the difference of k and m.

Seven	times	*n* squared	is	five	times	the difference of *k* and *m*.
7	$\cdot$	n^2	$=$	5	$\cdot$	$(k - m)$

The equation is $7n^2 = 5(k - m)$.

b. Fifteen times a number subtracted from 80 is 25.

You can rewrite the verbal sentence so it is easier to translate. *Fifteen times a number subtracted from 80 is 25* is the same as *80 minus 15 times a number is 25*. Let n represent the number.

80	minus	15	times	a number	is	25.
80	$-$	15	$\cdot$	n	$=$	25

The equation is $80 - 15n = 25$.

GuidedPractice

1A. Two plus the quotient of a number and 8 is the same as 16. $2 + \frac{n}{8} = 16$

1B. Twenty-seven times k is h squared decreased by 9. $27k = h^2 - 9$

1 Focus

VerticalAlignment

Before Lesson 2-1 Evaluate and simplify algebraic expressions.

Lesson 2-1 Translate sentences into equations.
Translate equations into sentences.

After Lesson 2-1 Transform and solve equations.

2 Teach

Scaffolding Questions

Have students read the **Why?** section of the lesson.

Ask:

- What is the length of the race? 500 miles
- What is the unknown that you want to find? the number of laps that equals 500 miles
- What do you know about the length of a lap? a lap is 2.5 miles
- What operation can you perform on the number of laps to equal the length of the race? Multiply the length of a lap, 2.5 miles, times the number of laps.

Lesson 2-1 Resources

Resource	Approaching Level AL	On Level OL	Beyond Level BL	English Learners ELL
Teacher Edition	▪ Differentiated Instruction, p. 77	▪ Differentiated Instruction, p. 77	▪ Differentiated Instruction, pp. 77, 80	▪ Differentiated Instruction, p. 77
Chapter Resource Masters	▪ Study Guide and Intervention, pp. 5–6 ▪ Skills Practice, p. 7 ▪ Practice, p. 8 ▪ Word Problem Practice, p. 9	▪ Study Guide and Intervention, pp. 5–6 ▪ Skills Practice, p. 7 ▪ Practice, p. 8 ▪ Word Problem Practice, p. 9 ▪ Enrichment, p. 10	▪ Practice, p. 8 ▪ Word Problem Practice, p. 9 ▪ Enrichment, p. 10	▪ Study Guide and Intervention, pp. 5–6 ▪ Skills Practice, p. 7 ▪ Practice, p. 8 ▪ Word Problem Practice, p. 9
Other	▪ 5-Minute Check 2-1 ▪ Study Notebook	▪ 5-Minute Check 2-1 ▪ Study Notebook	▪ 5-Minute Check 2-1 ▪ Study Notebook	▪ 5-Minute Check 2-1 ▪ Study Notebook

1 Write Equations

Example 1 shows how to translate sentences into equations. **Example 2** shows how the four-step problem-solving plan is used to solve a real-world problem. **Example 3** shows how to write a formula by translating a sentence.

Formative Assessment

Use the Guided Practice exercises after each Example to determine students' understanding of concepts.

Additional Examples

1 Translate each sentence into an equation.

a. A number b divided by three is six less than c.
$\frac{b}{3} = c - 6$

b. Fifteen more than z times 6 is 11 less than y times 2.
$15 + 6z = 2y - 11$

2 **JELLY BEANS** A jelly bean manufacturer produces 1,250,000 jelly beans per hour. How many hours does it take to produce 10,000,000 jelly beans? 8 hours

3 **GEOMETRY** Translate the sentence into a formula.
The perimeter of a square equals four times the length of a side.
$P = 4s$

Additional Examples also in Interactive Classroom PowerPoint® Presentations

IWB Interactive White Board READY

Translating sentences to algebraic expressions and equations is a valuable skill in solving real-world problems.

Real-WorldLink

In 1919, Britain and France offered a flight that carried two passengers at a time. Now there are more than 87,000 flights each day in the U.S.

Source: NATCA

Real-World Example 2 Use the Four-Step Problem-Solving Plan

AIR TRAVEL **Refer to the information at the left. In how many days will 261,000 flights have occurred in the United States?**

Understand The information given in the problem is that there are approximately 87,000 flights per day in the United States. We are asked to find how many days it will take for 261,000 flights to have occurred.

Plan Write an equation. Let d represent the number of days needed.

87,000	times	the number of days	equals	261,000.
87,000	$\cdot$	d	=	261,000

Solve $87{,}000\, d = 261{,}000$ Find d by asking, "What number times 87,000 is 261,000?"

$d = 3$

Check Check your answer by substituting 3 for d in the equation.

$87{,}000(3) \stackrel{?}{=} 261{,}000$ Substitute 3 for d.

$261{,}000 = 261{,}000$ ✓ Multiply.

The answer makes sense and works for the original problem.

GuidedPractice $50 = r - 70$; 120

2. **GOVERNMENT** There are 50 members in the North Carolina Senate. This is 70 fewer than the number in the North Carolina House of Representatives. How many members are in the North Carolina House of Representatives?

A rule for the relationship between certain quantities is called a **formula**. These equations use variables to represent numbers and form general rules.

Example 3 Write a Formula

GEOMETRY **Translate the sentence into a formula.**

The area of a triangle equals the product of $\frac{1}{2}$ the length of the base and the height.

Words	The	area of a triangle	equals	the product of $\frac{1}{2}$ the length of the base and the height.
Variables	Let A = area, b = base, and h = height.			
Equation		A	=	$\frac{1}{2}bh$

The formula for the area of a triangle is $A = \frac{1}{2}bh$.

GuidedPractice

3. **GEOMETRY** Translate the sentence into a formula.
In a right triangle, the square of the measure of the hypotenuse c is equal to the sum of the squares of the measures of the legs, a and b. $c^2 = a^2 + b^2$

Tips for New Teachers

Translating Tell students that when translating between sentences and equations, there is usually more than one way to write the result. The equation in Example 2 could also be written as $261{,}000 \div d = 87{,}000$.

Focus on Mathematical Content

Algebraic Expressions Algebraic expressions have one or more variables and usually contain some numbers and one or more operations. When writing an algebraic expression, variables are used to represent unknown numbers or measures.

Teach with Tech

Audio Recording Make an audio recording of reading several equations out loud. Play the recording for students and have them write the equations algebraically. You could post these audio recordings on your secure classroom Web site and have students complete this as homework.

76 | Lesson 2-1 | Writing Equations

Math HistoryLink

Ahmes (about 1680–1620 B.C.) Ahmes was the Egyptian mathematician and scribe who copied the Rhind Mathematical Papyrus. The papyrus contains 87 algebra problems of the same type. The first set of problems asks how to divide n loaves of bread among 10 people.

2 Write Sentences from Equations

If you are given an equation, you can write a sentence or create your own word problem.

Example 4 Translate Equations into Sentences

Translate each equation into a sentence.

a. $6z - 15 = 45$

$6z$	$-$	15	$=$	45
Six times z	minus	fifteen	equals	forty-five.

b. $y^2 + 3x = w$

y^2	$+$	$3x$	$=$	w
The sum of y squared	and	three times x	is	w.

GuidedPractice

4A. $15 = 25u^2 + 2$

4B. $\frac{3}{2}r - t^3 = 132$

4A. Sample answer: Fifteen is equal to the product of 25 and u squared plus two.
4B. Sample answer: Three halves times r minus t cubed is the same as one hundred thirty-two.

When given a set of information, you can create a problem that relates a story.

Example 5 Write a Problem

Write a problem based on the given information.

t = the time that Maxine drove in each turn; $t + 4$ = the time that Tia drove in each turn; $2t + (t + 4) = 28$

Sample problem:

Maxine and Tia went on a trip, and they took turns driving. During her turn, Tia drove 4 hours more than Maxine. Maxine took 2 turns, and Tia took 1 turn. Together they drove for 28 hours. How many hours did Maxine drive?

GuidedPractice

5. p = Beth's salary; $0.1p$ = bonus; $p + 0.1p = 525$

5. Beth gets paid at her job by both salary and a bonus. Her bonus is 10% of her salary. Her paycheck was \$525. How much is Beth's salary?

Check Your Understanding

○ = Step-by-Step Solutions begin on page R13.

Example 1 **Translate each sentence into an equation.**

1. Three times r less than 15 equals 6. $15 - 3r = 6$
2. The sum of q and four times t is equal to 29. $q + 4t = 29$
3. A number n squared plus 12 is the same as the quotient of p and 4. $n^2 + 12 = p \div 4$
4. Half of j minus 5 is the sum of k and 13. $\frac{1}{2}j - 5 = k + 13$
5. The sum of 8 and three times k equals the difference of 5 times k and 3. $8 + 3k = 5k - 3$
6. Three fourths of w plus 5 is one half of w increased by nine. $\frac{3}{4}w + 5 = \frac{1}{2}w + 9$
7. The quotient of 25 and t plus 6 is the same as twice t plus 1. $\frac{25}{t} + 6 = 2t + 1$
8. Thirty-two divided by y is equal to the product of three and y minus four. $\frac{32}{y} = 3y - 4$

DifferentiatedInstruction AL OL BL ELL

If some students are having trouble translating sentences into equations,

Then pair those students with students who are able to translate sentences into equations easily. Have the pairs work through several problems in Check Your Understanding.

2 Write Sentences from Equations

Example 4 shows how to translate equations into verbal sentences. **Example 5** shows how to write a verbal problem from information given in equations.

Additional Examples

4 Translate each equation into a sentence.

a. $12 - 2x = -5$ Sample answer: Twelve minus two times x equals negative five.

b. $a^2 + 3b = \frac{c}{6}$ Sample answer: a squared plus three times b equals c divided by 6.

5 Write a problem based on the given information.

f = cost of fries
$f + 1.50$ = cost of burger
$4(f + 1.50) - f = 8.25$

Sample answer: The cost of a burger is \$1.50 more than the cost of fries. Four times the cost of a burger minus the cost of fries equals \$8.25. How much do fries cost?

Tips for New Teachers

Sense-Making Remind students that there is often more than one way to translate an equation into a verbal sentence. For example, $y^2 + 3x = w$ could also be translated as, "y squared plus 3 times x equals w."

3 Practice

Formative Assessment

Use Exercises 1–20 to check for understanding.

Use the chart at the bottom of the next page to customize assignments for your students.

WatchOut!

Preventing Errors Explain that π is not a variable. The symbol π always represents the same nonterminating, nonrepeating decimal number.

Teaching the Process Standards

Modeling Mathematically proficient students can apply the mathematics they know to solve problems arising in everyday life. In Exercise 10, students should begin by identifying what they know and what they are looking to find.

Reasoning Mathematically proficient students make sense of quantities and their relationships in problem situations. In Exercise 48, ask students to analyze how the length of a side is related to area of a face and how the area of each face is related to the surface area of the cube.

Additional Answers

15. Sample answer: The product of seven and *m* minus *q* is equal to 23.
16. Sample answer: Six plus the product of nine and *k* plus the product 5 and *j* is fifty-four.
17. Sample answer: Three times the sum of *g* and eight is the same as 4 times *h* minus 10.
18. Sample answer: Six times *d* squared minus the product of seven and *f* is identical to eight times *d* plus *f* squared.
19. Sample answer: A team of gymnasts competed in a regional meet. Each member of the team won 3 medals. There were a total of 45 medals won by the team. How many team members were there?
20. A store receives a shipment of notebooks that costs the store *c* dollars per notebook. To sell the notebooks, the store marks them up by 25%. If the store charges \$3.75 for each notebook, what was the original cost of the notebook?

Example 2

9. **FINANCIAL LITERACY** Samuel has \$1900 in the bank. He wishes to increase his account to a total of \$2500 by depositing \$30 per week from his paycheck. Write and solve an equation to find how many weeks he needs to reach his goal. **$1900 + 30w = 2500$; 20**
10. **MODELING** Miguel is earning extra money by painting houses. He charges a \$200 fee plus \$12 per can of paint needed to complete the job. Write and use an equation to find how many cans of paint he needs for a \$260 job. **$12c + 200 = 260$; 5**

Translate each sentence into a formula.

Example 3

11. The perimeter of a regular pentagon is 5 times the length of each side. **$P = 5s$**
12. The area of a circle is the product of π and the radius *r* squared. **$A = \pi r^2$**
13. Four times π times the radius squared is the surface area of a sphere. **$4\pi r^2 = S$**
14. One third the product of the length of the side squared and the height is the volume of a pyramid with a square base. **$\frac{1}{3}s^2h = V$**

Example 4

Translate each equation into a sentence. **15–18. See margin.**

15. $7m - q = 23$
16. $6 + 9k + 5j = 54$
17. $3(g + 8) = 4h - 10$
18. $6d^2 - 7f = 8d + f^2$

Example 5

Write a problem based on the given information. **19–20. See margin.**

19. g = gymnasts on a team; $3g = 45$
20. c = cost of a notebook; $0.25c$ = markup; $c + 0.25c = 3.75$

Practice and Problem Solving

Extra Practice is on page R2.

Example 1

Translate each sentence into an equation.

21. The difference of *f* and five times *g* is the same as 25 minus *f*. **$f - 5g = 25 - f$**
22. Three times *b* less than 100 is equal to the product of 6 and *b*. **$100 - 3b = 6b$**
23. Four times the sum of 14 and *c* is *a* squared. **$4(14 + c) = a^2$**

Example 2

24. **MUSIC** A piano has 52 white keys. Write and use an equation to find the number of octaves on a piano keyboard. **$8k = 52$ or $52 \div 8 = k$; $6\frac{1}{2}$ octaves**
25. **GARDENING** A flat of plants contains 12 plants. Yoshi wants a garden that has three rows with 10 plants per row. Write and solve an equation for the number of flats Yoshi should buy. **$3 \cdot 10 = 12f$; $2\frac{1}{2}$ flats**

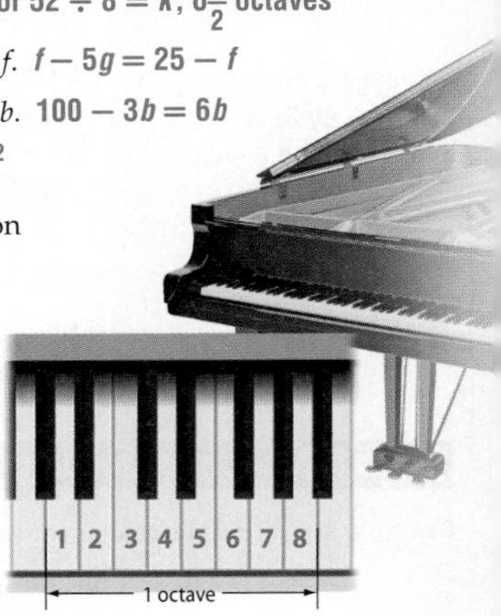

Example 3

Translate each sentence into a formula.

26. The perimeter of a rectangle is equal to 2 times the length plus twice the width. **$P = 2\ell + 2w$**
27. Celsius temperature *C* is five ninths times the difference of the Fahrenheit temperature *F* and 32. **$C = \frac{5}{9}(F - 32)$**
28. The density of an object is the quotient of its mass and its volume. **$D = \frac{m}{V}$**
29. Simple interest is computed by finding the product of the principal amount *p*, the interest rate *r*, and the time *t*. **$I = prt$**

Example 4

Translate each equation into a sentence. **30–35. See Ch. 2 Answer Appendix.**

30. $j + 16 = 35$
31. $4m = 52$
32. $7(p + 23) = 102$
33. $r^2 - 15 = t + 19$
34. $\frac{2}{5}v + \frac{3}{4} = \frac{2}{3}x^2$
35. $\frac{1}{3} - \frac{4}{5}z = \frac{4}{3}y^3$

Differentiated Homework Options

Level	Assignment	Two-Day Option	
AL Basic	21–39, 47–48, 50–61	21–39 odd, 51–54	22–38 even, 47–48, 50, 55–61
OL Core	21–39 odd, 40–48, 50–61	21–39, 51–54	40–48, 50, 55–61
BL Advanced	40–57, (optional: 58–61)		

Example 5 **Write a problem based on the given information.** **36–39. See Ch. 2 Answer Appendix.**

36. q = quarts of strawberries; $2.50q = 10$

37. p = the principal amount; $0.12p$ = the interest charged; $p + 0.12p = 224$

38. m = number of movies rented; $10 + 1.50m = 14.50$

39. p = the number of players in the game; $5p + 7$ = number of cards in a deck

B **For Exercises 40–43, match each sentence with an equation.**

A. $g^2 = 2(g - 10)$

B. $\frac{1}{2}g + 32 = 15 + 6g$

C. $g^3 = 24g + 4$

D. $3g^2 = 30 + 9g$

40. One half of g plus thirty-two is as much as the sum of fifteen and six times g. **B**

41. A number g to the third power is the same as the product of 24 and g plus 4. **C**

42. The square of g is the same as two times the difference of g and 10. **A**

43. The product of 3 and the square of g equals the sum of thirty and the product of nine and g. **D**

44. **FINANCIAL LITERACY** Tim's bank contains quarters, dimes, and nickels. He has three more dimes than quarters and 6 fewer nickels than quarters. If he has 63 coins, write and solve an equation to find how many quarters Tim has. **$q + (3 + q) + (q - 6) = 63$ or $3q - 3 = 63$; 22**

45. **SHOPPING** Pilar bought 17 items for her camping trip, including tent stakes, packets of drink mix, and bottles of water. She bought 3 times as many packets of drink mix as tent stakes. She also bought 2 more bottles of water than tent stakes. Write and solve an equation to discover how many tent stakes she bought. **$17 = t + 3t + (t + 2)$ or $17 = 5t + 2$; 3**

C 46. **MULTIPLE REPRESENTATIONS** In this problem, you will explore how to translate relations with powers.

x	2	3	4	5	6
y	5	10	17	26	37

a. **Verbal** Write a sentence to describe the relationship between x and y in the table. **The value of y is equal to the square of the x-value plus 1.**

b. **Algebraic** Write an equation that represents the data in the table. **$y = x^2 + 1$**

c. **Graphical** Graph each ordered pair and draw the function. Describe the graph as discrete or continuous. **See Ch. 2 Answer Appendix.**

H.O.T. Problems Use Higher-Order Thinking Skills

47. **OPEN ENDED** Write a problem about your favorite television show that uses the equation $x + 8 = 30$. **See Ch. 2 Answer Appendix.**

48. **REASONING** The surface area of a three-dimensional object is the sum of the areas of the faces. If ℓ represents the length of the side of a cube, write a formula for the surface area of the cube. **$S = 6\ell^2$**

49. **CHALLENGE** Given the perimeter P and width w of a rectangle, write a formula to find the length ℓ. **$\ell = \frac{P - 2w}{2}$**

50. **WRITING IN MATH** How can you translate a verbal sentence into an algebraic equation? **See Ch. 2 Answer Appendix.**

Multiple Representations

In Exercise 46, students use a table of values, an equation, and a graph in the coordinate plane to illustrate the nature of a quadratic function.

Study Guide and Intervention

AL OL ELL

NAME DATE PERIOD

2-1 Study Guide and Intervention

Writing Equations

Write Equations Writing equations is one strategy for solving problems. You can use a variable to represent an unspecified number or measure referred to in a problem. Then you can write a verbal expression as an algebraic expression.

Example 1 Translate each sentence into an equation or a formula.

a. Ten times a number x is equal to 2.8 times the difference y minus z.
$10 \times x = 2.8 \times (y - z)$
The equation is $10x = 2.8(y - z)$.

b. A number m minus 8 is the same as a number n divided by 2.
$m - 8 = n \div 2$
The equation is $m - 8 = \frac{n}{2}$.

c. The area of a rectangle equals the length times the width. Translate this sentence into a formula.
Let A = area, ℓ = length, and w = width.
Formula: Area equals length times width.
$A = \ell \times w$
The formula for the area of a rectangle is $A = \ell w$.

Example 2 Use the Four-Step Problem-Solving Plan.

POPULATION The population of the United States in July 2007 was about 301,000,000, and the land area of the United States is about 3,500,000 square miles. Find the average number of people per square mile in the United States.

Step 1 *Read* You know that there are 301,000,000 people. You want to know the number of people per square mile.

Step 2 *Plan* Write an equation to represent the situation. Let p represent the number of people per square mile.
$3,500,000 \times p = 301,000,000$

Step 3 *Solve* $3,500,000 \times p = 301,000,000$
$3,500,000p = 301,000,000$ Divide each side by 3,500,000.
$p = 86$
There are 86 people per square mile.

Step 4 *Check* If there are 86 people per square mile and there are 3,500,000 square miles, $86 \times 3,500,000 = 301,000,000$. The answer makes sense.

Exercises

Translate each sentence into an equation or formula.

1. Three times a number t minus twelve equals forty.

2. One-half of the difference of a and b is 54.

3. Three times the sum of d and 4 is 32.

4. The area A of a circle is the product of π and the radius r squared.

5. WEIGHT LOSS Lou wants to lose weight to audition for a part in a play. He weighs 160 pounds now. He wants to weigh 150 pounds.

a. If p represents the number of pounds he wants to lose, write an equation to represent this situation.

b. How many pounds does he need to lose to reach his goal?

Lesson 2-1

Practice

AL OL BL ELL

NAME DATE PERIOD

2-1 Practice

Writing Equations

Translate each sentence into an equation.

1. Fifty-three plus four times b is as much as 21.

2. The sum of five times h and twice g is equal to 23.

3. One fourth the sum of r and ten is identical to r minus 4.

4. Three plus the sum of the squares of w and x is 32.

Translate each sentence into a formula.

5. Degrees Kelvin K equals 273 plus degrees Celsius C.

6. The total cost C of gas is the price p per gallon times the number of gallons g.

7. The sum S of the measures of the angles of a polygon is equal to 180 times the difference of the number of sides n and 2.

Translate each equation into a sentence.

8. $r - (4 + p) = \frac{1}{3}r$

9. $\frac{3}{5}t + 2 = t$

10. $9(y^2 + x) = 18$

11. $2(m - n) = x + 7$

Write a problem based on the given information.

12. a = cost of one adult's ticket to zoo
$a - 4$ = cost of one children's ticket to zoo
$2a + 4(a - 4) = 38$

13. c = regular cost of one airline ticket
$0.20c$ = amount of 20% promotional discount
$3(c - 0.20c) = 330$

14. GEOGRAPHY About 15% of all federally-owned land in the 48 contiguous states of the United States is in Nevada. If F represents the area of federally-owned land in these states, and N represents the portion in Nevada, write an equation for this situation.

15. FITNESS Deanna and Pietra each go for walks around a lake a few times per week. Last week, Deanna walked 7 miles more than Pietra.

a. If p represents the number of miles Pietra walked, write an equation that represents the total number of miles T the two girls walked.

b. If Pietra walked 9 miles during the week, how many miles did Deanna walk?

c. If Pietra walked 11 miles during the week, how many miles did the two girls walk together?

Word Problem Practice

AL OL BL ELL

NAME DATE PERIOD

2-1 Word Problem Practice

Writing Equations

1. HOUSES The area of the Hartstein's kitchen is 182 square feet. This is 20% of the area of the first floor of their house. Let F represent the area of the first floor. Write an equation to represent the situation.

2. FAMILY Katie is twice as old as her sister Mara. The sum of their ages is 24. Write a one-variable equation to represent the situation.

3. GEOMETRY The formula $F + V = E + 2$ shows the relationship between the number of faces F, edges E, and vertices V of a polyhedron, such as a pyramid. Write the formula in words.

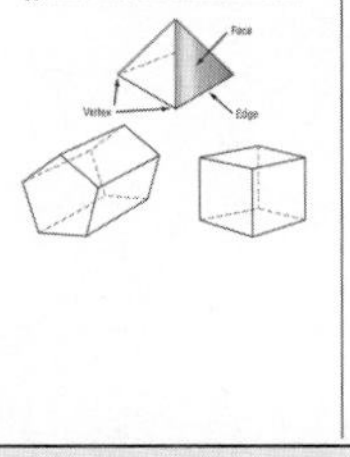

4. WIRELESS PHONE Spinfrog wireless phone company bills on a monthly basis. Each bill includes a $29.95 service fee for 1000 minutes plus a $2.95 federal communication tax. Additionally, there is a charge of $0.05 for each minute used over 1000. Let m represent the number of minutes over 1000 used during the month. Write an equation to describe the cost p of the wireless phone service per month.

5. TEMPERATURE The table below shows the temperature in Fahrenheit for some corresponding temperatures in Celsius.

Celsius	Fahrenheit
−20°	−4°
−10°	14°
0°	32°
10°	50°
20°	68°
30°	86°

a. Write a formula for converting Celsius temperatures to Fahrenheit temperatures.

b. Find the Fahrenheit equivalents for 25°C and 35°C.

Lesson 2-1

Enrichment

OL BL

NAME DATE PERIOD

2-1 Enrichment

Guess the Number

Think of a number. Add five to your number. Now, double your result. Double your result again. Divide you answer by four. Finally, subtract your original number. Your result is five.

How is it possible to know what the answer is without knowing the original number? Write the steps listed above as an expression in equation form. Then use algebra to show why this trick works.

Think of a number:	x
Add five to your number:	$x + 5$
Double your result:	$2(x + 5)$
Double your result again:	$2(2(x + 5))$
Divide you answer by four:	$\frac{2(2(x + 5))}{4}$
Subtract your original number:	$\frac{2(2(x + 5))}{4} - x$
Simplify the final expression:	$\frac{4(x + 5)}{4} - x$ Multiply.
	$x + 5 - x$ Divide.
	5 Simplify.

4 Assess

Ticket Out the Door Make several copies of five different equations. Give one equation to each student. As students leave, ask them to give a verbal sentence for the equation.

Follow-up

Students have explored translating sentences into equations.

Ask:

- Why is it helpful to represent a mathematical idea using an equation? Sample answer: You can rewrite an equation in numerous ways, as long as you preserve the relationship.

Additional Answers

55. Nonlinear; the graph intersects the y-axis at about (0, 0.8), so the y-intercept is about 0.8. This means that the population of Phoenix was about 800,000 in 1980. The graph has no symmetry. The graph does not intersect the x-axis, so there is no x-intercept. This means that the population will always have a positive value. The function is positive for all values of x. The function is increasing for all values of x. The y-intercept is a relative minimum, so the population was at its lowest in 1980. As x increases, y increases. As x decreases, y decreases.

56a.

Pairs of earrings	1	2	3	4	5
Total Cost	29	58	58	87	116

56c. Cost of Earrings

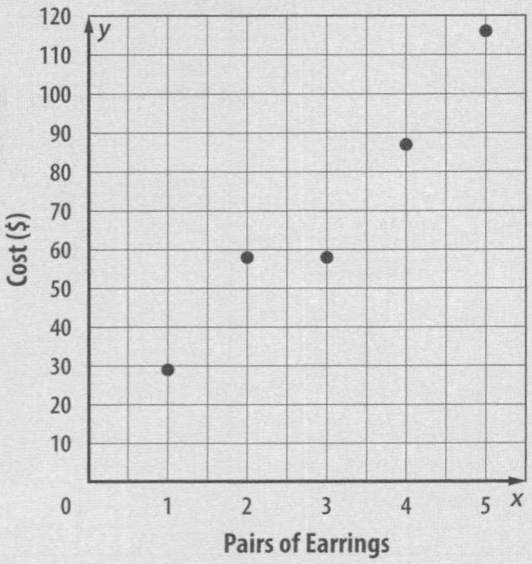

Standardized Test Practice

51. Which equation *best* represents the relationship between the number of hours an electrician works h and the total charges c? **C**

Cost of Electrician	
Emergency House Call	$30 one time fee
Rate	$55/hour

A $c = 30 + 55$
B $c = 30h + 55$
C $c = 30 + 55h$
D $c = 30h + 55h$

52. A car traveled at 55 miles per hour for 2.5 hours and then at 65 miles per hour for 3 hours. How far did the car travel in all? **J**

F 300.5 mi H 330 mi
G 305 mi J 332.5 mi

53. SHORT RESPONSE Suppose each dimension of rectangle $ABCD$ is doubled. What is the perimeter of the new $ABCD$? **180 m**

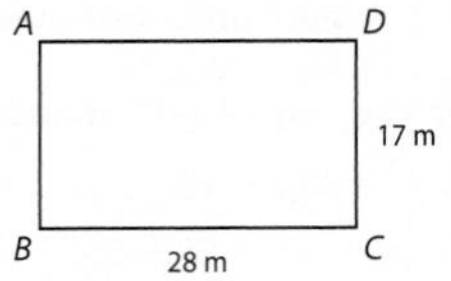

54. STATISTICS Stacy's first five science test scores were 95, 86, 83, 95, and 99. Which of the following is a true statement? **A**

A The mode is the same as the median.
B The median is the same as the mean.
C The range is the same as the mode.
D The mode is the same as the mean.

Spiral Review

55. POPULATION Identify the function graphed as *linear* or *nonlinear*. Then estimate and interpret the intercepts of the graph, any symmetry, where the function is positive, negative, increasing, and decreasing, the x-coordinate of any relative extrema, and the end behavior of the graph. (Lesson 1-8) **See margin.**

Phoenix Population

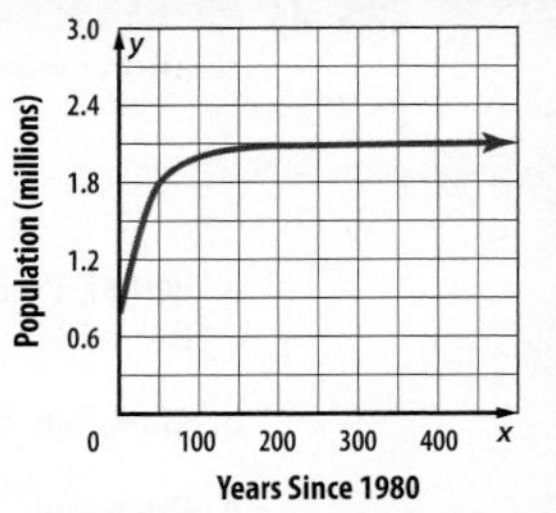

56. SHOPPING Cuties is having a sale on earrings that are regularly $29 for each pair. If you buy 2 pairs, you get 1 pair free. (Lesson 1-7) **a, c. See margin.**

a. Make a table that shows the cost of buying 1 to 5 pairs of earrings.

b. Write the data as a set of ordered pairs. **{(1, 29), (2, 58), (3, 58), (4, 87), (5, 116)}**

c. Graph the data.

57. GEOMETRY Refer to the table below. (Lesson 1-6)

Polygon	triangle	quadrilateral	pentagon	hexagon	heptagon
Number of Sides	3	4	5	6	7
Interior Angle Sum	180	360	540	720	900

a. Identify the independent and dependent variables.

b. Identify the domain and range for this situation.

c. State whether the function is *discrete* or *continuous*. Explain. **Discrete; sample answer: There cannot be a polygon with 3.5 sides, so the function cannot be continuous.**

57a. independent: number of sides; dependent: interior angle sum

57b. Domain: all integers greater than or equal to 3; Range: all positive integer multiples of 180

Skills Review

Evaluate each expression.

58. 9^2 **81** **59.** 10^6 **1,000,000** **60.** 3^5 **243** **61.** 5^3 **125**

80 | Lesson 2-1 | Writing Equations

Differentiated Instruction BL

Extension A pair of even numbers that are in order and differ by 2, such as 4 and 6, are called *consecutive even numbers*.

a. Write an equation for three consecutive even numbers with a sum of 60 if x is the least of the three numbers. $x + (x + 2) + (x + 4) = 60$

b. Write an equation for three consecutive even numbers with a sum of 108 if x is the least of the three numbers. $x + (x + 2) + (x + 4) = 108$

EXPLORE

2-2 Algebra Lab
Solving Equations

You can use **algebra tiles** to model solving equations. To **solve an equation** means to find the value of the variable that makes the equation true. An x tile represents the variable x. The 1 tile represents a positive 1. The −1 tile represents a negative 1. And, the −x tile represents the variable negative x. The goal is to get the x-tile by itself on one side of the mat by using the rules stated below.

Content Standards
AI.L.1

Rules for Equation Models When Adding or Subtracting:

- You can remove or add the same number of identical algebra tiles to each side of the mat without changing the equation.

- One positive tile and one negative tile of the same unit are called a zero pair. Since $1 + (-1) = 0$, you can remove or add zero pairs to either side of the equation mat without changing the equation.

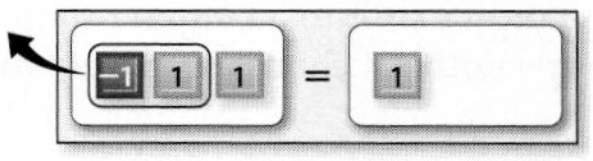

Activity 1 Addition Equation

Use an equation model to solve $x + 3 = -4$.

Step 1 Model the equation. Place 1 x-tile and 3 positive 1-tiles on one side of the mat. Place 4 negative 1-tiles on the other side of the mat.

Step 2 Isolate the x-term. Add 3 negative 1-tiles to each side. The resulting equation is $x = -7$.

$x + 3 = -4$
$x + 3 + (-3) = -4 + (-3)$
$x = -7$

Activity 2 Subtraction Equation

Use an equation model to solve $x - 2 = 1$.

Step 1

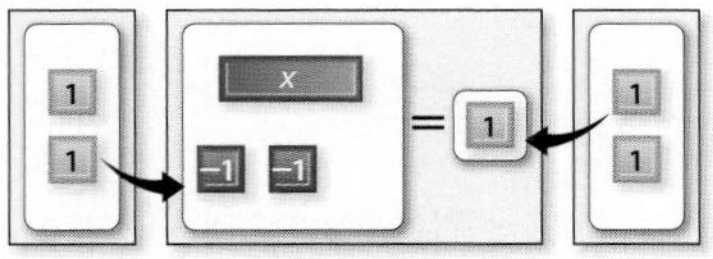

$x - 2 = 1$
$x - 2 + 2 = 1 + 2$

Place 1 x-tile and 2 negative 1-tiles on one side of the mat. Place 1 positive 1-tile on the other side of the mat. Then add 2 positive 1-tiles to each side.

Step 2

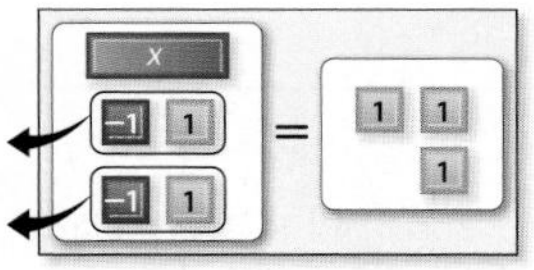

$x = 3$

Group the tiles to form zero pairs. Then remove all the zero pairs. The resulting equation is $x = 3$.

(continued on the next page)

- Why do you add 3 negative 1-tiles to each side of the equation? You need 3 negative 1-tiles to form 3 zero pairs on the left side of the equation mat.
- What do you do after you form zero pairs? Remove the zero pairs so that the x-tile is by itself.

1 Focus

Objective Use algebra tiles to solve addition, subtraction, and multiplication equations.

Materials for Each Group
- equation mats
- algebra tiles (x-tiles, 1-tiles)

Easy to Make Manipulatives
Teaching Algebra with Manipulatives templates for:
- algebra tiles, pp. 10–11
- equation mat, p. 16

Tips for New Teachers
Make sure students understand that zero pairs can be formed only after adding the same number of positive or negative tiles to each side of the equation mat. Point out that the number of positive or negative 1-tiles added to each side of the equation mat depends upon the 1-tiles on the side of the equation mat with the x-tile.

2 Teach

Working in Cooperative Groups
Put students in groups of two or three, mixing abilities to complete the Activities.

Ask:
In Activity 1,
- What does the x-tile represent? an unknown number that when added to 3 equals −4
- Is it possible to remove identical 1-tiles from each side of the equation mat? Explain. No; the 1-tiles on the left side are negative and the 1-tiles on the right side are positive, so there are no identical algebra tiles that can be removed from each side.

In Activity 2 remind students that when modeling subtraction with algebra tiles, they must add negative tiles.

Ask:

- Why do you add positive 1-tiles to each side of the equation mat? You need positive 1-tiles to form zero pairs with the negative 1-tiles on the left side of the equation mat.

In Activity 3, point out to students that what they do on one side of the equation mat, they must do on the other side. If they form one group of *x*-tiles on one side, they must form one group of 1-tiles on the other side and so on. If there is more than one *x*-tile, the number of 1-tiles paired with each *x*-tile must be the same for each group of 1-tiles.

Practice Have students complete Exercises 1–4 and 6–9.

3 Assess

Formative Assessment

Use Exercise 3 to assess whether students comprehend how to form zero-pairs in order to isolate the *x*-tile.

From Concrete to Abstract

Exercise 5 provides a symbolic representation for the addition and subtraction properties used in Examples 1 and 2. In Exercise 10, students should apply what they have learned to new situations.

Algebra Lab

Solving Equations *Continued*

Model and Analyze

Use algebra tiles to solve each equation.

1. $x + 4 = 9$ **5**

2. $x + (-3) = -4$ **−1**

3. $x + 7 = -2$ **−9**

4. $x + (-2) = 11$ **13**

5. **WRITING IN MATH** If $a = b$, what can you say about $a + c$ and $b + c$? about $a - c$ and $b - c$? $a + c = b + c$; $a - c = b - c$

When solving multiplication equations, the goal is still to get the *x*-tile by itself on one side of the mat by using the rules for dividing.

Rules for the Equation Models When Dividing:

- You can group the tiles on each side of the equation mat into an equal number of groups without changing the equation.

- You can place an equal grouping on each side of the equation mat without changing the equation.

Activity 3 Multiplication Equations

Use an equation model to solve $3x = 12$.

Step 1 Model the equation. Place 3 *x*-tiles on one side of the mat. Place 12 positive 1-tiles on the other side of the mat.

Step 2 Isolate the *x*-term. Separate the tiles into 3 equal groups to match the 3 *x*-tiles. Each *x*-tile is paired with 4 positive 1-tiles. The resulting equation is $x = 4$.

$$3x = 12$$
$$\frac{3x}{3} = \frac{12}{3}$$
$$x = 4$$

Model and Analyze

10. Sample answer: Since there is no $\frac{x}{4}$-tile, the equation cannot be solved using algebra tiles. To solve algebraically, multiply each side by 4.

Use algebra tiles to solve each equation.

6. $5x = -15$ **−3**

7. $-3x = -9$ **3**

8. $4x = 8$ **2**

9. $-6x = 18$ **−3**

10. **MAKE A CONJECTURE** How would you use algebra tiles to solve $\frac{x}{4} = 5$? Discuss the steps you would take to solve this equation algebraically.

Extending the Concept

Ask students how to use algebra tiles to solve $2x - 4 = 2$. Sample answer: After isolating the two *x*-tiles, separate the 1-tiles into 2 equal groups to correspond with each *x*-tile. The number of 1-tiles corresponding to one *x*-tile gives the solution. In this case, there should be three 1-tiles for each *x*-tile.

Teaching the Process Standards

Regularity Mathematically proficient students maintain oversight of the process, while attending to the details. Encourage students to look for general methods of solving equations as they solve multiple problems of the same type.

LESSON 2-2 Solving One-Step Equations

Then

- You translated sentences into equations.

Now

1. Solve equations by using addition and subtraction.
2. Solve equations by using multiplication and division.

Why?

- A record for the most snow angels made at one time was set in Michigan when 3784 people participated. North Dakota had 8910 people register to break the record. To determine how many more people North Dakota had than Michigan, solve the equation $3784 + x = 8910$.

NewVocabulary
solve an equation
equivalent equations

Content Standards
A1.L.1, A1.L.2

1 Solve Equations Using Addition or Subtraction

In an equation, the variable represents the number that satisfies the equation. To **solve an equation** means to find the value of the variable that makes the equation true.

The process of solving an equation requires assuming that the original equation has a solution and isolating the variable (with a coefficient of 1) on one side of the equation. Each step in this process results in equivalent equations. **Equivalent equations** have the same solution.

KeyConcept Addition Property of Equality

Words If an equation is true and the same number is added to each side of the equation, the resulting equivalent equation is also true.

Symbols For any real numbers a, b, and c, if $a = b$, then $a + c = b + c$.

Examples

$$14 = 14 \qquad -3 = -3$$
$$14 + 3 = 14 + 3 \qquad +9 = +9$$
$$17 = 17 \qquad 6 = 6$$

Example 1 Solve by Adding

Solve $c - 22 = 54$.

Horizontal Method

$c - 22 = 54$	Original equation
$c - 22 + 22 = 54 + 22$	Add 22 to each side.
$c = 76$	Simplify.

Vertical Method

$$c - 22 = 54$$
$$+22 = +22$$
$$c = 76$$

To check that 76 is the solution, substitute 76 for c in the original equation.

CHECK

$c - 22 = 54$	Original equation
$76 - 22 \stackrel{?}{=} 54$	Substitute 76 for c.
$54 = 54$ ✓	Subtract.

GuidedPractice

1A. $113 = g - 25$ **138**

1B. $j - 87 = -3$ **84**

1 Focus

VerticalAlignment

Before Lesson 2-2 Translate sentences into equations.

Lesson 2-2 Solve equations by using addition and subtraction. Solve equations by using multiplication and division.

After Lesson 2-2 Solve multi-step equations.

2 Teach

Scaffolding Questions

Have students read the **Why?** section of the lesson.

Ask:

- What is the Guinness World Record for the greatest number of snow angels made at one time? 8910
- What is the unknown quantity represented by x in the equation? how many more snow angels North Dakota made than Michigan at one time
- Is the value of x greater than or less than 8910? Explain. less than 8910 because $x + 3748$ is equal to 8910

Lesson 2-2 Resources

Resource	Approaching Level AL	On Level OL	Beyond Level BL	English Learners ELL
Teacher Edition	▪ Differentiated Instruction, p. 87	▪ Differentiated Instruction, pp. 87, 89	▪ Differentiated Instruction, p. 89	
Chapter Resource Masters	▪ Study Guide and Intervention, pp. 11–12 ▪ Skills Practice, p. 13 ▪ Practice, p. 14 ▪ Word Problem Practice, p. 15	▪ Study Guide and Intervention, pp. 11–12 ▪ Skills Practice, p. 13 ▪ Practice, p. 14 ▪ Word Problem Practice, p. 15 ▪ Enrichment, p. 16	▪ Practice, p. 14 ▪ Word Problem Practice, p. 15 ▪ Enrichment, p. 16	▪ Study Guide and Intervention, pp. 11–12 ▪ Skills Practice, p. 13 ▪ Practice, p. 14 ▪ Word Problem Practice, p. 15
Other	▪ 5-Minute Check 2-2 ▪ Study Notebook ▪ Teaching Algebra with Manipulatives	▪ 5-Minute Check 2-2 ▪ Study Notebook ▪ Teaching Algebra with Manipulatives	▪ 5-Minute Check 2-2 ▪ Study Notebook	▪ 5-Minute Check 2-2 ▪ Study Notebook ▪ Teaching Algebra with Manipulatives

1 Solve Equations Using Addition or Subtraction

Example 1 shows how to solve an equation by adding. **Example 2** shows how to solve an equation by subtracting.

Formative Assessment

Use the Guided Practice exercises after each Example to determine students' understanding of concepts.

Additional Examples

1 Solve $h - 12 = -27$ -15

2 Solve $c + 102 = 36$ -66

Additional Examples also in Interactive Classroom PowerPoint® Presentations

IWB Interactive White Board READY

WatchOut!

Preventing Errors Students may try to skip a step and solve the problem without first writing the equation. Tell students that they will make fewer mistakes in solving equations if they translate the sentence and write the equation before solving it.

Similar to the Addition Property of Equality, the **Subtraction Property of Equality** can also be used to solve equations.

StudyTip

Subtraction Subtracting a value is equivalent to adding the opposite of the value.

KeyConcept Subtraction Property of Equality

Words If an equation is true and the same number is subtracted from each side of the equation, the resulting equivalent equation is also true.

Symbols For any real numbers a, b, and c, if $a = b$, then $a - c = b - c$.

Examples

$$87 = 87$$
$$87 - 17 = 87 - 17$$
$$70 = 70$$

$$13 = 13$$
$$-28 = -28$$
$$-15 = -15$$

StudyTip

Solving an Equation When solving equations you can use either the horizontal method or the vertical method. Both methods will produce the same result.

Example 2 Solve by Subtracting

Solve $63 + m = 79$.

Horizontal Method

$63 + m = 79$ Original equation

$63 - 63 + m = 79 - 63$ Subtract 63 from each side.

$m = 16$ Simplify.

Vertical Method

$$63 + m = 79$$
$$-63 \quad = -63$$
$$m = 16$$

To check that 16 is the solution, replace m with 16 in the original equation.

CHECK $63 + m = 79$ Original equation

$63 + 16 \stackrel{?}{=} 79$ Substitution, $m = 16$

$79 = 79$ ✓ Simplify.

GuidedPractice

2A. $27 + k = 30$ **3**

2B. $-12 = p + 16$ **−28**

2 Solve Equations Using Multiplication or Division

In the equation $\frac{x}{3} = 9$, the variable x is divided by 3. To solve for x, undo the division by multiplying each side by 3. This is an example of the **Multiplication Property of Equality**.

KeyConcept Multiplication Property of Equality

Words If an equation is true and each side is multiplied by the same nonzero number, the resulting equation is equivalent.

Symbols For any real numbers a, b, and c, $c \neq 0$, if $a = b$, then $ac = bc$.

Example If $x = 5$, then $3x = 15$.

Division Property of Equality

Words If an equation is true and each side is divided by the same nonzero number, the resulting equation is equivalent.

Symbols For any real numbers a, b, and c, $c \neq 0$, if $a = b$, then $\frac{a}{c} = \frac{b}{c}$.

Example If $x = -20$, then $\frac{x}{5} = \frac{-20}{5}$ or -4.

Focus on Mathematical Content

Solving Equations The Subtraction Property of Equality may be used to isolate the variable when solving an equation. When the same number is subtracted from each side of a true equation, the resulting equation will also be true.

The reciprocal of a number can be used to solve equations.

Example 3 Solve by Multiplying or Dividing

Solve each equation.

a. $\frac{2}{3}q = \frac{1}{2}$

$\frac{2}{3}q = \frac{1}{2}$	Original equation
$\frac{3}{2}\left(\frac{2}{3}\right)q = \frac{3}{2}\left(\frac{1}{2}\right)$	Multiply each side by $\frac{3}{2}$, the reciprocal of $\frac{2}{3}$.
$q = \frac{3}{4}$	Check the result.

b. $39 = -3r$

$39 = -3r$	Original equation
$\frac{39}{-3} = \frac{-3r}{-3}$	Divide each side by −3.
$-13 = r$	Check the result.

Review Vocabulary

reciprocal the multiplicative inverse of a number

Guided Practice

3A. $\frac{3}{5}k = 6$ **10**

3B. $-\frac{1}{4} = \frac{2}{3}b$ $-\frac{3}{8}$

We can also use reciprocals and properties of equality to solve real-world problems.

Real-World Example 4 Solve by Multiplying

SURVEYS Of a group of 13- to 15-year-old girls surveyed, 225, or about $\frac{9}{20}$ said they talk on the telephone while they watch television. About how many girls were surveyed?

Words	Nine twentieths times those surveyed	is	225.
Variable	Let g = the number of girls surveyed.		
Equation	$\frac{9}{20}g$	=	225

$\frac{9}{20}g = 225$	Original equation
$\left(\frac{20}{9}\right)\frac{9}{20}g = \left(\frac{20}{9}\right)225$	Multiply each side by $\frac{20}{9}$.
$g = \frac{4500}{9}$	$\left(\frac{20}{9}\right)\left(\frac{9}{20}\right) = 1$
$g = 500$	Simplify.

About 500 girls were surveyed.

Ronnie Kaufman/Blend Images/Getty Images

Real-World Link

Almost half of 10- to 18-year-olds in the U.S. use a cell phone. Of those, 53% play games on their phones, more than 33% download games, 52% use the calendar/organizer, and nearly all teens with camera phones snap pictures.

Source: Lexdon Business Library

Guided Practice

4. STAINED GLASS Allison is making a stained glass window. Her pattern requires that one fifth of the glass should be blue. She has 288 square inches of blue glass. If she intends to use all of her blue glass, how much glass will she need for the entire project? **1440 square inches of glass**

2 Solve Equations Using Multiplication or Division

Example 3 shows how to solve an equation by multiplying or dividing each side by the same number. **Example 4** shows how to write and solve an equation for a real-world problem.

Additional Examples

3 Solve each equation.

a. $-1\frac{3}{8}k = \frac{2}{3}$ $-\frac{16}{33}$

b. $-75 = -15b$ 5

4 **TRAVEL** Ricardo is driving 780 miles to Memphis. He drove about $\frac{3}{5}$ of the distance on the first day. About how many miles did Ricardo drive? about 468 miles

Focus on Mathematical Content

Properties of Equality The Multiplication Property may be used to isolate the variable when solving an equation. When each side of a true equation is multiplied by the same nonzero number, the resulting equation will also be true. The Division Property may be used to isolate the variable when solving an equation. When each side of a true equation is divided by the same nonzero number, the resulting equation will also be true.

Teach with Tech

Blog On you secure classroom blog have students create a blog entry to summarize how to solve one-step equations. Make sure that students use the idea of inverse operations in their explanations.

The Math Forum

mathforum.org The Math Forum © Drexel University

Have your students refer to the Math Forum's Ask Dr. Math to learn how to set up an algebraic equation from a word problem. They can start their search at connectED.mcgraw-hill.com.

3 Practice

Formative Assessment

Use Exercises 1–17 to check for understanding.

Use the chart at the bottom of this page to customize assignments for your students.

Tips for New Teachers

Coefficients Students are sometimes confused about what to do with a variable in an equation such as $-x = 27$. Point out that the variable actually has a coefficient of -1. Remembering that the product of two negative numbers is a positive, you can multiply each side of the equation by -1. $(-1)(-x) = (-1)27$; $x = -27$

Teaching the Process Standards

Reasoning Mathematically proficient students attend to the meaning of quantities. In Exercise 17, point out to students that the amount donated to the shelter must be less than the cost of the pet bed. Is their answer reasonable?

Check Your Understanding

= Step-by-Step Solutions begin on page R13.

Examples 1–3 **Solve each equation. Check your solution.**

1. $g + 5 = 33$ **28**
2. $104 = y - 67$ **171**
3. $\frac{2}{3} + w = 1\frac{1}{2}$ **$\frac{5}{6}$**
4. $-4 + t = -7$ **-3**
5. $a + 26 = 35$ **9**
6. $-6 + c = 32$ **38**
7. $1.5 = y - (-5.6)$ **-4.1**
8. $3 + g = \frac{1}{4}$ **$-2\frac{3}{4}$**
9. $x + 4 = \frac{3}{4}$ **$-3\frac{1}{4}$**
10. $\frac{t}{7} = -5$ **-35**
11. $\frac{a}{36} = \frac{4}{9}$ **16**
12. $\frac{2}{3}n = 10$ **15**
13. $\frac{8}{9} = \frac{4}{5}k$ **$\frac{10}{9}$ or $1\frac{1}{9}$**
14. $12 = \frac{x}{-3}$ **-36**
15. $-\frac{r}{4} = \frac{1}{7}$ **$-\frac{4}{7}$**

Example 4

16. **FUNDRAISING** The television show "Idol Gives Back" raised money for relief organizations. During this show, viewers could call in and vote for their favorite performer. The parent company contributed \$5 million for the 50 million votes cast. What did they pay for each vote? **\$0.10**

17. **REASONING** Hana decides to buy her cat a bed from an online fund that gives $\frac{7}{8}$ of her purchase to shelters that care for animals. How much of Hana's money went to the animal shelter? **\$22.75**

Practice and Problem Solving

Extra Practice is on page R2.

Examples 1–3 **Solve each equation. Check your solution.**

18. $v - 9 = 14$ **23**
19. $44 = t - 72$ **116**
20. $-61 = d + (-18)$ **-43**
21. $18 + z = 40$ **22**
22. $-4a = 48$ **-12**
23. $12t = -132$ **-11**
24. $18 - (-f) = 91$ **73**
25. $-16 - (-t) = -45$ **-29**
26. $\frac{1}{3}v = -5$ **-15**
27. $\frac{u}{8} = -4$ **-32**
28. $\frac{a}{6} = -9$ **-54**
29. $-\frac{k}{5} = \frac{7}{5}$ **-7**
30. $\frac{3}{4} = w + \frac{2}{5}$ **$\frac{7}{20}$**
31. $-\frac{1}{2} + a = \frac{5}{8}$ **$1\frac{1}{8}$**
32. $-\frac{t}{7} = \frac{1}{15}$ **$-\frac{7}{15}$**
33. $-\frac{5}{7} = y - 2$ **$1\frac{2}{7}$**
34. $v + 914 = -23$ **-937**
35. $447 + x = -261$ **-708**
36. $-\frac{1}{7}c = 21$ **-147**
37. $-\frac{2}{3}h = -22$ **33**
38. $\frac{3}{5}q = -15$ **-25**
39. $\frac{n}{8} = -\frac{1}{4}$ **-2**
40. $\frac{c}{4} = -\frac{9}{8}$ **$-\frac{9}{2}$**
41. $\frac{2}{3} + r = -\frac{4}{9}$ **$-1\frac{1}{9}$**

Example 4

42. **CATS** A domestic cat can run at speeds of 27.5 miles per hour when chasing prey. A cheetah can run 42.5 miles per hour faster when chasing prey. How fast can the cheetah go? **70 mph**

43. **CARS** The average time t it takes to manufacture a car in the United States is 24.9 hours. This is 8.1 hours longer than the average time it takes to manufacture a car in Japan. Write and solve an equation to find the average time in Japan. **$24.9 = 8.1 + t$; 16.8 hours**

Differentiated Homework Options

Level	Assignment	Two-Day Option	
AL Basic	18–43, 72–74, 76, 78–88	19–43 odd, 79–82	18–42 even, 72–74, 76, 78, 83–88
OL Core	19–61 odd, 72–74, 76, 78–88	18–43, 79–82	44–74, 76, 78, 83–88
BL Advanced	44–90, (optional: 87, 88)		

86 | Lesson 2-2 | Solving One-Step Equations

B **Solve each equation. Check your solution.**

44. $\frac{x}{9} = 10$ **90** **45.** $\frac{b}{7} = -11$ **−77** **46.** $\frac{3}{4} = \frac{c}{24}$ **18**

47. $\frac{2}{3} = \frac{1}{8}y$ $\frac{16}{3}$ **48.** $\frac{2}{3}n = 14$ **21** **49.** $\frac{3}{5}g = -6$ **−10**

50. $4\frac{1}{5} = 3p$ $\frac{7}{5}$ or $1\frac{2}{5}$ **51.** $-5 = 3\frac{1}{2}x$ $-\frac{10}{7}$ or $-1\frac{3}{7}$ **52.** $6 = -\frac{1}{2}n$ **−12**

53. $-\frac{2}{5} = -\frac{z}{45}$ **18** **54.** $-\frac{g}{24} = \frac{5}{12}$ **−10** **55.** $-\frac{v}{5} = -45$ **225**

Write an equation for each sentence. Then solve the equation.

56. Six times a number is 132. $6n = 132$; **22**

57. Two thirds equals negative eight times a number.

58. Five elevenths times a number is 55.

59. Four fifths is equal to ten sixteenths of a number.

60. Three and two thirds times a number equals two ninths.

61 Four and four fifths times a number is one and one fifth.

57. $\frac{2}{3} = -8n$; $-\frac{1}{12}$

58. $\frac{5}{11}n = 55$; 121

59. $\frac{4}{5} = \frac{10}{16}n$; $\frac{32}{25}$

60. $3\frac{2}{3}n = \frac{2}{9}$; $\frac{2}{33}$

61. $4\frac{4}{5}n = 1\frac{1}{5}$; $\frac{1}{4}$

62. PRECISION Adelina is comparing prices for two brands of health and energy bars at the local grocery store. She wants to get the best price for each bar.

a. Write an equation to find the price for each bar of the Feel Great brand. $12p = 18$

b. Write an equation to find the price of each bar for the Super Power brand. $15p = 21.75$

c. Which bar should Adelina buy? Explain.

62c. Super Power bar; each bar is \$1.45, while Feel Great bars are \$1.50 each.

63. MEDIA The world's largest passenger plane, the Airbus A380, was first used by Singapore Airlines in 2005. The following description appeared on a news Web site after the plane was introduced.

"That airline will see the A380 transporting some 555 passengers, 139 more than a similarly set-up 747."

How many passengers will a similarly set-up 747 transport? $555 = 139 + p$; **416**

64. FUEL In 2004, approximately 5 million cars and trucks were classified as flex-fuel, which means they could run on gasoline or ethanol. In 2009, that number increased to about 8 million. How many more cars and trucks were flex-fuel in 2009? $5 + c = 8$; **3 million**

65. CHEERLEADING At a certain cheerleading competition, the maximum time per team, including the set up, is 3 minutes. The Ridgeview High School squad's performance time is 2 minutes and 34 seconds. How much time does the squad have left for their set up? $180 = t + 154$; **26 s**

66. COMIC BOOKS An X-Men #1 comic book in mint condition recently sold for \$45,000. An Action Comics #63 (Mile High), also in mint condition, sold for \$15,000. How much more did the X-Men comic book sell for than the Action Comics book? $45{,}000 = 15{,}000 + t$; **\$30,000**

67. MOVIES A certain movie made \$1.6 million in ticket sales. Its sequel made \$0.8 million in ticket sales. How much more did the first movie make than the sequel? $1.6 - m = 0.8$; **\$0.8 million**

68. CAMERAS An electronics store sells a certain digital camera for \$126. This is $\frac{2}{3}$ of the price that a photography store charges. What is the cost of the camera at the photography store? $126 = \frac{2}{3}c$; **\$189**

WatchOut!

Preventing Errors Remind students that the product of a fraction and its reciprocal is 1.

Tips for New Teachers

Isolating Variables Explain that when isolating a variable, it does not matter whether the variable ends up on the left or right side of an equation. For example, the solution of $8 = 15 + z$ is still -7, even though the final step may be $-7 = z$.

Teaching the Process Standards

Precision Mathematically proficient students express numerical answers with a degree of precision appropriate for the problem context. In Exercise 62, discuss the precision necessary for the situation. Must the calculations be accurate to the nearest cent, or is an estimate sufficient? Explain.

DifferentiatedInstruction AL OL

If students are having trouble solving equations by addition or subtraction,

Then write x and two numbers on the board. Give students the operation symbols + and −. Tell them to use both of the numbers, x, and the operation symbols to write two equations for which the value of x is the same. Have students solve for x in both equations. For example, suppose the two numbers were 23 and 45. Students could write $x + 23 = 45$ and $x = 45 - 23$. For both equations, the solution is 22.

69. **BLOGS** In 2006, 57 million American adults read online blogs. However, 45 million fewer American adults say that they maintain their own blog. How many American adults maintain a blog? **12 million**

70. **SCIENCE CAREERS** According to the Bureau of Labor and Statistics, approximately 140,000,000 people were employed in the United States in 2009. **a, b. See margin.**

 a. The number of people in production occupations times 20 is the number of working people. Write an equation to represent the number of people employed in production occupations in 2009. Then solve the equation.

 b. The number of people in repair occupations is 2,300,000 less than the number of people in production occupations. How many people are in repair occupations?

71. **DANCES** Student Council has a budget of \$1000 for the homecoming dance. So far, they have spent \$350 dollars for music. **a–c. See margin.**

 a. Write an equation to represent the amount of money left to spend. Then solve the equation.

 b. They then spent \$225 on decorations. Write an equation to represent the amount of money left.

 c. If the Student Council spent their entire budget, write an equation to represent how many \$6 tickets they must sell to make a profit.

72. $n - 16 = 29$ doesn't belong because for the other three, $n = 13$, and for this one, $n = 45$.

H.O.T. Problems Use Higher-Order Thinking Skills

72. **WHICH ONE DOESN'T BELONG?** Identify the equation that does not belong with the other three. Explain your reasoning.

$n + 14 = 27$	$12 + n = 25$	$n - 16 = 29$	$n - 4 = 9$

73. **OPEN ENDED** Write an equation involving addition and demonstrate two ways to solve it. **Sample answer: $12 + n = 25$; subtract 12 from each side or add -12 to each side.**

74. **REASONING** For which triangle is the height not $4\frac{1}{2}b$, where b is the length of the base? **$\triangle RST$**

Triangle	Base (cm)	Height (cm)
$\triangle ABC$	3.8	17.1
$\triangle MQP$	5.4	24.3
$\triangle RST$	6.3	28.5
$\triangle TRW$	1.6	7.2

75. **STRUCTURE** Determine whether each sentence is *sometimes*, *always*, or *never true*. Explain your reasoning.

 a. $x + x = x$ **Sometimes; $0 + 0 = 0$ but $2 + 2 \neq 2$.**

 b. $x + 0 = x$ **Always; this is the Additive Identity Property.**

76. **REASONING** Determine the value for each statement below.

 a. If $x - 7 = 14$, what is the value of $x - 2$? **19**

 b. If $t + 8 = -12$, what is the value of $t + 1$? **−19**

77. **CHALLENGE** Solve each equation for x. Assume that $a \neq 0$.

 a. $ax = 12$ **$x = \frac{12}{a}$**

 b. $x + a = 15$ **$x = 15 - a$**

 c. $-5 = x - a$ **$x = a - 5$**

 d. $\frac{1}{a}x = 10$ **$x = 10a$**

78. **WRITING IN MATH** Consider the Multiplication Property of Equality and the Division Property of Equality. Explain why they can be considered the same property. Which one do you think is easier to use? **Sample answer: Dividing by a nonzero number is the same as multiplying by its reciprocal, so the same rules would apply.**

Additional Answers

70a. $20p = 140{,}000{,}000$; 7,000,000

70b. $7{,}000{,}000 = n + 2{,}300{,}000$; 4,700,000

71a. $350 + m = 1000$; \$650

71b. $350 + 225 + m = 1000$; \$425

71c. $6t = 1000$; 167

Study Guide and Intervention
AL OL ELL

2-2 Study Guide and Intervention
Solving One-Step Equations

Solve Equations Using Addition and Subtraction If the same number is added to each side of an equation, the resulting equation is equivalent to the original one. In general if the original equation involves subtraction, this property will help you solve the equation. Similarly, if the same number is subtracted from each side of an equation, the resulting equation is equivalent to the original one. This property will help you solve equations involving addition.

Addition Property of Equality	For any numbers a, b, and c, if $a = b$, then $a + c = b + c$.
Subtraction Property of Equality	For any numbers a, b, and c, if $a = b$, then $a - c = b - c$.

Example 1 Solve $m - 32 = 18$.
$m - 32 = 18$ Original equation
$m - 32 + 32 = 18 + 32$ Add 32 to each side.
$m = 50$ Simplify.
The solution is 50.

Example 2 Solve $22 + p = -12$.
$22 + p = -12$ Original equation
$22 + p - 22 = -12 - 22$ Subtract 22 from each side.
$p = -34$ Simplify.
The solution is −34.

Exercises
Solve each equation. Check your solution.

1. $h - 3 = -2$ 2. $m - 8 = -12$ 3. $p - 5 = 15$
4. $20 = y - 8$ 5. $k - 0.5 = 2.3$ 6. $w - \frac{1}{2} = \frac{5}{8}$
7. $h - 18 = -17$ 8. $-12 = -24 + k$ 9. $j - 0.2 = 1.8$
10. $b - 40 = -40$ 11. $m - (-12) = 10$ 12. $w - \frac{3}{2} = \frac{1}{4}$
13. $x + 12 = 6$ 14. $w + 2 = -13$ 15. $-17 = b + 4$
16. $k + (-9) = 7$ 17. $-3.2 = \ell + (-0.2)$ 18. $-\frac{3}{8} + x = \frac{5}{8}$
19. $19 + h = -4$ 20. $-12 = k + 24$ 21. $j + 1.2 = 2.8$
22. $b + 80 = -80$ 23. $m + (-8) = 2$ 24. $w + \frac{3}{2} = \frac{5}{8}$

Practice
AL OL BL ELL

2-2 Practice
Solving One-Step Equations

Solve each equation. Check your solution.

1. $d - 8 = 17$ 2. $v + 12 = -5$ 3. $b - 2 = -11$
4. $-16 = m + 71$ 5. $29 = a - 76$ 6. $-14 + y = -2$
7. $8 - (-n) = 1$ 8. $78 + r = -15$ 9. $f + (-3) = -9$
10. $8j = 96$ 11. $-13z = -39$ 12. $-180 = 15m$
13. $243 = 27r$ 14. $\frac{y}{9} = -8$ 15. $-\frac{j}{12} = -8$
16. $\frac{a}{15} = \frac{4}{5}$ 17. $\frac{g}{27} = \frac{2}{9}$ 18. $\frac{q}{24} = \frac{1}{6}$

Write an equation for each sentence. Then solve the equation.

19. Negative nine times a number equals −117.
20. Negative one eighth of a number is $-\frac{3}{4}$.
21. Five sixths of a number is $-\frac{5}{9}$.
22. 2.7 times a number equals 8.37.

23. **HURRICANES** The day after a hurricane, the barometric pressure in a coastal town has risen to 29.7 inches of mercury, which is 2.9 inches of mercury higher than the pressure when the eye of the hurricane passed over.
 a. Write an addition equation to represent the situation.
 b. What was the barometric pressure when the eye passed over?

24. **ROLLER COASTERS** *Kingda Ka* in New Jersey is the tallest and fastest roller coaster in the world. Riders travel at an average speed of 61 feet per second for 3118 feet. They reach a maximum speed of 187 feet per second.
 a. If x represents the total time that the roller coaster is in motion for each ride, write an expression to represent the sitation. (*Hint:* Use the distance formula $d = rt$.)
 b. How long is the roller coaster in motion?

Word Problem Practice
AL OL BL ELL

2-2 Word Problem Practice
Solving One-Step Equations

1. **SUPREME COURT** Chief Justice William Rehnquist served on the Supreme Court for 33 years until his death in 2005. Write and solve an equation to determine the year he was confirmed as a justice on the Supreme Court.

2. **SALARY** In a recent year, the annual salary of the Governor of New York was \$179,000. During the same year, the annual salary of the Governor of Tennessee was \$94,000 less. Write and solve an equation to find the annual salary of the Governor of Tennessee in that year.

3. **WEATHER** On a cold January day, Mavis noticed that the temperature dropped 21 degrees over the course of the day to −9°C. Write and solve an equation to determine what the temperature was at the beginning of the day.

4. **FARMING** Mr. Hill's farm is 126 acres. Mr. Hill's farm is $\frac{1}{6}$ the size of Mr. Miller's farm. How many acres is Mr. Miller's farm?

5. **NAUTICAL** On the sea, distances are measured in nautical miles rather than miles.
 1 nautical mile = 6080 feet
 1 knot = 1 nautical mile / hour
 a. If a boat travels 16 knots in 1 hour, how far will it have traveled in feet? Write and solve an equation.
 b. About how fast was the boat traveling in miles per hour? Round your answer to the nearest hundredth.

Enrichment
OL BL

2-2 Enrichment

Elevator Puzzle
José gets on the elevator and rides without pushing any buttons. First, the elevator goes up 4 floors where Bob gets on. Bob goes down 6 floors and gets off. At that same floor Florence gets on and goes up one floor before getting off. The elevator then moves down 8 floors to pick up the Hartt family who ride down 3 floors and get off. Then the elevator goes up one floor, picks up Kris, and goes down 6 floors to the street level where José exits the elevator.

1. Suppose x is your starting point. Write an equation that represents José's elevator ride.

2. At what floor did José get on the elevator?

Now that you know the starting point of José, the starting point of every other person who rode the elevator can be determined.

Standardized Test Practice

79. Which of the following best represents the equation $w - 15 = 33$? **C**

A Jake added w ounces of water to his bottle, which originally contained 33 ounces of water. How much water did he add?

B Jake added 15 ounces of water to his bottle, for a total of 33 ounces. How much water w was originally in the bottle?

C Jake drank 15 ounces of water from his bottle and 33 ounces were left. How much water w was originally in the bottle?

D Jake drank 15 ounces of water from his water bottle, which originally contained 33 ounces. How much water w was left?

80. SHORT RESPONSE Charlie's company pays him for every mile that he drives on his trip. When he drives 50 miles, he is paid $30. To the nearest tenth, how many miles did he drive if he was paid $275? **458.3**

81. The table shows the results of a survey given to 500 international travelers. Based on the data, which statement is true? **F**

Vacation Plans

Destination	Percent
The Tropics	37
Europe	19
Asia	17
Other	17
No Vacation	10

F Fifty have no vacation plans.

G Fifteen are going to Asia.

H One third are going to the tropics.

J One hundred are going to Europe.

82. GEOMETRY The amount of water needed to fill a pool represents the pool's ____. **A**

A volume

B surface area

C circumference

D perimeter

Spiral Review

Translate each sentence into an equation. (Lesson 2-1)

83. The sum of twice r and three times k is identical to thirteen. **$2r + 3k = 13$**

84. The quotient of t and forty is the same as twelve minus half of u. **84. $\frac{t}{40} = 12 - \frac{1}{2}u$**

85. The square of m minus the cube of p is sixteen. **$m^2 - p^3 = 16$**

86. TOYS Identify the function graphed as *linear* or *nonlinear.* Then estimate and interpret the intercepts of the graph, any symmetry, where the function is positive, negative, increasing, and decreasing, the x-coordinate of any relative extrema, and the end behavior of the graph. (Lesson 1-8) **See margin.**

Distance from Toy Car

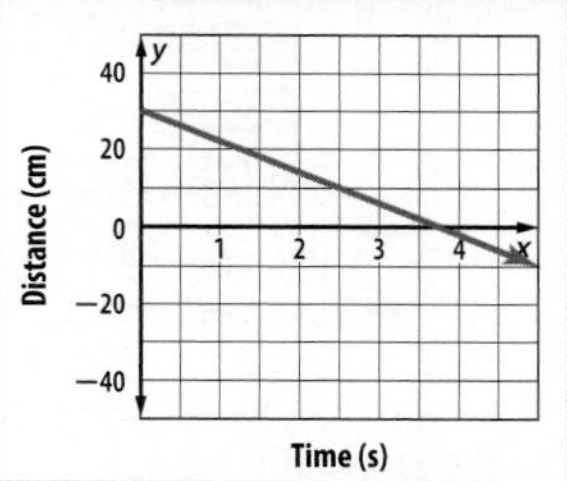

Skills Review

87. COMMUNICATION Sato communicates with friends for a project. He averages 5 hours using email, 8 hours on the phone, and 2 hours with them in person the first week. If this trend continues, write and evaluate an expression to predict how many hours he will spend communicating with friends over the next 12 weeks. **$12(5 + 8 + 2)$; 180 hours**

88. PETS The Poochie Pet supply store has the following items on sale. Write and evaluate an expression to find the total cost of purchasing 1 collar, 2 T-shirts, 3 kerchiefs, 1 leash, and 4 flying disks.
$4.50 + 2(6.25) + 3(3.00) + 5.50 + 4(3.25)$; $44.50

Item	Cost ($)
studded collar	4.50
kerchief	3.00
doggy T-shirt	6.25
leash	5.50
flying disk	3.25

DifferentiatedInstruction OL BL

Extension Write $\frac{30}{x} = 6$ on the board. Have students solve for x in two ways. Sample answers: Using mental math, think: 30 divided by what number is 6? Multiply each side by x, so $30 = 6x$; the solution is 5.

4 Assess

Name the Math Write an equation involving multiplication or division on the board. Have students identify the operation in the equation. Based on the operation they identify, have students suggest the operation that might be used to solve the equation.

Teaching the Process Standards

Structure Mathematically proficient students look closely to discern a pattern or structure. In Exercise 75, instruct students that when evaluating general equations they should experiment with both positive and negative values of x, and always consider 0.

Additional Answer

86. Linear; the y-intercept is 30, so the distance to the car was 30 centimeters when the measurement started. The x-intercept is about 3.75, so after about 3.75 seconds, the distance to the car was 0. A distance of 0 indicates that the toy car reaches the point of reference for the measurements. The graph has no line symmetry. The distance is greater than 0 for the first 3.75 seconds, and then less than 0 after 3.75 seconds. The distance is going down for the entire time. There are no extrema. As the time increases, the distance will continue to decrease. This indicates that the car passes the point of reference.

1 Focus

Objective Use algebra tiles to solve multi-step equations.

Materials for Each Group

- equation mats
- algebra tiles (*x*-tiles, 1-tiles)

Easy to Make Manipulatives

Teaching Algebra with Manipulatives templates for:

- algebra tiles, pp. 10–11
- equation mat, p. 16

Teaching Tip

You may need to review the method of forming zero pairs before beginning the activity.

2 Teach

Working in Cooperative Groups

Put students in groups of two or three, mixing abilities. Have groups complete the Activity and Exercises 1–4.

Point out that, in Step 4, separating the *x*-tiles and 1-tiles into 4 equivalent groups is a pictorial representation of dividing each side of the equation by 4.

Practice Have students complete Exercises 5–10.

From Concrete to Abstract

Ask students to discuss how the steps for solving an equation are similar to or different from the order of operations. Sample answer: When solving a multi-step equation, addition and subtraction are usually done before multiplication and division. This is the reverse of the order of operations.

EXPLORE 2-3

Algebra Lab
Solving Multi-Step Equations

You can use algebra tiles to model solving multi-step equations.

Content Standards
A1.L.1

Activity

Use an equation model to solve $4x + 3 = -5$.

Step 1 Model the equation.

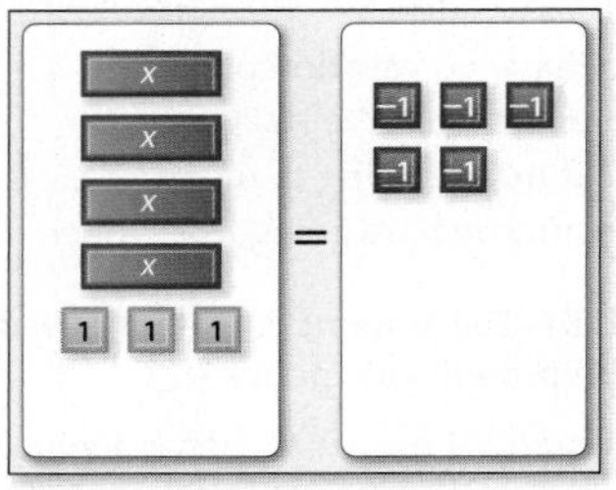

$4x + 3 = -5$

Place 4 *x*-tiles and 3 positive 1-tiles on one side of the mat. Place 5 negative 1-tiles on the other side.

Step 2 Isolate the *x*-term.

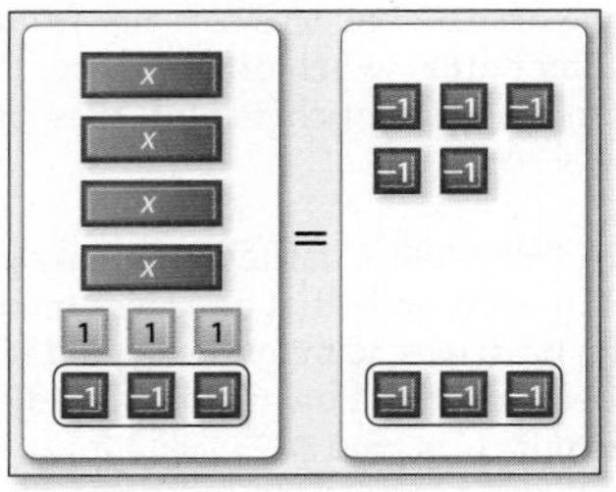

$4x + 3 - 3 = -5 - 3$

Since there are 3 positive 1-tiles with the *x*-tiles, add 3 negative 1-tiles to each side to form zero pairs.

Step 3 Remove zero pairs.

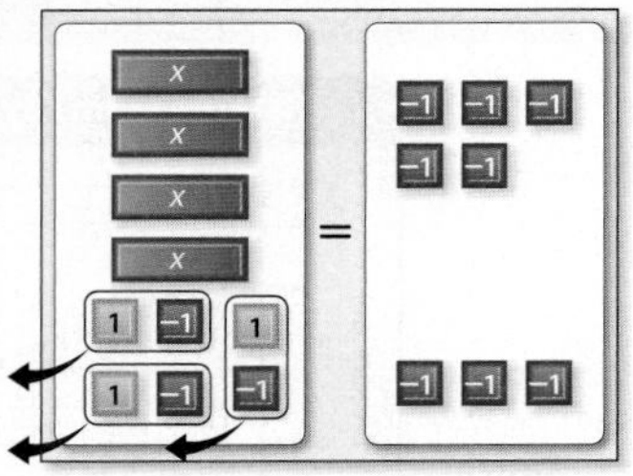

$4x = -8$

Group the tiles to form zero pairs and remove the zero pairs.

Step 4 Group the tiles.

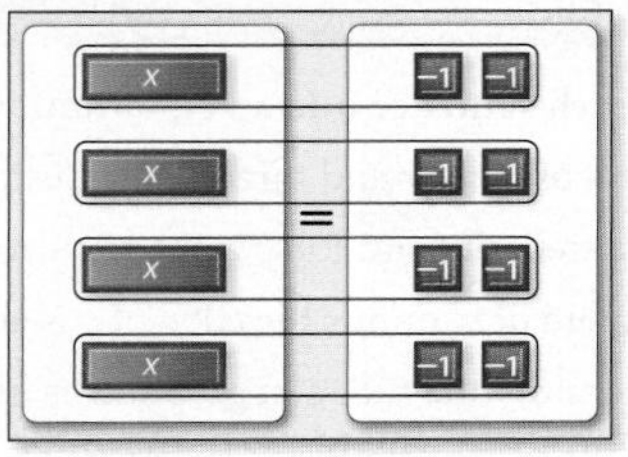

$\frac{4x}{4} = \frac{-8}{4}$

$x = -2$

Separate the remaining tiles into 4 equal groups to match the 4 *x*-tiles. Each *x*-tile is paired with 2 negative 1-tiles. The resulting equation is $x = -2$.

Model

Use algebra tiles to solve each equation. 10. First subtract 14 from each side, and then divide each side by 9.

1. $3x - 7 = -10$ **−1**
2. $2x + 5 = 9$ **2**
3. $5x - 7 = 8$ **3**
4. $-7 = 3x + 8$ **−5**
5. $5 + 4x = -11$ **−4**
6. $3x + 1 = 7$ **2**
7. $11 = 2x - 5$ **8**
8. $7 + 6x = -11$ **−3**
9. What would be your first step in solving $8x - 29 = 67$? **Add 29 to each side.**
10. What steps would you use to solve $9x + 14 = -49$?

3 Assess

Formative Assessment

Use Exercises 4 and 8 to assess whether students comprehend how to discover which side of the equation directs the method of solution.

Use Exercise 10 to assess whether students comprehend that addition and subtraction are done before multiplication and division when isolating the variable.

LESSON 2-3 Solving Multi-Step Equations

Then

- You solved one-step equations.

Now

1. Solve equations involving more than one operation.
2. Solve equations involving consecutive integers.

Why?

- The Tour de France is the premier cycling event in the world. The map shows the 2007 Tour de France course. If the length of the shortest portion of the race can be represented by k, the expression $4k + 20$ is the length of the longest stage or 236 kilometers. This can be described by the equation $4k + 20 = 236$.

NewVocabulary
multi-step equation
consecutive integers
number theory

Content Standards
AI.L.1, AI.L.2

1 Solve Multi-Step Equations

Since the above equation requires more than one step to solve, it is called a **multi-step equation**. To solve this equation, we must undo each operation by working backward.

Example 1 Solve Multi-Step Equations

Solve each equation. Check your solution.

a. $11x - 4 = 29$

$11x - 4 = 29$	Original equation
$11x - 4 + 4 = 29 + 4$	Add 4 to each side.
$11x = 33$	Simplify.
$\frac{11x}{11} = \frac{33}{11}$	Divide each side by 11.
$x = 3$	Simplify.

b. $\frac{a + 7}{8} = 5$

$\frac{a + 7}{8} = 5$	Original equation
$8\left(\frac{a + 7}{8}\right) = 8(5)$	Multiply each side by 8.
$a + 7 = 40$	Simplify.
$-7 = -7$	Subtract 7 from each side.
$a = 33$	Simplify.

You can check your solutions by substituting the results back into the original equations.

GuidedPractice

Solve each equation. Check your solution.

1A. $2a - 6 = 4$ **5**

1B. $\frac{n + 1}{-2} = 15$ **−31**

1 Focus

VerticalAlignment

Before Lesson 2-3 Solve one-step equations.

Lesson 2-3 Solve equations involving more than one operation. Solve equations involving consecutive integers.

After Lesson 2-3 Solve problems involving grouping symbols.

2 Teach

Scaffolding Questions

Have students read the **Why?** section of the lesson.

Ask:

- In the expression $4k + 20$, what does $4k$ represent? $4k$ represents four times the length of the shortest portion of the race; k represents the number of kilometers in the shortest portion of the race.
- What does the number 20 in the expression $4k + 20$ represent? an additional 20 kilometers in the longest portion of the race
- What is the expression $4k + 20$ equal to? 236 kilometers How do you write this as an equation? $4k + 20 = 236$

(continued on the next page)

Lesson 2-3 Resources

Resource	Approaching Level AL	On Level OL	Beyond Level BL	English Learners ELL
Teacher Edition	▪ Differentiated Instruction, pp. 92, 93	▪ Differentiated Instruction, pp. 93, 96	▪ Differentiated Instruction, pp. 93, 96	▪ Differentiated Instruction, p. 93
Chapter Resource Masters	▪ Study Guide and Intervention, pp. 17–18 ▪ Skills Practice, p. 19 ▪ Practice, p. 20 ▪ Word Problem Practice, p. 21	▪ Study Guide and Intervention, pp. 17–18 ▪ Skills Practice, p. 19 ▪ Practice, p. 20 ▪ Word Problem Practice, p. 21 ▪ Enrichment, p. 22	▪ Practice, p. 20 ▪ Word Problem Practice, p. 21 ▪ Enrichment, p. 22	▪ Study Guide and Intervention, pp. 17–18 ▪ Skills Practice, p. 19 ▪ Practice, p. 20 ▪ Word Problem Practice, p. 21
Other	▪ 5-Minute Check 2-3 ▪ Study Notebook ▪ Teaching Algebra with Manipulatives	▪ 5-Minute Check 2-3 ▪ Study Notebook ▪ Teaching Algebra with Manipulatives	▪ 5-Minute Check 2-3 ▪ Study Notebook	▪ 5-Minute Check 2-3 ▪ Study Notebook ▪ Teaching Algebra with Manipulatives

- What operations do you need to perform to isolate the variable in the equation? subtraction and division

1 Solve Multi-Step Equations

Example 1 shows how to undo operations to solve multi-step problems. **Example 2** shows how to write and solve a multi-step equation.

Formative Assessment

Use the Guided Practice exercises after each Example to determine students' understanding of concepts.

Additional Examples

1 Solve each equation. Check your solution.

a. $2q + 11 = 3$ -4

b. $\frac{k+9}{12} = -2$ -33

2 **SHOPPING** Susan had a \$10 coupon for the purchase of any item. She bought a coat that was on sale for $\frac{1}{2}$ its original price. After using the coupon, Susan paid \$125 for the coat before taxes. What was the original price of the coat? Write an equation for the problem. Then solve the equation.

$\frac{1}{2}p - 10 = 125$; $p = 270$, so the original price of the coat was \$270.

Additional Examples also in Interactive Classroom PowerPoint® Presentations

IWB Interactive White Board READY

Teach with Tech

Student Response System

Show students several different multi-step equations. Have a student state what operation should be done first, or next. Have students vote as to whether they agree or disagree. Save the results to track understanding.

Real-WorldLink

Shoppers in Shanghai, China, can pay for purchased items at a terminal that can match the buyers' fingerprints with their bank accounts.

Source: *Shanghai Daily*

Real-World Example 2 Write and Solve a Multi-Step Equation

SHOPPING Hiroshi is buying a pair of water skis that are on sale for $\frac{2}{3}$ of the original price. After he uses a \$25 gift certificate, the total cost before taxes is \$115. What was the original price of the skis? Write an equation for the problem. Then solve the equation.

Words	Two thirds	of	the price	minus	25	is	115.
Variable	Let p = original price of the skis.						
Equation	$\frac{2}{3}$	$\cdot$	p	$-$	25	$=$	115

$\frac{2}{3}p - 25 = 115$ Original equation

$\frac{2}{3}p - 25 + 25 = 115 + 25$ Add 25 to each side.

$\frac{2}{3}p = 140$ Simplify.

$\frac{3}{2}\left(\frac{2}{3}p\right) = \frac{3}{2}(140)$ Multiply each side by $\frac{3}{2}$.

$p = 210$ Simplify.

The original price of the skis was \$210.

GuidedPractice

2A. RETAIL A music store has sold $\frac{3}{5}$ of their hip-hop CDs, but 10 were returned. Now the store has 62 hip-hop CDs. How many were there originally? **130**

2B. READING Len read $\frac{3}{4}$ of a graphic novel over the weekend. Monday, he read 22 more pages. If he has read 220 pages, how many pages does the book have? **264**

2 Solve Consecutive Integer Problems

Consecutive integers are integers in counting order, such as 4, 5, and 6 or n, $n + 1$, and $n + 2$. Counting by two will result in *consecutive even integers* if the starting integer n is even and *consecutive odd integers* if the starting integer n is odd.

ConceptSummary Consecutive Integers

Type	Words	Symbols	Example
Consecutive Integers	Integers that come in counting order.	$n, n + 1, n + 2, \ldots$	$\ldots, -2, -1, 0, 1, 2, \ldots$
Consecutive Even Integers	Even integer followed by the next even integer.	$n, n + 2, n + 4, \ldots$	$\ldots, -2, 0, 2, 4, \ldots$
Consecutive Odd Integers	Odd integer followed by the next odd integer.	$n, n + 2, n + 4, \ldots$	$\ldots, -1, 1, -3, 5, \ldots$

Number theory is the study of numbers and the relationships between them.

DifferentiatedInstruction AL

If in Example 1b, some students do not understand why both sides of the equation are multiplied by 8 before subtracting 7 from each side,

Then use an example, such as $\frac{23 - 7}{8}$. Have a volunteer tell the steps used to simplify this expression. Explain that Example 1b is solved using the reverse of the steps used to simplify $\frac{23 - 7}{8}$. Then have students discuss the steps they would use to solve $\frac{b - 3}{-4} = 6$.

Example 3 Solve a Consecutive Integer Problem

NUMBER THEORY Write an equation for the following problem. Then solve the equation and answer the problem.

Find three consecutive odd integers with a sum of −51.

Let n = the least odd integer.

Then $n + 2$ = the next greater odd integer, and $n + 4$ = the greatest of the three integers.

StudyTip

Regularity You can use the same expressions to represent either consecutive even integers or consecutive odd integers. It is the value of n (odd or even) that differs between the two expressions.

Words	The sum of three consecutive odd integers	is	−51.
Equation	$n + (n + 2) + (n + 4)$	=	−51.

$n + (n + 2) + (n + 4) = -51$ Original equation

$3n + 6 = -51$ Simplify.

$-6 = -6$ Subtract 6 from each side.

$3n = -57$ Simplify.

$\frac{3n}{3} = \frac{-57}{3}$ Divide each side by 3.

$n = -19$ Simplify.

$n + 2 = -19 + 2$ or -17 $n + 4 = -19 + 4$ or -15

The consecutive odd integers are −19, −17, and −15.

CHECK −19, −17, and −15 are consecutive odd integers.
$-19 + (-17) + (-15) = -51$ ✓

GuidedPractice

3. Write an equation for the following problem. Then solve the equation and answer the problem. **$n + (n + 1) + (n + 2) = 21$; 6, 7, 8**

Find three consecutive integers with a sum of 21.

Check Your Understanding

= Step-by-Step Solutions begin on page R13.

Example 1 **Solve each equation. Check your solution.**

1. $3m + 4 = -11$ **−5**
2. $12 = -7f - 9$ **−3**
3. $-3 = 2 + \frac{a}{11}$ **−55**
4. $\frac{3}{2}a - 8 = 11$ **$12\frac{2}{3}$**
5. $8 = \frac{x - 5}{7}$ **61**
6. $\frac{c + 1}{-3} = -21$ **62**

Example 2

7. **NUMBER THEORY** Twelve decreased by twice a number equals −34. Write an equation for this situation and then find the number. **$12 - 2n = -34$; 23**

8. **BASEBALL** Among the career home run leaders for Major League Baseball, Hank Aaron has 175 fewer than twice the number that Dave Winfield has. Hank Aaron hit 755 home runs. Write an equation for this situation. How many home runs did Dave Winfield hit in his career? **$2h - 175 = 755$; 465 home runs**

Example 3 **Write an equation and solve each problem.**

9. Find three consecutive odd integers with a sum of 75. **$n + (n + 2) + (n + 4) = 75$; 23, 25, 27**
10. Find three consecutive integers with a sum of −36. **$n + (n + 1) + (n + 2) = -36$; −13, −12, −11**

Focus on Mathematical Content

Multi-Step Equations Multi-step equations include two or more operations. To solve a multi-step equation, "undo" the operations in reverse of the order of operations.

2 Solve Consecutive Integer Problems

Example 3 introduces students to number theory by showing how to solve a consecutive integer problem.

Additional Example

3. **NUMBER THEORY** Write an equation for the following problem. Then solve the equation and answer the problem.
Find three consecutive odd integers with a sum of 57.
$n + (n + 2) + (n + 4) = 57$, or $3n + 6 = 57$. The consecutive integers are 17, 19, and 21.

Teaching the Process Standards

Regularity Mathematically proficient students look both for general methods and for shortcuts. Ask students to explain why an equation to find consecutive odd integers looks like an equation to find consecutive even integers. Students should note that both odds and evens are calculated by adding 2 to the previous odd or even.

3 Practice

Formative Assessment

Use Exercises 1–10 to check for understanding.

Use the chart at the bottom of the next page to customize assignments for your students.

DifferentiatedInstruction AL OL BL ELL

Extension Hold a creativity competition for students. Each week, give students an equation and ask them to provide a context for the equation. Increase the difficulty level with each successive week and reward creativity for problems that accurately reflect the operations and variables in the equation. (Optional: Provide a prize for the winner each week.)

Teaching the Process Standards

Reasoning Mathematically proficient students consider the units involved in a problem. In Exercise 40, point out to students that ages must be positive.

Additional Answers

51b.

Visits	Cost for Members	Cost for Nonmembers
3	290	90
6	305	180
9	320	270
12	335	360
15	350	450

51c.

Park Costs

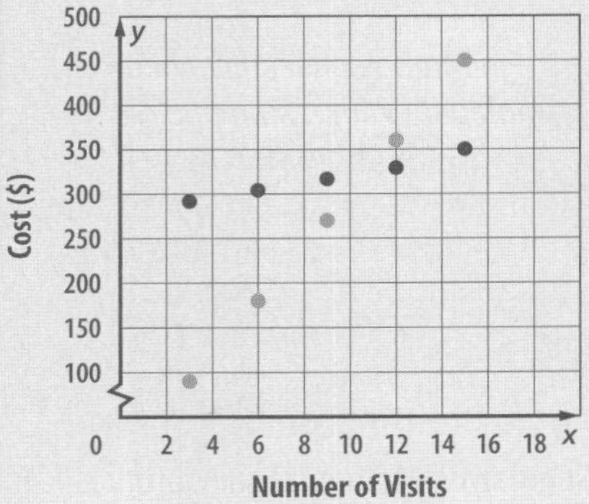

Both functions are linear. If a person is going to visit the park fewer than 11 times, it will be cheaper to be a nonmember.

55a. No; for there to be a solution there must be a number for which $a + 4 = a + 5$.

55b. Yes; for $b = 0$, $\frac{1+b}{1-b} = \frac{1+0}{1-0}$ or 1.

55c. No; $c - 5 = 5 - c$ when $c = 5$. However, $\frac{c-5}{5-c}$ is undefined for $c = 5$ since the fraction represents division by 0.

57. Sample answer: In order to solve the equation $4k + 20 = 236$, you would first subtract 20 from each side and then divide each side by 4.

Practice and Problem Solving

Extra Practice is on page R2.

Example 1 **Solve each equation. Check your solution.**

11. $3t + 7 = -8$ **−5**
12. $8 = 16 + 8n$ **−1**
13. $-34 = 6m - 4$ **−5**
14. $9x + 27 = -72$ **−11**
15. $\frac{y}{5} - 6 = 8$ **70**
16. $\frac{f}{-7} - 8 = 2$ **−70**
17. $1 + \frac{r}{9} = 4$ **27**
18. $\frac{k}{3} + 4 = -16$ **−60**
19. $\frac{n-2}{7} = 2$ **16**
20. $14 = \frac{6+z}{-2}$ **−34**
21. $-11 = \frac{a-5}{6}$ **−61**
22. $\frac{22-w}{3} = -7$ **43**

Example 2

23. FINANCIAL LITERACY The Cell+ Cellular Phone store offers the plans shown in the table. Raul chose the business plan and has budgeted $100 per month. Write an equation for this situation, and determine how many minutes per month he can use the phone and stay within budget. **$0.15m + 49.99 = 100$; $m \approx 333$; $650 + 333 = 983$ min**

Plan	Flat Monthly Fee	Anytime Minutes	Cost per Minute After Anytime Minutes
personal	$29.99	250	$0.20
business	$49.99	650	$0.15
executive	$59.99	1200	$0.10

Example 3 **Write an equation and solve each problem.**

24. Fourteen less than three fourths of a number is negative eight. Find the number.

25. Seventeen is thirteen subtracted from six times a number. What is the number?

26. Find three consecutive even integers with the sum of −84.

27. Find three consecutive odd integers with the sum of 141.

28. Find four consecutive integers with the sum of 54.

29. Find four consecutive integers with the sum of −142.

24. $\frac{3}{4}n - 14 = -8$; 8
25. $17 = 6x - 13$; 5
26. $n + (n + 2) + (n + 4) = -84$, −30, −28, −26
27. $n + (n + 2) + (n + 4) = 141$; 45, 47, 49
28. $n + (n + 1) + (n + 2) + (n + 3) = 54$; 12, 13, 14, 15
29. $n + (n + 1) + (n + 2) + (n + 3) = -142$; −37, −36, −35, −34

B **Solve each equation. Check your solution.**

30. $-6m - 8 = 24$ $-5\frac{1}{3}$
31. $45 = 7 - 5n$ $-7\frac{3}{5}$
32. $\frac{2b}{3} + 6 = 24$ **27**
33. $\frac{5x}{9} - 11 = -51$ **−72**
34. $65 = \frac{3}{4}c - 7$ **96**
35. $9 + \frac{2}{3}x = 81$ **108**
36. $-\frac{5}{2} = \frac{3}{4}z + \frac{1}{2}$ **−4**
37. $\frac{5}{6}k + \frac{2}{3} = \frac{4}{3}$ $\frac{4}{5}$
38. $-\frac{1}{5} - \frac{4}{9}a = \frac{2}{15}$ $-\frac{3}{4}$
39. $-\frac{3}{7} = \frac{3}{4} - \frac{b}{2}$ $\frac{33}{14}$

Write an equation and solve each problem.

40. REASONING The ages of three brothers are consecutive integers with the sum of 96. How old are the brothers? **$n + n + 1 + n + 2 = 96$; 31, 32, and 33**

41. VOLCANOES Moving lava can build up and form beaches at the coast of an island. The growth of an island in a seaward direction may be modeled as $8y + 2$ centimeters, where y represents the number of years that the lava flows. An island has expanded 60 centimeters seaward. How long has the lava flowed? **$7\frac{1}{4}$ yr or 7 yr 3 mo**

Differentiated Homework Options

Level	Assignment	Two-Day Option	
AL Basic	11–29, 53, 54, 57–78	11–29 odd, 58–61	12–28 even, 53, 54, 57, 62–78
OL Core	11–39 odd, 40, 41–51 odd, 52–54, 57–78	11–29, 58–61	30–54, 57, 62–78
BL Advanced	30–74, (optional: 75–78)		

C **Solve each equation. Check your solution.**

42. $-5x - 4.8 = 6.7$ **−2.3**

43. $3.7q + 26.2 = 111.67$ **23.1**

44. $0.6a + 9 = 14.4$ **9**

45. $\frac{c}{2} - 4.3 = 11.5$ **31.6**

46. $9 = \frac{-6p - (-3)}{-8}$ **12.5**

47. $3.6 - 2.4m = 12$ **−3.5**

48. If $7m - 3 = 53$, what is the value of $11m + 2$? **90**

49. If $13y + 25 = 64$, what is the value of $4y - 7$? **5**

50. If $-5c + 6 = -69$, what is the value of $6c - 15$? **75**

51. **AMUSEMENT PARKS** An amusement park offers a yearly membership of $275 that allows for free parking and admission to the park. Members can also use the water park for an additional $5 per day. Nonmembers pay $6 for parking, $15 for admission, and $9 for the water park.
   a. Write and solve an equation to find the number of visits it would take for the total cost to be the same for a member and a nonmember if they both use the water park at each visit. **$5x + 275 = x(6 + 15 + 9)$; 11 visits**
   b. Make a table for the costs of members and nonmembers after 3, 6, 9, 12, and 15 visits to the park. **See margin.**
   c. Plot these points on a coordinate graph and describe what you see. **See margin.**

52. **SHOPPING** At The Family Farm, you can pick your own fruits and vegetables.
   a. The cost of a bag of potatoes is $1.50 less than $\frac{1}{2}$ of the price of apples. Write and solve an equation to find the cost of potatoes. **$p = \frac{1}{2}a - 1.50$; $2.00**
   b. The price of each zucchini is 3 times the price of winter squash minus $7. Write and solve an equation to find the cost of zucchini. **$z = 3w - 7$; $1.97**
   c. Write an equation to represent the cost of a pumpkin using the cost of the blueberries. **Sample answer: $p = 2b - 0.98$**

The Family Farm	
Fruit	Price ($)
Apples	6.99/bag
Pumpkins	5.00 each
Blueberries	2.99/qt
Winter squash	2.99 each

53. Sample answer: A pair of designer jeans costs $60. This is $40 more than twice the cost of a T-shirt. How much is the T-shirt? The T-shirt costs $10.

H.O.T. Problems Use Higher-Order Thinking Skills

53. **OPEN ENDED** Write a problem that can be modeled by the equation $2x + 40 = 60$. Then solve the equation and explain the solution in the context of the problem.

54. **CHALLENGE** Solve each equation for x. Assume that $a \neq 0$.
   a. $ax + 7 = 5$ **$x = \frac{-2}{a}$**
   b. $\frac{1}{a}x - 4 = 9$ **$x = 13a$**
   c. $2 - ax = -8$ **$x = \frac{10}{a}$**

55. **REASONING** Determine whether each equation has a solution. Justify your answer.
   a. $\frac{a + 4}{5 + a} = 1$
   b. $\frac{1 + b}{1 - b} = 1$
   c. $\frac{c - 5}{5 - c} = 1$ **See margin.**

56. **REGULARITY** Determine whether the following statement is *sometimes*, *always*, or *never* true. Explain your reasoning. **Never; whenever three odd integers are added together, the sum is always odd.**
The sum of three consecutive odd integers equals an even integer.

57. **WRITING IN MATH** Write a paragraph explaining the order of the steps that you would take to solve a multi-step equation. **See margin.**

Teaching the Process Standards

Regularity Mathematically proficient students notice if calculations are repeated, and look for general methods. In Exercise 56, recommend that students add sets of three consecutive odd integers and note the result. Then write expressions for three consecutive integers and justify their conclusion.

Study Guide and Intervention
AL OL ELL

NAME ______ DATE ______ PERIOD ______

2-3 Study Guide and Intervention

Solving Multi-Step Equations

Work Backward **Working backward** is one of many problem-solving strategies that you can use to solve problems. To work backward, start with the result given at the end of a problem and undo each step to arrive at the beginning number.

Example 1 **A number is divided by 2, and then 8 is subtracted from the quotient. The result is 16. What is the number?**

Solve the problem by working backward.

The final number is 16. Undo subtracting 8 by adding 8 to get 24. To undo dividing 24 by 2, multiply 24 by 2 to get 48.

The original number is 48.

Example 2 **A bacteria culture doubles each half hour. After 3 hours, there are 6400 bacteria. How many bacteria were there to begin with?**

Solve the problem by working backward.

The bacteria have grown for 3 hours. Since there are 2 one-half hour periods in one hour, in 3 hours there are 6 one-half hour periods. Since the bacteria culture has grown for 6 time periods, it has doubled 6 times. Undo the doubling by halving the number of bacteria 6 times.

$6400 \times \frac{1}{2} \times \frac{1}{2} \times \frac{1}{2} \times \frac{1}{2} \times \frac{1}{2} \times \frac{1}{2} = 6400 \times \frac{1}{64}$
$= 100$

There were 100 bacteria to begin with.

Exercises

Solve each problem by working backward.

1. A number is divided by 3, and then 4 is added to the quotient. The result is 8. Find the number.
2. A number is multiplied by 5, and then 3 is subtracted from the product. The result is 12. Find the number.
3. Eight is subtracted from a number, and then the difference is multiplied by 2. The result is 24. Find the number.
4. Three times a number plus 3 is 24. Find the number.
5. **CAR RENTAL** Angela rented a car for $29.99 a day plus a one-time insurance cost of $5.00. Her bill was $124.96. For how many days did she rent the car?
6. **MONEY** Mike withdrew an amount of money from his bank account. He spent one fourth for gasoline and had $90 left. How much money did he withdraw?

Lesson 2-3

Practice
AL OL BL ELL

NAME ______ DATE ______ PERIOD ______

2-3 Practice

Solving Multi-Step Equations

Solve each problem by working backward.

1. Three is added to a number, and then the sum is multiplied by 4. The result is 16. Find the number.
2. A number is divided by 4, and the quotient is added to 3. The result is 24. What is the number?
3. Two is subtracted from a number, and then the difference is multiplied by 5. The result is 30. Find the number.
4. **BIRD WATCHING** While Michelle sat observing birds at a bird feeder, one fourth of the birds flew away when they were startled by a noise. Two birds left the feeder to go to another stationed a few feet away. Three more birds flew into the branches of a nearby tree. Four birds remained at the feeder. How many birds were at the feeder initially?

Solve each equation. Check your solution.

5. $-12n - 19 = 77$
6. $17 + 3f = 14$
7. $15t + 4 = 49$
8. $\frac{u}{5} + 6 = 2$
9. $\frac{d}{-4} + 3 = 15$
10. $\frac{b}{3} - 6 = -2$
11. $\frac{1}{2}y - \frac{1}{8} = \frac{7}{8}$
12. $-32 - \frac{3}{5}f = -17$
13. $8 - \frac{3}{8}k = -4$
14. $\frac{r + 13}{12} = 1$
15. $\frac{15 - a}{3} = -9$
16. $\frac{3k - 7}{5} = 16$
17. $\frac{x}{7} - 0.5 = 2.5$
18. $2.5g + 0.45 = 0.95$
19. $0.4m - 0.7 = 0.22$

Write an equation and solve each problem.

20. Seven less than four times a number equals 13. What is the number?
21. Find two consecutive odd integers whose sum is 116.
22. Find two consecutive even integers whose sum is 126.
23. Find three consecutive odd integers whose sum is 117.
24. **COIN COLLECTING** Jung has a total of 92 coins in his coin collection. This is 8 more than three times the number of quarters in the collection. How many quarters does Jung have in his collection?

Word Problem Practice
AL OL BL ELL

NAME ______ DATE ______ PERIOD ______

2-3 Word Problem Practice

Solving Multi-Step Equations

1. **TEMPERATURE** The formula for converting a Fahrenheit temperature to a Celsius temperature is $C = \frac{F - 32°}{1.8}$. Find the equivalent Celsius temperature for 68°F.
2. **HUMAN HEIGHT** It is a commonly used guideline that for the average American child, their maximum adult height will be about twice their height at age 2. Suppose that Micah's adult height fits the following equation $a = 2c - 1$, where a represents his adult height and c represents his height at age 2. At age 2 Micah was 35 inches tall. What is Micah's adult height? Write and solve an equation.
3. **CHEMISTRY** The half-life of a radioactive substance is the time required for half of a sample to undergo radioactive decay, or for the quantity to fall to half its original amount. Carbon 14 has a half-life of 5730 years. Suppose given samples of carbon 14 weigh $\frac{5}{8}$ of a pound and $\frac{7}{8}$ of a pound. What was the total weight of the samples 11,460 years ago?
4. **NUMBER THEORY** Write and solve an equation to find three consecutive odd integers whose sum is 3.
5. **GEOMETRY** A rectangular swimming pool is surrounded by a concrete sidewalk that is 3 feet wide. The dimensions of the rectangle created by the sidewalk are 21 feet by 31 feet.

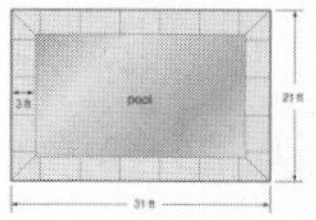

   a. Find the length and width of the pool.
   b. Find the area of the pool.
   c. Write and solve an equation to find the area of the sidewalk in square feet.

Lesson 2-3

Enrichment
OL BL

NAME ______ DATE ______ PERIOD ______

2-3 Enrichment

Consecutive Integer Problems

Many types of problems and puzzles involve the idea of consecutive integers. Knowing how to represent these integers algebraically can help to solve the problem.

Example **Find four consecutive odd integers whose sum is −80.**

An odd integer can be written as $2n + 1$, where n is any integer.

If $2n + 1$ is the first odd integer, then add 2 to get the next largest odd integer, and so on.

Now write an equation to solve this problem.

$(2n + 1) + (2n + 3) + (2n + 5) + (2n + 7) = -80$

Exercises

Write an equation for each problem. Then solve.

1. Complete the solution to the problem in the example.

4 Assess

Yesterday's News Have students write how yesterday's lesson helped them with today's new material.

Formative Assessment

Check for student understanding of Lessons 2-1 through 2-3.

Quiz 1, p. 63

Additional Answers

64. A number *f* minus 15 is 6.

65. Three times a number *h* is increased by 7 to equal 20.

66. A number *k* is squared and added to 18 to equal 54 decreased by *m*.

67. Three multiplied by a number *p* is the same as the difference of 8 times *p* and *r*.

68. Three fifths of *t* added to $\frac{1}{3}$ is *t*.

69. The product of $\frac{1}{2}$ and *v* is equal to the product of $\frac{2}{3}$ and *v* plus 4.

Standardized Test Practice

58. Which is the best estimate for the number of minutes on the calling card advertised below? **D**

A 10 min C 50 min
B 20 min D 200 min

59. GRIDDED RESPONSE The scale factor for two similar triangles is 2 : 3. The perimeter of the smaller triangle is 56 cm. What is the perimeter of the larger triangle in centimeters? **84**

60. Mr. Morrison is draining his cylindrical pool. The pool has a radius of 10 feet and a standard height of 4.5 feet. If the pool water is pumped out at a constant rate of 5 gallons per minute, about how long will it take to drain the pool? (1 ft^3 = 7.5 gal) **J**

F 37.8 min H 25.4 h
G 7 h J 35.3 h

61. STATISTICS Look at the golf scores for the five players in the table.

Player	1	2	3	4	5
Score	80	91	103	79	78

Which of these is the range of the golf scores? **B**

A 10 C 35
B 25 D 40

Spiral Review

62. GAS MILEAGE A midsize car with a 4-cylinder engine travels 34 miles on a gallon of gas. This is 10 miles more than a luxury car with an 8-cylinder engine travels on a gallon of gas. How many miles does a luxury car travel on a gallon of gas? (Lesson 2-2) **24 mi**

63. DEER In a recent year, 1286 female deer were born in Clark County. That is 93 fewer than the number of male deer born. How many male deer were born that year? (Lesson 2-2) **1379**

Translate each equation into a verbal sentence. (Lesson 2-1) **64–69. See margin.**

64. $f - 15 = 6$ **65.** $3h + 7 = 20$ **66.** $k^2 + 18 = 54 - m$

67. $3p = 8p - r$ **68.** $\frac{3}{5}t + \frac{1}{3} = t$ **69.** $\frac{1}{2}v = \frac{2}{3}v + 4$

70. GEOGRAPHY The Pacific Ocean covers about 46% of Earth. If *P* represents the surface area of the Pacific Ocean and *E* represents the surface area of Earth, write an equation for this situation. (Lesson 2-1) $P = 0.46E$

Find the value of *n* in each equation. Then name the property that is used. (Lesson 1-3)

71. $1.5 + n = 1.5$ **0; Additive Identity** **72.** $8n = 1$ $\frac{1}{8}$; **Multiplicative Inverse**

73. $4 - n = 0$ **4; Additive Inverse** **74.** $1 = 2n$ $\frac{1}{2}$; **Multiplicative Inverse**

Skills Review

Evaluate each expression.

75. $5 + 3(4^2)$ **53** **76.** $\frac{38 - 12}{2 \cdot 13}$ **1** **77.** $[5(1 + 1)]^3$ **1000** **78.** $[8(2) - 4^2] + 7(4)$ **28**

Differentiated Instruction OL BL

Extension Write $\frac{x}{10} + 3.2 = 4.7$ on the board. Ask students what would happen if each side of the equation were multiplied by 10. The result is an equivalent equation.

Ask a volunteer to explain why this might be a helpful first step in solving this type of equation. Multiplying by 10 changes all of the numbers in the equation to integers, and it might be easier to work with integers than with decimals and fractions.

Ask students to solve the equation both ways and confirm which way was easier. 15

LESSON 2-4 Solving Equations with the Variable on Each Side

Then	Now	Why?
You solved multi-step equations.	**1** Solve equations with the variable on each side. **2** Solve equations involving grouping symbols.	The equation $y = 1.3x + 19$ represents the number of times Americans eat in their cars each year, where x is the number of years since 1985, and y is the number of times that they eat in their car. The equation $y = -1.3x + 93$ represents the number of times Americans eat in restaurants each year, where x is the number of years since 1985, and y is the number of times that they eat in a restaurant. The equation $1.3x + 19 = -1.3x + 93$ represents the year when the number of times Americans eat in their cars will equal the number of times Americans eat in restaurants.

NewVocabulary
identity

Content Standards
AI.L.1, AI.L.2

Process Standards
PS.1, PS.5

Gen Nishino/The Image Bank/Getty Images

1 Variables on Each Side To solve an equation that has variables on each side, use the Addition or Subtraction Property of Equality to write an equivalent equation with the variable terms on one side.

PT

Example 1 Solve an Equation with Variables on Each Side

Solve $2 + 5k = 3k - 6$. Check your solution.

$2 + 5k = 3k - 6$	Original equation
$-3k = -3k$	Subtract $3k$ from each side.
$2 + 2k = -6$	Simplify.
$-2 \quad = -2$	Subtract 2 from each side.
$2k = -8$	Simplify.
$\frac{2k}{2} = \frac{-8}{2}$	Divide each side by 2.
$k = -4$	Simplify.
CHECK $2 + 5k = 3k - 6$	Original equation
$2 + 5(-4) \stackrel{?}{=} 3(-4) - 6$	Substitution, $k = -4$
$2 + -20 \stackrel{?}{=} -12 - 6$	Multiply.
$-18 = -18$ ✓	Simplify.

GuidedPractice

Solve each equation. Check your solution.

1A. $3w + 2 = 7w$ $\frac{1}{2}$

1B. $5a + 2 = 6 - 7a$ $\frac{1}{3}$

1C. $\frac{x}{2} + 1 = \frac{1}{4}x - 6$ -28

1D. $1.3c = 3.3c + 2.8$ -1.4

1 Focus

VerticalAlignment

Before Lesson 2-4 Solve multi-step equations.

Lesson 2-4 Solve equations with the variable on each side.
Solve equations involving grouping symbols.

After Lesson 2-4 Solve problems involving proportional change.

2 Teach

Scaffolding Questions

Have students read the **Why?** section of the lesson.

Ask:
- What does x represent in each equation? the number of years since 1985
- What is the value of x in the year 1985? 0
- If $x = 28$, what year would that be? 2013

Lesson 2-4 Resources

Resource	Approaching Level AL	On Level OL	Beyond Level BL	English Learners ELL
Teacher Edition	▪ Differentiated Instruction, p. 98		▪ Differentiated Instruction, p. 102	
Chapter Resource Masters	▪ Study Guide and Intervention, pp. 23–24 ▪ Skills Practice, p. 25 ▪ Practice, p. 26 ▪ Word Problem Practice, p. 27	▪ Study Guide and Intervention, pp. 23–24 ▪ Skills Practice, p. 25 ▪ Practice, p. 26 ▪ Word Problem Practice, p. 27 ▪ Enrichment, p. 28	▪ Practice, p. 26 ▪ Word Problem Practice, p. 27 ▪ Enrichment, p. 28	▪ Study Guide and Intervention, pp. 23–24 ▪ Skills Practice, p. 25 ▪ Practice, p. 26 ▪ Word Problem Practice, p. 27
Other	▪ 5-Minute Check 2-4 ▪ Study Notebook ▪ Teaching Algebra with Manipulatives	▪ 5-Minute Check 2-4 ▪ Study Notebook ▪ Teaching Algebra with Manipulatives	▪ 5-Minute Check 2-4 ▪ Study Notebook	▪ 5-Minute Check 2-4 ▪ Study Notebook ▪ Teaching Algebra with Manipulatives

1 Variables on Each Side

Example 1 shows how to solve an equation with variables on each side.

Formative Assessment

Use the Guided Practice exercises after each Example to determine students' understanding of concepts.

Additional Example

1 Solve $8 + 5c = 7c - 2$. Check your solution. 5

Additional Examples also in Interactive Classroom PowerPoint® Presentations

IWB Interactive White Board READY

2 Grouping Symbols

Example 2 shows how to use the Distributive Property to solve an equation containing grouping symbols. **Example 3** shows how to determine when an equation with the variable on each side has no solution and when it is an identity. **Example 4** shows how to write an equation to represent a situation.

Additional Examples

2 Solve $\frac{1}{3}(18 + 12q) = 6(2q - 7)$. Check your solution. 6

3 Solve each equation.

a. $8(5c - 2) = 10(32 + 4c)$ no solution

b. $4(t + 20) = \frac{1}{5}(20t + 400)$ all numbers

Teach with Tech

Video Recording Create a video showing how to solve equations with variables on each side. Post the video on a video sharing Web site so that your students have an additional reference outside of class.

2 Grouping Symbols If equations contain grouping symbols such as parentheses or brackets, use the Distributive Property first to remove the grouping symbols.

Example 2 Solve an Equation with Grouping Symbols

Solve $6(5m - 3) = \frac{1}{3}(24m + 12)$.

$6(5m - 3) = \frac{1}{3}(24m + 12)$	Original equation
$30m - 18 = 8m + 4$	Distributive Property
$30m - 18 - 8m = 8m + 4 - 8m$	Subtract $8m$ from each side.
$22m - 18 = 4$	Simplify.
$22m - 18 + 18 = 4 + 18$	Add 18 to each side.
$22m = 22$	Simplify.
$\frac{22m}{22} = \frac{22}{22}$	Divide each side by 22.
$m = 1$	Simplify.

StudyTip
Solving an Equation You may want to eliminate the terms with a variable from one side before eliminating a constant.

Guided Practice

Solve each equation. Check your solution.

2A. $8s - 10 = 3(6 - 2s)$ 2

2B. $7(n - 1) = -2(3 + n)$ $\frac{1}{9}$

Some equations may have no solution. That is, there is no value of the variable that will result in a true equation. Some equations are true for all values of the variables. These are called **identities**.

Example 3 Find Special Solutions

Solve each equation.

a. $5x + 5 = 3(5x - 4) - 10x$

$5x + 5 = 3(5x - 4) - 10x$	Original equation
$5x + 5 = 15x - 12 - 10x$	Distributive Property
$5x + 5 = 5x - 12$	Simplify.
$-5x \quad = -5x$	Subtract $5x$ from each side.
$5 \neq -12$	

Since $5 \neq -12$, this equation has no solution.

ReadingMath
No Solution The symbol that represents no solution is ∅.

b. $3(2b - 1) - 7 = 6b - 10$

$3(2b - 1) - 7 = 6b - 10$	Original equation
$6b - 3 - 7 = 6b - 10$	Distributive Property
$6b - 10 = 6b - 10$	Simplify.
$0 = 0$	Subtract $6b - 10$ from each side.

Since the expressions on each side of the equation are the same, this equation is an identity. It is true for all values of b.

Guided Practice

3A. $7x + 5(x - 1) = -5 + 12x$ all numbers

3B. $6(y - 5) = 2(10 + 3y)$ no solution

Differentiated Instruction AL

If some students are having trouble solving equations with a variable on each side,

Then those students may benefit from using an equation mat and algebra tiles. Have students model the equation, and then get them started by asking what they must do to remove the x-tiles from one side of the equation mat. Use questions to focus their attention on isolating the variable. Have them write out the steps they used after they solve for x.

The steps for solving an equation can be summarized as follows.

ConceptSummary Steps for Solving Equations

Step 1 Simplify the expressions on each side. Use the Distributive Property as needed.

Step 2 Use the Addition and/or Subtraction Properties of Equality to get the variables on one side and the numbers without variables on the other side. Simplify.

Step 3 Use the Multiplication or Division Property of Equality to solve.

There are many situations in which you must simplify expressions with grouping symbols in order to solve an equation.

Standardized Test Example 4 Write an Equation

Find the value of x so that the figures have the same area.

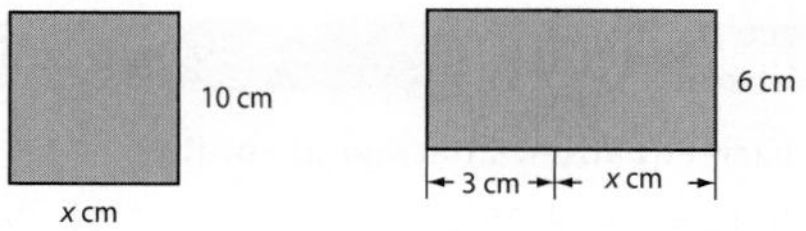

A 3 **C** 6.5

B 4.5 **D** 7

Test-TakingTip

Tools There is often more than one way to solve a problem. In this example, you can write an algebraic equation and solve for x. Or you can substitute each answer choice into the formulas to find the correct answer.

Read the Test Item

The area of the first rectangle is $10x$, and the area of the second is $6(3 + x)$. The equation $10x = 6(3 + x)$ represents this situation.

Solve the Test Item

A $10x = 6(3 + x)$

$10(3) \stackrel{?}{=} 6(3 + 3)$

$30 \stackrel{?}{=} 6(6)$

$30 \neq 36$ ✗

B $10x = 6(3 + x)$

$10(4.5) \stackrel{?}{=} 6(3 + 4.5)$

$45 \stackrel{?}{=} 6(7.5)$

$45 = 45$ ✓

Since the value 4.5 results in a true statement, you do not need to check 6.5 and 7. The answer is B.

GuidedPractice

4. **Find the value of x so that the figures have the same perimeter.** G

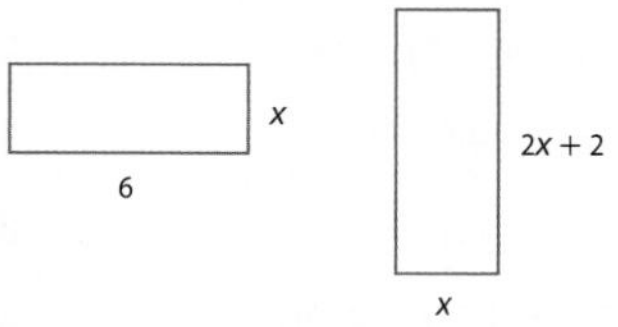

F 1.5 **G** 2 **H** 3.2 **J** 4

Tips for New Teachers

Eliminating the Variable Mathematically proficient students detect possible errors by strategically using estimation and other mathematical knowledge. Emphasize that there are only two possible outcomes under which the variable can be eliminated from an equation: either the equation has no solution (false statement) or the equation is an identity (true statement).

Focus on Mathematical Content

Grouping Symbols The Distributive Property may be used to simplify expressions with grouping symbols. When the expressions on each side of an equation are identical, the equation is true for every value of the variable. When the expressions simplify to a false statement, there are no solutions.

Additional Example

4 STANDARDIZED TEST PRACTICE Find the value of h so that the figures have the same area. D

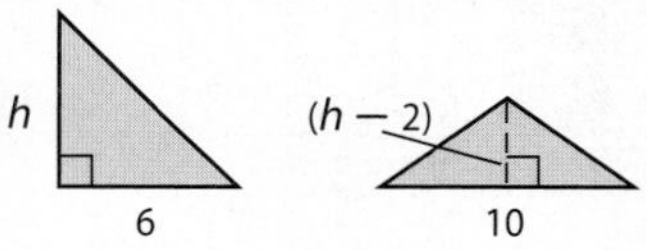

A 1 **C** 4

B 3 **D** 5

Teaching the Process Standards

Tools Mathematically proficient students detect possible errors by strategically using estimation and other mathematical knowledge. Caution students to be careful when checking possible answers on multiple-choice test items. Often, some of the incorrect possible answers are similar to the correct answer. A substitution or arithmetic error when checking possible answers could lead them to inadvertently choose the incorrect answer.

3 Practice

Formative Assessment

Use Exercises 1–9 to check for understanding.

Use the chart at the bottom of this page to customize assignments for your students.

Exercise Alert

Grid paper For Exercise 41, students need grid paper to graph ordered pairs.

Multiple Representations

In Exercise 41, students use a table of values and a graph in the coordinate plane to illustrate the solution of two simultaneous equations.

Additional Answers

41a. Sample answer: $y = 2x + 4$

x	−2	−1	0	1	2
y	0	2	4	6	8

$y = -x - 2$

x	−2	−1	0	1	2
y	0	−1	−2	−3	−4

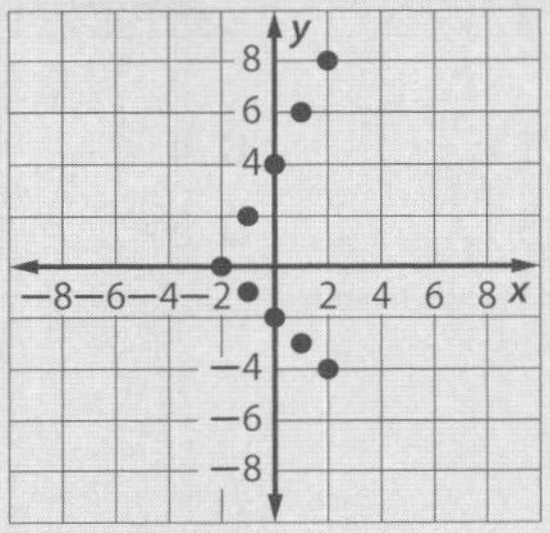

42. $5x + 2 = ax - 1$
Original equation
$5x + 2 - ax = -1$
Subtract ax from each side.
$5x - ax = -3$
Subtract 2 from each side.
$(5 - a)x = -3$
Distributive Property
$x = \frac{-3}{5 - a}$
Divide each side by 5 – a.

45a. Incorrect; the 2 must be distributed over both g and 5; 6.

45b. correct

45c. Incorrect; to eliminate $-6z$ on the left side of the equals sign, $6z$ must be added to each side of the equation; 1.

Check Your Understanding

● = Step-by-Step Solutions begin on page R13.

Examples 1–3 Solve each equation. Check your solution.

1. $13x + 2 = 4x + 38$ 4
2. $\frac{2}{3} + \frac{1}{6}q = \frac{5}{6}q + \frac{1}{3}$ $\frac{1}{2}$
3. $6(n + 4) = -18$ −7
4. $7 = -11 + 3(b + 5)$ 1
5. $5 + 2(n + 1) = 2n$ no solution
6. $7 - 3r = r - 4(2 + r)$ no solution
7. $14v + 6 = 2(5 + 7v) - 4$ all numbers
8. $5h - 7 = 5(h - 2) + 3$ all numbers

Example 4

9. **MULTIPLE CHOICE** Find the value of x so that the figures have the same perimeter. A

A 4 B 5 C 6 D 7

Practice and Problem Solving

Extra Practice is on page R2.

Examples 1–3 Solve each equation. Check your solution.

10. $7c + 12 = -4c + 78$ 6
11. $2m - 13 = -8m + 27$ 4
12. $9x - 4 = 2x + 3$ 1
13. $6 + 3t = 8t - 14$ 4
14. $\frac{b - 4}{6} = \frac{b}{2}$ −2
15. $\frac{5v - 4}{10} = \frac{4}{5}$ $2\frac{2}{5}$
16. $8 = 4(r + 4)$ −2
17. $6(n + 5) = 66$ 6
18. $5(g + 8) - 7 = 103$ 14
19. $12 - \frac{4}{5}(x + 15) = 4$ −5
20. $3(3m - 2) = 2(3m + 3)$ 4
21. $6(3a + 1) - 30 = 3(2a - 4)$ 1

Example 4

22. **GEOMETRY** Find the value of x so the rectangles have the same area. 8

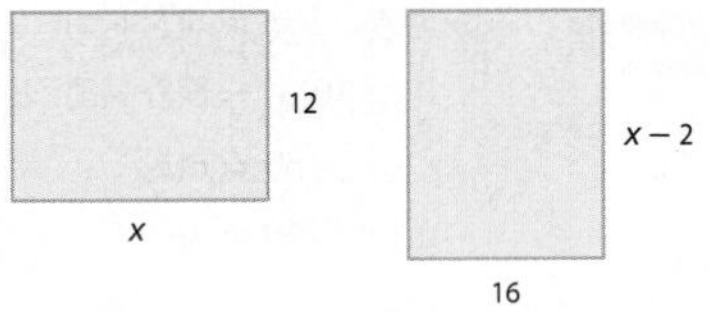

23. **NUMBER THEORY** Four times the lesser of two consecutive even integers is 12 less than twice the greater number. Find the integers. −4, −2
24. **SENSE-MAKING** Two times the least of three consecutive odd integers exceeds three times the greatest by 15. What are the integers? −27, −25, −23

B Solve each equation. Check your solution.

25. $2x = 2(x - 3)$ no solution
26. $\frac{2}{5}h - 7 = \frac{12}{5}h - 2h + 3$ no solution
27. $-5(3 - q) + 4 = 5q - 11$ all numbers
28. $2(4r + 6) = \frac{2}{3}(12r + 18)$ all numbers
29. $\frac{3}{5}f + 24 = 4 - \frac{1}{5}f$ −25
30. $\frac{1}{12} + \frac{3}{8}y = \frac{5}{12} + \frac{5}{8}y$ $-\frac{4}{3}$
31. $\frac{2m}{5} = \frac{1}{3}(2m - 12)$ 15
32. $\frac{1}{8}(3d - 2) = \frac{1}{4}(d + 5)$ 12
33. $6.78j - 5.2 = 4.33j + 2.15$ 3
34. $14.2t - 25.2 = 3.8t + 26.8$ 5
35. $3.2k - 4.3 = 12.6k + 14.5$ −2
36. $5[2p - 4(p + 5)] = 25$ −12.5

Differentiated Homework Options

Level	Assignment	Two-Day Option	
AL Basic	10–24, 42, 44, 45, 47–74	11–23 odd, 48–51	10–24 even, 42, 44, 45, 47, 52–74
OL Core	11–37 odd, 38–42, 44, 45, 47–74	10–24, 48–51	25–42, 44, 45, 52–74
BL Advanced	25–65, (optional: 66–74)		

100 | Lesson 2-4 | Solving Equations with the Variable on Each Side

37. **NUMBER THEORY** Three times the lesser of two consecutive even integers is 6 less than six times the greater number. Find the integers. **−2, 0**

38. **MONEY** Chris has saved twice the number of quarters that Nora saved plus 6. The number of quarters Chris saved is also five times the difference of the number of quarters and 3 that Nora has saved. Write and solve an equation to find the number of quarters they each have saved.
$2q + 6 = 5(q - 3)$; Nora saved 7 quarters, and Chris saved 20 quarters.

39. **DVD** A company that replicates DVDs spends \$1500 per day in building overhead plus \$0.80 per DVD in supplies and labor. If the DVDs sell for \$1.59 per disk, how many DVDs must the company sell each day before it makes a profit? **1899 DVDs/day**

40. **MOBILE PHONES** The table shows the number of mobile phone subscribers for two states for a recent year. How long will it take for the numbers of subscribers to be the same? **2.3 years or 2 years 4 months**

State	Mobile Phone Subscribers (thousands)	New Subscribers Each Year (thousands)
Alabama	3765	325
Wisconsin	3842	292

41. **MULTIPLE REPRESENTATIONS** In this problem, you will explore $2x + 4 = -x - 2$.

a. Graphical Make a table of values with five points for $y = 2x + 4$ and $y = -x - 2$. Graph the points from the tables. **See margin.**

b. Algebraic Solve $2x + 4 = -x - 2$. **−2**

c. Verbal Explain how the solution you found in part **b** is related to the intersection point of the graphs in part **a**. **Sample answer: The solution in part b is the *x*-coordinate for the point of intersection on the graph.**

H.O.T. Problems Use Higher-Order Thinking Skills

42. **REASONING** Solve $5x + 2 = ax - 1$ for x. Assume that $a \neq 0$. Describe each step. **See margin.**

43. **CHALLENGE** Write an equation with the variable on each side of the equals sign, at least one fractional coefficient, and a solution of −6. Discuss the steps you used. **See Ch. 2 Answer Appendix.**

44. **OPEN ENDED** Create an equation with at least two grouping symbols for which there is no solution. **Sample answer: $2(3x + 6) = 3(2x + 5)$**

45. **CRITIQUE** Determine whether each solution is correct. If the solution is not correct, describe the error and give the correct solution. **a–c. See margin.**

a.
$$\begin{aligned} 2(g + 5) &= 22 \\ 2g + 5 &= 22 \\ 2g + 5 - 5 &= 22 \\ 2g &= 17 \\ g &= 8.5 \end{aligned}$$

b.
$$\begin{aligned} 5d &= 2d - 18 \\ 5d - 2d &= 2d - 18 - 2d \\ 3d &= -18 \\ d &= -6 \end{aligned}$$

c.
$$\begin{aligned} -6z + 13 &= 7z \\ -6z + 13 - 6z &= 7z - 6z \\ 13 &= z \end{aligned}$$

46. **CHALLENGE** Find the value of k for which each equation is an identity.

a. $k(3x - 2) = 4 - 6x$ **−2**

b. $15y - 10 + k = 2(ky - 1) - y$ **8**

47. **WRITING IN MATH** Compare and contrast solving equations with variables on both sides of the equation to solving one-step or multi-step equations with a variable on one side of the equation.

47. Sample answer: If the equation has variables on both sides of the equation, you must first add or subtract one of the terms from both sides of the equation so that the variable is left on only one side of the equation. Then solving the equation uses the same steps.

Teaching the Process Standards

Sense-Making Mathematically proficient students analyze givens, constraints, relationships, and goals. In Exercise 24, point out that a constraint on the solutions is that they must be consecutive odd integers.

Critique Mathematically proficient students distinguish correct reasoning from that which is flawed, and explain any flaws. In Exercise 45, encourage students to analyze the reasoning in each step.

Study Guide and Intervention

AL OL ELL

2-4 Study Guide and Intervention

Solving Equations with the Variable on Each Side

Variables on Each Side To solve an equation with the same variable on each side, first use the Addition or the Subtraction Property of Equality to write an equivalent equation that has the variable on just one side of the equation. Then solve the equation.

Exercises

Solve each equation. Check your solution.

Practice

AL OL BL ELL

2-4 Practice

Solving Equations with the Variable on Each Side

Solve each equation. Check your solution.

Word Problem Practice

AL OL BL ELL

2-4 Word Problem Practice

Solving Equations with the Variable on Each Side

Enrichment

OL BL

2-4 Enrichment

Identities

An equation that is true for every value of the variable is called an **identity**. When you try to solve an identity, you end up with a statement that is always true. Here is an example.

Exercises

State whether each equation is an identity. If it is not, find its solution.

4 Assess

Name the Math On index cards, have students solve $3(x + 2) = 5(x - 8)$. Beside each step, have students write one or two sentences explaining and justifying their methods.

Additional Answers

60. 1; Multiplicative Identity

61. 2; Multiplicative Identity

62. 6; Reflexive Property

63. $\frac{2}{3}$; Additive Identity

64. 1; Multiplicative Inverse

65. 7; Transitive Property

Standardized Test Practice

48. A hang glider, 25 meters above the ground, starts to descend at a constant rate of 2 meters per second. Which equation shows the height h after t seconds of descent? **D**

A $h = 25t + 2t$
B $h = -25t + 2$
C $h = 2t + 25$
D $h = -2t + 25$

49. GEOMETRY Two rectangular walls each with a length of 12 feet and a width of 23 feet need to be painted. It costs $0.08 per square foot for paint. How much will it cost to paint the walls? **J**

F $22.08   H $34.50
G $23.04   J $44.16

50. SHORT RESPONSE Maddie works at Game Exchange. They are having a sale as shown.

Item	Price	Special
video games	$20	Buy 2 get 1 Free
DVDs	$15	Buy 1 get 1 Free

Her employee discount is 15%. If sales tax is 7.25%, how much does she spend for a total of 4 video games? **$54.70**

51. Solve $\frac{4}{5}x + 7 = \frac{3}{15}x - 3$. **A**

A $-16\frac{2}{3}$ C -10
B $-14\frac{4}{9}$ D $-6\frac{2}{3}$

Spiral Review

Solve each equation. Check your solution. (Lesson 2-3)

52. $5n + 6 = -4$ **-2**

53. $-1 = 7 + 3c$ **$-2\frac{2}{3}$**

54. $\frac{1}{2}z + 7 = 16 - \frac{3}{5}z$ **$8\frac{2}{11}$**

55. $\frac{2}{5}x + 6 = \frac{2}{3}x + 10$ **-15**

56. $\frac{a}{7} - 3 = -2$ **7**

57. $9 + \frac{y}{5} = 6$ **-15**

58. WORLD RECORDS In 1998, Winchell's House of Donuts in Pasadena, California, made the world's largest donut. It weighed 5000 pounds and had a circumference of 298.3 feet. What was the donut's diameter to the nearest tenth? (*Hint:* $C = \pi d$) (Lesson 2-2) **95.0 ft**

59. ZOO At a zoo, the cost of admission is posted on the sign. Find the cost of admission for two adults and two children. (Lesson 1-4) **$34**

Find the value of n. Then name the property used in each step. (Lesson 1-3)

60. $25n = 25$

61. $n \cdot 1 = 2$

62. $12 \cdot n = 12 \cdot 6$

63. $n + 0 = \frac{2}{3}$

64. $4 \cdot \frac{1}{4} = n$

65. $(10 - 8)(7) = 2(n)$

60–65. See margin.

Skills Review

Translate each sentence into an equation.

66. Twice a number t decreased by eight equals seventy. **$2t - 8 = 70$**

67. Five times the sum of m and k is the same as seven times k. **$5(m + k) = 7k$**

68. Half of p is the same as p minus 3. **$\frac{1}{2}p = p - 3$**

Evaluate each expression.

69. $-9 - (-14)$ **5**

70. $-10 + (20)$ **10**

71. $-15 - 9$ **-24**

72. $5(14)$ **70**

73. $-55 \div (-5)$ **11**

74. $-25(-5)$ **125**

Differentiated Instruction BL

Extension Remind students that they have learned that an equation can have 1, 0, or an endless number of solutions. Ask students to write an equation in which there are exactly two solutions for the variable. For example, in $|x| = 25$, $x = 25$ or -25 or in $x^2 = 25$, $x = 5$ or -5.

102 | Lesson 2-4 | Solving Equations with the Variable on Each Side

LESSON 2-5 Solving Equations Involving Absolute Value

Then
- You solved equations with the variable on each side.

Now
1. Evaluate absolute value expressions.
2. Solve absolute value equations.

Why?
- In 2007, a telephone poll was conducted to determine the reading habits of people in the U.S. People in this survey were allowed to select more than one type of book.

The survey had a margin of error of ±3%. This means that the results could be three points higher or lower. So, the percent of people who read religious material could be as high as 69% or as low as 63%.

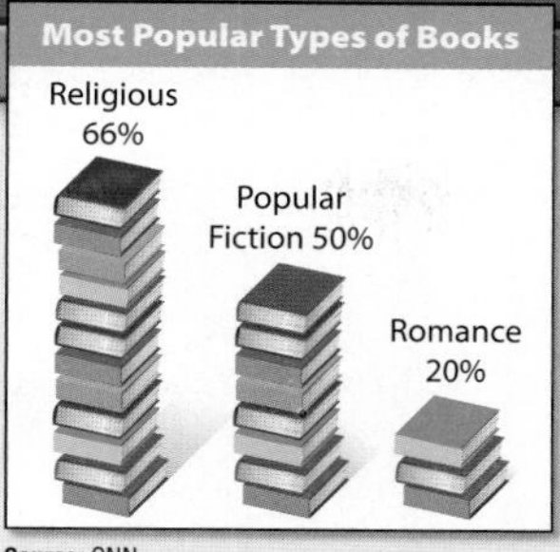

Source: CNN

Content Standards
A.I.L.9

Process Standards
PS.3, PS.7

1 Absolute Value Expressions

Expressions with absolute values define an upper and lower range in which a value must lie. Expressions involving absolute value can be evaluated using the given value for the variable.

Example 1 Expressions with Absolute Value

Evaluate $|m + 6| - 14$ if $m = 4$.

$|m + 6| - 14 = |4 + 6| - 14$ — Replace m with 4.

$= |10| - 14$ — $4 + 6 = 10$

$= 10 - 14$ — $|10| = 10$

$= -4$ — Simplify.

Guided Practice

1. Evaluate $23 - |3 - 4x|$ if $x = 2$. 18

2 Absolute Value Equations

The margin of error in the example at the top of the page is an example of absolute value. The distance between 66 and 69 on a number line is the same as the distance between 63 and 66.

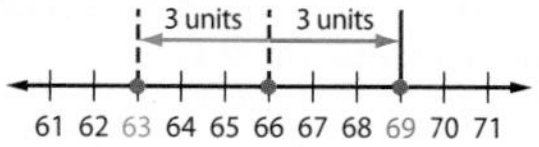

There are three types of open sentences involving absolute value, $|x| = n$, $|x| < n$, and $|x| > n$. In this lesson, we will consider only the first type. Look at the equation $|x| = 4$. This means that the distance between 0 and x is 4.

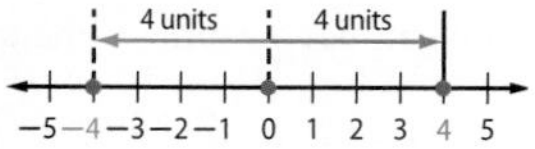

If $|x| = 4$, then $x = -4$ or $x = 4$. Thus, the solution set is $\{-4, 4\}$.

For each absolute value equation, we must consider both cases. To solve an absolute value equation, first isolate the absolute value on one side of the equals sign if it is not already by itself.

1 Focus

Vertical Alignment

Before Lesson 2-5 Solve equations with the variable on each side.

Lesson 2-5 Evaluate absolute value expressions.
Solve absolute value equations.

After Lesson 2-5 Solve inequalities involving absolute value.

2 Teach

Scaffolding Questions

Have students read the **Why?** section of the lesson.

Ask:

- Which type of book in the survey is the least popular? Romance
- With a 3-point margin of error, the number of people who chose popular fiction could be as high as what percent? as low as what percent? 53%; 47%
- How would you represent the margin of error in the percent of people who chose religious books with an absolute value equation? $|x - 66| = 3$

Lesson 2-5 Resources

Resource	Approaching Level AL	On Level OL	Beyond Level BL	English Learners ELL
Teacher Edition	▪ Differentiated Instruction, p. 104	▪ Differentiated Instruction, p. 104	▪ Differentiated Instruction, p. 109	
Chapter Resource Masters	▪ Study Guide and Intervention, pp. 30–31 ▪ Skills Practice, p. 32 ▪ Practice, p. 33 ▪ Word Problem Practice, p. 34	▪ Study Guide and Intervention, pp. 30–31 ▪ Skills Practice, p. 32 ▪ Practice, p. 33 ▪ Word Problem Practice, p. 34 ▪ Enrichment, p. 35	▪ Practice, p. 33 ▪ Word Problem Practice, p. 34 ▪ Enrichment, p. 35	▪ Study Guide and Intervention, pp. 30–31 ▪ Skills Practice, p. 32 ▪ Practice, p. 33 ▪ Word Problem Practice, p. 34
Other	▪ 5-Minute Check 2-5 ▪ Study Notebook	▪ 5-Minute Check 2-5 ▪ Study Notebook	▪ 5-Minute Check 2-5 ▪ Study Notebook	▪ 5-Minute Check 2-5 ▪ Study Notebook

1 Absolute Value Expressions

Example 1 shows how to evaluate an absolute value expression using a given value for the variable.

Formative Assessment

Use the Guided Practice exercises after each Example to determine students' understanding of concepts.

Additional Example

1 Evaluate $|a - 7| + 15$ if $a = 5$. 17

Additional Examples also in Interactive Classroom PowerPoint® Presentations

IWB Interactive White Board READY

2 Absolute Value Equations

Example 2 shows how to solve an absolute value equation, graph the solution set and how to recognize when the solution set is the empty set. **Example 3** shows how to solve an absolute value equation involving a real-world situation. **Example 4** shows how to write an equation involving absolute value for a given graph.

Additional Example

2 Solve each equation. Then graph the solution set.

a. $|2x - 1| = 7$ {−3, 4}

b. $|p + 6| = -5$ ∅

Teach with Tech

Interactive Whiteboard On the board, work through several examples solving absolute value equations. Save your work to a file and send it to your students so they can use it as an additional reference.

ReadingMath

Absolute Values The expression $|f + 5|$ is read the *absolute value of the quantity f plus 5.*

KeyConcept Absolute Value Equations

Words	When solving equations that involve absolute values, there are two cases to consider. **Case 1** The expression inside the absolute value symbol is positive or zero. **Case 2** The expression inside the absolute value symbol is negative.
Symbols	For any real numbers a and b, if $|a| = b$ and $b \geq 0$, then $a = b$ or $a = -b$.
Example	$|d| = 10$, so $d = 10$ or $d = -10$.

Example 2 Solve Absolute Value Equations

Solve each equation. Then graph the solution set.

a. $|f + 5| = 17$

$|f + 5| = 17$ Original equation

Case 1

$f + 5 = 17$

$f + 5 - 5 = 17 - 5$ Subtract 5 from each side.

$f = 12$ Simplify.

Case 2

$f + 5 = -17$

$f + 5 - 5 = -17 - 5$

$f = -22$

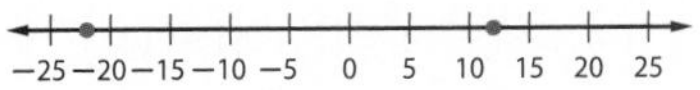

b. $|b - 1| = -3$

$|b - 1| = -3$ means the distance between b and 1 is −3. Since distance cannot be negative, the solution is the empty set ∅.

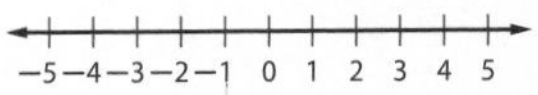

GuidedPractice

2A. $|y + 2| = 4$ {−6, 2}

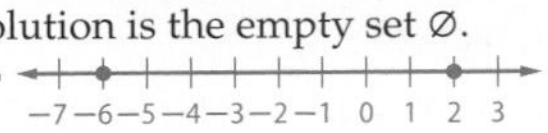

2B. $|3n - 4| = -1$ ∅

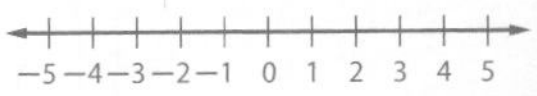

Absolute value equations occur in real-world situations that describe a range within which a value must lie.

Real-WorldLink

In 2001, the number of households in the U.S. that had either a turtle, snake, lizard, or other reptile as a pet was 1,678,000.

Source: American Veterinary Medical Association

Real-World Example 3 Solve an Absolute Value Equation

SNAKES **The temperature of an enclosure for a pet snake should be about 80°F, give or take 5°. Find the maximum and minimum temperatures.**

You can use a number line to solve.

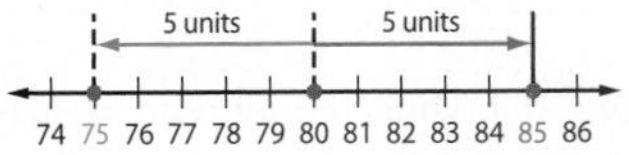

The distance from 80 to 75 is 5 units.
The distance from 80 to 85 is 5 units.

The solution set is {75, 85}. The maximum and minimum temperatures are 85° and 75°.

DifferentiatedInstruction AL OL

If some students are having trouble rewriting absolute value equations,

Then have them apply the two situations (positive and negative) to the expression within the absolute value symbols. For example, $|x| = 4$ can be written as $x = 4$ or as $-x = 4$, which yields $x = -4$.

104 | Lesson 2-5 | Solving Equations Involving Absolute Value

Guided Practice

3. **ICE CREAM** Ice cream should be stored at 5°F with an allowance for 5°. Write and solve an equation to find the maximum and minimum temperatures at which the ice cream should be stored. **$|t - 5| = 5$; 10°F and 0°F**

When given two points on a graph, you can write an absolute value equation for the graph.

> **Study Tip**
> **Find the Midpoint** To find the point midway between two points, add the values together and divide by 2. For Example 4, $11 + 19 = 30$, $30 \div 2 = 15$. So 15 is the point halfway between 11 and 19.

Example 4 Write an Absolute Value Equation

Write an equation involving absolute value for the graph.

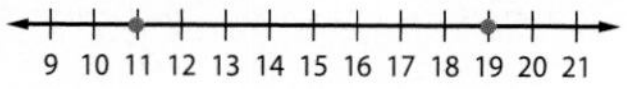

Find the point that is the same distance from 11 and from 19. This is the midpoint between 11 and 19, which is 15.

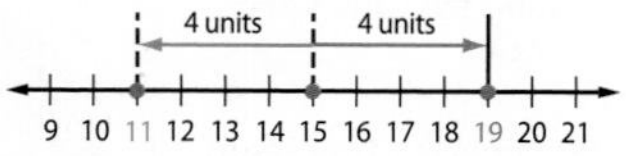

The distance from 15 to 11 is 4 units.
The distance from 15 to 19 is 4 units.

So an equation is $|x - 15| = 4$.

Guided Practice

4. Write an equation involving absolute value for the graph. **$|c - 22| = 5$**

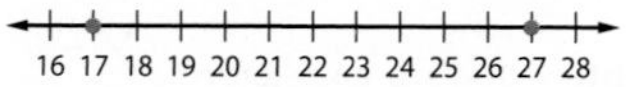

Check Your Understanding

= Step-by-Step Solutions begin on page R13.

Example 1 **Evaluate each expression if $f = 3$, $g = -4$, and $h = 5$.**

1. $|3 - h| + 13$ **15**
2. $16 - |g + 9|$ **11**
3. $|f + g| - h$ **−4**

Example 2 **Solve each equation. Then graph the solution set.** **4–9. See margin for graphs.**

4. $|n + 7| = 5$ **{−2, −12}**
5. $|3z - 3| = 9$ **{4, −2}**
6. $|4n - 1| = -6$ **∅**
7. $|b + 4| = 2$ **{−6, −2}**
8. $|2t - 4| = 8$ **{−2, 6}**
9. $|5h + 2| = -8$ **∅**

Example 3

10. **FINANCIAL LITERACY** For a company to invest in a product, they must believe they will receive a 12% return on investment (ROI) plus or minus 3%. Write an equation to find the least and the greatest ROI they believe they will receive. **$|x - 12| = 3$; {9, 15}**

Example 4 **Write an equation involving absolute value for each graph.**

11. 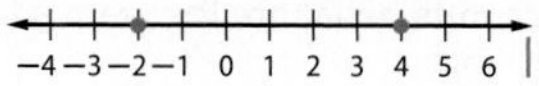

$|x - 1| = 3$

12. 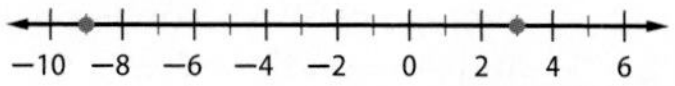

$|x + 3| = 6$

Focus on Mathematical Content

Absolute Value Equations Solve absolute value equations by graphing them on a number line or by writing a compound sentence and then solving it algebraically. Consider two cases: the expression inside the symbol is positive and the expression inside the symbol is negative.

Additional Examples

3. **WEATHER** The average January temperature in a northern Canadian city is 1°F. The actual January temperature for that city may be about 5°F warmer or colder. Write and solve an equation to find the maximum and minimum temperatures. $|t - 1| = 5$; {−4, 6}; the maximum and minimum temperatures are −4° and 6°.

4. Write an equation involving absolute value for the graph.

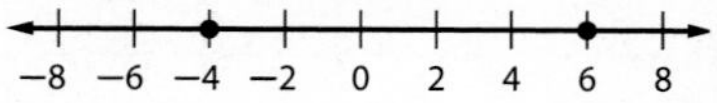

$|y - 1| = 5$

3 Practice

Formative Assessment

Use Exercises 1–12 to check for understanding.

Use the chart at the bottom of the next page to customize assignments for your students.

Additional Answers

4. 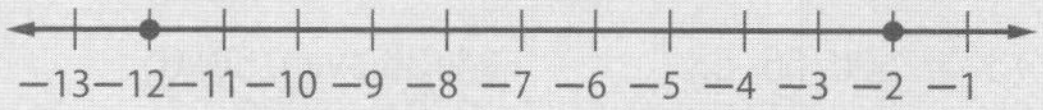

5. 

6. 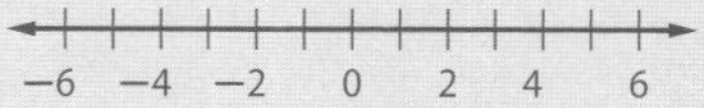

7. 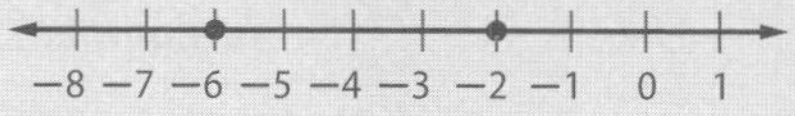

8. 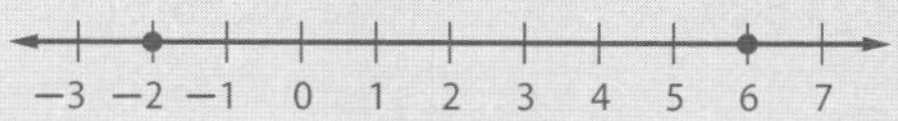

9. 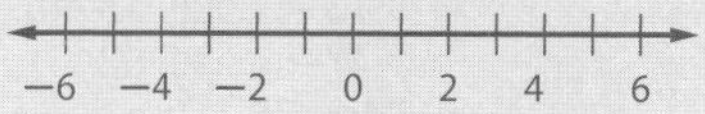

Teaching the Process Standards

Sense-Making Mathematically proficient students start by explaining to themselves the meaning of a problem and looking for entry points to its solution. In Exercise 43, point out that there is possible variation in each leg of the race.

Additional Answers

22. 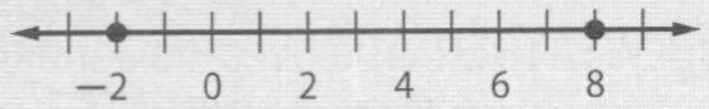

23. 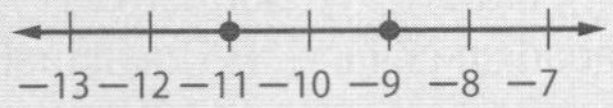

24. 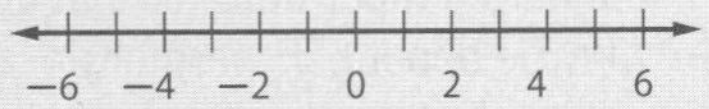

25. 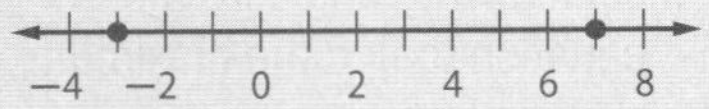

26. 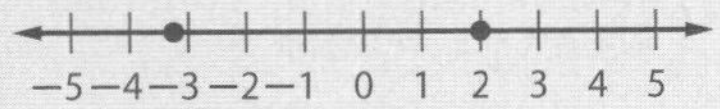

27. 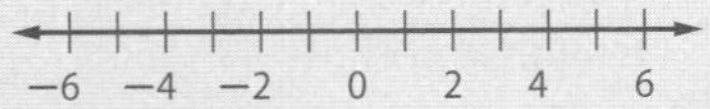

28. 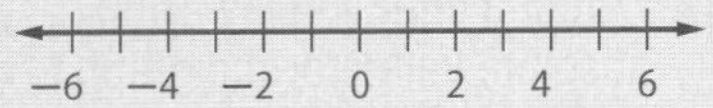

29. 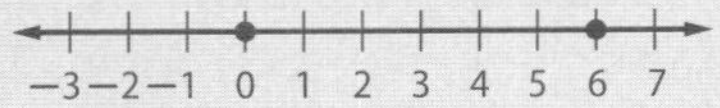

30. 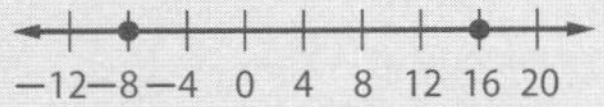

37. 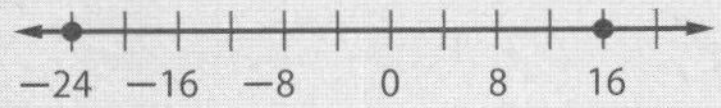

38. 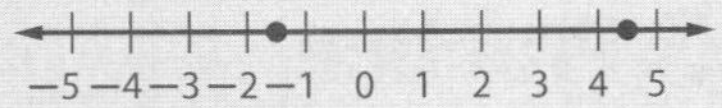

39. 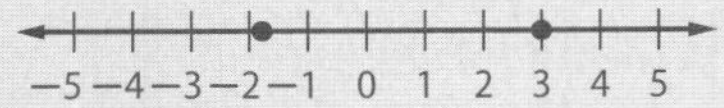

40. 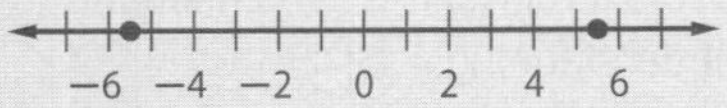

41. 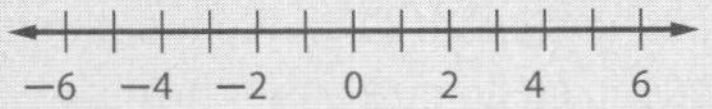

42. 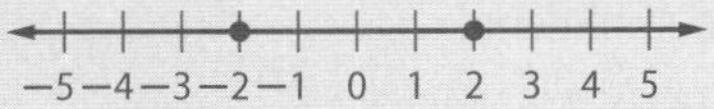

44a. $|t - 20| = 2$

44b. 18 in. to 22 in.

44c. No; the difference in heights of the models is greater than the difference in hem length of the skirt.

Practice and Problem Solving

Extra Practice is on page R2.

Example 1 **Evaluate each expression if $a = -2$, $b = -3$, $c = 2$, $x = 2.1$, $y = 3$, and $z = -4.2$.**

13. $|2x + z| + 2y$ **6**

14. $4a - |3b + 2c|$ **−13**

15. $-|5a + c| + |3y + 2z|$ **−7.4**

16. $-a + |2x - a|$ **8.2**

17. $|y - 2z| - 3$ **8.4**

18. $3|3b - 8c| - 3$ **72**

19. $|2x - z| + 6b$ **−9.6**

20. $-3|z| + 2(a + y)$ **−10.6**

21. $-4|c - 3| + 2|z - a|$ **0.4**

Example 2 **Solve each equation. Then graph the solution set.** **22–30. See margin for graphs.**

22. $|n - 3| = 5$ **{8, −2}**

23. $|f + 10| = 1$ **{−11, −9}**

24. $|v - 2| = -5$ **∅**

25. $|4t - 8| = 20$ **{7, −3}**

26. $|8w + 5| = 21$ **{2, −3.25}**

27. $|6y - 7| = -1$ **∅**

28. $\left|\frac{1}{2}x + 5\right| = -3$ **∅**

29. $|-2y + 6| = 6$ **{0, 6}**

30. $\left|\frac{3}{4}a - 3\right| = 9$ **{16, −8}**

Example 3

31. SURVEY The circle graph at the right shows the results of a survey that asked, "How likely is it that you will be rich some day?" If the margin of error is ±4%, what is the range of the percent of teens who say it is very likely that they will be rich? **11% to 19%**

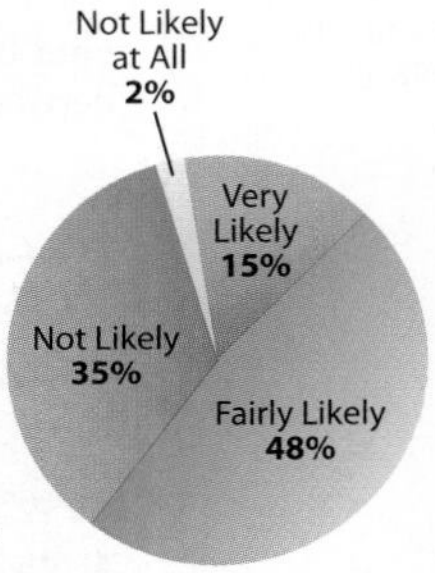

32. CHEERLEADING For competition, the cheerleading team is preparing a dance routine that must last 4 minutes, with a variation of ±5 seconds.

a. Find the least and greatest possible times for the routine in minutes and seconds. **4 min 5 s, 3 min 55 s**

b. Find the least and greatest possible times in seconds. **235 s, 245 s**

Example 4 **Write an equation involving absolute value for each graph.** **33–36. Sample answers given.**

33. 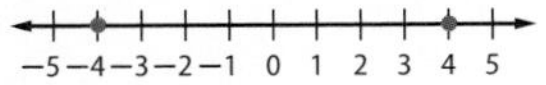

$|x| = 4$

34. 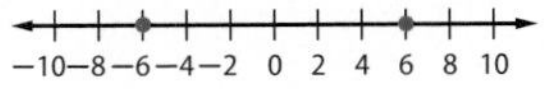

$|x| = 6$

35. 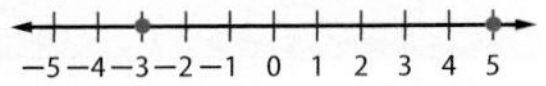

$|x - 1| = 4$

36. 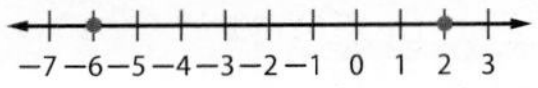

$|x + 2| = 4$

B **Solve each equation. Then graph the solution set.** **37–42. See margin for graphs.**

37. $\left|-\frac{1}{2}b - 2\right| = 10$ **{−24, 16}**

38. $|-4d + 6| = 12$ $\left\{-\frac{3}{2}, \frac{9}{2}\right\}$

39. $|5f - 3| = 12$ $\left\{3, -\frac{9}{5}\right\}$

40. $2|h| - 3 = 8$ **{5.5, −5.5}**

41. $4 - 3|q| = 10$ **no solution**

42. $\frac{4}{|p|} + 12 = 14$ **{2, −2}**

43. SENSE-MAKING The 4 × 400 relay is a race where 4 runners take turns running 400 meters, or one lap around the track.

a. If a runner runs the first leg in 52 seconds plus or minus 2 seconds, write an equation to find the fastest and slowest times. **$|x - 52| = 2$; {50, 54}**

b. If the runners of the second and third legs run their laps in 53 seconds plus or minus 1 second, write an equation to find the fastest and slowest times. **$|x - 53| = 1$; {52, 54}**

c. Suppose the runner of the fourth leg is the fastest on the team. If he runs an average of 50.5 seconds plus or minus 1.5 seconds, what are the team's fastest and slowest times? **203 seconds and 214 seconds**

Differentiated Homework Options

Level	Assignment	Two-Day Option	
AL Basic	13–36, 56–61, 63–75	13–35 odd, 65–68	14–36 even, 56–61, 63–64, 69–75
OL Core	13–41 odd, 43–45, 47–51 odd, 52–61, 63–75	13–36, 65–68	37–61, 63–64, 69–75
BL Advanced	37–71, (optional: 72–75)		

44. **FASHION** To allow for a model's height, a designer is willing to use models that require him to change hems either up or down 2 inches. The length of the skirts is 20 inches. **a–c. See margin.**

   a. Write an absolute value equation that represents the length of the skirts.

   b. What is the range of the lengths of the skirts?

   c. If a 20-inch skirt was fitted for a model that is 5 feet 9 inches tall, will the designer use a 6-foot-tall model?

45. **PRECISION** Speedometer accuracy can be affected by many details such as tire diameter and axle ratio. For example, there is variation of ± 3 miles per hour when calibrated at 50 miles per hour.

   a. What is the range of actual speeds of the car if calibrated at 50 miles per hour? **47 to 53 mph**

   b. A speedometer calibrated at 45 miles per hour has an accepted variation of ± 1 mile per hour. What can we conclude from this? **Sample answer: The speedometer was calibrated more accurately than the speedometer for part a.**

Write an equation involving absolute value for each graph. **46–51. Sample answers given.**

46. 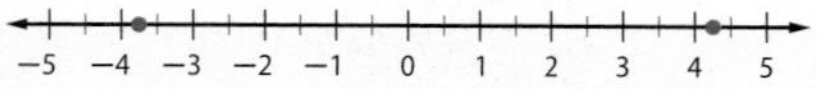

$\left|x - \frac{1}{4}\right| = 4$

47. 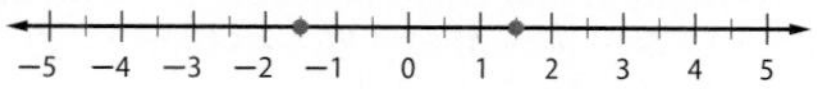

$|x| = 1\frac{1}{2}$

48. 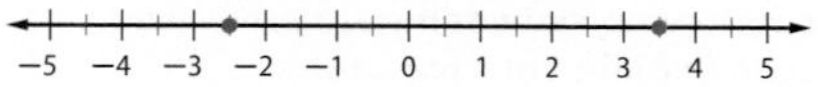

$\left|x - \frac{1}{2}\right| = 3$

49. 

$\left|x - \frac{1}{4}\right| = \frac{1}{4}$

50. 

$\left|x - \frac{2}{3}\right| = \frac{2}{3}$

51. 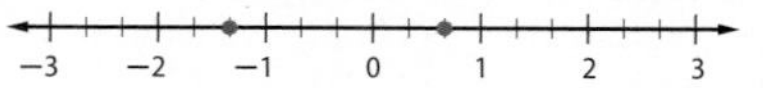

$\left|x + \frac{1}{3}\right| = 1$

52. **MUSIC** A CD will record an hour and a half of music plus or minus 3 minutes for time between tracks.

   a. Write an absolute value equation that represents the recording time. $|t - 90| = 3$

   b. What is the range of time in minutes that the CD could run? **87 to 93 minutes**

   c. Graph the possible times on a number line. **See Ch. 2 Answer Appendix.**

53a. Let h = the number of people that can clearly hear voices, $|h - 20{,}000| = 1000$.

53. **ACOUSTICS** The Red Rocks Amphitheater located in the Red Rock Park near Denver, Colorado, is the only naturally occurring amphitheater. The acoustic qualities here are such that a maximum of 20,000 people, plus or minus 1000, can hear natural voices clearly.

   a. Write an equation involving an absolute value that represents the number of people that can hear natural voices at Red Rocks Amphitheater.

   b. Find the maximum and minimum number of people that can hear natural voices clearly in the amphitheater. **21,000; 19,000**

   c. What is the range of people in part **b**? **2000**

Teaching the Process Standards

Precision Mathematically proficient students are careful about specifying units of measure. In Exercise 45, encourage students to state their answers clearly and think about the meaning of *miles per hour.*

Study Guide and Intervention

AL OL ELL

NAME ______ DATE ______ PERIOD ______

2-5 Study Guide and Intervention

Solving Equations Involving Absolute Value

Absolute Value Expressions Expressions with absolute values define an upper and lower range in which a value must lie. Expressions involving absolute value can be evaluated using the given value for the variable.

Example Evaluate $|t - 5| - 7$ if $t = 3$.

$|t - 5| - 7 = |3 - 5| - 7$ Replace t with 3.
$= |-2| - 7$ $3 - 5 = -2$
$= 2 - 7$ $|-2| = 2$
$= -5$ Simplify.

Exercises

Evaluate each expression if $r = -2$, $n = -3$, and $t = 3$.

1. $|8 - t| + 3$
2. $|t - 3| - 7$
3. $5 + |3 - n|$
4. $|r + n| - 7$
5. $|n - t| + 4$
6. $-|r + n + t|$

Evaluate each expression if $n = 2$, $q = -1.5$, $r = -3$, $v = -8$, $w = 4.5$, and $x = 4$.

7. $|2q + r|$
8. $10 - |2n + v|$
9. $|3x - 2w| - q$
10. $v - |3n + x|$
11. $1 + |5q - w|$
12. $2|3r - v|$
13. $|-2x + 5n| + (n - x)$
14. $4w - |2r + v|$
15. $3|w - n| - 5|q - r|$

Practice

AL OL BL ELL

NAME ______ DATE ______ PERIOD ______

2-5 Practice

Solving Equations Involving Absolute Value

Evaluate each expression if $x = -1$, $y = 3$, and $z = -4$.

1. $16 - |2z + 1|$
2. $|x - y| + 4$
3. $|-3y + z| - x$
4. $3|z - x| + |2 - y|$

Solve each equation. Then graph the solution set.

5. $|2x - 9| = 1$
6. $|3 - 2r| = 7$
7. $|3t + 6| = 9$
8. $|2g - 5| = 9$

Write an equation involving absolute value for each graph.

9. 10. 11. 12.

13. **FITNESS** Taisha uses the elliptical cross-trainer at the gym. Her general goal is to burn 280 Calories per workout, but she varies by as much as 25 Calories from this amount on any given day. Write and solve an equation to find the maximum and minimum number of Calories Taisha burns on the cross-trainer.

14. **TEMPERATURE** A thermometer is guaranteed to give a temperature no more than 1.2°F from the actual temperature. If the thermometer reads 28°F, write and solve an equation to find the maximum and minimum temperatures it could be.

Lesson 2-5

Word Problem Practice

AL OL BL ELL

NAME ______ DATE ______ PERIOD ______

2-5 Word Problem Practice

Solving Open Sentences Involving Absolute Value

1. **ENGINEERING** Tolerance in engineering is an allowance made for imperfections in a manufactured object. The manufacturer of an oven specifies a temperature tolerance of ±15°F. This means that the temperature inside the oven will be within 15°F of the temperature that it is set on. Write an absolute value expression to represent the maximum and minimum temperatures inside the oven when the thermostat is set on 400°F.

2. **AVIATION** The circle graph shows the results of a survey that asked 4300 students ages 7 to 18 what they thought would be the most important benefit of air travel in the future. There are about 40 million students in the United States. If the margin of error is ±3%, what is the range of the number of students ages 7 to 18 who would likely say that "finding new resources for Earth" is the most important benefit of future flight?

The Next Frontier for Flight

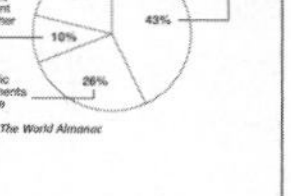

Source: *The World Almanac*

3. **COLLEGE** A certain scholarship and student loan fund uses a formula to determine whether or not a student qualifies for college funding. The formula is $|3k + 6| = 15$, where k is a need score determined by an interview. What are the possible need scores?

4. **STATISTICS** The most familiar statistical measure is the arithmetic mean, or average. A second important statistical measure is the standard deviation, which is a measure of how far the individual scores are from the mean. For example, the mean score on the Wechsler IQ test is 100 and the standard deviation is 15. This means that people within one deviation of the mean have IQ scores that are 15 points higher or lower than the mean.

   a. Write an absolute value equation to find the maximum and minimum test scores within one standard deviation if the mean was 80 and the standard deviation was 12.

   b. What is the range of Wechsler IQ test scores ±3 standard deviations from the mean?

Enrichment

OL BL

NAME ______ DATE ______ PERIOD ______

2-5 Enrichment

Precision of Measurement

The precision of a measurement depends both on your accuracy in measuring and the number of divisions on the ruler you use. Suppose you measured a length of wood to the nearest one-eighth of an inch and got a length of $6\frac{5}{8}$ in.

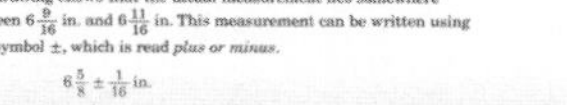

The drawing shows that the actual measurement lies somewhere between $6\frac{9}{16}$ in. and $6\frac{11}{16}$ in. This measurement can be written using the symbol ±, which is read *plus or minus.*

$$6\frac{5}{8} \pm \frac{1}{16} \text{ in.}$$

In this example, $\frac{1}{16}$ in. is the absolute error. The absolute error is one-half the smallest unit used in a measurement.

Teaching the Process Standards

Structure Mathematically proficient students look closely to discern structure. In Exercises 57–60, direct students' attention to the absolute value expressions. Guide them to think about the fact that an absolute value is nonnegative, and *x* may be negative, positive, or zero.

WatchOut!

Error Analysis In Exercise 63, suggest that students consider why Wesley thinks the solution set is the empty set. Students should see that the absolute value is equal to a negative number. Since absolute value represents the distance from zero on a number line and distance cannot be a negative number, there is no solution.

Additional Answers

55b. Sample answer:

Number of questions correct	Points
0	0
1	10
2	20
3	30
4	40
5	50

63. Wesley; the absolute value of a number cannot be a negative number.

64. Sample answer: There are two solutions when the absolute value is equal to a positive number. There is one solution if the equation indicates that the absolute value is equal to zero. There are no solutions if the absolute value is equal to a negative number. Absolute values are distances which can never be negative numbers. Two solutions: $|x| = 10$, because $|10| = 10$ and $|-10| = 10$. One solution: $|x| = 0$, because $|0| = 0$. No solution: $|x| = -10$, because the distance a number x is from 0 cannot be negative.

54. BOOK CLUB The members of a book club agree to read within ten pages of the last page of the chapter. The chapter ends on page 203.

a. Write an absolute value equation that represents the pages where club members could stop reading. **$|p - 203| = 10$**

b. Write the range of the pages where the club members could stop reading. **193 to 213**

55b. Let m be the score on the math section. $|m - 160| = 50$; 210, 110

55. SCHOOL Teams from Washington and McKinley High Schools are competing in an academic challenge. A correct response on a question earns 10 points and an incorrect response loses 10 points. A team earns 0 points on an unattempted question. There are 5 questions in the math section.

a. What are the maximum and minimum scores a team can earn on the math section? **50, −50**

b. Suppose the McKinley team has 160 points at the start of the math section. Write and solve an equation that represents the maximum and minimum scores the team could have at the end of the math section.

c. What are all of the possible scores that a school can earn on the math section? **50, 40, 30, 20, 10, 0, −10, −20, −30, −40, −50**

H.O.T. Problems Use Higher-Order Thinking Skills

C **56. OPEN ENDED** Describe a real-world situation that could be represented by the absolute value equation $|x - 4| = 10$. **Sample answer: Let x = the temperature at night. Then the temperature is 4 ± 10 degrees.**

STRUCTURE Determine whether the following statements are *sometimes*, *always*, or *never* true, if c is an integer. Explain your reasoning.

57. The value of $|x + 1|$ is greater than zero. **Sometimes; when $x = -1$, the value is 0.**

58. The solution of $|x + c| = 0$ is greater than 0.

59. The inequality $|x| + c < 0$ has no solution.

60. The value of $|x + c| + c$ is greater than zero.

58. Sometimes; when c is a negative value, x is a positive value.
59. Sometimes; when c is a negative value, the inequality is true.
60. Sometimes; when $c = 1$, $x > -2$.

61. REASONING Explain why an absolute value can never be negative.
An absolute value represents a distance from zero on a number line. A distance can never be a negative number.

62. CHALLENGE Use the sentence $x = 7 \pm 4.6$.

a. Describe the values of x that make the sentence true. **2.4, 11.6**

b. Translate the sentence into an equation involving absolute value. **$|x - 7| = 4.6$**

63. ERROR ANALYSIS Alex and Wesley are solving $|x + 5| = -3$. Is either of them correct? Explain your reasoning. **See margin.**

Alex	
$\lvert x + 5\rvert = 3$ or	$\lvert x + 5\rvert = -3$
$x + 5 = 3$	$x + 5 = -3$
$-5 \quad -5$	$-5 \quad -5$
$x = -2$	$x = -8$

Wesley
$\lvert x + 5\rvert = -3$
The solution is $\emptyset$.

64. WRITING IN MATH Explain why there are either two, one, or no solutions for absolute value equations. Demonstrate an example of each possibility. **See margin.**

108 | Lesson 2-5 | Solving Equations Involving Absolute Value

Standardized Test Practice

65. Which equation represents the second step of the solution process? **D**

Step 1: $4(2x + 7) - 6 = 3x$

Step 2: ________

Step 3: $5x + 28 - 6 = 0$

Step 4: $5x = -22$

Step 5: $x = -4.4$

A $4(2x - 6) + 7 = 3x$
B $4(2x + 1) = 3x$
C $8x + 7 - 6 = 3x$
D $8x + 28 - 6 = 3x$

66. GEOMETRY The area of a circle is 25π square centimeters. What is the circumference? **J**

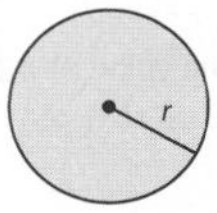

F 625π cm
G 50π cm
H 25π cm
J 10π cm

67. Tanya makes \$5 an hour and 15% commission of the total dollar value on cosmetics she sells. Suppose Tanya's commission is increased to 17%. How much money will she make if she sells \$300 worth of product and works 30 hours? **A**

A \$201 C \$255
B \$226 D \$283

68. EXTENDED RESPONSE John's mother has agreed to take him driving every day for two weeks. On the first day, John drives for 20 minutes. Each day after that, John drives 5 minutes more than the day before. **See margin.**

a. Write an expression for the minutes John drives on the nth day. Explain.

b. For how many minutes will John drive on the last day? Show your work.

c. John's driver's education teacher requires that each student drive for 30 hours with an adult outside of class. Will John's sessions with his mother fulfill this requirement?

Spiral Review

Write and solve an equation for each sentence. (Lesson 2-4)

69. One half of a number increased by 16 is four less than two thirds of the number. $\frac{1}{2}n + 16 = \frac{2}{3}n - 4$; **120**

70. The sum of one half of a number and 6 equals one third of the number. $\frac{1}{2}n + 6 = \frac{1}{3}n$; **−36**

71. SHOE If ℓ represents the length of a man's foot in inches, the expression $2\ell - 12$ can be used to estimate his shoe size. What is the approximate length of a man's foot if he wears a size 8? (Lesson 2-3) **10 in.**

Skills Review

Write an equation for each problem. Then solve the equation.

72. Seven times a number equals −84. What is the number? $7n = -84$; **−12**

73. Two fifths of a number equals −24. Find the number. $\frac{2}{5}n = -24$; **−60**

74. Negative 117 is nine times a number. Find the number. $-117 = 9n$; **−13**

75. Twelve is one fifth of a number. What is the number? $12 = \frac{1}{5}n$; **60**

DifferentiatedInstruction BL

Extension Have students solve the absolute value equation $|4b - 3| = 2b + 9$. Remind them to check the solutions. If necessary, give this hint: Use the opposite of the quantity of $2b + 9$ to solve for Case 2. {−1, 6}

4 Assess

Yesterday's News Ask students to write how yesterday's lesson on solving equations with variables on each side helped them with today's lesson on solving equations involving absolute value.

Formative Assessment

Check for student understanding of Lessons 2-4 and 2-5.

Quiz 2, p. 63

Additional Answers

68a. $15 + 5(n)$ where n represents the number of days, because John will drive 20 minutes on the first day and then an additional 5 minutes for each day after that.

68b. 85 min; $15 + 5(14) = 85$

68c. No; 30 hours is 1800 minutes. John drove a total of 735 minutes with his mother.

Formative Assessment

Use the Mid-Chapter Quiz to assess students' progress in the first half of the chapter.

For problems answered incorrectly, have students review the lessons indicated in parentheses.

Summative Assessment

Mid-Chapter Test, p. 65

McGraw-Hill eAssessment Customize and create multiple versions of your Mid-Chapter Quiz and their answer keys.

FOLDABLES StudyOrganizer

Dinah Zike's Foldables®

Before students complete the Mid-Chapter Quiz, encourage them to review the information for Lessons 2-1 through 2-5 in their Foldables.

CHAPTER 2 Mid-Chapter Quiz

Lessons 2-1 through 2-5

Translate each sentence into an equation. (Lesson 2-1)

1. The sum of three times *a* and four is the same as five times *a*. $3a + 4 = 5a$
2. One fourth of *m* minus six is equal to two times the sum of *m* and 9. $\frac{1}{4}m - 6 = 2(m + 9)$
3. The product of five and *w* is the same as *w* to the third power. $5w = w^3$

4. **MARBLES** Drew has 50 red, green, and blue marbles. He has six more red marbles than blue marbles and four fewer green marbles than blue marbles. Write and solve an equation to determine how many blue marbles Drew has. (Lesson 2-2) $3b + 2 = 50$; 16

Solve each equation. Check your solution. (Lesson 2-2)

5. $p + 8 = 13$ 5
6. $-26 = b - 3$ -23
7. $\frac{t}{6} = 3$ 18

8. **MULTIPLE CHOICE** Solve the equation $\frac{3}{5}a = \frac{1}{4}$. (Lesson 2-2) C

   A -3

   B $\frac{3}{20}$

   C $\frac{5}{12}$

   D 2

Solve each equation. Check your solution. (Lesson 2-3)

9. $2x + 5 = 13$ 4
10. $-21 = 7 - 4y$ 7
11. $\frac{m}{6} - 3 = 8$ 66
12. $-4 = \frac{d + 3}{5}$ -23

13. **FISH** The average length of a yellow-banded angelfish is 12 inches. This is 4.8 times as long as an average common goldfish. (Lesson 2-3)

    a. Write an equation you could use to find the length of the average common goldfish. $12 = 4.8g$

    b. What is the length of an average common goldfish? 2.5 in.

Write an equation and solve each problem. (Lesson 2-3)

14. Three less than three fourths of a number is negative 9. Find the number. $\frac{3}{4}n - 3 = -9$; -8
15. Thirty is twelve added to six times a number. What is the number? $30 = 12 + 6n$; 3
16. Find four consecutive integers with a sum of 106. $n + (n + 1) + (n + 2) + (n + 3) = 106$; 25, 26, 27, 28

Solve each equation. Check your solution. (Lesson 2-4)

17. $8p + 3 = 5p + 9$ 2
18. $\frac{3}{4}w + 6 = 9 - \frac{1}{4}w$ 3
19. $\frac{z + 6}{3} = \frac{2z}{4}$ 12

20. **PERIMETER** Find the value of *x* so that the triangles have the same perimeter. (Lesson 2-4) 20

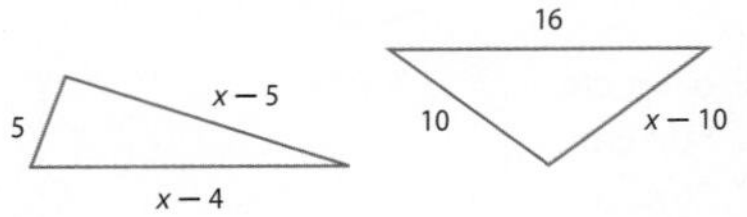

21. **PRODUCTION** ABC Sporting Goods Company produces baseball gloves. Their fixed monthly production cost is $8000 with a per glove cost of $5. XYZ Sporting Goods Company also produces baseball gloves. Their fixed monthly production cost is $10,000 with a per glove cost of $3. Find the value of *x*, the number of gloves produced monthly, so that the total monthly production cost is the same for both companies. (Lesson 2-4) 1000

Evaluate each expression if $x = -4$, $y = 7$, and $z = -9$. (Lesson 2-5)

22. $|3x - 2| + 2y$ 28
23. $|-4y + 2z| - 7z$ 109

24. **MULTIPLE CHOICE** Solve $|6m - 3| = 9$. (Lesson 2-5) G

    F {2} **H** {−3, 6}

    G {−1, 2} **J** {−3, 3}

25. **COFFEE** Some say to brew an excellent cup of coffee, you must have a brewing temperature of 200° F, plus or minus 5 degrees. Write and solve an equation describing the maximum and minimum brewing temperatures for an excellent cup of coffee. $|t - 200| = 5$; {205°, 195°}

InterventionPlanner

TIER 1 On Level OL	TIER 2 Strategic Intervention AL approaching grade level	TIER 3 Intensive Intervention 2 or more grades below level
If students miss about 25% of the exercises or less,	**If** students miss about 50% of the exercises,	**If** students miss about 75% of the exercises,
Then choose a resource: **SE** Lessons 2-1, 2-2, 2-3, 2-4, and 2-5 Skills Practice, pp. 7, 13, 19, 25, and 32 **TE** Chapter Project connectED.mcgraw-hill.com Self-Check Quiz	**Then** choose a resource: Study Guide and Intervention, Chapter 2, pp. 5, 11, 17, 23, and 30 *Quick Review Math Handbook* connectED.mcgraw-hill.com Extra Examples, Personal Tutor, Homework Help	**Then** use *Math Triumphs, Alg. 1,* Ch. 1–5 connectED.mcgraw-hill.com Extra Examples, Personal Tutor, Homework Help, Review Vocabulary

LESSON 2-6 Ratios and Proportions

Then

- You evaluated percents by using a proportion.

Now

1 Compare ratios.

2 Solve proportions.

Why?

- Ratios allow us to compare many items by using a common reference. The table below shows the number of restaurants a certain popular fast food chain has per 10,000 people in the United States as well as other countries. This allows us to compare the number of these restaurants using an equal reference.

Countries	United States	New Zealand	Canada	Australia	Japan	Singapore
Number of Restaurants per 10,000 People	0.433	0.369	0.352	0.349	0.282	0.273

NewVocabulary
ratio
proportion
means
extremes
rate
unit rate
scale
scale model

Content Standards
AI.L.3

1 Ratios and Proportions

The comparison between the number of restaurants and the number of people is a ratio. A **ratio** is a comparison of two numbers by division. The ratio of x to y can be expressed in the following ways.

$$x \text{ to } y \qquad x : y \qquad \frac{x}{y}$$

Suppose you wanted to determine the number of restaurants per 100,000 people in Australia. Notice that this ratio is equal to the original ratio.

$$\frac{0.349 \text{ restaurants}}{10{,}000 \text{ people}} = \frac{3.49 \text{ restaurants}}{100{,}000 \text{ people}} \quad (\times 10 \text{ top and bottom})$$

An equation stating that two ratios are equal is called a **proportion**. So, we can state that $\frac{0.349}{10{,}000} = \frac{3.49}{100{,}000}$ is a proportion.

Example 1 Determine Whether Ratios Are Equivalent

Determine whether $\frac{2}{3}$ and $\frac{16}{24}$ are equivalent ratios. Write *yes* or *no*. Justify your answer.

$$\frac{2}{3} = \frac{2}{3} \ (\div 1) \qquad \frac{16}{24} = \frac{2}{3} \ (\div 8)$$

When expressed in simplest form, the ratios are equivalent.

GuidedPractice

Determine whether each pair of ratios are equivalent ratios. Write *yes* or *no*. Justify your answer.

1A. $\frac{6}{10}, \frac{2}{5}$ no; $\frac{3}{5} \neq \frac{2}{5}$

1B. $\frac{1}{6}, \frac{5}{30}$ yes; $\frac{1}{6} = \frac{1}{6}$

1 Focus

VerticalAlignment

Before Lesson 2-6 Evaluate percents by using a proportion.

Lesson 2-6 Compare ratios. Solve proportions.

After Lesson 2-6 Describe functional relationships for given problem situations.

2 Teach

Scaffolding Questions

Have students read the **Why?** section of the lesson.

Ask:

- How can you use the information in the table to determine the number of fast food restaurants per 1,000,000 people? Multiply the number of fast food restaurants and the number of people by 100.
- Suppose you want to know the number of restaurants per 500,000 people. How can you determine this number? Multiply the number of restaurants and the number of people by 50.
- Which country has 1.41 fast food restaurants per 50,000 people? Japan

Lesson 2-6 Resources

Resource	Approaching Level AL	On Level OL	Beyond Level BL	English Learners ELL
Teacher Edition	▪ Differentiated Instruction, p. 113	▪ Differentiated Instruction, pp. 113, 114	▪ Differentiated Instruction, pp. 114, 117	
Chapter Resource Masters	▪ Study Guide and Intervention, pp. 36–37 ▪ Skills Practice, p. 38 ▪ Practice, p. 39 ▪ Word Problem Practice, p. 40	▪ Study Guide and Intervention, pp. 36–37 ▪ Skills Practice, p. 38 ▪ Practice, p. 39 ▪ Word Problem Practice, p. 40 ▪ Enrichment, p. 41	▪ Practice, p. 39 ▪ Word Problem Practice, p. 40 ▪ Enrichment, p. 41	▪ Study Guide and Intervention, pp. 36–37 ▪ Skills Practice, p. 38 ▪ Practice, p. 39 ▪ Word Problem Practice, p. 40
Other	▪ 5-Minute Check 2-6 ▪ Study Notebook ▪ Teaching Algebra with Manipulatives	▪ 5-Minute Check 2-6 ▪ Study Notebook ▪ Teaching Algebra with Manipulatives	▪ 5-Minute Check 2-6 ▪ Study Notebook	▪ 5-Minute Check 2-6 ▪ Study Notebook ▪ Teaching Algebra with Manipulatives

1 Ratios and Proportions

Example 1 shows how to determine whether ratios are equivalent.
Example 2 shows how to determine whether ratios form a proportion using cross products.

Formative Assessment

Use the Guided Practice exercises after each Example to determine students' understanding of concepts.

Additional Examples

1 Determine whether $\frac{7}{8}$ and $\frac{49}{56}$ are equivalent ratios. Write *yes* or *no*. Justify your answer. Yes; the ratios are equivalent when expressed in simplest form.

2 Use cross products to determine whether each pair of ratios forms a proportion.

a. $\frac{0.25}{0.6}, \frac{1.25}{2}$ not a proportion

b. $\frac{2}{2.5}, \frac{16}{20}$ a proportion

Additional Examples also in Interactive Classroom PowerPoint® Presentations

IWB Interactive White Board READY

Focus on Mathematical Content

Proportions One way to determine if two ratios form a proportion is to use cross products. In a proportion, the product of the extremes is equal to the product of the means.

Teach with Tech

Interactive Whiteboard Write two ratios on the board and show students how to determine if they form a proportion. Drag the numerators and denominators to show how to form the cross products and then simplify.

StudyTip

Means and Extremes To solve a proportion using cross products, write an equation that sets the product of the extremes equal to the product of the means.

There are special names for the terms in a proportion.

1.5 and 1.2 are called the **means**. They are the middle terms of the proportion.

$$0.2 : 1.5 \quad = \quad 1.2 : 9.0$$

0.2 and 9.0 are called the **extremes**. They are the first and last terms of the proportion.

KeyConcept Means-Extremes Property of Proportion

Words	In a proportion, the product of the extremes is equal to the product of the means.
Symbols	If $\frac{a}{b} = \frac{c}{d}$ and $b, d \neq 0$, then $ad = bc$.
Examples	Since $\frac{2}{4} = \frac{1}{2}$, $2(2) = 4(1)$ or $4 = 4$.

Another way to determine whether two ratios form a proportion is to use cross products. If the cross products are equal, then the ratios form a proportion.

This is the same as multiplying the means, and multiplying the extremes.

Example 2 Cross Products

Use cross products to determine whether each pair of ratios forms a proportion.

a. $\frac{2}{3.5}, \frac{8}{14}$

$\frac{2}{3.5} \stackrel{?}{=} \frac{8}{14}$ Original proportion

$2(14) \stackrel{?}{=} 3.5(8)$ Cross products

$28 = 28$ ✓ Simplify.

The cross products are equal, so the ratios form a proportion.

b. $\frac{0.3}{1.5}, \frac{0.5}{2.0}$

$\frac{0.3}{1.5} \stackrel{?}{=} \frac{0.5}{2.0}$ Original proportion

$0.3(2.0) \stackrel{?}{=} 1.5(0.5)$ Cross products

$0.6 \neq 0.75$ ✗ Simplify.

The cross products are not equal, so the ratios do not form a proportion.

GuidedPractice

2A. $\frac{0.2}{1.8}, \frac{1}{0.9}$ no **2B.** $\frac{15}{36}, \frac{35}{42}$ no

WatchOut!

Preventing Errors Point out that the definitions of extremes and means are not arbitrary. In the proportion $\frac{a}{b} = \frac{c}{d}$, *a* and *d* are the extremes, and *b* and *c* are the means. Remind students that the ratios can be written in the form $x:y$. If the proportions above are rewritten in this form, they are $a:b = c:d$. Looking at this proportion, *a* and *d* are the extremes because they are on the outside, and *extreme* is a synonym for outside. Similarly, *b* and *c* are the means because they are in the middle, and *mean* is often a synonym for middle.

StudyTip
Cross Products When you find cross products, you are said to be *cross multiplying*.

2 Solve Proportions

To solve proportions, use cross products.

Example 3 Solve a Proportion

Solve each proportion. If necessary, round to the nearest hundredth.

a. $\frac{x}{10} = \frac{3}{5}$

$\frac{x}{10} = \frac{3}{5}$	Original proportion
$x(5) = 10(3)$	Find the cross products.
$5x = 30$	Simplify.
$\frac{5x}{5} = \frac{30}{5}$	Divide each side by 5.
$x = 6$	Simplify.

b. $\frac{x-2}{14} = \frac{2}{7}$

$\frac{x-2}{14} = \frac{2}{7}$	Original proportion
$(x-2)7 = 14(2)$	Find the cross products.
$7x - 14 = 28$	Simplify.
$7x = 42$	Add 14 to each side.
$x = 6$	Divide each side by 7.

GuidedPractice

3A. $\frac{r}{8} = \frac{25}{40}$ 5

3B. $\frac{x+4}{5} = \frac{3}{8}$ −2.13

The ratio of two measurements having different units of measure is called a **rate**. For example, a price of $9.99 per 10 songs is a rate. A rate that tells how many of one item is being compared to 1 of another item is called a **unit rate**.

Real-WorldCareer
Retail Buyer A retail buyer purchases goods for stores, primarily from wholesalers, for resale to the general public. Buyers use math to determine the amount of each product to order. A bachelor's degree with an emphasis on business studies is usually required.

Real-World Example 4 Rate of Growth

RETAIL In the past two years, a retailer has opened 232 stores. If the rate of growth remains constant, how many stores will the retailer open in the next 3 years?

Understand Let r represent the number of retail stores.

Plan Write a proportion for the problem.

$$\frac{232 \text{ retail stores}}{2 \text{ years}} = \frac{r \text{ retail stores}}{3 \text{ years}}$$

Solve

$\frac{232}{2} = \frac{r}{3}$	Original proportion
$232(3) = 2r$	Find the cross products.
$696 = 2r$	Simplify.
$\frac{696}{2} = \frac{2r}{2}$	Divide each side by 2.
$348 = r$	Simplify.

The retailer will open 348 stores in 3 years.

Check If the clothing retailer continues to open 232 stores every 2 years, then in the next 3 years, it will open 348 stores.

DifferentiatedInstruction AL OL

If you have any doubt that your students have mastered the concept of proportions,

Then place students in small groups to work through the Check Your Understanding problems. Have a student from each group report on that group's progress and areas in which the group may need assistance. It is important for students to have a good understanding of writing and solving proportions before studying the next few lessons.

2 Solve Proportions

Example 3 shows how to solve a proportion involving a variable. **Example 4** shows how to write and solve a proportion for a problem involving rates (the ratio of two measurements having different units of measure). **Example 5** shows how to write and solve a problem using a ratio or rate called a scale.

Additional Examples

3 Solve each proportion. If necessary, round to the nearest hundredth.

a. $\frac{n}{12} = \frac{3}{8}$ $n = 4.5$

b. $\frac{x+4}{12} = \frac{3}{4}$ $x = 5$

4 **BICYCLING** The gear on a bicycle is 8:5. This means that for every 8 turns of the pedals, the wheel turns 5 times. Suppose the bicycle wheel turns about 2435 times during a trip. How many times would you have to crank the pedals during the trip? about 3896 times

Tips for New Teachers

Cross Products Point out to students that the cross products must be equal regardless of the location of the x in the proportion.

Additional Example

5 **MAP** In a road atlas, the scale for the map of Connecticut is 5 inches = 41 miles. What is the distance in miles represented by $2\frac{1}{2}$ inches on the map? $20\frac{1}{2}$ mi

3 Practice

Formative Assessment

Use Exercises 1–8 to check for understanding.

Use the chart at the bottom of the next page to customize assignments for your students.

GuidedPractice

4. **EXERCISE** It takes 7 minutes for Isabella to walk around the gym track twice. At this rate, how many times can she walk around the track in a half hour? about 8.6 times

A rate called a **scale** is used to make a **scale model** of something too large or too small to be convenient at actual size.

Real-WorldLink

The Great Smoky Mountains National Park in Tennessee is home to several waterfalls. The Ramsey Cascades is 100 feet tall. It is the tallest in the park.

Source: National Park Service

Real-World Example 5 Scale and Scale Models

MOUNTAIN TRAIL The Ramsey Cascades Trail is about $1\frac{1}{8}$ inches long on a map with scale 3 inches = 10 miles. What is the actual length of the trail?

Let ℓ represent the actual length.

$$\begin{matrix}\text{scale} \rightarrow \\ \text{actual} \rightarrow\end{matrix} \frac{3}{10} = \frac{1\frac{1}{8}}{\ell} \begin{matrix}\leftarrow \text{scale} \\ \leftarrow \text{actual}\end{matrix}$$

$3(\ell) = 1\frac{1}{8}(10)$ — Find the cross products.

$3\ell = \frac{45}{4}$ — Simplify.

$3\ell \div 3 = \frac{45}{4} \div 3$ — Divide each side by 3.

$\ell = \frac{15}{4}$ or $3\frac{3}{4}$ — Simplify.

The actual length is about $3\frac{3}{4}$ miles.

GuidedPractice

5. **AIRPLANES** On a model airplane, the scale is 5 centimeters = 2 meters. If the model's wingspan is 28.5 centimeters, what is the actual wingspan? 11.4 m

Check Your Understanding

◯ = Step-by-Step Solutions begin on page R13.

Examples 1–2 **Determine whether each pair of ratios are equivalent ratios. Write *yes* or *no*.**

1. $\frac{3}{7}, \frac{9}{14}$ no
2. $\frac{7}{8}, \frac{42}{48}$ yes
3. $\frac{2.8}{4.4}, \frac{1.4}{2.1}$ no

Example 3 **Solve each proportion. If necessary, round to the nearest hundredth.**

4. $\frac{n}{9} = \frac{6}{27}$ 2
5. $\frac{4}{u} = \frac{28}{35}$ 5
6. $\frac{3}{8} = \frac{b}{10}$ 3.75

Example 4

7. **RACE** Jennie ran the first 6 miles of a marathon in 58 minutes. If she is able to maintain the same pace, how long will it take her to finish the 26.2 miles? ≈ 253.3 min or ≈ 4 h 13.3 min

Example 5

8. **PRECISION** On a map of North Carolina, Raleigh and Asheville are about 8 inches apart. If the scale is 1 inch = 12 miles, how far apart are the cities? about 96 mi

DifferentiatedInstruction OL BL

Extension The development of proportional reasoning is crucial to future success in mathematics. While students typically find success with the process of cross multiplication, they rarely take the time to figure out why this procedure works. Engage mathematically talented students in other methods of solving proportions, such as multiplying the numerator and denominator by a common factor (focusing on non-integer factors).

Practice and Problem Solving

Extra Practice is on page R2.

Examples 1–2 **Determine whether each pair of ratios are equivalent ratios. Write *yes* or *no*.**

9. $\frac{9}{11}, \frac{81}{99}$ **yes**
10. $\frac{3}{7}, \frac{18}{42}$ **yes**
11. $\frac{8.4}{9.2}, \frac{8.8}{9.6}$ **no**
12. $\frac{4}{3}, \frac{6}{8}$ **no**
13. $\frac{29.2}{10.4}, \frac{7.3}{2.6}$ **yes**
14. $\frac{39.68}{60.14}, \frac{6.4}{9.7}$ **yes**

Example 3 **Solve each proportion. If necessary, round to the nearest hundredth.**

15. $\frac{3}{8} = \frac{15}{a}$ **40**
16. $\frac{t}{2} = \frac{6}{12}$ **1**
17. $\frac{4}{9} = \frac{13}{q}$ **29.25**
18. $\frac{15}{35} = \frac{g}{7}$ **3**
19. $\frac{7}{10} = \frac{m}{14}$ **9.8**
20. $\frac{8}{13} = \frac{v}{21}$ **12.92**
21. $\frac{w}{2} = \frac{4.5}{6.8}$ **1.32**
22. $\frac{1}{0.19} = \frac{12}{n}$ **2.28**
23. $\frac{2}{0.21} = \frac{8}{n}$ **0.84**
24. $\frac{2.4}{3.6} = \frac{k}{1.8}$ **1.2**
25. $\frac{t}{0.3} = \frac{1.7}{0.9}$ **0.57**
26. $\frac{7}{1.066} = \frac{z}{9.65}$ **63.37**
27. $\frac{x-3}{5} = \frac{6}{10}$ **6**
28. $\frac{7}{x+9} = \frac{21}{36}$ **3**
29. $\frac{10}{15} = \frac{4}{x-5}$ **11**

Example 4

30. **CAR WASH** The B-Clean Car Wash washed 128 cars in 3 hours. At that rate, how many cars can they wash in 8 hours? **about 341 cars**

Example 5

31. **GEOGRAPHY** On a map of Florida, the distance between Jacksonville and Tallahassee is 2.6 centimeters. If 2 centimeters = 120 miles, what is the distance between the two cities? **156 mi**

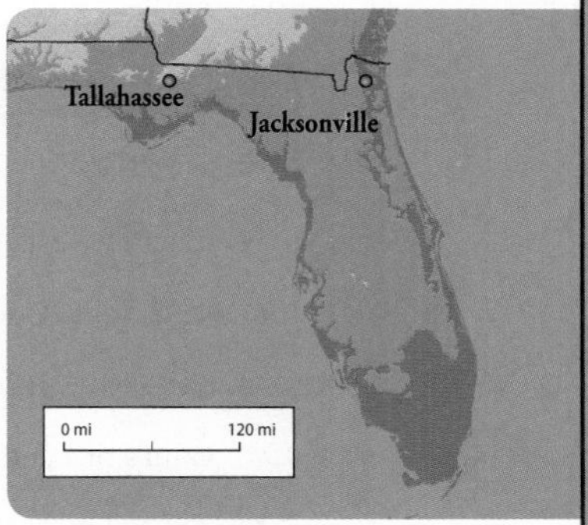

32. **PRECISION** An artist used interlocking building blocks to build a scale model of Kennedy Space Center, Florida. In the model, 1 inch equals 1.67 feet of an actual space shuttle. The model is 110.3 inches tall. How tall is the actual space shuttle? Round to the nearest tenth. **184.2 ft**

B

33. **MENU** On Monday, a restaurant made \$545 from selling 110 hamburgers. If they sold 53 hamburgers on Tuesday, how much did they make? **about \$262.59**

Solve each proportion. If necessary, round to the nearest hundredth.

34. $\frac{6}{14} = \frac{7}{x-3}$ **19.33**
35. $\frac{7}{4} = \frac{f-4}{8}$ **18**
36. $\frac{3-y}{4} = \frac{1}{9}$ **2.56**
37. $\frac{4v+7}{15} = \frac{6v+2}{10}$ **0.8**
38. $\frac{9b-3}{9} = \frac{5b+5}{3}$ **−3**
39. $\frac{2n-4}{5} = \frac{3n+3}{10}$ **11**

40. **ATHLETES** At Piedmont High School, 3 out of every 8 students are athletes. If there are 1280 students at the school, how many are not athletes? **800 students**

41. **BRACES** Two out of five students in the ninth grade have braces. If there are 325 students in the ninth grade, how many have braces? **130 students**

42. **PAINT** Joel used a half gallon of paint to cover 84 square feet of wall. He has 932 square feet of wall to paint. How many gallons of paint should he purchase? **6 gal**

Teaching the Process Standards

Precision Mathematically proficient students are careful about specifying units of measure. Remind students that while ratios often appear as fractions, a ratio is any comparison of two quantities by division. When using ratios to form proportions, students must make sure that the numerators and denominators of each ratio have the same units. In some cases, a conversion factor must be used.

Follow-up

Students have explored ratios and proportions.

Ask:

- How can you represent mathematical relationships using ratios and proportions? Sample answer: You can represent a relationship between two quantities by writing them as a ratio. You can represent the equivalence of two ratios by writing them as a proportion.

Differentiated Homework Options

Level	Assignment	Two-Day Option	
AL Basic	9–32, 46–47, 49–70	9–31 odd, 51–54	10–32 even, 46–47, 49–50, 55–70
OL Core	9–39 odd, 40–47, 49–70	9–32, 51–54	33–47, 49–50, 55–70
BL Advanced	33–67, (optional: 68–70)		

Study Guide and Intervention

AL OL ELL

NAME ______ DATE ______ PERIOD ______

2-6 Study Guide and Intervention

Ratios and Proportions

Ratios and Proportions A **ratio** is a comparison of two numbers by division. The ratio of x to y can be expressed as x to y, $x:y$ or $\frac{x}{y}$. Ratios are usually expressed in simplest form. An equation stating that two ratios are equal is called a **proportion**. To determine whether two ratios form a proportion, express both ratios in simplest form or check cross products.

Example 1 Determine whether the ratios $\frac{24}{36}$ and $\frac{12}{18}$ are equivalent ratios. Write *yes* or *no*. Justify your answer.

$\frac{24}{36} = \frac{2}{3}$ when expressed in simplest form.

$\frac{12}{18} = \frac{2}{3}$ when expressed in simplest form.

The ratios $\frac{24}{36}$ and $\frac{12}{18}$ form a proportion because they are equal when expressed in simplest form.

Example 2 Use cross products to determine whether $\frac{10}{18}$ and $\frac{25}{45}$ form a proportion.

$\frac{10}{18} \stackrel{?}{=} \frac{25}{45}$ Write the proportion.

$10(45) \stackrel{?}{=} 18(25)$ Cross products

$450 = 450$ Simplify.

The cross products are equal, so $\frac{10}{18} = \frac{25}{45}$. Since the ratios are equal, they form a proportion.

Exercises

Determine whether each pair of ratios are equivalent ratios. Write *yes* or *no*.

1. $\frac{1}{2}, \frac{16}{32}$ 2. $\frac{5}{8}, \frac{10}{15}$ 3. $\frac{10}{20}, \frac{25}{49}$
4. $\frac{25}{36}, \frac{15}{20}$ 5. $\frac{12}{32}, \frac{3}{16}$ 6. $\frac{4}{9}, \frac{12}{27}$
7. $\frac{0.1}{2}, \frac{5}{100}$ 8. $\frac{15}{20}, \frac{9}{12}$ 9. $\frac{14}{12}, \frac{20}{30}$
10. $\frac{2}{3}, \frac{20}{30}$ 11. $\frac{5}{9}, \frac{25}{45}$ 12. $\frac{72}{64}, \frac{9}{8}$
13. $\frac{5}{8}, \frac{20}{20}$ 14. $\frac{18}{24}, \frac{50}{75}$ 15. $\frac{100}{75}, \frac{44}{33}$
16. $\frac{0.05}{1}, \frac{1}{20}$ 17. $\frac{1.5}{2}, \frac{6}{8}$ 18. $\frac{0.1}{0.2}, \frac{0.45}{0.9}$

Practice

AL OL BL ELL

NAME ______ DATE ______ PERIOD ______

2-6 Practice

Ratios and Proportions

Determine whether each pair of ratios are equivalent ratios. Write *yes* or *no*.

1. $\frac{7}{8}, \frac{52}{48}$ 2. $\frac{3}{11}, \frac{15}{66}$ 3. $\frac{18}{24}, \frac{36}{48}$
4. $\frac{12}{11}, \frac{108}{99}$ 5. $\frac{8}{9}, \frac{72}{81}$ 6. $\frac{1.5}{9}, \frac{1}{6}$
7. $\frac{3.4}{5.2}, \frac{7.14}{10.92}$ 8. $\frac{1.7}{1.2}, \frac{2.8}{2.4}$ 9. $\frac{7.6}{1.8}, \frac{3.9}{0.9}$

Solve each proportion. If necessary, round to the nearest hundredth.

10. $\frac{5}{3} = \frac{30}{54}$ 11. $\frac{x}{46} = \frac{34}{23}$ 12. $\frac{40}{56} = \frac{k}{7}$
13. $\frac{28}{49} = \frac{4}{w}$ 14. $\frac{3}{6} = \frac{27}{162}$ 15. $\frac{7}{3} = \frac{48}{9}$
16. $\frac{2}{7} = \frac{10}{40}$ 17. $\frac{5}{11} = \frac{35}{x}$ 18. $\frac{3}{51} = \frac{z}{17}$
19. $\frac{6}{61} = \frac{12}{h}$ 20. $\frac{x}{16} = \frac{6}{4}$ 21. $\frac{14}{49} = \frac{2}{a}$
22. $\frac{7}{9} = \frac{8}{7}$ 23. $\frac{3}{8} = \frac{5}{6}$ 24. $\frac{m}{6} = \frac{5}{4}$
25. $\frac{x}{0.23} = \frac{7}{1.61}$ 26. $\frac{3}{0.72} = \frac{12}{b}$ 27. $\frac{6}{n} = \frac{3}{0.51}$
28. $\frac{7}{a-4} = \frac{14}{6}$ 29. $\frac{3}{12} = \frac{2}{y+6}$ 30. $\frac{m-1}{8} = \frac{2}{4}$
31. $\frac{5}{12} = \frac{x+1}{4}$ 32. $\frac{r+2}{7} = \frac{5}{7}$ 33. $\frac{3}{7} = \frac{x-2}{6}$

34. **PAINTING** Ysidra paints a room that has 400 square feet of wall space in $2\frac{1}{2}$ hours. At this rate, how long will it take her to paint a room that has 720 square feet of wall space?

35. **VACATION PLANS** Walker is planning a summer vacation. He wants to visit Petrified National Forest and Meteor Crater, Arizona, the 50,000-year-old impact site of a large meteor. On a map with a scale where 2 inches equals 75 miles, the two areas are about $1\frac{1}{2}$ inches apart. What is the distance between Petrified National Forest and Meteor Crater?

Lesson 2-6

Word Problem Practice

AL OL BL ELL

NAME ______ DATE ______ PERIOD ______

2-6 Word Problem Practice

Ratios and Proportions

1. **WATER** A dripping faucet wastes 3 cups of water every 24 hours. How much water is wasted in a week?

2. **GASOLINE** In November 2010 the average price of 5 gallons of regular unleaded gasoline in the United States was $14.40. What was the price for 16 gallons of gas?

3. **SHOPPING** Stevenson's Market is selling 3 packs of toothpicks for $0.87. How much will 10 packs of toothpicks cost at this price? Round your answer to the nearest cent.

4. **BUILDINGS** Willis Tower in Chicago is 1450 feet tall. The John Hancock Center in Chicago is 1127 feet tall. Suppose you are asked to build a small-scale replica of each. If you make the Willis Tower 3 meters tall, what would be the approximate height of the John Hancock replica? Round your answer to the nearest hundredth.

5. **MAPS** A map of Waco, Texas and neighboring towns is shown below.

a. Use a metric ruler to measure the distances between Robinson and Neale on the map.

b. Using the scale of the map, find the approximate actual distance by air (not by roads), between Robinson and Neale.

c. Approximately how many square miles are shown on this map?

C 43. **MOVIE THEATERS** Use the table at the right. **a, b. See margin.**

a. Write a ratio of the number of indoor theaters to the total number of theaters for each year.

b. Do any two of the ratios you wrote for part **a** form a proportion? If so, explain the real-world meaning of the proportion.

Year	Indoor	Drive-In	Total
2003	35,361	634	35,995
2004	36,012	640	36,652
2005	37,092	648	37,740
2006	37,776	649	38,425
2007	38,159	635	38,794
2008	38,201	633	38,834
2009	38,605	628	39,233

Source: North American Theater Owners

44. **DIARIES** In a survey, 36% of the students said that they kept an electronic diary. There were 900 students who kept an electronic diary. How many students were in the survey? **2500**

45. **MULTIPLE REPRESENTATIONS** In this problem, you will explore how changing the lengths of the sides of a shape by a factor changes the perimeter of that shape.

a. **Geometric** Draw a square *ABCD*. Draw a square *MNPQ* with sides twice as long as *ABCD*. Draw a square *FGHJ* with sides half as long as *ABCD*. **See margin.**

b. **Tabular** Complete the table below using the appropriate measures.

ABCD		*MNPQ*		*FGHJ*	
Side length	2	Side length	4	Side length	1
Perimeter	8	Perimeter	16	Perimeter	4

c. **Verbal** Make a conjecture about the change in the perimeter of a square if the side length is increased or decreased by a factor. **See margin.**

H.O.T. Problems Use Higher-Order Thinking Skills

46. **STRUCTURE** In 2007, organic farms occupied 2.6 million acres in the United States and produced goods worth about $1.7 billion. Divide one of these numbers by the other and explain the meaning of the result. **See margin.**

47. **REASONING** Compare and contrast ratios and rates.

48. **CHALLENGE** If $\frac{a+1}{b-1} = \frac{5}{1}$ and $\frac{a-1}{b+1} = \frac{1}{1}$, find the value of $\frac{b}{a}$. (*Hint:* Choose values of *a* and *b* for which the proportions are true and evaluate $\frac{b}{a}$.) $\frac{2}{4}$ **or** $\frac{1}{2}$

49. **WRITING IN MATH** On a road trip, Marcus reads a highway sign and then looks at his gas gauge.

Marcus's gas tank holds 10 gallons and his car gets 32 miles per gallon at his current speed of 65 miles per hour. If he maintains this speed, will he make it to Atlanta without having to stop and get gas? Explain your reasoning. **See Ch. 2 Answer Appendix.**

50. **WRITING IN MATH** Describe how businesses can use ratios. Write about a real-world situation in which a business would use a ratio. **See Ch. 2 Answer Appendix.**

47. Ratios and rates each compare two numbers by using division. However, rates compare two measurements that involve different units of measure.

Enrichment

OL BL

NAME ______ DATE ______ PERIOD ______

2-6 Enrichment

Angles of a Triangle

In geometry, many statements about physical space are proven to be true. Such statements are called **theorems**. Here are two examples of geometric theorems.

a. The sum of the measures of the angles of a triangle is 180°.

b. If two sides of a triangle have equal measure, then the two angles opposite those sides also have equal measure.

For each of the triangles, write an equation and then solve for *x*. (A tick mark on two or more sides of a triangle indicates that the sides have equal measure.)

1. 2.

3. 4.

Lesson 2-6

Teaching the Process Standards

Structure Mathematically proficient students recognize the significance of structure. In Exercise 46, point out to students that the same numbers can be used to form different ratios with different meanings. Each ratio is useful for interpreting quantities in different ways.

Standardized Test Practice

51. In the figure, $x : y = 2 : 3$ and $y : z = 3 : 5$. If $x = 10$, find the value of z. **C**

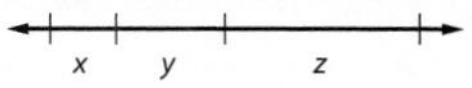

A 15
B 20
C 25
D 30

52. GRIDDED RESPONSE A race car driver records the finishing times for recent practice trials.

Trial	Time (seconds)
1	5.09
2	5.10
3	4.95
4	4.91
5	5.05

What is the mean time, in seconds, for the trials? **5.02**

53. GEOMETRY If $\triangle LMN$ is similar to $\triangle LPO$, what is z? **G**

F 240
G 140
H 120
J 70

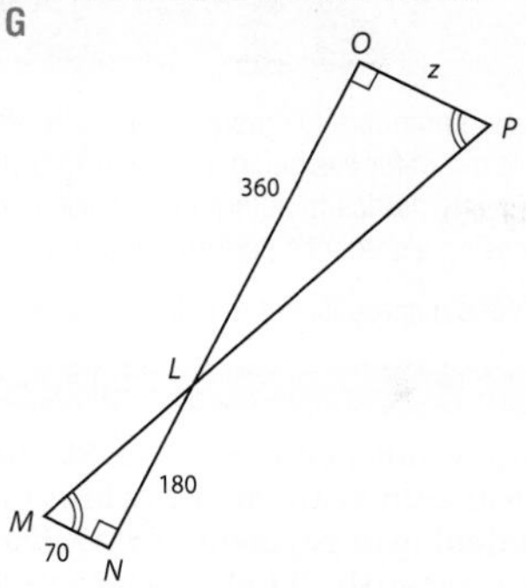

54. Which equation below illustrates the Commutative Property? **C**

A $(3x + 4y) + 2z = 3x + (4y + 2z)$
B $7(x + y) = 7x + 7y$
C $xyz = yxz$
D $x + 0 = x$

Spiral Review

Solve each equation. (Lesson 2-5)

55. $|x + 5| = -8$ $\varnothing$

56. $|b + 9| = 2$ $\{-7, -11\}$

57. $|2p - 3| = 17$ $\{10, -7\}$

58. $|5c - 8| = 12$ $\left\{4, -\frac{4}{5}\right\}$

59. HEALTH When exercising, a person's pulse rate should not exceed a certain limit. This maximum rate is represented by the expression $0.8(220 - a)$, where a is age in years. Find the age of a person whose maximum pulse rate is 122 more than their age. (Lesson 2-4) **30 years**

Solve each equation. Check your solution. (Lesson 2-3)

60. $15 = 4a - 5$ **5**

61. $7g - 14 = -63$ **−7**

62. $9 + \frac{y}{5} = 6$ **−15**

63. $\frac{t}{8} - 6 = -12$ **−48**

64. GEOMETRY Find the area of $\triangle ABC$ if each small triangle has a base of 5.2 inches and a height of 4.5 inches. (Lesson 1-4) **46.8 in²**

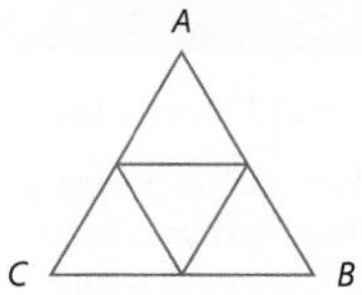

Evaluate each expression. (Lesson 1-2)

65. $3 + 16 \div 8 \cdot 5$ **13**

66. $4^2 \cdot 3 - 5(6 + 3)$ **3**

Skills Review

Solve each equation.

67. $4p = 22$ **5.5**

68. $5h = 33$ **6.6**

69. $1.25y = 4.375$ **3.5**

70. $9.8m = 30.87$ **3.15**

Differentiated Instruction BL

Extension Present students with the following problem: Kala made a scale drawing of a 12 m × 15 m room. The scale drawing is 9.6 cm × 12 cm. What scale did she use? Explain. Justify your answer. 1 cm = 1.25 m; Sample answer: To find the scale, simplify 9.6/12. Then use the scale to check that the length and width of the scale drawing and the original room are proportional: $\frac{1}{1.25} = \frac{9.6}{12}$; 12 = 12 and $\frac{1}{1.25} = \frac{12}{15}$; 15 = 15; since the cross products are equal, the scale is correct.

Multiple Representations

In Exercise 45, students use a geometric sketch, a table of values, and verbal analysis to show how the perimeter of a square is affected by a change in dimensions.

Exercise Alert

Ruler For Exercise 45, students need a ruler to draw and measure the sides of three squares.

4 Assess

Crystal Ball Have students write a sentence on how they think today's lesson will connect with tomorrow's lesson on finding the percent of change

Additional Answers

43a. 2003: $\frac{35,361}{35,995}$; 2004: $\frac{36,012}{36,652}$; 2005: $\frac{37,092}{37,740}$; 2006: $\frac{37,776}{38,425}$; 2007: $\frac{38,159}{38,794}$; 2008: $\frac{38,201}{38,834}$; 2009: $\frac{38,605}{39,233}$

43b. None of the ratios form a proportion.

45a.

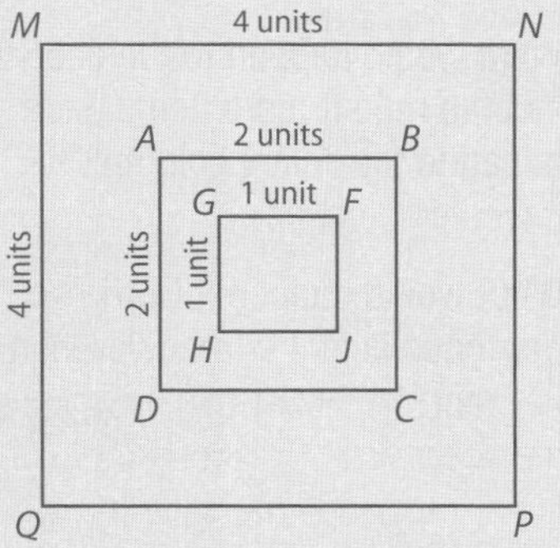

45c. If the length of a side is increased by a factor, the perimeter is also increased by that factor. If the length of the sides are decreased by a factor, the perimeter is also decreased by the same factor.

46. Sample answer: \$1.7 billion ÷ 2.6 million acres ≈ 653.85 dollars per acre, which represents the average production per acre. 2.6 million acres ÷ \$1.7 billion ≈ 0.0015 acres per dollar, which represents the average amount of land used to produce each dollar worth of goods.

1 Focus

Objective Use a spreadsheet to investigate different metrics.

Materials for Each Student

- computer
- spreadsheet software

Teaching Tip

You may want to explain that lending institutions use the debt-to-income ratio to determine their risk in lending money to an individual. Debt-to-income ratios are also used for car loans and other major purchases.

2 Teach

Working in Cooperative Groups

Have students work in pairs to complete the Activity.

Ask:

- What would happen to the debt-to-income ratio if more items were added to the expenses column? It would increase.
- What would happen to the debt-to-income ratio if more items were added to the salary column? It would decrease.
- What would happen if Dorrie's mortgage is higher or lower than her rent? A higher mortgage means a greater debt-to-income ratio; a lower mortgage means a lower debt-to-income ratio.

Practice Have students complete Exercises 1–4.

3 Assess

Formative Assessment

Use Exercise 2 to assess whether students understand how to use mortgage metrics.

EXTEND 2-6 Spreadsheet Lab: Descriptive Modeling

When using numbers to model a real-world situation, it is often helpful to have a metric. A **metric** is a rule for assigning a number to some characteristic or attribute. For example, teachers use metrics to determine grades. Each teacher determines an appropriate metric for assessing a student's performance and assigning a grade.

You can use a spreadsheet to calculate different metrics.

Activity

Dorrie wants to buy a house. She has the following expenses: rent of $650, credit card monthly bills of $320, a car payment of $410, and a student loan payment of $115. Dorrie has a yearly salary of $46,500. Use a spreadsheet to find Dorrie's debt-to-income ratio.

Step 1 Enter Dorrie's debts in column B.

Step 2 Add her debts using a function in cell B6. Go to Insert and then Function. Then choose Sum. The sum of 1495 appears in B6.

Step 3 Now insert Dorrie's salary in column C. Remember to find her monthly salary by dividing the yearly salary by 12.

A mortgage company will use the debt-to-income ratio as a metric to determine if Dorrie qualifies for a loan. The **debt-to-income ratio** is calculated as *how much she owes per month* divided by *how much she earns each month.*

Step 4 Enter a formula to find the debt-to-income ratio in cell C6. In the formula bar, enter =B6/C2.

The ratio of about 0.39 appears. An ideal ratio would be 0.36 or less. A ratio higher than 0.36 would cause an increased interest rate or may require a higher down payment.

The spreadsheet shows a debt-to-income ratio of about 0.39. Dorrie should try to eliminate or reduce some debts or try to earn more money in order to lower her debt-to-income ratio.

Lab 2-6 B Spreadsheet.xls

◇	A	B	C
1	Type of Debt	Expenses	Salary
2	Rent	650	3875
3	Credit Cards	320	
4	Car Payment	410	
5	Student Loan	115	
6		1495	0.385806
7			

Sheet 1 / Sheet 2 / Sheet 3

1. Sample answer: Reduce or eliminate credit card debt, reduce or eliminate car payments, or earn a higher salary.

Exercises

1. How could Dorrie improve her debt-to-income ratio?
2. Another metric mortgage companies use is the ratio of monthly mortgage to total monthly income. An ideal ratio is 0.28. Using this metric, how much could Dorrie afford to pay for a mortgage each month? **$1085**
3. How effective are each of these metrics as measures of whether Dorrie can afford to buy a house? Explain your reasoning. **See students' work.**
4. **MODELING** Metrics are used to compare athletes. For example, ERAs are used to compare pitchers. Find a metric and evaluate its effectiveness for modeling. Compare it to other metrics, and then define your own metric. **See students' work.**

Image Source/Punchstock

From Concrete to Abstract

Use Exercise 4 to assess whether students understand how to set up and use a spreadsheet to use metrics.

Teaching the Process Standards

Modeling Mathematically proficient students can apply the mathematics they know to solve problems arising in everyday life. In Exercise 4, encourage students to investigate metrics in their particular area of interest.

LESSON 2-7 Percent of Change

∴ Then	∴ Now	∴ Why?
● You solved proportions.	**1** Find the percent of change. **2** Solve problems involving percent of change.	● Every year, millions of people volunteer their time to improve their community. The difference in the number of volunteers from one year to the next can be used to determine a percent to represent the increase or decrease in volunteers.

NewVocabulary
percent of change
percent of increase
percent of decrease

Content Standards
AI.L.1, AI.L.2

Process Standards
PS.8

1 Percent of Change

Percent of change is the ratio of the change in an amount to the original amount expressed as a percent. If the new number is greater than the original number, the percent of change is a **percent of increase.** If the new number is less than the original number, the percent of change is a **percent of decrease.**

Example 1 Percent of Change

Determine whether each percent of change is a percent of *increase* or a percent of *decrease*. Then find the percent of change.

a. original: 20
final: 23

Subtract the original amount from the final amount to find the amount of change: $23 - 20 = 3$.

Since the new amount is greater than the original, this is a percent of increase.

Use the original number, 20, as the base.

change → original amount → $\frac{3}{20} = \frac{r}{100}$

$$3(100) = r(20)$$
$$300 = 20r$$
$$\frac{300}{20} = \frac{20r}{20}$$
$$15 = r$$

The percent of increase is 15%.

b. original: 25
final: 17

Subtract the original amount from the final amount to find the amount of change: $17 - 25 = -8$.

Since the new amount is less than the original, this is a percent of decrease.

Use the original number, 25, as the base.

change → original amount → $\frac{-8}{25} = \frac{r}{100}$

$$-8(100) = r(25)$$
$$-800 = 25r$$
$$\frac{-800}{25} = \frac{25r}{25}$$
$$-32 = r$$

The percent of decrease is 32%.

GuidedPractice

1A. original: 66
new: 30 **dec.; about 55%**

1B. original: 9.8
new: 12.1 **inc.; about 23.5%**

1C. original: 24
new: 40 **inc.; about 66.7%**

1D. original: 500
new: 131 **dec.; 73.8%**

Jim West/age fotostock

1 Focus

VerticalAlignment

Before Lesson 2-7 Solve proportions.

Lesson 2-7 Find the percent of change.
Solve problems involving percent of change.

After Lesson 2-7 Develop the concept of slope as rate of change.

2 Teach

Scaffolding Questions

Have students read the **Why?** section of the lesson.

Ask:

- In 2008 and 2009, about 61.8 and 63.4 million people volunteered their time, respectively. What was the change in the number of volunteers from 2008 to 2009? 1.6 million
- Does this change represent an increase or decrease in the number of volunteers? Why? An increase; the number of volunteers in 2009 was greater than the number of volunteers in 2008.
- Would the *percent* change in volunteers from 2008 to 2009 represent a percent increase or a percent decrease in the number of volunteers? percent increase

Lesson 2-7 Resources

Resource	Approaching Level AL	On Level OL	Beyond Level BL	English Learners ELL
Teacher Edition	▪ Differentiated Instruction, p. 121	▪ Differentiated Instruction, p. 121	▪ Differentiated Instruction, p. 124	
Chapter Resource Masters	▪ Study Guide and Intervention, pp. 42–43 ▪ Skills Practice, p. 44 ▪ Practice, p. 45 ▪ Word Problem Practice, p. 46	▪ Study Guide and Intervention, pp. 42–43 ▪ Skills Practice, p. 44 ▪ Practice, p. 45 ▪ Word Problem Practice, p. 46 ▪ Enrichment, p. 47	▪ Practice, p. 45 ▪ Word Problem Practice, p. 46 ▪ Enrichment, p. 47	▪ Study Guide and Intervention, pp. 42–43 ▪ Skills Practice, p. 44 ▪ Practice, p. 45 ▪ Word Problem Practice, p. 46
Other	▪ 5-Minute Check 2-7 ▪ Study Notebook ▪ Teaching Algebra with Manipulatives	▪ 5-Minute Check 2-7 ▪ Study Notebook ▪ Teaching Algebra with Manipulatives	▪ 5-Minute Check 2-7 ▪ Study Notebook	▪ 5-Minute Check 2-7 ▪ Study Notebook ▪ Teaching Algebra with Manipulatives

1 Percent of Change

Example 1 shows how to determine if a percent of change is a percent of increase or a percent of decrease and how to find the percent of change. **Example 2** shows how to write a percent of change proportion and use it to solve a real-world problem.

Formative Assessment

Use the Guided Practice exercises after each Example to determine students' understanding of concepts.

Additional Examples

1 Determine whether each percent of change is a percent of *increase* or a percent of *decrease*. Then find the percent of change.

a. original: 32
new: 40
percent of increase; 25%

b. original: 20
new: 4
percent of decrease; 80%

2 **SALES** The price a used-book store pays to buy a book is \$5. The store sells the book for 28% above the price that it pays for the book. What is the selling price of the book? \$6.40

Additional Examples also in Interactive Classroom PowerPoint® Presentations

IWB Interactive White Board READY

Real-WorldLink

In 2009, the total revenue earned by the North American cruise industry was more than \$15.16 billion.

Source: Cruise Market Watch

Real-World Example 2 Percent of Change

CRUISE **The total number of passengers on cruise ships increased 10% from 2007 to 2009. If there were 17.22 million passengers in 2009, how many were there in 2007?**

Let f = the number of passengers in 2009. Since 10% is a percent of increase, the number of passengers in 2007 is less than the number of passengers in 2009.

change → / original amount →	$\frac{17.22 - f}{f} = \frac{10}{100}$	Percent proportion
	$(1722 - f)100 = 10f$	Find the cross products.
	$1722 - 100f = 10f$	Distributive Property
	$1722 - 100f + 100f = 10f + 100f$	Add $100f$ to each side.
	$1722 = 110f$	Simplify.
	$\frac{1722}{110} = \frac{110f}{110}$	Divide each side by 110.
	$15.65 \approx f$	Simplify.

There were approximately 15.65 million passengers in 2007.

Guided Practice

2. **TUITION** A recent percent of increase in tuition at Northwestern University, in Evanston, Illinois, was 5.4%. If the new cost is \$33,408 per year, find the original cost per year. **\$31,696.39**

2 Solve Problems

Two applications of percent of change are sales tax and discounts. Sales tax is an example of a percent of increase. Discount is an example of a percent of decrease.

Example 3 Sales Tax

SHOPPING **Marta is purchasing wire and beads to make jewelry. Her merchandise is \$28.62 before tax. If the tax is 7.25% of the total sales, what is the final cost?**

Step 1 Find the tax.

The tax is 7.25% of the price of the merchandise.

7.25% of \$28.62 = 0.0725 × 28.62	7.25% = 0.0725
= 2.07495	Use a calculator.

Step 2 Find the cost with tax.

Round \$2.07495 to \$2.07 since tax is always rounded to the nearest cent. Add this amount to the original price: \$28.62 + \$2.07 = \$30.69.

The total cost of Marta's jewelry supplies is \$30.69.

Guided Practice

3. **SHOPPING** A new DVD costs \$24.99. If the sales tax is 6.85%, what is the total cost? **\$26.70**

To find a discounted amount, you will follow similar steps to those for sales tax.

Lloyd Sutton/Masterfile

Focus on Mathematical Content

Changing Percents to Decimals When changing a percent to a decimal, move the decimal point two places to the left and drop the percent sign.

Tips for New Teachers

Percent of Change Tell students to remember that the percent of change is relative to the original amount. So, the change in value is divided by the original amount.

Example 4 Discounts

DISCOUNT **Since Tyrell has earned good grades in school, he qualifies for the Good Student Discount on his car insurance. His monthly payment without the discount is $85. If the discount is 20%, what will he pay each month?**

Step 1 Find the discount.

The discount is 20% of the original payment.

20% of $85 = 0.20 × 85 — 20% = 0.20

= 17 — Use a calculator.

Step 2 Find the cost after discount.

Subtract $17 from the original payment: $85 − $17 = $68.

With the Good Student Discount, Tyrell will pay $68 per month.

StudyTip

Regularity When translating a problem from word sentences to math sentences, the word "is" translates to =, and the word "of" translates to ×.

GuidedPractice

4. **SALES** A picture frame originally priced at $14.89 is on sale for 40% off. What is the discounted price? **$8.93**

Check Your Understanding

= Step-by-Step Solutions begin on page R13.

Example 1 **State whether each percent of change is a percent of *increase* or a percent of *decrease*. Then find the percent of change. Round to the nearest whole percent.**

1. original: 78
new: 125 **inc.;60%**

2. original: 41
new: 24 **dec.;41%**

3. original: 6 candles
new: 8 candles **inc.;33%**

4. original: 35 computers
new: 32 computers **dec.;9%**

Example 2

5. **GEOGRAPHY** The distance from Phoenix to Tucson is 120 miles. The distance from Phoenix to Flagstaff is about 21.7% longer. To the nearest mile, what is the distance from Phoenix to Flagstaff? **146 mi**

Example 3 **Find the total price of each item.**

6. dress: $22.50
sales tax: 7.5% **$24.19**

7. video game: $35.99
sales tax: 6.75% **$38.42**

8. **PROM** A limo costs $85 to rent for 3 hours plus a 7% sales tax. What is the total cost to rent a limo for 6 hours? **$181.90**

9. **GAMES** A computer game costs $49.95 plus a 6.25% sales tax. What is the total cost of the game? **$53.07**

Example 4 **Find the discounted price of each item.**

10. guitar: $95.00
discount: 15% **$80.75**

11. DVD: $22.95
discount: 25% **$17.21**

12. **SKATEBOARD** A skateboard costs $99.99. If you have a coupon for 20% off, how much will you save? **$20**

13. **MODELING** Tickets to the county fair are $8 for an adult and $5 for a child. If you have a 15% discount card, how much will 2 adult tickets and 2 child tickets cost? **$22.10**

DifferentiatedInstruction AL OL

If students have difficulty recognizing patterns that involve percents,

Then pair these students with those who are able to recognize and work with patterns. After they complete Exercise 44, have them use the table in the exercise as a model to explore patterns using other numbers, such as 1% of 200 is 2, and so on.

2 Solve Problems

Example 3 shows how to solve real-world problems that deal with a percent of increase, such as sales tax. **Example 4** shows how to solve real-world problems that deal with a percent of decrease, such as a discounted price.

Teach with Tech

Web Search Ask students to research populations of different cities and states from the U.S. Census Bureau Web site. Have them calculate the percent of change in population over different time periods.

Additional Examples

3 **SALES TAX** A meal for two at a restaurant costs $32.75. If the sales tax is 5%, what is the total price of the meal? $34.39

4 **DISCOUNT** A dog toy is on sale for 20% off the original price. If the original price of the toy is $3.80, what is the discounted price? $3.04

3 Practice

Formative Assessment

Use Exercises 1–13 to check for understanding.

Use the chart at the bottom of the next page to customize assignments for your students.

Teaching the Process Standards

Regularity Mathematically proficient students look both for general methods and for shortcuts. Point out to students that key words in verbal problems are shortcuts to writing expressions and equations.

Modeling Mathematically proficient students are able to identify important quantities in a practical situation. In Exercise 13, encourage students to begin by identifying the quantities they know.

Teaching the Process Standards

Modeling Mathematically proficient students apply the mathematics they know to solve problems arising in everyday life. In Exercise 41, encourage students to estimate the discounts before doing the calculations. Making estimates like these is often useful in making consumer decisions.

Tools Mathematically proficient students consider the available tools when solving a mathematical problem. In Exercise 43, point out to students that a spreadsheet would be an excellent tool for calculating all of the percents of increase quickly.

WatchOut!

Error Analysis In Exercise 47, the only difference between Maddie's and Xavier's work is the number in the denominator of the first ratio in the proportion. Maddie has 28, which is the new amount in the problem, and Xavier has 25, which is the original amount in the problem. Suggest that students review Examples 1 and 2. Remind them that the ratio to use is the amount of change to the original amount.

Additional Answers

44c. 16% of 31.25 is 5.
6.25% of 320 is 20.
400% of 5 is 20.

48. Sometimes; the percent of change can be greater than 100%. If the original amount was 20 and the new amount was 40, then the percent of change is 100%

49. Sample answer: Retail stores use percents of decrease when the prices of items are discounted in a sale, salary increases are usually given as a percent of increase. To find the percent of change subtract the original from the new amount. Then write a proportion, comparing the change to the original amount. The answer should be written as a percent.

Practice and Problem Solving

Extra Practice is on page R2.

Example 1

State whether each percent of change is a percent of *increase* or a percent of *decrease*. Then find the percent of change. Round to the nearest whole percent.

14. original: 35
new: 40 **inc.; 14%**

15. original: 16
new: 10 **dec.; 38%**

16. original: 27
new: 73 **inc.; 170%**

17. original: 92
new: 21 **dec.; 77%**

18. original: 21.2 grams
new: 10.8 grams **dec.; 49%**

19. original: 11 feet
new: 25 feet **inc.; 127%**

20. original: $68
new: $76 **inc.; 12%**

21. original: 21 hours
new: 40 hours **inc.; 90%**

Example 2

22. GASOLINE The average cost of regular gasoline in North Carolina increased by 73% from 2006 to 2007. If the average cost of a gallon of gas in 2006 was $2.069, what was the average cost in 2007? Round to the nearest cent. **$3.58**

23. CARS Beng is shopping for a car. The cost of a new car is $15,500. This is 25% greater than the cost of a used car. What is the cost of the used car? **$12,400**

Example 3

Find the total price of each item.

24. messenger bag: $28.00
tax: 7.25% **$30.03**

25. software: $45.00
tax: 5.5% **$47.48**

26. vase: $5.50
tax: 6.25% **$5.84**

27. book: $25.95
tax: 5.25% **$27.31**

28. magazine: $3.50
tax: 5.75% **$3.70**

29. pillow: $9.99
tax: 6.75% **$10.66**

Example 4

Find the discounted price of each item.

30. computer: $1099.00
discount: 25% **$824.25**

31. CD player: $89.99
discount: 15% **$76.49**

32. athletic shoes: $59.99
discount: 40% **$35.99**

33. jeans: $24.50
discount: 33% **$16.42**

34. jacket: $125.00
discount: 25% **$93.75**

35. belt: $14.99
discount: 20% **$11.99**

B **Find the final price of each item.**

36. sweater: $14.99
discount: 12%
tax: 6.25% **$14.02**

37. printer: $60.00
discount: 25%
tax: 6.75% **$48.04**

38. board game: $25.00
discount: 15%
tax: 7.5% **$22.84**

39. CONSUMER PRICE INDEX An *index* measures the percent change of a value from a base year. An index of 115 means that there was a 15% increase from the base year. In 2000, the consumer price index of dairy products was 160.7. In 2007, it was 194.0. Determine the percent of change. **about 20.7% increase**

40. FINANCIAL LITERACY The current price of each share of a technology company is $135. If this represents a 16.2% increase over the past year, what was the price per share a year ago? **$116.18**

41. MODELING A group of girls are shopping for dresses to wear to the spring dance. One finds a dress priced $75 with a 20% discount. A second girl finds a dress priced $85 with a 30% discount.

a. Find the amount of discount for each dress. **first girl's dress = $15; second girl's dress = $25.50**

b. Which girl is getting the better price for the dress? **the second girl by $0.50**

42. RECREATIONAL SPORTS In 1995, there were 73,567 youth softball teams. By 2007, there were 86,049. Determine the percent of increase. **about 17%**

Differentiated Homework Options

Level	Assignment	Two-Day Option	
AL Basic	14–35, 45–47, 49–73	15–35 odd, 50–53	14–34 even, 45–47, 49, 54–73
OL Core	15–35 odd, 36–47, 49–73	14–35, 50–53	36–47, 49, 54–73
BL Advanced	36–67, (optional: 68–73)		

43. **TOOLS** Which grocery item had the greatest percent increase in cost from 2000 to 2007? **milk**

Average Retail Prices of Selected Grocery Items

Grocery Item	Cost in 2000 ($ per pound)	Cost in 2007 ($ per pound)
milk (gallon)	2.79	3.87
turkey (whole)	0.99	1.01
chicken (whole)	1.08	1.17
ground beef	1.63	2.23
apples	0.82	1.12
iceberg lettuce	0.85	0.95
peanut butter	1.96	1.88

Source: Statistical Abstract of the United States

44. **MULTIPLE REPRESENTATIONS** In this problem, you will explore patterns in percentages.

a. **Tabular** Copy and complete the following table.

1% of	500	is 5.	100% of	20	is 20.	25	% of 80 is 20.
2% of	250	is 5.	50% of	40	is 20.	50	% of 40 is 20.
4% of	125	is 5.	25% of	80	is 20.	100	% of 20 is 20.
8% of	62.5	is 5.	12.5% of	160	is 20.	200	% of 10 is 20.

b. **Verbal** Describe the patterns in the second and fifth columns.

c. **Analytical** Use the patterns to write the fifth row of the table. **See margin.**

44b. Sample answer: In the second column, as the percent doubles the amount is cut in half. In the fifth column, as the percent is cut in half the amount doubles.

H.O.T. Problems Use Higher-Order Thinking Skills

C 45. **OPEN ENDED** Write a real-world problem to find the total price of an item including sales tax. **Sample answer: A CD is on sale for $9.99. If tax is 6.5%, what will the CD cost?**

46. **REASONING** If you have 75% of a number n, what percent of decrease is it from the number n? If you have 40% of a number a, what percent of decrease do you have from the number a? What pattern do you notice? Is this always true?

47. **ERROR ANALYSIS** Maddie and Xavier are solving for the percent change if the original amount was $25 and the new amount is $28. Is either of them correct? Explain your reasoning. **Xavier; Maddie divided by the new amount instead of the original amount.**

46. 25%;60%; The percentage of the number and the decrease add to 100%; Yes

Maddie	Xavier
$\frac{3}{28} = \frac{r}{100}$	$\frac{3}{25} = \frac{r}{100}$
$3(100) = 28r$	$3(100) = 25r$
$300 = 28r$	$300 = 25r$
$10.7 = r$	$12 = r$

48. **CHALLENGE** Determine whether the following statement is *sometimes*, *always*, or *never* true. *The percent of change is less than 100%.* **See margin.**

49. **WRITING IN MATH** When is percent of change used in the real world? Explain how to find a percent of change between two values. **See margin.**

Multiple Representations

In Exercise 44, students use a table of values and verbal analysis to show patterns of percentages.

Study Guide and Intervention

AL OL ELL

NAME ______ DATE ______ PERIOD ______

2-7 Study Guide and Intervention

Percent of Change

Percent of Change When an increase or decrease in an amount is expressed as a percent, the percent is called the **percent of change**. If the new number is greater than the original number, the percent of change is a **percent of increase**. If the new number is less than the original number, the percent of change is the **percent of decrease.**

Example 1 **Find the percent of increase.**
original: 48
new: 60

First, subtract to find the amount of increase. The amount of increase is $60 - 48 = 12$.
Then find the percent of increase by using the original number, 48, as the base.

$\frac{12}{48} = \frac{r}{100}$ Percent proportion
$12(100) = 48(r)$ Cross products
$1200 = 48r$ Simplify.
$\frac{1200}{48} = \frac{48r}{48}$ Divide each side by 48.
$25 = r$ Simplify.

The percent of increase is 25%.

Example 2 **Find the percent of decrease.**
original: 30
new: 22

First, subtract to find the amount of decrease. The amount of decrease is $30 - 22 = 8$.
Then find the percent of decrease by using the original number, 30, as the base.

$\frac{8}{30} = \frac{r}{100}$ Percent proportion
$8(100) = 30(r)$ Cross products
$800 = 30r$ Simplify.
$\frac{800}{30} = \frac{30r}{30}$ Divide each side by 30.
$26\frac{2}{3} = r$ Simplify.

The percent of decrease is $26\frac{2}{3}$%, or about 27%.

Exercises

State whether each percent of change is a percent of *increase* or a percent of *decrease*. Then find each percent of change. Round to the nearest whole percent.

1. original: 50 new: 80
2. original: 90 new: 100
3. original: 45 new: 20
4. original: 77.5 new: 62
5. original: 140 new: 150
6. original: 135 new: 90
7. original: 120 new: 180
8. original: 90 new: 270
9. original: 27.5 new: 25
10. original: 84 new: 98
11. original: 12.5 new: 10
12. original: 250 new: 500

Practice

AL OL BL ELL

NAME ______ DATE ______ PERIOD ______

2-7 Practice

Percent of Change

State whether each percent of change is a percent of *increase* or a percent of *decrease*. Then find each percent of change. Round to the nearest whole percent.

1. original: 18 new: 10
2. original: 140 new: 160
3. original: 200 new: 320
4. original: 10 new: 25
5. original: 76 new: 60
6. original: 128 new: 120
7. original: 15 new: 35.5
8. original: 98.6 new: 64
9. original: 58.8 new: 65.7

Find the total price of each item.

10. concrete blocks: $95.00 tax: 6%
11. crib: $240.00 tax: 6.5%
12. jacket: $125.00 tax: 5.5%
13. class ring: $325.00 tax: 6%
14. blanket: $24.99 tax: 7%
15. kite: $18.90 tax: 5%

Find the discounted price of each item.

16. dry cleaning: $25.00 discount: 15%
17. computer game: $49.99 discount: 25%
18. luggage: $185.00 discount: 30%
19. stationery: $12.95 discount: 10%
20. prescription glasses: $149 discount: 20%
21. pair of shorts: $24.99 discount: 45%

Find the final price of each item.

22. television: $375.00 discount: 25% tax: 6%
23. DVD player: $269.00 discount: 20% tax: 7%
24. printer: $255.00 discount: 30% tax: 5.5%

25. **INVESTMENTS** The price per share of a stock decreased from $90 per share to $36 per share. By what percent did the price of the stock decrease?

26. **HEATING COSTS** Customers of a utility company received notices in their monthly bills that heating costs for the average customer had increased 125% over last year because of an unusually severe winter. In January of last year, the Garcia's paid $120 for heating. What should they expect to pay this January if their bill increased by 125%?

Lesson 2-7

Word Problem Practice

AL OL BL ELL

NAME ______ DATE ______ PERIOD ______

2-7 Word Problem Practice

Percent of Change

1. **SPORTS** A regulation girls' fast pitch softball diamond has bases that are 60 feet apart. A regulation professional baseball diamond has bases that are 50% farther apart. Label the distance between the bases on the regulation baseball diamond diagram.

2. **SALES TAX** Olivia purchases a DVD movie priced at $21.99. The sales tax is 6.5%. What is the total price of the movie, including tax?

3. **EDUCATION** The ACT is a college entrance exam taken by high school students. The maximum score that can be earned is 36. The average score in the United States was 21.2 during a recent year. The average score for Vermont students that year was 7.5% higher than the national average. What was the average ACT score for Vermont students? Round your answer to the nearest tenth.

4. **CARS** Mr. Thompson plans to purchase a used car priced at $8400. He will receive a 15% employee discount and then will have to pay a 5.5% sales tax. What will be the final price of the car?

5. **MUSIC** The table below shows the total number of CDs, downloaded singles, and music videos sold in 2004, 2006, and 2008.

Sales of Recorded Music and Music Videos (millions of units)

Format	2004	2006	2008
CD	767.0	614.9	368.4
Downloaded	139.4	586.4	1042.7
Video	32.8	23.1	20.8

Source: Recording Industry Association of America

a. Find the percent of change in the number of units sold between 2004 and 2006 and between 2006 and 2008 for each format. Round your answers to the nearest tenth.

b. Tell whether each percent of change in part **a** is a percent of increase or a percent of decrease.

c. Did these trends change from 2004 to 2008? Explain.

Enrichment

OL BL

NAME ______ DATE ______ PERIOD ______

2-7 Enrichment

Using Percent

Use what you have learned about percent to solve each problem.

A TV movie had a "rating" of 15 and a 25 "share." The rating is the percentage of the nation's total TV households that were tuned in to this show. The share is the percentage of homes with TVs turned on that were tuned to the movie. How many TV households had their TVs turned off at this time?

To find out, let T = the number of TV households
and x = the number of TV households with the TV off.
Then $T - x$ = the number of TV households with the TV on.
Since $0.15T$ and $0.25(T - x)$ both represent the number of households tuned to the movie,

$0.15T = 0.25(T - x)$
$0.15T = 0.25T - 0.25x$.
Solve for x. $0.25x = 0.10T$
$x = \frac{0.10T}{0.25}$ or $0.40T$

Forty percent of the TV households had their TVs off when the movie was aired.

Answer each question.

Lesson 2-7

4 Assess

Yesterday's News Have students write how yesterday's lesson on ratios and proportions has helped them with today's new material.

Formative Assessment

Check for student understanding of Lessons 2-6 and 2-7.

Quiz 3, p. 64

Additional Answers

68. Sample answer: A number *d* minus fourteen is five.
69. Sample answer: Six more than twice a number *f* equals nineteen.
70. Sample answer: Twelve less than *y* is the same as eight more than *y*.
71. Sample answer: The product of three and a number *a* when added to 5 is equal to the difference of 27 and two times *a*.
72. Sample answer: Negative six times a number *c* squared minus four times *c* is the same as twenty-five.
73. Sample answer: The fourth power of a number *d* increased by sixty-four is three times that number *d* to the third power plus seventy-seven.

Standardized Test Practice

50. GEOMETRY The rectangle has a perimeter of P centimeters. Which equation could be used to find the length ℓ of the rectangle? **D**

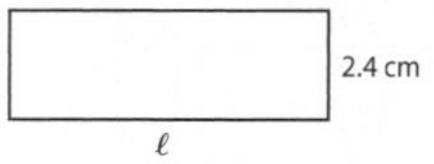

A $P = 2.4\ell$ C $P = 2.4 + 2\ell$
B $P = 4.8 + \ell$ D $P = 4.8 + 2\ell$

51. SHORT RESPONSE Henry is painting a room with four walls that are 12 feet by 14 feet. A gallon of paint costs \$18 and covers 350 square feet. If he uses two coats of paint, how much will it cost him to paint the room? **\$72**

52. The number of students at Franklin High School increased from 840 to 910 over a 5-year period. What was the percent of increase? **F**

F 8.3%
G 14.0%
H 18.5%
J 92.3%

53. PROBABILITY Two dice are rolled. What is the probability that the sum is 10? **C**

A $\frac{1}{3}$ B $\frac{1}{6}$ C $\frac{1}{12}$ D $\frac{1}{36}$

Spiral Review

54. TRAVEL The Chan's minivan requires 5 gallons of gasoline to travel 120 miles. How many gallons of gasoline will they need to travel 360 miles? (Lesson 2-6) **15 gal**

Evaluate each expression if $x = -2$, $y = 6$, and $z = 4$. (Lesson 2-5)

55. $|3 - x| + 7$ **12**
56. $12 - |z + 9|$ **−1**
57. $|y + x| - z + 4$ **4**

Solve each equation. Round to the nearest hundredth. Check your solution. (Lesson 2-4)

58. $1.03p - 4 = -2.15p + 8.72$ **4**
59. $18 - 3.8t = 7.36 - 1.9t$ **5.6**
60. $5.4w + 8.2 = 9.8w - 2.8$ **2.5**
61. $2[d + 3(d - 1)] = 18$ **3**

Solve each equation. Check your solution. (Lesson 2-3)

62. $5n + 6 = -4$ **−2**
63. $-11 = 7 + 3c$ **−6**
64. $15 = 4a - 5$ **5**
65. $-14 + 7g = -63$ **−7**

66. RIVERS The Congo River in Africa is 2900 miles long. That is 310 miles longer than the Niger River, which is also in Africa. (Lesson 2-2)

a. Write an equation you could use to find the length of the Niger River. **$n + 310 = 2900$**
b. What is the length of the Niger River? **2590 mi**

67. FOOD Cameron purchased x pounds of apples for \$0.99 per pound and y pounds of oranges for \$1.29 per pound. Write an algebraic expression that represents the cost of the purchase. (Lesson 1-1) **$0.99x + 1.29y$**

Skills Review

Translate each equation into a sentence. **68–73. See margin.**

68. $d - 14 = 5$
69. $2f + 6 = 19$
70. $y - 12 = y + 8$
71. $3a + 5 = 27 - 2a$
72. $-6c^2 - 4c = 25$
73. $d^4 + 64 = 3d^3 + 77$

Differentiated Instruction BL

Extension A DVD with an original price of \$10 is in the 20% off bin. If another reduction of 50% is taken at the cash register, is the total reduction 70%? If not, find the actual reduction. No, the reduction is not 70%, it is an actual reduction of 60% off.

124 | Lesson 2-7 | Percent of Change

EXTEND 2-7 Algebra Lab: Percentiles

A **percentile** is a measure that is often used to report test data, such as standardized test scores. It tells us what percent of the total scores were below a given score.

- Percentiles measure rank from the bottom.
- There is no 0 percentile rank. The lowest score is at the 1st percentile.
- There is no 100th percentile rank. The highest score is at the 99th percentile.

Activity

A talent show was held for the twenty finalists in the Teen Idol contest. Each performer received a score from 0 through 30 with 30 being the highest. What is Victor's percentile rank?

Name	Score	Name	Score
Arnold	17	Ishi	27
Benito	9	James	20
Brooke	25	Kat	16
Carmen	21	Malik	10
Daniel	14	Natalie	26
Delia	29	Pearl	4
Fernando	15	Twyla	6
Heather	12	Victor	28
Horatio	5	Warren	22
Ingrid	11	Yolanda	18

Step 1 Write one score on each of 20 slips of paper.

Step 2 Arrange the slips vertically from greatest to least score.

Step 3 Find Victor's percentile rank.

Victor had a score of 28. There are 18 scores below his score. To find his percentile rank, use the following formula.

$$\frac{\text{number of scores below 28}}{\text{total number of scores}} \cdot 100 = \frac{18}{20} \cdot 100 \text{ or } 90$$

Victor scored at the 90th percentile in the contest.

Analyze the Results

3. If you estimate the percentiles, Arnold is at the 50th percentile with a score of 17, Ingrid is at the 25th percentile with a score of 11, and Brooke is at the 75th percentile with a score of 25. The median of the data is 16.5, and the values for the lower and upper quartiles are 10.5 and 23.5 respectively.

1. Find the median, lower quartile, and upper quartile of the scores. **16.5, 10.5, 23.5**
2. Which performer was at the 50th percentile? the 25th percentile? the 75th percentile? **Arnold, Ingrid, Brooke**
3. Compare and contrast the values for the median, lower quartile, and upper quartile and the scores for the 25th, 50th, and 75th percentiles.
4. While Victor scored at the 90th percentile, what percent of the 30 possible points did he score? **about 93%**
5. **ARGUMENTS** Compare and contrast the percentile rank and the percent score. **The percentile rank tells where a score ranks among the rest of the scores. The percent is a comparison of a score to the highest score possible.**
6. Are there any outliers in the data that could alter the results of our computations? **no**
7. **Deciles** are values that divide a set of data into ten equal-sized parts. The 1st decile contains data up to but not including the 10th percentile; the 2nd decile contains data from the 10th percentile up to but not including the 20th percentile, and so on.
   a. Which contestants' scores fall in the 6th decile? **Arnold and Yolanda**
   b. In which decile are Heather and Daniel? **4th decile**

1 Focus

Objective Find the percentile rank of a data item in a set of scores.

Materials for Each Student

- paper (1 sheet)
- scissors

Teaching Tip

You may want to discuss the differences between percent and percentile. For example, a score at the 65th percentile means that 65% of the scores are either the same as the score at the 65th percentile or less than the score at that rank. It does not mean that the contestant scored 65% of the possible points.

2 Teach

Working in Cooperative Groups

Have students work in groups of three or four, mixing abilities, to complete Steps 1–3 in the Activity and Exercises 1–3.

Ask:

- What is the purpose of arranging the scores vertically from greatest to least score? to see the number of scores at or below a particular score
- What is the least score? 4 At what percentile rank is the least score? 1st percentile What is the score at the 99th percentile? 29

Teaching Tip

Review how to find the median, lower quartile, and upper quartile of a set of numbers for Exercise 1.

Practice Have students complete Exercises 1–6.

3 Assess

Formative Assessment

Use Exercise 5 to assess whether students understand the difference between percentile and percent.

From Concrete to Abstract

Exercise 6 asks students to consider factors that might affect the percentile ranking of a set of scores. Exercise 7 extends the concept to deciles.

Teaching the Process Standards

Arguments Mathematically proficient students understand and use definitions. In Exercise 5, ask students to identify similarities and differences between percentile rank and the percent score.

1 Focus

VerticalAlignment

Before Lesson 2-8 Solve equations with variables on each side.

Lesson 2-8 Solve equations for given variables.
Use formulas to solve real-world problems.

After Lesson 2-8 Solve systems of equations.

2 Teach

Scaffolding Questions

Have students read the **Why?** section of the lesson.

Ask:

- In the formula $A = P(1 + r)^t$, what operation do you perform to find A? Multiply P times $(1 + r)^t$.
- Suppose you know the quantities for A and r, but not P. How would you solve for P? Divide both sides of the equation by $(1 + r)^t$.
- Why solve a formula for a specific variable before you substitute quantities for the known variables? It makes it easier to solve the formula since you only need to perform operations on one side of the equation.

LESSON 2-8 Literal Equations and Dimensional Analysis

Then

- You solved equations with variables on each side.

Now

1. Solve equations for given variables.
2. Use formulas to solve real-world problems.

Why?

- Each year, more people use credit cards to make everyday purchases. If the entire balance is not paid by the due date, compound interest is applied. The formula for computing the balance of an account with compound interest added annually is $A = P(1 + r)^t$.
  - A represents the amount of money in the account including the interest,
  - P is the amount in the account before interest is added,
  - r is the interest rate written as a decimal,
  - t is the time in years.

NewVocabulary
literal equation
dimensional analysis
unit analysis

Content Standards
AI.L.11

Process Standards
PS.6

1 Solve for a Specific Variable

Some equations such as the one above contain more than one variable. At times, you will need to solve these equations for one of the variables.

Example 1 Solve for a Specific Variable

Solve $4m - 3n = 8$ for m.

$4m - 3n = 8$	Original equation
$4m - 3n + 3n = 8 + 3n$	Add $3n$ to each side.
$4m = 8 + 3n$	Simplify.
$\frac{4m}{4} = \frac{8 + 3n}{4}$	Divide each side by 4.
$m = \frac{8}{4} + \frac{3}{4}n$	Simplify.
$m = 2 + \frac{3}{4}n$	Simplify.

GuidedPractice

Solve each equation for the variable indicated.

1A. $15 = 3n + 6p$, for n **$5 - 2p$**

1B. $\frac{k - 2}{5} = 11j$, for k **$55j + 2$**

1C. $28 = t(r + 4)$, for t **$\frac{28}{r + 4}$**

1D. $a(q - 8) = 23$, for q **$\frac{23}{a} + 8$**

Sometimes we need to solve equations for a variable that is on both sides of the equation. When this happens, you must get all terms with that variable onto one side of the equation. It is then helpful to use the Distributive Property to isolate the variable for which you are solving.

Lesson 2-8 Resources

Resource	Approaching Level AL	On Level OL	Beyond Level BL	English Learners ELL
Teacher Edition	▪ Differentiated Instruction, p. 127	▪ Differentiated Instruction, p. 127	▪ Differentiated Instruction, p. 131	
Chapter Resource Masters	▪ Study Guide and Intervention, pp. 49–50 ▪ Skills Practice, p. 51 ▪ Practice, p. 52 ▪ Word Problem Practice, p. 53	▪ Study Guide and Intervention, pp. 49–50 ▪ Skills Practice, p. 51 ▪ Practice, p. 52 ▪ Word Problem Practice, p. 53 ▪ Enrichment, p. 54	▪ Practice, p. 52 ▪ Word Problem Practice, p. 53 ▪ Enrichment, p. 54	▪ Study Guide and Intervention, pp. 49–50 ▪ Skills Practice, p. 51 ▪ Practice, p. 52 ▪ Word Problem Practice, p. 53
Other	▪ 5-Minute Check 2-8 ▪ Study Notebook	▪ 5-Minute Check 2-8 ▪ Study Notebook	▪ 5-Minute Check 2-8 ▪ Study Notebook	▪ 5-Minute Check 2-8 ▪ Study Notebook

StudyTip

Solving for a Specific Variable When an equation has more than one variable, it can be helpful to highlight the variable for which you are solving on your paper.

Example 2 Solve for a Specific Variable

Solve $3x - 2y = xz + 5$ for x.

$3x - 2y = xz + 5$	Original equation
$3x - 2y + 2y = xz + 5 + 2y$	Add $2y$ to each side.
$3x - xz = xz - xz + 5 + 2y$	Subtract xz from each side.
$3x - xz = 5 + 2y$	Simplify.
$x(3 - z) = 5 + 2y$	Distributive Property
$\frac{x(3 - z)}{3 - z} = \frac{5 + 2y}{3 - z}$	Divide each side by $3 - z$.
$x = \frac{5 + 2y}{3 - z}$	Simplify.

Since division by 0 is undefined, $3 - z \neq 0$ so $z \neq 3$.

GuidedPractice

Solve each equation for the variable indicated.

2A. $d + 5c = 3d - 1$, for d $\frac{5c + 1}{2}$

2B. $6q - 18 = qr + t$, for q $\frac{18 + t}{6 - r}$

2 Use Formulas

An equation that involves several variables is called a formula or **literal equation**. To solve a literal equation, apply the process of solving for a specific variable.

Real-WorldLink

The largest yo-yo in the world is 32.7 feet in circumference. It was launched by crane from a height of 189 feet.

Source: *Guinness Book of World Records*

Real-World Example 3 Use Literal Equations

YO-YOS Use the information about the largest yo-yo at the left. The formula for the circumference of a circle is $C = 2\pi r$, where C represents circumference and r represents radius.

a. Solve the formula for r.

$C = 2\pi r$	Formula for circumference
$\frac{C}{2\pi} = \frac{2\pi r}{2\pi}$	Divide each side by 2π.
$\frac{C}{2\pi} = r$	Simplify.

b. Find the radius of the yo-yo.

$\frac{C}{2\pi} = r$	Formula for radius
$\frac{32.7}{2\pi} = r$	$C = 32.7$
$5.2 \approx r$	Use a calculator.

The yo-yo has a radius of about 5.2 feet.

GuidedPractice

3. GEOMETRY The formula for the volume of a rectangular prism is $V = \ell wh$, where ℓ is the length, w is the width, and h is the height.

A. Solve the formula for w. $\frac{V}{\ell h} = w$

B. Find the width of a rectangular prism that has a volume of 79.04 cubic centimeters, a length of 5.2 centimeters, and a height of 4 centimeters. **3.8 cm**

DifferentiatedInstruction AL OL

If students are confused by equations with more than one variable and with variables on both sides of the equation, such as Example 2,

Then have students work in pairs to analyze, discuss, and write out the steps necessary for solving the equation. They can then refer to and mark off the steps as they work through the solution.

1 Solve for a Specific Variable

Example 1 shows how to solve an equation with more than one variable for a specific variable. **Example 2** shows how the Distributive Property can be used to isolate the variable for which you are solving an equation or formula.

Formative Assessment

Use the Guided Practice exercises after each Example to determine students' understanding of concepts.

Additional Examples

1 Solve $5b + 12c = 9$ for b. $b = \frac{9 - 12c}{5}$

2 Solve $7x - 2z = 4 - xy$ for x. $x = \frac{4 + 2z}{7 + y}$

Additional Examples also in Interactive Classroom PowerPoint® Presentations

IWB Interactive White Board READY

Teach with Tech

Interactive Whiteboard Give students an equation that has several variables. Break the class into groups, and have each group solve the equation for a different variable. Then have one member from each group present and explain their work to the rest of the class on the board.

2 Use Formulas

Example 3 shows how to solve for a specific variable in a formula when solving a real-world problem. **Example 4** shows how to use dimensional analysis to convert units in a real-world problem.

Additional Examples

3 FUEL ECONOMY A car's fuel economy E (miles per gallon) is given by the formula $E = \frac{m}{g}$, where m is the number of miles driven and g is the number of gallons of fuel used.

a. Solve the formula for m. $m = Eg$

b. If Quanah's car has an average fuel consumption of 30 miles per gallon and she used 9.5 gallons, how far did she drive? 285 mi

4 CHIMPANZEES The average weight of the chimpanzees at a zoo is 52 kilograms. If 1 gram ≈ 0.0353 ounce, use dimensional analysis to find the average weight of the chimpanzees in pounds. (**Hint:** 1 lb = 16 oz) ≈115 lb

WatchOut!

Preventing Errors Encourage students to write the units for values they are substituting into an equation. Writing the units will help them to determine the reasonableness of an answer. If the problem asks for "miles" and they have "hours," they will know something is wrong.

3 Practice

Formative Assessment

Use Exercises 1–7 to check for understanding.

Use the chart at the bottom of the next page to customize assignments for your students.

When using formulas, you may want to use dimensional analysis. **Dimensional analysis** or **unit analysis** is the process of carrying units throughout a computation.

Example 4 Use Dimensional Analysis

RUNNING A 10K run is 10 kilometers long. If 1 meter = 1.094 yards, use dimensional analysis to find the length of the race in miles. (*Hint*: 1 mi = 1760 yd)

Since the given conversion relates meters to yards, first convert 10 kilometers to meters. Then multiply by the conversion factor such that the unit meters are divided out. To convert from yards to miles, multiply by $\frac{1\text{ mi}}{1760\text{ yd}}$.

length of run	×	kilometers to meters	×	meters to yards	×	yards to miles
10 km	×	$\frac{1000\text{ m}}{1\text{ km}}$	×	$\frac{1.094\text{ yd}}{1\text{ m}}$	×	$\frac{1\text{ mi}}{1760\text{ yd}}$

Notice how the units cancel, leaving the unit to which you are converting.

$$10\ \cancel{\text{km}} \times \frac{1000\ \cancel{\text{m}}}{1\ \cancel{\text{km}}} \times \frac{1.094\ \cancel{\text{yd}}}{1\ \cancel{\text{m}}} \times \frac{1\text{ mi}}{1760\ \cancel{\text{yd}}} = \frac{10{,}940\text{ mi}}{1760}$$
$$\approx 6.2\text{ mi}$$

A 10K race is approximately 6.2 miles.

StudyTip

Precision As you plan your method of solution, think about what the question is asking and what units of measure will apply to the solution.

GuidedPractice

4. A car travels a distance of 100 feet in about 2.8 seconds. What is the velocity of the car in miles per hour? Round to the nearest whole number. **24 mph**

Check Your Understanding

◯ = Step-by-Step Solutions begin on page R13.

Examples 1–2 **Solve each equation or formula for the variable indicated.**

1. $5a + c = -8a$, for a $a = -\frac{c}{13}$

2. $7h + f = 2h + g$, for g $5h + f = g$

3. $\frac{k + m}{-7} = n$, for k $k = -7n - m$

4. $q = p(r + s)$, for p $p = \frac{q}{r + s}$

Example 3

5. PACKAGING A soap company wants to use a cylindrical container to hold their new liquid soap.

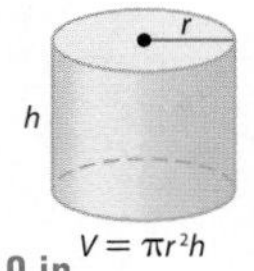

a. Solve the formula for h. $h = \frac{V}{\pi r^2}$

b. What is the height of a container if the volume is 56.52 cubic inches and the radius is 1.5 inches? Round to the nearest tenth. **8.0 in.**

Example 4

6. SHOPPING Scott found a rare video game on an online auction site priced at 35 Australian dollars. If the exchange rate is \$1 U.S. = \$1.24 Australian, find the cost of the game in United States dollars. Round to the nearest cent. **\$28.23**

7. PRECISION A fisheye lens has a minimum focus range of 13.5 centimeters. If 1 centimeter is equal in length to about 0.39 inch, what is the minimum focus range of the lens in feet? **about 0.43875 ft**

Focus on Mathematical Content

Using Formulas Many real-world problems require the use of formulas. Solving a formula for a specific variable may help to solve the problem.

Teaching the Process Standards

Precision Mathematically proficient students are careful about specifying units of measure. Encourage students to include the unit of measure in each numerator and denominator.

128 | Lesson 2-8 | Literal Equations and Dimensional Analysis

Practice and Problem Solving

Extra Practice is on page R2.

Examples 1–2 **Solve each equation or formula for the variable indicated.**

8. $u = vw + z$, for v $\quad v = \frac{u - z}{w}$

9. $x = b - cd$, for c $\quad c = \frac{x - b}{-d}$

10. $fg - 9h = 10j$, for g $\quad g = \frac{10j + 9h}{f}$

11. $10m - p = -n$, for m $\quad m = \frac{-n + p}{10}$

12. $r = \frac{2}{3}t + v$, for t $\quad t = \frac{3}{2}(r - v)$

13. $\frac{5}{9}v + w = z$, for v $\quad v = \frac{9}{5}(z - w)$

14. $\frac{10ac - x}{11} = -3$, for a $\quad a = \frac{-33 + x}{10c}$

15. $\frac{df + 10}{6} = g$, for f $\quad f = \frac{6g - 10}{d}$

Example 3

16. **FITNESS** The formula to compute a person's body mass index is $B = 703 \cdot \frac{w}{h^2}$. B represents the body mass index, w is the person's weight in pounds, and h represents the person's height in inches.
    a. Solve the formula for w. $\quad w = \frac{Bh^2}{703}$
    b. What is the weight to the nearest pound of a person who is 64 inches tall and has a body mass index of 21.45? **125 lb**

17. **PHYSICS** Acceleration is the measure of how fast a velocity is changing. The formula for acceleration is $a = \frac{v_f - v_i}{t}$. a represents the acceleration rate, v_f is the final velocity, v_i is the initial velocity, and t represents the time in seconds.
    a. Solve the formula for v_f. $\quad v_f = at + v_i$
    b. What is the final velocity of a runner who is accelerating at 2 feet per second squared for 3 seconds with an initial velocity of 4 feet per second? **10 ft/s²**

Example 4

18. **SWIMMING** If each lap in a pool is 100 meters long, how many laps equal one mile? Round to the nearest tenth. (*Hint*: 1 foot ≈ 0.3048 meter) **16.1 laps**

19. **PRECISION** How many liters of gasoline are needed to fill a 13.2-gallon tank? There are about 1.06 quarts per 1 liter. Round to the nearest tenth. **49.8 L**

Solve each equation or formula for the variable indicated.

B

20. $-14n + q = rt - 4n$, for n $\quad n = \frac{rt - q}{-10}$

21. $18t + 11v = w - 13t$, for t $\quad t = \frac{w - 11v}{31}$

22. $ax + z = aw - y$, for a $\quad a = \frac{-y - z}{x - w}$

23. $10c - f = -13 + cd$, for c $\quad c = \frac{-13 + f}{10 - d}$

Select an appropriate unit from the choices below and convert the rate to that unit.

ft/s	mph	mm/s	km/s

24. a car traveling at 36 ft/s **about 24.5 mph**

25. a snail moving at 3.6 m/h **1.0 mm/s**

26. a person walking at 3.4 mph **about 5.0 ft/s**

27. a satellite moving at 234,000 m/min **3.9 km/s**

28. **DANCING** The formula $P = \frac{1.2W}{H^2}$ represents the amount of pressure exerted on the floor by a ballroom dancer's heel. In this formula, P is the pressure in pounds per square inch, W is the weight of a person wearing the shoe in pounds, and H is the width of the heel of the shoe in inches.
    a. Solve the formula for W. $\quad W = \frac{H^2P}{1.2}$
    b. Find the weight of the dancer if the heel is 3 inches wide and the pressure exerted is 30 pounds per square inch. **225 lb**

Differentiated Homework Options

Level	Assignment	Two-Day Option	
AL Basic	8–19, 36–38, 40–61	9–19 odd, 41–44	8–18 even, 36–38, 40, 45–61
OL Core	9–19 odd, 20–34, 36–38, 40–61	8–19, 41–44	20–34, 36–38, 40, 45–61
BL Advanced	20–55, (optional: 56–61)		

Teaching the Process Standards

Precision In Exercises 7 and 19, point out to students that the final answers should be expressed in feet and liters respectively.

Study Guide and Intervention

AL OL ELL

NAME ______ DATE ______ PERIOD ______

2-8 Study Guide and Intervention

Literal Equations and Dimensional Analysis

Solve for Variables Sometimes you may want to solve an equation such as $V = \ell wh$ for one of its variables. For example, if you know the values of V, w, and h, then the equation $\ell = \frac{V}{wh}$ is more useful for finding the value of ℓ. If an equation that contains more than one variable is to be solved for a specific variable, use the properties of equality to isolate the specified variable on one side of the equation.

Example 1 Solve $2x - 4y = 8$, for y.

$$2x - 4y = 8$$
$$2x - 4y - 2x = 8 - 2x$$
$$-4y = 8 - 2x$$
$$\frac{-4y}{-4} = \frac{8 - 2x}{-4}$$
$$y = \frac{8 - 2x}{-4} \text{ or } \frac{2x - 8}{4}$$

The value of y is $\frac{2x - 8}{4}$.

Example 2 Solve $3m - n = km - 8$, for m.

$$3m - n = km - 8$$
$$3m - n - km = km - 8 - km$$
$$3m - n - km = -8$$
$$3m - n - km + n = -8 + n$$
$$3m - km = -8 + n$$
$$m(3 - k) = -8 + n$$
$$\frac{m(3 - k)}{3 - k} = \frac{-8 + n}{3 - k}$$
$$m = \frac{-8 + n}{3 - k} \text{ or } \frac{n - 8}{3 - k}$$

The value of m is $\frac{n - 8}{3 - k}$. Since division by 0 is undefined, $3 - k \neq 0$, or $k \neq 3$.

Lesson 2-8

Exercises

Solve each equation or formula for the variable indicated.

1. $ax - b = c$, for x
2. $15x + 1 = y$, for x
3. $(x + f) + 2 = j$, for x
4. $xy + w = 9$, for y
5. $x(4 - k) = p$, for k
6. $7x + 3y = m$, for y
7. $4(r + 3) = t$, for r
8. $2x + b = w$, for x
9. $x(1 + y) = z$, for x
10. $16w + 4x = y$, for x
11. $d = rt$, for r
12. $A = \frac{h(a + b)}{2}$, for h
13. $C = \frac{5}{9}(F - 32)$, for F
14. $P = 2\ell + 2w$, for w
15. $A = \ell w$, for ℓ

Practice

AL OL BL ELL

NAME ______ DATE ______ PERIOD ______

2-8 Practice

Literal Equations and Dimensional Analysis

Solve each equation or formula for the variable indicated.

1. $d = rt$, for r
2. $6w - y = 2z$, for w
3. $mx + 4y = 3t$, for x
4. $9s - 5g = -4u$, for s
5. $ab + 3c = 2x$, for b
6. $2p = kx - t$, for x
7. $\frac{2}{3}m + a = a + r$, for m
8. $\frac{2}{5}h + g = d$, for h
9. $\frac{2}{3}y + v = x$, for y
10. $\frac{3}{4}a - q = k$, for a
11. $\frac{rx + 9}{5} = h$, for x
12. $\frac{3b - 4}{2} = c$, for b
13. $2w - y = 7w - 2$, for w
14. $3\ell + y = 5 + 5\ell$, for ℓ

15. **ELECTRICITY** The formula for Ohm's Law is $E = IR$, where E represents voltage measured in volts, I represents current measured in amperes, and R represents resistance measured in ohms.
 a. Solve the formula for R.
 b. Suppose a current of 0.25 ampere flows through a resistor connected to a 12-volt battery. What is the resistance in the circuit?

16. **MOTION** In *uniform circular motion*, the speed v of a point on the edge of a spinning disk is $v = \frac{2\pi}{t}r$, where r is the radius of the disk and t is the time it takes the point to travel once around the circle.
 a. Solve the formula for r.
 b. Suppose a merry-go-round is spinning once every 3 seconds. If a point on the outside edge has a speed of 12.56 feet per second, what is the radius of the merry-go-round? (Use 3.14 for π.)

17. **HIGHWAYS** Interstate 90 is the longest interstate highway in the United States, connecting the cities of Seattle, Washington and Boston, Massachusetts. The interstate is 4,987,000 meters in length. If 1 mile = 1.609 kilometers, how many miles long is Interstate 90?

Word Problem Practice

AL OL BL ELL

NAME ______ DATE ______ PERIOD ______

2-8 Word Problem Practice

Literal Equations and Dimensional Analysis

1. **INTEREST** Simple interest that you may earn on money in a savings account can be calculated with the formula $I = prt$. I is the amount of interest earned, p is the principal or initial amount invested, r is the interest rate, and t is the amount of time the money is invested for. Solve the formula for p.

2. **DISTANCE** The distance d a car can travel is found by multiplying its rate of speed r by the amount of time t that it took to travel the distance. If a car has already traveled 5 miles, the total distance d is found by the formula $d = rt + 5$. Solve the formula for r.

3. **ENVIRONMENT** The United States released 5.877 billion metric tons of carbon dioxide into the environment through the burning of fossil fuels in a recent year. If 1 trillion pounds = 0.4536 billion metric tons, how many trillions of pounds of carbon dioxide did the United States release in that year?

4. **PHYSICS** The pressure exerted on an object is calculated by the formula $P = \frac{F}{A}$, where P is the pressure, F is the force, and A is the surface area of the object. Water shooting from a hose has a pressure of 75 pounds per square inch (psi). Suppose the surface area covered by the direct hose spray is 0.442 square inch. Solve the equation for F and find the force of the spray.

5. **GEOMETRY** The regular octagon is divided into 8 congruent triangles. Each triangle has an area of 21.7 square centimeters. The perimeter of the octagon is 48 centimeters.

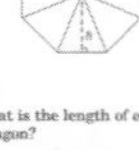

 a. What is the length of each side of the octagon?
 b. Solve the area of a triangle formula for h.
 c. What is the height of each triangle? Round to the nearest tenth.

Lesson 2-8

Write an equation and solve for the variable indicated.

29. Seven less than a number t equals another number r plus 6. Solve for t. **$t - 7 = r + 6$; $t = r + 13$**

30. Ten plus eight times a number a equals eleven times number d minus six. Solve for a.

31. Nine tenths of a number g is the same as seven plus two thirds of another number k. Solve for k. **$\frac{9}{10}g = 7 + \frac{2}{3}k$; $k = \frac{3}{2}\left[\frac{9}{10}g - 7\right]$**

32. Three fourths of a number p less two is five sixths of another number r plus five. Solve for r. **$\frac{3}{4}p - 2 = \frac{5}{6}r + 5$; $r = \frac{6}{5}\left[\frac{3}{4}p - 7\right]$**

30. $10 + 8a = 11d - 6$; $a = \frac{11d - 16}{8}$

33. **GIFTS** Ashley has 214 square inches of paper to wrap a gift box. The surface area S of the box can be found by using the formula $S = 2w(\ell + h) + 2\ell h$, where w is the width of the box, ℓ is the length of the box, and h is the height. If the length of the box is 7 inches and the width is 6 inches, how tall can Ashley's box be? **5 in.**

34. **DRIVING** A car is driven x miles a year and averages m miles per gallon.
 a. Write a formula for g, the number of gallons used in a year. **$g = \frac{x}{m}$**
 b. If the average price of gas is p dollars per gallon, write a formula for the total gas cost c in dollars for driving this car each year. **$c = \frac{px}{m}$**
 c. Car A averages 15 miles per gallon on the highway, while Car B averages 35 miles per gallon on the highway. If you average 15,000 miles each year, how much money would you save on gas per week by using Car B instead of Car A if the cost of gas averages \$3 per gallon? Explain. **See margin.**

H.O.T. Problems Use Higher-Order Thinking Skills

C 35. **CHALLENGE** The circumference of an NCAA women's basketball is 29 inches, and the rubber coating is $\frac{3}{16}$ inch thick. Use the formula $v = \frac{4}{3}\pi r^3$, where v represents the volume and r is the radius of the inside of the ball, to determine the volume of the air inside the ball. Round to the nearest whole number. **about 364 in^3**

36. **REASONING** Select an appropriate unit to describe the highway speed of a car and the speed of a crawling caterpillar. Can the same unit be used for both? Explain.

37. **ERROR ANALYSIS** Sandrea and Fernando are solving $4a - 5b = 7$ for b. Is either of them correct? Explain.

36. Sample answer: No; since the rate of a car is faster than a caterpillar, the rate of a car is best described by miles per hour and the caterpillar by inches per second.

Sandrea

$$4a - 5b = 7$$
$$-5b = 7 - 4a$$
$$\frac{-5b}{-5} = \frac{7 - 4a}{-5}$$
$$b = \frac{7 - 4a}{-5}$$

Fernando

$$4a - 5b = 7$$
$$5b = 7 - 4a$$
$$\frac{5b}{5} = \frac{7 - 4a}{5}$$
$$b = \frac{7 - 4a}{5}$$

Sandrea; she performed each step correctly; Fernando omitted the negative sign from $-5b$.

38. **OPEN ENDED** Write a formula for A, the area of a geometric figure such as a triangle or rectangle. Then solve the formula for a variable other than A.

38. Sample answer for a triangle: $A = \frac{1}{2}bh$; $b = \frac{2A}{h}$

39. **PERSEVERANCE** Solve each equation or formula for the variable indicated. **39a–b. See margin.**
 a. $n = \frac{x + y - 1}{xy}$ for x
 b. $\frac{x + y}{x - y} = \frac{1}{2}$ for y

40. **WRITING IN MATH** Why is it helpful to be able to represent a literal equation in different ways? **See margin.**

Enrichment

OL BL

NAME ______ DATE ______ PERIOD ______

2-8 Enrichment

Compound Interest

In most banks, interest on savings accounts is compounded at set time periods such as three or six months. At the end of each period, the bank adds the interest earned to the account. During the next period, the bank pays interest on all the money in the bank, including interest. In this way, the account earns interest on interest.

Suppose Ms. Tanner has \$1000 in an account that is compounded quarterly at 5%. Find the balance after the first two quarters.

Use $I = prt$ to find the interest earned in the first quarter if $p = 1000$ and $r = 5\%$. Why is t equal to $\frac{1}{4}$?

First quarter: $I = 1000 \times 0.05 \times \frac{1}{4}$

$I = 12.50$

The interest, \$12.50, earned in the first quarter is added to \$1000. The principal becomes \$1012.50.

Second quarter: $I = 1012.50 \times 0.05 \times \frac{1}{4}$

Additional Answer

34c. Car A would cost $\frac{3(15{,}000)}{15}$ or \$3000 per year, or about \$58 per week. Car B would cost $\frac{3(15{,}000)}{35}$, which is about \$1286 per year, or about \$24 per week, for a savings of about \$58 − 24 or \$34 per week.

Standardized Test Practice

41. Eula is investing \$6000, part at 4.5% interest and the rest at 6% interest. If d represents the amount invested at 4.5%, which expression represents the amount of interest earned in one year by the amount paying 6%? **D**

A $0.06d$
B $0.06(d - 6000)$
C $0.06(d + 6000)$
D $0.06(6000 - d)$

42. Todd drove from Boston to Cleveland, a distance of 616 miles. His breaks, gasoline, and food stops took 2 hours. If his trip took 16 hours altogether, what was Todd's average speed? **H**

F 38.5 mph
G 40 mph
H 44 mph
J 47.5 mph

43. SHORT RESPONSE Brian has 3 more books than Erika. Jasmine has triple the number of books that Brian has. Altogether Brian, Erika, and Jasmine have 22 books. How many books does Jasmine have? **15**

44. GEOMETRY Which of the following best describes a plane? **B**

A a location having neither size nor shape
B a flat surface made up of points having no depth
C made up of points and has no thickness or width
D a boundless, three-dimensional set of all points

Spiral Review

Find the final price of each item. (Lesson 2-7)

45. lamp: \$120.00 **\$101.76**
discount: 20%
tax: 6%

46. dress: \$70.00 **\$52.43**
discount: 30%
tax: 7%

47. camera: \$58.00 **\$46.33**
discount: 25%
tax: 6.5%

48. jacket: \$82.00 **\$73.88**
discount: 15%
tax: 6%

49. comforter: \$67.00 **\$56.95**
discount: 20%
tax: 6.25%

50. lawnmower: \$720.00 **\$500.76**
discount: 35%
tax: 7%

Solve each proportion. If necessary, round to the nearest hundredth. (Lesson 2-6)

51. $\frac{3}{4.5} = \frac{x}{2.5}$ **1.67**

52. $\frac{2}{0.36} = \frac{7}{p}$ **1.26**

53. $\frac{m}{9} = \frac{2.8}{4.9}$ **5.14**

54. JOBS Laurie mows lawns to earn extra money. She can mow at most 30 lawns in one week. She profits \$15 on each lawn she mows. Identify a reasonable domain and range for this situation and draw a graph. (Lesson 1-6) **See margin.**

55. ENTERTAINMENT Each member of the pit orchestra is selling tickets for the school musical. The trombone section sold 50 floor tickets and 90 balcony tickets. Write and evaluate an expression to find how much money the trombone section collected. (Lesson 1-4) **50(7.50)+90(5.00); \$825**

Skills Review

Solve each equation.

56. $8k + 9 = 7k + 6$ **−3**

57. $3 - 4q = 10q + 10$ **−0.5**

58. $\frac{3}{4}n + 16 = 2 - \frac{1}{8}n$ **−16**

59. $\frac{1}{4} - \frac{2}{3}y = \frac{3}{4} - \frac{1}{3}y$ **−1.5**

60. $4(2a - 1) = -10(a - 5)$ **3**

61. $2(w - 3) + 5 = 3(w - 1)$ **2**

Differentiated Instruction BL

Extension Write $\frac{1}{R} = \frac{1}{a} + \frac{1}{b}$ on the board. Tell students that the total resistance R in an electrical circuit consisting of two resistances of a ohms and b ohms connected in parallel is given by this equation. Ask students to explain how to solve this formula for R.

Multiply each side by R. $R\left(\frac{1}{R}\right) = \left(\frac{1}{a} + \frac{1}{b}\right)R$. Divide each side by $\frac{1}{a} + \frac{1}{b}$. $R = \frac{1}{\frac{1}{a} + \frac{1}{b}}$ or $\frac{ab}{b + a}$

WatchOut!

Error Analysis For Exercise 37, suggest that students work backward from the equation solution. In doing so, they should discover that the only difference in the solutions is the negative sign for 5 and that Fernando overlooked it when solving for b. Tell students this is a common error they should check for when solving equations.

Teaching the Process Standards

Perseverance Mathematically proficient students plan a solution pathway rather than simply jumping into a solution attempt. In Exercise 39, guide students to first find each occurrence of the variable to be isolated. Then plan to manipulate the equation to isolate the variable.

4 Assess

Ticket Out the Door Have students pick a formula that was not used in this lesson, perhaps from science class, and explain the variables in the formula and what it is used to find. Have students solve the formula for a different variable.

Additional Answers

39a. $x = \frac{y - 1}{yn - 1}$

39b. $y = -\frac{1}{3}x$

40. Sample answer: You can rewrite the equation to isolate the unknown variable, substitute the given information, and then simplify to find the solution.

54. D = whole numbers from 0 to 30; R = whole-number multiples of 15 from 0 to 450

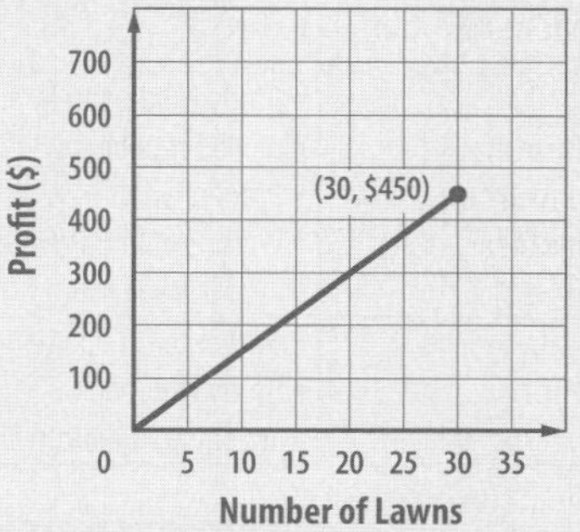

1 Focus

VerticalAlignment

Before Lesson 2-9 Translate sentences into equations.

Lesson 2-9 Solve mixture problems. Solve uniform motion problems.

After Lesson 2-9 Formulate linear equations to solve problems.

2 Teach

Scaffolding Questions

Have students read the **Why?** section of the lesson.

Ask:

- How is the slugging average weighted? The number of times a hitter gets to first base is counted once, to second base is counted twice, to third base is counted three times, and to home is counted four times.
- How would you calculate a slugging average that is not weighted? The number of times a hitter gets to each of the bases would be counted once and then divided by the number of times at bat.

LESSON 2-9 Weighted Averages

Then

- You translated sentences into equations.

Now

1. Solve mixture problems.
2. Solve uniform motion problems.

Why?

- Baseball players' performance is measured in large part by statistics. Slugging average (SLG) is a weighted average that measures the power of a hitter. The slugging average is calculated by using the following formula.

$$SLG = \frac{1B + (2 \times 2B) + (3 \times 3B) + (4 \times HR)}{\text{at bats}}$$

NewVocabulary
weighted average
mixture problem
uniform motion problem
rate problem

Process Standards
PS.4

1 Weighted Averages

The batter's slugging percentage is an example of a weighted average. The **weighted average** M of a set of data is found by multiplying each data value by its weight and then finding the mean of the new data set.

Mixture problems are problems in which two or more parts are combined into a whole. They are solved using weighted averages. In a mixture problem, the units are usually the number of gallons or pounds and the value is the cost, value, or concentration per unit.

Real-World Example 1 Mixture Problem

RETAIL **A tea company sells blended tea for $25 per pound. To make blackberry tea, dried blackberries that cost $10.50 per pound are blended with black tea that costs $35 per pound. How many pounds of black tea should be added to 5 pounds of dried blackberries to make blackberry tea?**

Step 1 Let w be the weight of the black tea. Make a table to organize the information.

	Number of Units (lb)	Price per Unit ($)	Total Price (price)(units)
Dried Blackberries	5	10.50	10.50(5)
Black Tea	w	35	$35w$
Blackberry Tea	$5 + w$	25	$25(5 + w)$

Write an equation using the information in the table.

Price of blackberries	plus	price of tea	equals	price of blackberry tea.
10.50(5)	+	$35w$	=	$25(5 + w)$

Step 2 Solve the equation.

$10.50(5) + 35w = 25(5 + w)$	Original equation
$52.5 + 35w = 125 + 25w$	Distributive Property
$52.5 + 35w - 25w = 125 + 25w - 25w$	Subtract $25w$ from each side.
$52.5 + 10w = 125$	Simplify.
$52.5 - 52.5 + 10w = 125 - 52.5$	Subtract 52.5 from each side.
$10w = 72.5$	Simplify.
$w = 7.25$	Divide each side by 10.

Lesson 2-9 Resources

Resource	Approaching Level AL	On Level OL	Beyond Level BL	English Learners ELL
Teacher Edition			▪ Differentiated Instruction, pp. 134, 138	
Chapter Resource Masters	▪ Study Guide and Intervention, pp. 55–56 ▪ Skills Practice, p. 57 ▪ Practice, p. 58 ▪ Word Problem Practice, p. 59	▪ Study Guide and Intervention, pp. 55–56 ▪ Skills Practice, p. 57 ▪ Practice, p. 58 ▪ Word Problem Practice, p. 59 ▪ Enrichment, p. 60	▪ Practice, p. 58 ▪ Word Problem Practice, p. 59 ▪ Enrichment, p. 60	▪ Study Guide and Intervention, pp. 55–56 ▪ Skills Practice, p. 57 ▪ Practice, p. 58 ▪ Word Problem Practice, p. 59
Other	▪ 5-Minute Check 2-9 ▪ Study Notebook ▪ Teaching Algebra with Manipulatives	▪ 5-Minute Check 2-9 ▪ Study Notebook ▪ Teaching Algebra with Manipulatives	▪ 5-Minute Check 2-9 ▪ Study Notebook	▪ 5-Minute Check 2-9 ▪ Study Notebook ▪ Teaching Algebra with Manipulatives

To make the blackberry tea, 7.25 pounds of black tea will need to be added to the dried blackberries.

Study Tip

Mixture Problems When you organize the information in mixture problems, remember that the final mixture must contain the sum of the parts in the correct quantities and at the correct percents.

Guided Practice

1. **COFFEE** How many pounds of Premium coffee beans should be mixed with 2 pounds of Supreme coffee to make the Blend coffee? **7 lb**

Sometimes mixture problems are expressed in terms of percents.

PT

Real-World Example 2 Percent Mixture Problem

FRUIT PUNCH Mrs. Matthews has 16 cups of punch that is 3% pineapple juice. She also has a punch that is 33% pineapple juice. How many cups of the 33% punch will she need to add to the 3% punch to obtain a punch that is 20% pineapple juice?

Step 1 Let x = the amount of 33% solution to be added. Make a table.

Problem-Solving Tip

Make a Table Using a table is a great way to organize the given information. It also helps you understand how to write an equation to solve for the missing value.

	Amount of Punch (cups)	Amount of Pineapple Juice
3% Punch	16	0.03(16)
33% Punch	x	$0.33x$
20% Punch	$16 + x$	$0.20(16 + x)$

Write an equation using the information in the table.

Amount of pineapple juice in 3% punch	plus	amount of pineapple juice in 33% punch	equals	amount of pineapple juice in 20% punch.
0.03(16)	+	$0.33x$	=	$0.20(16 + x)$

Step 2 Solve the equation.

$0.03(16) + 0.33x = 0.20(16 + x)$	Original equation
$0.48 + 0.33x = 3.2 + 0.20x$	Simplify.
$0.48 + 0.33x - 0.20x = 3.2 + 0.20x - 0.20x$	Subtract $0.20x$ from each side.
$0.48 + 0.13x = 3.2$	Simplify.
$0.48 - 0.48 + 0.13x = 3.2 - 0.48$	Subtract 0.48 from each side.
$0.13x = 2.72$	Simplify.
$\frac{0.13x}{0.13} = \frac{2.72}{0.13}$	Divide each side by 0.13.
$x \approx 20.9$	Round to the nearest tenth.

Mrs. Matthews should add about 20.9 cups of the 33% punch to the 16 cups of the 3% punch.

Guided Practice

2. **ANTIFREEZE** One type of antifreeze is 40% glycol, and another type of antifreeze is 60% glycol. How much of each kind should be used to make 100 gallons of antifreeze that is 48% glycol? **60 gal of 40% glycol, 40 gal of 60% glycol**

- Why is the slugging average weighted? The more powerful the hit, the more bases a hitter can get to, so the weighted average assigns a greater value to each subsequent base the hitter reaches.

1 Weighted Averages

Example 1 shows how to solve a real-world mixture problem using weighted averages. **Example 2** shows how to solve a real-world mixture problem expressed in terms of percents using weighted averages.

Formative Assessment

Use the Guided Practice exercises after each Example to determine students' understanding of concepts.

Additional Examples

1 **PETS** Mandisha feeds her cat gourmet cat food that costs \$1.75 per pound. She combines it with cheaper food that costs \$0.50 per pound. How many pounds of cheaper food should Mandisha buy to go with 5 pounds of gourmet food, if she wants the average price to be \$1.00 per pound? 7.5 lb of cheaper food

2 **AUTO MAINTENANCE** A car's radiator should contain a solution of 50% antifreeze. Bae has 2 gallons of 35% antifreeze. How many gallons of 100% antifreeze should he add to his solution to produce a solution of 50% antifreeze? 0.6 gal of 100% antifreeze

Additional Examples also in Interactive Classroom PowerPoint® Presentations

IWB **Interactive White Board READY**

Tips for New Teachers

Making a Connection Once students have learned the concept of weighted average, challenge them to describe a weighted average in terms of weights on a balance. How do the weights help to "tip" the balance?

Teach with Tech

Wiki Have groups of students create a wiki page about weighted averages. Tell students to include a description of weighted averages, and to use the page to keep a running list of examples of weighted averages. Have students maintain and update this page as they learn and think of additional examples.

2 Uniform Motion Problems

Example 3 shows how to solve a real-world, uniform motion problem using weighted averages. **Example 4** shows how to solve a real-world, uniform motion problem using weighted averages and making a table.

Additional Example

3 **AIR TRAVEL** Nita took a non-stop flight to visit her grandmother. The 750-mile trip took three hours and 45 minutes. Because of bad weather, the return trip took four hours and 45 minutes. What was her average speed for the round trip? The average speed for the round trip was about 176 mph.

Focus on Mathematical Content

Uniform Motion If an object moves without changing its speed, it is said to be in uniform motion. Uniform motion problems are solved using this formula:

Distance = rate × time

$d = r \times t$

Real-WorldLink

Inline skating is the fourth most popular recreational activity in the U.S.

Source: Statistical Abstract of the United States

2 Uniform Motion Problems

Uniform motion problems or **rate problems** are problems in which an object moves at a certain speed or rate. The formula $d = rt$ is used to solve these problems. In the formula, d represents distance, r represents rate, and t represents time.

Real-World Example 3 Speed of One Vehicle

INLINE SKATING **It took Travis and Tony 40 minutes to skate 5 miles. The return trip took them 30 minutes. What was their average speed for the trip?**

Understand We know that the boys did not travel the same amount of time on each portion of their trip. So, we will need to find the weighted average of their speeds. We are asked to find their average speed for both portions of the trip.

Plan First find the rate of the going portion, and then the return portion of the trip. Because the rate is in miles per hour we convert 40 minutes to about 0.667 hours and 30 minutes to 0.5 hours.

Going

$r = \frac{d}{t}$ Formula for rate

$\approx \frac{5 \text{ miles}}{0.667 \text{ hour}}$ or about 7.5 miles per hour Substitution $d = 5$ mi, $t = 0.667$ h

Return

$r = \frac{d}{t}$ Formula for rate

$= \frac{5 \text{ miles}}{0.5 \text{ hour}}$ or 10 miles per hour Substitution $d = 5$ mi, $t = 0.5$ h

Because we are looking for a weighted average we cannot just average their speeds. We need to find the weighted average for the round trip.

Solve $M = \frac{(\text{rate of going})(\text{time of going}) + (\text{rate of return})(\text{time of return})}{\text{time of going} + \text{time of return}}$

$\approx \frac{(7.5)(0.667) + (10)(0.5)}{0.667 + 0.5}$ Substitution

$\approx \frac{10.0025}{1.167}$ or about 8.6 Simplify.

Their average speed was about 8.6 miles per hour.

Check Our solution of 8.6 miles per hour is between the going portion rate, 7.5 miles per hour, and the return rate, 10 miles per hour. So, we know that our answer is reasonable.

GuidedPractice

3. **EXERCISE** Austin jogged 2.5 miles in 16 minutes and then walked 1 mile in 10 minutes. What was his average speed? **about 0.13 mi/min**

The formula $d = rt$ can also be used to solve real-world problems involving two vehicles in motion.

DifferentiatedInstruction BL

Logical Some students will appreciate the way in which weighted averages can be used to manipulate data. Challenge these students to create additional example problems using weighted averages. Share these problems with the class.

Real-World Example 4 Speeds of Two Vehicles

FREIGHT TRAINS Two trains are 550 miles apart heading toward each other on parallel tracks. Train A is traveling east at 35 miles per hour, while Train B travels west at 45 miles per hour. When will the trains pass each other?

> **StudyTip**
> **Sense-Making** Drawing a diagram is not just for geometry problems. You can use diagrams to visualize many problem situations that can be represented by equations.

Step 1 Draw a diagram.

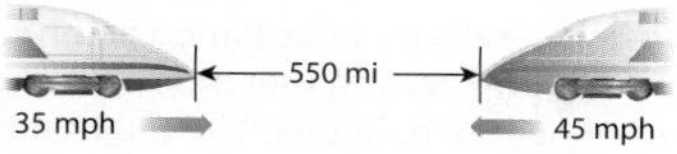

Step 2 Let t = the number of hours until the trains pass each other. Make a table.

	r	t	$d = rt$
Train A	35	t	$35t$
Train B	45	t	$45t$

Step 3 Write and solve an equation.

Distance traveled by Train A	plus	distance traveled by Train B	equals	550 miles.
$35t$	$+$	$45t$	$=$	550

$35t + 45t = 550$ Original equation

$80t = 550$ Simplify.

$\frac{80t}{80} = \frac{550}{80}$ Divide each side by 80.

$t = 6.875$ Simplify.

The trains will pass each other in about 6.875 hours.

GuidedPractice $\frac{1}{6}$ **hour or 10 min**

4. CYCLING Two cyclists begin traveling in opposite directions on a circular bike trail that is 5 miles long. One cyclist travels 12 miles per hour, and the other travels 18 miles per hour. How long will it be before they meet?

Check Your Understanding

= Step-by-Step Solutions begin on page R13.

Example 1

1. FOOD Tasha ordered soup and salad for lunch. If Tasha ordered 10 ounces of soup for lunch and the total cost was $3.30, how many ounces of salad did Tasha order? **9 oz**

Example 2

2. CHEMISTRY Margo has 40 milliliters of 25% solution. How many milliliters of 60% solution should she add to obtain the required 30% solution? **about 6.67 mL**

Example 3

3. TRAVEL A boat travels 16 miles due north in 2 hours and 24 miles due west in 2 hours. What is the average speed of the boat? **10 mph**

4. EXERCISE Felisa jogged 3 miles in 25 minutes and then jogged 3 more miles in 30 minutes. What was her average speed in miles per minute? **about 0.11 mi/min**

Example 4

5. CYCLING A cyclist begins traveling 18 miles per hour. At the same time and at the same starting point, an inline skater follows the cyclist's path and begins traveling 6 miles per hour. After how much time will they be 24 miles apart? **2 hours**

Additional Example

4 RESCUE A railroad switching operator has discovered that two trains are heading toward each other on the same track. Currently, the trains are 53 miles apart. One train is traveling at 75 miles per hour and the other 40 miles per hour. The faster train will require 5 miles to stop safely, and the slower train will require 3 miles to stop safely. About how many minutes does the operator have to warn the train engineers to stop their trains? about 23 min

3 Practice

Formative Assessment

Use Exercises 1–5 to check for understanding.

Use the chart at the bottom of the next page to customize assignments for your students.

Teaching the Process Standards

Sense-Making Mathematically proficient students can explain correspondences between equations, verbal descriptions, and tables, or draw diagrams of important relationships. Because uniform motion problems are often challenging for students, diagrams and tables are especially helpful tools.

connectED.mcgraw-hill.com 135

Teaching the Process Standards

Modeling Mathematically proficient students are able to identify important quantities in a practical situation and map their relationships. In problems like Exercise 12, encourage students to write each variable, draw diagrams, and use tables to organize information.

Additional Answers

16. 3.67

17. about 10.89 mph

18. 3.8 min

19a. 390 mi

19b. about 9.62 hours

26. Sample answer: Multiply the 1 gallon times 0.25. Then multiply the unknown amount by 0.10. Add these results together. This should equal the total amount times 0.15.

Practice and Problem Solving

Extra Practice is on page R2.

Example 1

6. CANDY A candy store wants to create a mix using two hard candies. One is priced at $5.45 per pound, and the other is priced at $7.33 per pound. How many pounds of the $7.33 candy should be mixed with 11 pounds of the $5.45 candy to sell the mixture for $6.14 per pound? **about 6.38 lb**

7. BUSINESS Party Supplies Inc. sells metallic balloons for $2 each and helium balloons for $3.50 per bunch. Yesterday, they sold 36 more metallic balloons than the number of bunches of helium balloons. The total sales for both types of balloons were $281. Let b represent the number of metallic balloons sold.

a. Copy and complete the table representing the problem.

	Number	Price	Total Price
Metallic Balloons	b	$2.00	$2.00b$
Bunches of Helium Balloons	$b - 36$	$3.50	$3.50(b - 36)$

b. Write an equation to represent the problem. $2.00b + 3.50(b - 36) = 281.00$

c. How many metallic balloons were sold? **74**

d. How many bunches of helium balloons were sold? **38**

8. FINANCIAL LITERACY Lakeisha spent $4.57 on color and black-and-white copies for her project. She made 7 more black-and-white copies than color copies. How many color copies did she make? **8 color copies**

Type of Copy	Cost per Page
color	$0.44
black-and-white	$0.07

Example 2

9. FISH Rosamaria is setting up a 20-gallon saltwater fish tank that needs to have a salt content of 3.5%. If Rosamaria has water that has 2.5% salt and water that has 3.7% salt, how many gallons of the water with 3.7% salt content should Rosamaria use? **about 16.67 gal**

10. CHEMISTRY Hector is performing a chemistry experiment that requires 160 milliliters of 40% sulfuric acid solution. He has a 25% sulfuric acid solution and a 50% sulfuric acid solution. How many milliliters of each solution should he mix to obtain the needed solution? **64 mL of the 25% solution and 96 mL of the 50% solution**

Example 3

11. TRAVEL A boat travels 36 miles in 1.5 hours and then 14 miles in 0.75 hour. What is the average speed of the boat? **about 22.2 mph**

12. MODELING A person walked 1.5 miles in 28 minutes and then jogged 1.2 more miles in 10 minutes. What was the average speed in miles per minute? **about 0.07 mi/min**

Example 4

13. AIRLINERS Two airliners are 1600 miles apart and heading toward each other at different altitudes. The first plane is traveling north at 620 miles per hour, while the second is traveling south at 780 miles per hour. When will the planes pass each other? **$1\frac{1}{7}$ hours or 1 h 8 min 34 s**

14. SAILING A ship is sailing due east at 20 miles per hour when it passes the lighthouse. At the same time a ship is sailing due west at 15 miles per hour when it passes a point. The point is 175 miles east of the lighthouse. When will these ships pass each other? **5 hours**

B

15. CHEMISTRY A lab technician has 40 gallons of a 15% iodine solution. How many gallons of a 40% iodine solution must he add to make a 20% iodine solution? **10 gal**

136 | Lesson 2-9 | Weighted Averages

Differentiated Homework Options

Level	Assignment	Two-Day Option	
AL Basic	6–14, 22–23, 26–47	7–13 odd, 27–30	6–14 even, 22–23, 26, 31–47
OL Core	7–13 odd, 16–23, 26–47	6–14, 27–30	15–23, 26, 31–47
BL Advanced	16–41, (optional: 42–47)		

16. **GRADES** At Westbridge High School, a student's grade point average (GPA) is based on the student's grade and the class credit rating. Brittany's grades for this quarter are shown. Find Brittany's GPA if a grade of A equals 4 and a B equals 3. **See margin.**

Class	Credit Rating	Grade
Algebra 1	1	A
Science	1	A
English	1	B
Spanish	1	A
Music	$\frac{1}{2}$	B

17. **SPORTS** In a triathlon, Steve swam 0.5 mile in 15 minutes, biked 20 miles in 90 minutes, and ran 4 miles in 30 minutes. What was Steve's average speed for the triathlon in miles per hour? **See margin.**

18. **MUSIC** Amalia has 10 songs on her digital media player. If 3 songs are 5 minutes long, 3 are 4 minutes long, 2 are 2 minutes long, and 2 are 3.5 minutes long, what is the average length of the songs? **See margin.**

19. **DISTANCE** Garcia is driving to Florida for vacation. The trip is a total of 625 miles.
   a. How far can he drive in 6 hours at 65 miles per hour?
   b. If Garcia maintains a speed of 65 miles per hour, how long will it take him to drive to Florida? **a–b. See margin.**

20. **TRAVEL** Two buses leave Smithville at the same time, one traveling north and the other traveling south. The northbound bus travels at 50 miles per hour, and the southbound bus travels at 65 miles per hour. Let t represent the amount of time since their departure.
   a. Copy and complete the table representing the situation.

	r	t	$d = rt$
Northbound bus	50 ?	t ?	$50t$?
Southbound bus	65 ?	t ?	$65t$?

   b. Write an equation to find when the buses will be 345 miles apart. **$50t + 65t = 345$**
   c. Solve the equation. Explain how you found your answer. **3 hours; combine like terms and solve for t.**

21. **TRAVEL** A subway travels 60 miles per hour from Glendale to Midtown. Another subway, traveling at 45 miles per hour, takes 11 minutes longer for the same trip. How far apart are Glendale and Midtown? **33 mi**

22. Sample answer: Miles and Tara live 15 miles apart. If Tara rides her bike towards Miles's house at 10 miles per hour and Miles rides his bike at 12 miles per hour towards her, when will they meet?

23. Sample answer: For a 50% solution being added to a 100% solution to produce a 75% resulting solution, the quantity of each must be the same.

H.O.T. Problems Use Higher-Order Thinking Skills

C 22. **OPEN ENDED** Write a problem that depicts motion in opposite directions.

23. **ARGUMENTS** Describe the conditions so that adding a 50% solution to a 100% solution would produce a 75% solution.

24. **CHALLENGE** Find five consecutive odd integers from least to greatest in which the sum of the first and the fifth is one less than three times the fourth. **−9, −7, −5, −3, −1**

25. **CHALLENGE** Describe a situation involving mixtures that could be represented by $1.00x + 0.15(36) = 0.50(x + 36)$.

26. **WRITING IN MATH** Describe how a gallon of 25% solution is added to an unknown amount of 10% solution to get a 15% solution. **See margin.**

25. Sample answer: How many grams of salt must be added to 36 grams of a 15% salt solution to obtain a 50% salt solution?

Teaching the Process Standards

Arguments Mathematically proficient students analyze situations by breaking them into cases. In Exercise 23, point out to students that it is easy to assume that adding a 50% solution and a 100% solution produces a 75% solution. Challenge them to find the cases when that is not true.

Enrichment

OL BL

NAME ________ DATE ______ PERIOD ______

2-9 Enrichment

Expected Value

Expected value is the average return of an event over repeated trial. Expected value is also a form of weighted average and can be used to determine whether or not you should play a game based on what the expected value of your winnings is. It can also be used to determine the expected length of a game.

Example **You are rolling a die to determine the number of candy bars you will win at a school fair. If you roll a one, you get 12 candy bars. If you roll a two or a three, you get 3 candy bars. If you roll a four, five or six, you get 2 candy bars.**

Since there are six possibilities for what you can roll:

- $\frac{1}{6}$ of the time, you will win 12 candy bars.
- $\frac{2}{6}$ or $\frac{1}{3}$ of the time, you will win 3 candy bars.
- $\frac{3}{6}$ or $\frac{1}{2}$ of the time, you will win 2 candy bars.

The expected value is $\frac{1}{6}(12) + \frac{1}{3}(3) + \frac{1}{2}(2)$ or 4 candy bars.

Study Guide and Intervention

AL OL ELL

NAME ________ DATE ______ PERIOD ______

2-9 Study Guide and Intervention

Weighted Averages

Mixture Problems **Mixture Problems** are problems where two or more parts are combined into a whole. They involve weighted averages. In a mixture problem, the weight is usually a price or a percent of something.

Weighted Average	The weighted average M of a set of data is the sum of the product of each number in the set and its weight divided by the sum of all the weights.

Example **COOKIES Delectable Cookie Company sells chocolate chip cookies for $6.95 per pound and white chocolate cookies for $5.95 per pound. How many pounds of chocolate chip cookies should be mixed with 4 pounds of white chocolate cookies to obtain a mixture that sells for $6.75 per pound.**

Let w = the number of pounds of chocolate chip cookies

	Number of Pounds	Price per Pound	Total Price
Chocolate Chip	w	6.95	$6.95w$
White Chocolate	4	5.95	4(5.95)
Mixture	$w + 4$	6.75	$6.75(w + 4)$

Equation: $6.95w + 4(5.95) = 6.75(w + 4)$

Solve the equation.

$6.95w + 4(5.95) = 6.75(w + 4)$	Original equation
$6.95w + 23.80 = 6.75w + 27$	Simplify.
$6.95w + 23.80 - 6.75w = 6.75w + 27 - 6.75w$	Subtract 6.75w from each side.
$0.2w + 23.80 = 27$	Simplify.
$0.2w + 23.80 - 23.80 = 27 - 23.80$	Subtract 23.80 from each side.
$0.2w = 3.2$	Simplify.
$w = 16$	Simplify.

16 pounds of chocolate chip cookies should be mixed with 4 pounds of white chocolate cookies.

Exercises

1. **SOLUTIONS** How many grams of sugar must be added to 60 grams of a solution that is 32% sugar to obtain a solution that is 50% sugar?
2. **NUTS** The Quik Mart has two kinds of nuts. Pecans sell for $1.55 per pound and walnuts sell for $1.95 per pound. How many pounds of walnuts must be added to 15 pounds of pecans to make a mixture that sells for $1.75 per pound?
3. **INVESTMENTS** Alice Gleason invested a portion of $32,000 at 9% interest and the balance at 11% interest. How much did she invest at each rate if her total income from both investments was $3200.
4. **MILK** Whole milk is 4% butterfat. How much skim milk with 0% butterfat should be added to 32 ounces of whole milk to obtain a mixture that is 2.5% butterfat?

Lesson 2-9

Practice

AL OL BL ELL

NAME ________ DATE ______ PERIOD ______

2-9 Practice

Weighted Averages

1. **GRASS SEED** A nursery sells Kentucky Blue Grass seed for $5.75 per pound and Tall Fescue seed for $4.50 per pound. The nursery sells a mixture of the two kinds of seed for $5.25 per pound. Let k represent the amount of Kentucky Blue Grass seed the nursery uses in 5 pounds of the mixture.
   a. Complete the table representing the problem.

	Number of Pounds	Price per Pound	Cost
Kentucky Blue Grass			
Tall Fescue			
Mixture			

   b. Write an equation to represent the problem.
   c. How much Kentucky Blue Grass does the nursery use in 5 pounds of the mixture?
   d. How much Tall Fescue does the nursery use in 5 pounds of the mixture?

2. **TRAVEL** Two commuter trains carry passengers between two cities, one traveling east, and the other west, on different tracks. Their respective stations are 150 miles apart. Both trains leave at the same time, one traveling at an average speed of 55 miles per hour and the other at an average speed of 65 miles per hour. Let t represent the time until the trains pass each other.
   a. Copy and complete the table representing the problem.

	r	t	$d = rt$
First Train			
Second Train			

   b. Write an equation using t that describes the distances traveled.
   c. How long after departing will the trains pass each other?

3. **TRAVEL** Two trains leave Raleigh at the same time, one traveling north, and the other south. The first train travels at 50 miles per hour and the second at 60 miles per hour. In how many hours will the trains be 275 miles apart?

4. **JUICE** A pineapple drink contains 15% pineapple juice. How much pure pineapple juice should be added to 8 quarts of the pineapple drink to obtain a mixture containing 50% pineapple juice?

Word Problem Practice

AL OL BL ELL

NAME ________ DATE ______ PERIOD ______

2-9 Word Problem Practice

Weighted Averages

1. **DRIVING** The drive from New York City to Boston is about 240 miles. It took Samir 5 hours to drive one way, but due to severe weather it took him 6.5 hours for the return trip. What was his average speed round trip? Round the answer to the nearest hundredth.

2. **GRADES** In math classes at Gorbine High School, all tests are given double the weight of a quiz or homework score when calculating grades. Use Donna's grade record sheet to determine her average grade so far this term.

Assignment	Grade
Homework chapter 1	95
Quiz chapter 1	80
Test chapter 1	92
Homework chapter 2	93
Quiz chapter 2	96
Test chapter 2	81

3. **MIXTURE** Keith wants to create a drink that is 40% juice. How much of a 10% juice solution should he add to 100 milliliters of 100% grape juice to obtain the 40% mixture?

4. **BUSINESS** Mrs. Winship sells chocolate fudge for $7.50 per pound and peanut butter fudge for $7.00 per pound. The total number of pounds sold on Saturday was 146 and the total amount of money collected was $1065. How many pounds of each type of fudge were sold?

5. **TRAINS** Two trains are 5000 feet apart, heading toward each other, but on separate parallel straight tracks. Train A is traveling at 45 miles per hour and Train B is traveling at 24 miles per hour.
   a. Change 45 miles per hour and 24 miles per hour into feet per second.
   b. About how far will each train travel before they meet? Round your answers to the nearest hundredth.
   c. In how many seconds will Train A and Train B meet?

Lesson 2-9

4 Assess

Name the Math Have students tell what mathematical procedures they would use to solve Exercise 7.

Formative Assessment

Check for student understanding of Lessons 2-8 and 2-9.

Quiz 4, p. 64

Additional Answers

35. Sample answer: The quotient of *n* and −6 is the same as the sum of two times *n* and one.

36. Sample answer: Eighteen decreased by five times *h* is the same as thirteen times *h*.

37. Sample answer: The sum of three and twice *x* squared is equal to twenty-one.

Standardized Test Practice

27. If $2x + y = 5$, what is the value of $4x$? **B**

A $10 - y$

B $10 - 2y$

C $\frac{5 - y}{2}$

D $\frac{10 - y}{2}$

28. Which expression is equivalent to $7x^2 3x^{-4}$? **J**

F $21x^{-8}$

G $21x^2$

H $21x^{-6}$

J $21x^{-2}$

29. GEOMETRY What is the base of the triangle if the area is 56 square meters? **C**

A 4 m

B 8 m

C 16 m

D 28 m

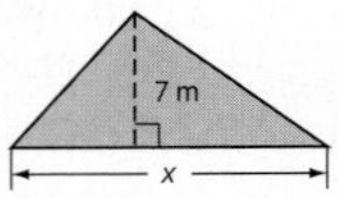

30. SHORT RESPONSE Brianne makes blankets for a baby store. She works on the blankets 30 hours per week. The store pays her $9.50 per hour plus 30% of the profit. If her hourly rate is increased by $0.75 and her commission is raised to 40%, how much will she earn for a week in which there was a $300 profit? **$427.50**

Spiral Review

Solve each equation or formula for x. (Lesson 2-8)

31. $2bx - b = -5$ $\frac{-5 + b}{2b}$

32. $3x - r = r(-3 + x)$ $\frac{-2r}{3 - r}$

33. $A = 2\pi r^2 + 2\pi rx$ $\frac{A}{2\pi r} - r$

34. SKIING Yuji is registering for ski camp. The cost of the camp is $1254, but there is a sales tax of 7%. What is the total cost of the camp including tax? (Lesson 2-7) **$1341.78**

Translate each equation into a sentence. (Lesson 2-1) **35–37. See margin.**

35. $\frac{n}{-6} = 2n + 1$

36. $18 - 5h = 13h$

37. $2x^2 + 3 = 21$

Refer to the graph. **38. (2, 15); Sample answer: If two cars are washed, $15 is earned.** **39. (4, 25); Sample answer: If four cars are washed, $25 is earned.**

38. Name the ordered pair at point *A* and explain what it represents. (Lesson 1-6)

39. Name the ordered pair at point *B* and explain what it represents. (Lesson 1-6)

40. Identify the independent and dependent variables for the function. (Lesson 1-6) **I: number of cars washed; D: amount earned**

41. BASEBALL Tickets to a baseball game cost $18.95, $12.95, or $9.95. A hot dog and soda combo costs $5.50. The Madison family is having a reunion. They buy 10 tickets in each price category and plan to buy 30 combos. What is the total cost for the tickets and meals? (Lesson 1-4) **$583.50**

Touchdown Club Car Wash

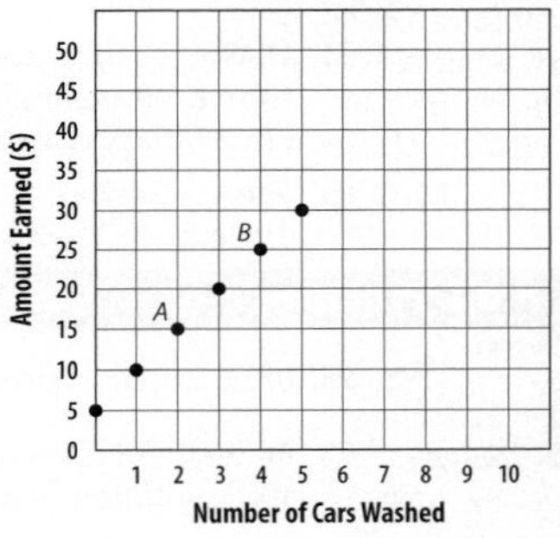

Skills Review

Solve each equation.

42. $a - 8 = 15$ **23**

43. $9m - 11 = -29$ **−2**

44. $18 - 2k = 24$ **−3**

45. $5 - 8y = 61$ **−7**

46. $7 = \frac{h}{2} + 3$ **8**

47. $\frac{n}{6} + 1 = 5$ **24**

Differentiated Instruction BL

Extension In many high schools, a special weight is assigned to the grades received in Advanced Placement classes when a student's GPA is calculated (A = 5 points; B = 4 points; C = 3 points). Have students pretend that one of their classes is an Advanced Placement class with a grade having special weight assigned to it. Have them use their current grades to calculate their GPAs. Ask students to explain how the class chosen as an Advanced Placement class made their GPA higher.

CHAPTER 2 Study Guide and Review

Study Guide

KeyConcepts

Writing Equations (Lesson 2-1)

- Identify the unknown you are looking for and assign a variable to it. Then, write the sentence as an equation.

Solving Equations (Lessons 2-2 to 2-4)

- Addition and Subtraction Properties of Equality: If an equation is true and the same number is added to or subtracted from each side, the resulting equation is true.
- Multiplication and Division Properties of Equality: If an equation is true and each side is multiplied or divided by the same nonzero number, the resulting equation is true.
- Steps for Solving Equations:
  - **Step 1** Simplify the expression on each side. Use the Distributive Property as needed.
  - **Step 2** Use the Addition and/or Subtraction Properties of Equality to get the variables on one side and the numbers without variables on the other side.
  - **Step 3** Use the Multiplication or Division Property of Equality to solve.

Absolute Value Equations (Lesson 2-5)

- For any real numbers a and b, if $|a| = b$ and $b \geq 0$, then $a = b$ or $a = -b$.

Ratios and Proportions (Lesson 2-6)

- The Means-Extremes Property of Proportion states that in a proportion, the product of the extremes is equal to the product of the means.

Percent of Change (Lesson 2-7)

- percent of change $= \frac{\text{the change in an amount}}{\text{the original amount}}$ expressed as a percent

Weighted Averages (Lesson 2-9)

- the weighted average M of a set of data $= \frac{\text{sum of (units} \times \text{the value per unit)}}{\text{the total number of units}}$

FOLDABLES StudyOrganizer

Be sure the Key Concepts are noted in your Foldable.

KeyVocabulary

consecutive integers (p. 92)	percent of decrease (p. 119)
dimensional analysis (p. 128)	percent of increase (p. 119)
equivalent equations (p. 83)	proportion (p. 111)
extremes (p. 112)	rate (p. 113)
formula (p. 76)	ratio (p. 111)
identity (p. 98)	scale (p. 114)
literal equation (p. 127)	scale model (p. 114)
means (p. 112)	solve an equation (p. 83)
multi-step equations (p. 91)	unit analysis (p. 128)
number theory (p. 92)	unit rate (p. 113)
percent of change (p. 119)	weighted average (p. 132)

VocabularyCheck

State whether each sentence is *true* or *false*. If *false*, replace the underlined term to make a true sentence.

1. In order to write an equation to solve a problem, identify the unknown for which you are looking and assign a(n) number to it. **false, variable**
2. To solve an equation means to find the value of the variable that makes the equation true. **true**
3. The numbers 10, 12, and 14 are an example of consecutive even integers. **true**
4. The absolute value of any number is simply the distance the number is away from zero on a number line. **true**
5. A(n) equation is a comparison of two numbers by division. **false, ratio**
6. An equation stating that two ratios are equal is called a(n) proportion. **true**
7. If the new number is less than the original number, the percent of change is a percent of increase. **false, decrease**
8. The weighted average of a set of data is the sum of the product of the number of units and the value per unit divided by the sum of the number of units. **true**

Formative Assessment

KeyVocabulary The page reference after each word denotes where that term was first introduced. If students have difficulty answering questions 1–8, remind them that they can use these page references to refresh their memories about the vocabulary terms.

Summative Assessment

Vocabulary Test, p. 66

Vocabulary Review

Vocabulary Review provides students the opportunity to check their understanding of important concepts and terminology in an online game format.

FOLDABLES StudyOrganizer

Dinah Zike's Foldables®

Have students look through the chapter to make sure they have included examples in their Foldables for each lesson of the chapter. Suggest that students keep their Foldables handy while completing the Study Guide and Review pages. Point out that their Foldables can serve as a quick review when studying for the chapter test.

Lesson-by-Lesson Review

Intervention If the given examples are not sufficient to review the topics covered by the questions, remind students that the lesson references tell them where to review that topic in their textbooks.

Two-Day Option Have students complete the Lesson-by-Lesson Review. Then you can use McGraw-Hill eAssessment to customize another review worksheet that practices all the objectives of this chapter or only the objectives on which your students need more help.

CHAPTER 2 Study Guide and Review *Continued*

Lesson-by-Lesson Review

2-1 Writing Equations

Translate each sentence into an equation.

9. The sum of five times a number x and three is the same as fifteen. **$5x + 3 = 15$**
10. Four times the difference of b and six is equal to b squared. **$4(b - 6) = b^2$**
11. One half of m cubed is the same as four times m minus nine. **$\frac{1}{2}m^3 = 4m - 9$**

Translate each equation into a sentence.

12. $3p + 8 = 20$
13. $h^2 - 5h + 6 = 0$
14. $\frac{3}{4}w^2 + \frac{2}{3}w - \frac{1}{5} = 2$
15. **FENCING** Adrianne wants to create an outdoor rectangular kennel. The length will be three feet more than twice the width. Write and use an equation to find the length and the width of the kennel if Adrianne has 54 feet of fencing. **width: 8 ft, length: 19 ft**

Example 1

Translate the following sentence into an equation.

Six times the sum of a number n and four is the same as the difference between two times n to the second power and ten.

$6(n + 4) = 2n^2 - 10$

Example 2

Translate $3d^2 - 9d + 8 = 4(d + 2)$ into a sentence.

Three times a number d squared minus nine times d increased by eight is equal to four times the sum of d and two.

12. The sum of three times p and eight is the same as twenty.
13. h squared minus five times h plus six is equal to zero.
14. Three-fourths w squared plus two-thirds w minus one fifth is equal to two.

2-2 Solving One-Step Equations

Solve each equation. Check your solution.

16. $x - 9 = 4$ **13**
17. $-6 + g = -11$ **−5**
18. $\frac{5}{9} + w = \frac{7}{9}$ **$\frac{2}{9}$**
19. $3.8 = m + 1.7$ **2.1**
20. $\frac{a}{12} = 5$ **60**
21. $8y = 48$ **6**
22. $\frac{2}{5}b = -4$ **−10**
23. $-\frac{t}{16} = -\frac{7}{8}$ **14**
24. **AGE** Max is four years younger than his sister Brenda. Max is 16 years old. Write and solve an equation to find Brenda's age. **$x - 4 = 16$; 20 years old**

Example 3

Solve $x - 13 = 9$. Check your solution.

$x - 13 = 9$		Original equation
$x - 13 + 13 = 9 + 13$		Add 13 to each side.
$x = 22$		$-13 + 13 = 0$ and $9 + 13 = 22$

To check that 22 is the solution, substitute 22 for x in the original equation.

CHECK $x - 13 = 9$		Original equation
$22 - 13 \stackrel{?}{=} 9$		Substitute 22 for x.
$9 = 9$ ✓		Subtract.

2-3 Solving Multi-Step Equations

Solve each equation. Check your solution.

25. $2d - 4 = 8$ 6
26. $-9 = 3t + 6$ -5
27. $14 = -8 - 2k$ -11
28. $\frac{n}{4} - 7 = -2$ 20
29. $\frac{r+4}{3} = 7$ 17
30. $-18 = \frac{9-a}{2}$ 45
31. $6g - 3.5 = 8.5$ 2
32. $0.2c + 4 = 6$ 10
33. $\frac{f}{3} - 9.2 = 3.5$ 38.1
34. $4 = \frac{-3u-(-7)}{-8}$ 13

35. CONSECUTIVE INTEGERS Find three consecutive odd integers with a sum of 63. 19, 21, 23

36. CONSECUTIVE INTEGERS Find three consecutive integers with a sum of -39. $-12, -13, -14$

Example 4

Solve $7y - 9 = 33$. Check your solution.

$7y - 9 = 33$	Original equation
$7y - 9 + 9 = 33 + 9$	Add 9 to each side.
$7y = 42$	Simplify.
$\frac{7y}{7} = \frac{42}{7}$	Divide each side by 7.
$y = 6$	Simplify.

CHECK	$7y - 9 = 33$	Original equation
	$7(6) - 9 \stackrel{?}{=} 33$	Substitute 6 for *y*.
	$42 - 9 \stackrel{?}{=} 33$	Multiply.
	$33 = 33$ ✓	Subtract.

2-4 Solving Equations with the Variable on Each Side

Solve each equation. Check your solution.

37. $8m + 7 = 5m + 16$ 3
38. $2h - 14 = -5h$ 2
39. $21 + 3j = 9 - 3j$ -2
40. $\frac{x-3}{4} = \frac{x}{2}$ -3
41. $\frac{6r-7}{10} = \frac{r}{4}$ 2
42. $3(p + 4) = 33$ 7
43. $-2(b - 3) - 4 = 18$ -8
44. $4(3w - 2) = 8(2w + 3)$ -8

Write an equation and solve each problem.

45. Find the sum of three consecutive odd integers if the sum of the first two integers is equal to twenty-four less than four times the third integer. 21

46. TRAVEL Mr. Jones drove 480 miles to a business meeting. His travel time to the meeting was 8 hours and from the meeting was 7.5 hours. Find his rate of travel for each leg of the trip. to meeting: 60 mph; from meeting: 64 mph

Example 5

Solve $9w - 24 = 6w + 18$.

$9w - 24 = 6w + 18$	Original equation
$9w - 24 - 6w = 6w + 18 - 6w$	Subtract 6*w* from each side.
$3w - 24 = 18$	Simplify.
$3w - 24 + 24 = 18 + 24$	Add 24 to each side.
$3w = 42$	Simplify.
$\frac{3w}{3} = \frac{42}{3}$	Divide each side by 3.
$w = 14$	Simplify.

Example 6

Write an equation to find three consecutive integers such that three times the sum of the first two integers is the same as thirteen more than four times the third integer.

Let x, $x + 1$, and $x + 2$ represent the three consecutive integers.

$3(x + x + 1) = 4(x + 2) + 13$

connectED.mcgraw-hill.com 141

Additional Answers

51. $\{-5, 17\}$

52. $\{-3, 4\}$

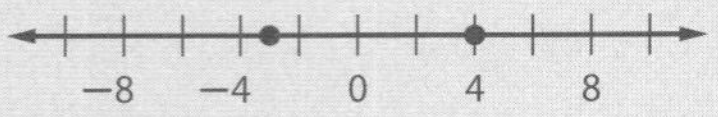

53. $\{-27, 63\}$

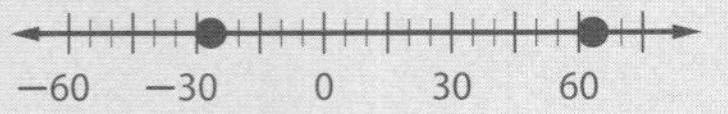

54. $\{18, -42\}$;

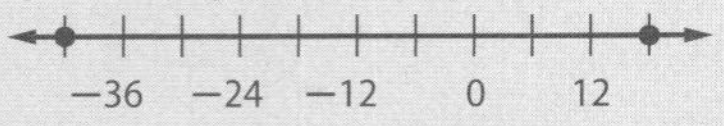

CHAPTER 2 Study Guide and Review *Continued*

2-5 Solving Equations Involving Absolute Value

Evaluate each expression if $m = -8$, $n = 4$, and $p = -12$.

47. $|3m - n|$ **28**

48. $|-2p + m| - 3n$ **4**

49. $-3|6n - 2p|$ **−144**

50. $4|7m + 3p| + 4n$ **384**

Solve each equation. Then graph the solution set. **51–54. See margin.**

51. $|x - 6| = 11$

52. $|-4w + 2| = 14$

53. $\left|\frac{1}{3}d - 6\right| = 15$

54. $\left|\frac{2b}{3} + 8\right| = 20$

Example 7

Solve $|y - 9| = 16$. Then graph the solution set.

Case 1

$y - 9 = 16$	Original equation
$y - 9 + 9 = 16 + 9$	Add 9 to each side.
$y = 25$	Simplify.

Case 2

$y - 9 = -16$	Original equation
$y - 9 + 9 = -16 + 9$	Add 9 to each side.
$y = -7$	Simplify.

The solution set is $\{-7, 25\}$.

Graph the points on a number line.

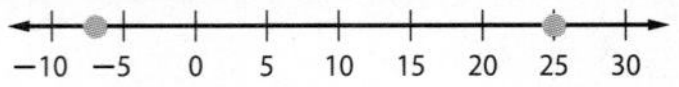

2-6 Ratios and Proportions

Determine whether each pair of ratios are equivalent ratios. Write *yes* or *no*.

55. $\frac{27}{45}, \frac{3}{5}$ **yes**

56. $\frac{18}{32}, \frac{3}{4}$ **no**

Solve each proportion. If necessary, round to the nearest hundredth.

57. $\frac{4}{9} = \frac{a}{45}$ **20**

58. $\frac{3}{8} = \frac{21}{t}$ **56**

59. $\frac{9}{12} = \frac{g}{16}$ **12**

60. **CONSTRUCTION** A new gym is being built at Greenfield Middle School. The length of the gym as shown on the builder's blueprints is 12 inches. Find the actual length of the new gym. **80 ft**

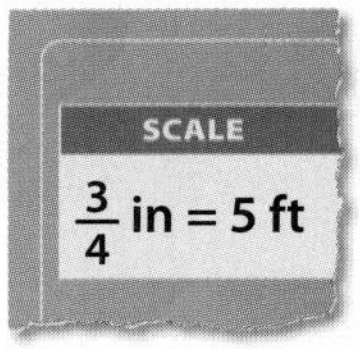

Example 8

Determine whether $\frac{7}{9}$ and $\frac{42}{54}$ are equivalent ratios. Write *yes* or *no*. Justify your answer.

First, simplify each ratio. $\frac{7}{9}$ is already in simplest form.

$$\frac{42}{54} = \frac{42 \div 6}{54 \div 6} = \frac{7}{9}$$

When expressed in simplest form, the ratios are equivalent. The answer is yes.

Example 9

Solve $\frac{r}{8} = \frac{3}{4}$. If necessary, round to the nearest hundredth.

$\frac{r}{8} = \frac{3}{4}$	Original equation
$r(4) = 3(8)$	Find the cross products.
$4r = 24$	Simplify.
$\frac{4r}{4} = \frac{24}{4}$	Divide each side by 4.
$r = 6$	Simplify.

2-7 Percent of Change

State whether each percent of change is a percent of *increase* or a percent of *decrease*. Then find the percent of change. Round to the nearest whole percent.

61. original: 40, new: 50 increase, 25%

62. original: 36, new: 24 decrease, 33%

63. original: \$72, new: \$60 decrease, 17%

Find the total price of each item.

64. boots: \$64, tax: 7% \$68.48

65. video game: \$49, tax: 6.5% \$52.19

66. hockey skates: \$199, tax: 5.25% \$209.45

Find the discounted price of each item.

67. digital media player: \$69.00, discount: 20% \$55.20

68. jacket: \$129, discount: 15% \$109.65

69. backpack: \$45, discount: 25% \$33.75

70. ATTENDANCE An amusement park recorded attendance of 825,000 one year. The next year, the attendance increased to 975,000. Determine the percent of increase in attendance. about 18.2%

Example 10

State whether the percent of change is a percent of *increase* or a percent of *decrease*. Then find the percent of change. Round to the nearest whole percent.

original: 80
final: 60

Subtract the original amount from the final amount to find the amount of change. $60 - 80 = -20$. Since the new amount is less than the original, this is a percent of decrease.

Use the original number, 80, as the base.

change → / original amount →	$\frac{20}{80} = \frac{r}{100}$	Percent proportion
	$20(100) = r(80)$	Find cross products.
	$2000 = 80r$	Simplify.
	$\frac{2000}{80} = \frac{80r}{80}$	Divide each side by 80.
	$25 = r$	Simplify.

The percent of decrease is 25%.

2-8 Literal Equations and Dimensional Analysis

Solve each equation or formula for the variable indicated.

71. $3x + 2y = 9$, for y $y = \frac{9 - 3x}{2}$

72. $P = 2\ell + 2w$, for ℓ $\ell = \frac{P - 2w}{2}$

73. $-5m + 9n = 15$, for m $m = \frac{15 - 9n}{-5}$

74. $14w + 15x = y - 21w$, for w $w = \frac{y - 15x}{35}$

75. $m = \frac{2}{5}y + n$, for y $y = \frac{5}{2}(m - n)$

76. $7d - 3c = f + 2d$, for d $d = \frac{f + 3c}{5}$ 77. $h = \frac{2A}{a + b}$

77. GEOMETRY The formula for the area of a trapezoid is $A = \frac{1}{2}h(a + b)$, where h represents the height and a and b represent the lengths of the bases. Solve for h.

Example 11

Solve $6p - 8n = 12$ for p.

$6p - 8n = 12$	Original equation
$6p - 8n + 8n = 12 + 8n$	Add $8n$ to each side.
$6p = 12 + 8n$	Simplify.
$\frac{6p}{6} = \frac{12 + 8n}{6}$	Divide each side by 6.
$\frac{6p}{6} = \frac{12}{6} + \frac{8}{6}n$	Simplify.
$p = 2 + \frac{4}{3}n$	Simplify.

connectED.mcgraw-hill.com 143

Anticipation Guide

Have students complete the Chapter 2 Anticipation Guide and discuss how their responses have changed now that they have completed Chapter 2.

CHAPTER 2 Study Guide and Review *Continued*

2-9 Weighted Averages

78. **CANDY** Michael is mixing two types of candy for a party. The chocolate pieces cost \$0.40 per ounce, and the hard candy costs \$0.20 per ounce. Michael purchases 20 ounces of the chocolate pieces, and the total cost of his candy was \$11. How many ounces of hard candy did he purchase? **15 oz**

79. **TRAVEL** A car travels 100 miles east in 2 hours and 30 miles north in half an hour. What is the average speed of the car? **52 mph**

80. **FINANCIAL LITERACY** A candle supply store sells votive wax and low-shrink wax. How many pounds of low-shrink wax should be mixed with 8 pounds of votive wax to obtain a blend that sells for \$0.98 a pound? **$10\frac{2}{3}$ lb**

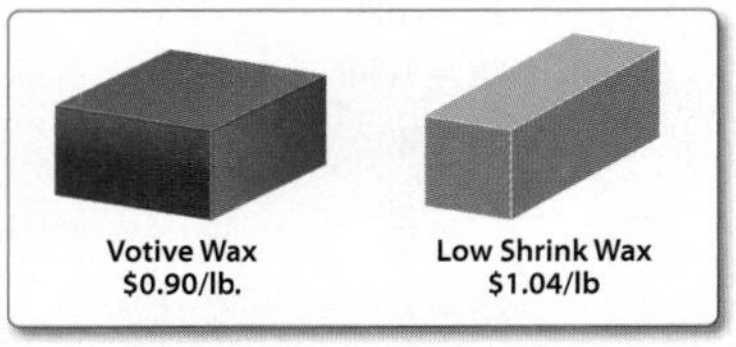

Example 12

METALS An alloy of metals is 25% copper. Another alloy is 50% copper. How much of each should be used to make 1000 grams of an alloy that is 45% copper?

Let x = the amount of the 25% copper alloy. Write and solve an equation.

$0.25x + 0.50(1000 - x) = 0.45(1000)$	Original Equation
$0.25x + 500 - 0.50x = 450$	Distributive Property
$-0.25x + 500 = 450$	Simplify.
$-0.25x + 500 - 500 = 450 - 500$	Subtract 500 from each side.
$-0.25x = -50$	Simplify.
$\frac{-0.25x}{-0.25} = \frac{-50}{-0.25}$	Divide each side by −0.25.
$x = 200$	Simplify.

200 grams of the 25% alloy and 800 grams of the 50% alloy should be used.

CHAPTER 2 Practice Test

Translate each sentence into an equation.

1. The sum of six and four times d is the same as d minus nine. **$6 + 4d = d - 9$**
2. Three times the difference of two times m and five is equal to eight times m to the second power increased by four. **$3(2m - 5) = 8m^2 + 4$**

Solve each equation. Check your solutions.

3. $x - 5 = -11$ **-6**
4. $\frac{2}{3} = w + \frac{1}{4}$ **$\frac{5}{12}$**
5. $\frac{t}{6} = -3$ **-18**

Solve each equation. Check your solution.

6. $2a - 5 = 13$ **9**
7. $\frac{p}{4} - 3 = 9$ **48**
8. **MULTIPLE CHOICE** At Mama Mia Pizza, the price of a large pizza is determined by $P = 9 + 1.5x$, where x represents the number of toppings added to a cheese pizza. Daniel spent $13.50 on a large pizza. How many toppings did he get? **C**

   A 0

   B 1

   C 3

   D 5

Solve each equation. Check your solution.

9. $5y - 4 = 9y + 8$ **-3**
10. $3(2k - 2) = -2(4k - 11)$ **2**
11. **GEOMETRY** Find the value of x so that the figures have the same perimeter. **7**

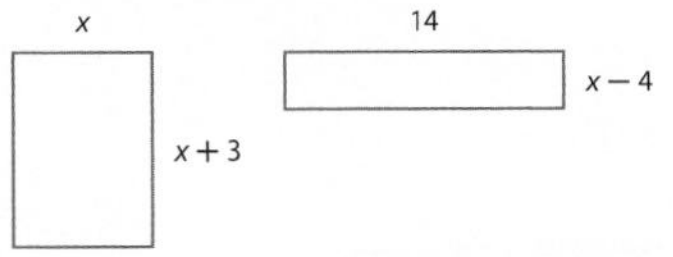

12. Evaluate the expression $|3t - 2u| + 5v$ if $t = 2$, $u = -5$, and $v = -3$. **1**

Solve each equation. Then graph the solution set.

13. $|p - 4| = 6$ **$\{-2, 10\}$**
14. $|2b + 5| = 9$ **$\{-7, 2\}$**

13–14. See margin for graphs.

Solve each proportion. If necessary, round to the nearest hundredth.

15. $\frac{a}{3} = \frac{16}{24}$ **2**
16. $\frac{9}{k + 3} = \frac{3}{5}$ **12**
17. **MULTIPLE CHOICE** Akiko uses 2 feet of thread for every three squares that she sews for her quilt. How many squares can she sew if she has 38 feet of thread? **G**

    F 19

    G 57

    H 76

    J 228

18. State whether the percent of change is a percent of *increase* or a percent of *decrease*. Then find the percent of change. Round to the nearest whole percent. **decrease; 17%**

    original: 54 new: 45

19. Find the total price of a sweatshirt that is priced at $48 and taxed at 6.5%. **$51.12**
20. **SHOPPING** Kirk wants to purchase a wide-screen TV. He sees an advertisement for a TV that was originally priced at $3200 and is 20% off. Find the discounted price of the TV. **$2560**
21. Solve $5x - 3y = 9$ for y. **$y = \frac{5}{3}x - 3$**
22. Solve $A = \frac{1}{2}bh$ for h. **$h = \frac{2A}{b}$**
23. **CHEMISTRY** Deon has 12 milliliters of a 5% solution. He also has a solution that has a concentration of 30%. How many milliliters of the 30% solution does Deon need to add to the 5% solution to obtain a 20% solution? **18 mL**
24. **BICYCLING** Shanee bikes 5 miles to the park in 30 minutes and 3 miles to the library in 45 minutes. What was her average speed? **6.4 mph**
25. **MAPS** On a map of North Carolina, the distance between Charlotte and Wilmington is 14.75 inches. If 2 inches equals 24 miles, what is the approximate distance between the two cities? **177 mi**

Summative Assessment

Use these alternate leveled chapter tests to differentiate assessment for your students.

Leveled Chapter 2 Tests

Form	Type	Level	Page(s)
1	MC	AL	67–68
2A	MC	OL	69–70
2B	MC	OL	71–72
2C	FR	OL	73–74
2D	FR	OL	75–76
3	FR	BL	77–78
Vocabulary Test			66
Extended-Response Test			79

MC = multiple-choice questions
FR = free-response questions

McGraw-Hill eAssessment Customize and create multiple versions of your chapter test and their answer keys. All of the questions from the leveled chapter tests in the *Chapter 2 Resource Masters* are also available on McGraw-Hill eAssessment.

Additional Answers

13.

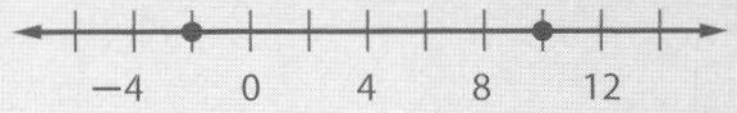

14.

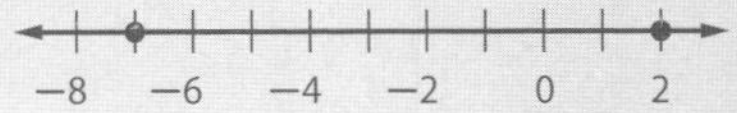

Intervention Planner

TIER 1 On Level OL

If students miss about 25% of the exercises or less,

Then choose a resource:

SE Lessons 2-1, 2-2, 2-3, 2-4, 2-5, 2-6, 2-7, 2-8 and 2-9

Skills Practice, pp. 7, 13, 19, 25, 32, 38, 44, 51, and 57

TE Chapter Project

connectED.mcgraw-hill.com Self-Check Quiz

TIER 2 Strategic Intervention AL approaching grade level

If students miss about 50% of the exercises,

Then choose a resource:

Study Guide and Intervention, Chapter 2, pp. 5, 11, 17, 23, 30, 36, 42, 49, and 55

Quick Review Math Handbook

connectED.mcgraw-hill.com Extra Examples, Personal Tutor, Homework Help

TIER 3 Intensive Intervention 2 or more grades below level

If students miss about 75% of the exercises,

Then use *Math Triumphs, Alg. 1*

connectED.mcgraw-hill.com Extra Examples, Personal Tutor, Homework Help, Review Vocabulary

1 Focus

Objective Use strategies for gridded response standardized test problems.

2 Teach

Scaffolding Questions

Ask:

- For what subjects have you filled in grids when taking a test? Answers will vary.
- What was most confusing about filling in the grids? Answers will vary.
- What can you do to avoid confusion when filling in grids? Sample answer: Make sure you understand the directions before filling in the grids.

CHAPTER 2 Preparing for Standardized Tests

Gridded Response Questions

In addition to multiple-choice, short-answer, and extended-response questions, you will likely encounter gridded-response questions on standardized tests. For gridded-response questions, you must print your answer on an answer sheet and mark in the correct circles on the grid to match your answer.

Strategies for Solving Gridded Response Questions

Step 1

Read the problem carefully.

- **Ask yourself:** "What information is given?" "What do I need to find?" "How do I solve this type of problem?"
- **Solve the Problem:** Use the information given in the problem to solve.
- **Check your answer:** If time permits, check your answer to make sure you have solved the problem correctly.

Step 2

Write your answer in the answer boxes.

- Print only one digit or symbol in each answer box.
- Do not write any digits or symbols outside the answer boxes.
- You may write your answer with the first digit in the left answer box, or with the last digit in the right answer box. You may leave blank any boxes you do not need on the right or the left side of your answer.

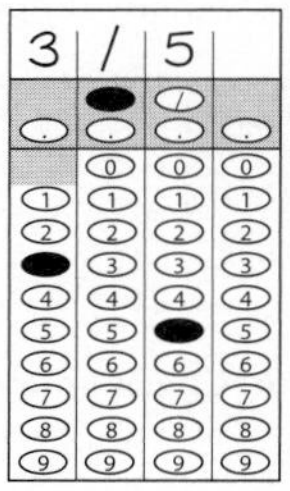

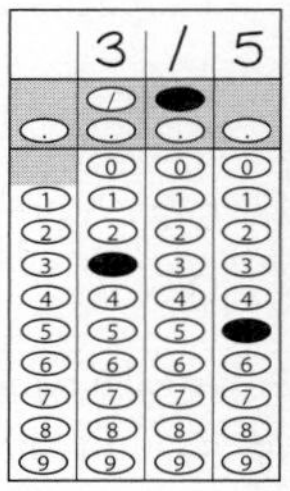

Step 3

Fill in the grid.

- Fill in only one bubble for every answer box that you have written in. Be sure not to fill in a bubble under a blank answer box.
- Fill in each bubble completely and clearly.

Standardized Test Example

Read the problem. Identify what you need to know. Then use the information in the problem to solve.

GRIDDED RESPONSE Ashley is 3 years older than her sister, Tina. Combined, the sum of their ages is 27 years. How old is Ashley?

146 | Chapter 2 | Preparing for Standardized Tests

Read the problem carefully. You are told that Ashley is 3 years older than her sister and that their ages combined equal 27 years. You need to find Ashley's age.

Solve the Problem

Words	Ashley's age plus Tina's age is equal to 27 years.
Variable	Let a represent Ashley's age. Then Tina's age is $a - 3$, since she is 3 years younger than Ashley.
Equation	$a \quad + \quad (a - 3) \quad = \quad 27$

Solve the equation for a.

$a + (a - 3) = 27$ Original equation.

$2a - 3 = 27$ Add like terms.

$2a = 30$ Add 3 to each side.

$a = 15$ Divide each side by 2.

Since we let a represent Ashley's age, we know that she is 15 years old.

Fill in the Grid

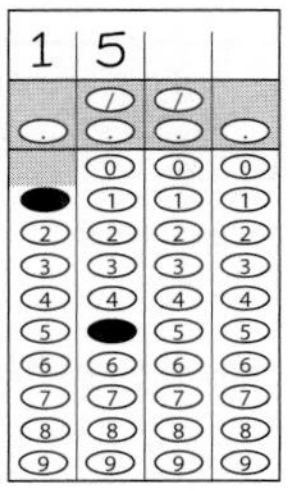

Additional Example

GRIDDED RESPONSE Derek and Tamara mailed a total of 86 invitations for the upcoming environmental fair. If Derek mailed 18 more invitations than Tamara did, how many invitations did Tamara mail?

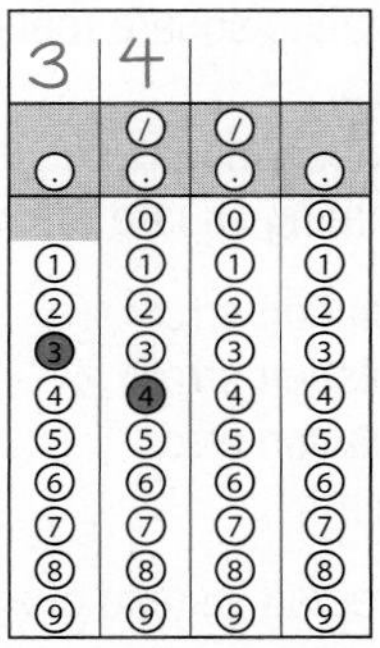

Exercises

Read each problem. Identify what you need to know. Then use the information in the problem to solve. Copy and complete an answer grid on your paper.

1. Orlando has \$1350 in the bank. He wants to increase his balance to a total of \$2550 by depositing \$40 each week from his paycheck. How many weeks will he need to save in order to reach his goal? **30**

2. Fourteen less than three times a number is equal to 40. Find the number. **18**

3. The table shows the regular prices and sale prices of certain items at a department store this week. What is the percent of discount during the sale? **20**

Item	Regular Price (\$)	Sale Price (\$)
pillows	25	20
sweaters	30	24
entertainment center	125	100

4. Maureen is driving from Raleigh, North Carolina, to Charlotte, North Carolina, to visit her brother at college. If she averages 65 miles per hour on the trip, then the equation $\frac{d}{2.65} = 65$ can be solved for the distance d. What is the distance to the nearest mile from Raleigh to Charlotte? **172**

5. Find the value of x so that the figures below have the same area. **5**

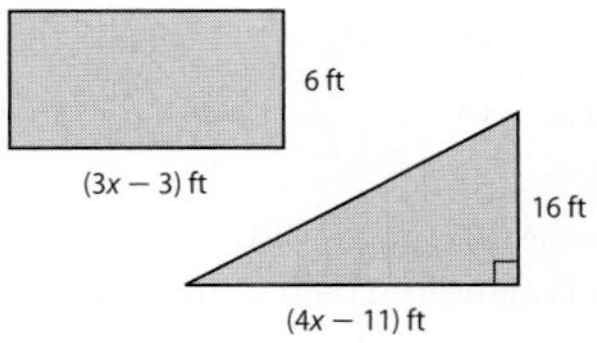

6. The sum of three consecutive whole numbers is 18. What is the greatest of the numbers? **7**

3 Assess

Use Exercises 1–6 to assess students' understanding.

Diagnose Student Errors

Survey student responses for each item. Class trends may indicate common errors and misconceptions.

1. A mistakenly chose estimate of the negative instead of positive square root
B misunderstood concept of estimating square roots
C correct
D misunderstood concept of estimating square roots

2. F calculation error
G calculation error
H calculation error
J correct

3. A subtracted instead of added 27
B guess
C correct
D guess

4. F correct
G calculation error: added $5x + 8x$ instead of $5x + (-8x)$ and $-12 + 18$ instead of $-12 + (-18)$
H multiple calculation errors
J calculation error: added $-12 + (-9)$)

5. A correct
B guess or calculation error
C guess or calculation error
D guess or calculation error

6. F confused Associative and Commutative Properties
G correct
H confused Associative and Distributive Properties
J confused Associative Property with Closure Property

7. A guess or calculation error: divided by $\frac{1}{10}$
B correct
C guess or calculation error: divided by $\frac{1}{5}$
D guess

8. F wrote expression for hours only
G does not understand how to write expressions
H transposed hours and fee to mow lawns
J correct

CHAPTER 2 Standardized Test Practice

Cumulative, Chapters 1 and 2

Multiple Choice

Read each question. Then fill in the correct answer on the answer document provided by your teacher or on a sheet of paper.

1. Which point on the number line best represents the position of $\sqrt{8}$? C

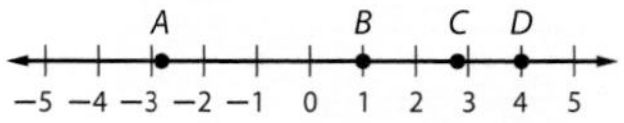

A -2.8
B 1
C 2.8
D 4

2. Find the value of x so that the figures have the same area. J

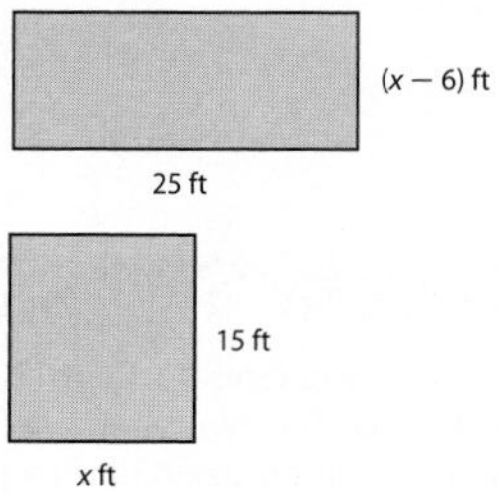

F 10
G 12
H 13
J 15

3. The elevation of Black Mountain is 27 feet more than 16 times the lowest point in the state. If the elevation of the lowest point in the state is 257 feet, what is the elevation of Black Mountain? C

A 4,085 feet
B 4,103 feet
C 4,139 feet
D 4,215 feet

4. The expression $(3x^2 + 5x - 12) - 2(x^2 + 4x + 9)$ is equivalent to which of the following? F

F $x^2 - 3x - 30$
G $x^2 + 13x + 6$
H $5x^2 + x - 18$
J $x^2 + 3x - 21$

5. The amount of soda, in fluid ounces, dispensed from a machine must satisfy the equation $|a - 0.4| = 20$. Which of the following graphs shows the acceptable minimum and maximum amounts that can be dispensed from the machine? A

A
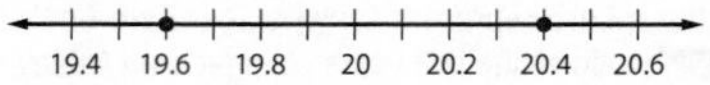

B
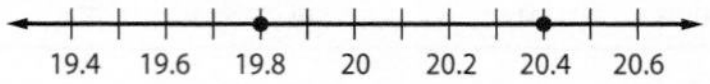

C
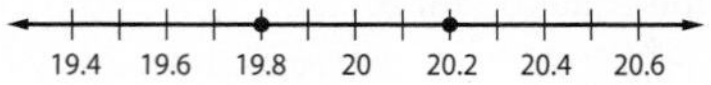

D
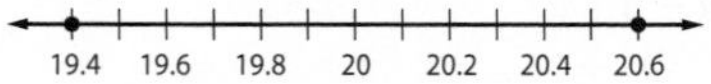

6. If a and b represent integers, $ab = ba$ is an example of which property? G

F Associative Property
G Commutative Property
H Distributive Property
J Closure Property

7. The sum of one fifth of a number and three is equal to half of the number. What is the number? B

A 5
B 10
C 15
D 20

8. Aaron charges \$15 to mow the lawn and \$10 per hour for other gardening work. Which expression represents his earnings? J

F $10h$
G $15h$
H $15h + 10$
J $15 + 10h$

Test-Taking Tip

Question 2 Use the figures and the formula for area to set up an equation. The product of the length and width of each figure should be equal.

Short Response/Gridded Response

Record your answers on the answer sheet provided by your teacher or on a sheet of paper.

9. The formula for the lateral area of a cylinder is $A = 2\pi rh$, where r is the radius and h is the height. Solve the equation for h. $h = \frac{A}{2\pi r}$

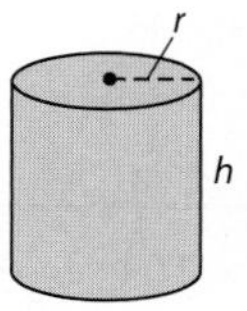

10. GRIDDED RESPONSE Solve the proportion $\frac{x}{18} = \frac{7}{21}$. 6

11. GRIDDED RESPONSE The table shows the cost of renting a moving van. If Miguel budgeted $75, how many miles could he drive the van and maintain his budget? 425

Moving Van Rentals	
Flat Fee	$50 for up to 300 miles
Variable Fee	$0.20 per mile over 300

12. Find the height of a soup can if the area of the label is 302 square centimeters and the radius of the can is 4 centimeters. Round to the nearest whole number. 12 cm

13. GRIDDED RESPONSE Lara's car needed a particular part that costs $75. The mechanic charges $50 per hour to install the part. If the total cost was $350, how many hours did it take to install the part? 5.5

14. Lucinda is buying a set of patio furniture that is on sale for $\frac{4}{5}$ of the original price. After she uses a $50 gift certificate, the total cost before sales tax is $222. What was the original price of the patio furniture? $340

Extended Response

Record your answers on a sheet of paper. Show your work.

15a. $120 + 2x = (12 + 5 + 5)x$ or $120 + 2x = 22x$; $x = 6$ visits

15. The city zoo offers a yearly membership that costs $120. A yearly membership includes free parking. Members can also purchase a ride pass for an additional $2 per day that allows them unlimited access to the rides in the park. Nonmembers pay $12 for admission to the park, $5 for parking, and $5 for a ride pass.

a. Write an equation that could be solved for the number of visits it would take for the total cost to be the same for a member and a nonmember if they both purchase a ride pass each day. Solve the equation.

b. What would the total cost be for members and nonmembers after this number of visits? $132

c. Georgena is deciding whether or not to purchase a yearly membership. Explain how she could use the results above to help make her decision.
Sample answer: If she will go more than 6 times, she should buy the membership. Otherwise, she should simply pay the daily fees.

Need ExtraHelp?

If you missed Question...	1	2	3	4	5	6	7	8	9	10	11	12	13	14	15
Go to Lesson...	0-2	2-4	2-3	1-4	2-5	1-3	2-4	1-1	2-8	2-6	2-3	2-8	2-3	2-3	2-4

Formative Assessment

You can use these pages to benchmark student progress.

Standardized Test Practice, pp. 80–82

Answer Sheet Practice

Have students simulate taking a standardized test by recording their answers on a practice recording sheet.

Student Recording Sheet

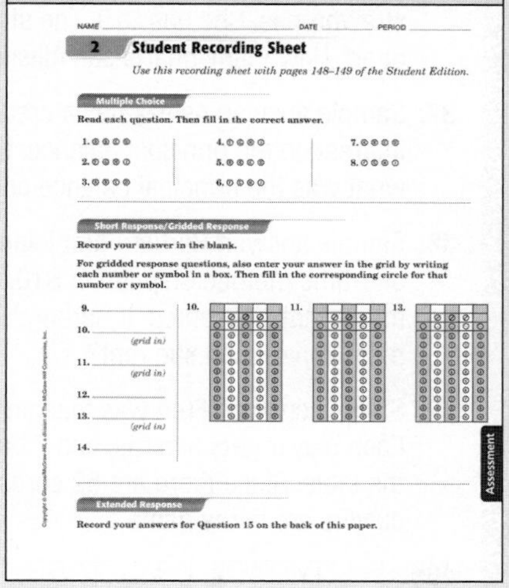

McGraw-Hill eAssessment Create practice tests that align to your state standards, the Common Core State Standards, and other national standards such as TIMSS and NAEP.

Homework Option

Get Ready for Chapter 3 Assign students the exercises on p. 151 as homework to assess whether they possess the prerequisite skills needed for the next chapter.

Lesson 2-1

30. Sample answer: The sum of *j* and sixteen is thirty-five.

31. Sample answer: Four times *m* is equal to fifty-two.

32. Sample answer: Seven times the sum of *p* and twenty-three is the same as one hundred two.

33. Sample answer: Fifteen less than the square of *r* equals the sum of *t* and nineteen.

34. Sample answer: Two fifths of *v* plus three fourths is identical to two thirds of *x* squared.

35. Sample answer: One third minus four fifths of *z* is four thirds of *y* cubed.

36. Sample answer: Allison is going to the market to buy some strawberries. She has $10. The strawberries cost $2.50 for each quart. How many quarts can Allison buy?

37. Sample answer: Ashley has a credit card that charges 12% interest on the principal balance. If Ashley's payment was $224, what was the principal balance on the credit card?

38. Sample answer: Barbara first joined a video club that charged a one-time membership fee of $10. She then paid $1.50 for each movie that she rented. If Barbara's first bill came to $14.50, how many movies did she rent?

39. Sample answer: Fred was teaching his friends a new card game. Each player gets 5 cards, and 7 cards are placed in the center of the table. Since there are 52 cards in a deck, find how many players are in the game.

46c.

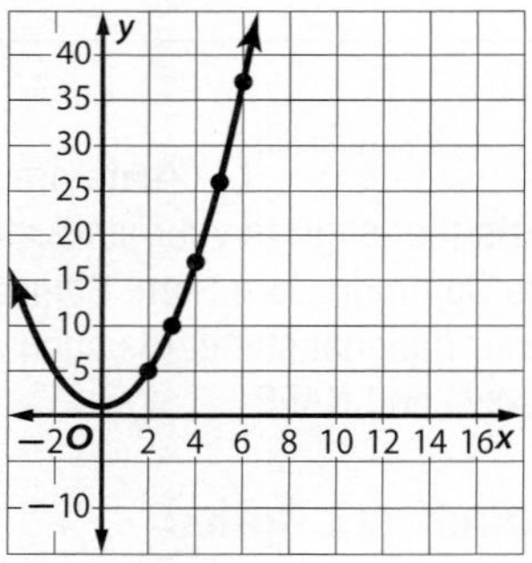

continuous

47. Sample answer: My favorite television show has 30 new episodes each year. So far eight have aired. How many new episodes are left?

50. Sample answer: First, you should identify the unknown quantity or quantities for which you are trying to solve, and assign variables. Then, you should look for key words or phrases that can help you to determine operations that are being used. You can then write the equation using the numbers that you are given and the variables and operations that you assigned.

Lesson 2-4

43. Sample answer: $2x + 1 = \frac{3}{2}x - 2$; First I chose $\frac{3}{2}$ as the fractional coefficient. Then I chose 2 for the coefficient for the variable on the other side of the equation. After substituting -6 in for x on both sides, 1 must be added to the left and 2 must be subtracted from the right to balance the equation.

Lesson 2-5

52c.

Lesson 2-6

49. If the tank is about $\frac{9}{16}$ full, he has about $\frac{9}{16} \times 10$ or $5\frac{5}{8}$ gal of gas left. At 32 miles per gallon, he will be able to travel $32 \times 5\frac{5}{8}$ or 180 miles. Since Atlanta is 200 miles away, he will run out of gas about 20 miles before reaching the city if he doesn't stop to get gas.

50. Sample answer: A business can use ratios to compare how many of the potential customers in an area use their business. Using ratios, a pizza business can find the number of potential customers in their area and compare them to how many they have. They can do the same with their competitors.

NOTES

Chapter 2 Answer Appendix

Chapter Planner

Diagnostic Assessment
Quick Check

	EXPLORE 3-1 (45 min: 0.5 day; 90 min: 0.5 day)	LESSON 3-1 (45 min: 0.5 day; 90 min: 0.5 day)	LESSON 3-2 (45 min: 1 day; 90 min: 0.5 day)
Title	**Algebra Lab: Analyzing Linear Graphs**	**Graphing Linear Equations**	**Solving Linear Equations by Graphing**
Objectives	▪ Analyze the key features of linear graphs.	▪ Identify linear equations, intercepts, and zeros. ▪ Graph linear equations.	▪ Solve linear equations by graphing. ▪ Estimate solutions to an equation by graphing.
Key Vocabulary	linear function constant function	linear equation standard form constant *x*-intercept *y*-intercept	linear function parent function family of graphs root zeros
Content Standards		PS.8	PS.4
Multiple Representations			
Lesson Resources	connectED.mcgraw-hill.com Animations Personal Tutor Vocabulary	connectED.mcgraw-hill.com Leveled Worksheets Vocabulary Animations Personal Tutor Virtual Manipulatives Self-Check Quiz ▪ *5-Minute Check* ▪ *Study Notebook* ▪ *Teaching Algebra with Manipulatives*	connectED.mcgraw-hill.com Leveled Worksheets Quiz 1 Vocabulary Animations Personal Tutor Virtual Manipulatives Self-Check Quiz ▪ *5-Minute Check* ▪ *Study Notebook*
Resources for Every Lesson	IWB eStudent Edition IWB Interactive Classroom	▪ eTeacher Edition ▪ eSolutions Manual ▪ McGraw-Hill eAssessment	
Differentiated Instruction		pp. 158, 162	pp. 164, 168

IWB All digital assets are Interactive Whiteboard ready.

Suggested Pacing			
Time Periods	Instruction	Review & Assess	Total
45-minute	9 days	2 days	11 days
90-minute	5 days	1 day	6 days

EXTEND 3-2 45 min: 0.5 day 90 min: 0.5 day	EXPLORE 3-3 45 min: 0.5 day 90 min: 0.5 day	LESSON 3-3 45 min: 1 day 90 min: 0.5 day	LESSON 3-4 45 min: 1 day 90 min: 0.5 day
Graphing Technology Lab: Graphing Linear Equations	**Algebra Lab: Rate of Change of a Linear Function**	**Rate of Change and Slope**	**Direct Variation**
▪ Change the viewing window so that a complete graph of a linear function can be displayed.	▪ Investigate the steepness of a line using concrete models.	▪ Use rate of change to solve problems. ▪ Find the slope of a line.	▪ Write and graph direct variation equations. ▪ Solve problems involving direct variation.
standard viewing window complete graph		rate of change slope	direct variation constant of variation constant of proportionality
PS.5		PS.2, AI.F.4, AI.L.5	PS.1, PS.6, AI.L.1, AI.L.2
connectED.mcgraw-hill.com Vocabulary Animations Personal Tutor **Materials:** ▪ TI-83/84 Plus or other graphing calculator	connectED.mcgraw-hill.com Animations ▪ *Teaching Algebra with Manipulatives* **Materials:** ▪ 2 rulers ▪ 5 books ▪ tape ▪ grid paper	connectED.mcgraw-hill.com Leveled Worksheets Quiz 2 Vocabulary Animations Personal Tutor Virtual Manipulatives Self-Check Quiz ▪ *5-Minute Check* ▪ *Study Notebook* ▪ *Teaching Algebra with Manipulatives*	connectED.mcgraw-hill.com Leveled Worksheets Vocabulary Animations Personal Tutor Virtual Manipulatives Self-Check Quiz ▪ *5-Minute Check* ▪ *Study Notebook*

IWB eStudent Edition
IWB Interactive Classroom
- eTeacher Edition
- eSolutions Manual
- McGraw-Hill eAssessment

		pp. 175, 176, 180	pp. 185, 188

Formative Assessment
Mid-Chapter Quiz

Chapter Planner

	LESSON 3-5 — 45 min: 2 days; 90 min: 0.5 day	EXTEND 3-5 — 45 min: 0.5 day; 90 min: 0.25 day	LESSON 3-6 — 45 min: 1.5 days; 90 min: 0.75 day
Title	**Arithmetic Sequences as Linear Functions**	**Algebra Lab: Inductive and Deductive Reasoning**	**Proportional and Nonproportional Relationships**
Objectives	▪ Recognize arithmetic sequences. ▪ Relate arithmetic sequences to linear functions.	▪ Investigate inductive and deductive reasoning.	▪ Write an equation for a proportional relationship. ▪ Write an equation for a nonproportional relationship.
Key Vocabulary	sequence terms arithmetic sequence common difference	inductive reasoning deductive reasoning	
Content Standards		PS.3	PS.7, AI.F.4, AI.L.3
Multiple Representations			
Lesson Resources	connectED.mcgraw-hill.com Leveled Worksheets Quiz 3 Vocabulary Animations Personal Tutor Virtual Manipulatives Self-Check Quiz ▪ *5-Minute Check* ▪ *Study Notebook*	connectED.mcgraw-hill.com Vocabulary ▪ *Teaching Algebra with Manipulatives*	connectED.mcgraw-hill.com Leveled Worksheets Quiz 4 Personal Tutor Virtual Manipulatives Self-Check Quiz ▪ *5-Minute Check* ▪ *Study Notebook*
Resources for Every Lesson	IWB eStudent Edition IWB Interactive Classroom	▪ eTeacher Edition ▪ eSolutions Manual ▪ McGraw-Hill eAssessment	
Differentiated Instruction	pp. 190, 192, 195		pp. 199, 202

Summative Assessment
Study Guide and Review
Practice Test

IWB All digital assets are Interactive Whiteboard ready.

Quick Review Math Handbook*

is Glencoe's mathematical handbook for students and parents.

HotWords includes a glossary of terms.

HotTopics consists of two parts:

- explanations of key mathematical concepts
- exercises to check students' understanding.

Lesson	Hot Topics Section	Lesson	Hot Topic Section
3-1	6.2, 6.4, 6.7	3-4	6.4, 6.8
3-2	6.2, 6.4, 6.7	3-5	6.7
3-3	2.4, 6.8	3-6	6.1

What the Research Says ...

The category of instructional strategies that affects student achievement most is *identifying similarities and differences.* (Marzano et al, 2001)

- Make comparisons and assign tasks that involve comparison. Encourage students to compare the key features of linear functions and equations of lines. Focus on slopes and intercepts.
- Classify topics and assign tasks that involve classification. Encourage students to examine many examples of equations and graphs of functions to develop categories. Then generalize types of functions.

[Source: Marzano, R.J., Pickering, D.J., & Pollock, J.E. (2001). *Classroom instruction that works: Research-based strategies for increasing students achievement.*, Alexandria, VA: Association for Supervision and Curriculum Development.]

Project CRISS℠

STUDY SKILL

Students can use a free-form map to create their own representation of the concepts they are learning. Free-form mapping is done as a cooperative activity after students have read about and discussed a lesson or chapter.

Give groups of students large sheets of paper or and markers. Have them present the important ideas from the lesson or chapter on paper using words, pictures, graphs, and diagrams.

The free-form map at the right represents the concepts in Lesson 3-1.

Graphing Linear Equations

Linear Equation Standard Form	Intercepts	Graphing with Intercepts
$Ax + By = C$ If it cannot be written in standard form, it is not a linear equation.	Linear graphs have no more than 1 intercept on each axis.	Use $x = 0$ to solve for the y-intercept and $y = 0$ to solve for the x-intercept. Then use those 2 points to graph the line.

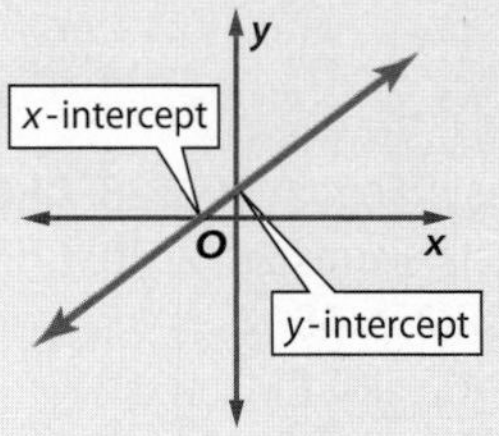

Creating Independence through Student-owned Strategies

Assessment and Intervention

SE = Student Edition, **TE** = Teacher Edition, **CRM** = Chapter Resource Masters

	Diagnosis	Prescription
DIAGNOSTIC ASSESSMENT	**Beginning Chapter 3**	
	Get Ready for Chapter 3 **SE**	Response to Intervention **TE**
	Beginning Every Lesson	
	Then, Now, Why? **SE** 5-Minute Check	Chapter 0 **SE** *Quick Review Math Handbook*
FORMATIVE ASSESSMENT	**During/After Every Lesson**	
	Guided Practice **SE**, every example Check Your Understanding **SE** H.O.T. Problems **SE** Spiral Review **SE** Additional Examples **TE** Watch Out! **TE** Step 4, Assess **TE** Chapter 3 Quizzes **CRM**, pp. 45–46 Self-Check Quizzes connectED.mcgraw-hill.com	**TIER 1 Intervention** Skills Practice **CRM**, Ch. 1–3 connectED.mcgraw-hill.com **TIER 2 Intervention** Differentiated Instruction **TE** Differentiated Homework Options **TE** Study Guide and Intervention **CRM**, Ch. 1–3 *Quick Review Math Handbook* **TIER 3 Intervention** *Math Triumphs, Alg. 1, Ch. 3*
	Mid-Chapter	
	Mid-Chapter Quiz **SE** Mid-Chapter Test **CRM**, p. 47 McGraw-Hill eAssessment	**TIER 1 Intervention** Skills Practice **CRM**, Ch. 1–3 connectED.mcgraw-hill.com **TIER 2 Intervention** Study Guide and Intervention **CRM**, Ch. 1–3; *Quick Review Math Handbook* **TIER 3 Intervention** *Math Triumphs, Alg. 1, Ch. 3*
	Before Chapter Test	
	Chapter Study Guide and Review **SE** Practice Test **SE** Standardized Test Practice **SE** Chapter Test connectED.mcgraw-hill.com Standardized Test Practice connectED.mcgraw-hill.com Vocabulary Review connectED.mcgraw-hill.com McGraw-Hill eAssessment	**TIER 1 Intervention** Skills Practice **CRM**, Ch. 1–3 connectED.mcgraw-hill.com **TIER 2 Intervention** Study Guide and Intervention **CRM**, Ch. 1–3; *Quick Review Math Handbook* **TIER 3 Intervention** *Math Triumphs, Alg. 1, Ch. 3*
SUMMATIVE ASSESSMENT	**After Chapter 3**	
	Multiple-Choice Tests, Forms 1, 2A, 2B **CRM**, pp. 49–54 Free-Response Tests, Forms 2C, 2D, 3 **CRM**, pp. 55–60 Vocabulary Test **CRM**, p. 48 Extended Response Test **CRM**, p. 61 Standardized Test Practice **CRM**, pp. 62–64 McGraw-Hill eAssessment	Study Guide and Intervention **CRM**, Ch. 1–3 *Quick Review Math Handbook* connectED.mcgraw-hill.com

Differentiated Instruction

Option 1 Reaching All Learners AL OL BL ELL

Visual/Spatial Provide students with four pipe-cleaners, glue, poster board, and grid paper. Ask students to glue the pipe-cleaners on the grids on their poster to demonstrates positive slope, negative slope, no slope, and zero slope. Have students find two points on each line and calculate the slope of each line.

Kinesthetic On the board write the following sentences, drawing three rectangles in each sentence as shown.

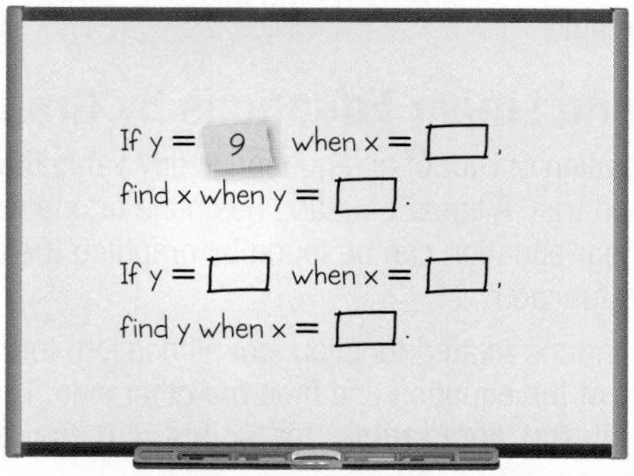

On self-sticking notes, write the digits 1–9. Ask one student to stick 1- or 2-digit numbers in the rectangles of one of the sentences. Then as a class, write a direct variation equation that relates *x* and *y*; then solve for either *x* or *y*.

Option 2 Approaching Level AL

Put students into groups of three. One student should write down a starting number (the first term of the sequence) and a value for *d*, the common difference. Ask the second student to use a calculator to add the common difference six times, making sure to proceed slowly enough so that the third student can record each sum showing on the calculator's screen. Then ask the group to write a formula that can be used to find the *n*th term of their sequence. Ask students to trade roles and then repeat this activity.

Option 3 English Learners ELL

Use floor tiles as a grid or use masking tape on the floor to create a grid. Have students walk the path from one point to another on the floor, allowing only one horizontal and vertical path. Ask them to describe their trip in terms of positive and negative movement and the number of squares traveled in each direction. Then have them write the description of their movement as the slope of the line connecting these two points.

Option 4 Beyond Level BL

Have small groups of students use a triple-beam balance and 4 stacks of identical washers. Each stack should contain a different number of washers tied together so that students cannot weigh just one washer. Record the number of washers, *n*, in each stack. Have students weigh one stack and then predict the weights, *W*, of the other stacks. How do they think this relates to the equation $W = kn$? See students' work. What does *k* represent? the weight of each washer

Focus on Mathematical Content

VerticalAlignment

Before Chapter 3

- locate and name points on a coordinate plane using ordered pairs
- simplify numeric expressions
- represent relationships among quantities using graphs

Related Topics from Grade 8

- use operations to solve problems involving rational numbers

Related Topics from Grade 8

- solve linear equations

Chapter 3

Related Topics from Algebra 1

- create, use, translate, and make connections among algebraic, tabular, graphical, or verbal descriptions of linear functions
- interpret the meaning of intercepts in situations using data, symbolic representation, or graphs
- determine the intercepts of the graphs of linear functions and zeros of linear functions from graphs, tables, and algebraic representations
- look for patterns and represent generalizations algebraically
- develop the concept of slope as rate of change and determine the slope from graphs, tables, and algebraic representations
- interpret the meaning of slope in situations using data, symbolic representations, or graphs
- relate direct variation to linear functions and solve problems involving proportional change

After Chapter 3

Preparation for Algebra 2

- use properties and attributes of functions and apply functions to problem situations
- identify mathematical domains and ranges and determine reasonable domain and range values for given situations, both continuous and discrete
- solve systems of equations
- use functions to model and make predictions involving direct variation

Lesson-by-Lesson Preview

3-1 Graphing Linear Equations

Linear equations can be written in the form $Ax + By = C$, the standard form of a linear equation. An equation is linear if the Properties of Equality can be applied to rewrite it in standard form. The graph of a linear function has at most one x-intercept (where the graph crosses the x-axis) and one y-intercept (where the graph crosses the y-axis). The intercepts can be found by alternately replacing x and y with 0. If these two points are graphed and then a line that connects them is drawn, all of the ordered pairs that lie on the line are solutions of the equation. Values of x for which $y = 0$ are called zeros. A zero is an x-intercept.

3-2 Solving Linear Equations by Graphing

The solution or root of an equation is any value that makes the equation true. A linear equation has none or one root. The root of a linear equation can be found by graphing the equation's related function.

- To find the related function, get all nonzero terms on one side of the equation and 0 on the other side. Then replace 0 with $f(x)$. For example, for $3x + 4 = 0$, the related function is $3x + 4 = f(x)$.
- To graph the function, make a table of values.
- When the graph is a line (horizontal) that does not intersect the x-axis, there is no solution.
- When the graph is a line that intersects the x-axis, there is one solution, the value of the x-intercept. This value is also called the *zero* of the function.
- When the x-intercept is not a whole number, an estimate can be made and checked using algebra.

3-3 Rate of Change and Slope

Rate of change is a ratio that describes, on average, how one quantity changes with respect to a change in another quantity. Slope can be used to describe rate of change.

The slope of a line is the ratio of the vertical change in the line to the horizontal change in the line. The slope can be expressed in several ways.

- slope $= \frac{\text{rise}}{\text{run}}$

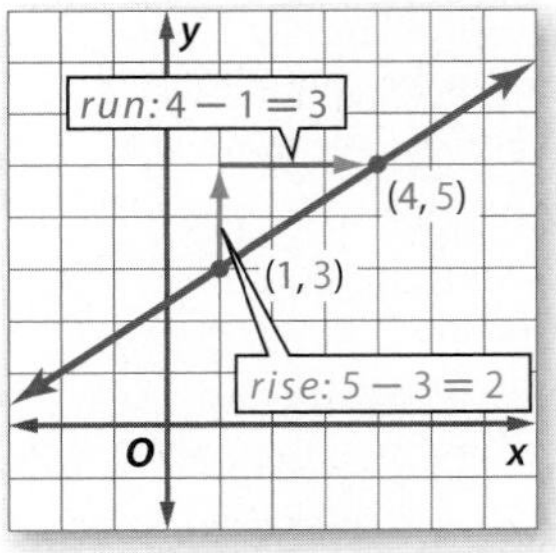

This can be observed from graphed lines, and it works well for whole number increments for the rise and run.

- $m = \frac{y_2 - y_1}{x_2 - x_1}$

This algebraic formula represents slope m using the coordinates of two points on a line (x_1, y_1) and (x_2, y_2). You can use this formula to determine the slope of a line without a graph if you know two points on the line.

3-4 Direct Variation

The concept of direct variation grows from the meaning of ratio (Lesson 2-6). If the ratio of two variables is a constant, then direct variation is the way of expressing the relationship between the two variables. That is, $\frac{y}{x} = k$, where y and x are variables and k is the constant (number) of variation. Multiply each side of the equation by x and you get $y = kx$. This represents an equation of a line. The constant k has the same value as the slope of the line. So, when you graph a direct variation, you are graphing lines with slope k. All of these lines pass through the origin. In real-world applications, most direct variation graphs are found in the first quadrant.

3-5 Arithmetic Sequences as Linear Functions

A sequence is a set of numbers in a specific order. The numbers in a sequence are called terms.

- If the terms of a sequence increase or decrease at a constant rate, it is called an arithmetic sequence.
- The difference between successive terms of an arithmetic sequence is called the common difference d.
- Any term of an arithmetic sequence can be found by adding the common difference to the preceding term.

The formula that can be used to find a specific term in an arithmetic sequence is $a_n = a_1 + (n - 1)d$. This means to find a specific term a_n find the sum of the first term a_1 and the product of the common difference, times one less than n, the number of the specific term.

3-6 Proportional and Nonproportional Relationships

When you solve a problem by making a conclusion based on a pattern, you are using inductive reasoning. Often patterns in sequences of figures or numbers can be found. Sometimes these patterns can lead to a general rule for the pattern. If the relationship between the domain and range of the relation is linear, a linear equation can be used to describe the relationship. Some linear relationships are proportional and can be modeled with an equation of the form $y = kx$. Other linear relationships are nonproportional.

To write an equation for a pattern that exhibits a linear relationship and is made up of a set of data with two variables (x and y) follow these steps:

- Use a ratio to compare the common difference of the range values to the common difference of the domain values. This ratio should be a constant ratio.
- Then, write the equation as this:
  dependant variable = constant ratio × independent variable. That is, $y =$ (constant ratio)x.
- Check to be sure this equation works for the set of data. If it does not, then check to see if the difference between the value obtained for the y using your equation and the given value of y is the same for each pair of x- and y-values in the pattern. If so, add that difference to one side of the equation to correctly describe the relation.

Mc Graw Hill Professional Development

Targeted professional development has been articulated throughout Algebra 1. More quality, customized professional development is available from McGraw-Hill Professional Development. Visit connectED.mcgraw-hill.com for details on each product.

- Online Lessons emphasize the strategies and techniques used to teach Algebra 1. Includes streaming video, interactive pages, and online tools.
- Video Workshops allow mentors, coaches, or leadership personnel to facilitate on-site workshops on educational strategies in mathematics and mathematical concepts.
- MHPD Online (www.mhpdonline.com) offers online professional development with video clips of instructional strategies, links, student activities, and news and issues in education.
- Teaching Today (teachingtoday.glencoe.com) gives secondary teachers practical strategies and materials that inspire excellence and innovation in teaching.

Chapter Project

Service with a Smile

Students use what they have learned about linear functions to complete a project.

This chapter project addresses financial literacy, as well as several specific skills identified as being essential to student success by the Framework for 21st Century Learning.

Visit connectED.mcgraw-hill.com for student and teacher handouts.

Key Vocabulary Introduce the key vocabulary in the chapter using the routine below.

Define: A term is a number, or variable, or a product or quotient of numbers and variables.

Example: $2x^2 + 6x + 5$, where each part of the expression, containing numbers or numbers and variables between operation signs, is called a term.

Ask: How many different terms are in this expression? three

CHAPTER 3 Linear Functions

Then

- You solved linear equations algebraically.

Now

In this chapter you will:

- Identify linear equations, intercepts, and zeros.
- Graph and write linear equations.
- Use rate of change to solve problems.

Why?

- **AMUSEMENT PARKS** The Magic Kingdom in Orlando, Florida, is one of the most popular amusement parks in the world. Yearly attendance figures increase steadily each year. Quantities like populations that change with respect to time can be described using rate of change. Often you can represent these situations with linear functions.

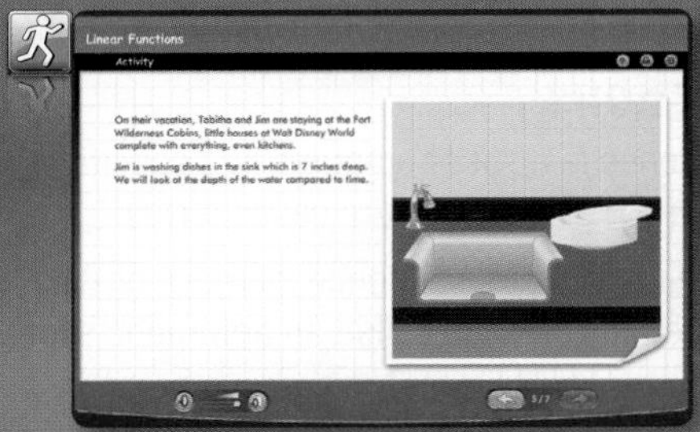

connectED.mcgraw-hill.com **Your Digital Math Portal**

Animation | Vocabulary | eGlossary | Personal Tutor | Virtual Manipulatives | Graphing Calculator | Audio | Foldables | Self-Check Practice | Worksheets

Content Standards
AI.F.4, AI.L.1, AI.L.2, AI.L.3, AI.L.5

Process Standards
PS.1, PS.2, PS.3, PS.4, PS.5, PS.6, PS.7, PS.8

Get Ready for the Chapter

Diagnose Readiness | You have two options for checking prerequisite skills.

1 Textbook Option

Take the Quick Check below. Refer to the Quick Review for help.

1–6. See Chapter 3 Answer Appendix.

QuickCheck

Graph each ordered pair on a coordinate grid.

1. $(-3, 3)$ **2.** $(-2, 1)$ **3.** $(3, 0)$

4. $(-5, 5)$ **5.** $(0, 6)$ **6.** $(2, -1)$

Write the ordered pair for each point.

7. A **(3, −1)** **8.** B **(−3, 1)**

9. C **(3, 2)** **10.** D **(−1, −4)**

11. F **(5, 0)** **12.** G **(−1, 2)**

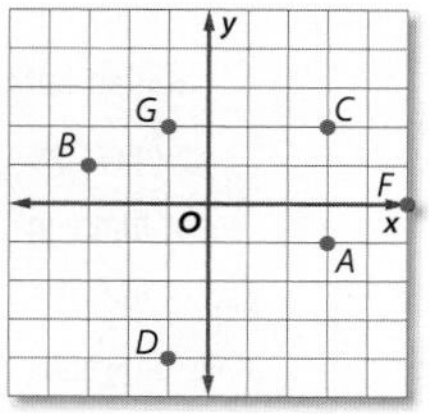

Solve each equation for y.

13. $3x + y = 1$ **14.** $8 - y = x$

15. $5x - 2y = 12$ **16.** $3x + 4y = 10$

17. $3 - \frac{1}{2}y = 5x$ **18.** $\frac{y+1}{3} = x + 2$

13. $y = -3x + 1$ **14.** $y = -x + 8$

15. $y = \frac{5}{2}x - 6$ **16.** $y = \frac{-3}{4}x + \frac{5}{2}$

17. $y = -10x + 6$ **18.** $y = 3x + 5$

Evaluate $\frac{a-b}{c-d}$ for each set of values.

19. $a = 7, b = 6, c = 9, d = 5$ $\frac{1}{4}$

20. $a = -3, b = 0, c = 3, d = -1$ $-\frac{3}{4}$

21. $a = -5, b = -5, c = 5, d = 8$ **0**

22. $a = -6, b = 3, c = 8, d = 2$ $-\frac{3}{2}$

23. **MOVIES** A movie made \$297.2 million in 22 weeks. How much did the movie make on average each week? **about \$13.5 million**

QuickReview

Example 1 (Used in Lessons 3-1 through 3-3)

Graph $(3, -2)$ on a coordinate grid.

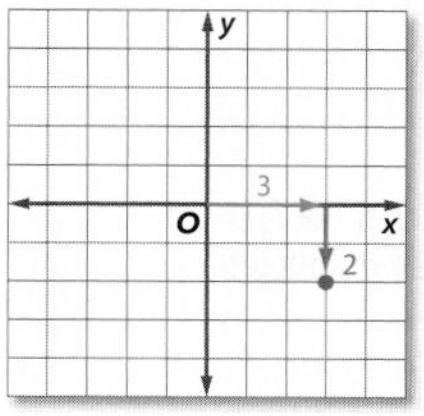

Example 2 (Used in Lessons 3-1 through 3-5)

Solve $x - 2y = 8$ for y.

$x - 2y = 8$	Original equation
$x - x - 2y = 8 - x$	Subtract x from each side.
$-2y = 8 - x$	Simplify.
$\frac{-2y}{-2} = \frac{8-x}{-2}$	Divide each side by −2.
$y = \frac{1}{2}x - 4$	Simplify.

Example 3 (Used in Lesson 3-4)

Evaluate $\frac{a-b}{c-d}$ for $a = 3$, $b = 5$, $c = -2$, and $d = -6$.

$\frac{a-b}{c-d}$	Original expression
$= \frac{3-5}{-2-(-6)}$	Substitute 3 for a, 5 for b, −2 for c, and −6 for d.
$= \frac{-2}{4}$	Simplify.
$= \frac{-2 \div 2}{4 \div 2}$	Divide −2 and 4 by their GCF, 2.
$= \frac{-1}{2}$ or $-\frac{1}{2}$	Simplify. The signs are different so the quotient is negative.

2 Online Option

Take an online self-check Chapter Readiness Quiz at connectED.mcgraw-hill.com.

Essential Question

- Why are graphs useful? Sample answer: They can help you visualize relationships between quantities. They can also be used to display data, identify trends, and make predictions.

Get Ready for the Chapter

Response to Intervention (RtI)

Use the *Quick Check* results and the Intervention Planner chart to help you determine your Response to Intervention. The If-Then statements in the chart below help you decide the appropriate tier of RtI and suggest intervention resources for each tier.

InterventionPlanner

TIER 1 On Level OL

If students miss about 25% of the exercises or less,

Then choose a resource:

SE Lessons 1-2, 1-6, and 2-8

Skills Practice, Chapter 1, pp. 13, 39, Chapter 2, p. 51

connectED.mcgraw-hill.com Self-Check Quiz

TIER 2 Strategic Intervention AL approaching grade level

If students miss about 50% of the exercises,

Then choose a resource:

Study Guide and Intervention, Chapter 1, pp. 11, 37, Chapter 2, p. 49

connectED.mcgraw-hill.com Extra Examples, Personal Tutor, Homework Help

TIER 3 Intensive Intervention 2 or more grades below level

If students miss about 75% of the exercises,

Then use *Math Triumphs, Alg. 1, Ch. 3*

connectED.mcgraw-hill.com Extra Examples, Personal Tutor, Homework Help, Review Vocabulary

FOLDABLES® StudyOrganizer

Dinah Zike's Foldables®

Focus Students write about linear functions as these concepts are presented in the lessons of this chapter.

Teach Have students make and label their Foldables as illustrated. Have students make notes under the appropriate tab as they cover each lesson in this chapter. Point out that the seventh tab should be used to list the Key Concepts in the chapter. The eighth tab should be used to note any Study Tips that are found in the chapter. Encourage students to write short descriptive paragraphs about each lesson and graph examples.

When to Use It Encourage students to add to their Foldables as they work through the chapter and to use them to review for the chapter test.

Differentiated Instruction

Student-Built Glossary, pp. 1–2

Students should complete the chart by providing the definition of each term and an example as they progress through Chapter 3. This study tool can also be used to review for the chapter test.

Get Started on the Chapter

You will learn several new concepts, skills, and vocabulary terms as you study Chapter 3. To get ready, identify important terms and organize your resources. You may wish to refer to Chapter 0 to review prerequisite skills.

FOLDABLES StudyOrganizer

Linear Functions Make this Foldable to help you organize your Chapter 3 notes about graphing relations and functions. Begin with four sheets of grid paper.

1 **Fold** each sheet of grid paper in half from top to bottom.

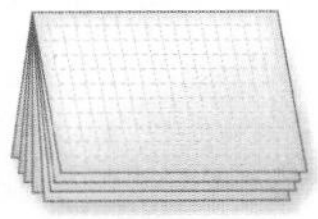

2 **Cut** along fold. Staple the eight half-sheets together to form a booklet.

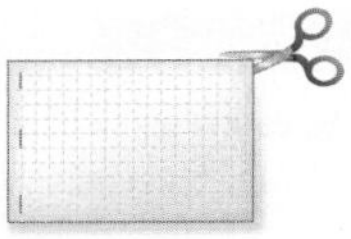

3 **Cut** tabs into margin. The top tab is 4 lines wide, the next tab is 8 lines wide, and so on. When you reach the bottom of a sheet, start the next tab at the top of the page.

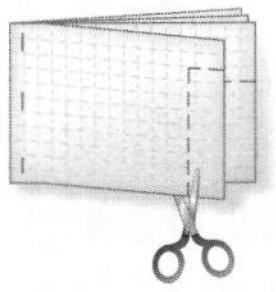

4 **Label** each of the tabs with a lesson number. Use the extra pages for vocabulary.

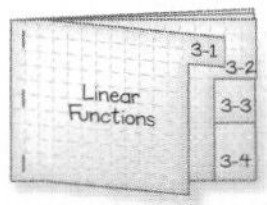

NewVocabulary

English		Español
linear equation	p. 155	ecuación lineal
standard form	p. 155	forma estándar
constant	p. 155	constante
x-intercept	p. 156	intersección *x*
y-intercept	p. 156	intersección *y*
linear function	p. 163	función lineal
parent function	p. 163	críe la función
family of graphs	p. 163	la familia de gráficas
root	p. 163	raiz
rate of change	p. 172	tasa de cambio
slope	p. 174	pendiente
direct variation	p. 182	variación directa
constant of variation	p. 182	constante de variación
arithmetic sequence	p. 189	sucesión arithmética
inductive reasoning	p. 196	razonamiento inductivo
deductive reasoning	p. 196	razonamiento deductivo

ReviewVocabulary

origin origen
the point where the two axes in a coordinate plane intersect with coordinates (0, 0)

x-axis eje *x* the horizontal number line on a coordinate plane

y-axis eje *y* the vertical number line on a coordinate plane

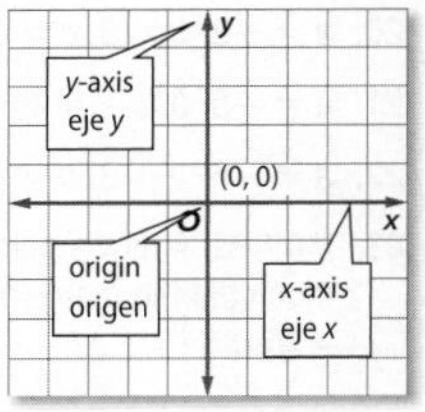

EXPLORE 3-1

Algebra Lab
Analyzing Linear Graphs

Analyzing a graph can help you learn about the relationship between two quantities. A **linear function** is a function for which the graph is a line. There are four types of linear graphs. Let's analyze each type.

Activity 1 Line that Slants Up

Analyze the function graphed at the right.

a. Describe the domain, range, and end behavior.

b. Describe the intercepts and any maximum or minimum points.

c. Identify where the function is positive, negative, increasing, and decreasing.

d. Describe any symmetry.

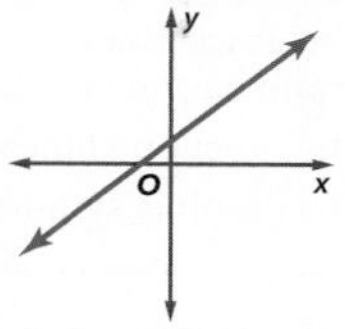

a. The domain and range are all real numbers. As you move left, the graph goes down. So as x decreases, y decreases. As you move right, the graph goes up. So as x increases, y increases.

b. There is one x-intercept and one y-intercept. There are no maximum or minimum points.

c. The function value is 0 at the x-intercept. The function values are negative to the left of the x-intercept and positive to the right. The function goes up from left to right, so it is increasing on the entire domain.

d. The graph has no symmetry.

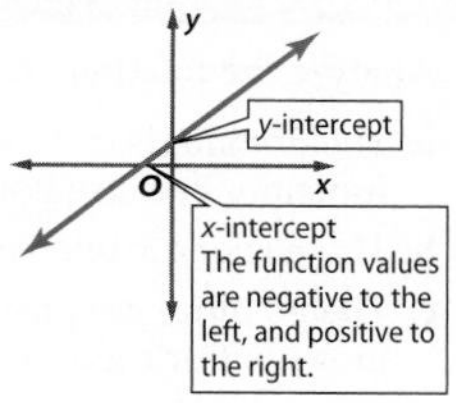

Lines that slant down from left to right have some different key features.

Activity 2 Line that Slants Down

Analyze the function graphed at the right.

a. Describe the domain, range, and end behavior.

b. Describe the intercepts and any maximum or minimum points.

c. Identify where the function is positive, negative, increasing, and decreasing.

d. Describe any symmetry.

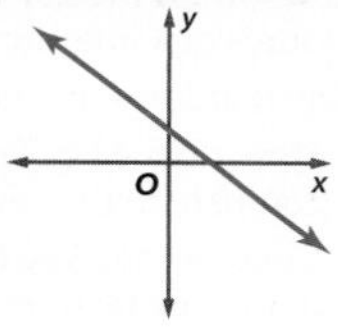

a. The domain and range are all real numbers. As you move left, the graph goes up. So as x decreases, y increases. As you move right, the graph goes down. So as x increases, y decreases.

b. There is one x-intercept and one y-intercept. There are no maximum or minimum points.

c. The function values are positive to the left of the x-intercept and negative to the right.
The function goes down from left to right, so it is decreasing on the entire domain.

d. The graph has no symmetry.

1 Focus

Objective
Analyze the key features of linear graphs.

Teaching Tips

- Students may find that placing a pencil on a coordinate plane to represent a line helps them visualize the key features of the graph. Suggest that students move the pencil to represent different lines and evaluate each feature.
- Have students experiment with their pencils on coordinate planes to verify that there are four general types of lines—slant up, slant down, horizontal, and vertical.

2 Teach

Working in Cooperative Groups

Divide the class into pairs. Work through Activities 1–4. Then ask students to work with their partners to complete Exercises 1–4.

Practice Have students complete Exercises 5–8.

3 Assess

Formative Assessment

Use Exercise 5 to assess each student's ability to analyze the key features of a linear graph.

From Concrete to Abstract

Ask students to summarize the key features of each type of linear graph.

connectED.mcgraw-hill.com 153

Algebra Lab
Analyzing Linear Graphs *Continued*

Horizontal lines represent special functions called **constant functions**.

Activity 3 Horizontal Line

Analyze the function graphed at the right.

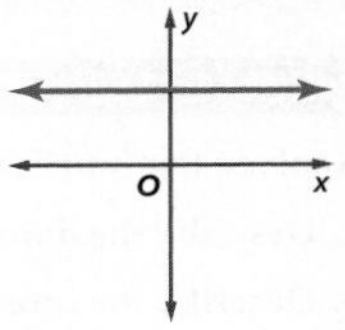

a. The domain is all real numbers, and the range is one value. As you move left or right, the graph stays constant. So as x decreases or increases, y is constant.

b. The graph does not intersect the x-axis, so there is no x-intercept. The graph has one y-intercept. There are no maximum or minimum points.

c. The function values are all positive. The function is constant on the entire domain.

d. The graph is symmetric about any vertical line.

Vertical lines represent linear relations that are *not* functions.

Activity 4 Vertical Line

Analyze the relation graphed at the right.

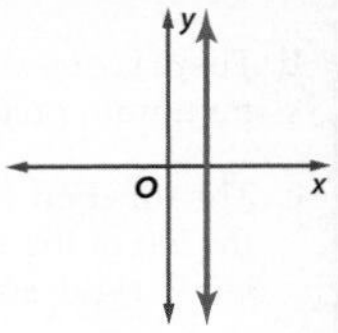

a. The domain is one value, and the range is all real numbers. This relation is not a function. Because you cannot move left or right on the graph, there is no end behavior.

b. There is one x-intercept and no y-intercept. There are no maximum or minimum points.

c. The y-values are positive above the x-axis and negative below. Because you cannot move left or right on the graph, the relation is neither increasing nor decreasing.

d. The graph is symmetric about itself.

Analyze the Results 1, 2. See Ch. 3 Answer Appendix.

1. Compare and contrast the key features of lines that slant up and lines that slant down.

2. How would the key features of a horizontal line below the x-axis differ from the features of a line above the x-axis?

3. Consider lines that pass through the origin. **a–c. See margin.**

a. How do the key features of a line that slants up and passes through the origin compare to the key features of the line in Activity 1?

b. Compare the key features of a line that slants down and passes through the origin to the key features of the line in Activity 2.

c. Describe a horizontal line that passes through the origin and a vertical line that passes through the origin. Compare their key features to those of the lines in Activities 3 and 4.

4. TOOLS Place a pencil on a coordinate plane to represent a line. Move the pencil to represent different lines and evaluate each conjecture.

a. *True* or *false*: A line can have more than one x-intercept. **true**

b. *True* or *false*: If the end behavior of a line is that as x increases, y increases, then the function values are increasing over the entire domain. **true**

c. *True* or *false*: Two different lines can have the same x- and y-intercepts. **false**

Sketch a linear graph that fits each description. 5–8. See margin.

5. as x increases, y decreases

6. one x-intercept and one y-intercept

7. has symmetry

8. is not a function

Additional Answers

3a. The key features are the same except that the x- and y-intercepts are the same point, (0, 0).

3b. The key features are the same except that the x- and y-intercepts are the same point, (0, 0).

3c. The horizontal line that passes through the origin is the x-axis. The key features of the graph are the same as those of the line in Activity 3 except that instead of no x-intercept, it has infinitely many x-intercepts. The vertical line that passes through the origin is the y-axis. The key features of the graph are the same as those of the line in Activity 4 except that instead of no y-intercept, it has infinitely many y-intercepts.

5. Sample answer: any line that slants down

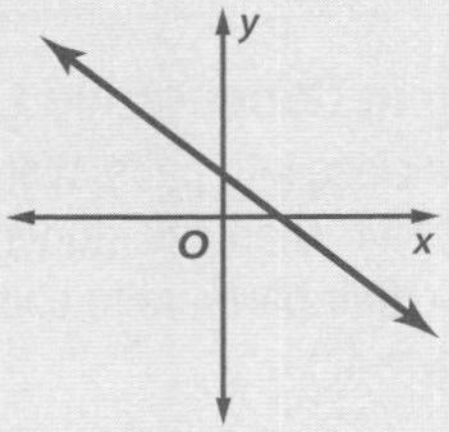

6. Sample answer: any nonvertical, nonhorizontal line

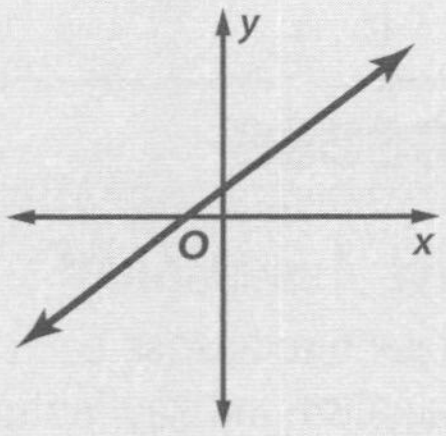

7. Sample answer: any vertical or horizontal line

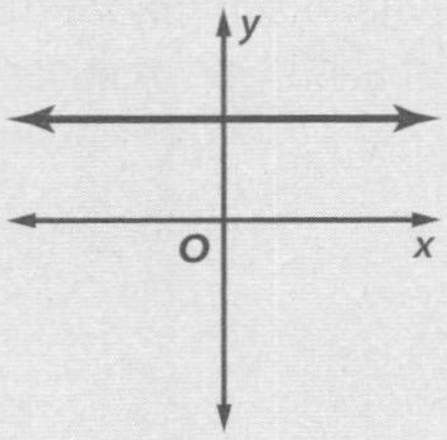

8. Sample answer: any vertical line

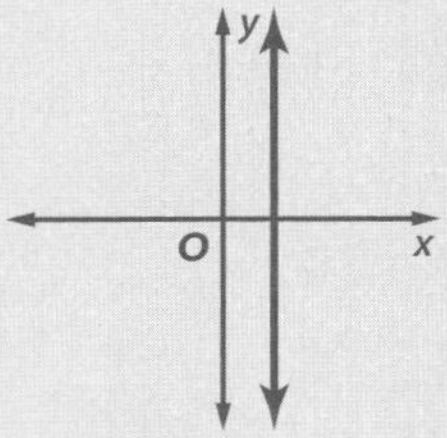

Teaching the Process Standards

Tools Mathematically proficient students use tools to explore and deepen their understanding of concepts. In Exercise 4, point out to students that a pencil is a model for a line that can be used often in their math study.

LESSON 3-1 Graphing Linear Equations

Then	Now	Why?
You represented relationships among quantities using equations.	**1** Identify linear equations, intercepts, and zeros. **2** Graph linear equations.	Recycling one ton of waste paper saves an average of 17 trees, 7000 gallons of water, 3 barrels of oil, and about 3.3 cubic yards of landfill space.

The relationship between the amount of paper recycled and the number of trees saved can be expressed with the equation $y = 17x$, where y represents the number of trees and x represents the tons of paper recycled.

NewVocabulary
linear equation
standard form
constant
x-intercept
y-intercept

Process Standards
PS.8

1 Linear Equations and Intercepts

A **linear equation** is an equation that forms a line when it is graphed. Linear equations are often written in the form $Ax + By = C$. This is called the **standard form** of a linear equation. In this equation, C is called a **constant**, or a number. Ax and By are variable terms.

KeyConcept Standard Form of a Linear Equation

Words The standard form of a linear equation is $Ax + By = C$, where $A \geq 0$, A and B are not both zero, and A, B, and C are integers with a greatest common factor of 1.

Examples In $3x + 2y = 5$, $A = 3$, $B = 2$, and $C = 5$.
In $x = -7$, $A = 1$, $B = 0$, and $C = -7$.

Example 1 Identify Linear Equations

Determine whether each equation is a linear equation. Write the equation in standard form.

a. $y = 4 - 3x$

Rewrite the equation so that it appears in standard form.

$y = 4 - 3x$	Original equation
$y + 3x = 4 - 3x + 3x$	Add $3x$ to each side.
$3x + y = 4$	Simplify.

The equation is now in standard form where $A = 3$, $B = 1$, and $C = 4$. This is a linear equation.

b. $6x - xy = 4$

Since the term xy has two variables, the equation cannot be written in the form $Ax + By = C$. Therefore, this is not a linear equation.

GuidedPractice

1A. $\frac{1}{3}y = -1$ yes; $y = -3$ **1B.** $y = x^2 - 4$ no

1 Focus

VerticalAlignment

Before Lesson 3-1 Represent relationships among quantities using equations.

Lesson 3-1 Identify linear equations, intercepts, and zeros. Graph linear equations.

After Lesson 3-1 Solve linear equations by graphing.

2 Teach

Scaffolding Questions

Have students read the **Why?** section of the lesson.

Ask:

- If a community recycles 6 tons of waste paper per year, how many trees are saved? about 102 trees
- What is the coefficient of x in the equation $y = 17x$? 17 What is the coefficient of y? 1
- How can you write $y = 17x$ so that the coefficient of y is -1? $17x - y = 0$

Lesson 3-1 Resources

Resource	Approaching Level AL	On Level OL	Beyond Level BL	English Learners ELL
Teacher Edition		▪ Differentiated Instruction, p. 158	▪ Differentiated Instruction, pp. 158, 162	
Chapter Resource Masters	▪ Study Guide and Intervention, pp. 5–6 ▪ Skills Practice, p. 7 ▪ Practice, p. 8 ▪ Word Problem Practice, p. 9 ▪ Spreadsheet Activity, p. 11	▪ Study Guide and Intervention, pp. 5–6 ▪ Skills Practice and Practice, pp. 7–8 ▪ Word Problem Practice, p. 9 ▪ Enrichment, p. 10 ▪ Spreadsheet Activity, p. 11	▪ Practice, p. 8 ▪ Word Problem Practice, p. 9 ▪ Enrichment, p. 10 ▪ Spreadsheet Activity, p. 11	▪ Study Guide and Intervention, pp. 5–6 ▪ Skills Practice, p. 7 ▪ Practice, p. 8 ▪ Word Problem Practice, p. 9 ▪ Spreadsheet Activity, p. 11
Other	▪ 5-Minute Check 3-1 ▪ Study Notebook ▪ Teaching Algebra with Manipulatives	▪ 5-Minute Check 3-1 ▪ Study Notebook ▪ Teaching Algebra with Manipulatives	▪ 5-Minute Check 3-1 ▪ Study Notebook	▪ 5-Minute Check 3-1 ▪ Study Notebook ▪ Teaching Algebra with Manipulatives

1 Identify Linear Equations and Intercepts

Example 1 shows how to identify a linear equation and write it in standard form. **Example 2** shows how to determine the *x*- and *y*-intercepts. **Example 3** shows how to determine and interpret the intercepts for real-world problems and describe what the intercepts mean in terms of the situation.

Formative Assessment

Use the Guided Practice exercises after each Example to determine students' understanding of concepts.

Additional Examples

1 Determine whether each equation is a linear equation. Write the equation in standard form.

a. $5x + 3 = xy + 2$ not linear

b. $\frac{3}{4}x = y + 8$ linear; $3x - 4y = 32$

2 **STANDARDIZED TEST PRACTICE** Find the *x*- and *y*-intercepts of the segment graphed below. B

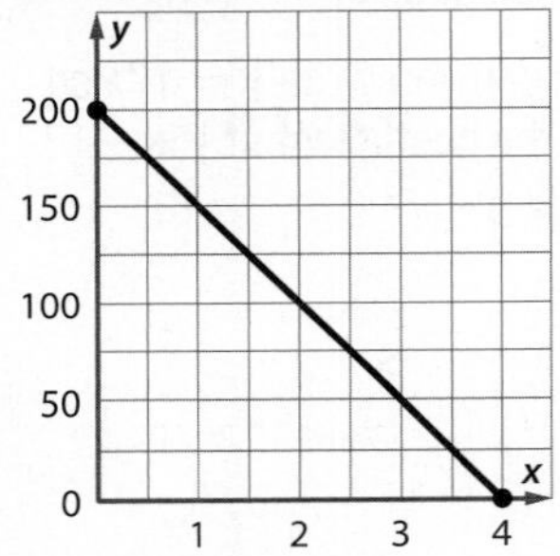

A *x*-intercept is 200; *y*-intercept is 4

B *x*-intercept is 4; *y*-intercept is 200

C *x*-intercept is 2; *y*-intercept is 100

D *x*-intercept is 4; *y*-intercept is 0

Additional Examples also in Interactive Classroom PowerPoint® Presentations

IWB Interactive White Board READY

A linear equation can be represented on a coordinate graph. The *x*-coordinate of the point at which the graph of an equation crosses the *x*-axis is an **x-intercept**. The *y*-coordinate of the point at which the graph crosses the *y*-axis is called a **y-intercept**.

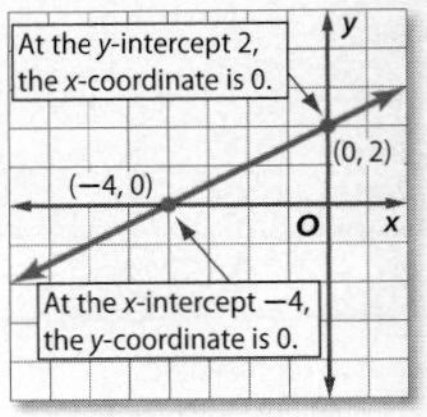

The graph of a linear equation has at most one *x*-intercept and one *y*-intercept, unless it is the equation $x = 0$ or $y = 0$, in which case every number is a *y*-intercept or an *x*-intercept, respectively.

Standardized Test Example 2 Find Intercepts from a Graph

Find the *x*- and *y*-intercepts of the line graphed at the right.

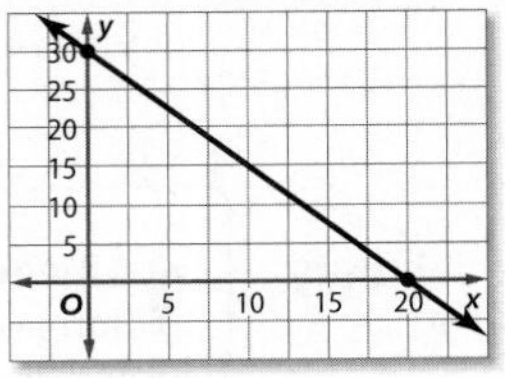

A *x*-intercept is 0; *y*-intercept is 30.

B *x*-intercept is 20; *y*-intercept is 30.

C *x*-intercept is 20; *y*-intercept is 0.

D *x*-intercept is 30; *y*-intercept is 20.

Read the Test Item

We need to determine the *x*- and *y*-intercepts of the line in the graph.

ReadingMath

Intercepts Usually, the individual coordinates are called the *x*-intercept and the *y*-intercept. The *x*-intercept 20 is located at (20, 0). The *y*-intercept 30 is located at (0, 30).

Solve the Test Item

Step 1 Find the *x*-intercept. Look for the point where the line crosses the *x*-axis.

The line crosses at (20, 0). The *x*-intercept is 20 because it is the *x*-coordinate of the point where the line crosses the *x*-axis.

Step 2 Find the *y*-intercept. Look for the point where the line crosses the *y*-axis.

The line crosses at (0, 30). The *y*-intercept is 30 because it is the *y*-coordinate of the point where the line crosses the *y*-axis.

Thus, the answer is B.

GuidedPractice

2. HEALTH Find the *x*- and *y*-intercepts of the graph. J

Gym Membership

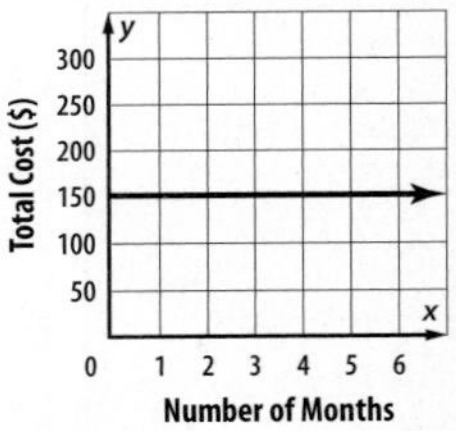

F *x*-intercept is 0; *y*-intercept is 150.

G *x*-intercept is 150; *y*-intercept is 0.

H *x*-intercept is 150; no *y*-intercept.

J No *x*-intercept; *y*-intercept is 150.

WatchOut!

Standard Form Students may assume that the standard form implies that linear equations must have positive coefficients on *x* and *y*. Point out that there are no restrictions on the value of *B*. This means that *B* could be negative. So, an equation like $3x - 4y = 7$ is a linear equation.

Focus on Mathematical Content

Linear Equations The standard form of a linear equation is $Ax + By = C$. If the properties of equality can be applied to an equation to rewrite it in standard form, then the equation is linear.

156 | Lesson 3-1 | Graphing Linear Equations

StudyTip

Defining Variables In Example 3, time is the *independent* variable, and volume of water is the *dependent* variable.

Real-World Example 3 Find Intercepts from a Table

SWIMMING POOL A swimming pool is being drained at a rate of 720 gallons per hour. The table shows the function relating the volume of water in a pool and the time in hours that the pool has been draining.

Draining a Pool	
Time (h)	Volume (gal)
x	y
0	10,080
2	8640
6	5760
10	2880
12	1440
14	0

a. Find the x- and y-intercepts of the graph of the function.

x-intercept = 14 — 14 is the value of x when $y = 0$.

y-intercept = 10,080 — 10,080 is the value of y when $x = 0$.

b. Describe what the intercepts mean in this situation.

The x-intercept 14 means that after 14 hours, the water has a volume of 0 gallons, or the pool is completely drained.

The y-intercept 10,080 means that the pool contained 10,080 gallons of water at time 0, or before it started to drain. This is shown in the graph.

Draining a Pool

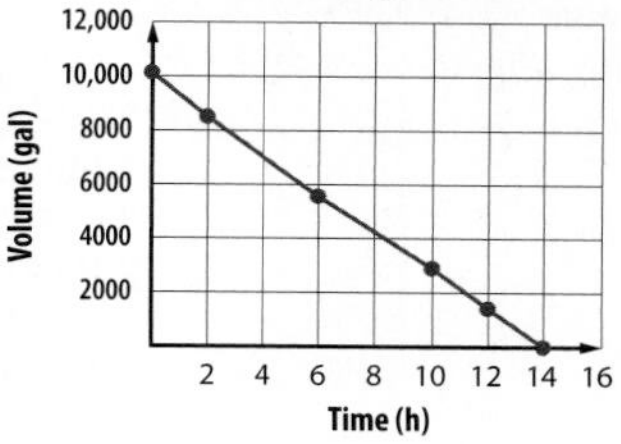

GuidedPractice

3. DRIVING The table shows the function relating the distance to an amusement park in miles and the time in hours the Torres family has driven. Find the x- and y-intercepts. Describe what the intercepts mean in this situation.

Time (h)	Distance (mi)
0	248
1	186
2	124
3	62
4	0

3. The x-intercept 4 means the Torrez family arrived at the amusement park after 4 hours of driving. The y-intercept 248 means their house is 248 mi away from the amusement park.

2 Graph Linear Equations

By first finding the x- and y-intercepts, you have the ordered pairs of two points through which the graph of the linear equation passes. This information can be used to graph the line because only two points are needed to graph a line.

StudyTip

Intercepts The x-intercept is where the graph crosses the x-axis. So the y-value is always 0. The y-intercept is where the graph crosses the y-axis. So, the x-value is always 0.

Example 4 Graph by Using Intercepts

Graph $2x + 4y = 16$ by using the x- and y-intercepts.

To find the x-intercept, let $y = 0$.

$2x + 4y = 16$ — Original equation

$2x + 4(0) = 16$ — Replace y with 0.

$2x = 16$ — Simplify.

$x = 8$ — Divide each side by 2.

The x-intercept is 8. This means that the graph intersects the x-axis at (8, 0).

Tips for New Teachers

Interpreting Graphs When discussing Example 3, take the opportunity to discuss what the points on the line with coordinates that are not part of the original data set represent.

Teach with Tech

Interactive Whiteboard Drag a coordinate grid onto the board. Use this as a template as you plot points and draw graphs for your class.

Additional Example

3 ANALYZE TABLES A box of peanuts is poured into bags at the rate of 4 ounces per second. The table shows the function relating the weight of peanuts in the box and the time in seconds the peanuts have been pouring out of the box.

Pouring Peanuts	
Time (s) x	Weight (oz) y
0	2000
125	1500
250	1000
375	500
500	0

a. Find the x- and y-intercepts of the graph of the function.

Pouring Peanuts

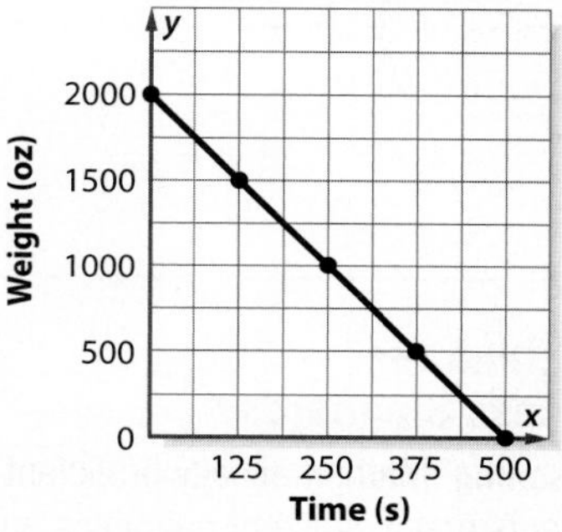

500; 2000

b. Describe what the intercepts mean in terms of this situation. x-intercept: 0 oz after 500 s; y-intercept: 2000 oz before pouring began

2 Graph Linear Equations

Example 4 shows how to graph a linear equation using the x- and y-intercepts. **Example 5** shows how to graph an equation by making a table.

Additional Examples

4 Graph $4x - y = 4$ by using the x- and y-intercepts.
x-intercept: 1; y-intercept: -4

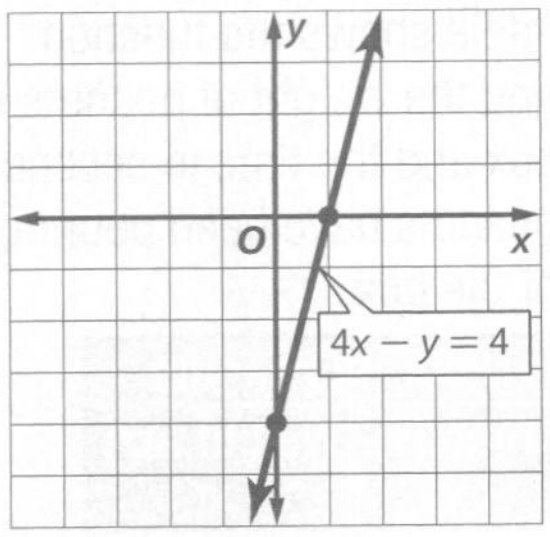

5 Graph $y = 2x + 2$.

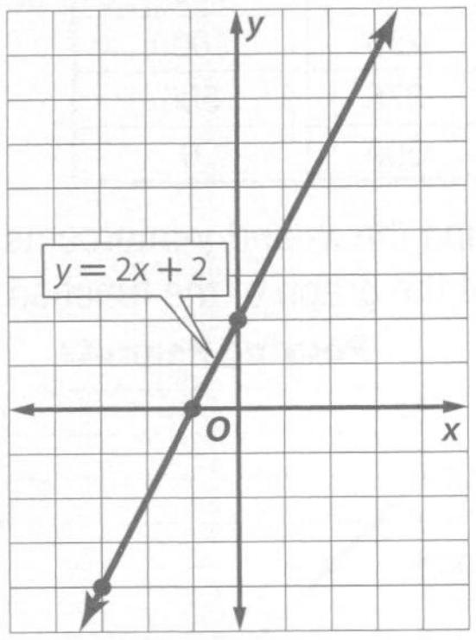

Teaching the Process Standards

Reasoning Mathematically proficient students make sense of quantities and their relationships in problem situations. In Exercise 12 part **b,** point out to students that interpreting solutions is as important to solving problems as accurately computing solutions.

Additional Answers (Guided Practice)

4A.

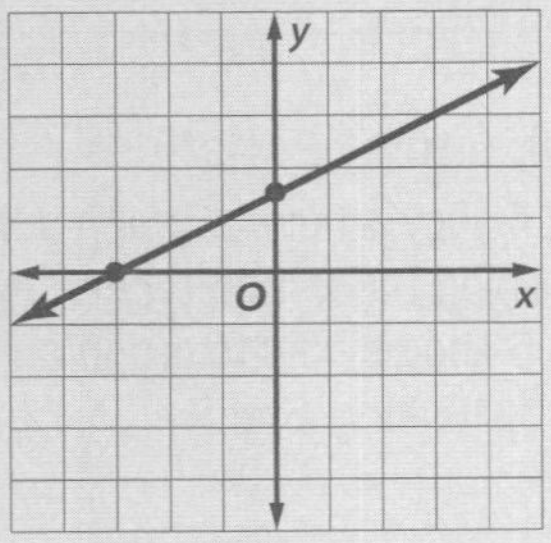

4B.

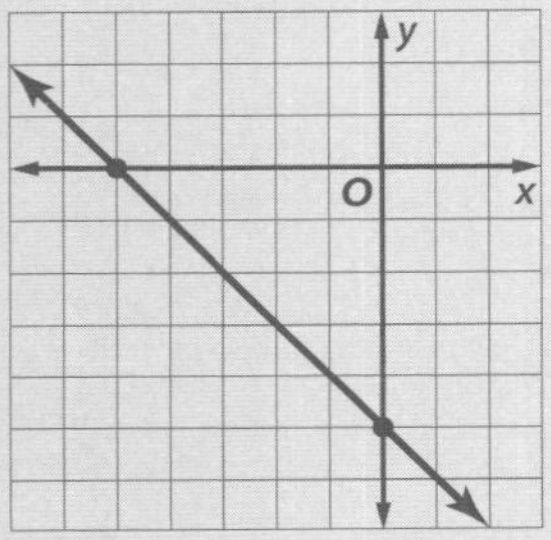

To find the y-intercept, let $x = 0$.

$2x + 4y = 16$	Original equation
$2(0) + 4y = 16$	Replace x with 0.
$4y = 16$	Simplify.
$y = 4$	Divide each side by 4.

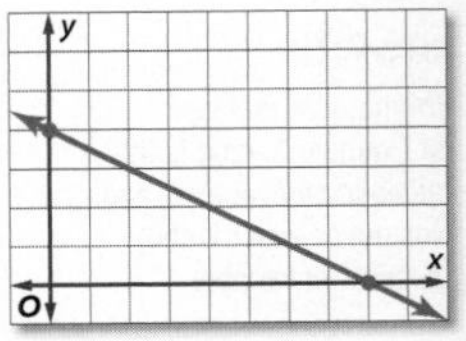

The y-intercept is 4. This means the graph intersects the y-axis at (0, 4).

Plot these two points and then draw a line through them.

StudyTip
Equivalent Equations Rewriting equations by solving for y may make it easier to find values for y.
$-x + 2y = 3 \rightarrow y = \frac{x+3}{2}$

GuidedPractice 4A–4B. See margin.

Graph each equation by using the x- and y-intercepts.

4A. $-x + 2y = 3$ **4B.** $y = -x - 5$

Note that the graph in Example 4 has both an x- and a y-intercept. Some lines have an x-intercept and no y-intercept or vice versa. The graph of $y = b$ is a horizontal line that only has a y-intercept (unless $b = 0$). The intercept occurs at $(0, b)$. The graph of $x = a$ is a vertical line that only has an x-intercept (unless $a = 0$). The intercept occurs at $(a, 0)$.

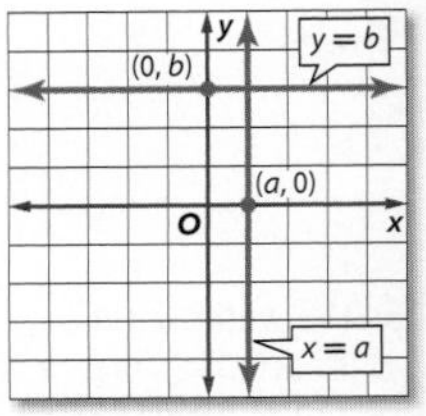

Every ordered pair that makes an equation true represents a point on the graph. So, the graph of an equation represents all of its solutions. Any ordered pair that does not make the equation true represents a point that is not on the line.

Example 5 Graph by Making a Table

Graph $y = \frac{1}{3}x + 2$.

The domain is all real numbers. Select values from the domain and make a table. When the x-coefficient is a fraction, select a number from the domain that is a multiple of the denominator. Create ordered pairs and graph them.

x	$\frac{1}{3}x + 2$	y	(x, y)
−3	$\frac{1}{3}(-3) + 2$	1	(−3, 1)
0	$\frac{1}{3}(0) + 2$	2	(0, 2)
3	$\frac{1}{3}(3) + 2$	3	(3, 3)
6	$\frac{1}{3}(6) + 2$	4	(6, 4)

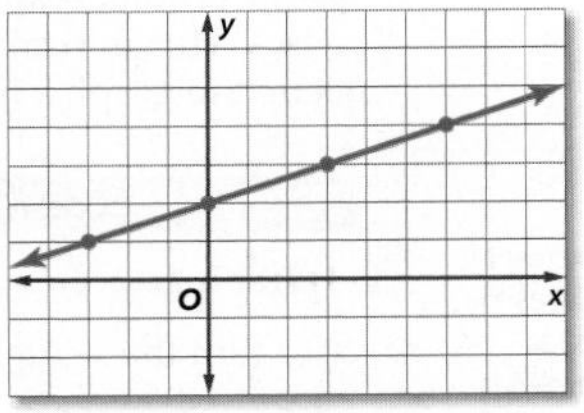

GuidedPractice

Graph each equation by making a table. 5A–5C. See margin.

5A. $2x - y = 2$ **5B.** $x = 3$ **5C.** $y = -2$

DifferentiatedInstruction OL BL

If students have mastered graphing with whole-number intercepts,

Then give students an equation with at least one of the intercepts of the graph not a whole number. Have students suggest an easier way to graph the equation.

Check Your Understanding

= Step-by-Step Solutions begin on page R13.

Example 1 Determine whether each equation is a linear equation. Write *yes* or *no*. If yes, write the equation in standard form.

1. $x = y - 5$ yes; $x - y = -5$
2. $-2x - 3 = y$ yes; $2x + y = -3$
3. $-4y + 6 = 2$ yes; $y = 1$
4. $\frac{2}{3}x - \frac{1}{3}y = 2$ yes; $2x - y = 6$

Examples 2–3 Find the x- and y-intercepts of the graph of each linear function. Describe what the intercepts mean.

5. **Increasing Temperature**

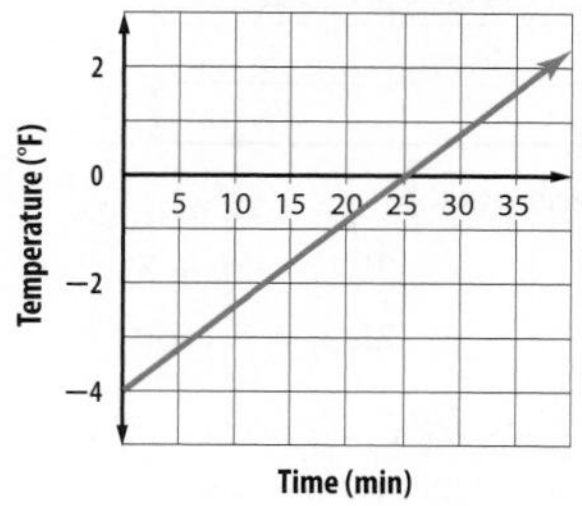

6.

Position of Scuba Diver	
Time (s)	Depth (m)
x	y
0	−24
3	−18
6	−12
9	−6
12	0

6. 12, −24; The x-intercept 12 means that after 12 seconds, the scuba diver is at a depth of 0 meters, or at the surface. The y-intercept −24 means that at time 0, the scuba diver is at a depth of −24 meters, or 24 meters below sea level.

5. 25, −4; The x-intercept 25 means that after 25 minutes, the temperature is 0°F. The y-intercept −4 means that at time 0, the temperature is −4°F.

Example 4 Graph each equation by using the x- and y-intercepts.

7. $y = 4 + x$
8. $2x - 5y = 1$

7–8. See Ch. 3 Answer Appendix.

Example 5 Graph each equation by making a table. 9–11. See Ch. 3 Answer Appendix.

9. $x + 2y = 4$
10. $-3 + 2y = -5$
11. $y = 3$

12. **REASONING** The equation $5x + 10y = 60$ represents the number of children x and adults y who can attend the rodeo for $60.

a. Use the x- and y-intercepts to graph the equation. See margin.

b. Describe what these values mean.

The x-intercept means that 12 children and 0 adults can attend for $60. The y-intercept means that 0 children and 6 adults can attend for $60.

Practice and Problem Solving

Extra Practice is on page R3.

Example 1 Determine whether each equation is a linear equation. Write *yes* or *no*. If yes, write the equation in standard form.

13. $5x + y^2 = 25$ no
14. $8 + y = 4x$ yes; $4x - y = 8$
15. $9xy - 6x = 7$ no
16. $4y^2 + 9 = -4$ no
17. $12x = 7y - 10y$ yes; $4x + y = 0$
18. $y = 4x + x$ yes; $5x - y = 0$

Example 2 Find the x- and y-intercepts of the graph of each linear function.

19.

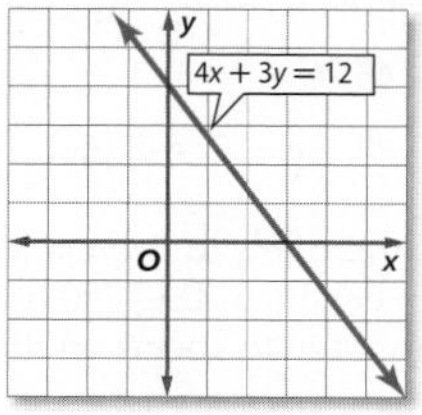

3, 4

20.

x	y
−3	−1
−2	0
−1	1
0	2
1	3

−2, 2

Differentiated Homework Options

Level	Assignment	Two-Day Option	
AL Basic	13–35, 60–77	13–35 odd, 65–68	14–34 even, 60–64, 69–77
OL Core	13–49 odd, 42, 50, 51–57 odd, 58, 60–77	13–35, 65–68	36–58, 60–64, 69–77
BL Advanced	36–73, (optional: 74–77)		

3 Practice

Formative Assessment

Use Exercises 1–12 to check for understanding.

Use the chart at the bottom of this page to customize assignments for your students.

Exercise Alert

Grid Paper For Exercises 42–48, 50, 57, and 58, students will need grid paper.

Straightedge For Exercise 58, students will need a straightedge.

Additional Answers (Guided Practice)

5A.

x	y
−2	−6
−1	−4
0	−2
1	0
2	2

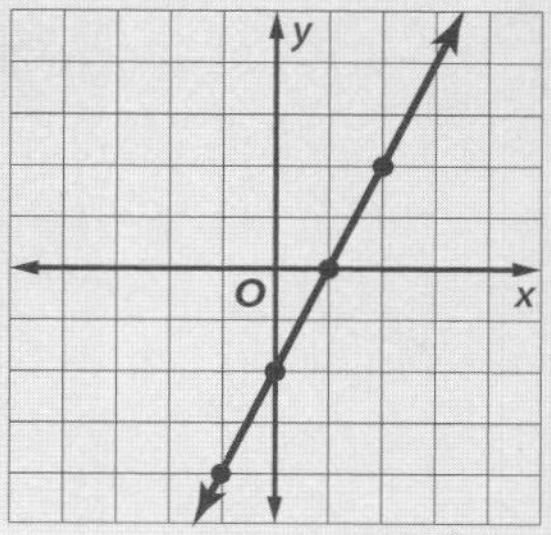

5B.

x	y
3	−2
3	−1
3	0
3	1
3	2

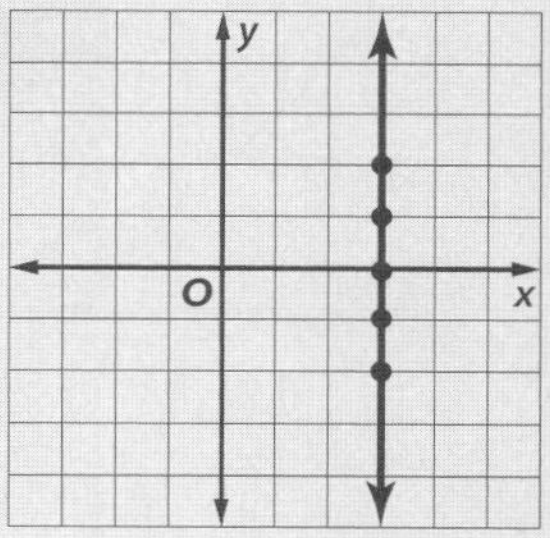

5C.

x	y
−2	−2
−1	−2
0	−2
1	−2
2	−2

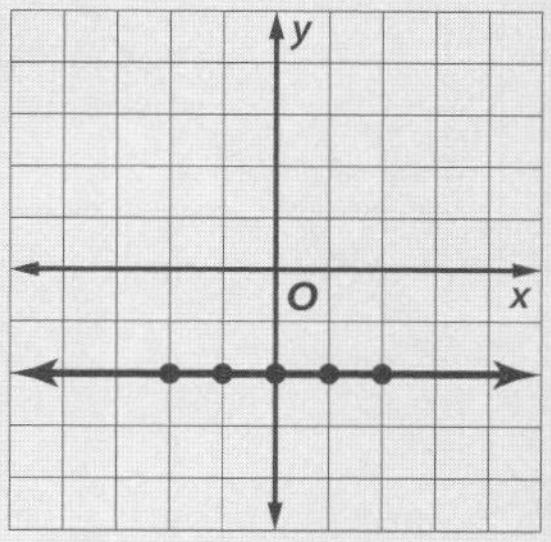

Additional Answer

12a.

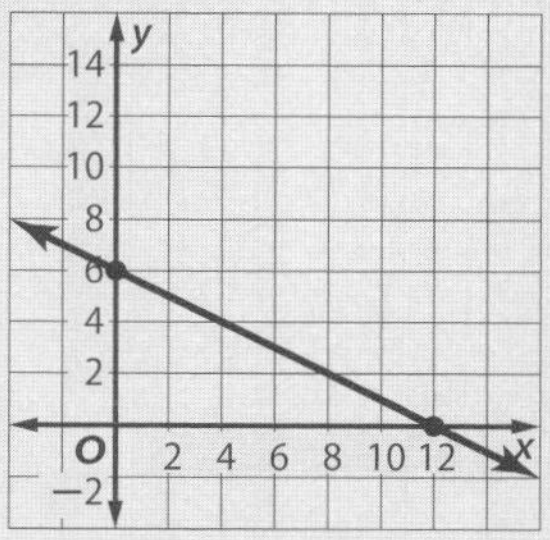

connectED.mcgraw-hill.com 159

Additional Answers

23.

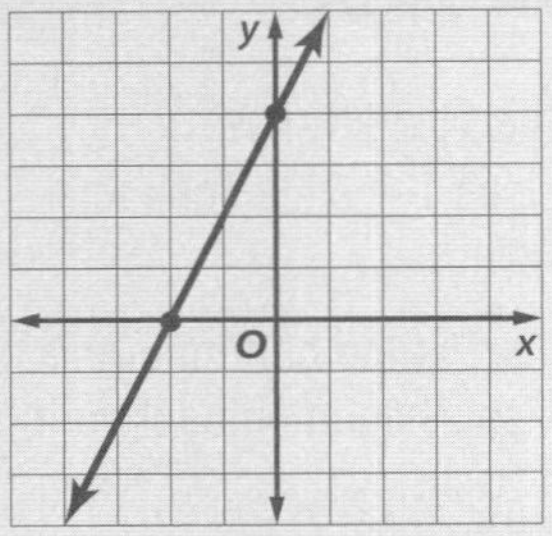

24.

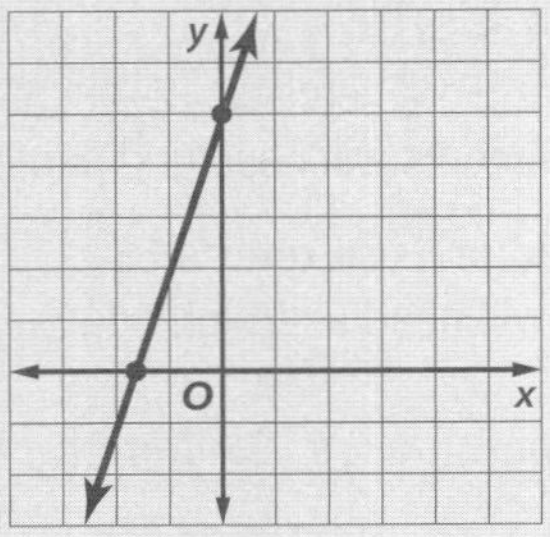

25.

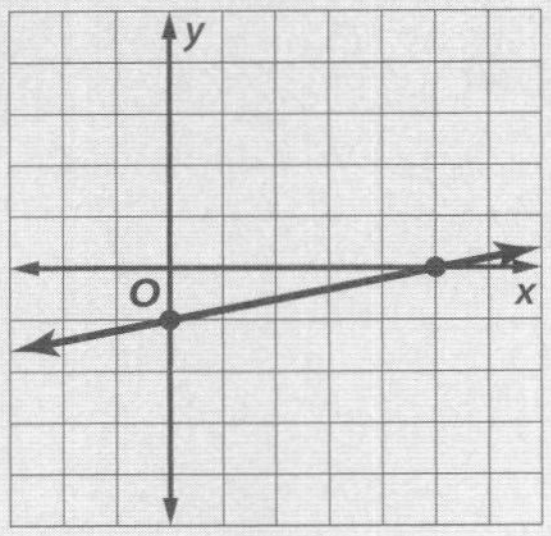

26.

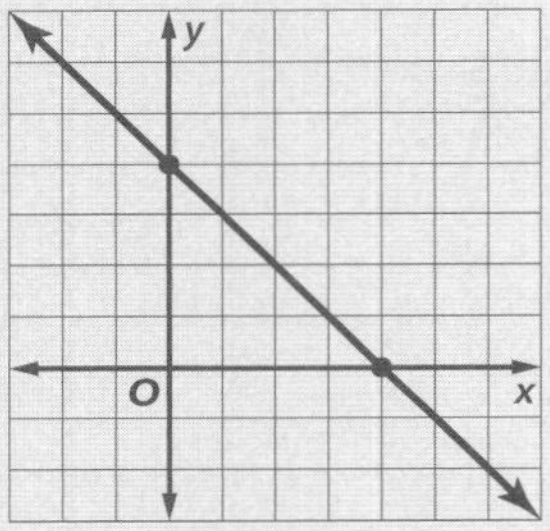

27.

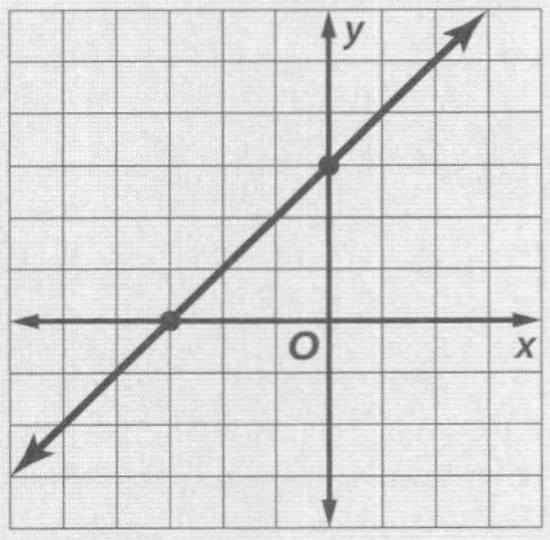

28.

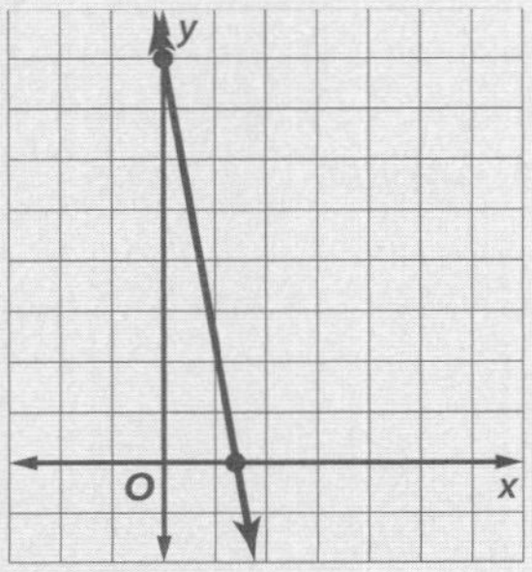

Example 3 **Find the x- and y-intercepts of each linear function. Describe what the intercepts mean.**

21. **Descent of Eagle**

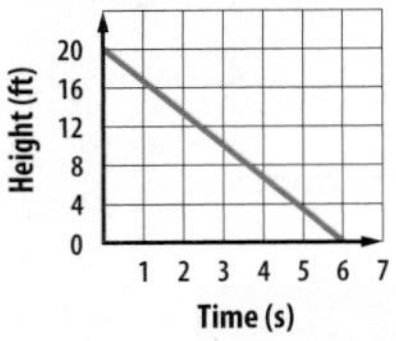

6, 20; The x-intercept represents the number of seconds that it takes the eagle to land. The y-intercept represents the initial height of the eagle.

22. Eva's Distance from Home

Time (min)	Distance (mi)
x	y
0	4
2	3
4	2
6	1
8	0

8, 4; The x-intercept 8 means that it took Eva 8 minutes to get home. The y-intercept 4 means that Eva was initially 4 miles from home.

Example 4 **Graph each equation by using the x- and y-intercepts.** **23–28. See margin.**

23. $y = 4 + 2x$ **24.** $5 - y = -3x$ **25.** $x = 5y + 5$

26. $x + y = 4$ **27.** $x - y = -3$ **28.** $y = 8 - 6x$

Example 5 **Graph each equation by making a table.** **29–34. See Chapter 3 Answer Appendix.**

29. $x = -2$ **30.** $y = -4$ **31.** $y = -8x$

32. $3x = y$ **33.** $y - 8 = -x$ **34.** $x = 10 - y$

35 **TV RATINGS** The number of people who watch a singing competition can be given by $p = 0.15v$, where p represents the number of people in millions who saw the show and v is the number of potential viewers in millions. **35a–b. See Chapter 3 Answer Appendix.**

a. Make a table of values for the points (v, p).

b. Graph the equation.

c. Use the graph to estimate the number of people who saw the show if there are 14 million potential viewers. **≈2.1 million**

d. Explain why it would not make sense for v to be a negative number. **There cannot be fewer than 0 viewers.**

Determine whether each equation is a linear equation. Write *yes* or *no*. If yes, write the equation in standard form. **38. yes; $6m - 7n = -4$**

B **36.** $x + \frac{1}{y} = 7$ **no** **37.** $\frac{x}{2} = 10 + \frac{2y}{3}$ **yes; $3x - 4y = 60$**

38. $7n - 8m = 4 - 2m$ **39.** $3a + b - 2 = b$ **yes; $3a = 2$**

40. $2r - 3rt + 5t = 1$ **no** **41.** $\frac{3m}{4} = \frac{2n}{3} - 5$ **yes, $9m - 8n = -60$**

42. **FINANCIAL LITERACY** James earns a monthly salary of \$1200 and a commission of \$125 for each car he sells.

a. Graph an equation that represents how much James earns in a month in which he sells x cars. **See Chapter 3 Answer Appendix.**

b. Use the graph to estimate the number of cars James needs to sell in order to earn \$5000. **about 30 cars**

Graph each equation. **43–48. See Chapter 3 Answer Appendix.**

43. $2.5x - 4 = y$ **44.** $1.25x + 7.5 = y$ **45.** $y + \frac{1}{5}x = 3$

46. $\frac{2}{3}x + y = -7$ **47.** $2x - 3 = 4y + 6$ **48.** $3y - 7 = 4x + 1$

49. No; sample answer: The rental car would cost \$176. Mrs. Johnson has only \$160 to spend.

49. **REASONING** Mrs. Johnson is renting a car for vacation and plans to drive a total of 800 miles. A rental car company charges \$153 for the week including 700 miles and \$0.23 for each additional mile. If Mrs. Johnson has only \$160 to spend on the rental car, can she afford to rent a car? Explain your reasoning.

59. Sample answer: Table 1: Yes; we used the formula $P = 4s$, which is linear. Table 2: No; we used the formula $A = s^2$, which is not linear. Table 3: No; we used the formula $V = s^3$, which is not linear.

Teaching the Process Standards

Reasoning Mathematically proficient students decontextualize information, represent it symbolically, and then contextualize to interpret the solution. In Exercise 49, ask students to start by defining the independent and dependent variables.

50. **AMUSEMENT PARKS** An amusement park charges \$50 for admission before 6 P.M. and \$20 for admission after 6 P.M. On Saturday, the park took in a total of \$20,000.

a. Write an equation that represents the number of admissions that may have been sold. Let x represent the admissions sold before 6 P.M., and let y represent the admissions sold after 6 P.M. **$20{,}000 = 50x + 20y$**

b. Graph the equation. **b–c. See Chapter 3 Answer Appendix.**

c. Find the x- and y-intercepts of the graph. What does each intercept represent?

Find the x-intercept and y-intercept of the graph of each equation.

51. $5x + 3y = 15$ **3; 5**
52. $2x - 7y = 14$ **7; −2**
53. $2x - 3y = 5$ **$2\frac{1}{2}$; $-1\frac{2}{3}$**
54. $6x + 2y = 8$ **$1\frac{1}{3}$; 4**
55. $y = \frac{1}{4}x - 3$ **12; −3**
56. $y = \frac{2}{3}x + 1$ **$-1\frac{1}{2}$; 1**

57. **ONLINE GAMES** The percent of teens who play online games can be modeled by $p = \frac{15}{4}t + 66$. p is the percent of students, and t represents time in years since 2000.

a. Graph the equation. **See Chapter 3 Answer Appendix.**

b. Use the graph to estimate the percent of students playing the games in 2008. **96%**

58. **MULTIPLE REPRESENTATIONS** In this problem, you will explore x- and y-intercepts of graphs of linear equations.

a. **Graphical** If possible, use a straightedge to draw a line on a coordinate plane with each of the following characteristics. **See Chapter 3 Answer Appendix.**

x- and y-intercept	x-intercept, no y-intercept	exactly 2 x-intercepts	no x-intercept, y-intercept	exactly 2 y-intercepts

b. **Analytical** For which characteristics were you able to create a line and for which characteristics were you unable to create a line? Explain.

c. **Verbal** What must be true of the x- and y-intercepts of a line?

58b. Sample answer: I was able to draw a line with an x- and a y-intercept, an x-intercept and no y-intercept, and no x-intercept and a y-intercept. I was unable to draw a line with 2 x-intercepts or 2 y-intercepts

58c. Lines that are neither vertical or horizontal cannot have more than one x- and/or y-intercept.

H.O.T. Problems Use Higher-Order Thinking Skills

59. **REGULARITY** Copy and complete each table. State whether any of the tables show a linear relationship. Explain. **See margin for explanation.**

Perimeter of a Square	
Side Length	**Perimeter**
1	4
2	8
3	12
4	16

Area of a Square	
Side Length	**Area**
1	1
2	4
3	9
4	16

Volume of a Cube	
Side Length	**Volume**
1	1
2	8
3	27
4	64

60. **REASONING** Compare and contrast the graphs of $y = 2x + 1$ with the domain $\{1, 2, 3, 4\}$ and $y = 2x + 1$ with the domain of all real numbers. **See Chapter 3 Answer Appendix.**

OPEN ENDED **Give an example of a linear equation of the form $Ax + By = C$ for each condition. Then describe the graph of the equation.**

61. $A = 0$
62. $B = 0$
63. $C = 0$

61. Sample answer: $y = 8$; horizontal line
62. Sample answer: $x = 5$; vertical line
63. Sample answer: $x - y = 0$; line through (0, 0)

64. **WRITING IN MATH** Explain how to find the x-intercept and y-intercept of a graph and summarize how to graph a linear equation. **See Chapter 3 Answer Appendix.**

Study Guide and Intervention
AL OL ELL

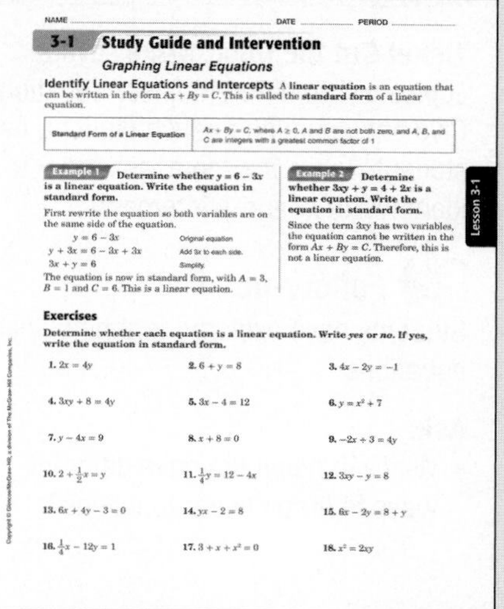
NAME DATE PERIOD
3-1 Study Guide and Intervention
Graphing Linear Equations
Identify Linear Equations and Intercepts A linear equation is an equation that can be written in the form $Ax + By = C$. This is called the standard form of a linear equation.
Exercises
Determine whether each equation is a linear equation. Write yes or no. If yes, write the equation in standard form.
1. $2x = 4y$ 2. $6 + y = 8$ 3. $4x - 2y = -1$
4. $3xy + 8 = 4y$ 5. $3x - 4 = 12$ 6. $y = x^2 + 7$
7. $y - 4x = 9$ 8. $x + 8 = 0$ 9. $-2x + 3 = 4y$

Practice
AL OL BL ELL

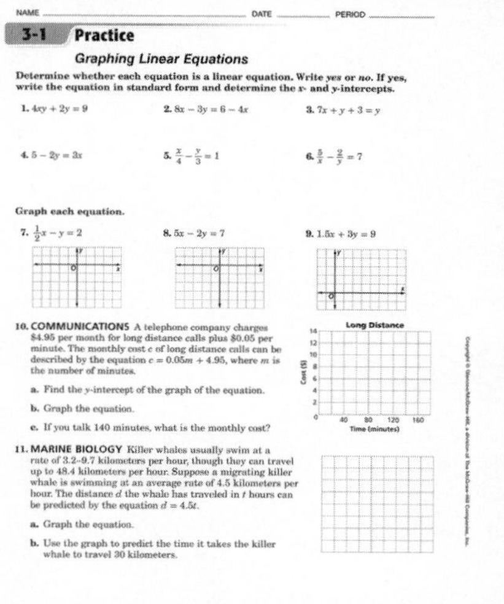
NAME DATE PERIOD
3-1 Practice
Graphing Linear Equations
Determine whether each equation is a linear equation. Write yes or no. If yes, write the equation in standard form and determine the x- and y-intercepts.
Graph each equation.
10. COMMUNICATIONS
11. MARINE BIOLOGY

Word Problem Practice
AL OL BL ELL

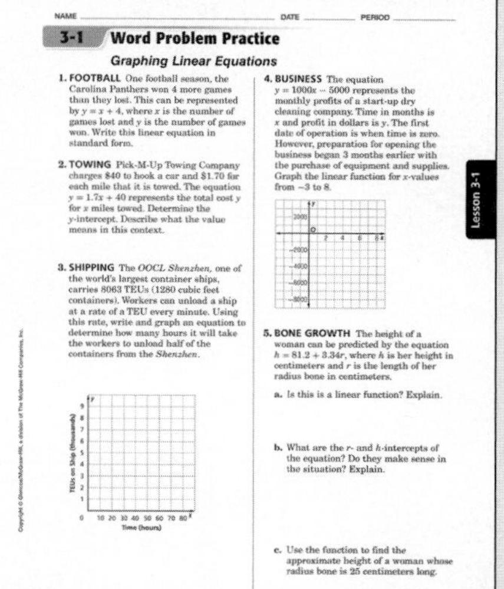
NAME DATE PERIOD
3-1 Word Problem Practice
Graphing Linear Equations
1. FOOTBALL
2. TOWING
3. SHIPPING
4. BUSINESS
5. BONE GROWTH

Multiple Representations

In Exercise 58, students will discover what types of intercepts are possible for the graph of a linear equation.

Teaching the Process Standards

Regularity In Exercise 59, challenge students to write an equation to represent each relationship. Then determine whether each equation is linear.

Enrichment
OL BL

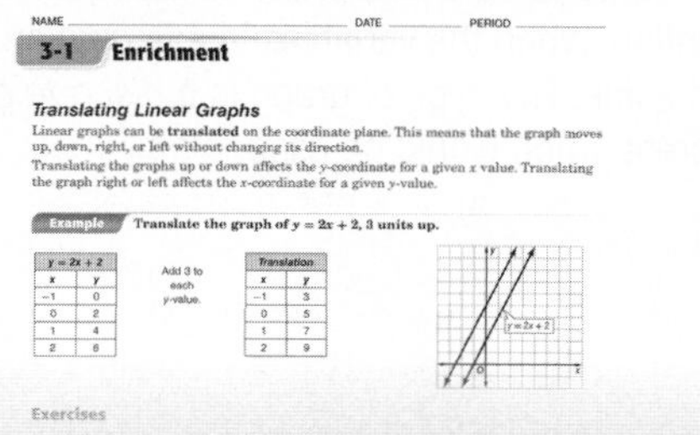
NAME DATE PERIOD
3-1 Enrichment
Translating Linear Graphs
Example Translate the graph of $y = 2x + 2$, 3 units up.
Exercises

4 Assess

Ticket Out the Door Make several copies of five different linear equations. Give one equation to each student. As students leave the room, ask them to identify the *x*- and *y*-intercepts.

Follow-up

Students have explored graphing linear equations.

Ask:

- Why is it helpful to have different ways to graph linear functions? Sample answer: Depending on the equation and how it is written, it may be easier to graph a function using the intercepts or it may be easier to create a table of points.

Standardized Test Practice

65. Sancho can ride 8 miles on his bicycle in 30 minutes. At this rate, about how long would it take him to ride 30 miles? D

A 8 hours

B 6 hours 32 minutes

C 2 hours

D 1 hour 53 minutes

66. GEOMETRY Which is a true statement about the relation graphed? H

Surface Area of Cube

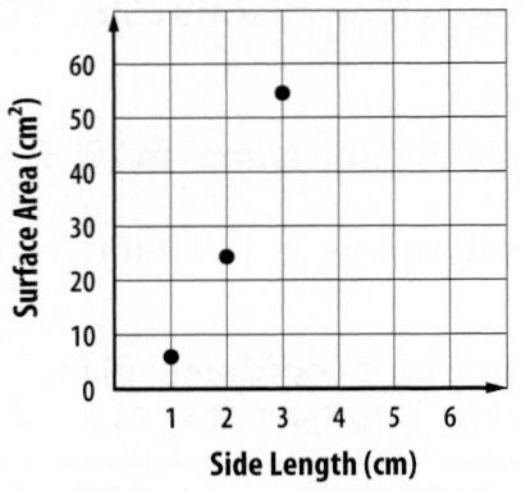

F The relation is not a function.

G Surface area is the independent quantity.

H The surface area of a cube is a function of the side length.

J As the side length of a cube increases, the surface area decreases.

67. SHORT RESPONSE Selena deposited \$2000 into a savings account that pays 1.5% interest compounded annually. If she does not deposit any more money into her account, how much will she earn in interest at the end of one year? \$30

68. A candle burns as shown in the graph.

Candle Height

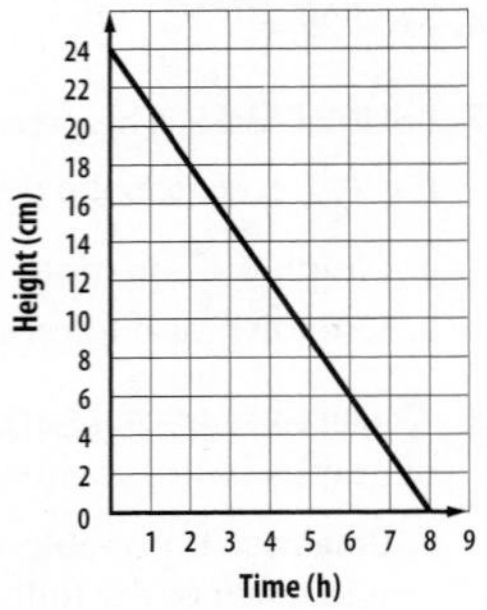

If the height of the candle is 8 centimeters, approximately how long has the candle been burning? D

A 0 hours

B 24 minutes

C 64 minutes

D $5\frac{1}{2}$ hours

Spiral Review

69. FUNDRAISING The Madison High School Marching Band sold solid-color gift wrap for \$4 per roll and print gift wrap for \$6 per roll. The total number of rolls sold was 480, and the total amount of money collected was \$2340. How many rolls of each kind of gift wrap were sold? (Lesson 2-9) 270 rolls of solid wrap, 210 rolls of print wrap

Solve each equation or formula for the variable specified. (Lesson 2-8)

70. $S = \frac{n}{2}(A + t)$, for A $A = \frac{2S}{n} - t$

71. $2g - m = 5 - gh$, for g $g = \frac{5 + m}{2 + h}$

72. $\frac{y + a}{3} = c$, for y $y = 3c - a$

73. $4z + b = 2z + c$, for z $z = \frac{c - b}{2}$

Skills Review

Evaluate each expression if $x = 2$, $y = 5$, and $z = 7$.

74. $3x^2 - 4y$ -8

75. $\frac{x - y^2}{2z}$ $-\frac{23}{14}$

76. $\left(\frac{y}{z}\right)^2 + \frac{xy}{2}$ $\frac{270}{49}$

77. $z^2 - y^3 + 5x^2$ -56

Differentiated Instruction BL

Extension Explain to students that the graph of a linear equation is called a *continuous graph*. It represents all solutions of the linear equation. Every ordered pair on a continuous line satisfies the equation. When the variables in an equation must be whole numbers, the points cannot be connected with a line. This type of graph is a *discrete graph*. Ask students to think of an example of when a discrete graph would be used. Sample answer: if *x* stood for the number of boys in a class and *y* stood for the number of girls in a class

LESSON 3-2 Solving Linear Equations by Graphing

Then

- You graphed linear equations by using tables and finding roots, zeros, and intercepts.

Now

1. Solve linear equations by graphing.
2. Estimate solutions to a linear equation by graphing.

Why?

- The cost of braces can vary widely. The graph shows the balance of the cost of treatments as payments are made. This is modeled by the function $b = -85p + 5100$, where p represents the number of \$85 payments made, and b is the remaining balance.

Orthodontic Payments

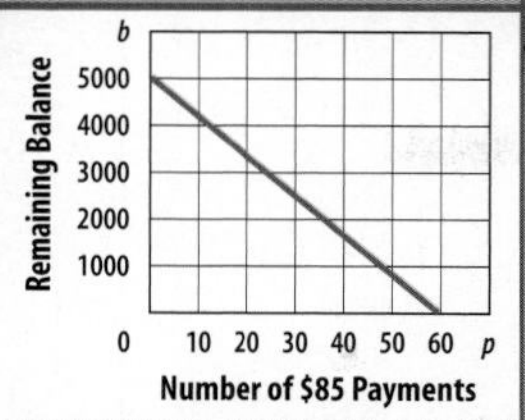

NewVocabulary

linear function
parent function
family of graphs
root
zeros

Process Standards
PS.4

1 Solve by Graphing

A **linear function** is a function for which the graph is a line. The simplest linear function is $f(x) = x$ and is called the **parent function** of the family of linear functions. A **family of graphs** is a group of graphs with one or more similar characteristics.

KeyConcept Linear Function

Parent function:	$f(x) = x$
Type of graph:	line
Domain:	all real numbers
Range:	all real numbers

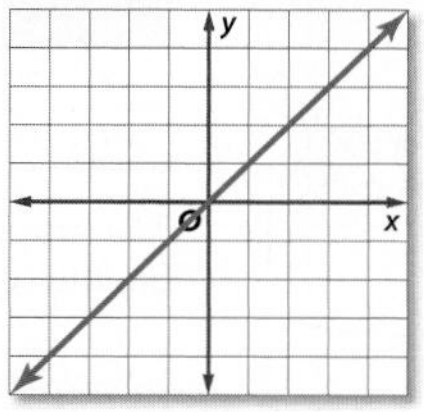

The solution or **root** of an equation is any value that makes the equation true. A linear equation has at most one root. You can find the root of an equation by graphing its related function. To write the related function for an equation, replace 0 with $f(x)$.

Linear Equation	Related Function
$2x - 8 = 0$	$f(x) = 2x - 8$ or $y = 2x - 8$

Values of x for which $f(x) = 0$ are called **zeros** of the function f. The zero of a function is located at the x-intercept of the function. The root of an equation is the value of the x-intercept. So:

- 4 is the x-intercept of $2x - 8 = 0$.
- 4 is the solution of $2x - 8 = 0$.
- 4 is the root of $2x - 8 = 0$.
- 4 is the zero of $f(x) = 2x - 8$.

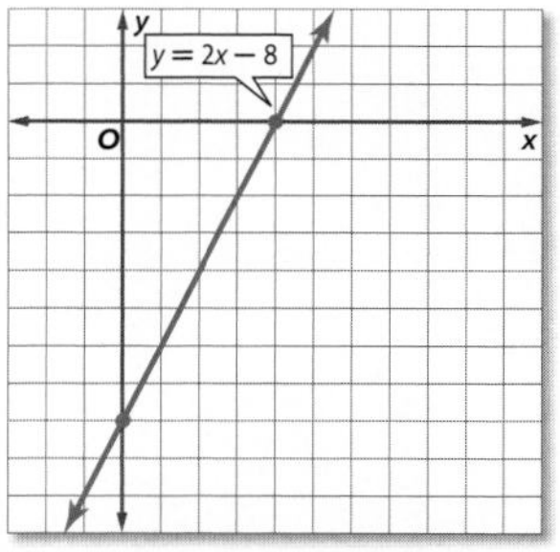

1 Focus

VerticalAlignment

Before Lesson 3-2 Graph linear equations by using tables and finding roots, zeros, and intercepts.

Lesson 3-2 Solve equations by graphing. Estimate solutions to an equation by graphing.

After Lesson 3-2 Determine the slope of a line.

2 Teach

Scaffolding Questions

Have students read the **Why?** section of the lesson.

Ask:

- If a parent has made 20 payments on her teenager's braces, what is the remaining balance to be paid? \$3400
- How can you use the graph to answer the question? Find 20 on the p-axis. Look to where the vertical line through 20 meets the line. Move to the b-axis to read the value.
- How can a parent use the graph to find how many payments there will be in all? Find where the graph meets the p-axis. The graph meets it at 60, so there will be a total of 60 payments.

Lesson 3-2 Resources

Resource	Approaching Level AL	On Level OL	Beyond Level BL	English Learners ELL
Teacher Edition	▪ Differentiated Instruction, p. 164	▪ Differentiated Instruction, pp. 164, 168	▪ Differentiated Instruction, p. 168	
Chapter Resource Masters	▪ Study Guide and Intervention, pp. 12–13 ▪ Skills Practice, p. 14 ▪ Practice, p. 15 ▪ Word Problem Practice, p. 16	▪ Study Guide and Intervention, pp. 12–13 ▪ Skills Practice, p. 14 ▪ Practice, p. 15 ▪ Word Problem Practice, p. 16 ▪ Enrichment, p. 17	▪ Practice, p. 15 ▪ Word Problem Practice, p. 16 ▪ Enrichment, p. 17	▪ Study Guide and Intervention, pp. 12–13 ▪ Skills Practice, p. 14 ▪ Practice, p. 15 ▪ Word Problem Practice, p. 16
Other	▪ 5-Minute Check 3-2 ▪ Study Notebook	▪ 5-Minute Check 3-2 ▪ Study Notebook	▪ 5-Minute Check 3-2 ▪ Study Notebook	▪ 5-Minute Check 3-2 ▪ Study Notebook

1 Solve by Graphing

Example 1 shows how to solve an equation with one root algebraically and by graphing. **Example 2** shows how to solve an equation that has no solution algebraically and by graphing.

Formative Assessment

Use the Guided Practice exercises after each example to determine students' understanding of concepts.

Additional Examples

1 Solve each equation.

a. $0 = \frac{1}{2}x + 3$ -6

b. $2 = \frac{1}{3}x + 3$ -3

2 Solve each equation.

a. $2x + 5 = 2x + 3$ no solution

b. $5x - 7 = 5x + 2$ no solution

Additional Examples also in Interactive Classroom PowerPoint® Presentations

IWB Interactive White Board READY

Focus on Mathematical Content

Identity Equations A linear equation in one variable has at most one root. There are equations with one variable that have infinitely many roots, but they are not linear equations. For example, $2x - 8 = 2(x - 4)$ when simplified becomes $2x - 8 = 2x - 8$ or $0 = 0$. This means any value chosen for x is a solution.

Tips for New Teachers

Function Notation Explain to students that $f(x)$ is a special notation, and is not "f" times "x."

Example 1 Solve an Equation with One Root

Solve each equation.

a. $0 = \frac{1}{3}x - 2$

Method 1 Solve algebraically.

$0 = \frac{1}{3}x - 2$	Original equation
$0 + 2 = \frac{1}{3}x - 2 + 2$	Add 2 to each side.
$3(2) = 3\left(\frac{1}{3}x\right)$	Multiply each side by 3.
$6 = x$	Solve.

The solution is 6.

b. $3x + 1 = -2$

Method 2 Solve by graphing.

Find the related function. Rewrite the equation with 0 on the right side.

$3x + 1 = -2$	Original equation
$3x + 1 + 2 = -2 + 2$	Add 2 to each side.
$3x + 3 = 0$	Simplify.

The related function is $f(x) = 3x + 3$. To graph the function, make a table.

x	$f(x) = 3x + 3$	$f(x)$	$(x, f(x))$
-2	$f(-2) = 3(-2) + 3$	-3	$(-2, -3)$
-1	$f(-1) = 3(-1) + 3$	0	$(-1, 0)$

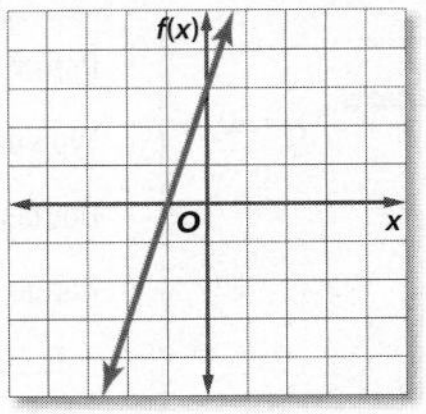

The graph intersects the x-axis at -1. So, the solution is -1.

StudyTip

Zeros from tables The zero is located at the x-intercept, so the value of y will equal 0. When looking at a table, the zero is the x-value when $y = 0$.

GuidedPractice

1A. $0 = \frac{2}{5}x + 6$ **−15**

1B. $-1.25x + 3 = 0$ **2.4 or $\frac{12}{5}$**

For equations with the same variable on each side of the equation, use addition or subtraction to get the terms with variables on one side. Then solve.

Example 2 Solve an Equation with No Solution

Solve each equation.

a. $3x + 7 = 3x + 1$

Method 1 Solve algebraically.

$3x + 7 = 3x + 1$	Original equation
$3x + 7 - 1 = 3x + 1 - 1$	Subtract 1 from each side.
$3x + 6 = 3x$	Simplify.
$3x - 3x + 6 = 3x - 3x$	Subtract $3x$ from each side.
$6 = 0$	Simplify.

The related function is $f(x) = 6$. The root of a linear equation is the value of x when $f(x) = 0$. Since $f(x)$ is always equal to 6, this equation has no solution.

DifferentiatedInstruction AL OL

If students have difficulty graphing equations,

Then consider having them work in small groups to work on problems like Example 1b. Make a large coordinate grid on a tiled floor. Assign one or two group members to make a table of values. Then have students stand on the grid on the ordered pairs and hold a string between them, close to the floor, to model the line. Have a student locate where the string crosses the x-axis.

b. $2x - 4 = 2x - 6$

Method 2 Solve by graphing.

$2x - 4 = 2x - 6$	Original equation
$2x - 4 + 6 = 2x - 6 + 6$	Add 6 to each side.
$2x + 2 = 2x$	Simplify.
$2x - 2x + 2 = 2x - 2x$	Subtract $2x$ from each side.
$2 = 0$	Simplify.

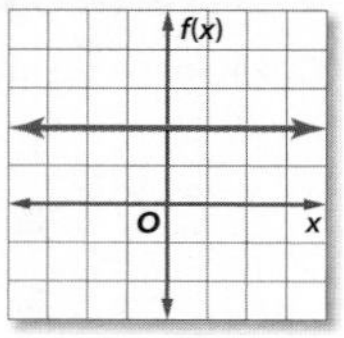

Graph the related function, which is $f(x) = 2$. The graph does not intersect the x-axis. Thus, there is no solution.

Guided Practice

2A. $4x + 3 = 4x - 5$ **no solution**

2B. $2 - 3x = 6 - 3x$ **no solution**

2 Estimate Solutions by Graphing

Graphing may provide only an estimate. In these cases, solve algebraically to find the exact solution.

Real-World Career

Entertainment Manager An entertainment manager supervises tech tests, calls show cues, schedules performances and performers, coaches employees and guest talent, and manages expenses. Entertainment managers need a college degree in a field such as communication or theater.

Real-World Example 3 Estimate by Graphing

CARNIVAL RIDES **Emily is going to a local carnival. The function $m = 20 - 0.75r$ represents the amount of money m she has left after r rides. Find the zero of this function. Describe what this value means in this context.**

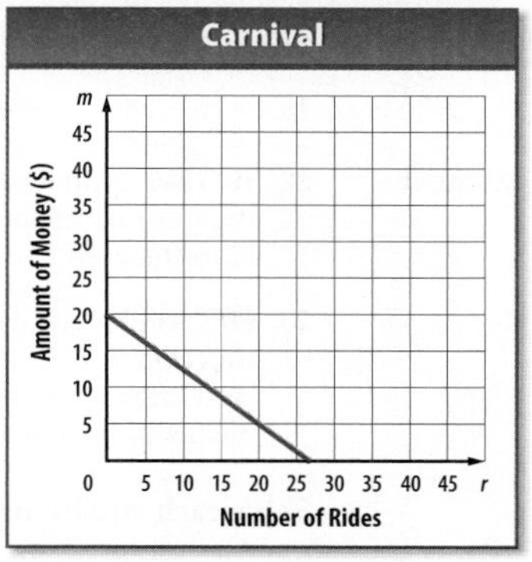

Make a table of values.

r	$m = 20 - 0.75r$	m	(r, m)
0	$m = 20 - 0.75(0)$	20	(0, 20)
5	$m = 20 - 0.75(5)$	16.25	(5, 16.25)

The graph appears to intersect the r-axis at 27.

Next, solve algebraically to check.

$m = 20 - 0.75r$	Original equation
$0 = 20 - 0.75r$	Replace m with 0.
$0 + 0.75r = 20 - 0.75r + 0.75r$	Add $0.75r$ to each side.
$0.75r = 20$	Simplify.
$\frac{0.75r}{0.75} = \frac{20}{0.75}$	Divide each side by 0.75.
$r \approx 26.67$	Simplify and round to the nearest hundredth.

The zero of this function is about 26.67. Since Emily cannot ride part of a ride, she can ride 26 rides before she will run out of money.

Guided Practice

3. Antoine's class must sell 30 candy bars before they make a profit.

3. FINANCIAL LITERACY Antoine's class is selling candy to raise money for a class trip. They paid \$45 for the candy, and they are selling each candy bar for \$1.50. The function $y = 1.50x - 45$ represents their profit y when they sell x candy bars. Find the zero and describe what it means in the context of this situation.

2 Estimate Solutions by Graphing

Example 3 shows how to estimate the zero of a function by graphing the function.

Additional Example

3 **FUNDRAISING** Kendra's class is selling greeting cards to raise money for new soccer equipment. They paid \$115 for the cards, and they are selling each card for \$1.75. The function $y = 1.75x - 115$ represents their profit y for selling x greeting cards. Find the zero of this function. Describe what this value means in this context. About 65.71; they must sell 66 cards to make a profit.

Tips for New Teachers

Reasoning Advise students to look for key words that describe situations in which it may be necessary to round an estimate up or down. For example, if you do not want to have *too few*, you need to round up. If you do not want to have *too much*, you round down.

Teach with Tech

Video Recording Have students work in groups to explain how to solve linear equations by graphing. Have them check their answers by solving the equations algebraically.

3 Practice

Formative Assessment

Use Exercises 1–9 to check for understanding.

Use the chart at the bottom of this page to customize assignments for your students.

Exercise Alert

Grid Paper Exercises 38–44 require the use of grid paper.

Teaching the Process Standards

Modeling Mathematically proficient students routinely interpret their mathematical results in the context of the situation. In Exercise 37, students must know or find the temperature when ice will begin to melt. Point out that t is the temperature in degrees Celsius.

WatchOut!

Error Analysis For Exercise 46, students should see that Clarissa did not simplify $x + 5 = 4$ correctly.

Additional Answers

22. 160; The text message is full after Sean has typed 160 characters.

36. $d \approx 1.67$; The water level in New Orleans has reached sea level after about 1.67 days of rain.

48. Sample answer: It is better to solve an equation algebraically if an exact answer is needed. It is better to solve graphically if an exact answer is not needed.

50. Sample answer: To solve a linear equation algebraically, solve the equation for x. To solve a linear equation graphically, find the related function by setting the equation equal to zero. Then, make a table and choose different values for x and find the corresponding y-coordinate. Determine where the graph intersects the x-axis. This is the solution. If the graph does not intersect the x-axis, there is no solution.

Check Your Understanding

= Step-by-Step Solutions begin on page R13.

Examples 1–2 Solve each equation by graphing. Verify your answer algebraically.

1. $-2x + 6 = 0$ **3**

2. $-x - 3 = 0$ **−3**

3. $4x - 2 = 0$ $\frac{1}{2}$

4. $9x + 3 = 0$ $-\frac{1}{3}$

5. $2x - 5 = 2x + 8$ **no solution**

6. $4x + 11 = 4x - 24$ **no solution**

7. $3x - 5 = 3x - 10$ **no solution**

8. $-6x + 3 = -6x + 5$ **no solution**

Example 3

9. **NEWSPAPERS** The function $w = 30 - \frac{3}{4}n$ represents the weight w in pounds of the papers in Tyrone's newspaper delivery bag after he delivers n newspapers. Find the zero and explain what it means in the context of this situation.
Tyrone must deliver 40 newspapers for the papers in his bag to weigh 0 pounds.

Practice and Problem Solving

Extra Practice is on page R3.

Solve each equation by graphing. Verify your answer algebraically.

12. no solution 13. no solution 17. no solution 18. no solution

10. $0 = x - 5$ **5**

11. $0 = x + 3$ **−3**

12. $5 - 8x = 16 - 8x$

13. $3x - 10 = 21 + 3x$

14. $4x - 36 = 0$ **9**

15. $0 = 7x + 10$ $-\frac{10}{7}$ or $-1\frac{3}{7}$

16. $2x + 22 = 0$ **−11**

17. $5x - 5 = 5x + 2$

18. $-7x + 35 = 20 - 7x$

19. $-4x - 28 = 3 - 4x$ **no solution**

20. $0 = 6x - 8$ $\frac{4}{3}$ or $1\frac{1}{3}$

21. $12x + 132 = 12x - 100$ **no solution**

Example 3

22. **TEXTING** Sean is sending texts to his friends. The function $y = 160 - x$ represents the number of characters y the message can hold after he has typed x characters. Find the zero and explain what it means in the context of this situation. **See margin.**

23. **GIFT CARDS** For her birthday Kwan receives a \$50 gift card to download songs. The function $m = -0.50d + 50$ represents the amount of money m that remains on the card after a number of songs d are downloaded. Find the zero and explain what it means in the context of this situation. **100; She can download a total of 100 songs before the gift card is completely used.**

B Solve each equation by graphing. Verify your answer algebraically.

24. $-7 = 4x + 1$ **−2**

25. $4 - 2x = 20$ **−8**

26. $2 - 5x = -23$ **5**

27. $10 - 3x = 0$ $\frac{10}{3}$ or $3\frac{1}{3}$

28. $15 + 6x = 0$ $-\frac{5}{2}$ or $-2\frac{1}{2}$

29. $0 = 13x + 34$ $-\frac{34}{13}$ or $-2\frac{8}{13}$

30. $0 = 22x - 10$ $\frac{5}{11}$

31. $25x - 17 = 0$ $\frac{17}{25}$

32. $0 = \frac{1}{2} + \frac{2}{3}x$ $-\frac{3}{4}$

33. $0 = \frac{3}{4} - \frac{2}{5}x$ $\frac{15}{8}$ or $1\frac{7}{8}$

34. $13x + 117 = 0$ **−9**

35. $24x - 72 = 0$ **3**

36. **SEA LEVEL** Parts of New Orleans lie 0.5 meter below sea level. After d days of rain the equation $w = 0.3d - 0.5$ represents the water level w in meters. Find the zero, and explain what it means in the context of this situation. **See margin.**

37. **MODELING** An artist completed an ice sculpture when the temperature was −10°C. The equation $t = 1.25h - 10$ shows the temperature h hours after the sculpture's completion. If the artist completed the sculpture at 8:00 A.M., at what time will it begin to melt? **4:00 P.M.**

38–43. See Chapter 3 Answer Appendix for graphs.

Solve each equation by graphing. Verify your answer algebraically.

38. $7 - 3x = 8 - 4x$ **1**

39. $19 + 3x = 13 + x$ **−3**

40. $16x + 6 = 14x + 10$ **2**

41. $15x - 30 = 5x - 50$ **−2**

42. $\frac{1}{2}x - 5 = 3x - 10$ **2**

43. $3x - 11 = \frac{1}{3}x - 8$ $\frac{9}{8}$ or $1\frac{1}{8}$

Differentiated Homework Options

Level	Assignment	Two-Day Option	
AL Basic	10–23, 46, 48–67	11–23 odd, 51–54	10–22 even, 46, 48–50, 55–67
OL Core	11–43 odd, 36, 44–46, 48–67	10–23, 51–54	24–46, 48–50, 55–67
BL Advanced	24–60, (optional: 61–67)		

44. **HAIR PRODUCTS** Chemical hair straightening makes curly hair straight and smooth. The percent of the process left to complete is modeled by $p = -12.5t + 100$, where t is the time in minutes that the solution is left on the hair, and p represents the percent of the process left to complete.

a. Find the zero of this function. **8**

b. Make a graph of this situation. **See Chapter 3 Answer Appendix.**

c. Explain what the zero represents in this context.

d. State the possible domain and range of this function. **D: $\{t \mid 0 \leq t \leq 8\}$, R: $\{p \mid 0 \leq p \leq 100\}$**

44c. The solution must remain on the hair for 8 minutes to be completely effective.

45. **MUSIC DOWNLOADS** In this problem, you will investigate the change between two quantities.

a. Copy and complete the table.

Number of Songs Downloaded	Total Cost ($)	Total Cost / Number of Songs Downloaded
2	4	2
4	8	2
6	12	2
8	16	2
10	20	2

b. As the number of songs downloaded increases, how does the total cost change? **increases by 4 for each 2 songs downloaded**

c. Interpret the value of the total cost divided by the number of songs downloaded. **It costs $2 per song to download.**

H.O.T. Problems Use Higher-Order Thinking Skills

46. Koko; Clarissa did not subtract the 5 from each side of the equation.

46. **ERROR ANALYSIS** Clarissa and Koko solve $3x + 5 = 2x + 4$ by graphing the related function. Is either of them correct? Explain your reasoning.

Clarissa

$3x + 5 = 2x + 4$

$x + 5 = 4$

$y = x + 5 + 4$

$y = x + 9$

$x = -9$

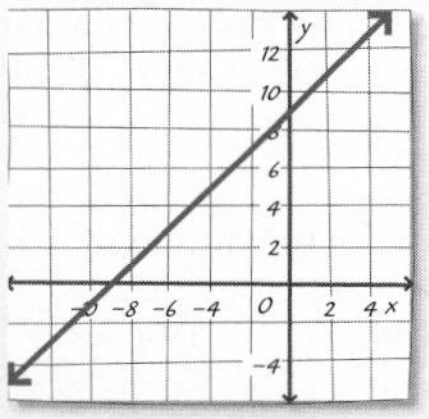

Koko

$3x + 5 = 2x + 4$

$x + 5 = 4$

$x + 1 = 0$

$y = x + 1$

$x = -1$

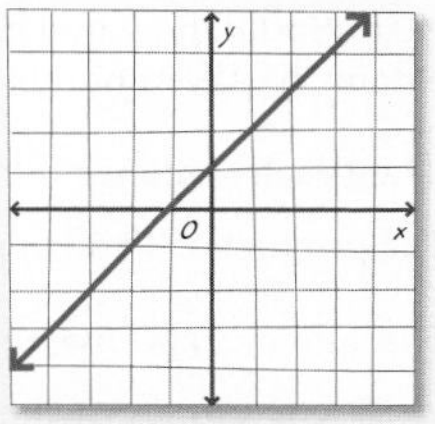

47. **CHALLENGE** Find the solution of $\frac{2}{3}(x + 3) = \frac{1}{2}(x + 5)$ by graphing. Verify your solution algebraically. **3**

48. **TOOLS** Explain when it is better to solve an equation using algebraic methods and when it is better to solve by graphing. **See margin.**

49. **OPEN ENDED** Write a linear equation that has a root of $-\frac{3}{4}$. Write its related function. **Sample answer: $3 + 4x = 0$; $y = 3 + 4x$ or $f(x) = 3 + 4x$**

50. **WRITING IN MATH** Summarize how to solve a linear equation algebraically and graphically. **See margin.**

Teaching the Process Standards

Tools Mathematically proficient students consider the available tools when solving a mathematical problem. In Exercise 48, point out to students that often multiple tools and methods are effective in solving a given problem.

Study Guide and Intervention
AL OL ELL

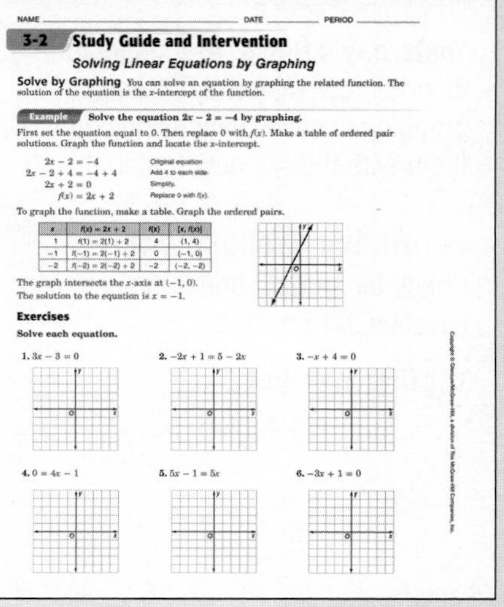
3-2 Study Guide and Intervention
Solving Linear Equations by Graphing

Practice
AL OL BL ELL

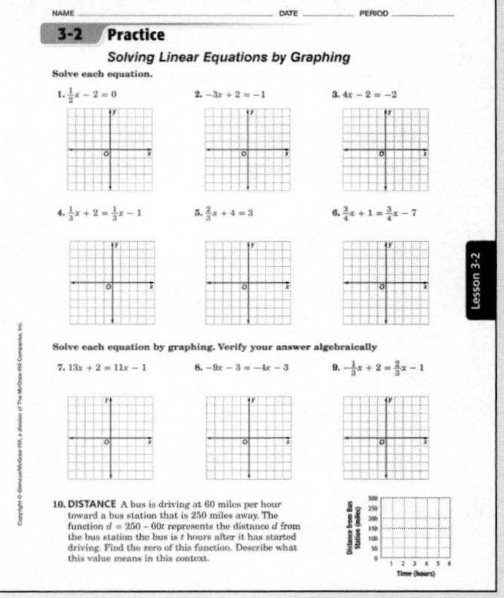
3-2 Practice
Solving Linear Equations by Graphing

Word Problem Practice
AL OL BL ELL

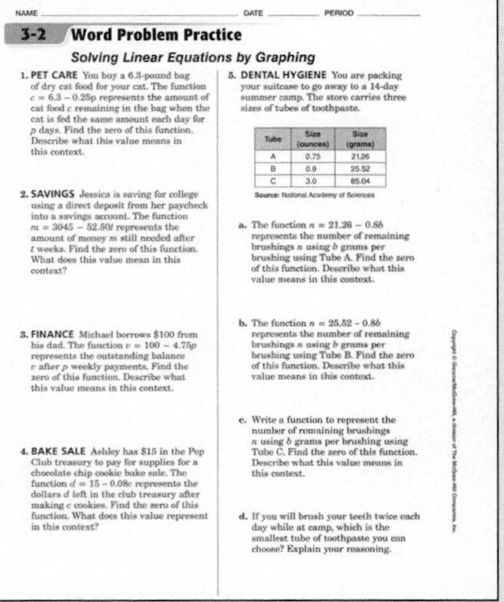
3-2 Word Problem Practice
Solving Linear Equations by Graphing

Enrichment
OL BL

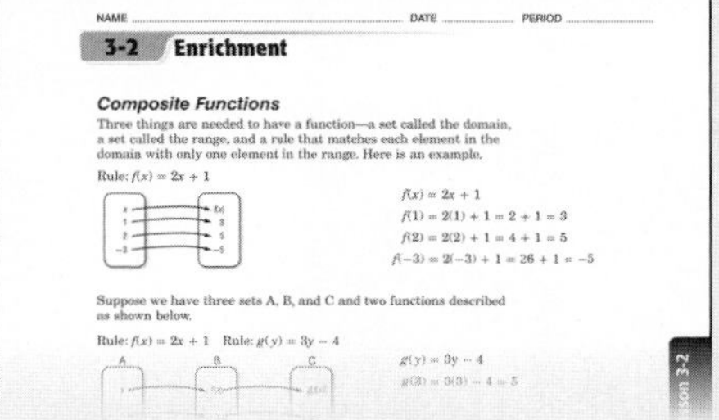
3-2 Enrichment
Composite Functions

4 Assess

Yesterday's News Ask students to write how yesterday's lesson on graphing linear equations helped them with today's new material.

Formative Assessment

Check for student understanding of Lessons 3-1 and 3-2.

Quiz 1, p. 45

Standardized Test Practice

51. What are the x- and y-intercepts of the graph of the function? **A**

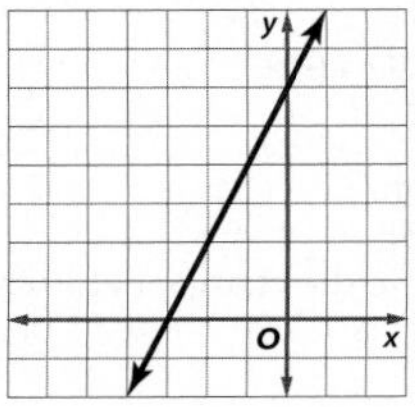

A $-3, 6$
B $6, -3$
C $3, -6$
D $-6, 3$

52. The table shows the cost C of renting a pontoon boat for h hours.

Hours	1	2	3
Cost ($)	7.25	14.5	21.75

Which equation best represents the data? **F**

F $C = 7.25h$
G $C = h + 7.25$
H $C = 21.75 - 7.25h$
J $C = 7.25h + 21.75$

53. Which is the best estimate for the x-intercept of the graph of the linear function represented in the table? **B**

x	y
0	5
1	3
2	1
3	−1
4	−3

A between 0 and 1
B between 2 and 3
C between 1 and 2
D between 3 and 4

54. EXTENDED RESPONSE Mr. Kauffmann has the following options for a backyard pool.

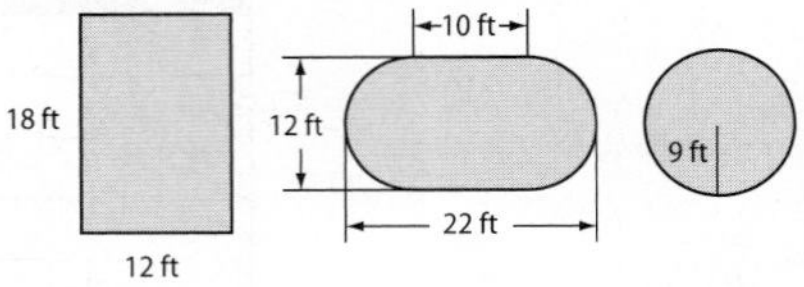

If each pool has the same depth, which pool would give the greatest area to swim? Explain your reasoning.
Circular pool; circular pool has an area ≈ 254.5 ft², which is greater than the rectangular pool with area = 216 ft² and the rounded pool with area ≈ 233 ft².

Spiral Review

Find the x- and y-intercepts of the graph of each linear equation. (Lesson 3-1)

55. $y = 2x + 10$ **−5, 10**

56. $3y = 6x - 9$ **$\frac{3}{2}$, −3**

57. $4x - 14y = 28$ **7, −2**

58. FOOD If 2% milk contains 2% butterfat and whipping cream contains 9% butterfat, how much whipping cream and 2% milk should be mixed to obtain 35 gallons of milk with 4% butterfat? (Lesson 2-9) **10 gal of cream, 25 gal of 2% milk**

Translate each sentence into an equation. (Lesson 2-1)

59. The product of 3 and m plus 2 times n is the same as the quotient of 4 and p. **$3m + 2n = \frac{4}{p}$**

60. The sum of x and five times y equals twice z minus 7. **$x + 5y = 2z - 7$**

Skills Review

Simplify.

61. $\frac{25}{10}$ **$\frac{5}{2}$**

62. $\frac{-4}{-12}$ **$\frac{1}{3}$**

63. $\frac{6}{-12}$ **$-\frac{1}{2}$**

64. $\frac{-36}{8}$ **$-\frac{9}{2}$**

Evaluate $\frac{a-b}{c-d}$ for the given values.

65. $a = 6, b = 2, c = 9, d = 3$ **$\frac{2}{3}$**

66. $a = -8, b = 4, c = 5, d = -3$ **$-\frac{3}{2}$**

67. $a = 4, b = -7, c = -1, d = -2$ **11**

Differentiated Instruction OL BL

Extension Solve $0 > \frac{1}{3}x - 1$. $3 > x$

Graphing Technology Lab
Graphing Linear Functions

The power of a graphing calculator is the ability to graph different types of equations accurately and quickly. By entering one or more equations in the calculator you can view features of a graph, such as the *x*-intercept, *y*-intercept, the origin, intersections, and the coordinates of specific points.

Process Standards
PS.5

Often linear equations are graphed in the **standard viewing window**, which is [−10, 10] by [−10, 10] with a scale of 1 on each axis. To quickly choose the standard viewing window on a TI-83/84 Plus, press ZOOM 6.

Activity 1 Graph a Linear Equation

Graph $3x - y = 4$.

Step 1 Enter the equation in the Y= list.

- The Y= list shows the equation or equations that you will graph.
- Equations must be entered with the y isolated on one side of the equation. Solve the equation for y, then enter it into the calculator.

The equals sign appears shaded for graphs that are selected to be displayed.

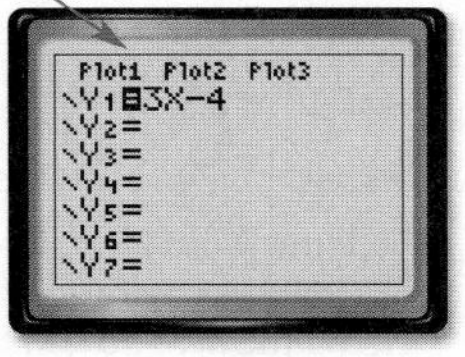

$3x - y = 4$	Original equation
$3x - y - 3x = 4 - 3x$	Subtract 3*x* from each side.
$-y = -3x + 4$	Simplify.
$y = 3x - 4$	Multiply each side by −1.

KEYSTROKES: Y= 3 X,T,θ,*n* − 4

Step 2 Graph the equation in the standard viewing window.

- Graph the selected equation.

KEYSTROKES: ZOOM 6

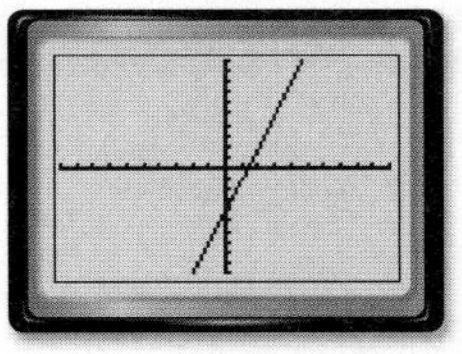

[−10, 10] scl: 1 by [−10, 10] scl: 1

Sometimes a complete graph is not displayed using the standard viewing window. A **complete graph** includes all of the important characteristics of the graph on the screen including the origin and the *x*- and *y*-intercepts. Note that the graph above is a complete graph because all of these points are visible.

When a complete graph is not displayed using the standard viewing window, you will need to change the viewing window to accommodate these important features. Use what you have learned about intercepts to help you choose an appropriate viewing window.

(continued on the next page)

1 Focus

Objective Change the viewing window so that a complete graph of a linear function can be displayed.

Materials for Each Group

- T1–83/84 Plus or other graphing calculator

Teaching Tip

- The graphing calculator has the ability to make graphs appear differently on the screen. The symbol before each **Y=** entry shows how the line will appear. Highlight the symbol and press ENTER repeatedly until the line type you want appears.
- The standard viewing window is selected by pressing ZOOM **6**. This is a [−10, 10] by [−10, 10] screen with scales, Xscl and Yscl, of 1.
- You can keep an equation in the **Y=** list and have it not appear on the graphing screen by highlighting the = sign and pressing ENTER.

2 Teach

Working in Cooperative Groups

Put students in groups of three or four, mixing abilities. Have groups help each other to complete Activities 1–2.

Make sure students have cleared or suppressed any equation in the Y= list other than those they wish to graph.

Ask:

- In what form must the equation be written to be entered into the calculator? with the *y* isolated on one side.
- How do you know you have a complete graph displayed in your window? The origin and the *x*- and *y*-intercepts are seen on the screen.

Practice Have students complete Exercises 1–15.

3 Assess

Formative Assessment

- Use Exercise 4 to assess whether students understand how to rewrite the equation with the *y* isolated on one side of the equation and enter it into their calculators.
- Use Exercise 10 to assess whether students understand how to modify the viewing window on their calculators.

From Concrete to Abstract

Ask:

How can the function $y = 3x + 15$ help you choose a viewing window for its graph? Sample answer: Since *b* is the *y*-intercept of the graph, you know that the window must at least include $y = 15$.

Teaching the Process Standards

Sense-Making Mathematically proficient students monitor and evaluate their progress and change course if necessary. In Exercises 7–12, students may need to change the viewing window on their graphing calculator to get the information they need. Stress that the *x*- and *y*-intercepts are key features of a linear graph to view.

Graphing Technology Lab
Graphing Linear Functions *Continued*

Activity 2 Graph a Complete Graph

Graph $y = 5x - 14$.

Step 1 Enter the equation in the Y= list and graph in the standard viewing window.

- Clear the previous equation from the Y= list. Then enter the new equation and graph.

KEYSTROKES: [Y=] [CLEAR] 5 [X,T,θ,n] [−] 14 [ZOOM] 6

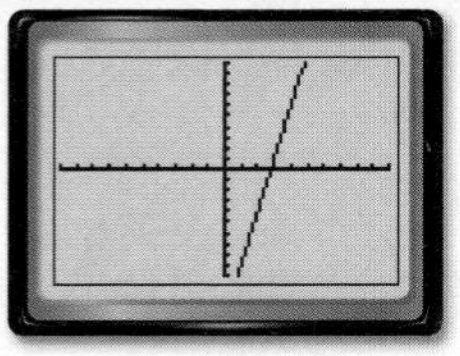

[−10, 10] scl: 1 by [−10, 10] scl: 1

Step 2 Modify the viewing window and graph again.

- The origin and the *x*-intercept are displayed in the standard viewing window. But notice that the *y*-intercept is outside of the viewing window.

Find the *y*-intercept.

$y = 5x - 14$ Original equation

$= 5(0) - 14$ Replace *x* with 0.

$= -14$ Simplify.

Since the *y*-intercept is −14, choose a viewing window that includes a number less than −14. The window [−10, 10] by [−20, 5] with a scale of 1 on each axis is a good choice.

KEYSTROKES: [WINDOW] −10 [ENTER] 10 [ENTER] 1 [ENTER] −20 [ENTER] 5 [ENTER] 1 [GRAPH]

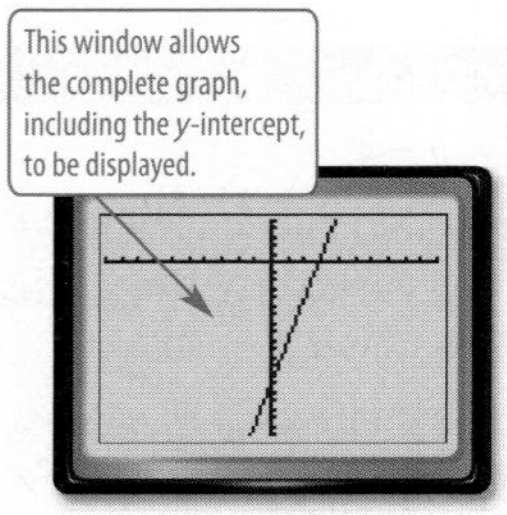

[−10, 10] scl: 1 by [−20, 5] scl: 1

Exercises

Use a graphing calculator to graph each equation in the standard viewing window. Sketch the result. 1–6. See Ch. 3 Answer Appendix.

1. $y = x + 5$ **2.** $y = 5x + 6$ **3.** $y = 9 - 4x$

4. $3x + y = 5$ **5.** $x + y = -4$ **6.** $x - 3y = 6$

SENSE-MAKING **Graph each equation in the standard viewing window. Determine whether the graph is complete. If the graph is not complete, adjust the viewing window and graph the equation again.** 7–12. See Ch. 3 Answer Appendix.

7. $y = 4x + 7$ **8.** $y = 9x - 5$ **9.** $y = 2x - 11$

10. $4x - y = 16$ **11.** $6x + 2y = 23$ **12.** $x + 4y = -36$

Consider the linear equation $y = 3x + b$.

13. Choose several different positive and negative values for *b*. Graph each equation in the standard viewing window. See students' work.

14. For which values of *b* is the complete graph in the standard viewing window? $-10 \leq b \leq 10$

15. How is the value of *b* related to the *y*-intercept of the graph of $y = 3x + b$? *b* is the *y*-intercept of the graph.

EXPLORE 3-3 Algebra Lab: Rate of Change of a Linear Function

In mathematics, you can measure the steepness of a line using a ratio.

Set Up the Lab

- Stack three books on your desk.
- Lean a ruler on the books to create a ramp.
- Tape the ruler to the desk.
- Measure the rise and the run. Record your data in a table like the one at the right.
- Calculate and record the ratio $\frac{\text{rise}}{\text{run}}$.

rise	run	$\frac{\text{rise}}{\text{run}}$

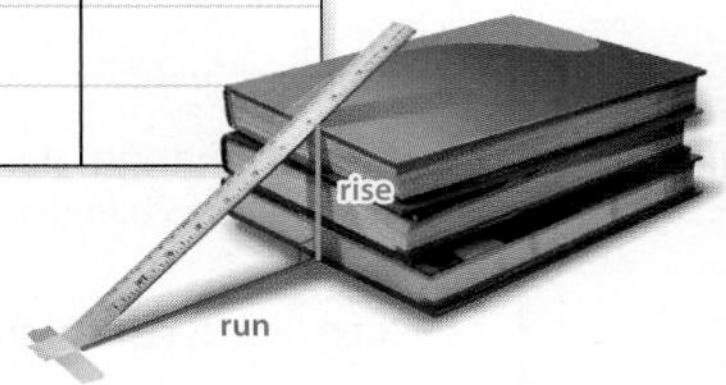

Activity

Step 1

Move the books to make the ramp steeper. Measure and record the rise and the run. Calculate and record $\frac{\text{rise}}{\text{run}}$.

Step 2

Add books to the stack to make the ramp even steeper. Measure, calculate, and record your data in the table.

Analyze the Results

1. Examine the ratios you recorded. How did they change as the ramp became steeper? **The ratios increased.**

2. **MAKE A PREDICTION** Suppose you want to construct a skateboard ramp that is not as steep as the one shown at the right. List three different sets of $\frac{\text{rise}}{\text{run}}$ measurements that will result in a less steep ramp. Verify your predictions by calculating the ratio $\frac{\text{rise}}{\text{run}}$ for each ramp. **Answers will vary.**

18 in.

24 in.

$m = \frac{18}{24} = \frac{3}{4}$

3. Copy the coordinate graph shown and draw a line through the origin with a $\frac{\text{rise}}{\text{run}}$ ratio greater than the original line. Then draw a line through the origin with a ratio less than that of the original line. Explain using the words *rise* and *run* why the lines you drew have a ratio greater or less than the original line. **Answers will vary.**

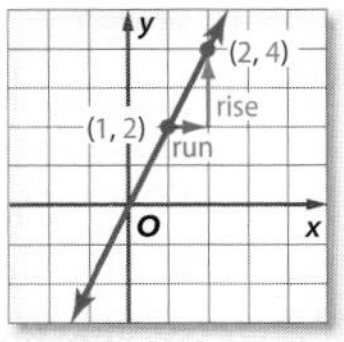

4. We have seen what happens on the graph as the $\frac{\text{rise}}{\text{run}}$ ratio gets closer to zero. What would you predict will happen when the ratio is zero? Explain your reasoning. Give an example to support your prediction.

Sample answer: If the ratio is zero, the rise must be zero. So, the line does not rise and would be horizontal. The line through (0, 2) and (2, 2) has a ratio of 0 and is horizontal.

1 Focus

Objective Investigate the steepness of a line using concrete materials.

Materials for Each Group

- 2 rulers
- 5 books
- a large piece of tape
- grid paper

Easy to Make Manipulatives

Teaching Algebra with Manipulatives

- Template for grid paper, p. 1

2 Teach

Working in Cooperative Groups

Put students in groups of three or four, mixing abilities. Have groups complete the Activity and Exercise 1.

Ask:

- Which measurement, rise or run, changes as you move the books? run
- In Step 2, which measurement changes when you add books? rise

Practice Have students complete Exercises 2 and 3.

3 Assess

Formative Assessment

Use Exercise 4 to assess whether students comprehend how to find slope from a coordinate graph.

From Concrete to Abstract

Give students a piece of uncooked spaghetti and a coordinate grid. Have them place the spaghetti on the grid and record the slope of the represented line. Repeat this activity five times.

Extending the Concept

Ask:

- If the run is not zero, is the $\frac{\text{rise}}{\text{run}}$ always a fraction? $\frac{\text{rise}}{\text{run}}$ can always be expressed as a fraction, even if it appears to be an integer.
- If the run is not zero, can $\frac{\text{rise}}{\text{run}}$ be negative? When? Yes; the $\frac{\text{rise}}{\text{run}}$ is negative when the line slopes down from left to right.

1 Focus

VerticalAlignment

Before Lesson 3-3 Graph ordered pairs in the coordinate plane.

Lesson 3-3 Use rate of change to solve problems. Find the slope of a line.

After Lesson 3-3 Write, graph, and solve direct variation equations.

2 Teach

Scaffolding Questions

Have students read the **Why?** section of the lesson.

Ask:

- How can you write the rate of change of the ride? $\frac{\text{change in distance}}{\text{change in time}}$
- What might the ratio be for a ride with a rate of change of 2? Sample answers: $\frac{10}{5}, \frac{6}{3}, \frac{2}{1}$
- Which has a steeper waterchute, a ride with a rate of change of $\frac{1}{2}$ or a ride with a rate of change of $\frac{5}{2}$? Why? $\frac{5}{2}$, because the change in distance is greater than in $\frac{1}{2}$ and both have the same change in time.

LESSON 3-3 Rate of Change and Slope

Then
- You graphed ordered pairs in the coordinate plane.

Now
1. Use rate of change to solve problems.
2. Find the slope of a line.

Why?
- The Daredevil Drop at Wet 'n Wild Emerald Pointe in Greensboro, North Carolina, is a thrilling ride that drops you 76 feet down a steep water chute. A *rate of change* of the ride might describe the distance a rider has fallen over a length of time.

NewVocabulary
rate of change
slope

Content Standards
AI.F.4, AI.L.5

Process Standards
PS.2

1 Rate of Change

Rate of change is a ratio that describes, on average, how much one quantity changes with respect to a change in another quantity.

KeyConcept Rate of Change

If x is the independent variable and y is the dependent variable, then

$$\text{rate of change} = \frac{\text{change in } y}{\text{change in } x}.$$

PT

Real-World Example 1 Find Rate of Change

ENTERTAINMENT Use the table to find the rate of change. Then explain its meaning.

Number of Computer Games	Total Cost ($)
x	y
2	78
4	156
6	234

$$\text{rate of change} = \frac{\text{change in } y}{\text{change in } x} \begin{matrix}\leftarrow \text{dollars}\\ \leftarrow \text{games}\end{matrix}$$

$$= \frac{\text{change in cost}}{\text{change in number of games}}$$

$$= \frac{156 - 78}{4 - 2}$$

$$= \frac{78}{2} \text{ or } \frac{39}{1}$$

The rate of change is $\frac{39}{1}$ or 39. This means that the cost per game is $39.

GuidedPractice

1. **REMODELING** The table shows how the tiled surface area changes with the number of floor tiles.

Number of Floor Tiles	Area of Tiled Surface (in^2)
x	y
3	48
6	96
9	144

A. Find the rate of change. 16

B. Explain the meaning of the rate of change. 16 in^2 of surface is tiled for each floor tile that is used.

Lesson 3-3 Resources

Resource	Approaching Level AL	On Level OL	Beyond Level BL	English Learners ELL
Teacher Edition	▪ Differentiated Instruction, p. 175	▪ Differentiated Instruction, pp. 175, 176, 180	▪ Differentiated Instruction, pp. 175, 176, 180	
Chapter Resource Masters	▪ Study Guide and Intervention, pp. 18–19 ▪ Skills Practice and Practice, pp. 20–21 ▪ Word Problem Practice, p. 22	▪ Study Guide and Intervention, pp. 18–19 ▪ Skills Practice and Practice, pp. 20–21 ▪ Word Problem Practice, p. 22 ▪ Enrichment, p. 23	▪ Practice, p. 21 ▪ Word Problem Practice, p. 22 ▪ Enrichment, p. 23	▪ Study Guide and Intervention, pp. 18–19 ▪ Skills Practice, p. 20 ▪ Practice, p. 21 ▪ Word Problem Practice, p. 22
Other	▪ 5-Minute Check 3-3 ▪ Study Notebook ▪ Teaching Algebra with Manipulatives	▪ 5-Minute Check 3-3 ▪ Study Notebook ▪ Teaching Algebra with Manipulatives	▪ 5-Minute Check 3-3 ▪ Study Notebook	▪ 5-Minute Check 3-3 ▪ Study Notebook ▪ Teaching Algebra with Manipulatives

So far, you have seen rates of change that are *constant*. Many real-world situations involve rates of change that are not constant.

Real-World Example 2 Compare Rates of Change

AMUSEMENT PARKS **The graph shows the number of people who visited U.S. theme parks in recent years.**

a. Find the rates of change for 2000–2002 and 2002–2004.

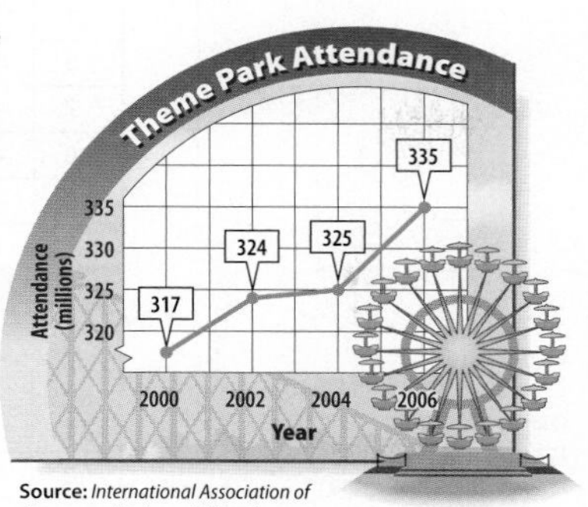

Source: *International Association of Amusement Parks and Attractions*

2000–2002:

$$\frac{\text{change in attendance}}{\text{change in time}} = \frac{324 - 317}{2002 - 2000} \begin{matrix}\leftarrow \text{people} \\ \leftarrow \text{years}\end{matrix} \quad \text{Substitute.}$$

$$= \frac{7}{2} \text{ or } 3.5 \quad \text{Simplify.}$$

Over this 2-year period, attendance increased by 7 million, for a rate of change of 3.5 million per year.

2002–2004:

$$\frac{\text{change in attendance}}{\text{change in time}} = \frac{325 - 324}{2004 - 2002} \quad \text{Substitute.}$$

$$= \frac{1}{2} \text{ or } 0.5 \quad \text{Simplify.}$$

Over this 2-year period, attendance increased by 1 million, for a rate of change of 0.5 million per year.

b. Explain the meaning of the rate of change in each case.

For 2000–2002, on average, 3.5 million more people went to a theme park each year than the last.

For 2002–2004, on average, 0.5 million more people attended theme parks each year than the last.

c. How are the different rates of change shown on the graph?

There is a greater vertical change for 2000–2002 than for 2002–2004. Therefore, the section of the graph for 2000–2002 is steeper.

GuidedPractice **2002–2004; Attendance increased by 0.5 million per year.**

2. Refer to the graph above. Without calculating, find the 2-year period that has the least rate of change. Then calculate to verify your answer.

StudyTip

Reasoning A positive rate of change indicates an increase over time. A negative rate of change indicates that a quantity is decreasing.

A rate of change is constant for a function when the rate of change is the same between any pair of points on the graph of the function. Linear functions have a constant rate of change.

1 Rate of Change

Example 1 shows how to find the rate of change given a table of values for a real-world situation. **Example 2** shows how to describe the rate of change for a real-world problem in which the difference between two *y*-values divided by the difference between their corresponding *x*-values is not constant. **Example 3** shows how to determine whether a function is linear or nonlinear.

Formative Assessment

Use the Guided Practice exercises after each Example to determine students' understanding of concepts.

Additional Example

1 **DRIVING TIME** Use the table to find the rate of change. Then explain its meaning.

Time Driving (h)	Distance Traveled (mi)
x	*y*
2	76
4	152
6	228

$\frac{38}{1}$; this means the car is traveling at a rate of 38 miles per hour.

Additional Examples also in Interactive Classroom PowerPoint® Presentations

IWB Interactive White Board READY

Teaching the Process Standards

Reasoning Mathematically proficient students make sense of quantities and their relationships in problem situations. Rate of change is an extremely important concept for students to master. Encourage students to relate the rate of change to the quantities a function represents.

Tips for New Teachers

Sense-Making Explain to students that linear functions have a constant rate of change or slope, regardless of which pair of points is used in the calculation, due to the properties of similar triangles. Demonstrate the idea by calculating the slopes of the sides of two triangles that can be formed from a line. Remind students that they have studied similar triangles in previous math courses.They will learn more in their Geometry course.

Additional Examples

2 **TRAVEL** The graph below shows the number of U.S. passports issued in 2002, 2004, and 2006.

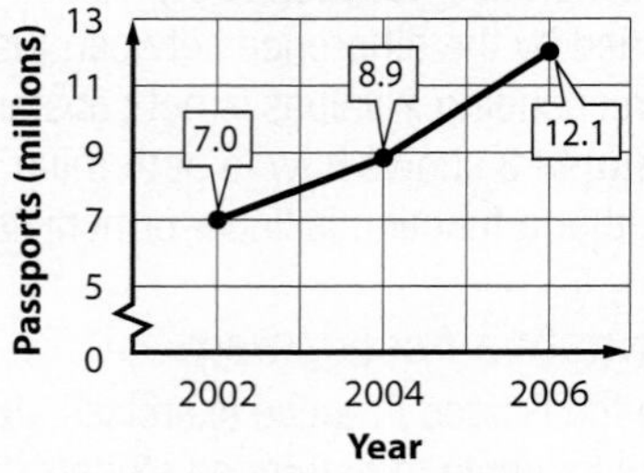

a. Find the rates of change for 2002–2004 and 2004–2006. 950,000/yr; 1,600,000/yr

b. Explain the meaning of the rate of change in each case. For 2002–2004, there was an average annual increase of 950,000 passports issued. Between 2004 and 2006, there was an average yearly increase of 1,600,000 passports issued.

c. How are the different rates of change shown on the graph? There is a greater vertical change for 2004–2006 than for 2002–2004. Therefore, the section of the graph for 2004–2006 is steeper.

3 Determine whether each function is linear. Explain.

a.

x	y
1	6
2	12
3	18
4	24

Yes; the rate of change is constant.

b.

x	y
−10	5
−2	1
6	−4
14	−10

No; the rate of change is not constant.

Example 3 Constant Rates of Change

Determine whether each function is linear. Explain.

a.

x	y
1	−6
4	−8
7	−10
10	−12
13	−14

x	y	rate of change
1	−6	
4	−8	$\frac{-8-(-6)}{4-1}$ or $-\frac{2}{3}$
7	−10	$\frac{-10-(-8)}{7-4}$ or $-\frac{2}{3}$
10	−12	$\frac{-12-(-10)}{10-7}$ or $-\frac{2}{3}$
13	−14	$\frac{-14-(-12)}{13-10}$ or $-\frac{2}{3}$

The rate of change is constant. Thus, the function is linear.

b.

x	y
−3	10
−1	12
1	16
3	18
5	22

x	y	rate of change
−3	10	
−1	12	$\frac{12-10}{-1-(-3)}$ or 1
1	16	$\frac{16-12}{1-(-1)}$ or 2
3	18	$\frac{18-16}{3-1}$ or 1
5	22	$\frac{22-18}{5-3}$ or 2

This rate of change is not constant. Thus, the function is not linear.

StudyTip

Linear or Nonlinear Function? Notice that the changes in x and y are not the same. For the rate of change to be linear, the change in x-values must be constant and the change in y-values must be constant.

GuidedPractice

3A.

x	y
−3	11
−2	15
−1	19
1	23
2	27

No; there is not a constant rate of change.

3B.

x	y
12	−4
9	1
6	6
3	11
0	16

Yes; the rate of change is constant.

2 Find Slope

The **slope** of a nonvertical line is the ratio of the change in the y-coordinates (rise) to the change in the x-coordinates (run) as you move from one point to another.

It can be used to describe a rate of change. Slope describes how steep a line is. The greater the absolute value of the slope, the steeper the line.

The graph shows a line that passes through (−1, 3) and (2, −2).

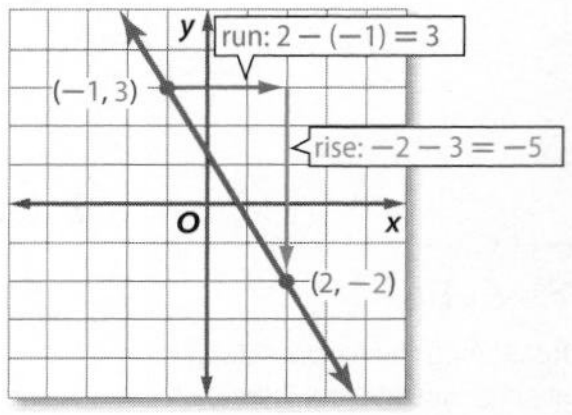

$$\text{slope} = \frac{\text{rise}}{\text{run}}$$

$$= \frac{\text{change in } y\text{-coordinates}}{\text{change in } x\text{-coordinates}}$$

$$= \frac{-2-3}{2-(-1)} \text{ or } -\frac{5}{3}$$

So, the slope of the line is $-\frac{5}{3}$.

Because a linear function has a constant rate of change, any two points on a nonvertical line can be used to determine its slope.

174 | Lesson 3-3 | Rate of Change and Slope

KeyConcept Slope

Words The slope of a nonvertical line is the ratio of the rise to the run.

Symbols The slope m of a nonvertical line through any two points, (x_1, y_1) and (x_2, y_2), can be found as follows.

$$m = \frac{y_2 - y_1}{x_2 - x_1} \begin{matrix} \leftarrow \text{change in } y \\ \leftarrow \text{change in } x \end{matrix}$$

Graph

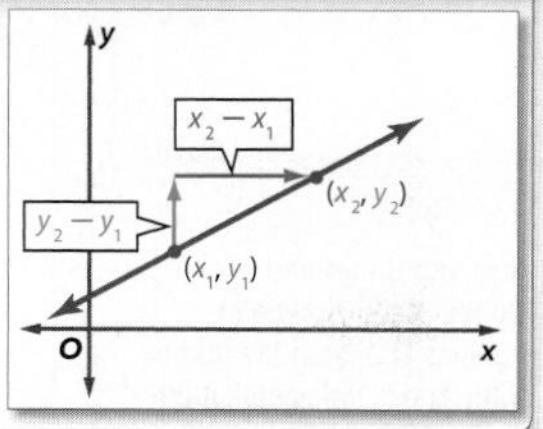

> **ReadingMath**
> Subscripts y_1 is read as *y sub one* and x_2 is read as *x sub two*. The 1 and 2 are subscripts and refer to the first and second point to which the *x*- and *y*-values correspond.

The slope of a line can be positive, negative, zero, or undefined. If the line is not horizontal or vertical, then the slope is either positive or negative.

Example 4 Positive, Negative and Zero Slope

Find the slope of a line that passes through each pair of points.

a. (−2, 0) and (1, 5)

$m = \frac{y_2 - y_1}{x_2 - x_1}$ rise/run

$= \frac{5 - 0}{1 - (-2)}$ $(-2, 0) = (x_1, y_1)$ and $(1, 5) = (x_2, y_2)$

$= \frac{5}{3}$ Simplify.

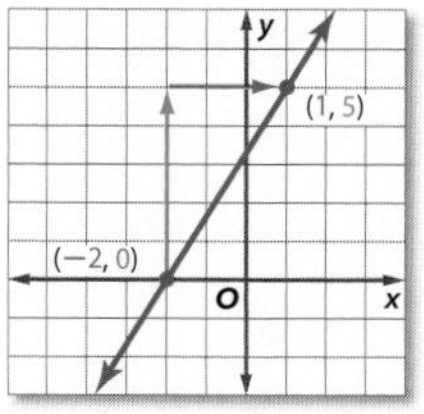

> **WatchOut!**
> Order Be careful not to transpose the order of the *x*-values or the *y*-values.

b. (−3, 4) and (2, −3)

$m = \frac{y_2 - y_1}{x_2 - x_1}$ rise/run

$= \frac{-3 - 4}{2 - (-3)}$ $(-3, 4) = (x_1, y_1)$ and $(2, -3) = (x_2, y_2)$

$= \frac{-7}{5}$ or $-\frac{7}{5}$ Simplify.

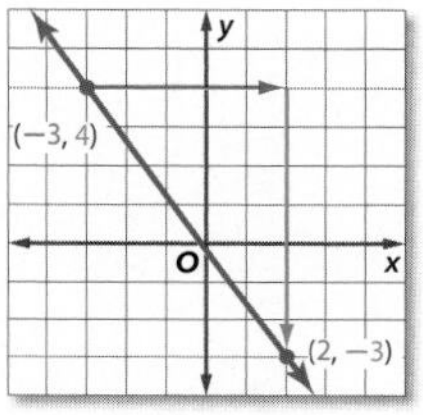

c. (−3, −1) and (2, −1)

$m = \frac{y_2 - y_1}{x_2 - x_1}$ rise/run

$= \frac{-1 - (-1)}{2 - (-3)}$ Substitute.

$= \frac{0}{5}$ or 0 Simplify.

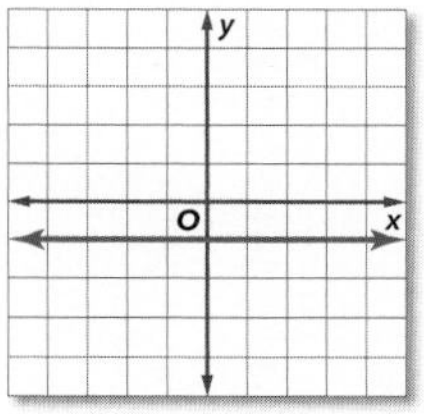

GuidedPractice

Find the slope of the line that passes through each pair of points.

4A. (3, 6), (4, 8) **2** **4B.** (−4, −2), (0, −2) **0** **4C.** (−4, 2), (−2, 10) **4**

4D. (6, 7), (−2, 7) **0** **4E.** (−2, 2), (−6, 4) $-\frac{1}{2}$ **4F.** (4, 3), (−1, 11) $-\frac{8}{5}$

DifferentiatedInstruction AL OL BL

If students automatically assume that the left-most point has to be (x_1, y_1) and the point farther right is (x_2, y_2),

Then explain that the designation of (x_1, y_1) and (x_2, y_2) is arbitrary. Write pairs of points on index cards. Give one card to each student. Have them find the slope both ways. Then ask which way made the subtraction easier.

2 Find Slope

Examples 4 and 5 show the four possible types when we try to find the slope of a line. **Example 6** shows how to use algebraic manipulation to find a missing coordinate when the slope is known.

Focus on Mathematical Content

Zero Slope A slope of 0 does not mean there is no slope. It means that the line has no steepness—that is, the line is horizontal.

Additional Example

4 Find the slope of the line that passes through each pair of points.

a. (−3, 2) and (5, 5) $\frac{3}{8}$

b. (−3, −4) and (−2, −8) −4

c. (−3, 4) and (4, 4) 0

Tips for New Teachers

Horizontal Lines After reviewing Example 4c, ask students how they would determine whether two points lie on a horizontal line without graphing the points.

Focus on Mathematical Content

Slope and Improper Fractions Slope is usually expressed as a fraction or an integer because it gives information about the direction of the line. A mixed number may not easily reveal that information.

Teach with Tech

Audio Recording Have students work in groups. Give each group graphs of several lines, without labels. Have students verbally describe real-world situations that could be shown by each graph.

Focus on Mathematical Content

Undefined Slope Undefined slope is not the same as slope of 0. The slope of a vertical line is undefined because the formula yields an expression with 0 as the denominator, and division by zero is undefined.

Additional Examples

5 Find the slope of the line that passes through $(-2, -4)$ and $(-2, 3)$. undefined

6 Find the value of r so that the line through $(6, 3)$ and $(r, 2)$ has a slope of $\frac{1}{2}$. 4

WatchOut!

Preventing Errors As students work through Example 6, watch for those who try to find the cross product mentally and forget to multiply both r and -4 by 3.

Example 5 Undefined Slope

Find the slope of the line that passes through $(-2, 4)$ and $(-2, -3)$.

$m = \frac{y_2 - y_1}{x_2 - x_1}$ — rise/run

$= \frac{-3 - 4}{-2 - (-2)}$ — Substitute.

$= \frac{-7}{0}$ or undefined — Simplify.

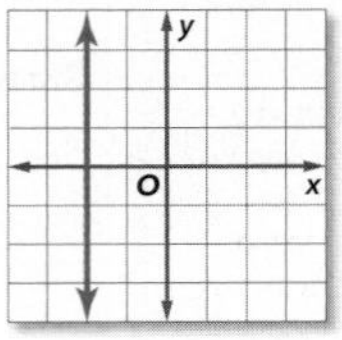

StudyTip

Zero and Undefined Slopes If the change in y-values is 0, then the graph of the line is horizontal. If the change in x-values is 0, then the slope is undefined. This graph is a vertical line.

GuidedPractice

Find the slope of the line that passes through each pair of points.

5A. $(6, 3), (6, 7)$ **undefined**

5B. $(-3, 2), (-3, -1)$ **undefined**

The graphs of lines with different slopes are summarized below.

ConceptSummary Slope

positive slope

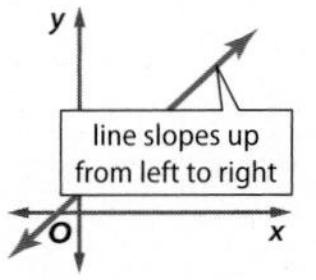

The function values are increasing over the entire domain.

negative slope

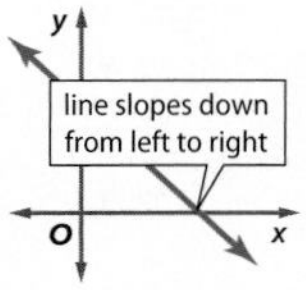

The function values are decreasing over the entire domain.

slope of 0

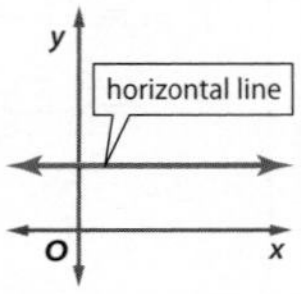

The function values are constant over the entire domain.

undefined slope

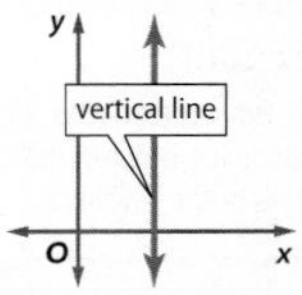

The relation is not a function.

Example 6 Find Coordinates Given the Slope

Find the value of r so that the line through $(1, 4)$ and $(-5, r)$ has a slope of $\frac{1}{3}$.

$m = \frac{y_2 - y_1}{x_2 - x_1}$ — Slope Formula

$\frac{1}{3} = \frac{r - 4}{-5 - 1}$ — Let $(1, 4) = (x_1, y_1)$ and $(-5, r) = (x_2, y_2)$.

$\frac{1}{3} = \frac{r - 4}{-6}$ — Subtract.

$3(r - 4) = 1(-6)$ — Find the cross products.

$3r - 12 = -6$ — Distributive Property

$3r = 6$ — Add 12 to each side and simplify.

$r = 2$ — Divide each side by 3 and simplify.

So, the line goes through $(-5, 2)$.

GuidedPractice

Find the value of r so the line that passes through each pair of points has the given slope.

6A. $(-2, 6), (r, -4); m = -5$ **0**

6B. $(r, -6), (5, -8); m = -8$ **4.75**

DifferentiatedInstruction OL BL

Extension Provide students with opportunities to analyze slope by giving contexts to graphs where the slope varies from point to point. Students can explore why graphs increase or decrease rapidly, steadily or slowly.

176 | Lesson 3-3 | Rate of Change and Slope

Check Your Understanding

◯ = Step-by-Step Solutions begin on page R13.

Example 1 **Find the rate of change represented in each table or graph.**

1. 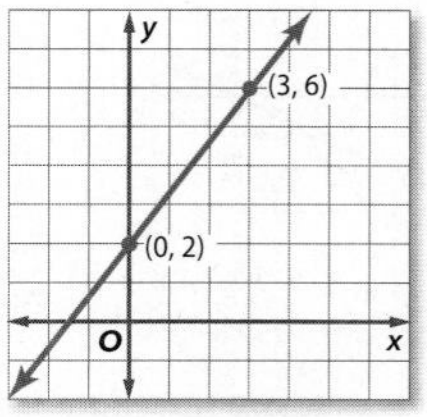

$\frac{4}{3}$

2.

x	y
3	−6
5	2
7	10
9	18
11	26

4

3a. 1.035; There was an average increase in ticket price of $1.035 per year.
3b. Sample answer: 1998–2000; A steeper segment means a greater rate of change.
4. Yes; the rate of change is constant.

Example 2 **3. SENSE-MAKING** Refer to the graph at the right.

- **a.** Find the rate of change of prices from 2006 to 2008. Explain the meaning of the rate of change.
- **b.** Without calculating, find a two-year period that had a greater rate of change than 2006–2008. Explain.
- **c.** Between which years would you guess the new stadium was built? Explain your reasoning. **Sample answer: 1998–2000; Ticket prices show a sharp increase.**

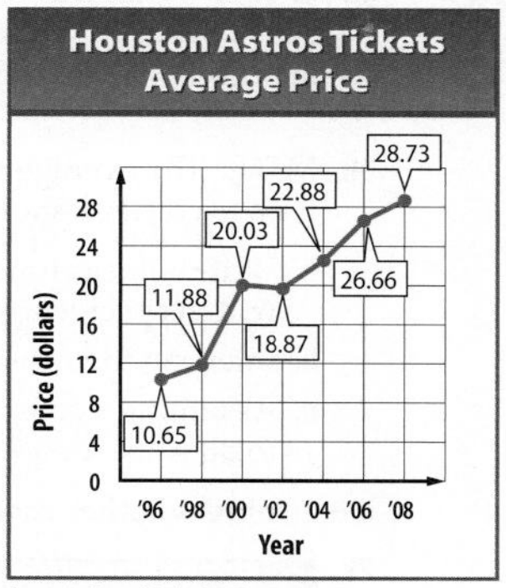

Source: *Team Marketing Report*

Example 3 **Determine whether each function is linear. Write *yes* or *no*. Explain.**

4.

x	−7	−4	−1	2	5
y	5	4	3	2	1

5.

x	8	12	16	20	24
y	7	5	3	0	−2

No; the rate of change is not constant.

Examples 4–5 **Find the slope of the line that passes through each pair of points.**

6. (5, 3), (6, 9) **6**
7. (−4, 3), (−2, 1) **−1**
8. (6, −2), (8, 3) $\frac{5}{2}$
9. (1, 10), (−8, 3) $\frac{7}{9}$
10. (−3, 7), (−3, 4) **undefined**
11. (5, 2), (−6, 2) **0**

Example 6 **Find the value of r so the line that passes through each pair of points has the given slope.**

12. $(-4, r), (-8, 3), m = -5$ **−17**
13. $(5, 2), (-7, r), m = \frac{5}{6}$ **−8**

Practice and Problem Solving

Extra Practice is on page R3.

Example 1 **Find the rate of change represented in each table or graph.**

14. $\frac{1}{5}$

x	y
5	2
10	3
15	4
20	5

(15) −6

x	y
1	15
2	9
3	3
4	−3

Differentiated Homework Options

Level	Assignment	Two-Day Option	
AL Basic	14–39, 48–49, 51–68	15–39 odd, 51–56	14–38 even, 48, 49, 57–68
OL Core	15–39 odd, 40–49, 51–68	14–39, 53–56	40–49, 51–52, 57–68
BL Advanced	40–62, (optional: 63–68)		

3 Practice

Formative Assessment

Use Exercises 1–13 to check for understanding.

Use the chart at the bottom of this page to customize assignments for your students.

Tips for New Teachers

Pacing Because slope is an important concept throughout this chapter, students should have a good understanding of it. If you are uncertain that your students have mastered the concept of slope, consider spending an extra day on this lesson.

Exercise Alert

Grid Paper For Exercises 46, 47, and 57–59, students will need grid paper.

Teaching the Process Standards

Sense-Making Mathematically proficient students can explain and use correspondences between various representations. In Exercise 3b, discuss how students can compare rates of change visually using a graph.

WatchOut!

Error Analysis For Exercise 52, if students have difficulty substituting the correct coordinates into the slope formula, show them the following diagram.

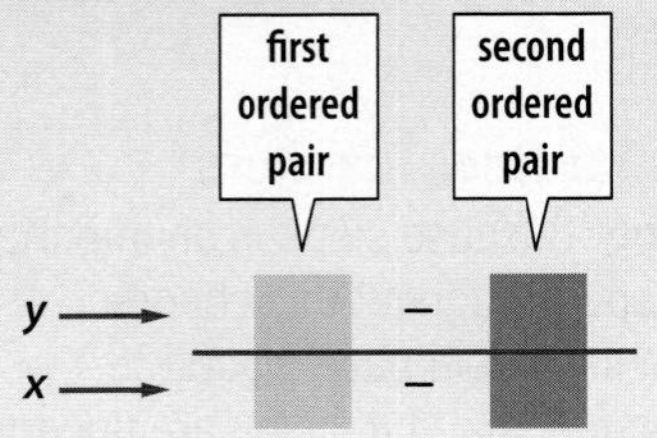

Additional Answers

46a-b.

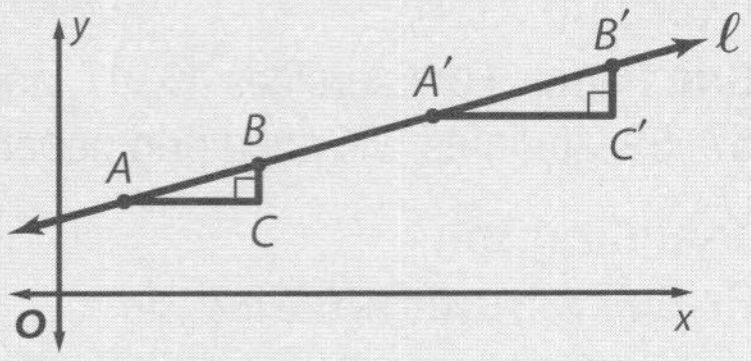

$\overline{AC}$ and $\overline{A'C'}$ are horizontal and $\overline{BC}$ and $\overline{B'C'}$ are vertical.

46c. Sample answer: Triangles ABC and $A'B'C'$ are similar because Line ℓ is a transversal of parallel segments $\overline{BC}$ and $\overline{B'C'}$, so $\angle ABC \cong \angle A'B'C'$ since corresponding angles of parallel lines are congruent. $\angle C \cong \angle C'$ because all right angles are congruent. Therefore, by AA Similarity, $\triangle ABC \cong \triangle A'B'C'$. So the slope of line $\frac{BC}{AC}$ through points A and B, is equal to $\frac{B'C'}{A'C'}$ the slope of line through points A' and B'.

48. The difference in the x-values is always 0, and division by 0 is undefined.

51. Sample answer: Slope can be used to describe a rate of change. Rate of change is a ratio that describes how much one quantity changes with respect to a change in another quantity. The slope of a line is also a ratio and it is the ratio of the change in the y-coordinates to the change in the x-coordinates.

Example 1 **Find the rate of change represented in each table or graph.**

16. 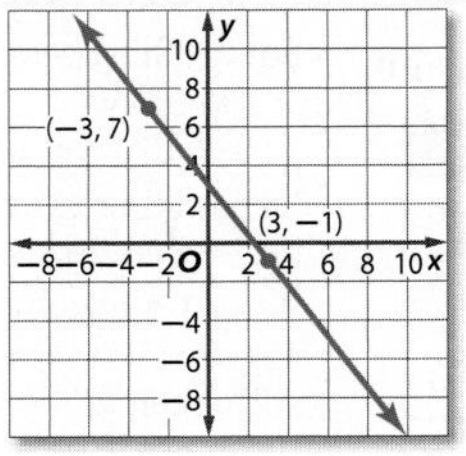

$-\frac{4}{3}$

17. 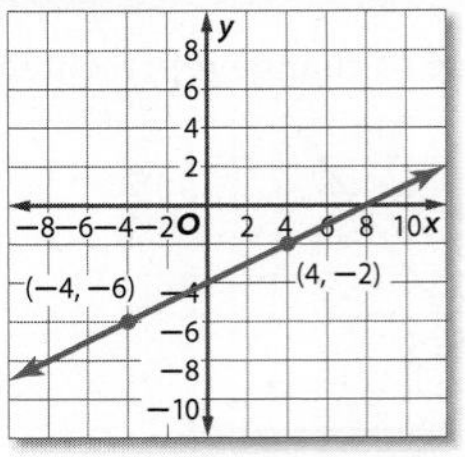

$\frac{1}{2}$

Example 2

18. SPORTS What was the annual rate of change from 2004 to 2008 for women participating in collegiate lacrosse? Explain the meaning of the rate of change.

Year	Number of Women
2004	5545
2008	6830

18. 321.25; There was an average increase of 321.25 women per year participating in lacrosse.

19. RETAIL The average retail price in the spring of 2009 for a used car is shown in the table at the right.

Age (years)	Value ($)
2	17,378
3	16,157

a. Write a linear function to model the price of the car with respect to age.

b. Interpret the meaning of the slope of the line.

c. Assuming a constant rate of change predict the average retail price for a 7-year-old car. **$11,273**

19a. Sample answer: $p = -1221t + 19{,}820$

19b. The car value depreciates by $1221 each year.

Example 3 **Determine whether each function is linear. Write *yes* or *no*. Explain.**

20.

x	4	2	0	−2	−4
y	−1	1	3	5	7

21.

x	−7	−5	−3	−1	0
y	11	14	17	20	23

22.

x	−0.2	0	0.2	0.4	0.6
y	0.7	0.4	0.1	0.3	0.6

23.

x	$\frac{1}{2}$	$\frac{3}{2}$	$\frac{5}{2}$	$\frac{7}{2}$	$\frac{9}{2}$
y	$\frac{1}{2}$	1	$\frac{3}{2}$	2	$\frac{5}{2}$

20–23. See Chapter 3 Answer Appendix.

Examples 4–5 **Find the slope of the line that passes through each pair of points.**

24. (4, 3), (−1, 6) $-\frac{3}{5}$

25. (8, −2), (1, 1) $-\frac{3}{7}$

26. (2, 2), (−2, −2) **1**

27. (6, −10), (6, 14)

28. (5, −4), (9, −4) **0**

29. (11, 7), (−6, 2) $\frac{5}{17}$

30. (−3, 5), (3, 6) $\frac{1}{6}$

31. (−3, 2), (7, 2) **0**

32. (8, 10), (−4, −6) $\frac{4}{3}$

33. (−8, 6), (−8, 4)

34. (−12, 15), (18, −13)

35. (−8, −15), (−2, 5) $\frac{10}{3}$

27. undefined
33. undefined
34. $-\frac{14}{15}$

Example 6 **Find the value of r so the line that passes through each pair of points has the given slope.**

36. (12, 10), (−2, r), $m = -4$ **66**

37. (r, −5), (3, 13), $m = 8$ $\frac{3}{4}$

38. (3, 5), (−3, r), $m = \frac{3}{4}$ $\frac{1}{2}$

39. (−2, 8), (r, 4), $m = -\frac{1}{2}$ **6**

B **TOOLS** Use a ruler to estimate the slope of each object.

40. 
Sample answer: about −0.5

41. 
Sample answer: about −1

Teaching the Process Standards

Tools Mathematically proficient students are sufficiently familiar with appropriate tools. In Exercises 40 and 41, discuss the units of measure used on the ruler and in the actual objects represented.

Teaching the Process Standards

Arguments Mathematically proficient students understand and use stated assumptions, definitions, and previously established results in constructing arguments. In Exercise 52, encourage students to supply a reason for each step in the solutions to detect any errors.

42. **DRIVING** When driving up a certain hill, you rise 15 feet for every 1000 feet you drive forward. What is the slope of the road? $\frac{3}{200}$

Find the slope of the line that passes through each pair of points.

43. $\frac{15}{4}$

x	y
4.5	−1
5.3	2

44. undefined

x	y
0.75	1
0.75	−1

45. $-\frac{2}{3}$

x	y
$2\frac{1}{2}$	$-1\frac{1}{2}$
$-\frac{1}{2}$	$\frac{1}{2}$

C 46. **MULTIPLE REPRESENTATIONS** In this problem, you will investigate why the slope of a line through any two points on that line is constant. **46a–c. See margin.**

a. **Visual** Sketch a line ℓ that contains points A, B, A' and B' on a coordinate plane.

b. **Geometric** Add segments to form right triangles ABC and $A'B'C'$ with right angles at C and C'. Describe $\overline{AC}$ and $\overline{A'C'}$, and $\overline{BC}$ and $\overline{B'C'}$.

c. **Verbal** How are triangles ABC and $A'B'C'$ related? What does that imply for the slope between any two distinct points on line ℓ?

47. **BASKETBALL** The table shown below shows the average points per game (PPG) Michael Redd has scored in each of his first 9 seasons with the NBA's Milwaukee Bucks. **a–c. See Ch. 3 Answer Appendix.**

Season	1	2	3	4	5	6	7	8	9
PPG	2.2	11.4	15.1	21.7	23.0	25.4	26.7	22.7	21.2

a. Make a graph of the data. Connect each pair of adjacent points with a line.

b. Use the graph to determine in which period Michael Redd's PPG increased the fastest. Explain your reasoning.

c. Discuss the difference in the rate of change from season 1 through season 4, from season 4 through season 7, from season 7 through season 9.

H.O.T. Problems Use Higher-Order Thinking Skills

48. **REASONING** Why does the Slope Formula not work for vertical lines? Explain. **See margin.**

49. **OPEN ENDED** Use what you know about rate of change to describe the function represented by the table.

Time (wk)	Height of Plant (in.)
4	9.0
6	13.5
8	18.0

49. See students' work. The rate of change is $2\frac{1}{4}$ inches of growth per week.

50. **CHALLENGE** Find the value of d so the line that passes through (a, b) and (c, d) has a slope of $\frac{1}{2}$. $\frac{c-a+2b}{2}$

51. **WRITING IN MATH** Explain how the rate of change and slope are related and how to find the slope of a line. **See margin.**

52. **ARGUMENTS** Kyle and Luna are finding the value of a so the line that passes through $(10, a)$ and $(-2, 8)$ has a slope of $\frac{1}{4}$. Is either of them correct? Explain.

Kyle

$\frac{-2-10}{8-a} = \frac{1}{4}$

$1(8-a) = 4(-12)$

$8 - a = -48$

$a = 56$

Luna

$\frac{8-a}{-2-10} = \frac{1}{4}$

$4(8-a) = 1(-12)$

$32 - 4a = -12$

$a = 11$

52. Luna; Kyle divided the change in x by the change in y.

Follow-up

Students have explored graphs of linear equations.

Ask:

- What can a linear graph tell you about the relationship that it represents? Sample answer: It can tell you about the rate of change, whether the relationship is positive or negative, the locations of the x- and y-intercepts, and what points fall on the graph.

Study Guide and Intervention

AL OL ELL

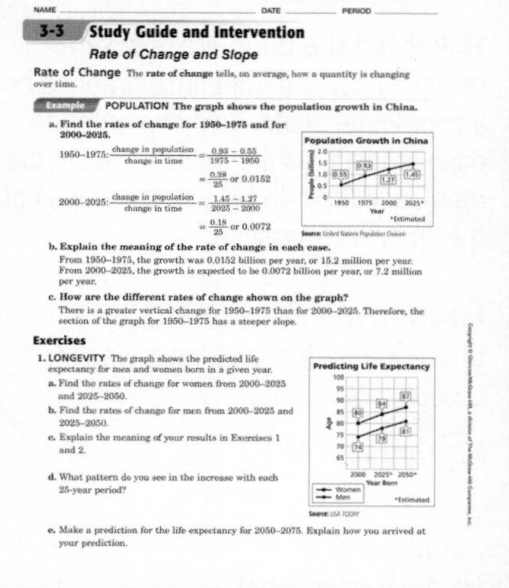
3-3 Study Guide and Intervention

Rate of Change and Slope

Rate of Change The rate of change tells, on average, how a quantity is changing over time.

Example POPULATION The graph shows the population growth in China.

a. Find the rates of change for 1950–1975 and for 2000–2025.

b. Explain the meaning of the rate of change in each case.

c. How are the different rates of change shown on the graph?

Exercises

1. LONGEVITY The graph shows the predicted life expectancy for men and women born in a given year.

e. Make a prediction for the life expectancy for 2050–2075. Explain how you arrived at your prediction.

Practice

AL OL BL ELL

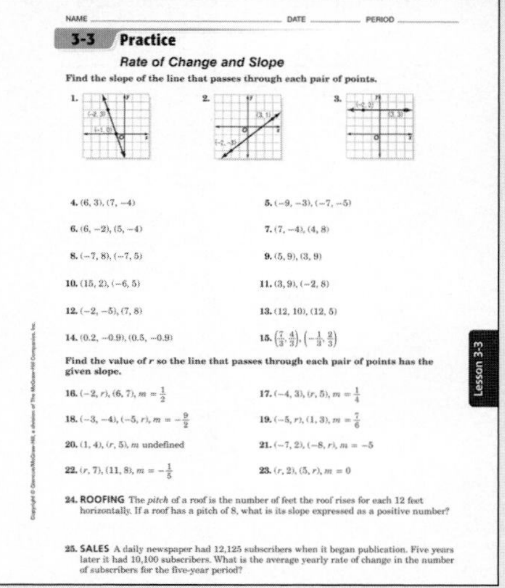
3-3 Practice

Rate of Change and Slope

Find the slope of the line that passes through each pair of points.

Find the value of r so the line that passes through each pair of points has the given slope.

24. ROOFING

25. SALES

Word Problem Practice

AL OL BL ELL

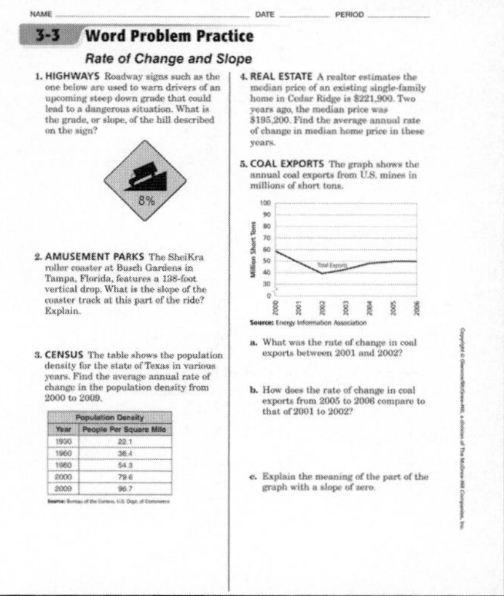
3-3 Word Problem Practice

Rate of Change and Slope

1. HIGHWAYS

2. AMUSEMENT PARKS

3. CENSUS

4. REAL ESTATE

5. COAL EXPORTS

Enrichment

OL BL

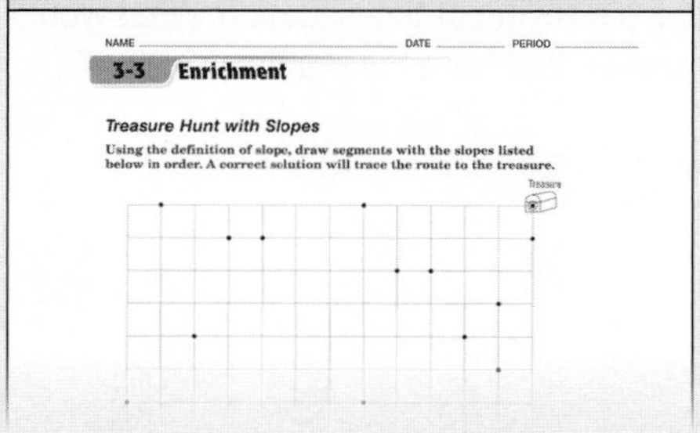
3-3 Enrichment

Treasure Hunt with Slopes

Using the definition of slope, draw segments with the slopes listed below in order. A correct solution will trace the route to the treasure.

4 Assess

Ticket Out the Door Make several copies of five different lines graphed on a coordinate plane. Give one graph to each student. As the students leave the room, ask them to tell you the slopes of the lines they possess.

Formative Assessment

Check for student understanding of Lesson 3-3.

Quiz 2, p. 45

Additional Answers (Mid-Chapter Quiz)

4.
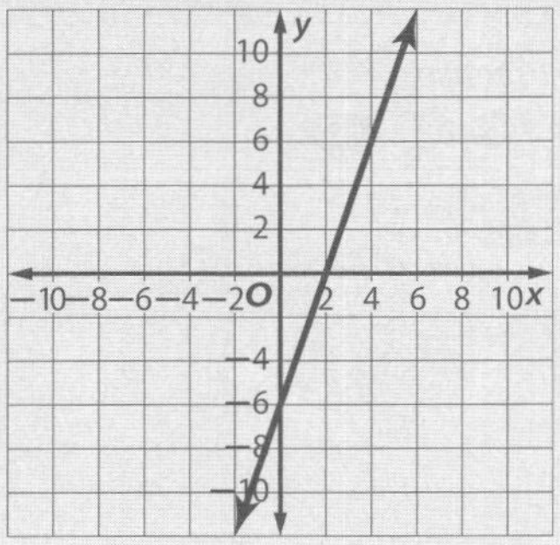

5.
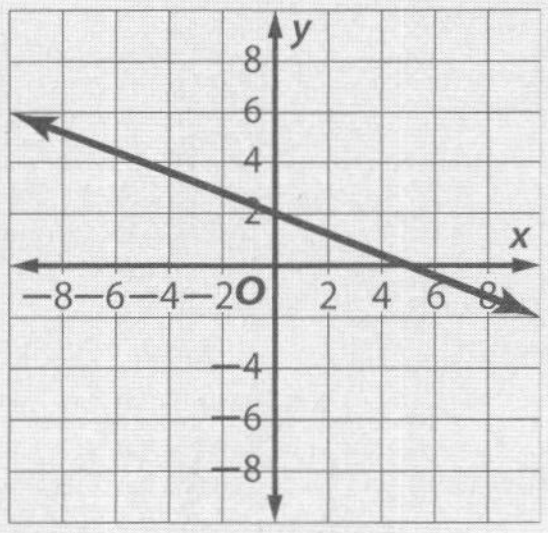

6.
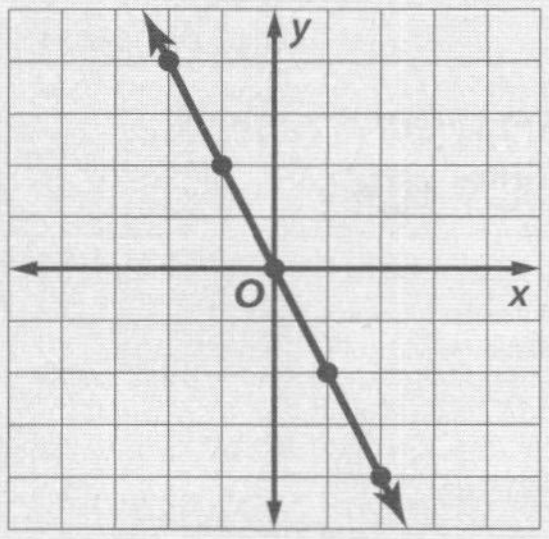

7.
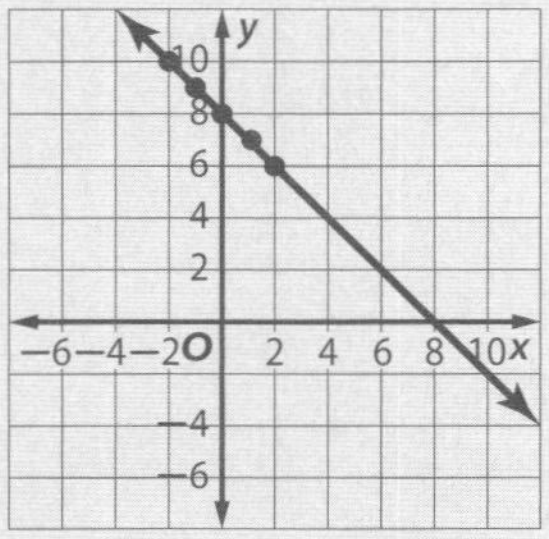

Standardized Test Practice

53. The cost of prints from an online photo processor is given by $C(p) = 29.99 + 0.13p$. \$29.99 is the cost of the membership, and p is the number of 4-inch by 6-inch prints. What does the slope represent? **A**

A cost per print

B cost of the membership

C cost of the membership and 1 print

D number of prints

54. Danita bought a computer for \$1200 and its value depreciated linearly. After 2 years, the value was \$250. What was the amount of yearly depreciation? **G**

F \$950

G \$475

H \$250

J \$225

55. SHORT RESPONSE The graph represents how much the Wright Brothers National Monument charges visitors. How much does the park charge each visitor? **\$4**

Wright Brothers National Monument

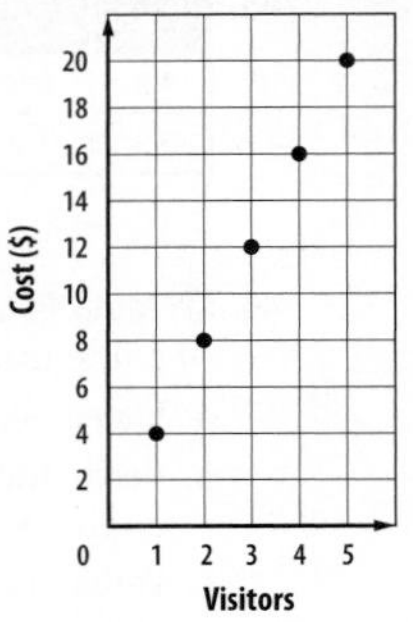

56. PROBABILITY At a gymnastics camp, 1 gymnast is chosen at random from each team. The Flipstars Gymnastics Team consists of 5 eleven-year-olds, 7 twelve-year-olds, 10 thirteen-year-olds, and 8 fourteen-year-olds. What is the probability that the age of the gymnast chosen is an odd number? **C**

A $\frac{1}{30}$ **B** $\frac{1}{15}$ **C** $\frac{1}{2}$ **D** $\frac{3}{5}$

Spiral Review

Solve each equation by graphing. (Lesson 3-2)

57. $3x + 18 = 0$ **−6**

58. $8x - 32 = 0$ **4**

59. $0 = 12x - 48$ **4**

Find the *x*- and *y*-intercepts of the graph of each linear function. (Lesson 3-1)

60.
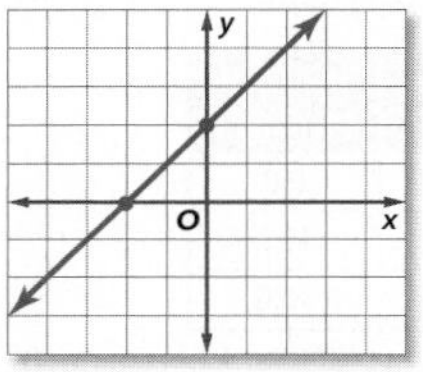
−2, 2

61.

x	y
−3	−4
−2	−2
−1	0
0	2
1	4

−1, 2

62. HOMECOMING Dance tickets are \$9 for one person and \$15 for two people. If a group of seven students wishes to go to the dance, write and solve an equation that would represent the least expensive price p of their tickets. (Lesson 1-3) $p = 15(3) + 9(1)$; **\$54**

Skills Review

Find each quotient.

63. $8 \div \frac{2}{3}$ **12**

64. $\frac{3}{8} \div \frac{1}{4}$ $\frac{3}{2}$

65. $\frac{5}{8} \div 2$ $\frac{5}{16}$

66. $\frac{12 \cdot 6}{9}$ **8**

67. $\frac{2 \cdot 15}{6}$ **5**

68. $\frac{18 \cdot 5}{15}$ **6**

Differentiated Instruction OL BL

Extension The road sign on a hill says 5% grade. The elevation of the road at that point is 1200 feet. Make a drawing of this situation. What would be the elevation of the road at an additional 2000 horizontal feet from the road sign? 1300 ft

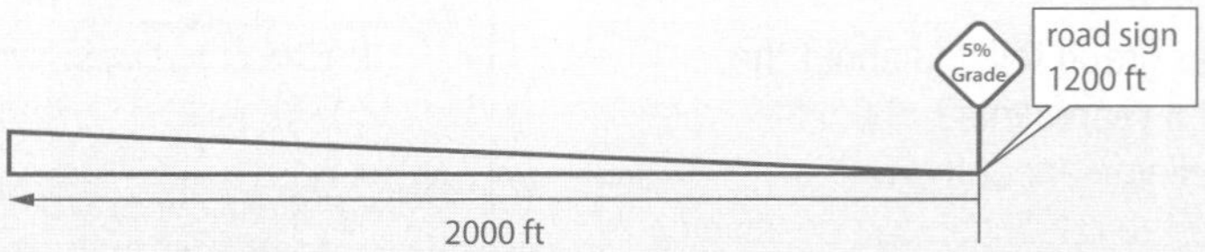

180 | Lesson 3-3 | Rate of Change and Slope

CHAPTER 3 Mid-Chapter Quiz
Lessons 3-1 through 3-3

Determine whether each equation is a linear equation. Write *yes* or *no*. If yes, write the equation in standard form. (Lesson 3-1)

1. $y = -4x + 3$ **yes, $4x + y = 3$**
2. $x^2 + 3y = 8$ **no**
3. $\frac{1}{4}x - \frac{3}{4}y = -1$ **yes, $x - 3y = -4$**

Graph each equation using the *x*- and *y*-intercepts. (Lesson 3-1) **4–5. See margin.**

4. $y = 3x - 6$
5. $2x + 5y = 10$

Graph each equation by making a table. (Lesson 3-1)

6. $y = -2x$
7. $x = 8 - y$

6–7. See margin.

8. **BOOK SALES** The equation $5x + 12y = 240$ describes the total amount of money collected when selling *x* paperback books at \$5 per book and *y* hardback books at \$12 per book. Graph the equation using the *x*- and *y*-intercepts. (Lesson 3-1) **See margin.**

Find the root of each equation. (Lesson 3-2)

9. $x + 8 = 0$ **−8**
10. $4x - 24 = 0$ **6**
11. $18 + 8x = 0$ $-\frac{9}{4}$
12. $\frac{3}{5}x - \frac{1}{2} = 0$ $\frac{5}{6}$

Solve each equation by graphing. (Lesson 3-2)

13. $-5x + 35 = 0$ **7**
14. $14x - 84 = 0$ **6**
15. $118 + 11x = -3$ **−11**

16. **MULTIPLE CHOICE** The function $y = -15 + 3x$ represents the outside temperature, in degrees Fahrenheit, in a small Alaskan town where *x* represents the number of hours after midnight. The function is accurate for *x* values representing midnight through 4:00 P.M. Find the zero of this function. (Lesson 3-2) **C**

A 0
B 3
C 5
D −15

17. Find the rate of change represented in the table. (Lesson 3-3) $\frac{4}{3}$

x	y
1	2
4	6
7	10
10	14

Find the slope of the line that passes through each pair of points. (Lesson 3-3)

18. (2, 6), (4, 12) **3**
19. (1, 5), (3, 8) $\frac{3}{2}$
20. (−3, 4), (2, −6) **−2**
21. $\left(\frac{1}{3}, \frac{3}{4}\right), \left(\frac{2}{3}, \frac{1}{4}\right)$ $-\frac{3}{2}$

22. **MULTIPLE CHOICE** Find the value of *r* so the line that passes through the pair of points has the given slope. (Lesson 3-3) **G**

$$(-4, 8), (r, 12), m = \frac{4}{3}$$

F −4
G −1
H 0
J 3

23. Find the slope of the line that passes through the pair of points. (Lesson 3-3) **12**

x	y
2.6	−2
3.1	4

24. **POPULATION GROWTH** The graph shows the population growth in Heckertsville since 2003. (Lesson 3-3)

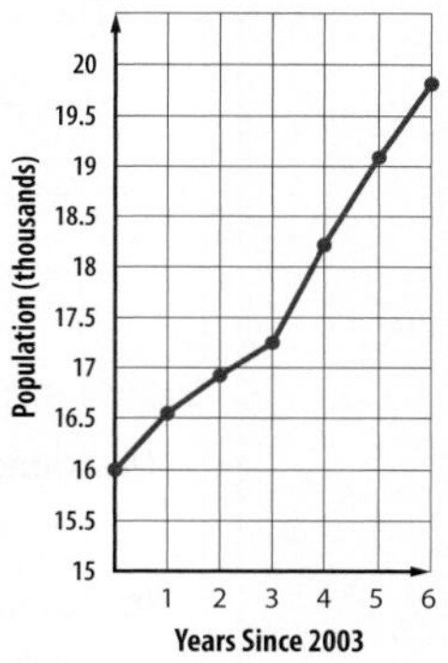

a. For which time period is the rate of change the greatest? **2006–2007**

b. Explain the meaning of the slope from 2003 to 2009. **b. The population of Heckertsville has increased by about 630 per year.**

Formative Assessment

Use the Mid-Chapter Quiz to assess students' progress in the first half of the chapter.

For problems answered incorrectly, have students review the lessons indicated in parentheses.

Summative Assessment

Mid-Chapter Test, p. 47

McGraw-Hill eAssessment Customize and create multiple versions of your Mid-Chapter Quiz and their answer keys.

FOLDABLES StudyOrganizer

Dinah Zike's Foldables®

Before students complete the Mid-Chapter Quiz, encourage them to review the information for Lessons 3-1 through 3-3 in their Foldables.

Additional Answer

8.

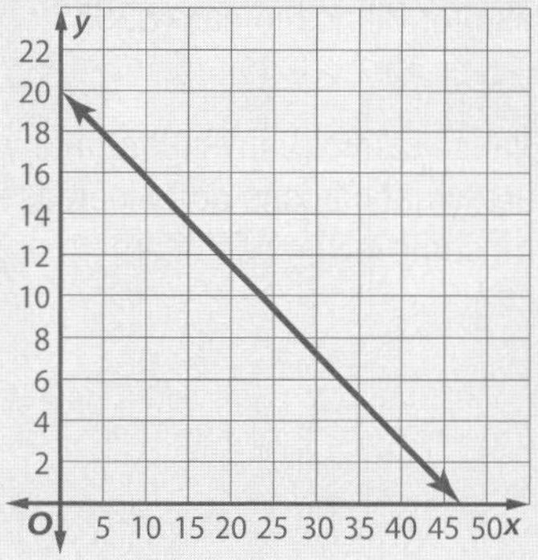

InterventionPlanner

TIER 1 On Level OL	TIER 2 Strategic Intervention AL approaching grade level	TIER 3 Intensive Intervention 2 or more grades below level
If students miss about 25% of the exercises or less,	**If** students miss about 50% of the exercises,	**If** students miss about 75% of the exercises,
Then choose a resource:	**Then** choose a resource:	**Then** use *Math Triumphs, Alg. 1, Ch. 3*
SE Lessons 3-1, 3-2, and 3-3 Skills Practice, pp. 7, 14 and 20 **TE** Chapter Project connectED.mcgraw-hill.com Self-Check Quiz	Study Guide and Intervention, Chapter 3, pp. 5, 12 and 18 *Quick Review Math Handbook* connectED.mcgraw-hill.com Extra Examples, Personal Tutor, Homework Help	connectED.mcgraw-hill.com Extra Examples, Personal Tutor, Homework Help, Review Vocabulary

1 Focus

VerticalAlignment

Before Lesson 3-4 Find rates of change of linear functions.

Lesson 3-4 Write and graph direct variation equations. Solve problems involving direct variation.

After Lesson 3-4 Write an equation for a proportional relationship.

2 Teach

Scaffolding Questions

Have students read the **Why?** section of the lesson.

Ask:

- How much money can Bianca earn in 5 hours of babysitting? $40
- How many hours of babysitting will it take for Bianca to earn $295? 37.25 or about 38 hours
- If Bianca cannot babysit that many hours, what can she do to increase her income? She can charge more per hour.

LESSON 3-4 Direct Variation

Then

- You found rates of change of linear functions.

Now

1. Write and graph direct variation equations.
2. Solve problems involving direct variation.

Why?

- Bianca is saving her money to buy a designer purse that costs $295. To help raise the money, she charges $8 per hour to babysit her neighbors' child. The slope of the line that represents the amount of money Bianca earns is 8, and the rate of change is constant.

NewVocabulary
direct variation
constant of variation
constant of proportionality

Content Standards
AI.L.1, AI.L.2

Process Standards
PS.1, PS.6

1 Direct Variation Equations

A **direct variation** is described by an equation of the form $y = kx$, where $k \neq 0$. The equation $y = kx$ illustrates a constant rate of change, and k is the **constant of variation**, also called the **constant of proportionality**.

Example 1 Slope and Constant of Variation

Name the constant of variation for each equation. Then find the slope of the line that passes through each pair of points.

a.

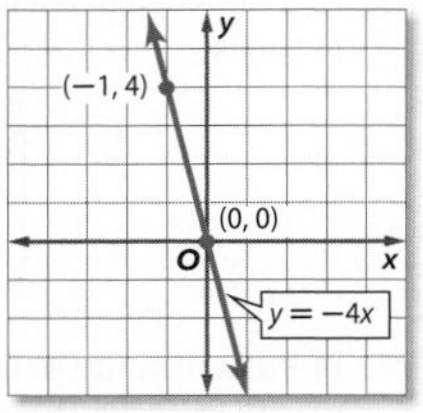

The constant of variation is −4.

$m = \frac{y_2 - y_1}{x_2 - x_1}$ Slope Formula

$= \frac{4 - 0}{-1 - 0}$ $(x_1, y_1) = (0, 0)$, $(x_2, y_2) = (-1, 4)$

$= -4$ The slope is −4.

b.

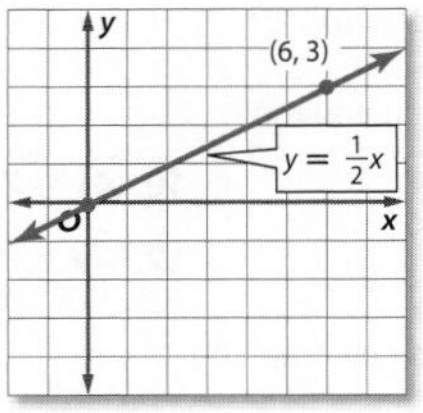

The constant of variation is $\frac{1}{2}$.

$m = \frac{y_2 - y_1}{x_2 - x_1}$ Slope Formula

$= \frac{3 - 0}{6 - 0}$ $(x_1, y_1) = (0, 0)$, $(x_2, y_2) = (6, 3)$

$= \frac{1}{2}$ The slope is $\frac{1}{2}$.

GuidedPractice

1A. Name the constant of variation for $y = \frac{1}{4}x$. Then find the slope of the line that passes through (0, 0) and (4, 1), two points on the line. $\frac{1}{4}; \frac{1}{4}$

1B. Name the constant of variation for $y = -2x$. Then find the slope of the line that passes through (0, 0) and (1, −2), two points on the line. −2; −2

The slope of the graph of $y = kx$ is k. Since $0 = k(0)$, the graph of $y = kx$ always passes through the origin. Therefore the x- and y-intercepts are zero.

Lesson 3-4 Resources

Resource	Approaching Level AL	On Level OL	Beyond Level BL	English Learners ELL
Teacher Edition	▪ Differentiated Instruction, p. 185		▪ Differentiated Instruction, p. 188	▪ Differentiated Instruction, p. 185
Chapter Resource Masters	▪ Study Guide and Intervention, pp. 24–25 ▪ Skills Practice, p. 26 ▪ Practice, p. 27 ▪ Word Problem Practice, p. 28	▪ Study Guide and Intervention, pp. 24–25 ▪ Skills Practice, p. 26 ▪ Practice, p. 27 ▪ Word Problem Practice, p. 28 ▪ Enrichment, p. 29	▪ Practice, p. 27 ▪ Word Problem Practice, p. 28 ▪ Enrichment, p. 29	▪ Study Guide and Intervention, pp. 24–25 ▪ Skills Practice, p. 26 ▪ Practice, p. 27 ▪ Word Problem Practice, p. 28
Other	▪ 5-Minute Check 3-4 ▪ Study Notebook	▪ 5-Minute Check 3-4 ▪ Study Notebook	▪ 5-Minute Check 3-4 ▪ Study Notebook	▪ 5-Minute Check 3-4 ▪ Study Notebook

StudyTip

Constant of Variation A line with a positive constant of variation will go up from left to right and a line with a negative constant of variation will go down from left to right.

Example 2 Graph a Direct Variation

Graph $y = -6x$.

Step 1 Write the slope as a ratio.

$-6 = \frac{-6}{1}$ rise / run

Step 2 Graph (0, 0).

Step 3 From the point (0, 0), move down 6 units and right 1 unit. Draw a dot.

Step 4 Draw a line containing the points.

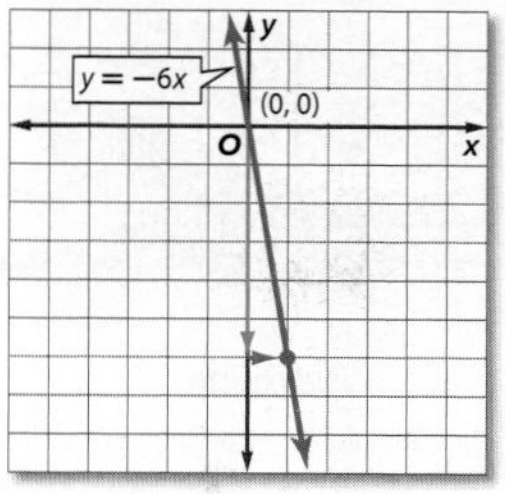

GuidedPractice **2A–2D. See Chapter 3 Answer Appendix.**

2A. $y = 6x$ **2B.** $y = \frac{2}{3}x$ **2C.** $y = -5x$ **2D.** $y = -\frac{3}{4}x$

The graphs of all direct variation equations share some common characteristics.

ConceptSummary Direct Variation Graphs

- Direct variation equations are of the form $y = kx$, where $k \neq 0$.
- The graph of $y = kx$ always passes through the origin.
- The slope is positive if $k > 0$.

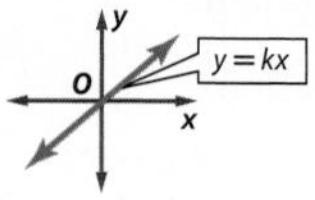

- The slope is negative if $k < 0$.

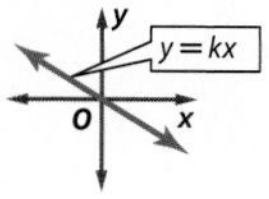

If the relationship between the values of y and x can be described by a direct variation equation, then we say that y varies directly as x.

Example 3 Write and Solve a Direct Variation Equation

Suppose y varies directly as x, and $y = 72$ when $x = 8$.

a. Write a direct variation equation that relates x and y.

$y = kx$	Direct variation formula
$72 = k(8)$	Replace y with 72 and x with 8.
$9 = k$	Divide each side by 8.

Therefore, the direct variation equation is $y = 9x$.

b. Use the direct variation equation to find x when $y = 63$.

$y = 9x$	Direct variation formula
$63 = 9x$	Replace y with 63.
$7 = x$	Divide each side by 9.

Therefore, $x = 7$ when $y = 63$.

GuidedPractice

3. Suppose y varies directly as x, and $y = 98$ when $x = 14$. Write a direct variation equation that relates x and y. Then find y when $x = -4$. **$y = 7x$; -28**

1 Direct Variation Equations

Example 1 shows how the constant of variation for an equation is related to the slope of the line. **Example 2** shows how to graph an equation of the form $y = kx$, for $k > 0$ or $k < 0$, by graphing (0, 0) and using the rise and run to find another point on the graph. **Example 3** shows how to use the definition of direct variation to write and solve direct variation equations.

Formative Assessment

Use the Guided Practice exercises after each Example to determine students' understanding of concepts.

Additional Examples

1 Name the constant of variation for each equation. Then find the slope of the line that passes through each pair of points.

a.

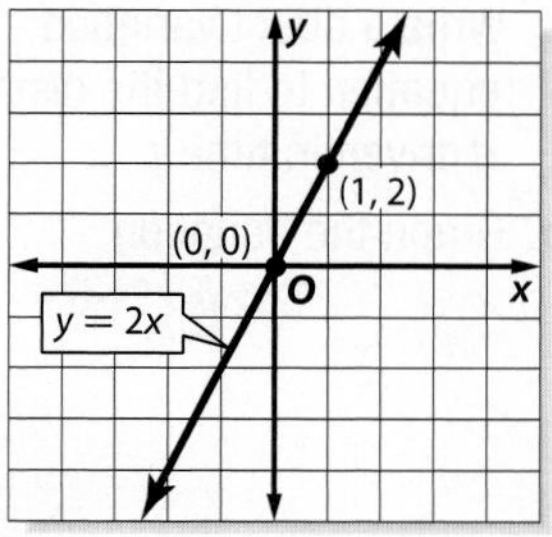

constant of variation: 2; slope: 2

b.

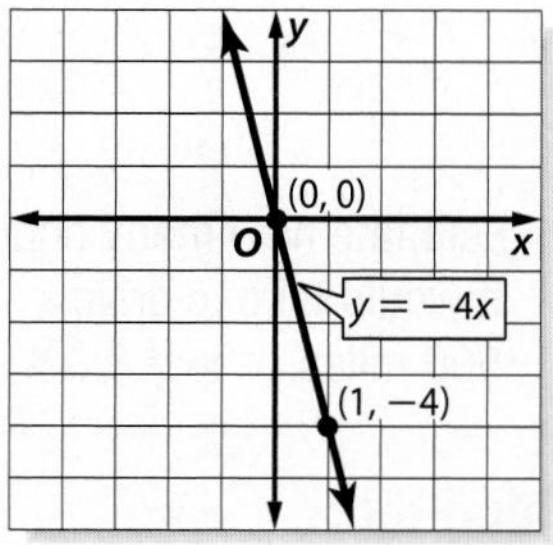

constant of variation: −4; slope: −4

2 Graph $y = -\frac{3}{2}x$. See bottom margin.

Additional Examples also in Interactive Classroom PowerPoint® Presentations

IWB Interactive White Board READY

Additional Answer (Additional Examples)

2.

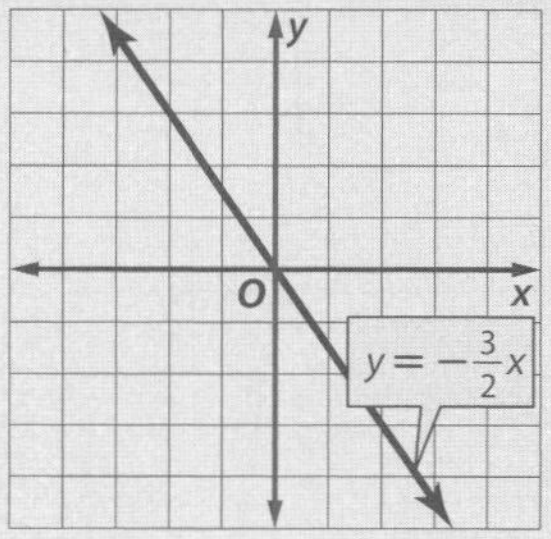

Teach with Tech

Interactive Whiteboard Choose a student to work through an example in front of the class. Give him or her an x-value and a y-value, and have the student find the constant of variation given that y varies directly with x.

Additional Example

3 Suppose y varies directly as x, and $y = 9$ when $x = -3$.

a. Write a direct variation equation that relates x and y. $y = -3x$

b. Use the direct variation equation to find x when $y = 15$. -5

2 Direct Variation Problems

Example 4 shows how to use a direct variation equation to solve a real-world problem.

Additional Example

4 **TRAVEL** The Ramirez family is driving cross-country on vacation. They drive 330 miles in 5.5 hours.

a. Write a direct variation equation to find the distance d driven in time t. $d = 60t$

b. Graph the equation.

Travel Time

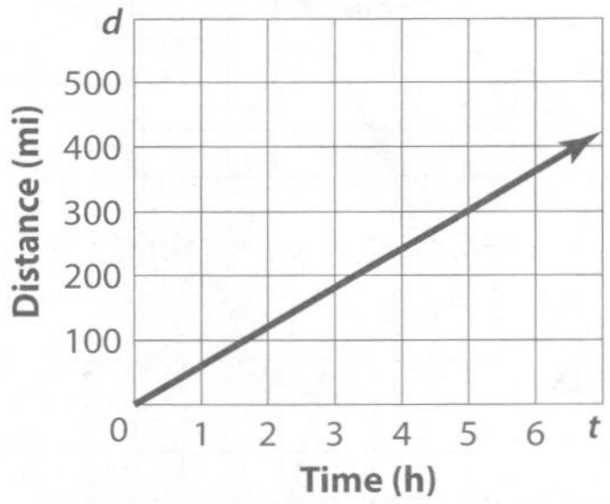

c. Estimate how many hours it would take to drive 500 miles. about 8.3 h

Teaching the Process Standards

Precision Mathematically proficient students calculate accurately and efficiently, and express numerical answers with a degree of precision appropriate for the problem context. Point out to students that a rough estimate can be made by observing that 6500 miles is less than twice 3420 miles, so the time should be less than twice 6 hours.

Real-WorldLink

In 2006, domestic airlines transported over 660 million passengers an average distance of 724 miles per flight.

Source: Bureau of Transportation Statistics

2 Direct Variation Problems

One of the most common applications of direct variation is the formula $d = rt$. Distance d varies directly as time t, and the rate r is the constant of variation.

Real-World Example 4 Estimate Using Direct Variation

TRAVEL The distance a jet travels varies directly as the number of hours it flies. A jet traveled 3420 miles in 6 hours.

a. Write a direct variation equation for the distance d flown in time t.

Words	Distance	equals	rate	times	time.
Variable	Let r = rate.				
Equation	3420	=	r	×	6

Solve for the rate.

$3420 = r(6)$ Original equation

$\frac{3420}{6} = \frac{r(6)}{6}$ Divide each side by 6.

$570 = r$ Simplify.

Therefore, the direct variation equation is $d = 570t$. The airliner flew at a rate of 570 miles per hour.

b. Graph the equation.

The graph of $d = 570t$ passes through the origin with slope 570.

$m = \frac{570}{1}$ $\frac{\text{rise}}{\text{run}}$

Distance Flown

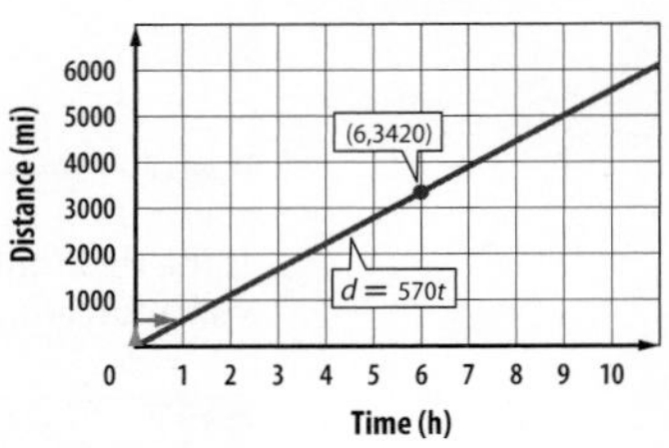

c. Estimate how many hours it will take for an airliner to fly 6500 miles.

$d = 570t$ Original equation

$6500 = 570t$ Replace d with 6500.

$\frac{6500}{570} = \frac{570t}{570}$ Divide each side by 570.

$t \approx 11.4$ Simplify.

It would take the airliner approximately 11.4 hours to fly 6500 miles.

Problem-SolvingTip

Precision Notice that the question asks for an estimate, not an exact answer.

GuidedPractice

4. HOT-AIR BALLOONS A hot-air balloon's height varies directly as the balloon's ascent time in minutes.

A. Write a direct variation for the distance d ascended in time t. $d = 70t$

B. Graph the equation. See Chapter 3 Answer Appendix.

C. Estimate how many minutes it would take to ascend 2100 feet. 30 min.

D. About how many minutes would it take to ascend 3500 feet? 50 min.

Additional Answers

3.

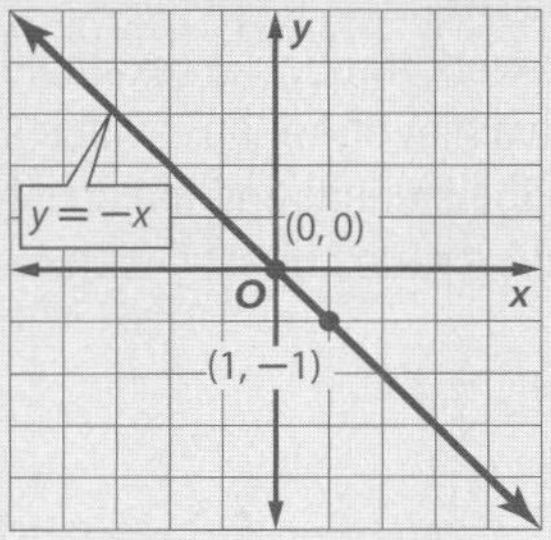

4.

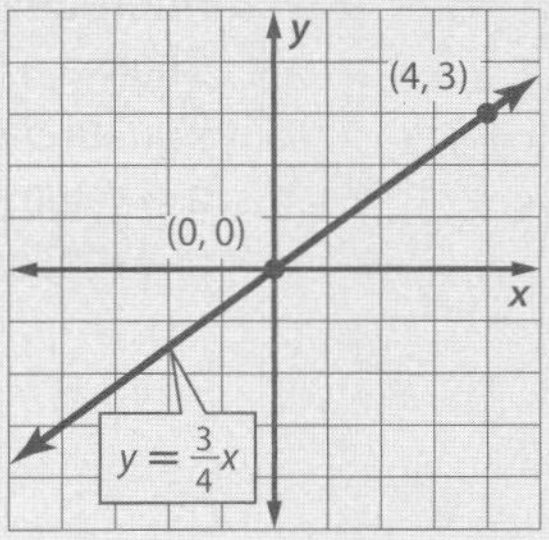

5.

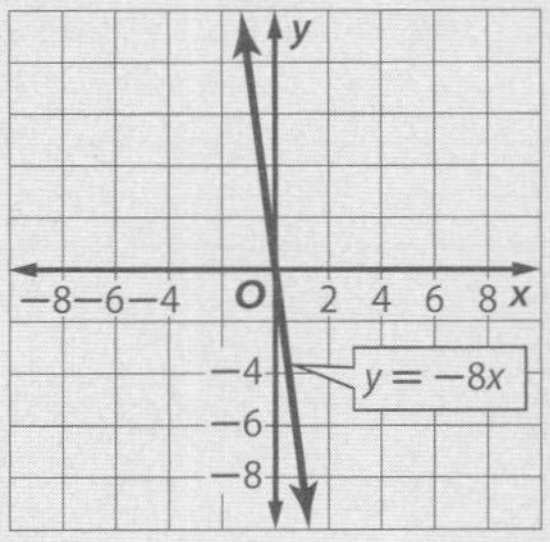

Check Your Understanding

= Step-by-Step Solutions begin on page R13.

Example 1 **Name the constant of variation for each equation. Then find the slope of the line that passes through each pair of points.**

1\.
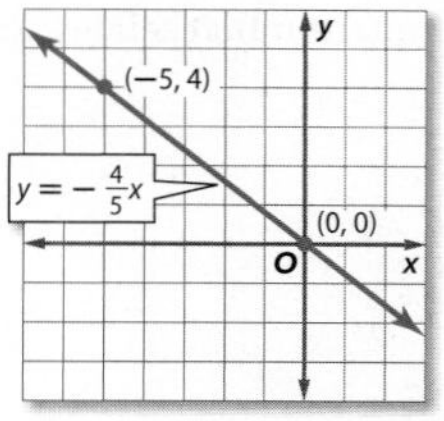

$-\frac{4}{5}; -\frac{4}{5}$

2\.
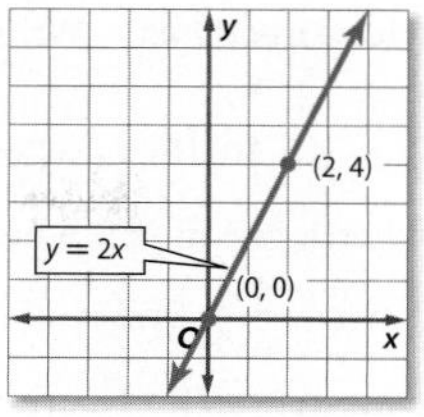

2; 2

Example 2 **Graph each equation.** 3–6. See margin.

3\. $y = -x$ 4. $y = \frac{3}{4}x$ 5. $y = -8x$ 6. $y = -\frac{8}{5}$

Example 3 **Suppose y varies directly as x. Write a direct variation equation that relates x and y. Then solve.**

7\. If $y = 15$ when $x = 12$, find y when $x = 32$. $y = \frac{5}{4}x$; 40

8\. If $y = -11$ when $x = 6$, find x when $y = 44$. $y = -\frac{11}{6}x$; −24

Example 4 9. **REASONING** You find that the number of messages you receive on your message board varies directly as the number of messages you post. When you post 5 messages, you receive 12 messages in return.

a. Write a direct variation equation relating your posts to the messages received. Then graph the equation. $y = \frac{12}{5}x$; see margin for graph.

b. Find the number of messages you need to post to receive 96 messages. 40

Practice and Problem Solving

Extra Practice is on page R3.

Example 1 **Name the constant of variation for each equation. Then find the slope of the line that passes through each pair of points.** 10–15. See margin.

10\.
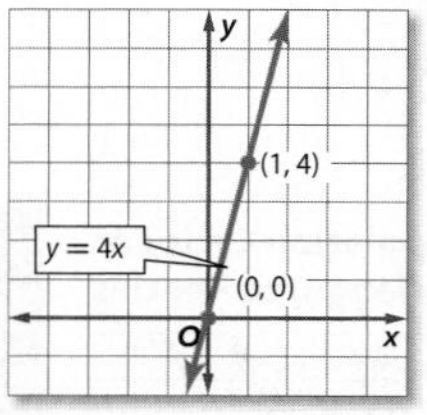

11\.
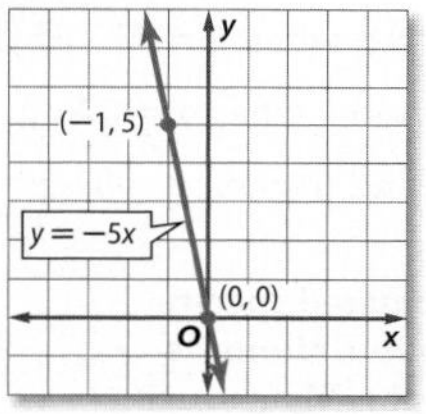

12\.
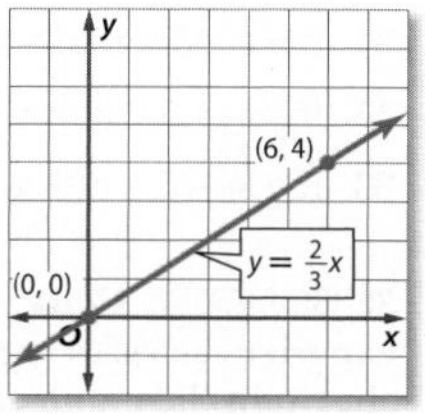

13\.
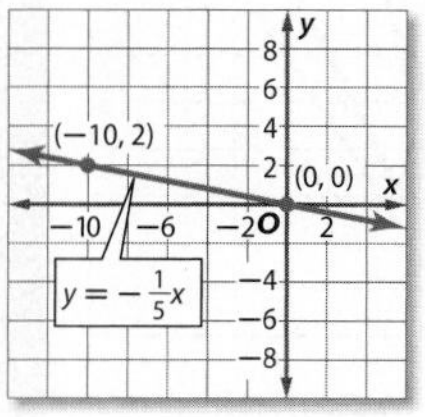

14\.
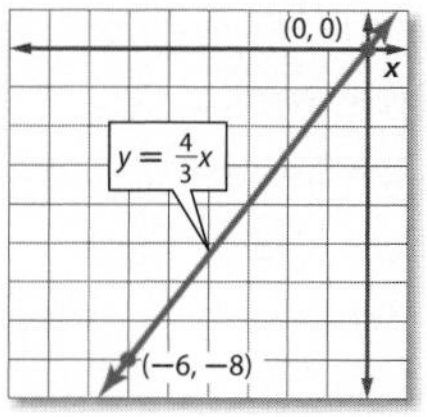

15\.
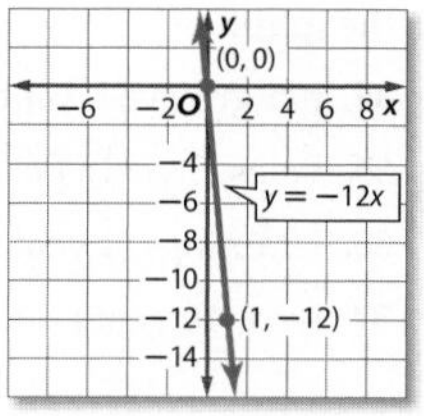

Differentiated Instruction AL ELL

If students have trouble with direct variation equations,

Then give students one function at a time. Have them read the function aloud, then tell if the function is a direct variation. If it is, ask them to tell the constant of variation.

WatchOut!

Preventing Errors Be sure students do not interchange the values of x and y when substituting them into an equation.

Exercise Alert

Grid Paper Students will need grid paper to answer Exercises 3–6, 9, 16–23, 28, 38–41, and 47.

3 Practice

Formative Assessment

Use Exercises 1–9 to check for understanding.

Use the chart at the bottom of the next page to customize assignments for your students.

Teaching the Process Standards

Reasoning Mathematically proficient students attend to the meaning of quantities. In Exercise 9, encourage students to begin by defining the variables.

Additional Answers

6\.
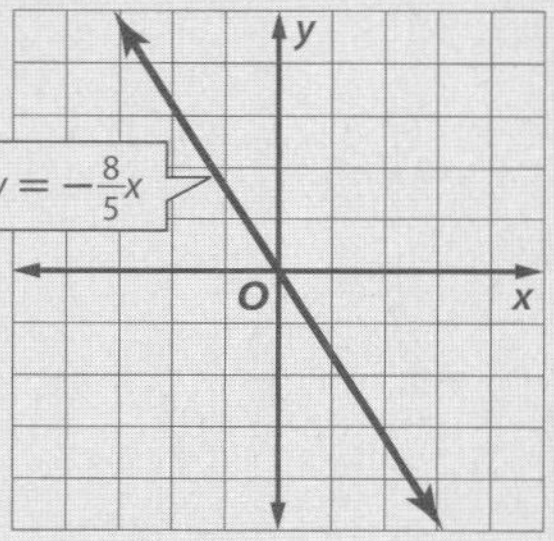

9a.
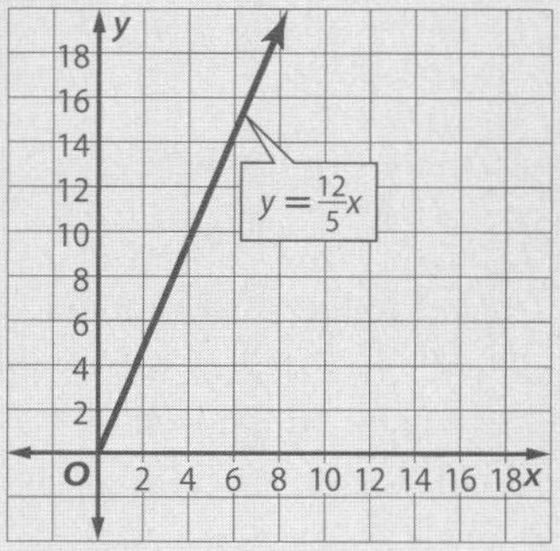

10\. 4; 4
11\. −5; −5
12\. $\frac{2}{3}; \frac{2}{3}$
13\. $-\frac{1}{5}; -\frac{1}{5}$
14\. $\frac{4}{3}; \frac{4}{3}$
15\. −12; −12

Multiple Representations

In Exercise 41, students investigate the relationship between the constant of variation, the slope, and the rate of change.

Teaching the Process Standards

Sense-Making Mathematically proficient students continually ask themselves, "Does this make sense?" In Exercises 34–37, discuss how a graph with more years per cycle compares to a graph with fewer years per cycle.

Structure In Exercise 48, encourage students to use the equation $y = kx$ and examine the effect of multiplying x by 2.

Additional Answers

38.

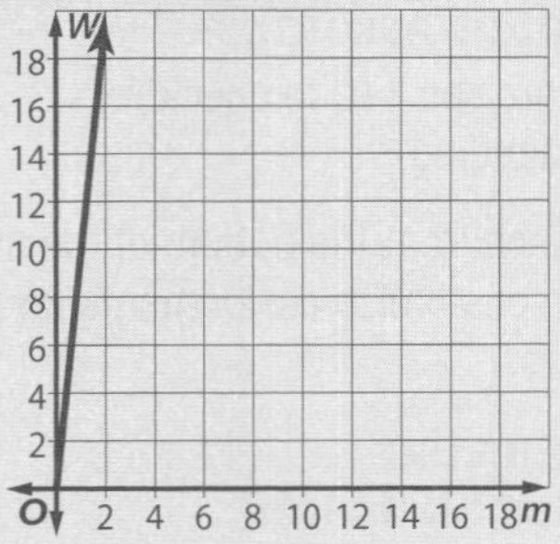

39.

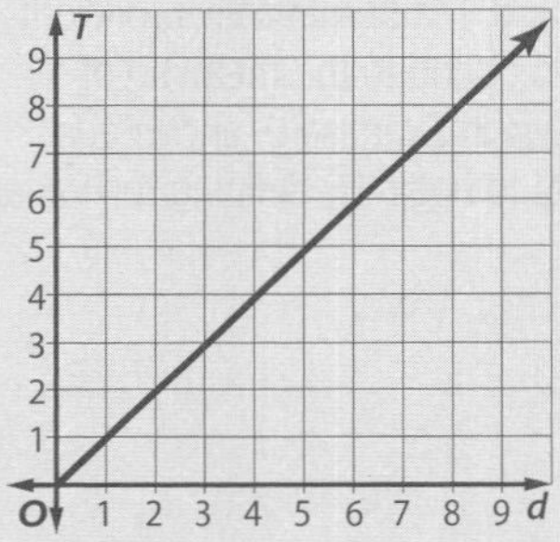

40.

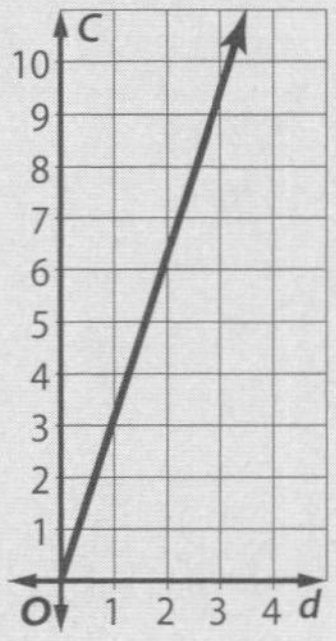

48. Always; if the equation is $y = kx$ $(k \neq 0)$, then the value of y when $x = a$ is ka, and the value of y when $x = 2a$ is $k(2a)$ or $2(ka)$.

49. Neither; the slope is constant, and it is k.

50. Sample answer: The graph of a direct variation equation $y = kx$ is a line that always passes through the origin.

Example 2 **Graph each equation.** **16–23. See Chapter 3 Answer Appendix.**

16. $y = 10x$
17. $y = -7x$
18. $y = x$
19. $y = \frac{7}{6}x$
20. $y = \frac{1}{6}x$
21. $y = \frac{2}{9}x$
22. $y = \frac{6}{5}x$
23. $y = -\frac{5}{4}x$

Example 3 **Suppose y varies directly as x. Write a direct variation equation that relates x and y. Then solve.**

24. If $y = 6$ when $x = 10$, find x when $y = 18$. **$y = \frac{3}{5}x$; 30**

25. If $y = 22$ when $x = 8$, find y when $x = -16$. **$y = \frac{11}{4}x$; -44**

26. If $y = 4\frac{1}{4}$ when $x = \frac{3}{4}$, find y when $x = 4\frac{1}{2}$. **$y = 5\frac{2}{3}x$; $25\frac{1}{2}$**

27. If $y = 12$ when $x = \frac{6}{7}$, find x when $y = 16$. **$y = 14x$; $1\frac{1}{7}$**

Example 4

28. **SPORTS** The distance a golf ball travels at an altitude of 7000 feet varies directly with the distance the ball travels at sea level, as shown.

Hitting a Golf Ball		
Altitude (ft)	0 (sea level)	7000
Distance (yd)	200	210

a. Write and graph an equation that relates the distance a golf ball travels at an altitude of 7000 feet y with the distance at sea level x. **$y = 1.05x$; See Chapter 3 Answer Appendix for graph.**

b. What would be a person's average driving distance at 7000 feet if his average driving distance at sea level is 180 yards? **189 yd**

29. **FINANCIAL LITERACY** Depreciation is the decline in a car's value over the course of time. The table below shows the values of a car with an average depreciation.

Age of Car (years)	1	2	3	4	5
Value (dollars)	12,000	10,200	8400	6600	4800

a. Write an equation that relates the age x of the car to the value y that it lost after each year. **$y = 1800x$**

b. Find the age of the car if the value is \$300. **7 yr 6 mo**

B **Suppose y varies directly as x. Write a direct variation equation that relates x and y. Then solve.**

30. If $y = 3.2$ when $x = 1.6$, find y when $x = 19$. **$y = 2x$; 38**

31. If $y = 15$ when $x = \frac{3}{4}$, find x when $y = 25$. **$y = 20x$; $\frac{5}{4}$**

32. If $y = 4.5$ when $x = 2.5$, find y when $x = 12$. **$y = 1.8x$; 21.6**

33. If $y = -6$ when $x = 1.6$, find y when $x = 8$. **$y = -3.75x$; -30**

SENSE-MAKING Certain endangered species experience cycles in their populations as shown in the graph at the right. Match each animal below to one of the colored lines in the graph.

34. red grouse, 8 years per cycle **red**

35. voles, 3 years per cycle **dark green**

36. lemmings, 4 years per cycle **blue**

37. lynx, 10 years per cycle **lime green**

Population Cycles of Endangered Species

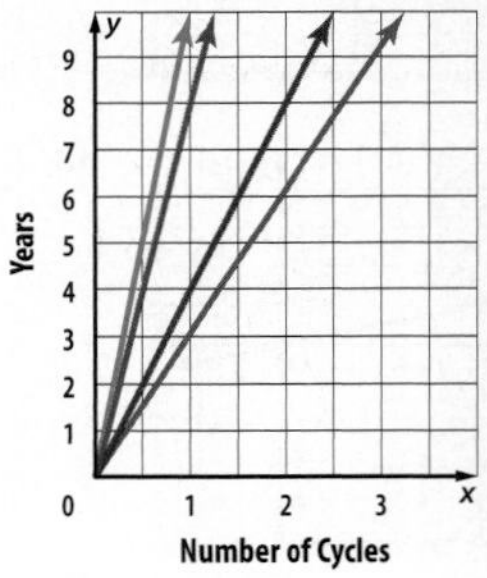

Differentiated Homework Options

Level	Assignment	Two-Day Option	
AL Basic	10–29, 45–47, 49–73	11–33 odd, 51–54	10–32 even, 45–47, 49, 50, 55–73
OL Core	11–37 odd, 35, 38–47, 49–73	10–33, 51–54	34–47, 49, 50, 55–73
BL Advanced	30–67, (optional: 68–73)		

In Exercises 38–40, write and graph a direct variation equation that relates the variables.

38. PHYSICAL SCIENCE The weight W of an object is 9.8 m/s^2 times the mass of the object m. $W = 9.8m$ **38–40. See margin for graphs.**

39. MUSIC Music downloads are \$0.99 per song. The total cost of d songs is T. $T = 0.99d$

40. GEOMETRY The circumference of a circle C is approximately 3.14 times the diameter d. $C = 3.14d$

41. MULTIPLE REPRESENTATIONS In this problem, you will investigate the family of direct variation functions. **41a–c. See Chapter 3 Answer Appendix.**

a. Graphical Graph $y = x$, $y = 3x$, and $y = 5x$ on the same coordinate plane.

b. Algebraic Describe the relationship among the constant of variation, the slope of the line, and the rate of change of the graph.

c. Verbal Make a conjecture about how you can determine without graphing which of two direct variation equations has the steeper graph.

42. TRAVEL A map of North Carolina is scaled so that 3 inches represents 93 miles. How far apart are Raleigh and Charlotte if they are 1.8 inches apart on the map? **55.8 mi**

43. INTERNET A company will design and maintain a Web site for your company for \$9.95 per month. Write a direct variation equation to find the total cost C for having a Web page for n months. $C = 9.95n$

44. BASEBALL Before their first game, high school student Todd McCormick warmed all 5200 seats in a new minor league stadium, by sitting in every seat. He started at 11:50 A.M. and finished around 3 P.M.

44a. $y = 27.3684t$; **Every minute Todd warms about 27 additional seats.**

a. Write a direct variation equation relating the number of seats to time. What is the meaning of the constant of variation in this situation?

b. About how many seats had Todd sat in by 1:00 P.M.? **about 1915 seats**

c. How long would you expect it to take Todd to sit in all of the seats at a major league stadium with more than 40,000 seats? **about 1461 min or 24 h and 21 min**

45. $z = \frac{1}{9}x$; **It is the only equation that is a direct variation.**

H.O.T. Problems Use Higher-Order Thinking Skills

45. WHICH ONE DOESN'T BELONG? Identify the equation that does not belong. Explain.

$9 = rt$	$9a = 0$	$z = \frac{1}{9}x$	$w = \frac{9}{t}$

46. REASONING How are the constant of variation and the slope related in a direct variation equation? Explain your reasoning. **See Chapter 3 Answer Appendix.**

47. OPEN ENDED Model a real-world situation using a direct variation equation. Graph the equation and describe the rate of change. **See Chapter 3 Answer Appendix.**

48. STRUCTURE Suppose y varies directly as x. If the value of x is doubled, then the value of y is also *always, sometimes* or *never* doubled. Explain your reasoning. **See margin.**

49. ERROR ANALYSIS Eddy says the slope between any two points on the graph of a direct variation equation $y = kx$ is $\frac{1}{k}$. Adelle says the slope depends on the points chosen. Is either of them correct? Explain. **See margin.**

50. WRITING IN MATH How can you identify the graph of a direct variation equation? **See margin.**

Study Guide and Intervention
AL OL ELL

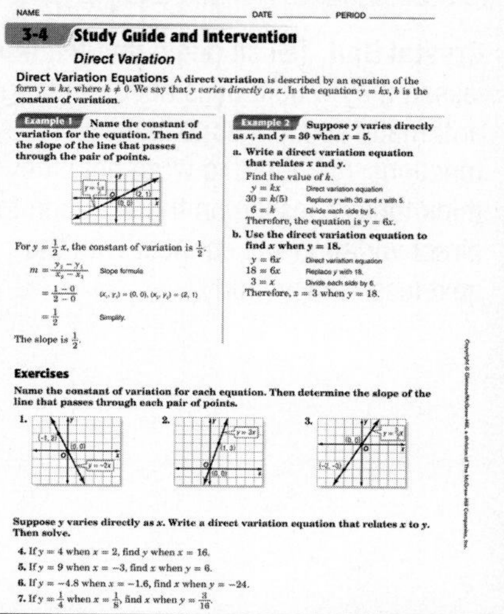
3-4 Study Guide and Intervention
Direct Variation
Direct Variation Equations A direct variation is described by an equation of the form $y = kx$, where $k \neq 0$. We say that y varies directly as x. In the equation $y = kx$, k is the constant of variation.
Exercises
Name the constant of variation for each equation. Then determine the slope of the line that passes through each pair of points.
Suppose y varies directly as x. Write a direct variation equation that relates x to y. Then solve.

Practice
AL OL BL ELL

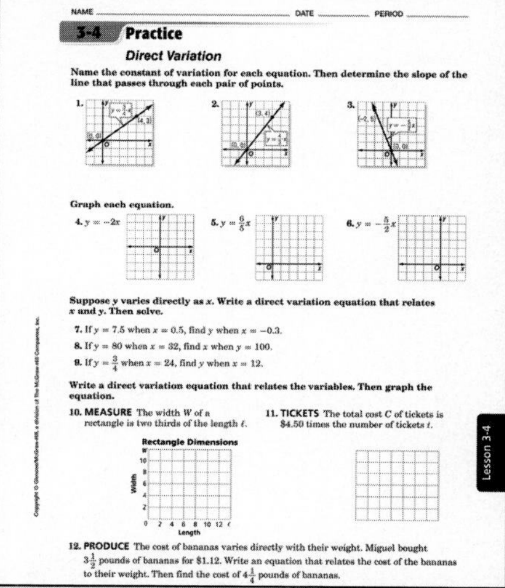
3-4 Practice
Direct Variation
Name the constant of variation for each equation. Then determine the slope of the line that passes through each pair of points.
Graph each equation.
Suppose y varies directly as x. Write a direct variation equation that relates x and y. Then solve.
Write a direct variation equation that relates the variables. Then graph the equation.

Word Problem Practice
AL OL BL ELL

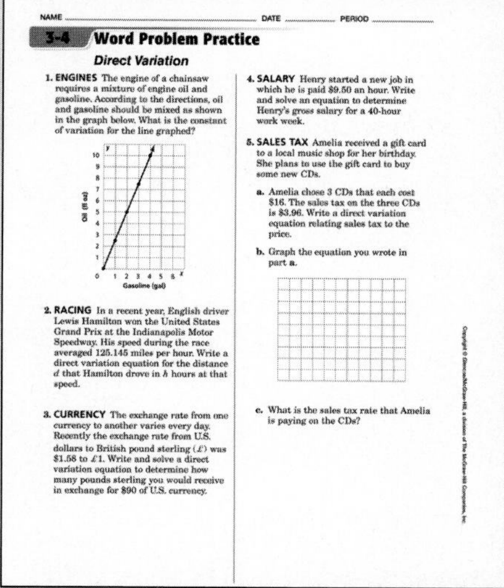
3-4 Word Problem Practice
Direct Variation

WatchOut!
Error Analysis For Exercise 49, suggest that students substitute different values for k, graph the equations, and then find the slopes.

Enrichment
OL BL

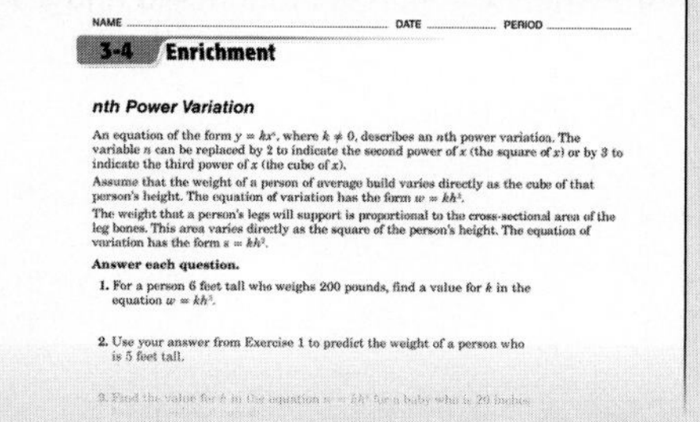
3-4 Enrichment
nth Power Variation

4 Assess

Crystal Ball Tell students that the next lesson they will study is about relating arithmetic sequences to linear functions. Ask them to write how they think today's lesson on the equation for direct variation will connect with the next lesson they study.

Standardized Test Practice

51. Patricia pays $1.19 each to download songs to her digital media player. If n is the number of downloaded songs, which equation represents the cost C in dollars? **A**

A $C = 1.19n$

B $n = 1.19C$

C $C = 1.19 \div n$

D $C = n + 1.19$

52. Suppose that y varies directly as x, and $y = 8$ when $x = 6$. What is the value of y when $x = 8$? **H**

F 6

G 12

H $10\frac{2}{3}$

J 16

53. What is the relationship between the input (x) and output (y)? **D**

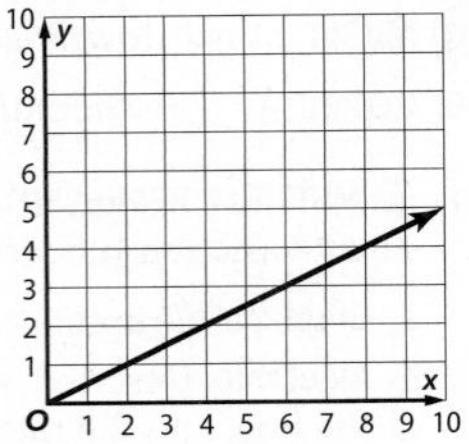

A The output is two more than the input.

B The output is two less than the input.

C The output is twice the input.

D The output is half the input.

54. **SHORT RESPONSE** A telephone company charges $40 per month plus $0.07 per minute. How much would a month of service cost a customer if the customer talked for 200 minutes? **$54**

Spiral Review

55. **TELEVISION** The graph shows the average number of television channels American households receive. What was the annual rate of change from 2004 to 2008? Explain the meaning of the rate of change. (Lesson 3-3)
6.5; There was an average increase of 6.5 channels per year.

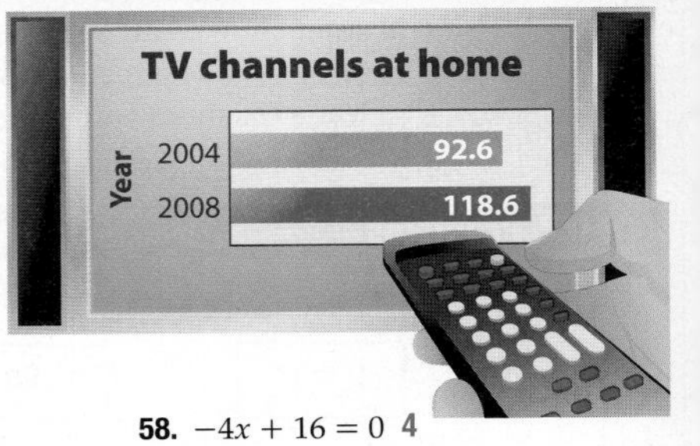

Solve each equation by graphing. (Lesson 3-2)

56. $0 = 18 - 9x$ **2**

57. $2x + 14 = 0$ **−7**

58. $-4x + 16 = 0$ **4**

59. $-5x - 20 = 0$ **−4**

60. $8x - 24 = 0$ **3**

61. $12x - 144 = 0$ **12**

Evaluate each expression if $a = 4$, $b = -2$, and $c = -4$. (Lesson 2-5)

62. $|2a + c| + 1$ **5**

63. $4a - |3b + 2|$ **12**

64. $-|a + 1| + |3c|$ **7**

65. $-a + |2 - a|$ **−2**

66. $|c - 2b| - 3$ **−3**

67. $-2|3b - 8|$ **−28**

Skills Review

Find each difference.

68. $13 - (-1)$ **14**

69. $4 - 16$ **−12**

70. $-3 - 3$ **−6**

71. $-8 - (-2)$ **−6**

72. $16 - (-10)$ **26**

73. $-8 - 4$ **−12**

Differentiated Instruction BL

Extension Write $y = kx^2$ on the board. Tell students that y varies directly as the *square* of x, and $y = 48$ when $x = 4$. Ask students to find y when $x = 10$. Since $k = 3$, $y = 300$.

LESSON 3-5 Arithmetic Sequences as Linear Functions

Then
- You indentified linear functions.

Now
1. Recognize arithmetic sequences.
2. Relate arithmetic sequences to linear functions.

Why?
- During a 2000-meter race, the coach of a women's crew team recorded the team's times at several intervals.
  - At 400 meters, the time was 1 minute 32 seconds.
  - At 800 meters, it was 3 minutes 4 seconds.
  - At 1200 meters, it was 4 minutes 36 seconds.
  - At 1600 meters, it was 6 minutes 8 seconds.

  They completed the race with a time of 7 minutes 40 seconds.

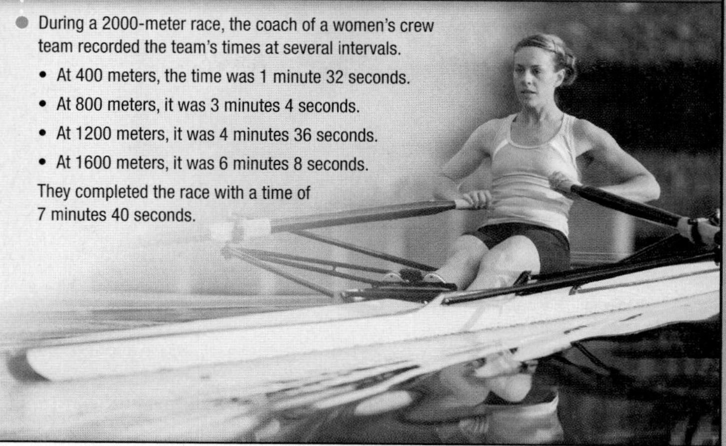

NewVocabulary
sequence
terms of the sequence
arithmetic sequence
common difference

1 Recognize Arithmetic Sequences

You can relate the pattern of team times to linear functions. A **sequence** is a set of numbers, called the **terms of the sequence**, in a specific order. Look for a pattern in the information given for the women's crew team. Make a table to analyze the data.

Distance (m)	400	800	1200	1600	2000
Time (min : sec)	1:32	3:04	4:36	6:08	7:40

+ 1:32   + 1:32   + 1:32   + 1:32

As the distance increases in regular intervals, the time increases by 1 minute 32 seconds. Since the difference between successive terms is constant, this is an **arithmetic sequence**. The difference between the terms is called the **common difference** d.

KeyConcept Arithmetic Sequence

Words An arithmetic sequence is a numerical pattern that increases or decreases at a constant rate called the *common difference.*

Examples

3, 5, 7, 9, 11, . . .
+2 +2 +2 +2
$d = 2$

33, 29, 25, 21, 17, . . .
−4 −4 −4 −4
$d = -4$

The three dots used with sequences are called an *ellipsis*. The ellipsis indicates that there are more terms in the sequence that are not listed.

connectED.mcgraw-hill.com 189

1 Focus

VerticalAlignment

Before Lesson 3-5 Identify linear functions.

Lesson 3-5 Recognize arithmetic sequences. Relate arithmetic sequences to linear functions.

After Lesson 3-5 Write equations in slope-intercept form.

2 Teach

Scaffolding Questions

Have students read the **Why?** section of the lesson.

Ask:
- What pattern do you see in the distances? The distances increase in regular intervals of 400 meters.
- What pattern do you see in the team's times? Each time is 1 minute 32 seconds more than the time before it.
- How could you find the team's time at 2000 meters? 6:08 + 1:32 = 7:40

Lesson 3-5 Resources

Resource	Approaching Level AL	On Level OL	Beyond Level BL	English Learners ELL
Teacher Edition	▪ Differentiated Instruction, p. 192	▪ Differentiated Instruction, pp. 190, 192	▪ Differentiated Instruction, pp. 190, 192, 195	
Chapter Resource Masters	▪ Study Guide and Intervention, pp. 30–31 ▪ Skills Practice, p. 32 ▪ Practice, p. 33 ▪ Word Problem Practice, p. 34	▪ Study Guide and Intervention, pp. 30–31 ▪ Skills Practice, p. 32 ▪ Practice, p. 33 ▪ Word Problem Practice, p. 34 ▪ Enrichment, p. 35	▪ Practice, p. 33 ▪ Word Problem Practice, p. 34 ▪ Enrichment, p. 35	▪ Study Guide and Intervention, pp. 30–31 ▪ Skills Practice, p. 32 ▪ Practice, p. 33 ▪ Word Problem Practice, p. 34
Other	▪ 5-Minute Check 3-5 ▪ Study Notebook	▪ 5-Minute Check 3-5 ▪ Study Notebook	▪ 5-Minute Check 3-5 ▪ Study Notebook	▪ 5-Minute Check 3-5 ▪ Study Notebook

1 Recognize Arithmetic Sequences

Example 1 shows how to determine whether a sequence is arithmetic.
Example 2 shows how to find the next term in an arithmetic sequence.
Example 3 shows how to write an equation for the *n*th term of an arithmetic sequence to find any term in the sequence or to find the term number of the term in the sequence.

Formative Assessment

Use the Guided Practice exercises after each Example to determine students' understanding of concepts.

Additional Examples

1 Determine whether each sequence is an arithmetic sequence. Explain.

a. $-15, -13, -11, -9, \ldots$ Yes; there is a common difference of 2.

b. $\frac{7}{8}, \frac{5}{8}, \frac{1}{8}, -\frac{5}{8}, \ldots$ No; there is no common difference.

2 Find the next three terms of the arithmetic sequence $-8, -11, -14, -17, \ldots$. $-20, -23, -26$

Additional Examples also in Interactive Classroom PowerPoint® Presentations

IWB Interactive White Board READY

Tips for New Teachers

Building on Prior Knowledge Ask a volunteer to count from zero by twos. Ask another to count from zero by threes. Ask a third to count from zero by fives. Explain to students that when they count by a certain number, whether 1, 2, 3, 5, or $\frac{1}{8}$, they are using an arithmetic sequence because there is a common difference.

Math HistoryLink

Mina Rees (1902–1997) Rees received the first award for Distinguished Service to Mathematics from the Mathematical Association of America. She was the first president of the Graduate Center at The City University of New York. Her work in analyzing patterns is still inspiring young women to study mathematics today.

PT

Example 1 Identify Arithmetic Sequences

Determine whether each sequence is an arithmetic sequence. Explain.

a. $-4, -2, 0, 2, \ldots$

$-4 \quad -2 \quad 0 \quad 2$

$+2 \quad +2 \quad +2$

The difference between terms in the sequence is constant. Therefore, this sequence is arithmetic.

b. $\frac{1}{2}, \frac{5}{8}, \frac{3}{4}, \frac{13}{16}, \ldots$

$\frac{1}{2} \quad \frac{5}{8} \quad \frac{3}{4} \quad \frac{13}{16}$

$+\frac{1}{8} \quad +\frac{1}{8} \quad +\frac{1}{16}$

This is not an arithmetic sequence. The difference between terms is not constant.

Guided Practice

1A. $-26, -22, -18, -14, \ldots$ Yes; the sequence has a common difference of 4.

1B. $1, 4, 9, 25, \ldots$

1B. No; the sequence does not have a common difference.

You can use the common difference of an arithmetic sequence to find the next term.

PT

Example 2 Find the Next Term

Find the next three terms of the arithmetic sequence $15, 9, 3, -3, \ldots$.

Step 1 Find the common difference by subtracting successive terms.

$15 \quad 9 \quad 3 \quad -3$

$-6 \quad -6 \quad -6$

The common difference is -6.

Step 2 Add -6 to the last term of the sequence to get the next term.

$-3 \quad -9 \quad -15 \quad -21$

$-6 \quad -6 \quad -6$

The next three terms in the sequence are -9, -15, and -21.

Guided Practice

2. Find the next four terms of the arithmetic sequence 9.5, 11.0, 12.5, 14.0, ... 15.5, 17.0, 18.5, 20.0

StudyTip

Regularity Notice the regularity in the way expressions in terms of a_1 and d change with each term of the sequence.

Each term in an arithmetic sequence can be expressed in terms of the first term a_1 and the common difference d.

Term	Symbol	In Terms of a_1 and d	Numbers
first term	a_1	a_1	8
second term	a_2	$a_1 + d$	$8 + 1(3) = 11$
third term	a_3	$a_1 + 2d$	$8 + 2(3) = 14$
fourth term	a_4	$a_1 + 3d$	$8 + 3(3) = 17$
⋮	⋮	⋮	⋮
*n*th term	a_n	$a_1 + (n-1)d$	$8 + (n-1)(3)$

KeyConcept *n*th Term of an Arithmetic Sequence

The *n*th term of an arithmetic sequence with first term a_1 and common difference d is given by $a_n = a_1 + (n-1)d$, where n is a positive integer.

Differentiated Instruction OL BL

Extension Arithmetic sequences can be programmed in graphing calculators and results displayed in lists. A good option for advanced learners or those who enjoy using technology might be locating a set of directions for programming a sequence and developing a lesson for their classmates on analyzing sequences using the calculator.

Example 3 Find the *n*th Term

a. Write an equation for the *n*th term of the arithmetic sequence −12, −8, −4, 0, … .

Step 1 Find the common difference.

−12   −8   −4   0

+4   +4   +4   The common difference is 4.

Step 2 Write an equation.

$a_n = a_1 + (n-1)d$	Formula for the *n*th term
$= -12 + (n-1)4$	$a_1 = -12$ and $d = 4$
$= -12 + 4n - 4$	Distributive Property
$= 4n - 16$	Simplify.

StudyTip

nth Terms Since *n* represents the number of the term, the inputs for *n* are the counting numbers.

b. Find the 9th term of the sequence.

Substitute 9 for *n* in the formula for the *n*th term.

$a_n = 4n - 16$	Formula for the *n*th term
$a_9 = 4(9) - 16$	$n = 9$
$a_9 = 36 - 16$	Multiply.
$a_9 = 20$	Simplify.

c. Graph the first five terms of the sequence.

n	$4n - 16$	a_n	(n, a_n)
1	4(1) − 16	−12	(1, −12)
2	4(2) − 16	−8	(2, −8)
3	4(3) − 16	−4	(3, −4)
4	4(4) − 16	0	(4, 0)
5	4(5) − 16	4	(5, 4)

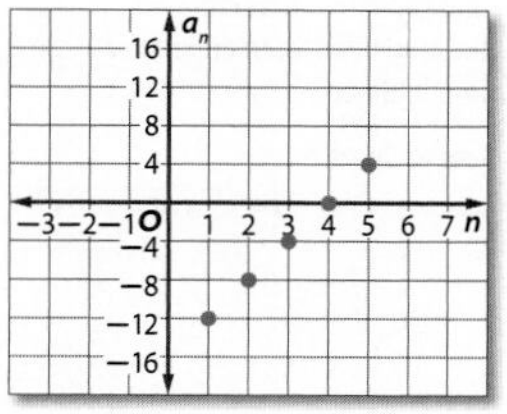

d. Which term of the sequence is 32?

In the formula for the *n*th term, substitute 32 for a_n.

$a_n = 4n - 16$	Formula for the *n*th term
$32 = 4n - 16$	$a_n = 32$
$32 + 16 = 4n - 16 + 16$	Add 16 to each side.
$48 = 4n$	Simplify.
$12 = n$	Divide each side by 4.

GuidedPractice

Consider the arithmetic sequence 3, −10, −23, −36, … .

3A. Write an equation for the *n*th term of the sequence. $a_n = -13n + 16$

3B. Find the 15th term in the sequence. −179

3C. Graph the first five terms of the sequence. **See margin.**

3D. Which term of the sequence is −114? 10

Additional Example

3 a. Write an equation for the *n*th term of the arithmetic sequence 1, 10, 19, 28,.... $a_n = 9n - 8$

b. Find the 12th term of the sequence. $a_{12} = 100$

c. Graph the first five terms of the sequence.

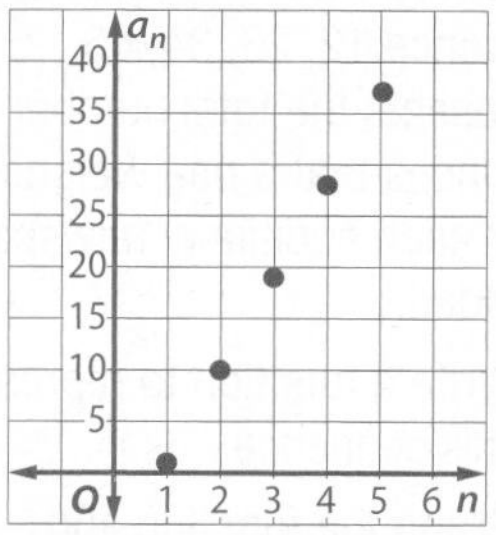

d. Which term of the sequence is 172? 20th term

Focus on Mathematical Content

Arithmetic Sequences After the first term, each term of an arithmetic sequence can be found by adding the common difference. The *n*th term of an arithmetic sequence with first term a_1 and a common difference d is given by $a_n = a_1 + (n - 1)d$, where n is a positive integer.

Teach with Tech

Blog On your secure classroom blog have students enter how to find a specific term of an arithmetic sequence. Make sure that students use the formula for finding the *n*th term of the sequence. Have each class select the best explanation to represent them and be posted on the classroom Web site for reference.

Teaching the Process Standards

Regularity Mathematically proficient students notice if calculations are repeated, and look both for general methods and for shortcuts. Encourage students to look for patterns in the sequences in Examples 1 and 2, before you present the formula for the *n*th term of an arithmetic sequence.

Additional Answer (Guided Practice)

3C.

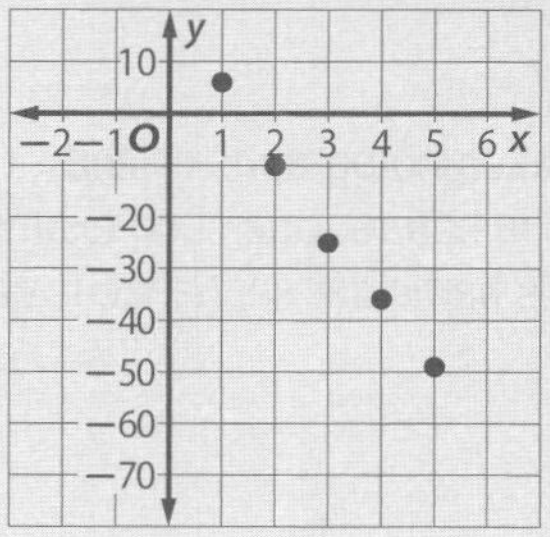

WatchOut!

Preventing Errors Make sure students carefully keep track of the variables in the function $a_n = a_1 + (n - 1)d$ as it is easy to substitute for the wrong variable when using this function.

2 Arithmetic Sequences and Functions

Example 4 shows how to solve a real-world problem by writing and graphing a function to represent an arithmetic sequence.

Additional Example

4 **NEWSPAPERS** The arithmetic sequence 12, 23, 34, 45 … represents the total number in ounces that a bag weighs after each additional newspaper is added.

a. Write a function to represent this sequence. $a_n = 11n + 1$

b. Graph the function and determine the domain.

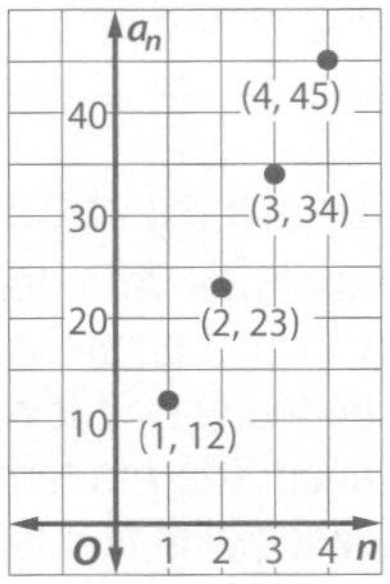

D = 0, 1, 2, 3, ...

Additional Answer (Guided Practice)

4B.

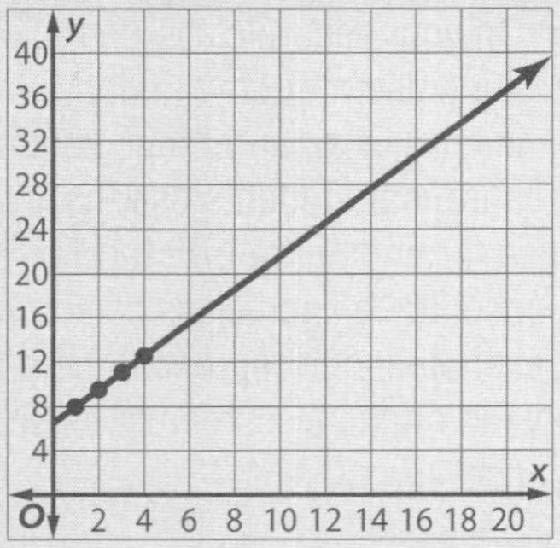

2 Arithmetic Sequences and Functions As you can see from Example 3, the graph of the first five terms of the arithmetic sequence lie on a line. An arithmetic sequence is a linear function in which n is the independent variable, a_n is the dependent variable, and d is the slope. The formula can be rewritten as the function $f(n) = (n - 1)d + a_1$, where n is a counting number.

While the domain of most linear functions are all real numbers, in Example 3 the domain of the function is the set of counting numbers and the range of the function is the set of integers on the line.

Real-WorldLink

When a Latina turns 15, her family may host a quinceañera for her birthday. The quinceañera is a traditional Hispanic ceremony and reception that signifies the transition from childhood to adulthood.

Source: Quince Girl

Real-World Example 4 Arithmetic Sequences as Functions

INVITATIONS Marisol is mailing invitations to her quinceañera. The arithmetic sequence \$0.42, \$0.84, \$1.26, \$1.68, … represents the cost of postage.

a. Write a function to represent this sequence.

The first term, a_1, is 0.42. Find the common difference.

0.42 0.84 1.26 1.68

+0.42 +0.42 +0.42

The common difference is 0.42.

$a_n = a_1 + (n - 1)d$	Formula for the *n*th term
$= 0.42 + (n - 1)0.42$	$a_1 = 0.42$ and $d = 0.42$
$= 0.42 + 0.42n - 0.42$	Distributive Property
$= 0.42n$	Simplify.

The function is $f(n) = 0.42n$.

b. Graph the function and determine the domain.

The rate of change of the function is 0.42. Make a table and plot points.

n	$f(n)$
1	0.42
2	0.84
3	1.26
4	1.68
5	2.10

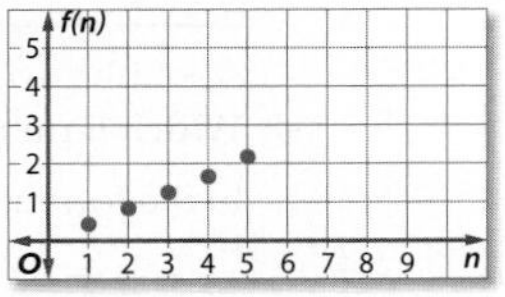

The domain of a function is the number of invitations Marisol mails. So, the domain is {1, 2, 3, 4, …}.

GuidedPractice

4. TRACK The chart below shows the length of Martin's long jumps.

Jump	1	2	3	4
Length (ft)	8	9.5	11	12.5

A. Write a function to represent this arithmetic sequence. $g(n) = 1.5n + 6.5$

B. Then graph the function. **See margin.**

DifferentiatedInstruction AL OL BL

If students have an interest in nature,

Then share that sequences are often visible in nature. Have students take photographs or find pictures in magazines or on calendars of examples of sequences in nature. One such example is the sequence found in the arrangement of seeds in a daisy. This particular sequence is called the Fibonacci sequence.

Check Your Understanding

= Step-by-Step Solutions begin on page R13.

Example 1 Determine whether each sequence is an arithmetic sequence. Write *yes* or *no*. Explain.

1. 18, 16, 15, 13, … No; there is no common difference.
2. 4, 9, 14, 19, … Yes; the common difference is 5.

Example 2 Find the next three terms of each arithmetic sequence.

3. 12, 9, 6, 3, … 0, −3, −6
4. −2, 2, 6, 10, … 14, 18, 22

Example 3 Write an equation for the *n*th term of each arithmetic sequence. Then graph the first five terms of the sequence. 5–6. See margin for graphs.

5. 15, 13, 11, 9, … $a_n = 17 - 2n$
6. −1, −0.5, 0, 0.5, … $a_n = 0.5n - 1.5$

Example 4

7. **SAVINGS** Kaia has \$525 in a savings account. After one month she has \$580 in the account. The next month the balance is \$635. The balance after the third month is \$690. Write a function to represent the arithmetic sequence. Then graph the function. $a(n) = 55n + 525$; See margin for graph.

Practice and Problem Solving

Extra Practice is on page R3.

Example 1 Determine whether each sequence is an arithmetic sequence. Write *yes* or *no*. Explain.

8. −3, 1, 5, 9, … Yes; the common difference is 4.
9. $\frac{1}{2}, \frac{3}{4}, \frac{5}{8}, \frac{7}{16}, \ldots$ No; there is no common difference.
10. −10, −7, −4, 1, … No; there is no common difference.
11. −12.3, −9.7, −7.1, −4.5, … Yes; the common difference is 2.6.

Example 2 Find the next three terms of each arithmetic sequence.

12. 0.02, 1.08, 2.14, 3.2, … 4.26, 5.32, 6.38
13. 6, 12, 18, 24, … 30, 36, 42
14. 21, 19, 17, 15, … 13, 11, 9
15. $-\frac{1}{2}, 0, \frac{1}{2}, 1, \ldots$ $1\frac{1}{2}, 2, 2\frac{1}{2}$
16. $2\frac{1}{3}, 2\frac{2}{3}, 3, 3\frac{1}{3}, \ldots$ $3\frac{2}{3}, 4, 4\frac{1}{3}$
17. $\frac{7}{12}, 1\frac{1}{3}, 2\frac{1}{12}, 2\frac{5}{6}, \ldots$ $3\frac{7}{12}, 4\frac{1}{3}, 5\frac{1}{12}$

Example 3 Write an equation for the *n*th term of the arithmetic sequence. Then graph the first five terms in the sequence. See Ch. 3 Answer Appendix for graphs.

18. −3, −8, −13, −18, … $a_n = -5n + 2$
19. −2, 3, 8, 13, … $a_n = 5n - 7$
20. −11, −15, −19, −23, … $a_n = -4n - 7$
21. −0.75, −0.5, −0.25, 0, … $a_n = 0.25n - 1$

Example 4

22. **AMUSEMENT PARKS** Shiloh and her friends spent the day at an amusement park. In the first hour, they rode two rides. After 2 hours, they had ridden 4 rides. They had ridden 6 rides after 3 hours.
    a. Write a function to represent the arithmetic sequence. $f(n) = 2n$
    b. Graph the function and determine the domain. See Ch. 3 Answer Appendix.

23. **MODELING** The table shows how Ryan is paid at his lumber yard job.

Number of 10-ft 2×4 Planks Cut	1	2	3	4	5	6	7
Amount Paid in Commission (\$)	8	16	24	32	40	48	56

    a. Write a function to represent Ryan's commission. $f(n) = 8n$
    b. Graph the function and determine the domain. See Ch. 3 Answer Appendix.

Differentiated Homework Options

Level	Assignment	Two-Day Option	
AL Basic	8–23, 32, 34, 36–55	9–23 odd, 37–40	8–22 even, 32, 34, 36, 41–55
OL Core	9–23 odd, 24–32, 34, 36–55	8–23, 37–40	24–32, 34, 36, 41–55
BL Advanced	24–49, (optional: 50–55)		

3 Practice

Formative Assessment

Use Exercises 1–7 to check for understanding.

Use the chart at the bottom of this page to customize assignments for your students.

Exercise Alert

Grid Paper Students will need grid paper to answer Exercises 5–7, 18–21, 22–23, and 50–55.

Teaching the Process Standards

Modeling Mathematically proficient students can apply the mathematics they know to solve problems arising in the workplace. In Exercise 23, encourage students to test their function by substitution.

Additional Answers

5.

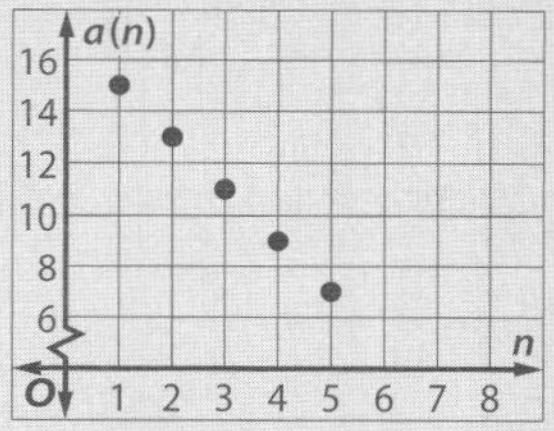

6.

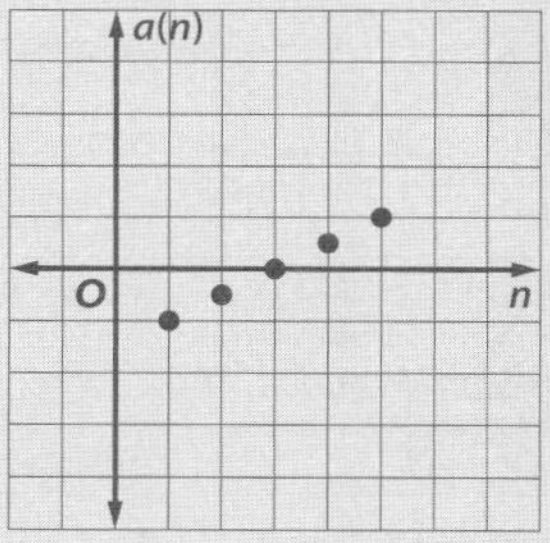

7.

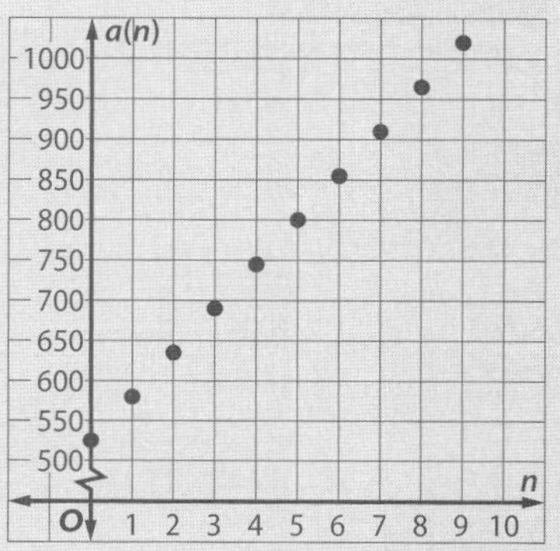

Study Guide and Intervention
AL OL ELL

NAME ______ DATE ______ PERIOD ______

3-5 Study Guide and Intervention

Arithmetic Sequences as Linear Functions

Recognize Arithmetic Sequences A sequence is a set of numbers in a specific order. If the difference between successive terms is constant, then the sequence is called an arithmetic sequence.

Arithmetic Sequence	a numerical pattern that increases or decreases at a constant rate or value called the common difference
Terms of an Arithmetic Sequence	If a_1 is the first term of an arithmetic sequence with common difference d, then the sequence is $a_1, a_1 + d, a_1 + 2d, a_1 + 3d, \ldots$
nth Term of an Arithmetic Sequence	$a_n = a_1 + (n - 1)d$

Example 1 Determine whether the sequence 1, 3, 5, 7, 9, 11, … is an arithmetic sequence. Justify your answer.

If possible, find the common difference between the terms. Since 3 − 1 = 2, 5 − 3 = 2, and so on, the common difference is 2.

Since the difference between the terms of 1, 3, 5, 7, 9, 11, … is constant, this is an arithmetic sequence.

Example 2 Write an equation for the nth term of the sequence 12, 15, 18, 21, … .

In this sequence, a_1 is 12. Find the common difference.

12 15 18 21 (+3 +3 +3)

The common difference is 3.

Use the formula for the nth term to write an equation.

$a_n = a_1 + (n - 1)d$ Formula for the nth term

$a_n = 12 + (n - 1)3$ $a_1 = 12, d = 3$

$a_n = 12 + 3n - 3$ Distributive Property

$a_n = 3n + 9$ Simplify.

The equation for the nth term is $a_n = 3n + 9$.

Exercises

Determine whether each sequence is an arithmetic sequence. Write *yes* or *no*. Explain.

1. 1, 5, 9, 13, 17, … 2. 8, 4, 0, −4, −8, … 3. 1, 3, 9, 27, 81, …

Find the next three terms of each arithmetic sequence.

4. 9, 13, 17, 21, 25, … 5. 4, 0, −4, −8, −12, … 6. 29, 35, 41, 47, …

Write an equation for the nth term of each arithmetic sequence. Then graph the first five terms of the sequence.

7. 1, 3, 5, 7, … 8. −1, −4, −7, −10, … 9. −4, −9, −14, −19, …

Practice
AL OL BL ELL

NAME ______ DATE ______ PERIOD ______

3-5 Practice

Arithmetic Sequences as Linear Functions

Determine whether each sequence is an arithmetic sequence. Write *yes* or *no*. Explain.

1. 21, 13, 5, −3, … 2. −5, 12, 29, 46, … 3. −2.2, −1.1, 0.1, 1.3, …

4. 1, 4, 9, 16, … 5. 9, 16, 23, 30, … 6. −1.2, 0.6, 1.8, 3.0, …

Find the next three terms of each arithmetic sequence.

7. 82, 76, 70, 64, … 8. −49, −35, −21, −7, … 9. $\frac{3}{4}, \frac{1}{2}, \frac{1}{4}, 0, \ldots$

10. −10, −3, 4, 11, … 11. 12, 10, 8, 6, … 12. 12, 7, 2, −3, …

Write an equation for the nth term of each arithmetic sequence. Then graph the first five terms of the sequence.

13. 9, 13, 17, 21, … 14. −5, −2, 1, 4, … 15. 19, 31, 43, 55, …

16. **BANKING** Chem deposited $115.00 in a savings account. Each week thereafter, he deposits $35.00 into the account.

a. Write a function to represent the total amount Chem has deposited for any particular number of weeks after his initial deposit.

b. How much has Chem deposited 30 weeks after his initial deposit?

17. **STORE DISPLAYS** Tamika is stacking boxes of tissue for a store display. Each row of tissues has 2 fewer boxes than the row below. The first row has 23 boxes of tissues.

a. Write a function to represent the arithmetic sequence.

b. How many boxes will there be in the tenth row?

Lesson 3-5

Word Problem Practice
AL OL BL ELL

NAME ______ DATE ______ PERIOD ______

3-5 Word Problem Practice

Arithmetic Sequences as Linear Functions

1. **POSTAGE** The price to send a large envelope first class mail is 88 cents for the first ounce and 17 cents for each additional ounce. The table below shows the cost for weights up to 5 ounces.

Weight (ounces)	1	2	3	4	5
Postage (dollars)	0.88	1.05	1.22	1.39	1.56

Source: United States Postal Service

How much did a large envelope weigh that cost $2.07 to send?

2. **SPORTS** Wanda is the manager for the soccer team. One of her duties is to hand out cups of water at practice. Each cup of water is 4 ounces. She begins practice with a 128-ounce cooler of water. How much water is remaining after she hands out the 14th cup?

3. **THEATER** A theater has 20 seats in the first row, 22 in the second row, 24 in the third row, and so on for 25 rows. How many seats are in the last row?

4. **NUMBER THEORY** One of the most famous sequences in mathematics is the Fibonacci sequence. It is named after Leonardo de Pisa (1170–1250) or Filius Bonacci, alias Leonardo Fibonacci. The first several numbers in the Fibonacci sequence are:
1, 1, 2, 3, 5, 8, 13, 21, 34, 55, 89, …
Does this represent an arithmetic sequence? Why or why not?

5. **SAVINGS** Inga's grandfather decides to start a fund for her college education. He makes an initial contribution of $3000 and each month deposits an additional $500. After one month he will have contributed $3500.

a. Write an equation for the nth term of the sequence.

b. How much money will Inga's grandfather have contributed after 24 months?

---

24. The graph is a representation of an arithmetic sequence.

a. List the first five terms. **−3, −1, 1, 3, 5**

b. Write the formula for the nth term. $a_n = 2n - 5$

c. Write the function. $f(n) = 2n - 5$

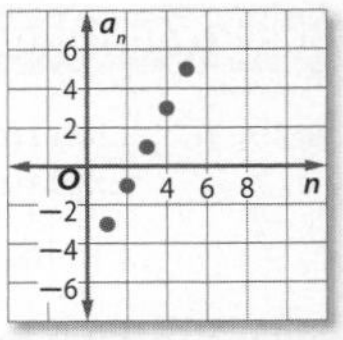

34. Sample answer: The domain of the function described by $Ax + By = C$ is the set of all real numbers, and the range is either the set of all real numbers or a set of just one number when the graph is a horizontal line. For an arithmetic sequence, the domain is the set of all counting numbers. The range will be an infinite discrete set of real numbers if $d \neq 0$. If $d \neq 0$, then the range will be $\{a_1\}$.

25. **NEWSPAPERS** A local newspaper charges by the number of words for advertising. Write a function to represent the advertising costs. $f(n) = 0.25n + 5$

DAILY NEWS ADVERTISING	
10 words $7.50	20 words $10.00
15 words $8.75	25 words $11.25

26. The fourth term of an arithmetic sequence is 8. If the common difference is 2, what is the first term? **2**

27. The common difference of an arithmetic sequence is −5. If a_{12} is 22, what is a_1? **77**

28. The first four terms of an arithmetic sequence are 28, 20, 12, and 4. Which term of the sequence is −36? **9**

29. **CARS** Jamal's odometer of his car reads 24,521. If Jamal drives 45 miles every day, what will the odometer reading be after 25 days? **25,646**

30. **YEARBOOKS** The yearbook staff is unpacking a box of school yearbooks. The arithmetic sequence 281, 270, 259, 248 … represents the total number of ounces that the box weighs as each yearbook is taken out of the box.

a. Write a function to represent this sequence. $f(n) = -11n + 292$

b. Determine the weight of each yearbook. **11 oz**

c. If the box weighs at least 17 ounces empty and 292 ounces when it is full, how many yearbooks were in the box? **25**

31. **SPORTS** To train for an upcoming marathon, Olivia plans to run 3 miles per day for the first week and then increase the daily distance by a half mile each of the following weeks.

a. Write an equation to represent the nth term of the sequence. $A_n = 2.5 + 0.5n$

b. If the pattern continues, during which week will she run 10 miles per day? **week 15**

c. Is it reasonable to think that this pattern will continue indefinitely? Explain. **Sample answer: No; eventually the number of miles ran per day will become unrealistic.**

H.O.T. Problems Use Higher-Order Thinking Skills

32. **OPEN ENDED** Create an arithmetic sequence with a common difference of −10. **Sample answer: 2, −8, −18, −28, …**

33. **PERSEVERANCE** Find the value of x that makes $x + 8$, $4x + 6$, and $3x$ the first three terms of an arithmetic sequence. **−1**

34. **REASONING** Compare and contrast the domain and range of the linear functions described by $Ax + By = C$ and $a_n = a_1 + (n - 1)d$.

35. **CHALLENGE** Determine whether each sequence is an arithmetic sequence. Write *yes* or *no*. Explain. If yes, find the common difference and the next three terms.

a. $2x + 1, 3x + 1, 4x + 1 \ldots$ **See margin.** b. $2x, 4x, 8x, \ldots$ **See margin.**

36. **WRITING IN MATH** How are graphs of arithmetic sequences and linear functions similar? different? **See margin.**

194 | Lesson 3-5 | Arithmetic Sequences as Linear Functions

Enrichment
OL BL

NAME ______ DATE ______ PERIOD ______

3-5 Enrichment

Arithmetic Series

An arithmetic series is a series in which each term after the first may be found by adding the same number to the preceding term. Let S stand for the following series in which each term is 3 more than the preceding one.

$S = 2 + 5 + 8 + 11 + 14 + 17 + 20$

The series remains the same if we reverse the order of all the terms. So let us reverse the order of the terms and add one series to the other, term by term. This is shown at the right.

$S = 2 + 5 + 8 + 11 + 14 + 17 + 20$
$S = 20 + 17 + 14 + 11 + 8 + 5 + 2$
$2S = 22 + 22 + 22 + 22 + 22 + 22 + 22$
$2S = 7(22)$
$S = \frac{7(22)}{2} = 7(11) = 77$

Let a represent the first term of the series.

Let ℓ represent the last term of the series.

Let n represent the number of terms in the series.

In the preceding example, $a = 2$, $\ell = 20$, and $n = 7$. Notice that when you add the two series, term by term, the sum of each pair of terms is 22. That sum can be found by adding the first and last terms, $2 + 20$ or $a + \ell$. Notice also that there are 7, or n, such sums. Therefore, the value of $2S$ is 7(22), or $n(a + \ell)$ in the general case. Since this is twice the sum of the series, you can use the formula $S = \frac{n(a + \ell)}{2}$ to find the sum of any arithmetic series.

Teaching the Process Standards

Perseverance Mathematically proficient students start by explaining to themselves the meaning of a problem and looking for entry points to its solution. In Exercise 33, remind students that the sequence is arithmetic. Encourage them to apply the definition of an arithmetic sequence.

Standardized Test Practice

37. GRIDDED RESPONSE The population of Westerville is about 35,000. Each year the population increases by about 400. This can be represented by the following equation, where n represents the number of years from now and p represents the population.

$$p = 35{,}000 + 400n$$

In how many years will the Westerville population be about 38,200? **8**

38. Which relation is a function? **D**

A $\{(-5, 6), (4, -3), (2, -1), (4, 2)\}$

B $\{(3, -1), (3, -5), (3, 4), (3, 6)\}$

C $\{(-2, 3), (0, 3), (-2, -1), (-1, 2)\}$

D $\{(-5, 6), (4, -3), (2, -1), (0, 2)\}$

39. Find the formula for the nth term of the arithmetic sequence. **H**

$$-7, -4, -1, 2, \ldots$$

F $a_n = 3n - 4$

G $a_n = -7n + 10$

H $a_n = 3n - 10$

J $a_n = -7n + 4$

40. STATISTICS A class received the following scores on the ACT. What is the difference between the median and the mode in the scores? **D**

18, 26, 20, 30, 25, 21, 32, 19, 22, 29, 29, 27, 24

A 1 C 3

B 2 D 4

Spiral Review

Name the constant of variation for each direct variation. Then find the slope of the line that passes through each pair of points. (Lesson 3-4)

41.

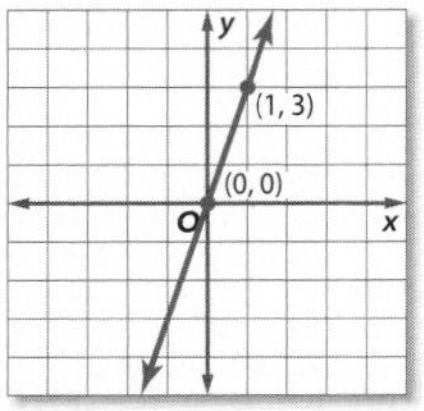

3, 3

42.

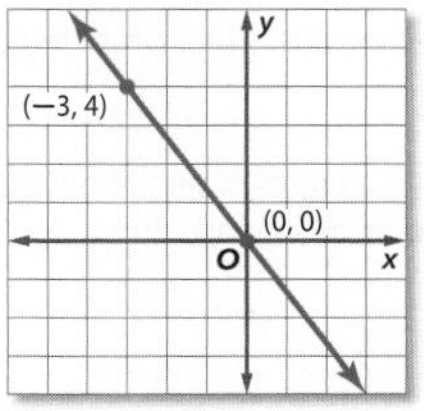

$-\frac{4}{3}, -\frac{4}{3}$

Find the slope of the line that passes through each pair of points. (Lesson 3-3)

43. $(5, 3), (-2, 6)$ $-\frac{3}{7}$

44. $(9, 2), (-3, -1)$ $\frac{1}{4}$

45. $(2, 8), (-2, -4)$ **3**

Solve each equation. Check your solution. (Lesson 2-3)

46. $5x + 7 = -8$ **−3**

47. $8 = 2 + 3n$ **2**

48. $12 = \frac{c - 6}{2}$ **30**

49. SPORTS The most popular sports for high school girls are basketball and softball. Write and use an equation to find how many more girls play on basketball teams than on softball teams. (Lesson 2-1)
Sample answer: 453,000 − d = 369,000; 84,000

Basketball
453,000 girls

Softball
369,000 girls

Skills Review

Graph each point on the same coordinate plane. 50–55. See margin.

50. $A(2, 5)$

51. $B(-2, 1)$

52. $C(-3, -1)$

53. $D(0, 4)$

54. $F(5, -3)$

55. $G(-5, 0)$

DifferentiatedInstruction BL

Extension Tell students that you applied a procedure that determines an arithmetic sequence in which the 4th term is 27 and the 8th term is 59. Ask students to find the starting number and the common difference. (Hint: Let the 4th term temporarily be the 1st term, which in turn makes the 8th term the 5th term.) $a_1 = 3, d = 8$

4 Assess

Name the Math Have students explain how they would find the 15th term of the arithmetic sequence −3, −1, 1, 1, −3 ....

Formative Assessment

Check for student understanding of Lessons 3-4 and 3-5.

Quiz 3, p. 46

Additional Answers

35a. Yes; there is a common difference; x; $5x + 1$, $6x + 1$, $7x + 1$.

35b. No; unless $x = 0$, there is no common difference.

36. Sample answer: They are similar in that the graph of the terms of an arithmetic sequence lies on a line. Therefore, an arithmetic sequence can be represented by a linear function. They are different in that the domain of an arithmetic sequence is the set of natural numbers, while the domain of a linear function is all real numbers. Thus, arithmetic sequences are discrete, while linear functions are continuous.

50–55.

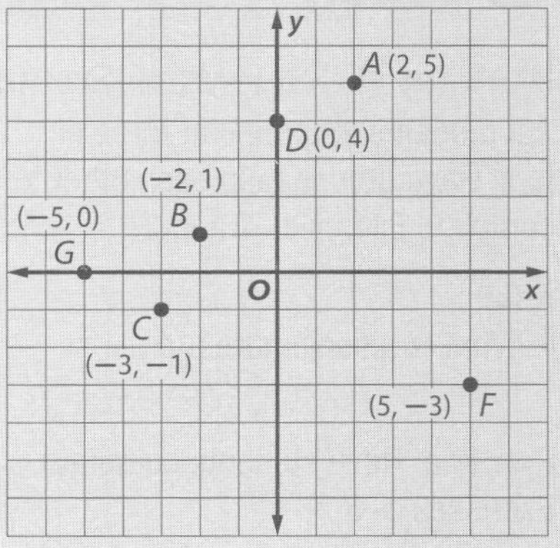

1 Focus

Objective Investigate inductive and deductive reasoning.

Teaching Tip

- Ask students to explain the types of thoughts they have when they solve a problem. If students have trouble coming up with ideas, give them a situation. Ask them how they would solve the problem of opening a locked door if they had a key ring with 100 keys on it.
- Explain to students that the root of inductive is *induce*. Induce is a verb that means *to call forth or bring about by influence*, or *to cause the formation of*. After students read the description of inductive reasoning, have them relate the principle of inductive reasoning to the definition of the word *induce*.
- Explain to students that the root of deductive is *deduce*. Deduce is a verb that means *to infer from a general principle*. Ask students to relate the principle of deductive reasoning to the definition of the word *deduce*.

2 Teach

Working in Cooperative Groups

Put students in groups of three or four. Have groups help each other to complete Exercises 1 and 2.

Ask:

- What is a conjecture? a guess based on incomplete information

Practice Have students complete Exercises 3–5.

3 Assess

Formative Assessment

Ask students whether predicting the next term in a sequence of numbers is done by trial and error, or by interpreting given information with a set of rules.

EXTEND 3-5

Algebra Lab
Inductive and Deductive Reasoning

Process Standards PS.3

If Jolene is not feeling well, she may go to a doctor. The doctor will ask her questions about how she is feeling and possibly run other tests. Based on her symptoms, the doctor can diagnose Jolene's illness. This is an example of inductive reasoning. **Inductive reasoning** is used to derive a general rule after observing many events.

To use inductive reasoning:

Step 1 Observe many examples.

Step 2 Look for a pattern.

Step 3 Make a conjecture.

Step 4 Check the conjecture.

Step 5 Discover a likely conclusion.

With **deductive reasoning**, you come to a conclusion by accepting facts. The results of the tests ordered by the doctor may support the original diagnosis or lead to a different conclusion. This is an example of deductive reasoning. There is no conjecturing involved. Consider the two statements below.

1) If the strep test is positive, then the patient has strep throat.

2) Jolene tested positive for strep.

If these two statements are accepted as facts, then the obvious conclusion is that Jolene has strep throat. This is an example of deductive reasoning.

Exercises

1. Explain the difference between *inductive* and *deductive* reasoning. Then give an example of each. **1–4. See Chapter 3 Answer Appendix.**
2. When a detective reaches a conclusion about the height of a suspect from the distance between footprints, what kind of reasoning is being used? Explain.
3. When you examine a finite number of terms in a sequence of numbers and decide that it is an arithmetic sequence, what kind of reasoning are you using? Explain.
4. Suppose you have found the common difference for an arithmetic sequence based on analyzing a finite number of terms, what kind of reasoning do you use to find the 100th term in the sequence?
5. **PERSEVERANCE**
   a. Copy and complete the table.

3^1	3^2	3^3	3^4	3^5	3^6	3^7	3^8	3^9
3	9	27	**81**	**243**	**729**	**2187**	**6561**	

19,683

   b. Write the sequence of numbers representing the numbers in the ones place. **3, 9, 7, 1, 3, 9, 7, 1, 3, …**

   c. Find the number in the ones place for the value of 3^{100}. Explain your reasoning. State the type of reasoning that you used. **See Chapter 3 Answer Appendix.**

From Concrete to Abstract

Use Exercises 3 and 4 to bridge the gap between using inductive and deductive reasoning in specific events and using this type of reasoning to solve problems concerning algebraic sequences.

Arguments Mathematically proficient students understand and use stated assumptions, definitions, and previously established results in constructing arguments. In Exercise 5, have students work in pairs to discuss their reasoning.

LESSON 3-6 Proportional and Nonproportional Relationships

Then

- You recognized arithmetic sequences and related them to linear functions.

Now

- 1 Write an equation for a proportional relationship.
- 2 Write an equation for a nonproportional relationship.

Why?

- Heather is planting flats of flowers. The table shows the number of flowers that she has planted and the amount of time that she has been working in the garden.

Number of flowers planted (p)	1	6	12	18
Number of minutes working (t)	5	30	60	90

The relationship between the flowers planted and the time that Heather worked in minutes can be graphed. Let p represent the number of flowers planted. Let t represent the number of minutes that Heather has worked.

When the ordered pairs are graphed, they form a linear pattern. This pattern can be described by an equation.

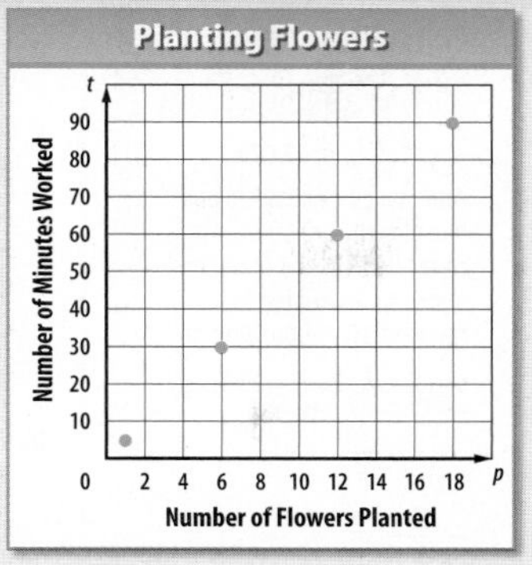

Content Standards
AI.F.4, AI.L.3

Process Standards
PS.7

1 Proportional Relationships

If the relationship between the domain and range of a relation is linear, the relationship can be described by a linear equation. If the equation is of the form $y = kx$, then the relationship is proportional. In a proportional relationship, the graph will pass through (0, 0). So, direct variations are proportional relationships.

KeyConcept Proportional Relationship

Words A relationship is proportional if its equation is of the form $y = kx$, $k \neq 0$. The graph passes through (0, 0).

Example $y = 3x$

x	0	1	2	3	4
y	0	3	6	9	12

The ratio of the value of x to the value of y is constant when $x \neq 0$.

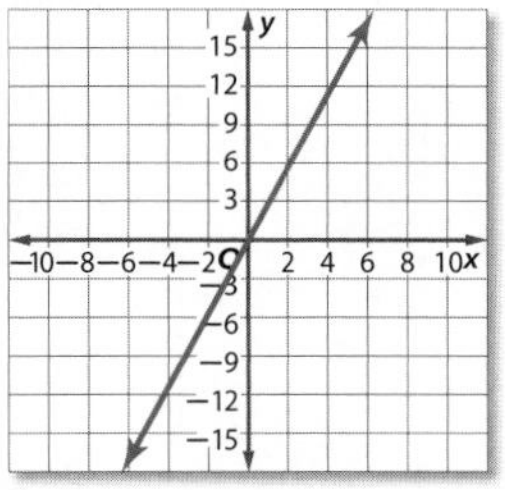

Proportional relationships are useful when analyzing real-world data. The pattern can be described using a table, a graph, and an equation.

1 Focus

VerticalAlignment

Before Lesson 3-6 Recognize arithmetic sequences and relate them to linear functions.

Lesson 3-6 Write an equation for a proportional relationship. Write an equation for a nonproportional relationship.

After Lesson 3-6 Write and graph linear functions in various forms.

2 Teach

Scaffolding Questions

Have students read the **Why?** section of the lesson.

Ask:

- If the linear pattern is extended, is (0, 0) part of the pattern? yes
- Is there an equation of the form $t = kp$ that describes the relationship? Yes, $t = 5p$.
- Based on your answer to the previous question, do you think there might be a way to predict the number of minutes it will take to plant 65 flowers? Yes, substitute 65 into the equation $t = 5p$ to get $t = 5(65)$. It will take 325 minutes.

Lesson 3-6 Resources

Resource	Approaching Level AL	On Level OL	Beyond Level BL	English Learners ELL
Teacher Edition	▪ Differentiated Instruction, p. 199	▪ Differentiated Instruction, p. 199	▪ Differentiated Instruction, p. 202	▪ Differentiated Instruction, p. 199
Chapter Resource Masters	▪ Study Guide and Intervention, pp. 37–38 ▪ Skills Practice, p. 39 ▪ Practice, p. 40 ▪ Word Problem Practice, p. 41	▪ Study Guide and Intervention, pp. 37–38 ▪ Skills Practice, p. 39 ▪ Practice, p. 40 ▪ Word Problem Practice, p. 41 ▪ Enrichment, p. 42	▪ Practice, p. 40 ▪ Word Problem Practice, p. 41 ▪ Enrichment, p. 42	▪ Study Guide and Intervention, pp. 37–38 ▪ Skills Practice, p. 39 ▪ Practice, p. 40 ▪ Word Problem Practice, p. 41
Other	▪ 5-Minute Check 3-6 ▪ Study Notebook	▪ 5-Minute Check 3-6 ▪ Study Notebook	▪ 5-Minute Check 3-6 ▪ Study Notebook	▪ 5-Minute Check 3-6 ▪ Study Notebook

Formative Assessment

Use the Guided Practice exercises after each Example to determine students' understanding of concepts.

1 Proportional Relationships

Example 1 shows how to write an equation for a real-world problem, given a table of data.

Additional Example

1 **ENERGY** The table shows the number of miles driven for each hour of driving.

Hours	1	2	3	4
Miles	50	100	150	200

a. Graph the data. What can you deduce from the pattern about the relationship between the number of hours of driving h and the number of miles driven m?

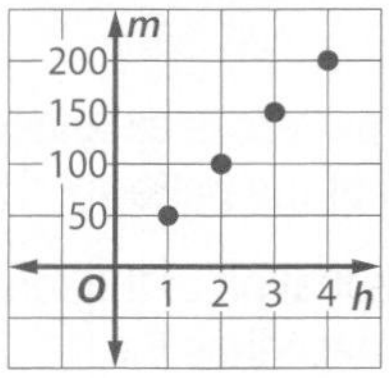

There is a linear relationship between hours of driving and miles driven.

b. Write an equation to describe this relationship. $m = 50h$

c. Use this equation to predict the number of miles driven in 8 hours of driving. 400 miles

Teaching the Process Standards

Structure Mathematically proficient students look closely to discern a pattern or structure. In Example 1b, point out to students that they need to examine the patterns in both the independent and dependent variables.

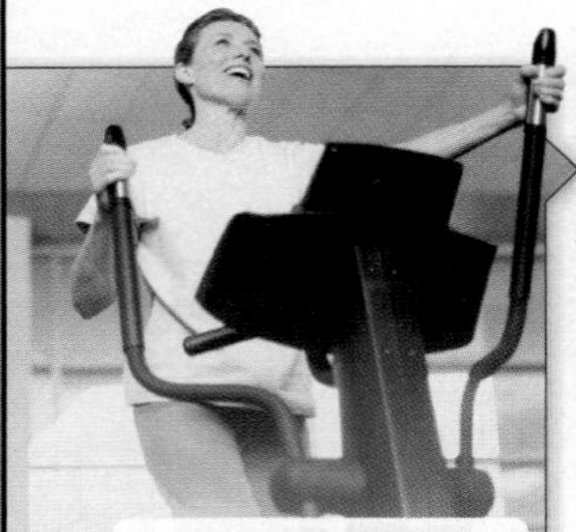

Real-WorldLink

Attendance at fitness clubs has steadily grown over the past fifteen years. Members' ages are expanding to a range of 15–34 on average.

Source: International Health, Racquet, and Sportsclub Association

StudyTip

Structure Look for a pattern that shows a constant rate of change between the terms.

Real-World Example 1 Proportional Relationships

BONUS PAY **Marcos is a personal trainer at a gym. In addition to his salary, he receives a bonus for each client he sees.**

Number of Clients	1	2	3	4	5
Bonus Pay ($)	45	90	135	180	225

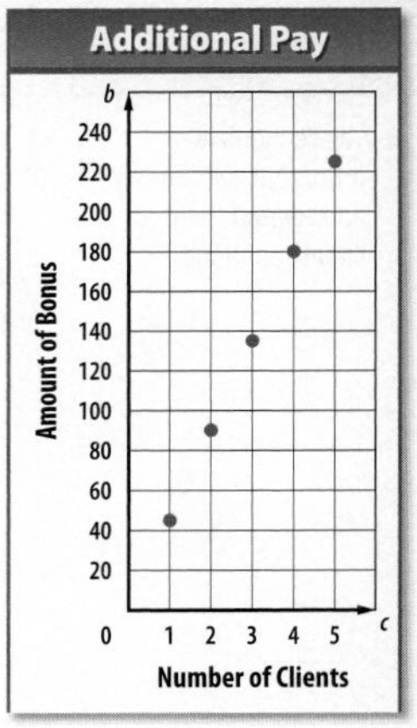

a. Graph the data. What can you deduce from the pattern about the relationship between the number of clients and the bonus pay?

The graph demonstrates a linear relationship between the number of clients and the bonus pay.

The graph also passes through the point (0, 0) because when Marcos sees 0 clients, he does not receive any bonus money. Therefore, the relationship is proportional.

b. Write an equation to describe this relationship.

Look for a pattern that can be described in an equation.

+1 +1 +1 +1

Number of Clients	1	2	3	4	5
Bonus Pay ($)	45	90	135	180	225

+45 +45 +45 +45

The difference between the values for the number of clients c is 1. The difference in the values for the bonus pay b is 45. This suggests that the k-value is $\frac{45}{1}$ or 45. So the equation is $b = 45c$. You can check this equation by substituting values for c into the equation.

CHECK If $c = 1$, then $b = 45(1)$ or 45. ✓
If $c = 5$, then $b = 45(5)$ or 225. ✓

c. Use this equation to predict the amount of Marcos's bonus if he sees 8 clients.

$b = 45c$ Original equation
$= 45(8)$ or 360 $c = 8$

Marcos will receive a bonus of $360 if he sees 8 clients.

GuidedPractice

1. CHARITY A professional soccer team is donating money to a local charity for each goal they score.

Number of Goals	1	2	3	4	5
Donation ($)	75	150	225	300	375

A. Graph the data. What can you deduce from the pattern about the relationship between the number of goals and the money donated? **See margin.**

B. Write an equation to describe this relationship. $d = 75g$

C. Use this equation to predict how much money will be donated for 12 goals. **$900**

Additional Answer (Guided Practice)

1A.

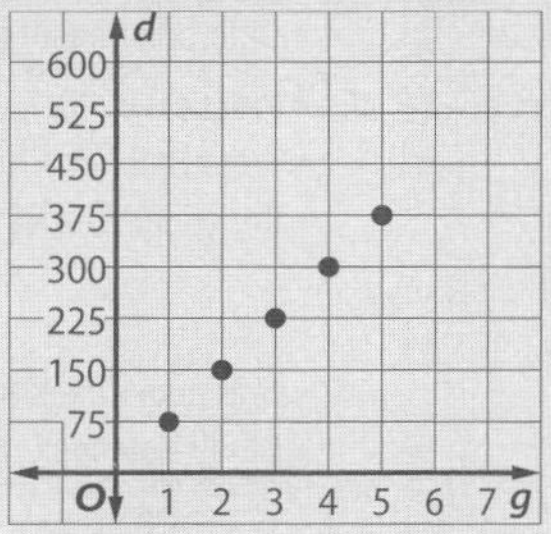

The graph demonstrates a linear pattern and passes through (0, 0). The relationship is proportional.

2 Nonproportional Relationships

Nonproportional Relationships Some linear equations can represent a nonproportional relationship. If the ratio of the value of x to the value of y is different for select ordered pairs that are on the line, the equation is nonproportional and the graph will not pass through (0, 0).

Example 2 Nonproportional Relationships

Write an equation in function notation for the graph.

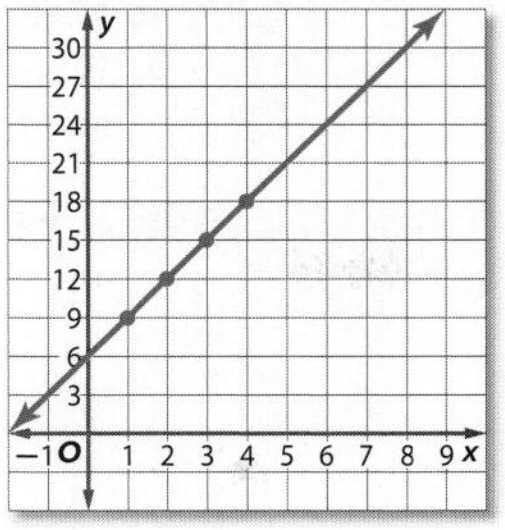

Understand You are asked to write an equation of the relation that is graphed in function notation.

Plan Find the difference between the x-values and the difference between the y-values.

Solve Select points from the graph and place them in a table.

+1 +1 +1

x	1	2	3	4
y	9	12	15	18

+3 +3 +3

Notice that $\frac{1}{9} \neq \frac{2}{12} \neq \frac{3}{15} \neq \frac{4}{18}$.

StudyTip

Graphs of Lines A value added to or subtracted from one side of the equation $y = ax$ will cause a shift along the y-axis for the graph of the line.

The difference between the x-values is 1, while the difference between the y-values is 3. This suggests that $y = 3x$ or $f(x) = 3x$.

If $x = 1$, then $y = 3(1)$ or 3. But the y-value for $x = 1$ is 9. Let's try some other values and see if we can detect a pattern.

x	1	2	3	4
$3x$	3	6	9	12
y	9	12	15	18

y is always 6 more than $3x$.

This pattern shows that 6 should be added to one side of the equation. Thus, the equation is $y = 3x + 6$ or $f(x) = 3x + 6$.

Check Compare the ordered pairs from the table to the graph. The points correspond. ✓

Guided Practice

2. Write an equation in function notation for the relation shown in the table.

A.

x	1	2	3	4
y	3	2	1	0

$y = -x + 4$ or $f(x) = -x + 4$

B. Write an equation in function notation for the graph. $y = 2x - 4$; $f(x) = 2x - 4$

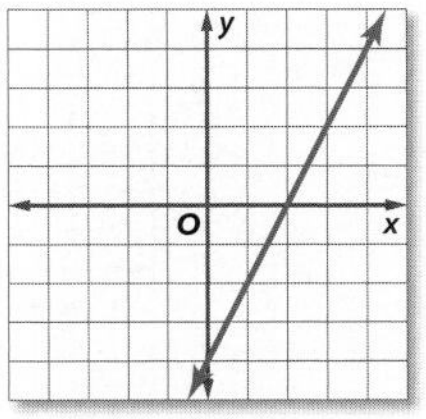

DifferentiatedInstruction AL OL ELL

If students need a concrete representation,

Then provide groups with posterboard. Have groups draw a large 10 × 10 coordinate grid on their posterboard. Next, have half of the groups draw a graph of a proportional relationship and the other half draw a graph of a nonproportional relationship. Then have groups explain which type of graph their example represents.

2 Nonproportional Relationships

Example 2 shows how to write an equation in function notation, given a graph of a relation.

Additional Example

2 Write an equation in function notation for the graph.

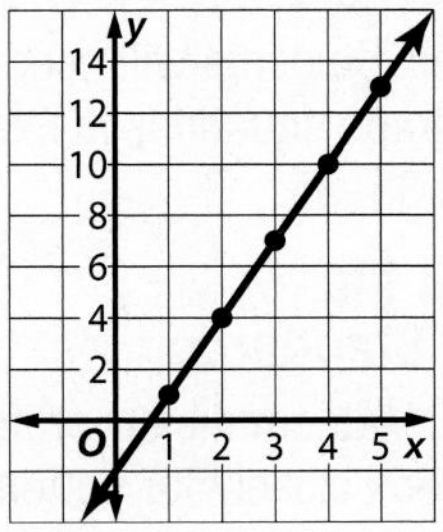

$f(x) = 3x - 2$

Additional Examples also in Interactive Classroom PowerPoint® Presentations

IWB Interactive White Board READY

Focus on Mathematical Content

Graphs The graph of a relation represented by $y = ax$ will be parallel to the graph of relations represented by $y = ax + b$ and $y = ax - b$.

Teach with Tech

Student Response System

Create a quiz that presents students with several relationships and ask them if each is a proportional or a nonproportional relationship. Have students respond with 1 for proportional or 2 for nonproportional.

3 Practice

Formative Assessment

Use Exercises 1–3 to check for understanding.

Use the chart at the bottom of this page to customize assignments for your students.

Exercise Alert

Grid Paper Students will need grid paper to graph equations in Exercises 1, 4, 13, and 33–35.

Teaching the Process Standards

Structure Mathematically proficient students look closely for patterns. Encourage students to use tables to organize their work.

Critique Mathematically proficient students understand and use definitions. For Exercise 14, remind students that equations of proportional relationships are in the form $y = kx$.

Additional Answers

1a.

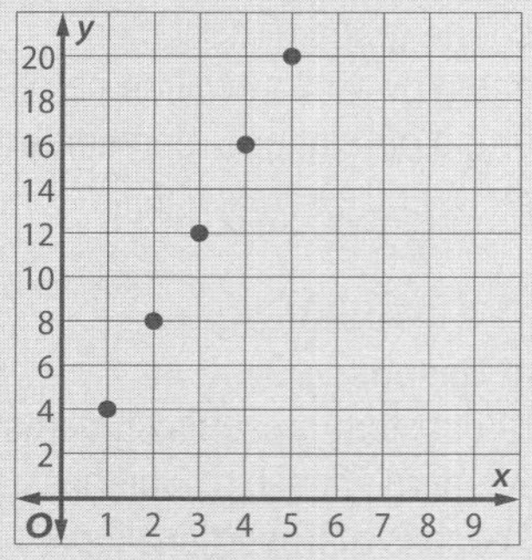

4a.

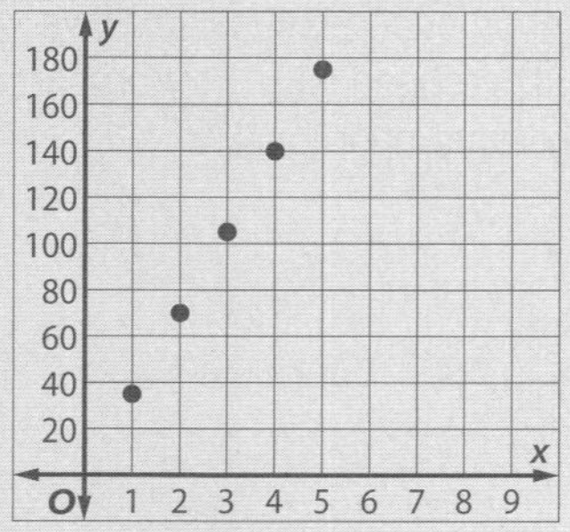

17. $f(n) = 3n + 2$ is the related function for the arithmetic sequence 5, 8, 11, 14, …, but it is not proportional. The line through (1, 5) and (2, 8) does not pass through (0, 0).

Check Your Understanding

= Step-by-Step Solutions begin on page R13.

Example 1

1. GEOMETRY The table shows the perimeter of a square with sides of a given length.

Side Length (in.)	1	2	3	4	5
Perimeter (in.)	4	8	12	16	20

a. Graph the data. **See margin.**

b. Write an equation to describe the relationship. $y = 4x$

c. What conclusion can you make regarding the relationship between the side and the perimeter? **The perimeter is 4 times the length of the side.**

Example 2

Write an equation in function notation for each relation.

2.

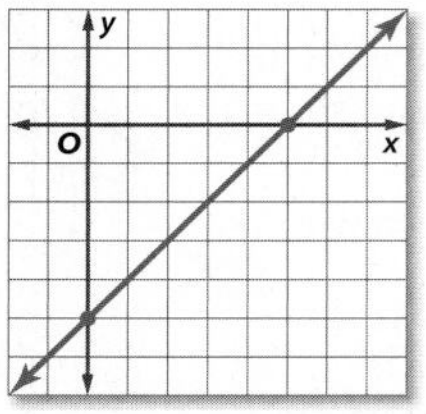

$f(x) = x - 5$

3.

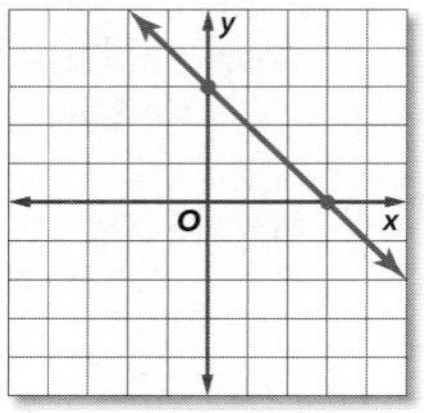

$f(x) = -x + 3$

Practice and Problem Solving

Extra Practice is on page R3.

Example 1

4. STRUCTURE The table shows the pages of comic books read.

Books Read	1	2	3	4	5
Pages Read	35	70	105	140	175

a. Graph the data. **See margin.**

b. Write an equation to describe the relationship. $y = 35x$

c. Find the number of pages read if 8 comic books were read. **280**

Example 2

Write an equation in function notation for each relation.

5.

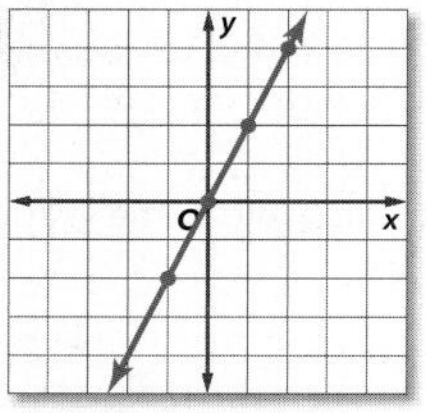

$f(x) = 2x$

6.

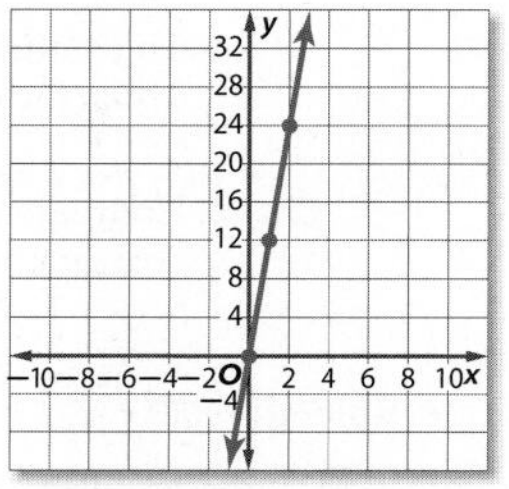

$f(x) = 12x$

7.

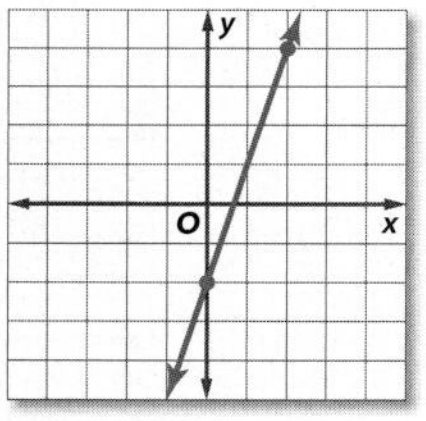

$f(x) = 3x - 2$

8.

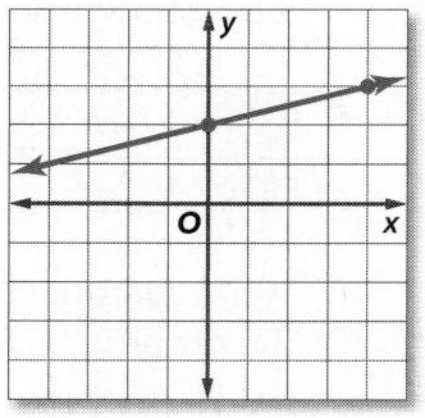

$f(x) = \frac{1}{4}x + 2$

Differentiated Homework Options

Level	Assignment	Two-Day Option	
AL Basic	4–8, 14, 15, 17–35	5, 7, 19–22	4–8 even, 14, 15, 17, 18, 23–35
OL Core	5, 7, 9–15, 17–35	4–8, 19–22	9–15, 17, 18, 23–35
BL Advanced	9–29, (optional: 30–35)		

B **For each arithmetic sequence, determine the related function. Then determine if the function is *proportional* or *nonproportional*. Explain.**

9. 0, 3, 6, …

10. −4, 0, 4, … $f(n) = 4n - 8$; nonproportional; the graph of the line does not pass through (0, 0).

11. BOWLING Marielle is bowling with her friends. The table shows prices for renting a pair of shoes and bowling. Write an equation to represent the total price y if Marielle buys x games. $y = 2.25x + 2.50$

Games Bowled	Total Price ($)
2	7.00
4	11.50
6	16.00
8	20.50

12. SNOWFALL The total snowfall each hour of a winter snowstorm is shown in the table below.

Hour	1	2	3	4
Inches of Snowfall	1.65	3.30	4.95	6.60

a. Write an equation to fit the data in the table. $a_n = 1.65n$

b. Describe the relationship between the hour and inches of snowfall. The relationship is proportional.

9. $f(n) = 3n - 3$; nonproportional; the function does not describe a direct variation.

13 FUNDRAISER The Cougar Pep Squad wants to sell T-shirts in the bookstore for the spring dance. The cost in dollars to order T-shirts in their school colors is represented by the equation $C = 2t + 3$.

a. Make a table of values that represents this relationship. See Chapter 3 Answer Appendix.

b. Rewrite the equation in function notation. $C(t) = 2t + 3$

c. Graph the function. See Chapter 3 Answer Appendix.

d. Describe the relationship between the number of T-shirts and the cost. This relationship is nonproportional.

H.O.T. Problems Use Higher-Order Thinking Skills

C **14. CRITIQUE** Quentin thinks that $f(x)$ and $g(x)$ are both proportional. Claudia thinks they are not proportional. Is either of them correct? Explain your reasoning.

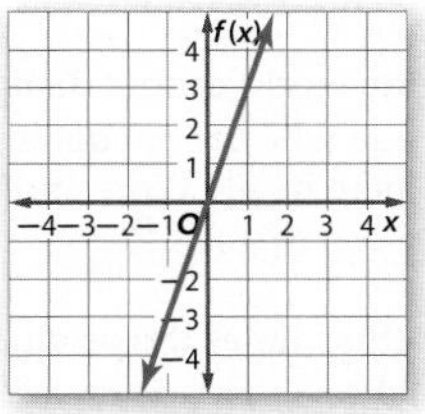

x	$g(x)$
−2	−7
−1	−4
0	−1
1	2
2	5

14. Neither; the graph represents $f(x) = 3x$ and the table represents $g(x) = 3x - 1$. Since $g(x)$ does not pass through the origin, it is not proportional. However, $f(x)$ is proportional.

15. Sample answer: 4, 7, 10, 13; add a common difference of 3; $a_n = 3n + 1$.

15. OPEN ENDED Create an arithmetic sequence in which the first term is 4. Explain the pattern that you used. Write an equation that represents your sequence.

16. CHALLENGE Describe how inductive reasoning can be used to write an equation from a pattern. Sample answer: Once you recognize a pattern, you can find a general rule that can be written as an algebraic expression.

17. REASONING A **counterexample** is a specific case that shows that a statement is false. Provide a counterexample to the following statement. *The related function of an arithmetic sequence is always proportional*. Explain your reasoning. See margin.

18. WRITING IN MATH Compare and contrast proportional relationships with nonproportional relationships. See margin.

Additional Answer

18. Sample answer: In a proportional relationship, the ratio of $\frac{y}{x}$ is the same for each ordered pair in the line for which $x \neq 0$. However, this is not the case in a nonproportional relationship. Both can be represented by a linear equation.

Study Guide and Intervention
AL OL ELL

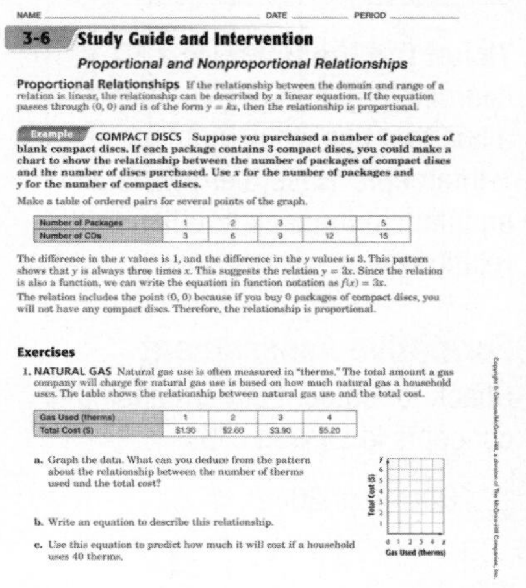

Practice
AL OL BL ELL

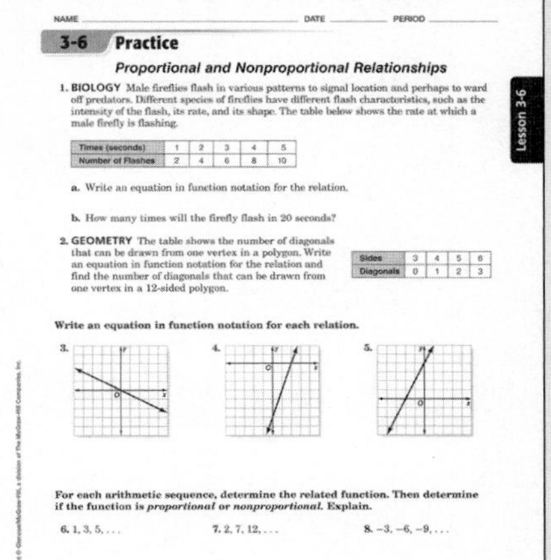

Word Problem Practice
AL OL BL ELL

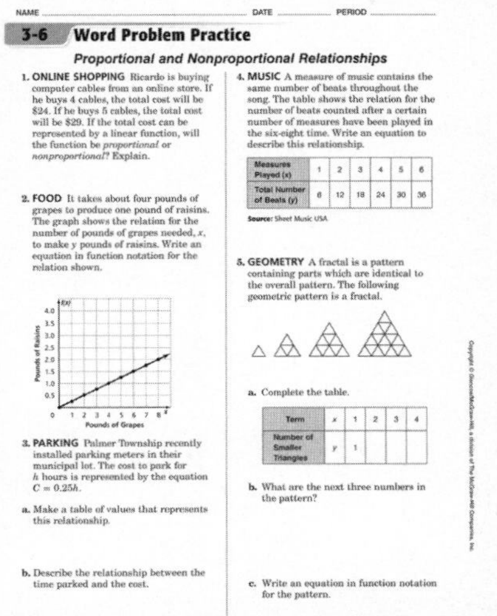

Enrichment
OL BL

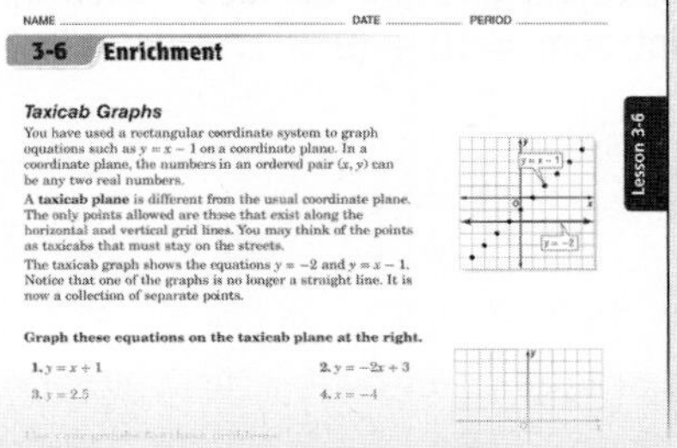

4 Assess

Ticket Out the Door On a 10×10 coordinate grid, have students draw a line that has whole number x- and y-intercepts. Have them write an equation in function notation for the relation.

Formative Assessment

Check for student understanding of concepts in Lesson 3-6.

Quiz 4, p. 46

Additional Answers

33.

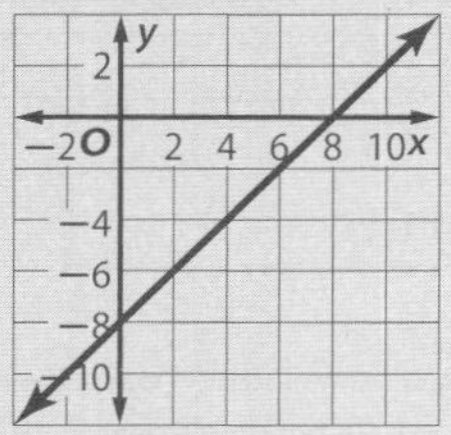

34.

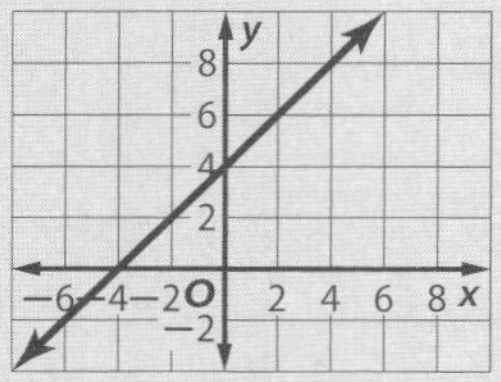

35.

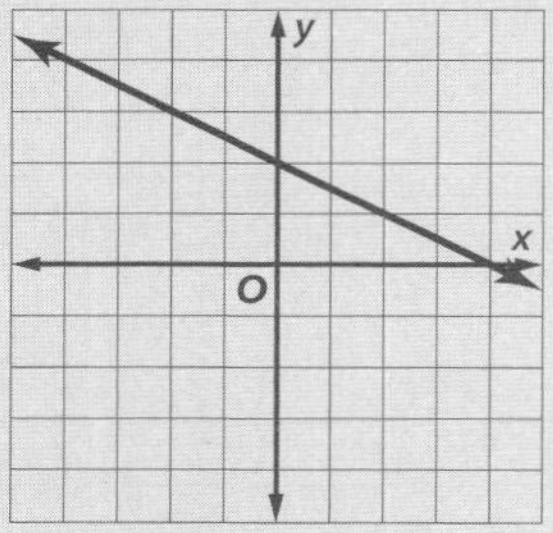

Standardized Test Practice

19. What is the slope of a line that contains the point $(1, -5)$ and has the same y-intercept as $2x - y = 9$? **D**

A -9 C 2

B -7 D 4

20. SHORT RESPONSE $\triangle FGR$ is an isosceles triangle. What is the measure of $\angle G$? **41°**

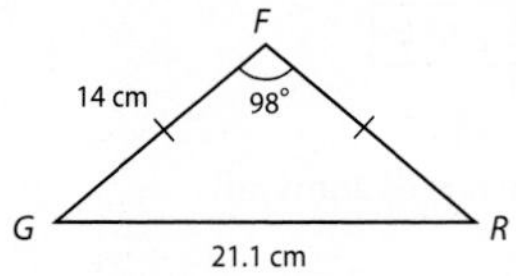

21. Luis deposits \$25 each week into a savings account from his part-time job. If he has \$350 in savings now, how much will he have in 12 weeks? **H**

F \$600 H \$650

G \$625 J \$675

22. GEOMETRY Omar and Mackenzie want to build a pulley system by attaching one end of a rope to their 8-foot-tall tree house and anchoring the other end to the ground 28 feet away from the base of the tree house. How long, to the nearest foot, does the piece of rope need to be? **D**

A 26 ft C 28 ft

B 27 ft D 29 ft

Spiral Review

Find the next three terms in each sequence. (Lesson 3-5)

23. 3, 13, 23, 33, … **43, 53, 63**

24. $-2, -1.4, -0.8, -0.2, \ldots$ **0.4, 1, 1.6**

25. $\frac{3}{4}, \frac{7}{8}, 1, \frac{9}{8}, \ldots$ $\frac{5}{4}, \frac{11}{8}, \frac{3}{2}$

Suppose y varies directly as x. Write a direct variation equation that relates x and y. Then solve. (Lesson 3-4)

26. If $y = 45$ when $x = 9$, find y when $x = 7$. $y = 5x$; **35**

27. If $y = -7$ when $x = -1$, find x when $y = -84$. $y = 7x$; **−12**

28. GENETICS About $\frac{2}{25}$ of the male population in the world cannot distinguish red from green. If there are 14 boys in the ninth grade who cannot distinguish red from green, about how many ninth-grade boys are there in all? Write and solve an equation to find the answer. (Lesson 2-2) $14 = \frac{2}{25}b$; **175 boys**

29. GEOMETRY The volume V of a cone equals one third times the product of π, the square of the radius r of the base, and the height h. (Lesson 2-1)

a. Write the formula for the volume of a cone. $V = \frac{1}{3}\pi r^2 h$

b. Find the volume of a cone if r is 10 centimeters and h is 30 centimeters. **about 3142 cm^3**

Skills Review

Solve each equation for y.

30. $3x = y + 7$ $y = 3x - 7$

31. $2y = 6x - 10$ $y = 3x - 5$

32. $9y + 2x = 12$ $y = -\frac{2}{9}x + \frac{4}{3}$

Graph each equation. **33–35. See margin.**

33. $y = x - 8$

34. $x - y = -4$

35. $2x + 4y = 8$

Differentiated Instruction BL

Extension Write 1, 2, 3, 4, 5, 6, 7, 8, 9, 10 on the board. Ask students to find the sum of the first 10 integers and then use inductive reasoning to find the sum of the first 100 positive integers. (Hint: sum = 10 + (9 + 1) + (8 + 2) + (7 + 3) + (6 + 4) + 5) 55; 5050

202 | Lesson 3-6 | Proportional and Nonproportional Relationships

CHAPTER 3 Study Guide and Review

Study Guide

KeyConcepts

Graphing Linear Equations (Lesson 3-1)

- The standard form of a linear equation is $Ax + By = C$, where $A \geq 0$, A and B are not both zero, and A, B, and C are integers whose greatest common factor is 1.

Solving Linear Equations by Graphing (Lesson 3-2)

- Values of x for which $f(x) = 0$ are called zeros of the function f. A zero of a function is located at an x-intercept of the graph of the function.

Rate of Change and Slope (Lesson 3-3)

- If x is the independent variable and y is the dependent variable, then rate of change equals
$$\frac{\text{change in } y}{\text{change in } x}.$$
- The slope of a line is the ratio of the rise to the run.
$$m = \frac{y_2 - y_1}{x_2 - x_1}$$

Direct Variation (Lesson 3-4)

- A direct variation is described by an equation of the form $y = kx$, where $k \neq 0$.

Arithmetic Sequences (Lesson 3-5)

- The nth term a_n of an arithmetic sequence with first term a_1 and common difference d is given by $a_n = a_1 + (n - 1)d$, where n is a positive integer.

Proportional and Nonproportional Relationships (Lesson 3-6)

- In a proportional relationship, the graph will pass through (0, 0).
- In a nonproportional relationship, the graph will not pass through (0, 0)

FOLDABLES StudyOrganizer

Be sure the Key Concepts are noted in your Foldable.

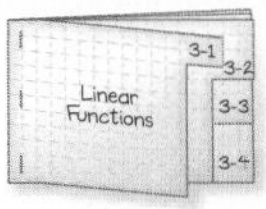

KeyVocabulary

arithmetic sequence (p. 189)	rate of change (p. 172)
common difference (p. 189)	root (p. 163)
constant (p. 155)	sequence (p. 189)
constant of variation (p. 182)	slope (p. 174)
deductive reasoning (p. 196)	standard form (p. 155)
direct variation (p. 182)	terms of the sequence (p. 189)
inductive reasoning (p. 196)	x-intercept (p. 156)
linear equation (p. 155)	y-intercept (p. 156)
linear function (p. 163)	zero of a function (p. 163)

VocabularyCheck

State whether each sentence is *true* or *false*. If *false*, replace the underlined word or number to make a true sentence.

1. The x-coordinate of the point at which the graph of an equation crosses the x-axis is an <u>x-intercept</u>. **true**
2. A <u>linear equation</u> is an equation of a line. **true**
3. The difference between successive terms of an arithmetic sequence is the <u>constant of variation</u>. **false; common difference**
4. The <u>regular form</u> of a linear equation is $Ax + By = C$. **false; standard form**
5. Values of x for which $f(x) = 0$ are called <u>zeros</u> of the function f. **true**
6. Any two points on a nonvertical line can be used to determine the <u>slope</u>. **true**
7. The slope of the line $y = 5$ is <u>5</u>. **false; 0**
8. The graph of any direct variation equation passes through <u>(0, 1)</u>. **false; (0, 0)**
9. A ratio that describes, on average, how much one quantity changes with respect to a change in another quantity is a <u>rate of change</u>. **true**
10. In the linear equation $4x + 3y = 12$, the constant term is <u>12</u>. **true**

Formative Assessment

KeyVocabulary The page reference after each word denotes where that term was first introduced. If students have difficulty answering questions 1–10, remind them that they can use these page references to refresh their memories about the vocabulary terms.

Summative Assessment

Vocabulary Test, p. 48

Vocabulary Review

Vocabulary Review provides students the opportunity to check their understanding of important concepts and terminology in an online game format.

FOLDABLES StudyOrganizer

Dinah Zike's Foldables®

Have students look through the chapter to make sure they have included examples in their Foldables for each lesson of the chapter. Suggest that students keep their Foldables handy while completing the Study Guide and Review pages. Point out that their Foldables can serve as a quick review when studying for the Chapter Test.

Lesson-by-Lesson Review

Intervention If the given examples are not sufficient to review the topics covered by the questions, remind students that the lesson references tell them where to review that topic in their textbooks.

Two-Day Option Have students complete the Lesson-by-Lesson Review. Then you can use McGraw-Hill eAssessment to customize another review worksheet that practices all the objectives of this chapter or only the objectives on which your students need more help.

Additional Answers

13. 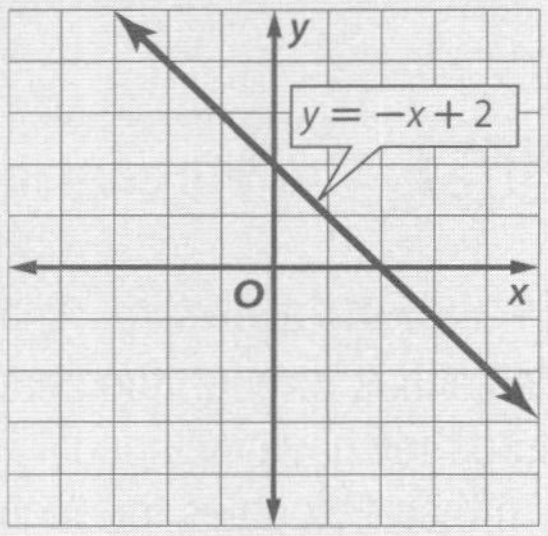

14. 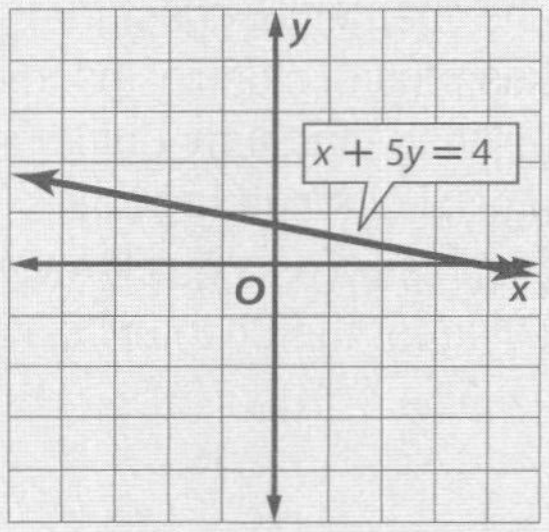

CHAPTER 3 Study Guide and Review *Continued*

Lesson-by-Lesson Review

3-1 Graphing Linear Equations

Find the x-intercept and y-intercept of the graph of each linear function.

11.

x	y
−8	0
−4	3
0	6
4	9
8	12

−8, 6

12. **3, −2**

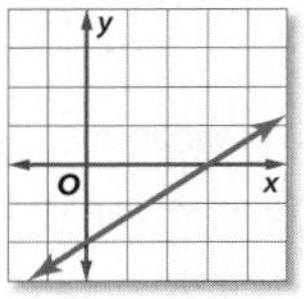

Graph each equation. **13–16. See margin.**

13. $y = -x + 2$
14. $x + 5y = 4$
15. $2x - 3y = 6$
16. $5x + 2y = 10$

17. **SOUND** The distance d in kilometers that sound waves travel through water is given by $d = 1.6t$, where t is the time in seconds. **See margin.**
   a. Make a table of values and graph the equation.
   b. Use the graph to estimate how far sound can travel through water in 7 seconds. **about 11 km**

Example 1

Graph $3x - y = 4$ by using the x- and y-intercepts.

Find the x-intercept.

$3x - y = 4$

$3x - 0 = 4$ Let $y = 0$.

$3x = 4$

$x = \frac{4}{3}$

Find the y-intercept.

$3x - y = 4$

$3(0) - y = 4$ Let $x = 0$.

$-y = 4$

$y = -4$

x-intercept: $\frac{4}{3}$

y-intercept: -4

The graph intersects the x-axis at $\left(\frac{4}{3}, 0\right)$ and the y-axis at $(0, -4)$. Plot these points. Then draw the line through them.

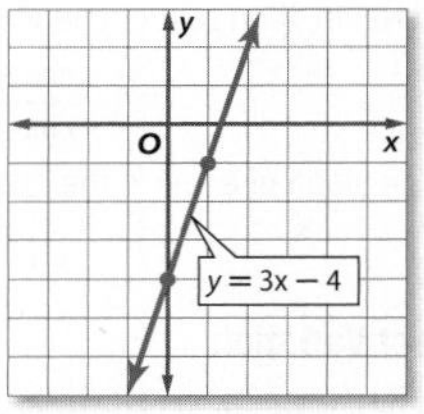

3-2 Solving Linear Equations by Graphing

Find the root of each equation.

18. $0 = 2x + 8$ **−4**
19. $0 = 4x - 24$ **6**
20. $3x - 5 = 0$ **$\frac{5}{3}$ or $1\frac{2}{3}$**
21. $6x + 3 = 0$ **$-\frac{1}{2}$**

Solve each equation by graphing.

22. $0 = 16 - 8x$ **2**
23. $0 = 21 + 3x$ **−7**
24. $-4x - 28 = 0$ **−7**
25. $25x - 225 = 0$ **9**

26. **FUNDRAISING** Sean's class is selling boxes of popcorn to raise money for a class trip. Sean's class paid $85 for the popcorn, and they are selling each box for $1. The function $y = x - 85$ represents their profit y for each box of popcorn sold x. Find the zero and describe what it means in this situation. **See margin.**

Example 2

Solve $3x + 1 = -2$ by graphing.

The first step is to find the related function.

$3x + 1 = -2$ Original equation

$3x + 1 + 2 = -2 + 2$ Add 2 to each side.

$3x + 3 = 0$ Simplify.

The related function is $y = 3x + 3$.

The graph intersects the x-axis at -1. So, the solution is -1.

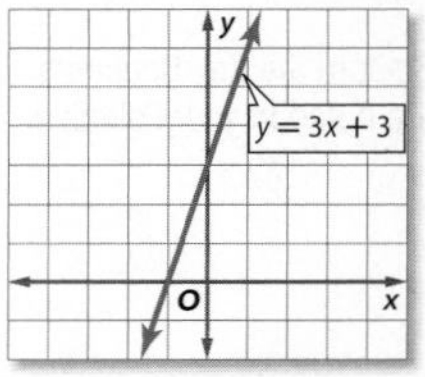

15. 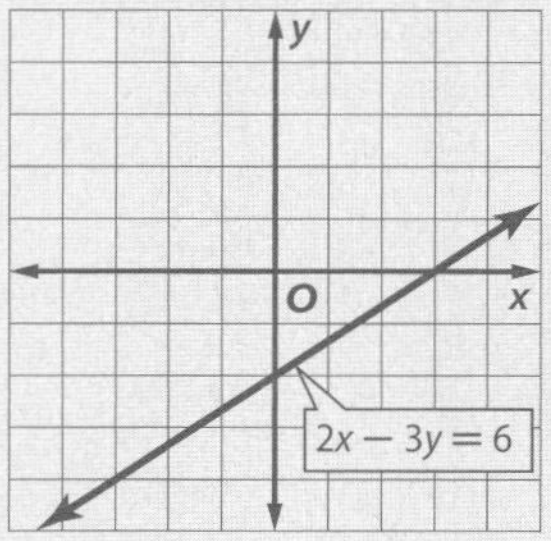

16. 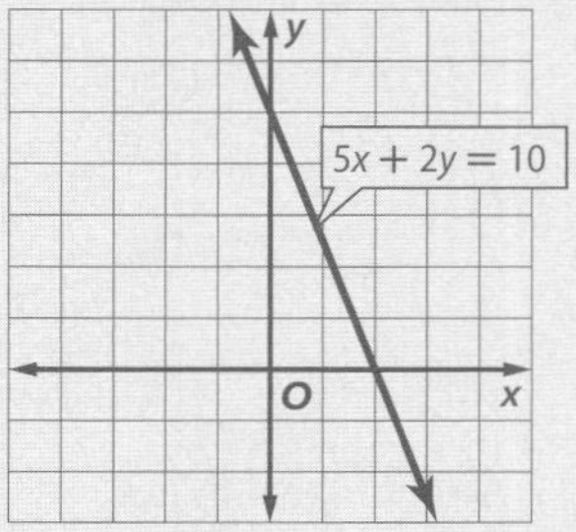

3-3 Rate of Change and Slope

Find the rate of change represented in each table or graph.

27. 3

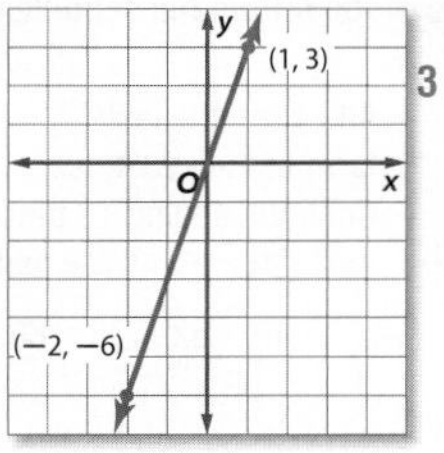

28. 0

x	y
−2	−3
0	−3
4	−3
12	−3

Find the slope of the line that passes through each pair of points.

29. (0, 5), (6, 2) $-\frac{1}{2}$

30. (−6, 4), (−6, −2) undefined

31. **PHOTOS** The average cost of online photos decreased from \$0.50 per print to \$0.15 per print between 2002 and 2009. Find the average rate of change in the cost. Explain what it means.

Example 3

Find the slope of the line that passes through (0, −4) and (3, 2).

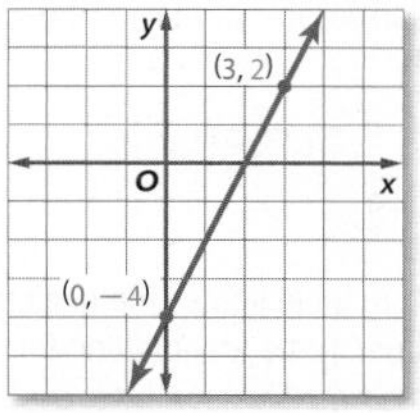

Let $(0, -4) = (x_1, y_1)$ and $(3, 2) = (x_2, y_2)$.

$m = \frac{y_2 - y_1}{x_2 - x_1}$ Slope formula

$= \frac{2 - (-4)}{3 - 0}$ $x_1 = 0, x_2 = 3, y_1 = -4, y_2 = 2$

$= \frac{6}{3}$ or 2 Simplify.

31. −0.05; an average decrease in cost of \$0.05 per year

3-4 Direct Variation

Graph each equation. **32–34. See margin.**

32. $y = x$ **33.** $y = \frac{4}{3}x$ **34.** $y = -2x$

Suppose y varies directly as x. Write a direct variation equation that relates x and y. Then solve.

35. If $y = 15$ when $x = 2$, find y when $x = 8$. **35.** $y = 7.5x$; $y = 60$

36. If $y = -6$ when $x = 9$, find x when $y = -3$.

37. If $y = 4$ when $x = -4$, find y when $x = 7$.

38. **JOBS** Suppose you earn \$127 for working 20 hours.

a. Write a direct variation equation relating your earnings to the number of hours worked. $y = 6.35x$

b. How much would you earn for working 35 hours? **\$222.25**

36. $y = -\frac{2}{3}x$; $x = 4\frac{1}{2}$ **37.** $y = -x$; $y = -7$

Example 4

Suppose y varies directly as x, and $y = -24$ when $x = 8$.

a. Write a direct variation equation that relates x and y.

$y = kx$ Direct variation equation

$-24 = k(8)$ Substitute −24 for y and 8 for x.

$\frac{-24}{8} = \frac{k(8)}{8}$ Divide each side by 8.

$-3 = k$ Simplify.

So, the direct variation equation is $y = -3x$.

b. Use the direct variation equation to find x when $y = -18$.

$y = -3x$ Direct variation equation

$-18 = -3x$ Replace y with −18.

$\frac{-18}{-3} = \frac{-3x}{-3}$ Divide each side by −3.

$6 = x$ Simplify.

Therefore, $x = 6$ when $y = -18$.

Additional Answers

17a.

t	d
0	0
1	1.6
2	3.2
3	4.8
4	6.4
5	8

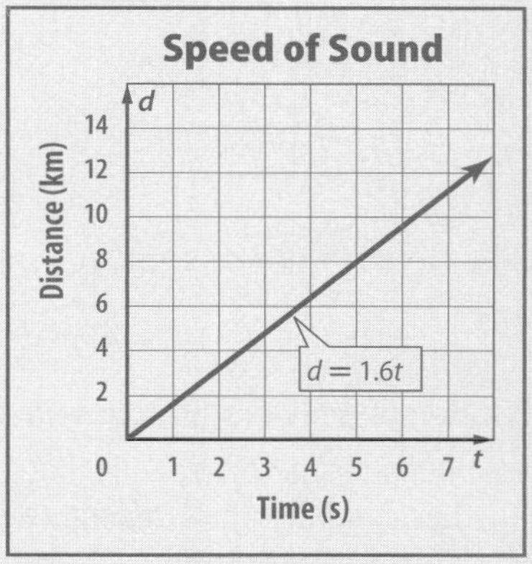

26. 85; Once they have sold 85 boxes of popcorn they will have earned back their initial investment.

32.

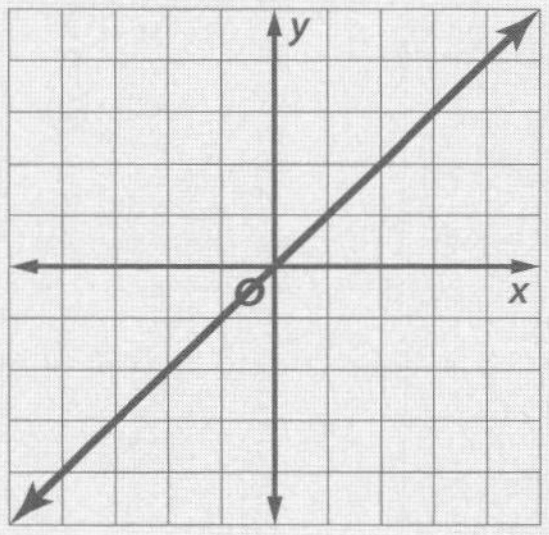

33.

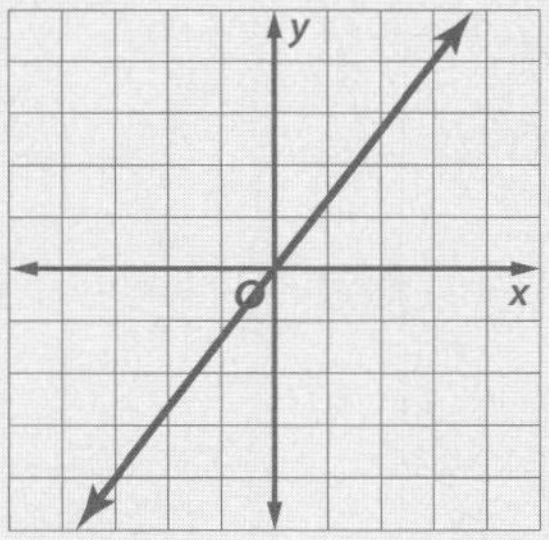

34.

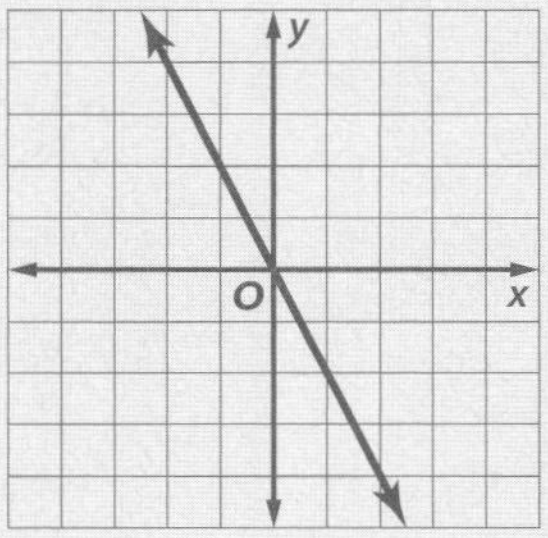

connectED.mcgraw-hill.com 205

Anticipation Guide

Have students complete the Chapter 3 Anticipation Guide and discuss how their responses have changed now that they have completed Chapter 3.

Additional Answers

45a.

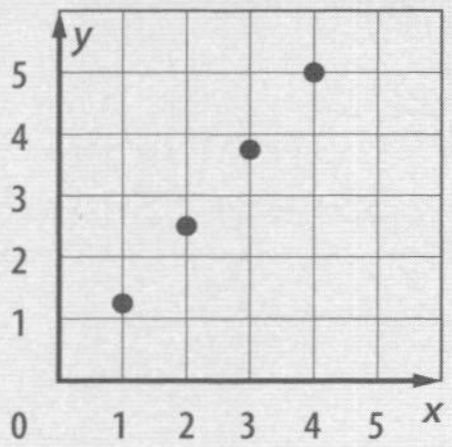

45b. $f(x) = 1.25x$

45c. $7.50

Additional Answers (Practice Test)

1a. Independent: *C*, dependent: *K*; Kelvin temperature depends on Celsius temperature.

1b. *C*-int: (−273, 0); −273°C is equal to 0°K; *K*-int: (0, 273); 0°C is equal to 273°K.

2.

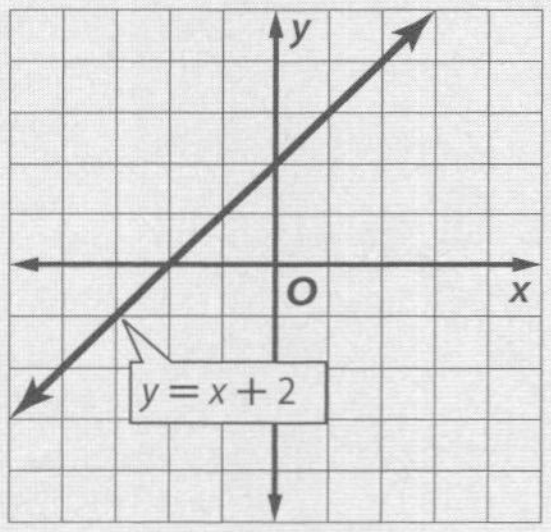

3.

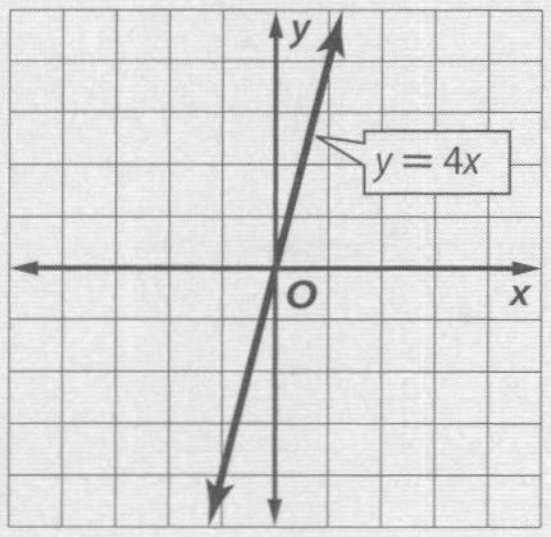

CHAPTER 3 Study Guide and Review *Continued*

3-5 Arithmetic Sequences as Linear Functions

Find the next three terms of each arithmetic sequence.

39. 6, 11, 16, 21, … **26, 31, 36**

40. 1.4, 1.2, 1.0, … **0.8, 0.6, 0.4**

Write an equation for the *n*th term of each arithmetic sequence.

41. $a_1 = 6, d = 5$ **$a_n = 5n + 1$**

42. 28, 25, 22, 19, … **$a_n = -3n + 31$**

43. **SCIENCE** The table shows the distance traveled by sound in water. Write an equation for this sequence. Then find the time for sound to travel 72,300 feet. **43. $a_n = 4820n$; 15 s**

Time (s)	1	2	3	4
Distance ft)	4820	9640	14,460	19,280

Example 5

Find the next three terms of the arithmetic sequence 10, 23, 36, 49, … .

Find the common difference.

10 23 36 49
+13 +13 +13

So, $d = 13$.

Add 13 to the last term of the sequence. Continue adding 13 until the next three terms are found.

49 62 75 88
+13 +13 +13

The next three terms are 62, 75, and 88.

3-6 Proportional and Nonproportional Relationships

44. Write an equation in function notation for this relation.

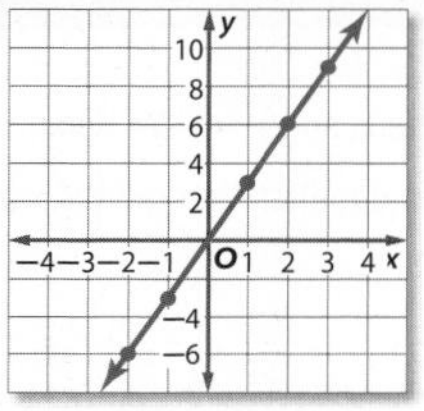

$f(x) = 3x$

45. **ANALYZE TABLES** The table shows the cost of picking your own strawberries at a farm.

Number of Pounds	1	2	3	4
Total Cost ($)	1.25	2.50	3.75	5.00

a. Graph the data. **a–c. See margin.**

b. Write an equation in function notation to describe this relationship.

c. How much would it cost to pick 6 pounds of strawberries?

Example 6

Write an equation in function notation for this relation.

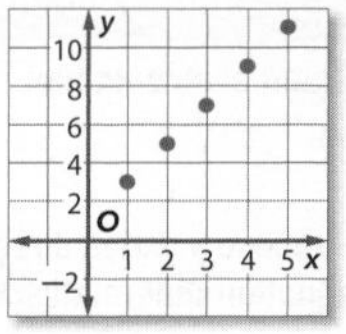

Make a table of ordered pairs for several points on the graph.

x	1	2	3	4	5
y	3	5	7	9	11

The difference in *y*-values is twice the difference of *x* values. This suggests that $y = 2x$. However, $3 \neq 2(1)$. Compare the values of *y* to the values of $2x$.

x	1	2	3	4	5
2x	2	4	6	8	10
y	3	5	7	9	11

The difference between *y* and $2x$ is always 1. So the equation is $y = 2x + 1$. Since this relation is also a function, it can be written as $f(x) = 2x + 1$.

4.

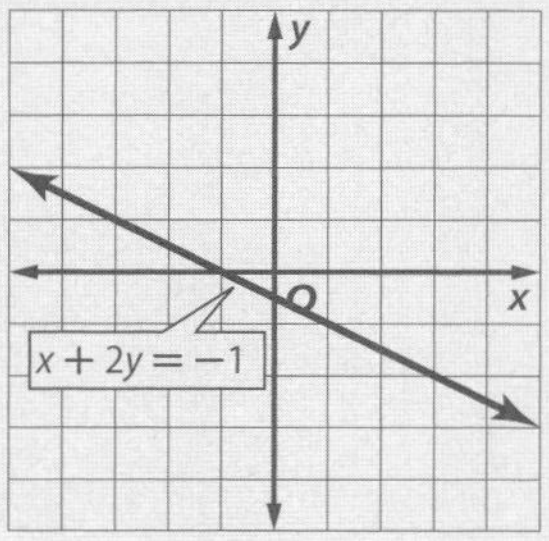

5.

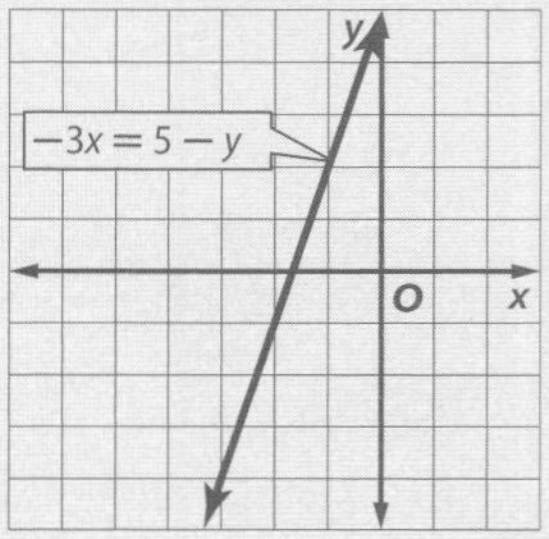

206 | Chapter 3 | Study Guide and Review

CHAPTER 3 Practice Test

1. **TEMPERATURE** The equation to convert Celsius temperature C to Kelvin temperature K is shown.

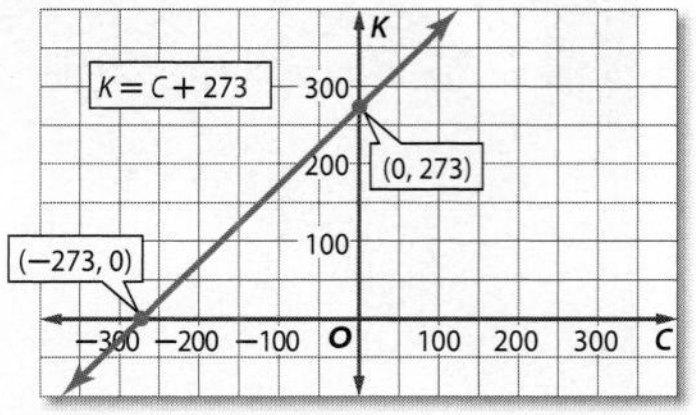

   a. State the independent and dependent variables. Explain. **See margin.**

   b. Determine the C- and K-intercepts and describe what the intercepts mean in this situation. **See margin.**

Graph each equation. **2–5. See margin.**

2. $y = x + 2$
3. $y = 4x$
4. $x + 2y = -1$
5. $-3x = 5 - y$

Solve each equation by graphing.

6. $4x + 2 = 0$ $-\frac{1}{2}$
7. $0 = 6 - 3x$ **2**
8. $5x + 2 = -3$ **−1**
9. $12x = 4x + 16$ **2**

Find the slope of the line that passes through each pair of points.

10. (5, 8), (−3, 7) $\frac{1}{8}$
11. (5, −2), (3, −2) **0**
12. (−4, 7), (8, −1) $-\frac{2}{3}$
13. (6, −3), (6, 4) **undefined**

14. **MULTIPLE CHOICE** Which is the slope of the linear function shown in the graph? **B**

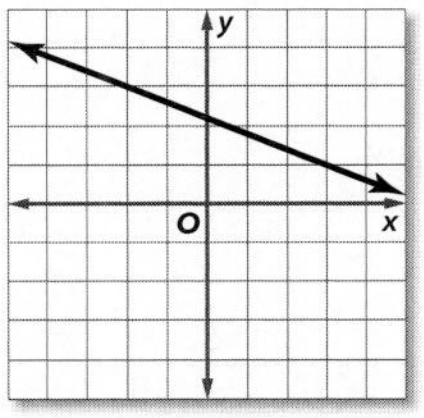

   A $-\frac{5}{2}$ C $\frac{2}{5}$

   B $-\frac{2}{5}$ D $\frac{5}{2}$

Suppose y varies directly as x. Write a direct variation equation that relates x and y. Then solve.

15. If $y = 6$ when $x = 9$, find x when $y = 12$.
16. When $y = -8$, $x = 8$. What is x when $y = -6$?
17. If $y = -5$ when $x = -2$, what is y when $x = 14$?
18. If $y = 2$ when $x = -12$, find y when $x = -4$.
15–18. See margin.

19. **BIOLOGY** The number of pints of blood in a human body varies directly with the person's weight. A person who weighs 120 pounds has about 8.4 pints of blood in his or her body.

   a. Write and graph an equation relating weight and amount of blood in a person's body.

   b. Predict the weight of a person whose body holds 12 pints of blood. **171 lbs**

19a. $y = 0.07w$**; See Chapter 3 Answer Appendix for graph.**

Find the next three terms of each arithmetic sequence.

20. 0, −15, −30, −45, −60, … **−75, −90, −105**
21. 5, 8, 11, 14, … **17, 20, 23**

Determine whether each sequence is an arithmetic sequence. If it is, state the common difference.

22. −40, −32, −24, −16, … **yes; 8**
23. 0.75, 1.5, 3, 6, 12, … **no**
24. 5, 17, 29, 41, … **yes; 12**

25. **MULTIPLE CHOICE** In each figure, only one side of each regular pentagon is shared with another pentagon. The length of each side is 1 centimeter. If the pattern continues, what is the perimeter of a figure that has 6 pentagons? **H**

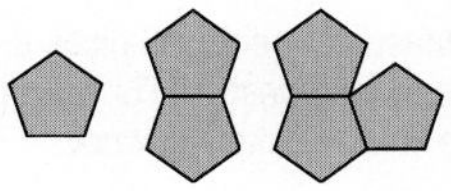

   F 30 cm

   G 25 cm

   H 20 cm

   J 15 cm

Summative Assessment

Use these alternate leveled chapter tests to differentiate assessment for your students.

Leveled Chapter 3 Tests

Form	Type	Level	Page(s)
1	MC	AL	49–50
2A	MC	OL	51–52
2B	MC	OL	53–54
2C	FR	OL	55–56
2D	FR	OL	57–58
3	FR	BL	59–60
Vocabulary Test			48
Extended-Response Test			61

MC = multiple-choice questions
FR = free-response questions

McGraw-Hill eAssessment Customize and create multiple versions of your chapter test and their answer keys. All of the questions from the leveled chapter tests in the *Chapter 3 Resource Masters* are also available on McGraw-Hill eAssessment.

Additional Answers

15. $y = \frac{2}{3}x;\ x = 18$
16. $y = -x;\ x = 6$
17. $y = \frac{5}{2}x;\ y = 35$
18. $y = -\frac{1}{6}x;\ y = \frac{2}{3}$

InterventionPlanner

TIER 1 On Level OL

If students miss about 25% of the exercises or less,

Then choose a resource:

SE Lessons 3-1, 3-2, 3-3, 3-4, 3-5, and 3-6

Skills Practice, pp. 7, 14, 20, 26, 32, and 39

TE Chapter Project

connectED.mcgraw-hill.com Self-Check Quiz

TIER 2 Strategic Intervention AL approaching grade level

If students miss about 50% of the exercises,

Then choose a resource:

Study Guide and Intervention, Chapter 3, pp. 5, 12, 18, 24, 30, and 37

Quick Review Math Handbook

connectED.mcgraw-hill.com Extra Examples, Personal Tutor, Homework Help

TIER 3 Intensive Intervention 2 or more grades below level

If students miss about 75% of the exercises,

Then use *Math Triumphs, Alg. 1, Ch.3*

connectED.mcgraw-hill.com Extra Examples, Personal Tutor, Homework Help, Review Vocabulary

1 Focus

Objective Use the strategy of reading the problem to solve standardized test problems.

2 Teach

Scaffolding Questions

Ask:

- Why would you skim or quickly read a report or article? Sample answer: to get an idea of what the report or article is about
- Why would you read a report or article more slowly? Sample answer: to find the details
- How would you combine these two strategies when reading a report or article? Sample answer: You might read the article or report quickly to jot down the major ideas, and then read it more slowly to fill in the details.

CHAPTER 3 Preparing for Standardized Tests

Reading Math Problems

The first step to solving any math problem is to read the problem. When reading a math problem to get the information you need to solve, it is helpful to use special reading strategies.

Strategies for Reading Math Problems

Step 1

Read the problem quickly to gain a general understanding of it.

- **Ask yourself:** "What do I know?" "What do I need to find out?"
- **Think:** "Is there enough information to solve the problem? Is there extra information?"
- **Highlight:** If you are allowed to write in your test booklet, underline or highlight important information. Cross out any information you don't need.

Step 2

Reread the problem to identify relevant facts.

- **Analyze:** Determine how the facts are related.
- **Key Words:** Look for keywords to solve the problem.
- **Vocabulary:** Identify mathematical terms. Think about the concepts and how they are related.
- **Plan:** Make a plan to solve the problem.
- **Estimate:** Quickly estimate the answer.

Step 3

Identify any obvious wrong answers.

- **Eliminate:** Eliminate any choices that are very different from your estimate.
- **Units of Measure:** Identify choices that are possible answers based on the units of measure in the question. For example, if the question asks for area, only answers in square units will work.

Step 4

Look back after solving the problem.

Check: Make sure you have answered the question.

Standardized Test Example

Read the problem. Identify what you need to know. Then use the information in the problem to solve.

Jamal, Gina, Lisa, and Renaldo are renting a car for a road trip. The cost of renting the car is given by the function $C = 12.5 + 21d$, where C is the total cost for renting the car for d days. What does the slope of the function represent?

A number of people
B cost per day
C number of days
D miles per gallon

Read the problem carefully. The number of people going on the trip is not needed information. You need to know what the slope of the function represents.

Slope is a ratio. The word "per" in answers B and D imply that they are both ratios. Since choices A and C are not ratios, eliminate them.

The problem says that C represents the cost of renting the car. So the slope cannot represent the miles per gallon of the car. The slope must represent the cost per day.

The correct answer is B.

Exercises

Read each problem. Identify what you need to know. Then use the information in the problem to solve.

1. What does the x-intercept mean in the context of the situation given below? A

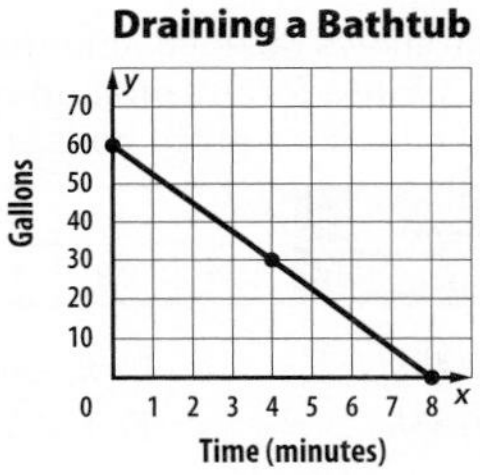

A amount of time needed to drain the bathtub
B number of gallons in the tub when the drain plug is pulled
C number of gallons in the tub after x minutes
D amount of water drained each minute

2. The amount of money raised by a charity carwash varies directly as the number of cars washed. When 11 cars are washed, \$79.75 is raised. How many cars must be washed to raise \$174.00? J

F 10 cars
G 16 cars
H 22 cars
J 24 cars

3. The function $C = 25 + 0.45(x - 450)$ represents the cost of a monthly cell phone bill, when x minutes are used. Which statement best represents the formula for the cost of the bill? C

A The cost consists of a flat fee of \$0.45 and \$25 for each minute used over 450.
B The cost consists of a flat fee of \$450 and \$0.45 for each minute used over 25.
C The cost consists of a flat fee of \$25 and \$0.45 for each minute used over 450.
D The cost consists of a flat fee of \$25 and \$0.45 for each minute used.

Additional Example

Manuel is filling an aquarium with water. The amount of water in the aquarium is given by the formula $G(t) = 2.5 + 3t$, where $G(t)$ is the total number of gallons of water in the aquarium and t is time in minutes. What does the slope of the function represent? C

A total number of gallons of water
B number of gallons of water after 3 minutes
C number of gallons per minute
D number of minutes per gallon

3 Assess

Use Exercises 1–3 to assess students' understanding.

Diagnose Student Errors

Survey student responses for each item. Class trends may indicate common errors and misconceptions.

1. A guess
B correct
C guess
D guess

2. F guess
G guess
H correct
J added 2^5 instead of subtracted

3. A did not read test-taking tip and does not understand the concept of slope
B guess or calculation error
C correct
D calculated change in *x*-coordinates to change in *y*-coordinates instead of change in *y*-coordinates to change in *x*-coordinates

4. F subtracted 11.00 − 5.50 incorrectly
G correct
H interpreted change as decrease instead of increase
J subtracted incorrectly and misinterpreted increase as decrease

5. A guess
B guess
C guess
D correct

6. F guess
G guess
H used wrong first term
J correct

7. A correct
B misunderstood how to write the function
C solved for 1 hour only
D misunderstood how to write the function

8. F correct
G guess
H guess
J guess or calculation error

CHAPTER 3 Standardized Test Practice

Cumulative, Chapters 1 through 3

Multiple Choice

Read each question. Then fill in the correct answer on the answer document provided by your teacher or on a sheet of paper.

1. Horatio is purchasing a computer cable for \$15.49. If the sales tax rate in his state is 5.25%, what is the total cost of the purchase? **B**

A \$16.42 C \$15.73
B \$16.30 D \$15.62

2. What is the value of the expression below? **H**

$$3^2 + 5^3 - 2^5$$

F 14 H 102
G 34 J 166

3. What is the slope of the linear function graphed below? **C**

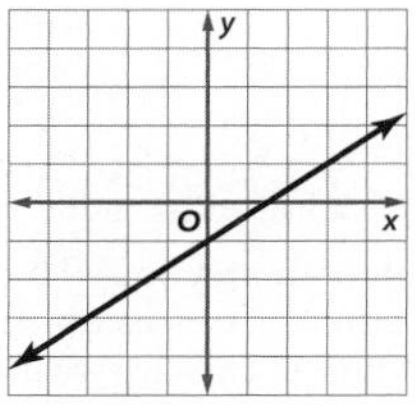

A $-\frac{1}{3}$ C $\frac{2}{3}$
B $\frac{1}{2}$ D $\frac{3}{2}$

4. Find the rate of change for the linear function represented in the table. **G**

Hours Worked	1	2	3	4
Money Earned (\$)	5.50	11.00	16.50	22.00

F increase \$6.50/h
G increase \$5.50/h
H decrease \$5.50/h
J decrease \$6.50/h

5. Suppose that y varies directly as x, and $y = 14$ when $x = 4$. What is the value of y when $x = 9$? **D**

A 25.5 C 29.5
B 27.5 D 31.5

6. Write an equation for the *n*th term of the arithmetic sequence shown below. **J**

$$-2, 1, 4, 7, 10, 13, \ldots$$

F $a_n = 2n - 1$ H $a_n = 3n + 2$
G $a_n = 2n + 4$ J $a_n = 3n - 5$

7. The table shows the labor charges of an electrician for jobs of different lengths.

Number of Hours (n)	Labor Charges (c)
1	\$60
2	\$85
3	\$110
4	\$135

Which function represents the situation? **A**

A $C(n) = 25n + 35$ C $C(n) = 35n + 25$
B $C(n) = 25n + 30$ D $C(n) = 35n + 40$

8. Find the value of x so that the figures have the same area. **F**

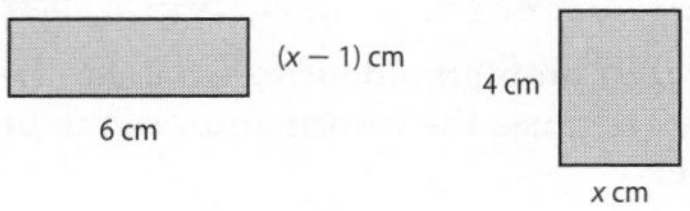

F 3 H 5
G 4 J 6

9. The table shows the total amount of rain during a storm. Write a formula to find out how much rain will fall after a given hour. **B**

Hours (h)	1	2	3	4
Inches (n)	0.45	9.9	1.35	1.8

A $h = 0.45n$ C $h = 0.9n$
B $n = 0.45h$ D $h = 1.8n$

Test-Taking Tip

Question 3 You can *eliminate unreasonable answers* to multiple choice items. The line slopes up from left to right, so the slope is positive. Answer choice A can be eliminated.

9. A interchanged *n* and *h*
B correct
C found wrong rate of change
D found wrong rate of change

Short Response/Gridded Response

Record your answers on the answer sheet provided by your teacher or on a sheet of paper.

10. The scale on a map is 1.5 inches = 6 miles. If two cities are 4 inches apart on the map, what is the actual distance between the cities? **16 miles**

11. Write a direct variation equation to represent the graph below. $y = 2x$

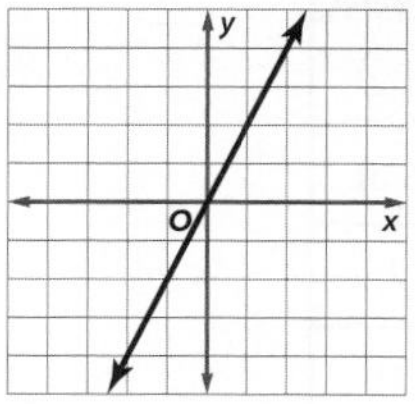

12. Justine bought a car for \$18,500 and its value depreciated linearly. After 3 years, the value was \$14,150. What is the amount of yearly depreciation? **\$1450**

13. GRIDDED RESPONSE Use the graph to determine the solution to the equation $-\frac{1}{3}x + 1 = 0$? **3**

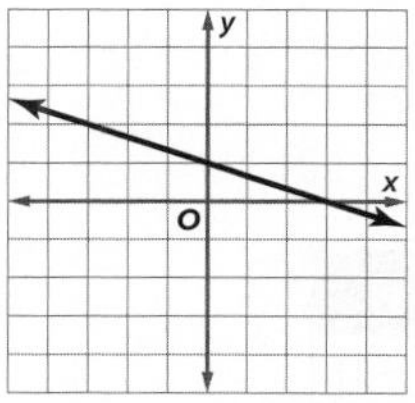

14. Write an expression that represents the total surface area (including the top and bottom) of a tower of n cubes each having a side length of s. (Do not include faces that cover each other.) $(4n + 2)s^2$

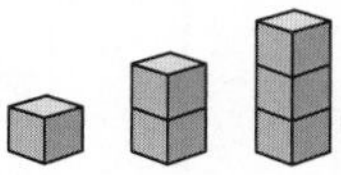

$n = 1$ $n = 2$ $n = 3$

15. GRIDDED RESPONSE There are 120 members in the North Carolina House of Representatives. This is 70 more than the number of members in the North Carolina Senate. How many members are in the North Carolina Senate? **50**

Extended Response

Record your answers on a sheet of paper. Show your work.

16. A hot air balloon was at a height of 60 feet above the ground when it began to ascend. The balloon climbed at a rate of 15 feet per minute.

a. Make a table that shows the height of the hot air balloon after climbing for 1, 2, 3, and 4 minutes. **75 ft, 90 ft, 105 ft, 120 ft**

b. Let t represent the time in minutes since the balloon began climbing. Write an algebraic equation for a sequence that can be used to find the height, h, of the balloon after t minutes. $h = 60 + 15t$

c. Use your equation from part b to find the height, in feet, of the hot air balloon after climbing for 8 minutes. **180 ft**

Need ExtraHelp?

If you missed Question...	1	2	3	4	5	6	7	8	9	10	11	12	13	14	15	16
Go to Lesson...	2-7	1-2	3-3	3-3	3-4	3-5	3-6	2-4	3-4	2-6	3-4	3-3	3-2	0-10	2-1	3-5

Formative Assessment

You can use these pages to benchmark student progress.

Standardized Test Practice, pp. 62–64

Answer Sheet Practice

Have students simulate taking a standardized test by recording their answers on a practice recording sheet.

Student Recording Sheet

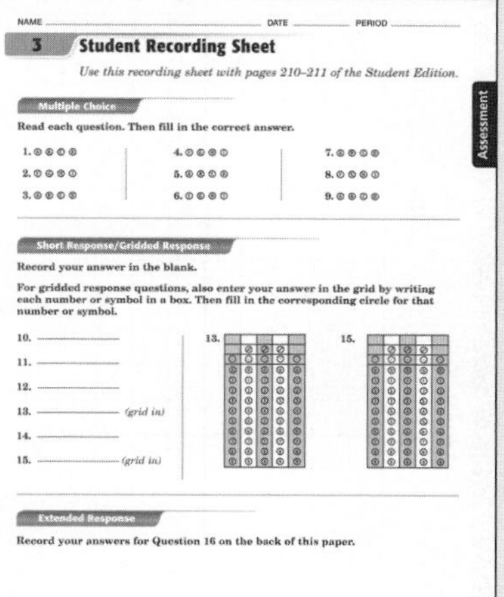

McGraw-Hill eAssessment Create practice tests that align to your state standards, the Common Core State Standards, and other national standards such as TIMSS and NAEP.

Homework Option

Get Ready for Chapter 4 Assign students the exercises on p. 213 as homework to assess whether they possess the prerequisite skills needed for the next chapter.

Get Ready for Chapter 3

1.
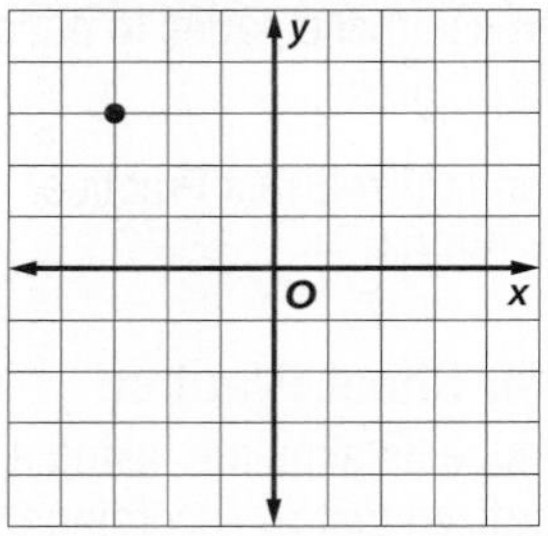

2.
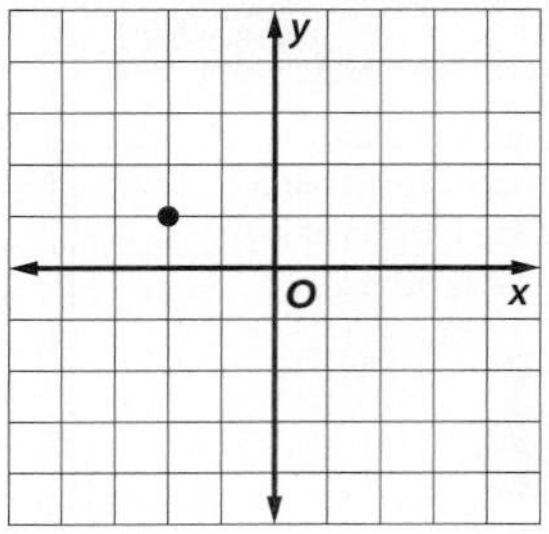

3.
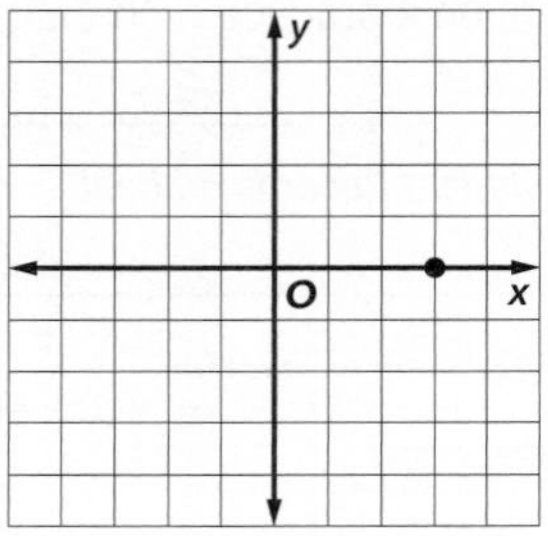

4.
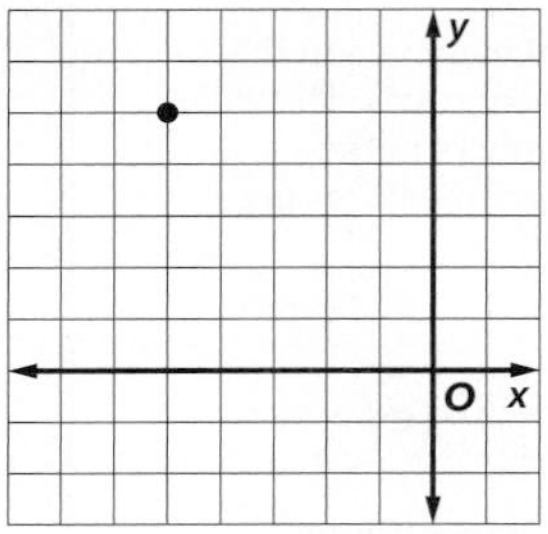

5.
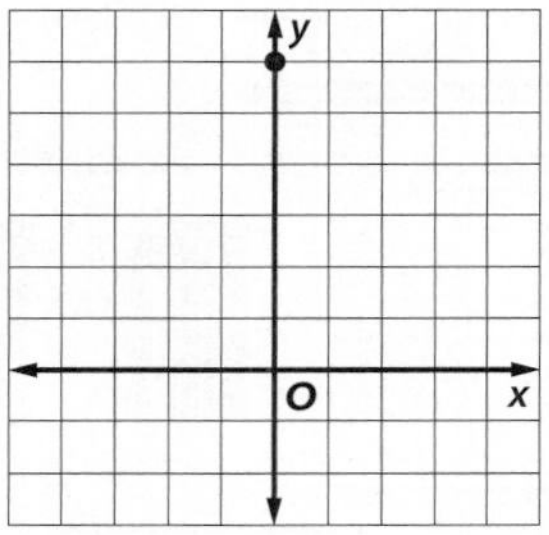

6.
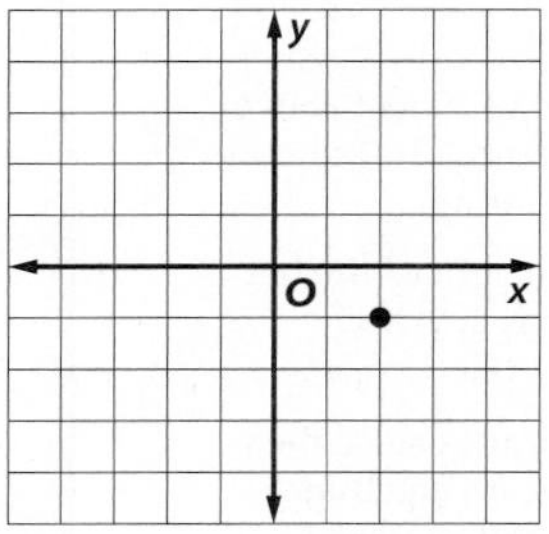

Explore 3-1

1. Sample answer: For both lines that slant up and lines that slant down, the domain and range are all real numbers, there is one x-intercept and one y-intercept, there are no maximum or minimum points, and the graph has no symmetry. For lines that slant up, the function values are negative to the left of the x-intercept and positive to the right. For lines that slant down, the function values are positive to the left of the x-intercept and negative to the right. For lines that slant up, the function is increasing on the entire domain. For lines that slant down, the function is decreasing on the entire domain. For lines that slant up, as x decreases, y decreases and as x increases, y increases. For lines that slant down, as x decreases, y increases and as x increases, y decreases.

2. Sample answer: The domain is still all real numbers. The range is one negative value instead of a positive value. The end behavior is the same. There is still no x-intercept. The one y-intercept is a negative value instead of a positive value. There are still no maximum or minimum points. The function values are all negative instead of all positive. The function is constant on the entire domain. The graph is still symmetric about any vertical line.

Lesson 3-1

7.
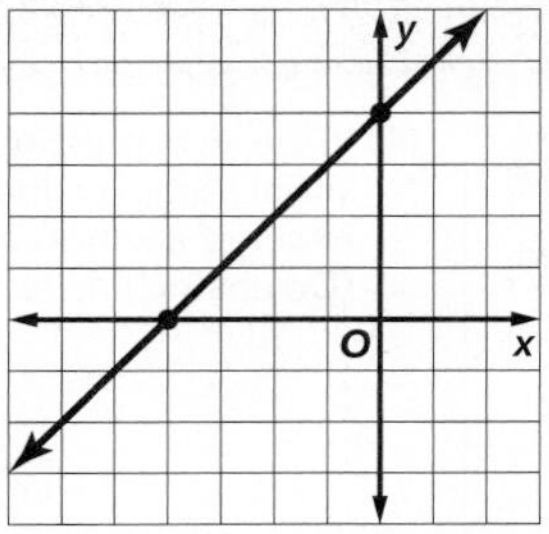

8.
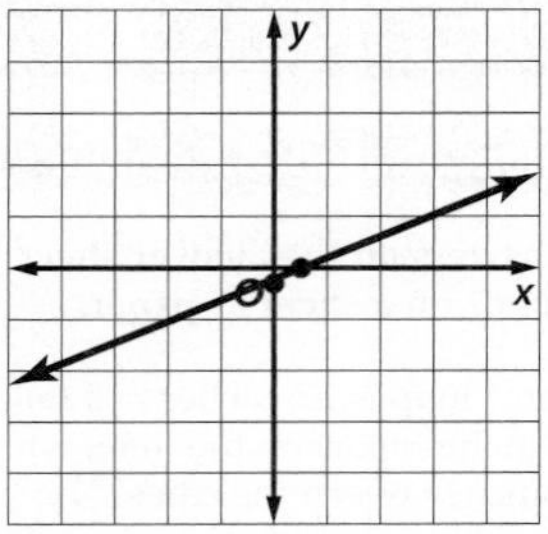

9.

x	$y = 2 - \frac{x}{2}$	y	(x, y)
−4	$y = 2 - \frac{(-4)}{2}$	4	(−4, 4)
−2	$y = 2 - \frac{(-2)}{2}$	3	(−2, 3)
0	$y = 2 - \frac{0}{2}$	2	(0, 2)
2	$y = 2 - \frac{2}{2}$	1	(2, 1)
4	$y = 2 - \frac{4}{2}$	0	(4, 0)

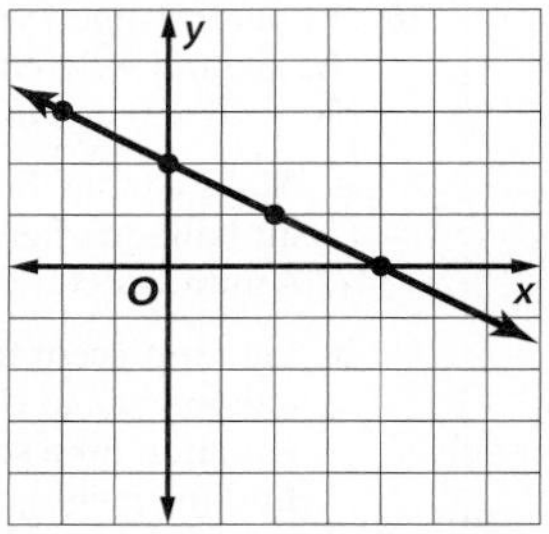

10.

x	$-3 + 2y = -5$	y	(x, y)
−2	$-3 + 2y = -5$	−1	(−2, −1)
−1	$-3 + 2y = -5$	−1	(−1, −1)
0	$-3 + 2y = -5$	−1	(0, −1)
1	$-3 + 2y = -5$	−1	(1, −1)
2	$-3 + 2y = -5$	−1	(2, −1)

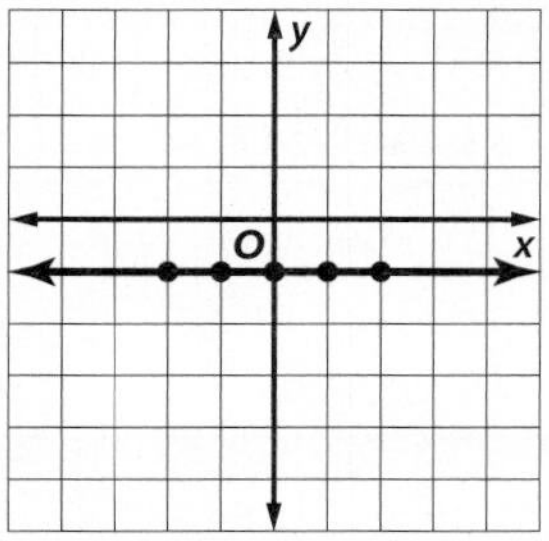

11.

x	$y = 3$	y	(x, y)
−2	$y = 3$	3	(−2, 3)
−1	$y = 3$	3	(−1, 3)
0	$y = 3$	3	(0, 3)
1	$y = 3$	3	(1, 3)
2	$y = 3$	3	(2, 3)

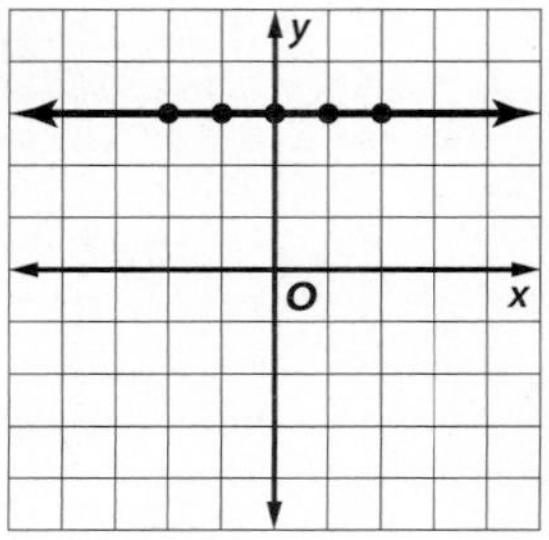

29.

x	y
−2	0
−2	1
−2	2

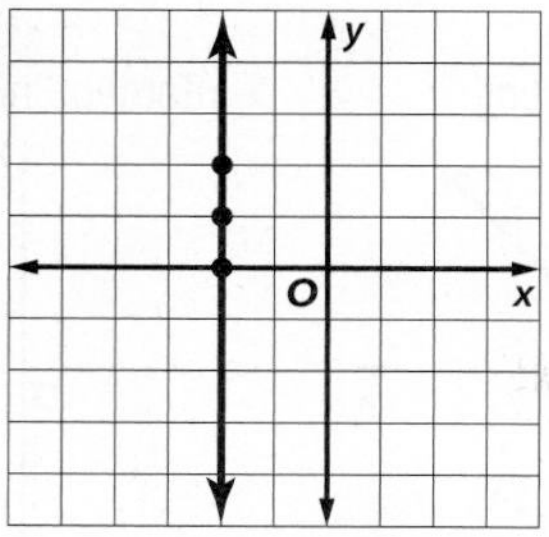

30.

x	y
0	−4
1	−4
2	−4

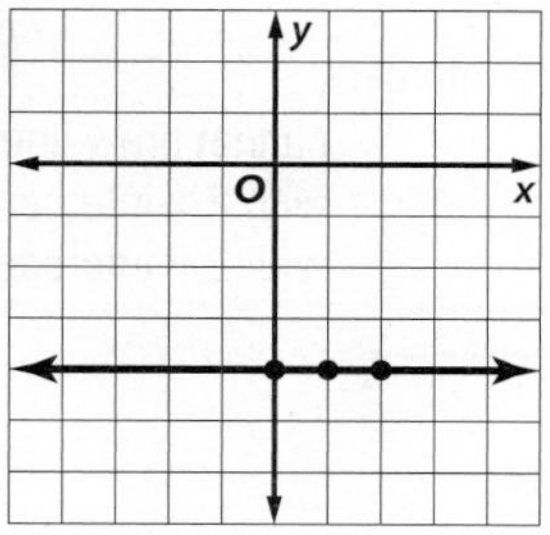

31.

x	y
−1	8
0	0
1	−8

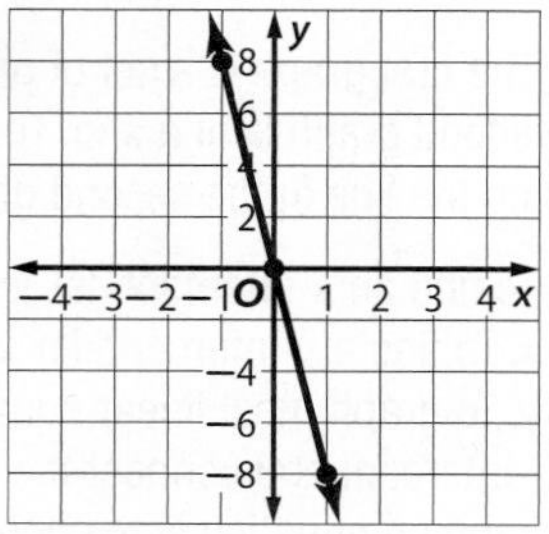

32.

x	y
0	0
1	3
2	6

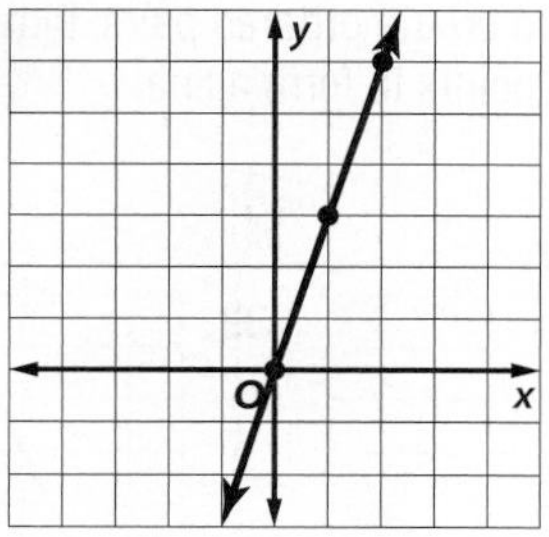

33.

x	y
0	8
1	7
2	6

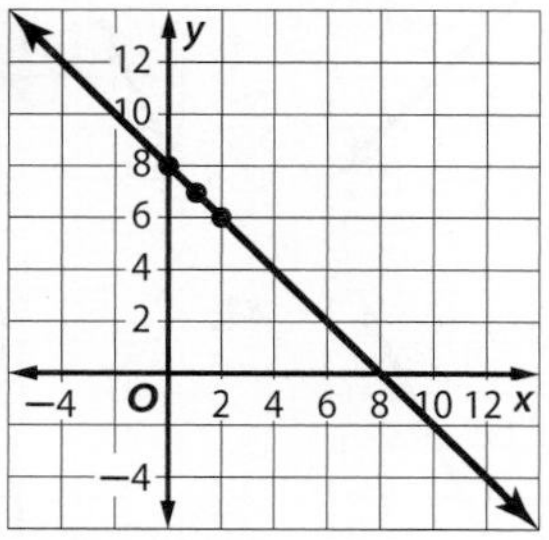

34.

x	y
0	10
1	9
2	8

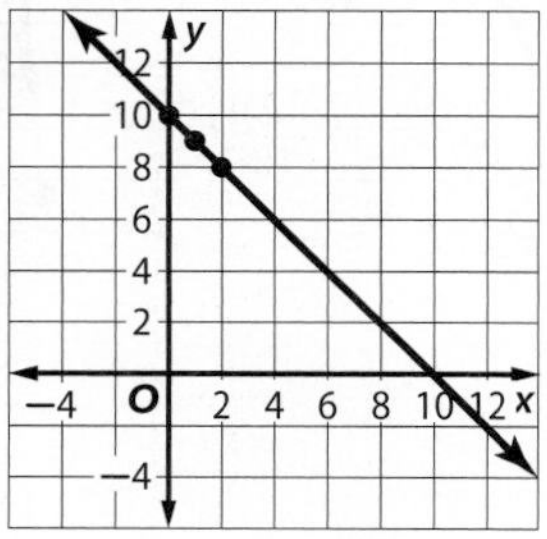

35a.

v	$p = 0.15v$	p	(v, p)
0	$p = 0.15(0)$	0	(0, 0)
2	$p = 0.15(2)$	0.3	(2, 0.3)
4	$p = 0.15(4)$	0.6	(4, 0.6)
6	$p = 0.15(6)$	0.9	(6, 0.9)
8	$p = 0.15(8)$	1.2	(8, 1.2)
10	$p = 0.15(10)$	1.5	(10, 1.5)

35b.

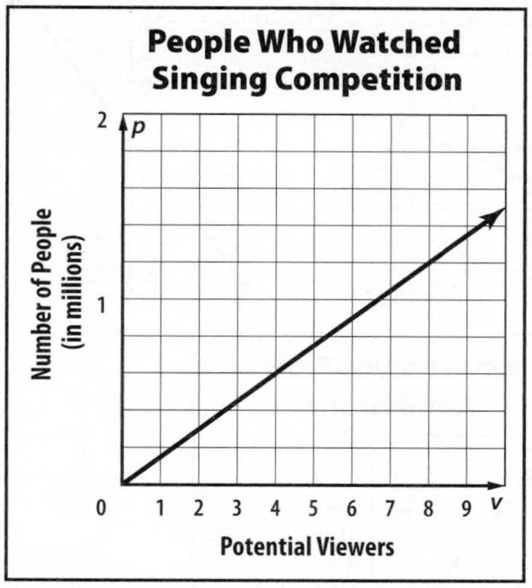

42a.

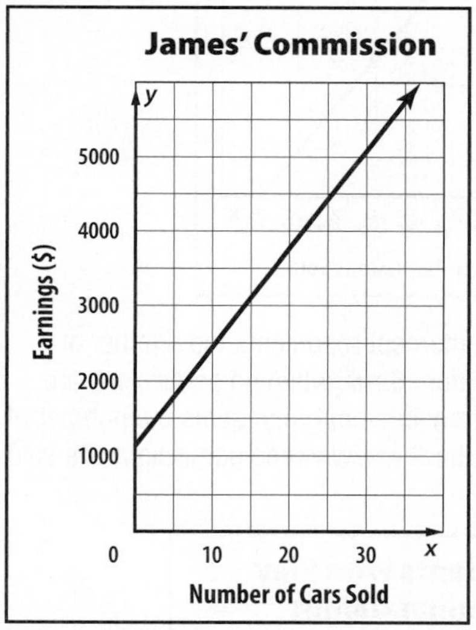

43.

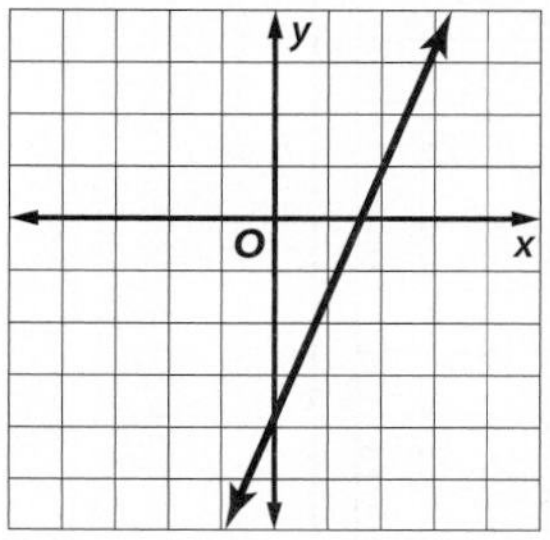

44.

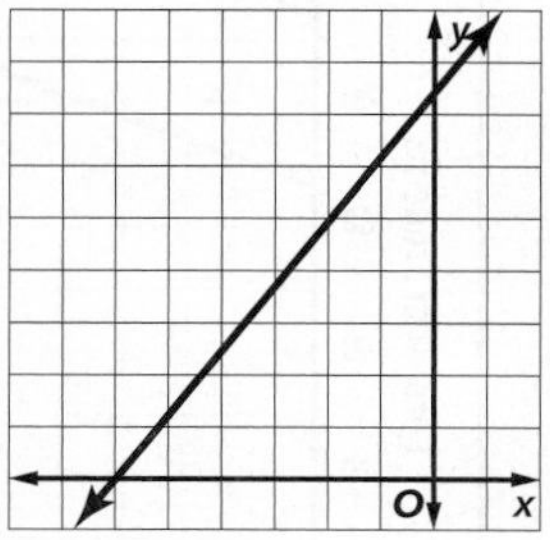

45.
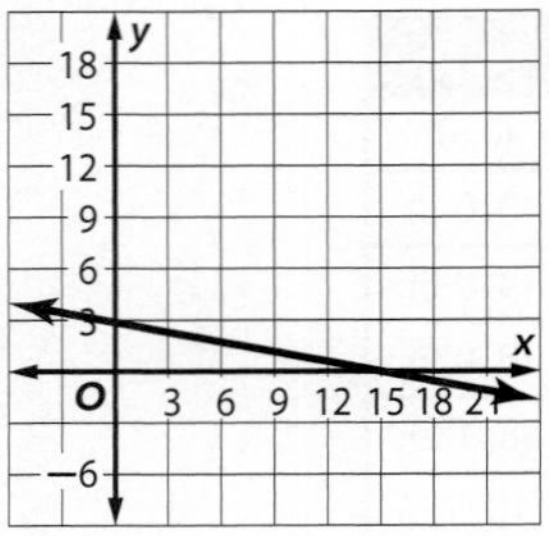

46.
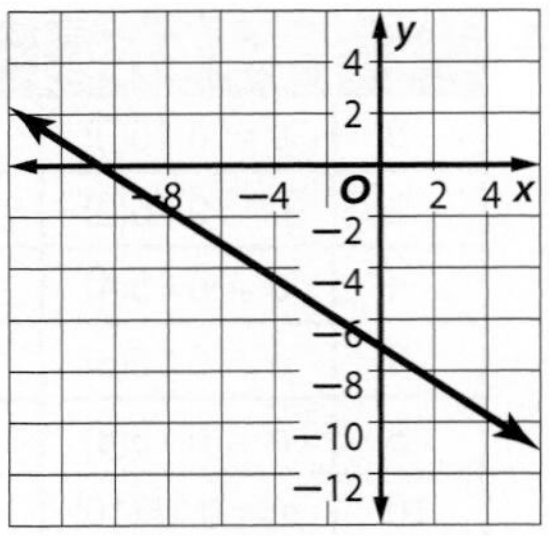

47.
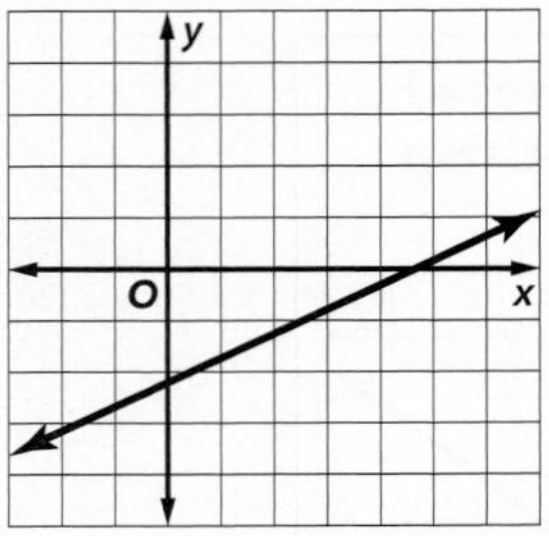

48.
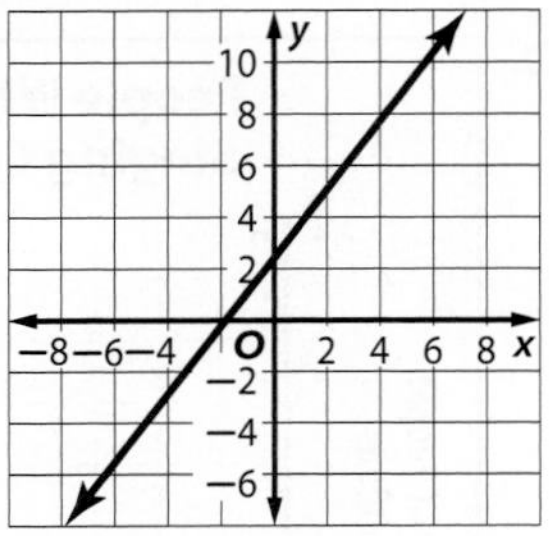

50b.
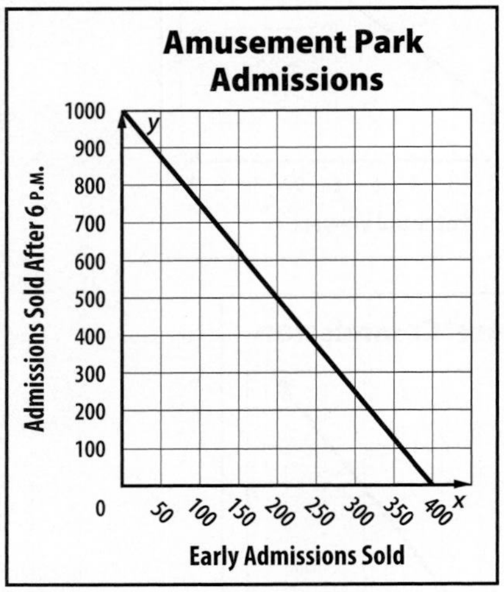

50c. 400; 1000; The x-intercept represents the number of admissions sold before 6 P.M. when no admissions are sold after 6 P.M. The y-intercept represents the number of admissions sold after 6 P.M. when no admissions are sold before 6 P.M.

57a.
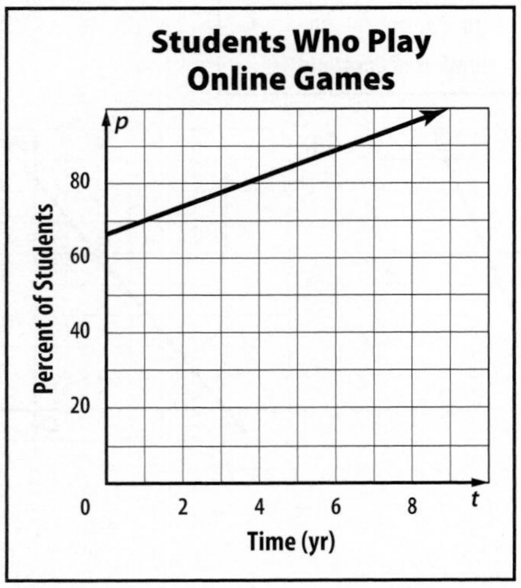

58a. Sample answer:

x- and y-intercept

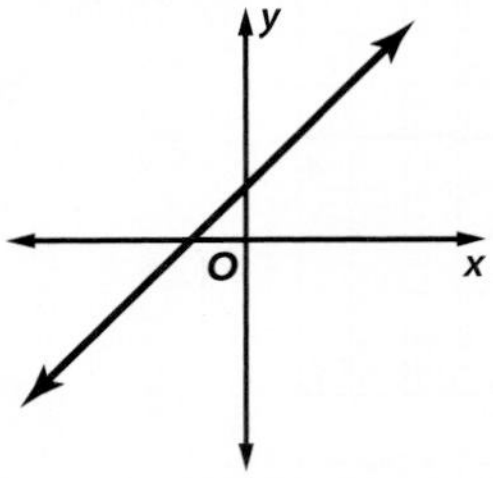

x-intercept, no y-intercept

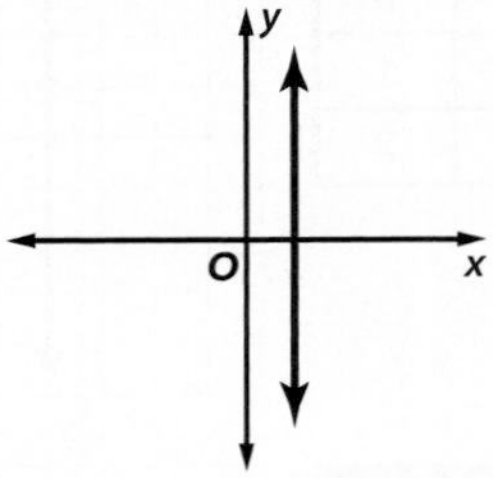

no x-intercept, y-intercept

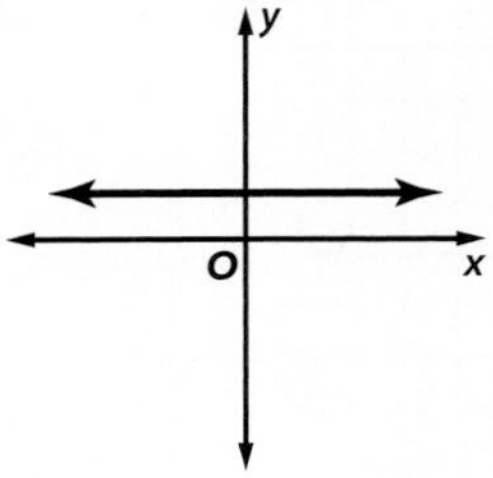

cannot draw lines with 2 x-intercepts or with 2 y-intercepts

60. Sample answer: The first graph is a set of points that are not connected. The second graph is of a line. The points of the first graph are points on the line in the second graph.

64. Sample answer: To find an x-intercept, let $y = 0$ and solve the equation for x. To find a y-intercept, let $x = 0$ and solve the equation for y. To graph most linear equations, plot the x-intercept and y-intercept and connect the points to form a line. Another way to graph an equation is to choose any value in the domain and create ordered pairs. Plot the ordered pairs and connect the points to form a line.

Lesson 3-2

38.
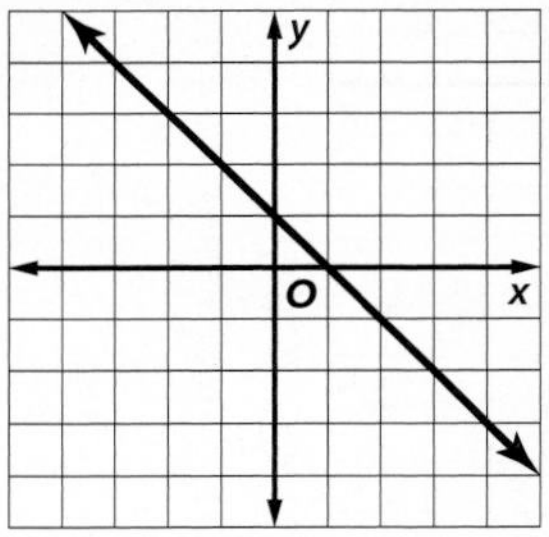

39.
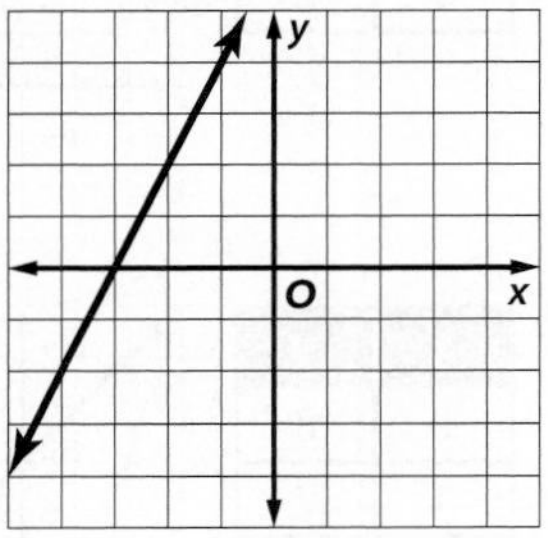

40.
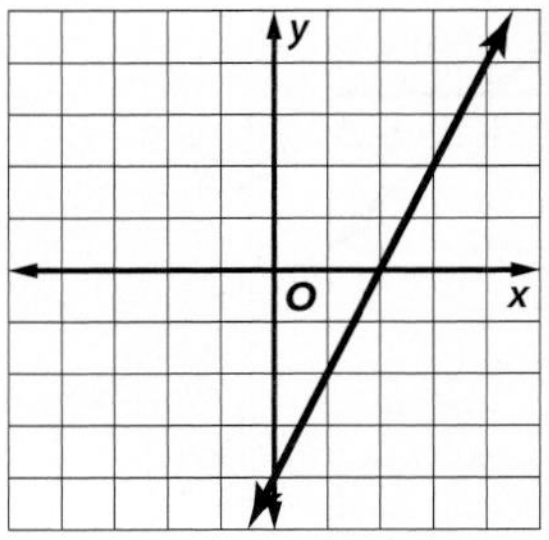

41.
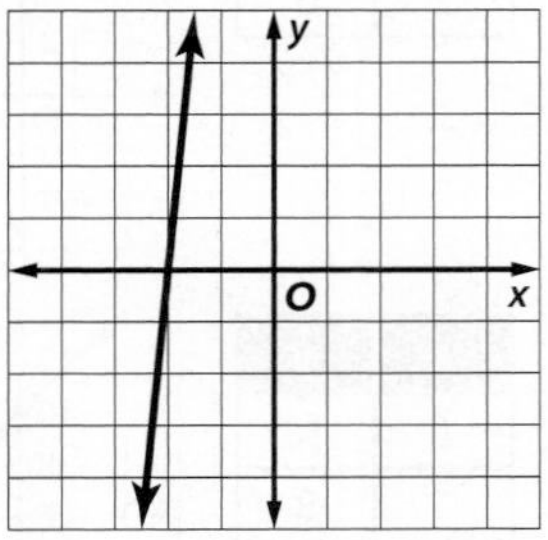

42.

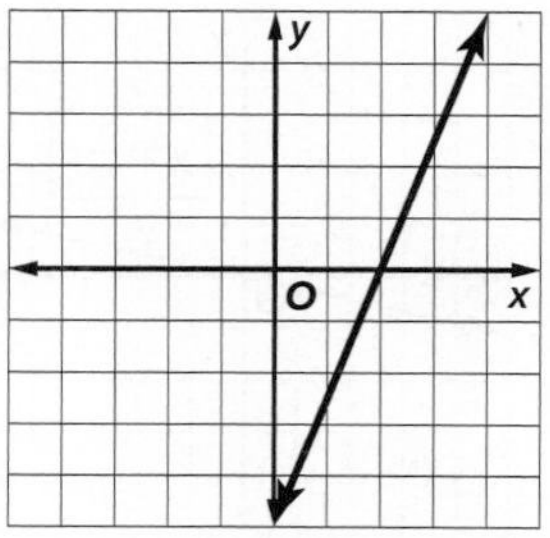

43.

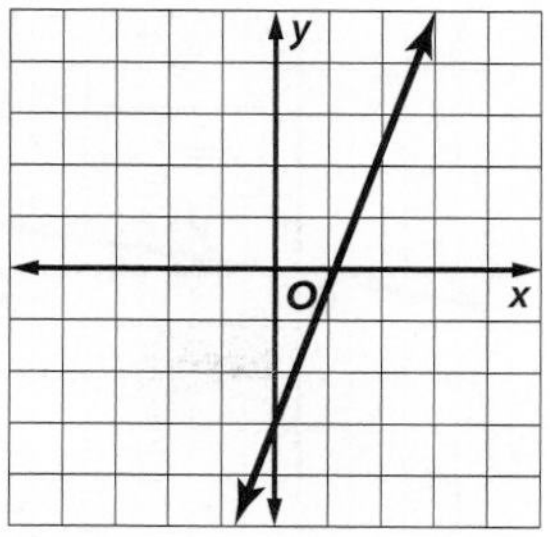

44b.

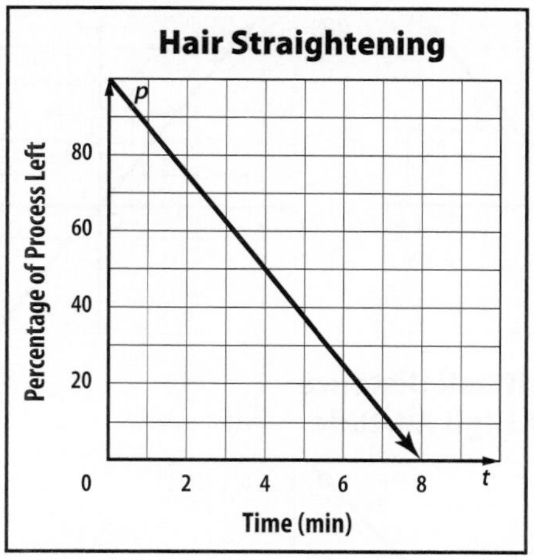

Extend 3-2

1.

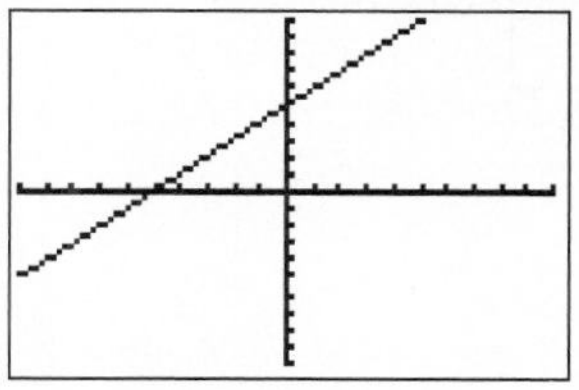

[−10, 10] scl: 1 by
[−10, 10] scl: 1

2.

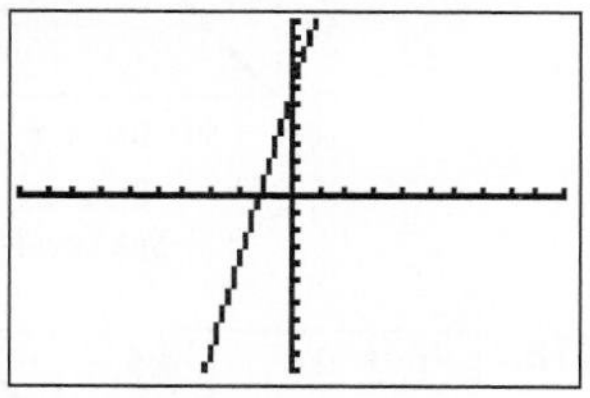

[−10, 10] scl: 1 by
[−10, 10] scl: 1

3.

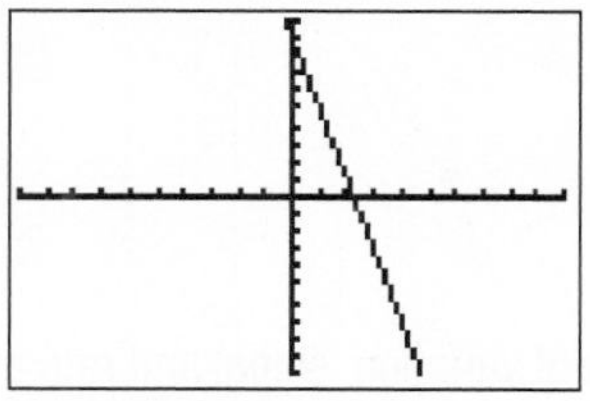

[−10, 10] scl: 1 by
[−10, 10] scl: 1

4.

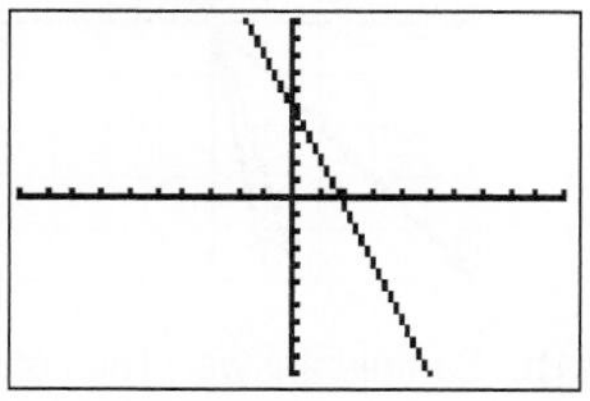

[−10, 10] scl: 1 by
[−10, 10] scl: 1

5.

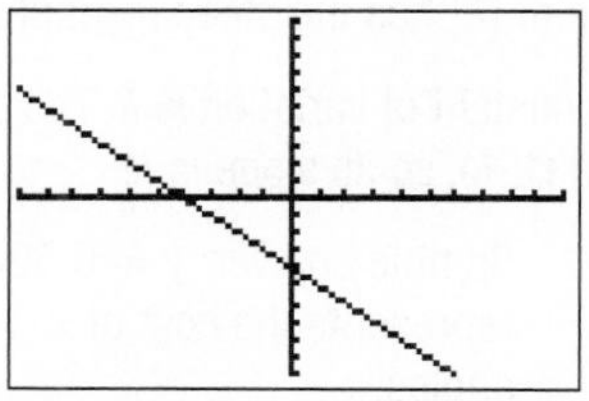

[−10, 10] scl: 1 by
[−10, 10] scl: 1

6.

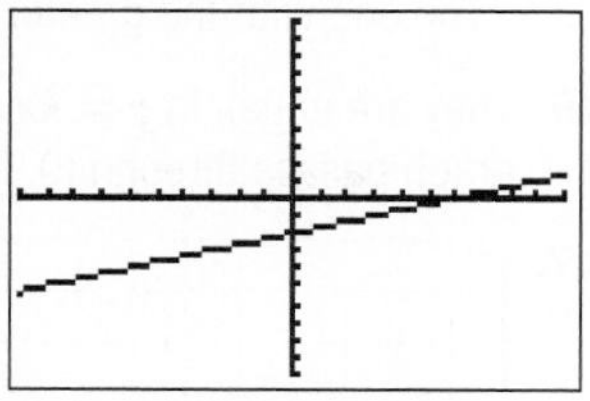

[−10, 10] scl: 1 by
[−10, 10] scl: 1

7.

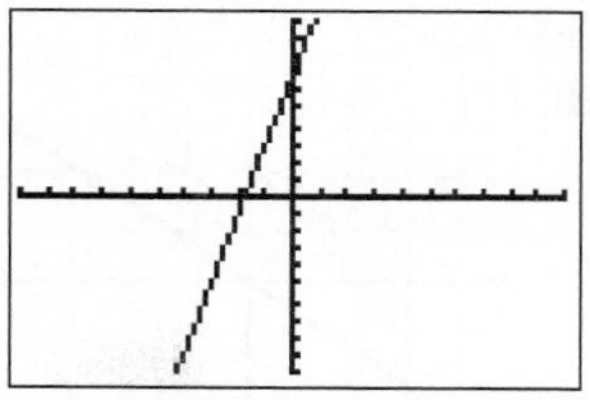

[−10, 10] scl: 1 by
[−10, 10] scl: 1

8.

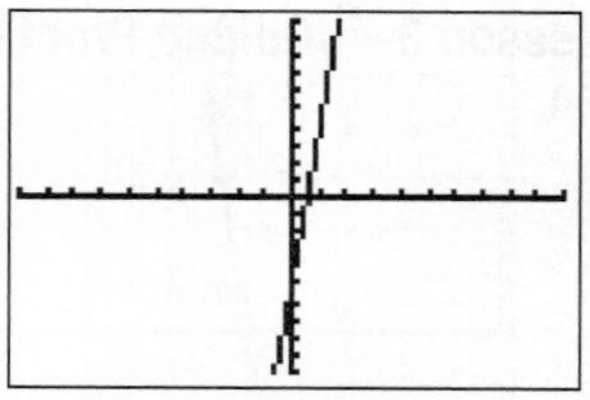

[−10, 10] scl: 1 by
[−10, 10] scl: 1

9.

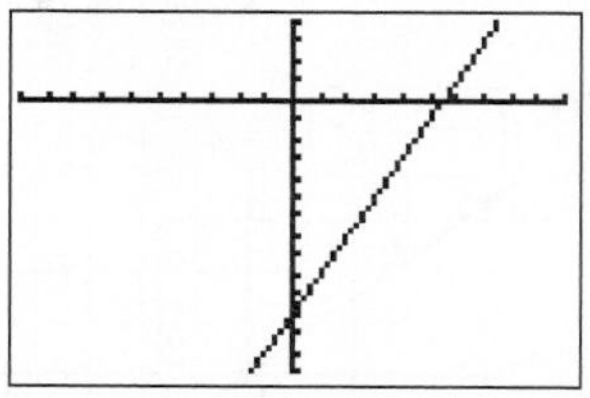

[−10, 10] scl: 1 by
[−15, 5] scl: 1

10.

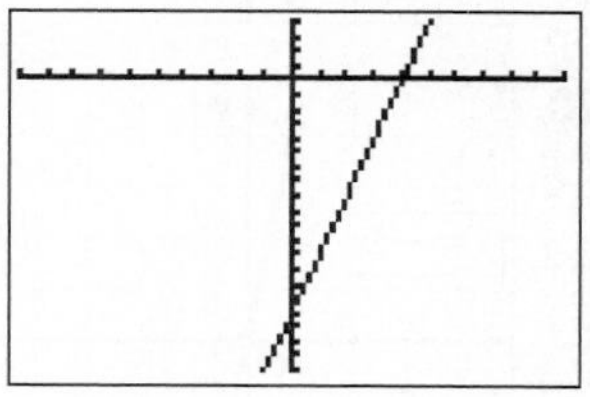

[−10, 10] scl: 1 by
[−20, 5] scl: 1

11.

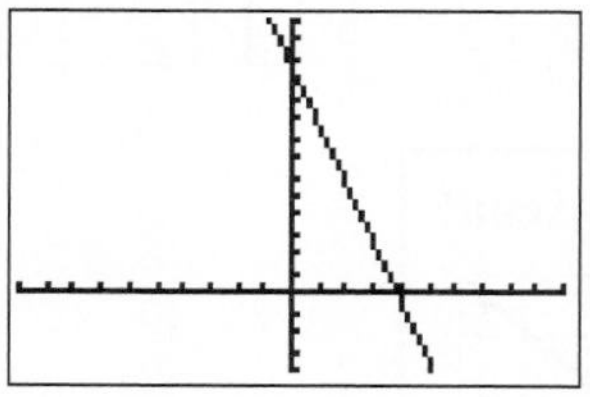

[−10, 10] scl: 1 by
[−5, 15] scl: 1

12.

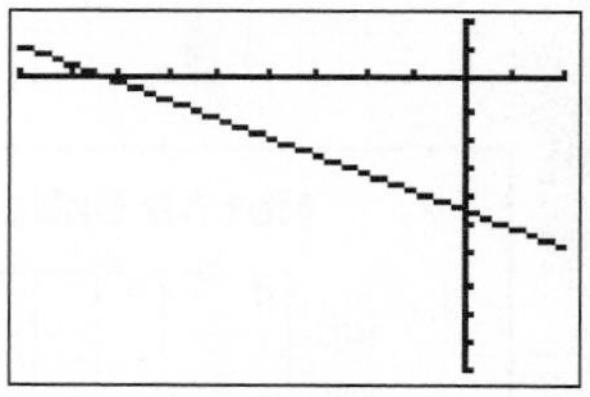

[−36, 8] scl: 4 by
[−20, 4] scl: 2

Lesson 3-3

20. Yes; the rate of change is constant.

21. No; the rate of change is not constant.

22. No; the rate of change is not constant.

23. Yes; the rate of change is constant.

47a.

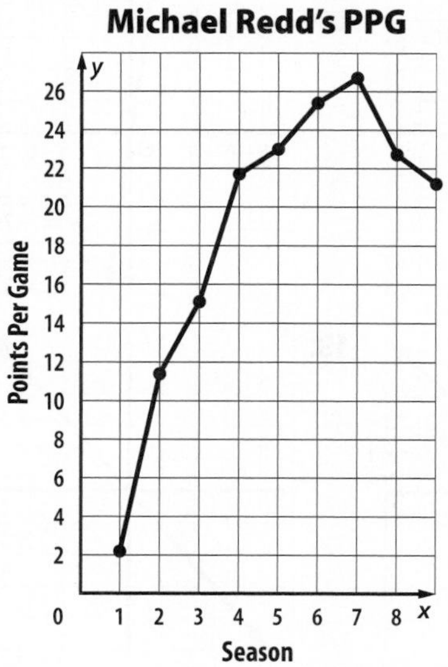

47b. Season 1 to Season 2; It is the steepest part of the graph.

47c. The rate of change was much more dramatic or steeper in the first four years, it leveled off the next three seasons, and was negative and steeper the last two seasons.

Lesson 3-4 (Guided Practice)

2A.

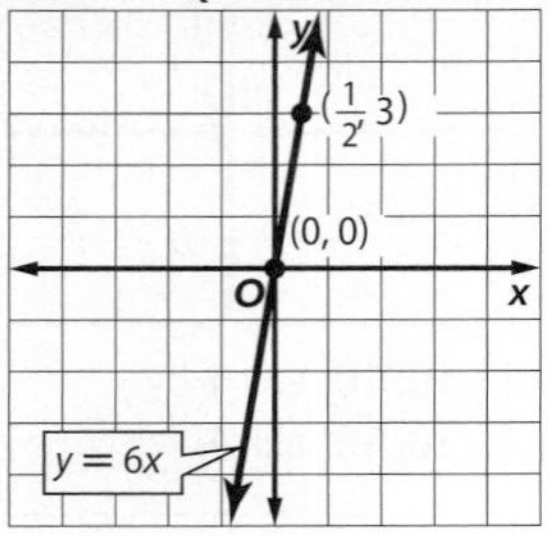

2B.

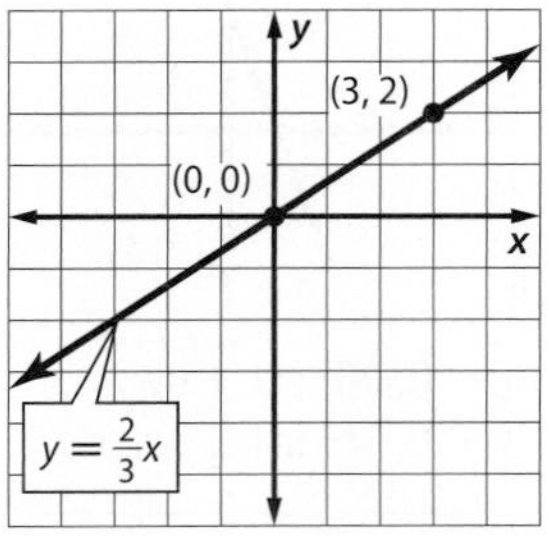

2C.

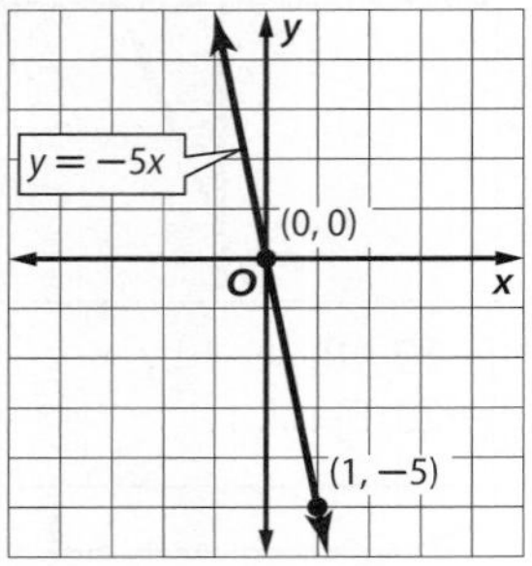

2D.

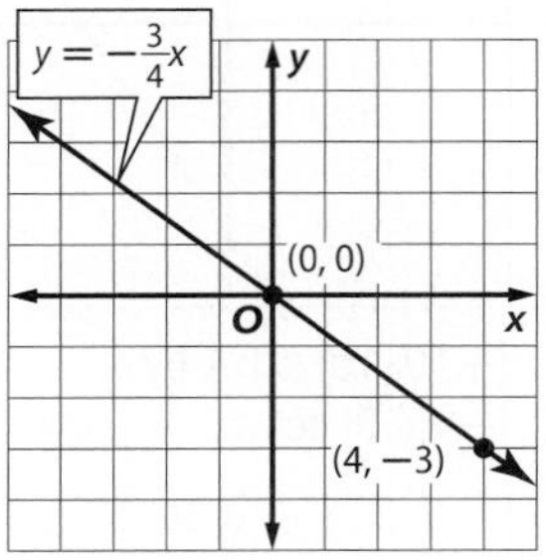

4B.

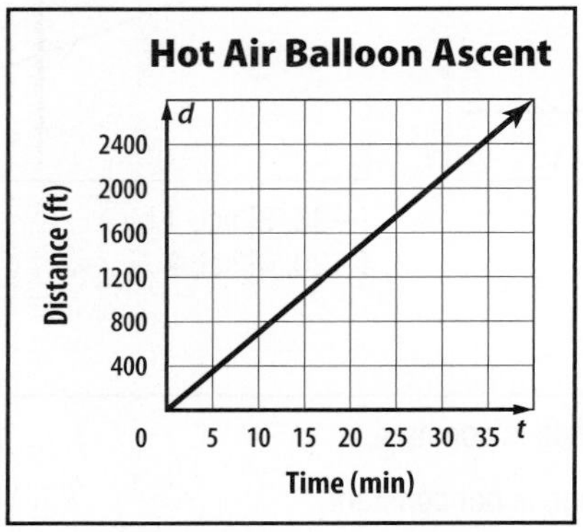

Lesson 3-4

16.

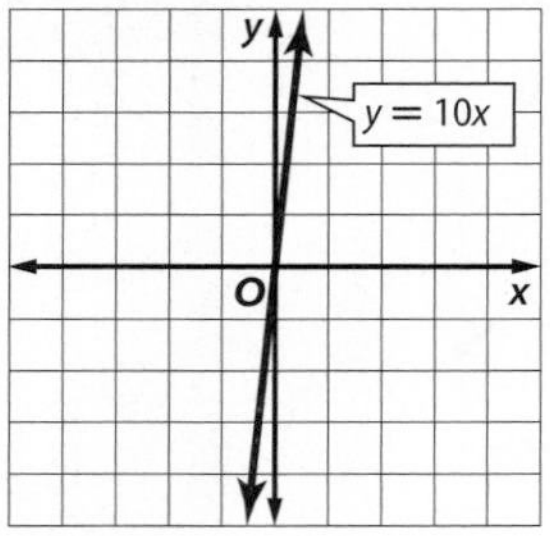

17.

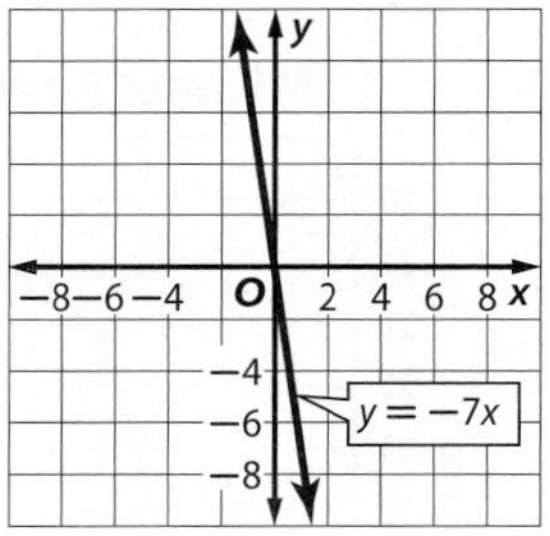

18.

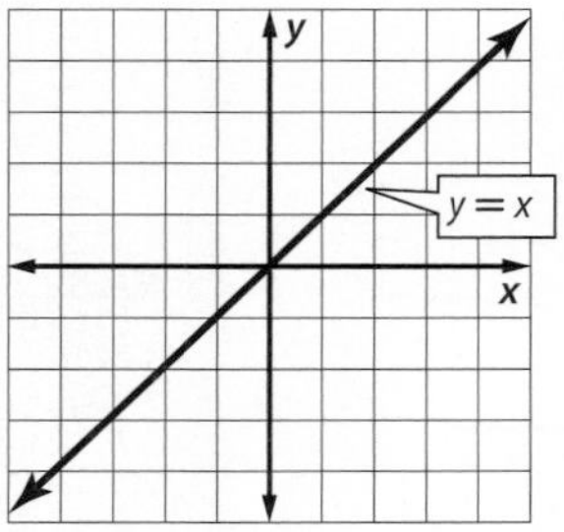

19.

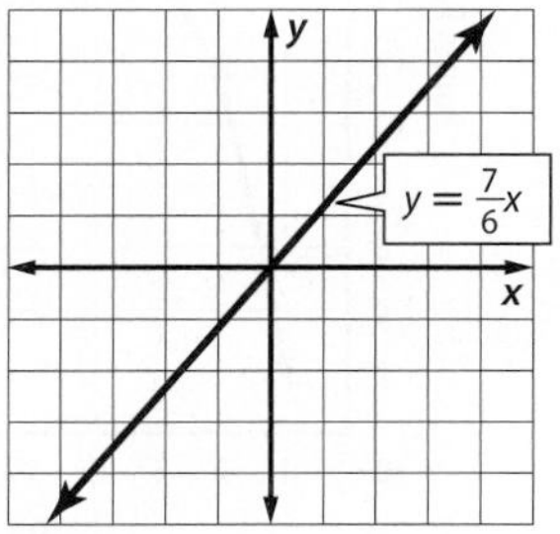

20.

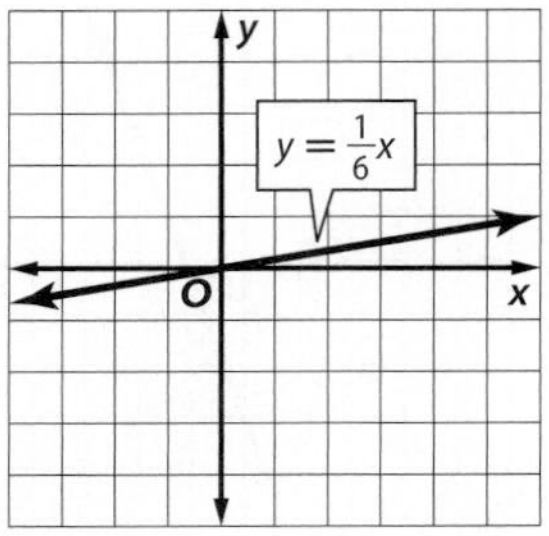

21.

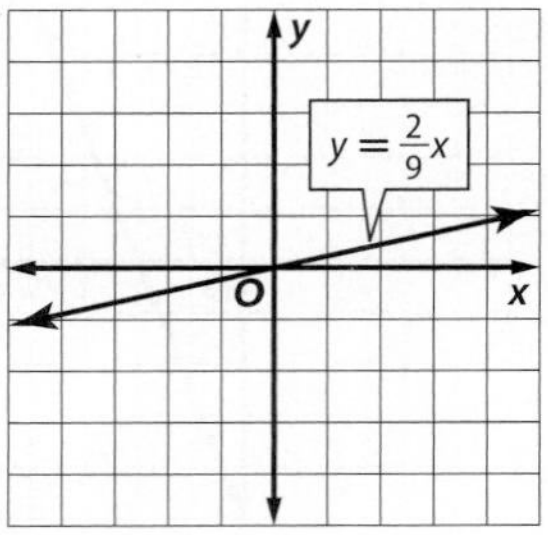

22.

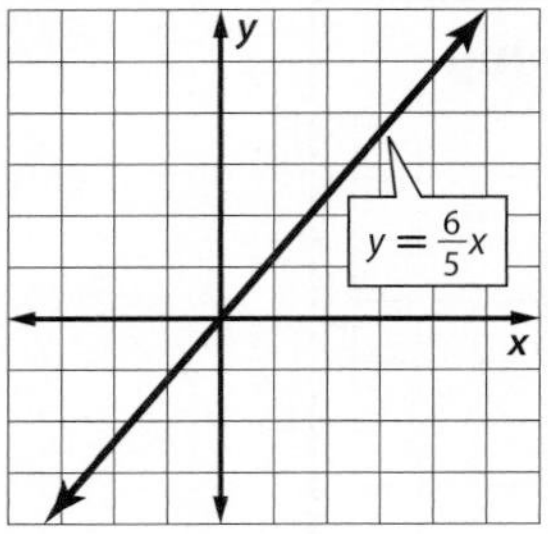

23.

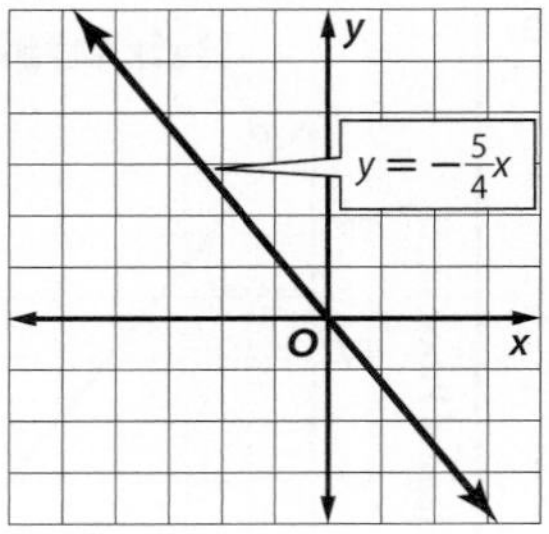

28a.

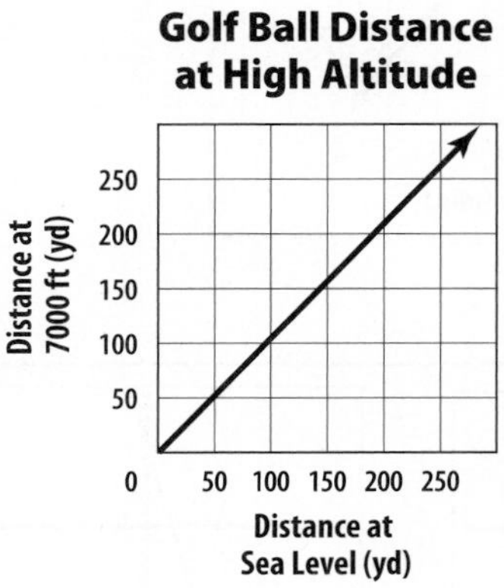

41a.

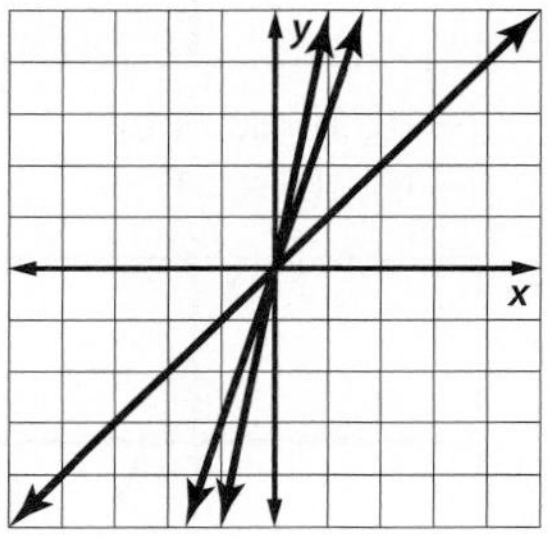

41b. Sample answer: The constant of variation, slope, and rate of change of a graph all have the same value.

41c. Sample answer: Find the absolute value of k in each equation. The one with the greater value of $|k|$ has the steeper graph.

46. They are equal; In $y = kx$, the constant of variation is k. The graph passes through (0, 0) and (1, k), so its slope is k.

47.

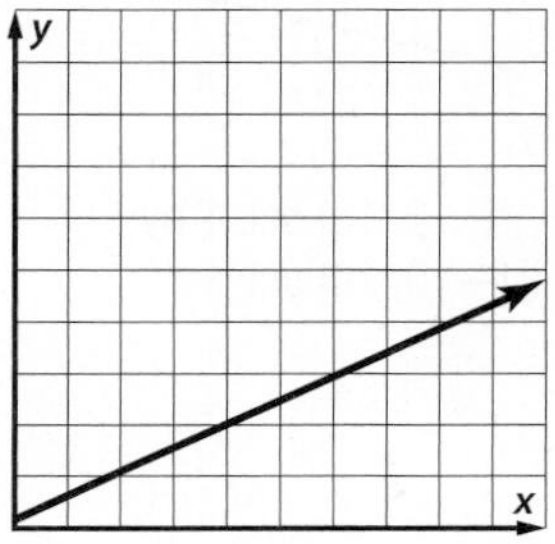

Sample answer: $y = 0.50x$ represents the cost of x apples.
The rate of change, 0.50, is the cost per apple.

Lesson 3-5

18.
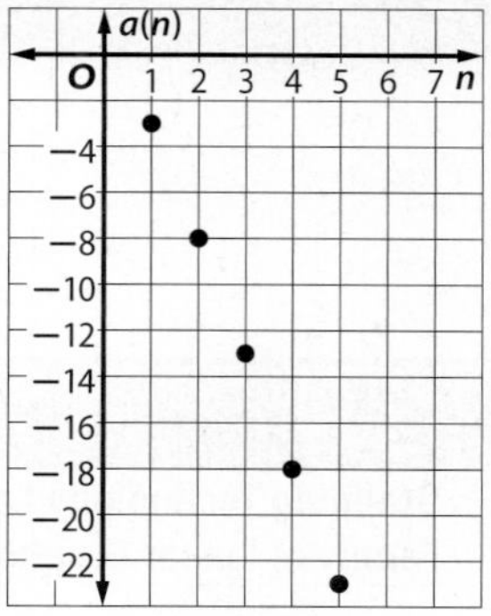

19.
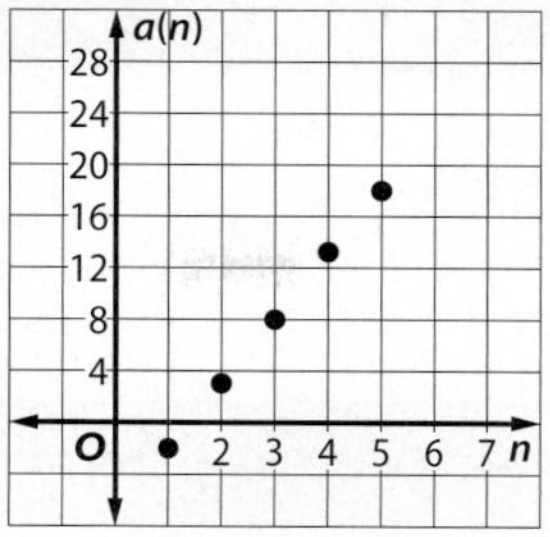

20.
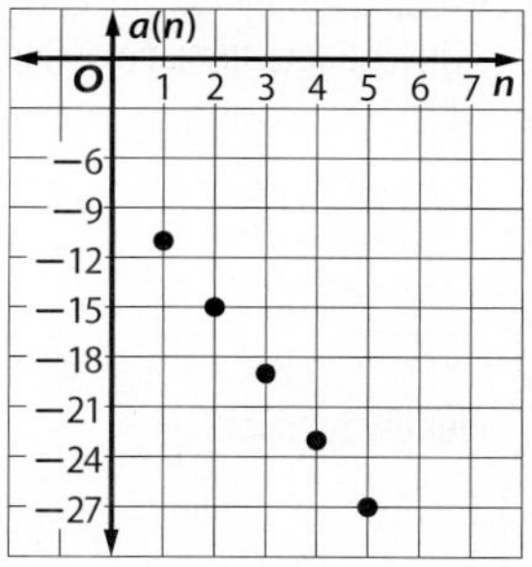

21.
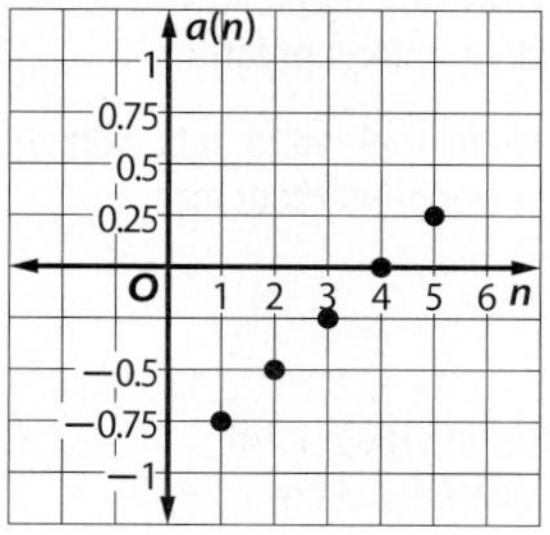

22b.
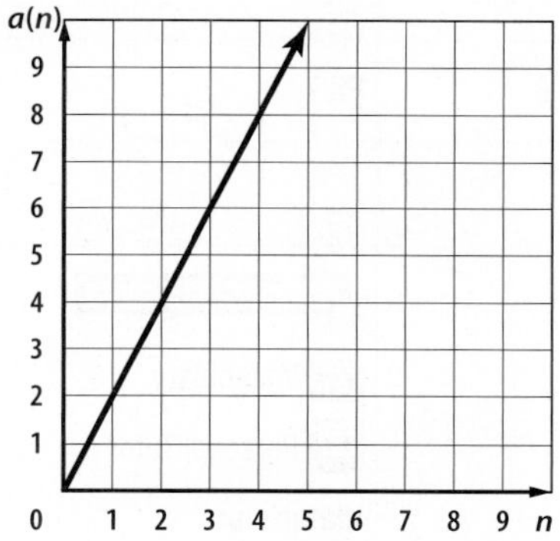

$D = \{1, 2, 3, 4, \ldots\}$

23b.
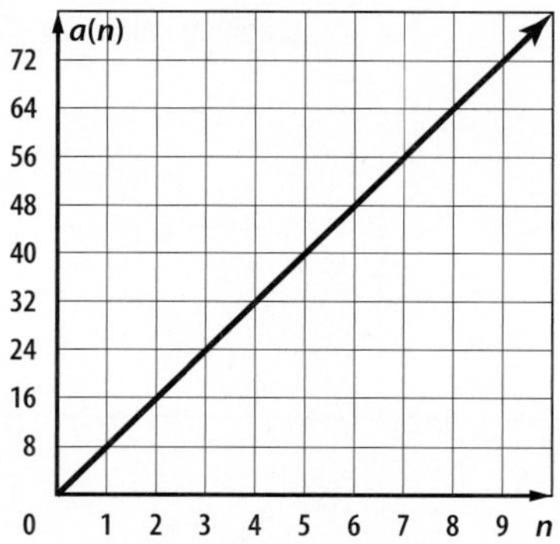

$D = \{1, 2, 3, 4, \ldots\}$

Extend 3-5

1. Sample answer: Inductive reasoning uses examples or past experience to make conclusions; deductive reasoning uses rules to make conclusions. Looking at a pattern of numbers to decide the next number is an example of inductive reasoning. Using the formula $A = \ell w$ and the length and width of a rectangle to find the area of a rectangle is an example of deductive reasoning.

2. Deductive reasoning; the detective is applying a general rule about height to a specific case.

3. Inductive reasoning; you are observing specific pairs of terms and discovering a common difference, and you conclude that the common difference applies to the sequence in general.

4. Deductive reasoning; you are using the general formula for the nth term and applying it to a particular term of a particular sequence.

5c. 1; 100 is divisible by 4. According to the pattern, all powers with exponents divisible by 4 have 1 in the ones place; inductive reasoning.

Lesson 3-6

13a. Sample answer:

Number of T-Shirts Ordered	5	10	15	20	25
Cost ($)	13	23	33	43	53

13c.
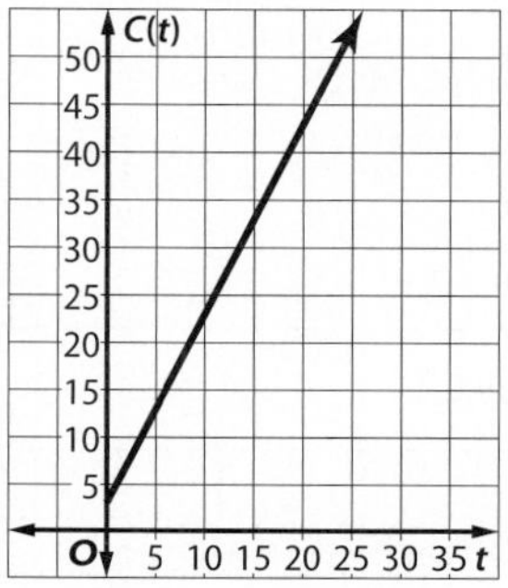

Practice Test

19a.
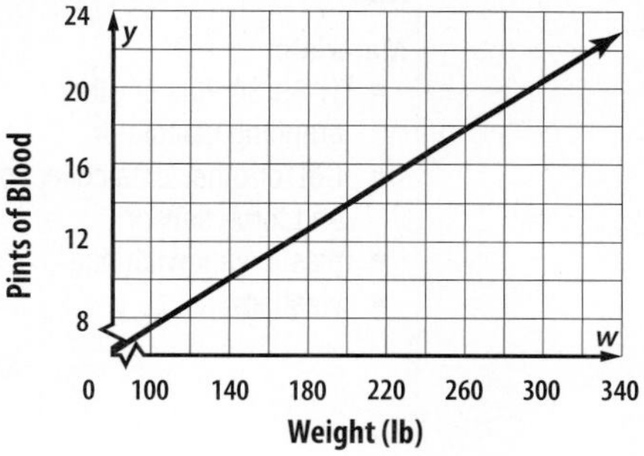

Chapter Planner

Diagnostic Assessment
Quick Check

	EXPLORE 4-1 (45 min: 0.5 day; 90 min: 0.25 day)	LESSON 4-1 (45 min: 1 day; 90 min: 0.5 day)	EXTEND 4-1 (45 min: 0.5 day; 90 min: 0.25 day)
Title	**Graphing Technology Lab: Investigating Slope-Intercept Form**	**Graphing Equations in Slope-Intercept Form**	**Graphing Technology Lab: The Family of Linear Graphs**
Objectives	▪ Use a graphing calculator to collect data and investigate slope-intercept form.	▪ Write and graph linear equations in slope-intercept form. ▪ Model real-world data with equations in slope-intercept form.	▪ Use a graphing calculator to investigate families of linear functions.
Key Vocabulary		slope-intercept form constant function	identity function
Content Standards	AI.L.4	PS.2, PS.8, AI.L.4, AI.L.5, AI.L.6	PS.7
Multiple Representations			
Lesson Resources	connectED.mcgraw-hill.com Animations **Materials:** ▪ TI-83/84 Plus or other graphing calculator ▪ CBL or other data collection devise and force sensor ▪ plastic sandwich bag ▪ washers	connectED.mcgraw-hill.com Leveled Worksheets Vocabulary Animations Personal Tutor Virtual Manipulatives Self-Check Quiz ▪ *5-Minute Check* ▪ *Study Notebook*	connectED.mcgraw-hill.com Vocabulary Personal Tutor **Materials:** ▪ TI-83/84 Plus or other graphing calculator
Resources for Every Lesson	IWB eStudent Edition IWB Interactive Classroom	▪ eTeacher Edition ▪ eSolutions Manual ▪ McGraw-Hill eAssessment	
Differentiated Instruction		pp. 219, 221	

IWB All digital assets are Interactive Whiteboard ready.

Suggested Pacing			
Time Periods	Instruction	Review & Assess	Total
45-minute	10 days	2 days	12 days
90-minute	7 days	1 day	8 days

LESSON 4-2 (45 min: 1 day; 90 min: 0.75 day)	LESSON 4-3 (45 min: 1 day; 90 min: 0.75 day)	LESSON 4-4 (45 min: 1 day; 90 min: 0.75 day)	LESSON 4-5 (45 min: 1 day; 90 min: 0.75 day)
Writing Equations in Slope-Intercept Form	**Writing Equations in Point-Slope Form**	**Parallel and Perpendicular Lines**	**Scatter Plots and Lines of Fit**
▪ Write an equation of a line in slope-intercept form given the slope and one point. ▪ Write an equation of a line in slope-intercept form given two points.	▪ Write equations of lines in point-slope form. ▪ Write linear equations in different forms.	▪ Write an equation of the line that passes through a given point, parallel to a given line. ▪ Write an equation of the line that passes through a given point, perpendicular to a given line.	▪ Investigate relationships between quantities by using points on scatter plots. ▪ Use lines of fit to make and evaluate predictions.
constraint linear extrapolation	point-slope form	parallel lines perpendicular lines	bivariate data scatter plot line of fit linear interpolation
PS.3, PS.6, AI.L.4, AI.L.5, AI.L.6	AI.L.4, AI.L.5, AI.L.6	PS.5	PS.1, PS.4, AI.L.4, AI.L.5, AI.DS.2, AI.DS.3
connectED.mcgraw-hill.com Leveled Worksheets Quiz 1 Vocabulary Personal Tutor Virtual Manipulatives Self-Check Quiz ▪ *5-Minute Check* ▪ *Study Notebook* ▪ *Teaching Algebra with Manipulatives*	connectED.mcgraw-hill.com Leveled Worksheets Vocabulary Personal Tutor Virtual Manipulatives Self-Check Quiz ▪ *5-Minute Check* ▪ *Study Notebook* ▪ *Teaching Algebra with Manipulatives*	connectED.mcgraw-hill.com Leveled Worksheets Quiz 2 Vocabulary Personal Tutor Virtual Manipulatives Self-Check Quiz ▪ *5-Minute Check* ▪ *Study Notebook* ▪ *Teaching Algebra with Manipulatives*	connectED.mcgraw-hill.com Leveled Worksheets Vocabulary Animations Personal Tutor Virtual Manipulatives Self-Check Quiz ▪ *5-Minute Check* ▪ *Study Notebook* ▪ *Teaching Algebra with Manipulatives*
IWB eStudent Edition IWB Interactive Classroom	▪ eTeacher Edition ▪ eSolutions Manual ▪ McGraw-Hill eAssessment		
pp. 228, 232	pp. 235, 238	pp. 241, 245	pp. 248, 251
		Formative Assessment Mid-Chapter Quiz	

Chapter Planner

	EXTEND 4-5 (45 min: 0.5 day; 90 min: 0.25 day)	LESSON 4-6 (45 min: 1.5 days; 90 min: 1 day)	LESSON 4-7 (45 min: 1.5 days; 90 min: 1.5 days)	EXTEND 4-7 (45 min: 0.5 day; 90 min: 0.25 day)
Title	**Algebra Lab: Correlation and Causation**	**Regression and Median-Fit Lines**	**Inverse Linear Functions**	**Algebra Lab: Drawing Inverses**
Objectives	▪ Explore the difference between correlation and causation.	▪ Write equations of best-fit lines using linear regression. ▪ Write equations of median-fit lines.	▪ Find the inverse of a relation. ▪ Find the inverse of a linear function.	▪ Draw the inverse of a relation and determine whether the inverse is a function.
Key Vocabulary	causation	best-fit line linear regression correlation coefficient residual median-fit line	inverse relation inverse function	
Content Standards	AI.DS.2, AI.DS.3, AI.DS.4, AI.DS.6	AI.L.4, AI.L.5, AI.DS.3		
Multiple Representations				
Lesson Resources	connectED.mcgraw-hill.com Animations Vocabulary Virtual Manipulatives ▪ *Teaching Algebra with Manipulatives* **Materials:** ▪ grid paper	connectED.mcgraw-hill.com Leveled Worksheets Quiz 3 Vocabulary Animations Personal Tutor Self-Check Quiz ▪ *5-Minute Check* ▪ *Study Notebook* ▪ *Teaching Algebra with Manipulatives*	connectED.mcgraw-hill.com Leveled Worksheets Quiz 4 Vocabulary Animations Personal Tutor Virtual Manipulatives Self-Check Quiz ▪ *5-Minute Check* ▪ *Study Notebook*	connectED.mcgraw-hill.com **Materials:** ▪ patty paper ▪ colored pencils
Resources for Every Lesson	IWB eStudent Edition IWB Interactive Classroom	▪ eTeacher Edition ▪ eSolutions Manual ▪ McGraw-Hill eAssessment		
Differentiated Instruction		pp. 257, 260	pp. 265, 270	

Summative Assessment
Study Guide and Review
Practice Test

IWB All digital assets are Interactive Whiteboard ready.

Quick Review Math Handbook*

is Glencoe's mathematical handbook for students and parents.

HotWords includes a glossary of terms.

HotTopics consists of two parts:

- explanations of key mathematical concepts
- exercises to check students' understanding

Lesson	Hot Topics Section	Lesson	Hot Topic Section
4-1	6.7, 6.8	4-5	4.2
4-2	6.8	4-6	4.3
4-3	6.8	4-7	6.8
4-4	6.7, 6.8		

**Also available in Spanish*

What the Research Says…

Good questioning includes challenging students to think about the main ideas in the lesson and go beyond simple recall or parroting of what has just been said. Questioning also increases student-to-student interaction so that students' ideas, expressed in their terminology are shared with the class. (Hiebert et al, 1997)

- Stress that the concept of slope is one that is used widely in mathematics through calculus.
- Understanding what slope represents will help students easily master skills in this chapter.

Source: Heibert, J., Carpenter, T.P., Fennema, E., Fuson, K.C., Murray, H., Olivier, A., Human, P., and Wearner, D. (1997) *Making Sense: Teaching and Learning Mathematics with Understanding,* Portsmouth, New Hampshire, Heinemann.

Project CRISS STUDY SKILL

A point-by-point format and example can be used to help students better understand the steps of many mathematical processes. In order to explain a process, they must understand how to perform a step as well as the reasoning behind each step.

Provide students with the description at the right as an example of using point-by-point format to explain how to write an equation of a line when two points are given. After reading Lesson 4-2, have students write a description of how to write an equation of a line when a point and slope are given.

Main Idea	Point-by-Point Steps	Example for the Points: (1, 5), (−1, 1)
Find an equation of a line when two points on the line are given.	Step 1 Find the slope of the line containing the points.	$m = \frac{y_2 - y_1}{x_2 - x_1}$ $m = \frac{1 - 5}{-1 - 1}$ $m = \frac{-4}{-2}$ or 2
	Step 2 Choose one of the points and find the *y*-intercept	$y = mx + b$ $1 = 2(-1) + b$ $3 = b$
	Step 3 Write the slope-intercept form of the equation using the slope and *y*-intercept.	Using $m = 2$ and $b = 3$, $y = mx + b$ $y = 2x + 3$

Creating Independence through Student-owned Strategies

Assessment and Intervention

SE = Student Edition, **TE** = Teacher Edition, **CRM** = Chapter Resource Masters

	Diagnosis	Prescription
DIAGNOSTIC ASSESSMENT	**Beginning Chapter 4**	
	Get Ready for Chapter 4 **SE**	Response to Intervention **TE**
	Beginning Every Lesson	
	Then, Now, Why? **SE** 5-Minute Check	Chapter 0 **SE** *Quick Review Math Handbook*
FORMATIVE ASSESSMENT	**During/After Every Lesson**	
	Guided Practice **SE**, every example Check Your Understanding **SE** H.O.T. Problems **SE** Spiral Review **SE** Additional Examples **TE** Watch Out! **TE** Step 4, Assess **TE** Chapter 4 Quizzes **CRM**, pp. 51–52 Self-Check Quizzes connectED.mcgraw-hill.com	TIER 1 Intervention Skills Practice **CRM**, Ch. 1–4 connectED.mcgraw-hill.com TIER 2 Intervention Differentiated Instruction **TE** Differentiated Homework Options **TE** Study Guide and Intervention **CRM**, Ch. 1–4 *Quick Review Math Handbook* TIER 3 Intervention *Math Triumphs, Alg. 1,* Ch. 4
	Mid-Chapter	
	Mid-Chapter Quiz **SE** Mid-Chapter Test **CRM**, p. 53 McGraw-Hill eAssessment	TIER 1 Intervention Skills Practice **CRM**, Ch. 1–4 connectED.mcgraw-hill.com TIER 2 Intervention Study Guide and Intervention **CRM**, Ch. 1–4 *Quick Review Math Handbook* TIER 3 Intervention *Math Triumphs, Alg. 1,* Ch. 4
	Before Chapter Test	
	Chapter Study Guide and Review **SE** Practice Test **SE** Standardized Test Practice **SE** Chapter Test connectED.mcgraw-hill.com Standardized Test Practice connectED.mcgraw-hill.com Vocabulary Review connectED.mcgraw-hill.com McGraw-Hill eAssessment	TIER 1 Intervention Skills Practice **CRM**, Ch. 1–4 connectED.mcgraw-hill.com TIER 2 Intervention Study Guide and Intervention **CRM**, Ch. 1–4 *Quick Review Math Handbook* TIER 3 Intervention *Math Triumphs, Alg. 1,* Ch. 4
SUMMATIVE ASSESSMENT	**After Chapter 4**	
	Multiple-Choice Tests, Forms 1, 2A, 2B **CRM**, pp. 55–60 Free-Response Tests, Forms 2C, 2D, 3 **CRM**, pp. 61–66 Vocabulary Test **CRM**, p. 54 Extended Response Test **CRM**, p. 67 Standardized Test Practice **CRM**, pp. 68–70 McGraw-Hill eAssessment	Study Guide and Intervention **CRM**, Ch. 1–4 *Quick Review Math Handbook* connectED.mcgraw-hill.com

Differentiated Instruction

Option 1 Reaching All Learners AL OL BL ELL

Interpersonal Place students in teams of three or four. Since there are several tasks involved in writing and graphing an equation in slope-intercept form, have the team members decide which tasks each will perform. For example, one member can be responsible for writing an equation given the slope and *y*-intercept, another can rewrite a given equation into slope-intercept form, and the remaining members can use the *y*-intercept and the slope to graph the equation.

Social Have each student plot (2, 1) on a coordinate grid. Then ask them to use a straightedge to draw a line through this point and crossing the *y*-axis. Then have students compare their lines. Discuss why so many different lines are drawn. Ask students what you would have had to give them, along with the original point, so that they would all have drawn the same line. slope or another point As a class, graph and write equations for the lines through (2, 1) with a slope of 3, and through (2, 1) and (1, 3).

Option 2 Approaching Level AL

Provide students with four equations in slope-intercept form that all have the same slope. Ask students to graph each equation, extending the lines so that each crosses the *y*-axis. Then have students write the equation for each line on the line itself. Discuss with students the relationships between the graph of the line and its equation, that is, the slope and the coefficient of *x* and the *y*-intercept and the value for *b*.

Option 3 English Learners ELL

Give students several exercises that ask them to write a particular type of equation. Have them describe or write how they would solve each type of problem. Then have them summarize the technique they think works best for each given situation (point and slope, two points, rewriting equations in various forms).

Option 4 Beyond Level BL

Have students research Galileo's Tower of Pisa experiment. Then have students conduct a similar experiment to determine if there is a correlation between the weight of an object and the speed at which it falls. Caution students to keep the distance the objects fall a constant, the size of the objects similar, but the mass of the objects different.

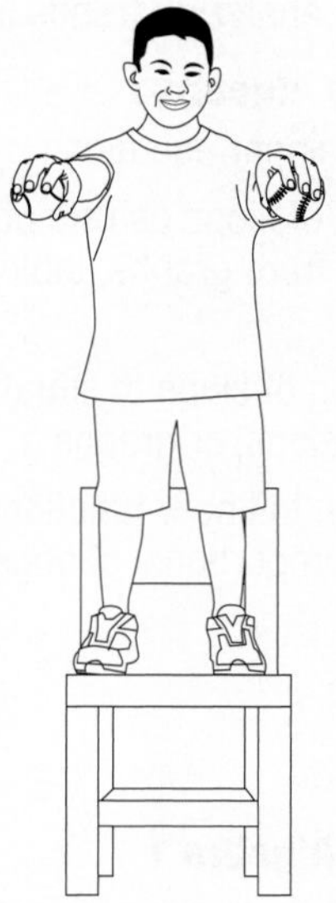

Focus on Mathematical Content

Vertical Alignment

Before Chapter 4

Related Topics before Grade 8

- represent relationships among quantities using graphs

Related Topics from Grade 8

- use operations to solve problems involving rational numbers
- make predictions by analyzing trends in scatter plots

Previous Topics from Algebra 1

- transform and solve linear equations
- develop the concept of slope as rate of change and determine the slope from graphs, tables, and algebraic representations
- interpret the meaning of slope in situations using data, symbolic representations, or graphs
- relate direct variation to linear functions and solve problems involving proportional change

Chapter 4

Related Topics from Algebra 1

- write equations of lines given specific characteristics
- interpret and predict the effects of changing the slope and *y*-intercept in applied situations
- interpret and make decisions, predictions, and critical judgments from functional relationships
- collect and organize data, make and interpret scatter plots, and model, predict, and make decisions and critical judgments in problem situations
- solve an equation of the form $f(x) = c$ for a simple function f that has an inverse and write an expression for the inverse.

After Chapter 4

Preparation for Algebra 2

- make and interpret scatter plots, fit the graph of a function to the data, and make predictions based on the function
- solve systems of equations
- use functions to model and make predictions

Lesson-by-Lesson Preview

4-1 Graphing Equations in Slope-Intercept Form

An equation of the form $y = mx + b$, in which m is the slope and b is the y-value where the graph of the equation crosses the y-axis, is said to be in slope-intercept form. The slope-intercept form of an equation offers two ways to graph a line.

- Select any two values for x, substitute the values into the equation, and then calculate the corresponding values of y to create two ordered pairs that can be graphed. Draw the line that contains these two points.
- Graph the y-intercept, use it as a starting point, and then use the slope to determine the distance and direction to move up/down and right/left to find another point on the line. Then draw the line.

4-2 Writing Equations in Slope-Intercept Form

The general equation for slope-intercept form is $y = mx + b$. This is the starting point for creating an equation from different types of information given.

- Given the slope m and one point (x, y)

Step 1: Substitute the values of m, x, and y into the slope-intercept form and solve for b.

Step 2: Write the slope-intercept form by substituting the values of m and b into $y = mx + b$.

- Given two points

Step 1: Use the two points to find m, the slope.

Step 2: Choose one of the two points to use.

Step 3: Follow the steps for writing an equation given the slope, m, and one point (x, y).

4-3 Writing Equations in Point-Slope Form

Point-slope form is derived from the definition of slope using the coordinates of two points on a line. Suppose the two points on a line are given as (x, y) and (x_1, y_1). Using the definition of the slope, $m = \frac{y - y_1}{x - x_1}$. If each side of the equation is multiplied by $(x - x_1)$, the result is $y - y_1 = m(x - x_1)$, the point-slope form of a linear equation.

4-4 Parallel and Perpendicular Lines

In coordinate geometry, graphing and properties of graphs are used to prove lines parallel or perpendicular.

- When two distinct lines lie in the same plane and have the same slope, they are parallel.
- When two lines do not have the same slope, they intersect. If two oblique lines intersect at right angles, forming perpendicular lines, the slopes of the two lines are negative reciprocals of each other, and the product of their slopes is -1.

4-5 Scatter Plots and Lines of Fit

A scatter plot consists of graphs of ordered pairs (x, y) that belong to a set in which the x-coordinate represents one real-world measurement and the y-coordinate represents another.

If a set of data exhibits a linear trend, a line of fit can be drawn to summarize the data. Once the line is drawn, an equation for the line can be written.

4-6 Regression and Median-Fit Lines

An equation for a best-fit line can be written for any set of data. The equation is only useful if the data exhibits a linear trend or pattern.

- The graphing calculator function LinReg($ax + b$) uses a least-squares fit method to determine the values for a, the slope, and b, the y-intercept. Once a and b are calculated, the equation for the line can be written.
- The values for a and b will be displayed in the calculator's window along with the value for the correlation coefficient. The closer the correlation coefficient is to 1 or -1, the more closely the equation for the best-fit line models the data inputted.
- Points on the best-fit line are used to estimate values that are not in the data set.

4-7 Inverse Linear Functions

An *inverse relation* is the set of ordered pairs obtained by exchanging the x-coordinate with the y-coordinate of each ordered pair of a relation.

A		***B***
$(-7, -12)$	$\longrightarrow$	$(-12, -7)$
$(-4, 6)$	$\longrightarrow$	$(6, -4)$
$(3, 18)$	$\longrightarrow$	$(18, 3)$
$(6, 39)$	$\longrightarrow$	$(39, 6)$

A and *B* are inverse relations.

A linear function $f(x)$ has an *inverse function* that can be written as $f^{-1}(x)$ and is read *f inverse* or *the inverse of f.*

To find the inverse function $f^{-1}(x)$ of the linear function $f(x)$, complete the following steps.

Step 1: Replace $f(x)$ with y in the equation for $f(x)$.

Step 2: Interchange y and x in the equation.

Step 3: Solve the equation for y.

Step 4: Replace y with $f^{-1}(x)$ in the new equation.

Professional Development

Targeted professional development has been articulated throughout Algebra 1. More quality, customized professional development is available from McGraw-Hill Professional Development. Visit connectED.mcgraw-hill.com for details on each product.

- Online Lessons emphasize the strategies and techniques used to teach Algebra 1. Includes streaming video, interactive pages, and online tools.
- Video Workshops allow mentors, coaches, or leadership personnel to facilitate on-site workshops on educational strategies in mathematics and mathematical concepts.
- MHPD Online (www.mhpdonline.com) offers online professional development with video clips of instructional strategies, links, student activities, and news and issues in education.
- Teaching Today (teachingtoday.glencoe.com) gives secondary teachers practical strategies and materials that inspire excellence and innovation in teaching.

Chapter Project

Statistically Speaking

Students use what they have learned about linear regression to complete a project.

This chapter project addresses civic literacy, as well as several specific skills identified as being essential to student success by the Framework for 21st Century Learning.

Visit connectED.mcgraw-hill.com for student and teacher handouts.

KeyVocabulary Introduce the key vocabulary in the chapter using the routine below.

Define: Slope-intercept form is an equation of the form $y = mx + b$, where m is the slope and b is the y-intercept.

Example: $y = 3x + 5$ has a slope of 3 and a y-intercept of 5.

Ask: Is the slope on the right side or the left side of the equation? right side

CHAPTER 4 Equations of Linear Functions

Then

You graphed linear functions.

Now

In this chapter, you will:

- Write and graph linear equations in various forms.
- Use scatter plots and lines of fit, and write equations of best-fit lines using linear regression.
- Find inverse linear functions.

Why? ▲

OIL The amount of oil drilled at an oil field changes from year to year. From the yearly data, patterns emerge. Rate of change can be applied to these data to determine a linear model. This can be used to predict the amount of oil drilled in future years.

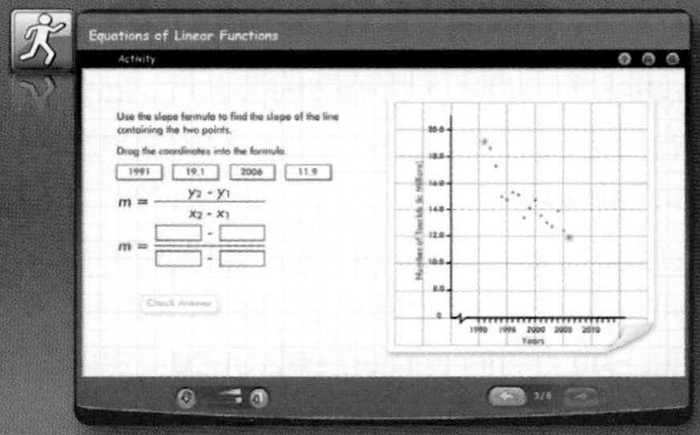

connectED.mcgraw-hill.com Your Digital Math Portal

Animation | Vocabulary | eGlossary | Personal Tutor | Virtual Manipulatives | Graphing Calculator | Audio | Foldables | Self-Check Practice | Worksheets

Content Standards
A1.L.4, A1.L.5, A1.L.6, A1.DS.2, A1.DS.3, A1.DS.4, A1.DS.6

Process Standards
PS.1, PS.2, PS.3, PS.4, PS.5, PS.6, PS.7, PS.8

Get Ready for the Chapter

Diagnose Readiness | You have two options for checking prerequisite skills.

1 Textbook Option Take the Quick Check below. Refer to the Quick Review for help.

QuickCheck

Evaluate $3a^2 - 2ab + c$ for the values given.

1. $a = 2, b = 1, c = 5$ 13
2. $a = -3, b = -2, c = 3$ 18
3. $a = -1, b = 0, c = 11$ 14
4. $a = 5, b = -3, c = -9$ 96
5. **CAR RENTAL** The cost of renting a car is given by $49x + 0.3y$. Let x represent the number of days rented, and let y represent the number of miles driven. Find the cost for a five-day rental over 125 miles. $282.50

Solve each equation for the given variable.

6. $x + y = 5$ for y $y = 5 - x$
7. $2x - 4y = 6$ for x $x = 3 + 2y$
8. $y - 2 = x + 3$ for y $y = x + 5$
9. $4x - 3y = 12$ for x
10. **GEOMETRY** The formula for the perimeter of a rectangle is $P = 2w + 2\ell$, where w represents width and ℓ represents length. Solve for w. $w = \frac{P}{2} - \ell$

9. $x = \frac{3}{4}y + 3$

Write the ordered pair for each point.

11. A (4, 2)
12. B (0, 3)
13. C (2, −4)
14. D (0, 0)
15. E (−3, −3)
16. F (−5, 2)

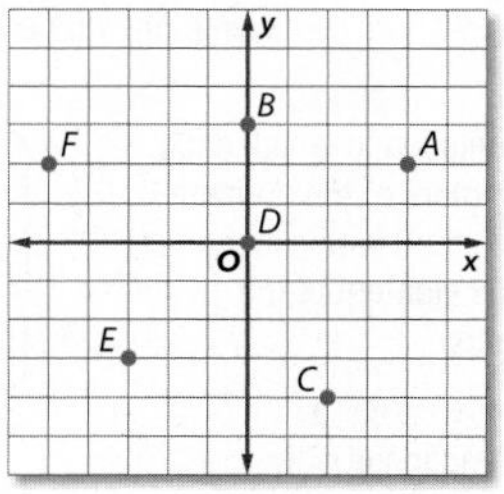

QuickReview

Example 1 (Used in Lessons 4-1 through 4-7)

Evaluate $2(m - n)^2 + 3p$ for $m = 5$, $n = 2$, and $p = -3$.

$2(m - n)^2 + 3p$	Original expression
$= 2(5 - 2)^2 + 3(-3)$	Substitute.
$= 2(3)^2 + 3(-3)$	Subtract.
$= 2(9) + 3(-3)$	Evaluate power.
$= 18 + (-9)$	Multiply.
$= 9$	Add.

Example 2 (Used in Lessons 4-1 through 4-3)

Solve $5x + 15y = 9$ for x.

$5x + 15y = 9$	Original equation
$5x + 15y - 15y = 9 - 15y$	Subtract $15y$ from each side.
$5x = 9 - 15y$	Simplify.
$\frac{5x}{5} = \frac{9 - 15y}{5}$	Divide each side by 5.
$x = \frac{9}{5} - 3y$	Simplify.

Example 3 (Used in Lessons 4-1 through 4-7)

Write the ordered pair for A.

Step 1 Begin at point A.

Step 2 Follow along a vertical line to the x-axis. The x-coordinate is −4.

Step 3 Follow along a horizontal line to the y-axis. The y-coordinate is 2.

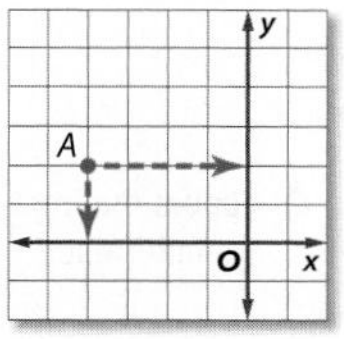

The ordered pair for point A is (−4, 2).

2 Online Option Take an online self-check Chapter Readiness Quiz at connectED.mcgraw-hill.com.

Essential Question

- Why is math used to model real-world situations?

Sample answer: in order to study trends, make predictions, understand phenomena in nature

Get Ready for the Chapter

Response to Intervention (RtI)

Use the *Quick Check* results and the Intervention Planner to help you determine your Response to Intervention. The If-Then statements in the chart below help you decide the appropriate tier of RtI and suggest intervention resources for each tier.

InterventionPlanner

TIER 1 On Level OL

If students miss about 25% of the exercises or less,

Then choose a resource:

SE Lessons 1-2, 1-6, and 2-8

Skills Practice, Chapter 1, pp. 13 and 39, Chapter 2, p. 51

connectED.mcgraw-hill.com Self-Check Quiz

TIER 2 Strategic Intervention AL approaching grade level

If students miss about 50% of the exercises,

Then choose a resource:

Study Guide and Intervention, Chapter 1, pp. 11 and 37, Chapter 2, p. 49

connectED.mcgraw-hill.com Extra Examples, Personal Tutor, Homework Help

TIER 3 Intensive Intervention 2 or more grades below level

If students miss about 75% of the exercises,

Then use *Math Triumphs, Alg. 1,* Ch. 4

connectED.mcgraw-hill.com Extra Examples, Personal Tutor, Homework Help, Review Vocabulary

FOLDABLES StudyOrganizer

Dinah Zike's Foldables®

Focus As students read and study this chapter, they should show examples and write notes about linear functions and relations.

Teach Have students make and label their Foldables as illustrated. Students should label the first three pockets with two lesson titles each. The fourth pocket should be labeled with the last lesson title. Students should list the vocabulary words on one index card per lesson. On the reverse of each card, students write the definitions of the vocabulary words. The cards are then placed in the appropriate pocket. The index cards can be used as flash cards for students to quiz each other.

When to Use It Encourage students to add to their Foldables as they work through the chapter and to use them to review for the chapter test.

Differentiated Instruction

Student-Built Glossary, pp. 1–2

Students should complete the chart by providing a definition of each term and an example as they progress through Chapter 4. This study tool can also be used to review for the chapter test.

Get Started on the Chapter

You will learn several new concepts, skills, and vocabulary terms as you study Chapter 4. To get ready, identify important terms and organize your resources. You may wish to refer to Chapter 0 to review prerequisite skills.

FOLDABLES StudyOrganizer

Equations of Linear Functions Make this Foldable to help you organize your Chapter 4 notes about linear functions. Begin with one sheet of 11" by 17" paper.

1. **Fold** each end of the paper in about 2 inches.

2. **Fold** along the width and the length. Unfold. Cut along the fold line from the top to the center.

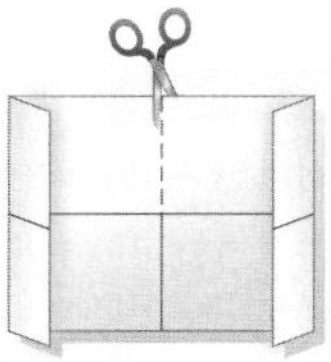

3. **Fold** the top flaps down. Then fold in half and turn to form a folder. Staple the flaps down to form pockets.

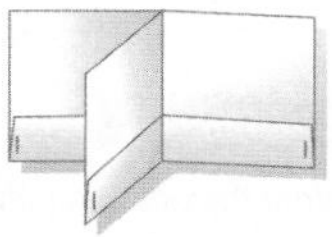

4. **Label** the front with the chapter title.

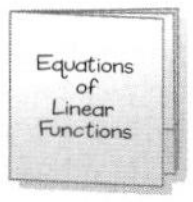

NewVocabulary

English		Español
slope-intercept form	p. 216	forma pendiente-intersección
linear extrapolation	p. 228	extrapolación lineal
point-slope form	p. 233	forma punto-pendiente
parallel lines	p. 239	rectas paralelas
perpendicular lines	p. 240	rectas perpendiculares
scatter plot	p. 247	gráfica de dispersión
line of fit	p. 248	recta de ajuste
linear interpolation	p. 249	interpolación lineal
best-fit line	p. 255	recta de ajuste óptimo
linear regression	p. 255	retroceso lineal
correlation coefficient	p. 255	coeficiente de correlación
median-fit line	p. 258	línea de mediana-ataque
inverse relation	p. 263	relación inversa
inverse function	p. 264	función inversa

ReviewVocabulary

coefficient coeficiente the numerical factor of a term

function función a relation in which each element of the domain is paired with exactly one element of the range

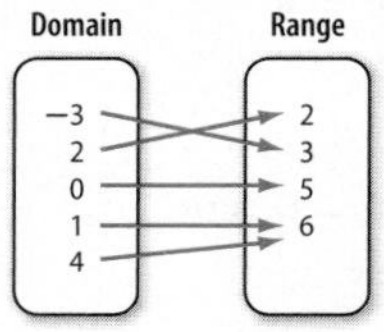

ratio razón a comparison of two numbers by division

214 | Chapter 4 | Equations of Linear Functions

EXPLORE 4-1

Graphing Technology Lab
Investigating Slope-Intercept Form

Set Up the Lab

Content Standards
A1.L.4

- Cut a small hole in a top corner of a plastic sandwich bag. Hang the bag from the end of the force sensor.
- Connect the force sensor to your data collection device.

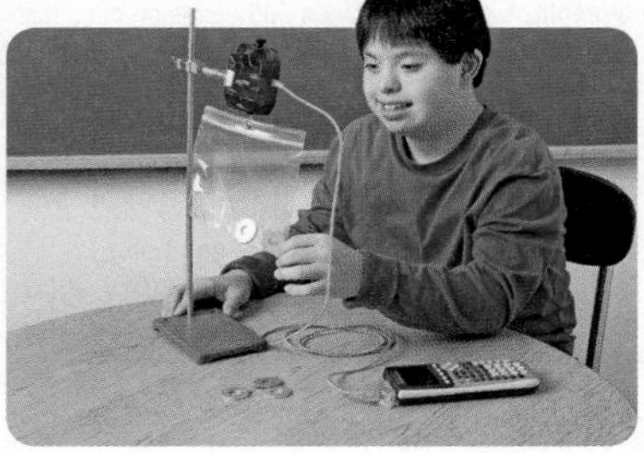

Activity Collect Data

Step 1 Use the sensor to collect the weight with 0 washers in the bag. Record the data pair in the calculator.

Step 2 Place one washer in the plastic bag. Wait for the bag to stop swinging, then measure and record the weight.

Step 3 Repeat the experiment, adding different numbers of washers to the bag. Each time, record the number of washers and the weight.

Analyze the Results

1. The domain contains values of the independent variable, number of washers. The range contains values of the dependent variable, weight. Use the graphing calculator to create a scatter plot using the ordered pairs (washers, weight). **See students' work.**
2. Write a sentence that describes the points on the graph. **Sample answer: It is a linear pattern.**
3. Describe the position of the point on the graph that represents the trial with no washers in the bag. **It is the y-intercept.**
4. The rate of change can be found by using the formula for slope.

$$\frac{\text{rise}}{\text{run}} = \frac{\text{change in weight}}{\text{change in number of washers}}$$

Find the rate of change in the weight as more washers are added. **See students' work. Sample answer: 0.025**

5. Explain how the rate of change is shown on the graph. **The slope represents the rate of change.**

6. Sample answer: The graph is the same as the one shown, shifted upward so that the y-intercept is at (0, 0.8).

Make a Conjecture

7. Sample answer: The graph has the same y-intercept, but the rate of change is greater.

The graph shows sample data from a washer experiment. Describe the graph for each situation.

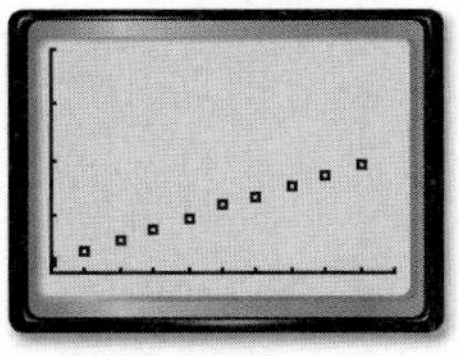

[0, 20] scl: 2 by [0, 1] scl: 0.25

6. a bag that hangs weighs 0.8 N when empty and increases in weight at the rate of the sample
7. a bag that has the same weight when empty as the sample and increases in weight at a faster rate
8. a bag that has the same weight when empty as the sample and increases in weight at a slower rate **Sample answer: The graph has the same y-intercept, but the rate of change is less.**

1 Focus

Objective Use a graphing calculator to collect data and investigate slope-intercept form.

Materials for Each Group

- T1–83/84 Plus or other graphing calculator
- CBL or other data collection device and force sensor
- plastic sandwich bag
- washers

Teaching Tip

Point out to students the features of the data collection device and show them how to weigh the washers. Urge students to record their data carefully. One careless recording will prevent students from seeing a pattern.

2 Teach

Working in Cooperative Groups

Have students work in groups of two or three, mixing abilities. Have groups complete the Activity and Exercises 1–5. In Step 1 of the Activity, suggest that students enter the number of washers in **L1** and the corresponding weights in **L2**. In Exercise 3, point out that the weight with no washers is the weight of the bag.

Practice Have students complete Exercises 6–8.

From Concrete to Abstract

- Ask students what they think the graph would look like if a bag had the same weight when empty as the sample and increased in weight at a slower and slower rate. Sample answer: the same y-intercept but the rate of change would be less and less
- Ask what the graph would look like if the slope were close to 0. Sample answer: a linear pattern that is close to horizontal

3 Assess

Formative Assessment

Use Exercise 4 to assess whether students can calculate the rate of change correctly. Use Exercise 7 to assess whether students understand that the rate of change is the slope of the line connecting the points.

1 Focus

VerticalAlignment

Before Lesson 4-1 Find rates of change and slopes.

Lesson 4-1 Write and graph linear equations in slope-intercept form. Model real-world data with equations in slope-intercept form.

After Lesson 4-1 Write an equation of a line given two points or a point and the slope in slope-intercept form.

2 Teach

Scaffolding Questions

Have students read the **Why?** section of the lesson.

Ask:

- How many songs could Jamil have on his digital media player after two months? 560
- How many songs could he have after four months? 620
- Would a graph of the equation $y = 30x + 500$ have a positive or negative slope? positive

LESSON 4-1 Graphing Equations in Slope-Intercept Form

Then

- You found rates of change and slopes.

Now

1. Write and graph linear equations in slope-intercept from.
2. Model real-world data with equations in slope-intercept form.

Why?

- Jamil has 500 songs on his digital media player. He joins a music club that lets him download 30 songs per month for a monthly fee. The number of songs that Jamil could eventually have in his player if he does not delete any songs is represented by $y = 30x + 500$.

NewVocabulary
slope-intercept form
constant function

Content Standards
AI.L.4, AI.L.5, AI.L.6

Process Standards
PS.2, PS.8

1 Slope-Intercept Form An equation of the form $y = mx + b$, where m is the slope and b is the y-intercept, is in **slope-intercept form**. The variables m and b are called *parameters* of the equation. Changing either value changes the equation's graph.

KeyConcept Slope-Intercept Form

Words The slope-intercept form of a linear equation is $y = mx + b$, where m is the slope and b is the y-intercept.

Example

$y = mx + b$

$y = 2x + 6$

slope (2) — y-intercept (6)

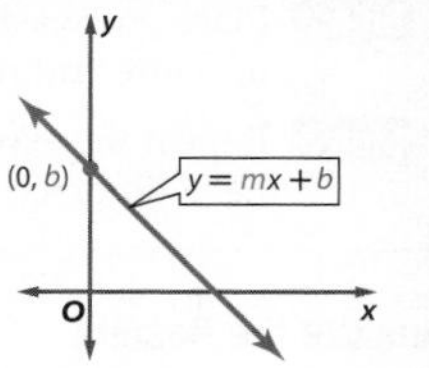

Example 1 Write and Graph an Equation

Write an equation in slope-intercept form for the line with a slope of $\frac{3}{4}$ and a y-intercept of −2. Then graph the equation.

$y = mx + b$ Slope-intercept form

$y = \frac{3}{4}x + (-2)$ Replace m with $\frac{3}{4}$ and b with −2.

$y = \frac{3}{4}x - 2$ Simplify.

Now graph the equation.

Step 1 Plot the y-intercept (0, −2).

Step 2 The slope is $\frac{\text{rise}}{\text{run}} = \frac{3}{4}$. From (0, −2), move up 3 units and right 4 units. Plot the point.

Step 3 Draw a line through the two points.

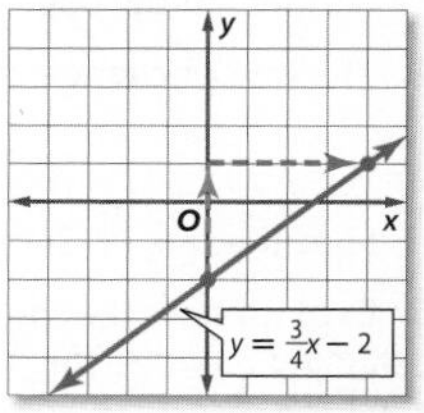

GuidedPractice

Write an equation of a line in slope intercept form with the given slope and y-intercept. Then graph the equation. 1A–1B. See Ch. 4 Answer Appendix for graphs.

1A. slope: $-\frac{1}{2}$, y-intercept: 3 $y = -\frac{1}{2}x + 3$ **1B.** slope: −3, y-intercept: −8 $y = -3x - 8$

216 | Lesson 4-1

Lesson 4-1 Resources

Resource	Approaching Level AL	On Level OL	Beyond Level BL	English Learners ELL
Teacher Edition	▪ Differentiated Instruction, p. 219	▪ Differentiated Instruction, p. 221	▪ Differentiated Instruction, p. 221	▪ Differentiated Instruction, p. 219
Chapter Resource Masters	▪ Study Guide and Intervention, pp. 5–6 ▪ Skills Practice, p. 7 ▪ Practice, p. 8 ▪ Word Problem Practice, p. 9	▪ Study Guide and Intervention, pp. 5–6 ▪ Skills Practice, p. 7 ▪ Practice, p. 8 ▪ Word Problem Practice, p. 9 ▪ Enrichment, p. 10	▪ Practice, p. 8 ▪ Word Problem Practice, p. 9 ▪ Enrichment, p. 10	▪ Study Guide and Intervention, pp. 5–6 ▪ Skills Practice, p. 7 ▪ Practice, p. 8 ▪ Word Problem Practice, p. 9
Other	▪ 5-Minute Check 4-1 ▪ Study Notebook	▪ 5-Minute Check 4-1 ▪ Study Notebook	▪ 5-Minute Check 4-1 ▪ Study Notebook	▪ 5-Minute Check 4-1 ▪ Study Notebook

When an equation is not written in slope-intercept form, it may be easier to rewrite it before graphing.

Example 2 Graph Linear Equations

Graph $3x + 2y = 6$.

Rewrite the equation in slope-intercept form.

$3x + 2y = 6$	Original equation
$3x + 2y - 3x = 6 - 3x$	Subtract $3x$ from each side.
$2y = 6 - 3x$	Simplify.
$2y = -3x + 6$	$6 - 3x = 6 + (-3x)$ or $-3x + 6$
$\frac{2y}{2} = \frac{-3x + 6}{2}$	Divide each side by 2.
$y = -\frac{3}{2}x + 3$	Slope-intercept form

Now graph the equation. The slope is $-\frac{3}{2}$, and the y-intercept is 3.

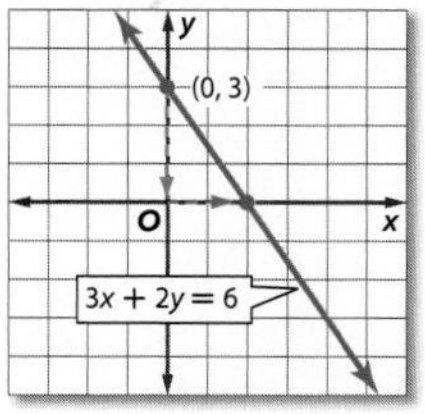

Step 1 Plot the y-intercept (0, 3).

Step 2 The slope is $\frac{\text{rise}}{\text{run}} = -\frac{3}{2}$. From (0, 3), move down 3 units and right 2 units. Plot the point.

Step 3 Draw a line through the two points.

StudyTip

Counting and Direction When counting rise and run, a negative sign may be associated with the value in the numerator or denominator. If with the numerator, begin by counting down for the rise. If with the denominator, count left when counting the run. The resulting line will be the same.

GuidedPractice

Graph each equation. **2A–2B. See Ch. 4 Answer Appendix.**

2A. $3x - 4y = 12$

2B. $-2x + 5y = 10$

Except for the graph of $y = 0$, which lies on the x-axis, horizontal lines have a slope of 0. They are graphs of **constant functions**, which can be written in slope-intercept form as $y = 0x + b$ or $y = b$, where b is any number. Constant functions do not cross the x-axis. Their domain is all real numbers, and their range is b.

Example 3 Graph Linear Equations

Graph $y = -3$.

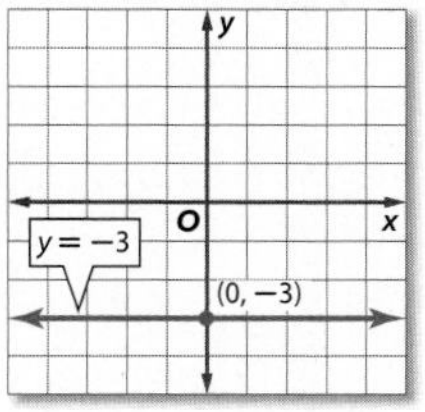

Step 1 Plot the y-intercept (0, −3).

Step 2 The slope is 0. Draw a line through the points with y-coordinate −3.

GuidedPractice

Graph each equation. **3A–3B. See Ch. 4 Answer Appendix.**

3A. $y = 5$

3B. $2y = 1$

Vertical lines have no slope. So, equations of vertical lines cannot be written in slope-intercept form.

1 Slope-Intercept Form

Example 1 shows how to write and graph a linear equation given the slope and y-intercept. **Example 2** shows how to rewrite a linear equation in slope-intercept form in order to graph it. **Example 3** shows how to graph a linear equation with a slope of 0. **Example 4** shows how to write an equation in slope-intercept form for a line on a graph.

Formative Assessment

Use the Guided Practice exercises after each Example to determine students' understanding of concepts.

Additional Examples

1 Write an equation in slope-intercept form of the line with a slope of $\frac{1}{4}$ and a y-intercept of −1. Then graph the equation. $y = \frac{1}{4}x - 1$

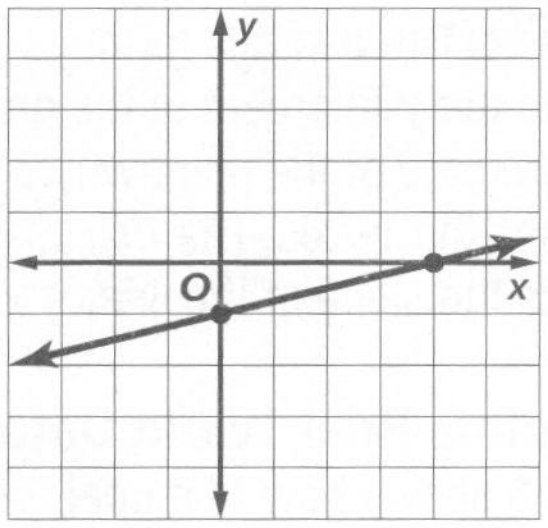

2 Graph $5x + 4y = 8$. (See bottom margin for graph.)

3 Graph $y = -7$. (See bottom margin for graph.)

Additional Examples also in Interactive Classroom PowerPoint® Presentations

IWB Interactive White Board READY

Additional Answers (Additional Examples)

2.

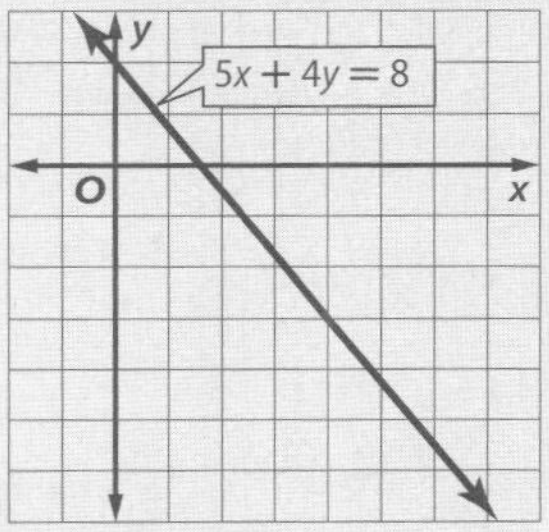

3.

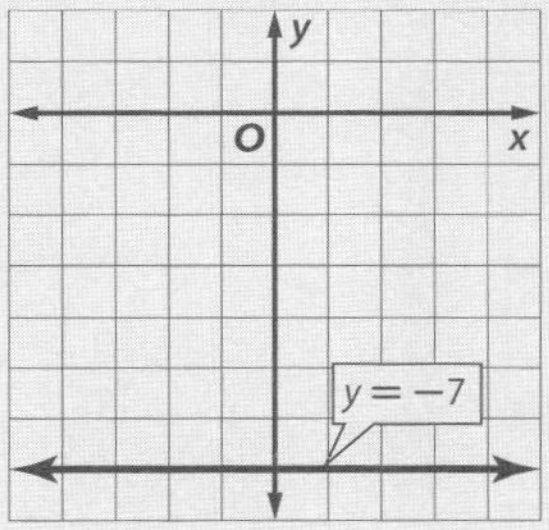

WatchOut!

Preventing Errors Remind students that b can be negative, so equations may not always have positive constants.

Additional Example

4 STANDARDIZED TEST PRACTICE Which of the following is an equation in slope-intercept form for the line shown in the graph? B

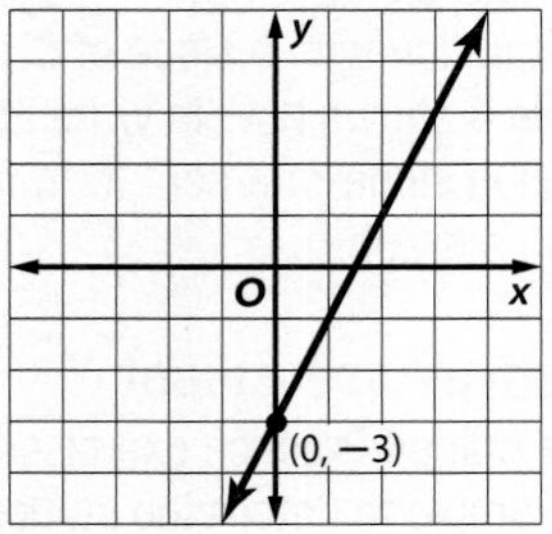

A $y = \frac{1}{2}x + 3$

B $y = 2x - 3$

C $y = \frac{1}{2}x + 3$

D $y = -2x - 3$

Focus on Mathematical Content

Slope-Intercept Form The slope-intercept form of a linear equation is $y = mx + b$. The b in this form represents the y-intercept of the graph, the y-coordinate of the point where the line crosses the y-axis. The m represents the slope of the line.

2 Modeling Real-World Data

Example 5 shows how to model real-world data with an equation in slope-intercept form and then use that equation to solve a problem.

Teach with Tech

Interactive Whiteboard Drag a coordinate grid on the board. Draw a line on the grid, and have students write the equation of the line in slope-intercept form. Then drag more lines from other locations on the board and again have students write the equation of the line. Discuss how the equations are similar and different.

Tips for New Teachers

Dependent Variables Remind students that y is the *dependent* variable because it *depends* on changes in x.

There are times when you will need to write an equation when given a graph. To do this, locate the y-intercept and use the rise and run to find another point on the graph. Then write the equation in slope-intercept form.

Test-Taking Tip

Eliminating Choices Analyze the graph to determine the slope and the y-intercept. Then you can save time by eliminating answer choices that do not match the graph.

Standardized Test Example 4 Write an Equation in Slope-Intercept Form

Which of the following is an equation in slope-intercept form for the line shown?

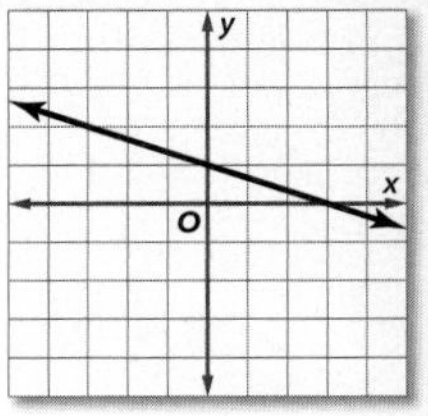

A $y = -3x + 1$

B $y = -3x + 3$

C $y = -\frac{1}{3}x + 1$

D $y = -\frac{1}{3}x + 3$

Read the Test Item

You need to find the slope and y-intercept of the line to write the equation.

Solve the Test Item

Step 1 The line crosses the y-axis at (0, 1), so the y-intercept is 1. The answer is either A or C.

Step 2 To get from (0, 1) to (3, 0), go down 1 unit and 3 units to the right. The slope is $-\frac{1}{3}$.

Step 3 Write the equation.

$y = mx + b$

$y = -\frac{1}{3}x + 1$

CHECK The graph also passes through (−3, 2). If the equation is correct, this should be a solution.

$y = -\frac{1}{3}x + 1$

$2 \stackrel{?}{=} -\frac{1}{3}(-3) + 1$

$2 \stackrel{?}{=} 1 + 1$

$2 = 2$ ✓ The answer is C.

Guided Practice

4. Which of the following is an equation in slope-intercept form for the line shown? F

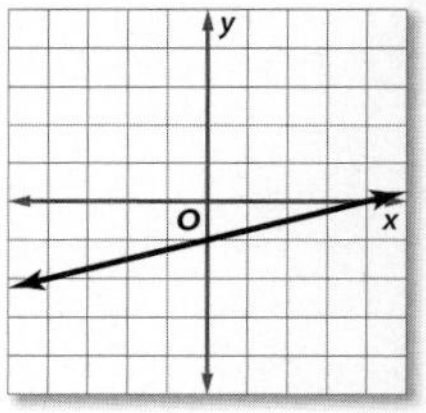

F $y = \frac{1}{4}x - 1$

G $y = \frac{1}{4}x + 4$

H $y = 4x - 1$

J $y = 4x + 4$

2 Modeling Real-World Data Real-world data can be modeled by a linear equation if there is a constant rate of change. The rate of change represents the slope. The y-intercept is the point where the value of the independent variable is 0.

Real-WorldLink

In 1997, about 2.6 million girls competed in high school sports. The number of girls competing in high school sports has increased by an average of 0.06 million per year since 1997.

Source: National Federation of High School Associations

Real-World Example 5 Write and Graph a Linear Equation

SPORTS **Use the information at the left about high school sports.**

a. Write a linear equation to find the number of girls in high school sports after 1997.

Words	Number of girls competing	equals	rate of change	times	number of years	plus	amount at start.
Variables	Let G = number of girls competing.			Let n = number of years since 1997.			
Equation	G	$=$	0.06	$\times$	n	$+$	2.6

The equation is $G = 0.06n + 2.6$.

b. Graph the equation.

The y-intercept is where the data begins. So, the graph passes through (0, 2.6).

The rate of change is the slope, so the slope is 0.06.

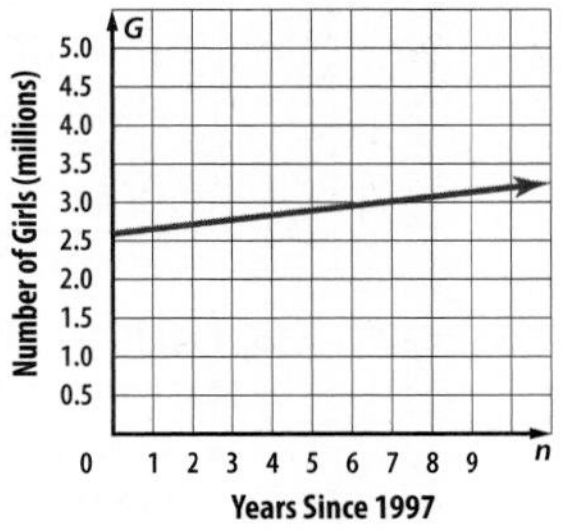

c. Estimate the number of girls competing in 2017.

The year 2017 is 20 years after 1997.

$G = 0.06n + 2.6$ Write the equation.

$= 0.06(20) + 2.6$ Replace n with 20.

$= 3.8$ Simplify.

There will be about 3.8 million girls competing in high school sports in 2017.

GuidedPractice

5. FUNDRAISERS The band boosters are selling sandwiches for \$5 each. They bought \$1160 in ingredients.

A. Write an equation for the profit P made on n sandwiches. $P = 5n - 1160$

B. Graph the equation. See margin.

C. Find the total profit if 1400 sandwiches are sold. \$5840

Check Your Understanding

= Step-by-Step Solutions begin on page R13.

Example 1 **Write an equation of a line in slope-intercept form with the given slope and y-intercept. Then graph the equation.** 1–4. See Ch. 4 Answer Appendix.

1. slope: 2, y-intercept: 4
2. slope: -5, y-intercept: 3
3. slope: $\frac{3}{4}$, y-intercept: -1
4. slope: $-\frac{5}{7}$, y-intercept: $-\frac{2}{3}$

Examples 2–3 **Graph each equation.** 5–10. See Ch. 4 Answer Appendix.

5. $-4x + y = 2$
6. $2x + y = -6$
7. $-3x + 7y = 21$
8. $6x - 4y = 16$
9. $y = -1$
10. $15y = 3$

Additional Example

5 HEALTH The ideal maximum heart rate for a 25-year-old exercising to burn fat is 117 beats per minute. For every five years older than 25, that ideal rate drops three beats per minute.

a. Write a linear equation to find the ideal maximum heart rate for anyone over 25 who is exercising to burn fat. $R = -\frac{3}{5}a + 117$, where R is the ideal maximum heart rate for a 25-year-old and a is the number of years older than 25

b. Graph the equation.

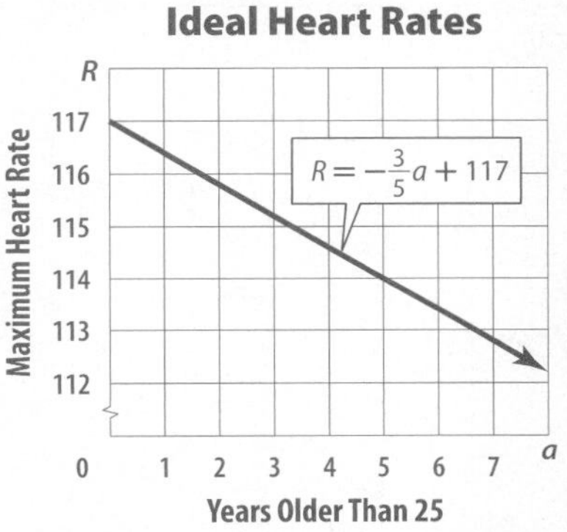

c. Find the ideal maximum heart rate for a 55-year-old person exercising to burn fat. 99 beats per minute

Additional Answer (Guided Practice)

5B.

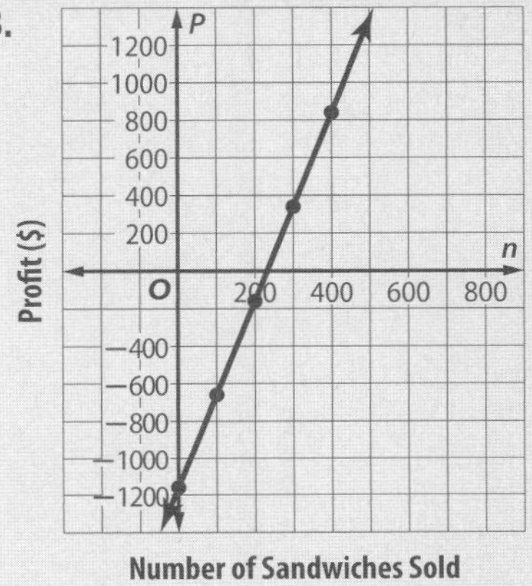

DifferentiatedInstruction AL ELL

If some students have difficulty with word problems because they cannot picture what the problem is trying to communicate,

Then sometimes it is easier for those students to graph or draw a picture of the given information before writing the equation. For Additional Example 5, you may wish to have students do part **b** first by using the starting point and the rate of change to determine other points on the graph. Then have students write the equation that describes the line formed.

3 Practice

Formative Assessment

Use Exercises 1–16 to check for understanding.

Use the chart at the bottom of this page to customize assignments for your students.

Teaching the Process Standards

Reasoning Mathematically proficient students make sense of quantities and their relationships in problem situations. Encourage students to start by identifying the independent and dependent variables.

Additional Answers

15b.

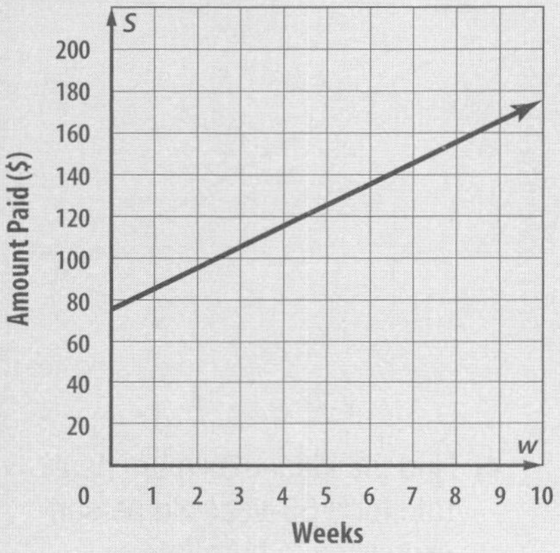

16b.

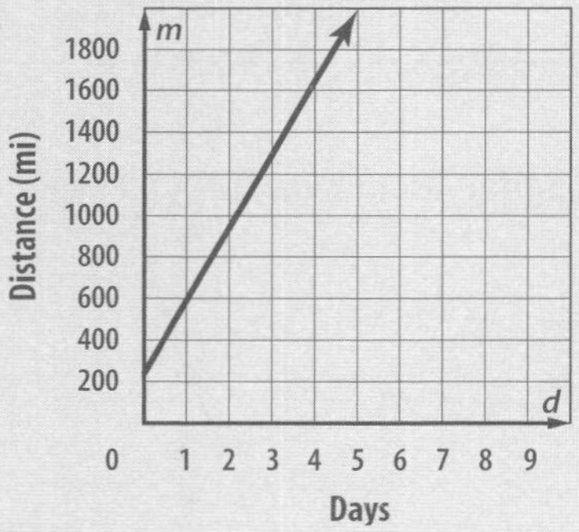

Example 4 **Write an equation in slope-intercept form for each graph shown.**

11.

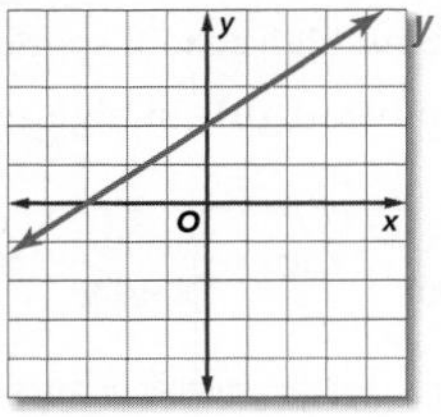

$y = \frac{2}{3}x + 2$

12.

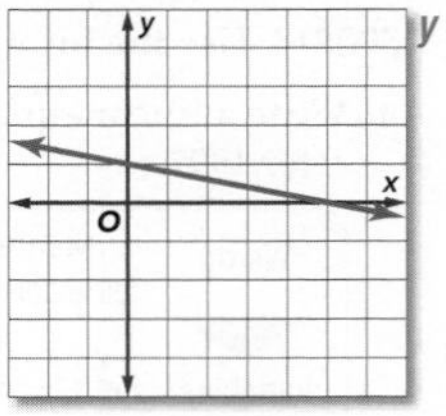

$y = -\frac{1}{5}x + 1$

13.

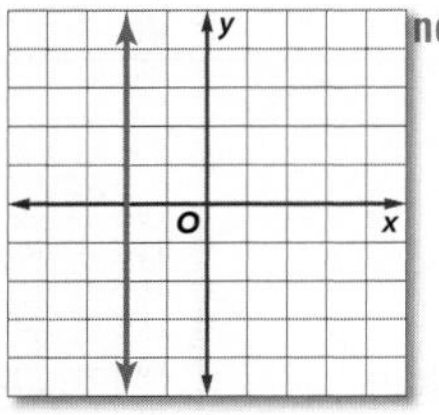

not possible

14.

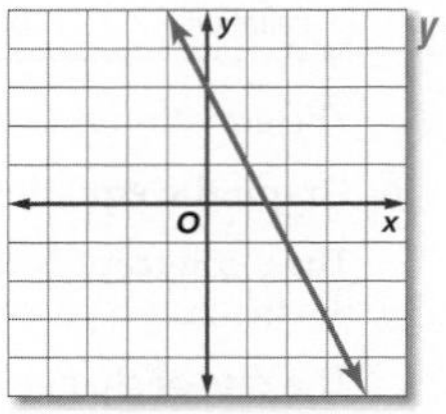

$y = -2x + 3$

Example 5 **15. FINANCIAL LITERACY** Rondell is buying a new stereo system for his car using Jack's Stereo layaway plan.

a. Write an equation for the total amount S that he has paid after w weeks. $S = 10w + 75$

b. Graph the equation. See margin.

c. Find out how much Rondell will have paid after 8 weeks. $155

16. REASONING Ana is driving from her home in Miami, Florida, to her grandmother's house in New York City. On the first day, she will travel 240 miles to Orlando, Florida, to pick up her cousin. Then they will travel 350 miles each day.

a. Write an equation that models the total number of miles m Ana has traveled, if d represents the number of days after she picks up her cousin. $m = 350d + 240$

b. Graph the equation. See margin.

c. How long will the drive take if the total length of the trip is 1343 miles? about 4 days

Practice and Problem Solving

Extra Practice is on page R4.

Example 1 **Write an equation of a line in slope-intercept form with the given slope and y-intercept. Then graph the equation.** 17–22. See Ch. 4 Answer Appendix.

17. slope: 5, y-intercept: 8

18. slope: 3, y-intercept: 10

19. slope: −4, y-intercept: 6

20. slope: −2, y-intercept: 8

21. slope: 3, y-intercept: −4

22. slope: 4, y-intercept: −6

Examples 2–3 **Graph each equation.** 23–32. See Ch. 4 Answer Appendix.

23. $-3x + y = 6$

24. $-5x + y = 1$

25. $-2x + y = -4$

26. $y = 7x - 7$

27. $5x + 2y = 8$

28. $4x + 9y = 27$

29. $y = 7$

30. $y = -\frac{2}{3}$

31. $21 = 7y$

32. $3y - 6 = 2x$

Differentiated Homework Options

Level	Assignment	Two-Day Option	
AL Basic	17–37, 62, 63, 65–83	17–37 odd, 67–70	18–36 even, 62, 63, 65, 66, 71–83
OL Core	17–49 odd, 50, 51, 53–57 odd, 58–63, 65–83	17–37, 67–70	38–63, 65, 66, 71–83
BL Advanced	38–79, (optional: 80–83)		

Example 4 **Write an equation in slope-intercept form for each graph shown.**

33. 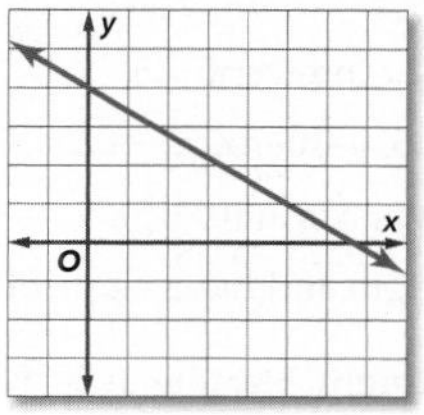

$y = -\frac{3}{5}x + 4$

34. 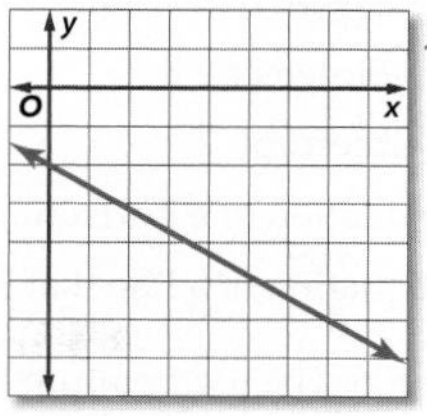

$y = -\frac{4}{7}x - 2$

35. 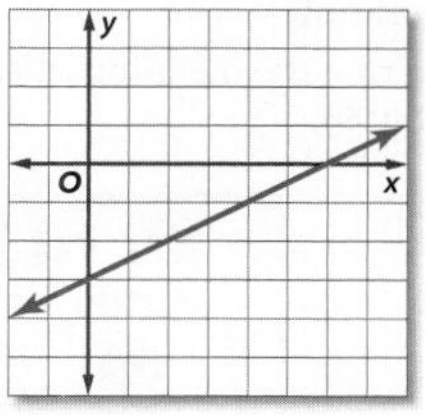

$y = \frac{1}{2}x - 3$

36. 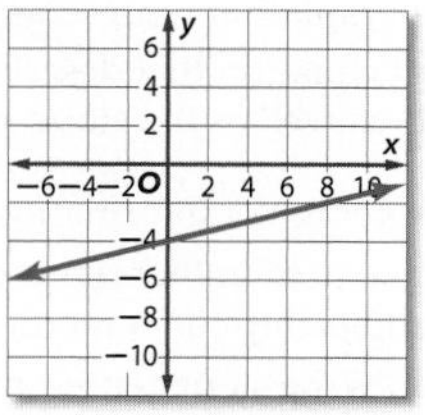

$y = \frac{1}{4}x - 4$

Example 5 **37** **MANATEES** In 1991, 1267 manatees inhabited Florida's waters. The manatee population has increased at a rate of 123 manatees per year.

a. Write an equation for the manatee population, P, t years since 1991. $P = 1267 + 123t$

b. Graph this equation. See margin.

c. In 2006, the manatee was removed from Florida's endangered species list. What was the manatee population in 2006? 3112 manatees

B **Write an equation of a line in slope-intercept form with the given slope and y-intercept.** 38–43. See margin.

38. slope: $\frac{1}{2}$, y-intercept: −3

39. slope: $\frac{2}{3}$, y-intercept: −5

40. slope: $-\frac{5}{6}$, y-intercept: 5

41. slope: $-\frac{3}{7}$, y-intercept: 2

42. slope: 1, y-intercept: 4

43. slope: 0, y-intercept: 5

Graph each equation. 44–49. See Ch. 4 Answer Appendix.

44. $y = \frac{3}{4}x - 2$

45. $y = \frac{5}{3}x + 4$

46. $3x + 8y = 32$

47. $5x - 6y = 36$

48. $-4x + \frac{1}{2}y = -1$

49. $3x - \frac{1}{4}y = 2$

50. **TRAVEL** A rental company charges \$8 per hour for a mountain bike plus a \$5 fee for a helmet.

a. Write an equation in slope-intercept form for the total rental cost C for a helmet and a bicycle for t hours. $C = 8t + 5$

b. Graph the equation. See margin.

c. What would the cost be for 2 helmets and 2 bicycles for 8 hours? \$138

51. **REASONING** For Illinois residents, the average tuition at Chicago State University is \$157 per credit hour. Fees cost \$218 per year.

a. Write an equation in slope-intercept form for the tuition T for c credit hours. $T = 157c + 218$

b. Find the cost for a student who is taking 32 credit hours. \$5242

Exercise Alert

Grid Paper Exercises 1–10, 15–32, 37, 44–49, 50, 58, and 62 require the use of grid paper.

Additional Answers

37b. 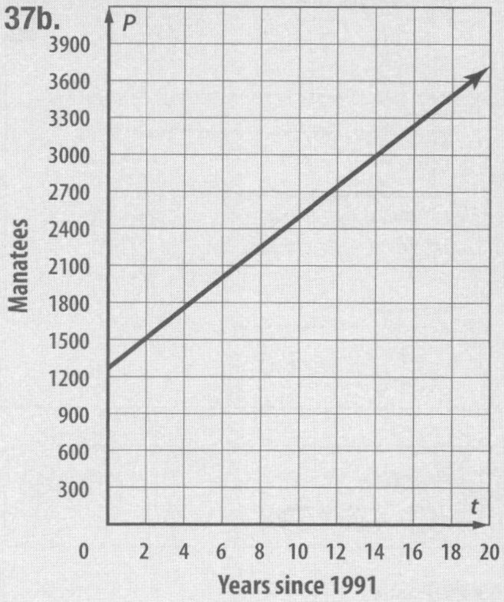

38. $y = \frac{1}{2}x - 3$

39. $y = \frac{2}{3}x - 5$

40. $y = -\frac{5}{6}x + 5$

41. $y = -\frac{3}{7}x + 2$

42. $y = x + 4$

43. $y = 5$

50b. 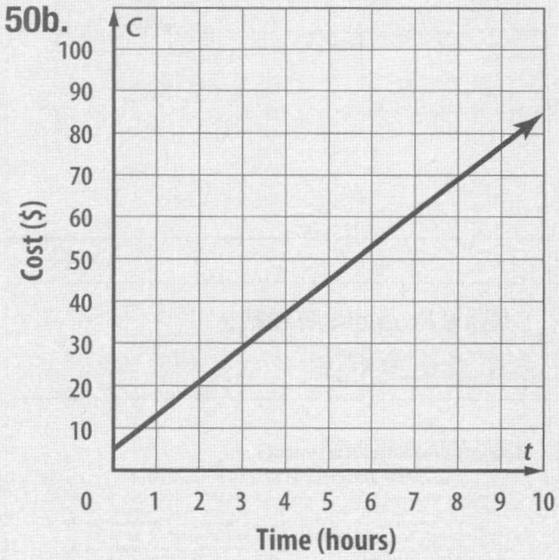

Differentiated Instruction OL BL

Extension Write $3x + 2y = 8$ and $-3x + 2y = 8$ on the board. Remind students that these equations are in the standard form for the equation of a line. Ask students to tell how the equations are alike and how they are different. Then, ask students to tell how the graphs of these two equations are alike and how they are different. The coefficients of x are additive inverses; the coefficients of y are the same, and the constant after the equals sign in each equation is the same. The slopes, $-\frac{3}{2}$ and $\frac{3}{2}$, are additive inverses of each other; they both have the same y-intercept, 4.

Write an equation of a line in slope-intercept form with the given slope and y-intercept. **52–55. See margin.**

52. slope: -1, y-intercept: 0

53. slope: 0.5, y-intercept: 7.5

54. slope: 0, y-intercept: 7

55. slope: -1.5, y-intercept: -0.25

56. Write an equation of a horizontal line that crosses the y-axis at $(0, -5)$. $y = -5$

57. Write an equation of a line that passes through the origin and has a slope of 3. $y = 3x$

C **58. TEMPERATURE** The temperature dropped rapidly overnight. Starting at 80°F, the temperature dropped 3° per minute.

a. Draw a graph that represents this drop from 0 to 8 minutes. **See margin.**

b. Write an equation that describes this situation. Describe the meaning of each variable as well as the slope and y-intercept. **See margin.**

59. FITNESS Refer to the information at the right.

a. Write an equation that represents the cost C of a membership for m months. $C = 45m + 145$

b. What does the slope represent?

c. What does the C-intercept represent? **the startup fee**

d. What is the cost of a two-year membership? **$1225**

GET FIT GYM
startup fee $145

$45 monthly fee

59b. the cost per month to maintain the membership

60. MAGAZINES A teen magazine began with a circulation of 500,000 in its first year. Since then, the circulation has increased an average of 33,388 per year.

a. Write an equation that represents the circulation c after t years. $c = 33{,}388t + 500{,}000$

b. What does the slope represent? **the increase in circulation each year**

c. What does the c-intercept represent? **the circulation in the first year**

d. If the magazine began in 1944, and this trend continues, in what year will the circulation reach 3,000,000? **2019**

61. SMART PHONES A telecommunications company sold 3305 smart phones in the first year of production. Suppose, on average, they expect to sell 25 phones per day.

a. Write an equation for the number of smart phones P sold t years after the first year of production, assuming 365 days per year. $P = 9125t + 3305$

b. If sales continue at this rate, how many years will it take for the company to sell 100,000 phones? **12 yr**

H.O.T. Problems Use Higher-Order Thinking Skills

62. OPEN ENDED Draw a graph representing a real-world linear function and write an equation for the graph. Describe what the graph represents. **See Ch. 4 Answer Appendix.**

63. REASONING Determine whether the equation of a vertical line can be written in slope-intercept form. Explain your reasoning. **No; because a vertical line has no slope, it cannot be written in slope-intercept form.**

64. CHALLENGE Summarize the characteristics that the graphs $y = 2x + 3$, $y = 4x + 3$, $y = -x + 3$, and $y = -10x + 3$ have in common. **Sample answer: All four graphs are lines that cross the y-axis at 3.**

65. REGULARITY If given an equation in standard form, explain how to determine the rate of change. **See margin.**

66. WRITING IN MATH Explain how you would use a given y-intercept and the slope to predict a y-value for a given x-value without graphing. **See margin.**

Study Guide and Intervention
AL OL ELL

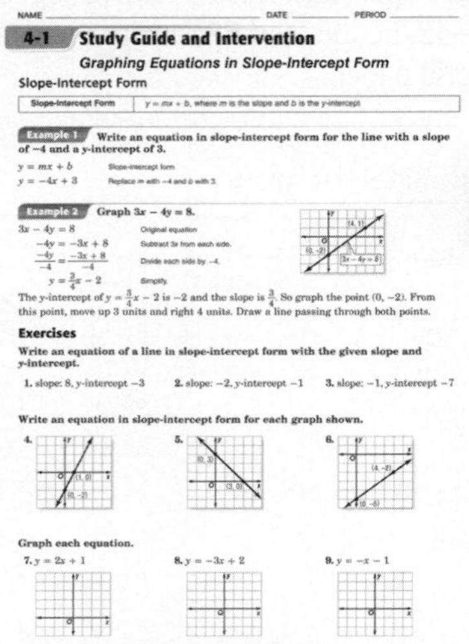
4-1 Study Guide and Intervention
Graphing Equations in Slope-Intercept Form
Slope-Intercept Form

Practice
AL OL BL ELL

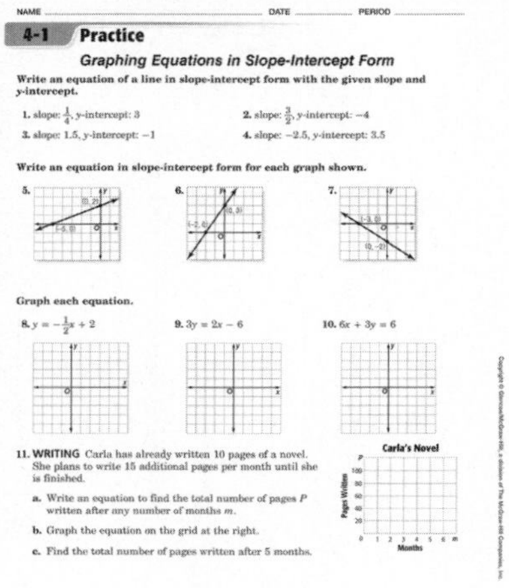
4-1 Practice
Graphing Equations in Slope-Intercept Form

Word Problem Practice
AL OL BL ELL

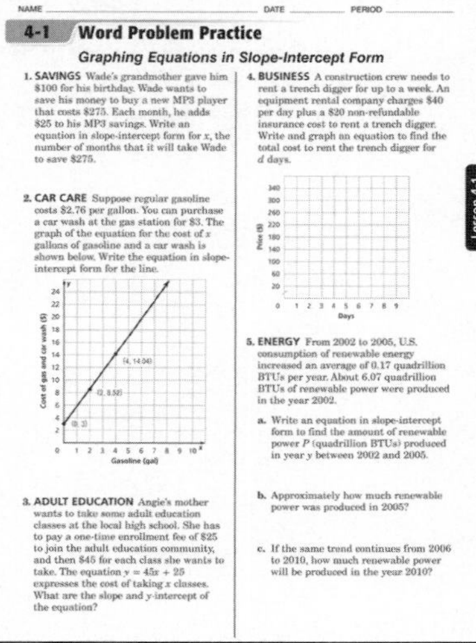
4-1 Word Problem Practice
Graphing Equations in Slope-Intercept Form

Enrichment
OL BL

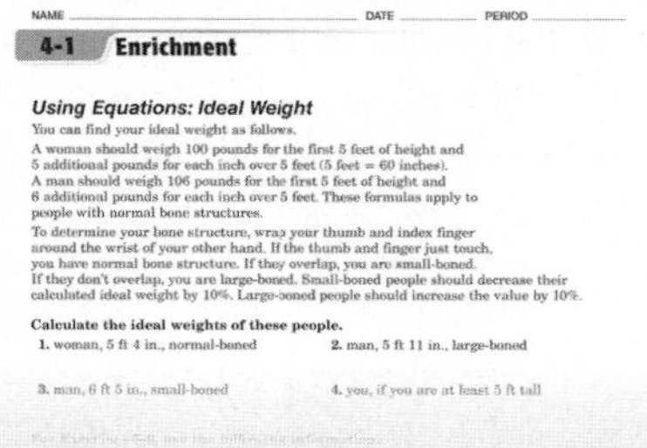
4-1 Enrichment
Using Equations: Ideal Weight

Additional Answers

52. $y = -x$

53. $y = 0.5x + 7.5$

54. $y = 7$

55. $y = -1.5x - 0.25$

Standardized Test Practice

67. A music store has x CDs in stock. If 350 are sold and $3y$ are added to stock, which expression represents the number of CDs in stock? **B**

A $350 + 3y - x$
C $x + 350 + 3y$
B $x - 350 + 3y$
D $3y - 350 - x$

68. PROBABILITY The table shows the result of a survey of favorite activities. What is the probability that a student's favorite activity is sports or drama club? **H**

Extracurricular Activity	Students
art club	24
band	134
choir	37
drama club	46
mock trial	19
school paper	26
sports	314

F $\frac{3}{8}$ G $\frac{4}{9}$ H $\frac{3}{5}$ J $\frac{2}{3}$

69. A recipe for fruit punch calls for 2 ounces of orange juice for every 8 ounces of lemonade. If Jennifer uses 64 ounces of lemonade, which proportion can she use to find x, the number of ounces of orange juice needed? **C**

A $\frac{2}{x} = \frac{64}{6}$
C $\frac{2}{8} = \frac{x}{64}$
B $\frac{8}{x} = \frac{64}{2}$
D $\frac{6}{2} = \frac{x}{64}$

70. EXTENDED RESPONSE The table shows the results of a canned food drive. 1225 cans were collected, and the 12th-grade class collected 55 more cans than the 10th-grade class. How many cans each did the 10th- and 12th-grade classes collect? Show your work. **See margin.**

Grade	Cans
9	340
10	x
11	280
12	y

Spiral Review

For each arithmetic sequence, determine the related function. Then determine if the function is *proportional* or *nonproportional*. (Lesson 3-6) **71–74. See margin.**

71. 3, 7, 11, … **72.** 8, 6, 4, … **73.** 0, 3, 6, … **74.** 1, 2, 3, …

75. GAME SHOWS Contestants on a game show win money by answering 10 questions. (Lesson 3-5)

a. Find the value of the 10th question. **$25,500**

b. If all questions are answered correctly, how much are the winnings? **$142,500**

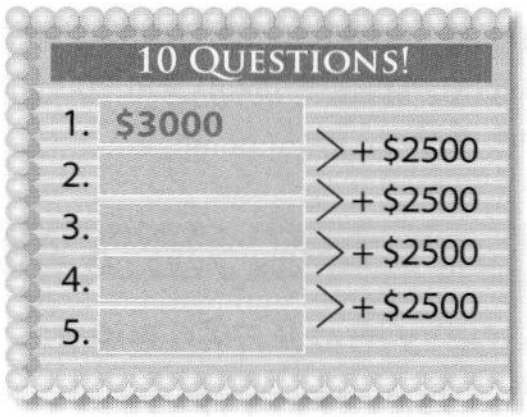

Suppose y varies directly as x. Write a direct variation equation that relates x and y. Then solve. (Lesson 3-4)

76. If $y = 10$ when $x = 5$, find y when $x = 6$. **$y = 2x$; 12**

77. If $y = -16$ when $x = 4$, find x when $y = 20$. **$y = -4x$; -5**

78. If $y = 6$ when $x = 18$, find y when $x = -12$. **$y = \frac{1}{3}x$; -4**

79. If $y = 12$ when $x = 15$, find x when $y = -6$. **$y = 0.8x$; -7.5**

Skills Review

Find the slope of the line that passes through each pair of points.

80. (2, 3), (9, 7) $\frac{4}{7}$ **81.** (−3, 6), (2, 4) $-\frac{2}{5}$ **82.** (2, 6), (−1, 3) **1** **83.** (−3, 3), (1, 3) **0**

71. $a_n = 4n - 1$; nonproportional, does not contain (0, 0)

72. $a_n = -2n + 10$; nonproportional, does not contain (0, 0)

73. $a_n = 3n - 3$; nonproportional, does not contain (0, 0)

74. $a_n = n$; proportional, contains (0, 0)

Teaching the Process Standards

Regularity Mathematically proficient students look for general methods. In Exercise 65, encourage students to look at problems they have solved in order to make a general statement.

4 Assess

Name the Math Have students summarize how they can draw the graph of an equation without finding points that satisfy the equation.

Additional Answers

58a.

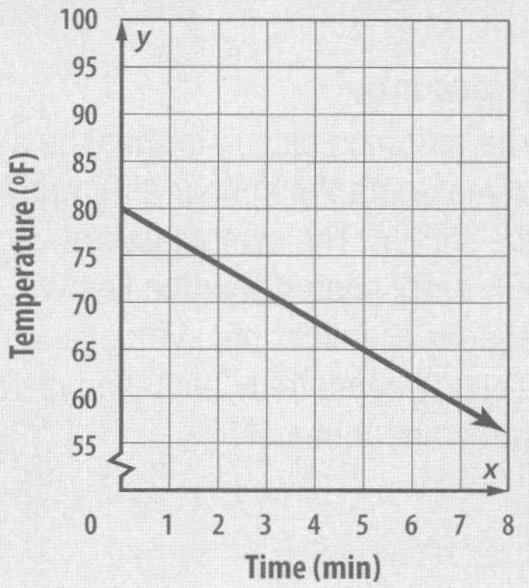

58b. $y = -3x + 80$; y represents the temperature, x represents the elapsed time, the slope represents the change in temperature per minute, and the y-intercept represents the temperature when the temperature started to drop.

65. Sample answer: Assume that the coefficient of y is not 0. We would first have to rewrite the equation in slope-intercept form. The rate of change is also the slope, so the coefficient for the x-variable is the rate of change.

66. Sample answer: If the slope is m and the y-intercept is b, substitute the given x-value for x in $y = mx + b$. Then simplify.

70. The 10th grade class collected 275, and the 12th grade class collected 330. First I found that the total number of cans collected by the 10th and 12th grade classes is 1225 − (340 + 280) or 605. Then, if x is the number of cans the 10th grade class collected, then the 12th grade class collected $x + 55$ cans. The sum of these is 605.
10th = x, 12th = $x + 55$,
$x + x + 55 = 605$; $x = 275$,
10th = 275, 12th = 330

1 Focus

Objective Use a graphing calculator to investigate families of linear functions.

Materials for Each Student

- T1–83/84 Plus or other graphing calculator

Teaching Tip

The graphing calculator has the ability to make graphs appear differently on the screen. The symbol before each **Y=** entry shows how the line will appear. Highlight the symbol and press [ENTER] repeatedly until the type of line you want appears.

2 Teach

Working in Cooperative Groups

Have students work in groups of two or three, mixing abilities. Have groups complete Activities 1–3 and Exercises 1–9.

- If necessary, remind students how to enter equations into the **Y=** list. Point out that by highlighting the = sign and pressing [ENTER], an equation will remain in the list but not appear on the screen.
- The standard viewing window is a [−10, 10] by [−10, 10] screen with **XScl** and **YScl** of 1. It is selected by pressing [ZOOM] 6.
- Before starting Activity 1, make sure students have cleared or suppressed any equations in the **Y=** list other than those they wish to graph.

Practice Have students complete Exercises 10–16.

Teaching the Process Standards

Structure Mathematically proficient students look closely to discern a pattern or structure. Point out to students that each Activity focuses on a specific parameter in a linear equation.

EXTEND 4-1 Graphing Technology Lab
The Family of Linear Graphs

A family of people is related by birth, marriage, or adoption. Often people in families share characteristics. The graphs in a family share at least one characteristic. Graphs in the linear family are all lines, with the simplest graph in the family being that of the parent function $y = x$. This parent function is also known as the **identity function**. Its graph contains all points with coordinates (a, a). Its domain and range are all real numbers.

Parent Graph
Identity Function

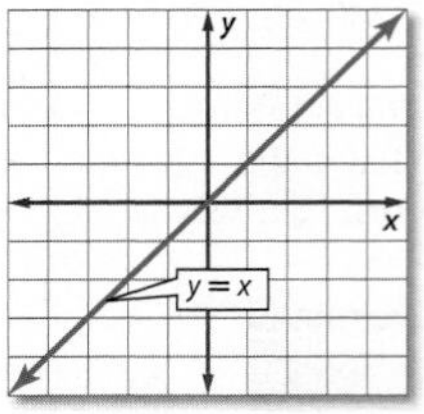

Process Standards
PS.7

You can use a graphing calculator to investigate how changing the parameters m and b in $y = mx + b$ affects the graphs in the family of linear functions.

Activity 1 Changing b in $y = mx + b$

Graph $y = x$, $y = x + 4$, and $y = x - 2$ in the standard viewing window.

Enter the equations in the **Y=** list as **Y1**, **Y2**, and **Y3**. Then graph the equations.

KEYSTROKES: [Y=] [X,T,θ,n] [ENTER] [X,T,θ,n] [+] 4 [ENTER] [X,T,θ,n] [−] 2 [ENTER] [ZOOM] 6

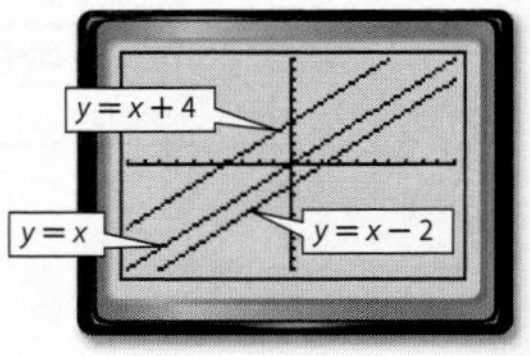

[−10, 10] scl: 1 by [−10, 10] scl: 1

1A. How do the slopes of the graphs compare? **They have the same slope.**

1B. Compare the graph of $y = x + 4$ and the graph of $y = x$. How would you obtain the graph of $y = x + 4$ from the graph of $y = x$? **Shift the graph of $y = x$ up 4 units.**

1C. How would you obtain the graph of $y = x - 2$ from the graph of $y = x$? **Shift the graph of $y = x$ down 2 units.**

Changing the y-intercept, b, translates, or moves, a linear function up or down the y-axis. Changing m in $y = mx + b$ affects the graphs in a different way. First, investigate positive values of m.

Activity 2 Changing m in $y = mx + b$, Positive Values

Graph $y = x$, $y = 2x$, and $y = \frac{1}{3}x$ in the standard viewing window.

Enter the equations in the **Y=** list and graph.

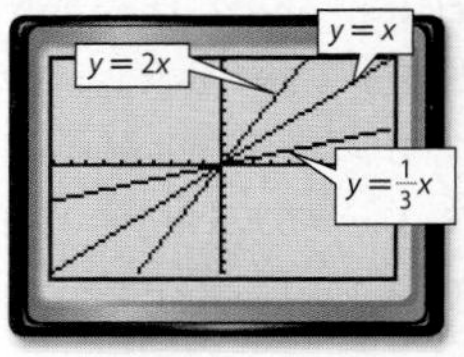

[−10, 10] scl: 1 by [−10, 10] scl: 1

2A. How do the y-intercepts of the graphs compare? **They have the same y-intercept.**

2B. Compare the graph of $y = 2x$ and the graph of $y = x$.

2C. Which is steeper, the graph of $y = \frac{1}{3}x$ or the graph of $y = x$? **The graph of $y = x$ is steeper.**

2B. The graph of $y = 2x$ is steeper than the graph of $y = x$.

Does changing m to a negative value affect the graph differently than changing it to a positive value?

Additional Answers

11. The value of m tells you how steep the graph should be compared to the graph of $y = x$ and the value of b tells you how many units higher or lower than $y = x$ the graph will be.

12. The graphs are all horizontal lines. They are all parallel. They intersect the y-axis at different points.

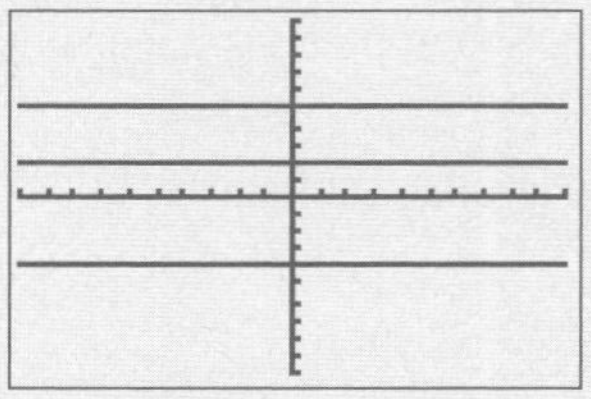

[−10, 10] scl: 1 by [−10, 10] scl: 1

Activity 3 Changing m in $y = mx + b$, Negative Values

Graph $y = x$, $y = -x$, $y = -3x$, and $y = -\frac{1}{2}x$ in the standard viewing window.

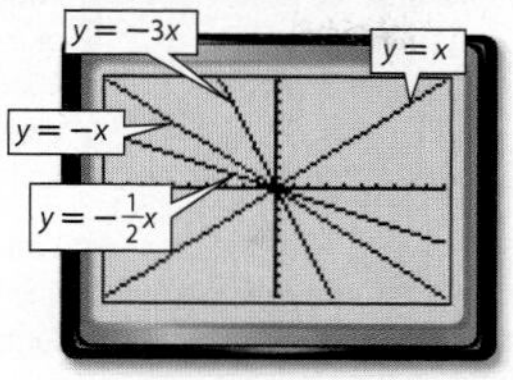

[−10, 10] scl: 1 by [−10, 10] scl: 1

Enter the equations in the **Y=** list and graph.

3A. How are the graphs with negative values of m different than graphs with a positive m?

3B. Compare the graphs of $y = -x$, $y = -3x$, and $y = -\frac{1}{2}x$. Which is steepest? $y = -3x$

3A. The graphs with negative values of m slope downward from left to right. Graphs with a positive m slope upward from left to right.

Analyze the Results

SENSE-MAKING AND PERSEVERANCE **Graph each set of equations on the same screen. Describe the similarities or differences.** 1–6. See Ch. 4 Answer Appendix.

1. $y = 2x$; $y = 2x + 3$; $y = 2x - 7$

2. $y = x + 1$; $y = 2x + 1$; $y = \frac{1}{4}x + 1$

3. $y = x + 4$; $y = 2x + 4$; $y = \frac{3}{4}x + 4$

4. $y = 0.5x + 2$; $y = 0.5x - 5$; $y = 0.5x + 4$

5. $y = -2x - 2$; $y = -4.2x - 2$; $y = -\frac{1}{3}x - 2$

6. $y = 3x$; $y = 3x + 6$; $y = 3x - 7$

7. Families of graphs have common characteristics. What do the graphs of all equations of the form $y = mx + b$ have in common? They all are nonvertical lines.

8. How does the value of b affect the graph of $y = mx + b$? The value of b determines the y-intercept.

9. What is the result of changing the value of m on the graph of $y = mx + b$ if m is positive?

10. How can you determine which graph is steepest by examining the following equations? $y = 3x$, $y = -4x - 7$, $y = \frac{1}{2}x + 4$

11. Explain how knowing about the effects of m and b can help you sketch the graph of an equation. See margin.

12. The equation $y = k$ can also be a parent graph. Graph $y = 5$, $y = 2$, and $y = -4$ on the same screen. Describe the similarities or differences among the graphs. See margin.

9. Changing the value of m changes the slope of the graph. If m is positive, then the greater the value of m the steeper the graph.

10. The graph of $y = -4x - 7$ is steepest because the absolute value of m is greatest.

Extension

Nonlinear functions can also be defined in terms of a family of graphs. Graph each set of equations on the same screen. Describe the similarities or differences. 13–15. See margin.

13. $y = x^2$; $y = -3x^2$; $y = (-3x)^2$

14. $y = x^2$; $y = x^2 + 3$; $y = (x - 2)^2$

15. $y = x^2$; $y = 2x^2 + 4$; $y = (3x)^2 - 5$

16. Describe the similarities and differences in the classes of functions $f(x) = x^2 + c$ and $f(x) = (x + c)^2$, where c is any real number. See margin.

3 Assess

Formative Assessment

Ask students to summarize what belonging to a family of graphs means.

- Use Exercise 1 to assess whether students understand how changing b affects the graphs in a family of linear functions.
- Use Exercises 3 and 5 to assess whether students understand how changing m affects the graphs in a family of linear functions.

From Concrete to Abstract

Ask: How can the graph of $y = mx + b$ be drawn from the graph of $y = mx$? Sample answer: Shift the graph of $y = mx$ up b units if b is positive and down $|b|$ units if b is negative.

Teaching the Process Standards

Sense-Making and Perseverance Mathematically proficient students consider analogous problems in order to gain insight into its solution. In Exercises 1–6, encourage students to change the viewing window on their graphing calculator to get the information they need.

Additional Answers

13. The graphs have the same y-intercept, but different widths.

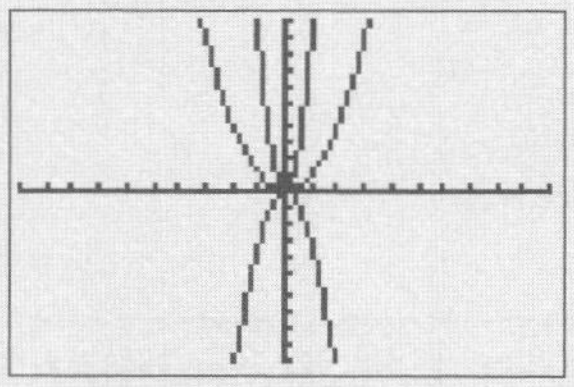

[−10, 10] scl: 1 by [−10, 10] scl: 1

14. The widths of each graph are the same, but each graph has different y-intercepts.

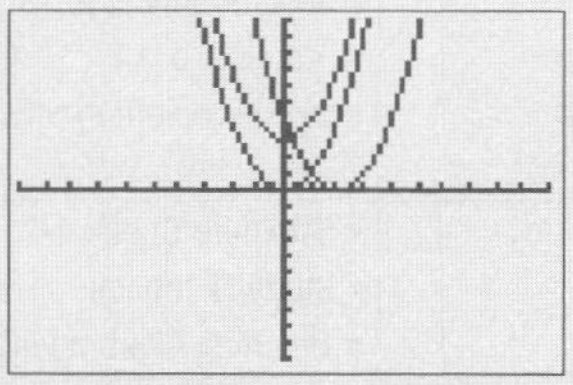

[−10, 10] scl: 1 by [−10, 10] scl: 1

15. The graphs have different widths and different y-intercepts.

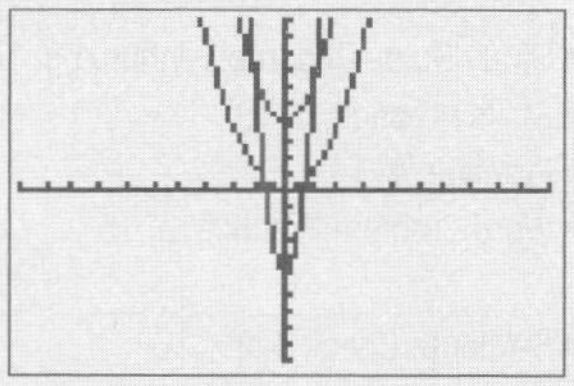

[−10, 10] scl: 1 by [−10, 10] scl: 1

16. In the graph of $f(x) = x^2 + c$, the graph is like $f(x) = x^2$, but shifted vertically $|c|$ units. In the graph of $f(x) = (x + c)^2$, the graph is like $f(x) = x^2$, but shifted horizontally $|c|$ units.

1 Focus

VerticalAlignment

Before Lesson 4-2 Graph lines given the slope and y-intercept.

Lesson 4-2 Write an equation of a line in slope-intercept form given the slope and one point or two points.

After Lesson 4-2 Write linear equations in point-slope form.

2 Teach

Scaffolding Questions

Have students read the **Why?** section of the lesson.

Ask:

- What two points would be on the graph of the data? (2006, 1.6) and (2009, 2.2)
- How could you find the slope of a line that would model the data? $\frac{2.2 - 1.6}{2009 - 2006} = \frac{0.6}{3} = 0.2$
- How could you use the equation that models this situation to predict the zoo attendance in any given year? Substitute the year for x, then solve for y.

LESSON 4-2 Writing Equations in Slope-Intercept Form

Then

- You graphed lines given the slope and the y-intercept.

Now

1. Write an equation of a line in slope-intercept form given the slope and one point.
2. Write an equation of a line in slope-intercept form given two points.

Why?

- In 2006, the attendance at the Columbus Zoo and Aquarium was about 1.6 million. In 2009, the zoo's attendance was about 2.2 million. You can find the average rate of change for these data. Then you can write an equation that would model the average attendance at the zoo for a given year.

NewVocabulary
constraint
linear extrapolation

Content Standards
AI.L.4, AI.L.5, AI.L.6

Process Standards
PS.3, PS.6

1 Write an Equation Given the Slope and a Point

The next example shows how to write an equation of a line if you are given a slope and a point other than the y-intercept.

Example 1 Write an Equation Given the Slope and a Point

Write an equation of the line that passes through (2, 1) with a slope of 3.

You are given the slope but not the y-intercept.

Step 1 Find the y-intercept.

$y = mx + b$	Slope-intercept form
$1 = 3(2) + b$	Replace m with 3, y with 1, and x with 2.
$1 = 6 + b$	Simplify.
$1 - 6 = 6 + b - 6$	Subtract 6 from each side.
$-5 = b$	Simplify.

Step 2 Write the equation in slope-intercept form.

$y = mx + b$	Slope-intercept form
$y = 3x - 5$	Replace m with 3 and b with −5.

Therefore, the equation of the line is $y = 3x - 5$.

GuidedPractice

Write an equation of a line that passes through the given point and has the given slope.

1A. (−2, 5), slope 3 $y = 3x + 11$

1B. (4, −7), slope −1 $y = -x - 3$

2 Write an Equation Given Two Points

If you are given two points through which a line passes, you can use them to find the slope first. Then follow the steps in Example 1 to write the equation.

Lesson 4-2 Resources

Resource	Approaching Level AL	On Level OL	Beyond Level BL	English Learners ELL
Teacher Edition	▪ Differentiated Instruction, p. 228	▪ Differentiated Instruction, pp. 228, 232	▪ Differentiated Instruction, p. 232	
Chapter Resource Masters	▪ Study Guide and Intervention, pp. 11–12 ▪ Skills Practice, p. 13 ▪ Practice, p. 14 ▪ Word Problem Practice, p. 15	▪ Study Guide and Intervention, pp. 11–12 ▪ Skills Practice, p. 13 ▪ Practice, p. 14 ▪ Word Problem Practice, p. 15 ▪ Enrichment, p. 16	▪ Practice, p. 14 ▪ Word Problem Practice, p. 15 ▪ Enrichment, p. 16	▪ Study Guide and Intervention, pp. 11–12 ▪ Skills Practice, p. 13 ▪ Practice, p. 14 ▪ Word Problem Practice, p. 15
Other	▪ 5-Minute Check 4-2 ▪ Study Notebook ▪ Teaching Algebra with Manipulatives	▪ 5-Minute Check 4-2 ▪ Study Notebook ▪ Teaching Algebra with Manipulatives	▪ 5-Minute Check 4-2 ▪ Study Notebook	▪ 5-Minute Check 4-2 ▪ Study Notebook ▪ Teaching Algebra with Manipulatives

Example 2 Write an Equation Given Two Points

Write an equation of the line that passes through each pair of points.

a. (3, 1) and (2, 4)

Step 1 Find the slope of the line containing the given points.

$m = \frac{y_2 - y_1}{x_2 - x_1}$ — Slope Formula

$= \frac{4-1}{2-3}$ — $(x_1, y_1) = (3, 1)$ and $(x_2, y_2) = (2, 4)$

$= \frac{3}{-1}$ or -3 — Simplify.

Step 2 Use either point to find the y-intercept.

$y = mx + b$ — Slope-intercept form

$4 = (-3)(2) + b$ — Replace m with -3, x with 2, and y with 4.

$4 = -6 + b$ — Simplify.

$4 - (-6) = -6 + b - (-6)$ — Subtract -6 from each side.

$10 = b$ — Simplify.

Step 3 Write the equation in slope-intercept form.

$y = mx + b$ — Slope-intercept form

$y = -3x + 10$ — Replace m with -3 and b with 10.

Therefore, the equation is $y = -3x + 10$.

b. (−4, −2) and (−5, −6)

Step 1 Find the slope of the line containing the given points.

$m = \frac{y_2 - y_1}{x_2 - x_1}$ — Slope Formula

$= \frac{-6-(-2)}{-5-(-4)}$ — $(x_1, y_1) = (-4, -2)$ and $(x_2, y_2) = (-5, -6)$

$= \frac{-4}{-1}$ or 4 — Simplify.

Step 2 Use either point to find the y-intercept.

$y = mx + b$ — Slope-intercept form

$-2 = 4(-4) + b$ — Replace m with 4, x with -4, and y with -2.

$-2 = -16 + b$ — Simplify.

$-2 - (-16) = -16 + b - (-16)$ — Subtract -16 from each side.

$14 = b$ — Simplify.

Step 3 Write the equation in slope-intercept form.

$y = mx + b$ — Slope-intercept form

$y = 4x + 14$ — Replace m with 4 and b with 14.

Therefore, the equation is $y = 4x + 14$.

StudyTip

Choosing a point Given two points on a line, you may select either point to be (x_1, y_1). Be sure to remain consistent throughout the problem.

StudyTip

Slope If the (x_1, y_1) coordinates are negative, be sure to account for both the negative signs and the subtraction symbols in the Slope Formula.

GuidedPractice

Write an equation of the line that passes through each pair of points.

2A. (−1, 12), (4, −8) $y = -4x + 8$

2B. (5, −8), (−7, 0) $y = -\frac{2}{3}x - \frac{14}{3}$

Teach with Tech

Audio Recording Have students record an explanation what each number of an equation in slope-intercept form represents in a real world situation. This recording can be replayed as review before beginning an assignment or a quiz.

1 Write an Equation Given the Slope and a Point

Example 1 shows how to write an equation for a line given the slope and a point on the line.

Formative Assessment

Use the Guided Practice exercises after each Example to determine students' understanding of concepts.

Additional Example

1 Write an equation of a line that passes through (2, −3) with a slope of $\frac{1}{2}$. $y = \frac{1}{2}x - 4$

Additional Examples also in Interactive Classroom PowerPoint® Presentations

IWB Interactive White Board READY

2 Write an Equation Given Two Points

Example 2 shows how to write an equation for a line given any two points on the line. **Example 3** shows how to solve a real-world problem by writing an equation for a line given two points on the line. **Example 4** shows how to use a linear equation to predict values for a real-world problem.

Additional Example

2 Write an equation of the line that passes through each pair of points.

a. (−3, −4) and (−2, −8) $y = -4x - 16$

b. (6, −2) and (3, 4) $y = -2x + 10$

Focus on Mathematical Content

Slope-Intercept Form When only the coordinates of two points on a line are known, use the two points to find the slope. Substitute the slope and the values of one of the points into $y = mx + b$ and solve for b, the y-intercept.

Additional Examples

3 **ECONOMY** During one year, Malik's cost for self-serve regular gasoline was $3.20 on the first of June and $3.42 on the first of July. Write a linear equation to predict Malik's cost of gasoline the first of any month during the year, using 1 to represent January. $y = 0.22x + 1.88$

4 **ECONOMY** On average, Malik uses 25 gallons of gasoline per month. He budgeted $100 for gasoline in October. Use the prediction equation in Additional Example 3 to determine if Malik will have to add to his budget. Explain. If gasoline prices increase at the same rate, a gallon will cost $4.08 in October. 25 gallons at this price is $102, so Malik will have to add at least $2 to his budget.

Teaching the Process Standards

Precision Mathematically proficient students express numerical answers with a degree of precision appropriate for the problem context. Discuss when estimates are appropriate and when problems require more exact answers.

In mathematics, a **constraint** is a condition that a solution must satisfy. Equations can be viewed as constraints in a problem situation. The solutions of the equation meet the constraints of the problem.

Real-WorldCareer

Ground Crew
Airline ground crew responsibilities include checking tickets, helping passengers with luggage, and making sure that baggage is loaded properly and secure. This job usually requires a high school diploma or GED.

Source: Airline Jobs

Real-World Example 3 Use Slope-Intercept Form

PT

FLIGHTS The table shows the number of domestic flights in the U.S. from 2004 to 2008. Write an equation that could be used to predict the number of flights if it continues to decrease at the same rate.

Year	Flights (millions)
2004	9.97
2005	10.04
2006	9.71
2007	9.84
2008	9.37

Understand You know the number of flights for 2004–2008.

Plan Let x represent the number of years since 2000, and let y represent the number of flights. Write an equation of the line that passes through (4, 9.97) and (8, 9.37).

Solve Find the slope.

$m = \frac{y_2 - y_1}{x_2 - x_1}$ — Slope formula

$= \frac{9.37 - 9.97}{8 - 4}$ — Let $(x_1, y_1) = (4, 9.97)$ and $(x_2, y_2) = (8, 9.37)$.

$= -\frac{0.6}{4}$ or -0.15 — Simplify.

Use (8, 9.37) to find the y-intercept of the line.

$y = mx + b$ — Slope-intercept form

$9.37 = -0.15(8) + b$ — Replace y with 9.37, m with −0.15, and x with 8.

$9.37 = -1.2 + b$ — Simplify.

$10.57 = b$ — Add 1.2 to each side.

Write the equation using $m = -0.15$ and $b = 10.57$.

$y = mx + b$ — Slope-intercept form

$y = -0.15x + 10.57$ — Replace m with −0.15 and b with 10.57.

Check Check your result by using the coordinates of the other point.

$y = -0.15x + 10.57$ — Original equation

$9.97 \stackrel{?}{=} -0.15(4) + 10.57$ — Replace y with 9.97 and x with 4.

$9.97 = 9.97$ ✓ — Simplify.

GuidedPractice

3. FINANCIAL LITERACY In addition to his weekly salary, Ethan is paid $16 per delivery. Last week, he made 5 deliveries, and his total pay was $215. Write a linear equation to find Ethan's total weekly pay T if he makes d deliveries. $T = 16d + 135$

You can use a linear equation to make predictions about values that are beyond the range of the data. This process is called **linear extrapolation**.

Problem-SolvingTip

Precision Deciding whether an answer is reasonable is useful when an exact answer is not necessary.

Real-World Example 4 Predict from Slope-Intercept Form

PT

FLIGHTS Estimate the number of domestic flights in 2020.

$y = -0.15x + 10.57$ — Original equation

$= -0.15(20) + 10.57$ or 7.57 million — Replace x with 20.

GuidedPractice

4. MONEY Use the equation in Guided Practice 3 to predict how much money Ethan will earn in a week if he makes 8 deliveries. $263

DifferentiatedInstruction AL OL

If students are confused by learning more than one way to write a linear equation,

Then have those students use the definition of slope to derive the slope-intercept form of an equation. This same approach can be used in Lesson 4-3 for the point-slope form of an equation. The logical learner does best when relating new concepts to concepts already learned.

Check Your Understanding

= Step-by-Step Solutions begin on page R13.

Example 1 **Write an equation of the line that passes through the given point and has the given slope.**

1. (3, −3), slope 3 $y = 3x - 12$
2. (2, 4), slope 2 $y = 2x$
3. (1, 5), slope −1 $y = -x + 6$
4. (−4, 6), slope −2 $y = -2x - 2$

Example 2 **Write an equation of the line that passes through each pair of points.**

5. (4, −3), (2, 3) $y = -3x + 9$
6. (−7, −3), (−3, 5) $y = 2x + 11$
7. (−1, 3), (0, 8) $y = 5x + 8$
8. (−2, 6), (0, 0) $y = -3x$

Examples 3, 4 9. **WHITEWATER RAFTING** Ten people from a local youth group went to Black Hills Whitewater Rafting Tour Company for a one-day rafting trip. The group paid $425.

a. Write an equation in slope-intercept form to find the total cost C for p people. $C = 35p + 75$

b. How much would it cost for 15 people? $600

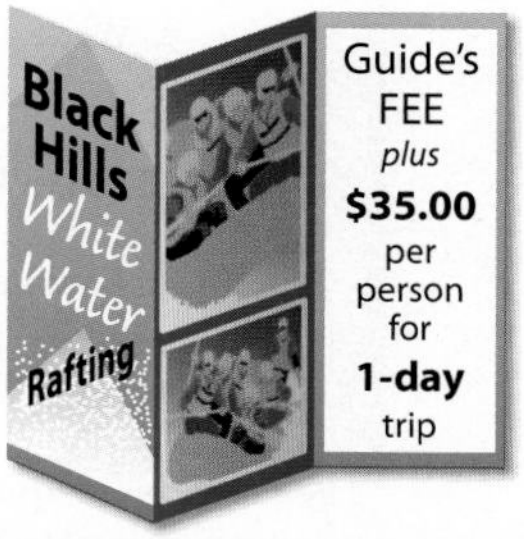

Practice and Problem Solving

Extra Practice is on page R4.

Example 1 **Write an equation of the line that passes through the given point and has the given slope.**

10. (3, 1), slope 2 $y = 2x - 5$
11. (−1, 4), slope −1 $y = -x + 3$
12. (1, 0), slope 1 $y = x - 1$
13. (7, 1), slope 8 $y = 8x - 55$
14. (2, 5), slope −2 $y = -2x + 9$
15. (2, 6), slope 2 $y = 2x + 2$

Example 2 **Write an equation of the line that passes through each pair of points.**

16. (9, −2), (4, 3) $y = -x + 7$
17. (−2, 5), (5, −2) $y = -x + 3$
18. (−5, 3), (0, −7) $y = -2x - 7$
19. (3, 5), (2, −2) $y = 7x - 16$
20. (−1, −3), (−2, 3) $y = -6x - 9$
21. (−2, −4), (2, 4) $y = 2x$

Examples 3, 4 22. **MODELING** Greg is driving a remote control car at a constant speed. He starts the timer when the car is 5 feet away. After 2 seconds the car is 35 feet away.

a. Write a linear equation to find the distance d of the car from Greg. $d = 15t + 5$

b. Estimate the distance the car has traveled after 10 seconds. 155 ft

23. **ZOOS** Refer to the beginning of the lesson.

a. Write a linear equation to find the attendance (in millions) y after x years. Let x be the number of years since 2000. $y = 0.2x + 0.4$

b. Estimate the zoo's attendance in 2020. 4.4 million

28. $y = \frac{2}{3}x - 4\frac{1}{3}$
29. $y = \frac{2}{7}x - 2\frac{4}{7}$

24. **BOOKS** In 1904, a dictionary cost 30¢. Since then the cost of a dictionary has risen an average of 6¢ per year.

a. Write a linear equation to find the cost C of a dictionary y years after 1904. $C = 30 + 6y$

b. If this trend continues, what will the cost of a dictionary be in 2020? $7.26

B **Write an equation of the line that passes through the given point and has the given slope.**

25. (4, 2), slope $\frac{1}{2}$ $y = \frac{1}{2}x$
26. (3, −2), slope $\frac{1}{3}$ $y = \frac{1}{3}x - 3$
27. (6, 4), slope $-\frac{3}{4}$ $y = -\frac{3}{4}x + 8\frac{1}{2}$
28. (2, −3), slope $\frac{2}{3}$
29. (2, −2), slope $\frac{2}{7}$
30. (−4, −2), slope $-\frac{3}{5}$ $y = -\frac{3}{5}x - 4\frac{2}{5}$

Differentiated Homework Options

Level	Assignment	Two-Day Option	
AL Basic	10–24, 47, 49–77	11–23 odd, 53–56	10–24 even, 47, 49–52, 57–77
OL Core	11–31 odd, 32, 33–39 odd, 40–47, 49–77	10–24, 53–56	25–47, 49–52, 57–77
BL Advanced	25–71, (optional: 72–77)		

WatchOut!

Student Misconceptions Remind students that the x and y in an equation represent any pairs of x- and y-values that satisfy the equation. The coordinates of the given point are one pair of these values.

Make sure students understand that while two points can be used to write an equation, real-life prediction equations involve many more data points.

3 Practice

Formative Assessment

Use Exercises 1–9 to check for understanding.

Use the chart at the bottom of this page to customize assignments for your students.

Tips for New Teachers

Sense-Making Remind students that the coefficient of x represents the slope only when the equation is in slope-intercept form. Demonstrate using an example with two equations, one that is not in slope-intercept form and one that is in slope-intercept form.

Teaching the Process Standards

Modeling Mathematically proficient students can analyze relationships mathematically to draw conclusions. In Exercise 22, encourage students to start by relating the motion of the car to how that can be modeled mathematically.

Exercise Alert

Grid Paper Students will need grid paper for Exercises 31, 45, 46, 57–62, and 65.

Teaching the Process Standards

Sense-Making Mathematically proficient students start by explaining to themselves the meaning of a problem. In Exercise 43, students should realize that because the waste is being reduced each year, the slope of the function is negative.

Arguments Mathematically proficient students are able to analyze situations by breaking them into cases. In Exercise 52, encourage students to list all of the combinations of information that could be used to write an equation of a line.

Additional Answers

31b.

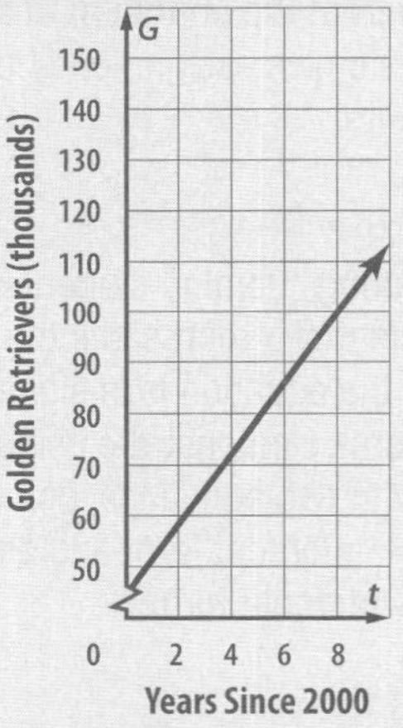

38. No; substituting 3 and −1 for x and y, respectively, results in an equation that is not true.

39. Yes; substituting 6 and −2 for x and y, respectively, results in and equation that is true.

---

31. DOGS In 2001, there were about 56.1 thousand golden retrievers registered in the United States. In 2002, the number was 62.5 thousand.

a. Write a linear equation to find the number of thousands of golden retrievers G that will be registered in year t, where $t = 0$ is the year 2000. $G = 6.4t + 49.7$

b. Graph the equation. See margin.

c. Estimate the number of golden retrievers that will be registered in 2017. 158,500

32. GYM MEMBERSHIPS A local recreation center offers a yearly membership for \$265. The center offers aerobics classes for an additional \$5 per class.

a. Write an equation that represents the total cost of the membership. $y = 5x + 265$

b. Carly spent \$500 one year. How many aerobics classes did she take? 47 classes

33. SUBSCRIPTION A magazine offers an online subscription that allows you to view up to 25 archived articles free. To view 30 archived articles, you pay \$49.15. To view 33 archived articles, you pay \$57.40.

a. What is the cost of each archived article for which you pay a fee? \$2.75

b. What is the cost of the magazine subscription? \$35.40

35. $y = -2\frac{2}{3}x + 10\frac{1}{3}$

36. $y = \frac{1}{6}x + \frac{19}{24}$

37. $y = -x - \frac{7}{12}$

C **Write an equation of the line that passes through the given points.**

34. (5, −2), (7, 1) $y = 1\frac{1}{2}x - 9\frac{1}{2}$

35. (5, −3), (2, 5)

36. $\left(\frac{5}{4}, 1\right), \left(-\frac{1}{4}, \frac{3}{4}\right)$

37. $\left(\frac{5}{12}, -1\right), \left(-\frac{3}{4}, \frac{1}{6}\right)$

Determine whether the given point is on the line. Explain why or why not. 38–39. See margin.

38. (3, −1); $y = \frac{1}{3}x + 5$

39. (6, −2); $y = \frac{1}{2}x - 5$

For Exercises 40–42, determine which equation best represents each situation. Explain the meaning of each variable.

A $y = -\frac{1}{3}x + 72$	**B** $y = 2x + 225$	**C** $y = 8x + 4$

40. CONCERTS Tickets to a concert cost \$8 each plus a processing fee of \$4 per order.

41. FUNDRAISING The freshman class has \$225. They sell raffle tickets at \$2 each to raise money for a field trip.

42. POOLS The current water level of a swimming pool in Tucson, Arizona, is 6 feet. The rate of evaporation is $\frac{1}{3}$ inch per day.

43. SENSE-MAKING A manufacturer implemented a program to reduce waste. In 1998 they sent 946 tons of waste to landfills. Each year after that, they reduced their waste by an average 28.4 tons.

a. How many tons were sent to the landfill in 2010? 605.2

b. In what year will it become impossible for this trend to continue? Explain.

44. COMBINING FUNCTIONS The parents of a college student open an account for her with a deposit of \$5000, and they set up automatic deposits of \$100 to the account every week. **44c.** $B(t) = 4400 - 150t$; the amount remaining in the account at time t

a. Write a function $d(t)$ to express the amount of money in the account t weeks after the initial deposit. $d(t) = 5000 + 100t$

b. The student plans on spending \$600 the first week and \$250 in each of the following weeks for room and board and other expenses. Write a function $w(t)$ to express the amount of money taken out of the account each week. $w(t) = 600 + 250t$

c. Find $B(t) = d(t) - w(t)$. What does this new function represent?

d. Will the student run out of money? If so, when? yes; in about 29 weeks

40. C; x represents the number of tickets per order and y represents the total cost of an order.

41. B; x represents the number of raffle tickets sold, y represents the total amount of money in the treasury.

42. A; x represents the number of days, y represents the total depth of water in inches of the pool.

43b. 2032; In that year, the waste would be 0 tons. After that, the waste would be a negative amount, which is impossible.

45 **CONCERT TICKETS** Jackson is ordering tickets for a concert online. There is a processing fee for each order, and the tickets are $52 each. Jackson ordered 5 tickets and the cost was $275. **b–c. See Ch. 4 Answer Appendix.**

a. Determine the processing fee. Write a linear equation to represent the total cost C for t tickets. **$15; $C = 52t + 15$**

b. Make a table of values for at least three other numbers of tickets.

c. Graph this equation. Predict the cost of 8 tickets.

46. **MUSIC** A music store is offering a Frequent Buyers Club membership. The membership costs $22 per year, and then a member can buy CDs at a reduced price. If a member buys 17 CDs in one year, the cost is $111.25.

a. Determine the cost of each CD for a member. **$5.25**

b. Write a linear equation to represent the total cost y of a one year membership, if x CDs are purchased. **$y = 5.25x + 22$**

c. Graph this equation. **See Ch. 4 Answer Appendix.**

H.O.T. Problems Use Higher-Order Thinking Skills

47. **ERROR ANALYSIS** Tess and Jacinta are writing an equation of the line through (3, −2) and (6, 4). Is either of them correct? Explain your reasoning.

Tess	Jacinta
$m = \frac{4-(-2)}{6-3} = \frac{6}{3}$ or 2	$m = \frac{4-(-2)}{6-3} = \frac{6}{3}$ or 2
$y = mx + b$	$y = mx + b$
$6 = 2(4) + b$	$-2 = 2(3) + b$
$6 = 8 + b$	$-2 = 6 + b$
$-2 = b$	$-8 = b$
$y = 2x - 2$	$y = 2x - 8$

Jacinta; Tess switched the x- and y-coordinates on the point that she entered in Step 3.

48. **CHALLENGE** Consider three points, (3, 7), (−6, 1) and (9, p), on the same line. Find the value of p and explain your steps. **11; Use the first two points to find the equation of the line, then replace x and y with 9 and p, respectively, to solve for p.**

49. **REASONING** Consider the standard form of a linear equation, $Ax + By = C$.

a. Rewrite the equation in slope-intercept form. **$y = -\frac{A}{B}x + \frac{C}{B}$**

b. What is the slope? **slope $= -\frac{A}{B}$**

c. What is the y-intercept? **y-intercept $= \frac{C}{B}$**

d. Is this true for all real values of A, B, and C? **No, $B \neq 0$.**

50. **OPEN ENDED** Create a real-world situation that fits the graph at the right. Define the two quantities and describe the functional relationship between them. Write an equation to represent this relationship and describe what the slope and y-intercept mean. **See Ch. 4 Answer Appendix.**

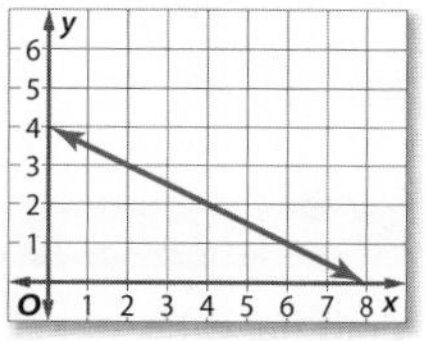

51. **WRITING IN MATH** Linear equations are useful in predicting future events. Describe some factors in real-world situations that might affect the reliability of the graph in making any predictions. **See Ch. 4 Answer Appendix.**

52. **ARGUMENTS** What information is needed to write the equation of a line? Explain. **You need to know the slope and y-intercept of the line, the slope and the coordinates of another point on the line, or the coordinates of two points on the line.**

WatchOut!

Error Analysis For Exercise 47, students should see that Tess and Jacinta have done something different in the equation they wrote under $y = mx + b$. Explain to students that it is very important to keep the values for x and y correctly identified.

Study Guide and Intervention

AL OL ELL

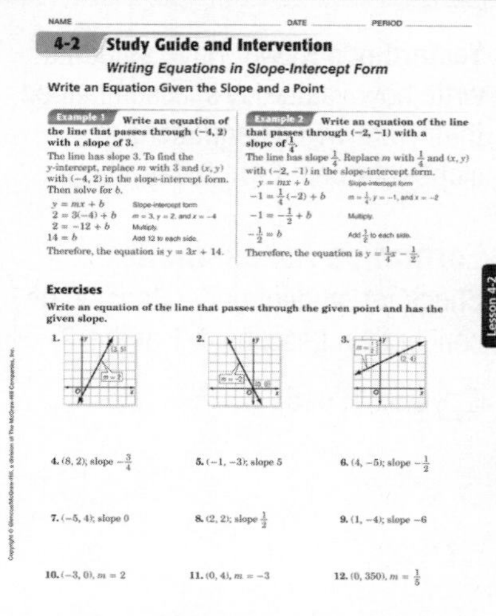

Practice

AL OL BL ELL

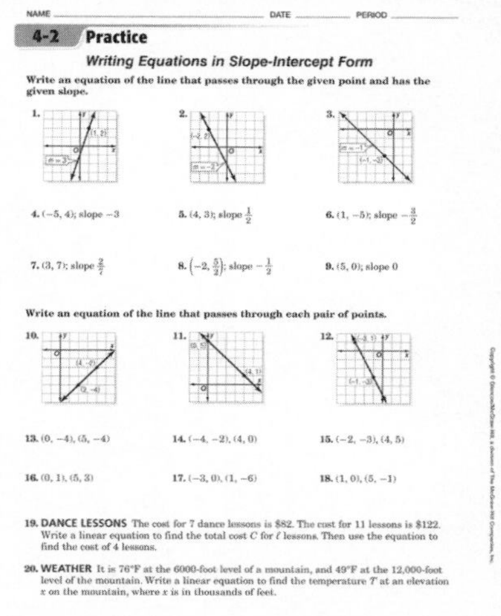

Word Problem Practice

AL OL BL ELL

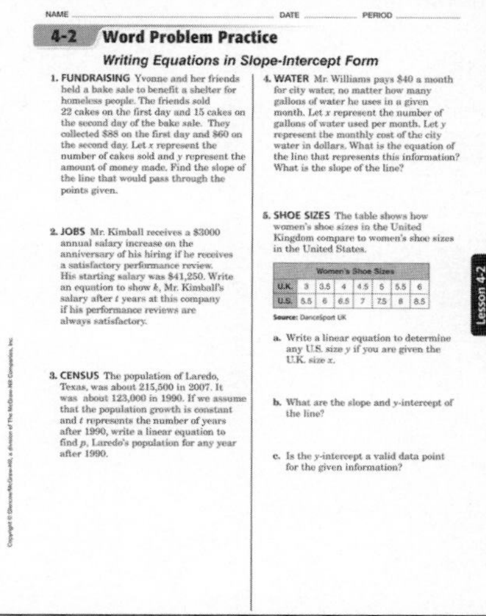

Enrichment

OL BL

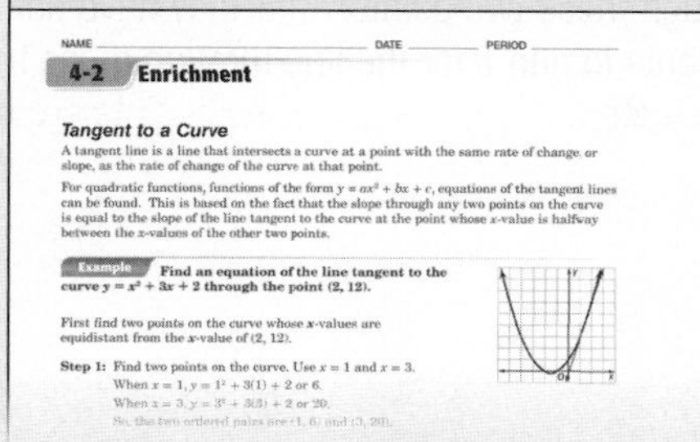

4 Assess

Yesterday's News Have students write how yesterday's lesson helped them with writing equations in slope-intercept form today.

Formative Assessment

Check for student understanding of concepts in Lessons 4-1 and 4-2.

Quiz 1, p. 51

Standardized Test Practice

53. Which equation *best* represents the graph? **D**

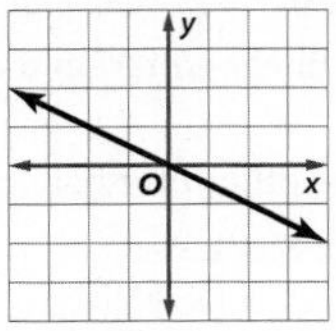

A $y = 2x$

B $y = -2x$

C $y = \frac{1}{2}x$

D $y = -\frac{1}{2}x$

54. Roberto receives an employee discount of 12%. If he buys a \$355 item at the store, what is his discount to the nearest dollar? **J**

F \$3 | H \$30

G \$4 | J \$43

55. GEOMETRY The midpoints of the sides of the large square are joined to form a smaller square. What is the area of the smaller square? **B**

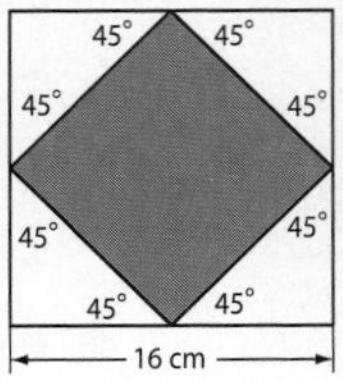

A 64 cm^2

B 128 cm^2

C 248 cm^2

D 256 cm^2

56. SHORT RESPONSE If $\frac{5(x+4)}{2} + 7 = 37$, what is the value of $3x - 9$? **15**

Spiral Review

Graph each equation. (Lesson 4-1) **57–62. See Ch. 4 Answer Appendix.**

57. $y = 3x + 2$ **58.** $y = -4x + 2$ **59.** $3y = 2x + 6$

60. $y = \frac{1}{2}x + 6$ **61.** $3x + y = -1$ **62.** $2x + 3y = 6$

Write an equation in function notation for each relation. (Lesson 3-6)

63.

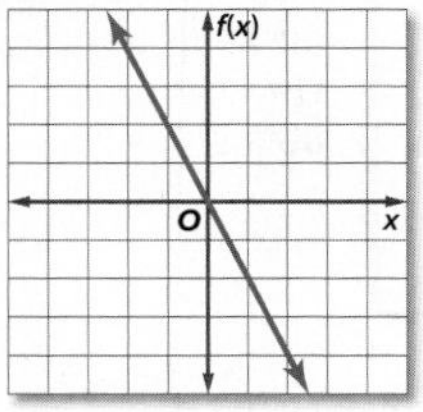

$f(x) = -2x$

64.

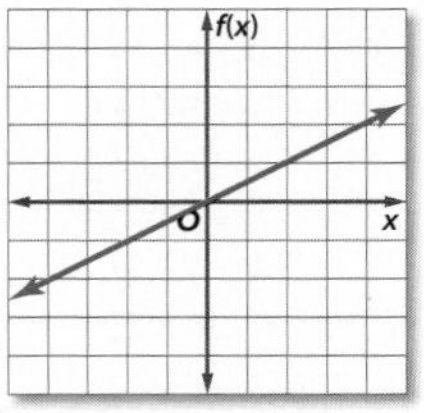

$f(x) = \frac{1}{2}x$

65a.

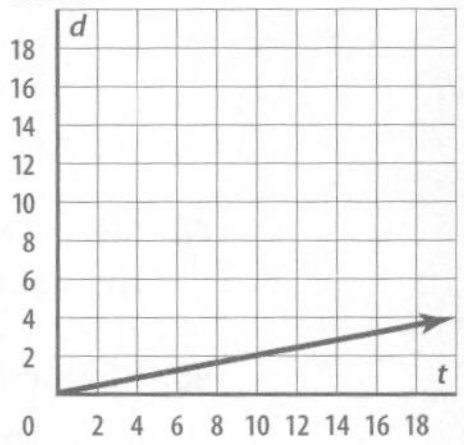

65. METEOROLOGY The distance d in miles that the sound of thunder travels in t seconds is given by the equation $d = 0.21t$. (Lesson 3-4)

a. Graph the equation.

b. Use the graph to estimate how long it will take you to hear thunder from a storm 3 miles away. **about 14 seconds**

Solve each equation. Check your solution. (Lesson 2-3)

66. $-5t - 2.2 = -2.9$ **0.14** **67.** $-5.5a - 43.9 = 77.1$ **−22** **68.** $4.2r + 7.14 = 12.6$ **1.3**

69. $-14 - \frac{n}{9} = 9$ **−207** **70.** $\frac{-8b - (-9)}{-10} = 17$ **22.375** **71.** $9.5x + 11 - 7.5x = 14$ **1.5**

Skills Review

Find the value of r so the line through each pair of points has the given slope.

72. $(6, -2), (r, -6), m = 4$ **5** **73.** $(8, 10), (r, 4), m = 6$ **7** **74.** $(7, -10), (r, 4), m = -3$ **$2\frac{1}{3}$**

75. $(6, 2), (9, r), m = -1$ **−1** **76.** $(9, r), (6, 3), m = -\frac{1}{3}$ **2** **77.** $(5, r), (2, -3), m = \frac{4}{3}$ **1**

Differentiated Instruction OL BL

Extension Write (3, 4) and (5, 4) on the board. Ask students to find b, the y-intercept, for the line through these two points. After they have done this, write (3, 5) and (3, 4) on the board and ask students to find b for the line through these two points and have them explain. $b = 4$; there is no y-intercept because these two points are on a vertical line.

LESSON 4-3 Writing Equations in Point-Slope Form

Then

- You wrote linear equations given either one point and the slope or two points.

Now

1. Write equations of lines in point-slope form.
2. Write linear equations in different forms.

Why?

- Most humane societies have foster homes for newborn puppies, kittens, and injured or ill animals. During the spring and summer, a large shelter can place 3000 animals in homes each month.

If a shelter had 200 animals in foster homes at the beginning of spring, the number of animals in foster homes at the end of the summer could be represented by $y = 3000x + 200$, where x is the number of months and y is the number of animals.

NewVocabulary
point-slope form

Content Standards
AI.L.4, AI.L.5, AI.L.6

1 Point-Slope Form

An equation of a line can be written in **point-slope form** when given the coordinates of one known point on a line and the slope of that line.

KeyConcept Point-Slope Form

Words The linear equation $y - y_1 = m(x - x_1)$ is written in point-slope form, where (x_1, y_1) is a given point on a nonvertical line and m is the slope of the line.

Symbols $y - y_1 = m(x - x_1)$

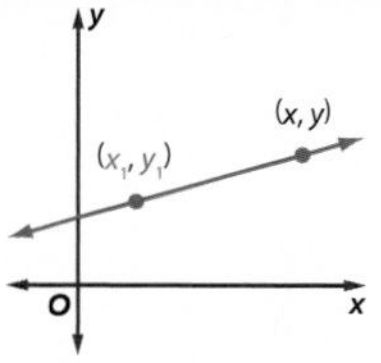

Example 1 Write and Graph an Equation in Point-Slope Form

Write an equation in point-slope form for the line that passes through (3, −2) with a slope of $\frac{1}{4}$. Then graph the equation.

$y - y_1 = m(x - x_1)$ Point-slope form

$y - (-2) = \frac{1}{4}(x - 3)$ $(x_1, y_1) = (3, -2), m = \frac{1}{4}$

$y + 2 = \frac{1}{4}(x - 3)$ Simplify.

Plot the point at (3, −2) and use the slope to find another point on the line. Draw a line through the two points.

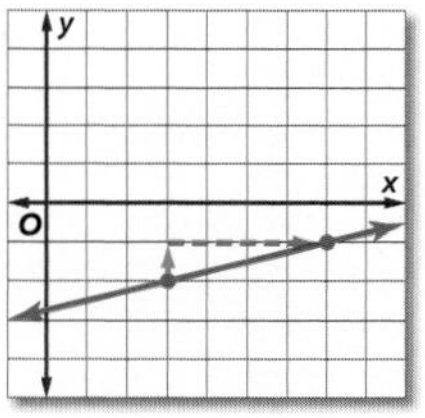

GuidedPractice See Ch 4. Answer Appendix for graph.

1. Write an equation in point-slope form for the line that passes through (−2, 1) with a slope of −6. Then graph the equation. $y - 1 = -6(x + 2)$

1 Focus

VerticalAlignment

Before Lesson 4-3 Write linear equations given either one point and the slope or two points.

Lesson 4-3 Write equations of lines in point-slope form. Write linear equations in different forms.

After Lesson 4-3 Use lines of fit on scatter plots to make and evaluate predictions.

2 Teach

Scaffolding Questions

Have students read the **Why?** section of the lesson.

Ask:

- What is the slope of the graph of the equation $y = 3000x + 200$? 3000
- What is one point on the graph of this line? Sample answer: (0, 200)
- Write an equation that relates the slope, the point you gave, and any point (x, y) on the line. Sample answer: $\frac{y - 200}{x - 0} = 3000$

Lesson 4-3 Resources

Resource	Approaching Level AL	On Level OL	Beyond Level BL	English Learners ELL
Teacher Edition	▪ Differentiated Instruction, p. 235	▪ Differentiated Instruction, pp. 235, 238	▪ Differentiated Instruction, p. 238	▪ Differentiated Instruction, p. 235
Chapter Resource Masters	▪ Study Guide and Intervention, pp. 17–18 ▪ Skills Practice, p. 19 ▪ Practice, p. 20 ▪ Word Problem Practice, p. 21 ▪ Graphing Calculator, p. 23	▪ Study Guide and Intervention, pp. 17–18 ▪ Skills Practice, p. 19 ▪ Practice, p. 20 ▪ Word Problem Practice, p. 21 ▪ Enrichment, p. 22 ▪ Graphing Calculator, p. 23	▪ Practice, p. 20 ▪ Word Problem Practice, p. 21 ▪ Enrichment, p. 22 ▪ Graphing Calculator, p. 23	▪ Study Guide and Intervention, pp. 17–18 ▪ Skills Practice, p. 19 ▪ Practice, p. 20 ▪ Word Problem Practice, p. 21 ▪ Graphing Calculator, p. 23
Other	▪ 5-Minute Check 4-3 ▪ Study Notebook ▪ Teaching Algebra with Manipulatives	▪ 5-Minute Check 4-3 ▪ Study Notebook ▪ Teaching Algebra with Manipulatives	▪ 5-Minute Check 4-3 ▪ Study Notebook	▪ 5-Minute Check 4-3 ▪ Study Notebook ▪ Teaching Algebra with Manipulatives

1 Point-Slope Form

Example 1 shows how to write an equation in point-slope form when the slope and a point on the line are known.

Formative Assessment

Use the Guided Practice exercises after each Example to determine students' understanding of concepts.

Additional Example

1 Write an equation in point-slope form for the line that passes through $(-2, 0)$ with a slope of $-\frac{3}{2}$. Then graph the equation. $y = -\frac{3}{2}(x + 2)$

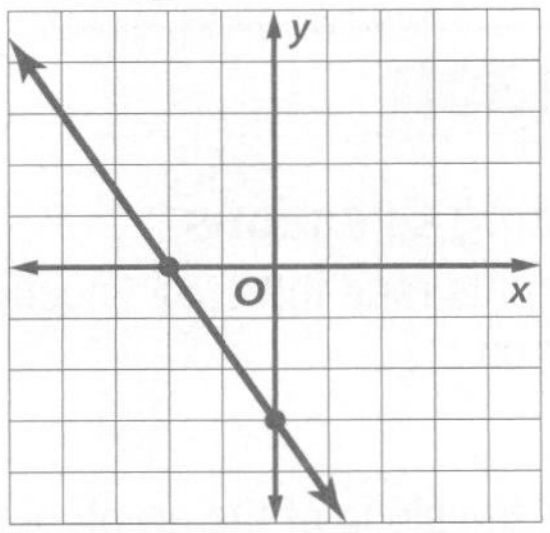

2 Forms of Linear Equations

Example 2 shows how to write an equation in standard form when given an equation in point-slope form. **Example 3** shows how to write an equation in slope-intercept form when given an equation in point-slope form. **Example 4** shows how to use the point-slope form to write an equation for the line making up a side of a geometric figure.

WatchOut!

Preventing Errors Emphasize that in standard form, A, B, and C are all integers. Example 2 is an exercise in algebraic manipulation.

2 Forms of Linear Equations

If you are given the slope and the coordinates of one or two points, you can write the linear equation in the following ways.

StudyTip

Slope The slope of the line remains unchanged throughout the line. You can go in either direction along the line using the same rise over run and you will always end at a point on the line.

ConceptSummary Writing Equations

Given the Slope and One Point	Given Two Points
Step 1 Substitute the value of m and let the x and y coordinates be (x_1, y_1). Or, substitute the value of m, x, and y into the slope-intercept form and solve for b.	**Step 1** Find the slope.
Step 2 Rewrite the equation in the needed form.	**Step 2** Choose one of the two points to use.
	Step 3 Follow the steps for writing an equation given the slope and one point.

ReviewVocabulary

Standard form of a linear equation $Ax + By = C$, where $A \geq 0$, A and B are not both zero, and A, B, and C are integers with a greatest common factor of 1

Example 2 Standard Form

Write $y - 1 = -\frac{2}{3}(x - 5)$ in standard form.

$y - 1 = -\frac{2}{3}(x - 5)$	Original equation
$3(y - 1) = 3\left(-\frac{2}{3}\right)(x - 5)$	Multiply each side by 3 to eliminate the fraction.
$3(y - 1) = -2(x - 5)$	Simplify.
$3y - 3 = -2x + 10$	Distributive Property
$3y = -2x + 13$	Add 3 to each side.
$2x + 3y = 13$	Add $2x$ to each side.

GuidedPractice

2. Write $y - 1 = 7(x + 5)$ in standard form. $7x - y = -36$

To find the y-intercept of an equation, rewrite the equation in slope-intercept form.

Example 3 Slope-Intercept Form

Write $y + 3 = \frac{3}{2}(x + 1)$ in slope-intercept form.

$y + 3 = \frac{3}{2}(x + 1)$	Original equation
$y + 3 = \frac{3}{2}x + \frac{3}{2}$	Distributive Property
$y = \frac{3}{2}x - \frac{3}{2}$	Subtract 3 from each side.

GuidedPractice

3. Write $y + 6 = -3(x - 4)$ in slope-intercept form. $y = -3x + 6$

Teach with Tech

Interactive Whiteboard Drag a coordinate plane onto the whiteboard. Plot two points on the plane and ask students to find the equation of the line that goes through these two points. Then, drag the points to other locations on the plane and repeat.

The Math Forum

Have your students refer to the Math Forum's Ask Dr. Math to learn more about the difference between slope intercept form and point slope form. They can start their search at connectED.mcgraw-hill.com.

234 | Lesson 4-3 | Writing Equations in Point-Slope Form

Being able to use a variety of forms of linear equations can be useful in other subjects as well.

StudyTip

Slopes in Squares Nonvertical opposite sides of a square have equal slopes. If the coordinates for one of the vertices are unavailable, use the slope of the opposite side.

Example 4 Point-Slope Form and Standard Form

GEOMETRY The figure shows square *RSTU*.

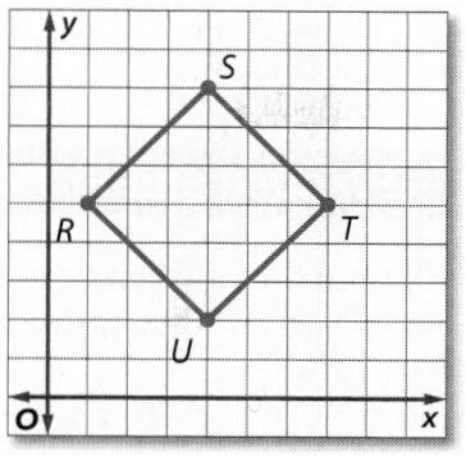

a. Write an equation in point-slope form for the line containing side $\overline{TU}$.

Step 1 Find the slope of $\overline{TU}$.

$m = \frac{y_2 - y_1}{x_2 - x_1}$ — Slope Formula

$= \frac{5-2}{7-4}$ or 1 — $(x_1, y_1) = (4, 2)$ and $(x_2, y_2) = (7, 5)$

Step 2 You can select either point for (x_1, y_1) in the point-slope form.

$y - y_1 = m(x - x_1)$ — Point-slope form

$y - 2 = 1(x - 4)$ — $(x_1, y_1) = (4, 2)$

$y - 5 = 1(x - 7)$ — $(x_1, y_1) = (7, 5)$

b. Write an equation in standard form for the same line.

$y - 2 = 1(x - 4)$	Original equation	$y - 5 = 1(x - 7)$
$y - 2 = 1x - 4$	Distributive Property	$y - 5 = 1x - 7$
$y = 1x - 2$	Add to each side.	$y = 1x - 2$
$-1x + y = -2$	Subtract 1*x* from each side.	$-1x + y = -2$
$x - y = 2$	Multiply each side by −1.	$x - y = 2$

GuidedPractice

4A. Write an equation in point-slope form of the line containing side $\overline{ST}$. **$y - 8 = -1(x - 4)$ or $y - 5 = -1(x - 7)$**

4B. Write an equation in standard form of the line containing $\overline{ST}$. **$x + y = 12$**

Check Your Understanding

○ = Step-by-Step Solutions begin on page R13.

Example 1 **Write an equation in point-slope form for the line that passes through the given point with the slope provided. Then graph the equation.** **1–3. See Ch. 4 Answer Appendix.**

1. $(-2, 5)$, slope -6
2. $(-2, -8)$, slope $\frac{5}{6}$
3. $(4, 3)$, slope $-\frac{1}{2}$

Example 2 **Write each equation in standard form.**

4. $y + 2 = \frac{7}{8}(x - 3)$ **$7x - 8y = 37$**
5. $y + 7 = -5(x + 3)$ **$5x + y = -22$**
6. $y + 2 = \frac{5}{3}(x + 6)$ **$5x - 3y = -24$**

Example 3 **Write each equation in slope-intercept form.**

7. $y - 10 = 4(x + 6)$ **$y = 4x + 34$**
8. $y - 7 = -\frac{3}{4}(x + 5)$ **$y = -\frac{3}{4}x + \frac{13}{4}$**
9. $y - 9 = x + 4$ **$y = x + 13$**

DifferentiatedInstruction AL OL ELL

If students have trouble remembering whether a vertical line or a horizontal line has slope 0,

Then tell them the word *horizontal* has an *o* to remind them of 0. A h**o**rizontal line has slope **0**. Challenge students to create a catchy phrase to help them remember the different forms for a linear equation.

Focus on Mathematical Content

Point-Slope Form You can derive the point-slope form of the equation of a line using the slope formula.

$m = \frac{y - y_1}{x - x_1}$	Slope Formula
$(x - x_1)m = y - y_1$	Multiply each side by $(x - x_1)$.
$y - y_1 = m(x - x_1)$	Solve for $y - y_1$.

Additional Examples

2 Write $y = \frac{3}{4}x - 5$ in standard form. $3x - 4y = 20$

3 Write $y - 5 = \frac{4}{3}(x - 3)$ in slope-intercept form. $y = \frac{4}{3}x + 1$

4 **GEOMETRY** The figure shows trapezoid *ABCD*, with bases $\overline{AB}$ and $\overline{CD}$.

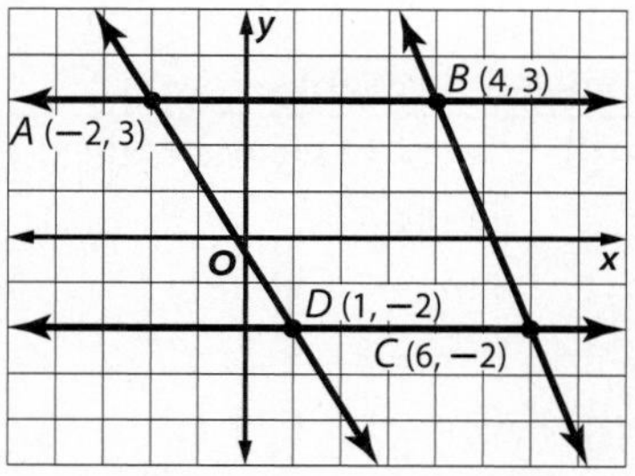

a. Write an equation in point-slope form for the line containing the side $\overline{BC}$.
$y - 3 = -\frac{5}{2}(x - 4)$ or
$y + 2 = -\frac{5}{2}(x - 6)$

b. Write an equation in standard form for the same line.
$5x + 2y = 26$

Additional Examples also in Interactive Classroom PowerPoint® Presentations

IWB Interactive White Board READY

3 Practice

Formative Assessment

Use Exercises 1–10 to check for understanding.

Use the chart at the bottom of this page to customize assignments for your students.

Exercise Alert

Grid Paper Students will need grid paper for Exercises 1–3 and 11–18.

Teaching the Process Standards

Reasoning Mathematically proficient students decontextualize information to represent it symbolically. In Exercise 36, students need to decontextualize the slope.

Critique Mathematically proficient students justify their conclusions, In Exercise 50, students may justify their conclusion by graphing or algebraically.

Additional Answers

11–18. See Ch. 4 Answer Appendix for graphs.

11. $y - 3 = 7(x - 5)$

12. $y + 1 = -3(x - 2)$

13. $y + 3 = -1(x + 6)$

14. $y - 6 = 0$

15. $y - 11 = \frac{4}{3}(x + 2)$

16. $y + 8 = -\frac{5}{8}(x + 6)$

17. $y + 9 = -\frac{7}{5}(x + 2)$

18. $y = 0$

51. Sample answer: Jocari spent \$14 to go to an amusement park and ride ponies. The price she paid included admission. The 5 pony rides cost \$2 each; $y - 14 = 2(x - 5)$, $-2x + y = 4$, $y = 2x + 4$.

52. $y = -\frac{15}{7}x - \frac{4}{7}$; $m = -\frac{15}{7}$; $-\frac{4}{15}$; $-\frac{4}{7}$

Example 4

10. GEOMETRY Use right triangle FGH.

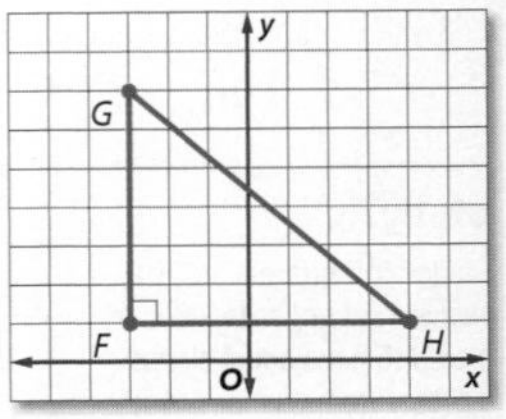

a. Write an equation in point-slope form for the line containing $\overline{GH}$. $y - 7 = -\frac{6}{7}(x + 3)$

b. Write the standard form of the line containing $\overline{GH}$. $6x + 7y = 31$

Practice and Problem Solving

Extra Practice is on page R4.

Example 1

Write an equation in point-slope form for the line that passes through each point with the given slope. Then graph the equation. 11–18. See margin.

11. $(5, 3)$, $m = 7$

12. $(2, -1)$, $m = -3$

13. $(-6, -3)$, $m = -1$

14. $(-7, 6)$, $m = 0$

15. $(-2, 11)$, $m = \frac{4}{3}$

16. $(-6, -8)$, $m = -\frac{5}{8}$

17. $(-2, -9)$, $m = -\frac{7}{5}$

18. $(-6, 0)$, horizontal line

Example 2

Write each equation in standard form.

19. $y - 10 = 2(x - 8)$ $2x - y = 6$

20. $y - 6 = -3(x + 2)$ $3x + y = 0$

21. $y - 9 = -6(x + 9)$ $6x + y = -45$

22. $y + 4 = \frac{2}{3}(x + 7)$ $2x - 3y = -2$

23. $y + 7 = \frac{9}{10}(x + 3)$ $9x - 10y = 43$

24. $y + 7 = -\frac{3}{2}(x + 1)$ $3x + 2y = -17$

25. $2y + 3 = -\frac{1}{3}(x - 2)$ $x + 6y = -7$

26. $4y - 5x = 3(4x - 2y + 1)$ $17x - 10y = -3$

Example 3

Write each equation in slope-intercept form.

27. $y - 6 = -2(x - 7)$ $y = -2x + 20$

28. $y - 11 = 3(x + 4)$ $y = 3x + 23$

29. $y + 5 = -6(x + 7)$ $y = -6x - 47$

30. $y - 1 = \frac{4}{5}(x + 5)$ $y = \frac{4}{5}x + 5$

31. $y + 2 = \frac{1}{6}(x - 4)$ $y = \frac{1}{6}x - \frac{8}{3}$

32. $y + 6 = -\frac{3}{4}(x + 8)$ $y = -\frac{3}{4}x - 12$

33. $y + 3 = -\frac{1}{3}(2x + 6)$ $y = -\frac{2}{3}x - 5$

34. $y + 4 = 3(3x + 3)$ $y = 9x + 5$

Example 4

35. MOVIE RENTALS The number of copies of a movie rented at a video kiosk decreased at a constant rate of 5 copies per week. The 6th week after the movie was released, 4 copies were rented. How many copies were rented during the second week? 24 copies

B

36. REASONING A company offers premium cable for \$39.95 per month plus a one-time setup fee. The total cost for setup and 6 months of service is \$264.70.

a. Write an equation in point-slope form to find the total price y for any number of months x. (*Hint*: The point (6, 264.70) is a solution to the equation.) $y - 264.70 = 39.95(x - 6)$

b. Write the equation in slope-intercept form. $y = 39.95x + 25$

c. What is the setup fee? \$25

Write an equation for the line described in standard form. 37. $x + y = 6$ 38. $3x + 4y = 0$

37. through $(-1, 7)$ and $(8, -2)$

38. through $(-4, 3)$ with y-intercept 0

39. with x-intercept 4 and y-intercept 5 $5x + 4y = 20$

Differentiated Homework Options

Level	Assignment	Two-Day Option	
AL Basic	11–35, 49–52, 54–75	11–35 odd, 55–58	12–34 even, 49–52, 54, 59–75
OL Core	11–35 odd, 36, 37, 39, 40–52, 54–75	11–35, 55–58	36–52, 54, 59–75
BL Advanced	36–71, (optional: 72–75)		

236 | Lesson 4-3 | Writing Equations in Point-Slope Form

C Write an equation in point-slope form for each line. **44.** $y = \frac{1}{2}x + \frac{3}{2}$

40.

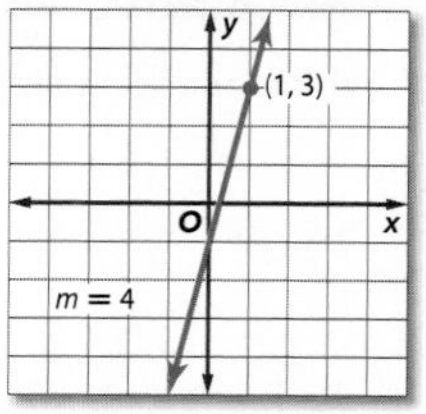

$y - 3 = 4(x - 1)$

41.

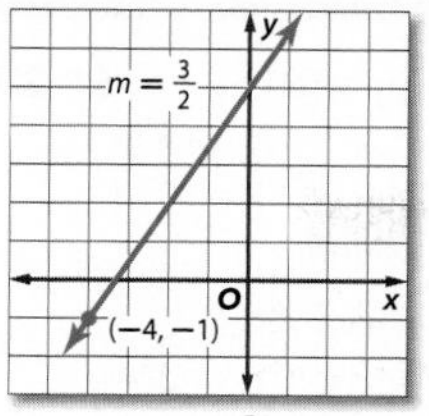

$y + 1 = \frac{3}{2}(x + 4)$

42.

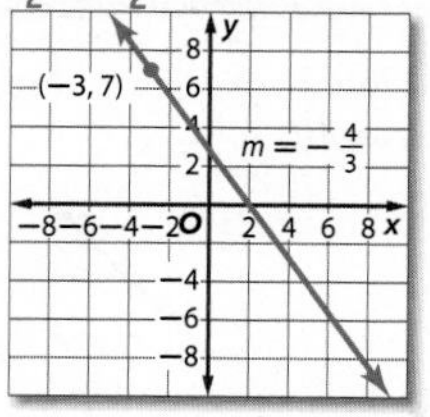

$y - 7 = -\frac{4}{3}(x + 3)$

Write each equation in slope-intercept form.

43. $y + \frac{3}{5} = x - \frac{2}{5}$ $y = x - 1$ **44.** $y - \frac{7}{2} = \frac{1}{2}(x - 4)$ **45.** $y + \frac{1}{3} = \frac{5}{6}\left(x + \frac{2}{5}\right)$ $y = \frac{5}{6}x$

46. Write an equation in point-slope form, slope-intercept form, and standard form for a line that passes through $(-2, 8)$ with slope $\frac{8}{5}$. $y - 8 = \frac{8}{5}(x + 2)$; $y = \frac{8}{5}x + \frac{56}{5}$; $8x - 5y = -56$

47. Line ℓ passes through $(-9, 4)$ with slope $\frac{4}{7}$. Write an equation in point-slope form, slope-intercept form, and standard form for line ℓ. $y - 4 = \frac{4}{7}(x + 9)$; $y = \frac{4}{7}x + \frac{64}{7}$; $4x - 7y = -64$

48. **WEATHER** The barometric pressure is 598 millimeters of mercury (mmHg) at an altitude of 1.8 kilometers and 577 millimeters of mercury at 2.1 kilometers. $f(x) = -70x + 724$

a. Write a formula for the barometric pressure as a function of the altitude.

b. What is the altitude if the pressure is 657 millimeters of mercury? 0.96 km

50. Juana; $f(x)$ and $g(x)$ both have the same slope. However, the x- and y-intercepts are different.

H.O.T. Problems Use Higher-Order Thinking Skills

49. **WHICH ONE DOESN'T BELONG?** Identify the equation that does not belong. Explain your reasoning. $y + 4 = 3(x + 1)$; The slope-intercept form is not $y = 3x + 2$.

$y - 5 = 3(x - 1)$	$y + 1 = 3(x + 1)$	$y + 4 = 3(x + 1)$	$y - 8 = 3(x - 2)$

50. **CRITIQUE** Juana thinks that $f(x)$ and $g(x)$ have the same slope but different intercepts. Sabrina thinks that $f(x)$ and $g(x)$ describe the same line. Is either of them correct? Explain your reasoning.

The graph of $g(x)$ is the line that passes through $(3, -7)$ and $(-6, 4)$.

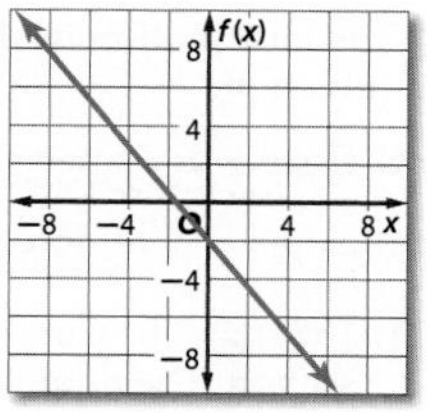

51. **OPEN ENDED** Describe a real-life scenario that has a constant rate of change and a value of y for a particular value of x. Represent this situation using an equation in point-slope form, an equation in standard form, and an equation in slope-intercept form. See margin.

52. **REASONING** Write an equation for the line that passes through $(-4, 8)$ and $(3, -7)$. What is the slope? Where does the line intersect the x-axis? the y-axis? See margin.

53. **CHALLENGE** Write an equation in point-slope form for the line that passes through the points (f, g) and (h, j). Sample answer: $y - g = \frac{j - g}{h - f}(x - f)$

54. **WRITING IN MATH** Why do we represent linear equations in more than one form? See Ch.4 Answer Appendix.

Study Guide and Intervention
AL OL ELL

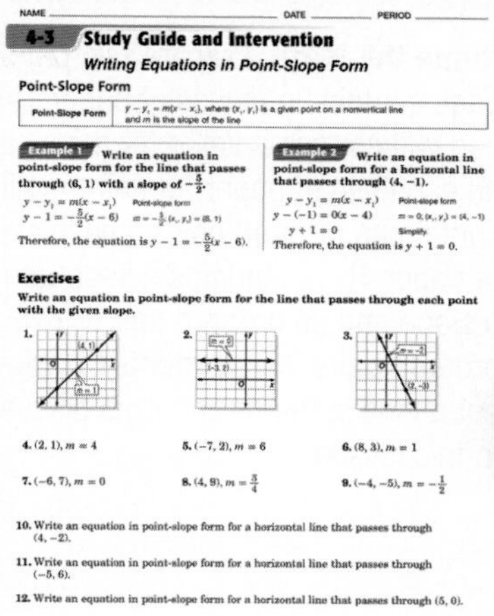

Practice
AL OL BL ELL

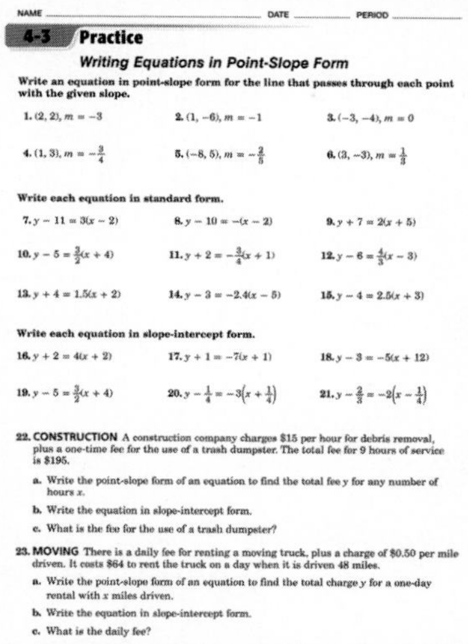

Word Problem Practice
AL OL BL ELL

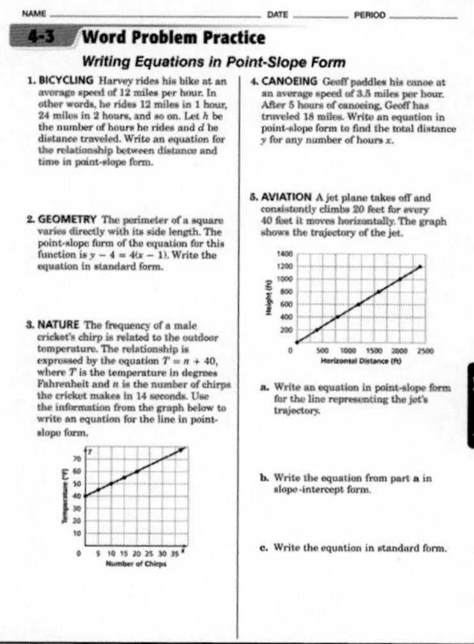

WatchOut!

Error Analysis For Exercise 50, suggest that students plot the two points on $g(x)$ and draw the line. Then they should see that the intercepts of $f(x)$ and $g(x)$ are different.

Enrichment
OL BL

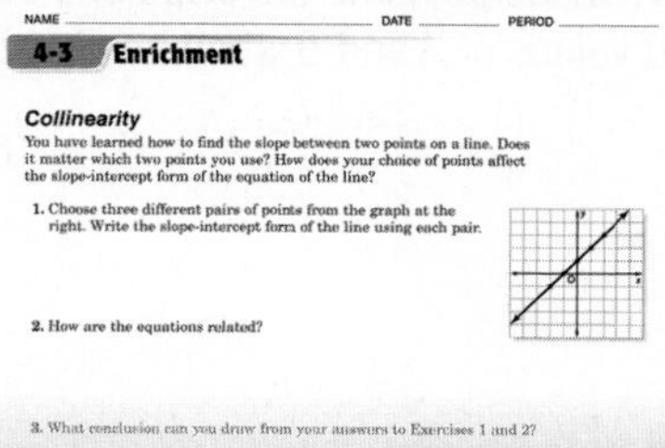

4 Assess

Name the Math Prepare two paper bags containing pieces of paper. One bag will contain a value for the slope on each slip of paper; the other will contain an ordered pair on each slip of paper. Have students select both a slope and an ordered pair or two ordered pairs. Ask students to write equations in the three forms discussed in this lesson.

Standardized Test Practice

55. Which statement is *most* strongly supported by the graph? **B**

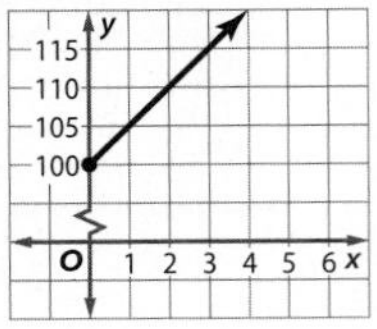

A You have \$100 and spend \$5 weekly.
B You have \$100 and save \$5 weekly.
C You need \$100 for a new CD player and save \$5 weekly.
D You need \$100 for a new CD player and spend \$5 weekly.

56. SHORT RESPONSE A store offers customers a \$5 gift certificate for every \$75 they spend. How much would a customer have to spend to earn \$35 worth of gift certificates? **\$525**

57. GEOMETRY Which triangle is similar to $\triangle ABC$? **J**

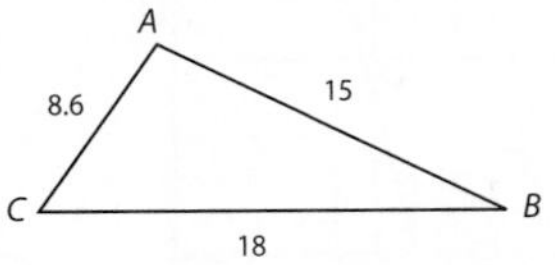

F
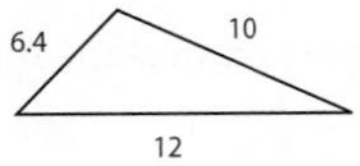

H
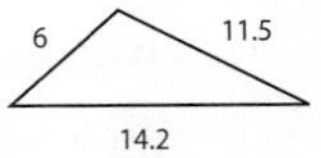

G
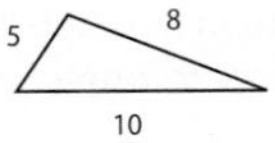

J
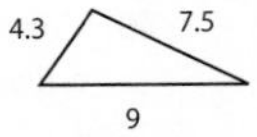

58. In a class of 25 students, 6 have blue eyes, 15 have brown hair, and 3 have blue eyes and brown hair. How many students have neither blue eyes nor brown hair? **B**

A 4 **C** 10
B 7 **D** 22

Spiral Review

Write an equation of the line that passes through each pair of points. (Lesson 4-2)

59. (4, 2), (−2, −4) $y = x - 2$
60. (3, −2), (6, 4) $y = 2x - 8$
61. (−1, 3), (2, −3) $y = -2x + 1$
62. (2, −2), (3, 2) $y = 4x - 10$
63. (7, −2), (−4, −2) $y = -2$
64. (0, 5), (−3, 5) $y = 5$

Write an equation in slope-intercept form of the line with the given slope and *y*-intercept. (Lesson 4-1)

65. slope: −2, *y*-intercept: 6 $y = -2x + 6$
66. slope: 3, *y*-intercept: −5 $y = 3x - 5$
67. slope: $\frac{1}{2}$, *y*-intercept: 3 $y = \frac{1}{2}x + 3$
68. slope: $-\frac{3}{5}$, *y*-intercept: 12 **68.** $y = -\frac{3}{5}x + 12$
69. slope: 0, *y*-intercept: 3 $y = 3$
70. slope: −1, *y*-intercept: 0 $y = -x$

71. THEATER The Coral Gables Actors' Playhouse has 7 rows of seats in the orchestra section. The number of seats in the rows forms an arithmetic sequence, as shown in the table. On opening night, 368 tickets were sold for the orchestra section. Was the section oversold? (Lesson 3-5) **Yes, there are only 364 seats.**

Rows	Number of Seats
7	76
6	68
5	60

Skills Review

Solve each equation or formula for the variable specified.

72. $y = mx + b$, for m $m = \frac{y - b}{x}$
73. $v = r + at$, for a $a = \frac{v - r}{t}$
74. $km + 5x = 6y$, for m $m = \frac{6y - 5x}{k}$
75. $4b - 5 = -t$, for b $b = \frac{-t + 5}{4}$

238 | Lesson 4-3 | Writing Equations in Point-Slope Form

Differentiated Instruction OL BL

Extension Write $4x + 3y = 8$ on the board. Ask students to rewrite the equation in slope-intercept form. Have students name the slope and then draw a conclusion about the relationship between the slope and values of A and B when an equation is written in standard form, $Ax + By = C$.
$y = -\frac{4}{3}x + \frac{8}{3}$; $-\frac{4}{3}$; The slope is $-\frac{4}{3}$; $m = -\frac{A}{B}$.

LESSON 4-4 Parallel and Perpendicular Lines

Then

- You wrote equations in point-slope form.

Now

1. Write an equation of the line that passes through a given point, parallel to a given line.
2. Write an equation of the line that passes through a given point, perpendicular to a given line.

Why?

- Notice the squares, rectangles and lines in the piece of art shown at the right. Some of the lines intersect forming right angles. Other lines do not intersect at all.

NewVocabulary
parallel lines
perpendicular lines

Process Standards
PS.5

1 Parallel Lines

Lines in the same plane that do not intersect are called **parallel lines**. Nonvertical parallel lines have the same slope.

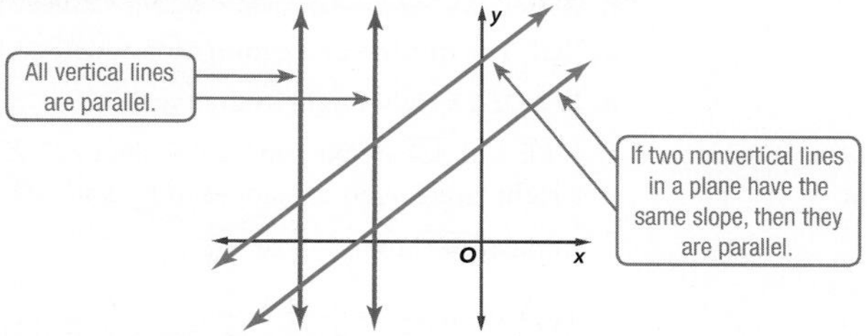

You can write an equation of a line parallel to a given line if you know a point on the line and an equation of the given line. First find the slope of the given line. Then, substitute the point provided and the slope from the given line into the point-slope form.

Example 1 Parallel Line Through a Given Point

PT

Write an equation in slope-intercept form for the line that passes through $(-3, 5)$ and is parallel to the graph of $y = 2x - 4$.

Step 1 The slope of the line with equation $y = 2x - 4$ is 2. The line parallel to $y = 2x - 4$ has the same slope, 2.

Step 2 Find the equation in slope-intercept form.

$y - y_1 = m(x - x_1)$	Point-slope form
$y - 5 = 2[x - (-3)]$	Replace m with 2 and (x_1, y_1) with $(-3, 5)$.
$y - 5 = 2(x + 3)$	Simplify.
$y - 5 = 2x + 6$	Distributive Property
$y - 5 + 5 = 2x + 6 + 5$	Add 5 to each side.
$y = 2x + 11$	Write the equation in slope-intercept form.

GuidedPractice

1. Write an equation in point-slope form for the line that passes through $(4, -1)$ and is parallel to the graph of $y = \frac{1}{4}x + 7$. $y + 1 = \frac{1}{4}(x - 4)$

1 Focus

VerticalAlignment

Before Lesson 4-4 Write equations in point-slope form.

Lesson 4-4 Write an equation of the line that passes through a given point, parallel to a given line. Write an equation of the line that passes through a given point, perpendicular to a given line.

After Lesson 4-4 Identify and graph absolute value and step functions.

2 Teach

Scaffolding Questions

Have students read the **Why?** section of the lesson.

Ask:

- How would you describe the relationship between the vertical lines in the art shown? They are parallel to each other. They have no slope.
- How would you describe the relationship between the horizontal lines in the art? They are parallel to each other. They have the same slope.

Lesson 4-4 Resources

Resource	Approaching Level AL	On Level OL	Beyond Level BL	English Learners ELL
Teacher Edition	▪ Differentiated Instruction, p. 241	▪ Differentiated Instruction, p. 245	▪ Differentiated Instruction, p. 245	▪ Differentiated Instruction, p. 241
Chapter Resource Masters	▪ Study Guide and Intervention, pp. 24–25 ▪ Skills Practice, p. 26 ▪ Practice, p. 27 ▪ Word Problem Practice, p. 28	▪ Study Guide and Intervention, pp. 24–25 ▪ Skills Practice, p. 26 ▪ Practice, p. 27 ▪ Word Problem Practice, p. 28 ▪ Enrichment, p. 29	▪ Practice, p. 27 ▪ Word Problem Practice, p. 28 ▪ Enrichment, p. 29	▪ Study Guide and Intervention, pp. 24–25 ▪ Skills Practice, p. 26 ▪ Practice, p. 27 ▪ Word Problem Practice, p. 28
Other	▪ 5-Minute Check 4-4 ▪ Study Notebook ▪ Teaching Algebra with Manipulatives	▪ 5-Minute Check 4-4 ▪ Study Notebook ▪ Teaching Algebra with Manipulatives	▪ 5-Minute Check 4-4 ▪ Study Notebook	▪ 5-Minute Check 4-4 ▪ Study Notebook ▪ Teaching Algebra with Manipulatives

1 Parallel Lines

Example 1 shows how to write the slope-intercept form of an equation for a line that passes through a particular point and is parallel to a given line.

Formative Assessment

Use the Guided Practice exercises after each Example to determine students' understanding of concepts.

Additional Example

1 Write an equation in slope-intercept form for the line that passes through (4, −2) and is parallel to the graph of $y = \frac{1}{2}x - 7$. $y = \frac{1}{2}x - 4$

Additional Examples also in Interactive Classroom PowerPoint® Presentations

IWB Interactive White Board READY

2 Perpendicular Lines

Example 2 shows how to determine whether two line segments in a real-world situation are perpendicular or parallel. **Example 3** shows how to determine whether the graphs of given equations are parallel or perpendicular. **Example 4** shows how to write an equation in slope-intercept form for a line perpendicular to a given line if you know a point on the line and the equation of the given line.

Teach with Tech

Interactive Whiteboard Give students an equation of a line and a point not on the line. Have one student show and explain how to find a line parallel to the given line that goes through that point. Have a second student show and explain how to find a line perpendicular to the given line that goes through that point.

ReviewVocabulary

opposite reciprocals

The opposite reciprocal of $\frac{a}{b}$ is $-\frac{b}{a}$. Their product is −1.

2 Perpendicular Lines Lines that intersect at right angles are called **perpendicular lines**. The slopes of nonvertical perpendicular lines are opposite reciprocals. That is, if the slope of a line is 4, the slope of the line perpendicular to it is $-\frac{1}{4}$.

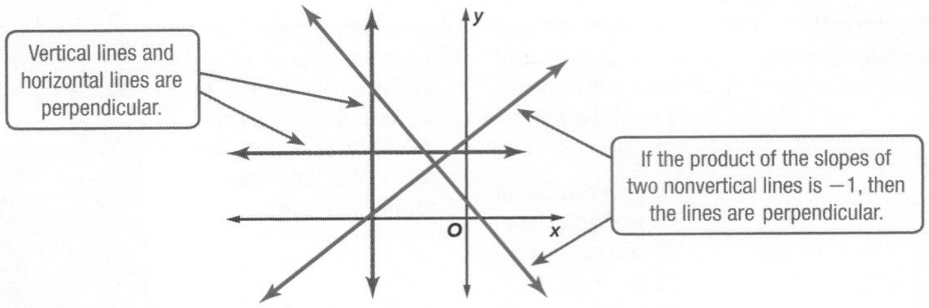

You can use slope to determine whether two lines are perpendicular.

Real-World Example 2 Slopes of Perpendicular Lines

DESIGN The outline of a company's new logo is shown on a coordinate plane.

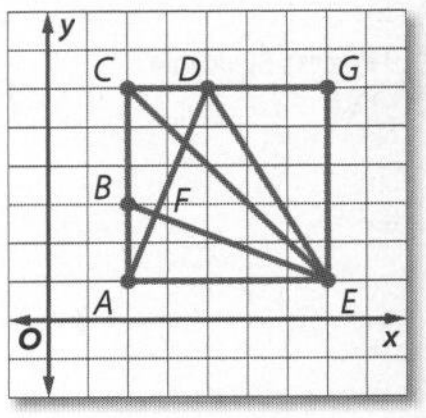

a. Is ∠DFE a right angle in the logo?

If $\overline{BE}$ and $\overline{AD}$ are perpendicular, then ∠DFE is a right angle. Find the slopes of $\overline{BE}$ and $\overline{AD}$.

slope of $\overline{BE}$: $m = \frac{1-3}{7-2}$ or $-\frac{2}{5}$

slope of $\overline{AD}$: $m = \frac{6-1}{4-2}$ or $\frac{5}{2}$

The line segments are perpendicular because $-\frac{2}{5} \times \frac{5}{2} = -1$. Therefore, ∠DFE is a right angle.

b. Is each pair of opposite sides parallel?

If a pair of opposite sides are parallel, then they have the same slope.

slope of $\overline{AC}$: $m = \frac{6-1}{2-2}$ or undefined

Since $\overline{AC}$ and $\overline{GE}$ are both parallel to the y-axis, they are vertical and are therefore parallel.

slope of $\overline{CG}$: $m = \frac{6-6}{7-2}$ or 0

Since $\overline{CG}$ and $\overline{AE}$ are both parallel to the x-axis, they are horizontal and are therefore parallel.

GuidedPractice

2. Slope of $\overline{QR} = \frac{6}{5}$; slope of $\overline{ST} = \frac{1}{5}$; the beams are not perpendicular since the product of their slopes is not −1.

2. CONSTRUCTION On the plans for a treehouse, a beam represented by $\overline{QR}$ has endpoints Q(−6, 2) and R(−1, 8). A connecting beam represented by $\overline{ST}$ has endpoints S(−3, 6) and T(−8, 5). Are the beams perpendicular? Explain.

Real-WorldLink

Though treehouses are typically built for recreational purposes, they were originally designed as a way to be protected from wild animals, dense population, and other threats.

Source: *The Treehouse Book*

You can determine whether the graphs of two linear equations are parallel or perpendicular by comparing the slopes of the lines.

Focus on Mathematical Content

Parallel and Perpendicular Lines All vertical lines are parallel, and all horizontal lines are parallel. All vertical lines are perpendicular to all horizontal lines and therefore, all horizontal lines are perpendicular to all vertical lines. Two nonvertical lines are parallel if their slopes are the same. They are perpendicular if the product of their slopes is −1.

Example 3 Parallel or Perpendicular Lines

Determine whether the graphs of $y = 5$, $x = 3$, and $y = -2x + 1$ are *parallel* or *perpendicular*. Explain.

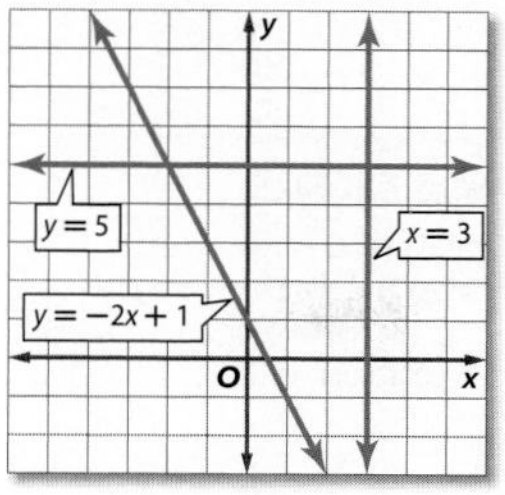

Graph each line on a coordinate plane.

From the graph, you can see that $y = 5$ is parallel to the x-axis and $x = 3$ is parallel to the y-axis. Therefore, they are perpendicular. None of the lines are parallel.

Guided Practice

3. Determine whether the graphs of $6x - 2y = -2$, $y = 3x - 4$, and $y = 4$ are *parallel* or *perpendicular*. Explain. $y = 3x - 4$ and $6x - 2y = -2$ are parallel since both have slope 3. None of the lines are perpendicular.

You can write the equation of a line perpendicular to a given line if you know a point on the line and the equation of the given line.

Study Tip

Tools Graph the given equation on a coordinate grid and plot the given point. Using a ruler, draw a line perpendicular to the given line that passes through the point.

Example 4 Perpendicular Line Through a Given Point

Write an equation in slope-intercept form for the line that passes through $(-4, 6)$ and is perpendicular to the graph of $2x + 3y = 12$.

Step 1 Find the slope of the given line by solving the equation for y.

$2x + 3y = 12$	Original equation
$2x - 2x + 3y = -2x + 12$	Subtract $2x$ from each side.
$3y = -2x + 12$	Simplify.
$\frac{3y}{3} = \frac{-2x + 12}{3}$	Divide each side by 3.
$y = -\frac{2}{3}x + 4$	Simplify.

The slope is $-\frac{2}{3}$.

Step 2 The slope of the perpendicular line is the opposite reciprocal of $-\frac{2}{3}$ or $\frac{3}{2}$. Find the equation of the perpendicular line.

$y - y_1 = m(x - x_1)$	Point-slope form
$y - 6 = \frac{3}{2}[x - (-4)]$	$(x_1, y_1) = (-4, 6)$ and $m = \frac{3}{2}$
$y - 6 = \frac{3}{2}(x + 4)$	Simplify.
$y - 6 = \frac{3}{2}x + 6$	Distributive Property
$y - 6 + 6 = \frac{3}{2}x + 6 + 6$	Add 6 to each side.
$y = \frac{3}{2}x + 12$	Simplify.

Guided Practice

4. Write an equation in slope-intercept form for the line that passes through $(4, 7)$ and is perpendicular to the graph of $y = \frac{2}{3}x - 1$. $y = -\frac{3}{2}x + 13$

Differentiated Instruction AL ELL

Kinesthetic Students may be familiar with the terms *parallel* and *perpendicular*. However, before covering the examples, you may want students to use rulers to draw parallel and perpendicular lines on graph paper.

Additional Examples

2 **GEOMETRY** The height of a trapezoid is the length of a segment that is perpendicular to both bases. In trapezoid *ARTP*, $\overline{AP}$ and $\overline{RT}$ are bases.

a. Can $\overline{EZ}$ be used to measure the height of the trapezoid? Explain.

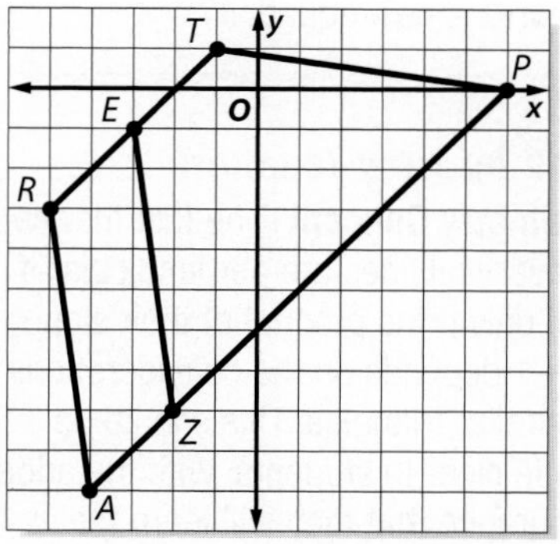

No, the slope of $\overline{RT}$ is 1, and the slope of $\overline{EZ}$ is -7. Since $1(-7) \neq -1$, $\overline{EZ}$ is not perpendicular to $\overline{RT}$. So, it cannot be used to measure the height of *ARTP*.

b. Are the bases parallel? Yes, both have a slope of 1.

3 Determine whether the graphs of $3x + y = 12$, $y = \frac{1}{3}x + 2$, and $2x - 6y = -5$ are *parallel* or *perpendicular*. Explain. $y = \frac{1}{3}x + 2$ is parallel to $2x - 6y = -5$ because they have equal slopes. $3x + y = 12$ is perpendicular to them both because the product of their slopes, $\frac{1}{3}$ and -3, is -1.

4 Write an equation in slope-intercept form for the line that passes through $(4, -1)$ and is perpendicular to the graph of $7x - 2y = 3$. $y = -\frac{2}{7}x + \frac{1}{7}$

Teaching the Process Standards

Tools Mathematically proficient students consider tools such as a ruler, a protractor, or technology, to solve a problem. Encourage students to keep tools in a convenient place to use while completing assignments.

WatchOut!

Preventing Errors Encourage students to understand the process used instead of simply the mechanics. For example, what do they know from the given information? What do they know about perpendicular lines? What do they need to know to write a new equation?

Tips for New Teachers

Geometry Concept The fact that two nonvertical lines are perpendicular if and only if the product of their slopes is −1 depends on the considerations of similar triangles. This should be made clear to students, with the added assurance that they will learn the concept in geometry.

Teaching the Process Standards

Precision Mathematically proficient students use clear definitions in discussion with others and in their own reasoning. In Exercise 4, point out to students that clear definitions will be especially important in the study of geometry.

3 Practice

Formative Assessment

Use Exercises 1–10 to check for understanding.

Use the chart at the bottom of the next page to customize assignments for your students.

Additional Answer

4. Since $\overline{EH}$ and $\overline{FG}$ are parallel to the y-axis, they are parallel. Since $\overline{EF}$ and $\overline{HG}$ are parallel to the x-axis they are parallel and $\overline{EH}$ is perpendicular to $\overline{EF}$ and $\overline{HG}$. Likewise, $\overline{FG}$ is perpendicular to $\overline{EF}$ and $\overline{HG}$. The slope of $\overline{EG}$ is −1 and the slope of $\overline{FH}$ is 1. Since the slopes are opposite reciprocals, $\overline{EG} \perp \overline{FH}$. The quadrilateral is a square.

ConceptSummary Parallel and Perpendicular Lines

	Parallel Lines	Perpendicular Lines
Words	Two nonvertical lines are parallel if they have the same slope.	Two nonvertical lines are perpendicular if the product of their slopes is −1.
Symbols	$\overleftrightarrow{AB} \parallel \overleftrightarrow{CD}$	$\overleftrightarrow{EF} \perp \overleftrightarrow{GH}$
Models	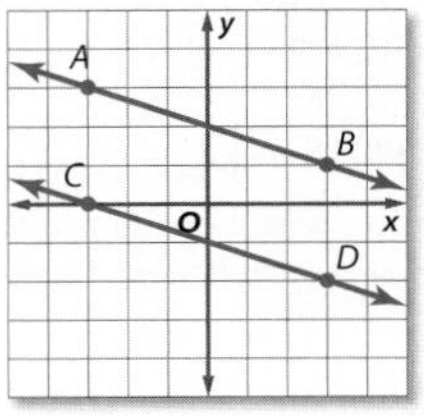	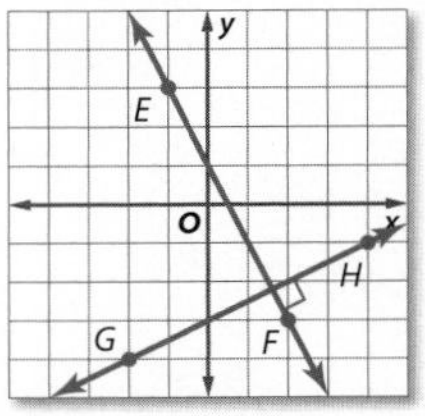

ReadingMath

Parallel and Perpendicular Lines The symbol for parallel is ∥. The symbol for perpendicular is ⊥.

3. Slope of $\overline{AC} = \frac{1-7}{-2-5}$ or $\frac{6}{7}$; slope of $\overline{BD} = \frac{-3-4}{3-(-3)}$ or $-\frac{7}{6}$; the paths are perpendicular.

5. $y = -2x$ and the other two graphs are perpendicular; slopes are opposite reciprocals; $2y = x$ and $4y = 2x + 4$ are parallel; equal slopes.

Check Your Understanding

○ = Step-by-Step Solutions begin on page R13.

Example 1 Write an equation in slope-intercept form for the line that passes through the given point and is parallel to the graph of the given equation.

1. $(-1, 2), y = \frac{1}{2}x - 3$ $y = \frac{1}{2}x + 2\frac{1}{2}$
2. $(0, 4), y = -4x + 5$ $y = -4x + 4$

Example 2

3. **GARDENS** A garden is in the shape of a quadrilateral with vertices $A(-2, 1)$, $B(3, -3)$, $C(5, 7)$, and $D(-3, 4)$. Two paths represented by $\overline{AC}$ and $\overline{BD}$ cut across the garden. Are the paths perpendicular? Explain.

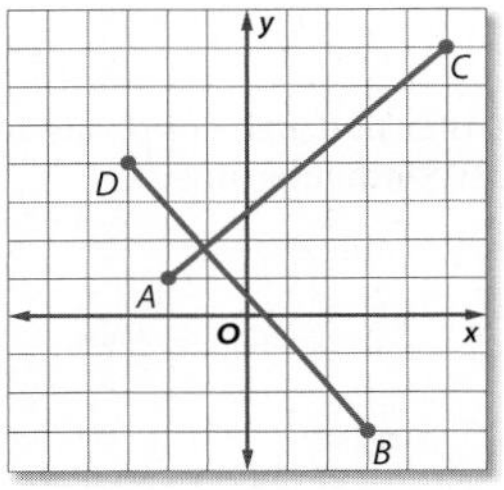

4. **PRECISION** A square is a quadrilateral that has opposite sides parallel, consecutive sides that are perpendicular, and diagonals that are perpendicular. Determine whether the quadrilateral is a square. Explain. **See margin.**

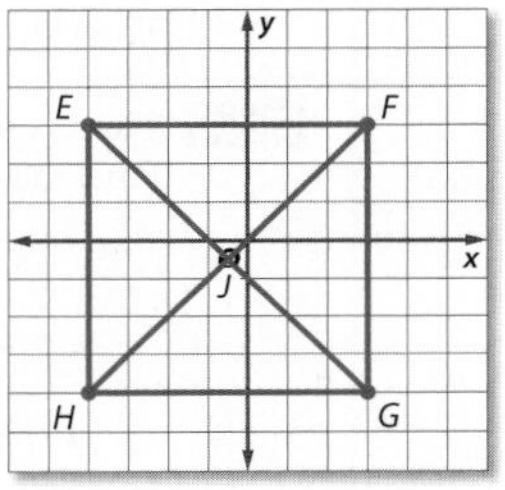

Example 3 Determine whether the graphs of the following equations are *parallel* or *perpendicular*. Explain.

5. $y = -2x, 2y = x, 4y = 2x + 4$
6. $y = \frac{1}{2}x, 3y = x, y = -\frac{1}{2}x$

6. None are parallel or perpendicular; none of the slopes are equal or opposite reciprocals.

Example 4 Write an equation in slope-intercept form for the line that passes through the given point and is perpendicular to the graph of the equation.

7. $(-2, 3), y = -\frac{1}{2}x - 4$ $y = 2x + 7$
8. $(-1, 4), y = 3x + 5$ $y = -\frac{1}{3}x + 3\frac{2}{3}$
9. $(2, 3), 2x + 3y = 4$ $y = \frac{3}{2}x$
10. $(3, 6), 3x - 4y = -2$ $y = -\frac{4}{3}x + 10$

Practice and Problem Solving

Extra Practice is on page R4.

Example 1 **Write an equation in slope-intercept form for the line that passes through the given point and is parallel to the graph of the given equation.**

11. $(3, -2), y = x + 4$ **12.** $(4, -3), y = 3x - 5$ **13.** $(0, 2), y = -5x + 8$

14. $(-4, 2), y = -\frac{1}{2}x + 6$ **15.** $(-2, 3), y = -\frac{3}{4}x + 4$ **16.** $(9, 12), y = 13x - 4$

Example 2 **17. GEOMETRY** A trapezoid is a quadrilateral that has exactly one pair of parallel opposite sides. Is *ABCD* a trapezoid? Explain your reasoning. **See margin.**

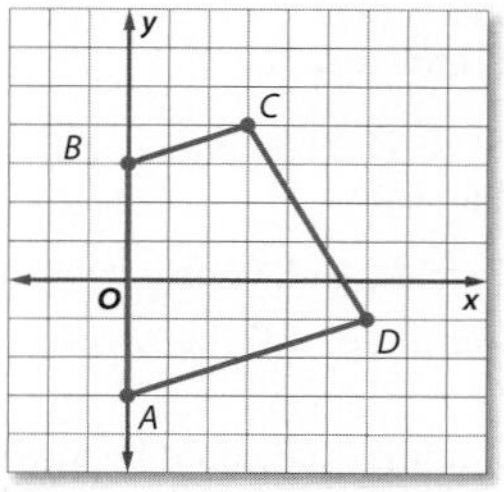

18. GEOMETRY *CDEF* is a kite. Are the diagonals of the kite perpendicular? Explain your reasoning.

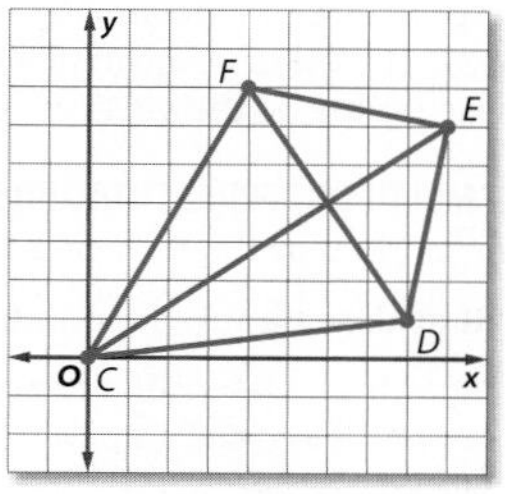

11. $y = x - 5$
12. $y = 3x - 15$
13. $y = -5x + 2$
14. $y = -\frac{1}{2}x$
15. $y = -\frac{3}{4}x + 1\frac{1}{2}$
16. $y = 13x - 105$
18. The slope of $\overline{CE}$ is $\frac{2}{3}$ and the slope of $\overline{DF}$ is $-\frac{3}{2}$. The diagonals are perpendicular because the slopes are opposite reciprocals.

19. Determine whether the graphs of $y = -6x + 4$ and $y = \frac{1}{6}x$ are perpendicular. Explain. **Yes; the slopes are -6 and $\frac{1}{6}$.**

20. MAPS On a map, Elmwood Drive passes through $R(4, -11)$ and $S(0, -9)$, and Taylor Road passes through $J(6, -2)$ and $K(4, -5)$. If they are straight lines, are the two streets perpendicular? Explain. **No; the slopes are $-\frac{1}{2}$ and $\frac{3}{2}$.**

Example 3 **PERSEVERANCE** **Determine whether the graphs of the following equations are *parallel* or *perpendicular*. Explain.**

21. $2x - 8y = -24, 4x + y = -2, x - 4y = 4$

22. $3x - 9y = 9, 3y = x + 12, 2x - 6y = 12$

21. $2x - 8y = -24$ and $4x + y = -2$ are perpendicular; $2x - 8y = -24$ and $x - 4y = 4$ are parallel.
22. All of the lines are parallel.

Example 4 **Write an equation in slope-intercept form for the line that passes through the given point and is perpendicular to the graph of the equation.** **23–28. See margin.**

23 $(-3, -2), y = -2x + 4$ **24.** $(-5, 2), y = \frac{1}{2}x - 3$ **25.** $(-4, 5), y = \frac{1}{3}x + 6$

26. $(2, 6), y = -\frac{1}{4}x + 3$ **27.** $(3, 8), y = 5x - 3$ **28.** $(4, -2), y = 3x + 5$

B **Write an equation in slope-intercept form for a line perpendicular to the graph of the equation that passes through the *x*-intercept of that line.** **29–31. See margin.**

29. $y = -\frac{1}{2}x - 4$ **30.** $y = \frac{2}{3}x - 6$ **31.** $y = 5x + 3$

32. Write an equation in slope-intercept form for the line that is perpendicular to the graph of $3x + 2y = 8$ and passes through the *y*-intercept of that line. $y = \frac{2}{3}x + 4$

Determine whether the graphs of each pair of equations are *parallel*, *perpendicular*, or *neither*.

33. $y = 4x + 3$, $4x + y = 3$ **neither** **34.** $y = -2x$, $2x + y = 3$ **parallel** **35.** $3x + 5y = 10$, $5x - 3y = -6$ **perpendicular**

36. $-3x + 4y = 8$, $-4x + 3y = -6$ **neither** **37.** $2x + 5y = 15$, $3x + 5y = 15$ **neither** **38.** $2x + 7y = -35$, $4x + 14y = -42$ **parallel**

Exercise Alert

Grid Paper For Exercises 43, 46 and 70–73, students will need grid paper.

Teaching the Process Standards

Perseverance Mathematically proficient students analyze givens and goals. In Exercises 21 and 22, point out to students that because there are three equations they will need to analyze all three possible pairs of lines.

Additional Answers

17. Yes; the line containing $\overline{AD}$ and the line containing $\overline{BC}$ have the same slope, $\frac{1}{3}$. Therefore, one pair of sides is parallel. The slope of $\overline{AB}$ is undefined and the slope of $\overline{CD}$ is $-\frac{5}{3}$.

23. $y = \frac{1}{2}x - \frac{1}{2}$
24. $y = -2x - 8$
25. $y = -3x - 7$
26. $y = 4x - 2$
27. $y = -\frac{1}{5}x + 8\frac{3}{5}$
28. $y = -\frac{1}{3}x - \frac{2}{3}$
29. $y = 2x + 16$
30. $y = -\frac{3}{2}x + \frac{27}{2}$
31. $y = -\frac{1}{5}x - \frac{3}{25}$

Differentiated Homework Options

Level	Assignment	Two-Day Option	
AL Basic	11–28, 45–73	11–27 odd, 49–52	12–28 even, 45–48, 53–73
OL Core	11–37 odd, 39–43, 45–73	11–28, 49–52	29–43, 45–48, 53–73
BL Advanced	29–69, (optional: 70–73)		

Study Guide and Intervention
AL OL ELL

NAME ______ DATE ______ PERIOD ______

4-4 Study Guide and Intervention

Parallel and Perpendicular Lines

Parallel Lines Two nonvertical lines are **parallel** if they have the same slope. All vertical lines are parallel.

Example Write an equation in slope-intercept form for the line that passes through (−1, 6) and is parallel to the graph of $y = 2x + 12$.

A line parallel to $y = 2x + 12$ has the same slope, 2. Replace m with 2 and (x_1, y_1) with (−1, 6) in the point-slope form.

$y - y_1 = m(x - x_1)$ Point-slope form
$y - 6 = 2[x - (-1)]$ $m = 2$; $(x_1, y_1) = (-1, 6)$
$y - 6 = 2(x + 1)$ Simplify.
$y - 6 = 2x + 2$ Distributive Property
$y = 2x + 8$ Slope-intercept form

Therefore, the equation is $y = 2x + 8$.

Exercises

Write an equation in slope-intercept form for the line that passes through the given point and is parallel to the graph of each equation.

1. 2. 3.

4. $(-2, 2), y = 4x - 2$ 5. $(6, 4), y = \frac{1}{3}x + 1$ 6. $(4, -2), y = -2x + 3$

7. $(-2, 4), y = -3x + 10$ 8. $(-1, 6), 3x + y = 12$ 9. $(4, -6), x + 2y = 5$

10. Find an equation of the line that has a y-intercept of 2 that is parallel to the graph of the line $4x + 2y = 8$.

11. Find an equation of the line that has a y-intercept of −1 that is parallel to the graph of the line $x - 3y = 6$.

12. Find an equation of the line that has a y-intercept of −4 that is parallel to the graph of the line $y = 6$.

Practice
AL OL BL ELL

NAME ______ DATE ______ PERIOD ______

4-4 Practice

Parallel and Perpendicular Lines

Write an equation in slope-intercept form for the line that passes through the given point and is parallel to the graph of the given equation.

1. $(3, 2), y = x + 5$ 2. $(-2, 5), y = -4x + 2$ 3. $(4, -6), y = -\frac{3}{4}x + 1$

4. $(5, 4), y = \frac{2}{5}x - 2$ 5. $(12, 3), y = \frac{4}{3}x + 5$ 6. $(3, 1), 2x + y = 5$

7. $(-3, 4), 3y = 2x - 3$ 8. $(-1, -2), 3x - y = 5$ 9. $(-8, 2), 5x - 4y = 1$

10. $(-1, -4), 9x + 3y = 8$ 11. $(-5, 6), 4x + 3y = 1$ 12. $(3, 1), 2x + 5y = 7$

Write an equation in slope-intercept form for the line that passes through the given point and is perpendicular to the graph of the given equation.

13. $(-2, -2), y = -\frac{1}{3}x + 9$ 14. $(-6, 5), x - y = 5$ 15. $(-4, -3), 4x + y = 7$

16. $(0, 1), x + 5y = 15$ 17. $(2, 4), x - 6y = 2$ 18. $(-1, -7), 3x + 12y = -6$

19. $(-4, 1), 4x + 7y = 6$ 20. $(10, 5), 5x + 4y = 8$ 21. $(4, -5), 2x - 5y = -10$

22. $(1, 1), 3x + 2y = -7$ 23. $(-6, -5), 4x + 3y = -6$ 24. $(-3, 5), 5x - 6y = 9$

25. **GEOMETRY** Quadrilateral $ABCD$ has diagonals $\overline{AC}$ and $\overline{BD}$. Determine whether $\overline{AC}$ is perpendicular to $\overline{BD}$. Explain.

26. **GEOMETRY** Triangle ABC has vertices $A(0, 4)$, $B(1, 2)$, and $C(4, 6)$. Determine whether triangle ABC is a right triangle. Explain.

Lesson 4-4

Word Problem Practice
AL OL BL ELL

NAME ______ DATE ______ PERIOD ______

4-4 Word Problem Practice

Parallel and Perpendicular Lines

1. **BUSINESS** Brady's Books is a retail store. The store's average daily profits y are given by the equation $y = 2x + 3$ where x is the number of hours available for customer purchases. Brady's adds an online shopping option. Write an equation in slope-intercept form to show a new profit line with the same profit rate containing the point (0, 12).

2. **ARCHITECTURE** The front view of a house is drawn on graph paper. The left side of the roof of the house is represented by the equation $y = x$. The rooflines intersect at a right angle and the peak of the roof is represented by the point (5, 5). Write the equation in slope-intercept form for the line that creates the right side of the roof.

3. **ARCHAEOLOGY** An archaeologist is comparing the location of a jeweled box she just found to the location of a brick wall. The wall can be represented by the equation $y = -\frac{3}{5}x + 13$. The box is located at the point (10, 9). Write an equation representing a line that is perpendicular to the wall and that passes through the location of the box.

4. **GEOMETRY** A parallelogram is created by the intersections of the lines $x = 2$, $x = 6$, $y = \frac{1}{2}x + 2$, and another line. Find the equation of the fourth line needed to complete the parallelogram. The line should pass through (2, 0). (*Hint:* Sketch a graph to help you see the lines.)

5. **INTERIOR DESIGN** Pamela is planning to install an island in her kitchen. She draws the shape she likes by specifying the vertices of the square tiles on her kitchen floor. She records the location of each corner in the table.

Corner	Distance from West Wall (tiles)	Distance from South Wall (tiles)
A	5	4
B	3	8
C	7	10
D	11	7

a. How many pairs of parallel sides are there in the shape $ABCD$ she designed? Explain.

b. How many pairs of perpendicular sides are there in the shape she designed? Explain.

c. What is the shape of her new island?

39. Write an equation of the line that is parallel to the graph of $y = 7x - 3$ and passes through the origin. $y = 7x$

40. **EXCAVATION** Scientists excavating a dinosaur mapped the site on a coordinate plane. If one bone lies from (−5, 8) to (10, −1) and a second bone lies from (−10, −3) to (−5, −6), are the bones parallel? Explain. **Yes; both have a slope of $-\frac{3}{5}$.**

41. **ARCHAEOLOGY** In the ruins of an ancient civilization, an archaeologist found pottery at (2, 6) and hair accessories at (4, −1). A pole is found with one end at (7, 10) and the other end at (14, 12). Is the pole perpendicular to the line through the pottery and the hair accessories? Explain.

42. **GRAPHICS** To create a design on a computer, Andeana must enter the coordinates for points on the design. One line segment she drew has endpoints of (−2, 1) and (4, 3). The other coordinates that Andeana entered are (2, −7) and (8, −3). Could these points be the vertices of a rectangle? Explain. **See margin.**

43. **MULTIPLE REPRESENTATIONS** In this problem, you will explore parallel and perpendicular lines. **a–c. See Ch. 4 Answer Appendix.**

a. **Graphical** Graph the points $A(-3, 3)$, $B(3, 5)$, and $C(-4, 0)$ on a coordinate plane.

b. **Analytical** Determine the coordinates of a fourth point D that would form a parallelogram. Explain your reasoning.

c. **Analytical** What is the minimum number of points that could be moved to make the parallelogram a rectangle? Describe which points should be moved, and explain why.

41. Yes; the slope of the line through the hair accessories and the pottery is $-\frac{7}{2}$. The slope of the line through the endpoints of the pole is $\frac{2}{7}$, so the lines are perpendicular.

H.O.T. Problems Use Higher-Order Thinking Skills

44. **CHALLENGE** If the line through (−2, 4) and (5, d) is parallel to the graph of $y = 3x + 4$, what is the value of d? **25**

45. **REASONING** Which key features of the graphs of two parallel lines are the same, and which are different? Which key features of the graphs of two perpendicular lines are the same, and which are different? **See margin.**

46. **OPEN ENDED** Graph a line that is parallel and a line that is perpendicular to $y = 2x - 1$. **See margin.**

Example 3

47. **CRITIQUE** Carmen and Chase are finding an equation of the line that is perpendicular to the graph of $y = \frac{1}{3}x + 2$ and passes through the point (−3, 5). Is either of them correct? Explain your reasoning.

Carmen	Chase
$y - 5 = -3[x - (-3)]$	$y - 5 = 3[x - (-3)]$
$y - 5 = -3(x + 3)$	$y - 5 = 3(x + 3)$
$y = -3x - 9 + 5$	$y = 3x + 9 + 5$
$y = -3x - 4$	$y = 3x + 14$

47. Carmen, she correctly determined the slope of the perpendicular line.

48. **WRITING IN MATH** Illustrate how you can determine whether two lines are parallel or perpendicular. Write an equation for the graph that is parallel and an equation for the graph that is perpendicular to the line shown. Explain your reasoning. **See Ch. 4 Answer Appendix.**

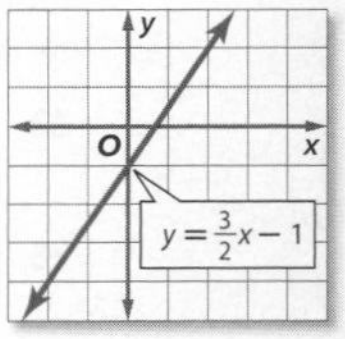

Enrichment
OL BL

NAME ______ DATE ______ PERIOD ______

4-4 Enrichment

Pencils of Lines

All of the lines that pass through a single point in the same plane are called a **pencil of lines**.

All lines with the same slope, but different intercepts, are also called a "pencil," a **pencil of parallel lines**.

Graph some of the lines in each pencil.

1. A pencil of lines through the point (1, 3)

2. A pencil of lines described by $y - 4 = m(x - 2)$, where m is any real number

Multiple Representations

In Exercise 43, students use a graph in the coordinate plane and analysis to compare parallelograms and rectangles.

Standardized Test Practice

49. Which of the following is an algebraic translation of the following phrase? **B**
5 less than the quotient of a number and 8

A $5 - \frac{n}{8}$ **C** $5 - \frac{8}{n}$

B $\frac{n}{8} - 5$ **D** $\frac{8}{n} - 5$

50. A line through which two points would be parallel to a line with a slope of $\frac{3}{4}$? **F**

F (0, 5) and (−4, 2) **H** (0, 0) and (0, −2)

G (0, 2) and (−4, 1) **J** (0, −2) and (−4, −2)

51. Which equation best fits the data in the table? **B**

A $y = x + 4$
B $y = 2x + 3$
C $y = 7$
D $y = 4x - 5$

x	y
1	5
2	7
3	9
4	11

52. SHORT RESPONSE Tyler is filling his 6000-gallon pool at a constant rate. After 4 hours, the pool contained 800 gallons. How many total hours will it take to completely fill the pool? **30 hours**

Spiral Review

Write each equation in standard form. (Lesson 4-3)

53. $y - 13 = 4(x - 2)$ **$4x - y = -5$**
54. $y - 5 = -2(x + 2)$ **$2x + y = 1$**
55. $y + 3 = -5(x + 1)$ **$5x + y = -8$**
56. $y + 7 = \frac{1}{2}(x + 2)$ **$x - 2y = 12$**
57. $y - 1 = \frac{5}{6}(x - 4)$ **$5x - 6y = 14$**
58. $y - 2 = -\frac{2}{5}(x - 8)$ **$2x + 5y = 26$**

59. CANOE RENTAL Latanya and her friends rented a canoe for 3 hours and paid a total of $45. (Lesson 4-2)

a. Write a linear equation to find the total cost C of renting the canoe for h hours. **$C = 10h + 15$**

b. How much would it cost to rent the canoe for 8 hours? **$95**

Write an equation of the line that passes through each point with the given slope. (Lesson 4-2)

60. $(5, -2), m = 3$ **$y = 3x - 17$**
61. $(-5, 4), m = -5$ **$y = -5x - 21$**
62. $(3, 0), m = -2$ **$y = -2x + 6$**
63. $(3, 5), m = 2$ **$y = 2x - 1$**
64. $(-3, -1), m = -3$ **$y = -3x - 10$**
65. $(-2, 4), m = -5$ **$y = -5x - 6$**

Simplify each expression. If not possible, write *simplified*. (Lesson 1-4)

66. $13m + m$ **$14m$**
67. $14a^2 + 13b^2 + 27$ **simplified**
68. $3(x + 2x)$ **$9x$**

69. FINANCIAL LITERACY At a Farmers' Market, merchants can rent a small table for $5.00 and a large table for $8.50. One time, 25 small and 10 large tables were rented. Another time, 35 small and 12 large were rented. (Lesson 1-2)

a. Write an algebraic expression to show the total amount of money collected. **25(5) + 10(8.5) + 35(5) + 12(8.5)**

b. Evaluate the expression. **$487**

Skills Review

Express each relation as a graph. Then determine the domain and range. **70–73. See Ch. 4 Answer Appendix.**

70. {(3, 8), (3, 7), (2, −9), (1, −9), (−5, −3)}
71. {(3, 4), (4, 3), (2, 2), (5, −4), (−4, 5)}
72. {(0, 2), (−5, 1), (0, 6), (−1, 9), (−4, −5)}
73. {(−7, 6), (−3, −4), (4, −5), (−2, 6), (−3, 2)}

Differentiated Instruction OL BL

Extension Write $A(-4, -1)$, $B(1, 4)$, $C(4, 1)$, and $D(-1, -4)$ on the board. Ask students to determine what geometric figure is made if they were to connect these points to get a polygon. Ask students to justify their answer. Rectangle; the slope of $\overline{AB}$ is 1. The slope of $\overline{CD}$ is 1. So $\overline{AB}$ is parallel to $\overline{CD}$. The slope of $\overline{AD}$ is −1. The slope of $\overline{BC}$ is −1. So $\overline{AD}$ is parallel to $\overline{BC}$. This makes the figure a parallelogram. Since the slopes of $\overline{AB}$ and $\overline{BC}$ are negative reciprocals of each other, $\overline{AB}$ and $\overline{BC}$ are perpendicular. This makes the figure a rectangle. Since the four sides are not of equal length, the figure is not a square.

Teaching the Process Standards

Critique Mathematically proficient students distinguish correct logic or reasoning from that which is flawed. For Exercise 47, students should see that Carmen and Chase have used different slopes in the first equation.

4 Assess

Ticket Out the Door Ask students to write and graph an equation of the form $Ax + By = C$. Have them draw two lines parallel to this line and describe those lines in terms of A, B, and C.

Formative Assessment

Check for student understanding of concepts in Lessons 4-3 and 4-4.

Quiz 2, p. 51

Additional Answers

42. No; The segment from (−2, 1) to (4, 3) is not perpendicular to the segment from (4, 3) to (8, −3).

45. Sample answer: Parallel lines: similarities: The domain and range are all real numbers, the functions are both either increasing or decreasing on the entire domain, the end behavior is the same; differences: x- and y-intercepts are different. Perpendicular lines: similarities: The domain and range are all real numbers; differences: One function is increasing and the other is decreasing on the entire domain, as x decreases, y increases for one function and decreases for the other and as x increases, y increases for one function and decreases for the other.

46. Sample answer:

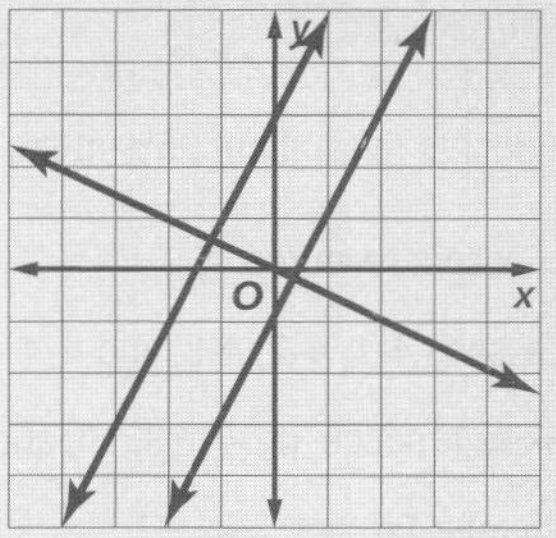

Formative Assessment

Use the Mid-Chapter Quiz to assess students' progress in the first half of the chapter.

For problems answered incorrectly, have students review the lessons indicated in parentheses.

Summative Assessment

Mid-Chapter Test, p. 53

McGraw-Hill eAssessment Customize and create multiple versions of your Mid-Chapter Test and their answer keys.

FOLDABLES StudyOrganizer

Dinah Zike's Foldables®

Before students complete the Mid-Chapter Quiz, encourage them to review the information for Lessons 4-1 through 4-4 in their Foldables.

CHAPTER 4 Mid-Chapter Quiz

Lessons 4-1 through 4-4

Write an equation in slope-intercept form for each graph shown. (Lesson 4-1)

1. 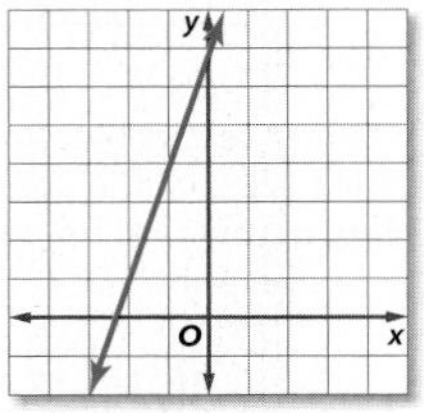 $y = 3x + 7$

2. 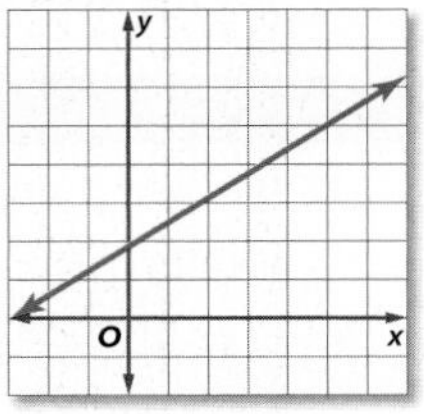 $y = \frac{3}{5}x + 2$

Graph each equation. (Lesson 4-1) **3–4. See Ch. 4 Answer Appendix.**

3. $y = 2x + 3$

4. $y = \frac{1}{3}x - 2$

5. BOATS Write an equation in slope-intercept form for the total rental cost C for a pontoon boat used for t hours. (Lesson 4-1) $C = 60t + 20$

Write an equation of the line with the given conditions. (Lesson 4-2)

6. (2, 5); slope 3 $y = 3x - 1$

7. (−3, −1), slope $\frac{1}{2}$ $y = \frac{1}{2}x + \frac{1}{2}$

8. (−3, 4), (1, 12) $y = 2x + 10$

9. (−1, 6), (2, 4) $y = -\frac{2}{3}x + \frac{16}{3}$

10. (2, 1), slope 0 $y = 1$

11. MULTIPLE CHOICE Write an equation of the line that passes through the point (0, 0) and has slope −4. (Lesson 4-2) **C**

A $y = x - 4$ **C** $y = -4x$

B $y = x + 4$ **D** $y = 4 - x$

12. $y - 4 = 6(x - 1)$ **13.** $y + 1 = -3(x + 2)$

Write an equation in point-slope form for the line that passes through each point with the given slope. (Lesson 4-3)

12. (1, 4), $m = 6$

13. (−2, −1), $m = -3$

14. Write an equation in point-slope form for the line that passes through the point (8, 3), $m = -2$. (Lesson 4-3)

15. Write $y + 3 = \frac{1}{2}(x - 5)$ in standard form. (Lesson 4-3)

16. Write $y + 4 = -7(x - 3)$ in slope-intercept form. (Lesson 4-3) $y = -7x + 17$

14. $y - 3 = -2(x - 8)$ **15.** $x - 2y = 11$

Write each equation in standard form. (Lesson 4-3)

17. $y - 5 = -2(x - 3)$ $2x + y = 11$

18. $y + 4 = \frac{2}{3}(x - 3)$ $2x - 3y = 18$

Write each equation in slope-intercept form. (Lesson 4-3)

19. $y - 3 = 4(x + 3)$ $y = 4x + 15$

20. $y + 1 = \frac{1}{2}(x - 8)$ $y = \frac{1}{2}x - 5$

21. MULTIPLE CHOICE Determine whether the graphs of the pair of equations are *parallel, perpendicular,* or *neither.* (Lesson 4-4) **F**

$$y = -6x + 8$$
$$3x + \frac{1}{2}y = -3$$

F parallel

G perpendicular

H neither

J not enough information

Write an equation in slope-intercept form for the line that passes through the given point and is perpendicular to the graph of the equation. (Lesson 4-4)

22. (3, −4); $y = -\frac{1}{3}x - 5$ $y = 3x - 13$

23. (0, −3); $y = -2x + 4$ $y = \frac{1}{2}x - 3$

24. (−4, −5); $-4x + 5y = -6$ $y = -\frac{5}{4}x - 10$

25. (−1, −4); $-x - 2y = 0$ $y = 2x - 2$

InterventionPlanner

TIER 1 On Level OL	TIER 2 Strategic Intervention AL approaching grade level	TIER 3 Intensive Intervention 2 or more grades below level
If students miss about 25% of the exercises or less,	**If** students miss about 50% of the exercises,	**If** students miss about 75% of the exercises,
Then choose a resource: **SE** Lessons 4-1, 4-2, 4-3, and 4-4 Skills Practice, pp. 7, 13, 19, and 26 **TE** Chapter Project connectED.mcgraw-hill.com Self-Check Quiz	**Then** choose a resource: Study Guide and Intervention, Chapter 4, pp. 5, 11, 17, and 24 *Quick Review Math Handbook* connectED.mcgraw-hill.com Extra Examples, Personal Tutor, Homework Help	**Then** use *Math Triumphs, Alg. 1,* Ch. 4 connectED.mcgraw-hill.com Extra Examples, Personal Tutor, Homework Help, Review Vocabulary

LESSON 4-5 Scatter Plots and Lines of Fit

Then
- You wrote linear equations given a point and the slope.

Now
- 1 Investigate relationships between quantities by using points on scatter plots.
- 2 Use lines of fit to make and evaluate predictions.

Why?
- The graph shows the number of people from the United States who travel to other countries. The points do not all lie on the same line; however, you may be able to draw a line that is close to all of the points. That line would show a linear relationship between the year x and the number of travelers each year y. Generally, international travel has increased.

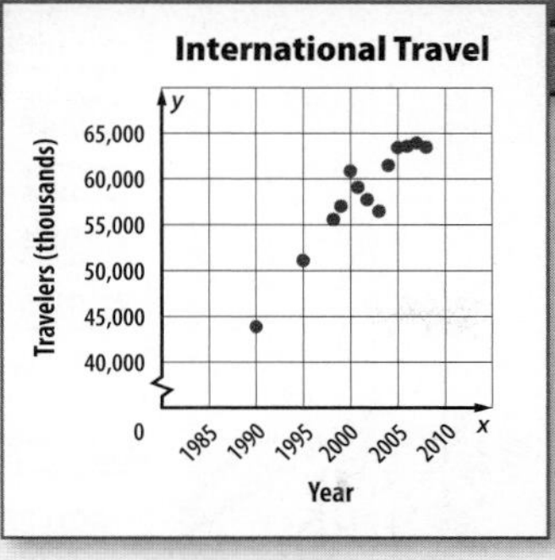

NewVocabulary
bivariate data
scatter plot
line of fit
linear interpolation

Content Standards
AI.L.4, AI.L.5, AI.DS.2, AI.DS.3

Process Standards
PS.1, PS.4

1 Investigate Relationships Using Scatter Plots

Data with two variables are called **bivariate data**. A **scatter plot** shows the relationship between a set of data with two variables, graphed as ordered pairs on a coordinate plane. Scatter plots are used to investigate a relationship between two quantities.

ConceptSummary Scatter Plots

Positive Correlation

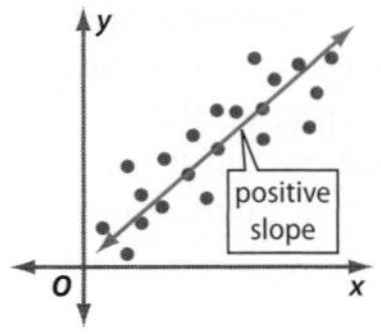

As x increases, y increases

Negative Correlation

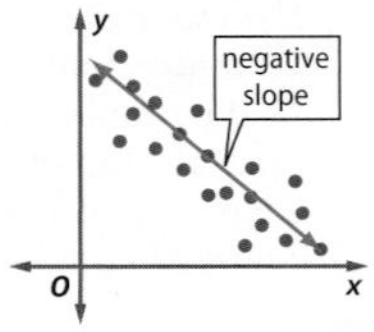

As x decreases, y decreases

No Correlation

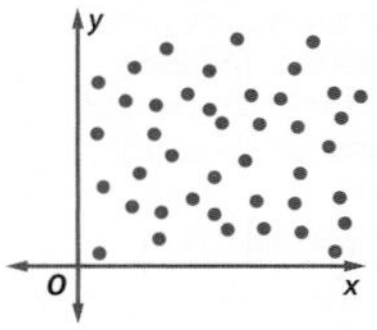

x and y are not related

Real-World Example 1 Evaluate a Correlation

WAGES Determine whether the graph shows a *positive*, *negative*, or *no* correlation. If there is a positive or negative correlation, describe its meaning in the situation.

The graph shows a positive correlation. As the number of hours worked increases, the wages usually increase.

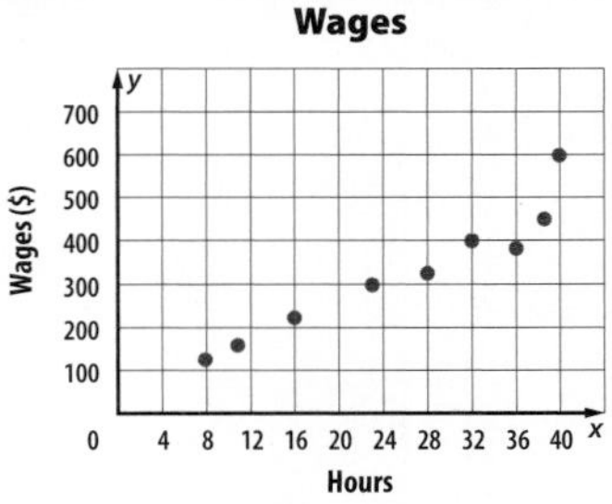

GuidedPractice

1. Positive, there are more travelers in the later years than in the early years.

1. Refer to the graph on international travel. Determine whether the graph shows a *positive*, *negative*, or *no* correlation. If there is a positive or negative correlation, describe its meaning.

1 Focus

VerticalAlignment

Before Lesson 4-5 Write linear equations given a point and the slope.

Lesson 4-5 Investigate relationships between quantities by using points on scatter plots. Use lines of fit to make and evaluate predictions.

After Lesson 4-5 Write equations of best-fit lines and median-fit lines using linear regression.

2 Teach

Scaffolding Questions

Have students read the **Why?** section of the lesson.

Ask:
- Would a line that is close to all of the points have a positive or negative slope? positive
- What would you do to find the equation of that line? Use two points on the line to write the equation.
- What type of graph would show that the relationship between the year and the number of travelers who travel to another country is decreasing? a line with a negative slope

Lesson 4-5 Resources

Resource	Approaching Level AL	On Level OL	Beyond Level BL	English Learners ELL
Teacher Edition	▪ Differentiated Instruction, p. 248	▪ Differentiated Instruction, pp. 248, 251	▪ Differentiated Instruction, p. 251	
Chapter Resource Masters	▪ Study Guide and Intervention, pp. 30–31 ▪ Skills Practice, p. 32 ▪ Practice, p. 33 ▪ Word Problem Practice, p. 34 ▪ Spreadsheet Activity, p. 36	▪ Study Guide and Intervention, pp. 30–31 ▪ Skills Practice, p. 32 ▪ Practice, p. 33 ▪ Word Problem Practice, p. 34 ▪ Enrichment, p. 35 ▪ Spreadsheet Activity, p. 36	▪ Practice, p. 33 ▪ Word Problem Practice, p. 34 ▪ Enrichment, p. 35 ▪ Spreadsheet Activity, p. 36	▪ Study Guide and Intervention, pp. 30–31 ▪ Skills Practice, p. 32 ▪ Practice, p. 33 ▪ Word Problem Practice, p. 34 ▪ Spreadsheet Activity, p. 36
Other	▪ 5-Minute Check 4-5 ▪ Study Notebook ▪ Teaching Algebra with Manipulatives	▪ 5-Minute Check 4-5 ▪ Study Notebook ▪ Teaching Algebra with Manipulatives	▪ 5-Minute Check 4-5 ▪ Study Notebook	▪ 5-Minute Check 4-5 ▪ Study Notebook ▪ Teaching Algebra with Manipulatives

1 Investigate Relationships Using Scatter Plots

Example 1 shows how to determine whether the graph of real-world data shows a *positive correlation*, a *negative correlation*, or *no correlation*.

Formative Assessment

Use the Guided Practice exercises after each Example to determine students' understanding of concepts.

Additional Example

1 TECHNOLOGY The graph shows the average number of students per computer in Maria's school. Determine whether the graph shows a *positive correlation*, a *negative correlation*, or *no correlation*. If there is a positive or negative correlation, describe its meaning in the situation.

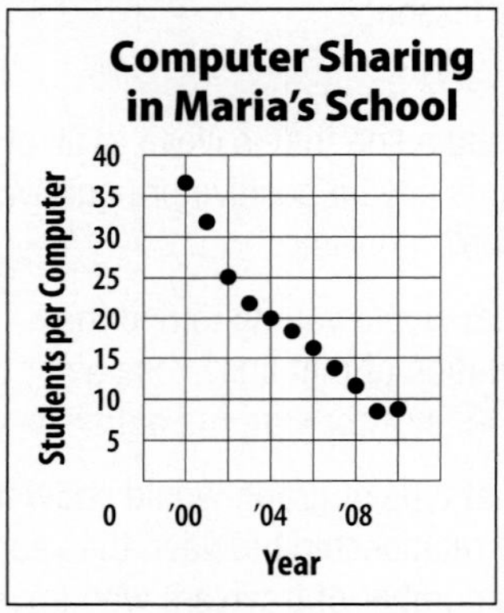

Negative correlation; sample answer: Each year, Maria's school has more computers, making the students-per-computer rate smaller.

Additional Examples also in Interactive Classroom PowerPoint® Presentations

IWB Interactive White Board READY

2 Use Lines of Fit

Scatter plots can show whether there is a trend in a set of data. When the data points all lie close to a line, a **line of fit** or *trend line* can model the trend.

KeyConcept Using a Linear Function to Model Data

Step 1 Make a scatter plot. Determine whether any relationship exists in the data.

Step 2 Draw a line that seems to pass close to most of the data points.

Step 3 Use two points on the line of fit to write an equation for the line.

Step 4 Use the line of fit to make predictions.

Real-WorldLink

The Kingda Ka roller coaster at Six Flags Great Adventure in Jackson, New Jersey, has broken three records: tallest roller coaster at 456 feet, fastest at 128 miles per hour, and largest vertical drop of 418 feet.

Source: Ultimate Roller Coaster

Real-World Example 2 Write a Line of Fit

ROLLER COASTERS The table shows the largest vertical drops of nine roller coasters in the United States and the number of years after 1988 that they were opened. Identify the independent and the dependent variables. Is there a relationship in the data? If so, predict the vertical drop in a roller coaster built 30 years after 1988.

Years Since 1988	1	3	5	8	12	12	12	13	15
Vertical Drop (ft)	151	155	225	230	306	300	255	255	400

Source: Ultimate Roller Coaster

Step 1 Make a scatter plot.

The independent variable is the year, and the dependent variable is the vertical drop. As the number of years increases, the vertical drop of roller coasters increases. There is a positive correlation between the two variables.

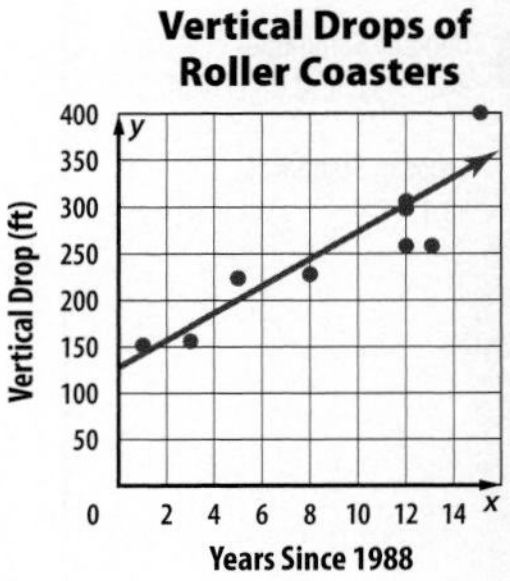

Step 2 Draw a line of fit.

No one line will pass through all of the data points. Draw a line that passes close to the points. A line of fit is shown.

Step 3 Write the slope-intercept form of an equation for the line of fit.

The line of fit passes close to (2, 150) and the data point (12, 300).

Find the slope.

$$m = \frac{y_2 - y_1}{x_2 - x_1} \quad (x_1, y_1) = (2, 150), (x_2, y_2) = (12, 300)$$

$$= \frac{300 - 150}{12 - 2}$$

$$= \frac{150}{10} \text{ or } 15$$

Use $m = 15$ and either the point-slope form or the slope-intercept form to write the equation of the line of fit.

$$y - y_1 = m(x - x_1)$$

$$y - 150 = 15(x - 2)$$

$$y - 150 = 15x - 30$$

$$y = 15x + 120$$

A slope of 15 means that the vertical drops increased an average of 15 feet per year. To predict the vertical drop of a roller coaster built 30 years after 1988, substitute 30 for x in the equation. The vertical drop is 15(30) + 120 or 570 feet.

DifferentiatedInstruction AL OL

If students need more practice making and interpreting scatter plots,

Then have them make a scatter plot of their height (*x*-values) and age (*y*-values) for the first ten years of their life. Students estimate their heights as needed, but check to be sure estimates are reasonable. Ask them to draw a line of fit and write the slope-intercept form of an equation for the line. Then ask students to compare their current height with that derived from their equation.

Guided Practice See Ch. 4 Answer Appendix.

2. MUSIC The table shows the dollar value in millions for the sales of CDs for the year. Make a scatter plot and determine what relationship exists, if any.

Year	2000	2001	2002	2003	2004	2005	2006	2007	2008
Sales	13,215	12,909	12,044	11,233	11,447	10,520	9373	7452	5471

Reading Math

Interpolation and Extrapolation The Latin prefix *inter-* means between, and the Latin prefix *extra-* means beyond.

In Lesson 4-2, you learned that linear extrapolation is used to predict values *outside* the range of the data. You can also use a linear equation to predict values *inside* the range of the data. This is called **linear interpolation**.

Real-World Example 3 Use Interpolation or Extrapolation

TRAVEL Use the scatter plot to find the approximate number of United States travelers to international countries in 1996.

International Travel

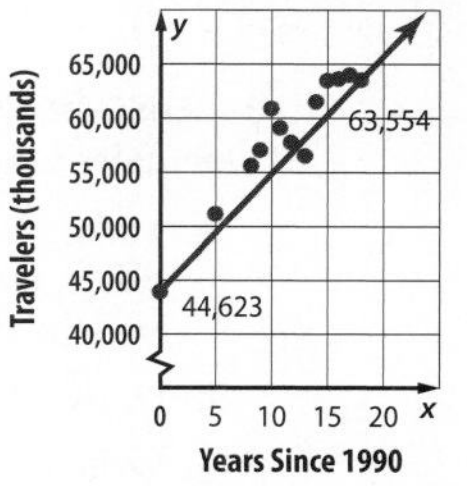

Source: *Statistical Abstract of the United States*

Step 1 Draw a line of fit. The line should be as close to as many points as possible.

Step 2 Write the slope-intercept form of the equation. The line of fit passes through (0, 44,623) and (18, 63,554).

Find the slope.

$m = \frac{y_2 - y_1}{x_2 - x_1}$ Slope Formula

$= \frac{63,554 - 44,623}{18 - 0}$ $(x_1, y_1) = (0, 44,623)$, $(x_2, y_2) = (18, 63,554)$

$= \frac{18,931}{18}$ Simplify.

Use $m = \frac{18,931}{18}$ and either the point-slope form or the slope-intercept form to write the equation of the line of fit.

$$y - y_1 = m(x - x_1)$$

$$y - 44,623 = \frac{18,931}{18}(x - 0)$$

$$y - 44,623 = \frac{18,931}{18}x$$

$$y = \frac{18,931}{18}x + 44,623$$

Step 3 Evaluate the function for $x = 1996 - 1990$ or 6.

$y = \frac{18,931}{18}x + 44,623$ Equation of best-fit line

$= \frac{18,931}{18}(6) + 44,623$ $x = 6$

$= 6310\frac{1}{3} + 44,623$ or $50,933\frac{1}{3}$ Add.

In 1996, there were approximately 50,933 thousand or 50,933,000 people who traveled from the United States to international countries.

Guided Practice

3. MUSIC Use the equation for the line of fit for the data in Guided Practice 2 to estimate CD sales in 2015. **$5715 million**

2 Use Lines of Fit

Example 2 shows how to draw a scatter plot for real-world data, draw a line of fit, and then write the slope-intercept form of an equation for the line of fit. **Example 3** shows how to use the equation for the line of fit to predict values inside the range of the data for a real-world situation.

Additional Examples

2 POPULATION The table shows the growth of the world population. Identify the independent and dependent variables.

Make a scatter plot and determine what relationship, if any, exists in the data.

Year	Populations (millions)
1650	500
1850	1000
1930	2000
1975	4000
2004	6400

independent variable: year; dependent variable: population; positive correlation; sample answer: $y = 35.1x - 63,870$

World Population

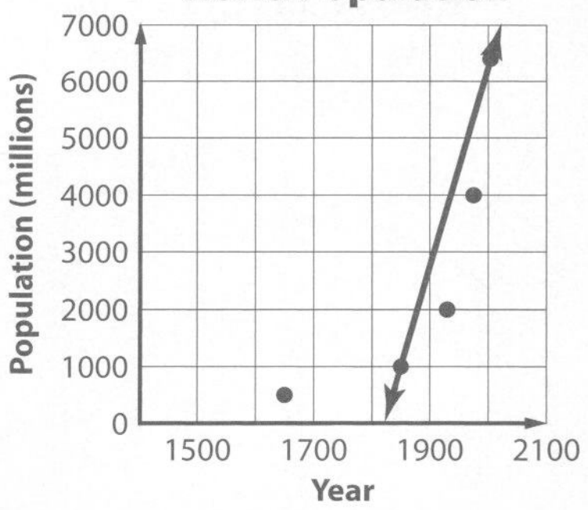

3 Use the equation for the line of fit in Additional Example 2 to predict the world's population in 2025. 7207.5 million

Focus on Mathematical Content

Scatter Plot A scatter plot is a graph that consists of points unconnected by a line. These points can show trends in the relationship between two quantities in a set of data. If the points show a linear trend, you can draw a line of fit to model that trend. Once a line is drawn, you can find an equation of the line and use that equation to make predictions.

Teach with Tech

Interactive Whiteboard Show a scatter plot on the board. Choose several students to draw lines that they believe fit the data. Have students explain why they chose to draw those particular lines.

Check Your Understanding

= Step-by-Step Solutions begin on page R13.

Example 1 **Determine whether each graph shows a *positive*, *negative*, or *no* correlation. If there is a positive or negative correlation, describe its meaning in the situation.**

1. **Free Throws**

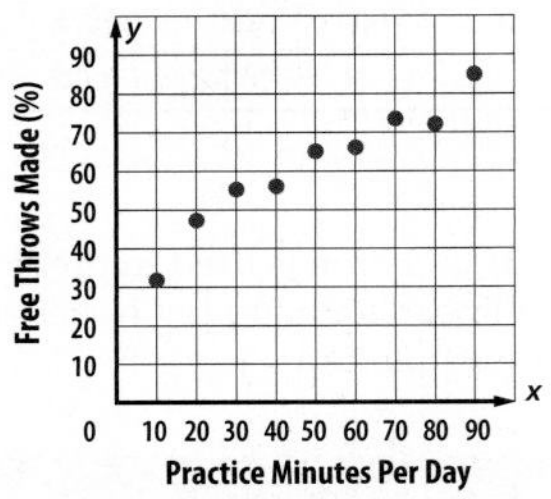

2. **Lemonade Sales**

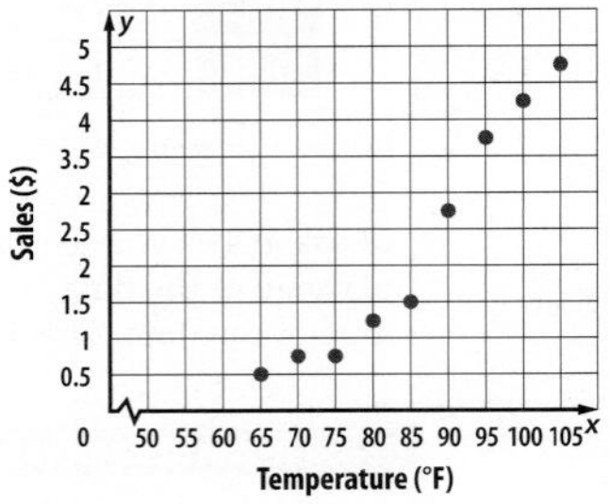

1. Positive; the longer you practice free throws, the more free throws you will make.
2. Positive; the warmer the temperature, the the more lemonade you sell.

Example 2 **3. SENSE-MAKING** The table shows the median age of females when they were first married.

a. Make a scatter plot and determine what relationship exists, if any, in the data. Identify the independent and the dependent variables. **a–b. See margin.**

b. Draw a line of fit for the scatter plot.

c. Write an equation in slope-intercept form for the line of fit.

Example 3 **d.** Predict what the median age of females when they are first married will be in 2016. **Sample answer: 27.0**

e. Do you think the equation can give a reasonable estimate for the year 2056? Explain.
Yes, according to the equation, the median age would be 31.4, which is likely.

Year	Age
1996	24.8
1997	25.0
1998	25.0
1999	25.1
2000	25.1
2001	25.1
2002	25.3
2003	25.3
2004	25.3
2005	25.5
2006	25.9

Source: U.S. Bureau of Census

3c. Sample answer: Using (1996, 24.8) and (2006, 25.9) and rounding, $y = 0.11x - 194.8$

Practice and Problem Solving

Extra Practice is on page R4.

Example 1 **Determine whether each graph shows a *positive*, *negative*, or *no* correlation. If there is a positive or negative correlation, describe its meaning in the situation.**

4. **Game Tickets at the Fair**

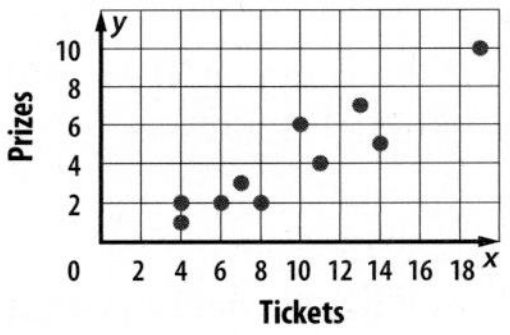

5 **NBA 3-Point Percentage**

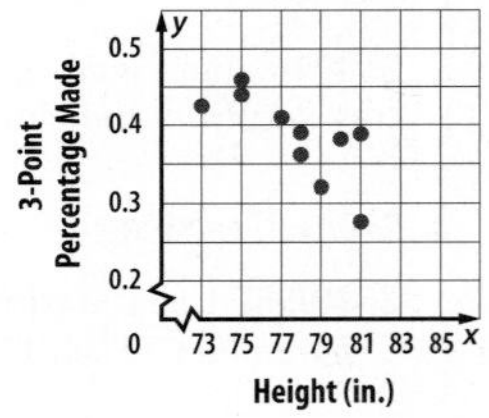

4. Positive; the more tickets you buy, the more game prizes you will win.
5. Negative; the taller the NBA player, the lower his 3-point shooting percentage.

WatchOut!

Student Misconceptions Remind students that predictions are only as valid as the equations used to find them. Therefore, there are as many predictions as there are equations that can be written from pairs of points.

3 Practice

Formative Assessment

Use Exercises 1–3 to check for understanding.

Use the chart at the bottom of this page to customize assignments for your students.

Exercise Alert

Grid Paper For Exercises 3, 10–12, 17, 32–34, 42 and 43 students will need grid paper.

Tape Measure Exercise 12 requires the use of a tape measure to measure foot size and height.

Additional Answers

3a, b.

Median Age of Females When First Married

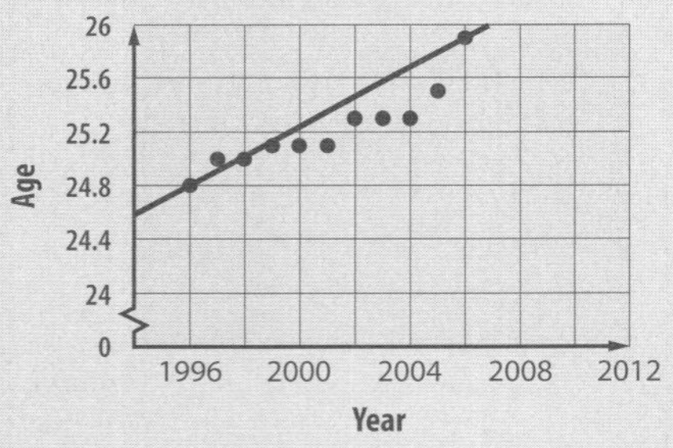

Positive; independent variable is the year and dependent variable is the median age of females when they were first married.

Differentiated Homework Options

Level	Assignment	Two-Day Option	
AL Basic	4–9, 13, 14, 16–43	5, 7, 18–21	4–8 even, 13, 14, 16, 17, 22–43
OL Core	5, 7, 9–14, 16–43	4–9, 18–21	10–14, 16, 17, 22–43
BL Advanced	10–41 (optional: 42, 43)		

6.

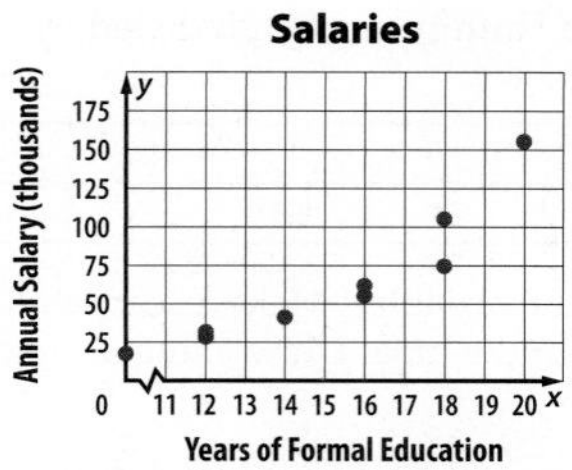

7

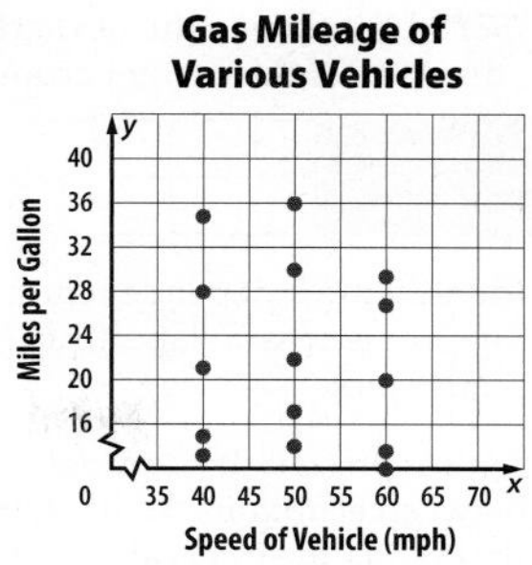

6. Positive; the more years of formal education you receive, the higher your salary will be.

7. No; various vehicles give too many varying results for there to be a correlation.

Examples 2–3 **8. MILK** Refer to the scatter plot of gallons of milk consumption per person for selected years.

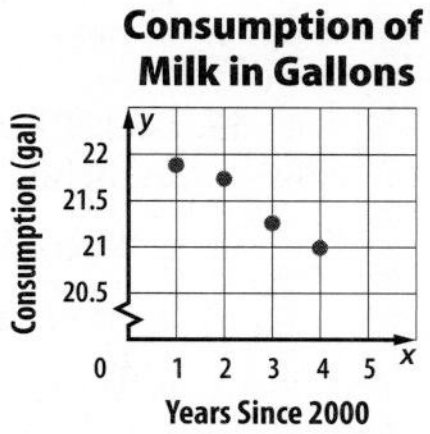

a. Use the points (2, 21.75) and (4, 21) to write the slope-intercept form of an equation for the line of fit. **$y = -0.375x + 22.5$**

b. Predict the milk consumption in 2020. **about 15 gal**

c. Predict in what year milk consumption will be 10 gallons. **2033**

d. Is it reasonable to use the equation to estimate the consumption of milk for any year? Explain. **Yes; if the current trend continues, the consumption of milk will continue to decrease.**

9. FOOTBALL Use the scatter plot.

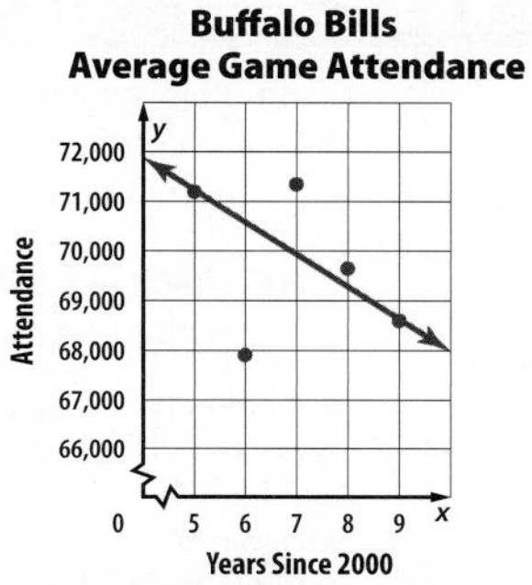

a. Use the points (5, 71,205) and (9, 68,611) to write the slope-intercept form of an equation for the line of fit shown in the scatter plot. **$y = -648.5x + 74{,}447.5$**

b. Predict the average attendance at a game in 2020. **61,478**

c. Can you use the equation to make a decision about the average attendance in any given year in the future? Explain. **No; the average attendance will fluctuate with other variables such as how good the team is that year.**

B **10. SENSE-MAKING** The Body Mass Index (BMI) is a measure of body fat using height and weight. The heights and weights of twelve men with normal BMI are given in the table at the right. **a–b. See Ch. 4 Answer Appendix.**

Height (in.)	Weight (lb)
62	115
63	124
65	120
67	134
67	140
68	138
68	144
68	152
69	147
72	155
73	168
73	166

a. Make a scatter plot comparing the height in inches to the weight in pounds.

b. Draw a line of fit for the data.

c. Write the slope-intercept form of an equation for the line of fit. **Sample answer: $y = 4.57x - 168.33$**

d. Predict the normal weight for a man who is 84 inches tall. **Sample answer: 215.6 lb**

e. A man's weight is 188 pounds. Use the equation of the line of fit to predict the height of the man. **Sample answer: about 78 in.**

Teaching the Process Standards

Sense-Making Mathematically proficient students search for regularity or trends. In Exercises 3 and 10, students should examine the data and use the scatter plot to observe the trends.

Tips for New Teachers

Reasoning Encourage students to think about why trends are occuring in the problems on which they are working. Then ask students how problems of this type could be important in other fields, such as engineering, marketing, and statistics.

Follow-up

Students have explored scatter plots and lines of fit.

Ask:

- When would a linear function be used to model a real-world situation? Sample answer: When the relationship that is modeled has a constant rate of change.

DifferentiatedInstruction OL BL

Extension Write (1, 10.1), (2, 9.8), (3, 10), (4, 10.5), (5, 10.4), (6, 10.8), and (7, 10.3) on the board. As a class, graph these data points on two separate graphs. Make the scale on the first graph such that the result is a scatter plot with no correlation. Make the scale on the second graph such that the result is a scatter plot with a positive correlation. Discuss how graphs can be manipulated to show different trends.

11. **GEYSERS** The time to the next eruption of Old Faithful can be predicted by using the duration of the current eruption.

Duration (min)	1.5	2	2.5	3	3.5	4	4.5	5
Interval (min)	48	55	70	72	74	82	93	100

11a. The independent variable is the interval between eruptions and the dependent variable is the duration of the eruptions. There is a positive correlation between the independent and dependent variables. See Ch.4 Answer Appendix for graph.

a. Identify the independent and the dependent variables. Make a scatter plot and determine what relationship, if any, exists in the data. Draw a line of fit for the scatter plot.

b. Let x represent the duration of the previous interval. Let y represent the time between eruptions. Write the slope-intercept form of the equation for the line of fit. Predict the interval after a 7.5-minute eruption.

c. Make a critical judgment about using the equation to predict the duration of the next eruption. Would the equation be a useful model?

12. **COLLECT DATA** Use a tape measure to measure both the foot size and the height in inches of ten individuals. **a–c. See students' work.**

a. Record your data in a table.

b. Make a scatter plot and draw a line of fit for the data.

c. Write an equation for the line of fit.

d. Make a conjecture about the relationship between foot size and height.

12d. Sample answer: There seems to be a general trend that taller people have larger feet.

11b. Sample answer using (2, 55) and (4, 82): $y = 13.5x + 28$; Sample answer: about 129.25 min

H.O.T. Problems Use Higher-Order Thinking Skills

13. **OPEN ENDED** Describe a real-life situation that can be modeled using a scatter plot. Decide whether there is a *positive*, *negative*, or *no* correlation. Explain what this correlation means. **See margin.**

14. **WHICH ONE DOESN'T BELONG?** Analyze the following situations and determine which one does not belong. **See margin.**

hours worked and amount of money earned	height of an athlete and favorite color
seedlings that grow an average of 2 centimeters each week	number of photos stored on a camera and capacity of camera

11c. Sample answer: The duration of an eruption is not dependent on the previous interval. Only the interval can be predicted by the length of the eruption.

15. **ARGUMENTS** Determine which line of fit is better for the scatter plot. Explain your reasoning. **See margin.**

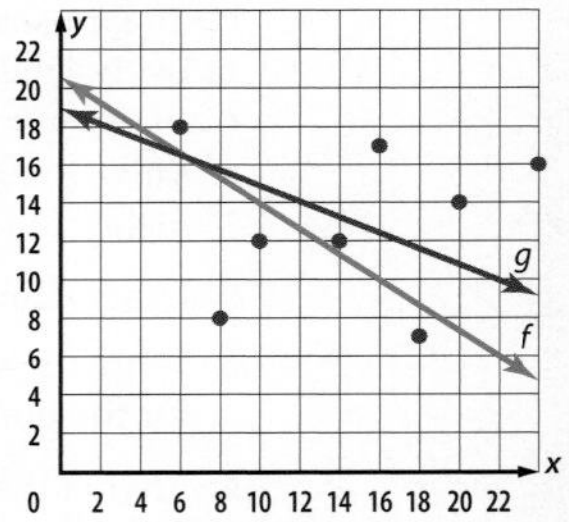

16. **REASONING** What can make a scatter plot and line of fit more useful for accurate predictions? Does an accurate line of fit always predict what will happen in the future? Explain. **See margin.**

17. **WRITING IN MATH** Make a scatter plot that shows the height of a person and age. Explain how you could use the scatter plot to predict the age of a person given his or her height. How can the information from a scatter plot be used to identify trends and make decisions? **See margin.**

Study Guide and Intervention

AL OL ELL

NAME ______ DATE ______ PERIOD ______

4-5 Study Guide and Intervention

Scatter Plots and Lines of Fit

Investigate Relationships Using Scatter Plots A **scatter plot** is a graph in which two sets of data are plotted as ordered pairs in a coordinate plane. If y increases as x increases, there is a **positive correlation** between x and y. If y decreases as x increases, there is a **negative correlation** between x and y. If x and y are not related, there is **no correlation**.

Example **EARNINGS The graph at the right shows the amount of money Carmen earned each week and the amount she deposited in her savings account that same week. Determine whether the graph shows a *positive correlation*, a *negative correlation*, or *no correlation*. If there is a positive or negative correlation, describe its meaning in the situation.**

The graph shows a positive correlation. The more Carmen earns, the more she saves.

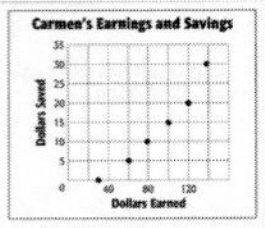

Exercises

Determine whether each graph shows a *positive correlation*, a *negative correlation*, or *no correlation*. If there is a positive or negative correlation, describe its meaning in the situation.

1. Average Weekly Work Hours in U.S.

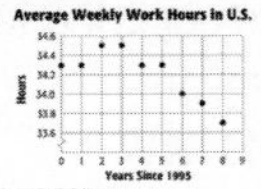

Source: *The World Almanac*

2. Average Jogging Speed

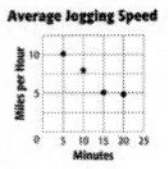

3. Average U.S. Hourly Earnings

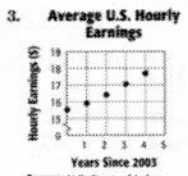

Source: U.S. Dept. of Labor

4. U.S. Imports from Mexico

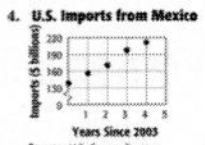

Source: U.S. Census Bureau

Practice

AL OL BL ELL

NAME ______ DATE ______ PERIOD ______

4-5 Practice

Scatter Plots and Lines of Fit

Determine whether each graph shows a *positive correlation*, a *negative correlation*, or *no correlation*. If there is a positive or negative correlation, describe its meaning in the situation.

1. Temperature versus Rainfall

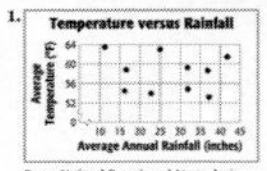

Source: National Oceanic and Atmospheric Administration

2. State Elevations

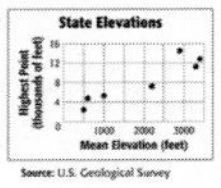

Source: U.S. Geological Survey

3. **DISEASE** The table shows the number of cases of Foodborne Botulism in the United States for the years 2001 to 2005.

U.S. Foodborne Botulism Cases					
Year	2001	2002	2003	2004	2005
Cases	39	28	20	16	18

Source: Centers for Disease Control

a. Draw a scatter plot and determine what relationship, if any, exists in the data.

b. Draw a line of fit for the scatter plot.

c. Write the slope-intercept form of an equation for the line of fit.

U.S. Foodborne Botulism Cases

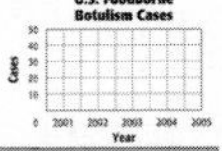

4. **ZOOS** The table shows the average and maximum longevity of various animals in captivity.

Longevity (years)								
Avg.	12	25	15	8	35	40	41	20
Max.	47	50	40	20	70	77	61	54

Source: Walker's Mammals of the World

a. Draw a scatter plot and determine what relationship, if any, exists in the data.

b. Draw a line of fit for the scatter plot.

c. Write the slope-intercept form of an equation for the line of fit.

d. Predict the maximum longevity for an animal with an average longevity of 33 years.

Animal Longevity (Years)

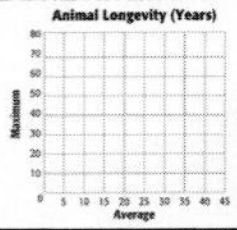

Lesson 4-5

Word Problem Practice

AL OL BL ELL

NAME ______ DATE ______ PERIOD ______

4-5 Word Problem Practice

Scatter Plots and Lines of Fit

1. **MUSIC** The scatter plot shows the number of CDs in millions that were sold from 1999 to 2005. If the trend continued, about how many CDs were sold in 2006?

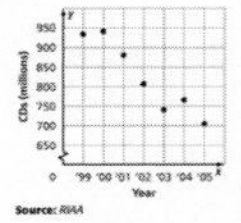

Source: *RIAA*

2. **FAMILY** The table shows the predicted annual cost for a middle income family to raise a child from birth until adulthood. Draw a scatter plot and describe what relationship exists within the data.

Cost of Raising a Child Born in 2003					
Child's Age	3	6	9	12	15
Annual Cost ($)	10,700	11,700	12,600	15,000	16,700

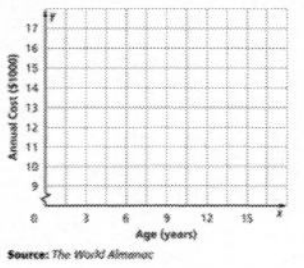

Source: *The World Almanac*

3. **HOUSING** The median price of an existing home was $160,000 in 2000 and $240,000 in 2007. If x represents the number of years since 2000, use these data points to determine a line of best fit for the trends in the price of existing homes. Write the equation in slope-intercept form.

4. **BASEBALL** The table shows the average length in minutes of professional baseball games in selected years.

Average Length of Major League Baseball Games							
Year	'92	'94	'96	'98	'00	'02	'04
Time (min)	170	174	171	168	178	172	167

Source: Elias Sports Bureau

a. Draw a scatter plot and determine what relationship, if any, exists in the data.

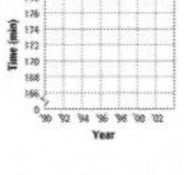

b. Explain what the scatter plot shows.

c. Draw a line of fit for the scatter plot.

Enrichment

OL BL

NAME ______ DATE ______ PERIOD ______

4-5 Enrichment

Latitude and Temperature

The *latitude* of a place on Earth is the measure of its distance from the equator. What do you think is the relationship between a city's latitude and its mean January temperature? At the right is a table containing the latitudes and January mean temperatures for fifteen U.S. cities.

U.S. City	Latitude	January Mean Temperature
Albany, New York	42:40 N	20.7°F
Albuquerque, New Mexico	35:07 N	34.3°F
Anchorage, Alaska	61:11 N	14.9°F
Birmingham, Alabama	33:32 N	41.7°F
Charleston, South Carolina	32:47 N	47.1°F
Chicago, Illinois	41:50 N	21.0°F
Columbus, Ohio	39:59 N	26.3°F
Duluth, Minnesota	46:47 N	7.0°F
Fairbanks, Alaska	64:50 N	−10.1°F
Galveston, Texas	29:14 N	52.9°F
Honolulu, Hawaii	21:19 N	72.9°F
Las Vegas, Nevada	36:12 N	45.1°F
Miami, Florida	25:47 N	67.3°F
[illegible]	[illegible]	[illegible]

Teaching the Process Standards

Arguments Mathematically proficient students justify their conclusions and communicate them to others. In Exercise 15, have students discuss why they chose the line they did.

Standardized Test Practice

18. Which equation best describes the relationship between the values of x and y in the table? **B**

A $y = x - 5$
B $y = 2x - 5$
C $y = 3x - 7$
D $y = 4x - 7$

x	y
−1	−7
0	−5
2	−1
4	3

19. STATISTICS Mr. Hernandez collected data on the heights and average stride lengths of a random sample of high school students. He then made a scatter plot. What kind of correlation did he most likely see? **F**

F positive
G constant
H negative
J no

20. GEOMETRY Mrs. Aguilar's rectangular bedroom measures 13 feet by 11 feet. She wants to purchase carpet for the bedroom that costs $2.95 per square foot, including tax. How much will the carpet cost? **D**

A $70.80
B $141.60
C $145.95
D $421.85

21. SHORT RESPONSE Nikia bought a one-month membership to a fitness center for $35. Each time she goes, she rents a locker for $0.25. If she spent $40.50 at the fitness center last month, how many days did she go? **22 days**

Spiral Review

Determine whether the graphs of each pair of equations are *parallel, perpendicular,* or *neither.* (Lesson 4-4)

22. $y = -2x + 11$ **parallel**
$y + 2x = 23$

23. $3y = 2x + 14$ **neither**
$2x + 3y = 2$

24. $y = -5x$ **neither**
$y = 5x - 18$

25. $y = 3x + 2$ **perpendicular**
$y = -\frac{1}{3}x - 2$

Write each equation in standard form. (Lesson 4-3)

26. $y - 13 = 4(x - 2)$ **$4x - y = -5$**

27. $y - 5 = -2(x + 2)$ **$2x + y = 1$**

28. $y + 3 = -5(x + 1)$ **$5x + y = -8$**

29. $y + 7 = \frac{1}{2}(x + 2)$ **$x - 2y = 12$**

30. $y - 1 = \frac{5}{6}(x - 4)$ **$5x - 6y = 14$**

31. $y - 2 = -\frac{2}{5}(x - 8)$ **$2x + 5y = 26$**

Graph each equation. (Lesson 4-1) **32–34. See margin.**

32. $y = 2x + 3$

33. $4x + y = -1$

34. $3x + 4y = 7$

Find the slope of the line that passes through each pair of points. (Lesson 3-3)

35. (3, 4), (10, 8) $\frac{4}{7}$

36. (−4, 7), (3, 5) $-\frac{2}{7}$

37. (3, 7), (−2, 4) $\frac{3}{5}$

38. (−3, 2), (−3, 4) **undefined**

39. (−2, −6), (−1, 10) **16**

40. (1, −5), (−3, −5) **0**

41. DRIVING Latisha drove 248 miles in 4 hours. At that rate, how long will it take her to drive an additional 93 miles? (Lesson 2-6) **1.5 h**

Skills Review

Express each relation as a graph. Then determine the domain and range. **42–43. See Ch. 4 Answer Appendix.**

42. {(4, 5), (5, 4), (−2, −2), (4, −5), (−5, 4)}

43. {(7, 6), (3, 4), (4, 5), (−2, 6), (−3, 2)}

32.

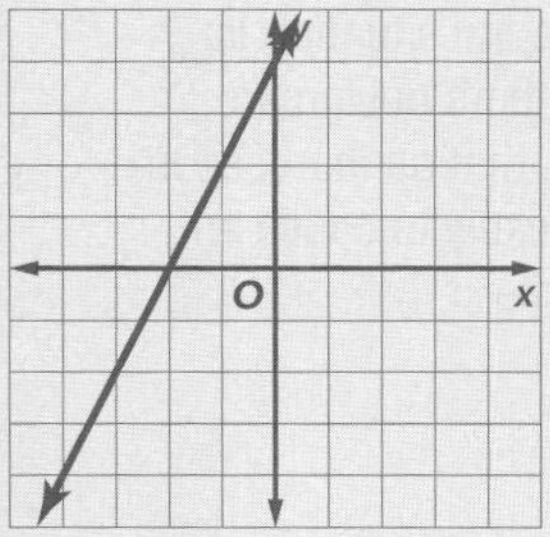

33.

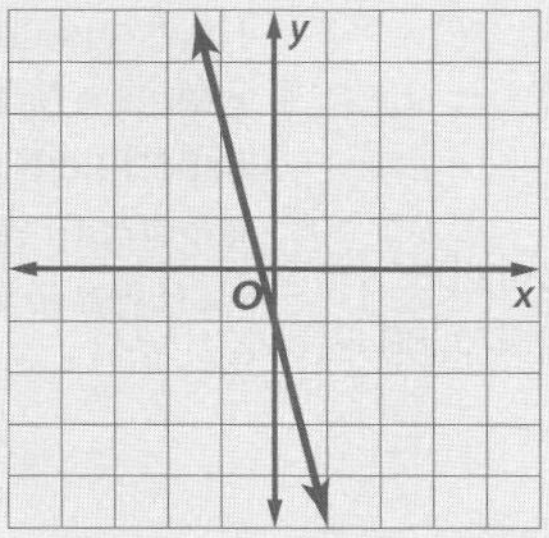

34.

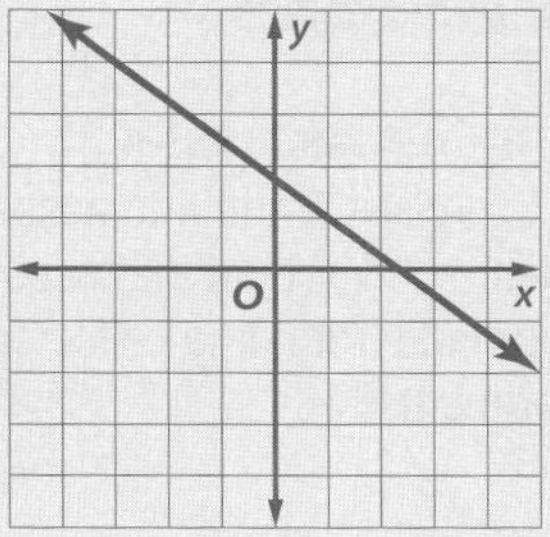

4 Assess

Crystal Ball Ask students to write how they think what they learned today about lines of fit will help them with tomorrow's lesson about finding the best-fit line for a set of data.

Additional Answers

13. Sample answer: The salary of an individual and the years of experience that they have; this would be a positive correlation because the more experience an individual has, the higher the salary would probably be.

14. Height and favorite color does not belong. The other situations have a positive correlation, this has no correlation.

15. Neither; line g has the same number of points above the line and below the line. Line f is close to 2 of the points; but for the rest of the data, there are 3 points above and 3 points below the line.

16. The more data you have, the more accurate the scatter plot and line of fit will be. No, trends can change and a line of fit assumes that the same pattern or trend will continue indefinitely.

17. Sample answer: You can visualize a line to determine whether the data has a positive or negative correlation. The graph below shows the ages and heights of people. To predict a person's age given his or her height, write a linear equation for the line of fit. Then substitute the person's height and solve for the corresponding age. You can use the pattern in the scatter plot to make decisions.

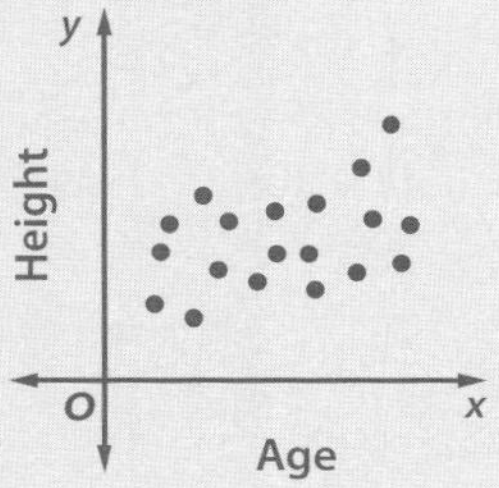

1 Focus

Objective Explore the difference between correlation and causation.

Materials for Each Student

- grid paper

Easy to Make Manipulatives

Teaching Algebra with Manipulatives

- grid paper, p. 1

Teaching Tip

Remind students that they have identified positive, negative, and no correlation between two variables. Some correlations may be purely coincidental, or they may have a common underlying cause. That is, the change in one variable may be the cause for the change in the other.

2 Teach

Working in Cooperative Groups

Suggest that students work in groups of three or four to allow for an exchange of ideas when answering the questions posed in the Activity. However, for Step 1 of the Activity, ask each group member to make his or her own graph.

- Can you think of another product that has had an increase in sales since 2001? Sample answers: computers, homes, gasoline, electricity
- Do you think it is possible that any one of those products might also be related to the increase in tuition? yes

Practice Have students complete Exercises 1–5.

EXTEND 4-5

Algebra Lab: Correlation and Causation

Content Standards
AI.DS.2, AI.DS.3, AI.DS.4, AI.DS.6

You may be considering attending a college or technical school in the future. What factors cause tuition to rise—increased building costs, higher employee salaries, or the amount of bottled water consumed?

Let's see how bottled water and college tuition are related. The table shows the average college tuition and fees for public colleges and the per person U.S. consumption of bottled water per year for 2003 through 2007.

Year	2003	2004	2005	2006	2007
Water Consumed (gallons)	21.6	23.2	25.4	27.6	29.3
Tuition ($)	4645	5126	5492	5804	6191

Source: *Beverage Marketing Corporation* and *College Board*

Activity Correlation and Causation

Follow the steps to learn about correlation and causation.

Step 1 Graph the ordered pairs (gallons, tuition) to create a scatter plot. For example, one ordered pair is (21.6, 4645). Describe the graph. **As the average cost of college tui increases, the amount of bottled w consumed in the United States also i See Ch. 4 Answer Appendix for grap**

Step 2 Is the correlation *positive* or *negative*? Explain. **Positive; the more bottled water consumed in the United States, the higher the average cost of college tuition.**

Step 3 Do you think drinking more bottled water *causes* college tuition costs to rise? Explain. **No; Sample Answer: both consumption of water and tuition have increased but one does not cause the other**

Step 4 **Causation** occurs when a change in one variable produces a change in another variable. Correlation can be observed between many variables, but causation can only be determined from data collected from a controlled experiment. Describe an experiment that could illustrate causation. **Sample Answer: class attendance and grade**

Exercises

For each exercise, determine whether each situation illustrates *correlation* or *causation*. Explain your reasoning, including other factors that might be involved. **1–5. See Ch. 4 Answer Appendix.**

1. A survey showed that sleeping with the light on was positively correlated to nearsightedness.
2. A controlled experiment showed a positive correlation between the number of cigarettes smoked and the probability of developing lung cancer.
3. A random sample of students found that owning a cell phone had a negative correlation with riding the bus to school.
4. A controlled experiment showed a positive correlation between the number of hours using headphones when listening to music and the level of hearing loss.
5. DeQuan read in the newspaper that shark attacks are positively correlated with monthly ice cream sales.

3 Assess

Formative Assessment

Use Exercises 3 and 4 to assess whether students understand that causation can only be determined from data collected from a controlled experiment.

From Concrete to Abstract

Have students examine the situation in Exercise 5. Then have them design an experiment that shows that an increase in ice cream sales is not likely to cause an increase in shark attacks.

LESSON 4-6 Regression and Median-Fit Lines

:: Then	:: Now	:: Why?
You used lines of fit and scatter plots to evaluate trends and make predictions.	1 Write equations of best-fit lines using linear regression. 2 Write equations of median-fit lines.	The table shows the total attendance, in millions of people, at the Minnesota State Fair from 2005 to 2009. You can use a graphing calculator to find the equation of a *best-fit line* and use it to make predictions about future attendance at the fair.

Year	Attendance (millions)
2005	1.633
2006	1.681
2007	1.682
2008	1.693
2009	1.790

NewVocabulary
best-fit line
linear regression
correlation coefficient
residual
median-fit line

Content Standards
AI.L.4, AI.L.5, AI.DS.3

1 Best-Fit Lines

You have learned how to find and write equations for lines of fit by hand. Many calculators use complex algorithms that find a more precise line of fit called the **best-fit line**. One algorithm is called **linear regression**.

Your calculator may also compute a number called the **correlation coefficient**. This number will tell you if your correlation is positive or negative and how closely the equation is modeling the data. The closer the correlation coefficient is to 1 or −1, the more closely the equation models the data.

Real-World Example 1 Best-Fit Line

MOVIES **The table shows the amount of money made by movies in the United States. Use a graphing calculator to write an equation for the best-fit line for that data.**

Year	2000	2001	2002	2003	2004	2005	2006	2007	2008	2009
Income ($ billion)	7.48	8.13	9.19	9.35	9.27	8.95	9.25	9.65	9.85	10.21

Before you begin, make sure that your Diagnostic setting is on. You can find this under the **CATALOG** menu. Press **D** and then scroll down and click **DiagnosticOn**. Then press ENTER.

Step 1 Enter the data by pressing STAT and selecting the **Edit** option. Let the year 2000 be represented by 0. Enter the years since 2000 into List 1 (L1). These will represent the *x*-values. Enter the income ($ billion) into List 2 (L2). These will represent the *y*-values.

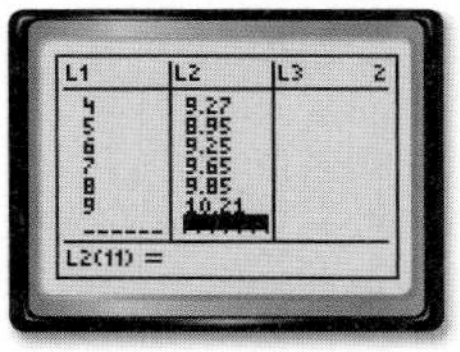

Step 2 Perform the regression by pressing STAT and selecting the **CALC** option. Scroll down to **LinReg (ax+b)** and press ENTER twice.

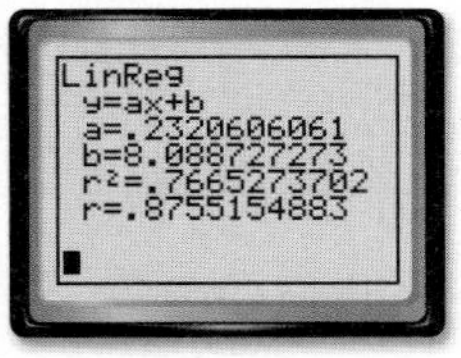

1 Focus

VerticalAlignment

Before Lesson 4-6 Use lines of fit and scatter plots to evaluate trends and make predictions.

Lesson 4-6 Write equations of best-fit lines using linear regression. Write equations of median-fit lines.

After Lesson 4-6 Find a curve of best-fit in the form of a polynomial function for data.

2 Teach

Scaffolding Questions

Have students read the **Why?** section of the lesson.

Ask:

- What type of correlation does the data in the table have? positive
- How could you estimate the Minnesota State Fair Attendance in 2012? Make a scatter plot of the data in the table. Draw a line that seems to be close to all the points, then use two points on that line to write an equation. Finally, substitute 2012 into the equation for *x* and solve for *y*.
- Is this the only line of fit for the data? No, other lines could be drawn that fit.

Lesson 4-6 Resources

Resource	Approaching Level AL	On Level OL	Beyond Level BL	English Learners ELL
Teacher Edition	▪ Differentiated Instruction, p. 257	▪ Differentiated Instruction, pp. 257, 260	▪ Differentiated Instruction, p. 260	
Chapter Resource Masters	▪ Study Guide and Intervention, pp. 37–38 ▪ Skills Practice, p. 39 ▪ Practice, p. 40 ▪ Word Problem Practice, p. 41	▪ Study Guide and Intervention, pp. 37–38 ▪ Skills Practice, p. 39 ▪ Practice, p. 40 ▪ Word Problem Practice, p. 41 ▪ Enrichment, p. 42	▪ Practice, p. 40 ▪ Word Problem Practice, p. 41 ▪ Enrichment, p. 42	▪ Study Guide and Intervention, pp. 37–38 ▪ Skills Practice, p. 39 ▪ Practice, p. 40 ▪ Word Problem Practice, p. 41
Other	▪ 5-Minute Check 4-6 ▪ Study Notebook ▪ Teaching Algebra with Manipulatives	▪ 5-Minute Check 4-6 ▪ Study Notebook ▪ Teaching Algebra with Manipulatives	▪ 5-Minute Check 4-6 ▪ Study Notebook	▪ 5-Minute Check 4-6 ▪ Study Notebook ▪ Teaching Algebra with Manipulatives

1 Equations of Best-Fit Lines

Examples 1–2 show how to use a calculator to write an equation for a best-fit line and how to analyze the applicable residual plot for a set of data.

Formative Assessment

Use the Guided Practice exercises after each Example to determine students' understanding of concepts.

Additional Examples

1 EARNINGS The table below shows Ariana's hourly earnings for 2001–2007. Use a graphing calculator to write an equation for the best-fit line for that data. Name the correlation coefficient. Let x be the number of years since 2000.

Year	Cost	Year	Cost
2001	$10	2005	$15
2002	$10.50	2006	$15.75
2003	$11	2007	$16.50
2004	$13		

$y = 1.21x + 8.25; \approx 0.9801$

2 Graph and analyze the residual plot for the data comparing the years since the 2000 and the cost of repairs.

Years	Cost
2	1236
3	1560
4	1423
5	1740
6	2230

The plot appears to have a curved pattern, so the regression line may not fit the data well.

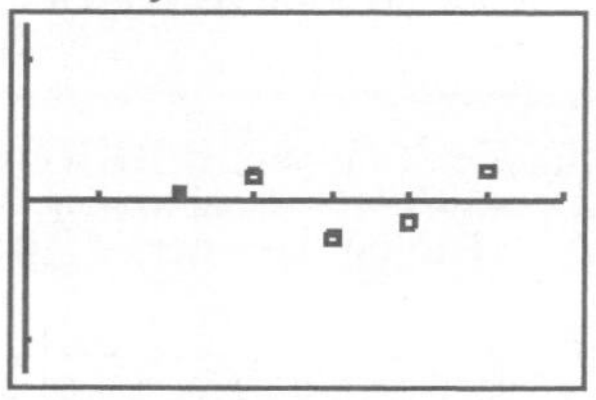

[0, 7] scl: 1 by [−1000, 1000] scl: 800

Additional Examples also in Interactive Classroom PowerPoint® Presentations

IWB Interactive White Board READY

Real-WorldLink

In 1994, Minnesota became the first state to sanction girls' ice hockey as a high school varsity sport.

Source: ESPNET SportsZone

Step 3 Write the equation of the regression line by rounding the a and b values on the screen. The form that we chose for the regression was $ax + b$, so the equation is $y = 0.23x + 8.09$. The correlation coefficient is about 0.8755, which means that the equation models the data fairly well.

Guided Practice

Write an equation of the best-fit line for the data in each table. Name the correlation coefficient. Round to the nearest ten-thousandth. Let x be the number of years since 2003.

1A. HOCKEY The table shows the number of goals of leading scorers for the Mustang Girls Hockey Team.

Year	2003	2004	2005	2006	2007	2008	2009	2010
Goals	30	23	41	35	31	43	33	45

1B. HOCKEY The table gives the number of goals scored by the team each season.

Year	2003	2004	2005	2006	2007	2008	2009	2010
Goals	63	44	55	63	81	85	93	84

1A. For x as years since 2003, $y = 1.87x + 28.58$; 0.6142
1B. For x as years since 2003, $y = 5.95x + 50.17$; 0.8495

We know that not all of the points will lie on the best-fit line. The difference between an observed y-value and its predicted y-value (found on the best-fit line) is called a **residual**. Residuals measure how much the data deviate from the regression line. When residuals are plotted on a scatter plot they can help to assess how well the best-fit line describes the data. If the best-fit line is a good fit, there is no pattern in the residual plot.

Real-World Example 2 Graph and Analyze a Residual Plot

HOCKEY Graph and analyze the residual plot for the data for Guided Practice 1A. Determine if the best-fit line models the data well.

After calculating the best-fit line in Guided Practice 1A, you can obtain the residual plot of the data. Turn on **Plot2** under the **STAT PLOT** menu and choose the scatter plot icon. Use **L1** for the **Xlist** and **RESID** for the **Ylist**. You can obtain **RESID** by pressing [2nd] **[STAT]** and selecting **RESID** from the list of names. Graph the scatter plot of the residuals by pressing [ZOOM] and choosing **ZoomStat**.

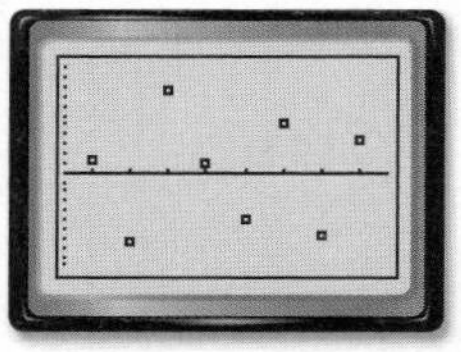

[0, 8] scl: 1 by [−10, 10] scl: 2

The residuals appear to be randomly scattered and centered about the line $y = 0$. Thus, the best-fit line seems to model the data well.

Guided Practice

2. UNEMPLOYMENT Graph and analyze the residual plot for the following data comparing graduation rates and unemployment rates.

Graduation Rate	73	85	64	81	68	82
Unemployment Rate	6.9	4.1	3.2	5.5	4.3	5.1

2. The plot appears to have a curved pattern, so the regression line may not fit the data well.

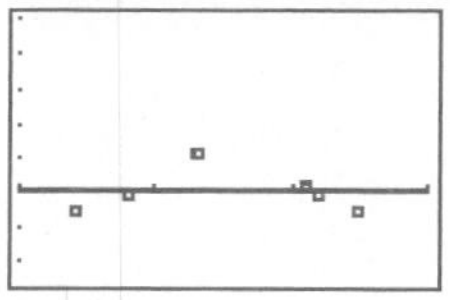

[60, 90] scl: 10 by [−5, 10] scl: 2

Focus on Mathematical Content

Equation of a Best-Fit Line The TI-83/84 Plus graphing calculator has two methods to compute the equation of a best-fit line:

- **LinReg($ax + b$)** for linear regression and
- **Med-Med** for a median-fit line.

The linear regression method uses a least-squares fit method to determine the values for a and b. This utilizes calculus involving the distance each point is from the best-fit line. The median-fit method calculates the medians of the coordinates of the data points.

256 | Lesson 4-6 | Regression and Median-Fit Lines

A residual is positive when the observed value is above the line, negative when the observed value is below the line, and zero when it is on the line. One common measure of goodness of fit is the sum of squared vertical distances from the points to the line. The best-fit line, which is also called the *least-squares regression line,* minimizes the sum of the squares of those distances.

We can use points on the best-fit line to estimate values that are not in the data. Recall that when we estimate values that are between known values, this is called *linear interpolation*. When we estimate a number outside of the range of the data, it is called *linear extrapolation*.

PT

Real-World Example 3 Use Interpolation and Extrapolation

PAINTBALL **The table shows the points received by the top ten paintball teams at a tournament. Estimate how many points the 20th-ranked team received.**

Rank	1	2	3	4	5	6	7	8	9	10
Score	100	89	96	99	97	98	78	70	64	80

Write an equation of the best-fit line for the data. Then extrapolate to find the missing value.

Step 1 Enter the data from the table into the lists. Let the ranks be the x-values and the scores be the y-values. Then graph the scatter plot.

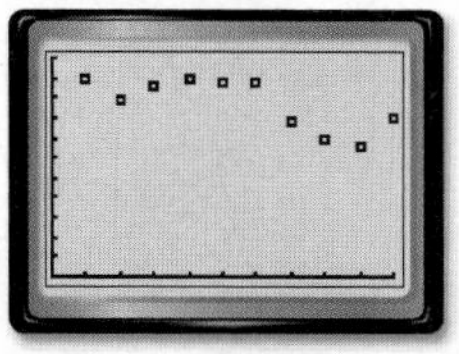

[0, 10] scl: 1 by [0, 110] scl: 10

Step 2 Perform the linear regression using the data in the lists. Find the equation of the best-fit line.

The equation is about $y = -3.32x + 105.3$.

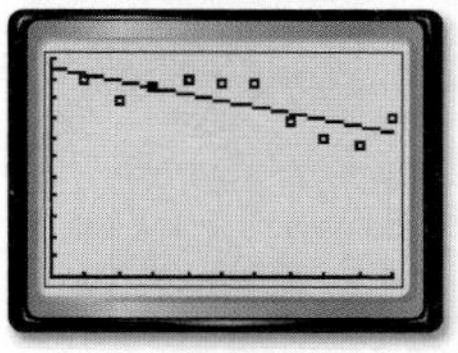

[0, 10] scl: 1 by [0, 110] scl: 10

Step 3 Graph the best-fit line. Press [Y=] [VARS] and choose **Statistics**. From the **EQ** menu, choose **RegEQ**. Then press [GRAPH].

Step 4 Use the graph to predict the points that the 20th-ranked team received. Change the viewing window to include the x-value to be evaluated. Press [2nd] **[CALC]** [ENTER] 20 [ENTER] to find that when $x = 20$, $y \approx 39$. It is estimated that the 20th ranked team received 39 points.

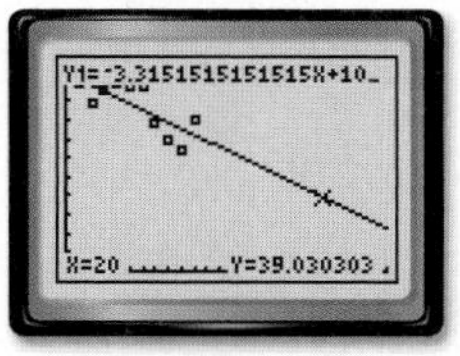

[0, 25] scl: 1 by [0, 110] scl: 1

DifferentiatedInstruction AL OL

If students have trouble remembering certain keystrokes on their graphing calculators,

Then have students make "recipe" cards for each calculator activity they study. For example, have them title a card "Best-fit Line" and then write the keystrokes for using their graphing calculator to find the best-fit line for data and correlation coefficient. Students can refer to these cards as needed until they commit the steps to memory. Be sure students include a card for how to clear all previous data lists using the following keystrokes: [2nd] [MEM] 4 [ENTER].

Tips for New Teachers

Graphing Calculator Make sure that students understand the keystrokes for the [STAT] menu. Make sure students have cleared the **L1** and **L2** lists before entering new data. If students enter their data into **L3** and **L4** instead of **L1** and **L2**, they must type in "**L3, L4**" after "**LinReg(ax+b)**" and then press [ENTER].

Correlation Coefficient With DiagnosticOn, the calculator also displays values for r^2 and r. The closer the value for $|r|$ is to 1, the better the equation fits the data.

Example 3 shows how to use a calculator and an equation of the best-fit line for data for estimating a number outside of the range of the data.

Additional Example

3 BOWLING The table below shows the points earned by the top ten bowlers in a tournament. Estimate how many points the 15th-ranked bowler earned.

Rank	Score	Rank	Score
1	210	6	147
2	197	7	144
3	164	8	142
4	158	9	134
5	151	10	132

about 83

Teach with Tech

Video Recording Have students work in pairs to create a video showing how to find a regression equation or median-fit line. Share each group's videos with the class.

2 Equations of Median-Fit Lines

Example 4 shows how to calculate the equation of a median-fit line using a graphing calculator and then use the equation to predict a value.

Additional Example

4 Find and graph the equation of a median-fit line for the data on the bowling tournament in Additional Example 2. Then predict the score of the 20th ranked bowler.
$y = -9x + 209.5$; ≈ 30

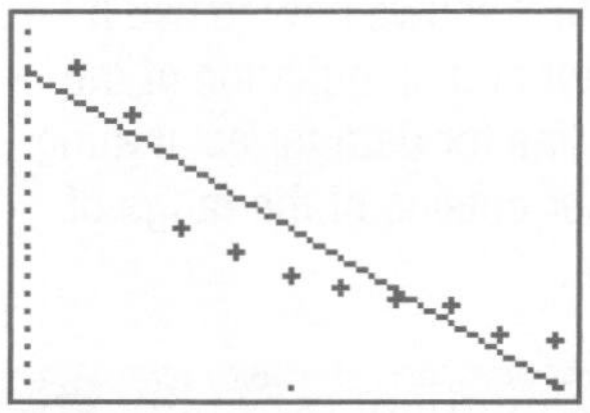

[0, 22] scl: 1 by [0, 225] scl: 10

3 Practice

Formative Assessment

Use Exercises 1–3 to check for understanding.

Use the chart at the bottom of this page to customize assignments for your students.

GuidedPractice

ONLINE GAMES **Use linear interpolation to estimate the percent of Americans that play online games for the following ages.**

Age	15	20	30	40	50
Percent	81	54	37	29	25

Source: Pew Internet & American Life Survey

3A. 35 years **≈39%** **3B.** 18 years **≈64%**

2 Median-Fit Lines A second type of fit line that can be found using a graphing calculator is a **median-fit line**. The equation of a median-fit line is calculated using the medians of the coordinates of the data points.

Real-WorldLink

Paintball is more popular with 12- to 17-year-olds than any other age group. In a recent year, 3,649,000 teens participated in paintball while 2,195,000 18- to 24-year-olds participated.

Source: *Statistical Abstract* of the *United States*

Example 4 Median-Fit Line

PAINTBALL **Find and graph the equation of a median-fit line for the data in Example 3. Then predict the score of the 15th ranked team.**

Step 1 Reenter the data if it is not in the lists. Clear the **Y=** list and graph the scatter plot.

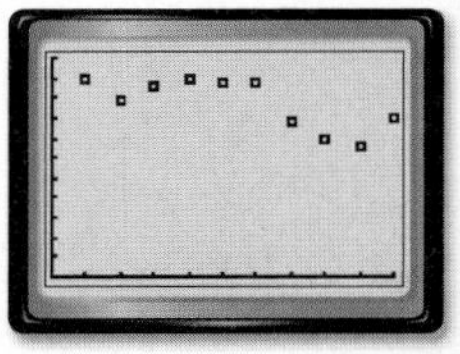

[0, 10] scl: 1 by [0, 110] scl: 10

Step 2 To find the median-fit equation, press the STAT key and select the **CALC** option. Scroll down to the **Med-Med** option and press ENTER. The value of a is the slope, and the value of b is the y-intercept.

The equation for the median-fit line is about $y = -3.71x + 108.26$.

Step 3 Copy the equation to the **Y=** list and graph. Use the **value** option to find the value of y when $x = 15$.

The 15th place team scored about 53 points.

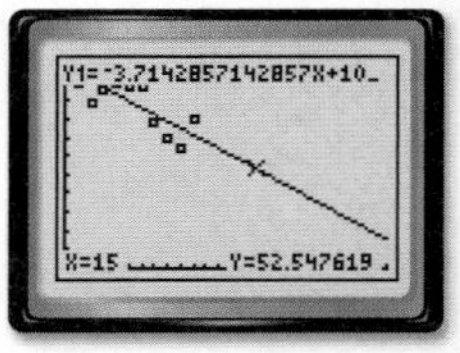

[0, 25] scl: 1 by [0, 110] scl: 1

Notice that the equations for the regression line and the median-fit line are very similar.

GuidedPractice

4. ≈63%, ≈38%; These values are relatively close to those in Guided Practice 3A and 3B.

4. Use the data from Guided Practice 3 and a median-fit line to estimate the numbers of 18- and 35-year-olds who play online games. Compare these values with the answers from the regression line.

Differentiated Homework Options

Level	Assignment	Two-Day Option	
AL Basic	4–7, 16–42	5, 7, 19–22	4–6 even, 16–18, 23–42
OL Core	5, 7, 9–14, 16–42	4–7, 19–22	8–14, 16–18, 23–42
BL Advanced	8–34, (optional: 35–42)		

Check Your Understanding

= Step-by-Step Solutions begin on page R13.

Examples 1, 2

1. POTTERY A local university is keeping track of the number of art students who use the pottery studio each day.

Day	1	2	3	4	5	6	7
Students	10	15	18	15	13	19	20

a. Write an equation of the regression line and find the correlation coefficient. $y = 1.18x + 11$; 0.7181

b. Graph the residual plot and determine if the regression line models the data well. **See margin.**

Example 3

2. COMPUTERS The table below shows the percent of Americans with a broadband connection at home in a recent year. Use linear extrapolation and a regression equation to estimate the percentage of 60-year-olds with broadband at home. **29%**

Age	25	30	35	40	45	50
Percent	40	42	36	35	36	32

Example 4

3. VACATION The Smiths want to rent a house on the lake that sleeps eight people. The cost of the house per night is based on how close it is to the water.

Distance from Lake (mi)	0.0 (houseboat)	0.3	0.5	1.0	1.25	1.5	2.0
Price/Night ($)	785	325	250	200	150	140	100

a. Find and graph an equation for the median-fit line.

b. What would you estimate is the cost of a rental 1.75 miles from the lake? **$78.69**

a. $y = -271.88x + 554.48$; **See margin for graph.**

Practice and Problem Solving

Extra Practice is on page R4.

Example 1

Write an equation of the regression line for the data in each table. Then find the correlation coefficient.

4. SKYSCRAPERS The table ranks the ten tallest buildings in the world. $y = -2.75x + 102.53$; -0.6071

Rank	1	2	3	4	5	6	7	8	9	10
Stories	101	88	110	88	88	80	69	102	78	70

5. MUSIC The table gives the number of annual violin auditions held by a youth symphony each year since 2004. Let x be the number of years since 2004.

5. $y = 3.54x + 19.68$; 0.9007

Year	2004	2005	2006	2007	2008	2009	2010
Auditions	22	19	25	37	32	35	42

Example 2

6. RETAIL The table gives the sales at a clothing chain since 2004. Let x be the number of years since 2004.

Year	2004	2005	2006	2007	2008	2009	2010
Sales (Millions of Dollars)	6.84	7.6	10.9	15.4	17.6	21.2	26.5

a. Write an equation of the regression line. $y = 3.32x + 5.20$

b. Graph and analyze the residual plot. **See margin.**

Exercise Alert

Grid Paper For Exercises 39–42, students will need grid paper.

Follow-up

Students have explored lines of best fit and linear regression.

Ask:

- How can you use a set of data to make predictions? Sample answer: You can create a scatter plot of the data and determine the line of best fit. You could also enter the data into a calculator and find the equation of the regression line. Then, you could use the equation to estimate values that are between known values or outside the range of the data.

Additional Answers

1b. The residuals appear to be randomly scattered, so the regression line fits the data reasonably well.

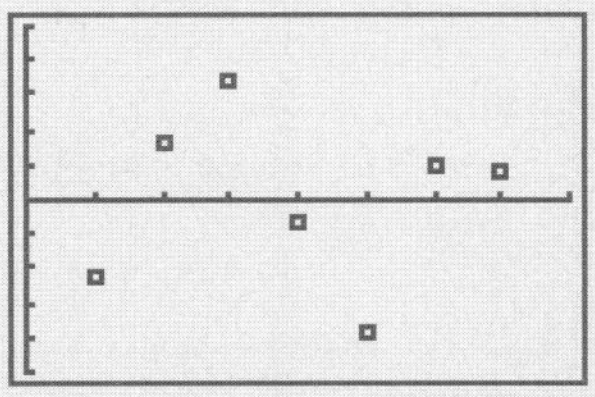

[0, 8] scl: 1.5 by [−5, 5] scl: 1.5

3a.

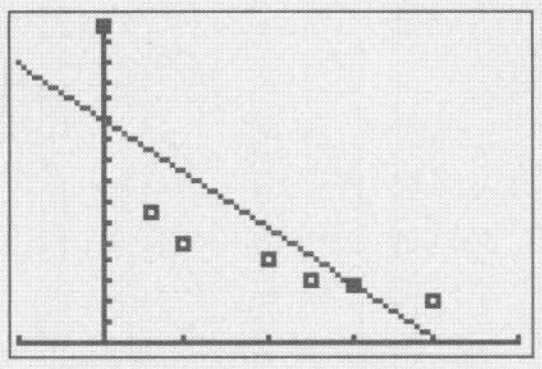

[−0.5, 2.5] scl: 1 by [0, 785] scl: 10

6b. The residuals appear to be randomly scattered, so the regression line fits the data well.

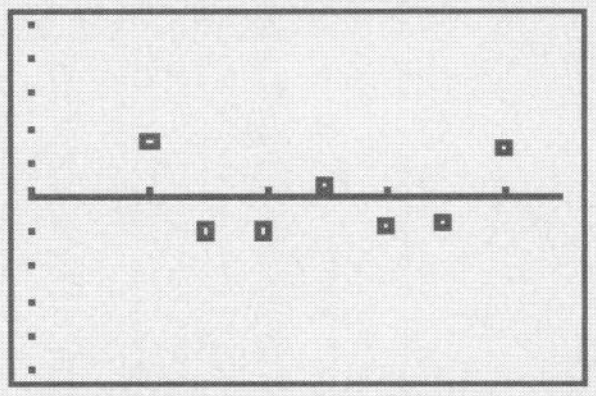

[2, 11] scl: 2 by [−5, 5]

Additional Answers

9b.

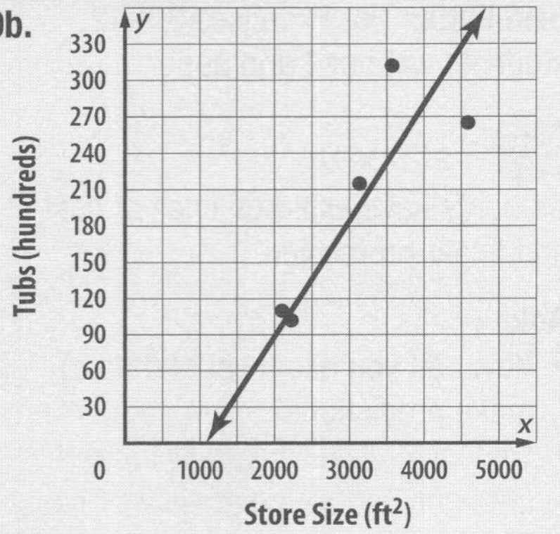

11a. $y = 0.0326x + 1.598$

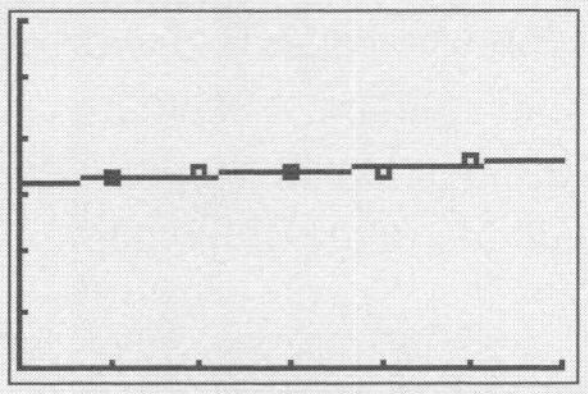

[0, 6] scl: 1 by [0, 3] scl: 0.5

11b. The regression line is a good fit as the residuals appear to almost be on the line.

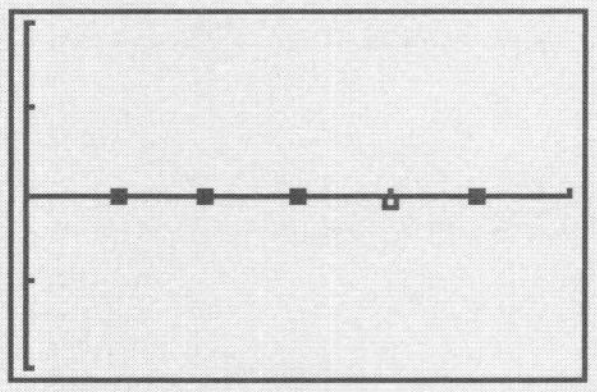

[0, 6] scl: 1 by [−2, 2] scl: 1

12a. $y = -841.42x + 223{,}288$

12b.

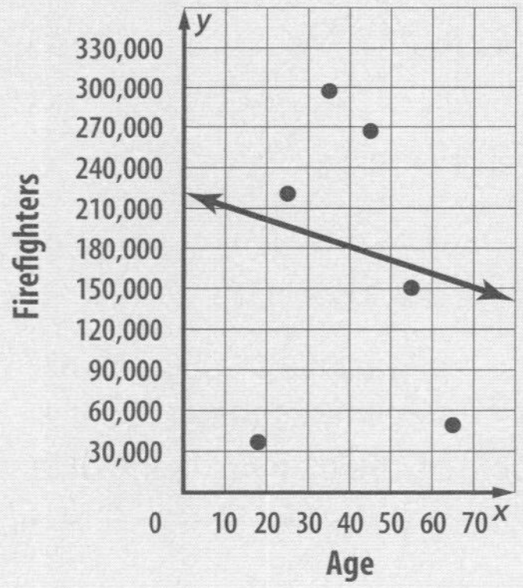

Examples 3, 4 **7. MARATHON** The number of entrants in the Boston Marathon every five years since 1975 is shown. Let x be the number of years since 1975.

Year	1975	1980	1985	1990	1995	2000	2005	2010
Entrants	2395	5417	5594	9412	9416	17,813	20,453	26,735

a. Find an equation for the median-fit line. **$y = 601.44x + 1236.13$**

b. According to the equation, how many entrants were there in 2003? **about 18,076**

B **8. CAMPING** A campground keeps a record of the number of campsites rented the week of July 4 for several years. Let x be the number of years since 2000.

Year	2002	2003	2004	2005	2006	2007	2008	2009	2010
Sites Rented	34	45	42	53	58	47	57	65	59

a. Find an equation for the regression line. **$y = 3.07x + 32.71$**

b. Predict the number of campsites that will be rented in 2012. **about 70 campsites**

c. Predict the number of campsites that will be rented in 2020. **about 94 campsites**

9. ICE CREAM An ice cream company keeps a count of the tubs of chocolate ice cream delivered to each of their stores in a particular area.

a. Find an equation for the median-fit line. **$y = 0.095x - 94.58$**

b. Graph the points and the median-fit line. **See margin.**

c. How many tubs would be delivered to a 1500-square-foot store? a 5000-square-foot store? **about 48 tubs; about 380 tubs**

Store Size (ft²)	2100	2225	3135	3569	4587
Tubs (hundreds)	110	102	215	312	265

10. CCSS SENSE-MAKING The prices of the eight top-selling brands of jeans at Jeanie's Jeans are given in the table below.

Sales Rank	1	2	3	4	5	6	7	8
Price ($)	43	44	50	61	64	135	108	78

a. Find the equation for the regression line. **$y = 9.8x + 28.79$**

b. According to the equation, what would be the price of a pair of the 12th best-selling brand? **$146.39**

c. Is this a reasonable prediction? Explain.

10c. Sample answer: No; the correlation between sales rank and price is too weak to make any reasonable prediction.

11. STATE FAIRS Refer to the beginning of the lesson. **a, b. See margin.**

a. Graph a scatter plot of the data, where $x = 1$ represents 2005. Then find and graph the equation for the best-fit line.

b. Graph and analyze the residual plot.

c. Predict the total attendance in 2020. **about 2.12 million people**

Differentiated Instruction OL BL

Extension Remind students that outliers are points that are significantly distant from the other data points. Ask students to determine if removing the outlier in Exercise 3 affects the estimated cost of a rental 1.75 miles from the lake. Yes, the outlier (0.0, 785) causes the estimate to be lower than it currently is. Removing the outlier and using the median-fit line for the remaining data points results in a more realistic estimated cost of $112 per night for renting a house 1.75 miles from the lake.

12. **FIREFIGHTERS** The table shows statistics from the U.S. Fire Administration.

Age	Number of Firefighters
18	40,919
25	245,516
35	330,516
45	296,665
55	167,087
65	54,559

a. Find an equation for the median-fit line. **See margin.**
b. Graph the points and the median-fit line. **See margin.**
c. Does the median-fit line give you an accurate picture of the number of firefighters? Explain.
No; sample answer: The points show no linear correlation; therefore a line cannot accurately portray the data.

13. **ATHLETICS** The table shows the number of participants in high school athletics.

Year Since 1970	1	10	20	30	35
Athletes	3,960,932	5,356,913	5,298,671	6,705,223	7,159,904

a. Find an equation for the regression line. $y = 87{,}390.5x + 4{,}018{,}431$
b. According to the equation, how many participated in 1988? **about 5,591,460**

14. **ART** A count was kept on the number of paintings sold at an auction by the year in which they were painted. Let x be the number of years since 1950.

Year Painted	1950	1955	1960	1965	1970	1975
Paintings Solds	8	5	25	21	9	22

a. Find the equation for the linear regression line. $y = 0.446x + 9.43$
b. How many paintings were sold that were painted in 1961? **about 14 paintings**
c. Is the linear regression equation an accurate model of the data? Explain why or why not. **No, the correlation coefficient is 0.48, so the linear model is not a good fit for the data.**

H.O.T. Problems Use Higher-Order Thinking Skills

15. **ARGUMENTS** Below are the results of the World Superpipe Championships in 2008.

Men	Score	Rank	Women	Score
Shaun White	93.00	1	Torah Bright	96.67
Mason Aguirre	90.33	2	Kelly Clark	93.00
Janne Korpi	85.33	3	Soko Yamaoka	85.00
Luke Mitrani	85.00	4	Ellery Hollingsworth	79.33
Keir Dillion	81.33	5	Sophie Rodriguez	71.00

Find an equation of the regression line for each, and graph them on the same coordinate plane. Compare and contrast the men's and women's graphs.
See Ch. 4 Answer Appendix.

16. **REASONING** For a class project, the scores that 10 randomly selected students earned on the first 8 tests of the school year are given. Explain how to find a line of best fit. Could it be used to predict the scores of other students? Explain your reasoning.
See Ch. 4 Answer Appendix.

17. **OPEN ENDED** For 10 different people, measure their heights and the lengths of their heads from chin to top. Use these data to generate a linear regression equation and a median-fit equation. Make a prediction using both of the equations. **See students' work.**

18. **WRITING IN MATH** How are lines of fit and linear regression similar? different?
See Ch. 4 Answer Appendix.

Teaching the Process Standards

Arguments Mathematically proficient students reason inductively about data. In Exercise 15, have students analyze each data set and then find similarities and differences.

Study Guide and Intervention
AL OL ELL

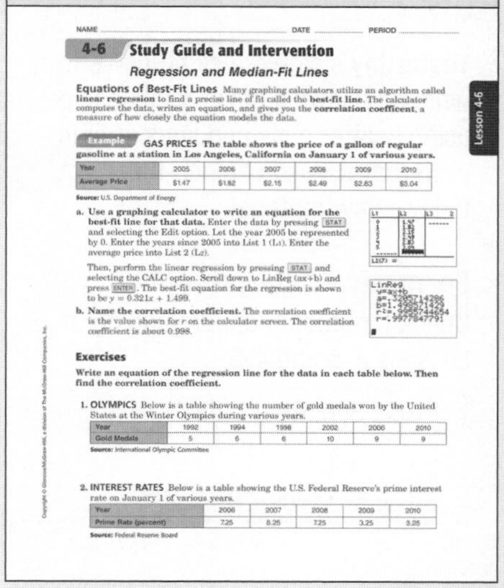
4-6 Study Guide and Intervention
Regression and Median-Fit Lines

Practice
AL OL BL ELL

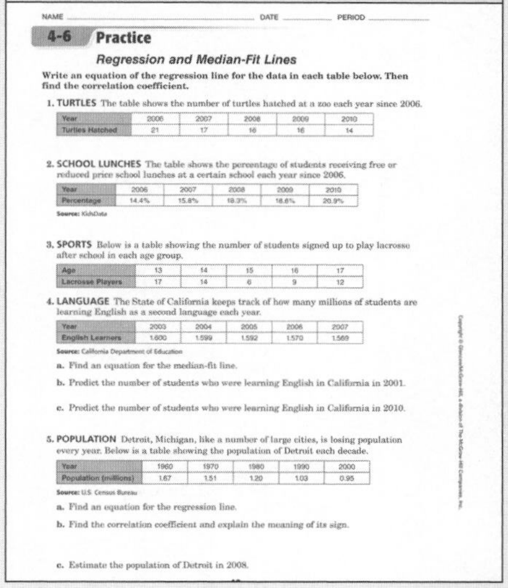
4-6 Practice
Regression and Median-Fit Lines

Word Problem Practice
AL OL BL ELL

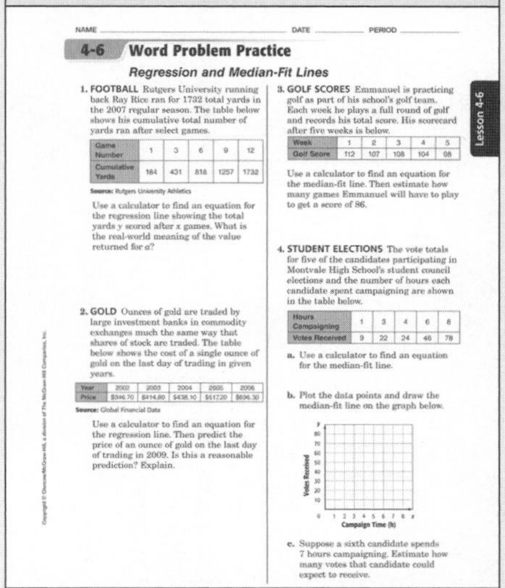
4-6 Word Problem Practice
Regression and Median-Fit Lines

Enrichment
OL BL

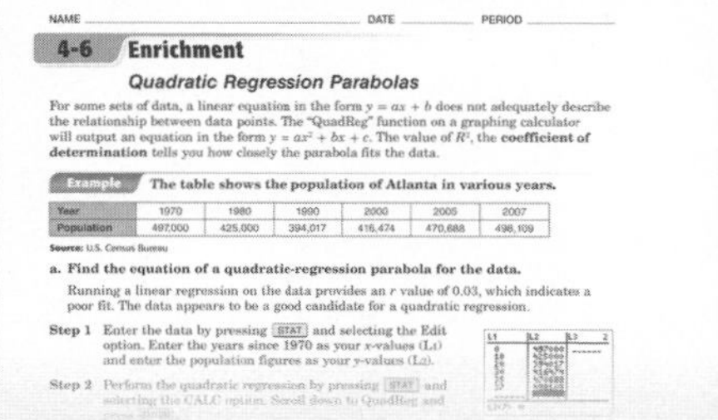
4-6 Enrichment
Quadratic Regression Parabolas

4 Assess

Yesterday's News Ask students to write how investigating relationships using scatter plots and lines of fit in yesterday's lesson helped them in today's new material.

Formative Assessment

Check for student understanding of Lessons 4-5 and 4-6.

Quiz 3, p. 52

Additional Answers

24. Yes; opposite sides have the same slope, so they are parallel. Consecutive sides have slopes that are opposite reciprocals, so they are perpendicular.

39.

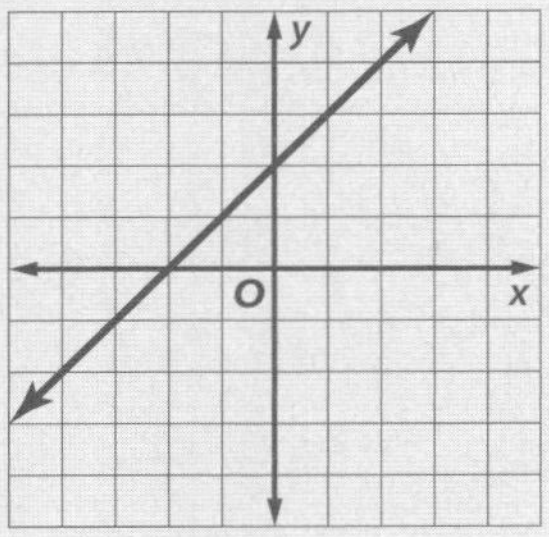

40.

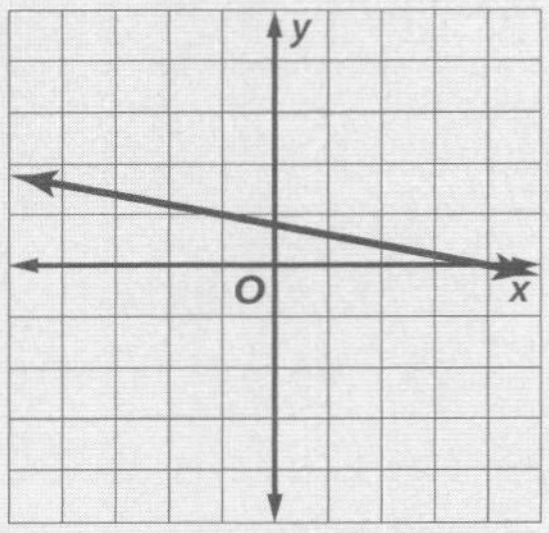

41.

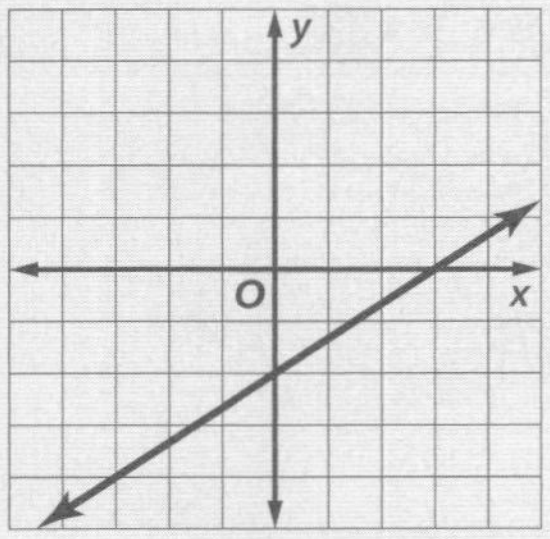

42.

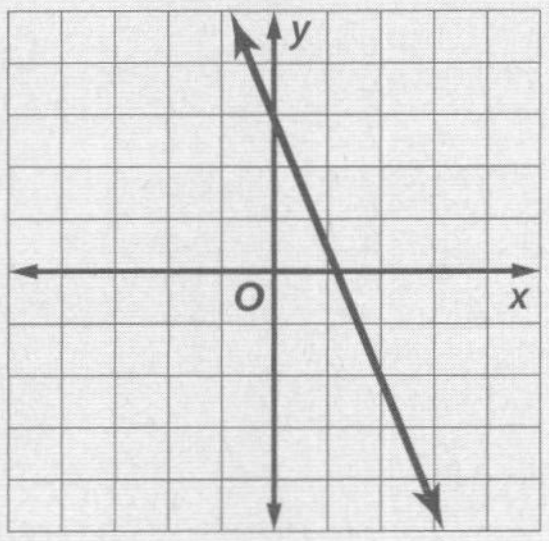

Standardized Test Practice

19. GEOMETRY Sam is putting a border around a poster. x represents the poster's width, and y represents the poster's length. Which equation represents how much border Sam will use if he doubles the length and the width? **C**

A $4xy$ C $4(x + y)$

B $(x + y)^4$ D $16(x + y)$

20. SHORT RESPONSE Tatiana wants to run 5 miles at an average pace of 9 minutes per mile. After 4 miles, her average pace is 9 minutes 10 seconds. In how many minutes must she complete the final mile to reach her goal? **8 min 20 s**

21. What is the slope of the line that passes through (1, 3) and (−3, 1)? **H**

F -2 H $\frac{1}{2}$

G $-\frac{1}{2}$ J 2

22. What is an equation of the line that passes through (0, 1) and has a slope of 3? **D**

A $y = 3x - 1$

B $y = 3x - 2$

C $y = 3x + 4$

D $y = 3x + 1$

Spiral Review

23. USED CARS Gianna wants to buy a specific make and model of a used car. She researched prices from dealers and private sellers and made the graph shown. (Lesson 4-5)

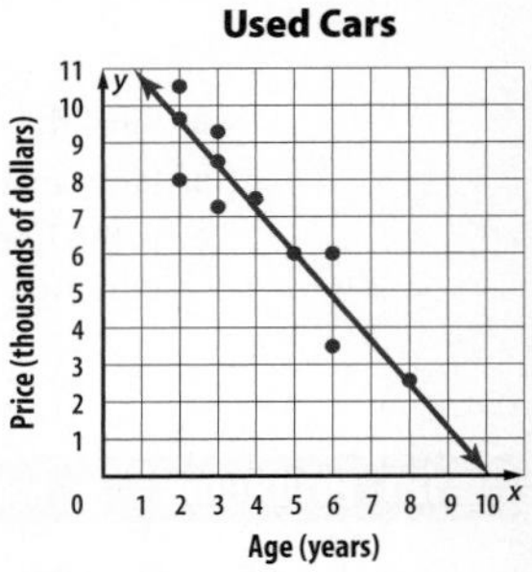

a. Describe the relationship in the data. **negative correlation**

b. Use the line of fit to predict the price of a car that is 7 years old. **$3600**

c. Is it reasonable to use this line of fit to predict the price of a 10-year-old car? Explain. **No, according to the line of fit, the price would be $0.**

24. GEOMETRY A quadrilateral has sides with equations $y = -2x$, $2x + y = 6$, $y = \frac{1}{2}x + 6$, and $x - 2y = 9$. Is the figure a rectangle? Explain your reasoning. (Lesson 4-4) **See margin.**

Write each equation in standard form. (Lesson 4-3)

25. $y - 2 = 3(x - 1)$ **$3x - y = 1$**

26. $y - 5 = 6(x + 1)$ **$6x - y = -11$**

27. $y + 2 = -2(x - 5)$ **$2x + y = 8$**

28. $y + 3 = \frac{1}{2}(x + 4)$ **$x - 2y = 2$**

29. $y - 1 = \frac{2}{3}(x + 9)$ **$2x - 3y = -21$**

30. $y + 3 = -\frac{1}{4}(x + 2)$ **$x + 4y = -14$**

Find the slope of the line that passes through each pair of points. (Lesson 3-3)

31. (3, 4), (10, 8) **$\frac{4}{7}$**

32. (−4, 7), (3, 5) **$-\frac{2}{7}$**

33. (3, 7), (−2, 4) **$\frac{3}{5}$**

34. (−3, 2), (−3, 4) **undefined**

Skills Review

If $f(x) = x^2 - x + 1$, find each value.

35. $f(-1)$ **3**

36. $f(5) - 3$ **18**

37. $f(a)$ **$a^2 - a + 1$**

38. $f(b^2)$ **$b^4 - b^2 + 1$**

Graph each equation. **39–42. See margin.**

39. $y = x + 2$

40. $x + 5y = 4$

41. $2x - 3y = 6$

42. $5x + 2y = 6$

LESSON 4-7 Inverse Linear Functions

Then

- You represented relations as tables, graphs, and mappings.

Now

1. Find the inverse of a relation.
2. Find the inverse of a linear function.

Why?

- Randall is writing a report on Santiago, Chile, and he wants to include a brief climate analysis. He found a table of temperatures recorded in degrees Celsius. He knows that a formula for converting degrees Fahrenheit to degrees Celsius is $C(x) = \frac{5}{9}(x - 32)$. He will need to find the *inverse* function to convert from degrees Celsius to degrees Fahrenheit.

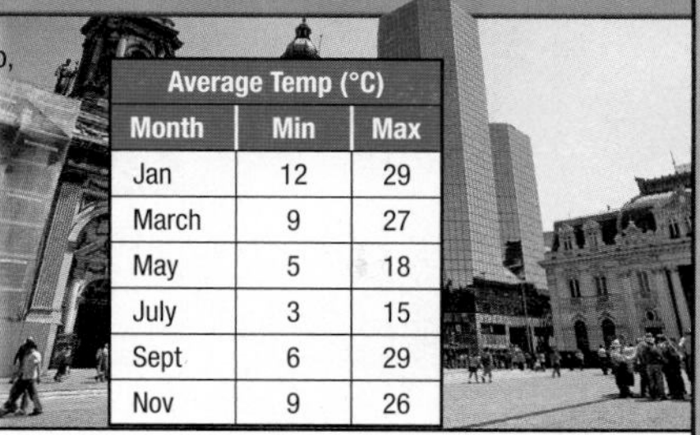

Average Temp (°C)		
Month	Min	Max
Jan	12	29
March	9	27
May	5	18
July	3	15
Sept	6	29
Nov	9	26

NewVocabulary
inverse relation
inverse function

1 Inverse Relations

An **inverse relation** is the set of ordered pairs obtained by exchanging the x-coordinates with the y-coordinates of each ordered pair in a relation. If (5, 3) is an ordered pair of a relation, then (3, 5) is an ordered pair of the inverse relation.

KeyConcept Inverse Relations

Words If one relation contains the element (a, b), then the inverse relation will contain the element (b, a).

Example A and B are inverse relations.

A		B
(−3, −16)	→	(−16, −3)
(−1, 4)	→	(4, −1)
(2, 14)	→	(14, 2)
(5, 32)	→	(32, 5)

Notice that the domain of a relation becomes the range of its inverse, and the range of the relation becomes the domain of its inverse.

Example 1 Inverse Relations

Find the inverse of each relation.

a. **{(4, −10), (7, −19), (−5, 17), (−3, 11)}**

To find the inverse, exchange the coordinates of the ordered pairs.

(4, −10) → (−10, 4) (−5, 17) → (17, −5)
(7, −19) → (−19, 7) (−3, 11) → (11, −3)

The inverse is {(−10, 4), (−19, 7), (17, −5), (11, −3)}.

b.

x	−4	−1	5	9
y	−13	−8.5	0.5	6.5

Write the coordinates as ordered pairs. Then exchange the coordinates of each pair.

(−4, −13) → (−13, −4) (5, 0.5) → (0.5, 5)
(−1, −8.5) → (−8.5, −1) (9, 6.5) → (6.5, 9)

The inverse is {(−13, −4), (−8.5, −1), (0.5, 5), (6.5, 9)}.

1 Focus

VerticalAlignment

Before Lesson 4-7 You represented relations as tables, graphs, and mappings.

Lesson 4-7 Find the inverse of a relation. Find the inverse of a linear function.

After Lesson 4-7 Find the inverse of a quadratic function.

2 Teach

Scaffolding Questions

Have students read the **Why?** section of the lesson.

Ask:

- What do $C(x)$ and x represent in the context of the function? $C(x)$ is degrees Celsius, and x is degrees Fahrenheit.
- How can the equation be used to convert 12° C to degree Fahrenheit? Sample answer: Substitute 12 for $C(x)$ in the given equation and then solve for x.
- Convert 12°C to degrees Fahrenheit. 53.6° F

Lesson 4-7 Resources

Resource	Approaching Level AL	On Level OL	Beyond Level BL	English Learners ELL
Teacher Edition	▪ Differentiated Instruction, p. 265	▪ Differentiated Instruction, p. 265	▪ Differentiated Instruction, p. 270	
Chapter Resource Masters	▪ Study Guide and Intervention, pp. 43–44 ▪ Skills Practice, p. 45 ▪ Practice, p. 46 ▪ Word Problem Practice, p. 47	▪ Study Guide and Intervention, pp. 43–44 ▪ Skills Practice, p. 45 ▪ Practice, p. 46 ▪ Word Problem Practice, p. 47 ▪ Enrichment, p. 48	▪ Practice, p. 46 ▪ Word Problem Practice, p. 47 ▪ Enrichment, p. 48	▪ Study Guide and Intervention, pp. 43–44 ▪ Skills Practice, p. 45 ▪ Practice, p. 46 ▪ Word Problem Practice, p. 47
Other	▪ 5-Minute Check 4-7 ▪ Study Notebook	▪ 5-Minute Check 4-7 ▪ Study Notebook	▪ 5-Minute Check 4-7 ▪ Study Notebook	▪ 5-Minute Check 4-7 ▪ Study Notebook

1 Inverse Relations

Example 1 shows how to find the inverses of relations. **Example 2** shows how to graph the inverse of a relation.

Formative Assessment

Use the Guided Practice exercises after each example to determine students' understanding of concepts.

Additional Examples

1 Find the inverse of each relation.

a. {(−3, 26), (2, 11), (6, −1), (−1, 20)} {(26, −3), (11, 2), (−1, 6), (20, −1)}

b.

x	y
−4	−3
−2	0
1	4.5
5	10.5

{(−3, −4), (0, −2), (4.5, 1), (10.5, 5)}

2 Graph the inverse of each relation.

a.

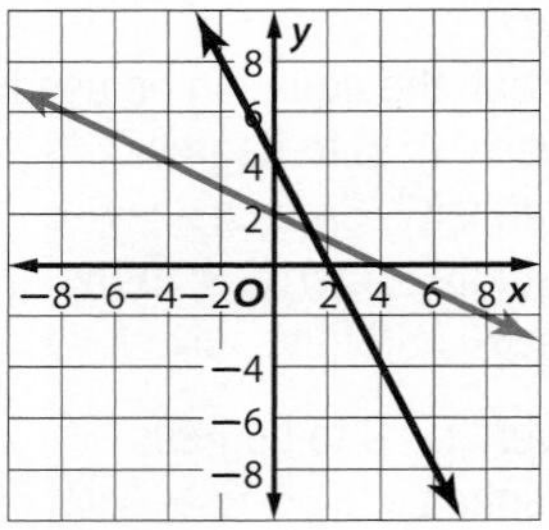

b.

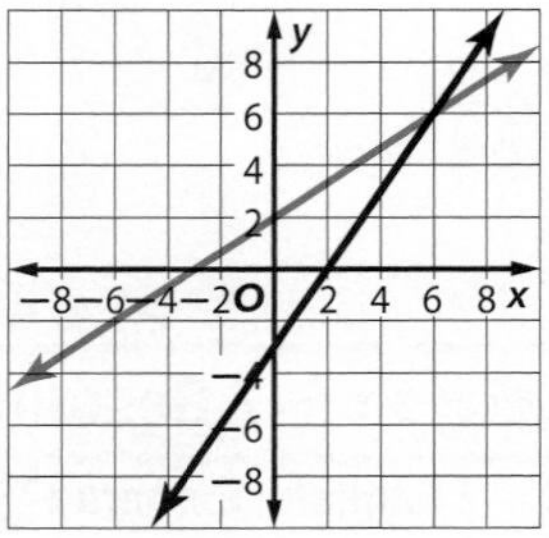

Additional Examples also in Interactive Classroom PowerPoint® Presentations

IWB Interactive White Board READY

GuidedPractice

1A. {(−6, 8), (−15, 11), (9, 3), (0, 6)}
{(8, −6), (11, −15), (3, 9), (6, 0)}

1B. {(5, −10), (11, −4), (12, −3), (15, 0)}

1B.

x	−10	−4	−3	0
y	5	11	12	15

The graphs of relations can be used to find and graph inverse relations.

Example 2 Graph Inverse Relations

Graph the inverse of the relation.

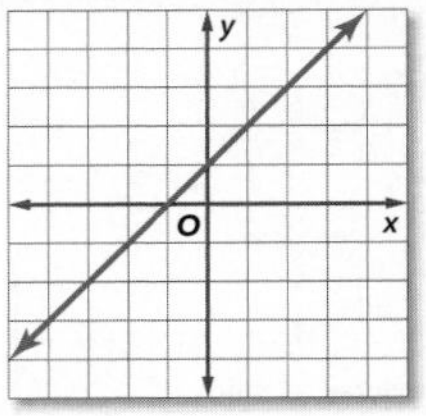

StudyTip

Precision Only two points are necessary to graph the inverse of a line, but several should be used to avoid possible error.

The graph of the relation passes through the points at (−4, −3), (−2, −1), (0, 1), (2, 3), and (3, 4). To find points through which the graph of the inverse passes, exchange the coordinates of the ordered pairs. The graph of the inverse passes through the points at (−3, −4), (−1, −2), (1, 0), (3, 2), and (4, 3). Graph these points and then draw the line that passes through them.

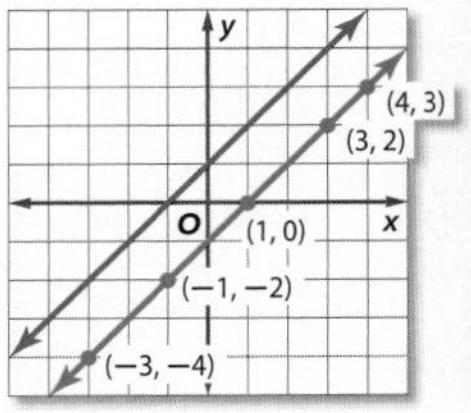

GuidedPractice

Graph the inverse of each relation.

2A.

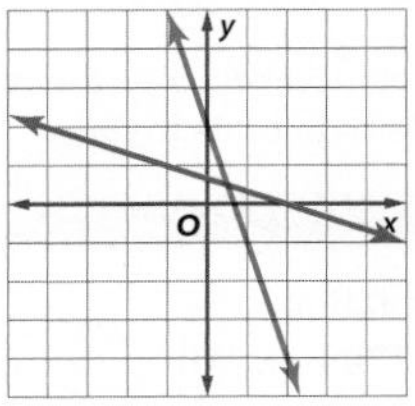

2B.

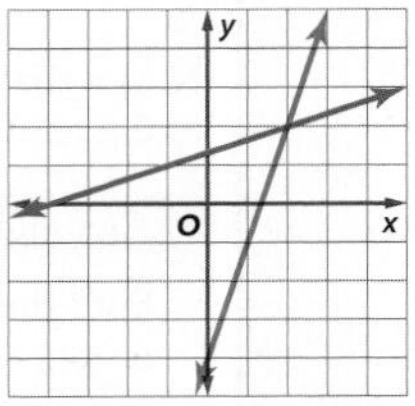

The graphs from Example 2 are graphed on the right with the line $y = x$. Notice that the graph of an inverse is the graph of the original relation reflected in the line $y = x$. For every point (x, y) on the graph of the original relation, the graph of the inverse will include the point (y, x).

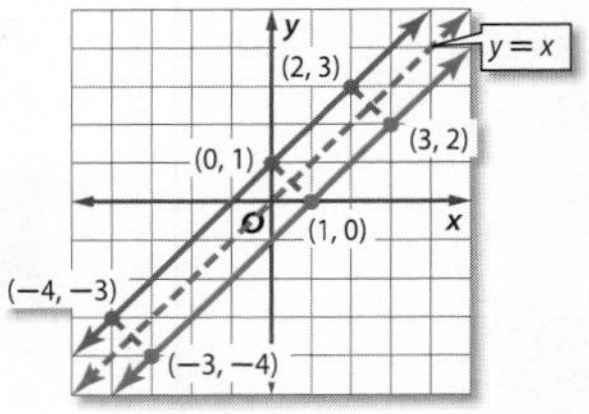

2 Inverse Functions

A linear relation that is described by a function has an **inverse function** that can generate ordered pairs of the inverse relation. The inverse of the linear function $f(x)$ can be written as $f^{-1}(x)$ and is read *f of x inverse* or *the inverse of f of x*.

Teaching the Process Standards

Precision Mathematically proficient students calculate accurately and efficiently. Emphasize that careful graphing ensures accurate answers.

Teach with Tech

Blog On your secure classroom blog, have students create a blog entry to list and describe real-world applications of inverse functions.

KeyConcept Finding Inverse Functions

To find the inverse function $f^{-1}(x)$ of the linear function $f(x)$, complete the following steps.

Step 1 Replace $f(x)$ with y in the equation for $f(x)$.

Step 2 Interchange y and x in the equation.

Step 3 Solve the equation for y.

Step 4 Replace y with $f^{-1}(x)$ in the new equation.

Example 3 Find Inverse Linear Functions

Find the inverse of each function.

a. $f(x) = 4x - 8$

Step 1	$f(x) = 4x - 8$	Original equation
	$y = 4x - 8$	Replace $f(x)$ with y.
Step 2	$x = 4y - 8$	Interchange y and x.
Step 3	$x + 8 = 4y$	Add 8 to each side.
	$\frac{x+8}{4} = y$	Divide each side by 4.
Step 4	$\frac{x+8}{4} = f^{-1}(x)$	Replace y with $f^{-1}(x)$.

The inverse of $f(x) = 4x - 8$ is $f^{-1}(x) = \frac{x+8}{4}$ or $f^{-1}(x) = \frac{1}{4}x + 2$.

CHECK Graph both functions and the line $y = x$ on the same coordinate plane. $f^{-1}(x)$ appears to be the reflection of $f(x)$ in the line $y = x$. ✓

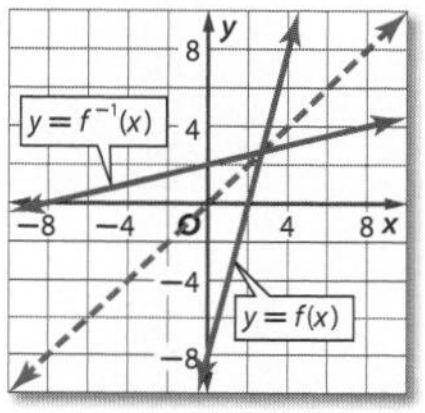

WatchOut!
Notation The -1 in $f^{-1}(x)$ is *not* an exponent.

b. $f(x) = -\frac{1}{2}x + 11$

Step 1	$f(x) = -\frac{1}{2}x + 11$	Original equation
	$y = -\frac{1}{2}x + 11$	Replace $f(x)$ with y.
Step 2	$x = -\frac{1}{2}y + 11$	Interchange y and x.
Step 3	$x - 11 = -\frac{1}{2}y$	Subtract 11 from each side.
	$-2(x - 11) = y$	Multiply each side by -2.
	$-2x + 22 = y$	Distributive Property
Step 4	$-2x + 22 = f^{-1}(x)$	Replace y with $f^{-1}(x)$.

The inverse of $f(x) = -\frac{1}{2}x + 11$ is $f^{-1}(x) = -2x + 22$.

GuidedPractice

3A. $f(x) = 4x - 12$ $f^{-1}(x) = \frac{1}{4}x + 3$ **3B.** $f(x) = \frac{1}{3}x + 7$ $f^{-1}(x) = 3x - 21$

2 Inverse Functions

Example 3 shows how to find inverses of functions. **Example 4** shows how to find and use an inverse function.

Additional Example

3 Find the inverse of each function.

a. $f(x) = -3x + 27$
$f^{-1}(x) = -\frac{1}{3}x + 9$

b. $f(x) = \frac{5}{4}x - 8$
$f^{-1}(x) = \frac{4}{5}x + \frac{32}{5}$

Tips for New Teachers

Inverse Functions If $f(x)$ and $g(x)$ are inverse functions, then $f(a) = b$ and $g(b) = a$. However, the converse of this statement is not necessarily true. Let $f(x) = 3x + 9$ and $g(x) = x - 13$. $f(2) = 15$ and $g(15) = 2$, but $f(x)$ and $g(x)$ are not inverse functions. Students will explore this in Exercises 40 and 41.

DifferentiatedInstruction AL OL

Interpersonal Learners Write the equation of a linear function on an index card. Sketch the graph of the function on a second card. On a third card, display a table of points for the function. Repeat this process for the inverse of the function. Create similar cards for several functions and their inverses. Have students work in groups of two or three. Give each group a copy of all of the cards. Have the groups divide the cards by matching each equation with its graph and table, and then with the equation, graph, and table of its inverse.

Additional Example

4 **SALES** Carter sells paper supplies and makes a base salary of \$2200 each month. He also earns 5% commission on his total sales. His total earnings $f(x)$ for a month in which he compiled x dollars in total sales is $f(x) = 2200 + 0.05x$.

a. Find the inverse function. $f^{-1}(x) = 20x - 44{,}000$

b. What do x and $f^{-1}(x)$ represent in the context of the inverse function? x is Carter's total earnings for the month, and $f^{-1}(x)$ is his total sales for the month.

c. Find Carter's total sales for last month if his earnings for that month were \$3450. \$25,000

Real-WorldLink

The winter months in Chile occur during the summer months in the U.S. due to Chile's location in the southern hemisphere. The average daily high temperature of Santiago during its winter months is about 60° F.

Source: World Weather Information Service

Real-World Example 4 Use an Inverse Function

TEMPERATURE **Refer to the beginning of the lesson. Randall wants to convert the temperatures from degrees Celsius to degrees Fahrenheit.**

a. Find the inverse function $C^{-1}(x)$.

Step 1 $C(x) = \frac{5}{9}(x - 32)$ Original equation

$y = \frac{5}{9}(x - 32)$ Replace $C(x)$ with y.

Step 2 $x = \frac{5}{9}(y - 32)$ Interchange y and x.

Step 3 $\frac{9}{5}x = y - 32$ Multiply each side by $\frac{9}{5}$.

$\frac{9}{5}x + 32 = y$ Add 32 to each side.

Step 4 $\frac{9}{5}x + 32 = C^{-1}(x)$ Replace y with $C^{-1}(x)$.

The inverse function of $C(x)$ is $C^{-1}(x) = \frac{9}{5}x + 32$.

b. What do x and $C^{-1}(x)$ represent in the context of the inverse function?

x represents the temperature in degrees Celsius. $C^{-1}(x)$ represents the temperature in degrees Fahrenheit.

c. Find the average temperatures for July in degrees Fahrenheit.

The average minimum and maximum temperatures for July are 3° C and 15° C, respectively. To find the average minimum temperature, find $C^{-1}(3)$.

$C^{-1}(x) = \frac{9}{5}x + 32$ Original equation

$C^{-1}(3) = \frac{9}{5}(3) + 32$ Substitute 3 for x.

$= 37.4$ Simplify.

To find the average maximum temperature, find $C^{-1}(15)$.

$C^{-1}(x) = \frac{9}{5}x + 32$ Original equation

$C^{-1}(15) = \frac{9}{5}(15) + 32$ Substitute 15 for x.

$= 59$ Simplify.

The average minimum and maximum temperatures for July are 37.4° F and 59° F, respectively.

GuidedPractice

4. **RENTAL CAR** Peggy rents a car for the day. The total cost $C(x)$ in dollars is given by $C(x) = 19.99 + 0.3x$, where x is the number of miles she drives.

A. Find the inverse function $C^{-1}(x)$. $C^{-1}(x) = \frac{x - 19.99}{0.3}$

B. What do x and $C^{-1}(x)$ represent in the context of the inverse function? **x is the total cost, and $C^{-1}(x)$ is the total number of miles driven.**

C. How many miles did Peggy drive if her total cost was \$34.99? **50**

266 | Lesson 4-7 | Inverse Linear Functions

Check Your Understanding

= Step-by-Step Solutions begin on page R13.

Example 1 Find the inverse of each relation.

1. {(4, −15), (−8, −18), (−2, −16.5), (3, −15.25)} {(−15, 4), (−18, −8), (−16.5, −2), (−15.25, 3)}

2.

x	−3	0	1	6
y	11.8	3.7	1	−12.5

{(11.8, −3), (3.7, 0), (1, 1), (−12.5, 6)}

Example 2 Graph the inverse of each relation.

3. 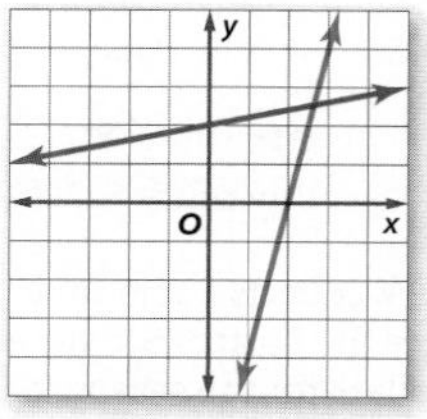

4. 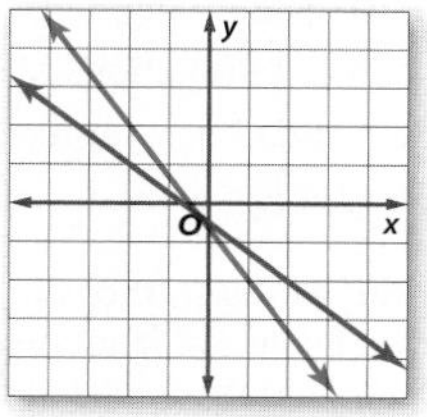

Example 3 Find the inverse of each function.

5. $f(x) = -2x + 7$ $f^{-1}(x) = -\frac{1}{2}x + \frac{7}{2}$

6. $f(x) = \frac{2}{3}x + 6$ $f^{-1}(x) = \frac{3}{2}x - 9$

Example 4

7. **REASONING** Dwayne and his brother purchase season tickets to the Cleveland Crusaders games. The ticket package requires a one-time purchase of a personal seat license costing $1200 for two seats. A ticket to each game costs $70. The cost $C(x)$ in dollars for Dwayne for the first season is $C(x) = 600 + 70x$, where x is the number of games Dwayne attends.

   a. Find the inverse function. $C^{-1}(x) = \frac{1}{70}x - \frac{60}{7}$

   b. What do x and $C^{-1}(x)$ represent in the context of the inverse function? **b.** x is Dwayne's total cost, and $C^{-1}(x)$ is the number of games Dwayne attended.

   c. How many games did Dwayne attend if his total cost for the season was $950? 5

Practice and Problem Solving

Extra Practice is on page R4.

Example 1 Find the inverse of each relation.

8. {(−5, 13), (6, 10.8), (3, 11.4), (−10, 14)} {(13, −5), (10.8, 6), (11.4, 3), (14, −10)}

9. {(−4, −49), (8, 35), (−1, −28), (4, 7)} {(−49, −4), (35, 8), (−28, −1), (7, 4)}

10.

x	y
−8	−36.4
−2	−15.4
1	−4.9
5	9.1
11	30.1

{(−36.4, −8), (−15.4, −2), (−4.9, 1), (9.1, 5), (30.1, 11)}

11.

x	y
−3	7.4
−1	4
1	0.6
3	−2.8
5	−6.2

{(7.4, −3), (4, −1), (0.6, 1), (−2.8, 3), (−6.2, 5)}

Example 2 Graph the inverse of each relation.

12. 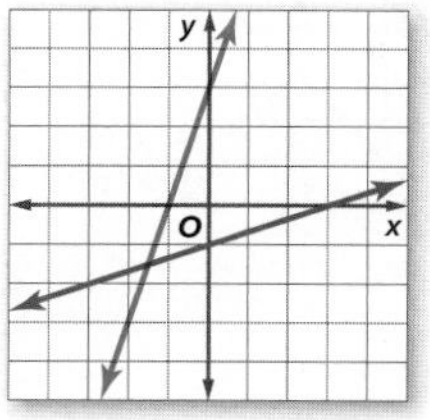

13. 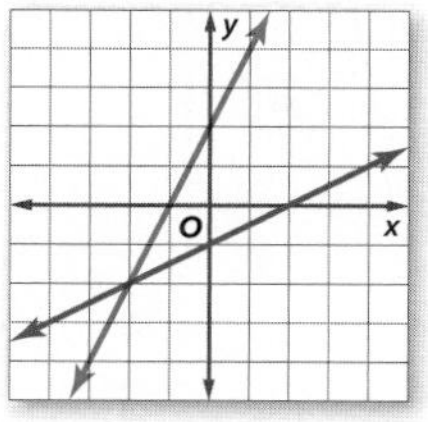

Differentiated Homework Options

Level	Assignment	Two-Day Option	
AL Basic	8–21, 40–62	9–21 (odd), 44–47	8–20 (even), 40–43, 48–62
OL Core	8–21 (odd), 22–37, 40–62	8–21, 44–47	22–37, 40–43, 48–62
BL Advanced	22–56, (optional: 57–62)		

3 Practice

Formative Assessment

Use Exercises 1–7 to check for understanding.

Use the chart at the bottom of this page to customize assignments for your students.

Teaching the Process Standards

Reasoning Mathematically proficient students make sense of quantities and their relationships in problem situations. In Exercise 7, encourage students to think about the relationship between the dependent and independent variables in both $C(x)$ and $C^{-1}(x)$.

Multiple Representations

In Exercise 37, students use graphs to investigate the domains and ranges of inverse functions.

connectED.mcgraw-hill.com 267

Teaching the Process Standards

Tools Mathematically proficient students consider available tools when solving a problem. In Exercises 28–31, point out that students could find the inverse of each function and then identify its graph, or graph each function by hand or using technology to match the functions and inverses.

Additional Answers

37b.

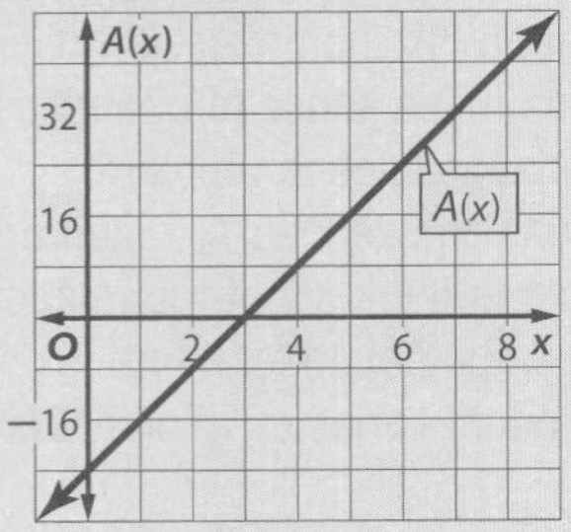

Sample answer: The domain represents possible values of x. The range represents the area of the rectangle and must be positive. This means that the domain of $A(x)$ is all real numbers greater than 3, and the range of $A(x)$ is all positive real numbers.

37d.

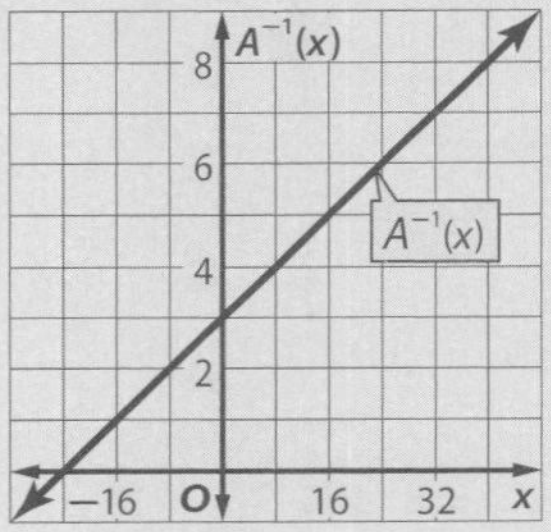

Sample answer: The domain represents the area of the rectangle and must be positive. The range represents possible values for x in the expression $x - 3$. This means that the domain of $A^{-1}(x)$ is all positive real numbers, and the range of $A^{-1}(x)$ is all real numbers greater than 3.

41. Sometimes; sample answer: $f(x)$ and $g(x)$ do not need to be inverse functions for $f(a) = b$ and $g(b) = a$. For example, if $f(x) = 2x + 10$, then $f(2) = 14$ and if $g(x) = x - 12$, then $g(14) = 2$, but $f(x)$ and $g(x)$ are not inverse functions. However, if $f(x)$ and $g(x)$ are inverse functions, then $f(a) = b$ and $g(b) = a$.

Example 3 Find the inverse of each function.

14. $f(x) = 25 + 4x$ $f^{-1}(x) = \frac{1}{4}x - \frac{25}{4}$

15. $f(x) = 17 - \frac{1}{3}x$ $f^{-1}(x) = -3x + 51$

16. $f(x) = 4(x + 17)$ $f^{-1}(x) = \frac{1}{4}x - 17$

17. $f(x) = 12 - 6x$ $f^{-1}(x) = -\frac{1}{6}x + 2$

18. $f(x) = \frac{2}{5}x + 10$ $f^{-1}(x) = \frac{5}{2}x - 25$

19. $f(x) = -16 - \frac{4}{3}x$ $f^{-1}(x) = -\frac{3}{4}x - 12$

Example 4

20. DOWNLOADS An online music subscription service allows members to download songs for \$0.99 each after paying a monthly service charge of \$3.99. The total monthly cost $C(x)$ of the service in dollars is $C(x) = 3.99 + 0.99x$, where x is the number of songs downloaded.

a. Find the inverse function. $C^{-1}(x) = \frac{x - 3.99}{0.99}$

b. What do x and $C^{-1}(x)$ represent in the context of the inverse function?

c. How many songs were downloaded if a member's monthly bill is \$27.75? 24

b. x is the total monthly cost of the service, and $C^{-1}(x)$ is the number of songs downloaded.

21. LANDSCAPING At the start of the mowing season, Chuck collects a one-time maintenance fee of \$10 from his customers. He charges the Fosters \$35 for each cut. The total amount collected from the Fosters in dollars for the season is $C(x) = 10 + 35x$, where x is the number of times Chuck mows the Fosters' lawn.

a. Find the inverse function. $C^{-1}(x) = \frac{1}{35}x - \frac{2}{7}$

b. What do x and $C^{-1}(x)$ represent in the context of the inverse function?

c. How many times did Chuck mow the Fosters' lawn if he collected a total of \$780 from them? 22

21b. x is the total amount collected from the Fosters, and $C^{-1}(x)$ is the number of times Chuck mowed the Fosters' lawn.

B Write the inverse of each equation in $f^{-1}(x)$ notation.

22. $3y - 12x = -72$ $f^{-1}(x) = \frac{1}{4}x + 6$

23. $x + 5y = 15$ $f^{-1}(x) = 15 - 5x$

24. $-42 + 6y = x$ $f^{-1}(x) = 6x - 42$

25. $3y + 24 = 2x$ $f^{-1}(x) = \frac{3}{2}x + 12$

26. $-7y + 2x = -28$ $f^{-1}(x) = \frac{7}{2}x - 14$

27. $3y - x = 3$ $f^{-1}(x) = 3x - 3$

TOOLS Match each function with the graph of its inverse.

A.

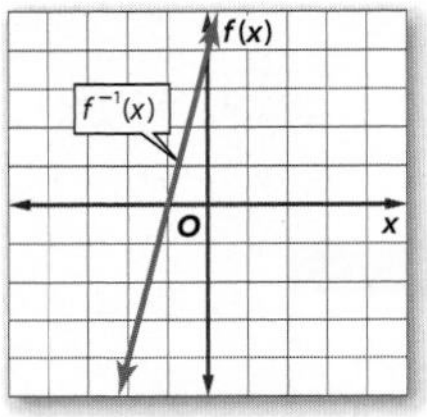

B.

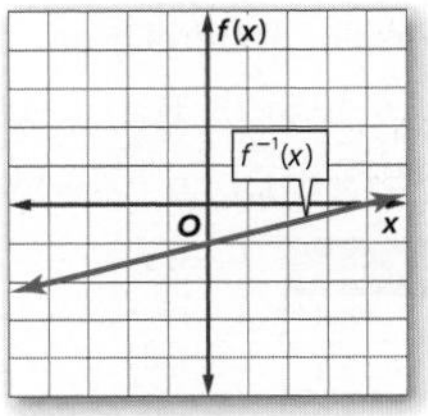

C.

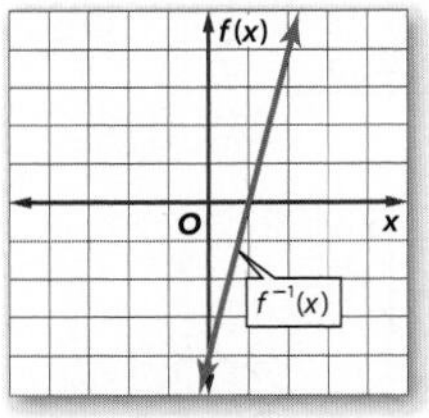

D.

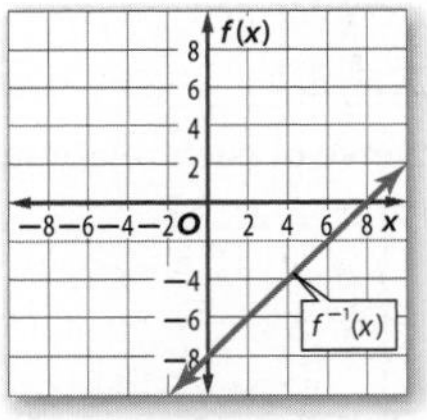

28. $f(x) = x + 4$ D

29. $f(x) = 4x + 4$ B

30. $f(x) = \frac{1}{4}x + 1$ C

31. $f(x) = \frac{1}{4}x - 1$ A

42. Sample answer: $f(x) = 2x + 6$, $f^{-1}(x) = \frac{1}{2}x - 3$

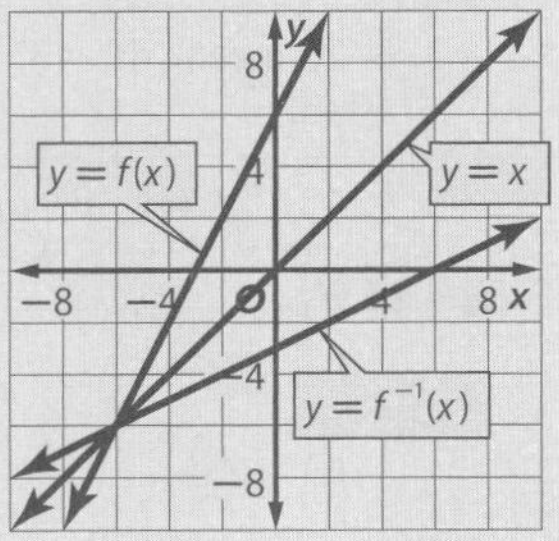

43. Sample answer: A situation may require substituting values for the dependent variable into a function. By finding the inverse of the function, the dependent variable becomes the independent variable. This makes the substitution an easier process.

Write an equation for the inverse function $f^{-1}(x)$ that satisfies the given conditions.

32. slope of $f(x)$ is 7; graph of $f^{-1}(x)$ contains the point (13, 1) $f^{-1}(x) = \frac{1}{7}x - \frac{6}{7}$

33. graph of $f(x)$ contains the points (−3, 6) and (6, 12) $f^{-1}(x) = \frac{3}{2}x - 12$

34. graph of $f(x)$ contains the point (10, 16); graph of $f^{-1}(x)$ contains the point (3, −16) $f^{-1}(x) = 2x - 22$

35. slope of $f(x)$ is 4; $f^{-1}(5) = 2$ $f^{-1}(x) = \frac{1}{4}x + \frac{3}{4}$

C **36. CELL PHONES** Mary Ann pays a monthly fee for her cell phone package which includes 700 minutes. She gets billed an additional charge for every minute she uses the phone past the 700 minutes. During her first month, Mary Ann used 26 additional minutes and her bill was \$37.79. During her second month, Mary Ann used 38 additional minutes and her bill was \$41.39.

a. Write a function that represents the total monthly cost $C(x)$ of Mary Ann's cell phone package, where x is the number of additional minutes used. $C(x) = 0.3x + 29.99$

b. Find the inverse function. $C^{-1}(x) = \frac{x - 29.99}{0.3}$

c. What do x and $C^{-1}(x)$ represent in the context of the inverse function?

d. How many additional minutes did Mary Ann use if her bill for her third month was \$48.89? 63

36c. x is Mary Ann's total monthly cost, and $C^{-1}(x)$ is the number of additional minutes used.

37. MULTIPLE REPRESENTATIONS In this problem, you will explore the domain and range of inverse functions. **b, d. See margin.**

a. **Algebraic** Write a function for the area $A(x)$ of the rectangle shown. $A(x) = 8(x - 3)$ or $A(x) = 8x - 24$

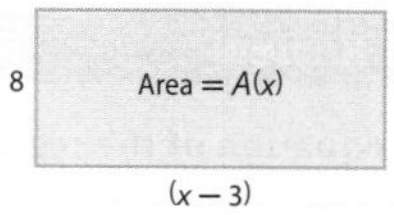

b. **Graphical** Graph $A(x)$. Describe the domain and range of $A(x)$ in the context of the situation.

c. **Algebraic** Write the inverse of $A(x)$. What do x and $A^{-1}(x)$ represent in the context of the situation?

d. **Graphical** Graph $A^{-1}(x)$. Describe the domain and range of $A^{-1}(x)$ in the context of the situation.

e. **Logical** Determine the relationship between the domains and ranges of $A(x)$ and $A^{-1}(x)$. Sample answer: The domain of $A(x)$ is the range of $A^{-1}(x)$, and the range of $A(x)$ is the domain of $A^{-1}(x)$.

$) = \frac{1}{8}x + 3;$
e area of
ctangle and
) is the
of x in the
ssion for
ngth of the
f the
gle $x - 3$.

40. True; sample answer: If $f(a) = b$, then the graph of $f(x)$ includes the point (a, b). If $f(x)$ and $g(x)$ are inverses, then the graph of $g(x)$ includes the point (b, a). If (b, a) is included on the graph of $g(x)$, then $g(b) = a$.

H.O.T. Problems Use Higher-Order Thinking Skills

38. CHALLENGE If $f(x) = 5x + a$ and $f^{-1}(10) = -1$, find a. 15

39. CHALLENGE If $f(x) = \frac{1}{a}x + 7$ and $f^{-1}(x) = 2x - b$, find a and b. $a = 2$; $b = 14$

ARGUMENTS Determine whether the following statements are *sometimes*, *always*, or *never* true. Explain your reasoning. 41–43. See margin.

40. If $f(x)$ and $g(x)$ are inverse functions, then $f(a) = b$ and $g(b) = a$.

41. If $f(a) = b$ and $g(b) = a$, then $f(x)$ and $g(x)$ are inverse functions.

42. OPEN ENDED Give an example of a function and its inverse. Verify that the two functions are inverses by graphing the functions and the line $y = x$ on the same coordinate plane.

43. WRITING IN MATH Explain why it may be helpful to find the inverse of a function.

Study Guide and Intervention

AL OL ELL

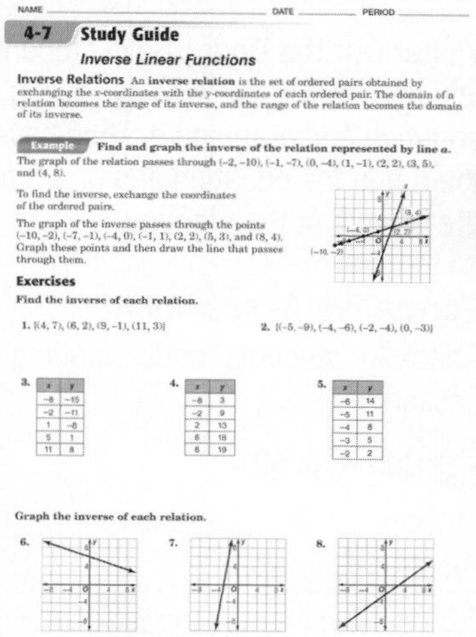

Practice

AL OL BL ELL

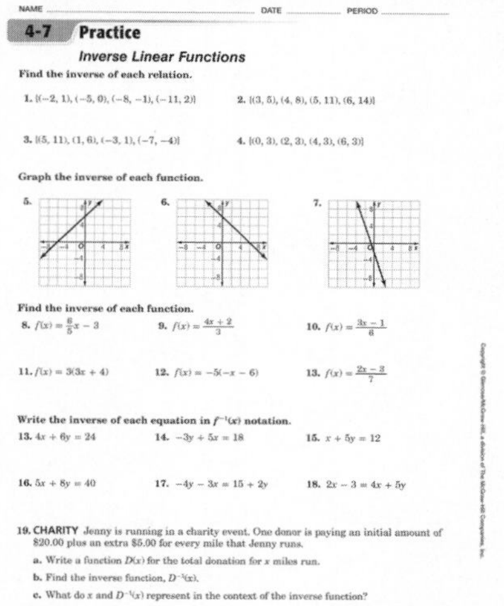

Word Problem Practice

AL OL BL ELL

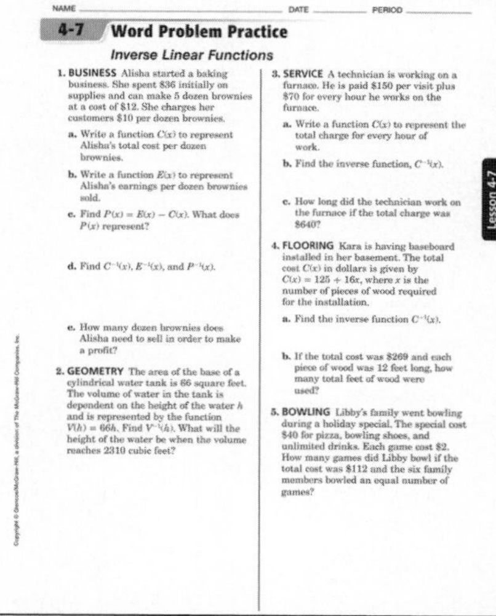

Teaching the Process Standards

Arguments Mathematically proficient students make conjectures and build a logical progression of statements to explore the truth of their conjectures. In Exercises 40 and 41, stress that students need to give mathematical reasons for their conclusions.

Enrichment

OL BL

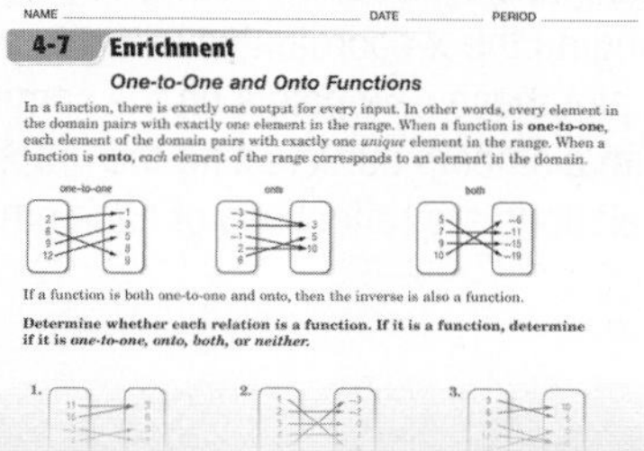

4 Assess

Ticket Out the Door Have students identify a linear function by writing its equation and graphing it. Then have them find the equation and graph for the inverse of the function.

Formative Assessment

Check for students' understanding of Lesson 4-7.

Quiz 4, p. 52

Additional Answer

52. Positive; it means the more you study, the better your test score.

Standardized Test Practice

44. Which equation represents a line that is perpendicular to the graph and passes through the point at (2, 0)? **C**

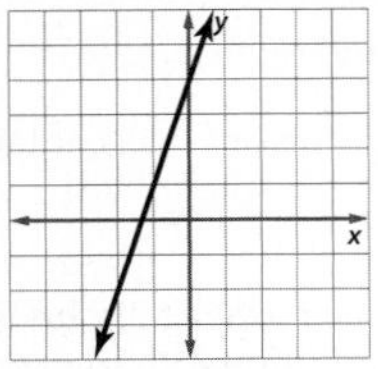

A $y = 3x - 6$

B $y = -3x + 6$

C $y = -\frac{1}{3}x + \frac{2}{3}$

D $y = \frac{1}{3}x - \frac{2}{3}$

45. A giant tortoise travels at a rate of 0.17 mile per hour. Which equation models the time t it would take the giant tortoise to travel 0.8 mile? **F**

F $t = \frac{0.8}{0.17}$ **H** $t = \frac{0.17}{0.8}$

G $t = (0.17)(0.8)$ **J** $0.8 = \frac{0.17}{t}$

46. GEOMETRY If $\triangle JKL$ is similar to $\triangle JNM$ what is the value of a? **B**

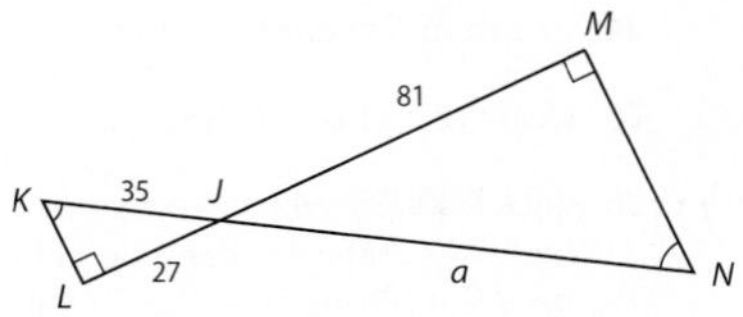

A 62.5

B 105

C 125

D 155.5

47. GRIDDED RESPONSE What is the difference in the value of $2.1(x + 3.2)$, when $x = 5$ and when $x = 3$? **4.2**

Spiral Review

Write an equation of the regression line for the data in each table. (Lesson 4-6)

48.

x	1	3	5	7	9
y	3	8	15	18	21

$y = 2.3x + 1.5$

49.

x	3	5	7	9	11
y	7.2	23.5	41.2	56.4	73.1

$y = 8.235x - 17.365$

50.

x	1	2	3	4	5
y	21	33	39	54	64

$y = 10.7x + 10.1$

51.

x	2	4	6	8	10
y	1.4	2.4	2.9	3.3	4.2

$y = 0.325x + 0.89$

52. TESTS Determine whether the graph at the right shows a *positive*, *negative*, or *no* correlation. If there is a correlation, describe its meaning. (Lesson 4-5) **See margin.**

Test Scores

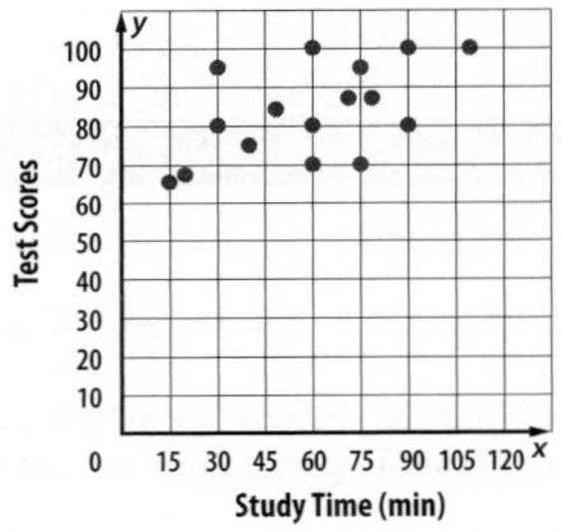

Suppose y varies directly as x. (Lesson 3-4)

53. If $y = 2.5$ when $x = 0.5$, find y when $x = 20$. **100**

54. If $y = -6.6$ when $x = 9.9$, find y when $x = 6.6$. **−4.4**

55. If $y = 2.6$ when $x = 0.25$, find y when $x = 1.125$. **11.7**

56. If $y = 6$ when $x = 0.6$, find x when $y = 12$. **1.2**

Skills Review

Solve each equation.

57. $104 = k - 67$ **171**

58. $-4 + x = -7$ **−3**

59. $\frac{m}{7} = -11$ **−77**

60. $\frac{2}{3}p = 14$ **21**

61. $-82 = 18 - n$ **100**

62. $\frac{9}{t} = -27$ $-\frac{1}{3}$

Differentiated Instruction BL

Extension Have students graph the inverse of $y = x^2$. First, have students graph $y = x^2$ on a coordinate plane by creating a table of points. Then, have them find points on the graph of the inverse by exchanging the x-coordinates with the y-coordinates of each ordered pair in the table. Have students plot these new points on the same coordinate plane. Finally, have students connect the new points with a smooth curve, using the graph of $y = x^2$ as a guide. Remind students that the graphs of inverse relations are reflections of each other in the line $y = x$.

4-7 Algebra Lab
Drawing Inverses

You can use patty paper to draw the graph of an inverse relation by reflecting the original graph in the line $y = x$.

Activity Draw an Inverse

Consider the graphs shown.

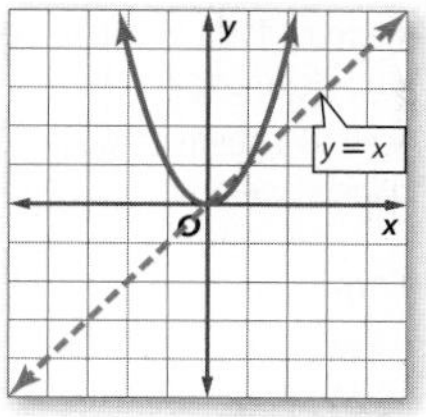

Step 1 Trace the graphs onto a square of patty paper, waxed paper, or tracing paper.

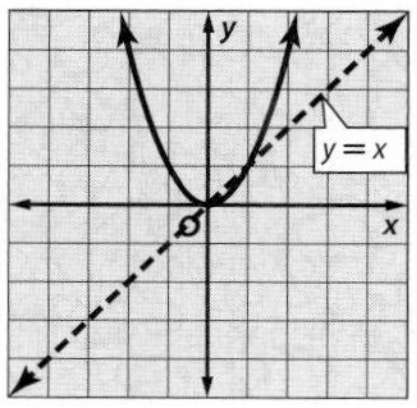

Step 2 Flip the patty paper over and lay it on the original graph so that the traced $y = x$ is on the original $y = x$.

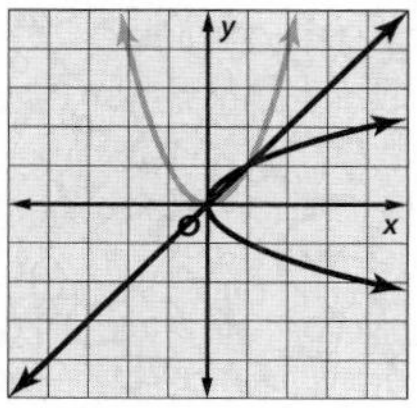

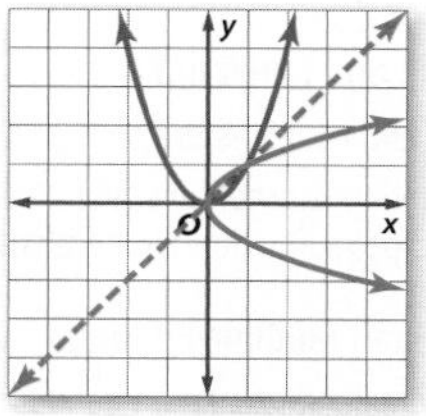

Notice that the result is the reflection of the graph in the line $y = x$ or the inverse of the graph.

Analyze The Results

6. Sample answer: Draw a horizontal line to see if the inverse represents a function. If a horizontal line intersects the graph more than once, then the inverse is not a function. If a horizontal line intersects the graph at only one point, the inverse is a function.

1. Is the graph of the original relation a function? Explain. **Yes; it passes the vertical line test.**
2. Is the graph of the inverse relation a function? Explain. **No; it does not pass the vertical line test.**
3. What are the domain and range of the original relation? of the inverse relation? **D = {all real numbers}, R = $\{y \mid y \geq 0\}$; D = $\{x \mid x \geq 0\}$; R = {all real numbers}**
4. If the domain of the original relation is restricted to D = $\{x \mid x \geq 0\}$, is the inverse relation a function? Explain. **Yes; none of the domain values would have more than one corresponding range value.**
5. If the graph of a relation is a function, what can you conclude about the graph of its inverse? **Nothing; its inverse may or may not be a function. However, if the domain of the original is restricted, the inverse will likely be a function.**
6. **CHALLENGE** The vertical line test can be used to determine whether a relation is a function. Write a rule that can be used to determine whether a function has an inverse that is also a function.

1 Focus

Objective Draw the inverse of a relation and determine whether the inverse is a function.

Materials for Each Student

- patty paper (1 sheet)
- colored pencils

Teach with Tech

Graphing Calculator Students may also be interested to know that most of their calculators have a draw inverse feature. They can access it by entering their original equation into the **Y=** list. Press 2nd **[DRAW]** 8. **DrawInv** will appear on the screen. Select the equation entered into **Y1** by pressing VARS ▶ 1 ENTER. Press ENTER once more to see the graph of the function and its inverse.

2 Teach

Working in Cooperative Groups

Divide the class into pairs to work through the Activity. Then ask students to work with their partners to complete Exercises 1–3.

Practice Have students complete Exercises 4–6.

3 Assess

Formative Assessment

Use Exercises 1–3 to assess each student's ability to determine the domain and range of a graph and its inverse and to determine if a relation and its inverse are functions.

From Concrete to Abstract

Exercise 4 asks about the specific case shown, Exercise 5 asks students to expand that knowledge to a general case, and Exercise 6 extends the concept to the horizontal line test.

Formative Assessment

KeyVocabulary The page reference after each word denotes where that term was first introduced. If students have difficulty answering questions 1–9, remind them that they can use these page references to refresh their memories about the vocabulary terms.

Summative Assessment

Vocabulary Test, p. 54

Vocabulary Review

Vocabulary Review provides students the opportunity to check their understanding of important concepts and terminology in an online game format.

FOLDABLES StudyOrganizer

Dinah Zike's Foldables®

Have students look through the chapter to make sure they have included examples in their Foldables for each lesson of the chapter. Suggest that students keep their Foldables handy while completing the Study Guide and Review pages. Point out that their Foldables can serve as a quick review when studying for the chapter test.

CHAPTER 4 Study Guide and Review

Study Guide

KeyConcepts

Slope-Intercept Form (Lessons 4-1 and 4-2)

- The slope-intercept form of a linear equation is $y = mx + b$, where m is the slope and b is the y-intercept.
- If you are given two points through which a line passes, use them to find the slope first.

Point-Slope Form (Lesson 4-3)

- The linear equation $y - y_1 = m(x - x_1)$ is written in point-slope form, where (x_1, y_1) is a given point on a nonvertical line and m is the slope of the line.

Parallel and Perpendicular Lines (Lesson 4-4)

- Nonvertical parallel lines have the same slope.
- Lines that intersect at right angles are called perpendicular lines. The slopes of perpendicular lines are opposite reciprocals.

Scatter Plots and Lines of Fit (Lesson 4-5)

- Data with two variables are called bivariate data.
- A scatter plot is a graph in which two sets of data are plotted as ordered pairs in a coordinate plane.

Regression and Median-Fit Lines (Lesson 4-6)

- A graphing calculator can be used to find regression lines and median-fit lines.

Inverse Linear Functions (Lesson 4-7)

- An inverse relation is the set of ordered pairs obtained by exchanging the x-coordinates with the y-coordinates of each ordered pair of a relation.
- A linear function $f(x)$ has an inverse function that can be written as $f^{-1}(x)$ and is read *f of x inverse* or *the inverse of f of x*.

FOLDABLES StudyOrganizer

Be sure the Key Concepts are noted in your Foldable.

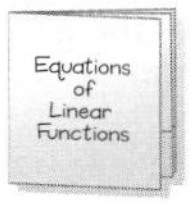

KeyVocabulary

best-fit line (p. 255)	linear interpolation (p. 249)
bivariate data (p. 247)	linear regression (p. 255)
constant function (p. 217)	line of fit (p. 248)
constraint (p. 228)	median-fit line (p. 258)
correlation coefficient (p. 255)	parallel lines (p. 239)
identity function (p. 224)	perpendicular lines (p. 240)
inverse function (p. 264)	point-slope form (p. 233)
inverse relation (p. 263)	scatter plot (p. 247)
linear extrapolation (p. 228)	slope-intercept form (p. 216)

VocabularyCheck

State whether each sentence is *true* or *false*. If *false*, replace the underlined term to make a true sentence.

1. The <u>y-intercept</u> is the y-coordinate of the point where the graph crosses the y-axis. **true**
2. The process of using a linear equation to make predictions about values that are beyond the range of the data is called <u>linear regression</u>. **false, linear extrapolation**
3. An <u>inverse relation</u> is the set of ordered pairs obtained by exchanging the x-coordinates with the y-coordinates of each ordered pair of a relation. **true**
4. The <u>correlation coefficient</u> describes whether the correlation between the variables is positive or negative and how closely the regression equation is modeling the data. **true**
5. Lines in the same plane that do not intersect are called <u>parallel</u> lines. **true**
6. Lines that intersect at <u>acute</u> angles are called perpendicular lines. **false, right**
7. A(n) <u>constant function</u> can generate ordered pairs for an inverse relation. **false, inverse function**
8. The <u>range</u> of a relation is the range of its inverse function. **false, domain**
9. An equation of the form $y = mx + b$ is in <u>point-slope form.</u> **false, slope-intercept form**

Additional Answers

10.

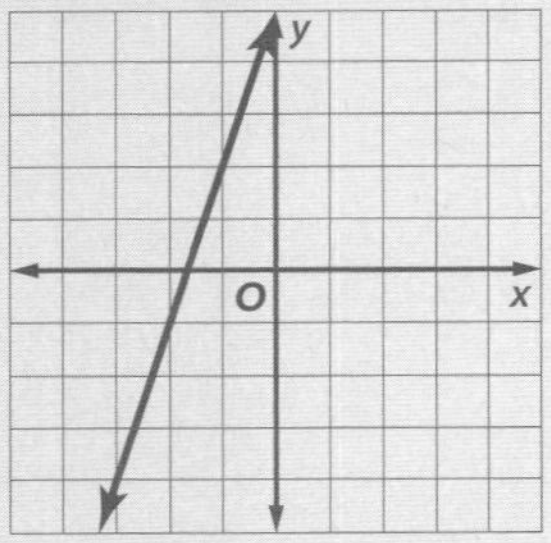

11.

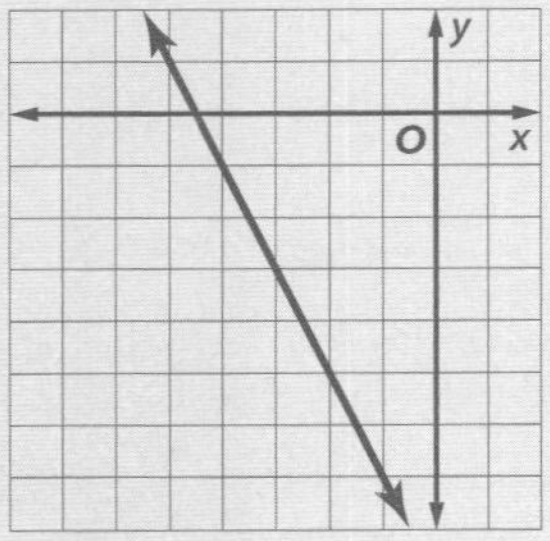

12.

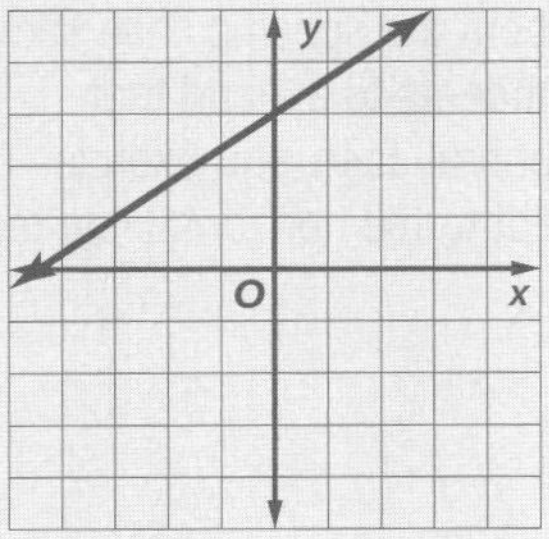

Lesson-by-Lesson Review

4-1 Graphing Equations in Slope-Intercept Form

Write an equation of a line in slope-intercept form with the given slope and *y*-intercept. Then graph the equation. **10–13. See margin for graphs.**

10. slope: 3, *y*-intercept: 5 $y = 3x + 5$

11. slope: −2, *y*-intercept: −9 $y = -2x - 9$

12. slope: $\frac{2}{3}$, *y*-intercept: 3 $y = \frac{2}{3}x + 3$

13. slope: $-\frac{5}{8}$, *y*-intercept: −2 $y = -\frac{5}{8}x - 2$

Graph each equation. **14–17. See margin.**

14. $y = 4x - 2$

15. $y = -3x + 5$

16. $y = \frac{1}{2}x + 1$

17. $3x + 4y = 8$

18. **SKI RENTAL** Write an equation in slope-intercept form for the total cost of skiing for *h* hours with one lift ticket. $y = 5h + 15$

Example 1

Write an equation of a line in slope-intercept form with slope −5 and *y*-intercept −3. Then graph the equation.

$y = mx + b$	Slope-intercept form
$y = -5x + (-3)$	$m = -5$ and $b = -3$
$y = -5x - 3$	Simplify.

To graph the equation, plot the *y*-intercept (0, −3).

Then move up 5 units and left 1 unit. Plot the point. Draw a line through the two points.

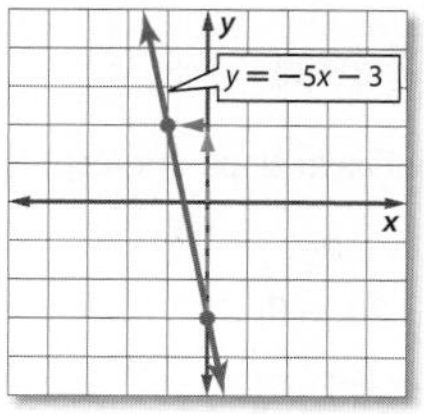

19. $y = 3x - 1$ **20.** $y = -4x + 2$

4-2 Writing Equations in Slope-Intercept Form

Write an equation of the line that passes through the given point and has the given slope.

19. (1, 2), slope 3

20. (2, −6), slope −4

21. (−3, −1), slope $\frac{2}{5}$ $y = \frac{2}{5}x + \frac{1}{5}$

22. (5, −2), slope $-\frac{1}{3}$ $y = -\frac{1}{3}x - \frac{1}{3}$

Write an equation of the line that passes through the given points. **23–26. See margin.**

23. (2, −1), (5, 2)

24. (−4, 3), (1, 13)

25. (3, 5), (5, 6)

26. (2, 4), (7, 2)

27. **CAMP** In 2005, a camp had 450 campers. Five years later, the number of campers rose to 750. Write a linear equation that represents the number of campers that attend camp. $y = 60x + 450$

Example 2

Write an equation of the line that passes through (3, 2) with a slope of 5.

Step 1 Find the *y*-intercept.

$y = mx + b$	Slope-intercept form
$2 = 5(3) + b$	$m = 5$, $y = 2$, and $x = 3$
$2 = 15 + b$	Simplify.
$-13 = b$	Subtract 15 from each side.

Step 2 Write the equation in slope-intercept form.

$y = mx + b$	Slope-intercept form
$y = 5x - 13$	$m = 5$ and $b = -13$

Lesson-by-Lesson Review

Intervention If the given examples are not sufficient to review the topics covered by the questions, remind students that the lesson references tell them where to review that topic in their textbooks.

Two-Day Option Have students complete the Lesson-by-Lesson Review. Then you can use McGraw-Hill eAssessment to customize another review worksheet that practices all the objectives of this chapter or only the objectives on which your students need more help.

Additional Answers

13.

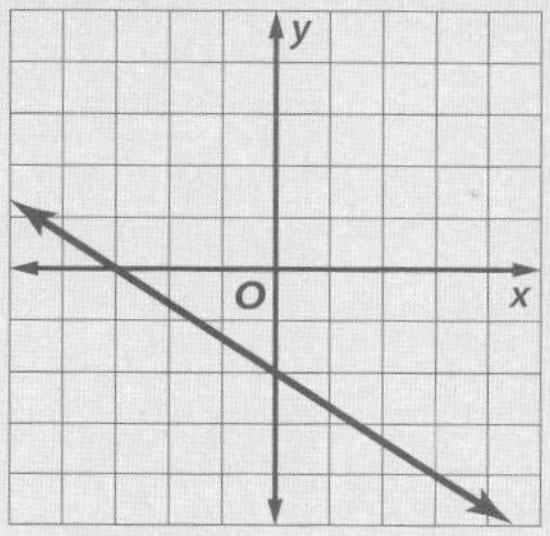

14.

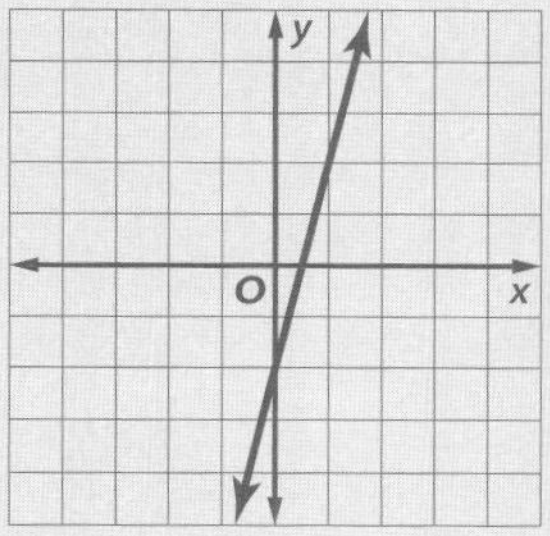

15.

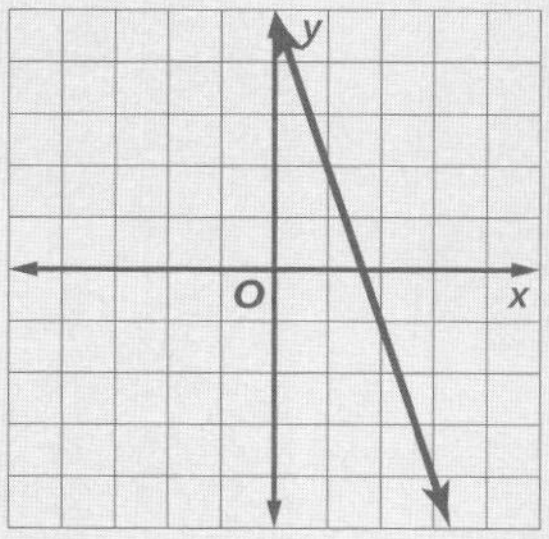

16.

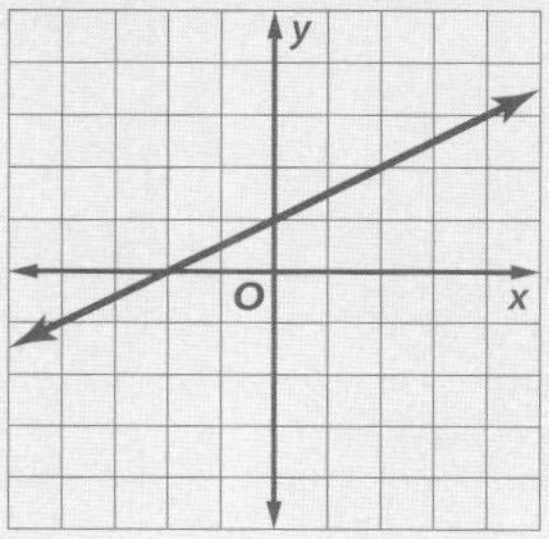

17.

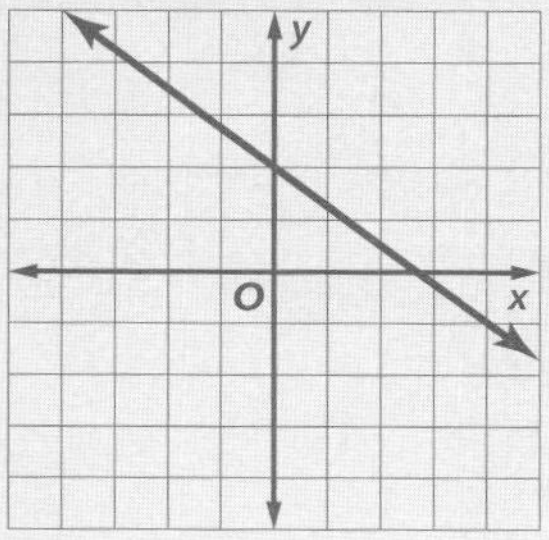

23. $y = x - 3$

24. $y = 2x + 11$

25. $y = \frac{1}{2}x + \frac{7}{2}$

26. $y = -\frac{2}{5}x + \frac{24}{5}$

CHAPTER 4

Study Guide and Review *Continued*

4-3 Writing Equations in Point-Slope Form

Write an equation in point-slope form for the line that passes through the given point with the slope provided.

28. (6, 3), slope 5 $y - 3 = 5(x - 6)$

29. (−2, 1), slope −3 $y - 1 = -3(x + 2)$

30. (−4, 2), slope 0 $y - 2 = 0$

Write each equation in standard form.

31. $y - 3 = 5(x - 2)$ $5x - y = 7$

32. $y - 7 = -3(x + 1)$ $3x + y = 4$

33. $y + 4 = \frac{1}{2}(x - 3)$ $x - 2y = 11$

34. $y - 9 = -\frac{4}{5}(x + 2)$ $4x + 5y = 37$

Write each equation in slope-intercept form.

35. $y - 2 = 3(x - 5)$ $y = 3x - 13$

36. $y - 12 = -2(x - 3)$ $y = -2x + 18$

37. $y + 3 = 5(x + 1)$ $y = 5x + 2$

38. $y - 4 = \frac{1}{2}(x + 2)$ $y = \frac{1}{2}x + 5$

Example 3

Write an equation in point-slope form for the line that passes through (3, 4) with a slope of −2.

$y - y_1 = m(x - x_1)$ Point-slope form

$y - 4 = -2(x - 3)$ Replace m with −2 and (x_1, y_1) with (3, 4).

Example 4

Write $y + 6 = -4(x - 3)$ in standard form.

$y + 6 = -4(x - 3)$ Original equation

$y + 6 = -4x + 12$ Distributive Property

$4x + y + 6 = 12$ Add $4x$ to each side.

$4x + y = 6$ Subtract 6 from each side.

4-4 Parallel and Perpendicular Lines

Write an equation in slope-intercept form for the line that passes through the given point and is parallel to the graph of each equation.

39. (2, 5), $y = x - 3$ $y = x + 3$

40. (0, 3), $y = 3x + 5$ $y = 3x + 3$

41. (−4, 1), $y = -2x - 6$ $y = -2x - 7$

42. (−5, −2), $y = -\frac{1}{2}x + 4$ $y = -\frac{1}{2}x - \frac{9}{2}$

Write an equation in slope-intercept form for the line that passes through the given point and is perpendicular to the graph of the given equation.

43. (2, 4), $y = 3x + 1$ $y = -\frac{1}{3}x + \frac{14}{3}$

44. (1, 3), $y = -2x - 4$ $y = \frac{1}{2}x + \frac{5}{2}$

45. (−5, 2), $y = \frac{1}{3}x + 4$ $y = -3x - 13$

46. (3, 0), $y = -\frac{1}{2}x$ $y = 2x - 6$

Example 5

Write an equation in slope-intercept form for the line that passes through (−2, 4) and is parallel to the graph of $y = 6x - 3$.

The slope of the line with equation $y = 6x - 3$ is 6. The line parallel to $y = 6x - 3$ has the same slope, 6.

$y - y_1 = m(x - x_1)$ Point-slope form

$y - 4 = 6[x - (-2)]$ Substitute.

$y - 4 = 6(x + 2)$ Simplify.

$y - 4 = 6x + 12$ Distributive Property

$y = 6x + 16$ Add 4 to each side.

4-5 Scatter Plots and Lines of Fit

47. Determine whether the graph shows a *positive*, *negative*, or *no* correlation. If there is a positive or negative correlation, describe its meaning. **Positive; as the number of hours spent studying increases, the test scores increase.**

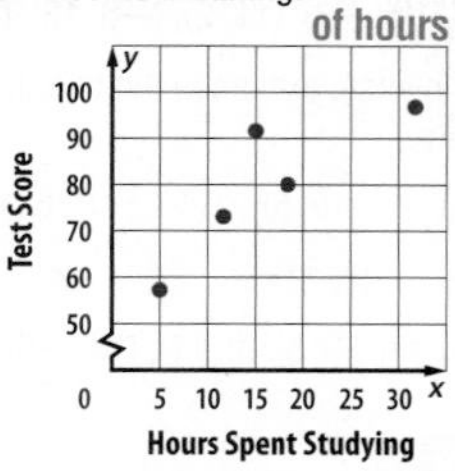

48. ATTENDANCE A scatter plot of data compares the number of years since a business has opened and its annual number of sales. It contains the ordered pairs (2, 650) and (5, 1280). Write an equation in slope-intercept form for the line of fit for this situation. $y = 210x + 230$

Example 6

The scatter plot displays the number of texts and the number of calls made daily. Write an equation for the line of fit.

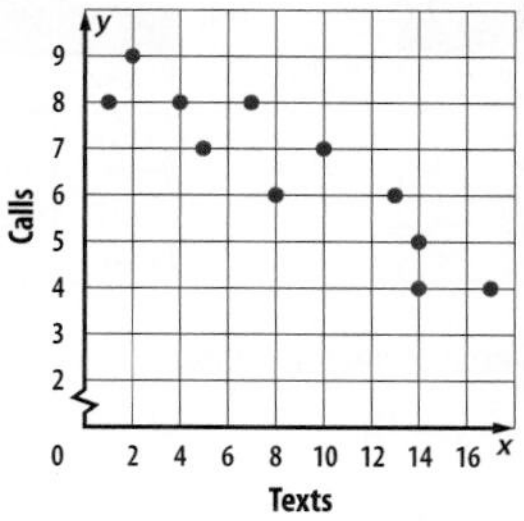

First, find the slope using (2, 9) and (17, 4).

$m = \frac{4 - 9}{17 - 2} = \frac{-5}{15}$ or $-\frac{1}{3}$ Substitute and simplify.

Then find the y-intercept.

$9 = -\frac{1}{3}(2) + b$ Substitute.

$9\frac{2}{3} = b$ Add $\frac{2}{3}$ to each side.

Write the equation. $y = -\frac{1}{3}x + 9\frac{2}{3}$

4-6 Regression and Median-Fit Lines

49. SALE The table shows the number of purchases made at an outerwear store during a sale. Write an equation of the regression line. Then estimate the daily purchases on day 10 of the sale. $y = 5.36x + 11$; 65

Days Since Sale Began	1	2	3	4	5	6	7
Daily Purchases	15	21	32	30	40	38	51

50. MOVIES The table shows ticket sales at a certain theater during the first week after a movie opened. Write an equation of the regression line. Then estimate the daily ticket sales on the 15th day. $y = -5.79x + 99.14$; \$12.29

Days Since Movie Opened	1	2	3	4	5	6	7
Daily Ticket Sales	85	92	89	78	65	68	55

Example 7

ATTENDANCE **The table shows the annual attendance at an amusement park. Write an equation of the regression line for the data.**

Years Since 2004	0	1	2	3	4	5	6
Attendance (thousands)	75	80	72	68	65	60	53

Step 1 Enter the data by pressing STAT and selecting the **Edit** option.

Step 2 Perform the regression by pressing STAT and selecting the **CALC** option. Scroll down to **LinReg (ax + b)** and press ENTER.

Step 3 Write the equation of the regression line by rounding the a- and b-values on the screen. $y = -4.04x + 79.68$

connectED.mcgraw-hill.com 275

Anticipation Guide

Have students complete the Chapter 4 Anticipation Guide and discuss how their responses have changed now that they have completed Chapter 4.

CHAPTER 4 Study Guide and Review *Continued*

4-7 Inverse Linear Functions

Find the inverse of each relation.

51. {(7, 3.5), (6.2, 8), (−4, 2.7), (−12, 1.4)} **51.** {(3.5, 7), (8, 6.2), (2.7, −4), (1.4, −12)}

52. {(1, 9), (13, 26), (−3, 4), (−11, −2)} **52.** {(9, 1), (26, 13), (4, −3), (−2, −11)}

53.

X	Y
−4	2.7
−1	3.8
0	4.1
3	7.2

{(2.7, −4), (3.8, −1), (4.1, 0), (7.2, 3)}

54.

X	Y
−12	4
−8	0
−4	−4
0	−8

{(4, −12), (0, −8), (−4, −4), (−8, 0)}

Find the inverse of each function.

55. $f(x) = \frac{5}{11}x + 10$ $f^{-1}(x) = \frac{11}{5}x - 22$

56. $f(x) = 3x + 8$ $f^{-1}(x) = \frac{1}{3}x - \frac{8}{3}$

57. $f(x) = -4x - 12$ $f^{-1}(x) = -\frac{1}{4}x - 3$

58. $f(x) = \frac{1}{4}x - 7$ $f^{-1}(x) = 4x + 28$

59. $f(x) = -\frac{2}{3}x + \frac{1}{4}$ $f^{-1}(x) = -\frac{3}{2}x + \frac{3}{8}$

60. $f(x) = -3x + 3$ $f^{-1}(x) = -\frac{1}{3}x + 1$

Example 8

Find the inverse of the relation.

{(5, −3), (11, 2), (−6, 12), (4, −2)}

To find the inverse, exchange the coordinates of the ordered pairs.

(5, −3) → (−3, 5) (−6, 12) → (12, −6)

(11, 2) → (2, 11) (4, −2) → (−2, 4)

The inverse is {(−3, 5), (2, 11), (12, −6), (−2, 4)}.

Example 9

Find the inverse of $f(x) = \frac{1}{4}x + 9$.

$f(x) = \frac{1}{4}x + 9$	Original equation
$y = \frac{1}{4}x + 9$	Replace $f(x)$ with y.
$x = \frac{1}{4}y + 9$	Interchange y and x.
$x - 9 = \frac{1}{4}y$	Subtract 9 from each side.
$4(x - 9) = y$	Multiply each side by 4.
$4x - 36 = y$	Distributive Property
$4x - 36 = f^{-1}(x)$	Replace y with $f^{-1}(x)$.

CHAPTER 4 Practice Test

1. Graph $y = 2x - 3$. See margin.

2. **MULTIPLE CHOICE** A popular pizza parlor charges \$12 for a large cheese pizza plus \$1.50 for each additional topping. Write an equation in slope-intercept form for the total cost C of a pizza with t toppings. C
   - A $C = 12t + 1.50$
   - B $C = 13.50t$
   - C $C = 12 + 1.50t$
   - D $C = 1.50t - 12$

Write an equation of a line in slope-intercept form that passes through the given point and has the given slope.

3. $(-4, 2)$; slope -3 $y = -3x - 10$
4. $(3, -5)$; slope $\frac{2}{3}$ $y = \frac{2}{3}x - 7$

Write an equation of the line in slope-intercept form that passes through the given points.

5. $(1, 4), (3, 10)$ $y = 3x + 1$
6. $(2, 5), (-2, 8)$ $y = -\frac{3}{4}x + \frac{13}{2}$
7. $(0, 4), (-3, 0)$ $y = \frac{4}{3}x + 4$
8. $(7, -1), (9, -4)$ $y = -\frac{3}{2}x + \frac{19}{2}$

9. **PAINTING** The data in the table show the size of a room in square feet and the time it takes to paint the room in minutes.

Room Size	100	150	200	400	500
Painting Time	160	220	270	500	680

   a. Use the points (100, 160) and (500, 680) to write an equation in slope-intercept form. $y = 1.3x + 30$

   b. Predict the amount of time required to paint a room measuring 750 square feet. 1005 min

10. **SALARY** The table shows the relationship between years of experience and teacher salary.

Years Experience	1	5	10	15	20
Salary (thousands of dollars)	28	31	42	49	64

   a. Write an equation for the best-fit line. $y = 1.89x + 23.57$

   b. Find the correlation coefficient and explain what it tells us about the relationship between experience and salary. 0.98; The equation fits the data well so experience affects salary.

Write an equation in slope-intercept form for the line that passes through the given point and is parallel to the graph of each equation.

11. $(2, -3), y = 4x - 9$ $y = 4x - 11$
12. $(-5, 1), y = -3x + 2$ $y = -3x - 14$

Write an equation in slope-intercept form for the line that passes through the given point and is perpendicular to the graph of the equation.

13. $(1, 4), y = -2x + 5$ 13. $y = \frac{1}{2}x + \frac{7}{2}$
14. $(-3, 6), y = \frac{1}{4}x + 2$ $y = -4x - 6$

15. **MULTIPLE CHOICE** The graph shows the relationship between outside temperature and daily ice cream cone sales. What type of correlation is shown? F

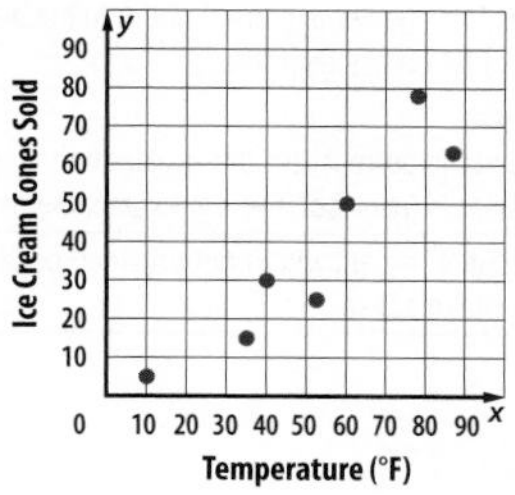

   - F positive correlation
   - G negative correlation
   - H no correlation
   - J not enough information

16. **ADOPTION** The table shows the number of children from Ethiopia adopted by U.S. citizens.

Years Since 2000	5	6	7	8	9
Number of Children	442	731	1254	1724	2277

   a. Write the slope-intercept form of the equation for the line of fit. $y = 466.3x - 1978.5$

   b. Predict the number of children from Ethiopia who will be adopted in 2025. about 9679

Find the inverse of each function.

17. $f(x) = -5x - 30$ $f^{-1}(x) = -\frac{1}{5}x - 6$
18. $f(x) = 4x + 10$ $f^{-1}(x) = \frac{1}{4}x - \frac{5}{2}$
19. $f(x) = \frac{1}{6}x - 2$ $f^{-1}(x) = 6x + 12$
20. $f(x) = \frac{3}{4}x + 12$ $f^{-1}(x) = \frac{4}{3}x - 16$

Summative Assessment

Use these alternate leveled chapter tests to differentiate assessment for your students.

Leveled Chapter 4 Tests

Form	Type	Level	Page(s)
1	MC	AL	55–56
2A	MC	OL	57–58
2B	MC	OL	59–60
2C	FR	OL	61–62
2D	FR	OL	63–64
3	FR	BL	65–66
Vocabulary Test			54
Extended-Response Test			67

MC = multiple-choice questions
FR = free-response questions

McGraw-Hill eAssessment Customize and create multiple versions of your chapter tests and their answer keys. All of the questions from the leveled chapter tests in the *Chapter 4 Resource Masters* are also available on McGraw-Hill eAssessment.

Additional Answer

1.

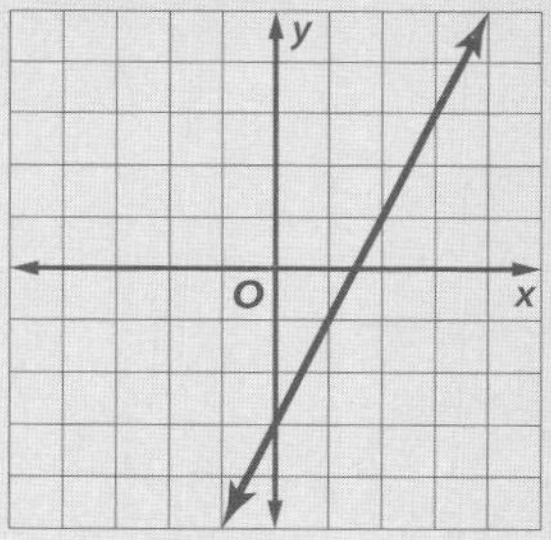

InterventionPlanner

TIER 1 On Level OL

If students miss about 25% of the exercises or less,

Then choose a resource:

SE Lessons 4-1, 4-2, 4-3, 4-4, 4-5, 4-6, and 4-7

Skills Practice, pp. 7, 13, 19, 26, 32, 39, and 45

TE Chapter Project, p. 210

connectED.mcgraw-hill.com Self-Check Quiz

TIER 2 Strategic Intervention AL approaching grade level

If students miss about 50% of the exercises,

Then choose a resource:

Study Guide and Intervention, Chapter 4, pp. 5, 11, 17, 24, 30, 37, and 43

Quick Review Math Handbook

connectED.mcgraw-hill.com Extra Examples, Personal Tutor, Homework Help

TIER 3 Intensive Intervention 2 or more grades below level

If students miss about 75% of the exercises,

Then use *Math Triumphs, Alg. 1* Ch. 4

connectED.mcgraw-hill.com Extra Examples, Personal Tutor, Homework Help, Review Vocabulary

1 Focus

Objective Use strategies for solving short answer standardized test problems.

2 Teach

Scaffolding Questions

Ask:

- How is a short answer question different from a multiple choice question? Sample answer: In a multiple choice question, you choose from several answers, but in a short answer question, your answer is the only answer.
- Why do you think math tests include short answer questions? Sample answer: To assess whether you understand a concept and know how to solve a problem.
- How can you show in a short answer response that you know how to solve a problem? Sample answer: Show the steps you used to solve the problem and/or explain how you solved it.

CHAPTER 4 Preparing for Standardized Tests

Short Answer Questions

Short answer questions require you to provide a solution to the problem, along with a method, explanation, and/or justification used to arrive at the solution.

Strategies for Solving Short Answer Questions

Step 1

Short answer questions are typically graded using a **rubric**, or a scoring guide. The following is an example of a short answer question scoring rubric.

Scoring Rubric	
Criteria	Score
Full Credit: The answer is correct and a full explanation is provided that shows each etep.	2
Partial Credit: • The answer is correct, but the explanation is incomplete. • The answer is incorrect, but the explanation is correct.	1
No Credit: Either an answer is not provided or the answer does not make sense.	0

Step 2

In solving short answer questions, remember to…

- explain your reasoning or state your approach to solving the problem.
- show all of your work or steps.
- check your answer if time permits.

Standardized Test Example

Read the problem. Identify what you need to know. Then use the information in the problem to solve. Show your work.

The table shows production costs for building different numbers of skateboards. Determine the missing value, x, that will result in a linear model.

Skateboards Built	Production Costs
14	$325
28	$500
x	$375
22	$425

278 | Chapter 4 | Preparing for Standardized Tests

Read the problem carefully. You are given several data points and asked to find the missing value that results in a linear model.

Example of a 2-point response:

Set up a coordinate grid and plot the three given points: (14, 325), (28, 500), (22, 425).

Then draw a straight line through them and find the x-value that produces a y-value of 375.

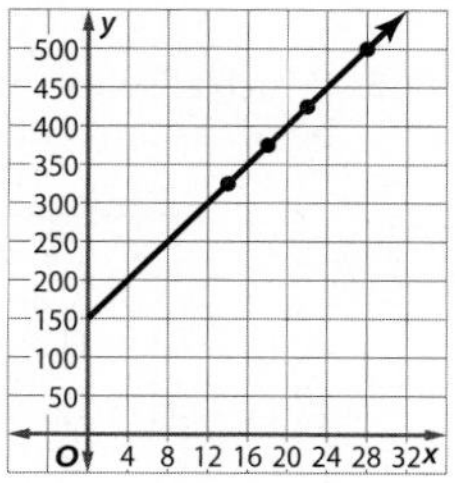

So, building 18 skateboards would result in production costs of $375. These data form a linear model.

The steps, calculations, and reasoning are clearly stated. The student also arrives at the correct answer. So, this response is worth the full 2 points.

Exercises

Read each problem. Identify what you need to know. Then use the information in the problem to solve. Show your work.

1. Given points $M(-1, 7)$, $N(3, -5)$, $O(6, 1)$, and $P(-3, -2)$, determine two segments that are perpendicular to each other. **$\overline{MN} \perp \overline{OP}$**

2. Write the equation of a line that is parallel to $4x + 2y = 8$ and has a y-intercept of 5. **$y = -2x + 5$**

3. Three vertices of a quadrilateral are shown on the coordinate grid. Determine a fourth vertex that would result in a trapezoid. **Sample answer: (2, 6)**

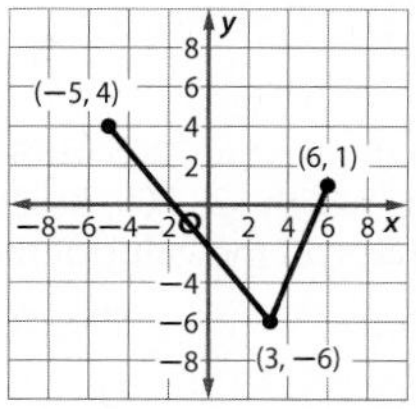

Additional Example

The table shows the earnings Nate makes in his job as a scuba diving instructor for a travel company. Write and use a linear equation to find the value of x in the table.

Hours	Earnings ($)
9	710
25	1750
x	1490
17	1230

Sample 2-point response: Use two points in the table to write an equation of the line in slope-intercept form. Find the slope using the slope formula, and then use the slope to find the y-intercept. Write the equation of the line and use it to find the value of x.

$$m = \frac{y_2 - y_1}{x_2 - x_1}$$

$$m = \frac{1750 - 710}{25 - 9} = \frac{1040}{16} \text{ or } 65$$

$$y = mx + b$$
$$710 = 65(9) + b$$
$$710 = 585 + b$$
$$710 - 585 = b$$
$$125 = b$$

The equation of the line is $y = 65x + 125$.

$$y = 65x + 125$$
$$1490 = 65x + 125$$
$$1490 - 125 = 65x$$
$$1365 = 65x$$
$$21 = x$$

So Nate works 21 hours to earn $1490.

3 Assess

Use Exercises 1–3 to assess students' understanding.

Diagnose Student Errors

Survey student responses for each item. Class trends may indicate common errors and misconceptions.

1. A incorrectly calculated $4 - (-2)$ or $-2 - 4$
B calculated the ratio of the run to the rise
C correct
D calculated the ratio of the run to the rise and incorrectly calculated $4 - (-2)$ or $-2 - 4$

2. F used *n* instead of $n - 1$ in the formula for the *n*th term
G correct
H guess
J guess

3. A correct
B guess
C calculation error, such as used 1400 instead of 1600 as the pattern for yearly decrease
D guess

4. F does not understand relationship between slope and intercepts
G does not understand relationship between slope and intercepts
H does not understand relationship between slope and intercepts
J correct

5. A partially correct for $x = 14$, but $x = -8$ not 8
B guess
C correct
D guess

6. F checked equation for 15° only
G checked equation for 10° only
H correct
J checked equation for 10° only

CHAPTER 4 Standardized Test Practice

Cumulative, Chapters 1 through 4

Multiple Choice

Read each question. Then fill in the correct answer on the answer document provided by your teacher or on a sheet of paper.

1. What is the rate of change represented in the graph? **C**

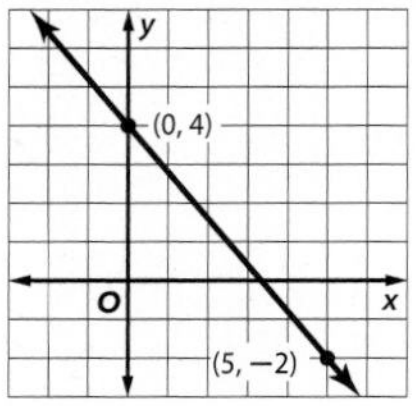

A $-\frac{2}{5}$
B $-\frac{5}{6}$
C $-\frac{6}{5}$
D $-\frac{5}{2}$

2. The table below shows the cost for renting a bicycle at a bike shop located in Venice Beach. What is a function that can represent this sequence? **G**

Number of Hours	Cost ($)
1	10
2	14
3	18
4	22

F $f(n) = 4n + 10$
G $f(n) = 4n + 6$
H $f(n) = 10n + 4$
J $f(n) = 10n - 6$

3. Jaime bought a car in 2005 for $28,500. By 2008, the car was worth $23,700. Based on a linear model, what will the value of the car be in 2012? **A**

A $17,300
B $17,550
C $18,100
D $18,475

4. If the graph of a line has a positive slope and a negative *y*-intercept, what happens to the *x*-intercept if the slope and the *y*-intercept are doubled? **J**

F The *x*-intercept becomes four times as great.
G The *x*-intercept becomes twice as great.
H The *x*-intercept becomes one-fourth as great.
J The *x*-intercept remains the same.

5. Which absolute value equation has the graph below as its solution? **C**

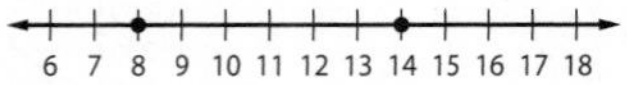

A $|x - 3| = 11$
B $|x - 4| = 12$
C $|x - 11| = 3$
D $|x - 12| = 4$

6. The table below shows the relationship between certain temperatures in degrees Fahrenheit and degrees Celsius. Which of the following linear equations correctly models this relationship? **H**

Celsius (C)	Fahrenheit (F)
10°	50°
15°	59°
20°	68°
25°	77°
30°	86°

F $F = \frac{8}{5}C + 35$
G $F = \frac{4}{5}C + 42$
H $F = \frac{9}{5}C + 32$
J $F = \frac{12}{5}C + 26$

Test-TakingTip

Question 3 Find the average annual depreciation between 2005 and 2008. Then extend the pattern to find the car's value in 2012.

Short Response/Gridded Response

Record your answers on the answer sheet provided by your teacher or on a sheet of paper.

7. What is the equation of the line graphed below?

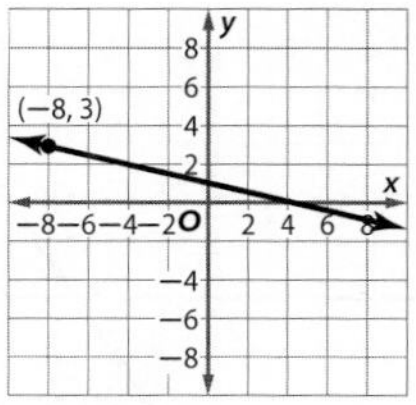

Express your answer in point slope form using the point (−8, 3). $y - 3 = -\frac{1}{4}(x + 8)$

8. GRIDDED RESPONSE The linear equation below is a best fit model for the peak depth of the Mad River when x inches of rain fall. What would you expect the peak depth of the river to be after a storm that produces $1\frac{3}{4}$ inches of rain? Round your answer to the nearest tenth of a foot if necessary. **1.6 ft**

$y = 2.5x + 14.8$

9. Jacob formed an advertising company in 1992. Initially, the company only had 14 employees. In 2008, the company had grown to a total of 63 employees. Find the percent of change in the number of employees working at Jacob's company. Round to the nearest tenth of a percent if necessary. **350%**

10. The table shows the total amount of rain during a storm. $y = 0.45x$

Hours	1	2	3	4
Inches	0.45	0.9	1.35	1.8

a. Write an equation to fit the data in the table.

b. Describe the relationship between the hour and the amount of rain received. **See margin.**

11. An electrician charges a $25 consultation fee plus $35 per hour for labor.

a. Copy and complete the following table showing the charges for jobs that take 1, 2, 3, 4, or 5 hours.

Hours, h	Total Cost, C
1	$60
2	$95
3	$130
4	$165
5	$200

b. Write an equation in slope-intercept form for the total cost of a job that takes h hours. $C = 35h + 25$

c. If the electrician bills in quarter hours, how much would it cost for a job that takes 3 hours 15 minutes to complete? **$138.75**

Extended Response

Record your answer on a sheet of paper. Show your work.

12. Explain how you can determine whether two lines are parallel or perpendicular.

12. Sample answer: Compare the slopes of the lines. If two lines have the same slope, they are parallel. If their slopes are opposite reciprocals, they are perpendicular. If two lines are vertical they are parallel. If one line is horizontal and one is vertical the two lines are perpendicular.

Need ExtraHelp?

If you missed Question...	1	2	3	4	5	6	7	8	9	10	11	12
Go to Lesson...	3-3	3-5	4-5	3-1	2-5	4-2	4-3	4-5	2-7	3-6	4-2	4-4

Additional Answer

10b. Sample answer: The amount of rain is proportional to the hour.

Formative Assessment

You can use these pages to benchmark student progress.

Standardized Test Practice, pp. 68–70

Answer Sheet Practice

Have students simulate taking a standardized test by recording their answers on a practice recording sheet.

Student Recording Sheet

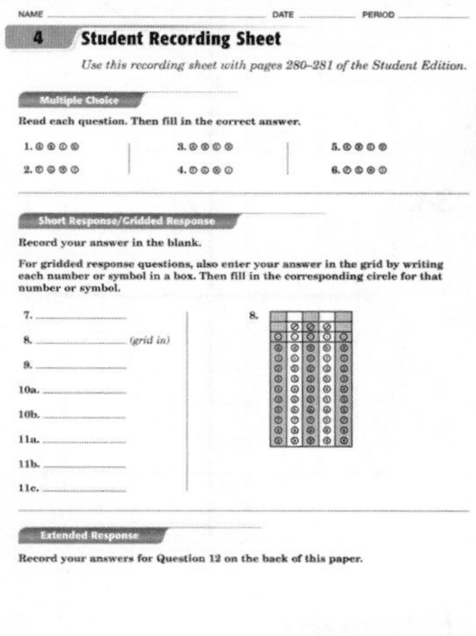

McGraw-Hill eAssessment Create practice tests that align to your state standards, the Common Core State Standards, and other national standards such as TIMSS and NAEP.

Homework Option

Get Ready for Chapter 5 Assign students the exercises on p. 283 as homework to assess whether they possess the prerequisite skills needed for the next chapter.

Lesson 4-1 (Guided Practice)

1A.

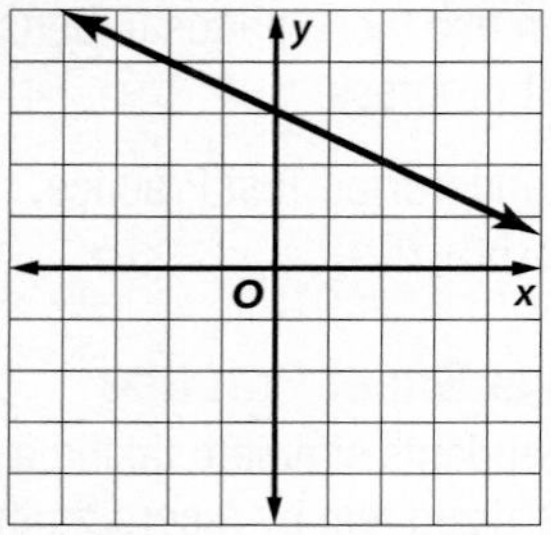

1B.

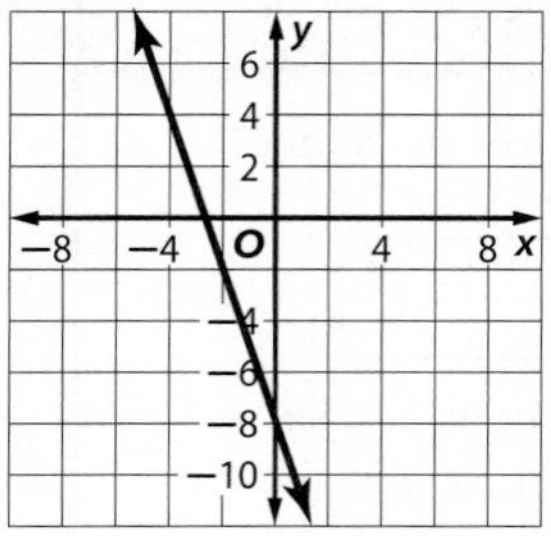

2A.

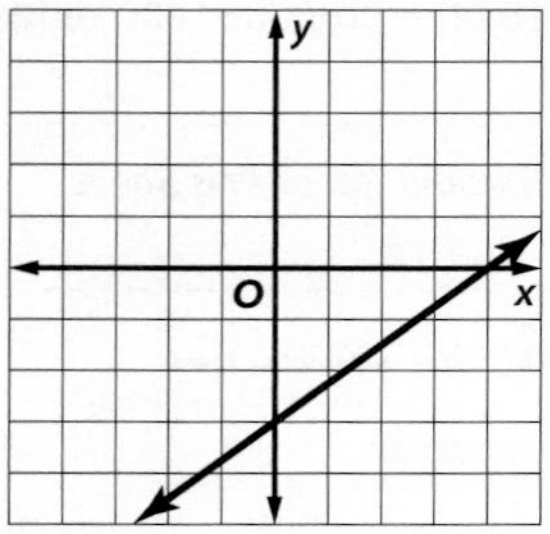

2B.

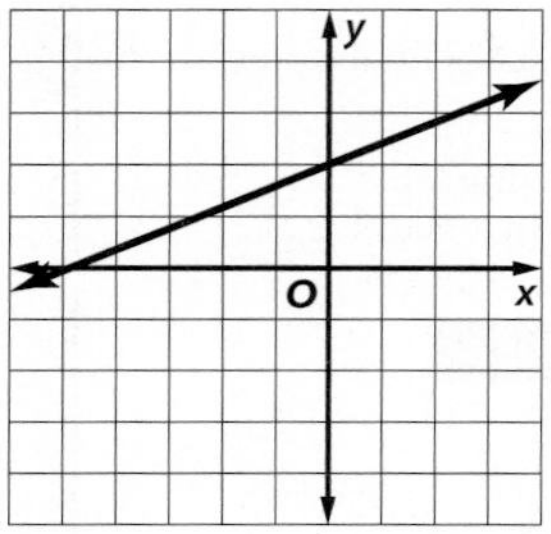

3A.

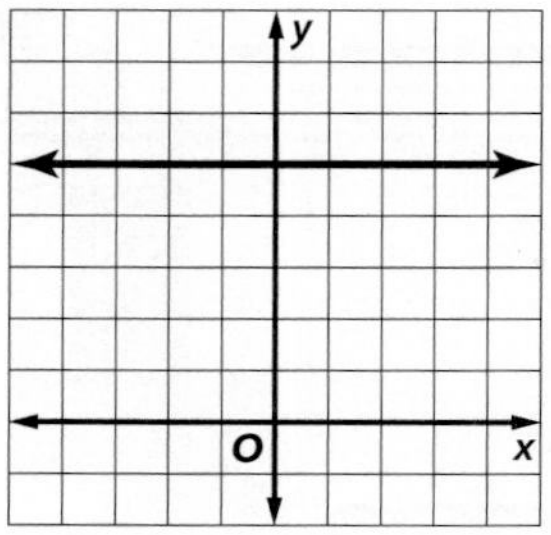

3B.

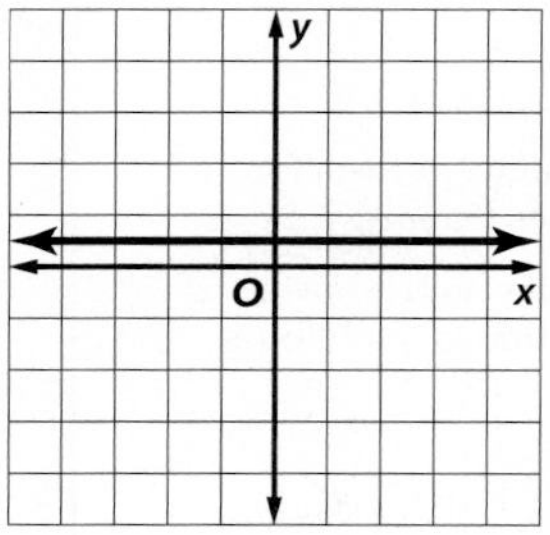

Lesson 4-1

1. $y = 2x + 4$

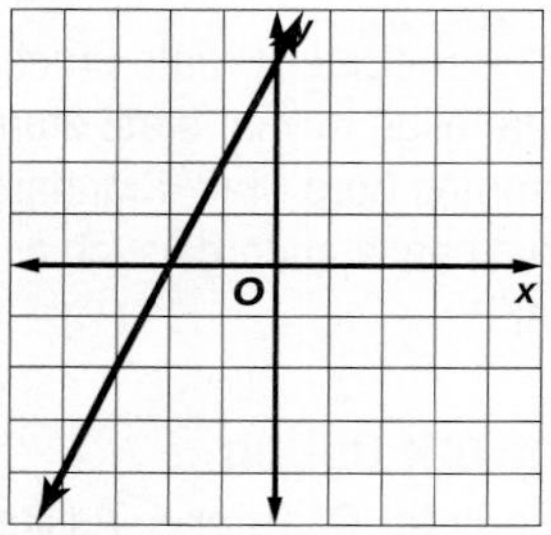

2. $y = -5x + 3$

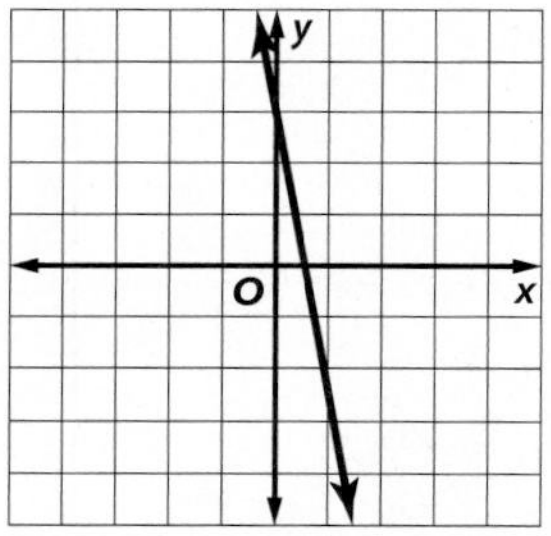

3. $y = \frac{3}{4}x - 1$

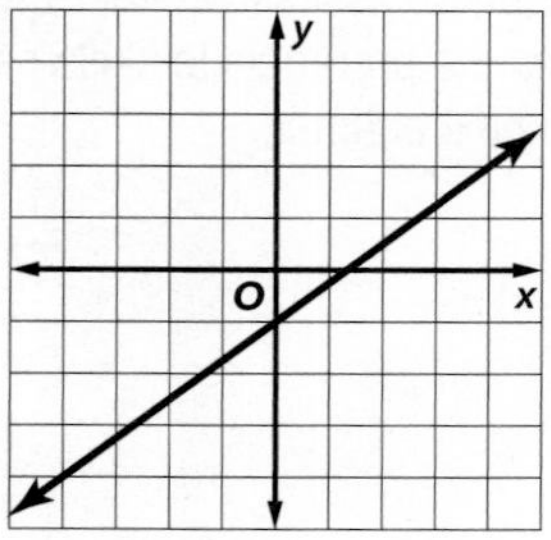

4. $y = -\frac{5}{7}x - \frac{2}{3}$

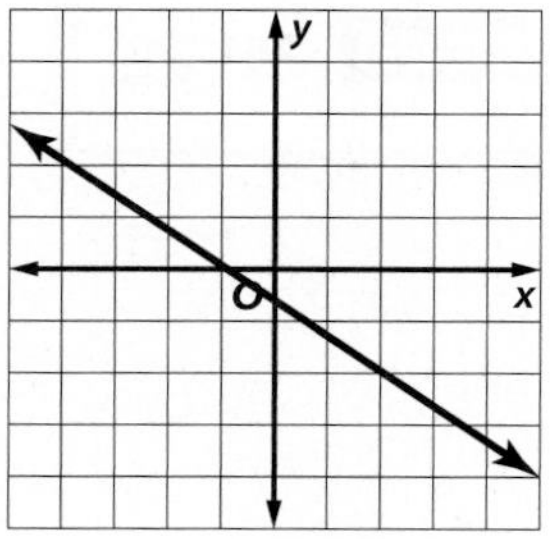

5.

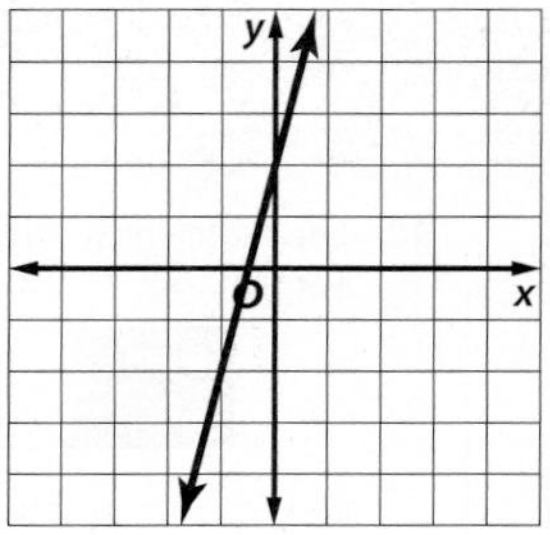

6.

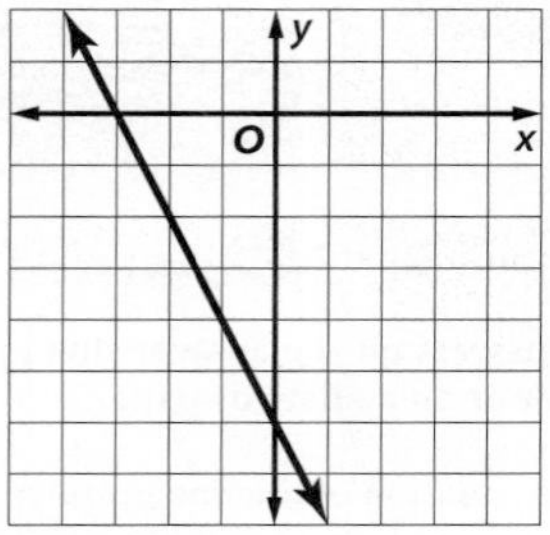

7.

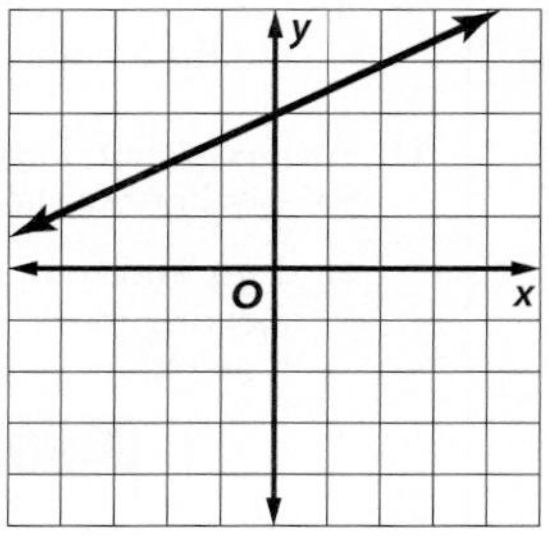

8.

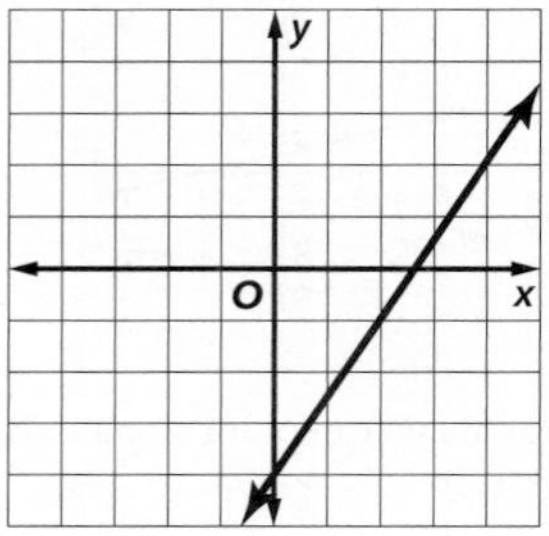

9.

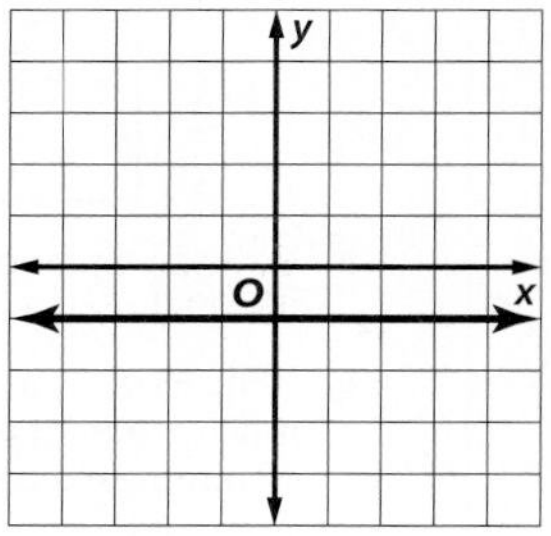

10.

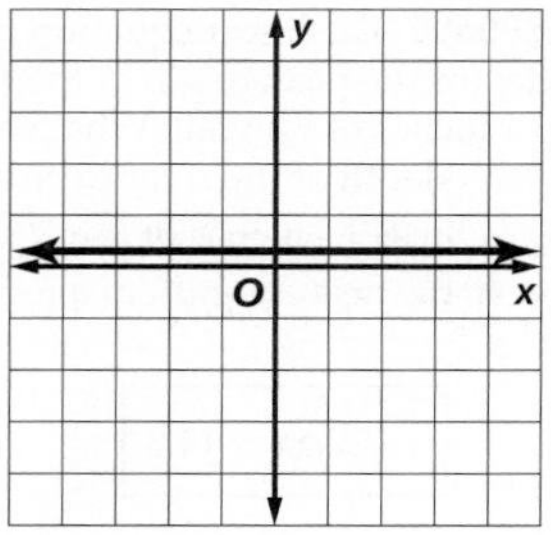

17. $y = 5x + 8$

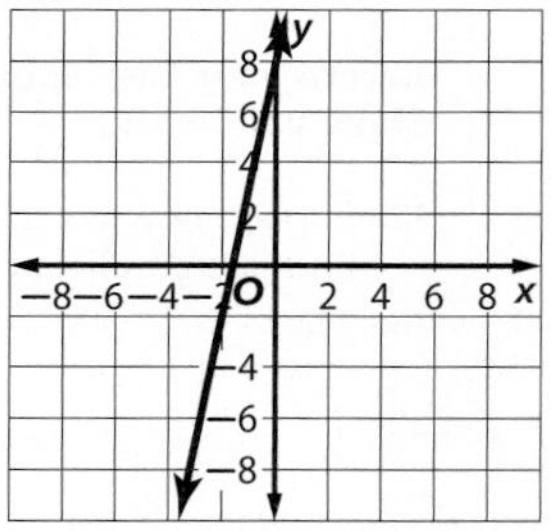

18. $y = 3x + 10$

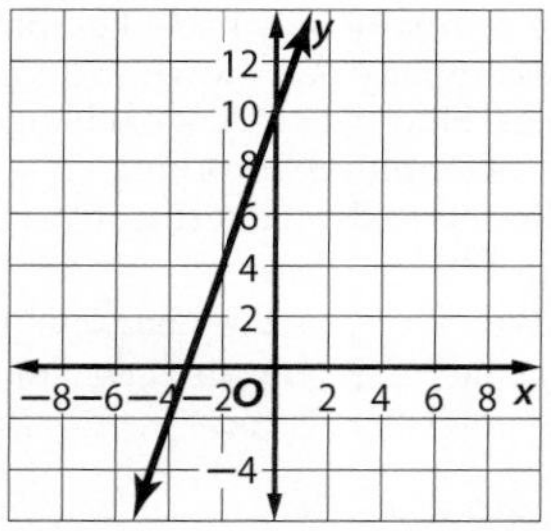

19. $y = -4x + 6$

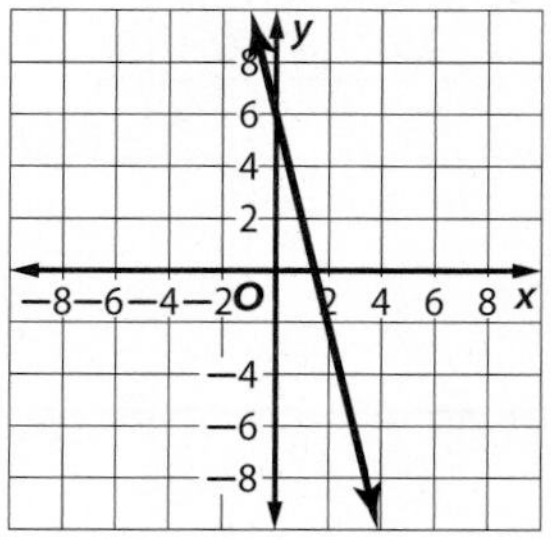

20. $y = -2x + 8$

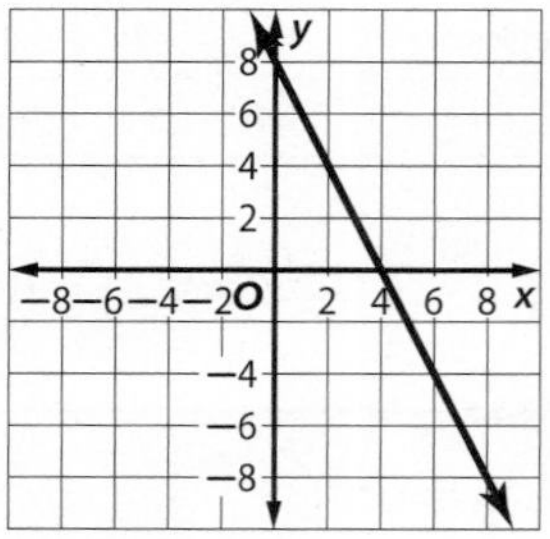

21. $y = 3x - 4$

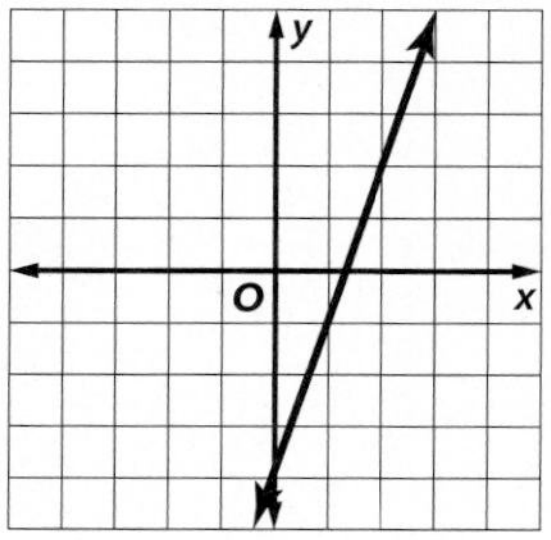

22. $y = 4x - 6$

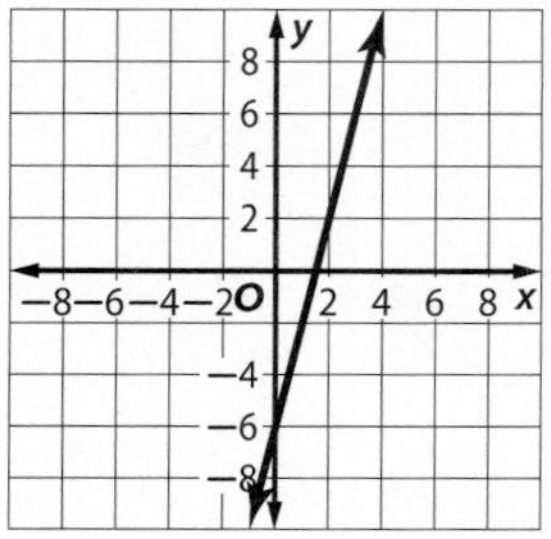

23.
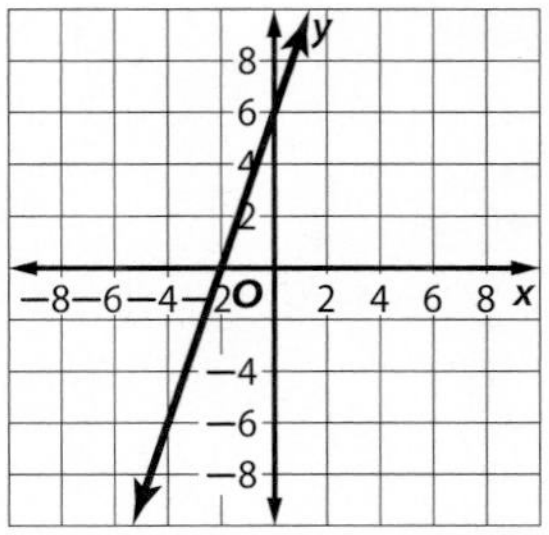

24.
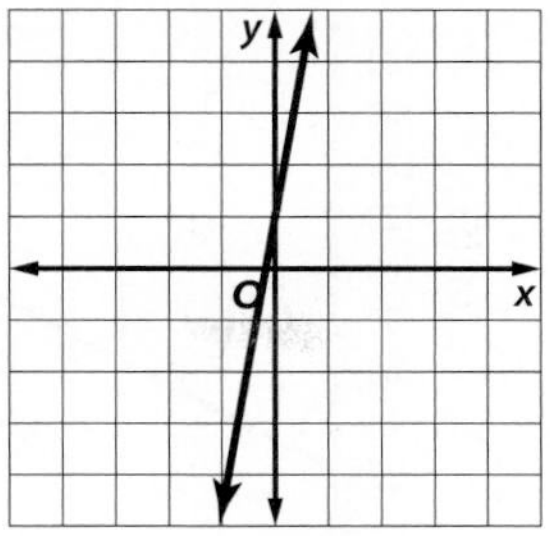

25.
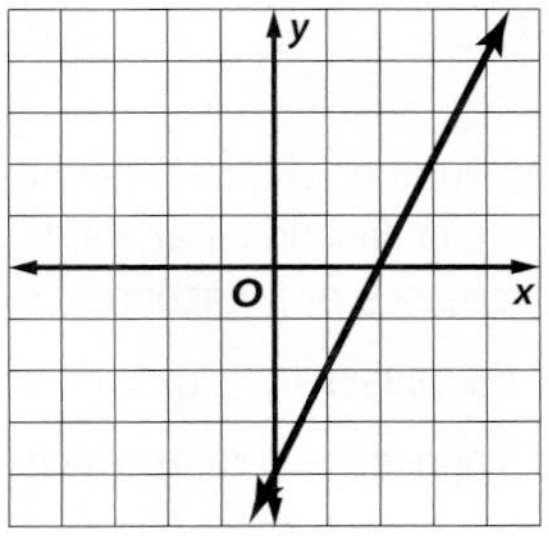

26.
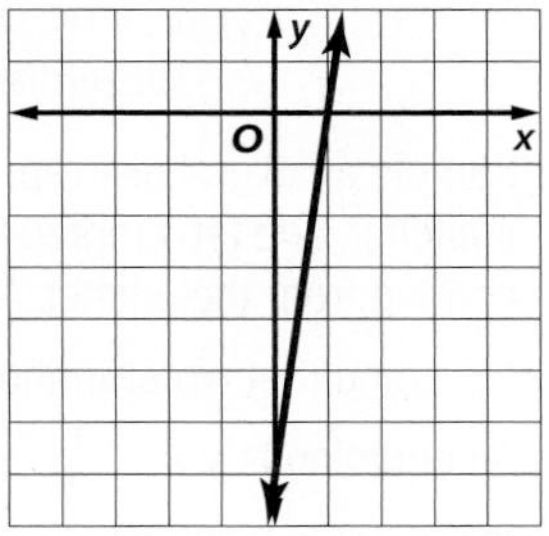

27.
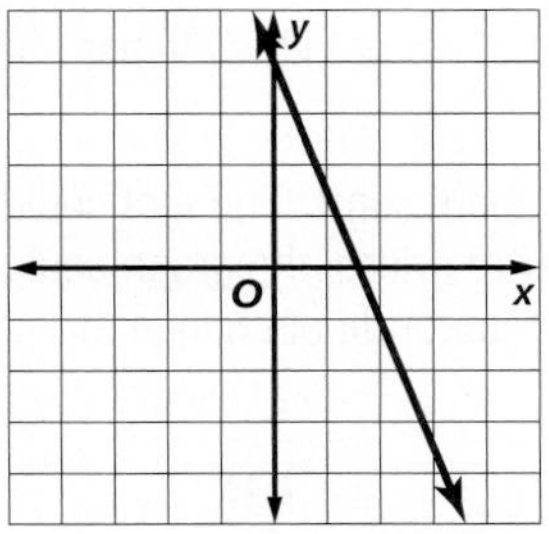

28.
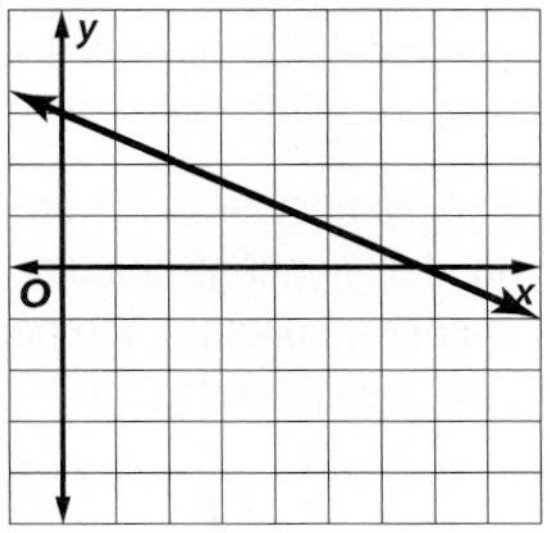

29.
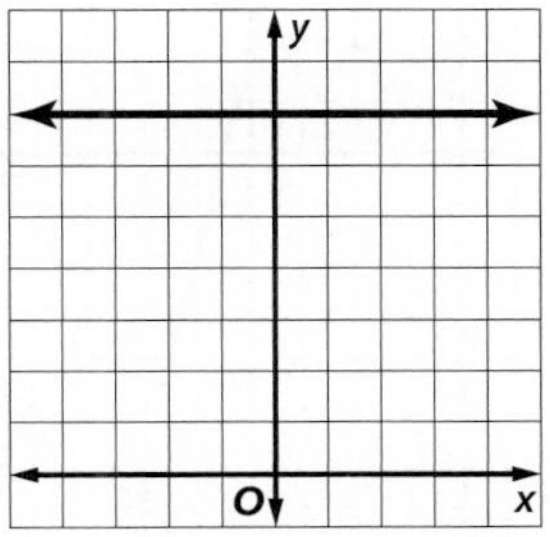

30.
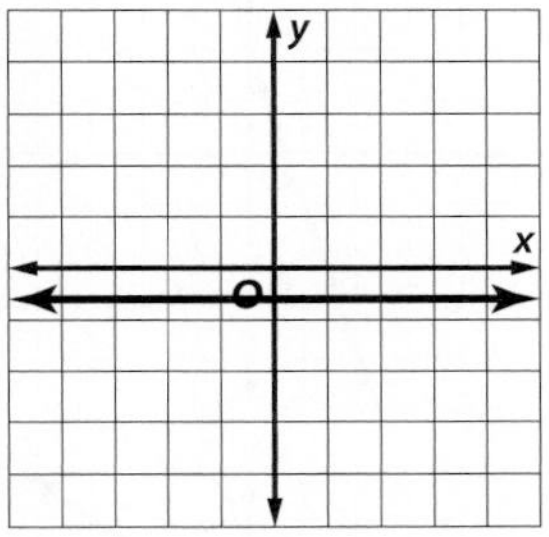

31.
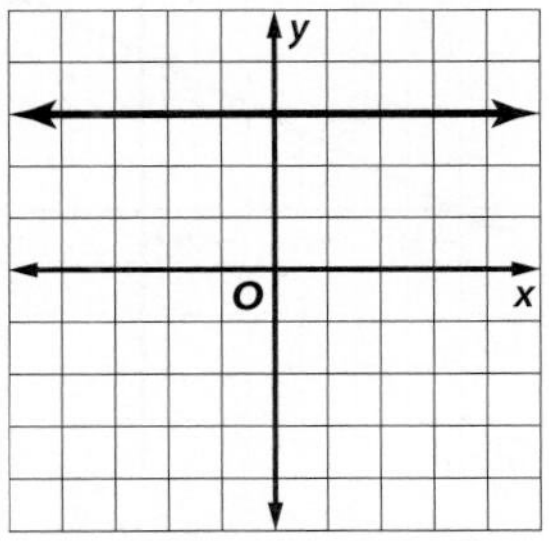

32.
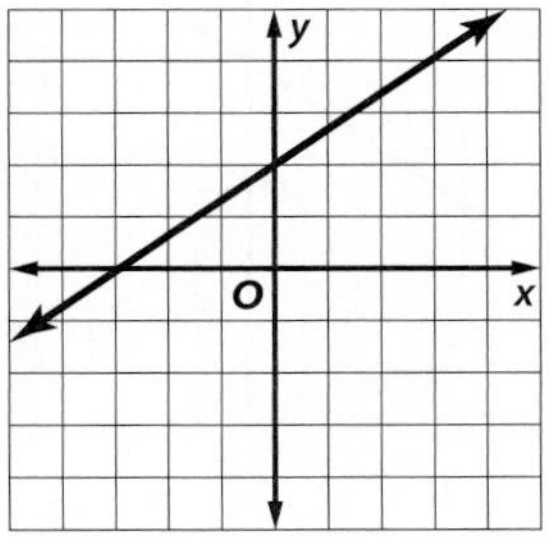

44.
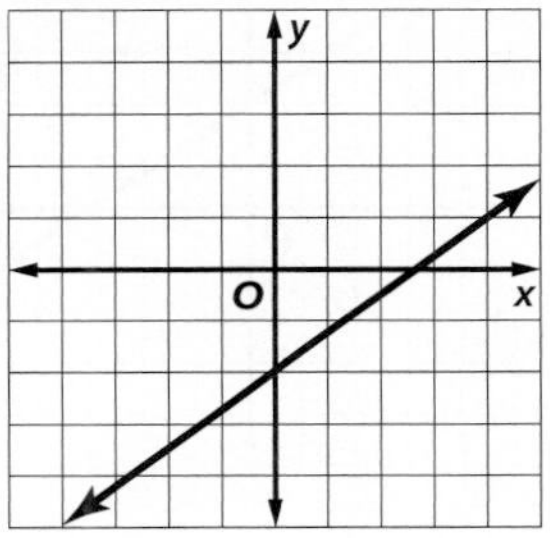

45.
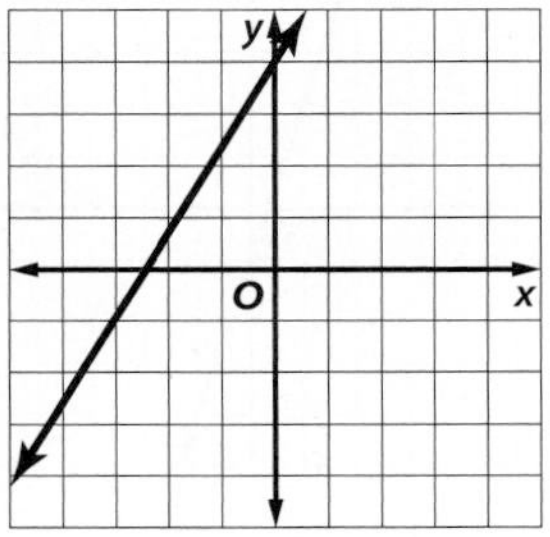

46.
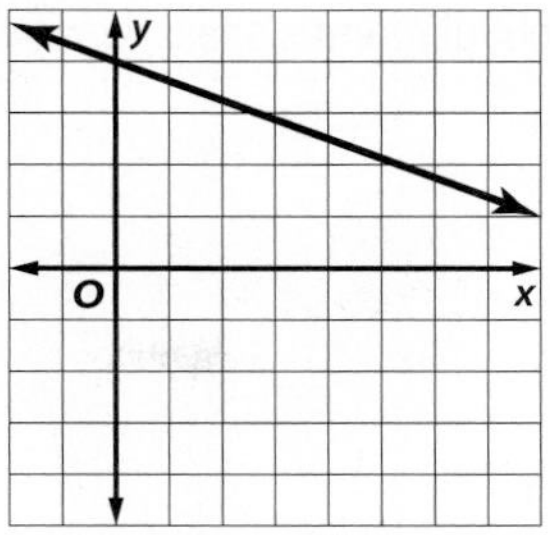

47.
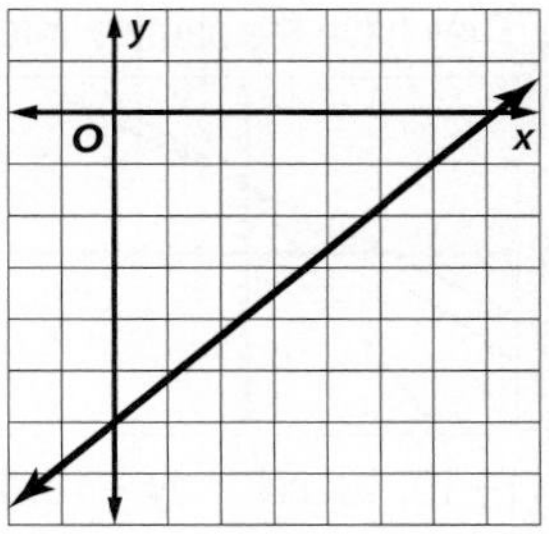

48.
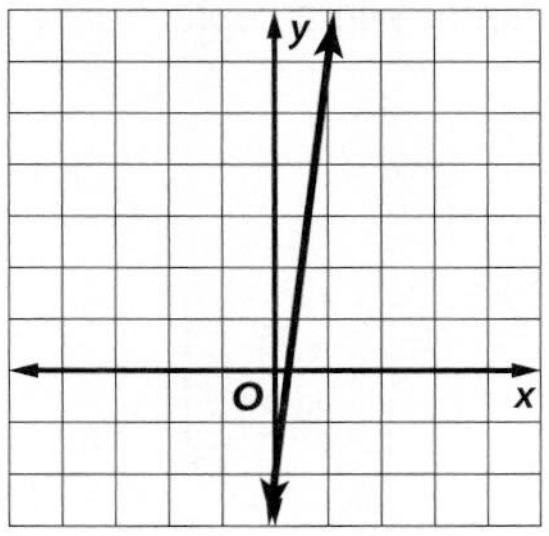

49.
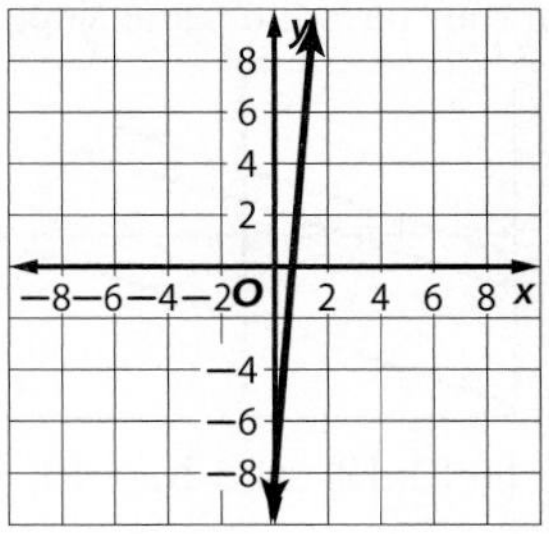

62. Sample answer: $y = x + 15$; The initial cost of joining a movie club is \$15. Then each movie costs \$1 for a 1-night rental.

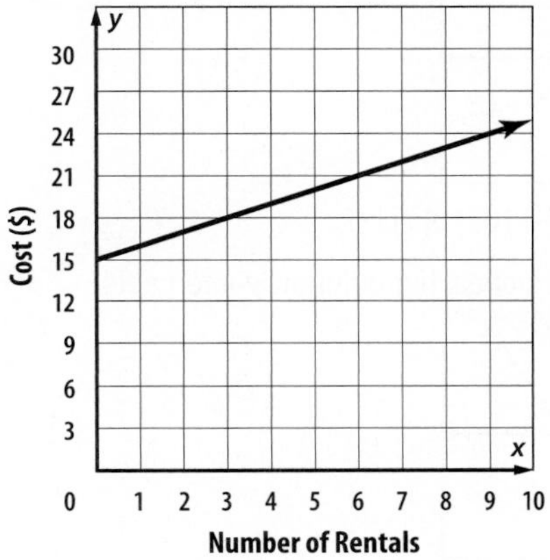

Extend 4-1

1. They have the same slope, but different *y*-intercepts.

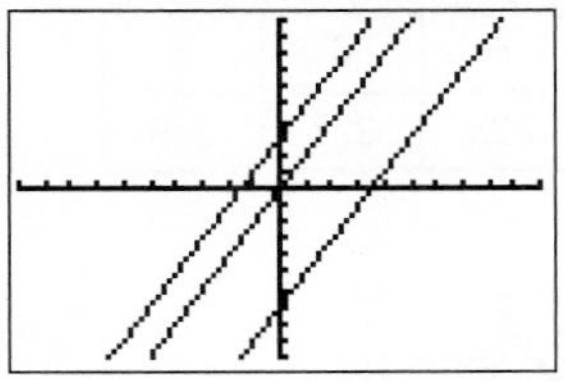

[−10, 10] scl: 1 by [−10, 10] scl: 1

2. They have the same *y*-intercept, but different slopes.

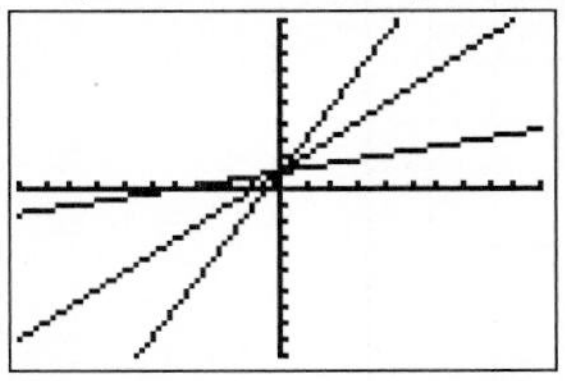

[−10, 10] scl: 1 by [−10, 10] scl: 1

3. They have the same y-intercept, but different slopes.

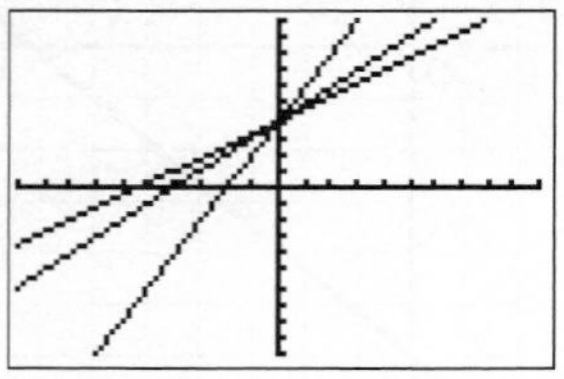

$[-10, 10]$ scl: 1 by $-10, 10]$ scl: 1

4. They have the same slope, but different y-intercepts.

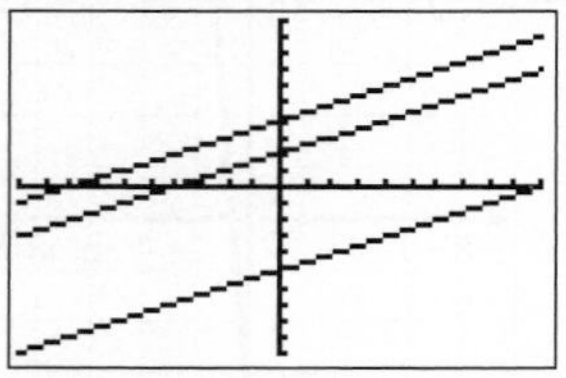

$[-10, 10]$ scl: 1 by $-10, 10]$ scl: 1

5. They have the same y-intercept, but different slopes.

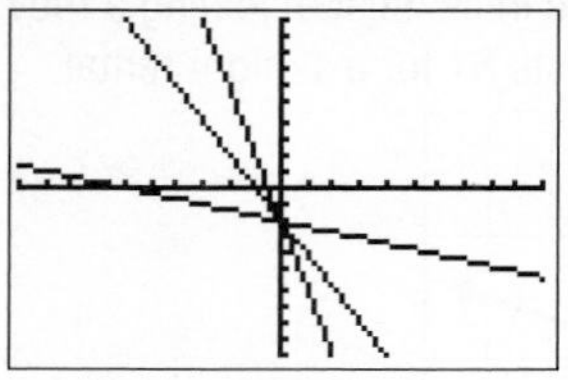

$[-10, 10]$ scl: 1 by $[-10, 10]$ scl: 1

6. They have the same slopes, but different y-intercepts.

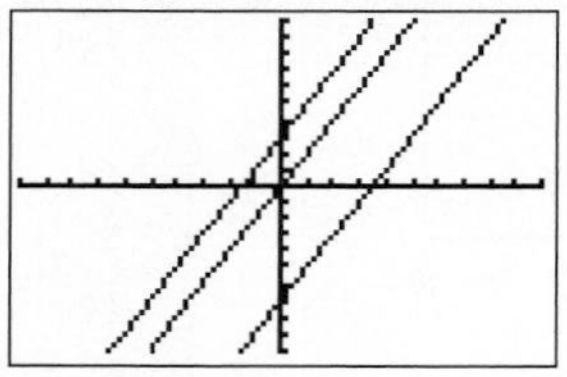

$[-10, 10]$ scl: 1 by $[-10, 10]$ scl: 1

Lesson 4-2

45b.

Number of Tickets	3	4	6	7
Cost ($)	171	223	327	379

45c. $431

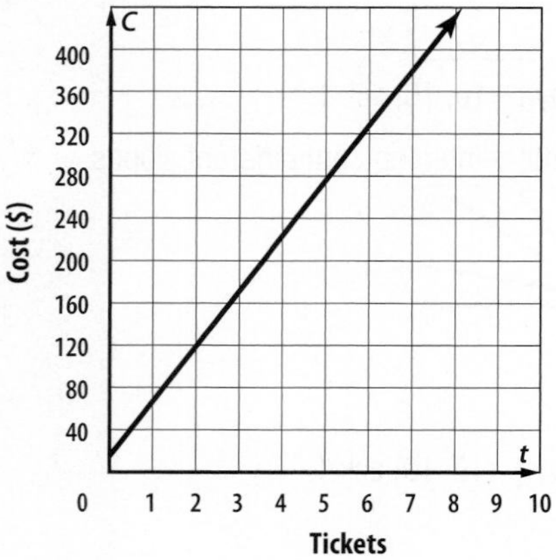

46c.

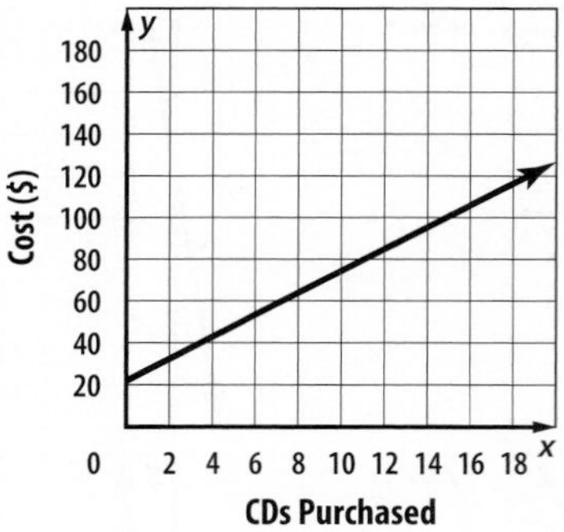

50. Sample answer: Let y represent the number of quarts of water in a pitcher, and let x represent the time in seconds that water is pouring from the pitcher. As time increases by 1 second, the amount of water in the pitcher decreases by $\frac{1}{2}$ qt. An equation is $y = -\frac{1}{2}x + 4$. The slope is the rate at which the water is leaving the pitcher, $\frac{1}{2}$ quart per second. The y-intercept represents the amount of water in the pitcher when it is full, 4 qt.

51. Sample answer: If the problem is about something that could suddenly change, such as weather or prices, the graph could suddenly spike up. You need a constant rate of change to produce a linear graph.

57.

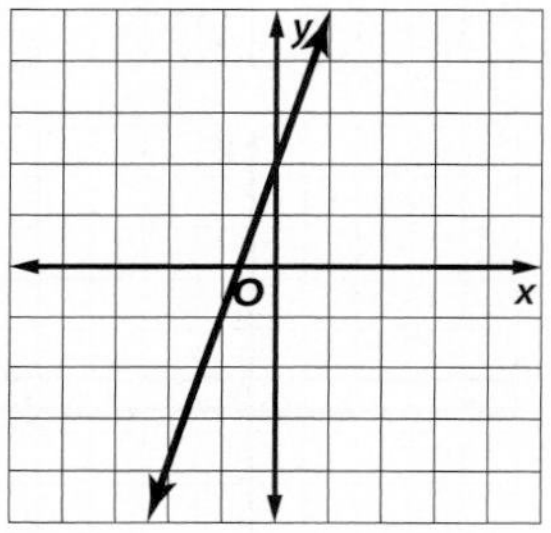

58.

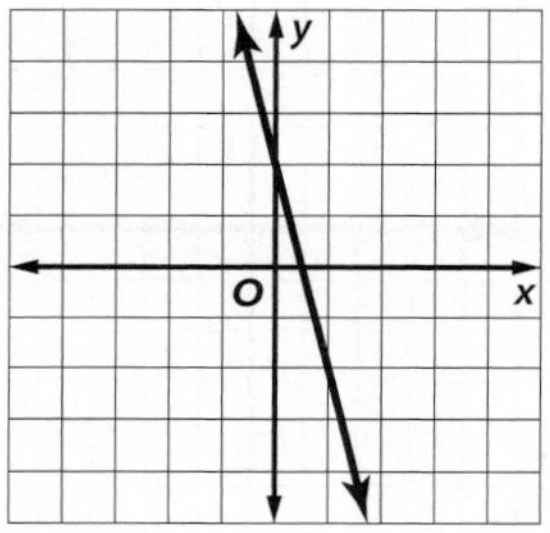

59.

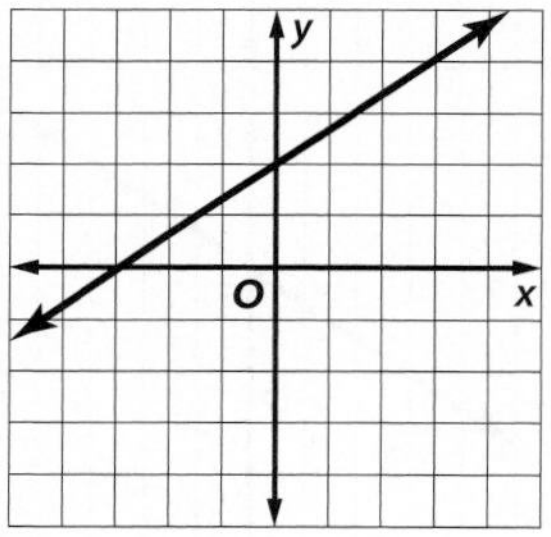

60.

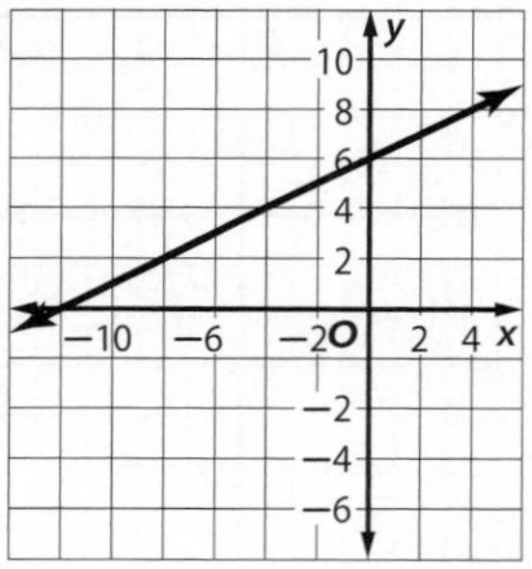

61.

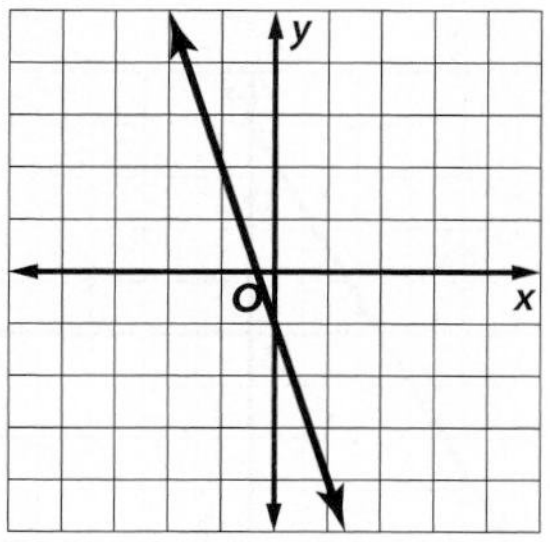

62.

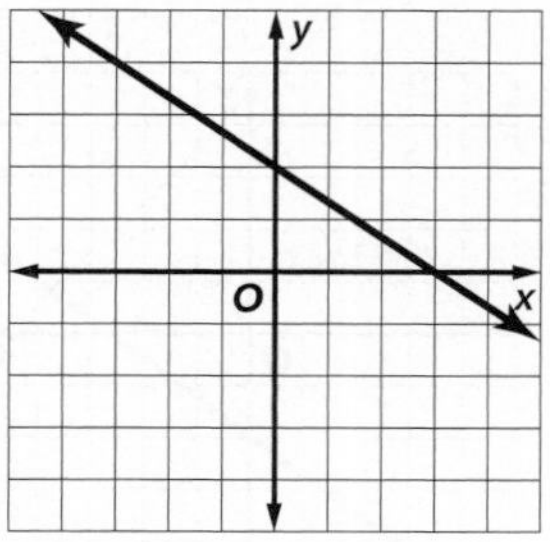

Lesson 4-3 (Guided Practice)

1.

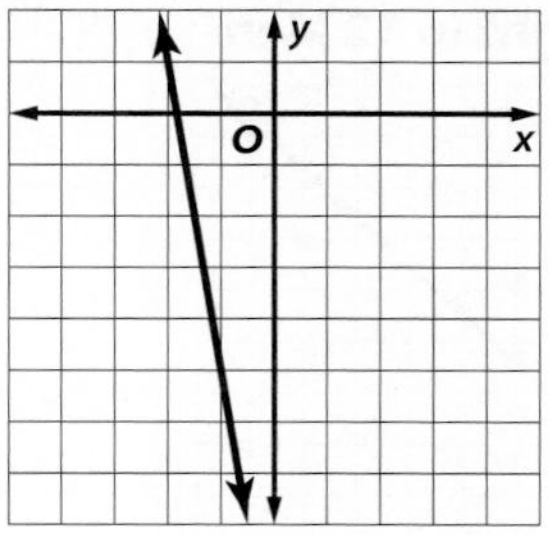

Lesson 4-3

1. $y - 5 = -6(x + 2)$

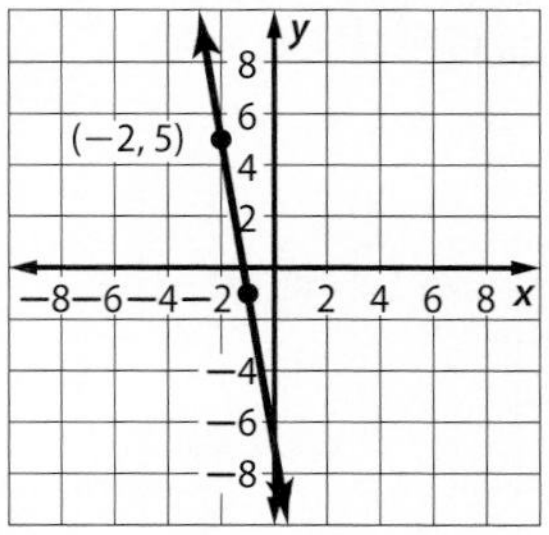

2. $y + 8 = \frac{5}{6}(x + 2)$

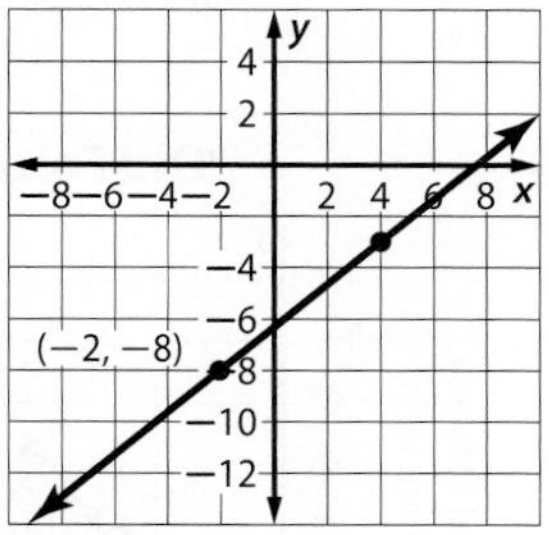

3. $y - 3 = -\frac{1}{2}(x - 4)$

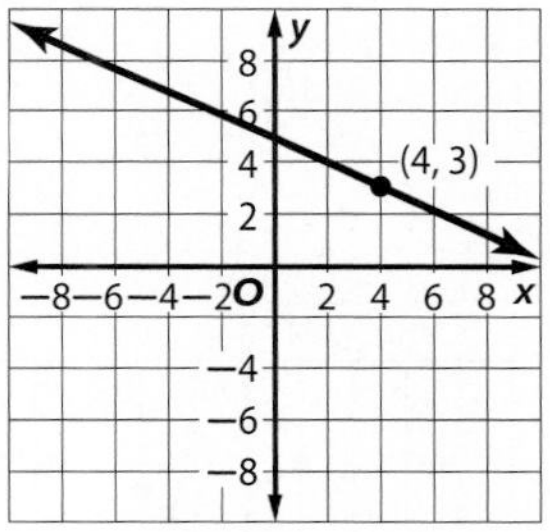

11.

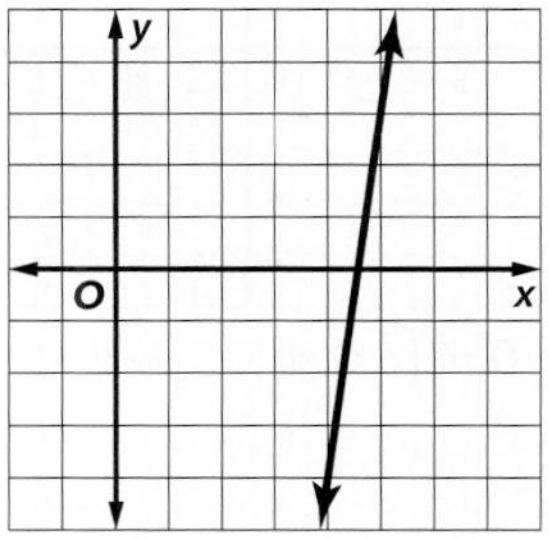

12.

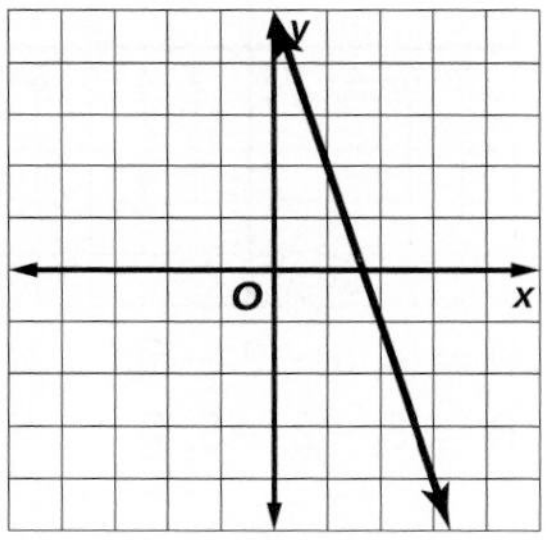

13.

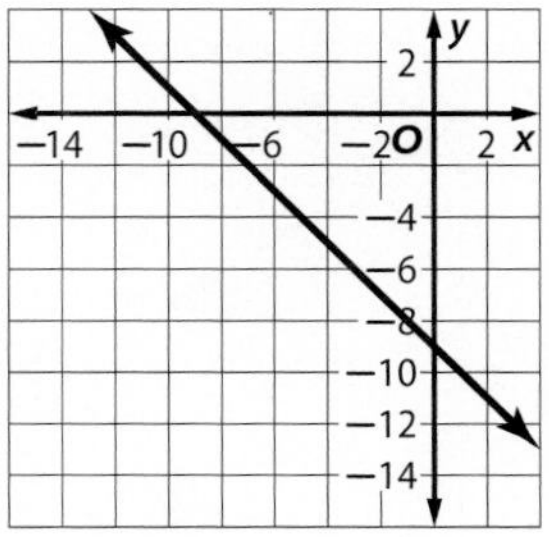

14.

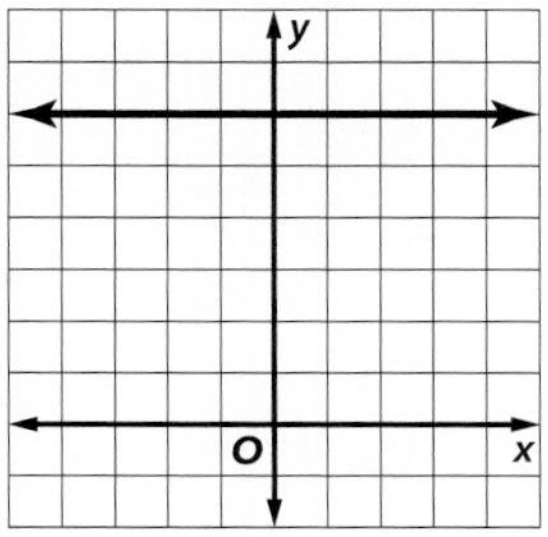

15.

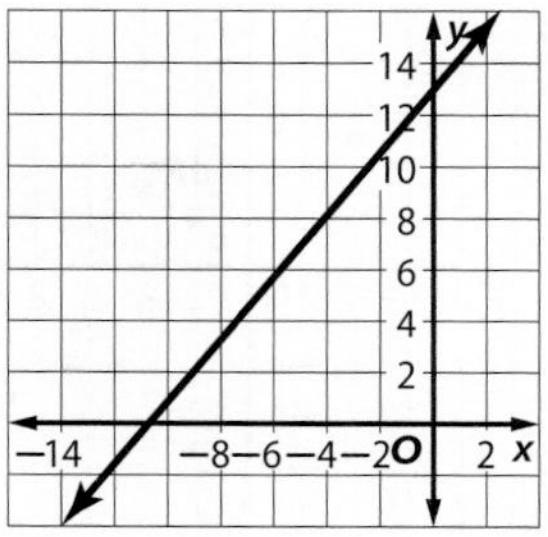

16.

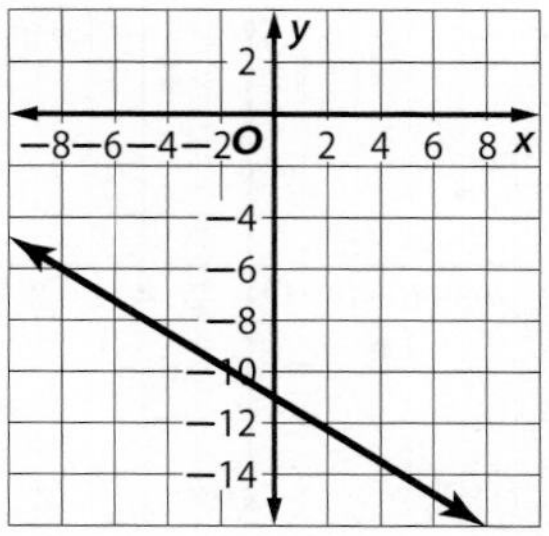

17.

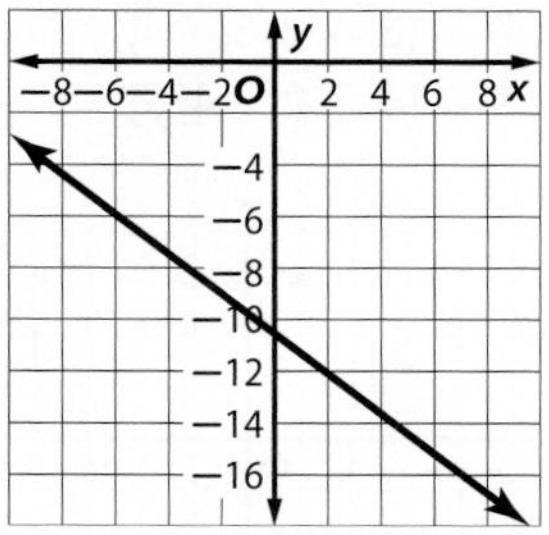

18.

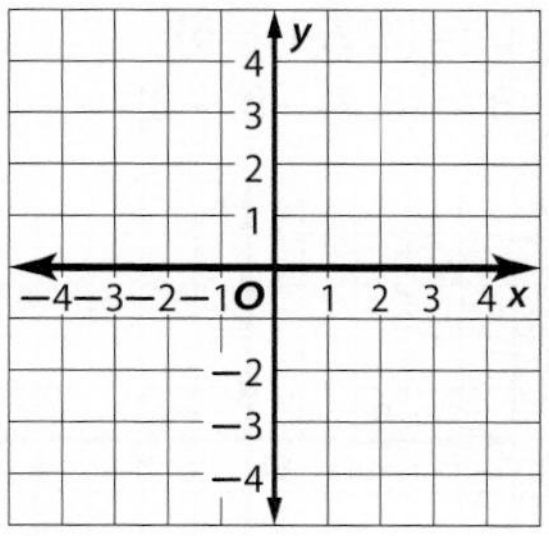

54. Sample answer: Depending on what information is given and what the problem is, it might be easier to represent a linear equation in one form over another. For example, if you are given the slope and the *y*-intercept, you could represent the equation in slope-intercept form. If you are given a point and the slope, you could represent the equation in point-slope form. If you are trying to graph an equation using the *x*- and *y*-intercepts, you could represent the equation in standard form.

Lesson 4-4

43a.

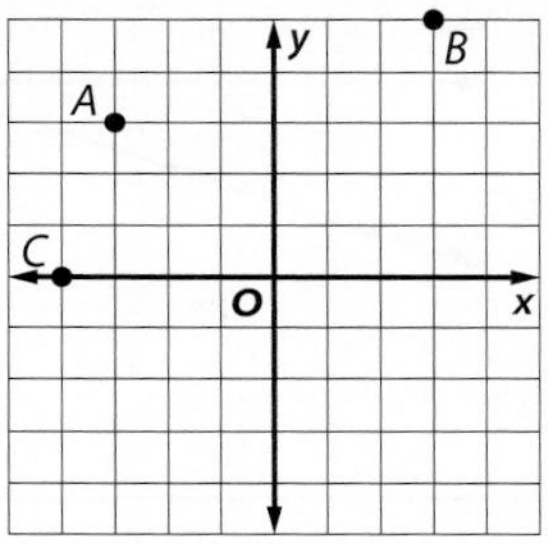

43b. Sample answer: (2, 2); $\overline{AB}$ and $\overline{CD}$ both have slope $\frac{1}{3}$, $\overline{AC}$ and $\overline{BD}$ both have slope 3.

43c. Two; sample answer: Move *C* to (−2, 0) and move *D* to (4, 2). Moving *C* changes the slope of $\overline{AC}$ to −3. This is the opposite reciprocal of the slope of $\overline{AB}$, $\frac{1}{3}$. Moving *D* also changes the slope of $\overline{BD}$ so $\overline{BD}$ is perpendicular to $\overline{AB}$ and $\overline{CD}$ and it is parallel to $\overline{AC}$.

48. Sample answer: If two lines have the same slope, then the lines are parallel. If the product of their slopes equals −1, then the lines are perpendicular. The graph of $y = \frac{3}{2}x$ is parallel to the graph of $y = \frac{2}{3}x - 1$ because they have the same slope, $\frac{3}{2}$. The graph of $y = -\frac{2}{3}x$ is perpendicular to the graph of $y = \frac{3}{2}x - 1$ because the slopes are opposite reciprocals of each other.

70.

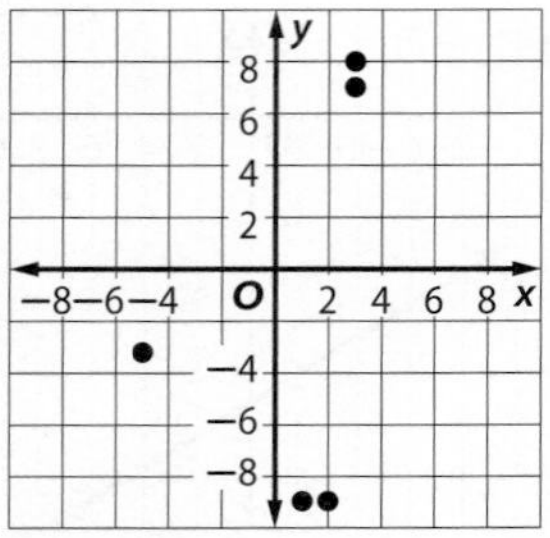

D = {3, 2, 1, −5};
R = {8, 7, −9, −3}

71.

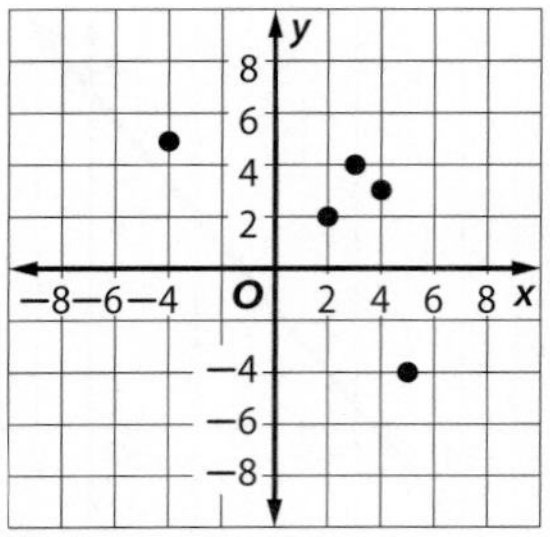

D = {3, 4, 2, 5, −4};
R = {4, 3, 2, −4, 5}

72.

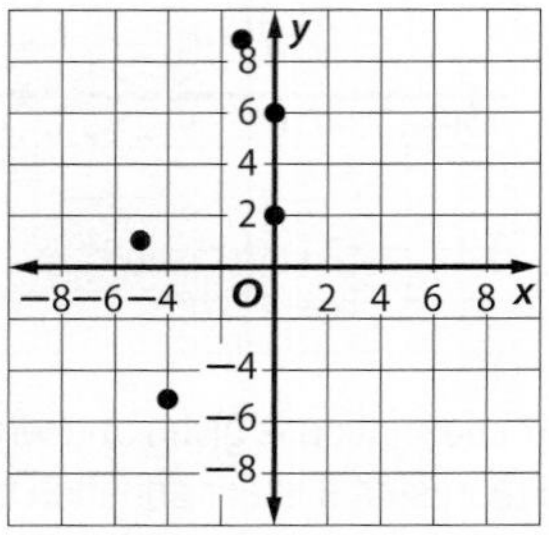

D = {0, −5, −1, −4}
R = {2, 1, 6, 9, −5}

73.

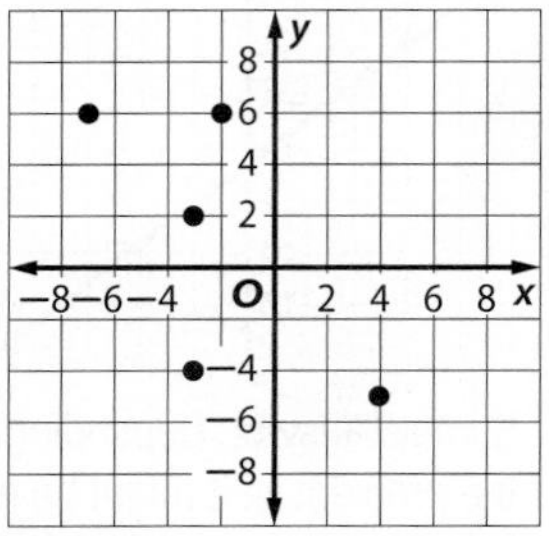

D = {−7, −3, 4, −2};
R = {6, −4, −5, 2}

Mid-Chapter Quiz

3.

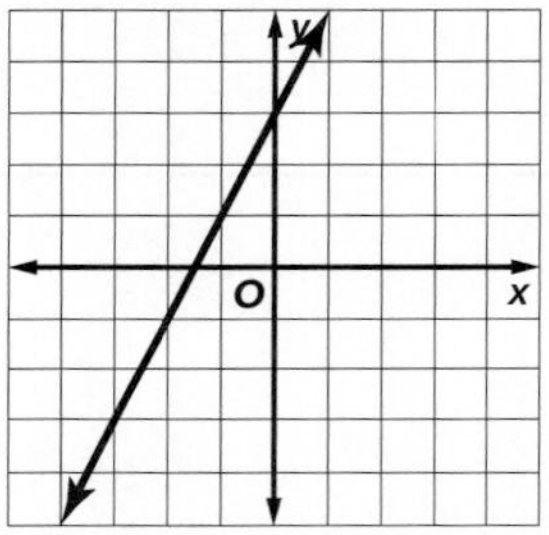

4.

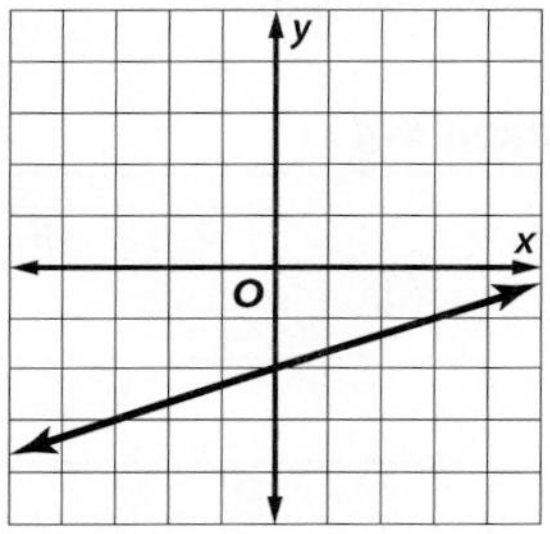

Lesson 4-5 (Guided Practice)

2. The independent variable is the year, and the dependent variable is the amount of sales; negative correlation.

CD Sales

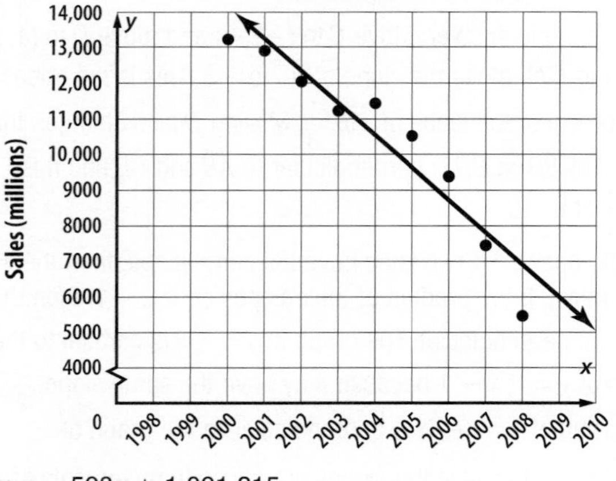

$y = -593x + 1{,}091{,}215$

Lesson 4-5

10a, b.

Height vs. Weight in 12 Men

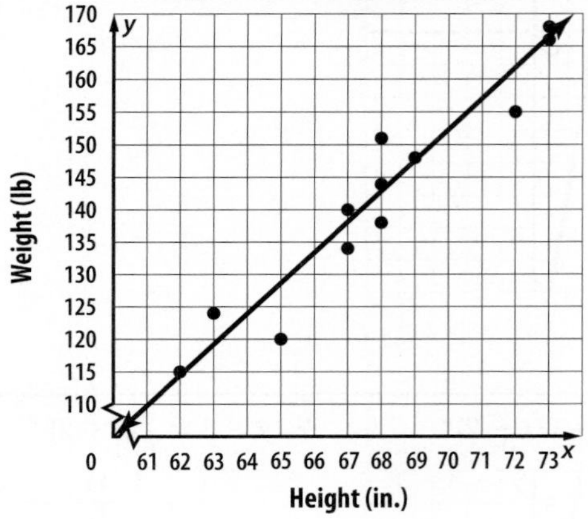

11a.

"Old Faithful"

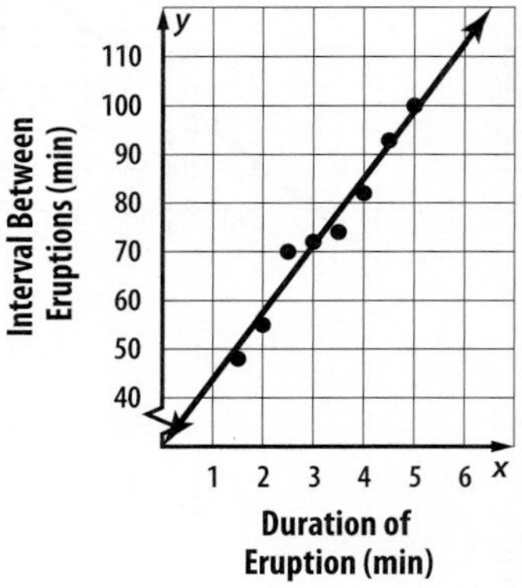

42.

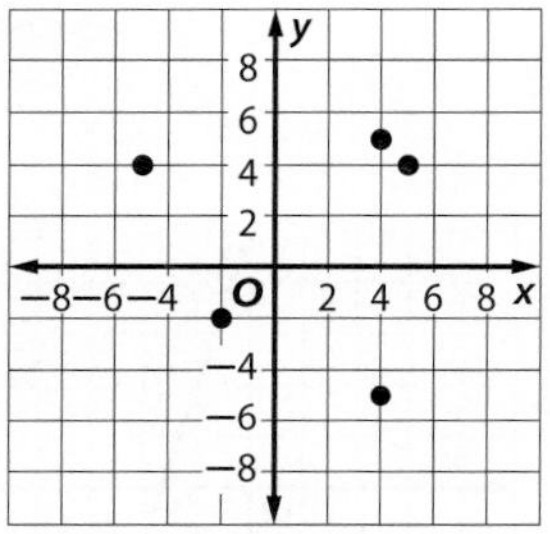

D = {4, 5, −2, −5};
R = {5, −2, −5, 4}

43.

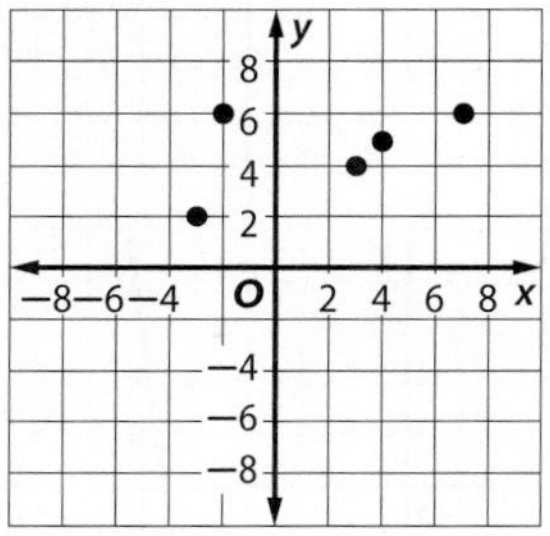

D = {7, 3, 4, −2, −3};
R = {6, 4, 5, 2}

Extend 4-5

Step 1

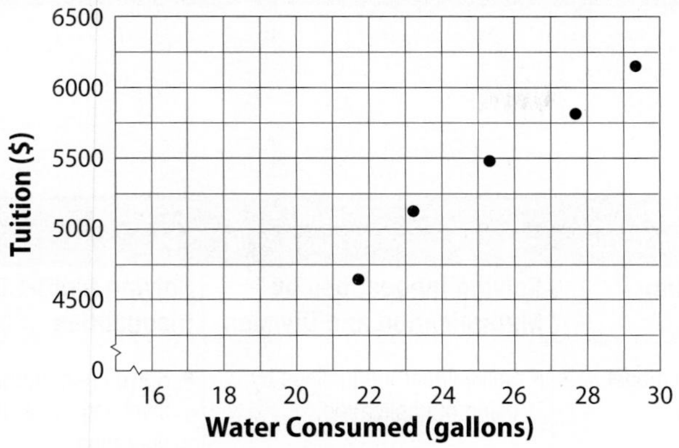

1. Correlation; a controlled experiment must be performed to show causation. This was just a survey. Other factors that might be involved could include an inherited trait from parents for nearsightedness or a disease.

2. Causation; this was a controlled experiment. Other factors that might be involved could include dangerous chemicals encountered in the environment or an inherited trait for developing cancer.

3. Correlation; a survey cannot show causation. Other factors that might be involved could be economic. Students riding the bus may come from families that do not have extra money to spare for alternate transportation or cell phones.

4. Causation; this was a controlled experiment. Other factors that might be involved could include loud noise encountered in the environment or workplace or an inherited trait for developing a hearing loss.

5. Correlation; it is not known if this was a controlled experiment or a survey. Other factors that might be involved include the fact the more people swim in the ocean and eat ice cream during hot months.

Lesson 4-6

15.

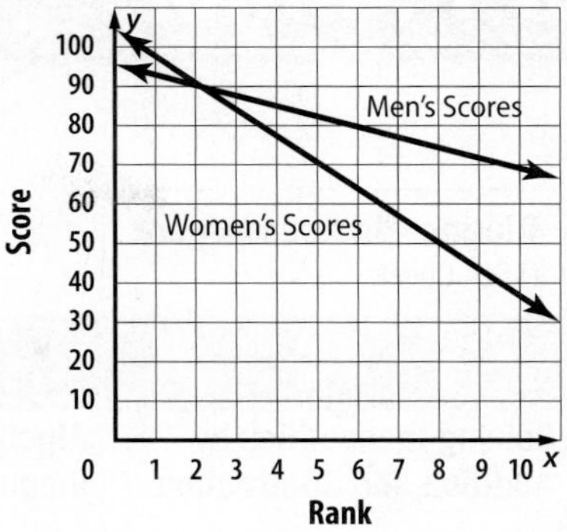

Sample answer: Men: $y = -2.92x + 95.92$; Women: $y = -7x + 106$; Women's scores have a steeper slope.

16. Apply a linear regression model to the data. Use the number of each test as the independent variable and the score on each test as the dependent variable. If there is no correlation, the r value will not be close to 1 or -1. If this is the case, the line of fit could not be used to predict the scores of the other students.

18. Sample answer: Both lines of fit and linear regression are used to model data. However, you could have numerous lines of fit, while linear regression results in one line of best fit. If linear regression is used, you can also use the correlation coefficient to see how closely the model fits the data.

Chapter Planner

Diagnostic Assessment
Quick Check

	LESSON 5-1 **45 min:** 1 day **90 min:** 0.5 day	EXPLORE 5-2 **45 min:** 0.5 day **90 min:** 0.5 day	LESSON 5-2 **45 min:** 1.5 days **90 min:** 0.75 day	LESSON 5-3 **45 min:** 1 day **90 min:** 0.5 day
Title	**Solving Inequalities by Addition and Subtraction**	**Algebra Lab: Solving Inequalities**	**Solving Inequalities by Multiplication and Division**	**Solving Multi-Step Inequalities**
Objectives	▪ Solve linear inequalities by using addition. ▪ Solve linear inequalities by using subtraction.	▪ Use algebra tiles to model solving inequalities.	▪ Solve linear inequalities by using multiplication. ▪ Solve linear inequalities by using division.	▪ Solve linear inequalities involving more than one operation. ▪ Solve linear inequalities involving the Distributive Property.
Key Vocabulary	set-builder notation			
Content Standards	PS.2, PS.4, AI.L.1, AI.L.2	AI.L.1	PS.6, AI.L.1, AI.L.2	AI.L.1, AI.L.2
Multiple Representations				
Lesson Resources	connectED.mcgraw-hill.com Leveled Worksheets Vocabulary Personal Tutor Virtual Manipulatives Self-Check Quiz ▪ *5-Minute Check* ▪ *Study Notebook* ▪ *Teaching Algebra with Manipulatives*	connectED.mcgraw-hill.com Animations Virtual Manipulatives ▪ *Teaching Algebra with Manipulatives* **Materials:** ▪ algebra tiles ▪ equation mats ▪ self-adhesive blank note	connectED.mcgraw-hill.com Leveled Worksheets Quiz 1 Animations Personal Tutor Virtual Manipulatives Self-Check Quiz ▪ *5-Minute Check* ▪ *Study Notebook* ▪ *Teaching Algebra with Manipulatives*	connectED.mcgraw-hill.com Leveled Worksheets Quiz 2 Animations Personal Tutor Virtual Manipulatives Self-Check Quiz ▪ *5-Minute Check* ▪ *Study Notebook*
Resources for Every Lesson	IWB eStudent Edition IWB Interactive Classroom	▪ eTeacher Edition ▪ eSolutions Manual ▪ McGraw-Hill eAssessment		
Differentiated Instruction	pp. 287, 290		pp. 293, 297	pp. 300, 303

Formative Assessment
Mid-Chapter Quiz

IWB All digital assets are Interactive Whiteboard ready.

Suggested Pacing			
Time Periods	Instruction	Review & Assess	Total
45-minute	9 days	2 days	11 days
90-minute	5 days	1 day	6 days

EXPLORE 5-4 **45 min:** 0.5 day **90 min:** 0.5 day	LESSON 5-4 **45 min:** 1.5 days **90 min:** 0.75 day	LESSON 5-5 **45 min:** 1 day **90 min:** 0.75 day	LESSON 5-6 **45 min:** 1.5 days **90 min:** 0.5 day	EXTEND 5-6 **45 min:** 0.5 day **90 min:** 0.25 day
Algebra Lab: Reading Compound Statements	**Solving Compound Inequalities**	**Inequalities Involving Absolute Value**	**Graphing Inequalities in Two Variables**	**Graphing Technology Lab: Graphing Inequalities**
▪ Identify compound statements connected by the word *and* or *or* as true or false.	▪ Solve compound inequalities containing the word *and* and graph their solution set. ▪ Solve compound inequalities containing the word *or* and graph their solution set.	▪ Solve and graph absolute value inequalities (<). ▪ Solve and graph absolute value inequalities (>).	▪ Graph linear inequalities on the coordinate plane. ▪ Solve inequalities by graphing.	▪ Use a graphing calculator to investigate the graphs of inequalities.
	compound inequality, intersection, union		boundary, half-plane closed (open) half-plane	
AI.L.8	PS.1, PS.8, AI.L.8	PS.3, PS.7	AI.L.7	PS.5, AI.L.7
connectED.mcgraw-hill.com ▪ *Teaching Algebra with Manipulatives*	connectED.mcgraw-hill.com Leveled Worksheets Vocabulary Animations Personal Tutor Virtual Manipulatives Self-Check Quiz ▪ *5-Minute Check* ▪ *Study Notebook* ▪ *Teaching Algebra with Manipulatives*	connectED.mcgraw-hill.com Leveled Worksheets Quiz 3 Animations Personal Tutor Virtual Manipulatives Self-Check Quiz ▪ *5-Minute Check* ▪ *Study Notebook*	connectED.mcgraw-hill.com Leveled Worksheets Quiz 4 Vocabulary Animations Personal Tutor Virtual Manipulatives Self-Check Quiz ▪ *5-Minute Check* ▪ *Study Notebook* ▪ *Teaching Algebra with Manipulatives*	connectED.mcgraw-hill.com Personal Tutor **Materials:** ▪ TI-83/84 Plus or other graphing calculator
IWB eStudent Edition IWB Interactive Classroom	▪ eTeacher Edition ▪ eSolutions Manual ▪ McGraw-Hill eAssessment			
	pp. 310, 311	pp. 313, 316	pp. 319, 322	

Summative Assessment
Study Guide and Review
Practice Test

Assessment and Intervention

SE = Student Edition, **TE** = Teacher Edition, **CRM** = Chapter Resource Masters

DIAGNOSTIC ASSESSMENT

Diagnosis	Prescription
Beginning Chapter 5	
Get Ready for Chapter 5 **SE**	Response to Intervention **TE**
Beginning Every Lesson	
Then, Now, Why? **SE** 5-Minute Check	Chapter 0 **SE** *Quick Review Math Handbook*

FORMATIVE ASSESSMENT

Diagnosis	Prescription
During/After Every Lesson	
Guided Practice **SE**, every example Check Your Understanding **SE** H.O.T. Problems **SE** Spiral Review **SE** Additional Examples **TE** Watch Out! **TE** Step 4, Assess **TE** Chapter 5 Quizzes **CRM**, pp. 45–46 Self-Check Quizzes connectED.mcgraw-hill.com	TIER 1 Intervention Skills Practice **CRM**, Ch. 1–5 connectED.mcgraw-hill.com TIER 2 Intervention Differentiated Instruction **TE** Differentiated Homework Options **TE** Study Guide and Intervention **CRM**, Ch. 1–5 *Quick Review Math Handbook* TIER 3 Intervention *Math Triumphs, Alg. 1*
Mid-Chapter	
Mid-Chapter Quiz **SE** Mid-Chapter Test **CRM**, p. 47 McGraw-Hill eAssessment	TIER 1 Intervention Skills Practice **CRM**, Ch. 1–5 connectED.mcgraw-hill.com TIER 2 Intervention Study Guide and Intervention **CRM**, Ch. 1–5; *Quick Review Math Handbook* TIER 3 Intervention *Math Triumphs, Alg. 1*
Before Chapter Test	
Chapter Study Guide and Review **SE** Practice Test **SE** Standardized Test Practice **SE** Chapter Test connectED.mcgraw-hill.com Standardized Test Practice connectED.mcgraw-hill.com Vocabulary Review connectED.mcgraw-hill.com McGraw-Hill eAssessment	TIER 1 Intervention Skills Practice **CRM**, Ch. 1–5 connectED.mcgraw-hill.com TIER 2 Intervention Study Guide and Intervention **CRM**, Ch. 1–5; *Quick Review Math Handbook* TIER 3 Intervention *Math Triumphs, Alg. 1*

SUMMATIVE ASSESSMENT

Diagnosis	Prescription
After Chapter 5	
Multiple-Choice Tests, Forms 1, 2A, 2B **CRM**, pp. 49–54 Free-Response Tests, Forms 2C, 2D, 3 **CRM**, pp. 55–60 Vocabulary Test **CRM**, p. 48 Extended Response Test **CRM**, p. 61 Standardized Test Practice **CRM**, pp. 62–64 McGraw-Hill eAssessment	Study Guide and Intervention **CRM**, Ch. 1–5 *Quick Review Math Handbook* connectED.mcgraw-hill.com

Differentiated Instruction

Option 1 Reaching All Learners AL OL BL ELL

Visual/Spatial On a transparency sheet draw a large number line with two dashed horizontal guide-lines above it. Alternatively, the number line and guide-lines could be drawn on a sheet of paper that is then laminated. Give students a compound inequality written as two sentences. Have students use a dry-erase marker to plot the solution for each inequality on one of the dashed guide-lines. If the inequality involves "and," have students wipe away any parts that are not on both dashed lines. This leaves a clear picture of what part of the number line should be used for the solution.

Logical Begin by writing $x - 12 = 8$ on the board. Review the Addition and Subtraction Properties of Equality as you solve for x. Then erase all the equals signs and replace them with $>$.

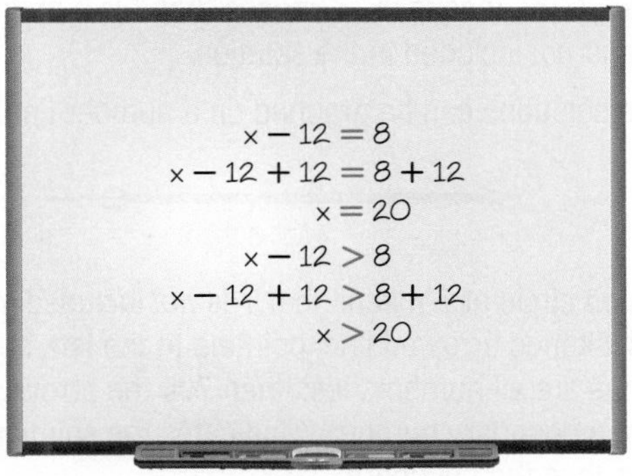

Discuss the similarities. Repeat using each of the inequality signs.

Option 2 Approaching Level AL

On self-sticking notes, write +, −, >, and <. Have students write an inequality involving a negative coefficient of x on their paper, such as [−] 4x [>] [+] 8, using the self-sticking notes for the symbols. Explain that since the coefficient of x is negative, all the signs in the inequality must change to their opposites, [+] 4x [<] [−] 8. Explain that by doing this they can solve for x without concern for the inequality sign.

Option 3 English Learners ELL

If students are having difficulty choosing the correct symbol for the problem's wording, have them use the chart on p. 287 to write each common inequality phrases on an index card and the appropriate inequality symbol on the back of the card. As students solve verbal problems, such as Example 4 on p. 287, they can pick the card that has the same wording as the problem. The back of the card will reveal the appropriate inequality symbol to use.

Option 4 Beyond Level BL

Have students work in pairs to develop two sets of inequalities. When graphed, the overlap of the solution sets of one pair form a triangle and the solution set of the other forms a square. This activity can be extended to include trapezoids and parallelograms. For example, when

$2x - y \geq -1$
$x + y \leq 4$ are graphed, a triangle is formed.
$x + 4y \geq 4$

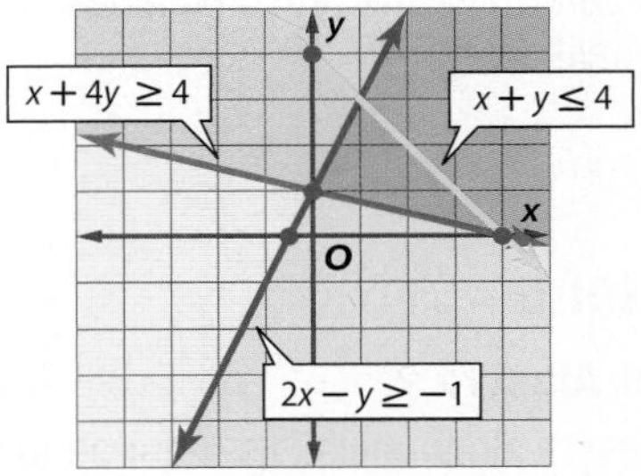

Students are often fascinated by the concept of infinity. Challenge students to think about the infinite nature of certain concepts using questions similar to the following:

- Is a half-plane really half of the plane or can it be more or less? Explain your reasoning.
- Does the solution set $\{x \mid x > 2\}$ contain an infinite set of numbers? Why or why not?
- Does the solution set $\{x \mid 2 < x < 2.5\}$ contain an infinite set of numbers? Why or why not?

Focus on Mathematical Content

VerticalAlignment

Before Chapter 5

Related Topics before Grade 8

- use Venn diagrams for displaying relationships

Previous Topics from Algebra 1

- use the Distributive Property to simplify algebraic equations
- transform and solve linear equations
- graph equations of lines

Chapter 5

Related Topics from Algebra 1

- formulate linear inequalities to solve problems
- investigate methods for solving linear inequalities using the Properties of Inequality
- solve linear inequalities
- interpret and determine the reasonableness of solutions to linear inequalities

After Chapter 5

Preparation for Algebra 2

- use the necessary algebraic skills required to solve equations and inequalities in problem situations
- use algebraic methods, graphs, or tables to solve systems of inequalities
- solve quadratic inequalities using graphs, tables, and algebraic methods

Lesson-by-LessonPreview

5-1 Solving Inequalities by Addition and Subtraction

Some equations are solved using the Addition and Subtraction Properties of Equality to isolate the variable, having a coefficient of 1, on one side of the equals sign (Lesson 2-2). Some inequalities are solved in much the same way.

The Addition and Subtraction Properties of Inequality state that any number added to or subtracted from each side of a true inequality, results in a true inequality.

The solution to inequalities can be expressed in more than one way.

- The solutions can be written in set-builder notation. For example: $\{x \mid x < 7\}$.

  This is read as *the set of all numbers x such that x is less than 7.* The inequality $<$ means that 7 is a boundary number and is *not* included in the solution.
- The solutions can be graphed on a number line. For example:

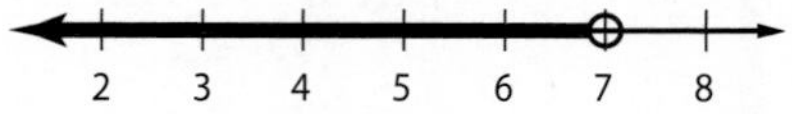

The open circle at 7 means that 7 is *not* included in the solution. The blackened arrowed line, pointing to the left, shows that the solutions are all numbers less than 7. If the arrow points to the right of a boundary number, it indicates the solutions are greater than the boundary.

If the inequality is $\geq$ or $\leq$, the boundary number is included in the solution, and a solid circle is placed at the boundary number on the number line.

5-2 Solving Inequalities by Multiplication and Division

Some equations are solved using the Multiplication and Division Properties of Equality to solve for a variable having a coefficient other than 1 (Lesson 2-2). Some inequalities are solved in much the same way, but there is one main difference.

When multiplying or dividing each side of an inequality by the same negative number, the direction of the inequality symbol must be reversed.

5-3 Solving Multi-Step Inequalities

Multi-step inequalities can be solved with the same process used for solving multi-step equations (Lesson 2-3). These equations can be solved using the Properties of Inequality and the strategy of undoing each operation by working backward. After each side is simplified using the Distributive Property and/or by combining like terms, work in the opposite order of the order of operations. The Addition and Subtraction Properties of Inequality are applied first, followed by the Multiplication or Division Property of Inequalities.

- If the inequality simplifies to a statement that is never true, such as $4 > 8$, the solution is the empty set, $\varnothing$, which has no members.
- If the solution results in a statement that is always true, such as $5 > 3$, then the solution is the set of all real numbers, $\{x \mid x \text{ is a real number}\}$.

5-4 Solving Compound Inequalities

If two inequalities are joined by the words *and* or *or*, the result is a compound inequality.

- If a compound inequality contains the word *and*, the solution must be a solution to both inequalities. The graph of the solution is the intersection of the graphs of the two inequalities.
- If the compound inequality contains the word *or*, the solution must be a solution to either *one* or *both* inequalities. The graph of the solution is the *union* of the graphs of the two inequalities.

The properties used to solve compound inequalities are the same as those used to solve any inequality.

5-5 Inequalities Involving Absolute Value

Absolute value inequalities can also be solved algebraically by writing them as compound inequalities.

When compound absolute inequalities are being solved, there are two cases to consider.

Case 1	The expression inside the absolute value symbol is positive or 0.
Case 2	The expression inside the absolute value symbol is negative.

If $n > 0$, then:
For $|x| < n$, the solution set is $\{x \mid -n < x < n\}$.
For $|x| \le n$, the solution set is $\{x \mid -n \le x \le n\}$.
For $|x| > n$, the solution set is $\{x \mid x > n \text{ or } x < -n\}$.
For $|x| \ge n$, the solution set is $\{x \mid x \ge n \text{ or } x \le -n\}$.

5-6 Graphing Inequalities in Two Variables

The solution set of a linear inequality, like that of a linear equation, is the set of all ordered pairs that makes the statement true. Like the solution set of an equation in two variables (Lesson 3-1), the solution set of an inequality in two variables is graphed on a coordinate plane. However, the solution set of a linear inequality is not linear. The graph of a linear inequality has the following characteristics.

- It has a linear boundary.

First graph the inequality as if it were an equation. This determines the boundary line. Use a solid line if the inequality is $\le$ or $\ge$. Use a dashed line if the inequality is $<$ or $>$.

- It covers a region called a half-plane.

Select a point in either half-plane determined by the boundary line and test it in the inequality. If the resulting statement is true, shade the half-plane that contains that point. If the statement is false, shade the other half-plane.

Professional Development

Targeted professional development has been articulated throughout Algebra 1. More quality, customized professional development is available from McGraw-Hill Professional Development. Visit connectED.mcgraw-hill.com for details on each product.

- Online Lessons emphasize the strategies and techniques used to teach Algebra 1. Includes streaming video, interactive pages, and online tools.
- Video Workshops allow mentors, coaches, or leadership personnel to facilitate on-site workshops on educational strategies in mathematics and mathematical concepts.
- MHPD Online (www.mhpdonline.com) offers online professional development with video clips of instructional strategies, links, student activities, and news and issues in education.
- Teaching Today (teachingtoday.glencoe.com) gives secondary teachers practical strategies and materials that inspire excellence and innovation in teaching.

Chapter Project

Caring For Our BFFs

Students use what they have learned about inequalities to complete a project.

This chapter project addresses entrepreneurial literacy, as well as several specific skills identified as being essential to student success by the Framework for 21st Century Learning.

Visit connectED.mcgraw-hill.com for student and teacher handouts.

KeyVocabulary Introduce the key vocabulary in the chapter using the routine below.

Define: A half-plane is a region on a coordinate plane where graphs of ordered pairs are filled.

Example:

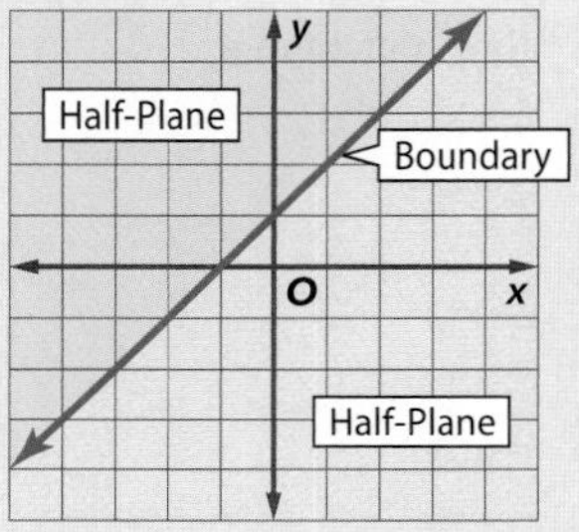

Ask: How many half-planes are in this graph? two

CHAPTER 5 Linear Inequalities

Then

You solved linear equations.

Now

In this chapter, you will:

- Solve one-step and multi-step inequalities.
- Solve compound inequalities and inequalities involving absolute value.
- Graph inequalities in two variables.

Why?

PETS In the United States, about 75 million dogs are kept as pets. Approximately 16% of these were adopted from animal shelters. About 14% of dog owners own more than 3 dogs.

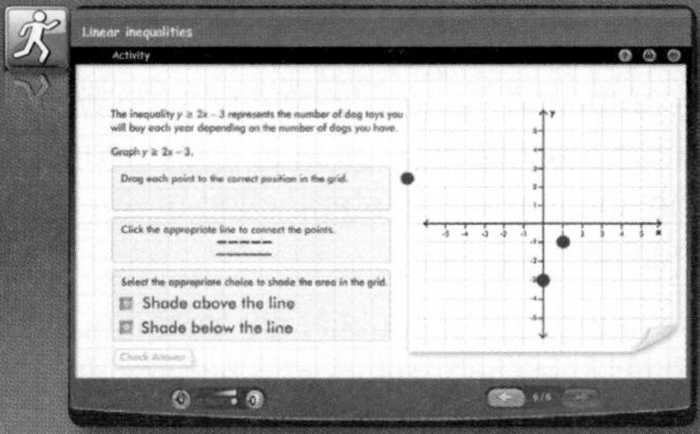

connectED.mcgraw-hill.com Your Digital Math Portal

Animation | Vocabulary | eGlossary | Personal Tutor | Virtual Manipulatives | Graphing Calculator | Audio | Foldables | Self-Check Practice | Worksheets

Content Standards
AI.L.1, AI.L.2, AI.L.7, AI.L.8

Process Standards
PS.1, PS.2, PS.3, PS.4, PS.5, PS.6, PS.7, PS.8

Get Ready for the Chapter

Diagnose Readiness | You have two options for checking prerequisite skills.

1 Textbook Option Take the Quick Check below. Refer to the Quick Review for help.

QuickCheck

Evaluate each expression for the given values.

1. $3x + y$ if $x = -4$ and $y = 2$ -10
2. $-2m + 3k$ if $m = -8$ and $k = 3$ 25
3. CARS The expression $\frac{m \text{ mi}}{g \text{ gal}}$ represents the gas mileage of a car. Find the gas mileage of a car that goes 295 miles on 12 gallons of gasoline. Round to the nearest tenth. 24.6

Solve each equation.

4. $x - 4 = 9$ 13
5. $x + 8 = -3$ -11
6. $4x = -16$ -4
7. $\frac{x}{3} = 7$ 21
8. $2x + 1 = 9$ 4
9. $4x - 5 = 15$ 5
10. $9x + 2 = 3x - 10$ -2
11. $3(x - 2) = -2(x + 13)$ -4
12. FINANCIAL LITERACY Claudia opened a savings account with $325. She saves $100 per month. Write an equation to determine how much money d, she has after m months. $d = 100m + 325$

Solve each equation.

13. $|x + 11| = 18$ $\{-29, 7\}$
14. $|3x - 2| = 16$ $\left\{-\frac{14}{3}, 6\right\}$
15. SURVEYS In a survey, 32% of the people chose pizza as their favorite food. The results were reported to within 2% accuracy. What is the maximum and minimum percent of people who chose pizza? 34%, 30%

QuickReview

Example 1 (Used in Lessons 5-1 through 5-6)

Evaluate $-3x^2 + 4x - 6$ if $x = -2$.

$-3x^2 + 4x - 6$	Original expression
$= -3(-2)^2 + 4(-2) - 6$	Replace x with -2.
$= -3(4) + 4(-2) - 6$	Evaluate the power.
$= -12 + (-8) - 6$	Multiply.
$= -26$	Add and subtract.

Example 2 (Used in Lessons 5-1 through 5-6)

Solve $-2(x - 4) = 7x - 19$.

$-2(x - 4) = 7x - 19$	Original equation
$-2x + 8 = 7x - 19$	Distributive Property
$-2x + 8 + 2x = 7x - 19 + 2x$	Add $2x$ to each side.
$8 = 9x - 19$	Simplify.
$8 + 19 = 9x - 19 + 19$	Add 19 to each side.
$27 = 9x$	Simplify.
$3 = x$	Divide each side by 3.

Example 3 (Used in Lesson 5-5)

Solve $|x - 4| = 9$.

If $|x - 4| = 9$, then $x - 4 = 9$ or $x - 4 = -9$.

$x - 4 = 9$	or	$x - 4 = -9$
$x - 4 + 4 = 9 + 4$		$x - 4 + 4 = -9 + 4$
$x = 13$		$x = -5$

So, the solution set is $\{-5, 13\}$.

2 Online Option Take an online self-check Chapter Readiness Quiz at connectED.mcgraw-hill.com.

Get Ready for the Chapter

Response to Intervention (RtI)

Use the *Quick Check* results and the Intervention Planner chart to help you determine your Response to Intervention. The If-Then statements in the chart below help you decide the appropriate tier of RtI and suggest intervention resources for each tier.

InterventionPlanner

TIER 1 On Level OL

If students miss about 25% of the exercises or less,

Then choose a resource:

SE Lessons 1-2, 2-2, 2-3, and 2-5

Skills Practice, Chapter 1, p. 13, Chapter 2, pp. 13, 19, 32,

TE Chapter Project

connectED.mcgraw-hill.com Self-Check Quiz

TIER 2 Strategic Intervention AL approaching grade level

If students miss about 50% of the exercises,

Then choose a resource:

Study Guide and Intervention, Chapter 1, pp. 11–12, Chapter 2, pp. 11–12, 17–18, 30–31

connectED.mcgraw-hill.com Extra Examples, Personal Tutor, Homework Help

TIER 3 Intensive Intervention 2 or more grades below level

If students miss about 75% of the exercises,

Then use *Math Triumphs, Alg. 1*

connectED.mcgraw-hill.com Extra Examples, Personal Tutor, Homework Help, Review Vocabulary

Essential Questions

- How are symbols useful in mathematics?
  Sample answer: Symbols allow you to express mathematical concepts in a condensed form.
- What mathematical symbols do you know?
  Sample answers: addition, subtraction, multiplication, division, equals sign, greater than, less than, grouping symbols, pi

FOLDABLES® StudyOrganizer

Dinah Zike's Foldables®

Focus Students write about the different ways inequalities can be solved as these methods are presented in the lessons of this chapter.

Teach Have students make label their Foldables as illustrated. Students should fill in the appropriate sections with their notes, diagrams, and examples as they cover each lesson in this chapter.

When to Use It Encourage students to add to their Foldables as they work through the chapter and to use them to review for the chapter test.

Differentiated Instruction

Student-Built Glossary, pp. 1–2

Students should complete the chart by providing a definition of each term and an example as they progress through Chapter 5. This study tool can also be used to review for the chapter test.

Get Started on the Chapter

You will learn several new concepts, skills, and vocabulary terms as you study Chapter 5. To get ready, identify important terms and organize your resources. You may wish to refer to Chapter 0 to review prerequisite skills.

FOLDABLES® StudyOrganizer

Linear Inequalities Make this Foldable to help you organize your Chapter 5 notes about linear inequalities. Begin with a sheet of 11" by 17" paper.

1 **Fold** each side so the edges meet in the center.

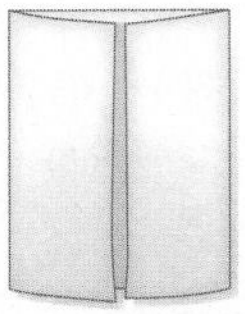

2 **Fold** in half.

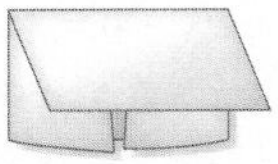

3 **Unfold** and cut from each end until you reach the vertical line.

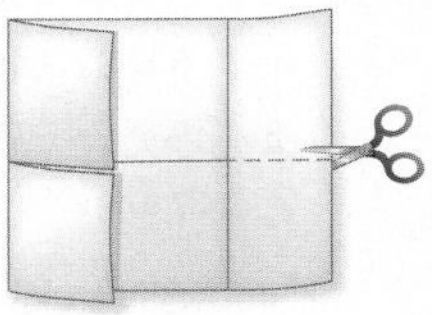

4 **Label** the front of each flap.

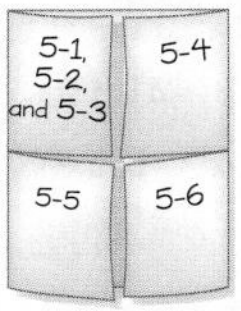

NewVocabulary

English		Español
inequality	p. 285	desigualdad
set-builder notation	p. 286	notación de construcción de conjuntos
compound inequality	p. 306	desigualdad compuesta
intersection	p. 306	intersección
union	p. 307	unión
boundary	p. 317	frontera
half-plane	p. 317	semiplano
closed half-plane	p. 317	semiplano cerrada
open half-plane	p. 317	semiplano abierto

ReviewVocabulary

equivalent equations ecuaciones equivalentes equations that have the same solution

linear equation ecuación lineal an equation in the form $Ax + By = C$, with a graph consisting of points on a straight line

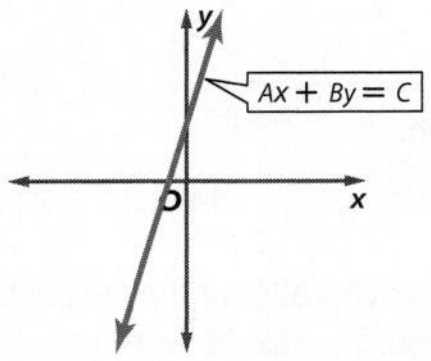

solution set conjunto solución the set of elements from the replacement set that makes an open sentence true

LESSON 5-1 Solving Inequalities by Addition and Subtraction

Then

- You solved equations by using addition and subtraction.

Now

1. Solve linear inequalities by using addition.
2. Solve linear inequalities by using subtraction.

Why?

- The data in the table show that the recommended daily allowance of Calories for girls 11–14 years old is less than that of girls between 15–18 years old.

Calories	
Girls 11–14 Years	Girls 15–18
1845	2110

Source: Vital Health Zone

$$1845 < 2110$$

If a 13-year-old girl and a 16-year-old girl each eat 150 more Calories in a day than is suggested, the 16-year-old will still eat more Calories.

$$1845 + 150 \ \underline{?}\ 2110 + 150$$
$$1995 < 2260$$

NewVocabulary
inequality
set-builder notation

Content Standards
AI.L.1, AI.L.2

Process Standards
PS.2, PS.4

1 Solve Inequalities by Addition

An open sentence that contains <, >, ≤, or ≥ is an **inequality**. The example above illustrates the Addition Property of Inequalities.

KeyConcept Addition Property of Inequalities

Words If the same number is added to each side of a true inequality, the resulting inequality is also true.

Symbols For all numbers *a*, *b*, and *c*, the following are true.

1. If $a > b$, then $a + c > b + c$.
2. If $a < b$, then $a + c < b + c$.

This property is also true for ≥ and ≤.

Example 1 Solve by Adding

Solve $x - 12 \geq 8$. Check your solution.

$x - 12 \geq 8$ — Original inequality

$x - 12 + 12 \geq 8 + 12$ — Add 12 to each side.

$x \geq 20$ — Simplify.

The solution is the set {all numbers greater than or equal to 20}.

CHECK To check, substitute three different values into the original inequality: 20, a number less than 20, and a number greater than 20.

GuidedPractice

Solve each inequality. Check your solution.

1A. $22 > m - 8$ {all numbers less than 30}

1B. $d - 14 \geq -19$ {all numbers greater than or equal to −5}

connectED.mcgraw-hill.com 285

1 Focus

VerticalAlignment

Before Lesson 5-1 Solve equations by using addition and subtraction.

Lesson 5-1 Solve linear inequalities by using addition and subtraction.

After Lesson 5-1 Solve systems of inequalities.

2 Teach

Scaffolding Questions

Have students read the **Why?** section of the lesson.

Ask:

- If both girls eat 200 fewer Calories than the recommended daily allowance, will the 13-year old eat fewer Calories than the 16-year old? Explain. Yes; $1845 - 200 = 1645$ and $2110 - 200 = 1910$, and $1645 < 1910$.
- If the two girls eat the same number of Calories over or under the daily allowance, is it ever possible that they will eat an equal number of Calories? Explain. No; the inequality between the two daily allowances is not changed by adding or subtracting the same amount on each side.

Lesson 5-1 Resources

Resource	Approaching Level AL	On Level OL	Beyond Level BL	English Learners ELL
Teacher Edition	▪ Differentiated Instruction, p. 287	▪ Differentiated Instruction, p. 289	▪ Differentiated Instruction, p. 290	▪ Differentiated Instruction, p. 287
Chapter Resource Masters	▪ Study Guide and Intervention, pp. 5–6 ▪ Skills Practice, p. 7 ▪ Practice, p. 8 ▪ Word Problem Practice, p. 9	▪ Study Guide and Intervention, pp. 5–6 ▪ Skills Practice, p. 7 ▪ Practice, p. 8 ▪ Word Problem Practice, p. 9 ▪ Enrichment, p. 10	▪ Practice, p. 8 ▪ Word Problem Practice, p. 9 ▪ Enrichment, p. 10	▪ Study Guide and Intervention, pp. 5–6 ▪ Skills Practice, p. 7 ▪ Practice, p. 8 ▪ Word Problem Practice, p. 9
Other	▪ 5-Minute Check 5-1 ▪ Study Notebook ▪ Teaching Algebra with Manipulatives	▪ 5-Minute Check 5-1 ▪ Study Notebook ▪ Teaching Algebra with Manipulatives	▪ 5-Minute Check 5-1 ▪ Study Notebook	▪ 5-Minute Check 5-1 ▪ Study Notebook ▪ Teaching Algebra with Manipulatives

1 Solve Inequalities by Addition

Example 1 shows how to solve a linear inequality using the Addition Property of Inequalities.

Formative Assessment

Use the Guided Practice exercises after each example to determine students' understanding of concepts.

Additional Example

1 Solve $c - 12 > 65$. Check your solution. $c > 77$ or {all numbers greater than 77}

Additional Examples also in Interactive Classroom PowerPoint® Presentations

IWB Interactive White Board READY

2 Solve Inequalities by Subtraction

Example 2 shows how to solve a linear inequality using the Subtraction Property of Inequalities. **Example 3** shows how to solve and graph a linear inequality with variables on each side. **Example 4** shows how to write and solve a linear inequality for a real-world problem.

Additional Example

2 STANDARDIZED TEST PRACTICE Solve the inequality $x + 23 < 14$.

A $\{x \mid x < -9\}$ **C** $\{x \mid x > -9\}$

B $\{x \mid x < 37\}$ **D** $\{x \mid x > 39\}$

A

ReadingMath

set-builder notation

$\{x \mid x \geq 20\}$ is read *the set of all numbers x such that x is greater than or equal to 20.*

A more concise way of writing a solution set is to use **set-builder notation**. In set-builder notation, the solution set in Example 1 is $\{x \mid x \geq 20\}$.

This solution set can be graphed on a number line. Be sure to check if the endpoint of the graph of an inequality should be a circle or a dot. If the endpoint is not included in the graph, use a circle, otherwise use a dot.

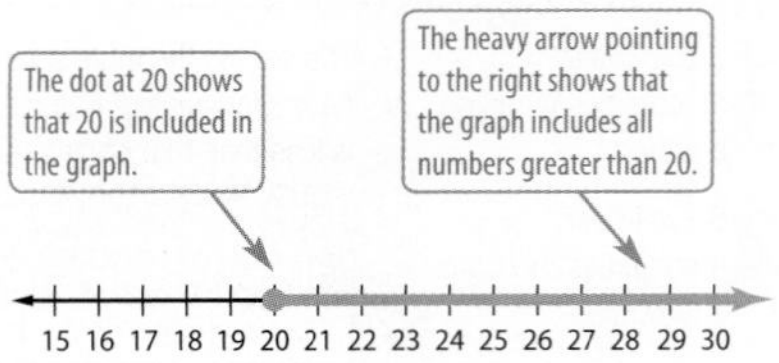

2 Solve Inequalities by Subtraction

Subtraction can also be used to solve inequalities.

KeyConcept Subtraction Property of Inequalities

Words	If the same number is subtracted from each side of a true inequality, the resulting inequality is also true.
Symbols	For all numbers *a*, *b*, and *c*, the following are true. **1.** If $a > b$, then $a - c > b - c$. **2.** If $a < b$, then $a - c < b - c$.

This property is also true for ≥ and ≤.

Test-TakingTip

Isolating the Variable When solving inequalities, the goal is to isolate the variable on one side of the inequality. This is the same as with solving equations.

Standardized Test Example 2 Solve by Subtracting

Solve $m + 19 > 56$.

A $\{m \mid m < 41\}$ **B** $\{m \mid m < 37\}$ **C** $\{m \mid m > 37\}$ **D** $\{m \mid m > 41\}$

Read the Test Item

You need to find the solution set for the inequality.

Solve the Test Item

Step 1 Solve the inequality.

$m + 19 > 56$	Original inequality
$m + 19 - \mathbf{19} > 56 - \mathbf{19}$	Subtract 19 from each side.
$m > 37$	Simplify.

Step 2 Write in set-builder notation: $\{m \mid m > 37\}$. The answer is C.

GuidedPractice

2. Solve $p + 8 \leq 18$. G

F $\{p \mid p \geq 10\}$ **G** $\{p \mid p \leq 10\}$ **H** $\{p \mid p \leq 26\}$ **J** $\{p \mid p \geq 126\}$

Tips for New Teachers

Set Builder Notation Reading set builder notation is new to students. Give them opportunities to practice reading sets aloud.

Tips for New Teachers

Sense-Making Advise students that an equation such as $5 = x$ can be written as $x = 5$ because of the Symmetric Property of Equality, but an inequality such as $3 > y$ cannot be written as $y > 3$. Remind students that the inequality sign always points to the lesser value, so in $3 > y$, the expression should be written as $y < 3$ if y is on the left side of the inequality.

Follow-up

Students have explored absolute value.

Ask:

- Why is it important to understand what the symbols in a mathematical sentence represent? Sample answer: If you are unsure of what the symbols represent, you may not translate a verbal representation into the correct algebraic representation.

Terms that are constants are not the only terms that can be subtracted. Terms with variables can also be subtracted from each side to solve inequalities.

StudyTip

Writing Inequalities Simplifying the inequality so that the variable is on the left side, as in $a \geq 6$, prepares you to write the solution set in set-builder notation.

Example 3 Variables on Each Side

Solve $3a + 6 \leq 4a$. Then graph the solution set on a number line.

$3a + 6 \leq 4a$ — Original inequality

$3a - 3a + 6 \leq 4a - 3a$ — Subtract $3a$ from each side.

$6 \leq a$ — Simplify.

Since $6 \leq a$ is the same as $a \geq 6$, the solution set is $\{a \mid a \geq 6\}$.

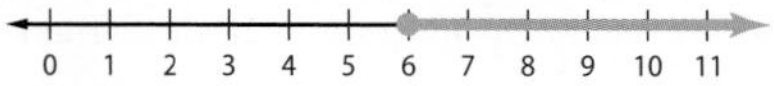

GuidedPractice

Solve each inequality. Then graph the solution set on a number line.

3A. $9n - 1 < 10n$ **3B.** $5h \leq 12 + 4h$ **3A–3B. See margin.**

Verbal problems containing phrases like *greater than* or *less than* can be solved by using inequalities. The chart shows some other phrases that indicate inequalities.

ConceptSummary Phrases for Inequalities

<	>	≤	≥
less than fewer than	greater than more than	at most, no more than, less than or equal to	at least, no less than, greater than or equal to

Real-World Example 4 Use an Inequality to Solve a Problem

Real-WorldLink

Leopard geckos are commonly yellow and white with black spots. They are nocturnal and easy to tame. They do not have toe pads like other geckos, so they do not climb.

Source: Exotic Pets

PETS **Felipe needs for the temperature of his leopard gecko's basking spot to be at least 82°F. Currently the basking spot is 62.5°F. How much warmer does the basking spot need to be?**

Words	The current temperature	needs to be	at least	82°F.
Variable	Let t = the number of degrees that the temperature needs to rise.			
Inequality	$62.5 + t$		$\geq$	82

$62.5 + t \geq 82$ — Original inequality

$62.5 + t - 62.5 \geq 82 - 62.5$ — Subtract 62.5 from each side.

$t \geq 19.5$ — Simplify.

Felipe needs to raise the temperature of the basking spot 19.5°F or more.

GuidedPractice

4. **SHOPPING** Sanjay has \$65 to spend at the mall. He bought a T-shirt for \$18 and a belt for \$14. If Sanjay wants a pair of jeans, how much can he spend? **no more than \$33**

DifferentiatedInstruction AL ELL

If students have trouble understanding some of the phrases used to indicate inequalities, such as *at most* or *no less than*,

Then have them work in pairs or groups to write word problems using the phrases. Have students write inequalities to represent the problem situations.

Additional Examples

3 Solve $12n - 4 \leq 13n$. Graph the solution set. $\{n \mid n \geq -4\}$

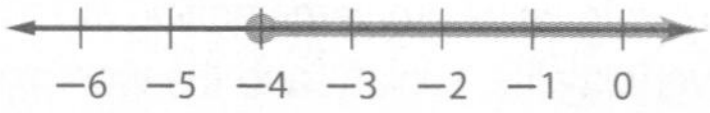

4 **ENTERTAINMENT** Panya wants to buy season passes to two theme parks. If one season pass costs \$54.99 and Panya has \$100 to spend on both passes, the second season pass must cost no more than what amount? The second season pass must cost no more than \$45.01.

Teach with Tech

Interactive Whiteboard Display a number line on the board. Give the class several exercises, and select students to come to the board to graph their solutions on the number line.

Focus on Mathematical Content

Producing Equivalent Inequalities You can substitute for either side of an inequality an expression equivalent to that side. For example, the inequality $2(3 + x) > 5$ is equivalent to the inequality $6 + 2x > 5$. You can also add (or subtract) the same real number to (or from) each side of an inequality.

3 Practice

Formative Assessment

Use Exercises 1–11 to check for understanding.

Use the chart at the bottom of the next page to customize assignments for your students.

Additional Answers (Guided Practice)

3A. $\{n \mid n > -1\}$

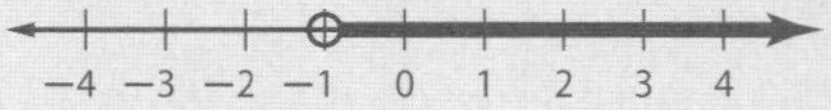

3B. $\{h \mid h \leq 12\}$

Check Your Understanding

= Step-by-Step Solutions begin on page R13.

Examples 1–3 Solve each inequality. Then graph the solution set on a number line. **1–8. See margin.**

1. $x - 3 > 7$
2. $5 \geq 7 + y$
3. $g + 6 < 2$
4. $11 \leq p + 4$
5. $10 > n - 1$
6. $k + 24 > -5$
7. $8r + 6 < 9r$
8. $8n \geq 7n - 3$

Example 4 Define a variable, write an inequality, and solve each problem. Check your solution.

9. Twice a number increased by 4 is at least 10 more than the number. **Sample answer: Let $n =$ the number, $2n + 4 \geq n + 10$; $\{n \mid n \geq 6\}$.**
10. Three more than a number is less than twice the number. **10. Sample answer: Let $n =$ the number, $3 + n < 2n$; $\{n \mid n > 3\}$.**
11. **AMUSEMENT** A thrill ride swings passengers back and forth, a little higher each time up to 137 feet. Suppose the height of the swing after 30 seconds is 45 feet. How much higher will the ride swing? **no more than 92 ft**

Practice and Problem Solving

Extra Practice is on page R5.

Examples 1–3 Solve each inequality. Then graph the solution set on a number line. **12–29. See Ch. 5 Answer Appendix.**

12. $m - 4 < 3$
13. $p - 6 \geq 3$
14. $r - 8 \leq 7$
15. $t - 3 > -8$
16. $b + 2 \geq 4$
17. $13 > 18 + r$
18. $5 + c \leq 1$
19. $-23 \geq q - 30$
20. $11 + m \geq 15$
21. $h - 26 < 4$
22. $8 \leq r - 14$
23. $-7 > 20 + c$
24. $2a \leq -4 + a$
25. $z + 4 \geq 2z$
26. $w - 5 \leq 2w$
27. $3y + 6 \leq 2y$
28. $6x + 5 \geq 7x$
29. $-9 + 2a < 3a$

34. Sample answer: Let $b =$ the amount of money that Keisha still needs; $b + 1300 \geq 5440$; $\{b \mid b \geq 4140\}$; Keisha needs to earn at least \$4140.

Example 4 Define a variable, write an inequality, and solve each problem. Check your solution. **30–33. Sample answers given.**

30. Twice a number is more than the sum of that number and 9. **Let $n =$ the number, $2n > n + 9$; $\{n \mid n > 9\}$.**
31. The sum of twice a number and 5 is at most 3 less than the number. **Let $n =$ the number, $2n + 5 \leq n - 3$; $\{n \mid n \leq -8\}$.**
32. The sum of three times a number and -4 is at least twice the number plus 8. **Let $n =$ the number, $3n + (-4) \geq 2n + 8$; $\{n \mid n \geq 12\}$.**
33. Six times a number decreased by 8 is less than five times the number plus 21. **Let $n =$ the number, $6n - 8 < 5n + 21$; $\{n \mid n < 29\}$.**

MODELING Define a variable, write an inequality, and solve each problem. Then interpret your solution.

34. **FINANCIAL LITERACY** Keisha is babysitting at \$8 per hour to earn money for a car. So far she has saved \$1300. The car that Keisha wants to buy costs at least \$5440. How much money does Keisha still need to earn to buy the car?
35. **TECHNOLOGY** A recent survey found that more than 21 million people between the ages of 12 and 17 use the Internet. Of those, about 16 million said they use the Internet at school. How many teens that are online do not use the Internet at school? **See margin.**

B

36. **MUSIC** A DJ added 20 more songs to his digital media player, making the total more than 61. How many songs were originally on the player? **See margin.**

Teaching the Process Standards

Modeling Mathematically proficient students can apply the mathematics they know to solve problems arising in everyday life, society, and the workplace. Encourage students to relate the problems in the text to their own experience.

Reasoning Mathematically proficient students flexibly use different properties of operations. In Exercises 46–51, point out that instead of isolating the variable they should apply the properties of inequalities to transform the inequality in a different way.

Additional Answers

1. $\{x \mid x > 10\}$

2. $\{y \mid y \leq -2\}$

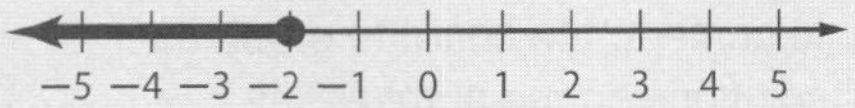

3. $\{g \mid g < -4\}$

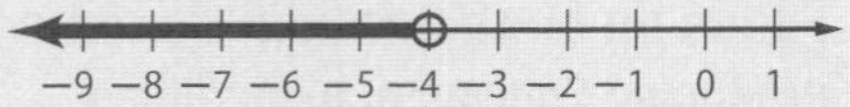

4. $\{p \mid p \geq 7\}$

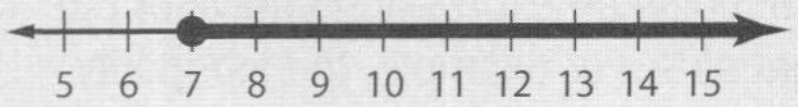

5. $\{n \mid n < 11\}$

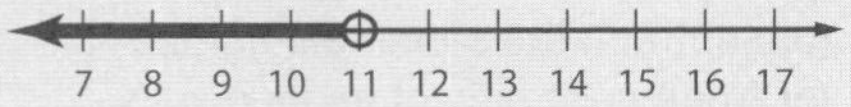

6. $\{k \mid k > -29\}$

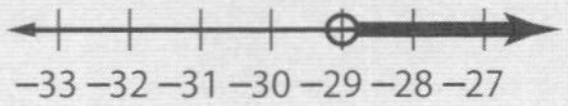

7. $\{r \mid r > 6\}$

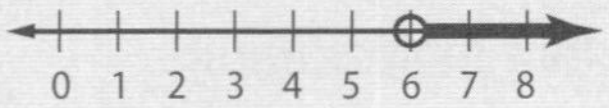

8. $\{n \mid n \geq -3\}$

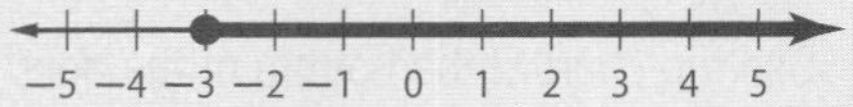

35. Sample answer: Let $n =$ the number of online teens that do not use the Internet at school in millions; $n > 21 - 16$; $\{n \mid n > 5\}$; at least 5 million teens use the Internet but not at school.
36. Sample answer: Let $n =$ the original number of songs; $n + 20 > 61$; $\{n \mid n > 41\}$; there were originally more than 41 songs on the player.

Differentiated Homework Options

Level	Assignment	Two-Day Option	
AL Basic	12–35, 52, 54–81	13–35 odd, 57–60	12–34 even, 52, 54–56, 61–81
OL Core	13–35 odd, 36–40, 41–51 odd, 52, 54–81	12–35, 57–60	36–52, 54–56, 61–81
BL Advanced	36–73, (optional: 74–81)		

39. Sample answer: Let m = the amount of money left on the gift card; $32 + 26 + m \leq 75$; $\{m \mid m \leq 17\}$; there will be no more than $17 left on her gift card.

37. TEMPERATURE The water temperature in a swimming pool increased 4°F this morning. The temperature is now less than 81°F. What was the water temperature this morning? **See Ch. 5 Answer Appendix.**

38. BASKETBALL A player's goal was to score at least 150 points this season. So far, she has scored 123 points. If there is one game left, how many points must she score to reach her goal? **See Ch. 5 Answer Appendix.**

39. SPAS Samantha received a $75 gift card for a local day spa for her birthday. She plans to get a haircut and a manicure. How much money will be left on her gift card after her visit?

Service	Cost ($)
haircut	at least 32
manicure	at least 26

40. VOLUNTEER Kono knows that he can only volunteer up to 25 hours per week. If he has volunteered for the times recorded at the right, how much more time can Kono volunteer this week?

Center	Time (h)
Shelter	3 h 15 min
Kitchen	2 h 20 min

Solve each inequality. Check your solution, and then graph it on a number line. **41–44. See Ch. 5 Answer Appendix.**

41. $c + (-1.4) \geq 2.3$ **42.** $9.1g + 4.5 < 10.1g$

43. $k + \frac{3}{4} > \frac{1}{3}$ **44.** $\frac{3}{2}p - \frac{2}{3} \leq \frac{4}{9} + \frac{1}{2}p$

C **45. MULTIPLE REPRESENTATIONS** In this problem, you will explore multiplication and division in inequalities.

a. **Geometric** Suppose a balance has 12 pounds on the left side and 18 pounds on the right side. Draw a picture to represent this situation. **a–d. See Ch. 5 Answer Appendix.**

b. **Numerical** Write an inequality to represent the situation.

c. **Tabular** Create a table showing the result of doubling, tripling, or quadrupling the weight on each side of the balance. Create a second table showing the result of reducing the weight on each side of the balance by a factor of $\frac{1}{2}$, $\frac{1}{3}$, or $\frac{1}{4}$. Include a column in each table for the inequality representing each situation.

d. **Verbal** Describe the effect multiplying or dividing each side of an inequality by the same positive value has on the inequality.

40. Sample answer: Let t = time remaining in hours; $3\frac{1}{4} + 2\frac{1}{3} + t \leq 25$; $\left\{t \mid t \leq 19\frac{5}{12}\right\}$; the time remaining is at most 19 h 25 min.

REASONING **If $m + 7 \geq 24$, then complete each inequality.**

46. $m \geq$ _?_ 17 **47.** $m +$ _?_ ≥ 27 10 **48.** $m - 5 \geq$ _?_ 12

49. $m -$ _?_ ≥ 14 3 **50.** $m - 19 \geq$ _?_ -2 **51.** $m +$ _?_ ≥ 43 26

52. In both graphs, the line is darkened to the left of 4. In the graph of $a < 4$, there is a circle at 4 to indicate that 4 is not included in the graph. In the graph of $a \leq 4$, there is a dot at 4 to indicate that 4 is included in the graph.

H.O.T. Problems Use Higher-Order Thinking Skills

52. REASONING Compare and contrast the graphs of $a < 4$ and $a \leq 4$.

53. CHALLENGE Suppose $b > d + \frac{1}{3}$, $c + 1 < a - 4$, and $d + \frac{5}{8} > a + 2$. Order a, b, c, and d from least to greatest. $c < a < d < b$

54. OPEN ENDED Write three linear inequalities that are equivalent to $y < -3$. **See Ch. 5 Answer Appendix.**

55. WRITING IN MATH Summarize the process of solving and graphing linear inequalities. **See Ch. 5 Answer Appendix.**

56. WRITING IN MATH Explain why $x - 2 > 5$ has the same solution set as $x > 7$. **See Ch. 5 Answer Appendix.**

Multiple Representations

In Exercise 45, students use a geometric sketch, a linear inequality, a table of values, and verbal analysis to show how inequalities are affected by multiplying or dividing each side by the same value.

Study Guide and Intervention

AL OL ELL

NAME ____ DATE ____ PERIOD ____

5-1 Study Guide and Intervention

Solving Inequalities by Addition and Subtraction

Solve Inequalities by Addition Addition can be used to solve inequalities. If any number is added to each side of a true inequality, the resulting inequality is also true.

Exercises

Solve each inequality. Check your solution, and then graph it on a number line.

Define a variable, write an inequality, and solve each problem. Check your solution.

13. A number decreased by 4 is less than 14.

14. The difference of two numbers is more than 12, and one of the numbers is 3.

15. Forty is no greater than the difference of a number and 2.

Practice

AL OL BL ELL

5-1 Practice

Solving Inequalities by Addition and Subtraction

Match each inequality with its corresponding graph.

Solve each inequality. Check your solution, and then graph it on a number line.

Define a variable, write an inequality, and solve each problem. Check your solution.

11. The sum of a number and 17 is no less than 26.

12. Twice a number minus 4 is less than three times the number.

13. Twelve is at most a number decreased by 7.

14. Eight plus four times a number is greater than five times the number.

Word Problem Practice

AL OL BL ELL

5-1 Word Problem Practice

Solving Inequalities by Addition and Subtraction

Enrichment

OL BL

5-1 Enrichment

Triangle Inequalities

Tips for New Teachers

Check Solutions Students should always check their solutions but often omit this step in their hurry to finish their assignments. Remind students that checking their solutions is especially important with inequalities because the direction of the inequality sign often is changed when writing solutions in set-builder notation.

4 Assess

Crystal Ball Have students write how they think today's lesson will connect to the next lesson on solving inequalities by multiplication and division.

Standardized Test Practice

57. Which equation represents the relationship shown? **C**

x	y
1	1
2	9
3	17
4	25
5	33
6	41

A $y = 7x - 8$
B $y = 7x + 8$
C $y = 8x - 7$
D $y = 8x + 7$

58. What is the solution set of the inequality $7 + x < 5$? **H**

F $\{x \mid x < 2\}$ H $\{x \mid x < -2\}$
G $\{x \mid x > 2\}$ J $\{x \mid x > -2\}$

59. Francisco has \$3 more than $\frac{1}{4}$ the number of dollars that Kayla has. Which expression represents how much money Francisco has? **B**

A $3\left(\frac{1}{4}k\right)$ C $3 - \frac{1}{4}k$
B $\frac{1}{4}k + 3$ D $\frac{1}{4} + 3k$

60. GRIDDED RESPONSE The mean score for 10 students on the chemistry final exam was 178. However, the teacher had made a mistake and recorded one student's score as ten points less than the actual score. What should the mean score be? **179**

Spiral Review

Find the inverse of each function. (Lesson 4-7)

61. $f(x) = 7x - 28$ $\mathbf{f(x)^{-1} = \frac{1}{7}x + 4}$

62. $f(x) = \frac{2}{5}x + 12$ $\mathbf{f(x)^{-1} = \frac{5}{2}x - 30}$

63. $f(x) = -\frac{1}{3}x - 8$ $\mathbf{f(x)^{-1} = -3x - 24}$

64. $f(x) = 12x + 16$ $\mathbf{f(x)^{-1} = \frac{1}{12}x - \frac{4}{3}}$

Write the slope-intercept form of an equation for the line that passes through the given point and is perpendicular to the graph of each equation. (Lesson 4-4)

65. $(-2, 0)$, $y = x - 6$ $\mathbf{y = -x - 2}$

66. $(-3, 1)$, $y = -3x + 7$ $\mathbf{y = \frac{1}{3}x + 2}$

67. $(1, -3)$, $y = \frac{1}{2}x + 4$ $\mathbf{y = -2x - 1}$

68. $(-2, 7)$, $2x - 5y = 3$ $\mathbf{y = -\frac{5}{2}x + 2}$

69. TRAVEL On an island cruise in Hawaii, each passenger is given a lei. A crew member hands out 3 red, 3 blue, and 3 green leis in that order. If this pattern is repeated, what color lei will the 50th person receive? (Lesson 3-6) **blue**

Find the nth term of each arithmetic sequence described. (Lesson 3-5)

70. $a_1 = 52, d = 12, n = 102$ **1264**

71. $-9, -7, -5, -3, \ldots$ for $n = 18$ **25**

72. $0.5, 1, 1.5, 2, \ldots$ for $n = 50$ **25**

73. JOBS Refer to the time card shown. Write a direct variation equation relating your pay to the hours worked and find your pay if you work 30 hours. (Lesson 3-4) $\mathbf{y = 7x}$**; \$210**

Weekly Time Card

Day	Hours
FRIDAY	2.0
SATURDAY	3.5
SUNDAY	2.0
TOTAL HOURS	7.5
PAY	\$52.50

Skills Review

Solve each equation.

74. $8y = 56$ **7**

75. $4p = -120$ **−30**

76. $-3a = -21$ **7**

77. $2c = \frac{1}{5}$ $\mathbf{\frac{1}{10}}$

78. $\frac{r}{2} = 21$ **42**

79. $-\frac{3}{4}g = -12$ **16**

80. $\frac{2}{5}w = -4$ **−10**

81. $-6x = \frac{2}{3}$ $\mathbf{-\frac{1}{9}}$

Differentiated Instruction OL BL

Extension Write these three linear inequalities on the board:

$$y > 3 \qquad y + 1 > 4 \qquad 5 < y + 2$$

Have students solve each linear inequality and compare the solutions. Ask students to formulate three more linear inequalities that are equivalent to $y > 3$.

Algebra Lab
Solving Inequalities

You can use algebra tiles to solve inequalities.

Content Standards
AI.L.1

Activity Solve Inequalities

Solve $-2x \leq 4$.

Step 1 Use a self-adhesive note to cover the equals sign on the equation mat. Then write a ≤ symbol on the note. Model the inequality.

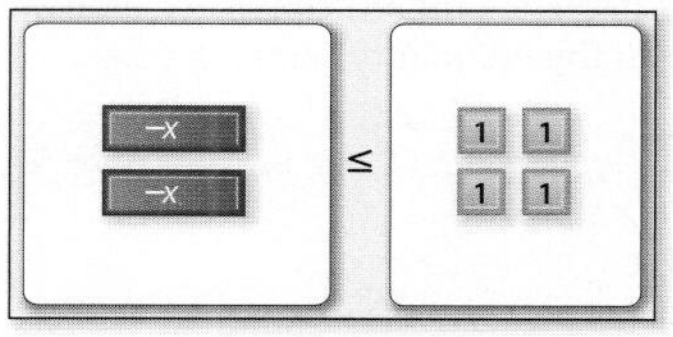

$-2x \leq 4$

Step 2 Since you do not want to solve for a negative x-tile, eliminate the negative x-tiles by adding 2 positive x-tiles to each side. Remove the zero pairs.

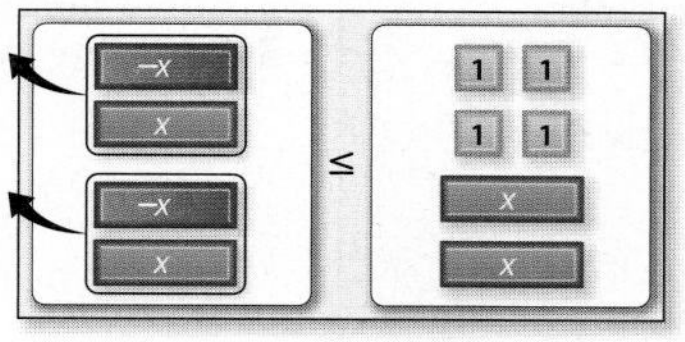

$-2x + 2x \leq 4 + 2x$

Step 3 Add 4 negative 1-tiles to each side to isolate the x-tiles. Remove the zero pairs.

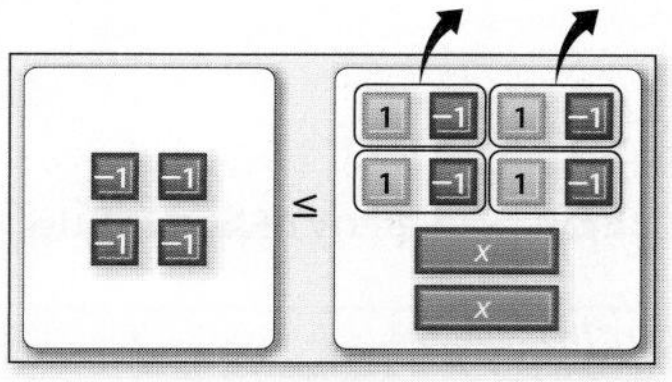

$-4 \leq 2x$

Step 4 Separate the tiles into 2 groups.

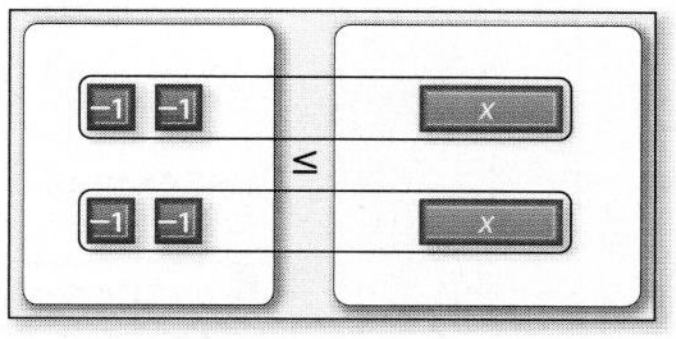

$-2 \leq x$ or $x \geq -2$

Model and Analyze

Use algebra tiles to solve each inequality.

1. $-3x < 9$ $\{x \mid x > -3\}$ **2.** $-4x > -4$ $\{x \mid x < 1\}$ **3.** $-5x \geq 15$ $\{x \mid x \leq -3\}$ **4.** $-6x \leq -12$ $\{x \mid x \geq 2\}$

5. In Exercises 1–4, is the coefficient of x in each inequality positive or negative? **negative**

6. Compare the inequality symbols and locations of the variable in Exercises 1–4 with those in their solutions. What do you find? **See Ch. 5 Answer Appendix.**

7. Model the solution for $3x \leq 12$. How is this different from solving $-3x \leq 12$? **See Ch. 5 Answer Appendix.**

8. Write a rule for solving inequalities involving multiplication and division. (*Hint:* Remember that dividing by a number is the same as multiplying by its reciprocal.) **See Ch. 5 Answer Appendix.**

1 Focus

Objective Use algebra tiles to model solving inequalities.

Materials for Each Group

- algebra tiles and equation mats
- self-adhesive blank notes

Easy to Make Manipulatives

Teaching Algebra with Manipulatives
Templates for:

- algebra tiles, pp. 10–11
- equation mat, p. 16

Teaching Tip Have students use a self-adhesive note to cover the equals sign on the equation mat. Write a ≤ symbol on the note. This will allow students to model inequalities with the equation mat and algebra tiles.

2 Teach

Working in Cooperative Groups

Put students in groups of two or three and demonstrate the Activity. Have groups complete Exercises 1 and 2.

- Make sure the inequality sign on the self-adhesive note is pointed in the correct direction to match the inequality.
- Once students have isolated the x-tiles, remind them to separate the 1-tiles into equal groups to correspond to the number of x-tiles.
- If the x-tiles end up on the right side of the inequality, students may rotate the mat 180 degrees to read the inequality with the variable on the left side.

Practice Have students complete Exercises 3–8.

3 Assess

Formative Assessment

Use Exercises 5 and 6 to assess whether students understand that when they multiply or divide both sides of an inequality by a negative number, the direction of the inequality sign changes.

From Concrete to Abstract

Exercise 8 asks students to generalize what happens to the inequality when multiplying or dividing by positive or negative numbers.

1 Focus

VerticalAlignment

Before Lesson 5-2 Solve equations by using multiplication and division.

Lesson 5-2 Solve linear inequalities by using multiplication.
Solve linear inequalities by using division.

After Lesson 5-2 Solve systems of inequalities.

2 Teach

Scaffolding Questions

Have students read the **Why?** section of the lesson.

Ask:

- In the inequality $0.89d \leq 20$, what does the variable d represent? the number of music downloads
- Why is the inequality symbol "≤" used to represent the situation? Terrell has $20 to spend, so the cost of music downloads times the number of downloads has to be less than or equal to $20.
- What operation can you perform to get the variable on one side of the inequality? divide each side by 0.89

LESSON 5-2 Solving Inequalities by Multiplication and Division

Then

- You solved equations by using multiplication and division.

Now

1. Solve linear inequalities by using multiplication.
2. Solve linear inequalities by using division.

Why?

- Terrell received a gift card for $20 of music downloads. If each download costs $0.89, the number of downloads he can purchase can be represented by the inequality $0.89d \leq 20$.

Content Standards
A1.L.1, A1.L.2

Process Standards
PS.6

1 Solve Inequalities by Multiplication

If you multiply each side of an inequality by a positive number, then the inequality remains true.

$4 > 2$	Original inequality
$4(3) \overset{?}{\_\_} 2(3)$	Multiply each side by 3.
$12 > 6$	Simplify.

Notice that the direction of the inequality remains the same.

If you multiply each side of an inequality by a negative number, the inequality symbol changes direction.

$7 < 9$	Original inequality
$7(-2) \overset{?}{\_\_} 9(-2)$	Multiply each side by −2.
$-14 > -18$	Simplify.

These examples demonstrate the **Multiplication Property of Inequalities**.

KeyConcept Multiplication Property of Inequalities

Words	Symbols	Examples
If both sides of an inequality that is true are multiplied by a positive number, the resulting inequality is also true.	For any real numbers a and b and any positive real number c, if $a > b$, then $ac > bc$. And, if $a < b$, then $ac < bc$.	$6 > 3.5$ $6(2) > 3.5(2)$ $12 > 7$ and $2.1 < 5$ $2.1(0.5) < 5(0.5)$ $1.05 < 2.5$
If both sides of an inequality that is true are multiplied by a negative number, the direction of the inequality sign is reversed to make the resulting inequality also true.	For any real numbers a and b and any negative real number c, if $a > b$, then $ac < bc$. And, if $a < b$, then $ac > bc$.	$7 > 4.5$ $7(-3) < 4.5(-3)$ $-21 < -13.5$ and $3.1 < 5.2$ $3.1(-4) > 5.2(-4)$ $-12.4 > -20.8$

This property also holds for inequalities involving ≤ and ≥.

Lesson 5-2 Resources

Resource	Approaching Level AL	On Level OL	Beyond Level BL	English Learners ELL
Teacher Edition		▪ Differentiated Instruction, pp. 293, 297	▪ Differentiated Instruction, pp. 293, 297	
Chapter Resource Masters	▪ Study Guide and Intervention, pp. 11–12 ▪ Skills Practice, p. 13 ▪ Practice, p. 14 ▪ Word Problem Practice, p. 15	▪ Study Guide and Intervention, pp. 11–12 ▪ Skills Practice, p. 13 ▪ Practice, p. 14 ▪ Word Problem Practice, p. 15 ▪ Enrichment, p. 16	▪ Practice, p. 14 ▪ Word Problem Practice, p. 15 ▪ Enrichment, p. 16	▪ Study Guide and Intervention, pp. 11–12 ▪ Skills Practice, p. 13 ▪ Practice, p. 14 ▪ Word Problem Practice, p. 15
Other	▪ 5-Minute Check 5-2 ▪ Study Notebook ▪ Teaching Algebra with Manipulatives	▪ 5-Minute Check 5-2 ▪ Study Notebook ▪ Teaching Algebra with Manipulatives	▪ 5-Minute Check 5-2 ▪ Study Notebook	▪ 5-Minute Check 5-2 ▪ Study Notebook ▪ Teaching Algebra with Manipulatives

2A.

2B.

2C.

2D.
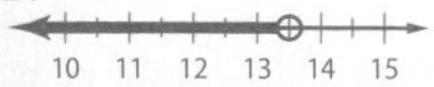

StudyTip

Sense-Making In Example 1, you could also check the solution by substituting a number greater than 672 and verifying that the resulting inequality is false.

Real-World Example 1 Write and Solve an Inequality

SURVEYS Of the students surveyed at Madison High School, fewer than eighty-four said they have never purchased an item online. This is about one eighth of those surveyed. How many students were surveyed?

Understand You know the number of students who have never purchased an item online and the portion this is of the number of students surveyed.

Plan Let n = the number of students surveyed. Write an open sentence that represents this situation.

Words	One eighth	times	the number of students surveyed	is less than	84.
Inequality	$\frac{1}{8}$	$\cdot$	n	$<$	84.

Solve Solve for n.

$\frac{1}{8}n < 84$ Original inequality

$(8)\frac{1}{8}n < (8)84$ Multiply each side by 8.

$n < 672$ Simplify.

Check Check the endpoint with 672 and the direction of the inequality with a value less than 672.

$\frac{1}{8}(672) \stackrel{?}{=} 84$ Check endpoint. $\frac{1}{8}(0) \stackrel{?}{<} 84$ Check direction.

$84 = 84$ ✓ $0 < 84$ ✓

The solution set is $\{n \mid n < 672\}$, so fewer than 672 students were surveyed.

GuidedPractice more than 3000 orchid species are in Malaysia

1. BIOLOGY Mount Kinabalue in Malaysia has the greatest concentration of wild orchids on Earth. It contains more than 750 species, or about one fourth of all orchid species in Malaysia. How many orchid species are there in Malaysia?

Real-WorldLink

More than 30,000 different orchid species flower in the wild on every continent except Antarctica.

Source: Aloha Orchid Nursery

You can also use multiplicative inverses with the Multiplication Property of Inequalities to solve an inequality.

Example 2 Solve by Multiplying

Solve $-\frac{3}{7}r < 21$. Graph the solution on a number line.

$-\frac{3}{7}r < 21$ Original inequality

$\left(-\frac{7}{3}\right)\left(-\frac{3}{7}r\right) > \left(-\frac{7}{3}\right)21$ Multiply each side by $-\frac{7}{3}$. Reverse the inequality symbol.

$r > -49$ Simplify. Check by substituting values.

The solution set is $\{r \mid r > -49\}$.

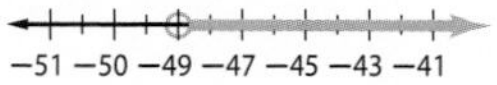

GuidedPractice **2A.** $\{n \mid n \geq -48\}$ **2B.** $\left\{p \mid p < 7\frac{1}{2}\right\}$ **2C.** $\{m \mid m \geq -15\}$ **2D.** $\left\{t \mid t < 13\frac{1}{3}\right\}$

Solve each inequality. Check your solution.

2A. $-\frac{n}{6} \leq 8$ **2B.** $-\frac{4}{3}p > -10$ **2C.** $\frac{1}{5}m \geq -3$ **2D.** $\frac{3}{8}t < 5$

DifferentiatedInstruction OL BL

If students understand how to solve inequalities by multiplication,

Then challenge students to explain how they might already know how to solve inequalities by division. Students should suggest that since they know how to solve inequalities by multiplying, and since division is the same as multiplying by the reciprocal, then they already know how to solve inequalities by division.

1 Solve Inequalities by Multiplication

Example 1 shows how to solve an inequality by multiplying each side by a positive number. **Example 2** shows how to solve an inequality by multiplying each side by a negative number.

Formative Assessment

Use the Guided Practice exercises after each example to determine students' understanding of concepts.

Additional Examples

1 HIKING Mateo walks at a rate of $\frac{3}{4}$ mile per hour. He knows that it is at least 9 miles to Onyx Lake. How long will it take Mateo to get there? Write and solve an inequality to find the time. $\frac{3}{4}t \geq 9$; $\{t \mid t \geq 12\}$; It will take Mateo at least 12 hours.

2 Solve $-\frac{3}{5}d \geq 6$. $\{d \mid d \leq -10\}$

Additional Examples also in Interactive Classroom PowerPoint® Presentations

IWB Interactive White Board READY

Focus on Mathematical Content

Inequality Symbols The Multiplication Property of Inequalities also holds for inequalities involving $\leq$ and $\geq$.

Teach with Tech

Interactive Whiteboard Have a student write an open sentence for a real-world situation. Highlight each value or key word. Have another student write the inequality and highlight the corresponding parts from the open sentence.

Teaching the Process Standards

Sense-Making Mathematically proficient students understand the approaches of others to solving complex problems. Encourage students to use the four-step plan and share their problem-solving strategies.

2 Solve Inequalities by Division

Example 3 shows how to solve an inequality by dividing each side by a positive number and by a negative number.

Additional Example

3 Solve each inequality.

a. $12k \geq 60$ $\{k \mid k \geq 5\}$

b. $-8q < 136$ $\{q \mid q > -17\}$

WatchOut!

Preventing Errors Point out to students that an inequality is easier to solve using division when the inequality involves whole numbers and easier to solve using multiplication by reciprocals when the inequality involves fractions.

Preventing Errors Point out that the rules for the Division Property of Inequalities state that each side of an inequality can be divided by a positive or negative number. In neither case is zero included because division by zero is an undefined operation.

Tips for New Teachers

Checking Solutions Discuss numbers that could be used as a check after an inequality is solved. For example, could $t = 0$ be used to check the solution to Example 3a?

WatchOut!

Negatives A negative sign in an inequality does not necessarily mean that the direction of the inequality should change. For example, when solving $\frac{x}{6} > -3$, do not change the direction of the inequality.

2 Solve Inequalities by Division

If you divide each side of an inequality by a positive number, then the inequality remains true.

$-10 < -5$	Original inequality
$\frac{-10}{5} \ ? \ \frac{-5}{5}$	Divide each side by −5.
$-2 < -1$	Simplify.

Notice that the direction of the inequality remains the same. If you divide each side of an inequality by a negative number, the inequality symbol changes direction.

$15 < 18$	Original inequality
$\frac{15}{-3} \ ? \ \frac{18}{-3}$	Divide each side by −3.
$-5 > -6$	Simplify.

These examples demonstrate the **Division Property of Inequalities**.

Math HistoryLink

Thomas Harriot (1560–1621) Harriot was a prolific astronomer. He was the first to map the Moon's surface and to see sunspots. Harriot is best known for his work in algebra.

KeyConcept Division Property of Inequalities

Words	Symbols	Examples
If both sides of a true inequality are divided by a positive number, the resulting inequality is also true.	For any real numbers a and b and any positive real number a, if $a > b$, then $\frac{a}{c} > \frac{b}{c}$. And, if $a < b$, then $\frac{a}{c} < \frac{b}{c}$.	$4.5 > 2.1$; $\frac{4.5}{3} > \frac{2.1}{3}$; $1.5 > 0.7$ and $1.5 < 5$; $\frac{1.5}{0.5} < \frac{5}{0.5}$; $3 < 10$
If both sides of a true inequality are divided by a negative number, the direction of the inequality sign is reversed to make the resulting inequality also true.	For any real numbers a and b, and any negative real number c, if $a > b$, then $\frac{a}{c} < \frac{b}{c}$. And, if $a < b$, then $\frac{a}{c} < \frac{b}{c}$.	$6 > 2.4$; $\frac{6}{-6} < \frac{2.4}{-6}$; $-1 < -0.4$ and $-1.8 < 3.6$; $\frac{-1.8}{-9} < \frac{3.6}{-9}$; $0.2 > -0.4$

This property also holds true for inequalities involving ≤ and ≥.

Example 3 Divide to Solve an Inequality

Solve each inequality. Graph the solution on a number line.

a. $60t > 8$

$60t > 8$	Original inequality
$\frac{60t}{60} > \frac{8}{60}$	Divide each side by 60.
$t > \frac{2}{15}$	Simplify.

$\left\{t \,\middle|\, t > \frac{2}{15}\right\}$

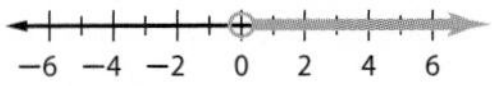

b. $-7d \leq 147$

$-7d \leq 147$	Original inequality
$\frac{-7d}{-7} \geq \frac{147}{-7}$	Divide each side by −7.
$d \geq -21$	Simplify.

$\{d \mid d \geq -21\}$

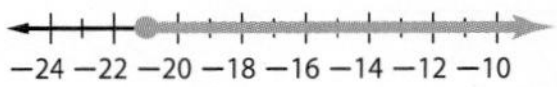

GuidedPractice

3A. $8p \leq 58$

3B. $-42 \geq 6r$

3C. $-12h > 15$

3D. $-\frac{1}{2}n \leq 6$

3A. $\left\{p \,\middle|\, p \leq 7\frac{1}{4}\right\}$

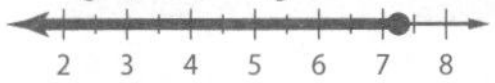

3B. $\{r \mid r \leq -7\}$

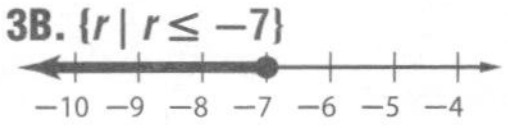

3C. $\left\{h \,\middle|\, h < -\frac{5}{4}\right\}$

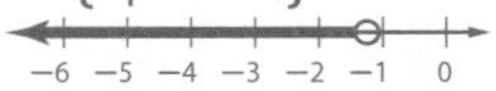

3D. $\{n \mid n \geq -12\}$

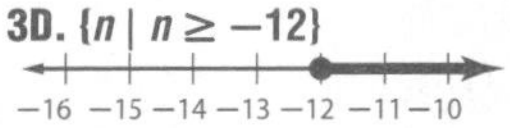

294 | Lesson 5-2 | Solving Inequalities by Multiplication and Division

Check Your Understanding

⬤ = Step-by-Step Solutions begin on page R13.

Example 1

1. **FUNDRAISING** The Jefferson Band Boosters raised more than \$5500 from sales of their \$15 band DVD. Define a variable, and write an inequality to represent the number of DVDs they sold. Solve the inequality and interpret your solution. Let d = the number of DVDs sold; $15d > 5500$; $d > 366.67$; the band sold at least 367 DVDs.

Examples 2–3 **Solve each inequality. Graph the solution on a number line.** 2–9. See margin for graphs.

2. $30 > \frac{1}{2}n$ $\{n \mid n < 60\}$
3. $-\frac{3}{4}r \leq -6$ $\{r \mid r \geq 8\}$
4. $-\frac{c}{6} \geq 7$ $\{c \mid c \leq -42\}$
5. $\frac{h}{2} < -5$ $\{h \mid h < -10\}$
6. $9t > 108$ $\{t \mid t > 12\}$
7. $-84 < 7v$ $\{v \mid v > -12\}$
8. $-28 \leq -6x$ $\left\{x \middle| x \leq 4\frac{2}{3}\right\}$
9. $40 \geq -5z$ $\{z \mid z \geq -8\}$

Practice and Problem Solving

Extra Practice is on page R5.

Example 1 **Define a variable, write an inequality, and solve each problem. Then interpret your solution.**

10. **CELL PHONE PLAN** Mario purchases a prepaid phone plan for \$50 at \$0.13 per minute. How many minutes can Mario talk on this plan? 10. Let m = the number of minutes that Mario can talk; $0.13m \leq 50$; $m \leq 384.6$; Mario can talk up to 384 minutes.

11. **FINANCIAL LITERACY** Rodrigo needs at least \$560 to pay for his spring break expenses, and he is saving \$25 from each of his weekly paychecks. How long will it be before he can pay for his trip? See margin.

Examples 2–3 **Solve each inequality. Graph the solution on a number line.** 12–29. See Chapter 5 Answer Appendix for graphs.

12. $\frac{1}{4}m \leq -17$ $\{m \mid m \leq -68\}$
13. $\frac{1}{2}a < 20$ $\{a \mid a < 40\}$
14. $-11 > -\frac{c}{11}$ $\{c \mid c > 121\}$
15. $-2 \geq -\frac{d}{34}$ $\{d \mid d \geq 68\}$
16. $-10 \leq \frac{x}{-2}$ $\{x \mid x \leq 20\}$
17. $-72 < \frac{f}{-6}$ $\{f \mid f < 432\}$
18. $\frac{2}{3}h > 14$ $\{h \mid h > 21\}$
19. $-\frac{3}{4}j \geq 12$ $\{j \mid j \leq -16\}$
20. $-\frac{1}{6}n \leq -18$ $\{n \mid n \geq 108\}$
21. $6p \leq 96$ $\{p \mid p \leq 16\}$
22. $4r < 64$ $\{r \mid r < 16\}$
23. $32 > -2y$ $\{y \mid y > -16\}$
24. $-26 < 26t$ $\{t \mid t > -1\}$
25. $-6v > -72$ $\{v \mid v < 12\}$
26. $-33 \geq -3z$ $\{z \mid z \geq 11\}$
27. $4b \leq -3$ $\left\{b \middle| b \leq -\frac{3}{4}\right\}$
28. $-2d < 5$ $\left\{d \middle| d > -2\frac{1}{2}\right\}$
29. $-7f > 5$ $\left\{f \middle| f < -\frac{5}{7}\right\}$

B

30. **CHEERLEADING** To remain on the cheerleading squad, Lakita must attend at least $\frac{3}{5}$ of the study table sessions offered. She attends 15 sessions. If Lakita met the requirements, what is the maximum number of study table sessions? 25

31. **BRACELETS** How many bracelets can Caitlin buy for herself and her friends if she wants to spend no more than \$22? no more than 4

32. **PRECISION** The National Honor Society at Pleasantville High School wants to raise at least \$500 for a local charity. Each student earns \$0.50 for every quarter of a mile walked in a walk-a-thon. How many miles will the students need to walk? at least 250 mi

33. **MUSEUM** The American history classes are planning a trip to a local museum. Admission is \$8 per person. Determine how many people can go for \$260. no more than 32 people

34. **GASOLINE** If gasoline costs \$3.15 per gallon, how many gallons of gasoline, to the nearest tenth, can Jan buy for \$24? no more than 7.6 gal

Differentiated Homework Options

Level	Assignment	Two-Day Option	
AL Basic	10–29, 42, 45–68	11–29 odd, 48–51	10–28 even, 42, 45–47, 52–68
OL Core	11–29 odd, 30–35, 37, 39–42, 45–68	10–29, 48–51	30–42, 45–47, 52–68
BL Advanced	30–62, (optional: 63–68)		

3 Practice

Formative Assessment

Use Exercises 1–9 to check for understanding.

Use the chart at the bottom of this page to customize assignments for your students.

Teaching the Process Standards

Precision Mathematically proficient students are careful about specifying units of measure. In Exercise 32, make sure students observe that the earnings are recorded for each quarter of a mile and the answer is to be given in miles.

Multiple Representations

In Exercise 41, students use a geometric sketch, an equation, a table of values, and numerical analysis to relate the dimensions of a square pyramid to its volume.

Additional Answers

2.
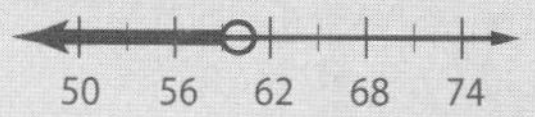

3.
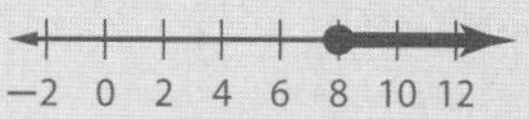

4.
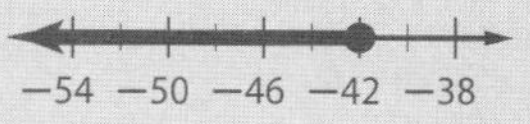

5.
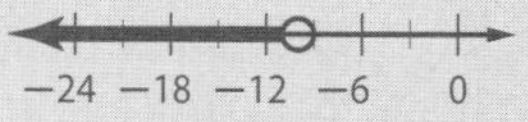

6.
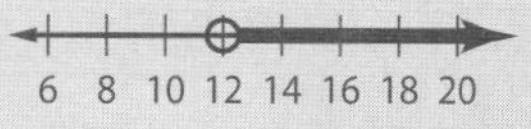

7.
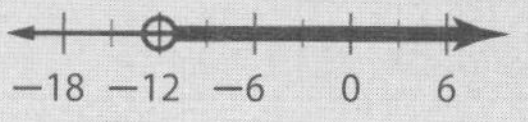

8.
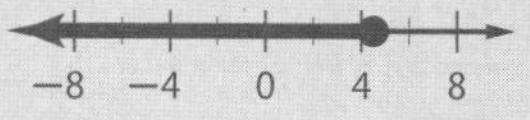

9.
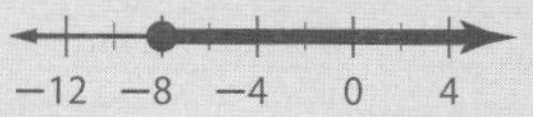

11. Let p = the number of pay periods for which Rodrigo will need to save; $25p \geq 560$; $p \geq 22.4$; Rodrigo will need to save for 23 weeks.

Study Guide and Intervention

AL OL ELL

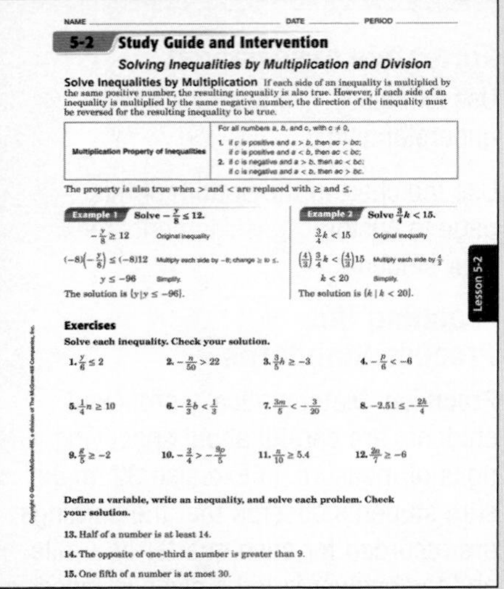
NAME ______ DATE ______ PERIOD ______

5-2 Study Guide and Intervention

Solving Inequalities by Multiplication and Division

Solve Inequalities by Multiplication If each side of an inequality is multiplied by the same positive number, the resulting inequality is also true. However, if each side of an inequality is multiplied by the same negative number, the direction of the inequality must be reversed for the resulting inequality to be true.

The property is also true when > and < are replaced with ≥ and ≤.

Exercises

Solve each inequality. Check your solution.

Define a variable, write an inequality, and solve each problem. Check your solution.

13. Half of a number is at least 14.

14. The opposite of one-third a number is greater than 9.

15. One fifth of a number is at most 30.

Practice

AL OL BL ELL

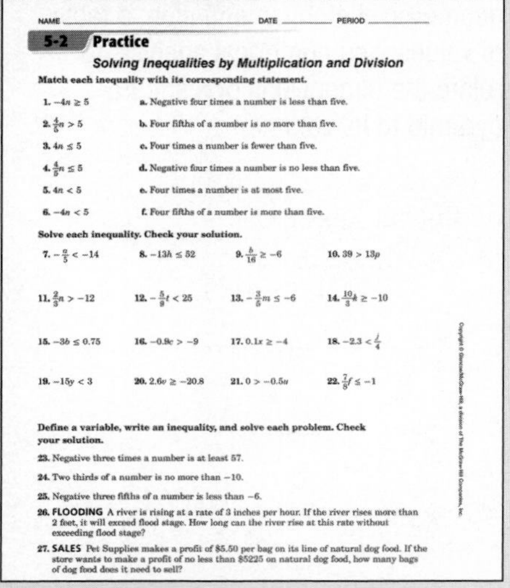
NAME ______ DATE ______ PERIOD ______

5-2 Practice

Solving Inequalities by Multiplication and Division

Match each inequality with its corresponding statement.

Solve each inequality. Check your solution.

Define a variable, write an inequality, and solve each problem. Check your solution.

Word Problem Practice

AL OL BL ELL

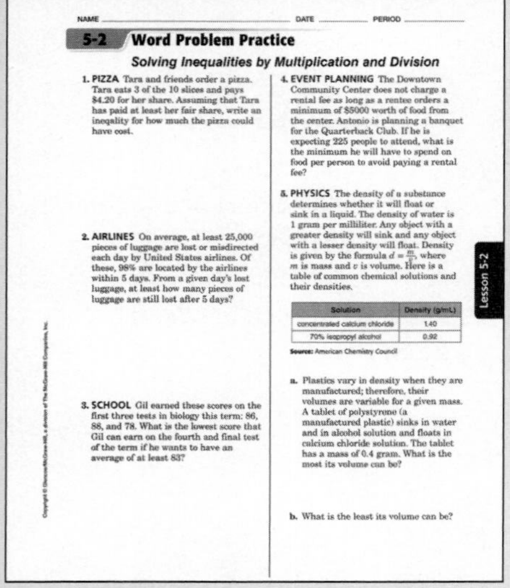
NAME ______ DATE ______ PERIOD ______

5-2 Word Problem Practice

Solving Inequalities by Multiplication and Division

Match each inequality to the graph of its solution.

35. $-\frac{2}{3}h \leq 9$ **b** **36.** $25j \geq 8$ **a** **37.** $3.6p < -4.5$ **d** **38.** $2.3 < -5t$ **c**

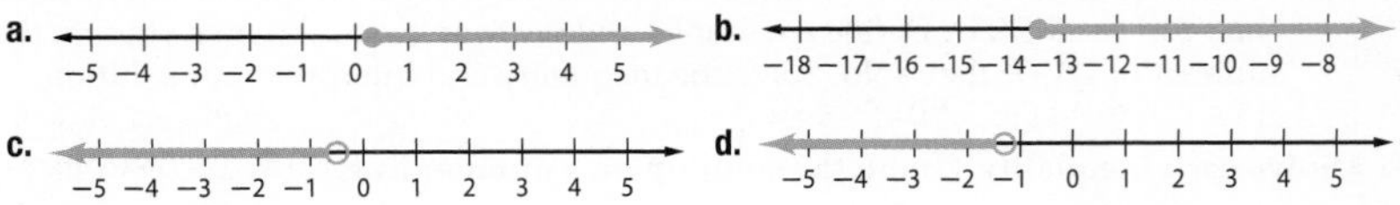

39. CANDY Fewer than 42 employees at a factory stated that they preferred fudge over fruit candy. This is about two thirds of the employees. How many employees are there? **fewer than 63 employees**

40. TRAVEL A certain travel agency employs more than 275 people at all of its branches. Approximately three fifths of all the people are employed at the west branch. How many people work at the west branch? **more than 165 employees**

41a.

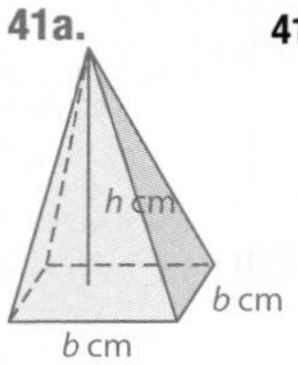

41. MULTIPLE REPRESENTATIONS The equation for the volume of a pyramid is $\frac{1}{3}$ the area of the base times the height.

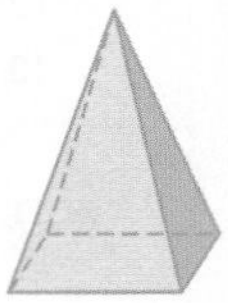

a. Geometric Draw a pyramid with a square base b cm long and a height of h cm.

b. Numerical Suppose the pyramid has a volume of 72 cm^3. Write an equation to find the height. $h = \frac{216}{b^2}$

c. Tabular Create a table showing the value of h when $b = 1, 3, 6, 9$, and 12. **See margin.**

d. Numerical Write an inequality for the possible lengths of b such that $b < h$. Write an inequality for the possible lengths of h such that $b > h$.

$b < h$ when $0 < b < 6$; $b > h$ when $h < 6$.

H.O.T. Problems Use Higher-Order Thinking Skills

42. ERROR ANALYSIS Taro and Jamie are solving $6d \geq -84$. Is either of them correct? Explain your reasoning.

Taro; the inequality does not need to be reversed when dividing by a positive number.

Taro	Jamie
$6d \geq -84$	$6d \geq -84$
$\frac{6d}{6} \geq \frac{-84}{6}$	$\frac{6d}{6} \leq \frac{-84}{6}$
$d \geq -14$	$d \leq -14$

43. CHALLENGE Solve each inequality for x. Assume that $a > 0$.

a. $-ax < 5$ $x > -\frac{5}{a}$ **b.** $\frac{1}{a}x \geq 8$ $x \geq 8a$ **c.** $-6 \geq ax$ $x \leq -\frac{6}{a}$

44. STRUCTURE Determine whether $x^2 > 1$ and $x > 1$ are equivalent. Explain.

No; the solution set of $x^2 > 1$ includes values of $x < -1$.

45. REASONING Explain whether the statement *If $a > b$, then $\frac{1}{a} > \frac{1}{b}$* is *sometimes, always,* or *never* true. **Sometimes; the statement is true when $a > 0$ and $b < 0$.**

46. OPEN ENDED Create a real-world situation to represent the inequality $-\frac{5}{8} \geq x$.

Sample answer: The temperature never exceeds $-\frac{5}{8}$°C.

47. WRITING IN MATH How are solving linear inequalities and linear equations similar? different? **See margin.**

Enrichment

OL BL

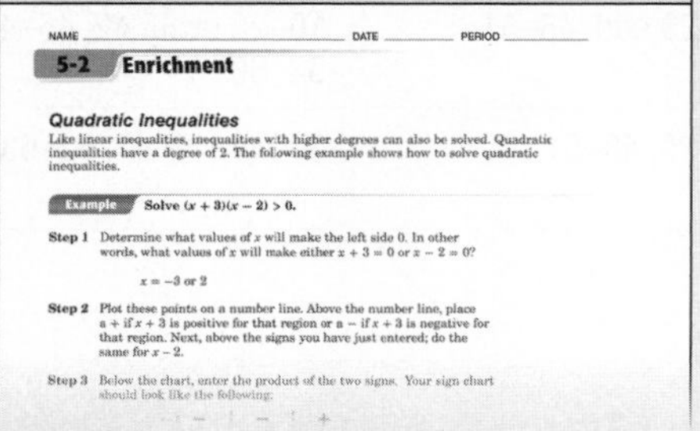
NAME ______ DATE ______ PERIOD ______

5-2 Enrichment

Quadratic Inequalities

Like linear inequalities, inequalities with higher degrees can also be solved. Quadratic inequalities have a degree of 2. The following example shows how to solve quadratic inequalities.

Example Solve $(x + 3)(x - 2) > 0$.

Step 1 Determine what values of x will make the left side 0. In other words, what values of x will make either $x + 3 = 0$ or $x - 2 = 0$?

$x = -3$ or 2

Teaching the Process Standards

Structure Mathematically proficient students look closely to discern structure. In Exercise 44, remind students that because the product of two negative numbers or two positive numbers is positive, if x is nonzero x^2 is always positive.

Standardized Test Practice

48. Juan's international calling card costs 9¢ for each minute. Which inequality can be used to find how long he can talk to a friend if he does not want to spend more than \$2.50 on the call? **D**

A $0.09 \geq 2.50m$

B $0.09 \leq 2.50m$

C $0.09m \geq 2.50$

D $0.09m \leq 2.50$

49. SHORT RESPONSE Find the value of x. **10 in.**

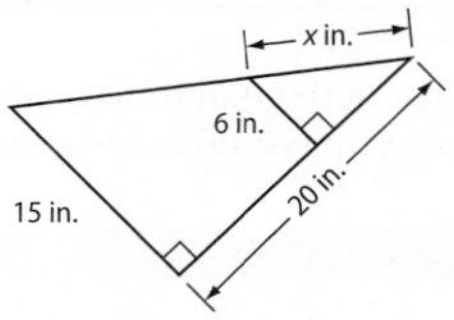

50. What is the greatest rate of decrease of this function? **F**

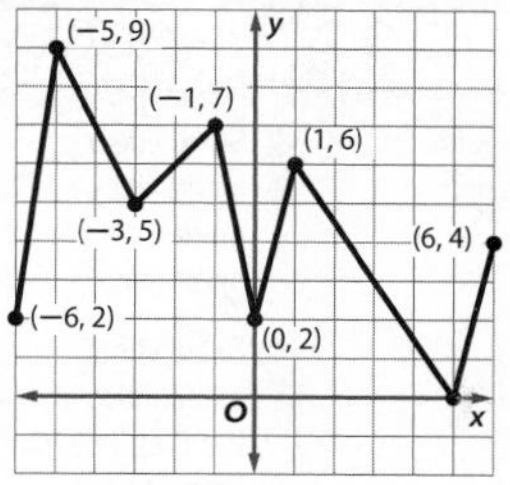

F -5 H -2

G -3 J 1

51. What is the value of x if $4x - 3 = -2x$? **C**

A -2 C $\frac{1}{2}$

B $-\frac{1}{2}$ D 2

Spiral Review

Solve each inequality. Check your solution, and then graph it on a number line. (Lesson 5-1) **52–54. See margin.**

52. $a + 8 > 4$ **53.** $6y \geq 5y + 21$ **54.** $b + \frac{1}{2} < 1$

Find the inverse of each function. (Lesson 4-7)

55. $f(x) = -6x + 18$ $f^{-1}(x) = -\frac{1}{6}x + 3$

56. $f(x) = \frac{3}{7}x + 9$ $f^{-1}(x) = \frac{7}{3}x - 21$

57. $f(x) = 4x - 5$ $f^{-1}(x) = \frac{1}{4}x + \frac{5}{4}$

58. HOME DECOR Pam is having blinds installed at her home. The cost c of installation for any number of blinds b can be described by $c = 25 + 6.5b$. Graph the equation and determine how much it would cost if Pam has 8 blinds installed. (Lesson 3-1) **See Ch. 5 Answer Appendix.**

59. RESCUE A boater radioed for a helicopter to pick up a sick crew member. At that time, the boat and the helicopter were at the positions shown. How long will it take for the helicopter to reach the boat? (Lesson 2-9) **2 hours**

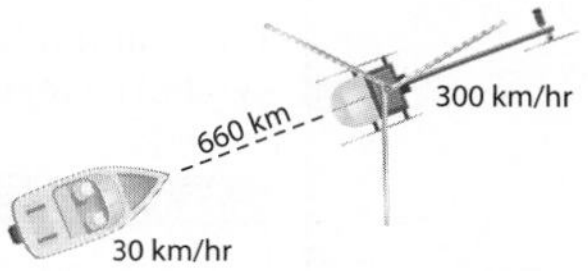

Solve each equation. (Lesson 2-5)

60. $|x + 3| = 10$ **{−13, 7}** **61.** $|2x - 8| = 6$ **{1, 7}** **62.** $|3x + 1| = -2$ **∅**

Skills Review

Solve each equation.

63. $4y + 11 = 19$ **2** **64.** $2x - 7 = 9 + 4x$ **−8** **65.** $\frac{1}{4} + 2x = 4x - 8$ $\frac{33}{8}$

66. $\frac{1}{3}(6w - 3) = 3w + 12$ **−13** **67.** $\frac{7r + 5}{2} = 13$ **3** **68.** $\frac{1}{2}a = \frac{a - 3}{4}$ **−3**

DifferentiatedInstruction OL BL

Extension Ask students to solve $2n + 4 \neq 12$. Have the students discuss the solution and write and solve a different inequality using the $\neq$ symbol. $\{n \mid n \neq 4\}$

WatchOut!

Error Analysis In Exercise 42, students should see that the only difference between Taro's and Jamie's solutions is the inequality symbol. Since the solution involves division by a positive number, the inequality symbol of the solution is not reversed from the original equality.

4 Assess

Ticket Out the Door Have students write a short statement about what they think is the most important thing to remember about solving inequalities by multiplication and division.

Formative Assessment

Check for student understanding of the concepts in Lessons 5-1 and 5-2.

Quiz 1, p. 45

Additional Answers

41c.

b	1	3	6	9	12
h	216	24	6	$\frac{8}{3}$	$\frac{3}{2}$

47. Sample answer: The same processes are used when solving linear inequalities and equations that involve addition, subtraction, multiplication, or division by a positive number. However, when a linear inequality is multiplied or divided by a negative number, the inequality symbol must change directions so that the inequality remains true.

52. $\{a \mid a > -4\}$

53. $\{y \mid y \geq 21\}$

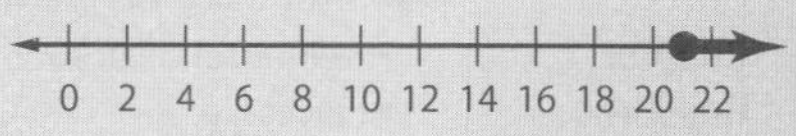

54. $\{b \mid b < \frac{1}{2}\}$

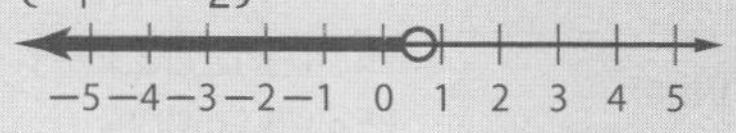

1 Focus

VerticalAlignment

Before Lesson 5-3 Solve multi-step equations.

Lesson 5-3 Solve linear inequalities involving more than one operation. Solve linear inequalities involving the Distributive Property.

After Lesson 5-3 Solve systems of inequalities.

2 Teach

Scaffolding Questions

Have students read the **Why?** section of the lesson.

Ask:

- What information is needed to solve the inequality for the number of sales? the base salary, the commission paid on each sale, and the income needed to pay the monthly bills
- Why is the inequality symbol "≥" used to represent the situation? The amount the salesperson earns from the base salary and commissions must be equal to at least the income needed to pay the bills.
- Which operations undo the operations represented in the inequality? subtraction and division

LESSON 5-3 Solving Multi-Step Inequalities

Then

- You solved multi-step equations.

Now

1. Solve linear inequalities involving more than one operation.
2. Solve linear inequalities involving the Distributive Property.

Why?

- A salesperson may make a base monthly salary and earn a commission on each of her sales. To find the number of sales she needs to make to pay her monthly bills, you can use a multi-step inequality.

Content Standards
AI.L.1, AI.L.2

1 Solve Multi-Step Inequalities

Multi–step inequalities can be solved by undoing the operations in the same way you would solve a multi-step equation.

PT

Real-World Example 1 Solve a Multi-Step Inequality

SALES **Write and solve an inequality to find the sales Mrs. Jones needs if she earns a monthly salary of $2000 plus a 10% commission on her sales. Her goal is to make at least $4000 per month. What sales does she need to meet her goal?**

base salary + (commission × sales) ≥ income needed

$2000 + 0.10x \geq 4000$	Substitution
$0.10x \geq 2000$	Subtract 2000 from each side.
$x \geq 20{,}000$	Divide each side by 0.10.

She must make at least $20,000 in sales to meet her monthly goal.

GuidedPractice

1. FINANCIAL LITERACY The Print Shop advertises a special to print 400 flyers for less than the competition. The price includes a $3.50 set-up fee. If the competition charges $35.50, what does the Print Shop charge for each flyer? **less than 8¢**

When multiplying or dividing by a negative number, the direction of the inequality symbol changes. This holds true for multi-step inequalities.

PT

Example 2 Inequality Involving a Negative Coefficient

Solve $-11y - 13 > 42$. Graph the solution on a number line.

$-11y - 13 > 42$	Original inequality
$-11y > 55$	Add 13 to each side and simplify.
$\frac{-11y}{-11} < \frac{55}{-11}$	Divide each side by −11, and reverse the inequality.
$y < -5$	Simplify.

The solution set is $\{y \mid y < -5\}$.

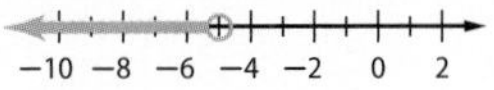

GuidedPractice **Solve each inequality.**

2A. $23 \geq 10 - 2w$ $\{w \mid w \geq -6.5\}$

2B. $43 > -4y + 11$ $\{y \mid y > -8\}$

Lesson 5-3 Resources

Resource	Approaching Level AL	On Level OL	Beyond Level BL	English Learners ELL
Teacher Edition	▪ Differentiated Instruction, p. 300	▪ Differentiated Instruction, pp. 300, 303	▪ Differentiated Instruction, pp. 300, 303	▪ Differentiated Instruction, p. 300
Chapter Resource Masters	▪ Study Guide and Intervention, pp. 17–18 ▪ Skills Practice, p. 19 ▪ Practice, p. 20 ▪ Word Problem Practice, p. 21	▪ Study Guide and Intervention, pp. 17–18 ▪ Skills Practice, p. 19 ▪ Practice, p. 20 ▪ Word Problem Practice, p. 21 ▪ Enrichment, p. 22	▪ Practice, p. 20 ▪ Word Problem Practice, p. 21 ▪ Enrichment, p. 22	▪ Study Guide and Intervention, pp. 17–18 ▪ Skills Practice, p. 19 ▪ Practice, p. 20 ▪ Word Problem Practice, p. 21
Other	▪ 5-Minute Check 5-3 ▪ Study Notebook	▪ 5-Minute Check 5-3 ▪ Study Notebook	▪ 5-Minute Check 5-3 ▪ Study Notebook	▪ 5-Minute Check 5-3 ▪ Study Notebook

You can translate sentences into multi-step inequalities and then solve them using the Properties of Inequalities.

Real-WorldCareer

Veterinarian Veterinarians take care of sick and injured animals. Vets can work anywhere from a zoo to a research facility to owning their own practice. Vets need to earn a bachelor's degree, attend vet college for 4 years, and take a test to get licensed.

Example 3 Write and Solve an Inequality

Define a variable, write an inequality, and solve the problem.

Five minus 6 times a number is more than four times the number plus 45.

Let n be the number.

Five	minus	six times a number	is more than	four times a number	plus	forty-five.
5	$-$	$6n$	$>$	$4n$	$+$	45

$5 - 10n > 45$ Subtract $4n$ from each side and simplify.

$-10n > 40$ Subtract 5 from each side and simplify.

$\frac{-10n}{-10} < \frac{40}{-10}$ Divide each side by -10, and reverse the inequality.

$n < -4$ Simplify.

The solution set is $\{n \mid n < -4\}$.

GuidedPractice

3. *Two more than half of a number is greater than twenty-seven.* **Sample answer: Let $n =$ the number; $\frac{1}{2}n + 2 > 27$; $\{n \mid n > 50\}$.**

2 Solve Inequalities Involving the Distributive Property

When solving inequalities that contain grouping symbols, use the Distributive Property to remove the grouping symbols first. Then use the order of operations to simplify the resulting inequality.

Example 4 Distributive Property

Solve $4(3t - 5) + 7 \geq 8t + 3$. Graph the solution on a number line.

$4(3t - 5) + 7 \geq 8t + 3$ Original inequality

$12t - 20 + 7 \geq 8t + 3$ Distributive Property

$12t - 13 \geq 8t + 3$ Combine like terms.

$4t - 13 \geq 3$ Subtract $8t$ from each side and simplify.

$4t \geq 16$ Add 13 to each side.

$\frac{4t}{4} \geq \frac{16}{4}$ Divide each side by 4.

$t \geq 4$ Simplify.

The solution set is $\{t \mid t \geq 4\}$.

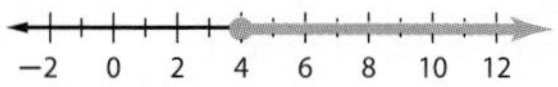

GuidedPractice

4A–4B. See margin for graphs.

Solve each inequality. Graph the solution on a number line.

4A. $6(5z - 3) \leq 36z$ **$\{z \mid z \geq -3\}$**

4B. $2(h + 6) > -3(8 - h)$ **$\{h \mid h < 36\}$**

WatchOut!

Distributive Property If a negative number is multiplied by a sum or difference, remember to distribute the negative sign along with the number to each term inside the parentheses.

If solving an inequality results in a statement that is always true, the solution set is the set of all real numbers. This solution set is written as $\{x \mid x$ is a real number.$\}$. If solving an inequality results in a statement that is never true, the solution set is the empty set, which is written as the symbol $\varnothing$. The empty set has no members.

1 Solve Multi-Step Inequalities

Example 1 shows how to solve a multi-step inequality. **Example 2** shows how to solve a multi-step inequality involving a negative coefficient. **Example 3** shows how to write and solve an inequality.

Formative Assessment

Use the Guided Practice exercises after each example to determine students' understanding of concepts.

Additional Examples

1 **FAXES** Adriana has a budget of \$115 for faxes. The fax service she uses charges \$25 to activate an account and \$0.08 per page to send faxes. How many pages can Adriana fax and stay within her budget? Use the inequality $25 + 0.08p \leq 115$. She can send at most 1125 faxes.

2 Solve $13 - 11d \geq 79$. Check your solution. $\{d \mid d \leq -6\}$

3 Define a variable, write an inequality, and solve the problem. Then check your solution. *Four times a number plus twelve is less than the number minus three.* Let $n =$ the number; $4n + 12 < n - 3$; $\{n \mid n < -5\}$.

Additional Examples also in Interactive Classroom PowerPoint® Presentations

IWB Interactive White Board READY

2 Solving Inequalities Involving the Distributive Property

Example 4 shows how to use the Distributive Property to solve a multi-step inequality. **Example 5** shows how to solve an inequality that results in the empty set or the set of all real numbers.

Additional Answers (Guided Practice)

4A.

4B.

Focus on Mathematical Content

Distributive Property When evaluating an expression that contains grouping symbols, you can distribute the term outside the grouping symbols to each term inside the symbols. This allows you to remove grouping symbols. For example, in the expression $3(4c + 2)$, use the Distributive Property to remove the grouping symbols: $12c + 6$.

Teaching the Process Standards

Structure Mathematically proficient students can see complicated things, such as some algebraic expressions, as single objects or as being composed of several objects. Encourage students to examine the expressions in each of the steps to solving an inequality, considering what type of number will solve an inequality. For example in Exercise 4, some number $\frac{2}{3}r$ plus 9 is greater than or equal to -3. So $\frac{2}{3}r$ must be negative.

Additional Examples

4 Solve $6c + 3(2 - c) \geq -2c + 1$. Check your solution. $\{c \mid c \geq -1\}$

5 Solve each inequality. Check your solution.

a. $-7(k + 4) + 11k \geq 8k - 2(2k + 1)$. $\varnothing$

b. $2(4r + 3) \leq 22 + 8(r - 2)$ $\{r \mid r \text{ is a real number.}\}$

WatchOut!

Student Misconceptions Students may incorrectly assume that the solution of all inequalities in which the variable has been eliminated is the empty set. Remind students that they must simplify the inequality to determine whether it is a true statement. If the inequality is true, the solution set is the set of all real numbers. Only when the inequality is untrue is the solution the empty set.

Teach with Tech

Wiki On your secure class wiki have students create a page explaining how they worked through solving a multi-step inequality. Be sure they explain how they decided whether or not to reverse the inequality sign. When all agree, save and have students use this as a reference.

PT

Example 5 Empty Set and All Reals

Solve each inequality. Check your solution.

a. $9t - 5(t - 5) \leq 4(t - 3)$

$9t - 5(t - 5) \leq 4(t - 3)$	Original inequality
$9t - 5t + 25 \leq 4t - 12$	Distributive Property
$4t + 25 \leq 4t - 12$	Combine like terms.
$4t + 25 - 4t \leq 4t - 12 - 4t$	Subtract $4t$ from each side.
$25 \leq -12$	Simplify.

Since the inequality results in a false statement, the solution set is the empty set, $\varnothing$.

b. $3(4m + 6) \leq 42 + 6(2m - 4)$

$3(4m + 6) \leq 42 + 6(2m - 4)$	Original inequality
$12m + 18 \leq 42 + 12m - 24$	Distributive Property
$12m + 18 \leq 12m + 18$	Combine like terms.
$12m + 18 - 12m \leq 12m + 18 - 12m$	Subtract $12m$ from each side.
$18 \leq 18$	Simplify.

All values of m make the inequality true. All real numbers are solutions.

StudyTip

Structure Notice that the inequality $4t + 25 < 4t - 12$ means *some number 4t plus 25 is less than or equal to that number minus 12.* No real number makes that inequality true. Observing the meaning of the expressions in each step in this way can lead you to solutions more quickly.

GuidedPractice

Solve each inequality. Check your solution. **5A.** $\{c \mid c \text{ is a real number.}\}$

5A. $18 - 3(8c + 4) \geq -6(4c - 1)$ **5B.** $46 \leq 8m - 4(2m + 5)$ $\varnothing$

3.
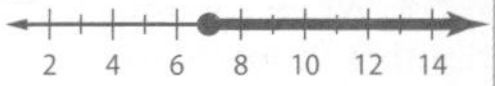

4.

5.
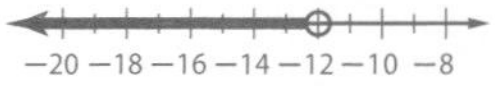

6.

Check Your Understanding

= Step-by-Step Solutions begin on page R13.

Example 1

1. CANOEING If four people plan to use the canoe with 60 pounds of supplies, write and solve an inequality to find the allowable average weight per person.

800-lb capacity

$4n + 60 \leq 800$; $n \leq 185$; at most 185 lb per person

2. SHOPPING Rita is ordering a movie for \$11.95 and a few CDs. She has \$50 to spend. Shipping and sales tax will be \$10. If each CD costs \$9.99, write and solve an inequality to find the greatest number of CDs that she can buy.
$9.99x + 11.95 + 10 \leq 50$; $x \leq 2.8$; Rita can buy 2 CDs.

Example 2

STRUCTURE Solve each inequality. Graph the solution on a number line.

3. $6h - 10 \geq 32$ $\{h \mid h \geq 7\}$

4. $-3 \leq \frac{2}{3}r + 9$ $\{r \mid r \geq -18\}$

5. $-3x + 7 > 43$ $\{x \mid x < -12\}$

6. $4m - 17 < 6m + 25$ $\{m \mid m > -21\}$

Example 3

Define a variable, write an inequality, and solve each problem. Then check your solution. **7.** Sample answer: Let $n =$ the number; $4n - 6 > 8 + 2n$; $\{n \mid n > 7\}$.

7. Four times a number minus 6 is greater than eight plus two times the number.

8. Negative three times a number plus 4 is less than five times the number plus 8.
Sample answer: Let $n =$ the number; $-3n + 4 < 5n + 8$; $\left\{n \middle| n > -\frac{1}{2}\right\}$

Examples 4–5 **Solve each inequality. Graph the solution on a number line.** **9–11.** See margin for graphs.

9. $-6 \leq 3(5v - 2)$ $\{v \mid v \geq 0\}$

10. $-5(g + 4) > 3(g - 4)$ $\{g \mid g < -1\}$

11. $3 - 8x \geq 9 + 2(1 - 4x)$ $\varnothing$

DifferentiatedInstruction AL OL BL ELL

If you have students who are interested in science,

Then point out that there are many natural settings, such as those in Exercises 36 and 41, that can be connected to linear inequalities. Have students write observations about possible connections in their notebooks and then share their observations with the class.

Practice and Problem Solving

Extra Practice is on page R5.

Examples 1 and 2

STRUCTURE Solve each inequality. Graph the solution on a number line.

12. $5b - 1 \geq -11$ $\{b \mid b \geq -2\}$
13. $21 > 15 + 2a$ $\{a \mid a < 3\}$
14. $-9 \geq \frac{2}{5}m + 7$ $\{m \mid m \leq -40\}$
15. $\frac{w}{8} - 13 > -6$ $\{w \mid w > 56\}$
16. $-a + 6 \leq 5$ $\{a \mid a \geq 1\}$
17. $37 < 7 - 10w$ $\{w \mid w < -3\}$
18. $8 - \frac{z}{3} \geq 11$ $\{z \mid z \leq -9\}$
19. $-\frac{5}{4}p + 6 < 12$ $\left\{p \mid p > -\frac{24}{5}\right\}$
20. $3b - 6 \geq 15 + 24b$ $\{b \mid b \leq -1\}$
21. $15h + 30 < 10h - 45$ $\{h \mid h < -15\}$

12–21. See Ch. 5 Answer Appendix for graphs.

22. Sample answer: Let n = the number; $\frac{3}{4}n - 9 \geq 42$; $\{n \mid n \geq 68\}$

23. Sample answer: Let n = the number; $\frac{2}{3}n + 6 \geq 22$; $\{n \mid n \geq 24\}$

Example 3

Define a variable, write an inequality, and solve each problem. Check your solution.

22. Three fourths of a number decreased by nine is at least forty-two.
23. Two thirds of a number added to six is at least twenty-two.
24. Seven tenths of a number plus 14 is less than forty-nine.
25. Eight times a number minus twenty-seven is no more than the negative of that number plus eighteen. Sample answer: Let n = the number; $8n - 27 \leq -n + 18$; $\{n \mid n \leq 5\}$
26. Ten is no more than 4 times the sum of twice a number and three. See margin.
27. Three times the sum of a number and seven is greater than five times the number less thirteen. Sample answer: Let n = the number; $3(n + 7) > 5n - 13$; $\{n \mid n < 17\}$
28. The sum of nine times a number and fifteen is less than or equal to the sum of twenty-four and ten times the number. Sample answer: Let n = the number; $9n + 15 \leq 24 + 10n$; $\{n \mid n \geq -9\}$

24. Sample answer: Let n = the number; $\frac{7}{10}n + 14 < 49$; $\{n \mid n < 50\}$

Examples 4 and 5

STRUCTURE Solve each inequality. Graph the solution on a number line.

29–34. See margin for graphs.

29. $-3(7n + 3) < 6n$ $\left\{n \mid n > -\frac{1}{3}\right\}$
30. $21 \geq 3(a - 7) + 9$ $\{a \mid a \leq 11\}$
31. $2y + 4 > 2(3 + y)$ $\varnothing$
32. $3(2 - b) < 10 - 3(b - 6)$ $\{b \mid b$ is a real number.$\}$
33. $7 + t \leq 2(t + 3) + 2$ $\{t \mid t \geq -1\}$
34. $8a + 2(1 - 5a) \leq 20$ $\{a \mid a \geq -9\}$

B **Define a variable, write an inequality, and solve each problem. Then interpret your solution.**

35. **CARS** A car salesperson is paid a base salary of \$35,000 a year plus 8% of sales. What are the sales needed to have an annual income greater than \$65,000? See margin.
36. **ANIMALS** Keith's dog weighs 90 pounds. A healthy weight for his dog would be less than 75 pounds. If Keith's dog can lose an average of 1.25 pounds per week on a certain diet, after how long will the dog reach healthy weight? See margin.

37, 38. See Ch. 5 Answer Appendix.

37. Solve $6(m - 3) > 5(2m + 4)$. Show each step and justify your work.
38. Solve $8(a - 2) \leq 10(a + 2)$. Show each step and justify your work.
39. **MUSICAL** A high school drama club is performing a musical to benefit a local charity. Tickets are \$5 each. They also received donations of \$565. They want to raise at least \$1500.
    39a. $5t + 565 \geq 1500$; $t \geq 187$
    a. Write an inequality that describes this situation. Then solve the inequality.
    b. Graph the solution. 39b.

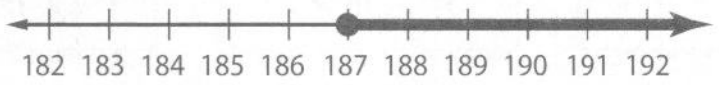

40. **ICE CREAM** Benito has \$6 to spend. A sundae costs \$3.25 plus \$0.65 per topping. Write and solve an inequality to find how many toppings he can order.
    Sample answer: $3.25 + 0.65t \leq 6$; 4 or fewer toppings

Differentiated Homework Options

Level	Assignment	Two-Day Option	
AL Basic	12–34, 55, 57–83	13–33 odd, 60–63	12–34 even, 55, 57–59, 64–83
OL Core	13–33 odd, 35–43, 45–53 odd, 54–55, 57–83	12–34, 60–63	35–55, 57–59, 64–83
BL Advanced	35–77, (optional: 78–83)		

3 Practice

Formative Assessment

Use Exercises 1–11 to check for understanding.

Use the chart at the bottom of this page to customize assignments for your students.

Additional Answers

9.

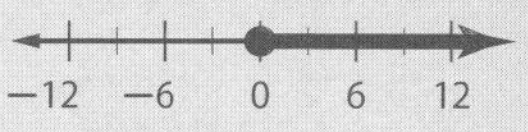

10.

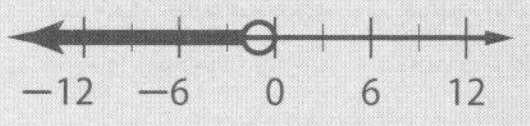

11.

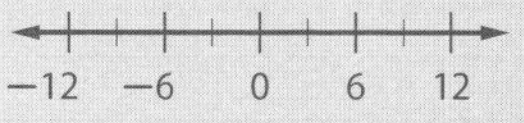

26. Sample answer: Let n = the number; $10 \leq 4(2n + 3)$; $\left\{n \mid n \geq -\frac{1}{4}\right\}$

29.

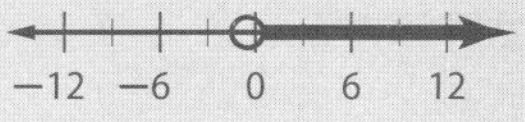

30.

31.

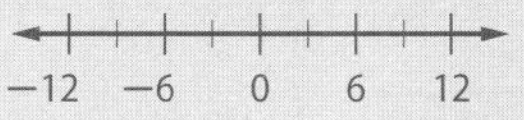

32.

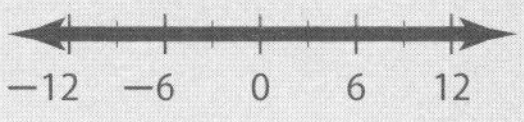

33.

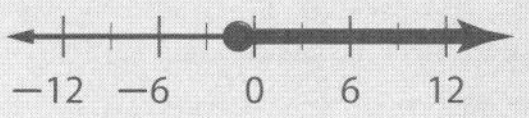

34.

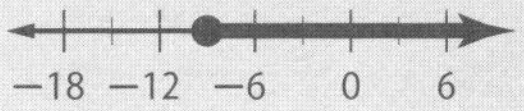

35. Sample answer: Let s = the amount of sales made; $35{,}000 + 0.08s > 65{,}000$; $\{s \mid s > 375{,}000\}$; the sales must be more than \$375,000.

36. Sample answer: Let w = the number of weeks; $1.25w > 90 - 75$; $\{w \mid w > 12\}$; it will take more than 12 weeks for the dog to reach a healthy weight.

41. **SCIENCE** The normal body temperature of a camel is 97.7°F in the morning. If it has had no water by noon, its body temperature can be greater than 104°F.

a. Write an inequality that represents a camel's body temperature at noon if the camel had no water. $t > 104$

b. If C represents degrees Celsius, then $F = \frac{9}{5}C + 32$. Write and solve an inequality to find the camel's body temperature at noon in degrees Celsius. $\frac{9}{5}C + 32 > 104$; $C > 40$

42. **NUMBER THEORY** Find all sets of three consecutive positive even integers with a sum no greater than 36. 2, 4, 6; 4, 6, 8; 6, 8, 10; 8, 10, 12; 10, 12, 14

43. **NUMBER THEORY** Find all sets of four consecutive positive odd integers with a sum that is less than 42. 1, 3, 5, 7; 3, 5, 7, 9; 5, 7, 9, 11; 7, 9, 11, 13

Solve each inequality. Check your solution.

44. $2(x - 4) \leq 2 + 3(x - 6)$ $\{x \mid x \geq 8\}$

45. $\frac{2x - 4}{6} \geq -5x + 2$ $\left\{x \mid x \geq \frac{1}{2}\right\}$

46. $5.6z + 1.5 < 2.5z - 4.7$ $\{z \mid z < -2\}$

47. $0.7(2m - 5) \geq 21.7$ $\{m \mid m \geq 18\}$

GRAPHING CALCULATOR **Use a graphing calculator to solve each inequality.**

48. $3x + 7 > 4x + 9$

49. $13x - 11 \leq 7x + 37$

50. $2(x - 3) < 3(2x + 2)$

51. $\frac{1}{2}x - 9 < 2x$

52. $2x - \frac{2}{3} \geq x - 22$

53. $\frac{1}{3}(4x + 3) \geq \frac{2}{3}x + 2$

48. $\{x \mid x < -2\}$
49. $\{x \mid x \leq 8\}$
50. $\{x \mid x > -3\}$
51. $\{x \mid x > -6\}$
52. $\left\{x \mid x \geq -\frac{64}{3}\right\}$
53. $\{x \mid x \geq 1.5\}$

C **54.** **MULTIPLE REPRESENTATIONS** In this problem, you will solve compound inequalities. A number x is greater than 4, and the same number is less than 9.

a. **Numerical** Write two separate inequalities for the statement. $x > 4$; $x < 9$

b. **Graphical** Graph the solution set for the first inequality in red. Graph the solution set for the second inequality in blue. Highlight where they overlap.

54b. See Ch. 5 Answer Appendix.

c. **Tabular** Make a table using ten points from your number line, including points from each section. Use one column for each inequality and a third column titled "Both are True." Complete the table by writing true or false. See Ch. 5 Answer Appendix.

d. **Verbal** Describe the relationship between the colored regions of the graph and the chart. See Ch. 5 Answer Appendix.

e. **Logical** Make a prediction of what the graph of $4 < x < 9$ looks like. The graph would be the highlighted section of the number line.

H.O.T. Problems Use Higher-Order Thinking Skills

55. **REASONING** Explain how you could solve $-3p + 7 \geq -2$ without multiplying or dividing each side by a negative number. See margin.

56. **CHALLENGE** If $ax + b < ax + c$ is true for all real values of x, what will be the solution of $ax + b > ax + c$? Explain how you know. See margin.

57. **CHALLENGE** Solve each inequality for x. Assume that $a > 0$.

a. $ax + 4 \geq -ax - 5$

b. $2 - ax < x$

c. $-\frac{2}{a}x + 3 > -9$ $\{x \mid x < 6a\}$

57a. $\left\{x \mid x \geq -\frac{9}{2a}\right\}$

57b. $\left\{x \mid x > \frac{2}{1 + a}\right\}$

58. **WHICH ONE DOESN'T BELONG?** Name the inequality that does not belong. Explain.

$4y + 9 > -3$	$3y - 4 > 5$	$-2y + 1 < -5$	$-5y + 2 < -13$

59. **WRITING IN MATH** Explain when the solution set of an inequality will be the empty set or the set of all real numbers. Show an example of each.

58, 59. See Ch. 5 Answer Appendix.

Study Guide and Intervention

AL OL ELL

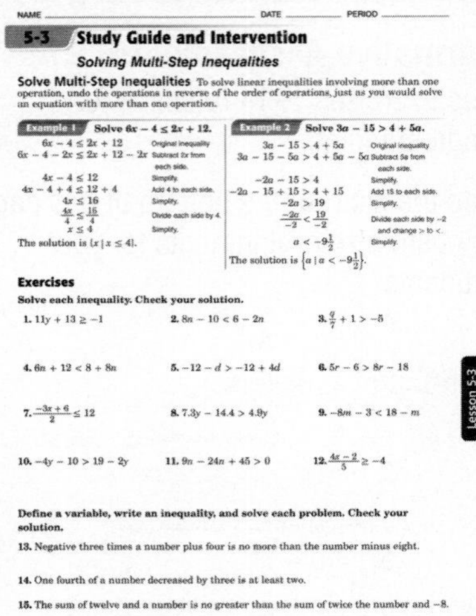

Practice

AL OL BL ELL

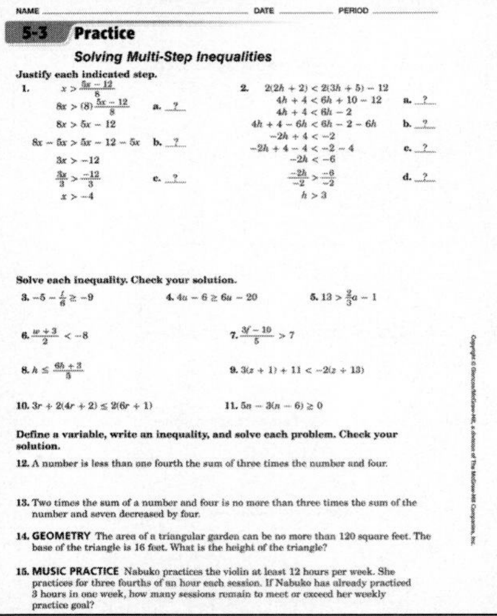

Word Problem Practice

AL OL BL ELL

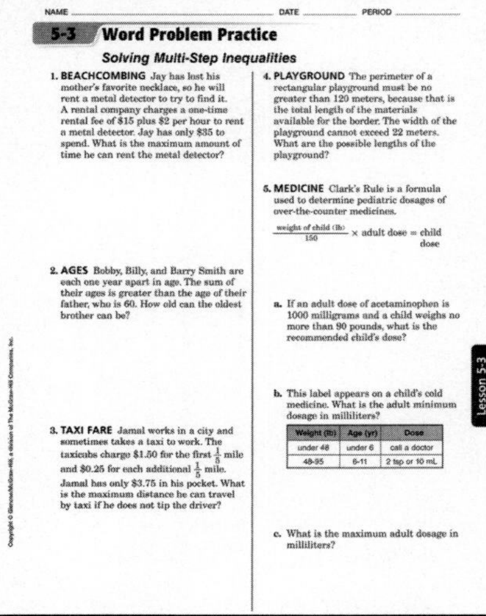

Enrichment

OL BL

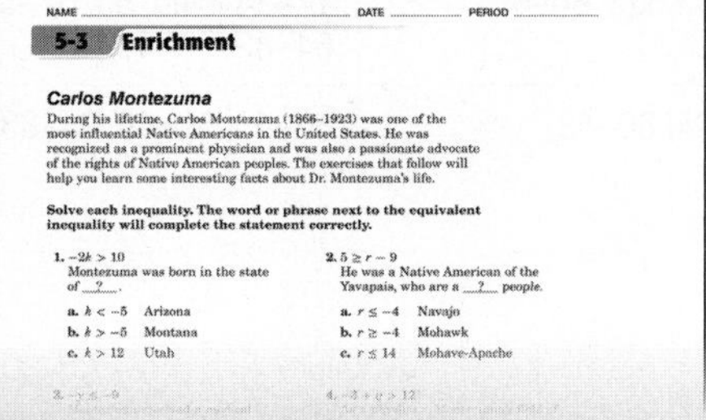

Multiple Representations

In Exercise 54, students use a number line, a table of values, and logical analysis to describe the solution of a compound inequality.

Standardized Test Practice

60. What is the solution set of the inequality $4t + 2 < 8t - (6t - 10)$? **C**

A $\{t \mid t < -6.5\}$ C $\{t \mid t < 4\}$
B $\{t \mid t > -6.5\}$ D $\{t \mid t > 4\}$

61. GEOMETRY The section of Liberty Ave. between 5th St. and King Ave. is temporarily closed. Traffic is being detoured right on 5th St., left on King Ave. and then back on Liberty Ave. How long is the closed section of Liberty Ave.? **G**

F 100 ft
G 120 ft
H 144 ft
J 180 ft

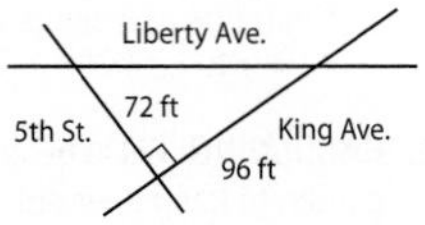

62. SHORT RESPONSE Rhiannon is paid $52 for working 4 hours. At this rate, how many hours will it take her to earn $845? **65 hours**

63. GEOMETRY Classify the triangle. **D**

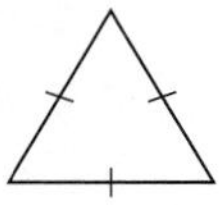

A right
B parallel
C obtuse
D equilateral

Spiral Review

Solve each inequality. Check your solution. (Lesson 5-2)

64. $\frac{y}{2} \leq -5$ **$\{y \mid y \leq -10\}$** **65.** $12b > -48$ **$\{b \mid b > -4\}$** **66.** $-\frac{2}{3}t \leq -30$ **$\{t \mid t \geq 45\}$**

Solve each inequality. Check your solution, and graph it on a number line. (Lesson 5-1) **67–69. See Ch. 5 Answer Appendix.**

67. $6 - h > -8$ **68.** $p - 9 < 2$ **69.** $3 \geq 4 - m$

Solve each equation by graphing. Verify your answer algebraically. (Lesson 3-2) **70–72. See Ch. 5 Answer Appendix.**

70. $2x - 7 = 4x + 9$ **71.** $5 + 3x = 7x - 11$ **72.** $2(x - 3) = 5x + 12$

73. THEME PARKS In a recent year, 70.9 million people visited the top 5 theme parks in North America. That represents an increase of about 1.14% in the number of visitors from the prior year. About how many people visited the top 5 theme parks in North America in the prior year? (Lesson 2-7) **about 70.1 million**

If $f(x) = 4x - 3$ and $g(x) = 2x^2 + 5$, find each value. (Lesson 1-7)

74. $f(-2)$ **−11** **75.** $g(2) - 5$ **8** **76.** $f(c + 3)$ **$4c + 9$**

77. COSMETOLOGY On average, a barber received a tip of $4 for each of 12 haircuts. Write and evaluate an expression to determine the total amount that she earned. (Lesson 1-4) **12(29.95 + 4) or 12(29.95) + 12(4); $407.40**

Skills Review

Graph each set of numbers on a number line. **78–83. See Ch. 5 Answer Appendix.**

78. $\{-4, -2, 2, 4\}$ **79.** $\{-3, 0, 1, 5\}$

80. {integers less than 3} **81.** {integers greater than or equal to −2}

82. {integers between −3 and 4} **83.** {integers less than −1}

DifferentiatedInstruction OL BL

Extension Ask students to explain how you can use the graph of $y = -2x + 6$ to solve the inequality $-2x + 6 < 0$. Sample explanation: The x-intercept ($x = 3$) is the value of x where $-2x + 6 = 0$. All values of x that are more than the x-intercept are solutions of $-2x + 6 < 0$. So, $x > 3$.

Teaching the Process Standards

Reasoning Mathematically proficient students flexibly use different properties of operations. In Exercise 55, have students list the properties of inequalities they know and then choose one to apply.

4 Assess

Yesterday's News Have students write an explanation of how the different methods they learned for solving multi-step linear inequalities relate to the methods learned in previous lessons, such as solving multi-step linear equations and using the Distributive Property.

Formative Assessment

Check for student understanding of Lesson 5-3.

Quiz 2, p. 45

Follow-up

Students have explored expressions, equations, and inequalities.

Ask:

- How are symbols used to write expressions, equations, and inequalities? Sample answer: If only operational symbols are used without a symbol that denotes equality or inequality, the statement is an expression. If an equals sign is used to show that two or more expressions are equal, the statement is an equation. If an inequality symbol is used to show that two or more expressions are unequal, the statement is an inequality.

Additional Answers

55. Add $3p$ and 2 to each side. The inequality becomes $9 \geq 3p$. Then divide each side by 3 to get $3 \geq p$.

56. ∅; if the first inequality is always true, the opposite inequality will always be false.

Formative Assessment

Use the Mid-Chapter Quiz to assess students' progress in the first half of the chapter.

For problems answered incorrectly, have students review the lessons indicated in parentheses.

Summative Assessment

Mid-Chapter Test, p. 47

McGraw-Hill eAssessment Customize and create multiple versions of your Mid-Chapter Test and their answer keys.

FOLDABLES® StudyOrganizer

Dinah Zike's Foldables®

Before students complete the Mid-Chapter Quiz, encourage them to review the information for Lessons 5-1 through 5-3 in their Foldables.

Additional Answers

1. $x > 12$

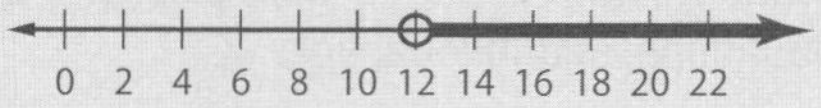

2. $m \geq 4$

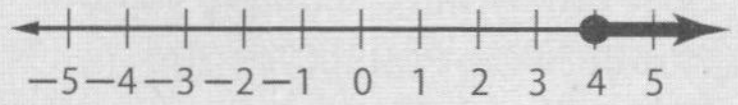

3. $p < -3$

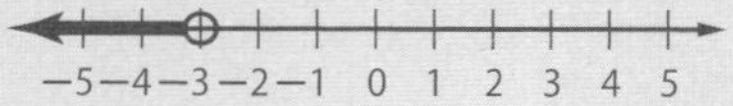

4. $t \geq 21$

CHAPTER 5 Mid-Chapter Quiz

Lessons 5-1 through 5-3

Solve each inequality. Then graph it on a number line. (Lesson 5-1) **1–4. See margin.**

1. $x - 8 > 4$
2. $m + 2 \geq 6$
3. $p - 4 < -7$
4. $12 \leq t - 9$

5. **CONCERTS** Lupe's allowance for the month is \$60. She wants to go to a concert for which a ticket costs \$45. (Lesson 5-1)

   a. Write and solve an inequality that shows how much money she can spend that month after buying a concert ticket. $m + 45 \leq 60;\ m \leq 15$

   b. She spends \$9.99 on music downloads and \$2 on lunch in the cafeteria. Write and solve an inequality that shows how much she can spend after these purchases and the concert ticket. $m + 45 + 9.99 + 2 \leq 60;\ m \leq 3.01$

Define a variable, write an inequality, and solve each problem. Check your solution. (Lesson 5-1) **6–8. See Ch. 5 Answer Appendix.**

6. The sum of a number and −2 is no more than 6.
7. A number decreased by 4 is more than −1.
8. Twice a number increased by 3 is less than the number decreased by 4.

9. **MULTIPLE CHOICE** Jane is saving money to buy a new cell phone that costs no more than \$90. So far, she has saved \$52. How much more money does Jane need to save? (Lesson 5-1) **C**

   A \$38

   B more than \$38

   C no more than \$38

   D at least \$38

Solve each inequality. Check your solution. (Lesson 5-2)

10. $\frac{1}{3}y \geq 5$ $y \geq 15$
11. $4 < \frac{c}{5}$ $c > 20$
12. $-8x > 24$ $x < -3$
13. $2m \leq -10$ $m \leq -5$
14. $\frac{x}{2} < \frac{5}{8}$ $x < \frac{5}{4}$
15. $-9a \geq -45$ $a \leq 5$
16. $\frac{w}{6} > -3$ $w > -18$
17. $\frac{k}{7} < -2$ $k < -14$

18. **ANIMALS** The world's heaviest flying bird is the great bustard. A male bustard can be up to 4 feet long and weigh up to 40 pounds. (Lesson 5-2)

    a. Write inequalities to describe the ranges of lengths and weights of male bustards. $0 < \ell \leq 4;\ 0 < w \leq 40$

    b. Male bustards are usually about four times as heavy as females. Write and solve an inequality that describes the range of weights of female bustards. $0 < 4w \leq 40;\ 0 < w \leq 10$

19. **GARDENING** Bill is building a fence around a square garden to keep deer out. He has 60 feet of fencing. Find the maximum length of a side of the garden. (Lesson 5-2) $x \leq 15$; at most 15 ft on each side

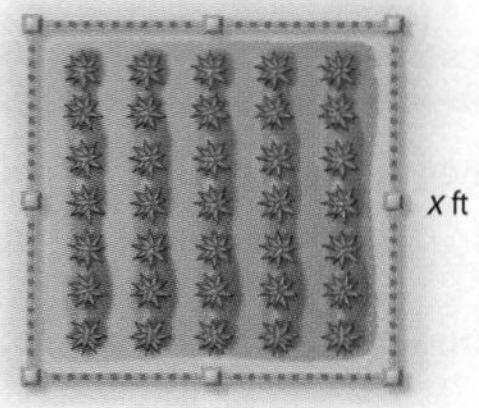

Solve each inequality. Check your solution. (Lesson 5-3)

20. $4a - 2 > 14$ $a > 4$
21. $2x + 11 \leq 5x - 10$ $x \geq 7$
22. $-p + 4 < -9$ $p > 13$
23. $\frac{d}{4} + 1 \geq -3$ $d \geq -16$
24. $-2(4b + 1) < -3b + 8$ $b > -2$

Define a variable, write an inequality, and solve each problem. Check your solution. (Lesson 5-3)

25. Three times a number increased by 8 is no more than the number decreased by 4.
26. Two thirds of a number plus 5 is greater than 17.

25–26. See Ch. 5 Answer Appendix.

27. **MULTIPLE CHOICE** Shoe rental costs \$2, and each game bowled costs \$3. How many games can Kyle bowl without spending more than \$15? (Lesson 5-3) **H**

    F 2

    G 3

    H 4

    J 5

InterventionPlanner

TIER 1 On Level OL	TIER 2 Strategic Intervention AL approaching grade level	TIER 3 Intensive Intervention 2 or more grades below level
If students miss about 25% of the exercises or less,	**If** students miss about 50% of the exercises,	**If** students miss about 75% of the exercises,
Then choose a resource:	**Then** choose a resource:	**Then** use *Math Triumphs, Alg. 1*
SE Lessons 5-1, 5-2, and 5-3 Skills Practice, pp. 7, 13, and 19 TE Chapter Project connectED.mcgraw-hill.com Self-Check Quiz	Study Guide and Intervention, Chapter 5, pp. 5, 11, and 17 *Quick Review Math Handbook* connectED.mcgraw-hill.com Extra Examples, Personal Tutor, Homework Help	connectED.mcgraw-hill.com Extra Examples, Personal Tutor, Homework Help, Review Vocabulary

EXPLORE 5-4 Algebra Lab Reading Compound Statements

A compound statement is made up of two simple statements connected by the word *and* or *or*. Before you can determine whether a compound statement is true or false, you must understand what the words *and* and *or* mean.

Content Standards A1.L.8

A spider has eight legs, *and* a dog has five legs.

For a compound statement connected by the word *and* to be true, both simple statements must be true.

A spider has eight legs. ⟶ true

A dog has five legs. ⟶ false

Since one of the statements is false, the compound statement is false.

A compound statement connected by the word *or* may be *exclusive* or *inclusive*. For example, the statement "With your lunch, you may have milk *or* juice," is exclusive. In everyday language, *or* means one or the other, but not both. However, in mathematics, *or* is inclusive. It means one or the other or both.

A spider has eight legs, *or* a dog has five legs.

For a compound statement connected by the word *or* to be true, at least one of the simple statements must be true. Since it is true that a spider has eight legs, the compound statement is true.

Exercises

1–10. See Ch. 5 Answer Appendix.

Is each compound statement *true* or *false*? Explain.

1. Most top 20 movies in 2007 were rated PG-13, *or* most top 20 movies in 2005 were rated G.
2. In 2008 more top 20 movies were rated PG than were rated G, *and* more were rated PG than rated PG-13.
3. For the years shown most top 20 movies are rated PG-13, *and* the least top 20 movies are rated G.
4. No top 20 movies in 2008 were rated G, *or* most top 20 movies in 2008 were *not* rated PG.

5. $11 < 5$ or $9 < 7$	6. $-2 > 0$ and $3 < 7$
7. $5 > 0$ and $-3 < 0$	8. $-2 > -3$ or $0 = 0$
9. $8 \neq 8$ or $-2 > -5$	10. $5 > 10$ and $4 > -2$

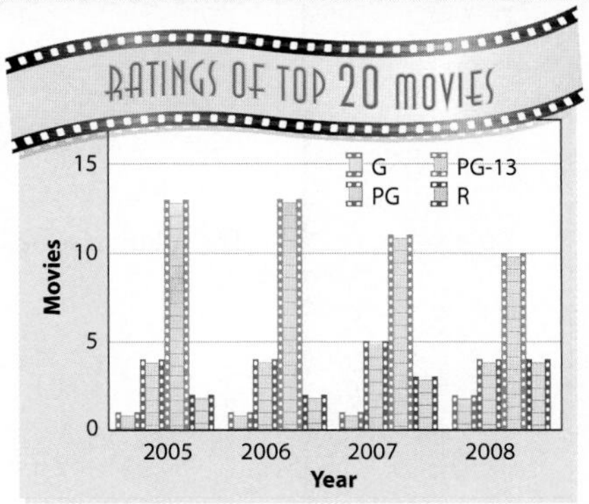

Source: National Association of Theater Owners

1 Focus

Objective Identify compound statements connected by the word *and* or *or* as true or false.

Teaching Tip

Before the activity, ask students to recall the definition of a compound sentence from their language arts studies. Students should know that a compound sentence is a sentence made up of two independent clauses joined by a coordinating conjunction, punctuation mark, or both. Explain that the compound statements in this activity are made up of two independent clauses joined by *and* or *or*.

2 Teach

Working in Cooperative Groups

Have students work in groups of three or four, mixing abilities, to complete Exercises 1–2 and 5–6.

Ask:

- What is a true compound statement that is connected by the word *and* that you can make about the legs of a spider and a dog? A spider has eight legs, *and* a dog has 4 legs.
- What is another true compound statement connected by the word *or* that you can make about the legs of a spider and a dog? A spider has eight legs, *or* a dog has 4 legs.
- Under what conditions is a compound statement that uses the word *or* false? It is false only if both statements are false.

Practice Have students complete Exercises 3–4 and 7–10.

3 Assess

Formative Assessment

Use Exercises 3 and 4 to assess whether students understand the conditions under which a compound statement using *and* or *or* is true or false.

From Concrete to Abstract

In Exercises 5–10, students apply their understanding of compound statements to compound inequalities.

1 Focus

VerticalAlignment

Before Lesson 5-4 Solve absolute value equations with two cases.

Lesson 5-4 Solve compound inequalities containing the word *and* and graph their solution sets. Solve compound inequalities containing the word *or* and graph their solution sets.

After Lesson 5-4 Solve and graph systems of inequalities.

2 Teach

Scaffolding Questions

Have students read the **Why?** section of the lesson.

Ask:

- What inequality symbol represents the term *at least* when we say that a rider must be at least 52 inches? $\geq$
- What is the minimum height a rider could be? 52 in.
- What is the maximum height a rider could be? 72 in.
- Could a rider who is 60 inches tall ride? Explain. Yes, because that rider would be more than 52 in. but less than 72 in.

LESSON 5-4 Solving Compound Inequalities

Then

- You solved absolute value equations with two cases.

Now

1. Solve compound inequalities containing the word *and*, and graph their solution set.
2. Solve compound inequalities containing the word *or*, and graph their solution set.

Why?

- Visitors 4 years of age and older have to purchase a ticket to visit a certain history museum. Visitors less than 18 years of age can purchase a youth ticket. If *v* represents the age of a visitor, we can write two inequalities to represent when a youth ticket can be purchased.

4 years of age and older	less than 18 years of age
$v \geq 4$	$v < 18$

The inequalities $v \geq 4$ and $v < 18$ can be combined and written without using *and* as $4 \leq v < 18$.

NewVocabulary
compound inequality
intersection
union

Content Standards
AI.L.8

Process Standards
PS.1, PS.8

1 Inequalities Containing *and*

When considered together, two inequalities such as $h \geq 52$ and $h \leq 72$ form a **compound inequality**. A compound inequality containing *and* is only true if both inequalities are true. Its graph is where the graphs of the two inequalities overlap. This is called the **intersection** of the two graphs.

The intersection can be found by graphing each inequality and then determining where the graphs intersect.

$x \geq 3$

$x < 7$

$x \geq 3$ and $x < 7$
$3 \leq x < 7$

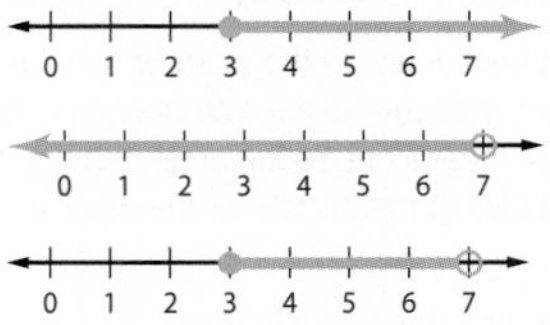

The statement $3 \leq x < 7$ can be read as *x is greater than or equal to 3 and less than 7* or *x is between 3 and 7 including 3.*

Example 1 Solve and Graph an Intersection

Solve $-2 \leq x - 3 < 4$. Then graph the solution set.

First, express $-2 \leq x - 3 < 4$ using *and*. Then solve each inequality.

$-2 \leq x - 3$	and	$x - 3 < 4$	Write the inequalities.
$-2 + 3 \leq x - 3 + 3$		$x - 3 + 3 < 4 + 3$	Add 3 to each side.
$1 \leq x$		$x < 7$	Simplify.

The solution set is $\{x \mid 1 \leq x < 7\}$. Now graph the solution set.

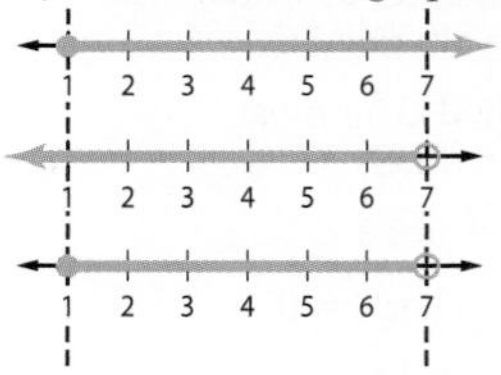

Graph $1 \leq x$ or $x \geq 1$.

Graph $x < 7$.

Find the intersection of the graphs.

Lesson 5-4 Resources

Resource	Approaching Level AL	On Level OL	Beyond Level BL	English Learners ELL
Teacher Edition	▪ Differentiated Instruction, p. 310	▪ Differentiated Instruction, p. 311	▪ Differentiated Instruction, pp. 310, 311	▪ Differentiated Instruction, p. 310
Chapter Resource Masters	▪ Study Guide and Intervention, pp. 23–24 ▪ Skills Practice, p. 25 ▪ Practice, p. 26 ▪ Word Problem Practice, p. 27	▪ Study Guide and Intervention, pp. 23–24 ▪ Skills Practice, p. 25 ▪ Practice, p. 26 ▪ Word Problem Practice, p. 27 ▪ Enrichment, p. 28	▪ Practice, p. 26 ▪ Word Problem Practice, p. 27 ▪ Enrichment, p. 28	▪ Study Guide and Intervention, pp. 23–24 ▪ Skills Practice, p. 26 ▪ Practice, p. 26 ▪ Word Problem Practice, p. 27
Other	▪ 5-Minute Check 5-4 ▪ Study Notebook ▪ Teaching Algebra with Manipulatives	▪ 5-Minute Check 5-4 ▪ Study Notebook ▪ Teaching Algebra with Manipulatives	▪ 5-Minute Check 5-4 ▪ Study Notebook	▪ 5-Minute Check 5-4 ▪ Study Notebook ▪ Teaching Algebra with Manipulatives

GuidedPractice

Solve each compound inequality. Then graph the solution set.

1A. $y - 3 \geq -11$ and $y - 3 \leq -8$ **1B.** $6 \leq r + 7 < 10$

1A. $\{y \mid -8 \leq y \leq -5\}$

1B. $\{r \mid -1 \leq r < 3\}$

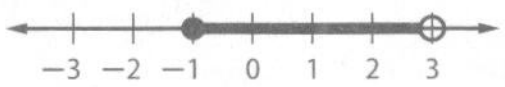

2 Inequalities Containing *or*

Another type of compound inequality contains the word *or*. A compound inequality containing *or* is true if at least one of the inequalities is true. Its graph is the **union** of the graphs of two inequalities.

$x > 2$

$x \leq -1$

$x > 2$ or $x \leq -1$

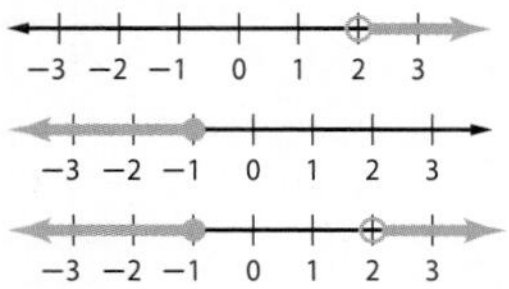

When solving problems involving inequalities, *within* is meant to be inclusive, so use $\geq$ or $\leq$. *Between* is meant to be exclusive, so use $<$ or $>$.

Real-World Example 2 Write and Graph a Compound Inequality

SOUND The human ear can only detect sounds between the frequencies 20 Hertz and 20,000 Hertz. Write and graph a compound inequality that describes the frequency of sounds humans cannot hear.

The problem states that humans can hear the frequencies between 20 Hz and 20,000 Hz. We are asked to find the frequencies humans cannot hear.

Words	The frequency	is at most	20 Hertz	or	The frequency	is at least	20,000 Hertz.
Variable	Let *f* be the frequency.						
Inequality	*f*	$\leq$	20	or	*f*	$\geq$	20,000

Now, graph the solution set.

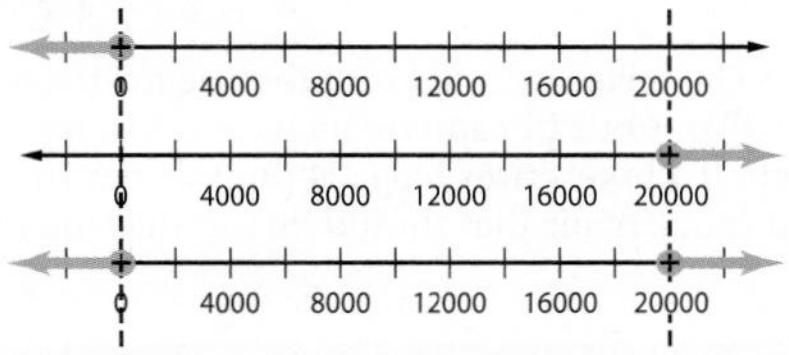

Notice that the graphs do not intersect. Humans cannot hear sounds at a frequency less than 20 Hertz or greater than 20,000 Hertz. The compound inequality is $\{f \mid f < 20 \text{ or } f > 20{,}000\}$.

2. $11.2 \leq h \leq 11.4$

GuidedPractice

2. MANUFACTURING A company is manufacturing an action figure that must be at least 11.2 centimeters and at most 11.4 centimeters tall. Write and graph a compound inequality that describes how tall the action figure can be.

ReadingMath

At Most The phrase *at most* in Example 2 indicates $\leq$. It could also have been phrased as *no more than* or *less than or equal to.*

1 Inequalities Containing *and*

Example 1 shows how to solve a compound inequality containing *and* and how to graph the solution set.

Formative Assessment

Use the Guided Practice exercises after each example to determine students' understanding of concepts.

WatchOut!

Student Misconceptions

Students may assume that the solution set for $\{x \mid 1 \leq x < 7\}$ includes 7. However, because less than 7 does not include 7, the solution set does not include 7.

Additional Examples

1 Solve $7 < z + 2 \leq 11$. Then graph the solution set. $\{z \mid 5 < z \leq 9\}$

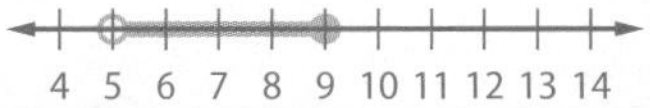

2 **TRAVEL** A ski resort has several types of hotel rooms and cabins. The hotel rooms cost at most \$89 per night, and the cabins cost at least \$109 per night. Write and graph a compound inequality that describes the amount a guest would pay per night at the resort. $\{n \mid n \leq 89$ or $n \geq 109\}$, where n is the amount a guest pays per night

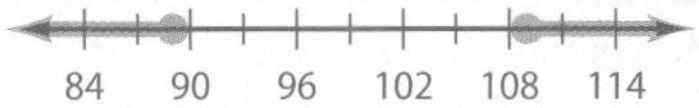

Additional Examples also in Interactive Classroom PowerPoint® Presentations

IWB Interactive White Board READY

2 Inequalities Containing *or*

Example 2 shows how to write and graph a compound inequality containing *or* for a real-world situation. **Example 3** shows how to solve and graph a compound inequality that involves *or.*

Tips for New Teachers

Intersection and Union Symbols Point out that the symbol for intersection is $\cap$. The solution set for Example 1 can be written as $\{x \mid x \geq 1\} \cap \{x \mid x < 7\}$. The symbol for union is $\cup$. The solution set for Example 3 can be written as $\{m \mid m \geq -3\} \cup \{m \mid m > 5\}$.

Focus on Mathematical Content

Conjunctions When the word *and* is used to join two inequalities to form a compound inequality, the resulting sentence is called a *conjunction.* To solve a conjunction, find the values of the variable for which *both* sentences are true.

Additional Example

3 Solve $4k - 7 \leq 25$ or $12 - 9k \geq 30$. Then graph the solution set. $\{k \mid k \leq 8\}$

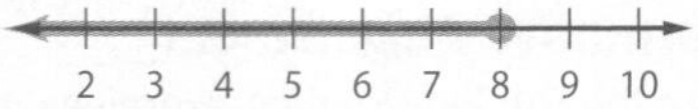

Teach with Tech

Document Camera Choose a student to work through an example using the document camera. Be sure the student uses a graph to find the solution to the inequality.

Tips for New Teachers

Reasoning Students may confuse the meaning of the words *intersection* and *union*. Have them compare the definitions of these two words in real-world situations. For intersection, students may suggest two roads overlapping at an intersection. For union, they might suggest the 50 states coming together to form a union.

3 Practice

Formative Assessment

Use Exercises 1–5 to check for understanding.

Use the chart at the bottom of this page to customize assignments for your students.

Additional Answers

16. Sample answer: Let r = rate of speed, then $40 \leq r \leq 70$.

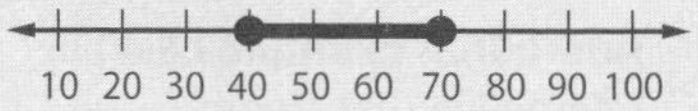

17. Sample answer: Let x = the smaller of two consecutive odd numbers, then $8 \leq 2x + 2 \leq 24$; $3 \leq x \leq 11$; 3, 5; 5, 7; 7, 9; 9, 11; 11, 13

Example 3 Solve and Graph a Union

Solve $-2m + 7 \leq 13$ or $5m + 12 > 37$. Then graph the solution set.

$-2m + 7 \leq 13$	or	$5m + 12 > 37$
$-2m + 7 - 7 \leq 13 - 7$	Subtract.	$5m + 12 - 12 > 37 - 12$
$-2m \leq 6$	Simplify.	$5m > 25$
$\frac{-2m}{-2} \geq \frac{6}{-2}$	Divide.	$\frac{5m}{5} > \frac{25}{5}$
$m \geq -3$	Simplify.	$m > 5$

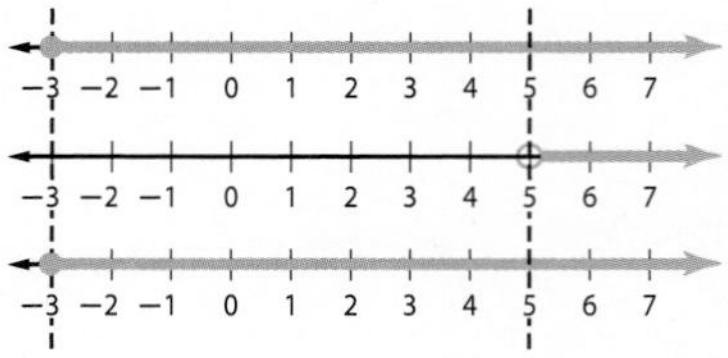

Graph $m \geq -3$.

Graph $m > 5$.

Find the union.

Notice that the graph of $m \geq -3$ contains every point in the graph of $m > 5$. So, the union is the graph of $m \geq -3$. The solution set is $\{m \mid m \geq -3\}$.

StudyTip

Intersections and Unions The graphs of compound inequalities containing *and* will be an intersection. The graphs of compound inequalities containing *or* will be a union.

3A. $\{a \mid a < 3$ or $a \geq 4\}$

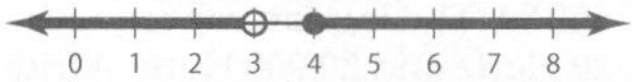

GuidedPractice

Solve each compound inequality. Then graph the solution set.

3A. $a + 1 < 4$ or $a - 1 \geq 3$

3B. $x \leq 9$ or $2 + 4x < 10$

3B. $\{x \mid x \leq 9\}$

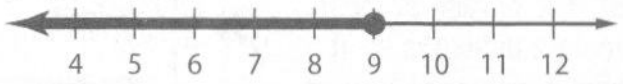

Check Your Understanding

● = Step-by-Step Solutions begin on page R13.

1–4. See Ch. 5 Answer Appendix.

Examples 1, 3 Solve each compound inequality. Then graph the solution set.

1. $4 \leq p - 8$ and $p - 14 \leq 2$

2. $r + 6 < -8$ or $r - 3 > -10$

3. $4a + 7 \geq 31$ or $a > 5$

4. $2 \leq g + 4 < 7$

Example 2

5. **SENSE-MAKING** The recommended air pressure for the tires of a mountain bike is at least 35 pounds per square inch (psi), but no more than 80 pounds per square inch. If a bike's tires have 24 pounds per square inch, what is the recommended range of air that should be put into the tires? **11 psi ≤ x ≤ 56 psi**

Practice and Problem Solving

Extra Practice is on page R5.

6–15. See Ch. 5 Answer Appendix.

Examples 1, 3 Solve each compound inequality. Then graph the solution set.

6. $f - 6 < 5$ and $f - 4 \geq 2$

7. $n + 2 \leq -5$ and $n + 6 \geq -6$

8. $y - 1 \geq 7$ or $y + 3 < -1$

9. $t + 14 \geq 15$ or $t - 9 < -10$

10. $-5 < 3p + 7 \leq 22$

11. $-3 \leq 7c + 4 < 18$

12. $5h - 4 \geq 6$ and $7h + 11 < 32$

13. $22 \geq 4m - 2$ or $5 - 3m \leq -13$

14. $-4a + 13 \geq 29$ and $10 < 6a - 14$

15. $-y + 5 \geq 9$ or $3y + 4 < -5$

Differentiated Homework Options

Level	Assignment	Two-Day Option	
AL Basic	6–17, 39–41, 43–72	7–17 odd, 44–47	6–16 even, 39–41, 43, 48–72
OL Core	7–27 odd, 28–41, 43–72	6–17, 44–47	18–41, 43, 48–72
BL Advanced	18–63, (optional: 64–72)		

Practice and Problem Solving

Extra Practice is on page R5.

Example 2

16. **SPEED** The posted speed limit on an interstate highway is shown. Write an inequality that represents the sign. Graph the inequality.

17. **NUMBER THEORY** Find all sets of two consecutive positive odd integers with a sum that is at least 8 and less than 24. **16–17. See margin.**

B **Write a compound inequality for each graph.**

18. 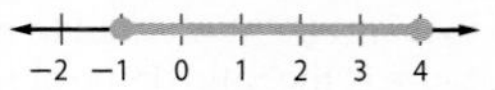 $-1 \le x \le 4$

19. 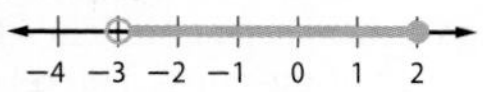 $-3 < x \le 2$

20. 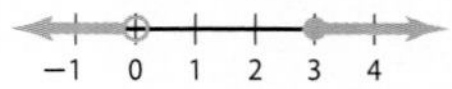 $x < 0$ or $x \ge 3$

21. 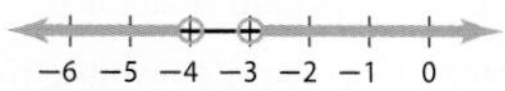 $x < -4$ or $x > -3$

22. 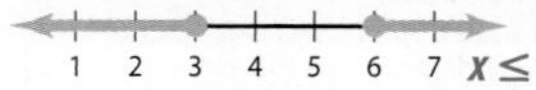 $x \le 3$ or $x \ge 6$

23. 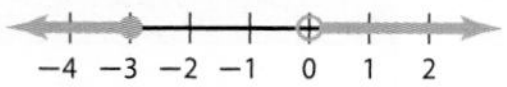 $x \le -3$ or $x > 0$

Solve each compound inequality. Then graph the solution set. **24–27. See Ch. 5 Answer Appendix.**

24. $3b + 2 < 5b - 6 \le 2b + 9$

25. $-2a + 3 \ge 6a - 1 > 3a - 10$

26. $10m - 7 < 17m$ or $-6m > 36$

27. $5n - 1 < -16$ or $-3n - 1 < 8$

28. **COUPON** Juanita has a coupon for 10% off any digital camera at a local electronics store. She is looking at digital cameras that range in price from \$100 to \$250.
    a. How much are the cameras after the coupon is used? **from \$90 to \$225 inclusive**
    b. If the tax amount is 6.5%, how much should Juanita expect to spend? **from \$95.85 to \$239.63 inclusive**

Define a variable, write an inequality, and solve each problem. Then check your solution. **29–32. Sample answers given. Let $n =$ the number.**

29. Eight less than a number is no more than 14 and no less than 5. **29.** $5 \le n - 8 \le 14$; $\{n \mid 13 \le n \le 22\}$

30. The sum of 3 times a number and 4 is between −8 and 10. **30.** $-8 < 3n + 4 < 10$; $\{n \mid -4 < n < 2\}$

31. The product of −5 and a number is greater than 35 or less than 10. **31.** $-5n > 35$ or $-5n < 10$; $\{n \mid n < -7$ or $n > -2\}$

32. One half a number is greater than 0 and less than or equal to 1. **32.** $0 < \frac{1}{2}n \le 1$; $\{n \mid 0 \le n \le 2\}$

33. **SNAKES** Most snakes live where the temperature ranges from 75°F to 90°F, inclusive. Write an inequality for temperatures where snakes will *not* thrive. $t < 75$ or $t > 90$

34. **FUNDRAISING** Yumas is selling gift cards to raise money for a class trip. He can earn prizes depending on how many cards he sells. So far, he has sold 34 cards. How many more does he need to sell to earn a prize in category 4? **from 12 to 26, inclusive**

Cards	Prize
1–15	1
16–30	2
31–45	3
46–60	4
+61	5

35. **TURTLES** Atlantic sea turtle eggs that incubate below 23°C or above 33°C rarely hatch. Write the temperature requirements in two ways: as a pair of simple inequalities, and as a compound inequality. $t \ge 23$ and $t \le 33$; $23 \le t \le 33$

36. **STRUCTURE** The *Triangle Inequality Theorem* states that the sum of the measures of any two sides of a triangle is greater than the measure of the third side. **a.** $x + 9 > 4$, $x > -5$; $x + 4 > 9$, $x > 5$; $4 + 9 > x$, $x < 13$
    a. Write and solve three inequalities to express the relationships among the measures of the sides of the triangle shown at the right.
    b. What are four possible lengths for the third side of the triangle? **36b. Sample answer: 6, 9, 10, 11**
    c. Write a compound inequality for the possible values of x. $5 < x < 13$

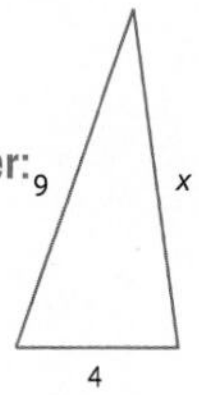

Teaching the Process Standards

Sense-Making Mathematically proficient students can explain the meaning of a problem. In Exercise 5, have students think about how much air pressure may be added.

Structure Mathematically proficient students can see complicated things as single objects or as being composed of several objects. In Exercise 36, encourage students to use number lines to visualize the possible values of x.

Enrichment

OL BL

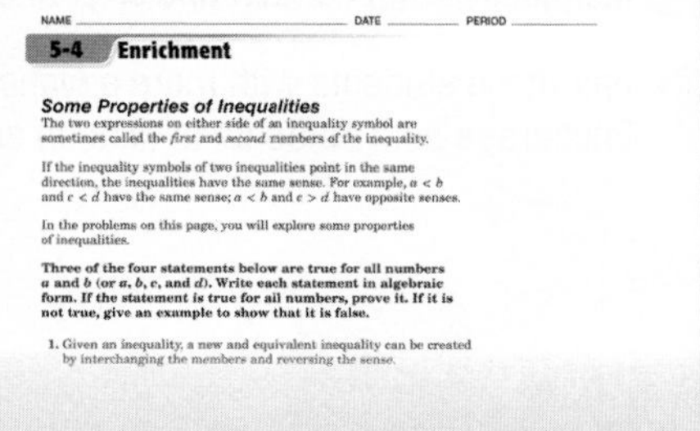
5-4 Enrichment

Some Properties of Inequalities

The two expressions on either side of an inequality symbol are sometimes called the *first* and *second* members of the inequality.

If the inequality symbols of two inequalities point in the same direction, the inequalities have the same sense. For example, $a < b$ and $c < d$ have the same sense; $a < b$ and $c > d$ have opposite senses.

In the problems on this page, you will explore some properties of inequalities.

Three of the four statements below are true for all numbers a and b (or a, b, c, and d). Write each statement in algebraic form. If the statement is true for all numbers, prove it. If it is not true, give an example to show that it is false.

1. Given an inequality, a new and equivalent inequality can be created by interchanging the members and reversing the sense.

Study Guide and Intervention

AL OL ELL

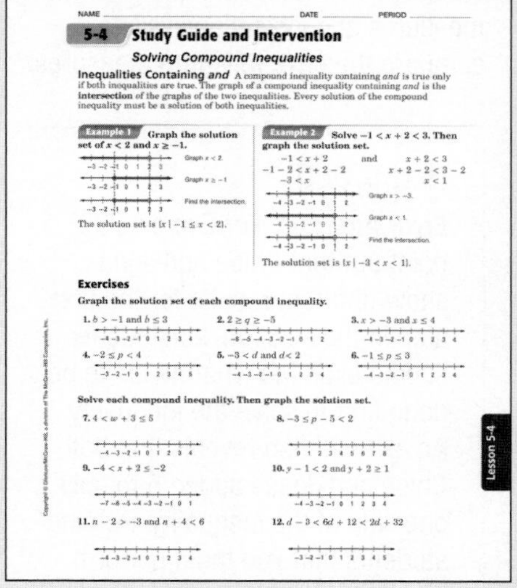
5-4 Study Guide and Intervention

Solving Compound Inequalities

Practice

AL OL BL ELL

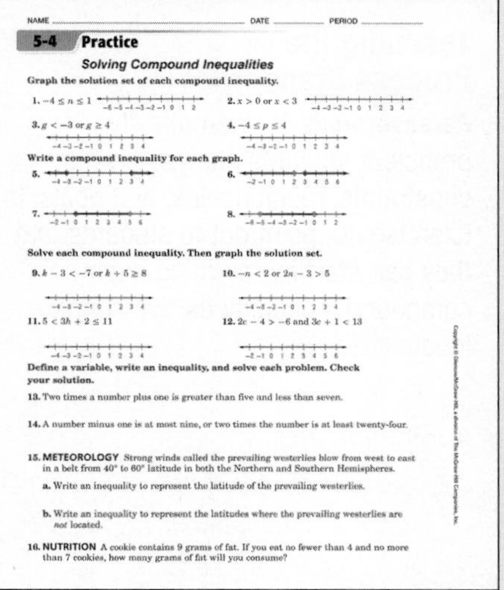
5-4 Practice

Solving Compound Inequalities

Word Problem Practice

AL OL BL ELL

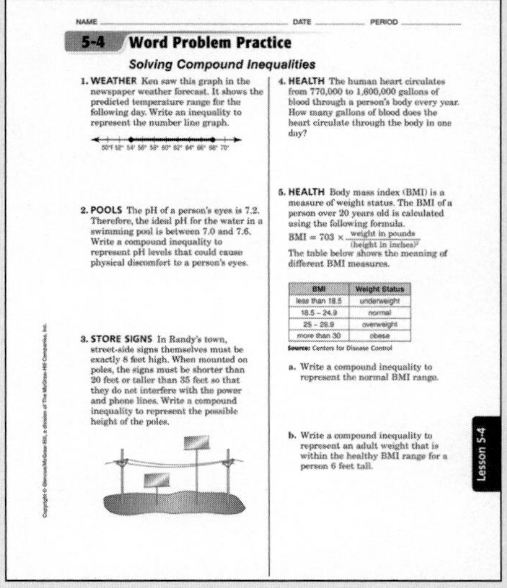
5-4 Word Problem Practice

Solving Compound Inequalities

Multiple Representations

In Exercise 38, students use a table of measures and logical analysis to compare the error in length measures.

WatchOut!

Error Analysis For Exercise 39, point out that Chloe and Jonas show different results for the first step in the solution, so students should examine what needs to be done first to solve the inequality. An examination reveals that both Chloe and Jonas added 5 to only one side of the inequality. Remind students that you must perform the same operation on both sides of the inequality for the inequality to remain true.

Teaching the Process Standards

Perseverance Mathematically proficient students analyze givens, constraints, relationships, and goals. In Exercise 40, point out to students that they can start by rewriting each compound inequality as two simpler inequalities.

Additional Answers

42. Sometimes; the graph of $x > 2$ or $x < 5$ includes the entire number line.

43. Sample answer: The speed at which a roller coaster runs while staying on the track could represent a compound inequality that is an intersection.

37 **HURRICANES** The Saffir-Simpson Hurricane Scale rates hurricanes on a scale from 1 to 5 based on their wind speed.

Category	Wind Speed (mph)	Example (year)
1	74–95	Gaston (2004)
2	96–110	Frances (2004)
3	111–130	Ivan (2004)
4	131–155	Charley (2004)
5	> 155	Andrew (1992)

a. Write a compound inequality for the wind speeds of a category 3 and a category 4 hurricane. **$111 \le x \le 130$; $131 \le x \le 155$**

b. What is the intersection of the two graphs of the inequalities you found in part **a**? **$\varnothing$**

38. **MULTIPLE REPRESENTATIONS** In this problem, you will investigate measurements. The **absolute error** of a measurement is equal to one half the unit of measure. The **relative error** of a measure is the ratio of the absolute error to the expected measure.

a. Tabular Copy and complete the table.

Measure	Absolute Error	Relative Error
14.3 cm	$\frac{1}{2}(0.1) = 0.05$ cm	$\frac{\text{absolute error}}{\text{expected measure}} = \frac{0.05 \text{ cm}}{14.3 \text{ cm}}$ ≈ 0.0035 or 0.4%
1.85 cm	**0.005 cm**	**≈ 0.0027 or 0.3%**
61.2 cm	**0.05 cm**	**≈ 0.00082 or 0.08%**
237 cm	**0.5 cm**	**≈ 0.0021 or 0.2%**

b. Analytical You measured a length of 12.8 centimeters. Compute the absolute error and then write the range of possible measures. **0.05 cm; 12.75 cm – 12.85 cm**

c. Logical To what precision would you have to measure a length in centimeters to have an absolute error of less than 0.05 centimeter? **to the nearest hundredths place**

d. Analytical To find the relative error of an area or volume calculation, add the relative errors of each linear measure. If the measures of the sides of a rectangular box are 6.5 centimeters, 7.2 centimeters, and 10.25 centimeters, what is the relative error of the volume of the box? **0.015 cm**

H.O.T. Problems Use Higher-Order Thinking Skills

39. **ERROR ANALYSIS** Chloe and Jonas are solving $3 < 2x - 5 < 7$. Is either of them correct? Explain your reasoning. **Neither; Chloe did not add 5 to 3, and Jonas did not add 5 to 7.**

Chloe

$3 < 2x - 5 < 7$

$3 < 2x < 12$

$\frac{3}{2} < x < 6$

Jonas

$3 < 2x - 5 < 7$

$8 < 2x < 7$

$4 < x < \frac{7}{2}$

40. **PERSEVERANCE** Solve each inequality for x. Assume a is constant and $a > 0$.

a. $-3 < ax + 1 \le 5$ **$x > -\frac{4}{a}$ and $x \le \frac{4}{a}$**

b. $-\frac{1}{a}x + 6 < 1$ or $2 - ax > 8$ **$x < -\frac{6}{a}$ or $x > 5a$**

41. **OPEN ENDED** Create an example of a compound inequality containing *or* that has infinitely many solutions. **Sample answer: $x \le 2$ or $x \ge 4$**

42. **CHALLENGE** Determine whether the following statement is *always, sometimes,* or *never* true. Explain. *The graph of a compound inequality that involves an* or *statement is bounded on the left and right by two values of x.* **42–43. See margin.**

43. **WRITING IN MATH** Give an example of a compound inequality you might encounter at an amusement park. Does the example represent an intersection or a union?

310 | Lesson 5-4 | Solving Compound Inequalities

Differentiated Instruction AL BL ELL

If some students are overwhelmed trying to discern whether word problems represent compound inequalities that contain *and* or *or* and whether the inequalities are inclusive or exclusive,

Then pair these students with more advanced students to discuss and solve Exercises 33–37. Encourage both students to take an active role in solving the problems.

Standardized Test Practice

44. What is the solution set of the inequality $-7 < x + 2 < 4$? **C**

A $\{x \mid -5 < x < 6\}$ C $\{x \mid -9 < x < 2\}$
B $\{x \mid -5 < x < 2\}$ D $\{x \mid -9 < x < 6\}$

45. GEOMETRY What is the surface area of the rectangular solid? **H**

F 249.6 cm^2
G 278.4 cm^2
H 313.6 cm^2
J 371.2 cm^2

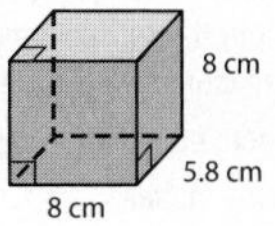

46. GRIDDED RESPONSE What is the next term in the sequence? **38/17**

$\frac{13}{2}, \frac{18}{5}, \frac{23}{8}, \frac{28}{11}, \frac{33}{14}, \ldots$

47. After paying a \$15 membership fee, members of a video club can rent movies for \$2. Nonmembers can rent movies for \$4. What is the least number of movies which must be rented for it to be less expensive for members? **B**

A 9 C 7
B 8 D 6

Spiral Review

48. BABYSITTING Marilyn earns \$150 per month delivering newspapers plus \$7 an hour babysitting. If she wants to earn at least \$300 this month, how many hours will she have to babysit? (Lesson 5-3) **at least 22 hours**

49. MAGAZINES Carlos has earned more than \$260 selling magazine subscriptions. Each subscription was sold for \$12. How many did Carlos sell? (Lesson 5-2) **at least 22 subscriptions**

50. PUNCH Raquel is mixing lemon-lime soda and a fruit juice blend that is 45% juice. If she uses 3 quarts of soda, how many quarts of fruit juice must be added to produce punch that is 30% juice? (Lesson 2-9) **6 qt**

Solve each proportion. If necessary, round to the nearest hundredth. (Lesson 2-6)

51. $\frac{14}{x} = \frac{20}{8}$ **5.6** **52.** $\frac{0.47}{6} = \frac{1.41}{m}$ **18** **53.** $\frac{16}{7} = \frac{9}{b}$ **3.94**

54. $\frac{2 + y}{5} = \frac{10}{3}$ **14.67** **55.** $\frac{8}{9} = \frac{2r - 3}{4}$ **3.28** **56.** $\frac{6 - 2y}{8} = \frac{2}{18}$ **2.56**

Determine whether each relation is a function. Explain. (Lesson 1-7) **57–60. See margin.**

57.

Domain	2	6	10	7
Range	5	0	5	0

58.

Domain	−5	2	−3	2
Range	−10	−7	−5	−3

59. $\{(-4, 11), (-2, 7), (1, 3), (-4, -1)\}$

60. $\{(2, 7), (5, -3), (7, 6), (10, 7)\}$

Evaluate each expression. (Lesson 1-2) **61–63. See margin.**

61. $5 + (4 - 2^2)$ **62.** $\frac{3}{8}[8 \div (7 - 4)]$ **63.** $2(4 \cdot 9 - 3) + 5 \cdot \frac{1}{5}$

Skills Review

Solve each equation.

64. $4p - 2 = -6$ **−1** **65.** $18 = 5p + 3$ **3** **66.** $9 = 1 + \frac{m}{7}$ **56**

67. $1.5a - 8 = 11$ **$12\frac{2}{3}$** **68.** $20 = -4c - 8$ **−7** **69.** $\frac{b + 4}{-2} = -17$ **30**

70. $\frac{n - 3}{8} = 20$ **163** **71.** $6y - 16 = 44$ **10** **72.** $130 = 11k + 9$ **11**

4 Assess

Name the Math Have each student tell a partner the difference between a compound inequality that contains *or* and a compound inequality that contains *and*.

Additional Answers

57. Yes; for each input there is exactly one output.

58. No; the domain value 2 is paired with both −7 and −3.

59. No; the domain value −4 is paired with both −1 and 11.

60. Yes; for each input there is exactly one output.

61. $5 + (4 - 2^2)$
$= 5 + (4 - 4)$
$= 5 + 0$
$= 5$

62. $\frac{3}{8}[8 \div (7 - 4)]$
$= \frac{3}{8}[8 \div 3]$
$= \frac{3}{8} \cdot \frac{8}{3}$
$= 1$

63. $2(4 \cdot 9 - 3) + 5 \cdot \frac{1}{5}$
$= 2(36 - 3) + 5 \cdot \frac{1}{5}$
$= 2(33) + 5 \cdot \frac{1}{5}$
$= 66 + 5 \cdot \frac{1}{5}$
$= 66 + 1$
$= 67$

Differentiated Instruction (OL) (BL)

Extension Have students find a value of k so that the solution set of $k - 5 \leq x - 6 \leq 3$ is $\{x \mid 6 \leq x \leq 9\}$. 5

1 Focus

VerticalAlignment

Before Lesson 5-5 Solve equations involving absolute value.

Lesson 5-5 Solve and graph absolute value inequalities (<). Solve and graph absolute value inequalities (>).

After Lesson 5-5 Graph inequalities in two variables.

2 Teach

Scaffolding Questions

Have students read the **Why?** section of the lesson.

Ask:

- How would you represent the length of a baby carrot x sliced by the machine with an absolute value inequality? $|x - 3| \leq \frac{1}{8}$
- What graph would represent the length of baby carrots sliced by the machine?

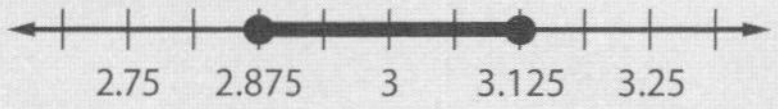

- If the accuracy of the machine were within $\frac{1}{4}$ of an inch, would the margin of error be less or greater? greater

LESSON 5-5 Inequalities Involving Absolute Value

Then

- You solved equations involving absolute value.

Now

1. Solve and graph absolute value inequalities (<).
2. Solve and graph absolute value inequalities (>).

Why?

- Some companies use absolute value inequalities to control the quality of their product. To make baby carrots, long carrots are sliced into 3-inch sections and peeled. If the machine is accurate to within $\frac{1}{8}$ of an inch, the length ranges from $2\frac{7}{8}$ inches to $3\frac{1}{8}$ inches.

Process Standards PS.3, PS.7

1 Absolute Value Inequalities (<)

The inequality $|x| < 3$ means that the distance between x and 0 is less than 3.

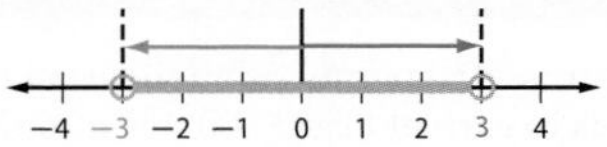

So, $x > -3$ and $x < 3$. The solution set is $\{x \mid -3 < x < 3\}$.

When solving absolute value inequalities, there are two cases to consider.

Case 1 The expression inside the absolute value symbols is nonnegative.

Case 2 The expression inside the absolute value symbols is negative.

The solution is the intersection of the solutions of these two cases.

Example 1 Solve Absolute Value Inequalities (<)

Solve each inequality. Then graph the solution set.

a. $|m + 2| < 11$

Rewrite $|m + 2| < 11$ for Case 1 *and* Case 2.

Case 1 $m + 2$ is nonnegative. **and** **Case 2** $m + 2$ is negative.

$$m + 2 < 11$$
$$m + 2 - 2 < 11 - 2$$
$$m < 9$$

$$-(m + 2) < 11$$
$$m + 2 > -11$$
$$m + 2 - 2 > -11 - 2$$
$$m > -13$$

So, $m < 9$ and $m > -13$. The solution set is $\{m \mid -13 < m < 9\}$.

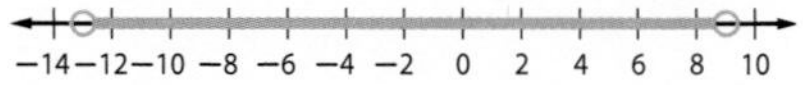

b. $|y - 1| < -2$

$|y - 1|$ cannot be negative. So it is not possible for $|y - 1|$ to be less than −2. Therefore, there is no solution, and the solution set is the empty set, Ø.

GuidedPractice

1A. $|n - 8| \leq 2$ **1A.** $\{n \mid 6 \leq n \leq 10\}$

1B. $|2c - 5| < -3$ Ø

Lesson 5-5 Resources

Resource	Approaching Level AL	On Level OL	Beyond Level BL	English Learners ELL
Teacher Edition	▪ Differentiated Instruction, p. 313	▪ Differentiated Instruction, pp. 313, 316	▪ Differentiated Instruction, p. 316	
Chapter Resource Masters	▪ Study Guide and Intervention, pp. 29–30 ▪ Skills Practice, p. 31 ▪ Practice, p. 32 ▪ Word Problem Practice, p. 33	▪ Study Guide and Intervention, pp. 29–30 ▪ Skills Practice, p. 31 ▪ Practice, p. 32 ▪ Word Problem Practice, p. 33 ▪ Enrichment, p. 34 ▪ Graphing Calculator, p. 35	▪ Practice, p. 32 ▪ Word Problem Practice, p. 33 ▪ Enrichment, p. 34	▪ Study Guide and Intervention, pp. 29–30 ▪ Skills Practice, p. 31 ▪ Practice, p. 32 ▪ Word Problem Practice, p. 33
Other	▪ 5-Minute Check 5-5 ▪ Study Notebook	▪ 5-Minute Check 5-5 ▪ Study Notebook	▪ 5-Minute Check 5-5 ▪ Study Notebook	▪ 5-Minute Check 5-5 ▪ Study Notebook

Real-World Example 2 Apply Absolute Value Inequalities

INTERNET A recent survey showed that 65% of young adults watched online video clips. The margin of error was within 3 percentage points. Find the range of young adults who use video sharing sites.

The difference between the actual number of viewers and the number from the survey is less than or equal to 3. Let x be the actual number of viewers. Then $|x - 65| \le 3$.

Solve each case of the inequality.

Case 1 $x - 65$ is nonnegative. **and** **Case 2** $x - 65$ is negative.

$x - 65 \le 3$ | $-(x - 65) \le 3$

$x - 65 + 65 \le 3 + 65$ | $x - 65 \ge -3$

$x \le 68$ | $x \ge 62$

The range of young adults who use video sharing sites is $\{x \mid 62 \le x \le 68\}$.

Real-WorldLink

One in five Americans use the Internet to view videos. Young adults tend to watch funny videos, while other age groups tend to watch the news.

Source: Pew Internet and American Life Project

GuidedPractice

2. **CHEMISTRY** The melting point of ice is 0°C. During a chemistry experiment, Jill observed ice melting within 2°C of this measurement. Write the range of temperatures that Jill observed. $\{t \mid 0 \le t \le 2\}$

2 Absolute Value Inequalities (>)

The inequality $|x| > 3$ means that the distance between x and 0 is greater than 3.

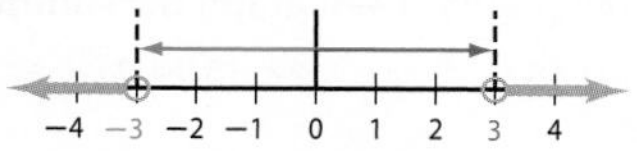

So, $x < -3$ or $x > 3$. The solution set is $\{x \mid x < -3 \text{ or } x > 3\}$.

As in the previous example, we must consider both cases.

Case 1 The expression inside the absolute value symbols is nonnegative.

Case 2 The expression inside the absolute value symbols is negative.

Example 3 Solve Absolute Value Inequalities (>)

Solve $|3n + 6| \ge 12$. Then graph the solution set.

Rewrite $|3n + 6| \ge 12$ for Case 1 *or* Case 2.

Case 1 $3n + 6$ is nonnegative. **or** **Case 2** $3n + 6$ is negative.

$3n + 6 \ge 12$ | $-(3n + 6) \ge 12$

$3n + 6 - 6 \ge 12 - 6$ | $3n + 6 \le -12$

$3n \ge 6$ | $3n \le -18$

$n \ge 2$ | $n \le -6$

So, $n \ge 2$ or $n \le -6$. The solution set is $\{n \mid n \ge 2 \text{ or } n \le -6\}$.

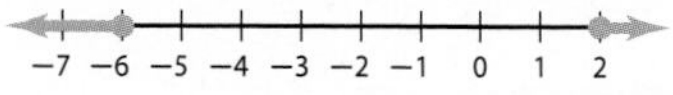

StudyTip

Structure For $|a| \ge b$, where a is any linear expression in one variable and b is a negative number, the solution set will always be the set of all real numbers. Since $|a|$ is always greater than or equal to zero, $|a|$ is always greater than or equal to b.

GuidedPractice

Solve each inequality. Then graph the solution set. 3A–3B. See margin.

3A. $|2k + 1| > 7$

3B. $|r - 6| \ge -5$

1 Absolute Value Inequalities (<)

Example 1 shows how to solve an absolute value inequality of the form $|x| < n$. **Example 2** shows how to solve an absolute value inequality involving a real-world situation.

Formative Assessment

Use the Guided Practice exercises after each Example to determine students' understanding of concepts.

Additional Example

1 Solve each inequality. Then graph the solution set.

a. $|n - 3| \le 12$

$\{n \mid -9 \le n \le 15\}$

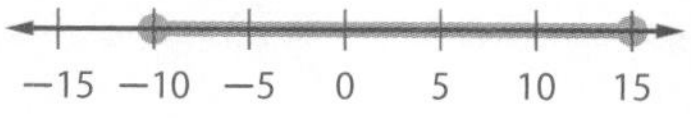

b. $|x + 6| < -8$ $\varnothing$

Additional Examples also in Interactive Classroom PowerPoint® Presentations

IWB Interactive White Board READY

2 Absolute Value Inequalities (>)

Example 3 shows how to solve an absolute value inequality of the form $|x| > n$.

Teaching the Process Standards

Structure Mathematically proficient students can see complicated things as single objects or as being composed of several objects. Stress that any expression in absolute value bars represents a nonnegative number.

Additional Answers (Guided Practice)

3A. $\{k \mid k > 3 \text{ or } k < -4\}$

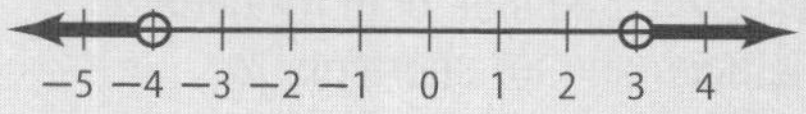

3B. $\{r \mid r \text{ is a real number.}\}$

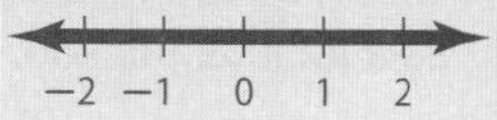

DifferentiatedInstruction AL OL

If students do not understand why $|m + 2| < 11$ is rewritten as $m + 2 < 11$ and $m + 2 > -11$,

Then have them rewrite the second inequality as $-(m + 2) < 11$ and multiply each side by -1 to yield $m + 2 > -11$. This method makes the switch of the direction of the inequality more obvious, as students must make the switch when they multiply each side by -1.

Additional Examples

2 **RAINFALL** The average annual rainfall in California for the last 100 years is 23 inches. However, the annual rainfall can differ by 10 inches from the 100 year average. What is the range of annual rainfall for California?
$\{x \mid 13 \leq x \leq 33\}$

3 Solve each inequality. Then graph the solution set.

a. $|3y - 3| > 9$
$\{y \mid y < -2 \text{ or } y > 4\}$

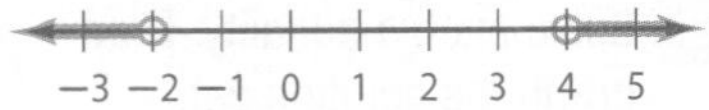

b. $|2x + 7| \geq -11$
$\{x \mid x \text{ is a real number.}\}$

Teach with Tech

Digital Camera Have students use a camera to take step-by-step photos of their work. Then choose several students to display their photos as a slide show, and explain their work in each step.

3 Practice

Formative Assessment

Use Exercises 1–7 to check for understanding.

Use the chart at the bottom of this page to customize assignments for your students.

Teaching the Process Standards

Regularity Mathematically proficient students notice if calculations are repeated, and look both for general methods and for shortcuts. In Exercises 32–35, ask students to examine their method and verbalize their thinking as a general method.

Multiple Representations

In Exercise 42, students use a table of values and a graph in the coordinate plane to describe inequalities.

Check Your Understanding

= Step-by-Step Solutions begin on page R13.

Examples 1–3 **Solve each inequality. Then graph the solution set.** **1–6. See Ch. 5 Answer Appendix.**

1. $|a - 5| < 3$
2. $|u + 3| < 7$
3. $|t + 4| \leq -2$
4. $|c + 2| > -2$
5. $|n + 5| \geq 3$
6. $|p - 2| \geq 8$

Example 2

7. **FINANCIAL LITERACY** Jerome bought stock in his favorite fast-food restaurant chain at $70.85. However, it has fluctuated up to $0.75 in a day. Find the range of prices for which the stock could trade in a day. $\{m \mid 70.10 \leq m \leq 71.60\}$

Practice and Problem Solving

Extra Practice is on page R5.

Examples 1–3 **Solve each inequality. Then graph the solution set.** **8–19. See Ch. 5 Answer Appendix.**

8. $|x + 8| < 16$
9. $|r + 1| \leq 2$
10. $|2c - 1| \leq 7$
11. $|3h - 3| < 12$
12. $|m + 4| < -2$
13. $|w + 5| < -8$
14. $|r + 2| > 6$
15. $|k - 4| > 3$
16. $|2h - 3| \geq 9$
17. $|4p + 2| \geq 10$
18. $|5v + 3| > -9$
19. $|-2c - 3| > -4$

Example 2

20. **SCUBA DIVING** The pressure of a scuba tank should be within 500 pounds per square inch (psi) of 2500 psi. Write the range of optimum pressures. $\{p \mid 2000 \leq p \leq 3000\}$

B **Solve each inequality. Then graph the solution set.** **21–29. See Ch. 5 Answer Appendix.**

21. $|4n + 3| \geq 18$
22. $|5t - 2| \leq 6$
23. $\left|\frac{3h + 1}{2}\right| < 8$
24. $\left|\frac{2p - 8}{4}\right| \geq 9$
25. $\left|\frac{7c + 3}{2}\right| \leq -5$
26. $\left|\frac{2g + 3}{2}\right| > -7$
27. $|-6r - 4| < 8$
28. $|-3p - 7| > 5$
29. $|-h + 1.5| < 3$

30. **MUSIC DOWNLOADS** Kareem is allowed to download $10 worth of music each month. This month he has spent within $3 of his allowance.
    a. What is the range of money he has spent on music downloads this month? $\{m \mid 7 \leq m \leq 13\}$
    b. Graph the range of the money that he spent. **See Ch. 5 Answer Appendix.**

31. **CHEMISTRY** Water can be present in our atmosphere as a solid, liquid, or gas. Water freezes at 32°F and vaporizes at 212°F.
    a. Write the range of temperatures in which water is not a liquid. $\{t \mid t < 32 \text{ or } t > 212\}$
    b. Graph this range.

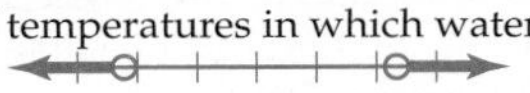

    c. Write the absolute value inequality that describes this situation. $|t - 122| > 90$

REGULARITY **Write an open sentence involving absolute value for each graph.**

32. 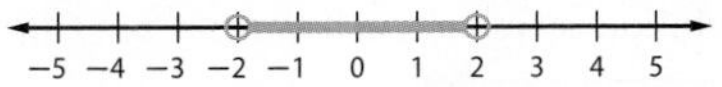

$|x| < 2$

33. 

$|x + 1| \leq 4$

34. 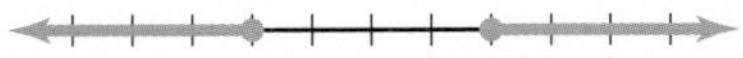

$|x + 1| \geq 2$

35. 

$|x - 5.5| > 4.5$

Differentiated Homework Options

Level	Assignment	Two-Day Option	
AL Basic	8–20, 43, 44, 46–68	9–19 odd, 48–51	8–20 even, 43, 44, 46, 47, 52–68
OL Core	9–29 odd, 30, 31–35 odd, 36–44, 46–68	8–20, 48–51	21–47, 52–68
BL Advanced	21–60, (optional: 61–68)		

36. **ANIMALS** A sheep's normal body temperature is 39°C. However, a healthy sheep may have body temperatures 1°C above or below this temperature. What is the range of body temperatures for a sheep? **$\{t \mid 38 \leq t \leq 40\}$**

37. **MINIATURE GOLF** Ginger's score was within 5 strokes of her average score of 52. Determine the range of scores for Ginger's game. **$\{g \mid 47 \leq g \leq 57\}$**

Express each statement using an inequality involving absolute value. Do *not* solve.

38. The pH of a swimming pool must be within 0.3 of a pH of 7.5. **$|p - 7.5| \leq 0.3$**

39. The temperature inside a refrigerator should be within 1.5 degrees of 38°F. **$|t - 38| \leq 1.5$**

40. Ramona's bowling score was within 6 points of her average score of 98. **$|b - 98| \leq 6$**

41. The cruise control of a car should keep the speed within 3 miles per hour of 55. **$|c - 55| \leq 3$**

C 42. **MULTIPLE REPRESENTATIONS** In this problem, you will investigate the graphs of linear inequalities on a coordinate plane.

a. **Tabular** Copy and complete the table. Substitute the x and $f(x)$ values for each point into each inequality. Mark whether the resulting statement is *true* or *false*.

Point	$f(x) \geq x - 1$	true/false	$f(x) \leq x - 1$	true/false
(−4, 2)	$2 \geq -5$	true	$2 \leq -5$	false
(−2, 2)	$2 \geq -3$	true	$2 \leq -3$	false
(0, 2)	$2 \geq -1$	true	$2 \leq -1$	false
(2, 2)	$2 \geq 1$	true	$2 \leq 1$	false
(4, 2)	$2 \geq 3$	false	$2 \leq 3$	true

b. **Graphical** Graph $f(x) = x - 1$. **b–d. See Ch. 5 Answer Appendix.**

c. **Graphical** Plot each point from the table that made $f(x) \geq x - 1$ a true statement on the graph in red. Plot each point that made $f(x) \leq x - 1$ a true statement in blue.

d. **Logical** Make a conjecture about what the graphs of $f(x) \geq x - 1$ and $f(x) \leq x - 1$ look like. Complete the table with other points to verify your conjecture.

e. **Logical** Use what you discovered to describe the graph of a linear inequality. **Sample answer: The graph of a linear inequality is a boundary line and the region above or below it.**

H.O.T. Problems Use Higher-Order Thinking Skills

43. **ERROR ANALYSIS** Lucita sketched a graph of her solution to $|2a - 3| > 1$. Is she correct? Explain your reasoning. **No; Sample answer: Lucita forgot to change the direction of the inequality sign for the negative case of the absolute value.**

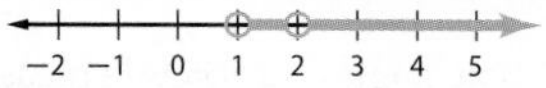

44. **REASONING** The graph of an absolute value inequality is *sometimes, always,* or *never* the union of two graphs. Explain. **Sometimes; the graph could be the intersection of two graphs, the empty set, or all real numbers.**

45. **ARGUMENTS** Demonstrate why the solution of $|t| > 0$ is not all real numbers. Explain your reasoning. **Sample answer: If $t = 0$, then the absolute value is equal to 0, not greater than 0.**

46. **WRITING IN MATH** How are symbols used to represent mathematical ideas? Use an example to justify your reasoning. **46–47. See Ch. 5 Answer Appendix.**

47. **WRITING IN MATH** Explain how to determine whether an absolute value inequality uses a compound inequality with *and* or a compound inequality with *or*. Then summarize how to solve absolute value inequalities.

Study Guide and Intervention
AL OL ELL

5-5 Study Guide and Intervention
Inequalities Involving Absolute Value

Practice
AL OL BL ELL

5-5 Practice
Inequalities Involving Absolute Value

Word Problem Practice
AL OL BL ELL

5-5 Word Problem Practice
Inequalities Involving Absolute Value

Teaching the Process Standards

Arguments Mathematically proficient students can recognize and use counterexamples. In Exercise 45, point out that only one counterexample is needed to show that the solution is not all real numbers.

Enrichment
OL BL

5-5 Enrichment

Precision of Measurement

The precision of a measurement depends both on your accuracy in measuring and the number of divisions on the ruler you use. Suppose you measured a length of wood to the nearest one-eighth of an inch and got a length of $6\frac{5}{8}$ inches.

4 Assess

Crystal Ball Have students write how they think what they learned in today's lesson will connect to the next lesson *Graphing Inequalities in Two Variables.*

Formative Assessment

Check for student understanding of concepts in Lessons 5-4 and 5-5.

Quiz 3, p. 46

Additional Answers

52. $\{b \mid -5 < b < 8\}$

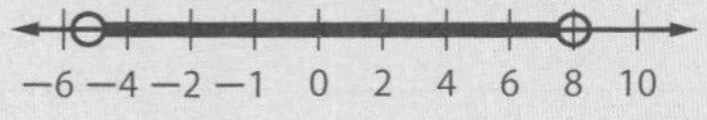

53. $\{t \mid 5 \leq t \leq 6\}$

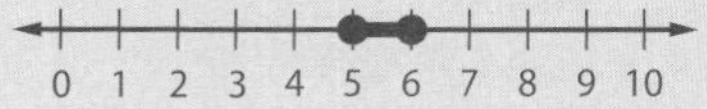

54. $\{c \mid c \geq 4 \text{ or } c \leq -4\}$

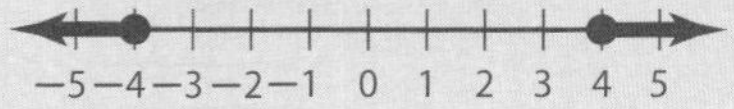

Standardized Test Practice

48. The formula for acceleration in a circle is $a = \frac{v^2}{r}$. Which of the following shows the equation solved for r? **B**

A $r = v$

B $r = \frac{v^2}{a}$

C $r = av^2$

D $r = \frac{\sqrt{a}}{v}$

49. An engraver charges a \$3 set-up fee and \$0.25 per word. Which table shows the total price p for w words? **J**

F

w	p
15	\$3
20	\$4.25
25	\$5.50
30	\$7.75

H

w	p
15	\$3.75
20	\$5
25	\$6.25
30	\$8.50

G

w	p
15	\$6.75
20	\$7
25	\$7.25
30	\$7.50

J

w	p
15	\$6.75
20	\$8
25	\$9.25
30	\$10.50

50. SHORT RESPONSE The table shows the items in stock at the school store the first day of class. What is the probability that an item chosen at random was a notebook? $\frac{1}{8}$

Item	Number Purchased
pencil	57
pen	38
eraser	6
folder	25
notebook	18

51. Solve for n. **B**

$$|2n - 3| = 5$$

A $\{-4, -1\}$

B $\{-1, 4\}$

C $\{1, 1\}$

D $\{4, 4\}$

Spiral Review

Solve each compound inequality. Then graph the solution set. (Lesson 5-4) **52–54. See margin.**

52. $b + 3 < 11$ and $b + 2 > -3$

53. $6 \leq 2t - 4 \leq 8$

54. $2c - 3 \geq 5$ or $3c + 7 \leq -5$

55. FINANCIAL LITERACY Jackson's bank charges him a monthly service fee of \$6 for his checking account and \$2 for each out-of-network ATM withdrawal. Jackson's account balance is \$87. Write and solve an inequality to find how many out-of-network ATM withdrawals of \$20 Jackson can make without overdrawing his account. (Lesson 5-3) **Sample answer: $6 + 22w \leq 87$; up to 3 withdrawals**

56. GEOMETRY One angle of a triangle measures 10° more than the second. The measure of the third angle is twice the sum of the measure of the first two angles. Find the measure of each angle. (Lesson 2-4) **25°, 35°, 120°**

Solve each equation. Then check your solution. (Lesson 2-2)

57. $c - 7 = 11$ **18**

58. $2w = 24$ **12**

59. $9 + p = -11$ **−20**

60. $\frac{t}{5} = 20$ **100**

Skills Review

Graph each equation. **61–68. See Ch. 5 Answer Appendix.**

61. $y = 4x - 1$

62. $y - x = 3$

63. $2x - y = -4$

64. $3y + 2x = 6$

65. $4y = 4x - 16$

66. $2y - 2x = 8$

67. $-9 = -3x - y$

68. $-10 = 5y - 2x$

Differentiated Instruction OL BL

Extension Draw a number line on the board or overhead. Have a student use your number line to create the graph of an absolute value inequality. Ask the rest of the class to write the inequality that the graph models.

316 | Lesson 5-5 | Inequalities Involving Absolute Value

LESSON 5-6 Graphing Inequalities in Two Variables

Then	Now	Why?
You graphed linear equations.	1 Graph linear inequalities on the coordinate plane. 2 Solve inequalities by graphing.	Hannah has budgeted \$35 every three months for car maintenance. From this she must buy oil costing \$3 and filters that cost \$7 each. How much oil and how many filters can Hannah buy and stay within her budget?

NewVocabulary
boundary
half-plane
closed half-plane
open half-plane

Content Standards
A1.L.7

1 Graph Linear Inequalities

The graph of a linear inequality is the set of points that represent all of the possible solutions of that inequality. An equation defines a **boundary**, which divides the coordinate plane into two **half-planes**.

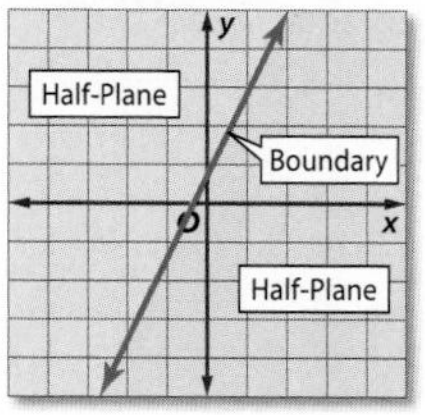

The boundary may or may not be included in the solution. When it is included, the solution is a **closed half-plane**. When not included, the solution is an **open half-plane**.

KeyConcept Graphing Linear Inequalities

Step 1 Graph the boundary. Use a solid line when the inequality contains $\leq$ or $\geq$. Use a dashed line when the inequality contains $<$ or $>$.

Step 2 Use a test point to determine which half-plane should be shaded.

Step 3 Shade the half-plane that contains the solution.

Example 1 Graph an Inequality ($<$ or $>$)

Graph $3x - y < 2$.

Step 1 First, solve for y in terms of x.

$$3x - y < 2$$
$$-y < -3x + 2$$
$$y > 3x - 2$$

Then, graph $y = 3x - 2$. Because the inequality involves $>$, graph the boundary with a dashed line.

Step 2 Select (0, 0) as a test point.

$3x - y < 2$ Original inequality

$3(0) - 0 < 2$ $x = 0$ and $y = 0$

$0 < 2$ true

Step 3 So, the half-plane containing the origin is the solution. Shade this half-plane.

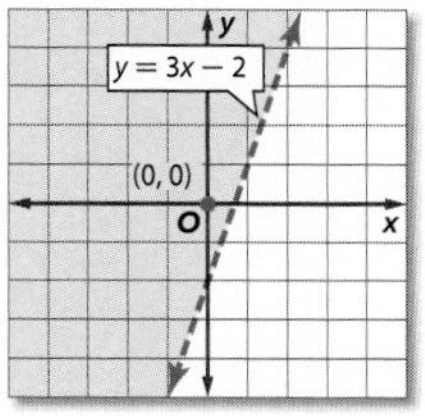

1A–1B. See Ch. 5 Answer Appendix.

GuidedPractice Graph each inequality.

1A. $y > \frac{1}{2}x + 3$ **1B.** $x - 1 > y$

1 Focus

VerticalAlignment

Before Lesson 5-6 Graph linear equations.

Lesson 5-6 Graph linear inequalities on the coordinate plane. Solve inequalities by graphing.

After Lesson 5-6 Graph systems of linear inequalities.

2 Teach

Scaffolding Questions

Have students read the **Why?** section of the lesson.

Ask:

- How many variables do you need if you want to write an inequality for Hannah's budget? Explain. Two; you need a variable to represent the number of units of oil and a variable to represent the number of filters.
- Which inequality symbol would you use to write the inequality? Explain. the symbol for less than or equal to, $\leq$, because Hannah can spend up to \$35
- What inequality can you write to represent the situation? $3x + 7y \leq 35$, where x is the number of units of oil, and y is the number of filters.

Lesson 5-6 Resources

Resource	Approaching Level AL	On Level OL	Beyond Level BL	English Learners ELL
Teacher Edition	▪ Differentiated Instruction, p. 319	▪ Differentiated Instruction, p. 322	▪ Differentiated Instruction, p. 322	
Chapter Resource Masters	▪ Study Guide and Intervention, pp. 36–37 ▪ Skills Practice, p. 38 ▪ Practice, p. 39 ▪ Word Problem Practice, p. 40	▪ Study Guide and Intervention, pp. 36–37 ▪ Skills Practice, p. 38 ▪ Practice, p. 39 ▪ Word Problem Practice, p. 40 ▪ Enrichment, p. 41 ▪ Spreadsheet Activity, p. 42	▪ Practice, p. 39 ▪ Word Problem Practice, p. 40 ▪ Enrichment, p. 41	▪ Study Guide and Intervention, pp. 36–37 ▪ Skills Practice, p. 38 ▪ Practice, p. 39 ▪ Word Problem Practice, p. 40
Other	▪ 5-Minute Check 5-6 ▪ Study Notebook	▪ 5-Minute Check 5-6 ▪ Study Notebook	▪ 5-Minute Check 5-6 ▪ Study Notebook	▪ 5-Minute Check 5-6 ▪ Study Notebook

1 Graph Linear Inequalities

Example 1 shows how to graph an inequality that contains < or >. **Example 2** shows how to graph an inequality that contains ≤ or ≥.

Formative Assessment

Use the Guided Practice exercises after each example to determine students' understanding of concepts.

WatchOut!

Preventing Errors Students may need a quick refresher on slope-intercept form before they graph inequalities. Remind students that slope-intercept form is $y = mx + b$.

Additional Examples

1 Graph $2y - 4x > 6$.

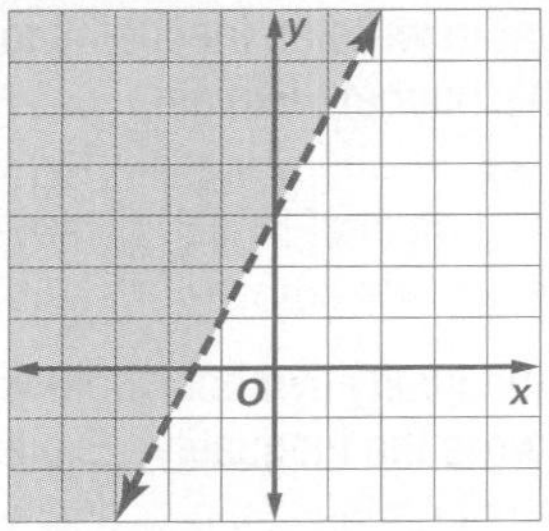

2 Graph $x + 4y \geq 2$.

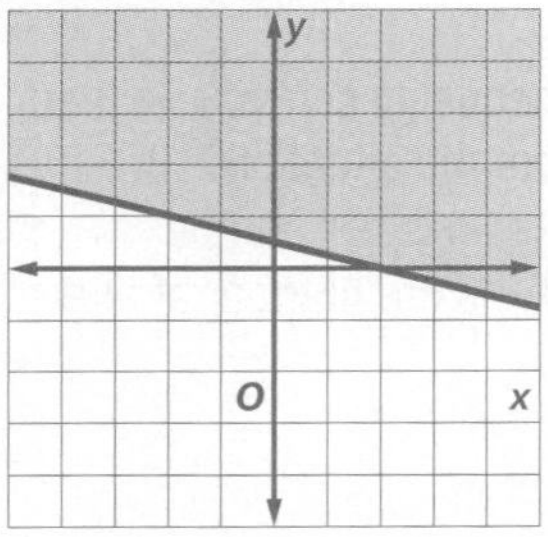

Additional Examples also in Interactive Classroom PowerPoint® Presentations

IWB Interactive White Board READY

Example 2 Graph an Inequality (≤ or ≥)

Graph $x + 5y \leq 10$.

Step 1 Solve for y in terms of x.

$x + 5y \leq 10$	Original inequality
$5y \leq -x + 10$	Subtract x from each side and simplify.
$y \leq -\frac{1}{5}x + 2$	Divide each side by 5.

Graph $y = -\frac{1}{5}x + 2$. Because the inequality symbol is ≤, graph the boundary with a solid line.

StudyTip

Selecting a Test Point When selecting a test point, a standard choice is the origin because it offers easy calculations. However, if it lies on the border, you must choose another point that is not on the border.

Step 2 Select a test point. Let's use (3, 3). Substitute the values into the original inequality.

$x + 5y \leq 10$	Original inequality
$3 + 5(3) \leq 10$	$x = 3$ and $y = 3$
$18 \nleq 10$	Simplify.

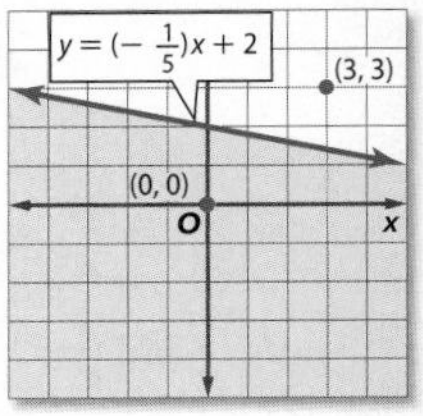

Step 3 Since this statement is false, shade the other half-plane.

GuidedPractice

Graph each inequality. **2A–2B. See Ch. 5 Answer Appendix.**

2A. $x - y \leq 3$ **2B.** $2x + 3y \geq 18$

2 Solve Linear Inequalities

We can use a coordinate plane to solve inequalities with one variable.

Example 3 Solve Inequalities From Graphs

Use a graph to solve $3x + 5 < 14$.

Step 1 First graph the boundary, which is the related equation. Replace the inequality sign with an equals sign, and solve for x.

$3x + 5 < 14$	Original inequality
$3x + 5 = 14$	Change < to =.
$3x = 9$	Subtract 5 from each side and simplify.
$x = 3$	Divide each side by 3.

Graph $x = 3$ with a dashed line.

Step 2 Choose (0, 0) as a test point. These values in the original inequality give us $5 < 14$.

Step 3 Since this statement is true, shade the half-plane that contains the point (0, 0).

Notice that the x-intercept of the graph is at 3. Since the half-plane to the left of the x-intercept is shaded, the solution is $x < 3$.

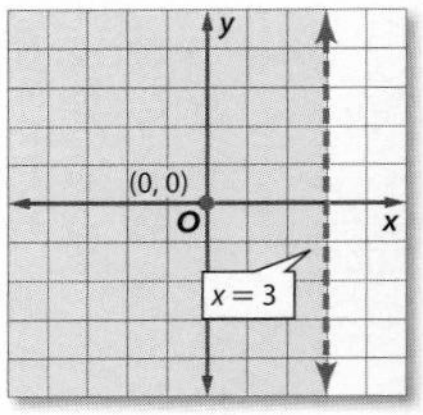

GuidedPractice

Use a graph to solve each inequality.

3A–3B. See Ch. 5 Answer Appendix for graphs.

3A. $4x - 3 \geq 17$ **$x \geq 5$** **3B.** $-2x + 6 > 12$ **$x < -3$**

318 | Lesson 5-6 | Graphing Inequalities in Two Variables

Focus on Mathematical Content

Graphing Inequalities To graph an inequality, begin by solving the inequality for y in terms of x. Then graph the related equation $y = mx + b$. Use a dashed line when the boundary is not part of the solution set and use a solid line when the boundary is included. If the origin is not on the boundary line, use it as a test point to determine which half-plane is the graph of the solution set of the inequality.

An inequality can be viewed as a constraint in a problem situation. Each solution of the inequality represents a combination that meets the constraint. In real-world problems, the domain and range are often restricted to nonnegative or whole numbers.

Real-WorldLink

As a supplement to traditional yearbooks, many schools are producing digital versions. They include features that allow you to click on a picture and see a short video clip.

Source: eSchool News

Real-World Example 4 Write and Solve an Inequality

CLASS PICNIC **A yearbook company promises to give the junior class a picnic if they spend at least $28,000 on yearbooks and class rings. Each yearbook costs $35, and each class ring costs $140. How many yearbooks and class rings must the junior class buy to get their picnic?**

Understand You know the cost of each item and the minimum amount the class needs to spend.

Plan Let $x =$ the number of yearbooks and $y =$ the number of class rings the class must buy. Write an inequality.

$35	times	the number of yearbooks	plus	$140	times	the number of rings	is at least	$28,000.
35	$\cdot$	x	$+$	140	$\cdot$	y	$\geq$	28,000

Solve Solve for y in terms of x.

$35x + 140y - 35x \geq 28{,}000 - 35x$ Subtract $35x$ from each side.

$140y \geq -35x + 28{,}000$ Divide each side by 140.

$\frac{140y}{140} \geq \frac{-35x}{140} + \frac{28000}{140}$ Simplify.

$y \geq -0.25x + 200$ Simplify.

Because the yearbook company cannot sell a negative number of items, the domain and range must be nonnegative numbers. Graph the boundary with a solid line. If we test (0, 0), the result is $0 \geq 28{,}000$, which is false. Shade the closed half-plane that does not include (0, 0).

One solution is (500, 100), or 500 yearbooks and 100 class rings.

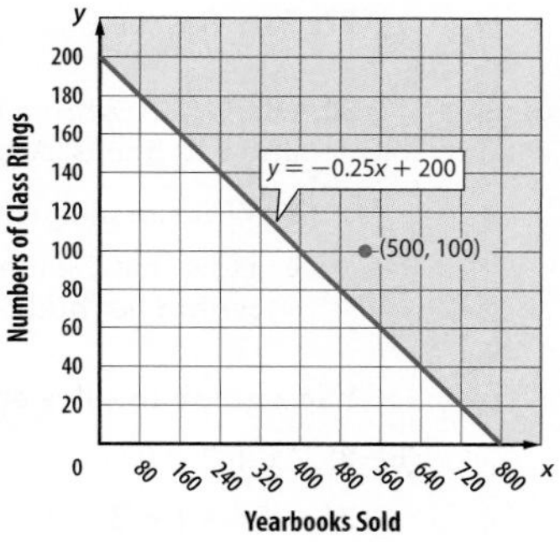

Problem-SolvingTip

Use a Graph You can use a graph to visualize data, analyze trends, and make predictions.

Check If we test (500, 100), the result is $100 \geq 75$, which is true. Because the company cannot sell a fraction of an item, only points with whole-number coordinates can be solutions.

GuidedPractice

4. MARATHONS Neil wants to run a marathon at a pace of at least 6 miles per hour. Write and graph an inequality for the miles y he will run in x hours.

4. $y \geq 6x$

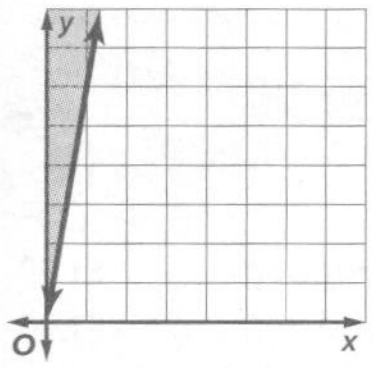

DifferentiatedInstruction AL

If some students have trouble working with the numbers in Example 4,

Then as an alternative problem, have them write and solve an inequality for the budget situation in the *Why?* section at the beginning of the lesson. The inequality they should write, solve, and then graph is $3x + 7y \leq 35$.

2 Solve Linear Inequalities

Example 3 shows how to use a graph to solve an inequality. **Example 4** shows how to write, solve, and graph an inequality involving a real-world situation.

Additional Examples

3 Use a graph to solve $2x + 3 \leq 7$. $x \leq 2$

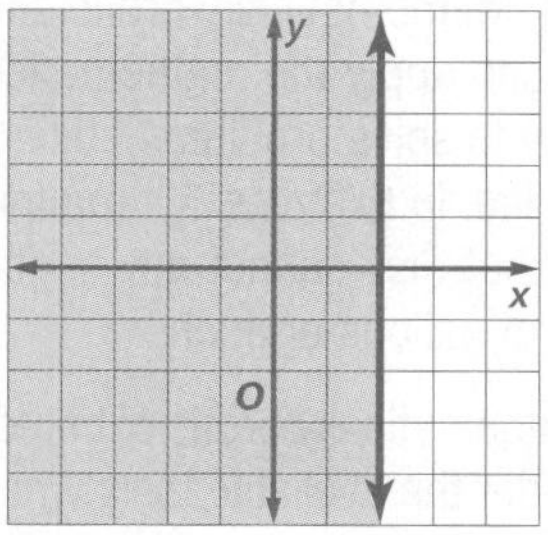

4 **JOURNALISM** Ranjan writes and edits short articles for a local newspaper. It takes him about an hour to write an article and about a half-hour to edit an article. If Ranjan works up to 8 hours a day, how many articles can he write and edit in one day?

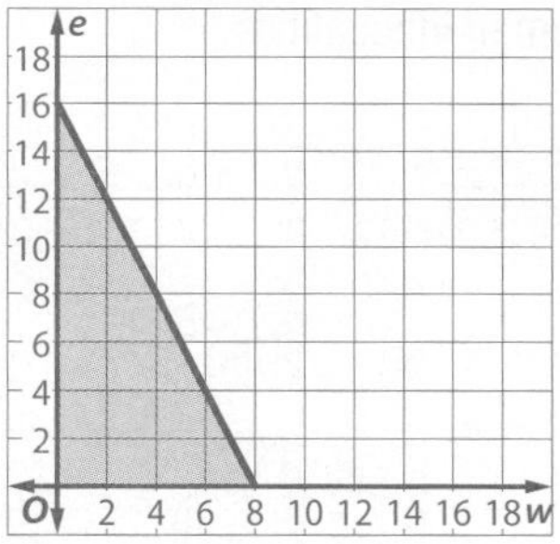

$e \leq -2w + 16$

One solution is (2, 3) or write 2 articles and edit 3. Consider other possibilities.

Teach with Tech

Portable Media Player Create a video showing your students how to graph inequalities in two variables. Post the video on your class Web page for students to download onto their portable media players for use as an additional reference outside of class.

3 Practice

Formative Assessment

Use Exercises 1–11 to check for understanding.

Use the chart at the bottom of this page to customize assignments for your students.

Teaching the Process Standards

Modeling Mathematically proficient students can apply the mathematics they know to solve problems arising in everyday life. In Exercise 30, remind students that they cannot buy negative numbers of gallons or linens.

Tools Mathematically proficient students can consider the available tools when solving a mathematical problem. In Exercise 47, point out that a graphing calculator or spreadsheet may be helpful in testing possible solutions.

Multiple Representations

In Exercise 45, students use graphing and shading in the coordinate plane along with algebraic analysis to solve a system of inequalities.

Additional Answers

11b. Sample answer: 1 skim board and 4 surfboards

37a. $x + 1.25y \geq 2000$

37b.

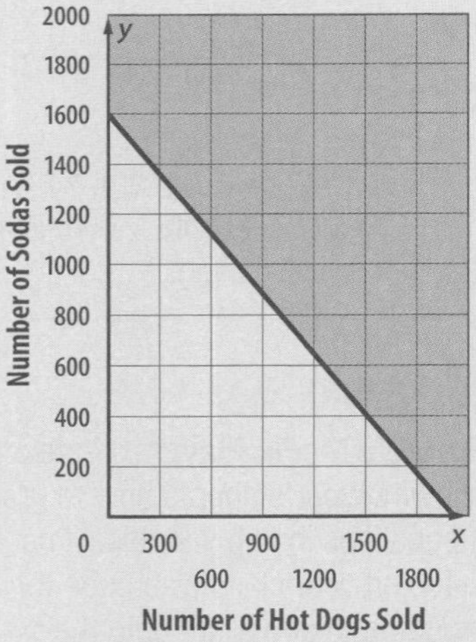

37c. Sample answer: (400, 1600), (200,1500), (300, 1400), (400, 1300), (1000, 1000)

37d. Sample points should be in the shaded region of the graph in part **b**.

Check Your Understanding

● = Step-by-Step Solutions begin on page R13.

Examples 1–2 **Graph each inequality.** **1–6. See Ch. 5 Answer Appendix.**

1. $y > x + 3$ **2.** $y \geq -8$ **3.** $x + y > 1$

4. $y \leq x - 6$ **5.** $y < 2x - 4$ **6.** $x - y \leq 4$

Example 3 **Use a graph to solve each inequality.** **7–10. See Ch. 5 Answer Appendix for graphs.**

7. $7x + 1 < 15$ $x < 2$ **8.** $-3x - 2 \geq 11$ $x \leq -4\frac{1}{3}$

9. $3y - 5 \leq 34$ $y \leq 13$ **10.** $4y - 21 > 1$ $y > 5\frac{1}{2}$

Example 4 **11. FINANCIAL LITERACY** The surf shop has a weekly overhead of $2300.

a. Write an inequality to represent the number of skimboards and longboards the shop sells each week to make a profit. $115x + 685y > 2300$

b. How many skimboards and longboards must the shop sell each week to make a profit? **See margin.**

Practice and Problem Solving

Extra Practice is on page R5.

Examples 1–2 **Graph each inequality.** **12–23. See Ch. 5 Answer Appendix.**

12. $y < x - 3$ **13.** $y > x + 12$ **14.** $y \geq 3x - 1$

15. $y \leq -4x + 12$ **16.** $6x + 3y > 12$ **17.** $2x + 2y < 18$

18. $5x + y > 10$ **19.** $2x + y < -3$ **20.** $-2x + y \geq -4$

21. $8x + y \leq 6$ **22.** $10x + 2y \leq 14$ **23.** $-24x + 8y \geq -48$

Example 3 **Use a graph to solve each inequality.** **24–29. See Ch. 5 Answer Appendix for graphs.**

24. $10x - 8 < 22$ $x < 3$ **25.** $20x - 5 > 35$ $x > 2$ **26.** $4y - 77 \geq 23$ $y \geq 25$

27. $5y + 8 \leq 33$ $y \leq 5$ **28.** $35x + 25 < 6$ $x < -\frac{19}{35}$ **29.** $14x - 12 > -31$ $x > -\frac{19}{14}$

Example 4 **30. MODELING** Sybrina is decorating her bedroom. She has $300 to spend on paint and bed linens. A gallon of paint costs $14, while a set of bed linens costs $60.

a. Write an inequality for this situation. $14x + 60y \leq 300$

b. How many gallons of paint and bed linen sets can Sybrina buy and stay within her budget? **Sample answer: 5 gallons of paint and 3 bed linen sets**

Use a graph to solve each inequality. **31–36. See Ch. 5 Answer Appendix for graphs.**

B **31.** $3x + 2 < 0$ $x < -\frac{2}{3}$ **32.** $4x - 1 > 3$ $x > 1$ **33.** $-6x - 8 \geq -4$ $x \leq -\frac{2}{3}$

34. $-5x + 1 < 3$ $x > -\frac{2}{5}$ **35.** $-7x + 13 < 10$ $x > \frac{3}{7}$ **36.** $-4x - 4 \leq -6$ $x \geq \frac{1}{2}$

37. SOCCER The girls' soccer team wants to raise $2000 to buy new goals. How many of each item must they sell to buy the goals? **a–d. See margin.**

a. Write an inequality that represents this situation.

b. Graph this inequality.

c. Make a table of values that shows at least five possible solutions.

d. Plot the solutions from part **c**.

Differentiated Homework Options

Level	Assignment	Two-Day Option	
AL Basic	12–30, 46, 48–65	13–29 odd, 51–54	12–30 even, 46, 48–50, 55–65
OL Core	13–43 odd, 44–46, 48–65	12–30, 51–54	31–46, 48–50, 55–65
BL Advanced	31–64, (optional: 65)		

320 | Lesson 5-6 | Graphing Inequalities in Two Variables

Graph each inequality. Determine which of the ordered pairs are part of the solution set for each inequality. **38–43. See Ch. 5 Answer Appendix.**

38. $y \geq 6$; {(0, 4), (−2, 7), (4, 8), (−4, −8), (1, 6)}

39. $x < -4$; {(2, 1), (−3, 0), (0, −3), (−5, −5), (−4, 2)}

40. $2x - 3y \leq 1$; {(2, 3), (3, 1), (0, 0), (0, −1), (5, 3)}

41. $5x + 7y \geq 10$; {(−2, −2), (1, −1), (1, 1), (2, 5), (6, 0)}

42. $-3x + 5y < 10$; {(3, −1), (1, 1), (0, 8), (−2, 0), (0, 2)}

43. $2x - 2y \geq 4$; {(0, 0), (0, 7), (7, 5), (5, 3), (2, −5)}

44. RECYCLING Mr. Jones would like to spend no more than $37.50 per week on recycling. A curbside recycling service will remove up to 50 pounds of plastic bottles and paper products per week. They charge $0.25 per pound of plastic and $0.75 per pound of paper products.

a. Write an inequality that describes the number of pounds of each product that can be included in the curbside service. $x + y \leq 50$

b. Write an inequality that describes Mr. Jones' weekly cost for the service if he stays within his budget. $0.25x + 0.75y \leq 37.50$

c. Graph an inequality for the weekly costs for the service. **See Ch. 5 Answer Appendix.**

45. MULTIPLE REPRESENTATIONS Use inequalities A and B to investigate graphing compound inequalities on a coordinate plane.

A. $7(y + 6) \leq 21x + 14$ **B.** $-3y \leq 3x - 12$

a. Numerical Solve each inequality for y. $y \leq 3x - 4$; $y \geq -x + 4$

b. Graphical Graph both inequalities on one graph. Shade the half-plane that makes A true in red. Shade the half-plane that makes B true in blue. **See Ch. 5 Answer Appendix.**

c. Verbal What does the overlapping region represent? **The overlapping region represents the solutions that make both A and B true.**

H.O.T. Problems Use Higher-Order Thinking Skills

46. ERROR ANALYSIS Reiko and Kristin are solving $4y \leq \frac{8}{3}x$ by graphing. Is either of them correct? Explain your reasoning.

Reiko

$4y \leq \frac{8}{3}x$

$y \leq \frac{2}{3}x$

test point (1, 1)

$1 \leq \frac{2}{3}$ false

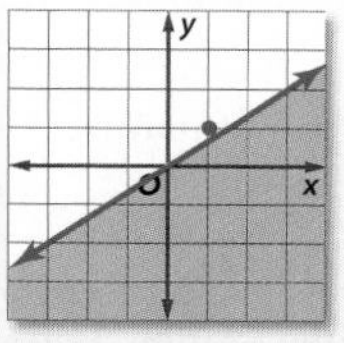

Kristin

$4y \leq \frac{8}{3}x$

$y \leq \frac{2}{3}x$

test point (0, 0)

$0 \leq 0$ true

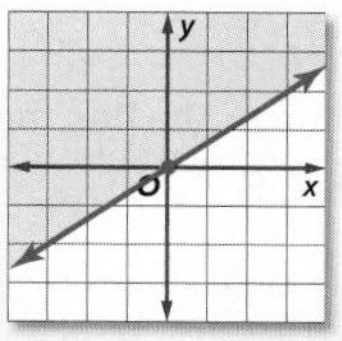

Reiko; Kristin used a test point located on the line and shaded the incorrect half-plane.

47. TOOLS Write a linear inequality for which (−1, 2), (0, 1), and (3, −4) are solutions but (1, 1) is not. **Sample answer:** $y < -x + 1$

48. REASONING Explain why a point on the boundary should not be used as a test point. **48–50. See Ch. 5 Answer Appendix.**

49. OPEN ENDED Write a two-variable inequality with a restricted domain and range to represent a real-world situation. Give the domain and range, and explain why they are restricted.

50. WRITING IN MATH Summarize the steps to graph an inequality in two variables.

WatchOut!

Error Analysis In Exercise 46, since Reiko and Kristin graphed the same solutions, have students examine the two graphs to find any differences. They should see that Reiko and Kristin shaded different half-planes. They should also notice that the test points they used are different. Ask students why one set of test points is better than the other.

Study Guide and Intervention
AL OL ELL

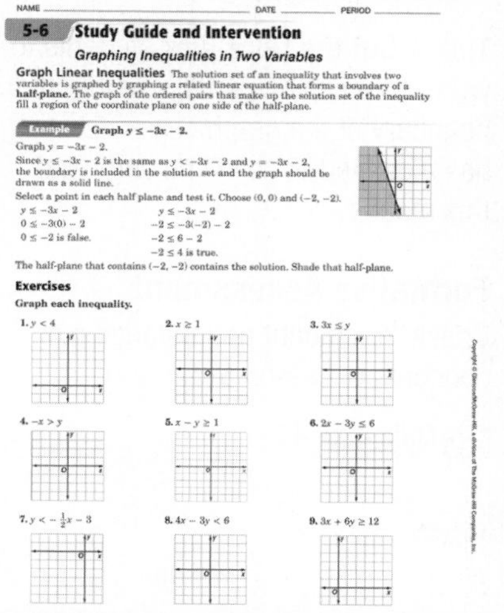

5-6 Study Guide and Intervention

Graphing Inequalities in Two Variables

Practice
AL OL BL ELL

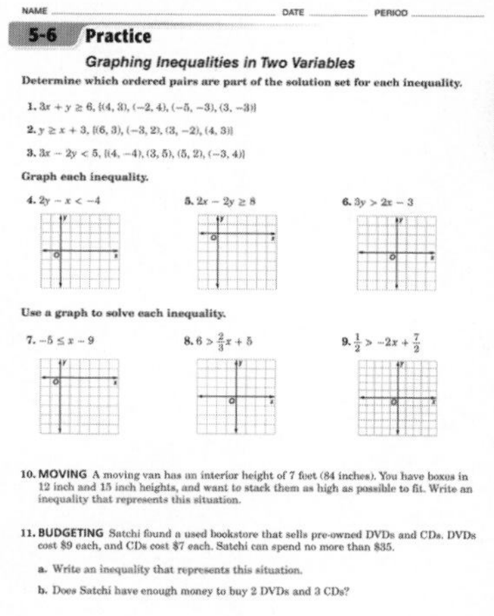

5-6 Practice

Graphing Inequalities in Two Variables

Word Problem Practice
AL OL BL ELL

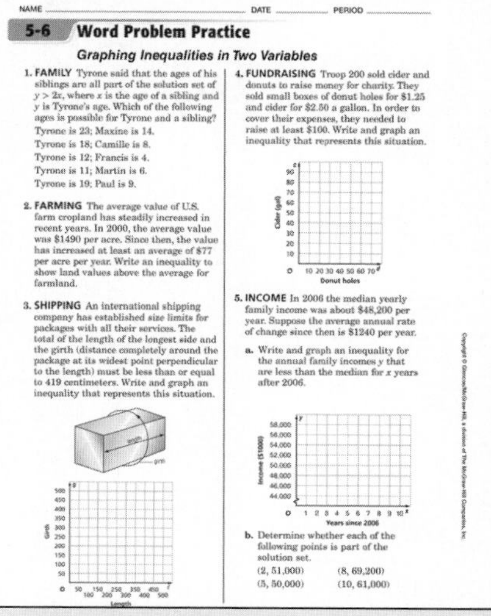

5-6 Word Problem Practice

Graphing Inequalities in Two Variables

Enrichment
OL BL

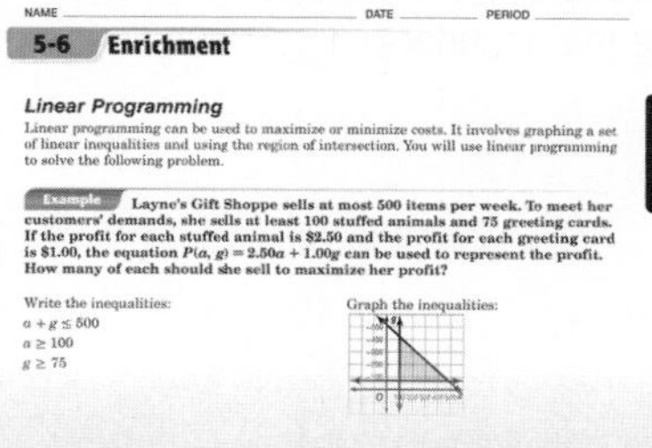

5-6 Enrichment

Linear Programming

4 Assess

Ticket Out the Door Ask students to write, on a slip on paper, whether the boundary of the graph of $y < 2x + 1$ has a dashed or solid line and what this means.

Formative Assessment

Check for student understanding of concepts in Lesson 5-6.

Quiz 4, p. 46

Additional Answers

52b. 390; the y-intercept represents the number of trees with leaves in the arboretum on day 0.

52c. The arboretum will close after 30 days; I found the solution of $0 = 390 - 13d$.

Standardized Test Practice

51. What is the domain of this function? **B**

A $\{x \mid 0 \le x \le 3\}$
B $\{x \mid 0 \le x \le 9\}$
C $\{y \mid 0 \le y \le 9\}$
D $\{y \mid 0 \le y \le 3\}$

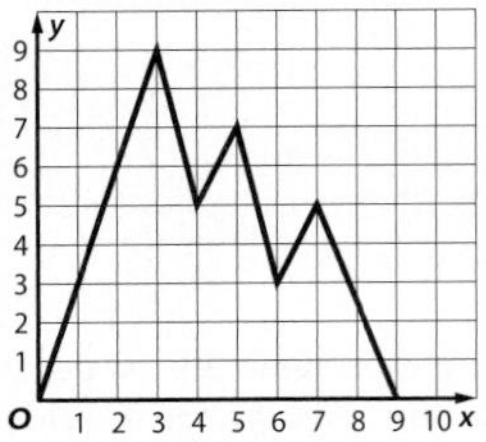

52. EXTENDED RESPONSE An arboretum will close for the winter when all of the trees have lost their leaves. The table shows the number of trees each day that still have leaves.

Day	5	10	15	20
Trees with Leaves	325	260	195	130

a. Write an equation that represents the number of trees with leaves y after d days. $y = 390 - 13d$

b. Find the y-intercept. What does it mean in the context of this problem? **b–c. See margin.**

c. After how many days will the arboretum close? Explain how you got your answer.

53. Which inequality best represents the statement below? **F**

A jar contains 832 gumballs. Ebony's guess was within 46 pieces.

F $|g - 832| \le 46$
G $|g + 832| \le 46$
H $|g - 832| \ge 46$
J $|g + 832| \ge 46$

54. GEOMETRY If the rectangular prism has a volume of 10,080 cm³, what is the value of x? **D**

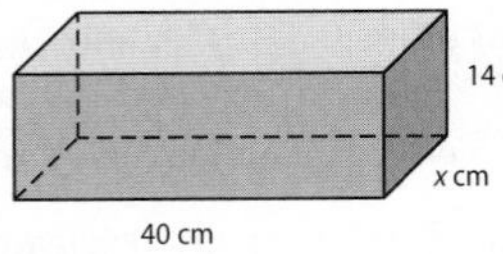

A 12
B 14
C 16
D 18

Spiral Review

Solve each open sentence. (Lesson 5-5)

55. $|y - 2| > 4$ $\{y \mid y > 6 \text{ or } y < -2\}$

56. $|t - 6| \le 5$ $\{t \mid 1 \le t \le 11\}$

57. $|3 + d| < -4$ $\varnothing$

Solve each compound inequality. (Lesson 5-4)

58. $4c - 4 < 8c - 16 < 6c - 6$ $\{c \mid 3 < c < 5\}$

59. $5 < \frac{1}{2}p + 3 < 8$ $\{p \mid 4 < p < 10\}$

60. $0.5n \ge -7$ or $2.5n + 2 \le 9$ $\{n \mid n \text{ is a real number.}\}$

Write an equation of the line that passes through each pair of points. (Lesson 4-2)

61. (1, −3) and (2, 5) $y = 8x - 11$

62. (−2, −4) and (−7, 3)

63. (−6, −8) and (−8, −5)

62. $y = -\frac{7}{5}x - \frac{34}{5}$

63. $y = -\frac{3}{2}x - 17$

64. FITNESS The table shows the maximum heart rate to maintain during aerobic activities. Write an equation in function notation for the relation. Determine what would be the maximum heart rate to maintain in aerobic training for an 80-year-old. (Lesson 3-5)

Age (yr)	20	30	40	50	60	70
Pulse rate (beats/min)	175	166	157	148	139	130

$f(a) = -0.9a + 193$; 121 beats/min

Skills Review

65. WORK The formula $s = \frac{w - 10r}{m}$ is used to find keyboarding speeds. In the formula, s represents the speed in words per minute, w the number of words typed, r the number of errors, and m the number of minutes typed. Solve for r. $r = \frac{w - sm}{10}$

322 | Lesson 5-6 | Graphing Inequalities in Two Variables

Differentiated Instruction OL BL

Extension Challenge students to write an inequality for the graph whose boundary passes through the points at (4, −2) and (−3, −2) and whose solution set contains the boundary and all the points above the boundary. $y \ge -2$

EXTEND 5-6 Graphing Technology Lab
Graphing Inequalities

You can use a graphing calculator to investigate the graphs of inequalities.

Content Standards
AI.L.7

Process Standards
PS.5

Activity 1 Less Than

Graph $y \le 2x + 5$.

Clear all functions from the **Y=** list.

KEYSTROKES: [Y=] [CLEAR]

Graph $y \le 2x + 5$ in a standard viewing window.

KEYSTROKES: 2 [X,T,θ,n] [+] 5 [◄] [◄] [◄] [◄] [◄] [◄] [ENTER] [ENTER] [ENTER] [ZOOM] 6

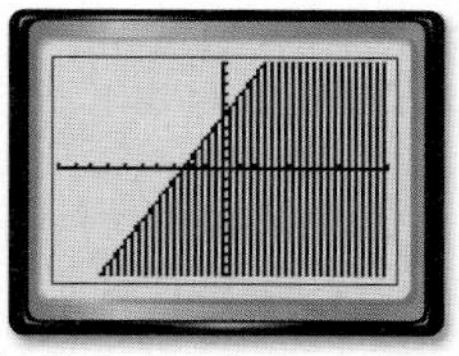

[−10, 10] scl: 1 by [−10, 10] scl: 1

All ordered pairs for which y is *less than or equal to* $2x + 5$ lie *below or on* the line and are solutions.

Activity 2 Greater Than

Graph $y - 2x \ge 5$.

Clear the graph that is currently displayed.

KEYSTROKES: [Y=] [CLEAR]

Rewrite $y - 2x \ge 5$ as $y \ge 2x + 5$ and graph it.

KEYSTROKES: 2 [X,T,θ,n] [+] 5 [◄] [◄] [◄] [◄] [◄] [◄] [ENTER] [ENTER] [ZOOM] 6

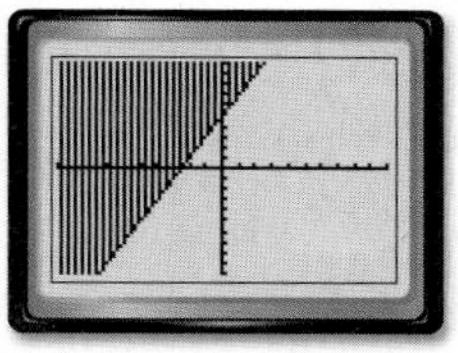

[−10, 10] scl: 1 by [−10, 10] scl: 1

All ordered pairs for which y is *greater than or equal to* $2x + 5$ lie *above or on* the line and are solutions.

1. Both graphs contain the line $y = 2x + 5$. The first graph is shaded below $y = 2x + 5$, while the second graph is shaded above $y = 2x + 5$.

Exercises

1. Compare and contrast the two graphs shown above.
2. Graph $y \ge -3x + 1$ in the standard viewing window. Using your graph, name four solutions of the inequality. **Sample answer: {(0, 1), (−1, 7), (2, 6), (4.2, −1.5)}**
3. Suppose student water park tickets cost \$16, and adult water park tickets cost \$20. You would like to buy at least 10 tickets but spend no more than \$200.
   - **a.** Let x = number of student tickets and y = number of adult tickets. Write two inequalities, one representing the total number of tickets and the other representing the total cost of the tickets. $x + y \ge 10$; $16x + 20y \le 200$
   - **b.** Graph the inequalities. Use the viewing window [0, 20] scl: 1 by [0, 20] scl: 1. **See margin.**
   - **c.** Name four possible combinations of student and adult tickets. **Sample answer: {(0, 10), (6, 5), (8, 3), (11, 1)}**

1 Focus

Objective Use a graphing calculator to investigate the graphs of inequalities.

Materials for Each Group

- TI–83/84 Plus or other graphing calculator

Teaching Tip

You may also need students to reset the viewing windows. Have them enter [ZOOM] 6 to graph in the standard viewing window.

2 Teach

Working in Cooperative Groups

Put students in groups of two or three, mixing abilities. Have groups complete the Activities and Exercise 1.

- To graph inequalities, enter the function in the **Y=** table editor at **Y1=**. Then highlight the symbol in front of the **Y1** entry and press [ENTER] until either shading above or below the symbol appears.

Practice Have students complete Exercises 2 and 3.

3 Assess

Formative Assessment

Use Exercise 2 to assess whether students understand that the coordinates of all the points on the line or in the shaded region are solutions of the inequality.

Additional Answer

3b.

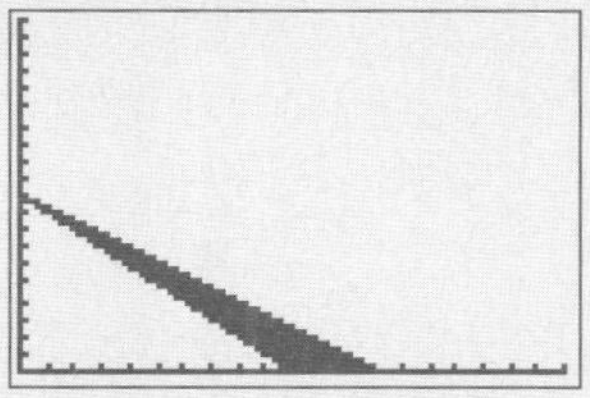

[0, 20] scl: 1 by [0, 20] scl: 1

From Concrete to Abstract

Ask:

- Why do the ordered pairs that lie on the line belong to the solution set of the inequality for Exercise 2? Sample answer: The equals sign is included with the inequality.

Formative Assessment

KeyVocabulary The page references after each word denote where that term was first introduced. If students have difficulty answering questions 1–10, remind them that they can use these page references to refresh their memories about the vocabulary.

Summative Assessment

Vocabulary Test, p. 48

Vocabulary Review

Vocabulary Review provides students the opportunity to check their understanding of important concepts and terminology in an online game format.

FOLDABLES StudyOrganizer

Dinah Zike's Foldables®

Have students look through the chapter to make sure they have included examples in their Foldables. Suggest that students keep their Foldables handy while completing the Study Guide and Review pages. Point out that their Foldables can serve as a quick review when studying for the chapter test.

Additional Answers

11. $\{w \mid w > 13\}$

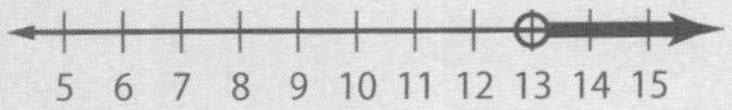

12. $\{x \mid x \leq -5\}$

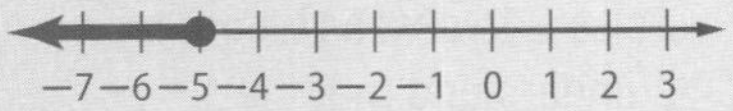

13. $\{h \mid h < -5\}$

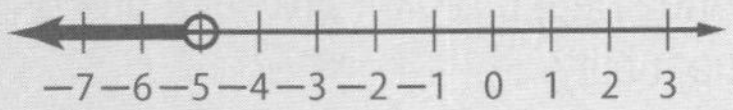

14. $\{a \mid a > -7\}$

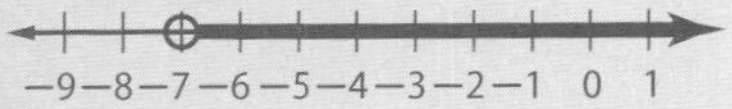

15. $\{p \mid p \leq -2\}$

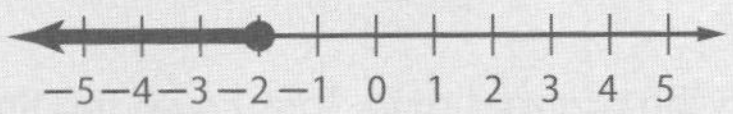

16. $\{y \mid y \leq 7\}$

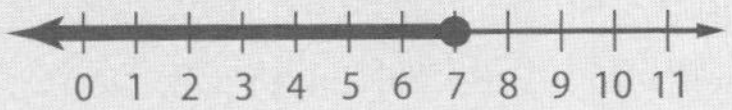

CHAPTER 5 Study Guide and Review

Study Guide

KeyConcepts

Solving One-Step Inequalities (Lessons 5-1 and 5-2)

For all numbers *a*, *b*, and *c*, the following are true.

- If $a > b$ and c is positive, $ac > bc$.
- If $a > b$ and c is negative, $ac < bc$.

Multi-Step and Compound Inequalities (Lessons 5-3 and 5-4)

- Multi-step inequalities can be solved by undoing the operations in the same way you would solve a multi-step equation.
- A compound inequality containing *and* is only true if both inequalities are true.
- A compound inequality containing *or* is true if at least one of the inequalities is true.

Absolute Value Inequalities (Lesson 5-5)

- The absolute value of any number x is its distance from zero on a number line and is written as $|x|$. If $x \geq 0$, then $|x| = x$. If $x < 0$, then $|x| = -x$.
- If $|x| < n$ and $n > 0$, then $-n < x < n$.
- If $|x| > n$ and $n > 0$, then $x > n$ or $x < -n$.

Inequalities in Two Variables (Lesson 5-6)

To graph an inequality:

Step 1 Graph the boundary. Use a solid line when the inequality contains $\leq$ or $\geq$. Use a dashed line when the inequality contains $<$ or $>$.

Step 2 Use a test point to determine which half-plane should be shaded.

Step 3 Shade the half-plane.

FOLDABLES StudyOrganizer

Be sure the Key Concepts are noted in your Foldable.

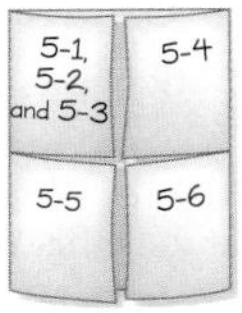

KeyVocabulary

boundary (p. 317)
closed half-plane (p. 317)
compound inequality (p. 306)
half-plane (p. 317)
inequality (p. 285)
intersection (p. 306)
open half-plane (p. 317)
set-builder notation (p. 286)
union (p. 307)

VocabularyCheck

State whether each sentence is *true* or *false*. If *false*, replace the underlined term to make a true sentence.

1. Set-builder notation is a <u>less</u> concise way of writing a solution set. **false; more**
2. There are <u>two</u> types of compound inequalities. **true**
3. The graph of a compound inequality containing *and* shows the <u>union</u> of the individual graphs. **false; intersection**
4. A compound inequality containing *or* is true if one or both of the inequalities is true. Its graph is the <u>union</u> of the graphs of the two inequalities. **true**
5. The graph of an inequality of the form $y < ax + b$ is a region on the coordinate plane called a <u>half-plane</u>. **true**
6. A <u>point</u> defines the boundary of an open half-plane. **false; line**
7. The <u>boundary</u> is the graph of the equation of the line that defines the edge of each half-plane. **true**
8. The solution set to the inequality $y \geq x$ includes the <u>boundary</u>. **true**
9. When solving an inequality, <u>multiplying</u> each side by a negative number reverses the inequality symbol. **true**
10. The graph of a compound inequality that contains <u>*and*</u> is the intersection of the graphs of the two inequalities. **true**

Lesson-by-Lesson Review

5-1 Solving Inequalities by Addition and Subtraction

Solve each inequality. Then graph it on a number line. 11–16. See margin.

11. $w - 4 > 9$ **12.** $x + 8 \leq 3$

13. $6 + h < 1$ **14.** $-5 < a + 2$

15. $13 - p \geq 15$ **16.** $y + 1 \leq 8$

17. **FIELD TRIP** A bus can hold 44 people. If there are 35 students in Samantha's class, how many more people can ride on the bus? no more than 9

Example 1

Solve $x - 9 < -4$. Then graph it on a number line.

$x - 9 < -4$	Original inequality
$x - 9 + 9 < -4 + 9$	Add 9 to each side.
$x < 5$	Simplify.

The solution set is $\{x \mid x < 5\}$.

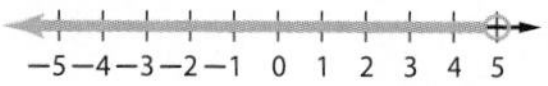

5-2 Solving Inequalities by Multiplication and Division

Solve each inequality. Graph the solution on a number line.

18. $\frac{1}{3}x > 6$ $\{x \mid x > 18\}$ **19.** $\frac{1}{5}g \geq -4$ $\{g \mid g \geq -20\}$

20. $4p < 32$ $\{p \mid p < 8\}$ **21.** $-55 \leq -5w$ $\{w \mid w \leq 11\}$

22. $-2m > 100$ $\{m \mid m < -50\}$ **23.** $\frac{2}{3}t < -48$ $\{t \mid t < -72\}$

24. **MOVIE RENTAL** Jack has no more than $24 to spend on DVDs for a party. Each DVD rents for $4. Find the maximum number of DVDs Jack can rent for his party. 6

18–23. See margin for graphs.

Example 2

Solve $-14h < 56$. Check your solution.

$-14h < 56$	Original inequality
$\frac{-14h}{-14} > \frac{56}{-14}$	Divide each side by −14.
$h > -4$	Simplify.
$\{h \mid h > -4\}$	

CHECK To check, substitute three different values into the original inequality: −4, a number less than −4, and a number greater than −4.

5-3 Solving Multi-Step Inequalities

Solve each inequality. Graph the solution on a number line.

25. $3h - 7 < 14$ $\{h \mid h < 7\}$ **26.** $4 + 5b > 34$ $\{b \mid b > 6\}$

27. $18 \leq -2x + 8$ $\{x \mid x \leq -5\}$ **28.** $\frac{t}{3} - 6 > -4$ $\{t \mid t > 6\}$

29. Four times a number decreased by 6 is less than −2. Define a variable, write an inequality, and solve for the number. See margin.

30. **TICKET SALES** The drama club collected $160 from ticket sales for the spring play. They need to collect at least $400 to pay for new lighting for the stage. If tickets sell for $3 each, how many more tickets need to be sold? at least 80 more

25–28. See margin for graphs.

Example 3

Solve $-6y - 13 > 29$. Check your solution.

$-6y - 13 > 29$	Original inequality
$-6y - 13 + 13 > 29 + 13$	Add 13 to each side.
$-6y > 42$	Simplify.
$\frac{-6y}{-6} < \frac{42}{-6}$	Divide each side by −6 and change > to <.
$y < -7$	Simplify.

The solution set is $\{y \mid y < -7\}$.

CHECK	$-6y - 13 > 29$	Original inequality
	$-6(-10) - 13 \overset{?}{>} 29$	Substitute −10 for y.
	$47 > 29$ ✓	Simplify.

Lesson-by-Lesson Review

Intervention If the given examples are not sufficient to review the topics covered by the questions, remind students that the lesson references tell them where to review that topic in their textbook.

Two-Day Option Have students complete the Lesson-by-Lesson Review. Then you can use McGraw-Hill eAssessment to customize another review worksheet that practices all the objectives of this chapter or only the objectives on which your students need more help.

Additional Answers

18.
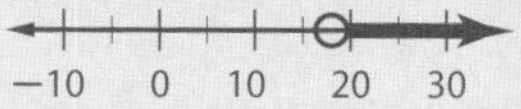

19.
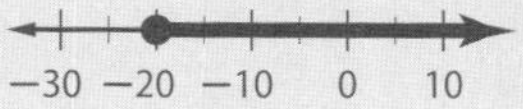

20.
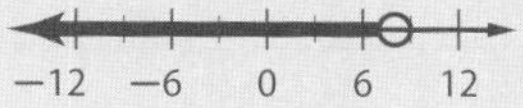

21.
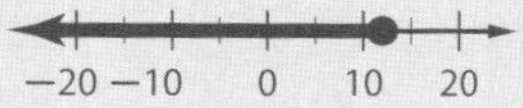

22.
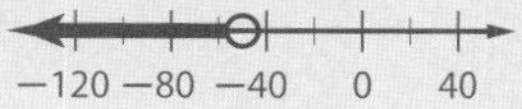

23.
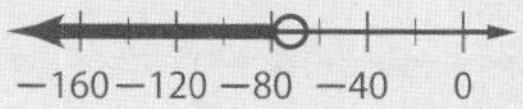

25.
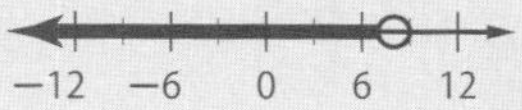

26.
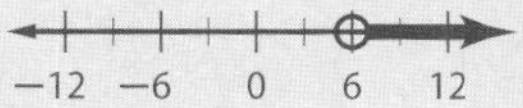

27.
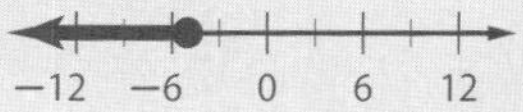

28.
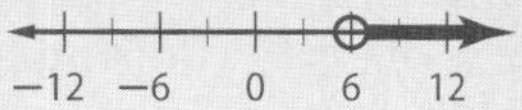

29. Sample answer: Let $x =$ the number, $4x - 6 < -2$; $x < 1$; $\{x \mid x < 1\}$

Anticipation Guide

Have students complete the Chapter 5 Anticipation Guide and discuss how their responses have changed now that they have completed Chapter 5.

Additional Answers

31. $\{m \mid 2 < m < 9\}$

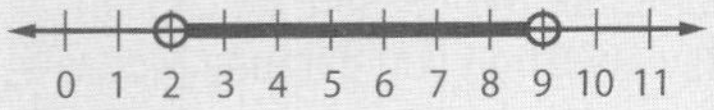

32. $\{t \mid 1 < t < 7\}$

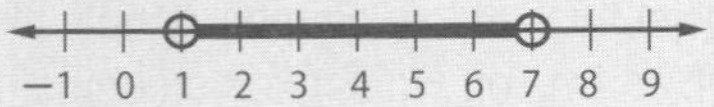

33. $\{x \mid x \leq 3 \text{ or } x > 6\}$

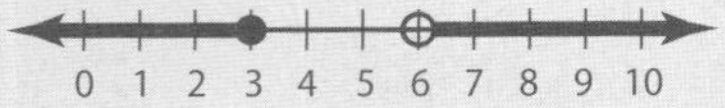

35. $\{x \mid -5 < x < 13\}$

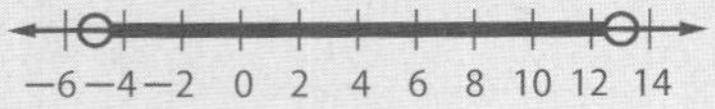

36. $\{p \mid p < -9 \text{ or } p > 5\}$

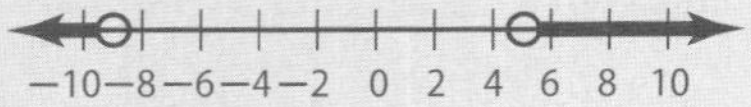

37. $\{c \mid -7 \leq c \leq 4\}$

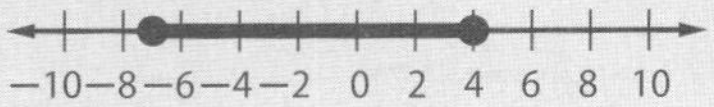

38. $\{f \mid f \leq 7 \text{ or } f \geq 11\}$

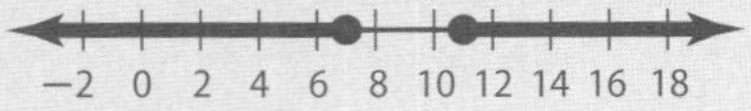

39. $\left\{d \mid -\frac{7}{3} \leq d \leq 3\right\}$

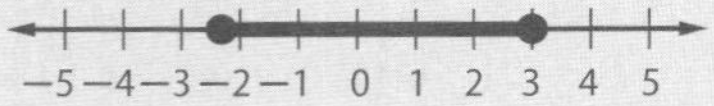

40. $\left\{b \mid -\frac{17}{2} < b < \frac{19}{2}\right\}$

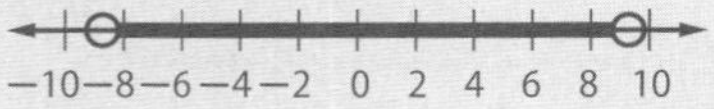

CHAPTER 5 Study Guide and Review *Continued*

5-4 Solving Compound Inequalities

Solve each compound inequality. Then graph the solution set. **31–33. See margin.**

31. $m - 3 < 6$ and $m + 2 > 4$

32. $-4 < 2t - 6 < 8$

33. $3x + 2 \leq 11$ or $5x - 8 > 22$

34. KITES A kite can be flown in wind speeds no less than 7 miles per hour and no more than 16 miles per hour. Write an inequality for the wind speeds at which the kite can fly. **$7 \leq x \leq 16$**

Example 4

Solve $-3w + 4 > -8$ and $2w - 11 > -19$. Then graph the solution set.

$-3w + 4 > -8$ and $2w - 11 > -19$

$w < 4$ $\qquad$ $w > -4$

To graph the solution set, graph $w < 4$ and graph $w > -4$. Then find the intersection.

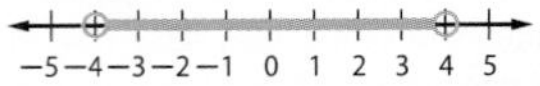

5-5 Inequalities Involving Absolute Value

Solve each inequality. Then graph the solution set. **35–44. See margin.**

35. $|x - 4| < 9$

36. $|p + 2| > 7$

37. $|2c + 3| \leq 11$

38. $|f - 9| \geq 2$

39. $|3d - 1| \leq 8$

40. $\left|\frac{4b - 2}{3}\right| < 12$

41. $\left|\frac{2t + 6}{2}\right| > 10$

42. $|-4y - 3| < 13$

43. $|m + 19| \leq 1$

44. $|-k - 7| \geq 4$

Example 5

Solve $|x - 6| < 9$. Then graph the solution set.

Case 1 $x - 6$ is nonnegative.

$x - 6 < 9$

$x < 15$

Case 2 $x - 6$ is negative.

$-(x - 6) < 9$

$x > -3$

The solution set is $\{x \mid -3 < x < 15\}$.

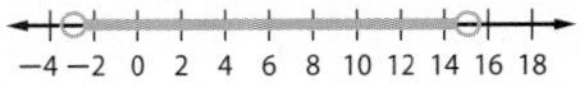

5-6 Graphing Inequalities in Two Variables

Graph each inequality. **45–50. See Ch. 5 Answer Appendix.**

45. $y > x - 3$

46. $y < 2x + 1$

47. $3x - y \leq 4$

48. $y \geq -2x + 6$

49. $5x - 2y < 10$

50. $x + y \geq 1$

Graph each inequality. Determine which of the ordered pairs are part of the solution set for each inequality.

51. $y \leq 4$; $\{(3, 6), (1, 2), (-4, 8), (3, -2), (1, 7)\}$ **(1, 2), (3, −2)**

52. $-2x + 3y \geq 12$; $\{(-2, 2), (-1, 1), (0, 4), (2, 2)\}$ **(0, 4)**

53. BAKERY Ben has \$24 to spend on cookies and cupcakes. Write and graph an inequality that represents what Ben can buy. **$2x + 3y \leq 24$**

51–53. See Ch. 5 Answer Appendix for graphs.

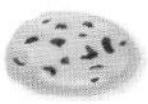

$2

$3

Example 6

Graph $2x - y > 3$.

Solve for y in terms of x.

$2x - y > 3$ — Original inequality

$-y > -2x + 3$ — Subtract $2x$ from each side.

$y < 2x - 3$ — Multiply each side by -1.

Graph the boundary using a dashed line. Choose (0, 0) as a test point.

$2(0) - 0 \stackrel{?}{>} 3$

$0 \not> 3$

Since 0 is not greater than 3, shade the plane that does not contain (0, 0).

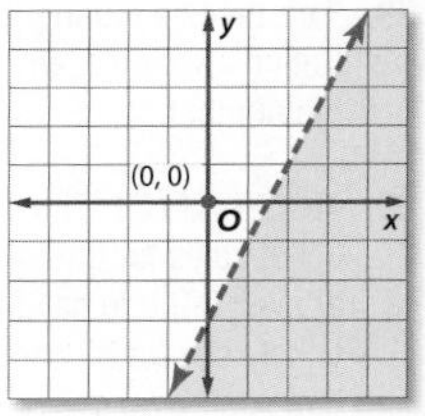

41. $\{t \mid t < -13 \text{ or } t > 7\}$

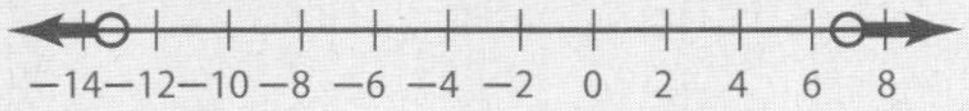

42. $\left\{y \mid -4 < y < \frac{5}{2}\right\}$

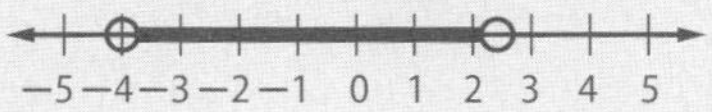

43. $\{m \mid -20 \leq m \leq -18\}$

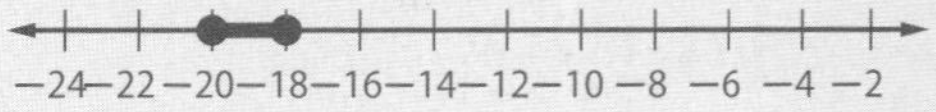

44. $\{k \mid k \geq -3 \text{ or } k \leq -11\}$

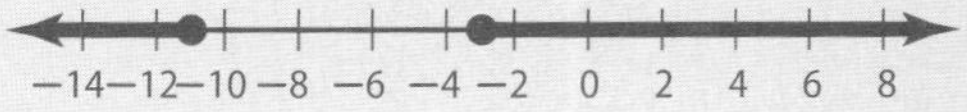

CHAPTER 5 Practice Test

Solve each inequality. Then graph it on a number line.

1. $x - 9 < -4$ $\{x \mid x < 5\}$

2. $6p \geq 5p - 3$ $\{p \mid p \geq -3\}$

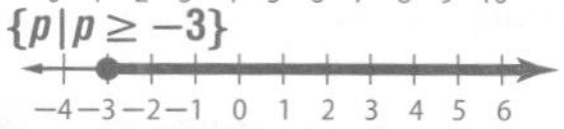

3. MULTIPLE CHOICE Drew currently has 31 comic books in his collection. His friend Connor has 58 comic books. How many more comic books does Drew need to add to his collection in order to have a larger collection than Connor? C

A no more than 21

B 27

C at least 28

D more than 30

Solve each inequality. Graph the solution on a number line. 4–10. See Ch. 5 Answer Appendix for graphs.

4. $\frac{1}{5}h > 3$ $\{h \mid h > 15\}$

5. $7w \leq -42$ $\{w \mid w \leq -6\}$

6. $-\frac{2}{3}t \geq 24$ $\{t \mid t \leq -36\}$

7. $-9m < -36$ $\{m \mid m > 4\}$

8. $3c - 7 < 11$ $\{c \mid c < 6\}$

9. $\frac{g}{4} + 3 \leq -9$ $\{g \mid g \leq -48\}$

10. $-2(x - 4) > 5x - 13$ $\{x \mid x < 3\}$

11. ZOO The 8th grade science class is going to the zoo. The class can spend up to $300 on admission.

Zoo Admission	
Visitor	**Cost**
student	$8
adult	$10

a. Write an inequality for this situation. $8s + 10a \leq 300$

b. If there are 32 students in the class and 1 adult will attend for every 8 students, can the entire class go to the zoo? yes

Solve each compound inequality. Then graph the solution set. 12–13. See margin.

12. $y - 8 < -3$ or $y + 5 > 19$

13. $-11 \leq 2h - 5 \leq 13$

14. $3z - 2 > -5$ and $7z + 4 < -17$ Ø

Define a variable, write an inequality, and solve the problem. Check your solution.

15. The difference of a number and 4 is no more than 8. 15–16. See Ch. 5 Answer Appendix.

16. Nine times a number decreased by four is at least twenty-three.

17. MULTIPLE CHOICE Write a compound inequality for the graph shown below. G

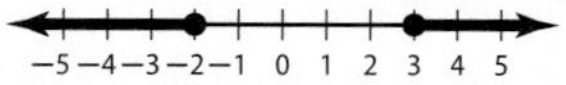

F $-2 \leq x < 3$

G $x \leq -2$ or $x \geq 3$

H $x < -2$ or $x \geq 3$

J $-2 < x \leq 3$

Solve each inequality. Then graph the solution set.

18. $|p - 5| < 3$

19. $|2f + 7| \geq 21$

20. $|-4m + 3| \leq 15$

21. $\left|\frac{x - 3}{4}\right| > 5$

18–21. See Ch. 5 Answer Appendix.

22. RETAIL A sporting goods store is offering a $15 coupon on any pair of shoes.

a. The most and least expensive pairs of shoes are $149.95 and $24.95. What is the range of costs for customers with coupons? $9.95 \leq p \leq 134.95$

b. When buying a pair of $109.95 shoes, you can use a coupon or a 15% discount. Which option is best? 15% discount

Graph each inequality.

23. $y < 4x - 1$

24. $2x + 3y \geq 12$

23–24. See Ch. 5 Answer Appendix.

25. Graph $y > -2x + 5$. Then determine which of the ordered pairs in {(−2, 0), (−1, 5), (2, 3), (7, 3)} are in the solution set. See Ch. 5 Answer Appendix.

26. $6x + 4y \leq 96$; see Ch. 5 Answer Appendix for graph.

26. PRESCHOOL Mrs. Jones is buying new books and puzzles for her preschool classroom. Each book costs $6, and each puzzle costs $4. Write and graph an inequality to determine how many books and puzzles she can buy for $96.

Summative Assessment

Use these alternate leveled chapter tests to differentiate assessment for your students.

Leveled Chapter 5 Tests			
Form	**Type**	**Level**	**Page(s)**
1	MC	AL	49–50
2A	MC	OL	51–52
2B	MC	OL	53–54
2C	FR	OL	55–56
2D	FR	OL	57–58
3	FR	BL	59–60
Vocabulary Test			48
Extended-Response Test			61

MC = multiple-choice questions
FR = free-response questions

McGraw-Hill eAssessment Customize and create multiple versions of your chapter tests and their answer keys. All of the questions from the leveled chapter tests in the *Chapter 5 Resource Masters* are also available on McGraw-Hill eAssessment.

Additional Answers

12. $\{y \mid y < 5$ or $y > 14\}$

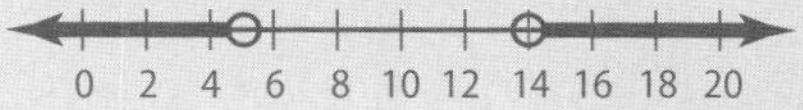

13. $\{h \mid -3 \leq h \leq 9\}$

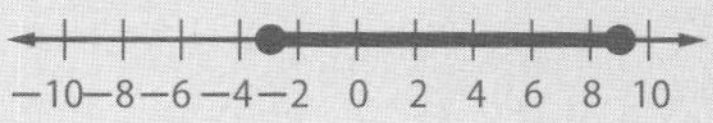

InterventionPlanner

TIER 1 On Level OL

If students miss about 25% of the exercises or less,

Then choose a resource:

SE Lessons 5-1, 5-2, 5-3, 5-4, 5-5, and 5-6

Skills Practice, pp. 7, 13, 19, 25, 31, and 38

TE Chapter Project

connectED.mcgraw-hill.com Self-Check Quiz

TIER 2 Strategic Intervention AL approaching grade level

If students miss about 50% of the exercises,

Then choose a resource:

Study Guide and Intervention, Chapter 5, p. 5, 11, 17, 23, 29, and 36

Quick Review Math Handbook

connectED.mcgraw-hill.com Extra Examples, Personal Tutor, Homework Help

TIER 3 Intensive Intervention 2 or more grades below level

If students miss about 75% of the exercises,

Then use *Math Triumphs, Alg. 1*

connectED.mcgraw-hill.com Extra Examples, Personal Tutor, Homework Help, Review Vocabulary

1 Focus

Objective Use the strategy of writing and solving an inequality to solve standardized test problems.

2 Teach

Scaffolding Questions

Ask:

- What are some situations in which you could use an inequality to represent the situation? Answers will vary.
- What are the symbols used to indicate an inequality and what do they mean? The symbols are $<$, which means less than, $>$, which means greater than, $\leq$, which means less than or equal to, and $\geq$, which means greater than or equal to.
- What are some clues in a word problem that suggest that writing and solving an inequality will solve the problem? Answers will vary.

CHAPTER 5 Preparing for Standardized Tests

Write and Solve an Inequality

Many multiple-choice items will require writing and solving inequalities. Follow the steps below to help you successfully solve these types of problems.

Strategies for Writing and Solving Inequalities

Step 1

Read the problem statement carefully.

Ask yourself:

- What am I being asked to solve?
- What information is given in the problem?
- What are the unknowns for which I need to solve?

Step 2

Translate the problem statement into an inequality.

- Assign variables to the unknown(s).
- Write the word sentence as a mathematical number sentence looking for words such as *greater than, less than, no more than, up to*, or *at least* to indicate the type of inequality as well as where to place the inequality sign.

Step 3

Solve the inequality.

- Solve for the unknowns in the inequality.
- Remember that multiplying or dividing each side by a negative number reverses the direction of the inequality.
- Check your answer to make sure it makes sense.

Standardized Test Example

Read the problem. Identify what you need to know. Then use the information in the problem to solve. Show your work.

Pedro has earned scores of 89, 74, 79, 85, and 88 on his tests this semester. He needs a test average of at least 85 in order to earn an A for the semester. There will be one more test given this semester.

A Write an inequality to model the situation.

B What score must he have on his final test to earn an A for the semester?

Read the problem carefully. You are given Pedro's first 5 test scores and told that he needs an average of *at least* 85 after his next test to earn an A for the semester.

a. Write the inequality.

Words	Pedro needs a test average of at *least* 85.
Variable	Let t represent Pedro's score on the final test.
Equation	$\frac{89 + 74 + 79 + 85 + 88 + t}{6} \geq 85$

b. Solve the inequality for *t*.

$$\frac{89 + 74 + 79 + 85 + 88 + t}{6} \geq 85$$
$$89 + 74 + 79 + 85 + 88 + t \geq 85(6)$$
$$415 + t \geq 510$$
$$t \geq 95$$

So, Pedro's final test score must be greater than or equal to 95 in order for him to earn an A for the semester.

Exercises

Read each problem. Identify what you need to know. Then use the information in the problem to solve.

1. Craig has $20 to order a pizza. The pizza costs $12.50 plus $0.95 per topping. If there is also a $3 delivery fee, how many toppings can Craig order? **up to 4 toppings**

2. To join an archery club, Nina had to pay an initiation fee of $75, plus $40 per year in membership dues.
   a. Write an equation to model the total cost, y, of belonging to the club for x years. $y = 40x + 75$
   b. How many years will it take her to spend more than $400 to belong to the club? **9 years**

3. The area of the triangle below is no more than 84 square millimeters. What is the height of the triangle? **no more than 12 mm**

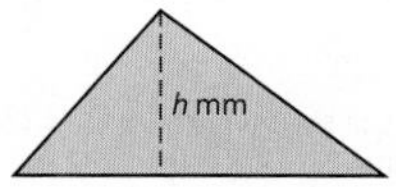

4. Rosa earns $200 a month delivering newspapers, plus an average of $11 per hour babysitting. If her goal is to earn at least $295 this month, how many hours will she have to babysit? **at least 9 hours**

5. To earn money for a new bike, Ethan is selling some of his baseball cards. He has saved $245. If the bike costs $1400, and he can sell 154 cards, for how much money will he need to sell each card to reach his goal? **at least $7.50 per card**

6. In a certain lacrosse league, there can be no more than 22 players on each team, and no more than 10 teams per age group. There are 6 age groups.
   a. Write an inequality to represent this situation. $p \leq 22 \cdot 10 \cdot 6$
   b. What is the greatest number of players that can play lacrosse in this league? **1320 players**

7. Sarah has $120 to shop for herself and to buy some gifts for 6 of her friends. She has purchased a shirt for herself for $32. Assuming that she spends an equal amount on each friend, what is the maximum that she can spend per person? **$14.66**

Additional Example

SHORT RESPONSE A company plans to buy, at most, 115 spots of radio airtime to advertise a new line of sporting goods. The company will use 40 spots to advertise the new line and 5 weeks of spots to advertise sales of the new line. The company plans to run an equal number of spots each week.

a. Write an inequality to model the situation.

b. What is the greatest number of spots the company will run each week?

Sample 2-point response:

a. Let a equal the number of advertising spots per week. Let the symbol $\leq$ represent the inequality *at most*. The inequality $5a + 40 \leq 115$ models the situation.

b. Solve the inequality for a to find the greatest number of spots the company will run per week.

$$5a + 40 \leq 115$$
$$5a \leq 115 - 40$$
$$5a \leq 75$$
$$4 \leq 15$$

So, the company will run at most 15 spots per week.

3 Assess

Use Exercises 1–7 to assess students' understanding.

connectED.mcgraw-hill.com 329

Diagnose Student Errors

Survey student responses for each item. Class trends may indicate common errors and misconceptions.

1. A rounded answer up instead of down
B used the inequality symbol for *at least* instead of *at most*
C used the inequality symbol for *less than* instead of *at most* or *less than* or *equal to*
D correct

2. F chose hours that represent less than \$600
G chose hours that represent less than \$600
H correct
J chose hours that represent at least \$600, but not the minimum hours

3. A confused slope and *y*-intercept and chose positive instead of negative slope
B chose negative instead of positive *y*-intercept
C correct
D confused slope and *y*-intercept

4. F chose highest score only
G chose lowest score only
H misunderstood difference between *greater than* and *greater than* or *equal to* and *less than* and *less than* or *equal to*
J correct

5. A misinterpreted *over* to mean *less than* instead of *greater than*
B correct
C calculation error
D calculation error and misinterpreted over to mean *less than* instead of *greater than*

6. F chose result for *less than* instead of *at least*
G chose result for *less than* instead of *at least*
H correct
J exactly \$250, not more than

CHAPTER 5 Standardized Test Practice

Cumulative, Chapters 1 through 5

Multiple Choice

Read each question. Then fill in the correct answer on the answer document provided by your teacher or on a sheet of paper.

1. Miguel received a \$100 gift certificate for a graduation gift. He wants to buy a CD player that costs \$38 and CDs that cost \$12 each. Which of the following inequalities represents how many CDs Miguel can buy? **D**

A $n \leq 6$

B $n \geq 5$

C $n < 5$

D $n \leq 5$

2. Craig is paid time-and-a-half for any additional hours over 40 that he works.

Time	Pay Rate
Up to 40 hours	\$12.80/hr
Additional hours worked over 40	\$19.20/hr

If Craig's goal is to earn at least \$600 next week, what is the minimum number of hours he needs to work? **H**

F 43 hours

G 44 hours

H 45 hours

J 46 hours

3. Which equation has a slope of $-\frac{2}{3}$ and a y-intercept of 6? **C**

A $y = 6x + \frac{2}{3}$

B $y = -\frac{2}{3}x - 6$

C $y = -\frac{2}{3}x + 6$

D $y = 6x - \frac{2}{3}$

4. The highest score that is on record on a video game is 10,219 points. The lowest score on record is 257 points. Which of the following inequalities best shows the range of scores recorded on the game? **J**

F $x \leq 10{,}219$

G $x \geq 257$

H $257 < x < 10{,}219$

J $257 \leq x \leq 10{,}219$

5. The current temperature is 82°. If the temperature rises more than 4 degrees, there will be a new record high for the date. Which number line represents the temperatures that would set a new record high? **B**

A 

B 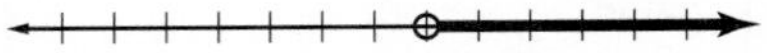

C 

D 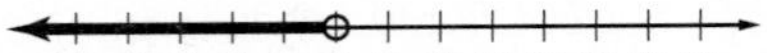

6. The girls' volleyball team is selling T-shirts and pennants to raise money for new uniforms. The team hopes to raise more than \$250.

Item	Price
T-shirt	\$10
Pennant	\$4

Which of the following combinations of items sold would meet this goal? **H**

F 16 T-shirts and 20 pennants

G 20 T-shirts and 12 pennants

H 18 T-shirts and 18 pennants

J 15 T-shirts and 20 pennants

7. What type of line does not have a defined slope? **D**

A horizontal

B parallel

C perpendicular

D vertical

8. Which expression below illustrates the Associative Property? **H**

F $abc = bac$

G $2(x - 3) = 2x - 6$

H $(p + 3) - t = p + (3 - t)$

J $5 + (-5) = 0$

Test-TakingTip

Question 2 You can check your answer by finding Craig's earnings for the hours worked.

7. A misunderstood concept of undefined slope
B misunderstood concept of undefined slope
C misunderstood concept of undefined slope
D correct

8. F chose Commutative Property instead of Associative Property
G chose Distributive Property instead of Associative Property
H correct
J chose Additive Inverse Property instead of Associative Property

Short Response/Gridded Response

Record your answers on the answer sheet provided by your teacher or on a sheet of paper.

9. Solve $-4 < 3x + 8 \leq 23$. $-4 < x \leq 5$

10. GRIDDED RESPONSE Tien is saving money for a new television. She needs to save at least $720 to pay for her expenses. Each week Tien saves $50 toward her new television. How many weeks will it take so she can pay for the television? **15 weeks**

11. Write an inequality that best represents the graph. $y \leq -\frac{2}{3}x + 1$

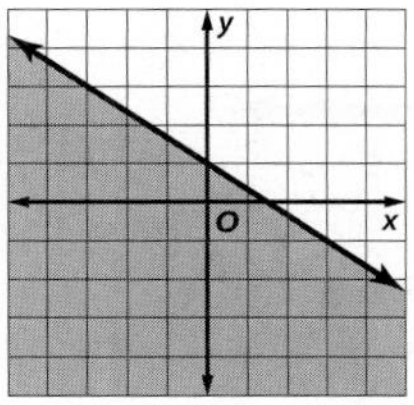

12. Solve $|x - 4| < 2$. $2 < x < 6$

13. GRIDDED RESPONSE Daniel wants to ship a set of golf clubs and several boxes of golf balls in a box that can hold up to 20 pounds. If the set of clubs weighs 9 pounds and each box of golf balls weighs 12 ounces, how many boxes of golf balls can Daniel ship? **14 boxes**

14. Graph the solution set for the inequality $3x - 6 \leq 4x - 4 \leq 3x + 1$.

15. Write an equation that represents the data in the table. $y = 3.5x + 2$

x	y
3	12.5
4	16
5	19.5
6	23
7	26.5

16. A sporting goods company near the beach rents bicycles for $10 plus $5 per hour. Write an equation in slope-intercept form that shows the total cost, y, of renting a bicycle for x hours. How much would it cost Emily to rent a bicycle for 6 hours? $y = 5x + 10$; **$40**

Extended Response

Record your answers on a sheet of paper. Show your work.

17. Theresa is saving money for a vacation. She needs to save at least $640 to pay for her expenses. Each week, she puts $35 towards her vacation savings.

a. Let w represent the number of weeks Theresa saves money. Write an inequality to model the situation. $35w \geq 640$

b. Solve the inequality from part a. What is the minimum number of weeks Theresa must save money in order to reach her goal? **19 weeks**

c. If Theresa were to save $45 each week instead, by how many weeks would the minimum savings time be decreased? **by 4 weeks**

Need ExtraHelp?

If you missed Question...	1	2	3	4	5	6	7	8	9	10	11	12	13	14	15	16	17
Go to Lesson...	5-3	5-3	4-1	5-4	5-1	5-6	3-3	1-3	5-4	5-2	5-6	5-5	5-3	5-4	3-5	4-2	5-2

Formative Assessment

You can use these pages to benchmark student progress.

Standardized Test Practice, pp. 62–64

Answer Sheet Practice

Have students simulate taking a standardized test by recording their answers on a practice recording sheet.

Student Recording Sheet

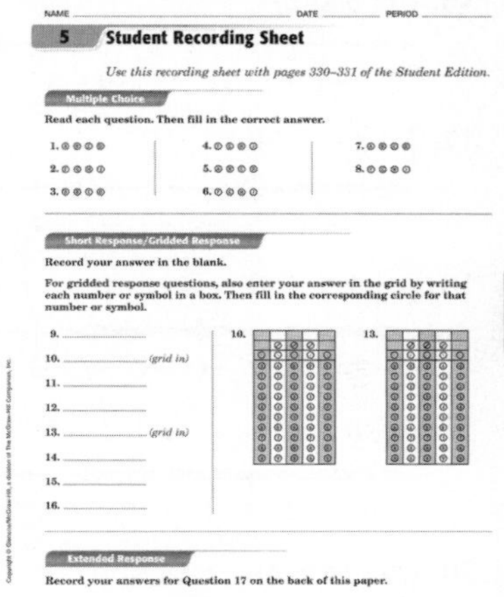
NAME DATE PERIOD

5 Student Recording Sheet

Use this recording sheet with pages 330–331 of the Student Edition.

Multiple Choice

Read each question. Then fill in the correct answer.

1. 2. 3. 4. 5. 6. 7. 8.

Short Response/Gridded Response

Record your answer in the blank.

For gridded response questions, also enter your answer in the grid by writing each number or symbol in a box. Then fill in the corresponding circle for that number or symbol.

9. 10. (grid in) 11. 12. 13. (grid in) 14. 15. 16.

Extended Response

Record your answers for Question 17 on the back of this paper.

McGraw-Hill eAssessment Create practice tests that align to your state standards, the Common Core State Standards, and other national standards such as TIMSS and NAEP.

Homework Option

Get Ready for Chapter 6 Assign students the exercises on p. 333 as homework to assess whether they possess the prerequisite skills needed for the next chapter.

Lesson 5-1

12. $\{m \mid m < 7\}$

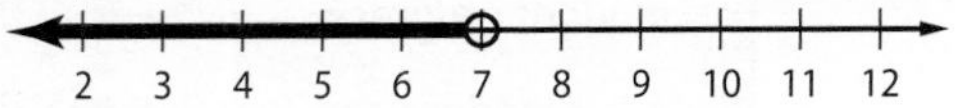

13. $\{p \mid p \geq 9\}$

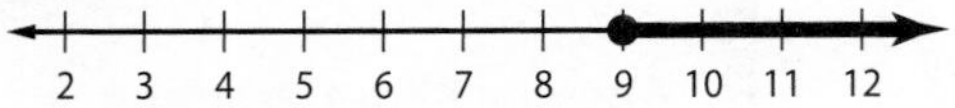

14. $\{r \mid r \leq 15\}$

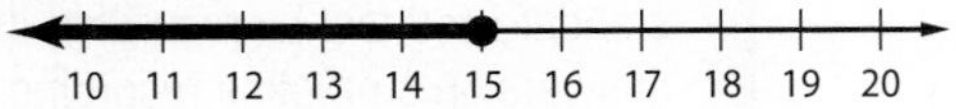

15. $\{t \mid t > -5\}$

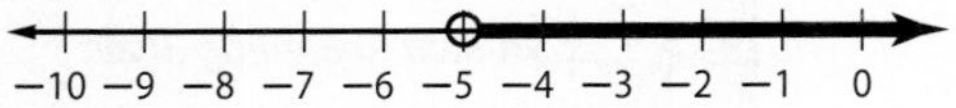

16. $\{b \mid b \geq 2\}$

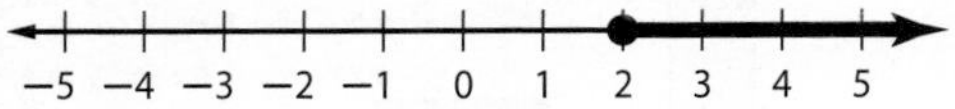

17. $\{r \mid r < -5\}$

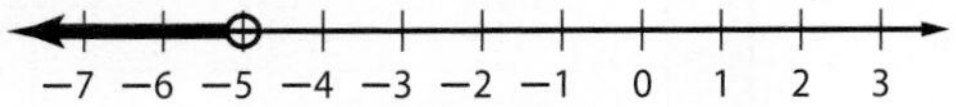

18. $\{c \mid c \leq -4\}$

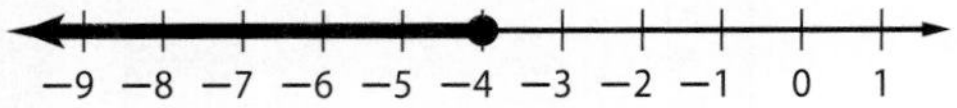

19. $\{q \mid q \leq 7\}$

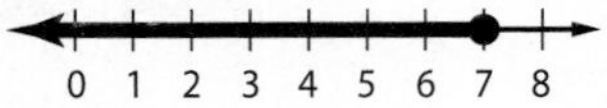

20. $\{m \mid m \geq 4\}$

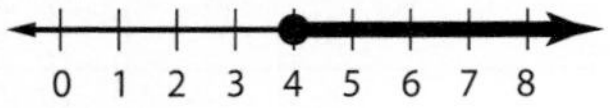

21. $\{h \mid h < 30\}$

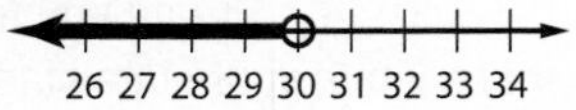

22. $\{r \mid r \geq 22\}$

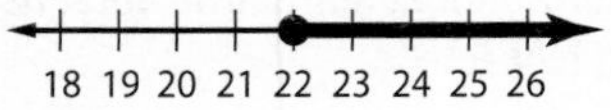

23. $\{c \mid c < -27\}$

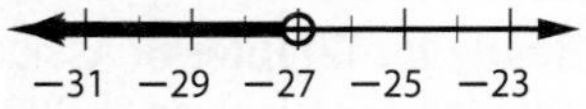

24. $\{a \mid a \leq -4\}$

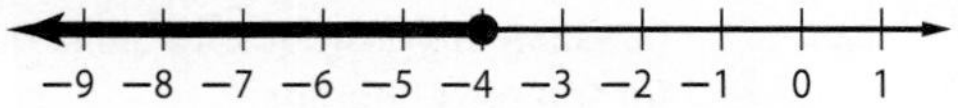

25. $\{z \mid z \leq 4\}$

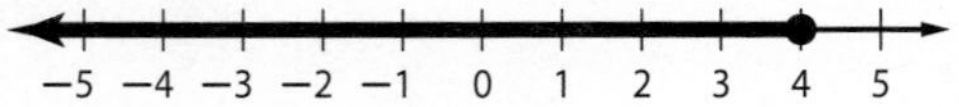

26. $\{w \mid w \geq -5\}$

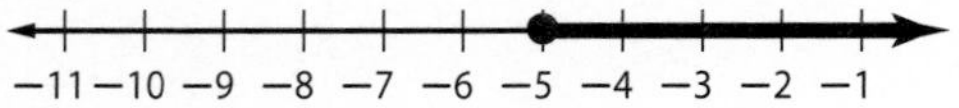

27. $\{y \mid y \leq -6\}$

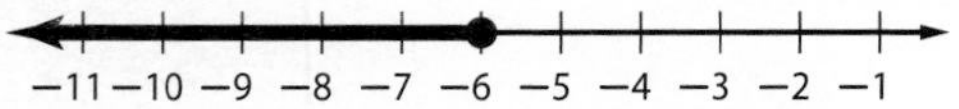

28. $\{x \mid x \leq 5\}$

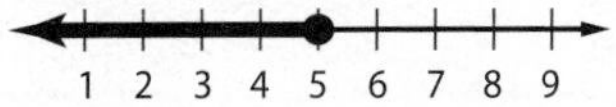

29. $\{a \mid a > -9\}$

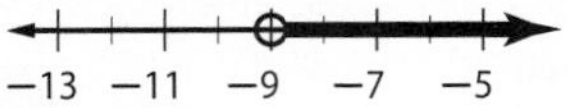

37. Sample answer: Let $t =$ the original water temperature; $t + 4 < 81$; $\{t \mid t < 77\}$; the water temperature was originally less than 77°.

38. Sample answer: Let $p =$ points needed to score; $p + 123 \geq 150$; $\{p \mid p \geq 27\}$; she must score at least 27 points.

41. $\{c \mid c \geq 3.7\}$

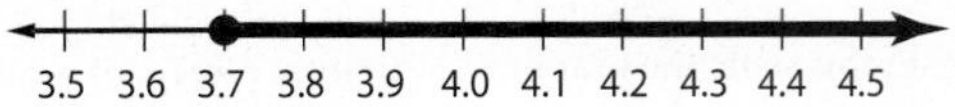

42. $\{g \mid g > 4.5\}$

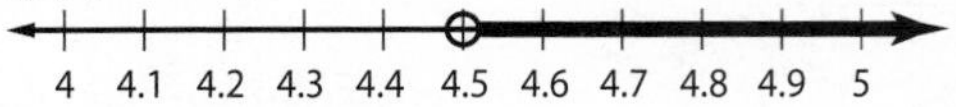

43. $\left\{k \mid k > -\frac{5}{12}\right\}$

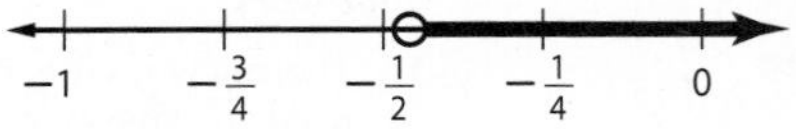

44. $\left\{p \mid p \leq 1\frac{1}{9}\right\}$

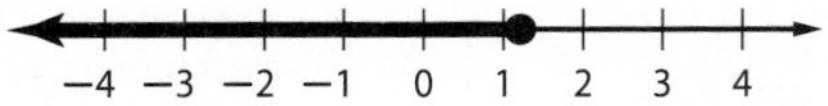

45a.

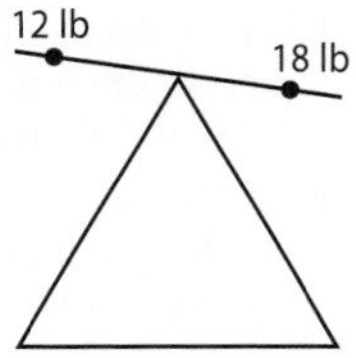

45b. 12 lb < 18 lb

45c.

	12	<	18
2×	24	<	36
3×	36	<	54
4×	48	<	72
$\frac{1}{2}$×	6	<	9
$\frac{1}{3}$×	4	<	6
$\frac{1}{4}$×	3	<	$4\frac{1}{2}$

45d. If a true inequality is multiplied by a positive number, the resulting inequality is also true. If a true inequality is divided by a positive number, the resulting inequality is also true.

54. Sample answers: $y + 1 < -2$, $y - 1 < -4$, $y + 3 < 0$

55. Solving linear inequalities is similar to solving linear equations. You must isolate the variable on one side of the inequality. To graph, if the problem is a less than or a greater than inequality, an open circle is used. Otherwise a dot is used. If the variable is on the left hand side of the inequality, and the inequality sign is less than (or less than or equal to), the graph extends to the left; otherwise it extends to the right.

56. The inequalities are equivalent. By adding 2 to each side of the first inequality, you get the second inequality.

Explore 5-2

6. Sample answer: When the solution is written so that the variable remains on the same side as in the original inequality, the inequality symbol is reversed in the solution.

7. Sample answer: $x \leq 4$; The inequality symbol remains the same in the solution for $3x \leq 12$, but is reversed in the solution for $-3x \leq 12$.

8. Sample answer: When solving inequalities involving multiplication, the inequality symbol remains unchanged when multiplying by a positive number, but is reversed when multiplying by a negative number. When solving inequalities involving division, the inequality symbol remains unchanged when dividing by a positive number, but is reversed when dividing by a negative number or multiplying by a negative reciprocal.

Lesson 5-2

12. 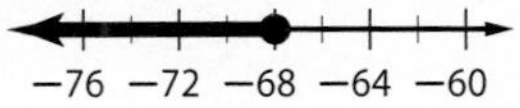

13. 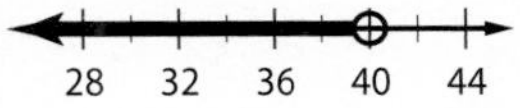

14. 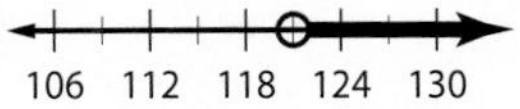

15. 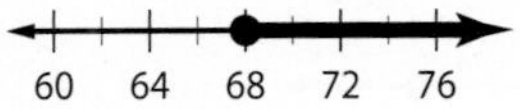

16. 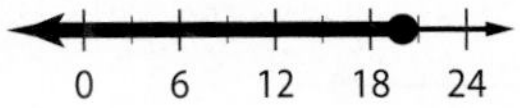

17. 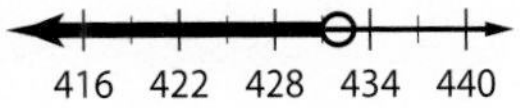

18. 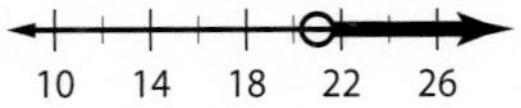

19. 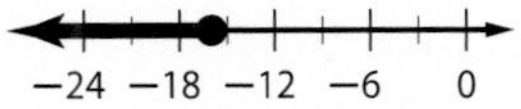

20. 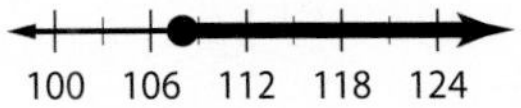

21. 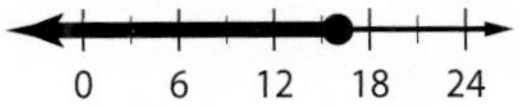

22. 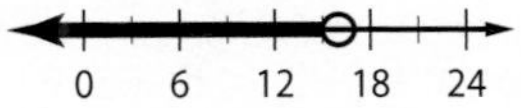

23. 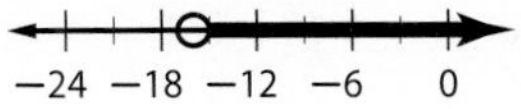

24. 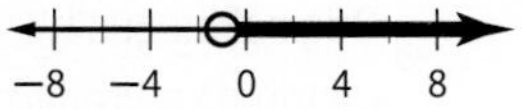

25. 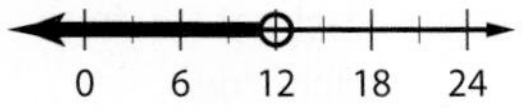

26. 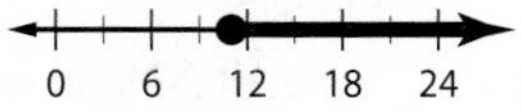

27. 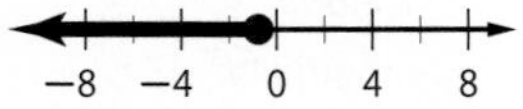

28. 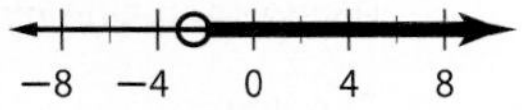

29. 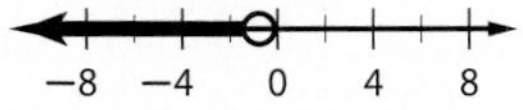

58. 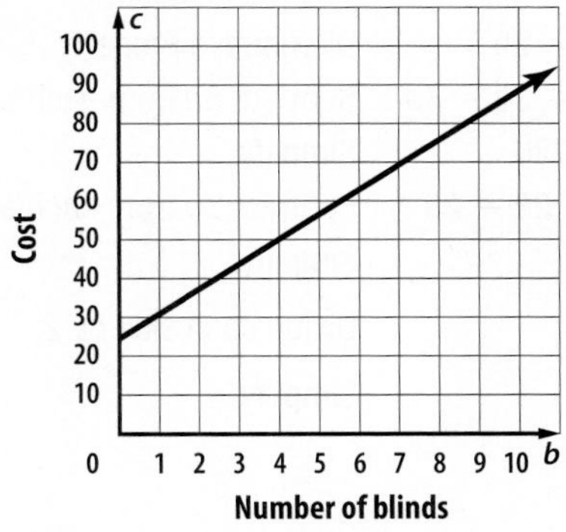

$77

Lesson 5-3

12. 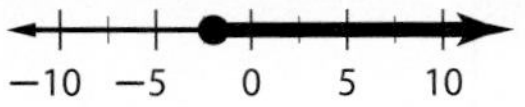

13. 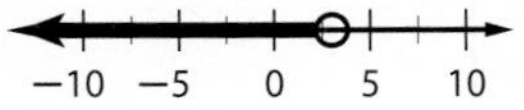

14. 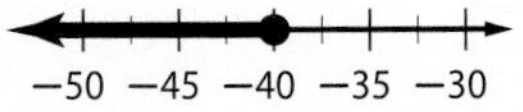

15. 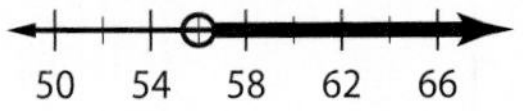

16. 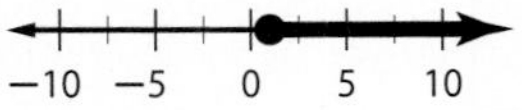

17. 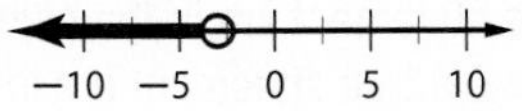

18. 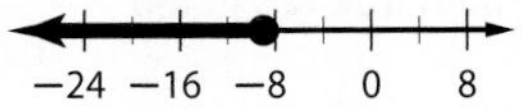

19. 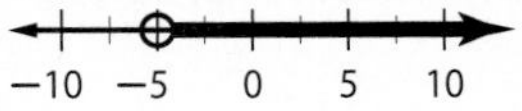

20. 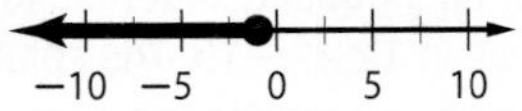

21. 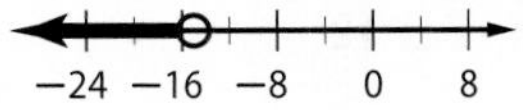

37.

$6(m-3) > 5(2m+4)$	Original inequality
$6m - 18 > 10m + 20$	Distributive Property
$6m - 18 - 6m > 10m + 20 - 6m$	Subtract 6*m* from each side.
$-18 > 4m + 20$	Simplify.
$-18 - 20 > 4m + 20 - 20$	Subtract 20 from each side.
$-38 > 4m$	Simplify.
$-\frac{38}{4} > \frac{4m}{4}$	Divide each side by 4.
$-9.5 > m$	Simplify.
$\{m \mid m < -9.5\}$	

38.

$8(a-2) \leq 10(a+2)$	Original inequality
$8a - 16 \leq 10a + 20$	Distributive Property
$8a - 16 - 8a \leq 10a + 20 - 8a$	Subtract 8*a* from each side.
$-16 \leq 2a + 20$	Simplify.
$-16 - 20 \leq 2a + 20 - 20$	Subtract 20 from each side.
$-36 \leq 2a$	Simplify.
$\frac{-36}{2} \leq \frac{2a}{2}$	Divide each side by 2.
$-18 \leq a$	Simplify.
$\{a \mid a \geq -18\}$	

54b.

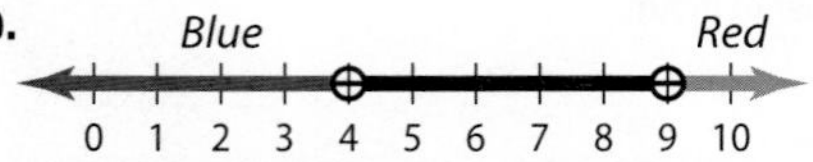

54c.

Point	$x > 4$	$x < 9$	Both are True
1	false	true	false
2	false	true	false
3	false	true	false
4	false	true	false
5	true	true	true
6	true	true	true
7	true	true	true
8	true	true	true
9	true	false	false
10	true	false	false

54d. The points that make $x > 4$ a true statement are in the blue section. The points that make $x < 9$ a true statement are in the red section. The points that make both true are in the highlighted section.

58. $4y + 9 > -3$; it is the only inequality that does not have a solution set of $\{y \mid y > 3\}$.

59. Sample answer: The solution set for an inequality that results in a false statement is the empty set, as in $12 < -15$. The solution set for an inequality in which any value of x results in a true statement is all real numbers, as in $12 \leq 12$.

67. $\{h \mid h < 14\}$

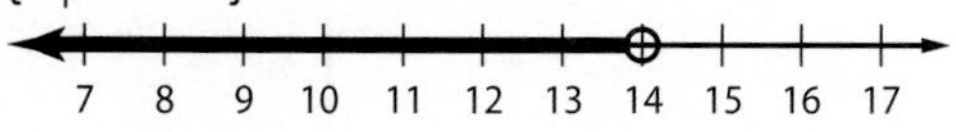

68. $\{p \mid p < 11\}$

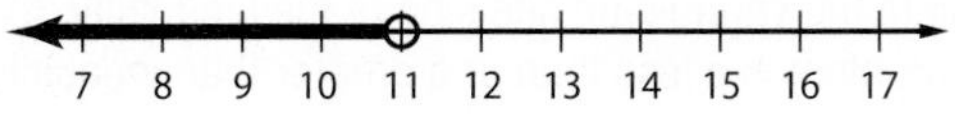

69. $\{m \mid m \geq 1\}$

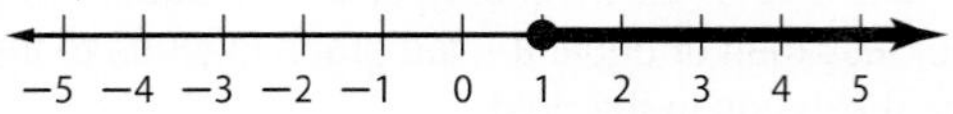

70. -8

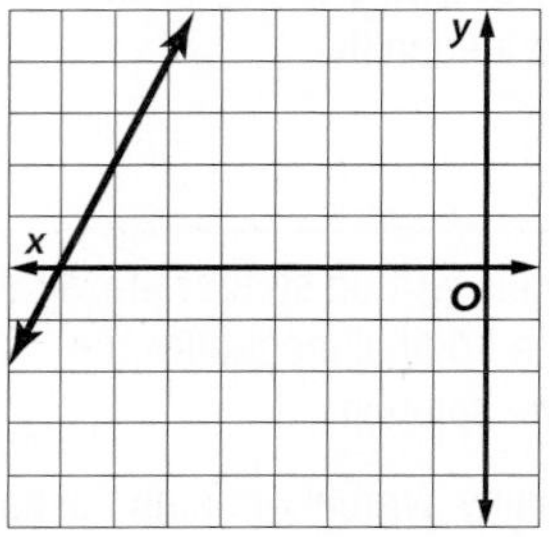

71. 4

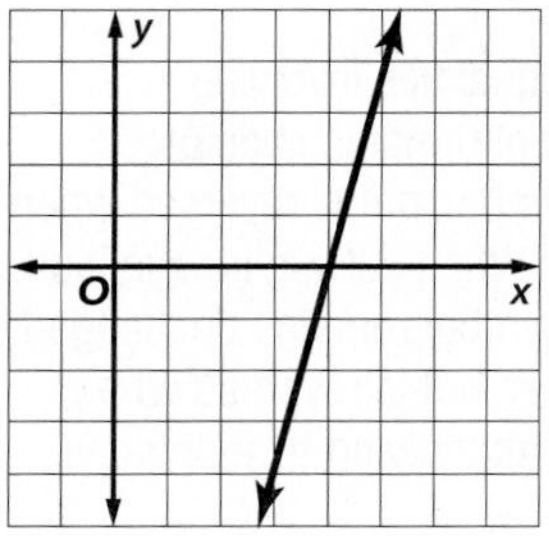

72. -6

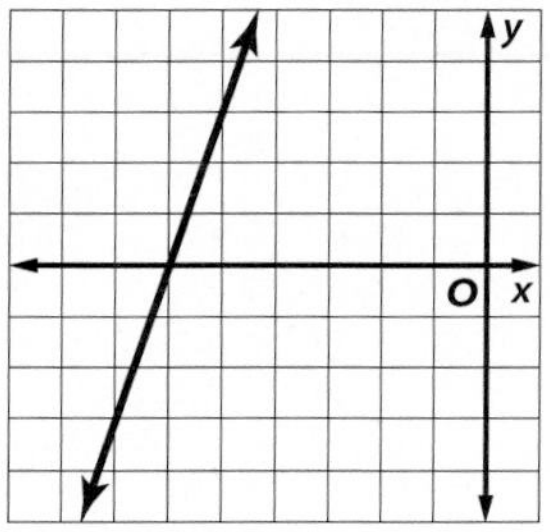

78.

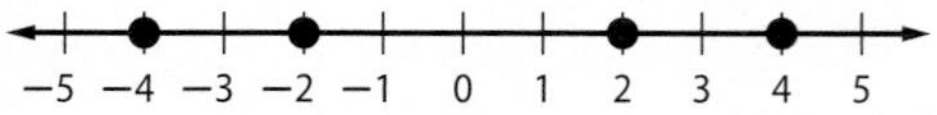

79.

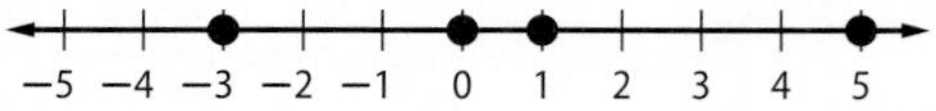

80.

81.

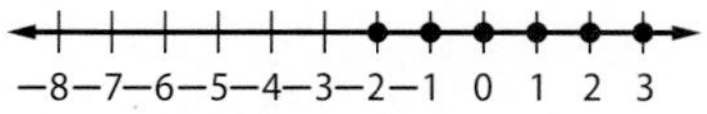

82.

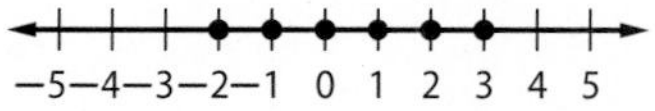

83.

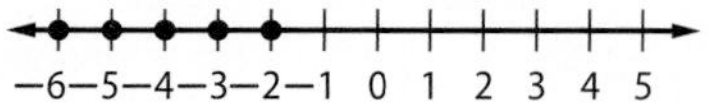

Mid-Chapter Quiz

6. Sample answer: Let x = the number; $x + (-2) \leq 6$; $x \leq 8$

7. Sample answer: Let x = the number; $x - 4 > -1$; $x > 3$

8. Sample answer: Let $x =$ the number; $2x + 3 < x - 4$; $x < -7$

25. Sample answer: Let $x =$ the number; $3x + 8 \leq x - 4$; $x \leq -6$

26. Sample answer: Let $x =$ the number; $\frac{2}{3}x + 5 > 17$; $x > 18$

Explore 5-4

1. True; since most top 20 movies in 2007 were rated PG-13, one of the statements is true. Thus the compound statement is true.
2. False; since more movies were not rated PG than rated PG-13, one of the statements is false. Thus the compound statement is false.
3. True; both parts of the compound statement are true. Thus the compound statement is true.
4. True; most top 20 movies in 2008 were not rated PG, one of the statements is true. Thus the compound statement is true.
5. False; both statements are false. Thus the compound statement is false.
6. False; since (−2) is not greater than 0, one of the statements is false. Thus the compound statement is false.
7. True; both parts of the compound statement are true. Thus the compound statement is true.
8. True; both parts of the compound statement are true. Thus the compound statement is true.
9. True; since −2 is greater than −5, one of the statements is true. Thus the compound statement is true.
10. False; since 5 is not greater than 10, one of the statements is false. Thus the compound statement is false.

Lesson 5-4

1. $\{p \mid 12 \leq p \leq 16\}$

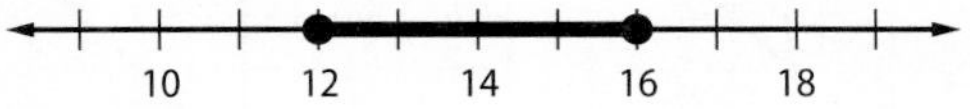

2. $\{r \mid r < -14 \text{ or } r > -7\}$

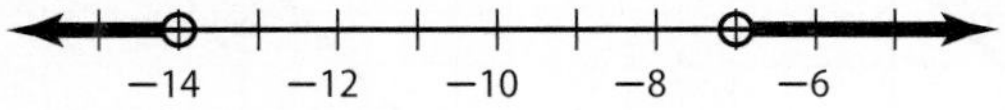

3. $\{a \mid a > 5\}$

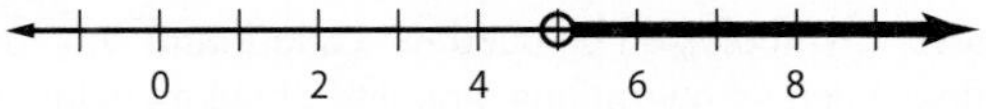

4. $\{g \mid -2 \leq g < 3\}$

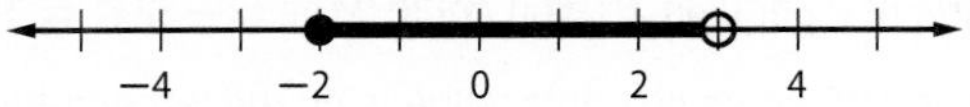

6. $\{f \mid 6 \leq f < 11\}$

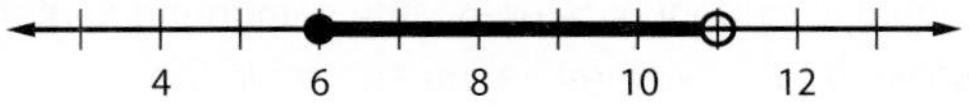

7. $\{n \mid -12 \leq n \leq -7\}$

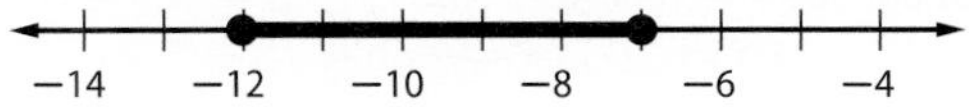

8. $\{y \mid y \geq 8 \text{ or } y < -4\}$

9. $\{t \mid t \geq 1 \text{ or } t < -1\}$

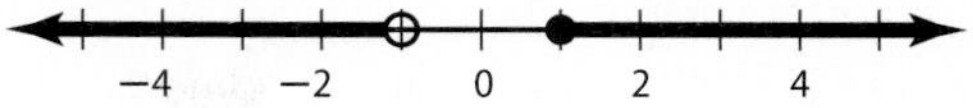

10. $\{p \mid -4 < p \leq 5\}$

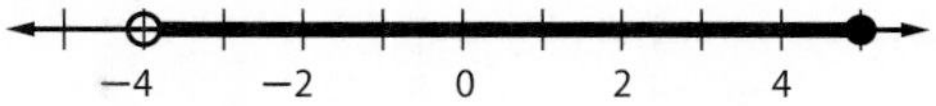

11. $\{c \mid -1 \leq c < 2\}$

12. $\{h \mid 2 \leq h < 3\}$

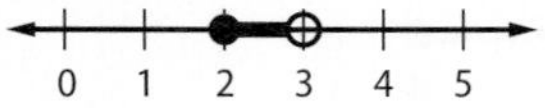

13. $\{m \mid m \text{ is a real number.}\}$

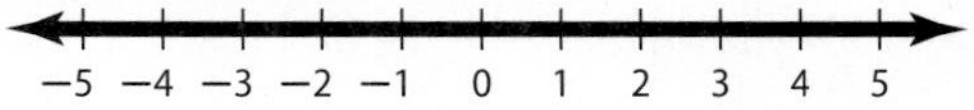

14. $\varnothing$

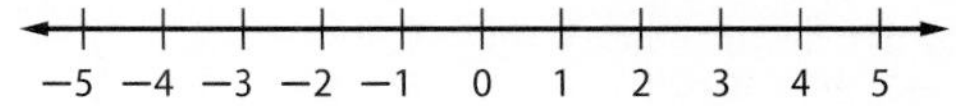

15. $\{y \mid y < -3\}$

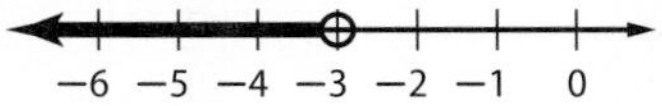

24. $\{b \mid 4 < b \leq 5\}$

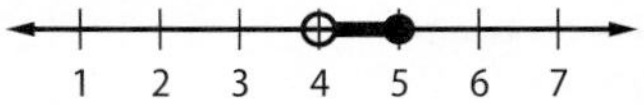

25. $\left\{a \mid -3 < a \leq \frac{1}{2}\right\}$

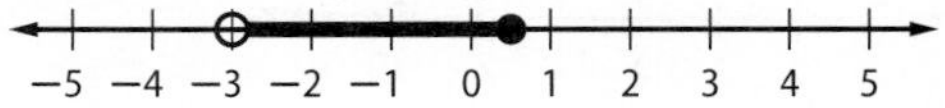

26. $\{m \mid m < -6 \text{ or } m > -1\}$

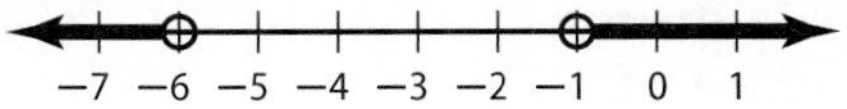

27. $\{n \mid n < -3 \text{ or } n > -3\}$

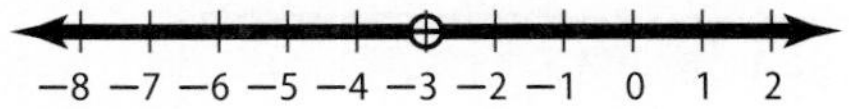

Lesson 5-5

1. $\{a \mid 2 < a < 8\}$

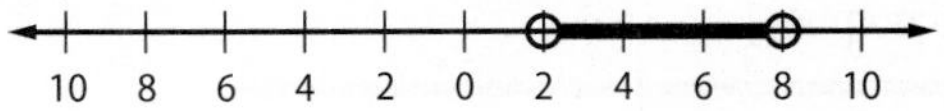

2. $\{u \mid -10 < u < 4\}$

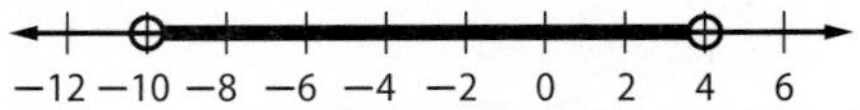

3. $\varnothing$

4. $\{c \mid c \text{ is a real number.}\}$

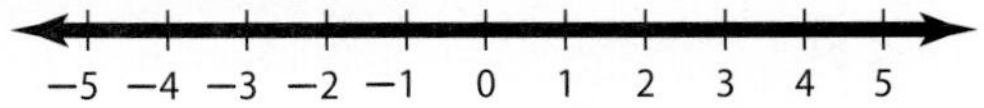

5. $\{n \mid n \leq -8 \text{ or } n \geq -2\}$

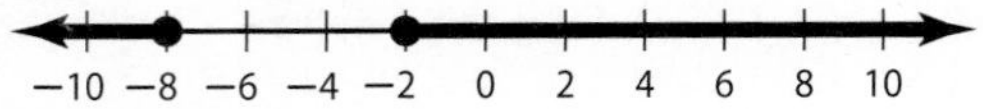

6. $\{p \mid p \leq -6 \text{ or } p \geq 10\}$

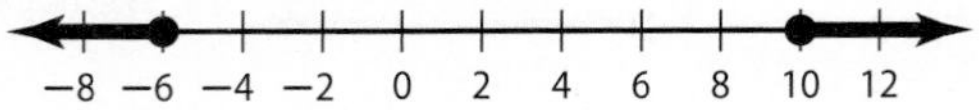

8. $\{x \mid -24 < x < 8\}$

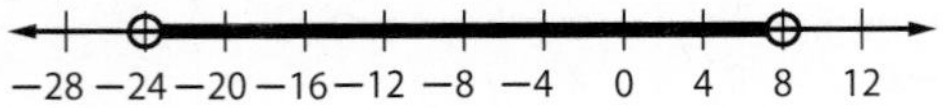

9. $\{r \mid -3 \leq r \leq 1\}$

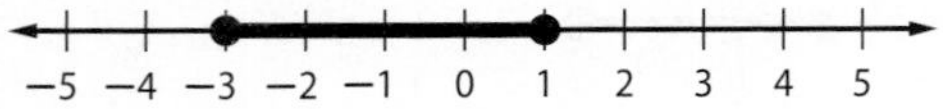

10. $\{c \mid -3 \leq c \leq 4\}$

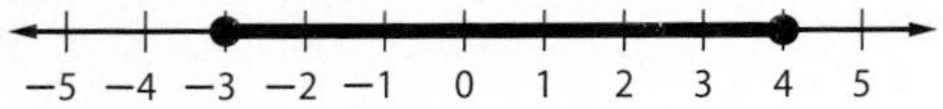

11. $\{h \mid -3 < h < 5\}$

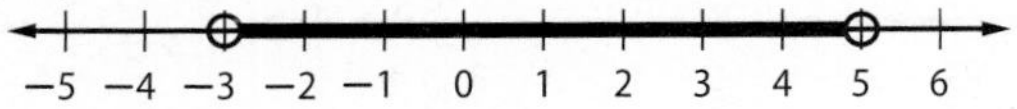

12. $\varnothing$

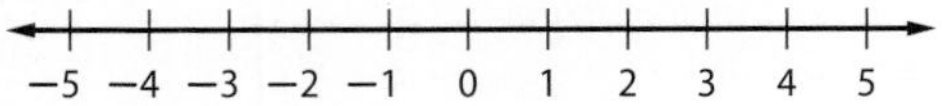

13. $\varnothing$

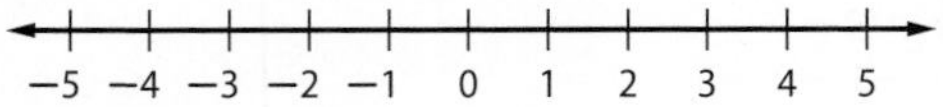

14. $\{r \mid r < -8 \text{ or } r > 4\}$

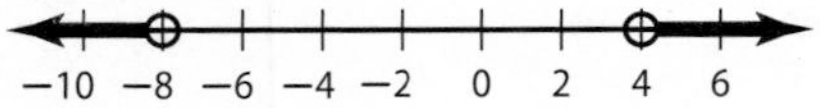

15. $\{k \mid k < 1 \text{ or } k > 7\}$

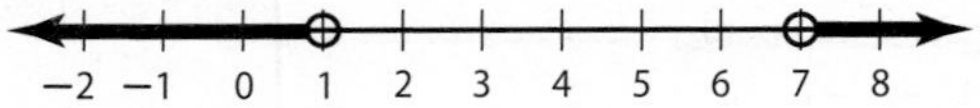

16. $\{h \mid h \leq -3 \text{ or } h \geq 6\}$

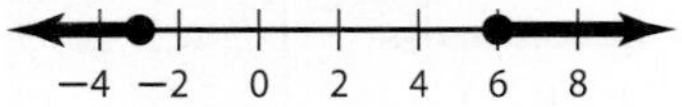

17. $\{p \mid p \leq -3 \text{ or } p \geq 2\}$

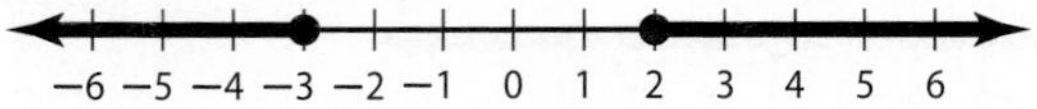

18. $\{v \mid v \text{ is a real number.}\}$

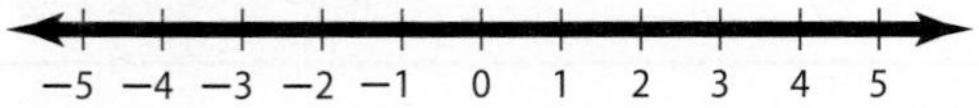

19. $\{c \mid c \text{ is a real number.}\}$

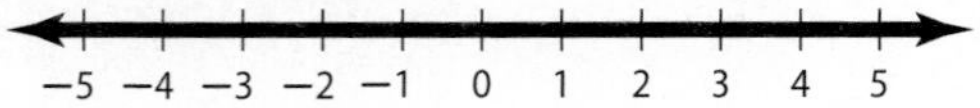

21. $\left\{n \mid n \leq -5\frac{1}{4} \text{ or } n \geq 3\frac{3}{4}\right\}$

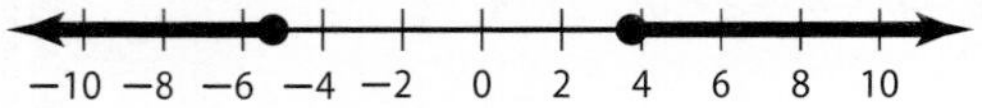

22. $\left\{t \mid -\frac{4}{5} \leq t \leq 1\frac{3}{5}\right\}$

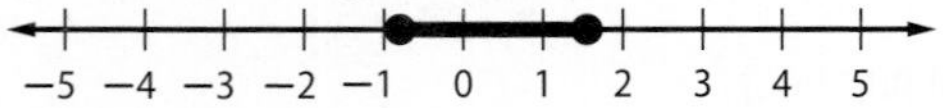

23. $\left\{h \mid -5\frac{2}{3} < h < 5\right\}$

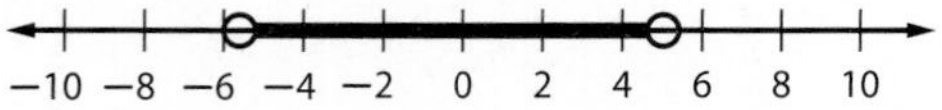

24. $\{p \mid p \leq -14 \text{ or } p \geq 22\}$

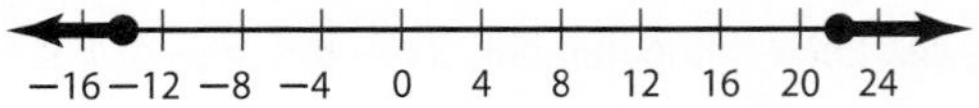

25. $\varnothing$

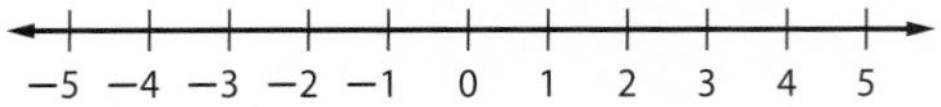

26. $\{g \mid g \text{ is a real number.}\}$

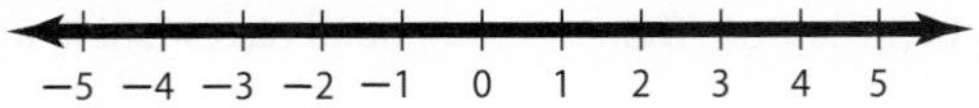

27. $\left\{r \mid -2 < r < \frac{2}{3}\right\}$

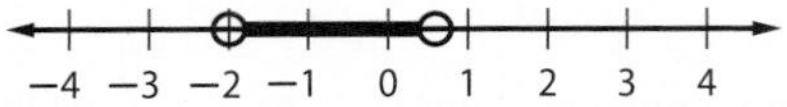

28. $\left\{p \mid p < -4 \text{ or } p > -\frac{2}{3}\right\}$

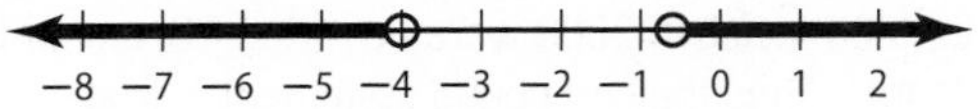

29. $\{h \mid -1.5 < h < 4.5\}$

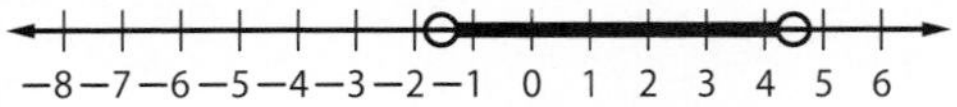

30b.

42b.

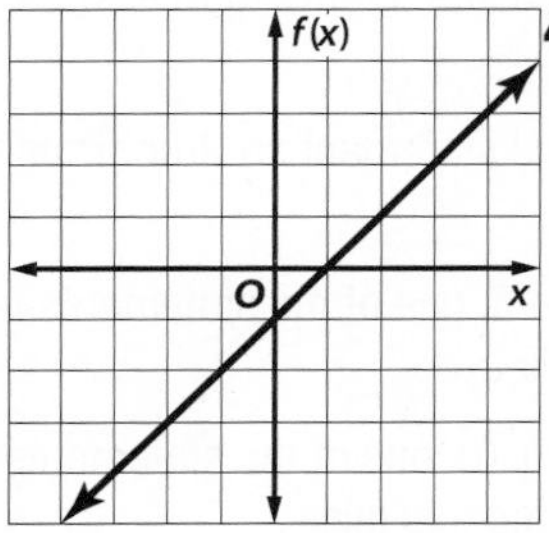

42c.

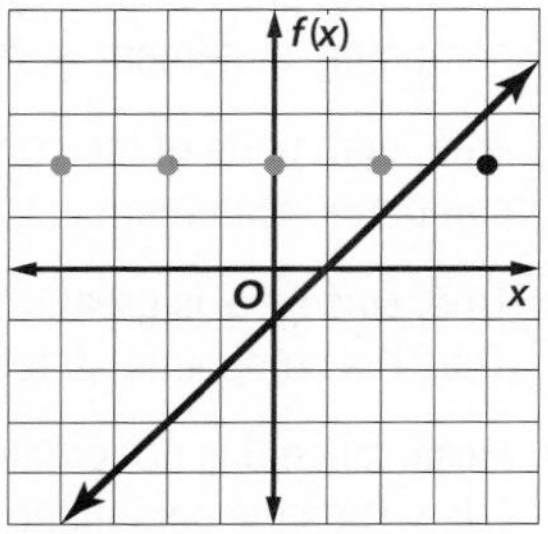

42d. See students' tables.

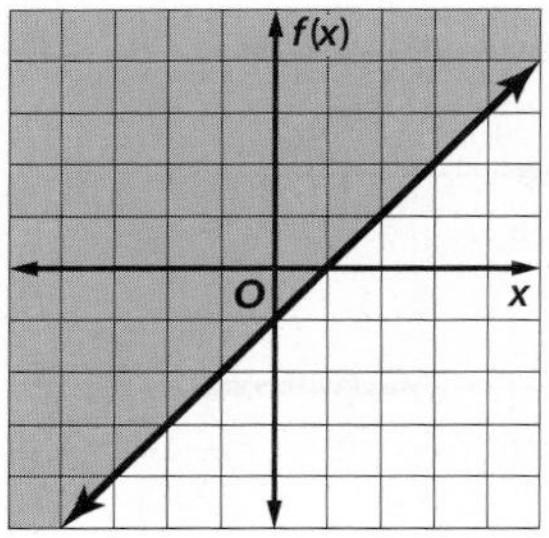

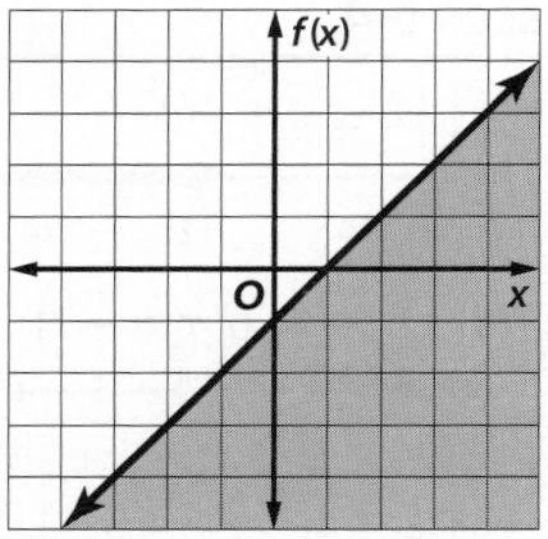

46. Sample answer: Symbols can be used as a shorthand way to represent ideas such as operations, equality, absolute value, and the empty set. For example, instead of writing 5 minus the absolute value of $2x$ equals 10, you could write $5 - |2x| = 10$.

47. Sample answer: When an absolute value is on the left and the inequality symbol is $<$ or $\leq$, the compound sentence uses *and*, and if the inequality symbol is $>$ or $\geq$, the compound sentence uses *or*. To solve, if $|x| < n$, then set up and solve the inequalities $x < n$ and $x > -n$, and if $|x| > n$, then set up and solve the inequalities $x > n$ or $x < -n$.

61.
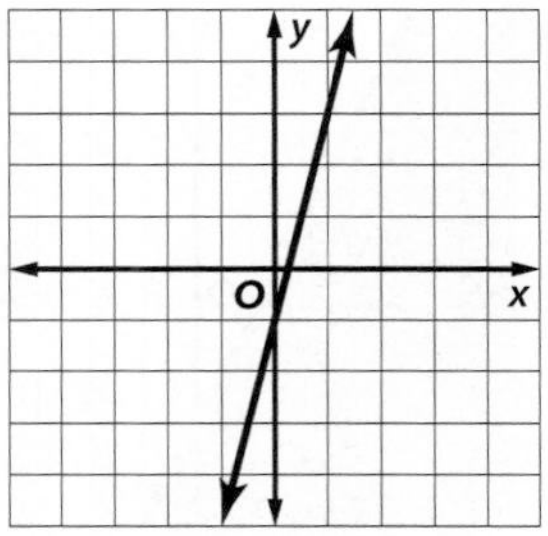

62.
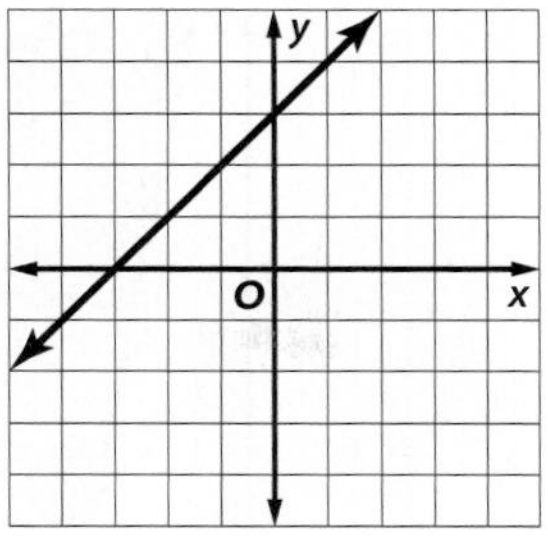

63.
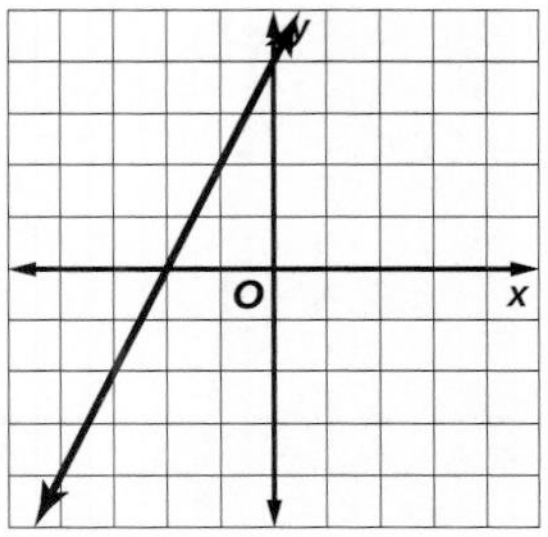

64.
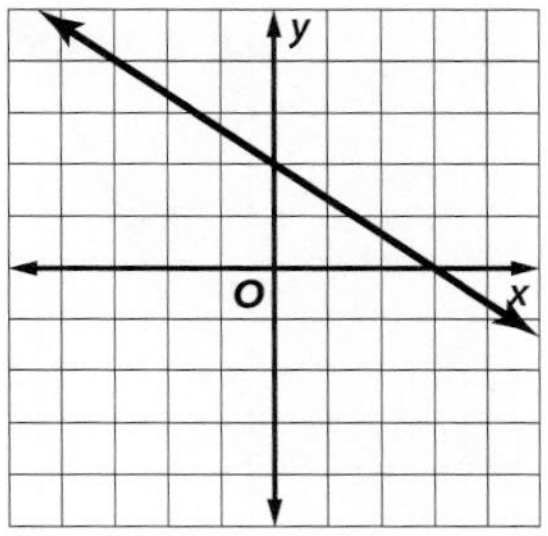

65.
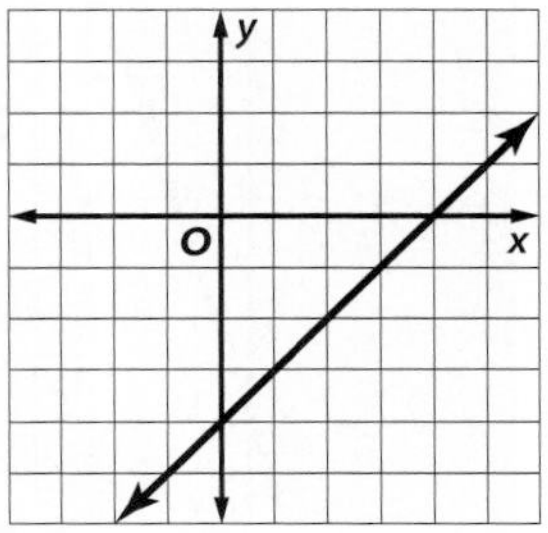

66.
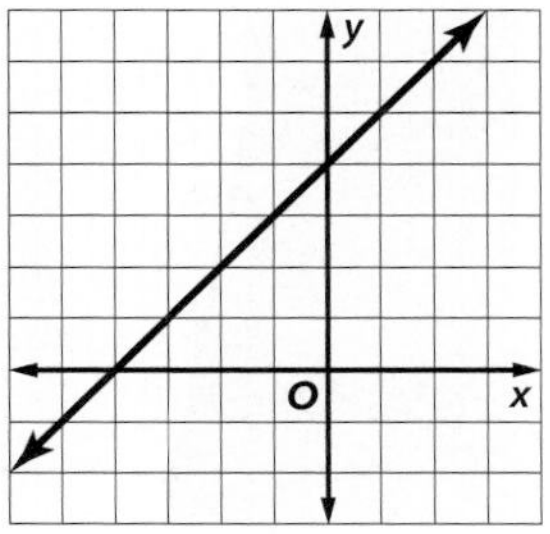

67.
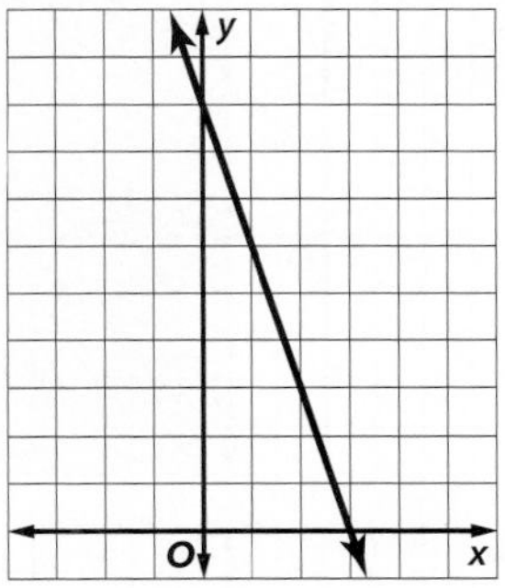

68.
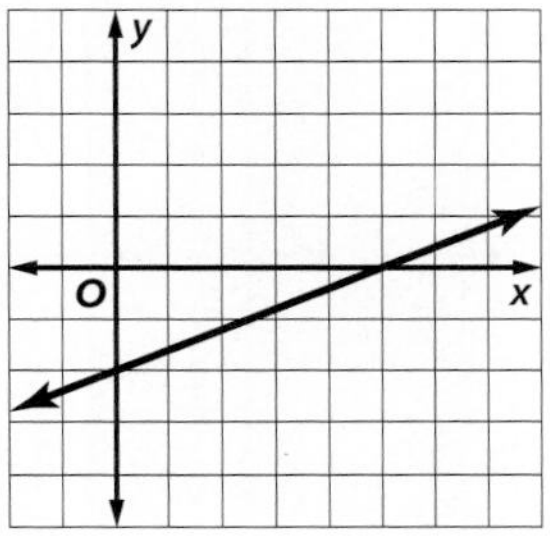

Lesson 5-6 (Guided Practice)

1A.
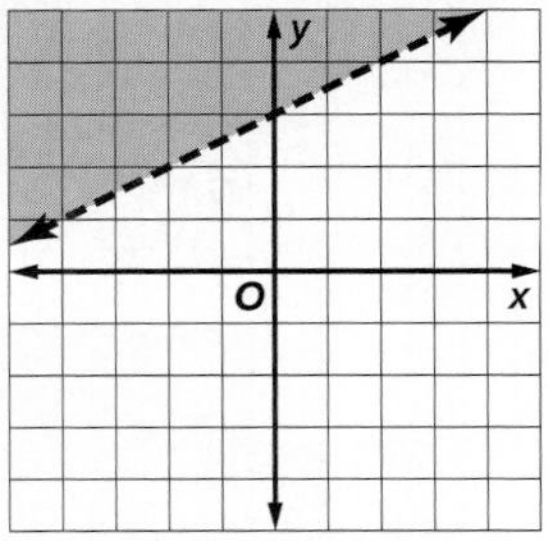

1B.
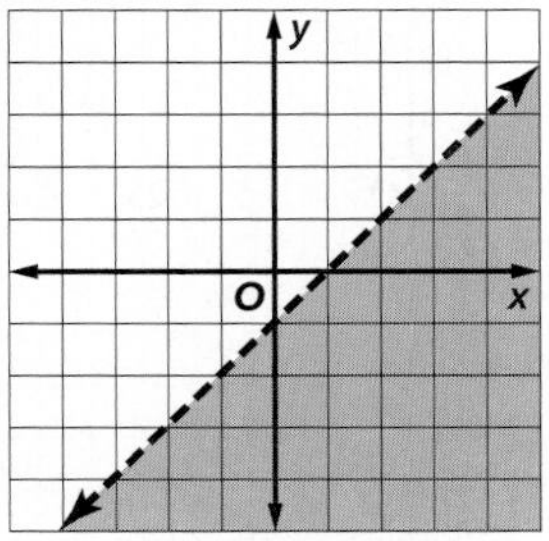

2A.
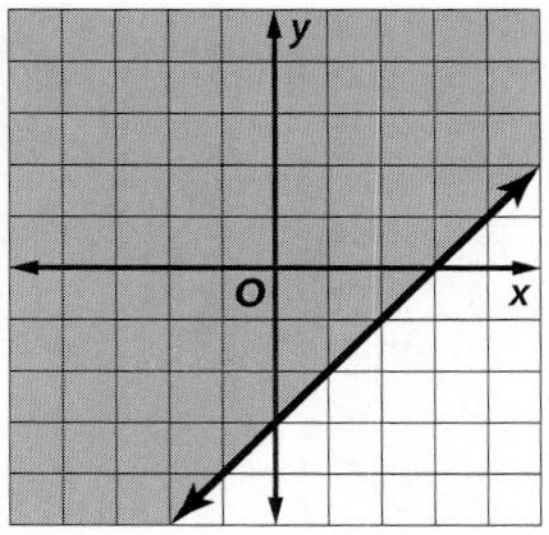

2B.
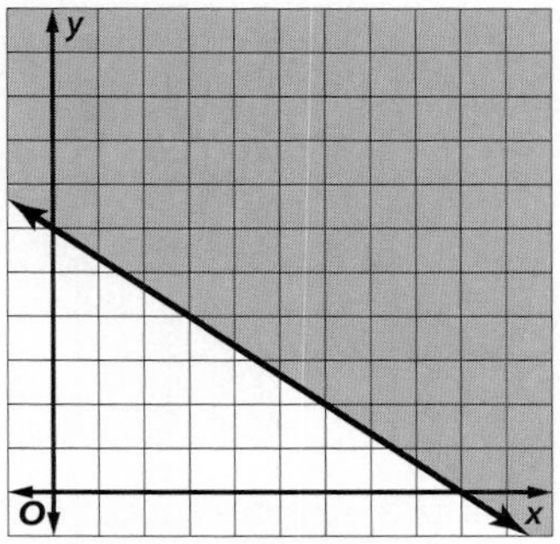

3A.
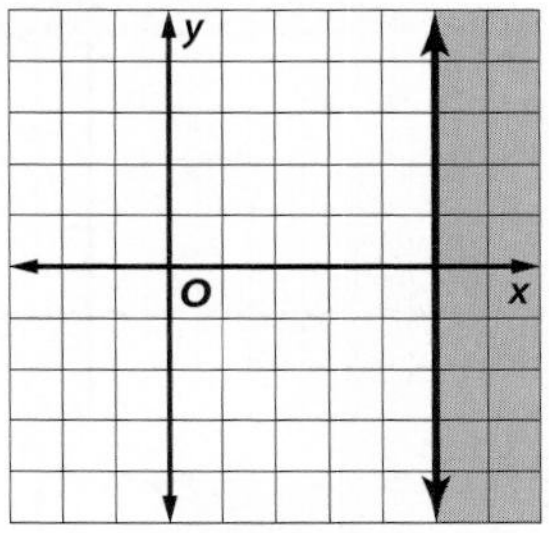

3B.
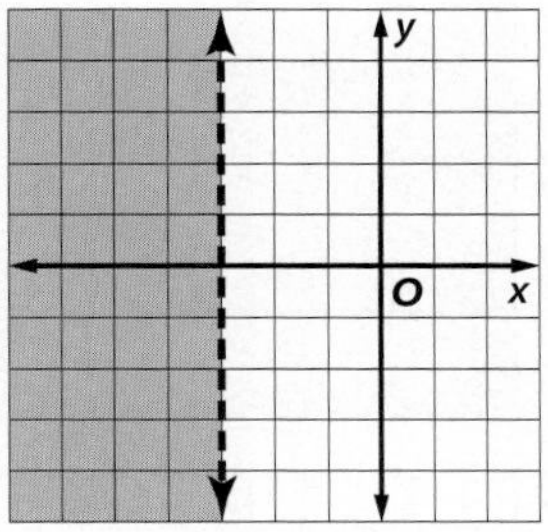

Lesson 5-6

1.
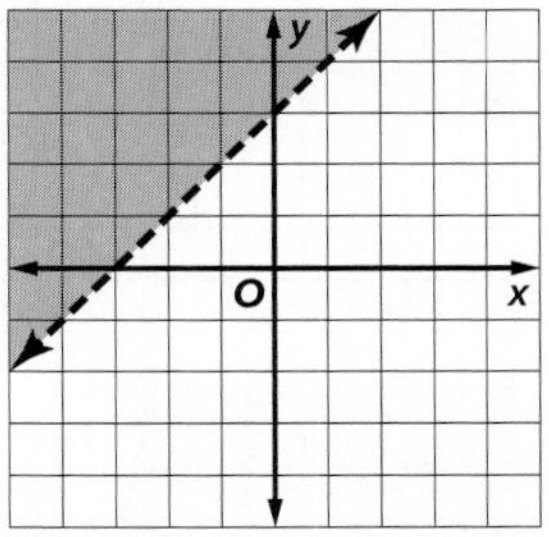

2.
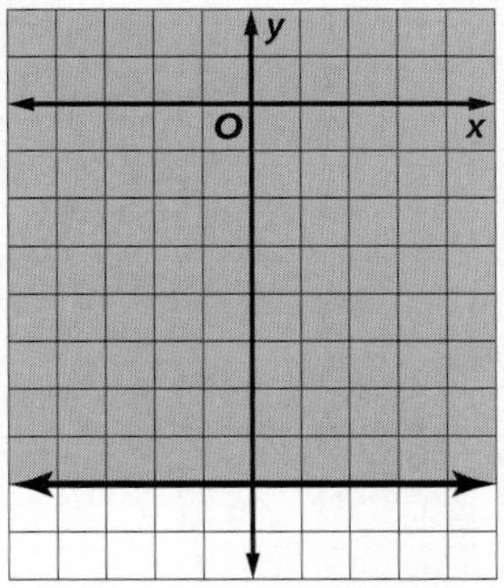

3.
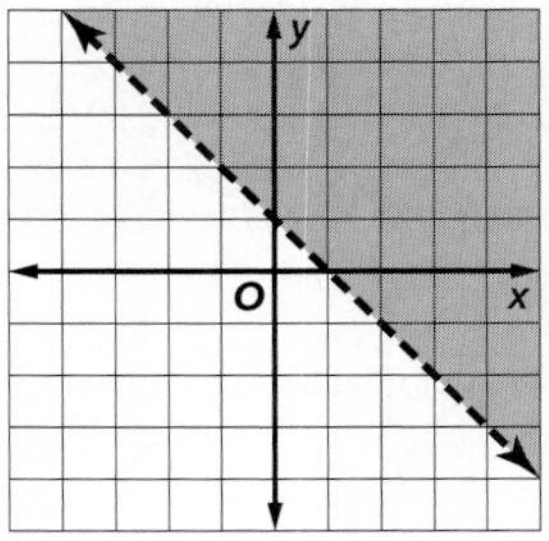

4.
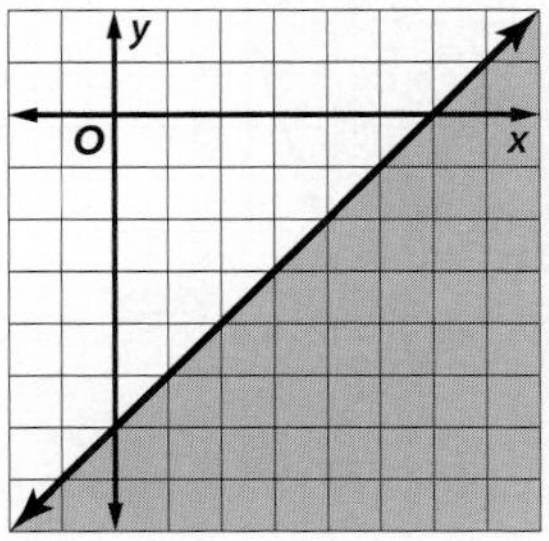

5.
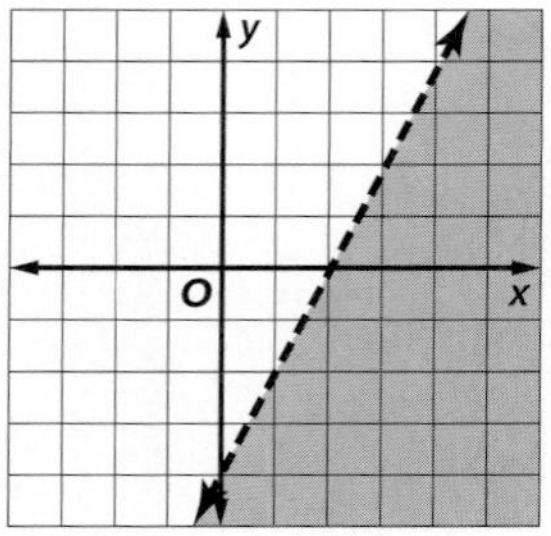

6.
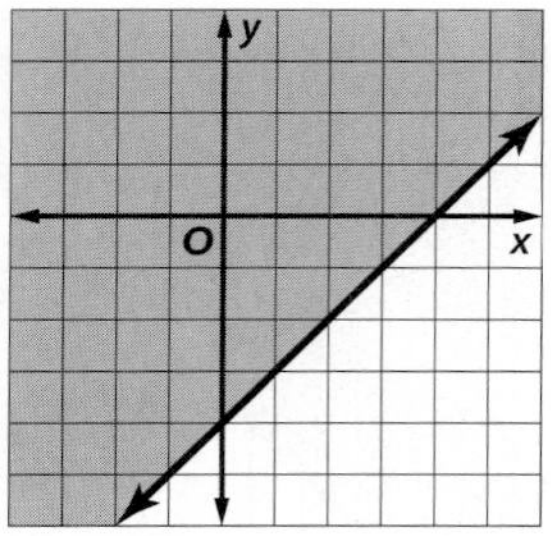

7.
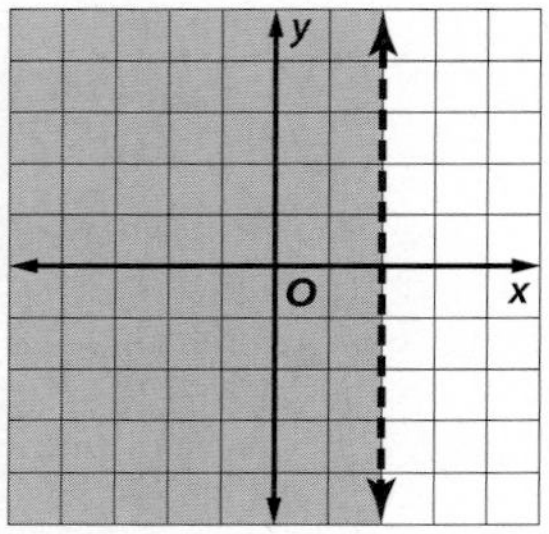

8.
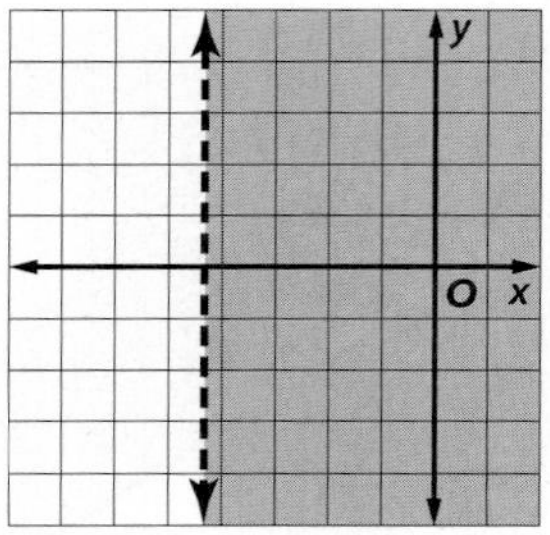

9.
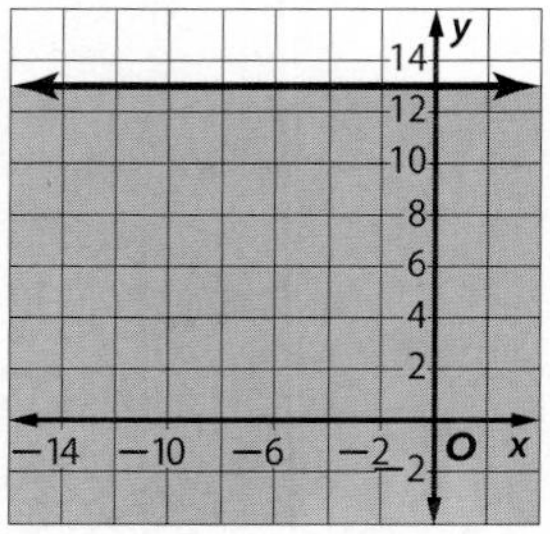

10.
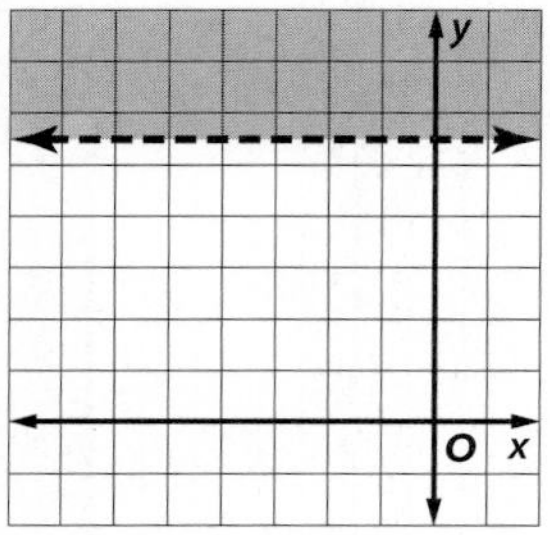

12.
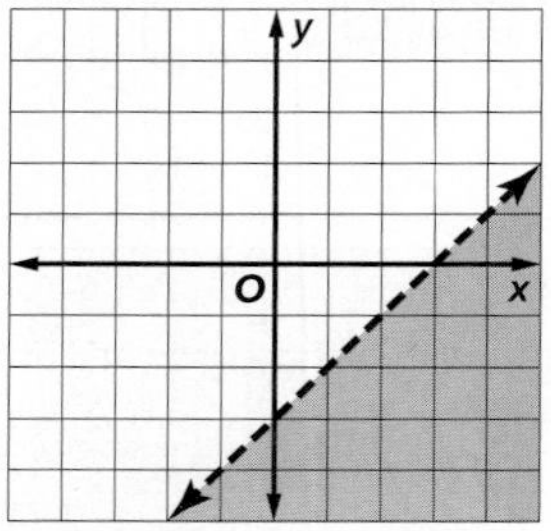

13.
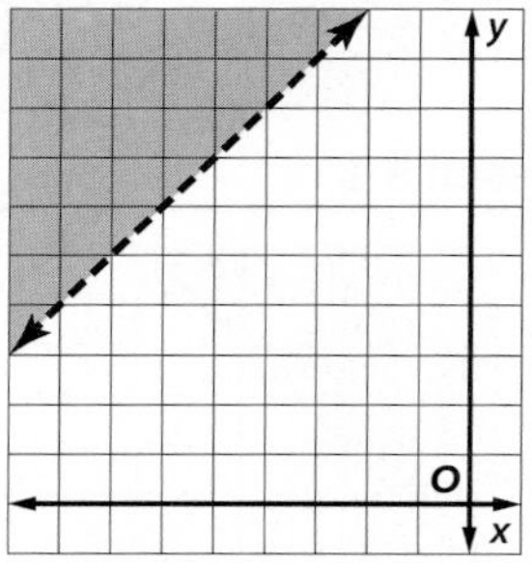

14.
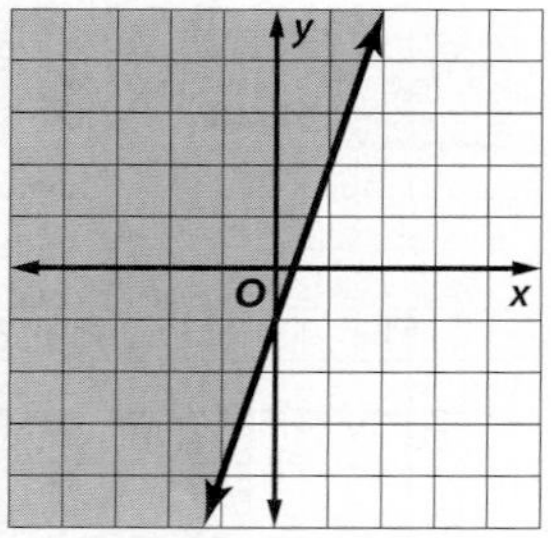

15.
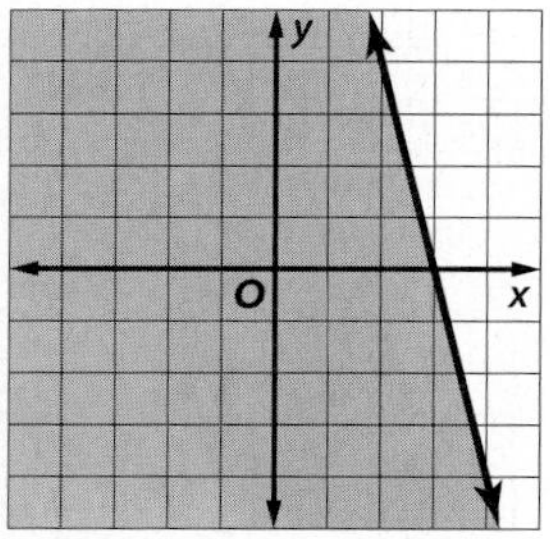

16.
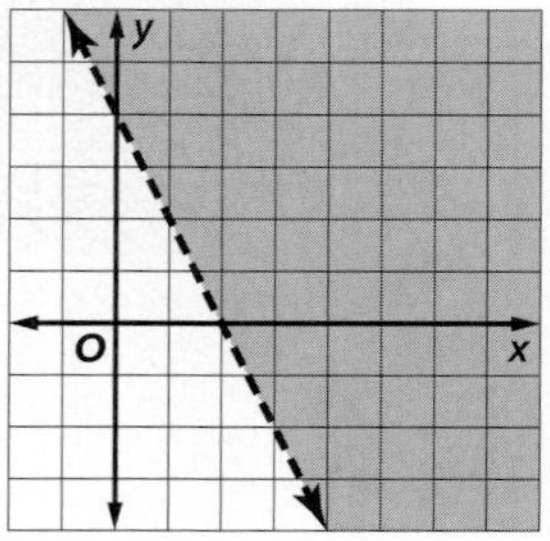

17.
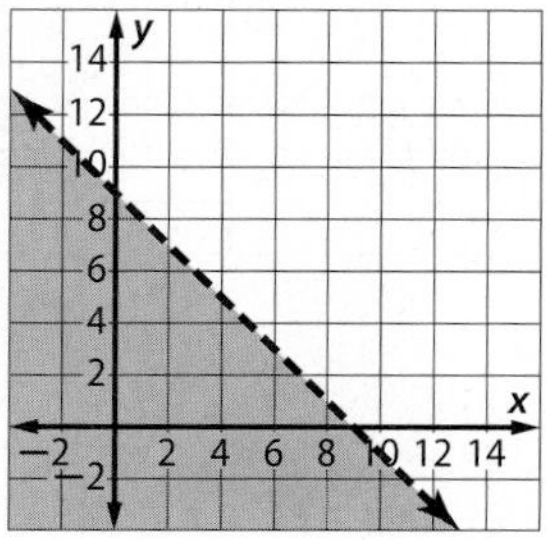

18.
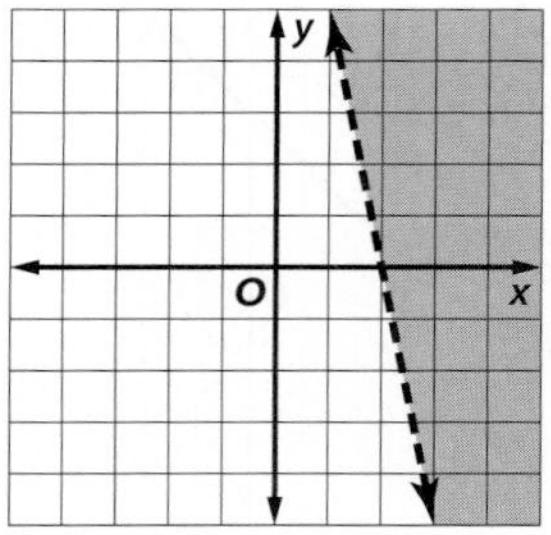

19.
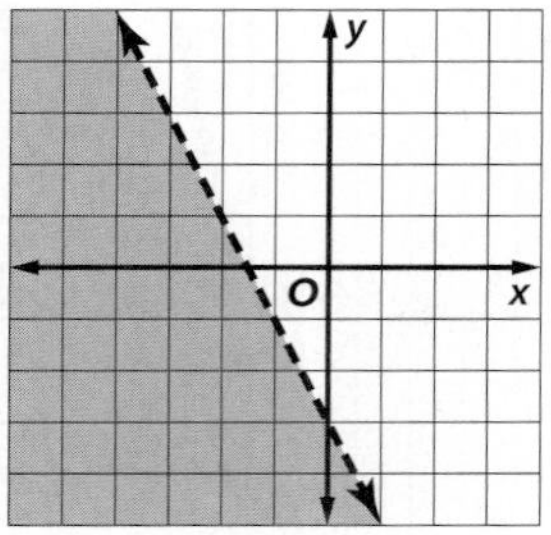

20.
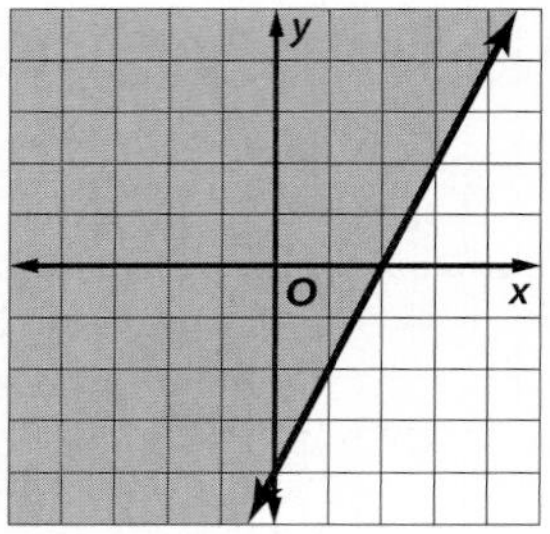

21.
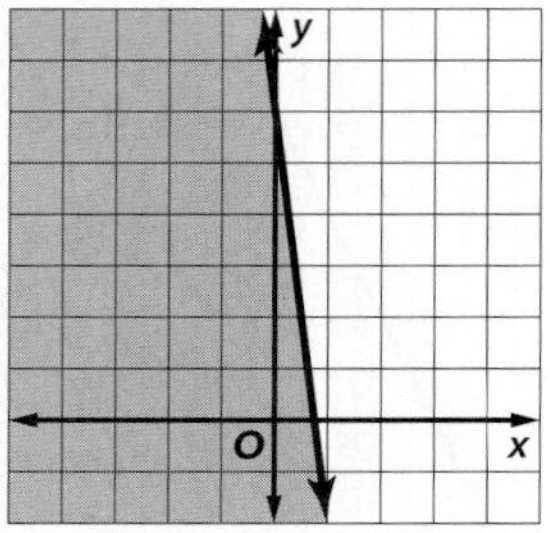

22.
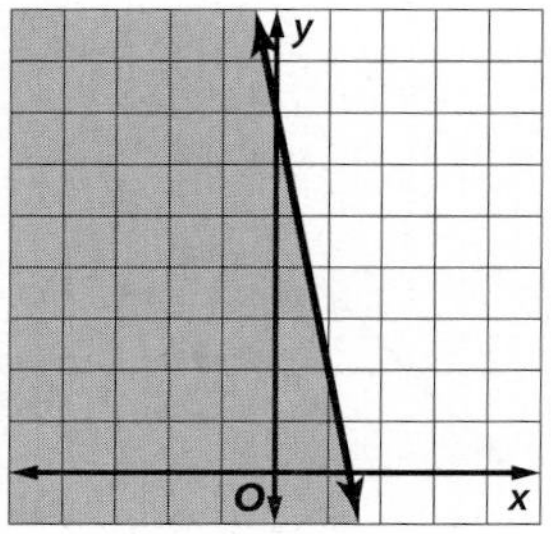

23.
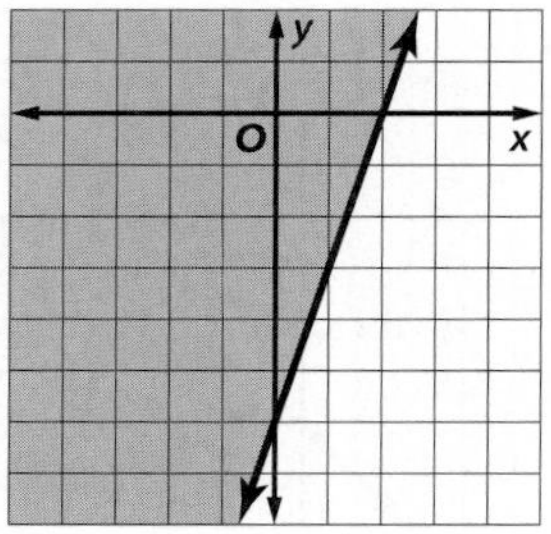

24.
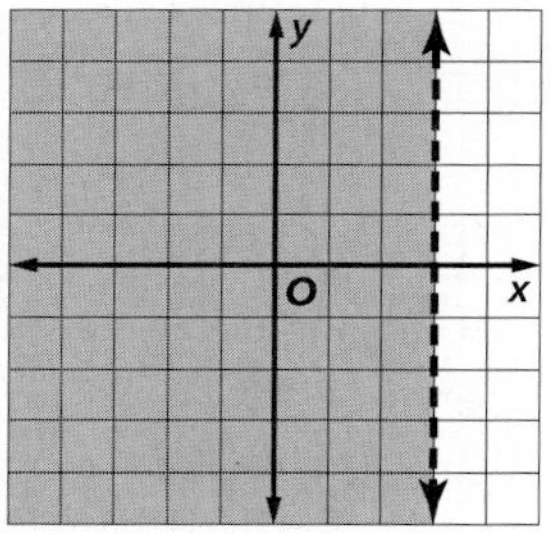

25.
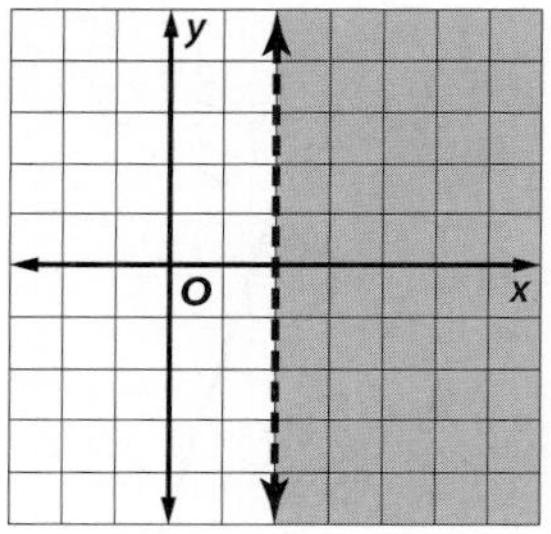

26.
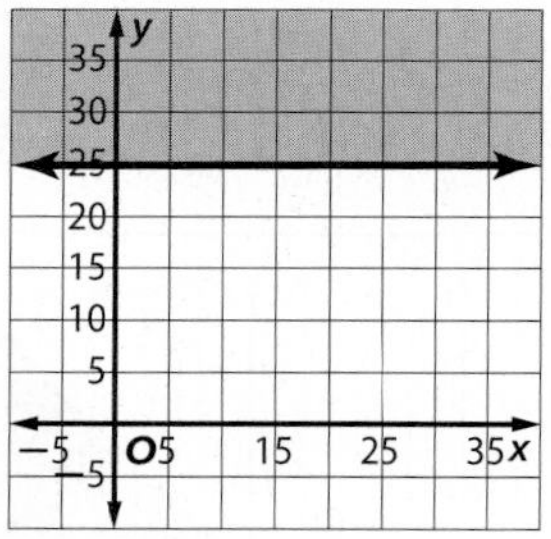

27.
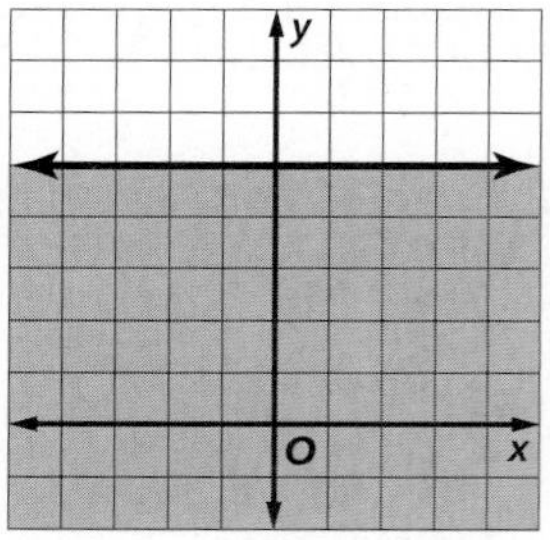

28.
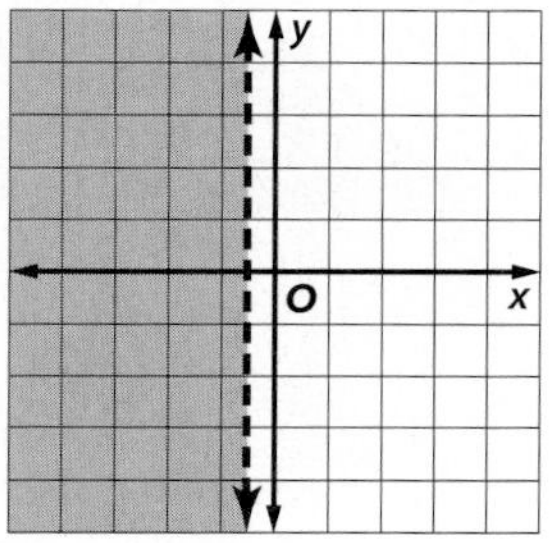

29.
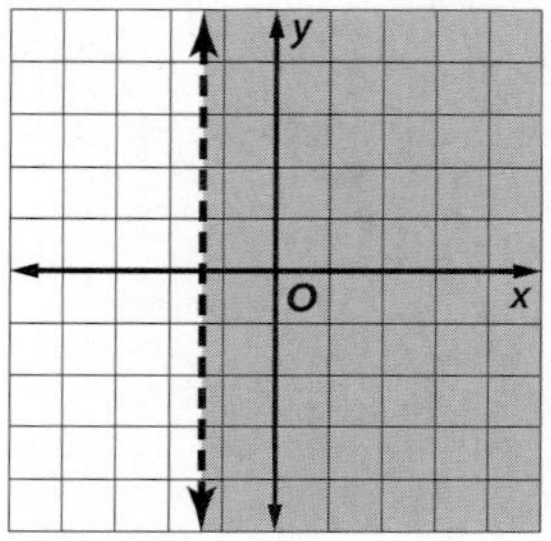

31.

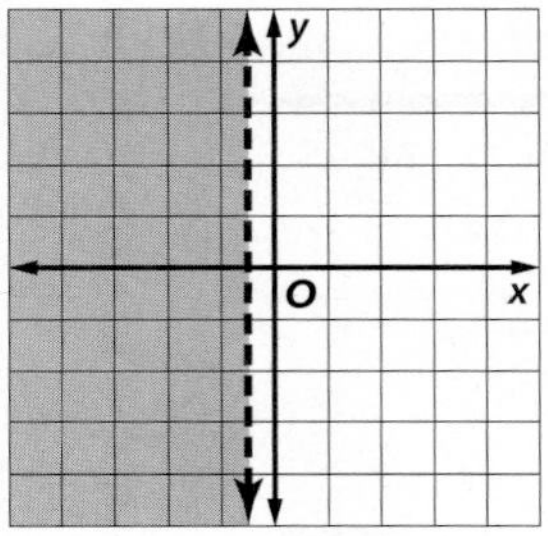

32.

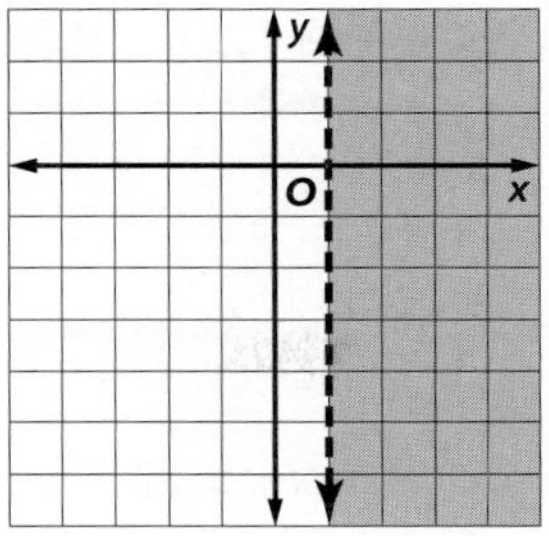

33.

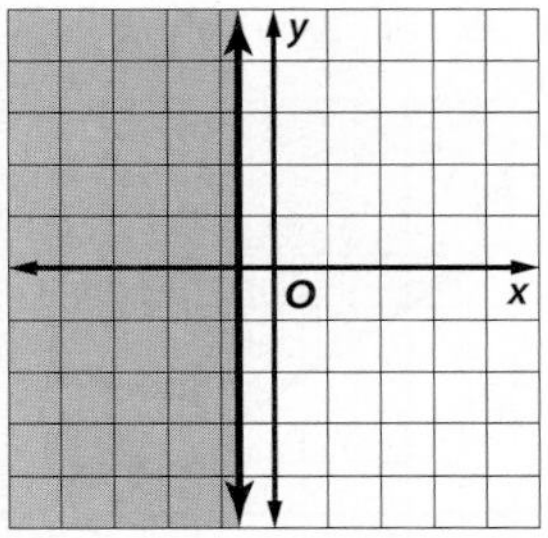

34.

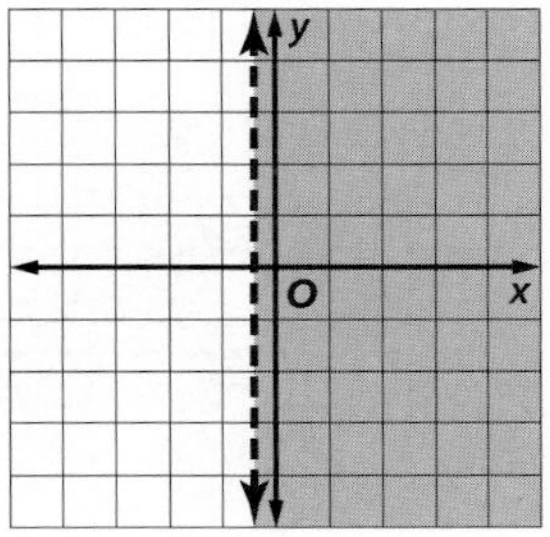

35.

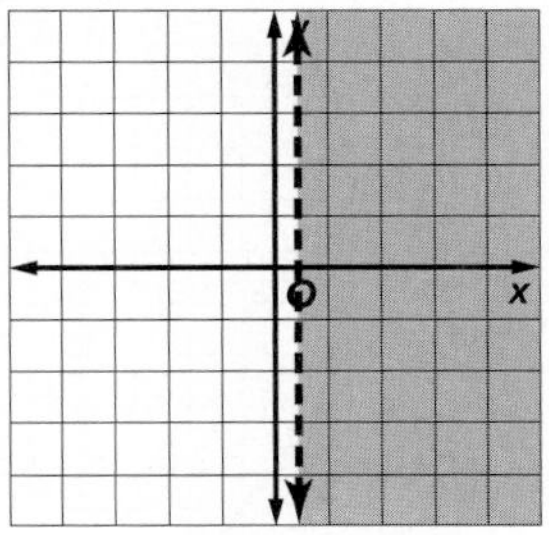

36.

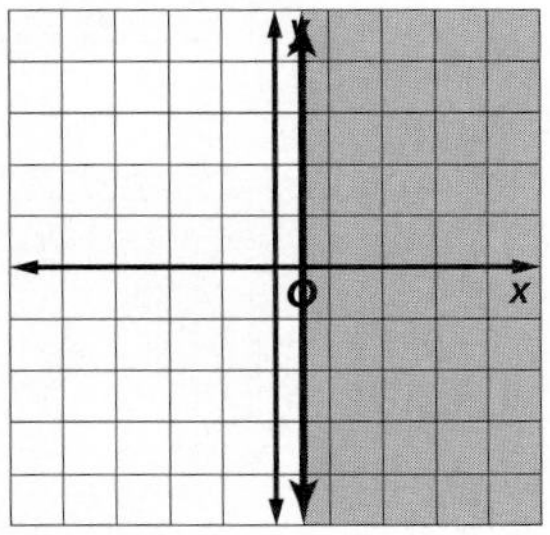

38. (−2, 7), (4, 8), (1, 6)

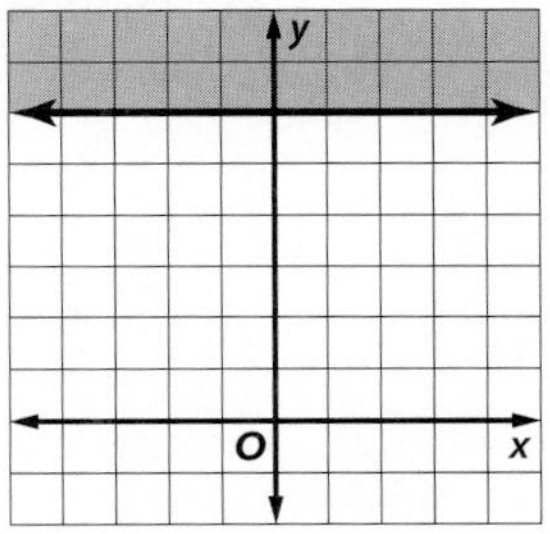

39. (−5, −5)

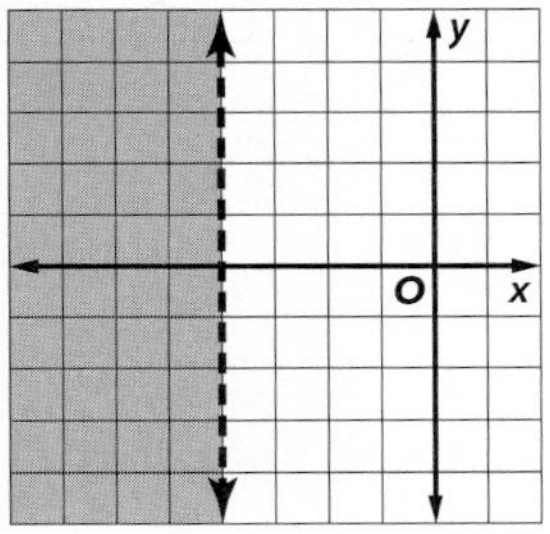

40. (2, 3), (0, 0), (5, 3)

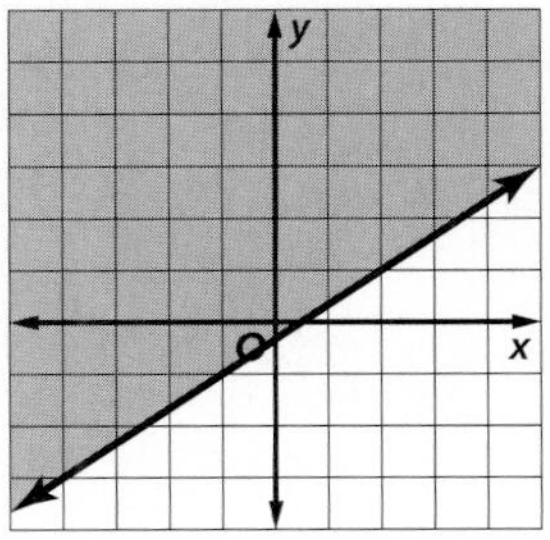

41. (1, 1), (2, 5), (6, 0)

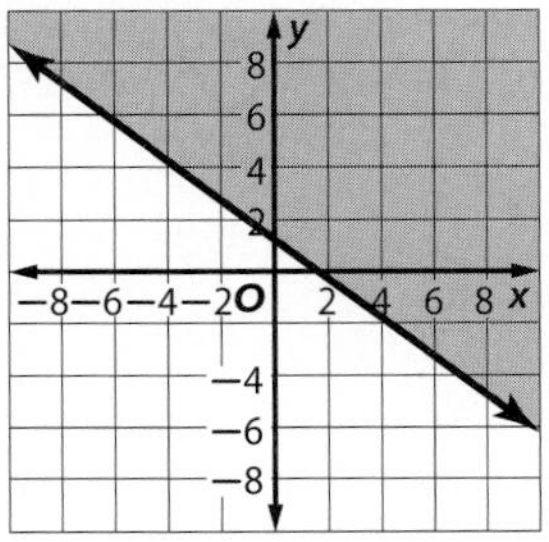

42. (3, −1), (1, 1), (−2, 0)

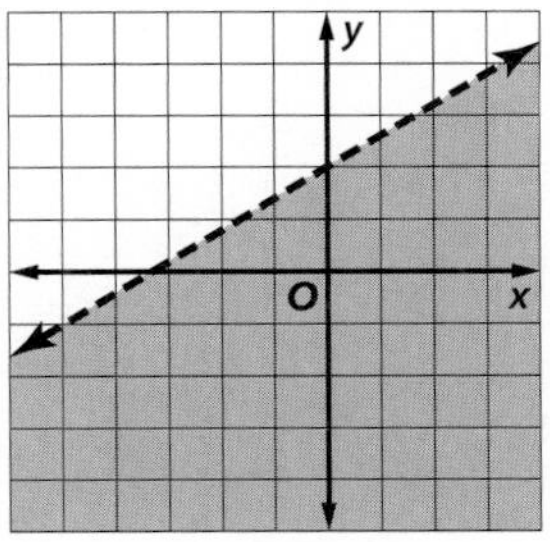

43. (7, 5), (5, 3), (2, −5)

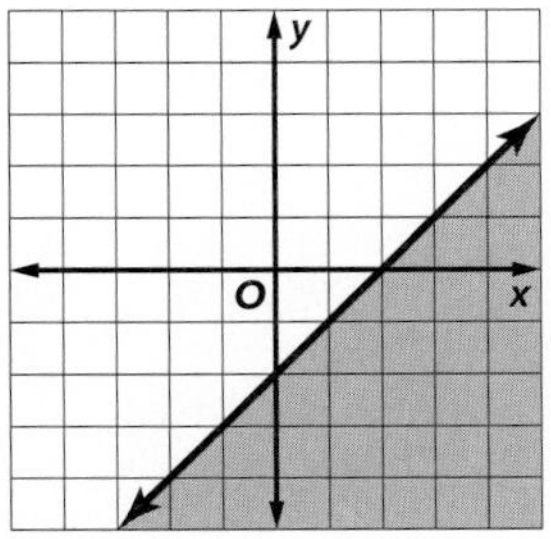

44c.

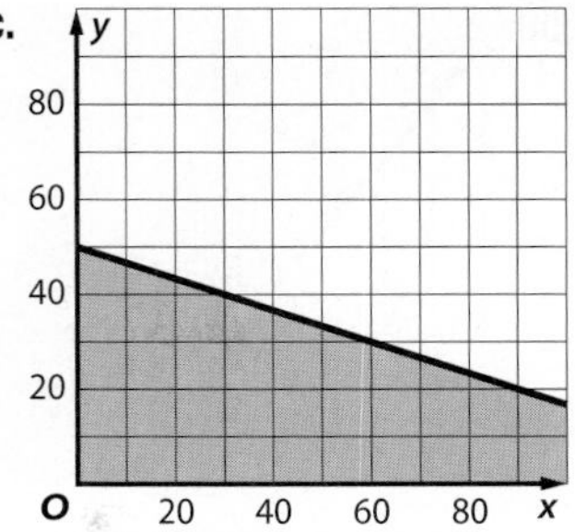

45b.

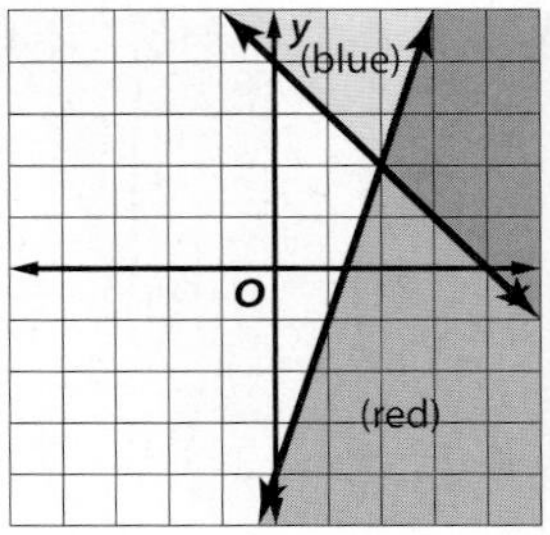

48. A test point on the boundary does not show which half-plane contains points that make the inequality true.

49. Sample answer: The inequality $y > 10x + 45$ represents the cost of a monthly smartphone data plan with a flat rate of $45 for the first 2 GB of data used, plus $10 per each additional GB of data used. Both the domain and range are nonnegative real numbers because GB used, and the total cost cannot be negative.

50. Sample answer: First solve the inequality for y. Then change the inequality sign to an equal sign and graph the boundary. If $<$ or $>$ is used, the boundary is not included in the graph and the line is dashed. Otherwise, the boundary is included and the line is solid. Then choose a test point not on the boundary. Substitute the coordinates of the test point into the original inequality. If the result makes the inequality true, then shade the half-plane that includes the test point. If the result makes the inequality false, shade the half-plane that does not include the test point. Lastly, check your solution by choosing a test point that is in the half-plane that is not shaded. This second test point should make the inequality false if the solution is correct.

Study Guide and Review

45.

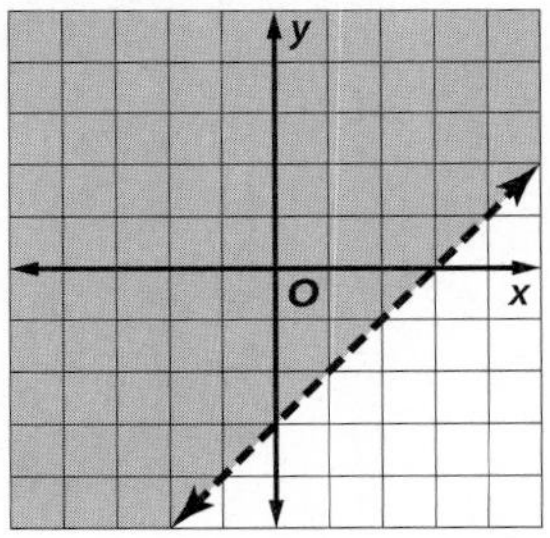

46.

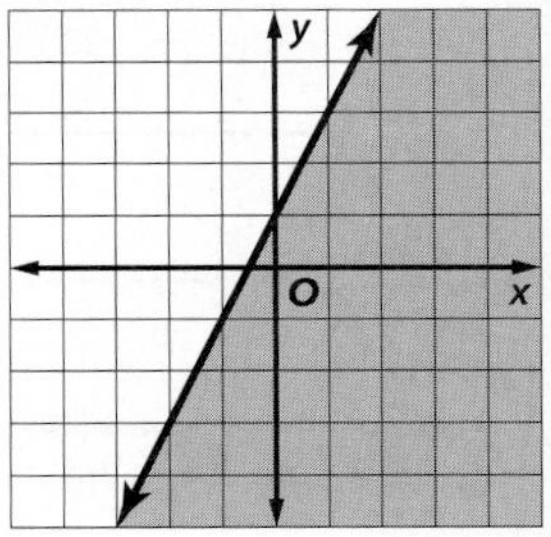

47.

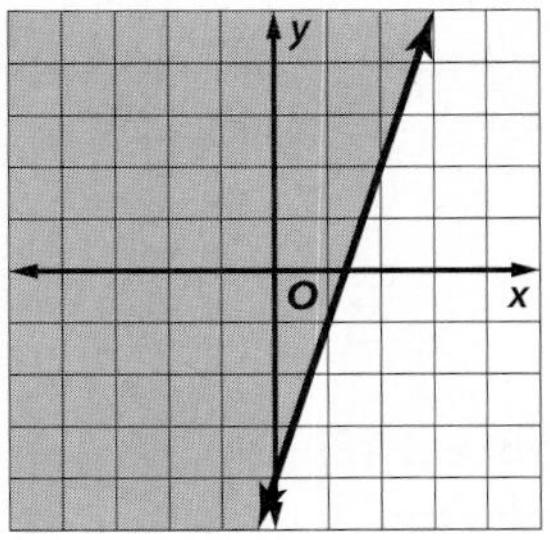

48.

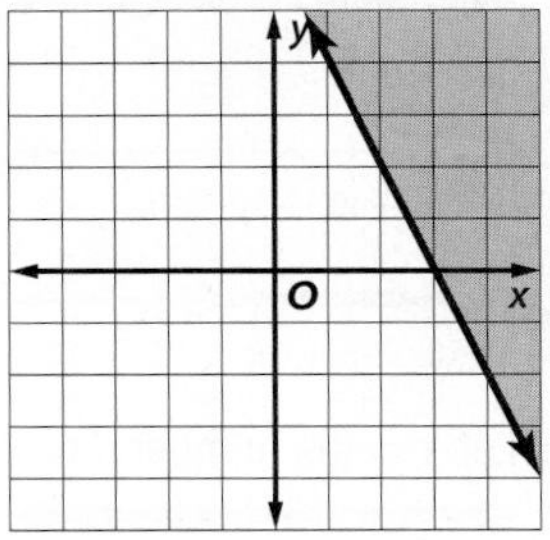

49. 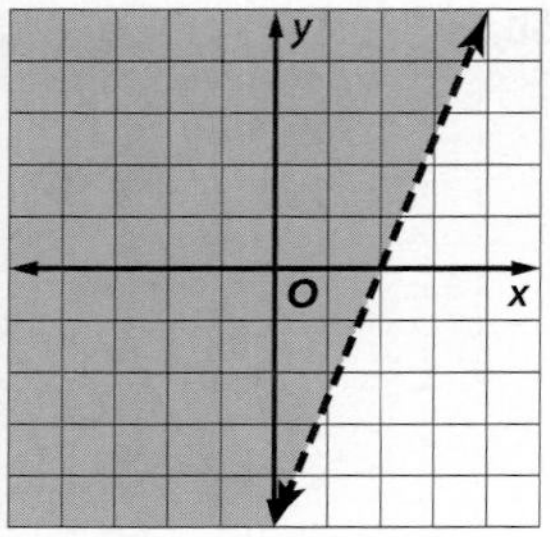

50. 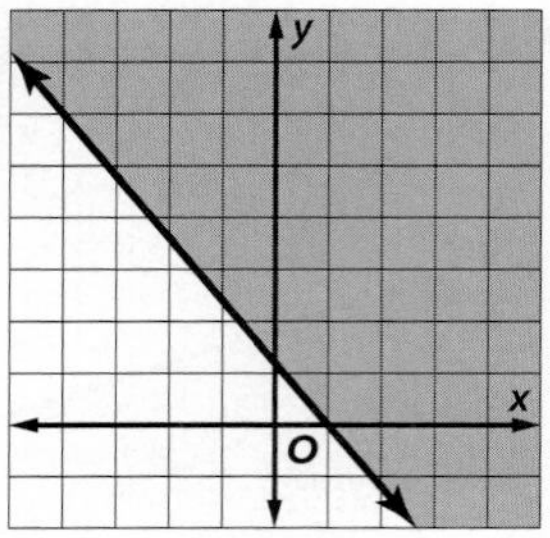

51. 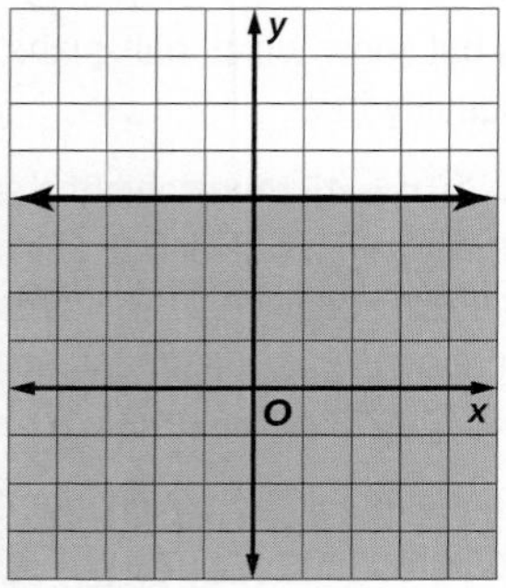

52. 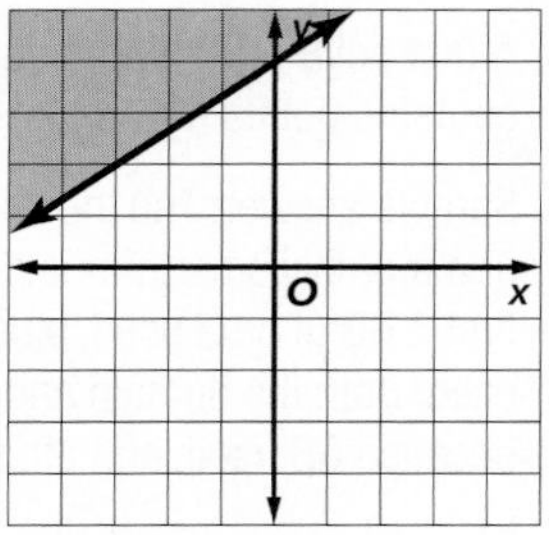

53. 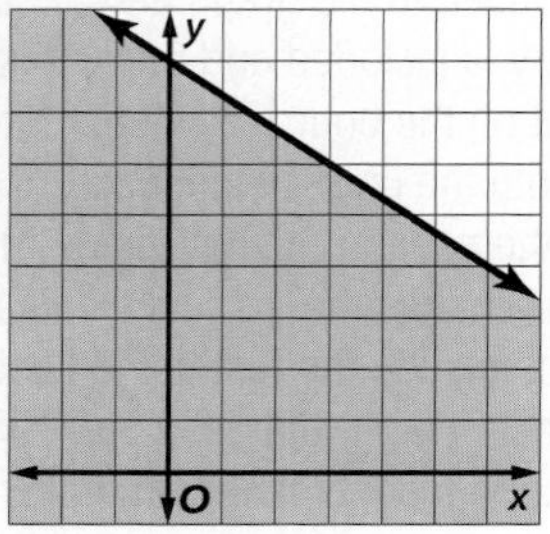

Practice Test

4. 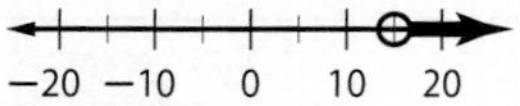

5. 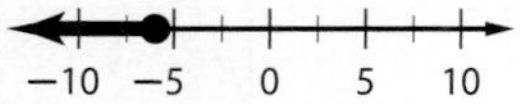

6. 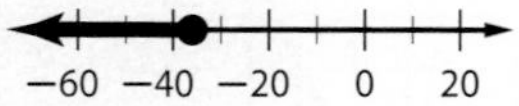

7. 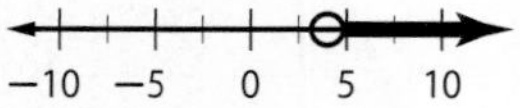

8. 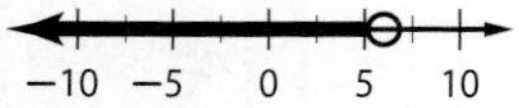

9. 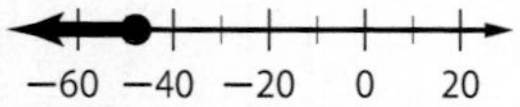

10. 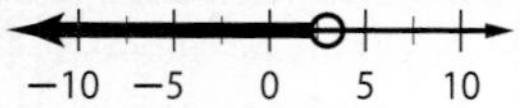

15. Let x = the number; $\{x \mid x - 4 \leq 8; x \leq 12\}$.

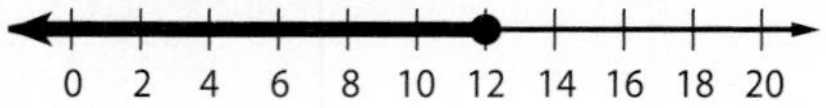

16. Let x = the number; $\{x \mid 9x - 4 \geq 23; x \geq 3\}$

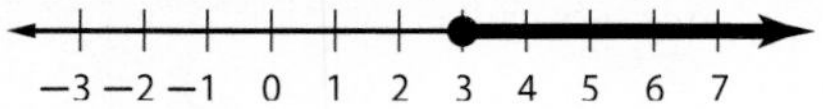

18. $2 < p < 8$

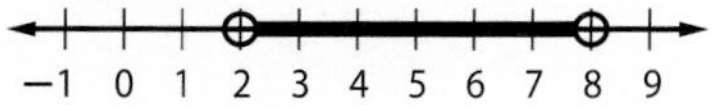

19. $f \leq -14$ or $f \geq 7$

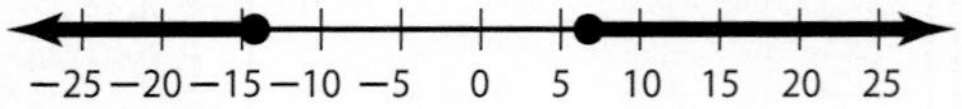

20. $-3 \leq m \leq \frac{9}{2}$

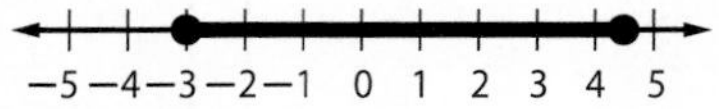

21. $x < -17$ or $x > 23$

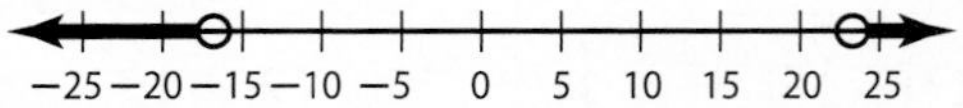

23. 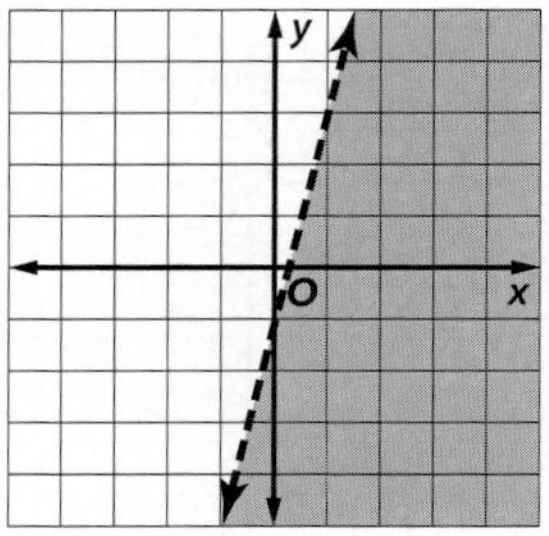

24. 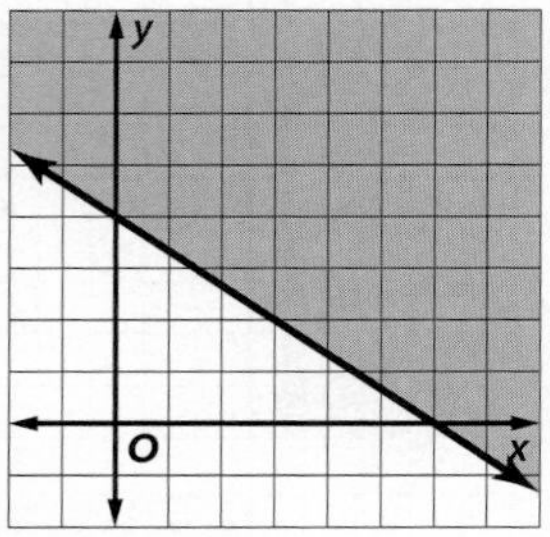

25. (2, 3), (7, 3)

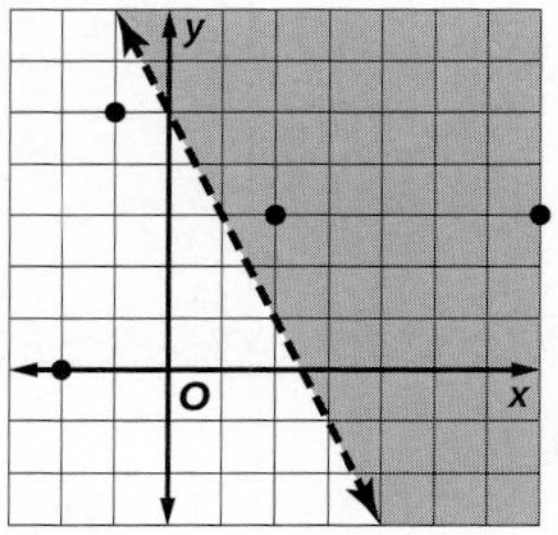

26. 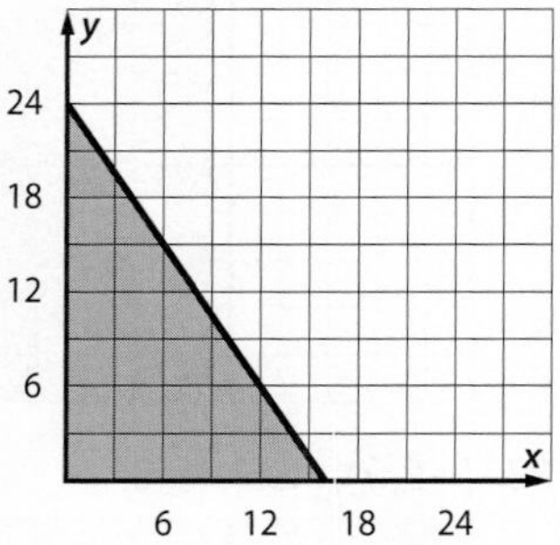

NOTES

Chapter Planner

	Diagnostic Assessment Quick Check		
	LESSON 6-1 45 min: 1.5 days 90 min: 0.75 day	EXTEND 6-1 45 min: 0.5 day 90 min: 0.25 day	LESSON 6-2 45 min: 1 day 90 min: 0.5 day
Title	**Graphing Systems of Equations**	**Graphing Technology Lab: Systems of Equations**	**Substitution**
Objectives	▪ Determine the number of solutions a system of linear equations has, if any. ▪ Solve systems of linear equations by graphing.	▪ Use a graphing calculator to solve a system of equations.	▪ Solve systems of equations by using substitution. ▪ Solve real-world problems involving systems of equations by using substitution.
Key Vocabulary	system of equations consistent independent dependent inconsistent		substitution
Content Standards	PS.3, PS.8, AI.SEI.1, AI.SEI.3	PS.5, AI.SEI.1	AI.SEI.2, AI.SEI.3
Multiple Representations			
Lesson Resources	connectED.mcgraw-hill.com Leveled Worksheets Vocabulary Animations Personal Tutor Virtual Manipulatives Self-Check Quiz ▪ *5-Minute Check* ▪ *Study Notebook* ▪ *Teaching Algebra with Manipulatives*	connectED.mcgraw-hill.com Personal Tutor **Materials:** ▪ TI-83/84 Plus or other graphing calculator	connectED.mcgraw-hill.com Leveled Worksheets Quiz 1 Vocabulary Animations Personal Tutor Virtual Manipulatives Self-Check Quiz ▪ *5-Minute Check* ▪ *Study Notebook*
Resources for Every Lesson	IWB eStudent Edition IWB Interactive Classroom	▪ eTeacher Edition ▪ eSolutions Manual ▪ McGraw-Hill eAssessment	
Differentiated Instruction	pp. 336, 340		pp. 345, 349

IWB All digital assets are Interactive Whiteboard ready.

Suggested Pacing			
Time Periods	Instruction	Review & Assess	Total
45-minute	10 days	2 days	12 days
90-minute	5 days	1 day	6 days

LESSON 6-3 (45 min: 2 days; 90 min: 1 day)	LESSON 6-4 (45 min: 1 day; 90 min: 0.5 day)	LESSON 6-5 (45 min: 1.5 days; 90 min: 0.75 day)	EXTEND 6-5 (45 min: 0.5 day; 90 min: 0.25 day)
Elimination Using Addition and Subtraction	**Elimination Using Multiplication**	**Applying Systems of Linear Equations**	**Algebra Lab: Using Matrices to Solve Systems of Equations**
■ Solve systems of equations by using elimination with addition. ■ Solve systems of equations by using elimination with subtraction.	■ Solve systems of equations by using elimination with multiplication. ■ Solve real-world problems involving systems of equations.	■ Determine the best method for solving systems of equations. ■ Apply systems of equations.	■ Use matrices to solve systems of equations.
elimination			matrix elements dimensions augmented matrix row reduction identity matrix
PS.7, AI.SEI.2, AI.SEI.3	PS.1, AI.SEI.2, AI.SEI.3	PS.2, PS.4, AI.SEI.3	
connectED.mcgraw-hill.com Leveled Worksheets Vocabulary Animations Personal Tutor Self-Check Quiz ■ *5-Minute Check* ■ *Study Notebook* ■ *Teaching Algebra with Manipulatives*	connectED.mcgraw-hill.com Leveled Worksheets Quiz 2 Animations Personal Tutor Self-Check Quiz ■ *5-Minute Check* ■ *Study Notebook*	connectED.mcgraw-hill.com Leveled Worksheets Quiz 3 Animations Personal Tutor Virtual Manipulatives Self-Check Quiz ■ *5-Minute Check* ■ *Study Notebook*	connectED.mcgraw-hill.com Vocabulary Animations
IWB eStudent Edition IWB Interactive Classroom	■ eTeacher Edition ■ eSolutions Manual ■ McGraw-Hill eAssessment		
pp. 352, 355, 356	pp. 359, 362	pp. 366, 369	
	Formative Assessment Mid-Chapter Quiz		

Chapter Planner

	LESSON 6-6 (45 min: 1 day; 90 min: 0.5 day)	EXTEND 6-6 (45 min: 1 day; 90 min: 0.5 day)
Title	**Systems of Inequalities**	**Graphing Technology Lab: Systems of Inequalities**
Objectives	■ Solve systems of linear inequalities by graphing. ■ Apply systems of linear inequalities.	■ Use a graphing calculator to explore systems of inequalities.
Key Vocabulary	system of inequalities	
Content Standards	PS.6, AI.SEI.4	AI.SEI.4
Multiple Representations		
Lesson Resources	connectED.mcgraw-hill.com Leveled Worksheets Quiz 4 Vocabulary Animations Personal Tutor Virtual Manipulatives Self-Check Quiz ■ *5-Minute Check* ■ *Study Notebook* ■ *Teaching Algebra with Manipulatives*	connectED.mcgraw-hill.com Personal Tutor **Materials:** ■ TI-Nspire Technology
Resources for Every Lesson	IWB eStudent Edition IWB Interactive Classroom	■ eTeacher Edition ■ eSolutions Manual ■ McGraw-Hill eAssessment
Differentiated Instruction	pp. 373, 376	

Summative Assessment
Study Guide and Review
Practice Test

IWB All digital assets are Interactive Whiteboard ready.

Professional Development

Targeted professional development has been articulated throughout Algebra 1. More quality, customized professional development is available from McGraw-Hill Professional Development. Visit connectED.mcgraw-hill.com for details on each product.

- Online Lessons emphasize the strategies and techniques used to teach Algebra 1. Includes streaming video, interactive pages, and online tools.
- Video Workshops allow mentors, coaches, or leadership personnel to facilitate on-site workshops on educational strategies in mathematics and mathematical concepts.
- MHPD Online (www.mhpdonline.com) offers online professional development with video clips of instructional strategies, links, student activities, and news and issues in education.
- Teaching Today (teachingtoday.glencoe.com) gives secondary teachers practical strategies and materials that inspire excellence and innovation in teaching.

What the Research Says...

According to Smith (1997), current technology allows readily accessible representations of systems of equations in algebraic, numeric, and geometric forms. Integrating these different representations into the curriculum helps students to think more critically about systems, to foster new perspectives, and to feel more confident in their results.

- In Extend 6-1, students use graphing calculators to visualize systems, based on concepts discussed in Lesson 6-1.
- Throughout Chapter 6, algebraic methods for solving systems are related to graphical representations.

Source: Smith, K.B. (1997). "Exploration and Visualization: Making Critical Connections About Linear Systems of Equations," *School Science and Mathematics*, 97(1), pp. 13–19.

Project CRISS

STUDY SKILL

Students may find it helpful to organize information they are learning in a frame. A sample concept frame that shows the major concepts about systems of two liner equations is shown at the right. Have students complete this sample or develop their own frames to explain other concepts from Chapter 6.

Term	Sample Graph	Description	Definition (own words)
Consistent and independent system	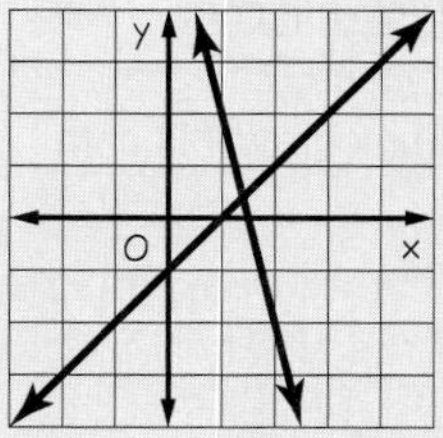	intersecting lines	a system of equations that has exactly one solution
Inconsistent	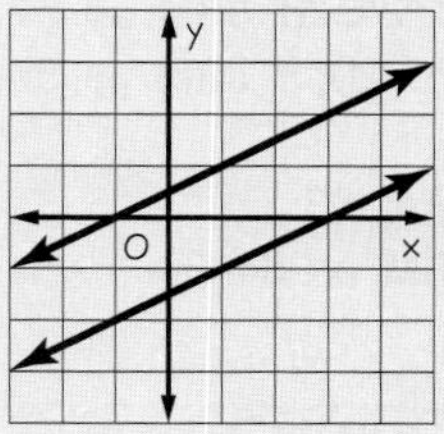	parallel lines	a system of equations that has no solution

Creating Independence through Student-owned Strategies

Assessment and Intervention

SE = Student Edition, **TE** = Teacher Edition, **CRM** = Chapter Resource Masters

	Diagnosis	Prescription
DIAGNOSTIC ASSESSMENT	**Beginning Chapter 6**	
	Get Ready for Chapter 6 **SE**	Response to Intervention **TE**
	Beginning Every Lesson	
	Then, Now, Why? **SE** 5-Minute Check	Chapter 0 **SE** *Quick Review Math Handbook*
FORMATIVE ASSESSMENT	**During/After Every Lesson**	
	Guided Practice **SE**, every example Check Your Understanding **SE** H.O.T. Problems **SE** Spiral Review **SE** Additional Examples **TE** Watch Out! **TE** Step 4, Assess **TE** Chapter 6 Quizzes **CRM**, pp. 47, 48 Self-Check Quizzes connectED.mcgraw-hill.com	TIER 1 Intervention Skills Practice **CRM**, Ch. 1–6 connectED.mcgraw-hill.com TIER 2 Intervention Differentiated Instruction **TE** Differentiated Homework Options **TE** Study Guide and Intervention **CRM**, Ch. 1–6 *Quick Review Math Handbook* TIER 3 Intervention *Math Triumphs, Alg. 1*
	Mid-Chapter	
	Mid-Chapter Quiz **SE** Mid-Chapter Test **CRM**, p. 49 McGraw-Hill eAssessment	TIER 1 Intervention Skills Practice **CRM**, Ch. 1–6 connectED.mcgraw-hill.com TIER 2 Intervention Study Guide and Intervention **CRM**, Ch. 1–6; *Quick Review Math Handbook* TIER 3 Intervention *Math Triumphs, Alg. 1*
	Before Chapter Test	
	Chapter Study Guide and Review **SE** Practice Test **SE** Standardized Test Practice **SE** Chapter Test connectED.mcgraw-hill.com Standardized Test Practice connectED.mcgraw-hill.com Vocabulary Review connectED.mcgraw-hill.com McGraw-Hill eAssessment	TIER 1 Intervention Skills Practice **CRM**, Ch. 1–6 connectED.mcgraw-hill.com TIER 2 Intervention Study Guide and Intervention **CRM**, Ch. 1–6; *Quick Review Math Handbook* TIER 3 Intervention *Math Triumphs, Alg. 1*
SUMMATIVE ASSESSMENT	**After Chapter 6**	
	Multiple-Choice Tests, Forms 1, 2A, 2B **CRM**, pp. 51–56 Free-Response Tests, Forms 2C, 2D, 3 **CRM**, pp. 57–62 Vocabulary Test **CRM**, p. 50 Extended Response Test **CRM**, p. 63 Standardized Test Practice **CRM**, pp. 64–66 McGraw-Hill eAssessment	Study Guide and Intervention **CRM**, Ch. 1–6 *Quick Review Math Handbook* connectED.mcgraw-hill.com

Differentiated Instruction

Option 1 Reaching All Learners AL OL BL ELL

Interpersonal Place students in pairs or small groups and assign systems of equations for them to solve. Tell students to use the Concept Summary on p. 364 or discuss which method is best to use to solve the system of equations they have been assigned. Make sure all group members participate in the discussion.

Visual Write several linear equations on the board. Graph each of these equations on a separate transparency coordinate grid. Then take a pair of equations and write them as a system of equations. Overlap the transparencies of their graphs to find their point of intersection. Repeat for a different pair of equations.

Then, change all the equations to inequalities. Shade their corresponding graphs to reflect the inequality. Then take a pair of inequalities and write them as a system of inequalities. Overlap the transparencies of their graphs to find their points of intersection.

Option 2 Approaching Level AL

Provide students with a copy of the graph of a system of linear equations and write the equations of the system on the board. Ask students to identify which line belongs to which equation. Then ask students to check that the solution works for both equations. Similarly, provide students with a graph of a system of linear inequalities. Ask students to identify which line and shading belongs to which inequality. Then ask students to check that several solutions within the overlapped shading work for both inequalities.

Option 3 English Learners ELL

Help students understand the vocabulary in the first lesson of this chapter by creating a set of flashcards. On one side of the card draw a graph of intersecting lines, one line, or a pair of parallel lines. On the flip side, write *consistent and independent*, *consistent and dependent*, or *inconsistent*.

Option 4 Beyond Level BL

Ask students to write a sentence about a two-digit number on one side of an index card. On the back of the card, students write and solve a system of equations to find the number. Have students trade cards and solve each other's number puzzle.

The sum of the digits of a two-digit number is 7. If the digits are reversed, the new number is 9 more than the original number."

$t + u = 7$

$10u + t = 9 + 10t + u$

$u = 4, t = 3$

The original number is 34.

Focus on Mathematical Content

VerticalAlignment

Before Chapter 6

Related Topics before Grade 8
- use a coordinate system to graph ordered pairs
- use Venn diagrams for displaying relationships

Previous Topics from Algebra 1
- graph equations of lines
- use properties of equality to solve equations
- analyze situations involving linear functions and formulate linear equations to solve problems

Chapter 6

Related Topics from Algebra 1
- analyze situations and formulate systems of linear equations in two unknowns to solve problems
- solve systems of linear equations and linear inequalities using graphs and algebraic methods
- interpret and determine the reasonableness of solutions to systems of linear equations and linear inequalities

After Chapter 6

Preparation for Algebra 2
- analyze situations and formulate systems of equations in two or more unknowns, or inequalities in two unknowns to solve problems
- use algebraic methods, graphs, tables, or matrices to solve systems of equations or inequalities
- interpret and determine the reasonableness of solutions to systems of equations or inequalities for given contexts

Lesson-by-LessonPreview

6-1 Graphing Systems of Equations

A system of equations can be solved by graphing the equations on the same coordinate plane. A solution of a system of two linear equations is an ordered pair that satisfies both equations in the system. A system of two linear equations can have the following:

- *exactly one solution*—The graphs of the equations intersect at one point. This system is said to be consistent and independent.
- *no solution*—The graphs of the equation are parallel. There are no ordered pairs that satisfy both equations. This system is said to be inconsistent.
- *infinite number of solutions*—The graphs of the equations are the same line. An infinite number of points will satisfy both equations. This system is said to be consistent and dependent.

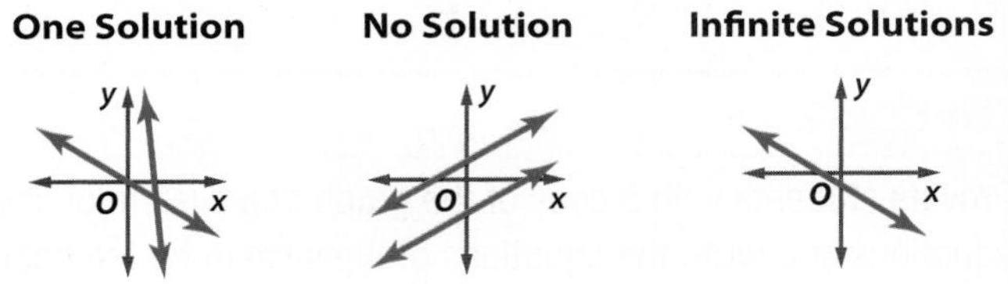

6-2 Substitution

Determining the exact solution to a system of equations from a graph can be difficult at times. When an exact solution is needed, algebraic methods can be used. Substitution is one method. To use substitution,

- Solve one equation for one variable in terms of the other variable.
- Next, substitute this expression into the other equation, thus eliminating one of the variables.
- Solve the resulting equation for the other variable.
- Substitute this value into either original equation to find the value of the eliminated variable.

If the system has *one solution*, the two values are written as an ordered pair.

The system has an *infinite number of solutions* if solving the system results in a true statement (such as $3 = 3$). There is *no solution* if solving the system results in a false statement (such as $-2 = 4$).

6-3 Elimination Using Addition and Subtraction

Elimination using addition or subtraction is another algebraic method used in solving a system of equations. When using this method, the two equations are combined to eliminate one of the variables. One equation can be added or subtracted from the other using the Addition/Subtraction Properties of Equality.

To use this method of elimination,

- Add the two equations if the coefficients of one of the variables are additive inverses, or opposites.
- Subtract the two equations if the coefficients of one of the variables are the same.

After eliminating one of the variables, solve for the remaining variable. Then substitute this value back into either original equation to find the value of the eliminated variable. The solution to the system is the two values written as an ordered pair.

6-4 Elimination Using Multiplication

When the coefficients of one of the variables are neither the same nor additive inverses, multiplication is used. This method requires that either one or both equations be changed using the Multiplication Property of Equality.

To use multiplication,

- multiply each term of one equation by the same number, or multiply both equations by different numbers in order to get one of the variables to have coefficients that are additive inverses of each other or the same number
- then solve the system by following the steps for solving a system by elimination using addition or subtraction.

6-5 Applying Systems of Linear Equations

Five methods of solving systems of equations have been studied. Each method works best for certain systems.

- Graphing can be used when an estimate will do.
- Substitution is used when one of the variables in either equation has a coefficient of 1 or -1.
- Elimination using addition is used if the coefficients of one of the variables are additive inverses.
- Elimination using subtraction is used if the coefficients of one of the variables are the same.
- Elimination using multiplication is used when none of the coefficients are 1 or -1 and neither of the variables can be eliminated by addition or subtraction.
- For real-world problems, check solutions in the context of the situation.

6-6 Systems of Inequalities

A solution of a system of inequalities is the set of all points that satisfy both inequalities. To solve the system, graph each inequality. The points that are solutions lie in the region where the graphs overlap, or intersect. There are two possibilities.

- *no solution*—The boundary lines are parallel, and the shaded regions have no points in common.
- *infinitely many solutions*—The overlapping shaded region extends on indefinitely.

Chapter Project

Save the Date

Students use what they have learned about systems of equations to complete a project.

This chapter project addresses global awareness, as well as several specific skills identified as being essential to student success by the Framework for 21st Century Learning.

Visit connectED.mcgraw-hill.com for student and teacher handouts.

KeyVocabulary Introduce the key vocabulary in the chapter using the routine below.

Define: A system of equations is a set of equations with the same variables.

Example: $y = 34.2 - 14.9x$ and $y = 3.3 + 4.7x$

Ask: What variables do both equations have in common? x and y

CHAPTER 6 Systems of Linear Equations and Inequalities

Then

You solved linear equations in one variable.

Now

In this chapter, you will:

- Solve systems of linear equations by graphing, substitution, and elimination.
- Solve systems of linear inequalities by graphing.

Why?

MUSIC \$1500 worth of tickets were sold for a marching band competition. Adult tickets were \$12 each, and student tickets were \$8 each. If you knew how many total tickets were sold, you could use a system of equations to determine how many adult tickets and how many student tickets were sold.

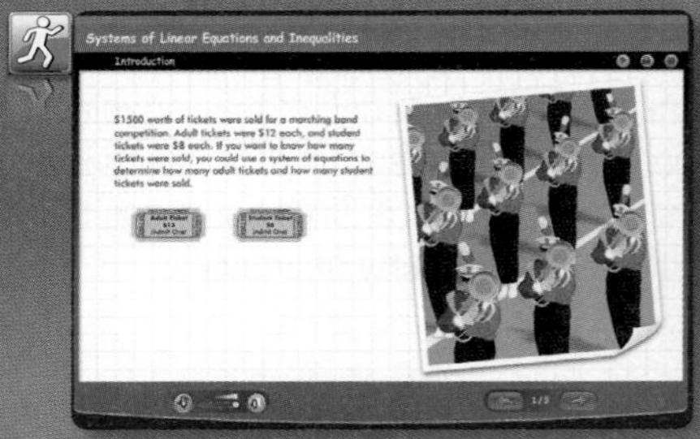

connectED.mcgraw-hill.com **Your Digital Math Portal**

Animation | Vocabulary | eGlossary | Personal Tutor | Virtual Manipulatives | Graphing Calculator | Audio | Foldables | Self-Check Practice | Worksheets

Content Standards
AI.SEI.1, AI.SEI.2, AI.SEI.3, AI.SEI.4

Process Standards
PS.1, PS.2, PS.3, PS.4, PS.5, PS.6, PS.7, PS.8

Get Ready for the Chapter

Diagnose Readiness | You have two options for checking prerequisite skills.

1 Textbook Option

Take the Quick Check below. Refer to the Quick Review for help.

QuickCheck

Name the ordered pair for each point on the coordinate plane.

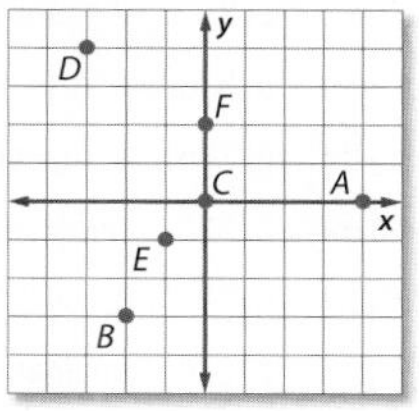

1. A (4, 0)
2. D (−3, 4)
3. B (−2, −3)
4. C (0, 0)
5. E (−1, −1)
6. F (0, 2)

QuickReview

Example 1 (Used in Lessons 6-1 and 6-5.)

Name the ordered pair for Q on the coordinate plane.

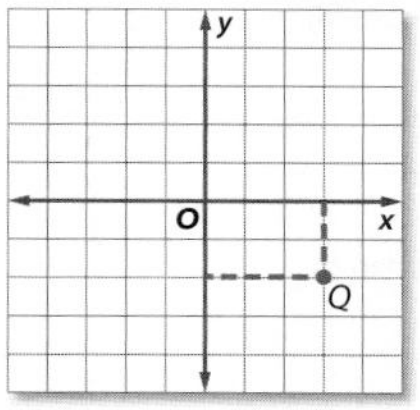

Follow a vertical line from the point to the x-axis. This gives the x-coordinate, 3.

Follow a horizontal line from the point to the y-axis. This gives the y-coordinate, −2.

The ordered pair is (3, −2).

QuickCheck

Solve each equation or formula for the variable specified.

7. $2x + 4y = 12$, for x $x = 6 - 2y$
8. $x = 3y - 9$, for y $y = \frac{x+9}{3}$
9. $m - 2n = 6$, for m $m = 2n + 6$
10. $y = mx + b$, for x $x = \frac{y-b}{m}$
11. $P = 2\ell + 2w$, for ℓ $\ell = \frac{P-2w}{2}$
12. $5x - 10y = 40$, for y $y = \frac{x-8}{2}$
13. **GEOMETRY** The formula for the area of a triangle is $A = \frac{1}{2}bh$, where A represents the area, b is the base, and h is the height of the triangle. Solve the equation for b. $b = \frac{2A}{h}$

QuickReview

Example 2 (Used in Lessons 6-1 through 6-5.)

Solve $12x + 3y = 36$ for y.

$12x + 3y = 36$	Original equation
$12x + 3y - 12x = 36 - 12x$	Subtract $12x$ from each side.
$3y = 36 - 12x$	Simplify.
$\frac{3y}{3} = \frac{36-12x}{3}$	Divide each side by 3.
$y = 12 - 4x$	Simplify.

2 Online Option

Take an online self-check Chapter Readiness Quiz at connectED.mcgraw-hill.com.

Essential Question

- How can you find the solution to a math problem?

Sample answer: Use a graph; analyze a table of values; solve an equation; guess and check.

Get Ready for the Chapter

Response to Intervention (RtI)

Use the *Quick Check* results and the Intervention Planner chart to help you determine your Response to Intervention. The If-Then statements in the chart below help you decide the appropriate tier of RtI and suggest intervention resources for each tier.

InterventionPlanner

TIER 1 On Level OL

If students miss about 25% of the exercises or less,

Then choose a resource:

- SE Lessons 1-6 and 2-8
- Skills Practice, Chapter 1, p. 39, Chapter 2, p. 51
- TE Chapter Project
- connectED.mcgraw-hill.com Self-Check Quiz

TIER 2 Strategic Intervention AL approaching grade level

If students miss about 50% of the exercises,

Then choose a resource:

- Study Guide and Intervention, Chapter 1, p. 37, Chapter 2, p. 49
- *Quick Review Math Handbook*
- connectED.mcgraw-hill.com Extra Examples, Personal Tutor, Homework Help

TIER 3 Intensive Intervention 2 or more grades below level

If students miss about 75% of the exercises,

Then use *Math Triumphs, Alg. 1*

- connectED.mcgraw-hill.com Extra Examples, Personal Tutor, Homework Help, Review Vocabulary

FOLDABLES StudyOrganizer

Dinah Zike's Foldables®

Focus Students write notes about solving systems of linear equations and inequalities as they are presented in the lessons of this chapter.

Teach Have students make and label their Foldables as illustrated. Have students write a word or concept from the lesson on the back of each lesson's tab. Under the word or concept, ask students to include a definition and an example.

When to Use It Encourage students to add to their Foldables as they work through the chapter and to use them to review for the chapter test.

Differentiated Instruction

Student-Built Glossary, pp. 1–2

Students should complete the chart by providing the definition of each term and an example as they progress through Chapter 6. This study tool can also be used to review for the chapter test.

Get Started on the Chapter

You will learn several new concepts, skills, and vocabulary terms as you study Chapter 6. To get ready, identify important terms and organize your resources. You may wish to refer to Chapter 0 to review prerequisite skills.

FOLDABLES StudyOrganizer

Systems of Linear Equations and Inequalities Make this Foldable to help you organize your Chapter 6 notes about solving systems of equations and inequalities. Begin with a sheet of notebook paper.

1 **Fold** lengthwise to the holes.

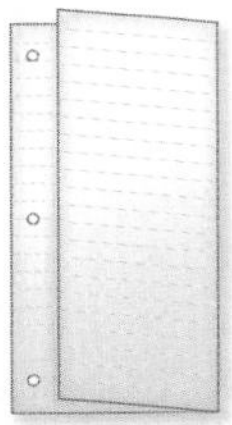

2 **Cut** 6 tabs.

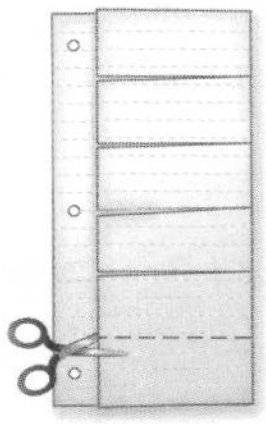

3 **Label** the tabs using the lesson titles.

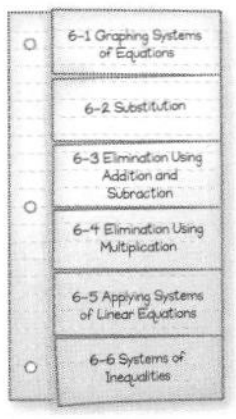

NewVocabulary

English		Español
system of equations	p. 335	sistema de ecuaciones
consistent	p. 335	consistente
independent	p. 335	independiente
dependent	p. 335	dependiente
inconsistent	p. 335	inconsistente
substitution	p. 344	sustitución
elimination	p. 350	eliminación
matrix	p. 370	matriz
element	p. 370	elemento
dimension	p. 370	dimensión
augmented matrix	p. 370	matriz ampliada
row reduction	p. 371	reducción de fila
identity matrix	p. 371	matriz
system of inequalities	p. 372	sistema de desigualdades

ReviewVocabulary

domain dominio the set of the first numbers of the ordered pairs in a relation

intersection intersección the graph of a compound inequality containing *and*; the solution is the set of elements common to both graphs

proportion proporción an equation stating that two ratios are equal

Proportion

$$\frac{24}{30} = \frac{4}{5}$$

(÷ 6 numerator, ÷ 6 denominator)

334 | Chapter 6 | Systems of Linear Equations and Inequalities

LESSON 6-1 Graphing Systems of Equations

:: Then	:: Now	:: Why?
You graphed linear equations.	**1** Determine the number of solutions a system of linear equations has. **2** Solve systems of linear equations by graphing.	The cost to begin production on a band's CD is \$1500. Each CD costs \$4 to produce and will sell for \$10. The band wants to know how many CDs they will have to sell to earn a profit. Graphing a system can show when a company makes a profit. The cost of producing the CD can be modeled by the equation $y = 4x + 1500$, where y represents the cost of production and x is the number of CDs produced.

Band's CD Sales

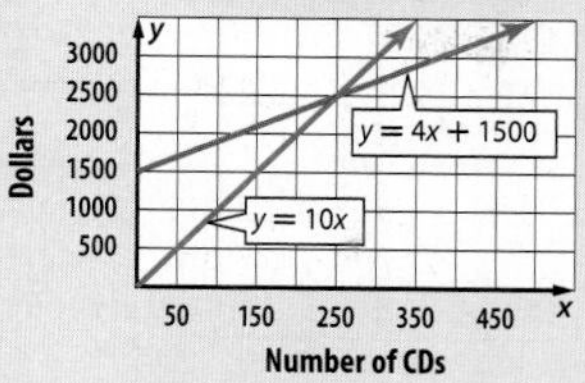

New Vocabulary
system of equations
consistent
independent
dependent
inconsistent

Content Standards
AI.SEI.1, AI.SEI.3

Process Standards
PS.3, PS.8

1 Possible Number of Solutions

The income from the CDs sold can be modeled by the equation $y = 10x$, where y represents the total income of selling the CDs, and x is the number of CDs sold.

If we graph these equations, we can see at which point the band begins making a profit. The point where the two graphs intersect is where the band breaks even. This happens when the band sells 250 CDs. If the band sells more than 250 CDs, they will make a profit.

The two equations, $y = 4x + 1500$ and $y = 10x$, form a **system of equations**. The ordered pair that is a solution of both equations is the solution of the system. A system of two linear equations can have one solution, an infinite number of solutions, or no solution.

- If a system has at least one solution, it is said to be **consistent**. The graphs intersect at one point or are the same line.
- If a consistent system has exactly one solution, it is said to be **independent**. If it has an infinite number of solutions, it is **dependent**. This means that there are unlimited solutions that satisfy both equations.
- If a system has no solution, it is said to be **inconsistent**. The graphs are parallel.

Concept Summary Possible Solutions

Number of Solutions	exactly one	infinite	no solution
Terminology	consistent and independent	consistent and dependent	inconsistent
Graph	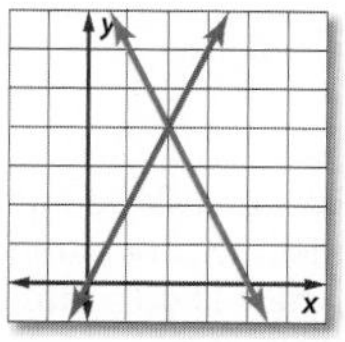	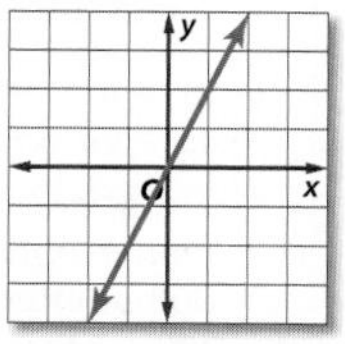	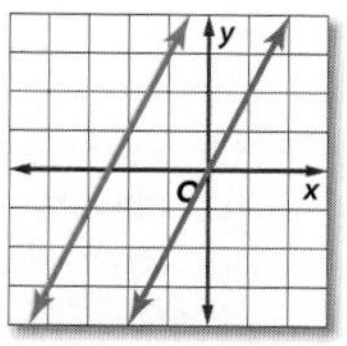

1 Focus

Vertical Alignment

Before Lesson 6-1 Graph linear functions.

Lesson 6-1 Determine the number of solutions a system of linear equations has, if any.
Solve systems of linear equations by graphing.

After Lesson 6-1 Solve systems of linear equations using algebraic methods.

2 Teach

Scaffolding Questions

Have students read the **Why?** section of the lesson.

- What does it mean to *break even* in this situation? The income from CD sales and the cost of producing the CDs are equal.
- What is the break-even dollar amount? \$2500
- How many solutions does the system have? Explain. One; there can be only one break-even point, and that is where the graphs intersect.

Lesson 6-1 Resources

Resource	Approaching Level AL	On Level OL	Beyond Level BL	English Learners ELL
Teacher Edition	Differentiated Instruction, p. 340	Differentiated Instruction, pp. 336, 340	Differentiated Instruction, p. 336	Differentiated Instruction, p. 340
Chapter Resource Masters	Study Guide and Intervention, pp. 5–6 Skills Practice, p. 7 Practice, p. 8 Word Problem Practice, p. 9 Graphing Calculator Activity, p. 11	Study Guide and Intervention, pp. 5–6 Skills Practice, p. 7 Practice, p. 8 Word Problem Practice, p. 9 Enrichment, p. 10 Graphing Calculator Activity, p. 11	Practice, p. 8 Word Problem Practice, p. 9 Enrichment, p. 10 Graphing Calculator Activity, p. 11	Study Guide and Intervention, pp. 5–6 Skills Practice, p. 7 Practice, p. 8 Word Problem Practice, p. 9 Graphing Calculator Activity, p. 11
Other	5-Minute Check 6-1 Study Notebook Teaching Algebra with Manipulatives	5-Minute Check 6-1 Study Notebook Teaching Algebra with Manipulatives	5-Minute Check 6-1 Study Notebook	5-Minute Check 6-1 Study Notebook Teaching Algebra with Manipulatives

1 Possible Number of Solutions

Example 1 shows how to find the number of solutions of a system of equations, and if it is consistent, inconsistent, dependent, or independent.

Formative Assessment

Use the Guided Practice exercises after each Example to determine students' understanding of concepts.

Additional Example

1 Use the graph to determine whether each system is *consistent* or *inconsistent* and if it is *independent* or *dependent*.

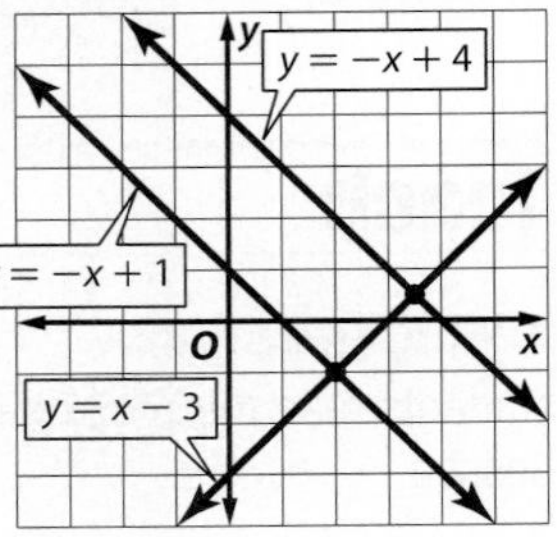

a. $y = -x + 1$
$y = -x + 4$
inconsistent

b. $y = x - 3$
$y = -x + 1$
consistent and independent

Additional Examples also in Interactive Classroom PowerPoint® Presentations

IWB Interactive White Board READY

Tips for New Teachers

Interactive Whiteboard

Create a table with columns: *no solutions*, *1 solution*, and *infinitely many solutions*. Write several systems of equations on the board. Have students drag each system to the correct column.

StudyTip

Number of Solutions When both equations are of the form $y = mx + b$, the values of m and b can determine the number of solutions.

Compare m and b	Number of Solutions
different m values	one
same m value, but different b values	none
same m value, and same b value	infinite

Example 1 Number of Solutions

Use the graph at the right to determine whether each system is *consistent* or *inconsistent* and if it is *independent* or *dependent*.

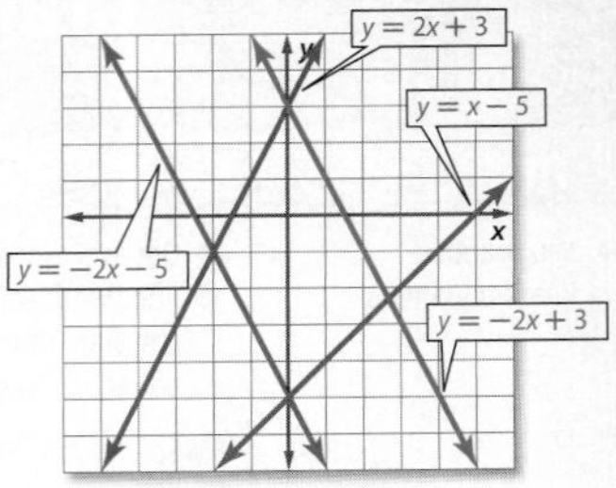

a. $y = -2x + 3$
$y = x - 5$

Since the graphs of these two lines intersect at one point, there is exactly one solution. Therefore, the system is consistent and independent.

b. $y = -2x - 5$
$y = -2x + 3$

Since the graphs of these two lines are parallel, there is no solution of the system. Therefore, the system is inconsistent.

GuidedPractice

1A. $y = 2x + 3$
$y = -2x - 5$ **consistent and independent**

1B. $y = x - 5$
$y = -2x - 5$ **consistent and independent**

2 Solve by Graphing One method of solving a system of equations is to graph the equations carefully on the same coordinate grid and find their point of intersection. This point is the solution of the system.

Example 2 Solve by Graphing

Graph each system and determine the number of solutions that it has. If it has one solution, name it.

a. $y = -3x + 10$
$y = x - 2$

The graphs appear to intersect at the point (3, 1). You can check this by substituting 3 for x and 1 for y.

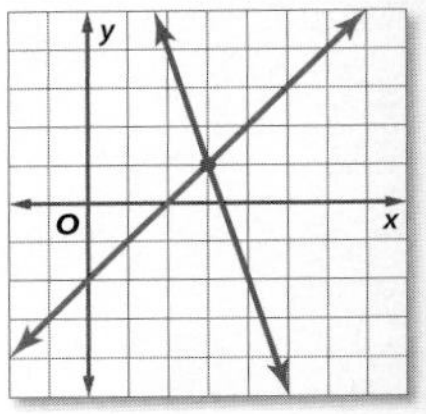

CHECK

CHECK	$y = -3x + 10$	Original equation
	$1 \stackrel{?}{=} -3(3) + 10$	Substitution
	$1 \stackrel{?}{=} -9 + 10$	Multiply.
	$1 = 1$ ✓	
	$y = x - 2$	Original equation
	$1 \stackrel{?}{=} 3 - 2$	Substitution
	$1 = 1$ ✓	Multiply.

The solution is (3, 1).

b. $2x - y = -1$
$4x - 2y = 6$

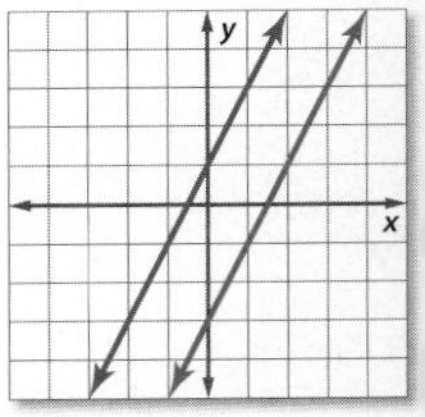

The lines have the same slope but different y-intercepts, so the lines are parallel. Since they do not intersect, there is no solution of this system. The system is inconsistent.

ReviewVocabulary

parallel lines never intersect and have the same slope

DifferentiatedInstruction OL BL

Extension Write a system of three equations in two variables on the board. Have the students determine if the system has *one* solution, *no* solution, or *infinitely many* solutions. If it has one solution, name it. For example,

$x + y = 2$
$x - y = 0$
$y = -2$

has *no* solution because the three lines do not intersect at one point.

Guided Practice

Graph each system and determine the number of solutions that it has. If it has one solution, name it. 2A–2B. See Ch. 6 Answer Appendix for graphs.

2A. $x - y = 2$
$3y + 2x = 9$ 1 solution; (3, 1)

2B. $y = -2x - 3$
$6x + 3y = -9$ infinitely many

We can use what we know about systems of equations to solve many real-world problems involving constraints that are modeled by two or more different functions.

Real-WorldLink

In 2008, 3.1 million girls participated in high school sports. This was an all-time high for female participation.

Source: National Federation of State High School Associations

Real-World Example 3 Write and Solve a System of Equations

SPORTS **The number of girls participating in high school soccer and track and field has steadily increased over the past few years. Use the information in the table to predict the approximate year when the number of girls participating in these two sports will be the same.**

High School Sport	Number of Girls Participating in 2008 (thousands)	Average rate of increase (thousands per year)
soccer	345	8
track and field	458	3

Source: National Federation of State High School Associations

Words	Number of girls participating	equals	rate of increase	times	number of years after 2008	plus	number participating in 2008.

Variables: Let y = number of girls competing. Let x = number of years after 2008.

Equations:
Soccer: $y = 8 \cdot x + 345$
Track and field: $y = 3 \cdot x + 458$

Graph $y = 8x + 345$ and $y = 3x + 458$. The graphs appear to intersect at approximately (22.5, 525).

CHECK Use substitution to check this answer.

$y = 8x + 345$ | $y = 3x + 458$

$525 \stackrel{?}{=} 8(22.5) + 345$ | $525 \stackrel{?}{=} 3(22.5) + 458$

$525 = 525$ ✓ | $525 \approx 525.5$ ✓

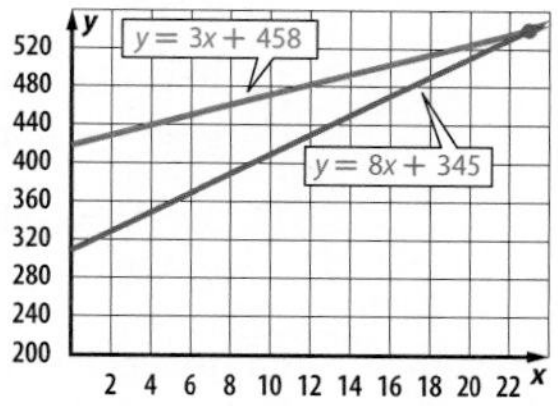

The solution means that approximately 22 years after 2008, or in 2030, the number of girls participating in high school soccer and track and field will be the same, about 525,000.

Guided Practice

3. **VIDEO GAMES** Joe and Josh each want to buy a video game. Joe has \$14 and saves \$10 a week. Josh has \$26 and saves \$7 a week. In how many weeks will they have the same amount? 4 weeks

2 Solve By Graphing

Example 2 shows how to solve a system of equations by graphing. **Example 3** shows how to use a system of equations to solve a real-world problem.

Additional Examples

2 Graph each system and determine the number of solutions that it has. If it has one solution, name it.

a. $y = 2x + 3$
$8x - 4y = -12$ infinitely many solutions

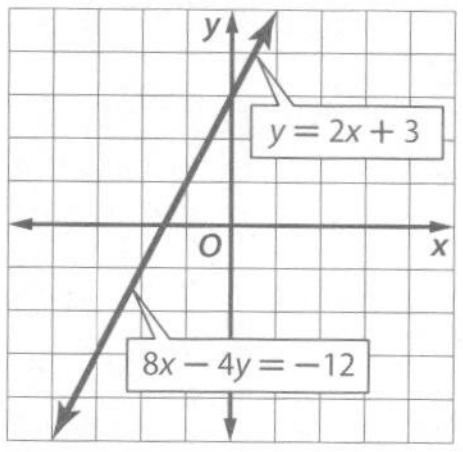

b. $x - 2y = 4$
$x - 2y = -2$ no solution

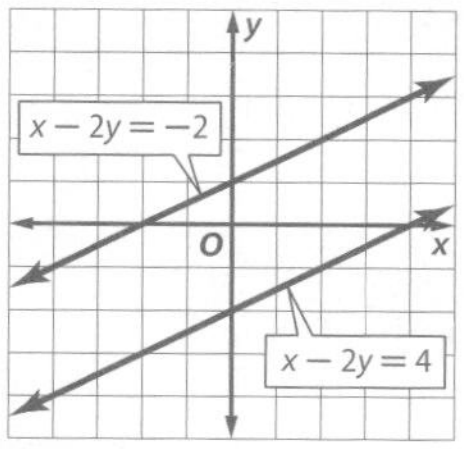

3 **BICYCLING** Naresh rode 20 miles last week and plans to ride 35 miles per week. Diego rode 50 miles last week and plans to ride 25 miles per week. Predict the week in which Naresh and Diego will have ridden the same number of miles. week 3

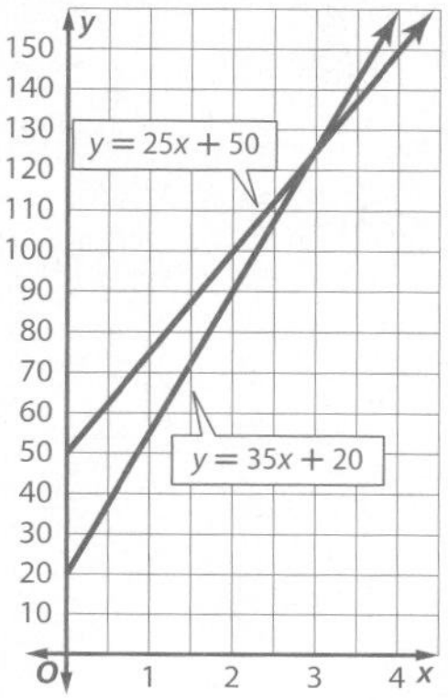

Focus on Mathematical Content

Graphing Systems of Equations If the graphs of a system intersect in one point, the system is consistent and independent and has one solution. If the graphs coincide or lie on the same line, the system is consistent and dependent, and the system has an infinite number of solutions. If the graphs are parallel, the system is inconsistent, there are no points of intersection, and there is no solution. In their study of geometry, students will extend their understanding of equations of parallel lines when they prove the slope criteria for parallel lines.

3 Practice

Formative Assessment

Use Exercises 1–9 to check for understanding.

Use the chart at the bottom of this page to customize assignments for your students.

Additional Answers

7. 1 solution, (−4, 0)

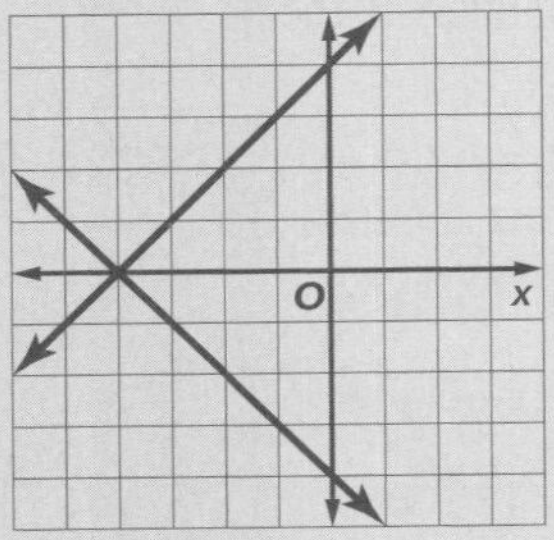

8. 1 solution, (−1, 2)

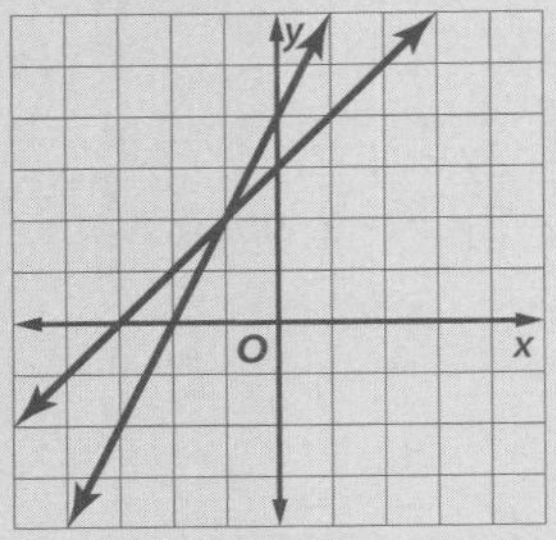

9b.

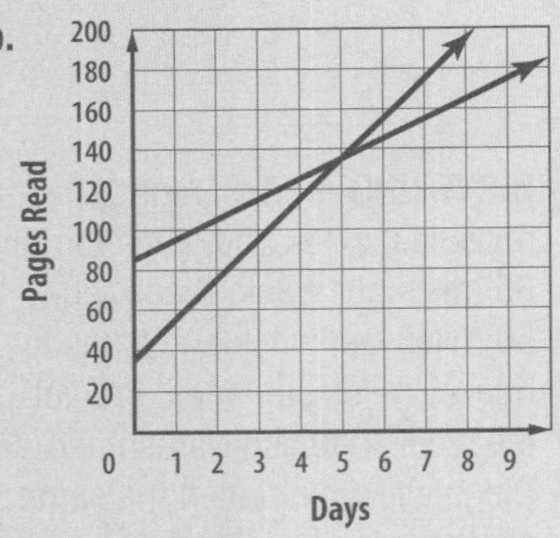

16–24. See Ch. 6 Answer Appendix for graphs.

16. 1 solution, (0, −3)

17. 1 solution; $\left(-\frac{5}{6}, -\frac{4}{3}\right)$

18. no solution

19. infinitely many

20. infinitely many

21. 1 solution; (5, −1)

22. 1 solution; (3, 2)

23. no solution

24. infinitely many

Check Your Understanding

(circle) = Step-by-Step Solutions begin on page R13.

Example 1 Use the graph at the right to determine whether each system is *consistent* or *inconsistent* and if it is *independent* or *dependent*.

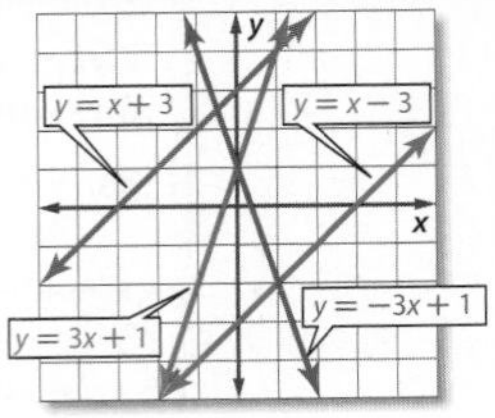

1. $y = -3x + 1$, $y = 3x + 1$ **consistent and independent**

2. $y = 3x + 1$, $y = x - 3$ **consistent and independent**

3. $y = x - 3$, $y = x + 3$ **inconsistent**

4. $y = x + 3$, $x - y = -3$ **consistent and dependent**

5. $x - y = -3$, $y = -3x + 1$ **consistent and independent**

6. $y = -3x + 1$, $y = x - 3$ **consistent and independent**

Example 2 Graph each system and determine the number of solutions that it has. If it has one solution, name it. **7–8. See margin.**

7. $y = x + 4$, $y = -x - 4$

8. $y = x + 3$, $y = 2x + 4$

Example 3

9. MODELING Alberto and Ashanti are reading a graphic novel. **9a. Alberto: $y = 20x + 35$; Ashanti: $y = 10x + 85$**

a. Write an equation to represent the pages each boy has read.

b. Graph each equation. **See margin.**

c. How long will it be before Alberto has read more pages than Ashanti? Check and interpret your solution. **(5, 135); Alberto will have read more after 5 days.**

Practice and Problem Solving

Extra Practice is on page R6.

Example 1 Use the graph at the right to determine whether each system is *consistent* or *inconsistent* and if it is *independent* or *dependent*.

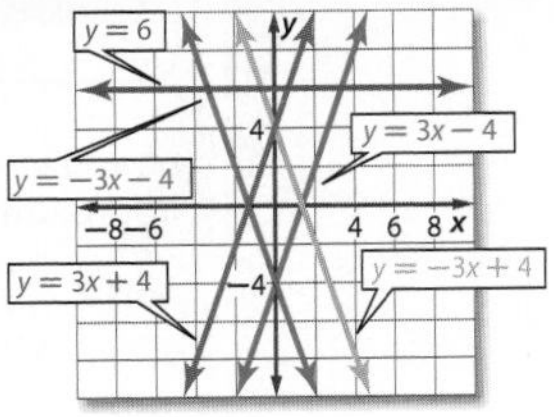

10. $y = 6$, $y = 3x + 4$

11. $y = 3x + 4$, $y = -3x + 4$

12. $y = -3x + 4$, $y = -3x - 4$

13. $y = -3x - 4$, $y = 3x - 4$

14. $3x - y = -4$, $y = 3x + 4$

15. $3x - y = 4$, $3x + y = 4$

10. consistent and independent
11. consistent and independent
12. inconsistent
13. consistent and independent
14. consistent and dependent
15. consistent and independent

Example 2 Graph each system and determine the number of solutions that it has. If it has one solution, name it. **16–24. See margin.**

16. $y = -3$, $y = x - 3$

17. $y = 4x + 2$, $y = -2x - 3$

18. $y = x - 6$, $y = x + 2$

19. $x + y = 4$, $3x + 3y = 12$

20. $x - y = -2$, $-x + y = 2$

21. $x + 2y = 3$, $x = 5$

22. $2x + 3y = 12$, $2x - y = 4$

23. $2x + y = -4$, $y + 2x = 3$

24. $2x + 2y = 6$, $5y + 5x = 15$

Differentiated Homework Options

Level	Assignment	Two-Day Option	
AL Basic	10–26, 47, 49–76	11–25 odd, 53–56	10–26 even, 47, 49–52, 57–76
OL Core	11–25 odd, 26, 27–41 odd, 42–47, 49–76	10–26, 53–56	27–47, 49–52, 57–76
BL Advanced	27–68, (optional: 69–76)		

Example 3

25. **SCHOOL DANCE** Akira and Jen are competing to see who can sell the most tickets for the Winter Dance. On Monday, Akira sold 22 and then sold 30 per day after that. Jen sold 53 on Monday and then sold 20 per day after that.

    a. Write equations for the number of tickets each person has sold. **Akira: $y = 30x + 22$; Jen: $y = 20x + 53$**

    b. Graph each equation. **See Ch. 6 Answer Appendix.**

    c. Solve the system of equations. Check and interpret your solution. **(3.1, 115); After about 3 days, Akira will have sold more tickets.**

26. **MODELING** If x is the number of years since 2000 and y is the percent of people using travel services, the following equations represent the percent of people using travel agents and the percent of people using the Internet to plan travel.

    Travel agents: $y = -2x + 30$ Internet: $y = 6x + 41$

    a. Graph the system of equations. **See Ch. 6 Answer Appendix.**

    b. Estimate the year travel agents and the Internet were used equally. **1999**

B **Graph each system and determine the number of solutions that it has. If it has one solution, name it. 27–41. See Ch. 6 Answer Appendix for graphs.**

27. $y = \frac{1}{2}x$, $y = x + 2$ **1 solution; (−4, −2)**

28. $y = 6x + 6$, $y = 3x + 6$ **1 solution; (0, 6)**

29. $y = 2x - 17$, $y = x - 10$ **1 solution; (7, −3)**

30. $8x - 4y = 16$, $-5x - 5y = 5$ **1 solution; (1, −2)**

31. $3x + 5y = 30$, $3x + y = 18$ **1 solution; (5, 3)**

32. $-3x + 4y = 24$, $4x - y = 7$ **1 solution; (4, 9)**

33. $2x - 8y = 6$, $x - 4y = 3$ **infinitely many**

34. $4x - 6y = 12$, $-2x + 3y = -6$ **infinitely many**

35. $2x + 3y = 10$, $4x + 6y = 12$ **no solution**

36. $3x + 2y = 10$, $2x + 3y = 10$ **1 solution; (2, 2)**

37. $3y - x = -2$, $y - \frac{1}{3}x = 2$ **no solution**

38. $\frac{8}{5}y = \frac{2}{5}x + 1$, $\frac{2}{5}y = \frac{1}{10}x + \frac{1}{4}$ **infinitely many**

39. $\frac{1}{3}x + \frac{1}{3}y = 1$, $x + y = 1$ **no solution**

40. $\frac{3}{4}x + \frac{1}{2}y = \frac{1}{4}$, $\frac{2}{3}x + \frac{1}{6}y = \frac{1}{2}$ **1 solution; (1, −1)**

41. $\frac{5}{6}x + \frac{2}{3}y = \frac{1}{2}$, $\frac{2}{5}x + \frac{1}{5}y = \frac{3}{5}$ **1 solution; (3, −3)**

42d. The domain of each of these equations is the set of real numbers greater than or equal to 0. The range of each of these equations is the set of real numbers greater than or equal to 0.

42. **PHOTOGRAPHY** Suppose x represents the number of cameras sold and y represents the number of years since 2000. Then the number of digital cameras sold each year since 2000, in millions, can be modeled by the equation $y = 12.5x + 10.9$. The number of film cameras sold each year since 2000, in millions, can be modeled by the equation $y = -9.1x + 78.8$.

    a. Graph each equation. **See Ch. 6 Answer Appendix.**

    b. In which year did digital camera sales surpass film camera sales? **2003**

    c. In what year did film cameras stop selling altogether? **2008**

    d. What are the domain and range of each of the functions in this situation?

C **Graph each system and determine the number of solutions that it has. If it has one solution, name it. 43–44. See Ch. 6 Answer Appendix for graphs.**

43. $2y = 1.2x - 10$, $4y = 2.4x$ **no solution**

44. $x = 6 - \frac{3}{8}y$, $4 = \frac{2}{3}x + \frac{1}{4}y$ **infinitely many**

Study Guide and Intervention

AL OL ELL

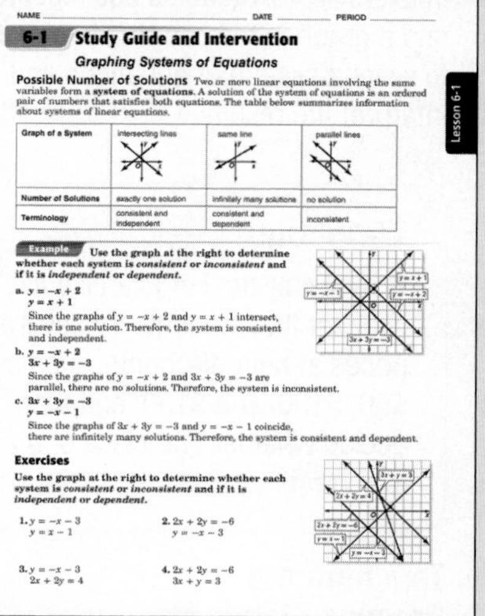

Practice

AL OL BL ELL

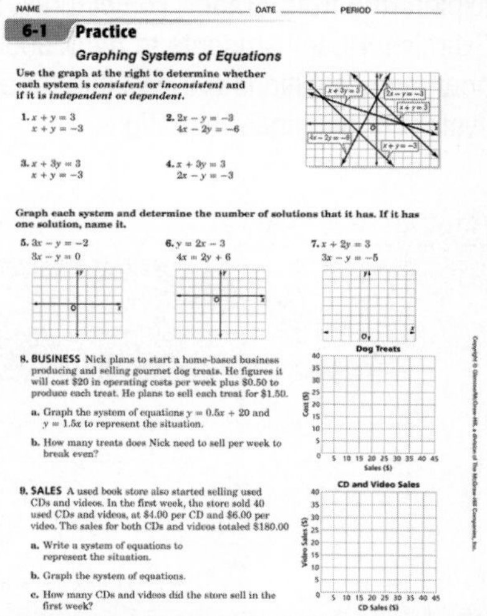

Word Problem Practice

AL OL BL ELL

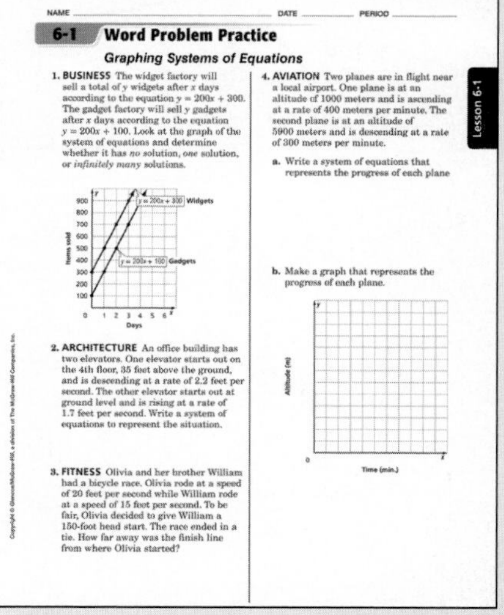

Teaching the Process Standards

Modeling Mathematically proficient students apply the mathematics they know to solve problems arising in everyday life. In Exercise 9, point out that Ashanti starts with more pages read but since Alberto is reading faster he will catch up. In Exercise 26, ask students what the slope in each equation represents in the context of the problem.

Enrichment

OL BL

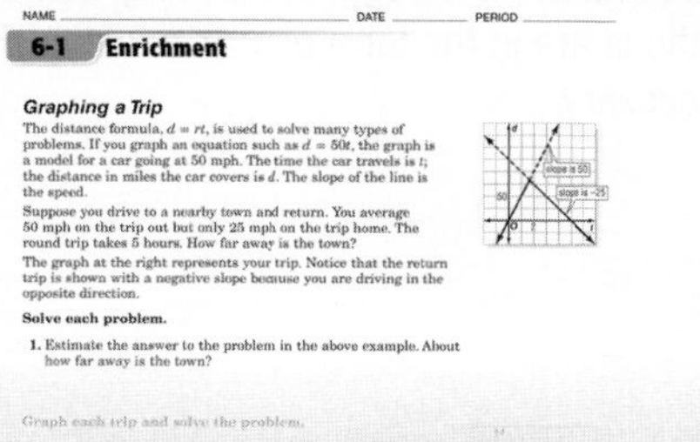

Multiple Representations

In Exercise 46, students use algebra and a graph in the coordinate plane to solve a system of equations and interpret the results.

WatchOut!

Error Analysis For Exercise 47, suggest that students try several prices at both discounts, such as \$50, \$100, and \$150, and then decide whether Francisca or Alan is correct.

Teaching the Process Standards

Arguments Mathematically proficient students make conjectures and build a logical progression of statements to explore the truth of their conjectures. In Exercise 49, tell students to think about how many solutions are possible for a system of two linear equations.

Additional Answers

45b.

Years Since 2009	Lookatme Visitors (mln)	Buyourstuff Visitors (mln)
0	2.5	59
1	15.6	57
2	28.7	55
3	41.8	53
4	54.9	51

45c.

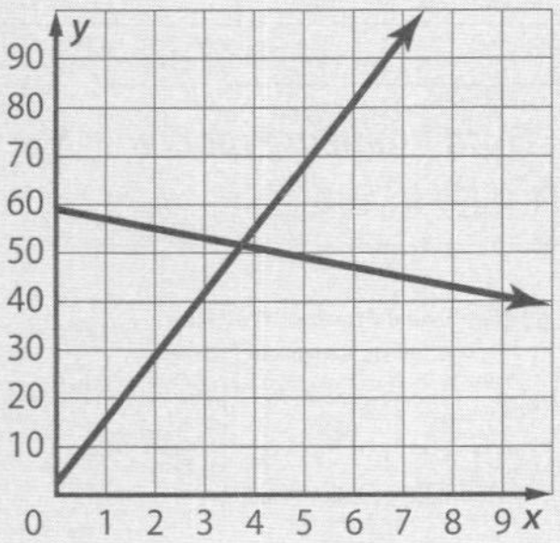

46b. (6, 6)

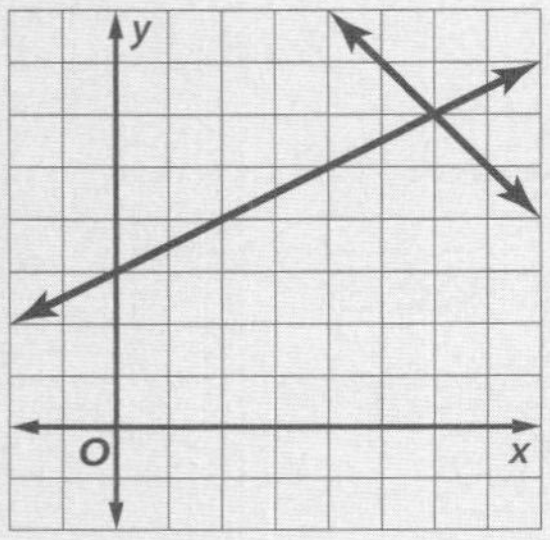

46c. Both sides of the equation in part a are set equal to y in the system of linear equations in part b.

46d. You can find the solution from the x-coordinate of the intersection of the two lines in the system of equation.

45 **WEB SITES** Personal publishing site *Lookatme* had 2.5 million visitors in 2009. Each year after that, the number of visitors rose by 13.1 million. Online auction site *Buyourstuff* had 59 million visitors in 2009, but each year after that the number of visitors fell by 2 million.

a. Write an equation for each of the companies. **Lookatme: $y = 13.1x + 2.5$; Buyourstuff: $y = -2x + 59$**

b. Make a table of values for 5 years for each of the companies. **See margin.**

c. Graph each equation. **See margin.**

d. When will *Lookatme* and *Buyourstuff's* sites have the same number of visitors? **sometime during 2012**

e. Name the domain and range of these functions in this situation. **$D = \{x \mid x \geq 0\}$; $R = \{y \mid y \geq 0\}$**

46. **MULTIPLE REPRESENTATIONS** In this problem, you will explore different methods for finding the intersection of the graphs of two linear equations.

a. **Algebraic** Use algebra to solve the equation $\frac{1}{2}x + 3 = -x + 12$. **6**

b. **Graphical** Use a graph to solve $y = \frac{1}{2}x + 3$ and $y = -x + 12$. **See margin.**

c. **Analytical** How is the equation in part **a** related to the system in part **b**?

d. **Verbal** Explain how to use the graph in part **b** to solve the equation in part **a**.

H.O.T. Problems Use Higher-Order Thinking Skills

49. Always; if the equations are linear and have more than one common solution, they must be consistent and dependent, which means that they have an infinite number of solutions in common.

50. Sample answer: $4x + 2y = 14$, $12x + 6y = 18$; This system is inconsistent while the others are consistent and independent.

47. **ERROR ANALYSIS** Store A is offering a 10% discount on the purchase of all electronics in their store. Store B is offering \$10 off all the electronics in their store. Francisca and Alan are deciding which offer will save them more money. Is either of them correct? Explain your reasoning.

47. Francisca; if the item is less than \$100, then \$10 off is better. If the item is more than \$100, then the 10% is better.

Francisca	Alan
You can't determine which store has the better offer unless you know the price of the items you want to buy.	Store A has the better offer because 10% of the sale price is a greater discount than \$10.

48. **CHALLENGE** Use graphing to find the solution of the system of equations $2x + 3y = 5$, $3x + 4y = 6$, and $4x + 5y = 7$. **(−2, 3); See Ch. 6 Answer Appendix for graph.**

49. **ARGUMENTS** Determine whether a system of two linear equations with (0, 0) and (2, 2) as solutions *sometimes*, *always*, or *never* has other solutions. Explain.

50. **WHICH ONE DOESN'T BELONG?** Which one of the following systems of equations doesn't belong with the other three? Explain your reasoning.

$4x - y = 5$	$-x + 4y = 8$	$4x + 2y = 14$	$3x - 2y = 1$
$-2x + y = -1$	$3x - 6y = 6$	$12x + 6y = 18$	$2x + 3y = 18$

51. **OPEN ENDED** Write three equations such that they form three systems of equations with $y = 5x - 3$. The three systems should be inconsistent, consistent and independent, and consistent and dependent, respectively. **Sample answers: $y = 5x + 3$; $y = -5x - 3$; $2y = 10x - 6$**

52. **WRITING IN MATH** Describe the advantages and disadvantages to solving systems of equations by graphing. **See margin.**

340 | Lesson 6-1 | Graphing Systems of Equations

Differentiated Instruction AL OL ELL

Interpersonal Learners Have students work in pairs or groups to check the solutions for Exercises 16–24 and 27–41. Suggest that they use the Study Tip (p. 336) on comparing m and b when both equations are in the form of $y = mx + b$. Have students write equations in slope-intercept form, if necessary.

Standardized Test Practice

53. SHORT RESPONSE Certain bacteria can reproduce every 20 minutes, doubling the population. If there are 450,000 bacteria in a population at 9:00 A.M., how many bacteria will be in the population at 2:00 P.M.? **14,745,600,000 bacteria**

54. GEOMETRY An 84-centimeter piece of wire is cut into equal segments and then attached at the ends to form the edges of a cube. What is the volume of the cube? **B**

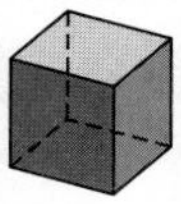

A 294 cm^3 C 1158 cm^3
B 343 cm^3 D 2744 cm^3

55. What is the solution of the inequality $-9 < 2x + 3 < 15$? **H**

F $-x \geq 0$ H $-6 < x < 6$
G $x \leq 0$ J $-5 < x < 5$

56. What is the solution of the system of equations? **D**

$$x + 2y = -1$$
$$2x + 4y = -2$$

A $(-1, -1)$ C no solution
B $(2, 1)$ D infinitely many solutions

Spiral Review

Graph each inequality. (Lesson 5-6) **57–62. See margin.**

57. $3x + 6y > 0$

58. $4x - 2y < 0$

59. $3y - x \leq 9$

60. $4y - 3x \geq 12$

61. $y < -4x - 8$

62. $3x - 1 > y$

63. LIBRARY To get a grant from the city's historical society, the number of history books must be within 25 of 1500. What is the range of the number of historical books that must be in the library? (Lesson 5-5) **1475 to 1525 books**

64. SCHOOL Camilla's scores on three math tests are shown in the table. The fourth and final test of the grading period is tomorrow. She needs an average of at least 92 to receive an A for the grading period. (Lesson 5-3)

Test	Score
1	91
2	95
3	88

a. If m represents her score on the fourth math test, write an inequality to represent this situation. $\frac{91 + 95 + 88 + m}{4} \geq 92$

b. If Camilla wants an A in math, what must she score on the test? **94 or higher**

c. Is your solution reasonable? Explain. **Yes; the score is attainable and Camilla has scored higher than that before.**

Write the slope-intercept form of an equation for the line that passes through the given point and is perpendicular to the graph of the equation. (Lesson 4-4)

65. $(-3, 1), y = \frac{1}{3}x + 2$ $y = -3x - 8$

66. $(6, -2), y = \frac{3}{5}x - 4$ $y = -\frac{5}{3}x + 8$

67. $(2, -2), 2x + y = 5$ $y = \frac{1}{2}x - 3$

68. $(-3, -3), -3x + y = 6$ $y = -\frac{1}{3}x - 4$

Skills Review

Find the solution of each equation using the given replacement set.

69. $f - 14 = 8$; {12, 15, 19, 22} **22**

70. $15(n + 6) = 165$; {3, 4, 5, 6, 7} **5**

71. $23 = \frac{d}{4}$; {91, 92, 93, 94, 95} **92**

72. $36 = \frac{t - 9}{2}$; {78, 79, 80, 81} **81**

Evaluate each expression if $a = 2$, $b = -3$, and $c = 11$.

73. $a + 6b$ **−16**

74. $7 - ab$ **13**

75. $(2c + 3a) \div 4$ **7**

76. $b^2 + (a^3 - 8)5$ **9**

4 Assess

Ticket Out the Door Give students a small piece of grid paper. Have them draw a graph that represents a system of equations that is consistent and dependent.

Additional Answers

52. Graphing clearly shows whether a system of equations has one solution, no solution, or infinitely many solutions. However, finding the exact values of x and y from a graph can be difficult.

57.

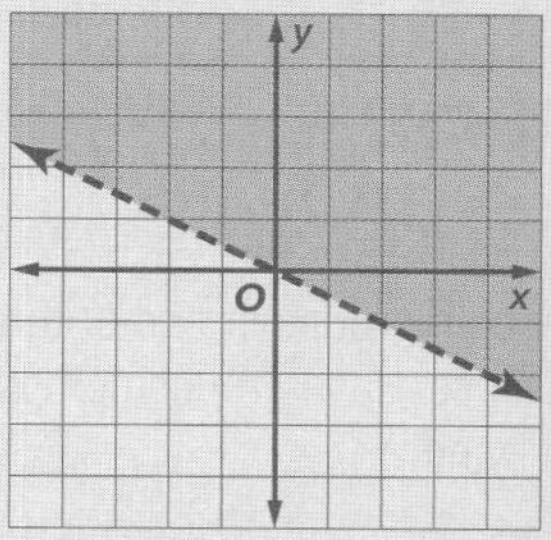

58.

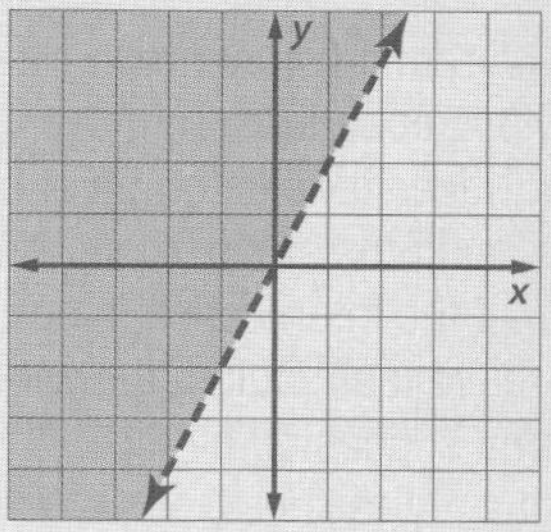

59.

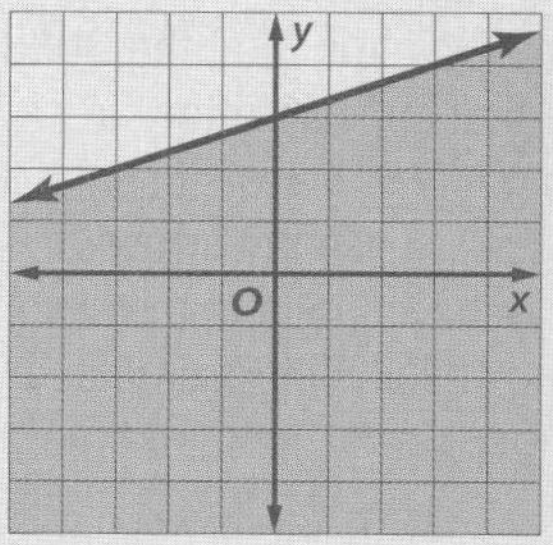

60.

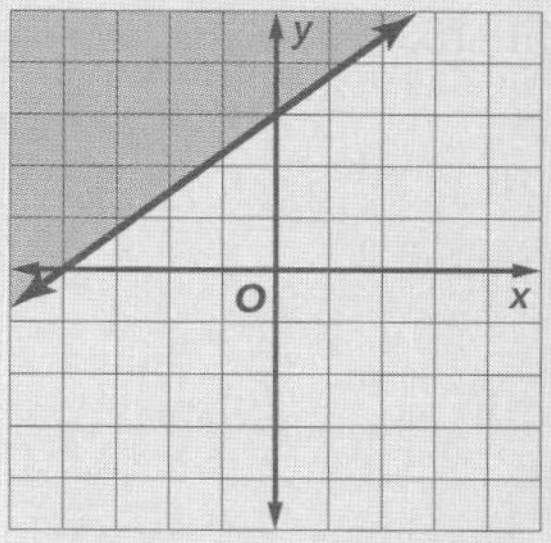

61.

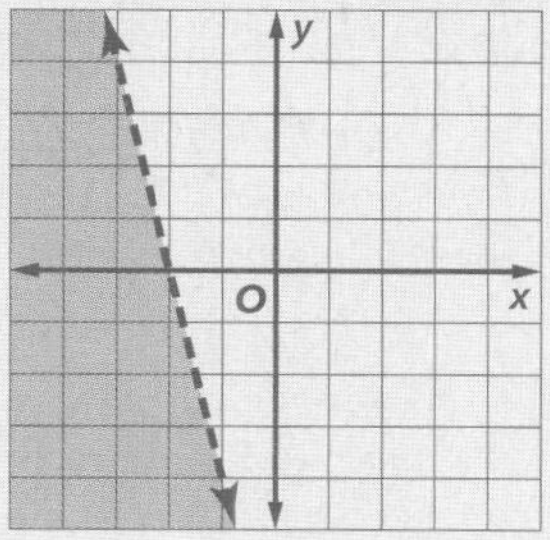

62.

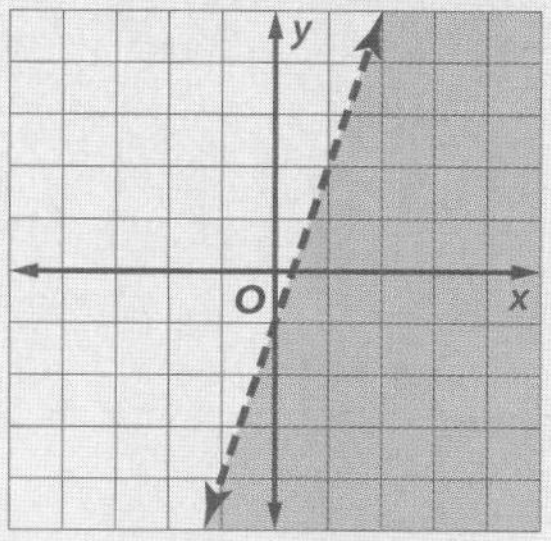

1 Focus

Objective Use a graphing calculator to solve a system of equations.

Materials

- TI–83/84 Plus or other graphing calculator

Teaching Tip

Remind students that the equations must be solved for *y* before they are entered in the calculator.

2 Teach

Working in Cooperative Groups

Put students in groups of two or three, mixing abilities. Have groups complete Activities 1 and 2.

Activity 1

- In Step 2, remind students to clear all previous equations from the Y= list. Have students graph each system using the standard viewing window. If the intersection is not visible, have them adjust the window to an area suggested by the directions of the lines.
- In Step 3, point out that the **GUESS** feature that appears after the second [ENTER] gives students an opportunity to use the arrow keys to estimate the solution to the system and then check their estimates by pressing [ENTER] the third time.

Practice Have students complete Exercises 1–10.

EXTEND 6-1 Graphing Technology Lab
Systems of Equations

You can use a graphing calculator to graph and solve a system of equations.

Activity 1 Solve a System of Equations

Solve the system of equations. State the decimal solution to the nearest hundredth.

$5.23x + y = 7.48$
$6.42x - y = 2.11$

Content Standards
AI.SEI.1

Process Standards
PS.5

Step 1 Solve each equation for y to enter them into the calculator.

$5.23x + y = 7.48$	First equation
$5.23x + y - 5.23x = 7.48 - 5.23x$	Subtract 5.23*x* from each side.
$y = 7.48 - 5.23x$	Simplify.
$6.42x - y = 2.11$	Second equation
$6.42x - y - 6.42x = 2.11 - 6.42x$	Subtract 6.42*x* from each side.
$-y = 2.11 - 6.42x$	Simplify.
$(-1)(-y) = (-1)(2.11 - 6.42x)$	Multiply each side by −1.
$y = -2.11 + 6.42x$	Simplify.

Step 2 Enter these equations in the **Y=** list and graph in the standard viewing window.

KEYSTROKES: [Y=] 7.48 [−] 5.23 [X,T,θ,*n*] [ENTER] [(−)] 2.11 [+] 6.42 [X,T,θ,*n*] [ZOOM] 6

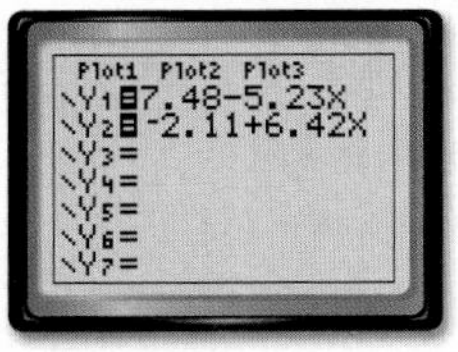

Step 3 Use the **CALC** menu to find the point of intersection.

KEYSTROKES: [2nd] [CALC] 5 [ENTER] [ENTER] [ENTER]

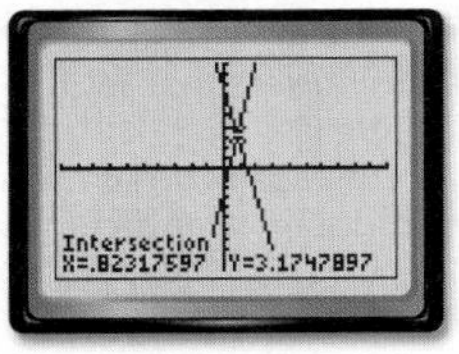

[−10, 10] scl: 1 by [−10, 10] scl: 1

The solution is approximately (0.82, 3.17).

When you solve a system of equations with $y = f(x)$ and $y = g(x)$, the solution is an ordered pair that satisfies both equations. The solution always occurs when $f(x) = g(x)$. Thus, the *x*-coordinate of the solution is the value of *x* where $f(x) = g(x)$.

One method you can use to solve an equation with one variable is by graphing and solving a system of equations based on the equation. To do this, write a system using both sides of the equation. Then use a graphing calculator to solve the system.

Activity 2 Use a System to Solve a Linear Equation

Use a system of equations to solve $5x + 6 = -4$.

Step 1 Write a system of equations. Set each side of the equation equal to y.

$y = 5x + 6$ First equation
$y = -4$ Second equation

Step 2 Enter these equations in the **Y=** list and graph.

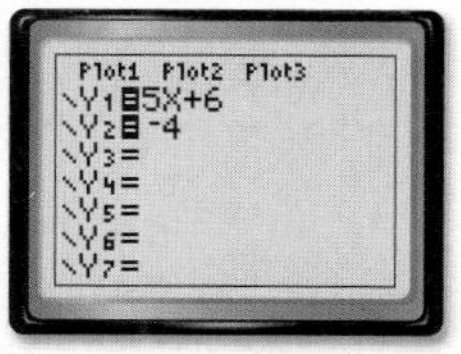

Step 3 Use the **CALC** menu to find the point of intersection.

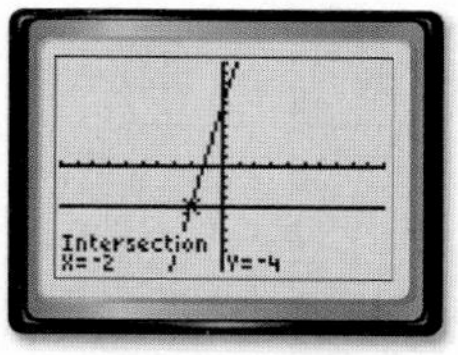

[−10, 10] scl: 1 by [−10, 10] scl: 1

The solution is −2.

Exercises

Use a graphing calculator to solve each system of equations. Write decimal solutions to the nearest hundredth.

1. $y = 2x - 3$
$y = -0.4x + 5$ **(3.33, 3.67)**

2. $y = 6x + 1$
$y = -3.2x - 4$ **(−0.54, −2.26)**

3. $x + y = 9.35$
$5x - y = 8.75$ **(3.02, 6.33)**

4. $2.32x - y = 6.12$
$4.5x + y = -6.05$ **(0.01, −6.10)**

5. $5.2x - y = 4.1$
$1.5x + y = 6.7$ **(1.61, 4.28)**

6. $1.8 = 5.4x - y$
$y = -3.8 - 6.2x$ **(−0.17, −2.73)**

7. $7x - 2y = 16$
$11x + 6y = 32.3$ **(2.51, 0.78)**

8. $3x + 2y = 16$
$5x + y = 9$ **(0.29, 7.57)**

9. $0.62x + 0.35y = 1.60$
$-1.38x + y = 8.24$ **(−1.16, 6.63)**

10. $75x - 100y = 400$
$33x - 10y = 70$ **(1.18, −3.12)**

Use a graphing calculator to solve each equation. Write decimal solutions to the nearest hundredth.

11. $4x - 2 = -6$ **−1**

12. $3 = 1 + \frac{x}{2}$ **4**

13. $\frac{x+4}{-2} = -1$ **−2**

14. $\frac{3}{2}x + \frac{1}{2} = 2x - 3$ **7**

15. $4x - 9 = 7 + 7x$ **−5.33**

16. $-2 + 10x = 8x - 1$ **0.5**

17. **WRITING IN MATH** Explain why you can solve an equation like $r = ax + b$ by solving the system of equations $y = r$ and $y = ax + b$. **17. At the intersection of the graphs of $y = r$ and $y = ax + b$, the y-values are equal. Therefore, at that point $r = ax + b$.**

Activity 2

- For Activity 2, students will need to clear the **Y=** list to begin the activity. Remind students to press [(−)] to enter −4 rather than the key for the subtraction symbol.
- In Step 3, students should use the same keystrokes used in Activity 1, Step 3.

Ask:

- What does the solution in Step 3 mean? For the equation $y = 5x + 6$, $x = -2$ when $y = -4$.
- How can you check your solution? Substitute −2 for x in the original equation to check whether the equation is true.

Practice Have students complete Exercises 11–17.

3 Assess

Formative Assessment

- Use Exercise 7 to assess whether students can use a graphing calculator to solve a system of equations.
- Use Exercise 15 to assess whether students can graph a system to solve an equation with one variable.

From Concrete to Abstract

Exercise 17 asks students to give an algebraic justification for using a system of equations to solve a linear equation with one variable.

Extending the Concept

Ask:

- When would a system of two linear equations not have a point of intersection? Sample answer: Two linear equations will not have a point of intersection if their graphs are parallel.

1 Focus

VerticalAlignment

Before Lesson 6-2 Solve systems of equations by graphing.

Lesson 6-2 Solve systems of equations by using substitution. Solve real-world problems involving systems of equations by using substitution.

After Lesson 6-2 Solve systems of equations by using elimination.

2 Teach

Scaffolding Questions

Have students read the **Why?** section of the lesson.

Ask:

- What are the rates of decrease for Movies A and B? $16 million per week; $10 million per week
- If $x =$ the number of weeks from the opening week, and $y =$ total earnings, what equation represents the earnings in week x for Movie A? $y = -16x + 31$ for Movie B? $y = -10x + 21$

LESSON 6-2 Substitution

Then

- You solved systems of equations by graphing.

Now

1. Solve systems of equations by using substitution.
2. Solve real-world problems involving systems of equations by using substitution.

Why?

- Two movies were released at the same time. Movie A earned $31 million in its opening week, but fell to $15 million the following week. Movie B opened earning $21 million and fell to $11 million the following week. If the earnings for each movie continue to decrease at the same rate, when will they earn the same amount?

NewVocabulary
substitution

Content Standards
AI.SEI.2, AI.SEI.3

1 Solve by Substitution

You can use a system of equations to find when the movie earnings are the same. One method of finding an exact solution of a system of equations is called **substitution**.

KeyConcept Solving by Substitution

Step 1 When necessary, solve at least one equation for one variable.

Step 2 Substitute the resulting expression from Step 1 into the other equation to replace the variable. Then solve the equation.

Step 3 Substitute the value from Step 2 into either equation, and solve for the other variable. Write the solution as an ordered pair.

Example 1 Solve a System by Substitution

Use substitution to solve the system of equations.

$y = 2x + 1$ ← **Step 1** The first equation is already solved for y.
$3x + y = -9$

Step 2 Substitute $2x + 1$ for y in the second equation.

$3x + y = -9$	Second equation
$3x + 2x + 1 = -9$	Substitute $2x + 1$ for y.
$5x + 1 = -9$	Combine like terms.
$5x = -10$	Subtract 1 from each side.
$x = -2$	Divide each side by 5.

Step 3 Substitute -2 for x in either equation to find y.

$y = 2x + 1$	First equation
$= 2(-2) + 1$	Substitute -2 for x.
$= -3$	Simplify.

The solution is $(-2, -3)$.

CHECK You can check your solution by graphing.

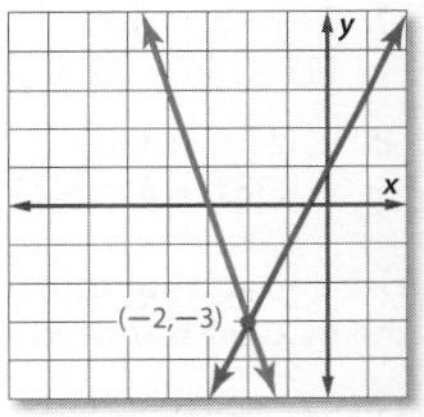

GuidedPractice

1A. $y = 4x - 6$
$5x + 3y = -1$ (1, −2)

1B. $2x + 5y = -1$
$y = 3x + 10$ (−3, 1)

Lesson 6-2 Resources

Resource	Approaching Level AL	On Level OL	Beyond Level BL	English Learners ELL
Teacher Edition	▪ Differentiated Instruction, p. 345	▪ Differentiated Instruction, pp. 345, 349	▪ Differentiated Instruction, p. 349	
Chapter Resource Masters	▪ Study Guide and Intervention, pp. 12–13 ▪ Skills Practice, p. 14 ▪ Practice, p. 15 ▪ Word Problem Practice, p. 16	▪ Study Guide and Intervention, pp. 12–13 ▪ Skills Practice, p. 14 ▪ Practice, p. 15 ▪ Word Problem Practice, p. 16 ▪ Enrichment, p. 17	▪ Practice, p. 15 ▪ Word Problem Practice, p. 16 ▪ Enrichment, p. 17	▪ Study Guide and Intervention, pp. 12–13 ▪ Skills Practice, p. 14 ▪ Practice, p. 15
Other	▪ 5-Minute Check 6-2 ▪ Study Notebook	▪ 5-Minute Check 6-2 ▪ Study Notebook	▪ 5-Minute Check 6-2 ▪ Study Notebook	▪ 5-Minute Check 6-2 ▪ Study Notebook

StudyTip

Slope-Intercept Form If both equations are in the form $y = mx + b$, they can simply be set equal to each other and then solved for x. The solution for x can then be used to find the value of y.

If a variable is not isolated in one of the equations in a system, solve an equation for a variable first. Then you can use substitution to solve the system.

Example 2 Solve and then Substitute

Use substitution to solve the system of equations.

$x + 2y = 6$
$3x - 4y = 28$

Step 1 Solve the first equation for x since the coefficient is 1.

$x + 2y = 6$	First equation
$x + 2y - 2y = 6 - 2y$	Subtract $2y$ from each side.
$x = 6 - 2y$	Simplify.

Step 2 Substitute $6 - 2y$ for x in the second equation to find the value of y.

$3x - 4y = 28$	Second equation
$3(6 - 2y) - 4y = 28$	Substitute $6 - 2y$ for x.
$18 - 6y - 4y = 28$	Distributive Property
$18 - 10y = 28$	Combine like terms.
$18 - 10y - 18 = 28 - 18$	Subtract 18 from each side.
$-10y = 10$	Simplify.
$y = -1$	Divide each side by -10.

Step 3 Find the value of x.

$x + 2y = 6$	First equation
$x + 2(-1) = 6$	Substitute -1 for y.
$x - 2 = 6$	Simplify.
$x = 8$	Add 2 to each side.

Guided Practice

2A. $4x + 5y = 11$
$y - 3x = -13$ **(4, −1)**

2B. $x - 3y = -9$
$5x - 2y = 7$ **(3, 4)**

Generally, if you solve a system of equations and the result is a false statement such as $3 = -2$, there is no solution. If the result is an identity, such as $3 = 3$, then there are an infinite number of solutions.

Example 3 No Solution or Infinitely Many Solutions

Use substitution to solve the system of equations.

$y = 2x - 4$
$-6x + 3y = -12$

Substitute $2x - 4$ for y in the second equation.

$-6x + 3y = -12$	Second equation
$-6x + 3(2x - 4) = -12$	Substitute $2x - 4$ for y.
$-6x + 6x - 12 = -12$	Distributive Property
$-12 = -12$	Combine like terms.

This statement is an identity. Thus, there are an infinite number of solutions.

StudyTip

Dependent Systems There are infinitely many solutions of the system in Example 3 because the equations in slope-intercept form are equivalent, and they have the same graph.

Differentiated Instruction AL OL

If students have difficulty solving a system using substitution,

Then suggest that they use the Study Tip to write both equations in slope-intercept form, set the expressions in x equal to each other, solve for x, and then use the value for x to find y. Have students compare the methods and decide which method they prefer.

- Why might solving the system of equations using substitution be better than graphing the equations to determine when the movies have the same earnings? Sample answer: Using substitution might give a more exact answer since the graphs might intersect between weeks.

1 Solve by Substitution

Example 1 shows how to solve a system of equations using substitution. **Example 2** shows how to solve one of the equations for one variable and then substitute to solve the system of equations. **Example 3** shows how to solve a system of equations that has an infinite number of solutions.

Formative Assessment

Use the Guided Practice exercises after each example to determine students' understanding of concepts.

Additional Examples

1 Use substitution to solve the system of equations.
$y = -4x + 12$
$2x + y = 2$ (5, −8)

2 Use substitution to solve the system of equations.
$x - 2y = -3$
$3x + 5y = 24$ (3, 3)

Additional Examples also in Interactive Classroom PowerPoint® Presentations

IWB Interactive White Board READY

WatchOut!

Preventing Errors Point out that if neither of the equations gives one variable in terms of the other, you must solve for one variable first. The easiest choice in Example 2 is to solve the first equation for x by subtracting $2y$ from both sides.

Additional Example

3 Use substitution to solve the system of equations.

$2x + 2y = 8$

$x + y = -2$ no solution

2 Solve Real-World Problems

Example 4 shows how to write and solve a system of equations for a real-world problem that can be solved by substitution.

Additional Example

4 **NATURE CENTER** A nature center charges $35.25 for a yearly membership and $6.25 for a single admission. Last week it sold a combined total of 50 yearly memberships and single admissions for $660.50. How many memberships and how many single admissions were sold? 12 memberships and 38 single admissions

Focus on Mathematical Content

Infinitely Many or No Solutions

If solving a system of equations results in a true sentence (such as $3 = 3$), then the system has infinitely many solutions. This happens when the two equations represent the same line. When solving a system of equations results in a false sentence (such as $3 = 2$), the system has no solution. The equations represent two parallel lines. If both equations are solved for y, the equations will have the same slope but different y-intercepts.

GuidedPractice **Use substitution to solve each system of equations.**

3A. $2x - y = 8$
$y = 2x - 3$ **no solution**

3B. $4x - 3y = 1$
$6y - 8x = -2$ **infinite number**

2 Solve Real-World Problems

You can use substitution to find the solution of a real-world problem involving constraints modeled by a system of equations.

PT

Real-World Example 4 Write and Solve a System of Equations

MUSIC **A store sold a total of 125 car stereo systems and speakers in one week. The stereo systems sold for $104.95, and the speakers sold for $18.95. The sales from these two items totaled $6926.75. How many of each item were sold?**

Number of Units Sold	c	t	125
Sales ($)	$104.95c$	$18.95t$	6926.75

Let c = the number of car stereo systems sold, and let t = the number of speakers sold.

So, the two equations are $c + t = 125$ and $104.95c + 18.95t = 6926.75$.

Notice that $c + t = 125$ represents combinations of car stereo systems and speakers with a sum of 125. The equation $104.95c + 18.95t = 6926.75$ represents the combinations of car stereo systems and speakers with a sales of $6926.75. The solution of the system of equations represents the option that meets both of the constraints.

Step 1 Solve the first equation for c.

$c + t = 125$ First equation

$c + t - t = 125 - t$ Subtract t from each side.

$c = 125 - t$ Simplify.

Step 2 Substitute $125 - t$ for c in the second equation.

$104.95c + 18.95t = 6926.75$ Second equation

$104.95(125 - t) + 18.95t = 6926.75$ Substitute $125 - t$ for c.

$13{,}118.75 - 104.95t + 18.95t = 6926.75$ Distributive Property

$13{,}118.75 - 86t = 6926.75$ Combine like terms.

$-86t = -6192$ Subtract 13,118.75 from each side.

$t = 72$ Divide each side by -86.

Step 3 Substitute 72 for t in either equation to find the value of c.

$c + t = 125$ First equation

$c + 72 = 125$ Substitute 72 for t.

$c = 53$ Subtract 72 from each side.

The store sold 53 car stereo systems and 72 speakers.

Real-WorldLink

Sound Engineering Technician Sound engineering technicians record, synchronize, mix, and reproduce music, voices, and sound effects in recording studios, sporting arenas, and theater, movie, or video productions. They need to have at least a 2-year associate's degree in electronics.

GuidedPractice

4. BASEBALL As of 2009, the New York Yankees and the Cincinnati Reds together had won a total of 32 World Series. The Yankees had won 5.4 times as many as the Reds. How many World Series had each team won? **Cincinnati, 5; New York, 27**

Teach with Tech

Audio Recording Have students work in groups to record a song to a common tune about how to solve a system of equations by substitution. Have students use each song to solve a problem to determine if it really explains how to solve systems by substitution.

Check Your Understanding

= Step-by-Step Solutions begin on page R13.

Examples 1–3 Use substitution to solve each system of equations.

1. $y = x + 5$
   $3x + y = 25$ **(5, 10)**
2. $x = y - 2$
   $4x + y = 2$ **(0, 2)**
3. $3x + y = 6$
   $4x + 2y = 8$ **(2, 0)**
4. $2x + 3y = 4$
   $4x + 6y = 9$ **no solution**
5. $x - y = 1$
   $3x = 3y + 3$ **infinitely many**
6. $2x - y = 6$
   $-3y = -6x + 18$ **infinitely many**

Example 4

7. **GEOMETRY** The sum of the measures of angles X and Y is 180°. The measure of angle X is 24° greater than the measure of angle Y.
   a. Define the variables, and write equations for this situation. **$x = m\angle X$, $y = m\angle Y$; $x + y = 180$, $x = 24 + y$**
   b. Find the measure of each angle. **$x = 102°$, $y = 78°$**

Practice and Problem Solving

Extra Practice is on page R6.

Examples 1–3 Use substitution to solve each system of equations.

8. $y = 5x + 1$
   $4x + y = 10$ **(1, 6)**
9. $y = 4x + 5$
   $2x + y = 17$ **(2, 13)**
10. $y = 3x - 34$
    $y = 2x - 5$ **(29, 53)**
11. $y = 3x - 2$
    $y = 2x - 5$ **(−3, −11)**
12. $2x + y = 3$
    $4x + 4y = 8$ **(1, 1)**
13. $3x + 4y = -3$
    $x + 2y = -1$ **(−1, 0)**
14. $y = -3x + 4$
    $-6x - 2y = -8$ **infinitely many**
15. $-1 = 2x - y$
    $8x - 4y = -4$ **infinitely many**
16. $x = y - 1$
    $-x + y = -1$ **no solution**
17. $y = -4x + 11$
    $3x + y = 9$ **(2, 3)**
18. $y = -3x + 1$
    $2x + y = 1$ **(0, 1)**
19. $3x + y = -5$
    $6x + 2y = 10$ **no solution**
20. $5x - y = 5$
    $-x + 3y = 13$ **(2, 5)**
21. $2x + y = 4$
    $-2x + y = -4$ **(2, 0)**
22. $-5x + 4y = 20$
    $10x - 8y = -40$ **infinitely many**

Example 4

23. **ECONOMICS** In 2000, the demand for nurses was 2,000,000, while the supply was only 1,890,000. The projected demand for nurses in 2020 is 2,810,414, while the supply is only projected to be 2,001,998.
    a. Define the variables, and write equations to represent these situations.
    b. Use substitution to determine during which year the supply of nurses was equal to the demand. **during 1996**

23a. Let x = number of years since 2000, and let y = the number of nurses; supply, $y = 5599.9x + 1{,}890{,}000$; demand, $y = 40{,}520.7x + 2{,}000{,}000$

B 24. **REASONING** The table shows the approximate number of tourists in two areas of the world during a recent year and the average rates of change in tourism.

Destination	Number of Tourists	Average Rates of Change in Tourists (millions per year)
South America and the Caribbean	40.3 million	increase of 0.8
Middle East	17.0 million	increase of 1.8

a. Define the variables, and write an equation for each region's tourism rate. **See margin.**
b. If the trends continue, in how many years would you expect the number of tourists in the regions to be equal? **in 23.3 yr, or about 23 yr 4 mo**

3 Practice

Formative Assessment

Use Exercises 1–7 to check for understanding.

Use the chart at the bottom of this page to customize assignments for your students.

Teaching the Process Standards

Reasoning Mathematically proficient students attend to the meaning of quantities, not just how to compute them. In Exercise 24, point out that the table headings tell the meanings of the values in the table.

WatchOut!

Error Analysis In Exercise 27, remind students that both Guillermo and Cara could be wrong, and that errors can be made in interpreting a solution as well as finding it.

Additional Answer

24a. Let x = number of years since base year, and y = number of tourists in millions; South America and Caribbean, $y = 0.8x + 40.3$; Middle East, $y = 1.8x + 17.0$.

Differentiated Homework Options

Level	Assignment	Two-Day Option	
AL Basic	8–23, 27, 29–50	9–23 odd, 32–35	18–22 even, 27, 29–31, 36–50
OL Core	9–23 odd, 25–27, 29–50	8–23, 32–35	24–27, 29–31, 36–50
BL Advanced	24–46, (optional: 47–50)		

Study Guide and Intervention

AL OL ELL

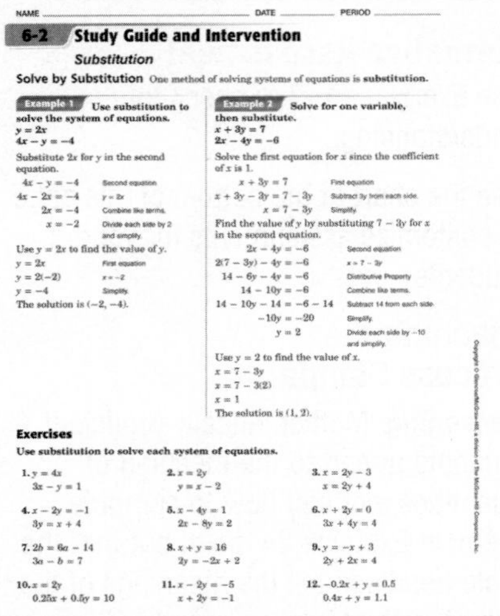

Practice

AL OL BL ELL

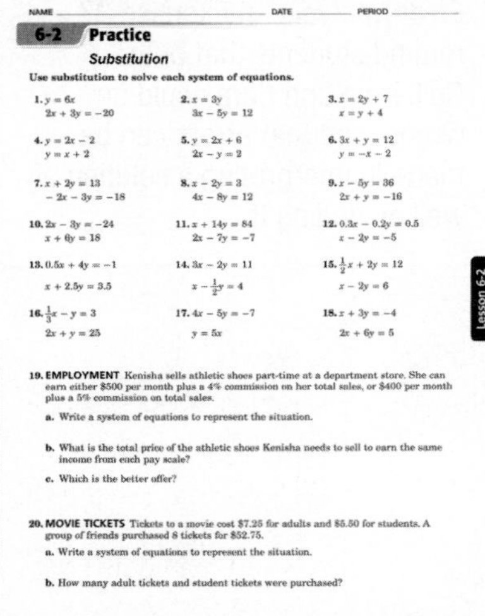

Word Problem Practice

AL OL BL ELL

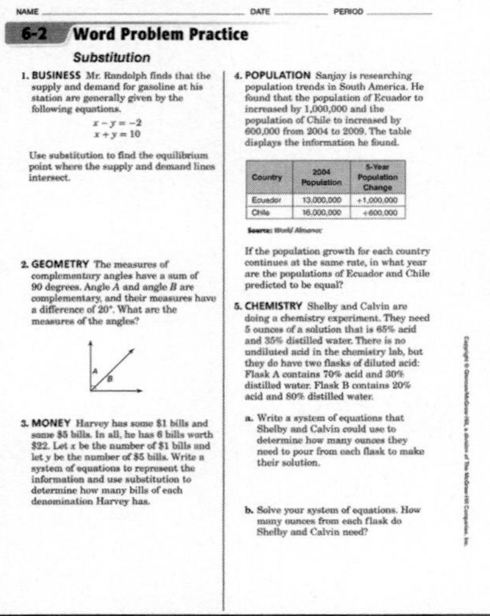

25. SPORTS The table shows the winning times for the Triathlon World Championship.

Year	Men's	Women's
2000	1:51:39	1:54:43
2009	1:44:51	1:59:14

a. The times are in hours, minutes, and seconds. Rewrite the times rounded to the nearest minute. **men: 112, 105; women: 115, 119**

b. Let the year 2000 be 0. Assume that the rate of change remains the same for years after 2000. Write an equation to represent each of the men's and women's winning times y in any year x. **$y = -0.8x + 112$; $y = 0.4x + 115$**

c. If the trend continues, when would you expect the men's and women's winning times to be the same? Explain your reasoning. **Never; the graphs never intersect for $x > 0$.**

26. CONCERT TICKETS Booker is buying tickets online for a concert. He finds tickets for himself and his friends for \$65 each plus a one-time fee of \$10. Paula is looking for tickets to the same concert. She finds them at another Web site for \$69 and a one-time fee of \$13.60. **a–d. See Ch. 6 Answer Appendix.**

a. Define the variables, and write equations to represent this situation.

b. Create a table of values for 1 to 5 tickets for each person's purchase.

c. Graph each of these equations.

d. Use the graph to determine who received the better deal? Explain why.

27. Neither; Guillermo substituted incorrectly for b. Cara solved correctly for b, but misinterpreted the pounds of apples bought.

H.O.T. Problems Use Higher-Order Thinking Skills

27. ERROR ANALYSIS In the system $a + b = 7$ and $1.29a + 0.49b = 6.63$, a represents pounds of apples and b represents pounds of bananas. Guillermo and Cara are finding and interpreting the solution. Is either of them correct? Explain.

Guillermo

$1.29a + 0.49b = 6.63$

$1.29a + 0.49(a + 7) = 6.63$

$1.29 + 0.49a + 3.43 = 6.63$

$0.49a = 3.2$

$a = 1.9$

$a + b = 7$, so $b = 5$. The solution (2, 5) means that 2 pounds of apples and 5 pounds of bananas were bought.

Cara

$1.29a + 0.49b = 6.63$

$1.29(7 - b) + 0.49b = 6.63$

$9.03 - 1.29b + 0.49b = 6.63$

$-0.8b = -2.4$

$b = 3$

The solution $b = 3$ means that 3 pounds of apples and 3 pounds of bananas were bought.

28. PERSEVERANCE A local charity has 60 volunteers. The ratio of boys to girls is 7:5. Find the number of boy and the number of girl volunteers. **25 girls and 35 boys**

29. REASONING Compare and contrast the solution of a system found by graphing and the solution of the same system found by substitution.

30. OPEN ENDED Create a system of equations that has one solution. Illustrate how the system could represent a real-world situation and describe the significance of the solution in the context of the situation. **See Ch. 6 Answer Appendix.**

31. WRITING IN MATH Explain how to determine what to substitute when using the substitution method of solving systems of equations.

29. Sample answer: The solutions found by each of these methods should be the same. However, it may be necessary to estimate using a graph. So, when a precise solution is needed, you should use substitution.

31. An equation containing a variable with a coefficient of 1 can easily be solved for the variable. That expression can then be substituted into the second equation for the variable.

Enrichment

OL BL

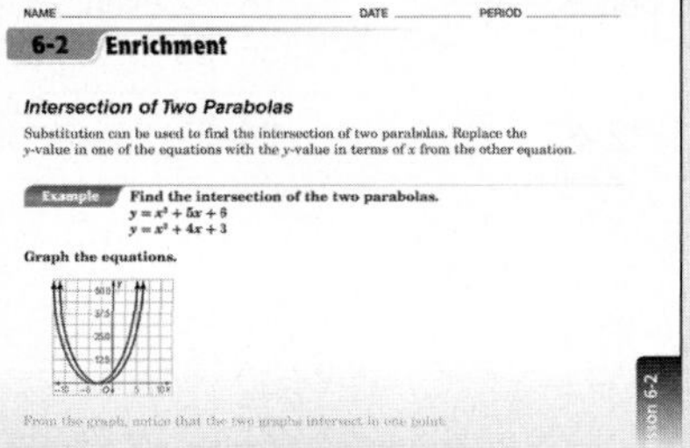

Additional Answer

36.

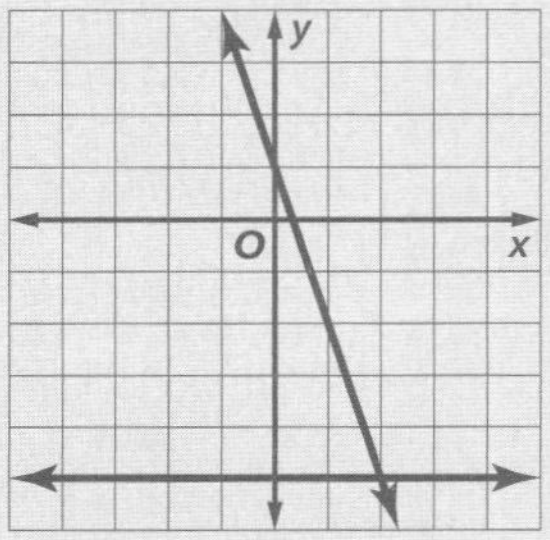

one solution; (2, −5)

Standardized Test Practice

32. The debate team plans to make and sell trail mix. They can spend \$34.

Item	Cost Per Pound
sunflower seeds	\$4.00
raisins	\$1.50

The pounds of raisins in the mix are to be 3 times the pounds of sunflower seeds. Which system can be used to find r, the pounds of raisins, and p, pounds of sunflower seeds, they should buy? **A**

A $3p = r$
 $4p + 1.5r = 34$

B $3p = r$
 $4r + 1.5p = 34$

C $3r = p$
 $4p + 1.5r = 34$

D $3r = p$
 $4r + 1.5p = 34$

33. GRIDDED RESPONSE The perimeters of two similar polygons are 250 centimeters and 300 centimeters, respectively. What is the scale factor between the first and second polygons? **5/6**

34. Based on the graph, which statement is true? **G**

Sports Drinks Supply

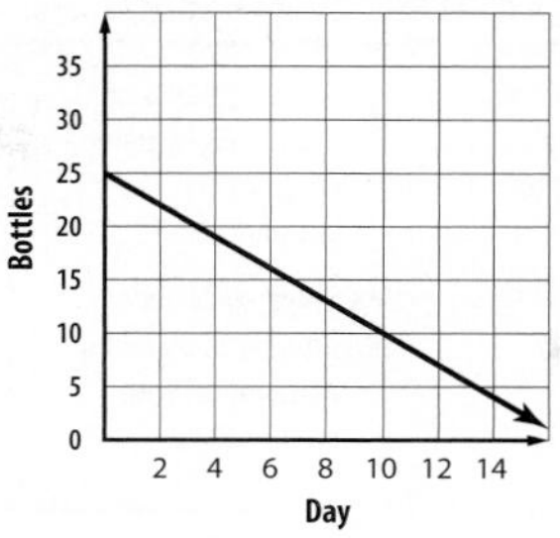

F Mary started with 30 bottles.
G On day 10, Mary will have 10 bottles left.
H Mary will be out of sports drinks on day 14.
J Mary drank 5 bottles the first two days.

35. If p is an integer, which of the following is the solution set for $2|p| = 16$? **C**

A $\{0, 8\}$ **C** $\{-8, 8\}$
B $\{-8, 0\}$ **D** $\{-8, 0, 8\}$

40a. Let p represent the number of pizzas, and let d represent the number of pitchers of soft drinks; $12p + 2d \le 70$.

Spiral Review

Graph each system and determine how many solutions it has. If it has one solution, name it. (Lesson 6-1) **36–39. See margin.**

36. $y = -5$, $3x + y = 1$

37. $x = 1$, $2x - y = 7$

38. $y = x + 5$, $y = x - 2$

39. $x + y = 1$, $3y + 3x = 3$

40. ENTERTAINMENT Coach Ross wants to take the soccer team out for pizza after their game. Her budget is at most \$70. (Lesson 5-6)

a. Using the sign, write an inequality that represents this situation.

b. Are there any restrictions on the variables? Explain.

Solve each inequality. Check your solution. (Lesson 5-3)

41. $6v + 1 \ge -11$ $v \ge -2$

42. $24 > 18 + 2n$ $n < 3$

43. $-11 \ge \frac{2}{5}q + 5$ $q \le -40$

44. $\frac{a}{8} - 10 > -3$ $a > 56$

45. $-3t + 9 \le 0$ $t \ge 3$

46. $54 > -10 - 8n$ $n > -8$

40b. $0 \le p < 6$, $0 \le d \le 35$, and p and d are integers; The coach cannot purchase a fractional part of a pizza or pitcher of drinks.

Skills Review

Rewrite each product using the Distributive Property. Then simplify.

47. $10b + 5(3 + 9b)$ $55b + 15$

48. $5(3t^2 + 4) - 8t$ $15t^2 - 8t + 20$

49. $7h^2 + 4(3h + h^2)$ $11h^2 + 12h$

50. $-2(7a + 5b) + 5(2a - 7b)$ $-4a - 45b$

Differentiated Instruction OL BL

Extension Have students write a system of equations that produces one solution using $y = \frac{1}{3}x - 2$ as one of the equations. Ask them to solve the system. Sample answer: Using the equation $2x - y = 7$, the solution is $(3, -1)$.

Teaching the Process Standards

Perseverance Mathematically proficient students look for entry points to the solution of a problem. In Exercise 28, encourage students to write a few ratios equivalent to 7:5. Then ask them to write an expression for all the ratios in terms of a variable.

4 Assess

Name the Math Write a system of equations on the board. Have students pair up and tell each other how they would solve the system.

Formative Assessment

Check for student understanding of concepts in Lessons 6-1 and 6-2.

Quiz 1, p. 59

Additional Answers

37.

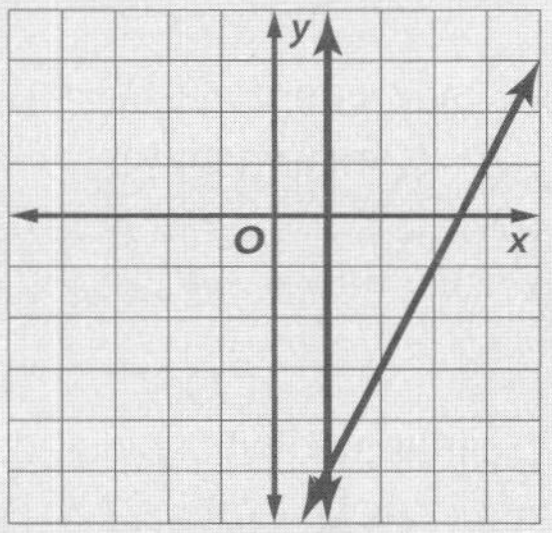

one solution; $(1, -5)$

38.

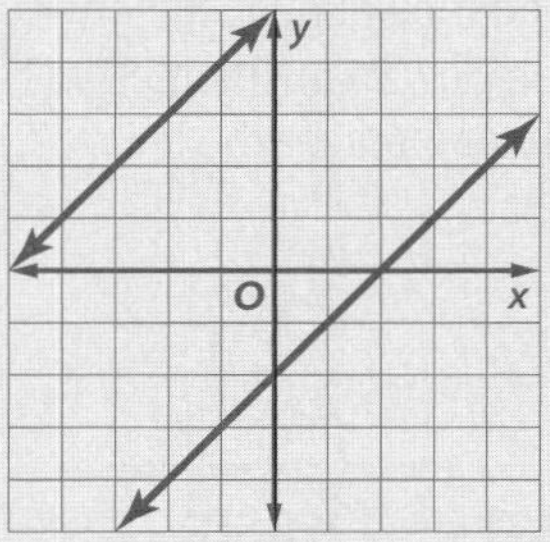

no solution

39.

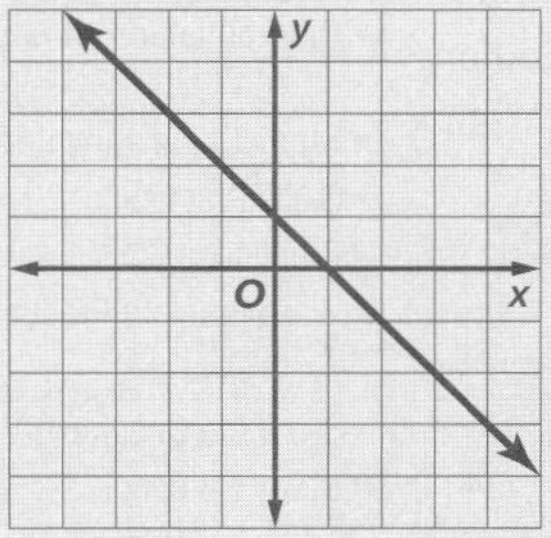

infinitely many solutions

1 Focus

VerticalAlignment

Before Lesson 6-3 Use properties of equality to solve equations.

Lesson 6-3 Solve systems of equations by using elimination with addition.
Solve systems of equations by using elimination with subtraction.

After Lesson 6-3 Solve systems of equations by using elimination with multiplication.

2 Teach

Scaffolding Questions

Have students read the **Why?** section of the lesson.

Ask:

- Why does the system $a + b = 12$ and $a - b = 2$ represent the situation? There are 12 months in a year and the difference between a and b is 2.
- Why is b eliminated when you add $a + b = 12$ and $a - b = 2$? b is eliminated because $b + (-b) = 0$
- If you add the equations, then $2a = 14$. How many months will the high temperature be below 70° F? 7 months

LESSON 6-3 Elimination Using Addition and Subtraction

Then	Now	Why?
You solved systems of equations by using substitution.	**1** Solve systems of equations by using elimination with addition. **2** Solve systems of equations by using elimination with subtraction.	In Chicago, Illinois, there are two more months a when the mean high temperature is below 70°F than there are months b when it is above 70°F. The system of equations, $a + b = 12$ and $a - b = 2$, represents this situation.

NewVocabulary
elimination

Content Standards
AI.SEI.2, AI.SEI.3

Process Standards
PS.7

1 Elimination Using Addition

If you add these equations, the variable b will be eliminated. Using addition or subtraction to solve a system is called **elimination**.

KeyConcept Solving by Elimination

Step 1 Write the system so like terms with the same or opposite coefficients are aligned.

Step 2 Add or subtract the equations, eliminating one variable. Then solve the equation.

Step 3 Substitute the value from Step 2 into one of the equations and solve for the other variable. Write the solution as an ordered pair.

Example 1 Elimination Using Addition

Use elimination to solve the system of equations.

$4x + 6y = 32$
$3x - 6y = 3$ ← **Step 1** $6y$ and $-6y$ have opposite coefficients.

Step 2 Add the equations.

$$\begin{aligned} 4x + 6y &= 32 \\ (+)\ 3x - 6y &= 3 \\ \hline 7x \quad &= 35 && \text{The variable } y \text{ is eliminated.} \\ \frac{7x}{7} &= \frac{35}{7} && \text{Divide each side by 7.} \\ x &= 5 && \text{Simplify.} \end{aligned}$$

Step 3 Substitute 5 for x in either equation to find the value of y.

$$\begin{aligned} 4x + 6y &= 32 && \text{First equation} \\ 4(5) + 6y &= 32 && \text{Replace } x \text{ with 5.} \\ 20 + 6y &= 32 && \text{Multiply.} \\ 20 + 6y - 20 &= 32 - 20 && \text{Subtract 20 from each side.} \\ 6y &= 12 && \text{Simplify.} \\ \frac{6y}{6} &= \frac{12}{6} && \text{Divide each side by 6.} \\ y &= 2 && \text{Simplify.} \end{aligned}$$

The solution is (5, 2).

Lesson 6-3 Resources

Resource	Approaching Level AL	On Level OL	Beyond Level BL	English Learners ELL
Teacher Edition	▪ Differentiated Instruction, p. 352	▪ Differentiated Instruction, pp. 352, 355, 356	▪ Differentiated Instruction, pp. 355, 356	▪ Differentiated Instruction, p. 352
Chapter Resource Masters	▪ Study Guide and Intervention, pp. 18–19 ▪ Skills Practice, p. 20 ▪ Practice, p. 21 ▪ Word Problem Practice, p. 22	▪ Study Guide and Intervention, pp. 18–19 ▪ Skills Practice, p. 20 ▪ Practice, p. 21 ▪ Word Problem Practice, p. 22 ▪ Enrichment, p. 23	▪ Practice, p. 21 ▪ Word Problem Practice, p. 22 ▪ Enrichment, p. 23	▪ Study Guide and Intervention, pp. 18–19 ▪ Skills Practice, p. 20 ▪ Practice, p. 21 ▪ Word Problem Practice, p. 22
Other	▪ 5-Minute Check 6-3 ▪ Study Notebook ▪ Teaching Algebra with Manipulatives	▪ 5-Minute Check 6-3 ▪ Study Notebook ▪ Teaching Algebra with Manipulatives	▪ 5-Minute Check 6-3 ▪ Study Notebook	▪ 5-Minute Check 6-3 ▪ Study Notebook ▪ Teaching Algebra with Manipulatives

Guided Practice

1A. $-4x + 3y = -3$
$4x - 5y = 5$ (0, −1)

1B. $4y + 3x = 22$
$3x - 4y = 14$ (6, 1)

We can use elimination to find specific numbers that are described as being related to each other.

Example 2 Write and Solve a System of Equations

Negative three times one number plus five times another number is −11. Three times the first number plus seven times the other number is −1. Find the numbers.

Negative three times one number	plus	five times another number	is	−11.
$-3x$	+	$5y$	=	−11
Three times the first number	plus	seven times the other number	is	−1.
$3x$	+	$7y$	=	−1

Steps 1 and 2 Write the equations vertically and add.

$$\begin{aligned} -3x + 5y &= -11 \\ (+)\ 3x + 7y &= -1 \\ \hline 12y &= -12 \quad \text{The variable } x \text{ is eliminated.} \\ \frac{12y}{12} &= \frac{-12}{12} \quad \text{Divide each side by 12.} \\ y &= -1 \quad \text{Simplify.} \end{aligned}$$

Step 3 Substitute −1 for y in either equation to find the value of x.

$$\begin{aligned} 3x + 7y &= -1 && \text{Second equation} \\ 3x + 7(-1) &= -1 && \text{Replace } y \text{ with } -1. \\ 3x + (-7) &= -1 && \text{Simplify.} \\ 3x + (-7) + 7 &= -1 + 7 && \text{Add 7 to each side.} \\ 3x &= 6 && \text{Simplify.} \\ \frac{3x}{3} &= \frac{6}{3} && \text{Divide each side by 3.} \\ x &= 2 && \text{Simplify.} \end{aligned}$$

The numbers are 2 and −1.

CHECK

$$\begin{aligned} -3x + 5y &= -11 && \text{First equation} \\ -3(2) + 5(-1) &\stackrel{?}{=} -11 && \text{Substitute 2 for } x \text{ and } -1 \text{ for } y. \\ -11 &= -11\ \checkmark && \text{Simplify.} \\ 3x + 7y &= -1 && \text{Second equation} \\ 3(2) + 7(-1) &\stackrel{?}{=} -1 && \text{Substitute 2 for } x \text{ and } -1 \text{ for } y. \\ -1 &= -1\ \checkmark && \text{Simplify.} \end{aligned}$$

Guided Practice

2. The sum of two numbers is −10. Negative three times the first number minus the second number equals 2. Find the numbers. 4, −14

Study Tip

Coefficients When the coefficients of a variable are the same, subtracting the equations will eliminate the variable. When the coefficients are opposites, adding the equations will eliminate the variable.

Problem-Solving Tip

Perseverance Checking your answers in both equations of a system helps ensure there are no calculation errors.

Focus on Mathematical Content

Elimination Using Addition Solving a system of equations by using elimination with addition requires adding the two equations together to eliminate one of the variables. The resulting equation is then solved for the remaining variable. Once the value of one variable is known, it can be substituted into one of the original equations to determine the value of the other variable. In order to use this method, the coefficients of either x or y need to be additive inverses.

- If you know the value of a, how can you find the value of b? Substitute the value of a for a in one of the equations and solve for b.
- When might you use elimination with addition to solve a system of equations? when the coefficients of one variable are opposites

1 Elimination Using Addition

Example 1 shows how to solve a system of equations by using elimination with addition. **Example 2** shows how to write a system of equations and then use elimination with addition to solve it.

Formative Assessment

Use the Guided Practice exercises after each example to determine students' understanding of concepts.

Additional Examples

1 Use elimination to solve the system of equations.
$-3x + 4y = 12$
$3x - 6y = 18$ (−24, −15)

2 Four times one number minus three times another number is 12. Two times the first number added to three times the second number is 6. Find the numbers. The numbers are 3 and 0.

Additional Examples also in Interactive Classroom PowerPoint® Presentations

IWB Interactive White Board READY

Teaching the Process Standards

Perseverance Mathematically proficient check their answers. Encourage students to check their answers in both equations, stressing that they should use the original equations.

2 Elimination Using Subtraction

Example 3 shows how to solve a system of equations using elimination with subtraction. **Example 4** shows how to write and solve a system of equations by elimination for a real-world problem.

Additional Examples

3 Use elimination to solve the system of equations.

$4x + 2y = 28$

$4x - 3y = 18$ (6, 2)

4 **RENTALS** A hardware store earned \$956.50 from renting ladders and power tools last week. The store charged customers for a total of 36 days for ladders and 85 days for power tools. This week the store charged 36 days for ladders, 70 days for power tools, and earned \$829. How much does the store charge per day for ladders and for power tools? \$6.50 per day for ladders and \$8.50 per day for power tools

Focus on Mathematical Content

Elimination Using Subtraction Solving a system of equations by subtraction requires subtracting one equation from the other to eliminate one of the variables. The coefficients of either *x* or *y* must be the same in order to use this method.

WatchOut!

Preventing Errors When using elimination with subtraction to solve systems of equations, many students forget to distribute the negative sign over every term of the equation that is subtracted. Since subtraction is the same as adding the inverse, you might suggest that students change the signs of the terms and then add to eliminate the variable.

2 Elimination Using Subtraction

Sometimes we can eliminate a variable by subtracting one equation from another.

Standardized Test Example 3

PT

Solve the system of equations. $2t + 5r = 6$
$9r + 2t = 22$

A $(-7, 15)$ **B** $\left(7, \frac{8}{9}\right)$ **C** $(4, -7)$ **D** $\left(4, -\frac{2}{5}\right)$

Read the Test Item

Since both equations contain $2t$, use elimination by subtraction.

Solve the Test Item

Step 1 Subtract the equations.

$5r + 2t = 6$	Write the system so like terms are aligned.
$(-)\ 9r + 2t = 22$	
$-4r = -16$	The variable *t* is eliminated.
$r = 4$	Simplify.

Step 2 Substitute 4 for *r* in either equation to find the value of *t*.

$5r + 2t = 6$	First equation
$5(4) + 2t = 6$	$r = 4$
$20 + 2t = 6$	Simplify.
$20 + 2t - 20 = 6 - 20$	Subtract 20 from each side.
$2t = -14$	Simplify.
$t = -7$	Simplify.

The solution is $(4, -7)$. The correct answer is C.

GuidedPractice

3. Solve the system of equations. H $8b + 3c = 11$
$8b + 7c = 7$

F $(1.5, -1)$ **G** $(1.75, -1)$ **H** $(1.75, 1)$ **J** $(1.5, 1)$

Real-WorldLink

The five most dangerous jobs for teens are: delivery and other driving jobs, working alone in cash-based businesses, traveling youth crews, cooking, and construction.

Source: National Consumers League

Real-World Example 4 Write and Solve a System of Equations

PT

JOBS Cheryl and Jackie work at an ice cream shop. Cheryl earns \$8.50 per hour and Jackie earns \$7.50 per hour. During a typical week, Cheryl and Jackie earn \$299.50 together. One week, Jackie doubles her work hours, and the girls earn \$412. How many hours does each girl work during a typical week?

Understand You know how much Cheryl and Jackie each earn per hour and how much they earned together.

Plan Let c = Cheryl's hours and j = Jackie's hours.

Cheryl's pay	plus	Jackie's pay	equals	\$299.50.
$8.50c$	$+$	$7.50j$	$=$	299.50
Cheryl's pay	plus	Jackie's pay	equals	\$412.
$8.50c$	$+$	$7.50(2)j$	$=$	412

DifferentiatedInstruction AL OL ELL

Kinesthetic Learners Students may benefit from using concrete models to solve systems of equations with elimination. Have students write the terms of the equations on pieces of paper or use algebra tiles or other models to represent the equations. When they eliminate a variable, have them remove the model for that variable. The act of removing the terms should help them remember eliminating the variable.

StudyTip

Another Method Instead of subtracting the equations, you could also multiply one equation by −1 and then add the equations.

Solve Subtract the equations to eliminate one of the variables. Then solve for the other variable.

$$\begin{array}{rl} 8.50c + 7.50j = 299.50 & \text{Write the equations vertically.} \\ (-)\ 8.50c + 7.50(2)j = 412 & \\ \hline \end{array}$$

$$\begin{array}{rl} 8.50c + 7.50j = 299.50 & \\ (-)\ 8.50c + 15j = 412 & \text{Simplify.} \\ \hline -7.50j = -112.50 & \text{Subtract. The variable } c \text{ is eliminated.} \\ \frac{-7.50j}{-7.50} = \frac{-112.50}{-7.50} & \text{Divide each side by } -7.50. \\ j = 15 & \text{Simplify.} \end{array}$$

Now substitute 15 for j in either equation to find the value of c.

$$\begin{array}{rl} 8.50c + 7.50j = 299.50 & \text{First equation} \\ 8.50c + 7.50(15) = 299.50 & \text{Substitute 15 for } j. \\ 8.50c + 112.50 = 299.50 & \text{Simplify.} \\ 8.50c = 187 & \text{Subtract 112.50 from each side.} \\ c = 22 & \text{Divide each side by 8.50.} \end{array}$$

Check Substitute both values into the other equation to see if the equation holds true. If $c = 22$ and $j = 15$, then $8.50(22) + 15(15)$ or 412.

Cheryl works 22 hours, while Jackie works 15 hours during a typical week.

GuidedPractice

4. PARTIES Tamera and Adelina are throwing a birthday party for their friend. Tamera invited 5 fewer friends than Adelina. Together they invited 47 guests. How many guests did each girl invite? **Tamera, 21; Adelina, 26**

6. recycling and reuse, 1,150,000; waste management, 125,000

Check Your Understanding

◯ = Step-by-Step Solutions begin on page R13.

Examples 1, 3 **Use elimination to solve each system of equations.**

1. $5m - p = 7$
$7m - p = 11$ **(2, 3)**

2. $8x + 5y = 38$
$-8x + 2y = 4$ **(1, 6)**

3. $7f + 3g = -6$
$7f - 2g = -31$ **(−3, 5)**

4. $6a - 3b = 27$
$2a - 3b = 11$ **(4, −1)**

Example 2 **5. REASONING** The sum of two numbers is 24. Five times the first number minus the second number is 12. What are the two numbers? **6, 18**

Example 4 **6. RECYCLING** The recycling and reuse industry employs approximately 1,025,000 more workers than the waste management industry. Together they provide 1,275,000 jobs. How many jobs does each industry provide?

3 Practice

Formative Assessment

Use Exercises 1–6 to check for understanding.

Use the chart at the bottom of this page to customize assignments for your students.

Teach with Tech

Video Recording Have students work in groups, and record themselves teaching each other how to solve an equation using elimination. Then share all of the videos with the class.

Teaching the Process Standards

Reasoning Mathematically proficient students create a coherent representation of the problem at hand. In Exercise 5, make sure students use different variables for the two numbers.

Differentiated Homework Options

Level	Assignment	Two-Day Option	
AL Basic	7–23, 34–37, 39–59	7–23 odd, 40–43	8–22 even, 34–37, 39, 44–59
OL Core	7–29 odd, 30–37, 39–59	7–23, 40–43	24–37, 39, 44–59
BL Advanced	24–55, (optional: 56–59)		

Study Guide and Intervention

AL OL ELL

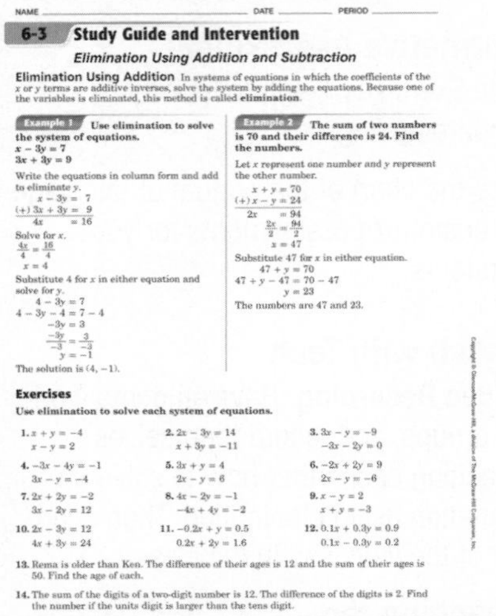
6-3 Study Guide and Intervention
Elimination Using Addition and Subtraction

Practice

AL OL BL ELL

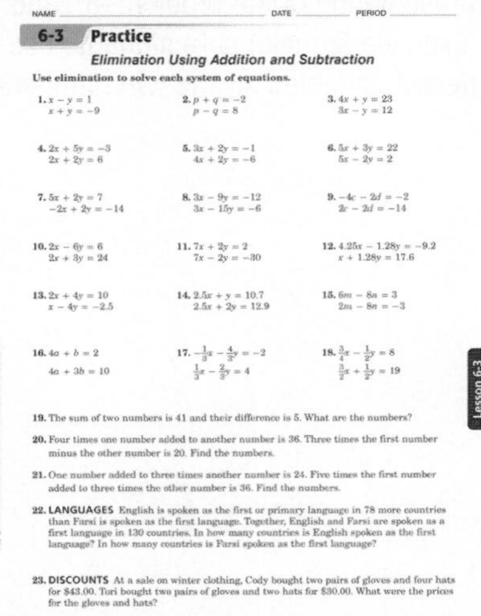
6-3 Practice
Elimination Using Addition and Subtraction

Word Problem Practice

AL OL BL ELL

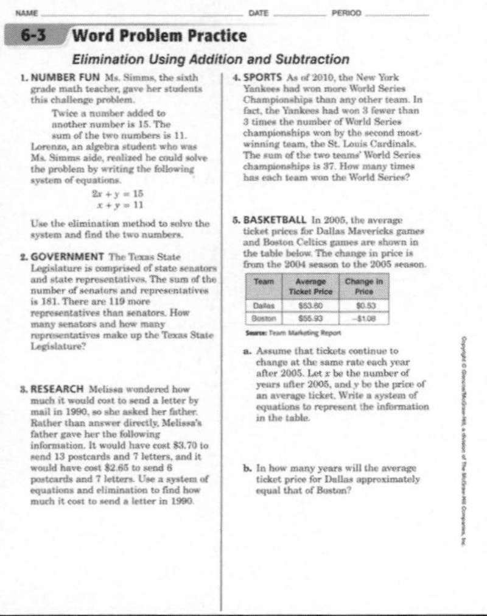
6-3 Word Problem Practice
Elimination Using Addition and Subtraction

Practice and Problem Solving

Extra Practice is on page R6.

Examples 1, 3 Use elimination to solve each system of equations.

7. $-v + w = 7$
$v + w = 1$ **(−3, 4)**

8. $y + z = 4$
$y - z = 8$ **(6, −2)**

9. $-4x + 5y = 17$
$4x + 6y = -6$ **(−3, 1)**

10. $5m - 2p = 24$
$3m + 2p = 24$ **(6, 3)**

11. $a + 4b = -4$
$a + 10b = -16$ **(4, −2)**

12. $6r - 6t = 6$
$3r - 6t = 15$ **(−3, −4)**

13. $6c - 9d = 111$
$5c - 9d = 103$ **(8, −7)**

14. $11f + 14g = 13$
$11f + 10g = 25$ **(5, −3)**

15. $9x + 6y = 78$
$3x - 6y = -30$ **(4, 7)**

16. $3j + 4k = 23.5$
$8j - 4k = 4$ **(2.5, 4)**

17. $-3x - 8y = -24$
$3x - 5y = 4.5$ **(4, 1.5)**

18. $6x - 2y = 1$
$10x - 2y = 5$ **(1, 2.5)**

Example 2

19. The sum of two numbers is 22, and their difference is 12. What are the numbers? **5, 17**

20. Find the two numbers with a sum of 41 and a difference of 9. **25, 16**

21. Three times a number minus another number is −3. The sum of the numbers is 11. Find the numbers. **2, 9**

22. A number minus twice another number is 4. Three times the first number plus two times the second number is 12. What are the numbers? **4, 0**

Example 4

23. **TOURS** The Blackwells and Joneses are going to Hershey's Really Big 3D Show in Pennsylvania. Find the adult price and the children's price of the show. **Adult, $5.95; children, $3.95**

Family	Number of Adults	Number of Children	Total Cost
Blackwell	2	5	$31.65
Jones	2	3	$23.75

B Use elimination to solve each system of equations.

24. $4(x + 2y) = 8$
$4x + 4y = 12$ **(4, −1)**

25. $3x - 5y = 11$
$5(x + y) = 5$ **(2, −1)**

26. $4x + 3y = 6$
$3x + 3y = 7$ $\left(-1, 3\frac{1}{3}\right)$

27. $6x - 7y = -26$
$6x + 5y = 10$ $\left(-\frac{5}{6}, 3\right)$

28. $\frac{1}{2}x + \frac{2}{3}y = 2\frac{3}{4}$
$\frac{1}{4}x - \frac{2}{3}y = 6\frac{1}{4}$ $\left(12, -4\frac{7}{8}\right)$

29. $\frac{3}{5}x + \frac{1}{2}y = 8\frac{1}{3}$
$-\frac{3}{5}x + \frac{3}{4}y = 8\frac{1}{3}$ $\left(2\frac{7}{9}, 13\frac{1}{3}\right)$

30. **SENSE-MAKING** The total height of an office building b and the granite statue that stands on top of it g is 326.6 feet. The difference in heights between the building and the statue is 295.4 feet.
   a. How tall is the statue? **15.6 ft**
   b. How tall is the building? **311 ft**

31. **BIKE RACING** Professional Mountain Bike Racing currently has 66 teams. The number of non-U.S. teams is 30 more than the number of U.S. teams.
   a. Let x represent the number of non-U.S. teams and y represent the number of U.S. teams. Write a system of equations that represents the number of U.S. teams and non-U.S. teams. $x + y = 66$; $x = 30 + y$
   b. Use elimination to find the solution of the system of equations. **(48, 18)**
   c. Interpret the solution in the context of the situation. **See margin.**
   d. Graph the system of equations to check your solution. **See margin.**

Enrichment

OL BL

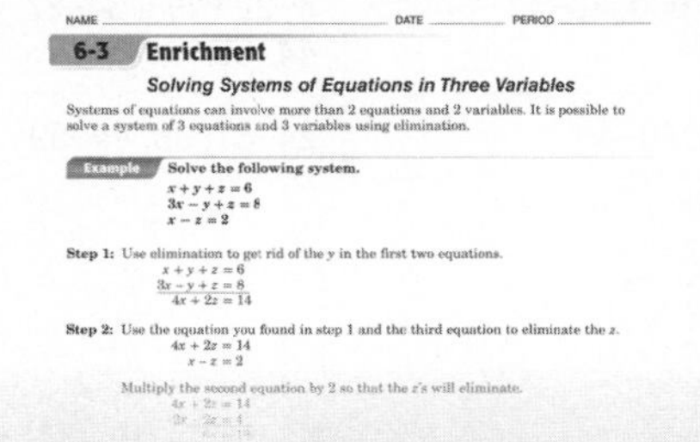
6-3 Enrichment
Solving Systems of Equations in Three Variables

Teaching the Process Standards

Sense-Making Mathematically proficient students can draw diagrams of important features and relationships. In Exercise 30, encourage students to draw a diagram of the statue and the building to help in writing the system of equations.

32. **SHOPPING** Let x represent the number of years since 2004 and y represent the number of catalogs.

Catalogs	Number in 2004	Growth Rate (number per year)
online	7440	1293
print	3805	−1364

Source: MediaPost Publications

a. Write a system of equations to represent this situation. **$y = 1293x + 7440$; $y = -1364x + 3805$**

b. Use elimination to find the solution to the system of equations. **about (−1.4, 5671.1)**

c. Analyze the solution in terms of the situation. Determine the reasonableness of the solution. **About 1.4 years before 2004, or in 2002, the number of online catalogs and the number of print catalogs were both 5671.**

C 33. **MULTIPLE REPRESENTATIONS** Collect 9 pennies and 9 paper clips. For this game, you use objects to score points. Each paper clip is worth 1 point and each penny is worth 3 points. Let p represent the number of pennies and c represent the number of paper clips.

9 points = 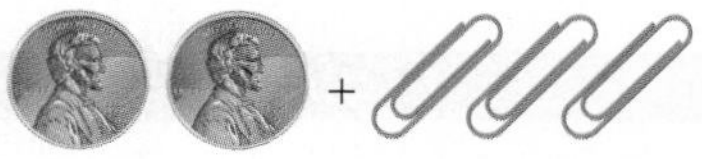 $= 3p + c$
$= 3(2) + 3$

a. **Concrete** Choose a combination of 9 objects and find your score. **Sample answer: If you choose 4 pennies and 5 paper clips, the score will be 4(3) + 5 or 17**

b. **Analytical** Write and solve a system of equations to find the number of paper clips and pennies used for 15 points, if 9 total objects are used. **Sample answer: $p + c = 9$, $3p + c = 15$, $p = 3$, $c = 6$**

c. **Tabular** If 9 total objects are used, make a table showing the number of paper clips used and the total number of points when the number of pennies is 0, 1, 2, 3, 4, or 5. **See margin.**

d. **Verbal** Does the result in the table match the results in part **b**? Explain. **See margin.**

37. Sample answer: $-x + y = 5$; I used the solution to create another equation with the coefficient of the x-term being the opposite of its corresponding coefficient.

H.O.T. Problems Use Higher-Order Thinking Skills

34. **REASONING** Describe the solution of a system of equations if after you added two equations the result was 0 = 0. **If the result is a true statement such as 0 = 0, then there would be an infinite number of solutions.**

35. **REASONING** What is the solution of a system of equations if the sum of the equations is 0 = 2? **See margin.**

36. **OPEN ENDED** Create a system of equations that can be solved by using addition to eliminate one variable. Formulate a general rule for creating such systems.

36. Sample answer: $2a + b = 5$, $a - b = 4$; a system that can be solved by using addition to eliminate one variable must have one variable with coefficients that are additive inverses.

37. **STRUCTURE** The solution of a system of equations is (−3, 2). One equation in the system is $x + 4y = 5$. Find a second equation for the system. Explain how you derived this equation.

38. **CHALLENGE** The sum of the digits of a two-digit number is 8. The result of subtracting the units digit from the tens digit is −4. Define the variables and write the system of equations that you would use to find the number. Then solve the system and find the number. **See margin.**

39. **WRITING IN MATH** Describe when it would be most beneficial to use elimination to solve a system of equations. **See margin.**

DifferentiatedInstruction OL BL

Visual Learners Have students find the missing value. The values represent the sums of each row and column.

Hint: Let each symbol or set of symbols represent one variable.

※※	◆◆	◁▷	ՕՕ	?15
※※	※※	◆◆	◆◆	10
◁▷	ՕՕ	◁▷	ՕՕ	20
◆◆	◆◆	◁▷	◁▷	16
14	11	20	16	

※※ = 3, ◆◆ = 2, ◁▷ = 6, ՕՕ = 4

Multiple Representations

In Exercise 33, students use a concrete model and a table of values to illustrate the solution of a system of equations.

Teaching the Process Standards

Structure Mathematically proficient students look closely to discern a structure. In Exercise 37, encourage students to think about the lines that fit the criteria of the problem and how they can be represented mathematically. They should see that using the point-slope form with (−3, 2) and any slope different than that of the given line will produce a correct system.

Additional Answers

31c. There are 48 teams that are not from the U.S. and 18 teams that are from the U.S.

31d.

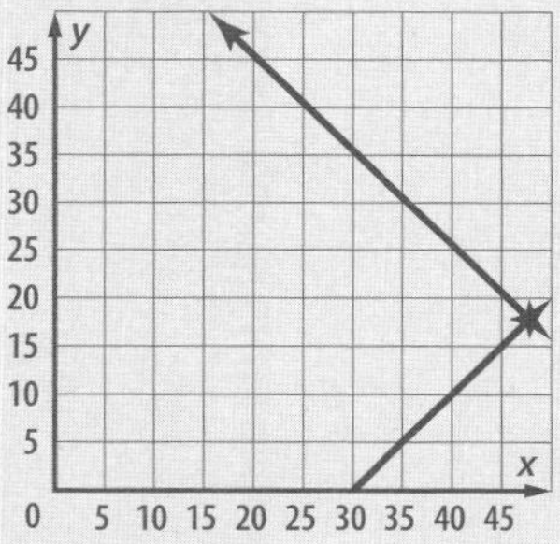

33c. Sample answer:

Pennies (p)	0	1	2	3	4	5
Paper clips ($9 - p$)	9	8	7	6	5	4
Points ($3p + c$)	9	11	13	15	17	19

33d. Yes; since the pennies are 3 points each, 3 of them makes 9 points. Add the 6 points from 6 paper clips and you get 15 points. Using 9 objects, there is no other way of obtaining a score of 15 points.

35. The result of the statement is false, so there is no solution.

38. Let a = the tens digit of the number, and let b = the ones digit of the number; $a - b = -4$; $a + b = 8$; 26 is the number.

39. Sample answer: It would be most beneficial when one variable has either the same coefficient or opposite coefficients in the equations.

4 Assess

Ticket Out the Door Have students write a system of equations that can be solved by using elimination with subtraction.

Standardized Test Practice

40. SHORT RESPONSE Martina is on a train traveling at a speed of 188 mph between two cities 1128 miles apart. If the train has been traveling for an hour, how many more hours is her train ride? **5 hours**

41. GEOMETRY Ms. Miller wants to tile her rectangular kitchen floor. She knows the dimensions of the floor. Which formula should she use to find the area? **A**

A $A = \ell w$
B $V = Bh$
C $P = 2\ell + 2w$
D $c^2 = a^2 + b^2$

42. If the pattern continues, what is the 8th number in the sequence? **F**

$$2, 3, \frac{9}{2}, \frac{27}{4}, \frac{81}{8}, \ldots$$

F $\frac{2187}{64}$
G $\frac{2245}{64}$
H $\frac{2281}{64}$
J $\frac{2445}{64}$

43. What is the solution of this system of equations? **B**

$$x + 4y = 1$$
$$2x - 3y = -9$$

A $(2, -8)$
B $(-3, 1)$
C no solution
D infinitely many solutions

Spiral Review

Use substitution to solve each system of equations. If the system does not have exactly one solution, state whether it has no solution or infinitely many solutions. (Lesson 6-2)

44. $y = 6x$
$2x + 3y = 40$ **(2, 12)**

45. $x = 3y$
$2x + 3y = 45$ **(15, 5)**

46. $x = 5y + 6$
$x = 3y - 2$ **(−14, −4)**

47. $y = 3x + 2$
$y = 4x - 1$ **(3, 11)**

48. $3c = 4d + 2$
$c = d - 1$ **(−6, −5)**

49. $z = v + 4$
$2z - v = 6$ **(−2, 2)**

50. FINANCIAL LITERACY Gregorio and Javier each want to buy a bicycle. Gregorio has already saved \$35 and plans to save \$10 per week. Javier has \$26 and plans to save \$13 per week. (Lesson 6-1)

a. In how many weeks will Gregorio and Javier have saved the same amount of money? **3 wk**

b. How much will each person have saved at that time? **\$65**

51. GEOMETRY A *parallelogram* is a quadrilateral in which opposite sides are parallel. Determine whether *ABCD* is parallelogram. Explain your reasoning. (Lesson 4-4)

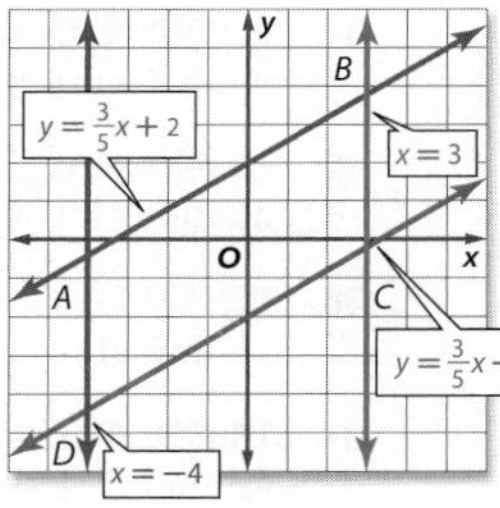

Solve each equation. Check your solution. (Lesson 2-2)

52. $6u = -48$ **−8**

53. $75 = -15p$ **−5**

54. $\frac{2}{3}a = 8$ **12**

55. $-\frac{3}{4}d = 15$ **−20**

51. Yes; each pair of opposite sides have the same or an undefined slope, so they are parallel.

Skills Review

Simplify each expression. If not possible, write *simplified*.

56. $6q - 3 + 7q + 1$ **$13q - 2$**

57. $7w^2 - 9w + 4w^2$ **$11w^2 - 9w$**

58. $10(2 + r) + 3r$ **$13r + 20$**

59. $5y - 7(y + 5)$ **$-2y - 35$**

Differentiated Instruction OL BL

Extension Write two equations on the board with the constants missing. Have students find the missing constants that ensure the given solution. For example, write the system $3x + 2y = ?$, $5x - 2y = ?$ and tell students that the solution is (1.5, 0.25). $3x + 2y = 5, 5x - 2y = 7$

356 | Lesson 6-3 | Elimination Using Addition and Subtraction

LESSON 6-4 Elimination Using Multiplication

Then

- You used elimination with addition and subtraction to solve systems of equations.

Now

1. Solve systems of equations by using elimination with multiplication.
2. Solve real-world problems involving systems of equations.

Why?

- The table shows the number of cars at Scott's Auto Repair Shop for each type of service.

Item	Repairs	Maintenance
body	3	4
engine	2	2

The manager has allotted 1110 minutes for body work and 570 minutes for engine work. The system $3r + 4m = 1110$ and $2r + 2m = 570$ can be used to find the average time for each service.

Content Standards
AI.SEI.2, AI.SEI.3

Process Standards
PS.1

1 Elimination Using Multiplication

In the system above, neither variable can be eliminated by adding or subtracting. You can use multiplication to solve.

KeyConcept Solving by Elimination Using Multiplication

Step 1 Multiply at least one equation by a constant to get two equations that contain opposite terms.

Step 2 Add the equations, eliminating one variable. Then solve the equation.

Step 3 Substitute the value from Step 2 into one of the equations and solve for the other variable. Write the solution as an ordered pair.

PT

Example 1 Multiply One Equation to Eliminate a Variable

Use elimination to solve the system of equations.
$5x + 6y = -8$
$2x + 3y = -5$

Steps 1 and 2

$5x + 6y = -8$
$2x + 3y = -5$ — Multiply each term by −2. →

$$\begin{aligned} 5x + 6y &= -8 \\ (+)\ -4x - 6y &= 10 \quad \text{Add.} \\ \hline x &= 2 \quad y \text{ is eliminated.} \end{aligned}$$

Step 3

$2x + 3y = -5$	Second equation
$2(2) + 3y = -5$	Substitution, $x = 2$
$4 + 3y = -5$	Simplify.
$3y = -9$	Subtract 4 from each side and simplify.
$y = -3$	Divide each side by 3 and simplify.

The solution is $(2, -3)$.

GuidedPractice

1A. $6x - 2y = 10$
$3x - 7y = -19$ **(3, 4)**

1B. $9r + q = 13$
$3r + 2q = -4$ **(2, −5)**

1 Focus

VerticalAlignment

Before Lesson 6-4 Use properties of equality to solve equations.

Lesson 6-4 Solve systems of equations by using elimination with multiplication.
Solve real-world problems involving systems of equations.

After Lesson 6-4 Apply systems of equations.

2 Teach

Scaffolding Questions

Have students read the **Why?** section of the lesson.

Ask:

- What does the first equation in the system of equations represent? the amount of time to perform body repair for 3 cars and body maintenance for 4 cars
- What does the second equation in the system represent? the amount of time to perform engine repair for 2 cars and engine maintenance for 2 cars

(continued on the next page)

Lesson 6-4 Resources

Resource	Approaching Level AL	On Level OL	Beyond Level BL	English Learners ELL
Teacher Edition	▪ Differentiated Instruction, p. 359	▪ Differentiated Instruction, p. 362	▪ Differentiated Instruction, p. 362	▪ Differentiated Instruction, p. 359
Chapter Resource Masters	▪ Study Guide and Intervention, pp. 24–25 ▪ Skills Practice, p. 26 ▪ Practice, p. 27 ▪ Word Problem Practice, p. 28	▪ Study Guide and Intervention, pp. 24–25 ▪ Skills Practice, p. 26 ▪ Practice, p. 27 ▪ Word Problem Practice, p. 28 ▪ Enrichment, p. 29	▪ Practice, p. 27 ▪ Word Problem Practice, p. 28 ▪ Enrichment, p. 29	▪ Study Guide and Intervention, pp. 24–25 ▪ Skills Practice, p. 26 ▪ Practice, p. 27 ▪ Word Problem Practice, p. 28
Other	▪ 5-Minute Check 6-4 ▪ Study Notebook	▪ 5-Minute Check 6-4 ▪ Study Notebook	▪ 5-Minute Check 6-4 ▪ Study Notebook	▪ 5-Minute Check 6-4 ▪ Study Notebook

- What will the solution to the system represent? the average number of minutes allotted per repair and the average number of minutes allotted per maintenance
- If you multiply the second equation by −2, what variable could you eliminate by adding the equations? the variable m

1 Elimination Using Multiplication

Example 1 shows how to multiply one equation of a system by a number to eliminate a variable. **Example 2** shows how to multiply both equations of a system to eliminate a variable.

Formative Assessment

Use the Guided Practice exercises after each example to determine students' understanding of concepts.

Additional Examples

1 Use elimination to solve the system of equations.

$2x + y = 23$

$3x + 2y = 37$ (9, 5)

2 Use elimination to solve the system of equations.

$4x + 3y = 8$

$3x - 5y = -23$ (−1, 4)

Additional Examples also in Interactive Classroom PowerPoint® Presentations

IWB Interactive White Board READY

Teach with Tech

Blog On your secure classroom blog have students write a blog entry explaining how they decide when to use each of the different methods for solving a system of equations.

Sometimes you have to multiply each equation by a different number in order to solve the system.

StudyTip

Choosing a Variable to Eliminate Unless the problem is asking for the value of a specific variable, you may use multiplication to eliminate either variable.

Example 2 Multiply Both Equations to Eliminate a Variable

Use elimination to solve the system of equations.

$4x + 2y = 8$

$3x + 3y = 9$

Method 1 Eliminate x.

$4x + 2y = 8$ → Multiply by 3. → $12x + 6y = 24$

$3x + 3y = 9$ → Multiply by −4. → $(+)\ -12x - 12y = -36$ Add equations.

$-6y = -12$ x is eliminated.

$\frac{-6y}{-6} = \frac{-12}{-6}$ Divide each side by −6.

$y = 2$ Simplify.

Now substitute 2 for y in either equation to find the value of x.

$3x + 3y = 9$	Second equation
$3x + 3(2) = 9$	Substitute 2 for y.
$3x + 6 = 9$	Simplify.
$3x = 3$	Subtract 6 from each side and simplify.
$\frac{3x}{3} = \frac{3}{3}$	Divide each side by 3.
$x = 1$	The solution is (1, 2).

Method 2 Eliminate y.

$4x + 2y = 8$ → Multiply by 3. → $12x + 6y = 24$

$3x + 3y = 9$ → Multiply by −2. → $(+)\ -6x - 6y = -18$ Add equations.

$6x = 6$ y is eliminated.

$\frac{6x}{6} = \frac{6}{6}$ Divide each side by 6.

$x = 1$ Simplify.

Now substitute 1 for x in either equation to find the value of y.

$3x + 3y = 9$	Second equation
$3(1) + 3y = 9$	Substitute 1 for x.
$3 + 3y = 9$	Simplify.
$3y = 6$	Subtract 3 from each side and simplify.
$\frac{3y}{3} = \frac{6}{3}$	Divide each side by 3.
$y = 2$	Simplify.

The solution is (1, 2), which matches the result obtained with Method 1.

CHECK Substitute 1 for x and 2 for y in the first equation.

$4x + 2y = 8$	Original equation
$4(1) + 2(2) \stackrel{?}{=} 8$	Substitute (1, 2) for (x, y).
$4 + 4 \stackrel{?}{=} 8$	Multiply.
$8 = 8$ ✓	Add.

Math HistoryLink

Leonardo Pisano (1170–1250) Leonardo Pisano is better known by his nickname *Fibonacci*. His book introduced the Hindu-Arabic place-valued decimal system. Systems of linear equations are studied in this work.

GuidedPractice

2A. $5x - 3y = 6$
$2x + 5y = -10$ **(0, −2)**

2B. $6a + 2b = 2$
$4a + 3b = 8$ **(−1, 4)**

Focus on Mathematical Content

Elimination Using Multiplication This method of solving a system must be used when neither x nor y can be eliminated by adding or subtracting the two equations. The Multiplication Property of Equality is used in order to add or subtract the equations to eliminate one of the variables. Multiply one or both of the equations by numbers so that a variable will be eliminated when the equations of the new system are added or subtracted.

2 Solve Real-World Problems

Sometimes it is necessary to use multiplication before elimination in real-world problem solving too.

Real-World Example 3 Solve a System of Equations

FLIGHT **A personal aircraft traveling with the wind flies 520 miles in 4 hours. On the return trip, the airplane takes 5 hours to travel the same distance. Find the speed of the airplane if the air is still.**

You are asked to find the speed of the airplane in still air.

Let a = the rate of the airplane if the air is still.
Let w = the rate of the wind.

	r	t	d	$r \cdot t = d$
With the Wind	$a + w$	4	520	$(a + w)4 = 520$
Against the Wind	$a - w$	5	520	$(a - w)5 = 520$

So, our two equations are $4a + 4w = 520$ and $5a - 5w = 520$.

$4a + 4w = 520$ → Multiply by 5. → $20a + 20w = 2600$
$5a - 5w = 520$ → Multiply by 4. → $(+)\ 20a - 20w = 2080$

$40a = 4680$ — w is eliminated.

$\frac{40a}{40} = \frac{4680}{40}$ — Divide each side by 40.

$a = 117$ — Simplify.

The rate of the airplane in still air is 117 miles per hour.

Guided Practice $3\frac{1}{3}$ mi/h

3. **CANOEING** A canoeist travels 4 miles downstream in 1 hour. The return trip takes the canoeist 1.5 hours. Find the rate of the boat in still water.

Check Your Understanding

= Step-by-Step Solutions begin on page R13.

Examples 1–2 **Use elimination to solve each system of equations.**

1. $2x - y = 4$
$7x + 3y = 27$ **(3, 2)**

2. $2x + 7y = 1$
$x + 5y = 2$ **(−3, 1)**

3. $4x + 2y = -14$
$5x + 3y = -17$ **(−4, 1)**

4. $9a - 2b = -8$
$-7a + 3b = 12$ **(0, 4)**

Example 3

5. **SENSE-MAKING** A kayaking group with a guide travels 16 miles downstream, stops for a meal, and then travels 16 miles upstream. The speed of the current remains constant throughout the trip. Find the speed of the kayak in still water. **6 mph**

6. **PODCASTS** Steve subscribed to 10 podcasts for a total of 340 minutes. He used his two favorite tags, Hobbies and Recreation and Soliloquies. Each of the Hobbies and Recreation episodes lasted about 32 minutes. Each Soliloquies episode lasted 42 minutes. To how many of each tag did Steve subscribe?
8 Hobbies and Recreation, 2 Soliloquies

Differentiated Instruction AL ELL

If students have trouble solving Exercises 1–4,

Then suggest that they form groups of two or three to discuss the best strategy for solving each problem and then work through the solution together. Encourage all students to participate and remind students to check their solutions.

2 Solve Real-World Problems

Example 3 shows how to write and solve a system of equations by elimination for a real-world situation.

Additional Example

3 **TRANSPORTATION** A fishing boat travels 10 miles downstream in 30 minutes. The return trip takes the boat 40 minutes. Find the rate in miles per hour of the boat in still water. 17.5 mi/h

WatchOut!

Common Errors When using elimination with multiplication, many students forget to multiply each term on both sides of the equation by the number. Suggest that they include an extra step in the solutions that shows the multiplication:

$$3x + 2y = 7$$
$$2x - 7y = -12$$
$$\Downarrow$$
$$2(3x + 2y) = 2(7)$$
$$-3(2x - 7y) = -3(-12)$$

3 Practice

Formative Assessment

Use Exercises 1–6 to check for understanding.

Use the chart at the bottom of the next page to customize assignments for your students.

Teaching the Process Standards

Sense-Making Mathematically proficient students consider analogous problems. In Exercise 5, encourage students to reference Example 3 as they write and solve the system of equations.

Teaching the Process Standards

Modeling Mathematically proficient students apply the mathematics they know to solve problems arising in the workplace. In Exercise 25, encourage students to think about why this would be an important issue in a workplace setting.

Critique Mathematically proficient students critique the reasoning of others. In Exercise 30, tell students to look at the original system of equations before they evaluate Jason's and Daniela's work. Did they both find a way to eliminate one variable completely?

Additional Answers

26b.

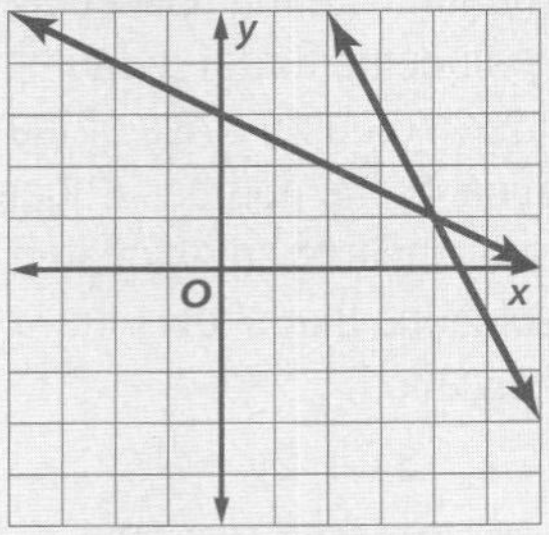

26c.

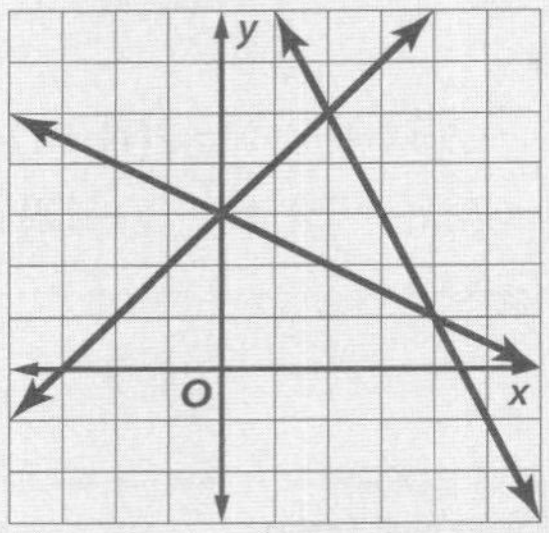

32. $a = -2$, $b = 22$; Substitute 3 for x and a for y in the first equation and then solve for a to get $a = -2$. Then substitute 3 for x and -2 for y in the second equation and simplify to get $b = 22$.

33. Sample answer: It is more helpful to use substitution when one of the variables has a coefficient of 1 or if a coefficient can be reduced to 1 without turning other coefficients into fractions. Otherwise, elimination is more helpful because it will avoid the use of fractions when solving the system.

Practice and Problem Solving

Extra Practice is on page R6.

Examples 1–2 Use elimination to solve each system of equations.

7. $x + y = 2$
$-3x + 4y = 15$ **(−1, 3)**

8. $x - y = -8$
$7x + 5y = 16$ **(−2, 6)**

9. $x + 5y = 17$
$-4x + 3y = 24$ **(−3, 4)**

10. $6x + y = -39$
$3x + 2y = -15$ **(−7, 3)**

11. $2x + 5y = 11$
$4x + 3y = 1$ **(−2, 3)**

12. $3x - 3y = -6$
$-5x + 6y = 12$ **(0, 2)**

13. $3x + 4y = 29$
$6x + 5y = 43$ **(3, 5)**

14. $8x + 3y = 4$
$-7x + 5y = -34$ **(2, −4)**

15. $8x + 3y = -7$
$7x + 2y = -3$ **(1, −5)**

16. $4x + 7y = -80$
$3x + 5y = -58$ **(−6, −8)**

17. $12x - 3y = -3$
$6x + y = 1$ **(0, 1)**

18. $-4x + 2y = 0$
$10x + 3y = 8$ $\left(\frac{1}{2}, 1\right)$

Example 3

19. **NUMBER THEORY** Seven times a number plus three times another number equals negative one. The sum of the two numbers is negative three. What are the numbers? **2, −5**

20. **FOOTBALL** A field goal is 3 points and the extra point after a touchdown is 1 point. In a recent post-season, Adam Vinatieri of the Indianapolis Colts made a total of 21 field goals and extra point kicks for 49 points. Find the number of field goals and extra points that he made. **14 field goals; 7 extra points**

B Use elimination to solve each system of equations.

21. $2.2x + 3y = 15.25$
$4.6x + 2.1y = 18.325$ **(2.5, 3.25)**

22. $-0.4x + 0.25y = -2.175$
$2x + y = 7.5$ **(4.5, −1.5)**

23. $\frac{1}{4}x + 4y = 2\frac{3}{4}$
$3x + \frac{1}{2}y = 9\frac{1}{4}$ $\left(3, \frac{1}{2}\right)$

24. $\frac{2}{5}x + 6y = 24\frac{1}{5}$
$3x + \frac{1}{2}y = 3\frac{1}{2}$ $\left(\frac{1}{2}, 4\right)$

25. **MODELING** A staffing agency for in-home nurses and support staff places necessary personnel at locations on a daily basis. Each placed nurse works 240 minutes per day at a daily rate of \$90. Each support staff employee works 360 minutes per day at a daily rate of \$120.

a. On a given day, 3000 total minutes are worked by the nurses and support staff that were placed. Write an equation that represents this relationship. **$240n + 360s = 3000$**

b. On the same day, earnings for placed nurses and support staff totaled \$1050. Write an equation that represents this relationship. **$90n + 120s = 1050$**

c. Solve the system of equations, and interpret the solution in the context of the situation. **(5, 5); 5 nurses and 5 support staff employees were placed.**

26. **GEOMETRY** The graphs of $x + 2y = 6$ and $2x + y = 9$ contain two of the sides of a triangle. A vertex of the triangle is at the intersection of the graphs.

a. What are the coordinates of the vertex? **(4, 1)**

b. Draw the graph of the two lines. Identify the vertex of the triangle. **See margin.**

c. The line that forms the third side of the triangle is the line $x - y = -3$. Draw this line on the previous graph. **See margin.**

d. Name the other two vertices of the triangle. **(0, 3); (2, 5)**

Differentiated Homework Options

Level	Assignment	Two-Day Option	
AL Basic	7–20, 29–31, 33–54	7–19 odd, 34–37	8–20 even, 29–31, 33, 38–54
OL Core	7–25 odd, 26–31, 33–54	7–20, 34–37	21–31, 33, 38–54
BL Advanced	21–48, (optional: 49–54)		

27 **ENTERTAINMENT** At an entertainment center, two groups of people bought batting tokens and miniature golf games, as shown in the table.

27a. Let x = the cost of a batting token and let y = the cost of a miniature golf game; $16x + 3y = 30$ and $22x + 5y = 43$.

27b. (1.5, 2); A batting token costs $1.50 and a game of miniature golf costs $2.00.

Group	Number of Batting Tokens	Number of Miniature Golf Games	Total Cost
A	16	3	$30
B	22	5	$43

a. Define the variables, and write a system of linear equations from this situation.

b. Solve the system of equations, and explain what the solution represents.

28. **TESTS** Mrs. Henderson discovered that she had accidentally reversed the digits of a test score and did not give a student 36 points. Mrs. Henderson told the student that the sum of the digits was 14 and agreed to give the student his correct score plus extra credit if he could determine his actual score. What was his correct score? **95**

H.O.T. Problems Use Higher-Order Thinking Skills

29. **REASONING** Explain how you could recognize a system of linear equations with infinitely many solutions. **One of the equations will be a multiple of the other.**

30. **CRITIQUE** Jason and Daniela are solving a system of equations. Is either of them correct? Explain your reasoning.

Jason

$2r + 7t = 11$
$r - 9t = -7$

$2r + 7t = 11$
$(-)\ 2r - 18t = -14$
$25t = 25$
$t = 1$

$2r + 7t = 11$
$2r + 7(1) = 11$
$2r + 7 = 11$
$2r = 4$
$\frac{2r}{2} = \frac{4}{2}$
$r = 2$

The solution is (2, 1).

Daniela

$2r + 7t = 11$
$(-)\ r - 9t = -7$
$r = 18$

$2r + 7t = 11$
$2(18) + 7t = 11$
$36 + 7t = 11$
$7t = -25$
$\frac{7t}{7} = -\frac{25}{7}$
$t = -3.6$

The solution is (18, -3.6).

30. Jason; in order to eliminate the r-terms, you can multiply the second equation by 2 and then subtract, or multiply the equation by −2 and then add. Daniela did not subtract the equations correctly.

31. Sample answer: $2x + 3y = 6$, $4x + 9y = 5$

31. **OPEN ENDED** Write a system of equations that can be solved by multiplying one equation by −3 and then adding the two equations together.

32. **CHALLENGE** The solution of the system $4x + 5y = 2$ and $6x - 2y = b$ is $(3, a)$. Find the values of a and b. Discuss the steps that you used. **See margin.**

33. **WRITING IN MATH** Why is substitution sometimes more helpful than elimination, and vice versa? **See margin.**

Study Guide and Intervention

AL OL ELL

NAME ______ DATE ______ PERIOD ______

6-4 Study Guide and Intervention

Elimination Using Multiplication

Elimination Using Multiplication Some systems of equations cannot be solved simply by adding or subtracting the equations. In such cases, one or both equations must first be multiplied by a number before the system can be solved by elimination.

Example 1 Use elimination to solve the system of equations.
$x + 10y = 3$
$4x + 5y = 5$

If you multiply the second equation by −2, you can eliminate the y terms.

$x + 10y = 3$
$(+)\ -8x - 10y = -10$
$-7x = -7$
$\frac{-7x}{-7} = \frac{-7}{-7}$
$x = 1$

Substitute 1 for x in either equation.

$1 + 10y = 3$
$1 + 10y - 1 = 3 - 1$
$10y = 2$
$\frac{10y}{10} = \frac{2}{10}$
$y = \frac{1}{5}$

The solution is $\left(1, \frac{1}{5}\right)$.

Example 2 Use elimination to solve the system of equations.
$3x - 2y = -7$
$2x - 5y = 10$

If you multiply the first equation by 2 and the second equation by −3, you can eliminate the x terms.

$6x - 4y = -14$
$(+)\ -6x + 15y = -30$
$11y = -44$
$\frac{11y}{11} = -\frac{44}{11}$
$y = -4$

Substitute −4 for y in either equation.

$3x - 2(-4) = -7$
$3x + 8 = -7$
$3x + 8 - 8 = -7 - 8$
$3x = -15$
$\frac{3x}{3} = -\frac{15}{3}$
$x = -5$

The solution is (−5, −4).

Exercises

Use elimination to solve each system of equations.

1. $2x + 3y = 6$, $x + 2y = 5$
2. $2m + 3n = 4$, $-m + 2n = 5$
3. $3a - b = 2$, $a + 2b = 3$
4. $4x + 5y = 6$, $6x - 7y = -20$
5. $4x - 3y = 22$, $2x - y = 10$
6. $3x - 4y = -4$, $x + 3y = -10$
7. $4x - y = 9$, $5x + 2y = 8$
8. $4a - 3b = -8$, $2a + 2b = 3$
9. $2x + 2y = 5$, $4x - 4y = 10$
10. $6x - 4y = -8$, $4x + 2y = -3$
11. $4x + 2y = -5$, $-2x - 4y = 1$
12. $2x + y = 3.5$, $-x + 2y = 2.5$

13. **GARDENING** The length of Sally's garden is 4 meters greater than 3 times the width. The perimeter of her garden is 72 meters. What are the dimensions of Sally's garden?

Practice

AL OL BL ELL

NAME ______ DATE ______ PERIOD ______

6-4 Practice

Elimination Using Multiplication

Use elimination to solve each system of equations.

1. $2x - y = -1$, $3x - 2y = 1$
2. $5x - 2y = -10$, $3x + 6y = 66$
3. $7x + 4y = -4$, $5x + 8y = 28$
4. $2x - 4y = -22$, $3x + 3y = 30$
5. $3x + 2y = -9$, $5x - 3y = 4$
6. $4x - 2y = 32$, $-3x - 5y = -11$
7. $3x + 4y = 27$, $5x - 3y = 16$
8. $0.5x + 0.5y = -2$, $x - 0.25y = 6$
9. $2x - \frac{3}{4}y = -7$, $x + \frac{1}{2}y = 0$
10. $6x - 3y = 21$, $2x + 2y = 22$
11. $3x + 2y = 11$, $2x + 6y = -2$
12. $-3x + 2y = -15$, $2x - 4y = 26$

13. Eight times a number plus five times another number is −13. The sum of the two numbers is 1. What are the numbers?

14. Two times a number plus three times another number equals 4. Three times the first number plus four times the other number is 7. Find the numbers.

15. **FINANCE** Gunther invested $10,000 in two mutual funds. One of the funds rose 6% in one year, and the other rose 9% in one year. If Gunther's investment rose a total of $684 in one year, how much did he invest in each mutual fund?

16. **CANOEING** Laura and Brent paddled a canoe 6 miles upstream in four hours. The return trip took three hours. Find the rate at which Laura and Brent paddled the canoe in still water.

17. **NUMBER THEORY** The sum of the digits of a two-digit number is 11. If the digits are reversed, the new number is 45 more than the original number. Find the number.

Lesson 6-4

Word Problem Practice

AL OL BL ELL

NAME ______ DATE ______ PERIOD ______

6-4 Word Problem Practice

Elimination Using Multiplication

1. **SOCCER** Suppose a youth soccer field has a perimeter of 320 yards and its length measures 40 yards more than its width. Ms. Hughey asks her players to determine the length and width of their field. She gives them the following system of equations to represent the situation. Use elimination to solve the system to find the length and width of the field.

$2L + 2W = 320$
$L - W = 40$

2. **SPORTS** The Fan Cost Index (FCI) tracks the average costs for attending sporting events, including tickets, drinks, food, parking, programs, and souvenirs. According to the FCI, a family of four would spend a total of $592.30 to attend two Major League Baseball (MLB) games and one National Basketball Association (NBA) game. The family would spend $691.31 to attend one MLB and two NBA games. Write and solve a system of equations to find the family's costs for each kind of game according to the FCI.

3. **ART** Mr. Santos, the curator of the children's museum, recently made two purchases of clay and wood for a visiting artist to sculpt. Use the table to find the cost of each product per kilogram.

Clay (kg)	Wood (kg)	Total Cost
5	4	$35.50
3.5	6	$50.45

4. **TRAVEL** Antonio flies from Houston to Philadelphia, a distance of about 1340 miles. His plane travels with the wind and takes 2 hours and 20 minutes. At the same time, Paul is on a plane from Philadelphia to Houston. Since his plane is heading against the wind, Paul's flight takes 2 hours and 50 minutes. What was the speed of the wind in miles per hour?

5. **BUSINESS** Suppose you start a business assembling and selling motorized scooters. It costs you $1500 for tools and equipment to get started, and the materials cost $200 for each scooter. Your scooters sell for $300 each.

a. Write and solve a system of equations representing the total costs and revenue of your business.

b. Describe what the solution means in terms of the situation.

c. Give an example of a reasonable number of scooters you could assemble and sell in order to make a profit, and find the profit you would make for that number of scooters.

Enrichment

OL BL

NAME ______ DATE ______ PERIOD ______

6-4 Enrichment

George Washington Carver and Percy Julian

In 1990, George Washington Carver and Percy Julian became the first African Americans elected to the National Inventors Hall of Fame. Carver (1864–1943) was an agricultural scientist known worldwide for developing hundreds of uses for the peanut and the sweet potato. His work revitalized the economy of the southern United States because it was no longer dependent solely upon cotton. Julian (1898–1975) was a research chemist who became famous for inventing a method of making a synthetic cortisone from soybeans. His discovery has had many medical applications, particularly in the treatment of arthritis.

There are dozens of other African American inventors whose accomplishments are not as well known. Their inventions range from common household items like the ironing board to complex devices that have revolutionized manufacturing. The exercises that follow will help you identify just a few of these inventors and their inventions.

Match the inventors with their inventions by matching each system with its solution. (Not all the solutions will be used.)

1. Sara Boone $x + y = 2$, $x - y = 10$ A. (1, 4) automatic traffic signal

2. Sarah Goode B. (4, −2)

4 Assess

Crystal Ball Have students write how they think what they learned today about using multiplication before elimination to solve a system of equations will help them in the next lesson on applying systems of linear equations.

Formative Assessment

Check for student understanding of the concepts in Lessons 6-3 and 6-4.

Quiz 2, p. 59

Follow-up

Students have explored solving systems of linear equations by graphing and using algebra.

Ask:

- What are the benefits of having different strategies for solving systems of equations? Sample answer: You can use the strategy that is most efficient. For example, if an estimate of the solution is sufficient, graphing can be used. You can use algebraic methods to find exact solutions.

Additional Answers

45. $m \leq 13$ and $m \geq -3$

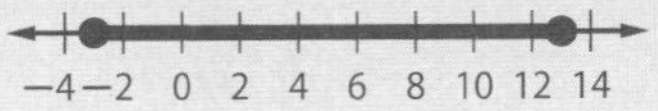

46. $q < -6$ and $q > -16$

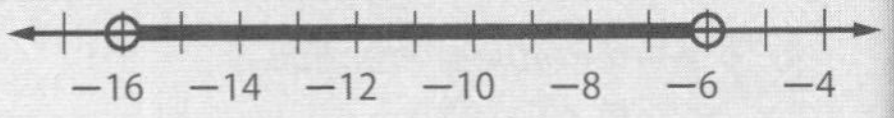

47. $w > 1$ or $w < -10$

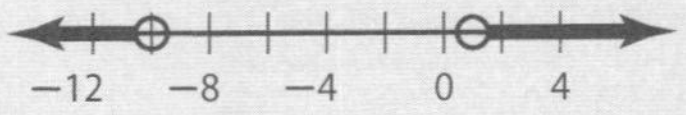

48. $r \geq 4$ or $r \leq -5$

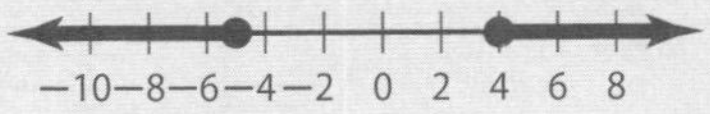

Standardized Test Practice

34. What is the solution of this system of equations? **C**

$2x - 3y = -9$
$-x + 3y = 6$

A (3, 3)   C (−3, 1)
B (−3, 3)   D (1, −3)

35. A buffet has one price for adults and another for children. The Taylor family has two adults and three children, and their bill was \$40.50. The Wong family has three adults and one child. Their bill was \$38. Which system of equations could be used to determine the price for an adult and for a child? **G**

F $x + y = 40.50$, $x + y = 38$
H $2x + 3y = 40.50$, $x + 3y = 38$
G $2x + 3y = 40.50$, $3x + y = 38$
J $2x + 2y = 40.50$, $3x + y = 38$

36. SHORT RESPONSE A customer at the paint store has ordered 3 gallons of ivy green paint. Melissa mixes the paint in a ratio of 3 parts blue to one part yellow. How many quarts of blue paint does she use? **9 qt**

37. PROBABILITY The table shows the results of a number cube being rolled. What is the experimental probability of rolling a 3? **D**

Outcome	Frequency
1	4
2	8
3	2
4	0
5	5
6	1

A $\frac{2}{3}$ B $\frac{1}{3}$ C 0.2   D 0.1

Spiral Review

Use elimination to solve each system of equations. (Lesson 6-3)

38. $f + g = -3$, $f - g = 1$ **(−1, −2)**

39. $6g + h = -7$, $6g + 3h = -9$ **(−1, −1)**

40. $5j + 3k = -9$, $3j + 3k = -3$ **(−3, 2)**

41. $2x - 4z = 6$, $x - 4z = -3$ **(9, 3)**

42. $-5c - 3v = 9$, $5c + 2v = -6$ **(0, −3)**

43. $4b - 6n = -36$, $3b - 6n = -36$ **(0, 6)**

44. JOBS Brandy and Adriana work at an after-school child care center. Together they cared for 32 children this week. Brandy cared for 0.6 times as many children as Adriana. How many children did each girl care for? (Lesson 6-2) **Brandy: 12; Adriana: 20**

Solve each inequality. Then graph the solution set. (Lesson 5-5) **45–48. See margin.**

45. $|m - 5| \leq 8$ **46.** $|q + 11| < 5$ **47.** $|2w + 9| > 11$ **48.** $|2r + 1| \geq 9$

Skills Review

Translate each sentence into a formula.

49. The area A of a triangle equals one half times the base b times the height h. $A = \frac{1}{2}bh$

50. The circumference C of a circle equals the product of 2, π, and the radius r. $C = 2\pi r$

51. The volume V of a rectangular box is the length ℓ times the width w multiplied by the height h. $V = \ell wh$

52. The volume of a cylinder V is the same as the product of π and the radius r to the second power multiplied by the height h. $V = \pi r^2 h$

53. The area of a circle A equals the product of π and the radius r squared. $A = \pi r^2$

54. Acceleration A equals the increase in speed s divided by time t in seconds. $A = \frac{s}{t}$

Differentiated Instruction OL BL

Extension Have students solve this system or a similar system using elimination.

$\frac{1}{2}x - \frac{2}{3}y = \frac{7}{3}$

$\frac{3}{2}x + 2y = -25$

(−6, −8)

CHAPTER 6 Mid-Chapter Quiz
Lessons 6-1 through 6-4

Use the graph to determine whether each system is *consistent* or *inconsistent* and if it is *independent* or dependent. (Lesson 6-1)

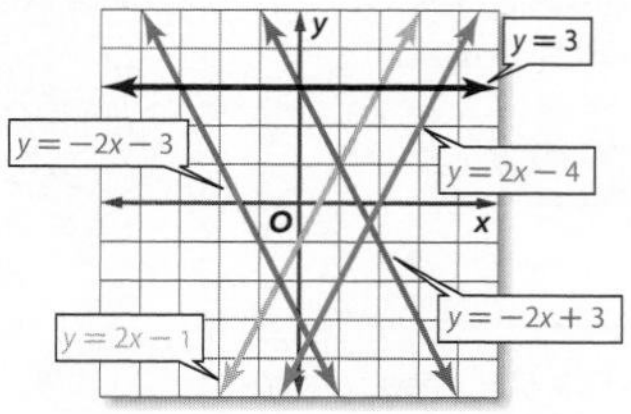

1. $y = 2x - 1$
   $y = -2x + 3$
   consistent, independent

2. $y = -2x + 3$
   $y = -2x - 3$
   inconsistent

Graph each system and determine the number of solutions that it has. If it has one solution, name it. (Lesson 6-1)

3. $y = 2x - 3$ (7, 11)
   $y = x + 4$

4. $x + y = 6$ (5, 1)
   $x - y = 4$

5. $x + y = 8$ infinitely many solutions
   $3x + 3y = 24$

6. $x - 4y = -6$ (−10, −1)
   $y = -1$

7. $3x + 2y = 12$ no solutions
   $3x + 2y = 6$

8. $2x + y = -4$ (−6, 8)
   $5x + 3y = -6$

3–8. See Ch. 6 Answer Appendix for graphs.

Use substitution to solve each system of equations. (Lesson 6-2)

9. $y = x + 4$ (4, 8)
   $2x + y = 16$

10. $y = -2x - 3$ (−12, 21)
    $x + y = 9$

11. $x + y = 6$ (7, −1)
    $x - y = 8$

12. $y = -4x$ (3, −12)
    $6x - y = 30$

13. **FOOD** The cost of two meals at a restaurant is shown in the table below. (Lesson 6-2)

Meal	Total Cost
3 tacos, 2 burritos	\$7.40
4 tacos, 1 burrito	\$6.45

a. Define variables to represent the cost of a taco and the cost of a burrito. a–c. See margin.

b. Write a system of equations to find the cost of a single taco and a single burrito.

c. Solve the systems of equations, and explain what the solution means.

d. How much would a customer pay for 2 tacos and 2 burritos? \$6.30

14. **AMUSEMENT PARKS** The cost of two groups going to an amusement park is shown in the table. (Lesson 6-3) a–c. See Ch. 6 Answer Appendix.

Group	Total Cost
4 adults, 2 children	\$184
4 adults, 3 children	\$200

a. Define variables to represent the cost of an adult ticket and the cost of a child ticket.

b. Write a system of equations to find the cost of an adult ticket and a child ticket.

c. Solve the system of equations, and explain what the solution means.

d. How much will a group of 3 adults and 5 children be charged for admission? \$194

15. **MULTIPLE CHOICE** Angelina spent \$16 for 12 pieces of candy to take to a meeting. Each chocolate bar costs \$2, and each lollipop costs \$1. Determine how many of each she bought. (Lesson 6-3) B

A 6 chocolate bars, 6 lollipops

B 4 chocolate bars, 8 lollipops

C 7 chocolate bars, 5 lollipops

D 3 chocolate bars, 9 lollipops

Use elimination to solve each system of equations. (Lessons 6-3 and 6-4)

16. $x + y = 9$ (3, 6)
    $x - y = -3$

17. $x + 3y = 11$ (5, 2)
    $x + 7y = 19$

18. $9x - 24y = -6$ (2, 1)
    $3x + 4y = 10$

19. $-5x + 2y = -11$ (3, 2)
    $5x - 7y = 1$

20. **MULTIPLE CHOICE** The Blue Mountain High School Drama Club is selling tickets to their spring musical. Adult tickets are \$4 and student tickets are \$1. A total of 285 tickets are sold for \$765. How many of each type of ticket are sold? (Lesson 6-4) J

F 145 adult, 140 student

G 120 adult, 165 student

H 180 adult, 105 student

J 160 adult, 125 student

Formative Assessment

Use the Mid-Chapter Quiz to assess students' progress in the first half of the chapter.

For problems answered incorrectly, have students review the lessons indicated in parentheses.

Summative Assessment

Mid-Chapter Test, p. 61

McGraw-Hill eAssessment Customize and create multiple versions of your Mid-Chapter Quiz and their answer keys.

FOLDABLES StudyOrganizer

Dinah Zike's Foldables®

Before students complete the Mid-Chapter Quiz, encourage them to review the information for Lessons 6-1 through 6-4 in their Foldables.

Additional Answers

13a. Let $t =$ the cost of a taco and $b =$ the cost of a burrito.

13b. $3t + 2b = 7.4$
$4t + b = 6.45$

13c. (1.10, 2.05); The cost of a single taco is \$1.10, and the cost of a single burrito is \$2.05

InterventionPlanner

TIER 1 On Level OL

If students miss about 25% of the exercises or less,

Then choose a resource:

SE Lessons 6-1, 6-2, 6-3, and 6-4

Skills Practice, pp. 7, 14, 20, and 26

TE Chapter Project

connectED.mcgraw-hill.com Self-Check Quiz

TIER 2 Strategic Intervention AL approaching grade level

If students miss about 50% of the exercises,

Then choose a resource:

Study Guide and Intervention, Chapter 6, pp. 5, 12, 18, 24

Quick Review Math Handbook

connectED.mcgraw-hill.com Extra Examples, Personal Tutor, Homework Help

TIER 3 Intensive Intervention 2 or more grades below level

If students miss about 75% of the exercises,

Then use *Math Triumphs, Alg. 1*

connectED.mcgraw-hill.com Extra Examples, Personal Tutor, Homework Help, Review Vocabulary

1 Focus

VerticalAlignment

Before Lesson 6-5 Solve systems of equations by using substitution and elimination.

Lesson 6-5 Determine the best method for solving systems of equations.
Apply systems of equations.

After Lesson 6-5 Graph and solve linear inequalities.

2 Teach

Scaffolding Questions

Have students read the **Why?** section of the lesson.

Ask:

- What do the variables *x* and *y* represent in the problem? The length of the official track is represented by *x* and the length of the short track by *y* in meters.
- What method could you use to solve the system? substitution or elimination

LESSON 6-5 Applying Systems of Linear Equations

Then

- You solved systems of equations by using substitution and elimination.

Now

1. Determine the best method for solving systems of equations.
2. Apply systems of equations.

Why?

- In speed skating, competitors race two at a time on a double track. Indoor speed skating rinks have two track sizes for race events: an official track and a short track.

Speed Skating Tracks	
official track	x
short track	y

The total length of the two tracks is 511 meters. The official track is 44 meters less than four times the short track. The total length is represented by $x + y = 511$. The length of the official track is represented by $x = 4y - 44$.

You can solve the system of equations to find the length of each track.

Content Standards
AI.SEI.3

Process Standards
PS.2, PS.4

1 Determine the Best Method You have learned five methods for solving systems of linear equations. The table summarizes the methods and the types of systems for which each method works best.

ConceptSummary Solving Systems of Equations

Method	The Best Time to Use
Graphing	To estimate solutions, since graphing usually does not give an exact solution.
Substitution	If one of the variables in either equation has a coefficient of 1 or -1.
Elimination Using Addition	If one of the variables has opposite coefficients in the two equations.
Elimination Using Subtraction	If one of the variables has the same coefficient in the two equations.
Elimination Using Multiplication	If none of the coefficients are 1 or -1 and neither of the variables can be eliminated by simply adding or subtracting the equations.

Substitution and elimination are algebraic methods for solving systems of equations. An algebraic method is best for an exact solution. Graphing, with or without technology, is a good way to estimate a solution.

A system of equations can be solved using each method. To determine the best approach, analyze the coefficients of each term in each equation.

Lesson 6-5 Resources

Resource	Approaching Level AL	On Level OL	Beyond Level BL	English Learners ELL
Teacher Edition	▪ Differentiated Instruction, p. 366	▪ Differentiated Instruction, pp. 366, 369	▪ Differentiated Instruction, p. 369	▪ Differentiated Instruction, p. 366
Chapter Resource Masters	▪ Study Guide and Intervention, pp. 30–31 ▪ Skills Practice, p. 32 ▪ Practice, p. 33 ▪ Word Problem Practice, p. 34	▪ Study Guide and Intervention, pp. 30–31 ▪ Skills Practice, p. 32 ▪ Practice, p. 33 ▪ Word Problem Practice, p. 34 ▪ Enrichment, p. 35	▪ Practice, p. 33 ▪ Word Problem Practice, p. 34 ▪ Enrichment, p. 35	▪ Study Guide and Intervention, pp. 30–31 ▪ Skills Practice, p. 32 ▪ Practice, p. 33 ▪ Word Problem Practice, p. 34
Other	▪ 5-Minute Check 6-5 ▪ Study Notebook	▪ 5-Minute Check 6-5 ▪ Study Notebook	▪ 5-Minute Check 6-5 ▪ Study Notebook	▪ 5-Minute Check 6-5 ▪ Study Notebook

Example 1 Choose the Best Method

Determine the best method to solve the system of equations. Then solve the system.

$4x - 4y = 8$
$-8x + y = 19$

Understand To determine the best method to solve the system of equations, look closely at the coefficients of each term.

Plan Neither the coefficients of x nor y are the same or additive inverses, so you cannot add or subtract to eliminate a variable. Since the coefficient of y in the second equation is 1, you can use substitution.

Solve First, solve the second equation for y.

$-8x + y = 19$	Second equation
$-8x + y + 8x = 19 + 8x$	Add $8x$ to each side.
$y = 19 + 8x$	Simplify.

Next, substitute $19 + 8x$ for y in the first equation.

$4x - 4y = 8$	First equation
$4x - 4(19 + 8x) = 8$	Substitution
$4x - 76 - 32x = 8$	Distributive Property
$-28x - 76 = 8$	Simplify.
$-28x - 76 + 76 = 8 + 76$	Add 76 to each side.
$-28x = 84$	Simplify.
$\frac{-28x}{-28} = \frac{84}{-28}$	Divide each side by -28.
$x = -3$	Simplify.

Last, substitute -3 for x in the second equation.

$-8x + y = 19$	Second equation
$-8(-3) + y = 19$	$x = -3$
$y = -5$	Simplify.

The solution of the system of equations is $(-3, -5)$.

Check Use a graphing calculator to check your solution. If your algebraic solution is correct, then the graphs will intersect at $(-3, -5)$.

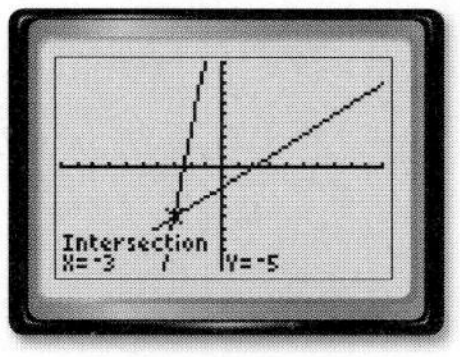

$[-10, 10]$ scl: 1 $[-10, 10]$ scl: 1

GuidedPractice

1A. $5x + 7y = 2$, $-2x + 7y = 9$ **elimination (−); (−1, 1)**

1B. $3x - 4y = -10$, $5x + 8y = -2$ **elimination (×); (−2, 1)**

1C. $x - y = 9$, $7x + y = 7$ **elimination (+); (2, −7)**

1D. $5x - y = 17$, $3x + 2y = 5$ **substitution; (3, −2)**

StudyTip

Reasoning The system of equations in Example 1 can also be solved by using elimination with multiplication. You can multiply the first equation by 2 and then add to eliminate the x-term.

1 Determine the Best Method

Example 1 shows how to determine the best method to use in solving a system of equations.

Formative Assessment

Use the Guided Practice exercises after each example to determine students' understanding of concepts.

Additional Example

1 Determine the best method to solve the system of equations. Then solve the system.

$2x + 3y = 23$
$4x + 2y = 34$

The best method is elimination using multiplication. The solution is (7, 3).

Additional Examples also in Interactive Classroom PowerPoint® Presentations

IWB Interactive White Board READY

Tips for New Teachers

Reasoning Encourage students to take time to plan a problem-solving strategy before starting calculations. Advise students that taking this time may provide them with insight into the best strategy.

Teaching the Process Standards

Reasoning Mathematically proficient knowing and flexibly using different properties of operations and objects. Encourage students to think of various ways to solve a system of equations before choosing the one that they think is best.

Focus on Mathematical Content

Best Method for Solving a System of Equations Systems of equations can be solved by graphing, substitution, or elimination. Graphing can be used to approximate a solution and to provide a visual model of the problem. To find an exact solution, substitution or elimination should be used. Use substitution if one of the variables has a 1 or −1 for its coefficient. Use elimination with addition if the coefficients of one of the variables are opposites. Use elimination with subtraction if the coefficients of one of the variables are the same. Use elimination with multiplication in all other situations.

2 Apply Systems of Linear Equations

Example 2 shows how to solve a real-world problem by writing and solving a system of equations.

Additional Example

2 **CAR RENTAL** Ace Car Rental rents a car for $45 and $0.25 per mile. Star Car Rental rents a car for $35 and $0.30 per mile. How many miles would a driver need to drive before the cost of renting a car at Ace Car Rental and renting a car at Star Car Rental were the same?
Let x = number of miles and y = cost of renting car.
$y = 45 + 0.25x$
$y = 35 + 0.30x$
The solution is (200, 95). This means that when the car has been driven 200 miles, the cost of renting a car will be the same ($95) at both rental companies.

Teach with Tech

Digital Camera Have students find the capacity of the memory card in their camera, and the file size of photos of different resolutions. Use this information to create an in class example. For example, if the camera has 64MB of memory and photos can be either 2MB or 3MB, have students find the number of each type of photo that can be taken to have a total of 30 photos and fill the memory card.

The Math Forum

Have your students refer to the Math Forum's Ask Dr. Math to learn more about different ways to solve systems of linear equations. They can start their search at connectED.mcgraw-hill.com.

Real-WorldLink

Four species of penguins are on the endangered species list. The colonies of penguins that live closest to human inhabitants are the most at risk for extinction.

Source: PBS

2 Apply Systems of Linear Equations

When applying systems of linear equations to problems, it is important to analyze each solution in the context of the situation.

Real-World Example 2 Apply Systems of Linear Equations

PENGUINS Of the 17 species of penguins in the world, the largest species is the emperor penguin. One of the smallest is the Galapagos penguin. The total height of the two penguins is 169 centimeters. The emperor penguin is 22 centimeters more than twice the height of the Galapagos penguin. Find the height of each penguin.

The total height of the two species can be represented by $p + g = 169$, where p represents the height of the emperor penguin and g the height of the Galapagos penguin. Next write an equation to represent the height of the emperor penguin.

Words	The emperor penguin	is	22 centimeters	more than	twice the height of the Galapagos penguin.
Variables	Let p = the height of the emperor penguin and g = the height of the Galapagos penguin.				
Equation	p	=	22	+	$2g$

First rewrite the second equation.

$p = 22 + 2g$ — Second equation
$p - 2g = 22$ — Subtract $2g$ from each side.

You can use elimination by subtraction to solve this system of equations.

$p + g = 169$ — First equation
$(-)\ p - 2g = 22$ — Subtract the second equation.
$3g = 147$ — Eliminate p.
$\frac{3g}{3} = \frac{147}{3}$ — Divide each side by 3.
$g = 49$ — Simplify.

Next substitute 49 for g in one of the equations.

$p = 22 + 2g$ — Second equation
$= 22 + 2(49)$ — $g = 49$
$= 120$ — Simplify.

The height of the emperor penguin is 120 centimeters, and the height of the Galapagos penguin is 49 centimeters.

Does the solution make sense in the context of the problem?

Check by verifying the given information. The penguins' heights added together would be 120 + 49 or 169 centimeters and 22 + 2(49) is 120 centimeters.

GuidedPractice

2. **VOLUNTEERING** Jared has volunteered 50 hours and plans to volunteer 3 hours in each coming week. Clementine is a new volunteer who plans to volunteer 5 hours each week. Write and solve a system of equations to find how long it will be before they will have volunteered the same number of hours.
$y = 50 + 3x$, $y = 5x$; 25 wk

DifferentiatedInstruction AL OL ELL

If students have trouble writing the necessary equations for a system in a real-world situation,

Then give them these steps to help them explore, plan, solve, and check.

- Determine the question.
- Describe the variables used for the unknowns.
- Translate the conditions in the problem into two equations.
- Solve the system by the best method.
- Analyze the solution in the context of the situation.

Check Your Understanding

= Step-by-Step Solutions begin on page R13.

Example 1 Determine the best method to solve each system of equations. Then solve the system.

1. $2x + 3y = -11$
$-8x - 5y = 9$
elim (×); (2, −5)

2. $3x + 4y = 11$
$2x + y = -1$
subst.; (−3, 5)

3. $3x - 4y = -5$
$-3x + 2y = 3$
elim (+); $\left(-\frac{1}{3}, 1\right)$

4. $3x + 7y = 4$
$5x - 7y = -12$
elim (+); (−1, 1)

Example 2 **5. SHOPPING** At a sale, Salazar bought 4 T-shirts and 3 pairs of jeans for \$181. At the same store, Jenna bought 1 T-shirt and 2 pairs of jeans for \$94. The T-shirts were all the same price, and the jeans were all the same price.

a. Write a system of equations that can be used to represent this situation. See margin.

b. Determine the best method to solve the system of equations. substitution

c. Solve the system. Each T-shirt cost \$16 and each pair of jeans cost \$39.

Practice and Problem Solving

Extra Practice is on page R6.

Example 1 Determine the best method to solve each system of equations. Then solve the system. 6–11. See margin.

6. $-3x + y = -3$
$4x + 2y = 14$

7. $2x + 6y = -8$
$x - 3y = 8$

8. $3x - 4y = -5$
$-3x - 6y = -5$

9. $5x + 8y = 1$
$-2x + 8y = -6$

10. $y + 4x = 3$
$y = -4x - 1$

11. $-5x + 4y = 7$
$-5x - 3y = -14$

Example 2 **12. FINANCIAL LITERACY** For a Future Teachers of America fundraiser, Denzell sold food as shown in the table. He sold 11 more subs than pizzas and earned a total of \$233. Write and solve a system of equations to represent this situation. Then describe what the solution means.

Item	Selling Price
pizza	\$5.00
sub	\$3.00

12. Sample answer: $3s + 5p = 233$ and $s = p + 11$; (25, 36); Denzell sold 25 pizzas and 36 subs.

13. DVDs Manuela has a total of 40 DVDs of movies and television shows. The number of movies is 4 less than 3 times the number of television shows. Write and solve a system of equations to find the numbers of movies and television shows that she has on DVD. $m + t = 40$ and $m = 3t - 4$; 29 movies, 11 television shows

14. CAVES The Caverns of Sonora have two different tours: the Crystal Palace tour and the Horseshoe Lake tour. The total length of both tours is 3.25 miles. The Crystal Palace tour is a half-mile less than twice the distance of the Horseshoe Lake tour. Determine the length of each tour. See margin.

15. MODELING The *break-even point* is the point at which income equals expenses. Ridgemont High School is paying \$13,200 for the writing and research of their yearbook plus a printing fee of \$25 per book. If they sell the books for \$40 each, how many will they have to sell to break even? Explain. See margin.

B **16. PAINTBALL** Clara and her friends are planning a trip to a paintball park. Find the cost of lunch and the cost of each paintball. What would be the cost for 400 paintballs and lunch? The cost of lunch is \$10 and the cost of each paintball is \$0.03. The cost of 400 paintballs and lunch would be \$22.

Differentiated Homework Options

Level	Assignment	Two-Day Option	
AL Basic	6–15, 21, 22, 24–44	7–15 odd, 27–30	6–14 even, 21, 22, 24–26, 31–44
OL Core	7–15 odd, 16–22, 24–44	6–15, 27–30	16–22, 24–26, 31–44
BL Advanced	16–38, (optional: 39–44)		

3 Practice

Formative Assessment

Use Exercises 1–5 to check for understanding.

Use the chart at the bottom of this page to customize assignments for your students.

WatchOut!

Preventing Errors Students frequently do not understand what their answers mean in the context of the problem. Stress that they should go back and read the problem again to make sure they have answered the question. It is also helpful to have them give their answers to a word problem in sentence form.

Teaching the Process Standards

Modeling Mathematically proficient students apply the mathematics they know to solve problems arising in everyday life. In Exercise 15, point out to students that because 400 paintballs is between 200 and 500, the cost of lunch and 400 paintballs should be between the cost for lunch and 200 paintballs and the cost for lunch and 500 paintballs.

Additional Answers

5a. $4t + 3j = 181$; $t + 2j = 94$

6. subst.; (2, 3)

7. subst.; (2, −2)

8. elim (+); $\left(-\frac{1}{3}, 1\right)$

9. elim (−); $\left(1, -\frac{1}{2}\right)$

10. subst.; no solution

11. elim (−); (1, 3)

14. Horseshoe Lake = 1.25 mi, Crystal Palace = 2 mi

15. 880 books; If they sell this number, then their income and expenses both equal \$35,200.

Study Guide and Intervention

AL OL ELL

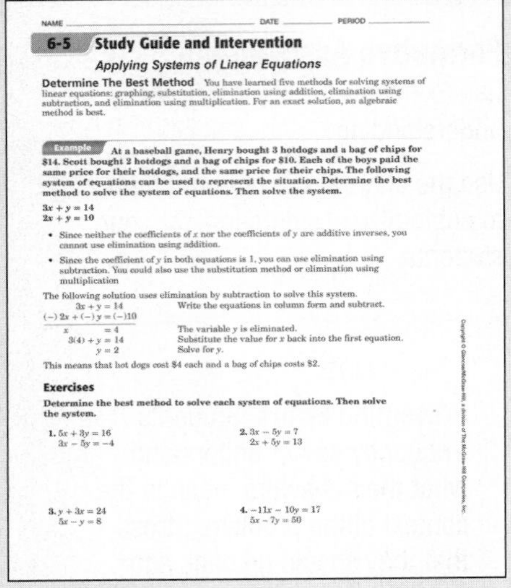
NAME ______ DATE ______ PERIOD ______

6-5 Study Guide and Intervention

Applying Systems of Linear Equations

Practice

AL OL BL ELL

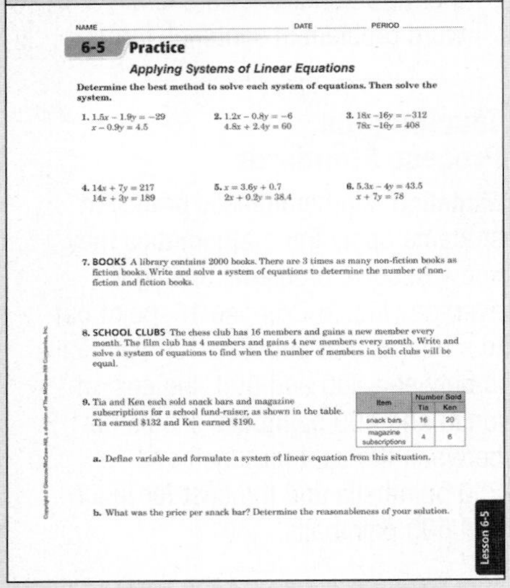
NAME ______ DATE ______ PERIOD ______

6-5 Practice

Applying Systems of Linear Equations

Word Problem Practice

AL OL BL ELL

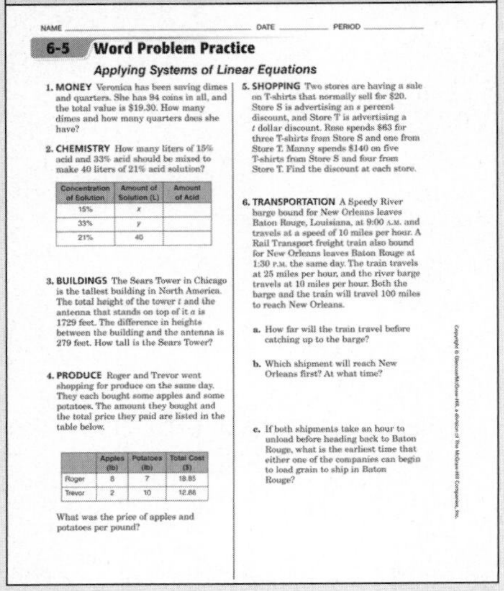
NAME ______ DATE ______ PERIOD ______

6-5 Word Problem Practice

Applying Systems of Linear Equations

17. RECYCLING Mara and Ling each recycled aluminum cans and newspaper, as shown in the table. Mara earned \$3.77, and Ling earned \$4.65.

Materials	Pounds Recycled	
	Mara	Ling
aluminum cans	9	9
newspaper	26	114

a. Define variables and write a system of linear equations from this situation.

17a. Let x = the cost per pound of aluminum cans, and let y = the cost per pound of newspaper; $9x + 26y = 3.77$ and $9x + 114y = 4.65$.

b. What was the price per pound of aluminum? Determine the reasonableness of your solution. **\$0.39; This solution is reasonable.**

18. BOOKS The library is having a book sale. Hardcover books sell for \$4 each, and paperback books are \$2 each. If Connie spends \$26 for 8 books, how many hardcover books did she buy? **5**

C **19. MUSIC** An online music club offers individual songs for one price or entire albums for another. Kendrick pays \$14.90 to download 5 individual songs and 1 album. Geoffrey pays \$21.75 to download 3 individual songs and 2 albums.

a. How much does the music club charge to download a song? **\$1.15**

b. How much does the music club charge to download an entire album? **\$9.15**

20. CANOEING Malik canoed against the current for 2 hours and then with the current for 1 hour before resting. Julio traveled against the current for 2.5 hours and then with the current for 1.5 hours before resting. If they traveled a total of 9.5 miles against the current, 20.5 miles with the current, and the current is 3 miles per hour, how fast do Malik and Julio travel in still water? **Malik: 6 mph; Julio: 4 mph**

H.O.T. Problems Use Higher-Order Thinking Skills

21. OPEN ENDED Formulate a system of equations that represents a situation in your school. Describe the method that you would use to solve the system. Then solve the system and explain what the solution means. **See margin.**

22. REASONING In a system of equations, x represents the time spent riding a bike, and y represents the distance traveled. You determine the solution to be $(-1, 7)$. Use this problem to discuss the importance of analyzing solutions in the context of real-world problems.

22. Sample answer: You should always check that the answer makes sense in the context of the original problem. If it does not, you may have made an incorrect calculation. If $(-1, 7)$ was the solution, then it is probably incorrect, since time in this case cannot be a negative number. The solution should be recalculated.

23. CHALLENGE Solve the following system of equations by using three different methods. Show your work. **See margin.**

$$4x + y = 13$$
$$6x - y = 7$$

24. WRITE A QUESTION A classmate says that elimination is the best way to solve a system of equations. Write a question to challenge his conjecture. **See margin.**

25. WHICH ONE DOESN'T BELONG? Which system is different? Explain.

$x - y = 3$ $x + \frac{1}{2}y = 1$	$-x + y = 0$ $5x = 2y$	$y = x - 4$ $y = \frac{2}{x}$	$y = x + 1$ $y = 3x$

25. The third system; this system is the only one that is not a system of linear equations.

26. E **WRITING IN MATH** How do you know what method to use when solving a system of equations? **See Ch. 6 Answer Appendix.**

Enrichment

OL BL

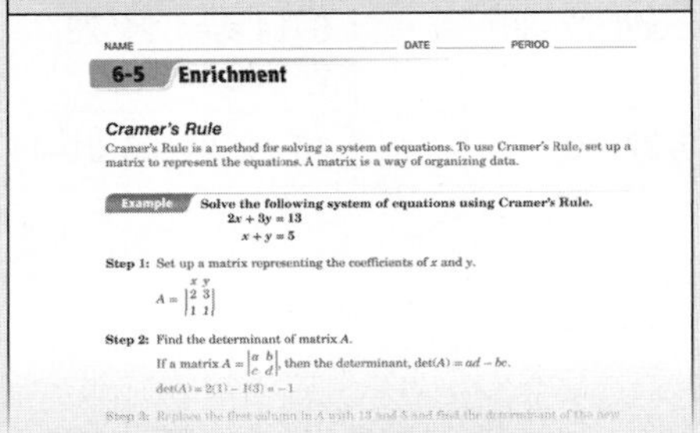
NAME ______ DATE ______ PERIOD ______

6-5 Enrichment

Cramer's Rule

Additional Answer

21. Sample answer: $x + y = 12$ and $3x + 2y = 29$, where x represents the cost of a student ticket for the basketball game and y represents the cost of an adult ticket; substitution could be used to solve the system; (5, 7) means the cost of a student ticket is \$5 and the cost of an adult ticket is \$7.

Standardized Test Practice

27. If $5x + 3y = 12$ and $4x - 5y = 17$, what is y? **A**

A -1 **B** 3 **C** $(-1, 3)$ **D** $(3, -1)$

28. STATISTICS The scatter plot shows the number of hay bales used on the Bostwick farm during the last year. **J**

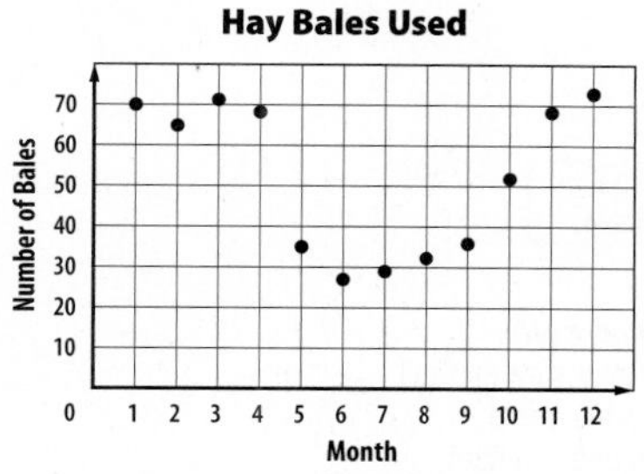

Which is an invalid conclusion?

F The Bostwicks used less hay in the summer than they did in the winter.

G The Bostwicks used about 629 bales of hay during the year.

H On average, the Bostwicks used about 52 bales each month.

J The Bostwicks used the most hay in February.

29. SHORT RESPONSE At noon, Cesar cast a shadow 0.15 foot long. Next to him a streetlight cast a shadow 0.25 foot long. If Cesar is 6 feet tall, how tall is the streetlight? **10 ft**

30. The graph shows the solution to which of the following systems of equations? **A**

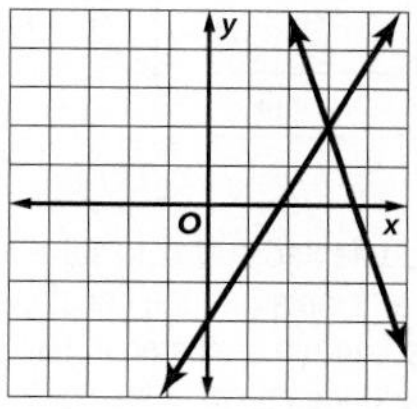

A $y = -3x + 11$
$3y = 5x - 9$

B $y = 5x - 15$
$2y = x + 7$

C $y = -3x + 11$
$2y = 4x - 5$

D $y = 5x - 15$
$3y = 2x + 18$

Spiral Review

Use elimination to solve each system of equations. (Lesson 6-4)

31. $x + y = 3$
$3x - 4y = -12$ **(0, 3)**

32. $-4x + 2y = 0$
$2x - 3y = 16$ **(−4, −8)**

33. $4x + 2y = 10$
$5x - 3y = 7$ **(2, 1)**

34. TRAVELING A youth group is traveling in two vans to visit an aquarium. The number of people in each van and the cost of admission for that van are shown. What are the adult and student prices? (Lesson 6-3) **\$16; \$9**

Van	Number of Adults	Number of Students	Total Cost
A	2	5	\$77
B	2	7	\$95

Graph each inequality. (Lesson 5-6) **35–38. See Ch. 6 Answer Appendix.**

35. $y < 4$ **36.** $x \geq 3$ **37.** $7x + 12y > 0$ **38.** $y - 3x \leq 4$

Skills Review

Find each sum or difference.

39. $(-3.81) + (-8.5)$ **−12.31**

40. $12.625 + (-5.23)$ **7.395**

41. $21.65 + (-15.05)$ **6.6**

42. $(-4.27) + 1.77$ **−2.5**

43. $(-78.94) - 14.25$ **−93.19**

44. $(-97.623) - (-25.14)$ **−72.483**

Differentiated Instruction OL BL

Extension Have students make up their own real-world problem that can be solved using a system of linear equations. This will help all students understand the concept of solving systems of linear equations.

4 Assess

Yesterday's News Have students write how yesterday's concept of using elimination with multiplication to solve systems of equations helped them with today's concept of determining the best method for solving systems of equations.

Teaching the Process Standards

Reasoning Mathematically proficient students make sense of quantities and their relationships in problem situations. In Exercise 22, point out to students that a time of −1 makes sense if x is hours since 12:00, but a negative number of hours riding a bike does not make sense.

Additional Answers

23. Graphing: (2, 5);

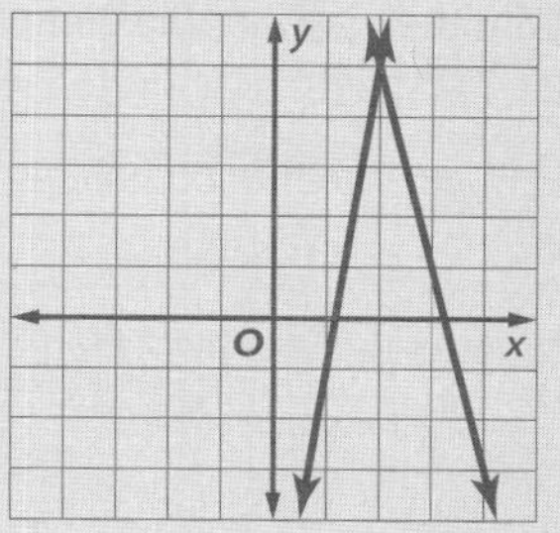

elimination by addition:

$4x + y = 13$
$\underline{6x - y = 7}$
$10x = 20$
$x = 2$
$4(2) + y = 13$
$y = 5$

substitution:

$y = -4x + 13$
$6x - (-4x + 13) = 7$
$6x + 4x - 13 = 7$
$10x = 20$
$x = 2$

$4(2) + y = 13$
$y = 5$

24. Sample answer: Would another method work better if one of the equations is in the form $y = mx + b$?

1 Focus

Objective Use matrices to solve systems of equations.

Teaching Tips

- Remind students that multiplying a row does not involve multiplying every row in the matrix.
- Student may also perform row operations and check their solutions using a graphing calculator. Type 2nd **[MATRIX]** to access the **Matrix** menu.

2 Teach

Working in Cooperative Groups

Divide the class into pairs. Work through Activity 1 as a class. Then ask students to work with their partners to complete Activity 2.

Practice Have students complete Exercises 1–6.

EXTEND 6-5

Algebra Lab: Using Matrices to Solve Systems of Equations

A **matrix** is a rectangular arrangement of numbers, called **elements**, in rows and columns enclosed in brackets. Usually named using an uppercase letter, a matrix can be described by its **dimensions** or by the number of rows and columns in the matrix. A matrix with m rows and n columns is an $m \times n$ matrix (read "m by n").

$$A = \begin{bmatrix} 7 & -9 & 5 & 3 \\ -1 & 3 & -3 & 6 \\ 0 & -4 & 8 & 2 \end{bmatrix}$$

A is a 3 × 4 matrix.

3 rows

4 columns

The element 2 is in Row 3, Column 4.

You can use an augmented matrix to solve a system of equations. An **augmented matrix** consists of the coefficients and the constant terms of a system of equations. Make sure that the coefficients of the x-terms are listed in one column, the coefficients of the y-terms are in another column, and the constant terms are in a third column. The coefficients and constant terms are usually separated by a dashed line.

Linear System	Augmented Matrix
$x - 3y = 8$ $-9x + 2y = -4$	$\left[\begin{array}{cc:c} 1 & -3 & 8 \\ -9 & 2 & -4 \end{array}\right]$

Activity 1 Write an Augmented Matrix

Write an augmented matrix for each system of equations.

a. $-2x + 7y = 11$
$6x - 4y = 2$

Place the coefficients of the equations and the constant terms into a matrix.

$$\begin{aligned} -2x + 7y &= 11 \\ 6x - 4y &= 2 \end{aligned} \quad \rightarrow \quad \left[\begin{array}{cc:c} -2 & 7 & 11 \\ 6 & -4 & 2 \end{array}\right]$$

b. $x - 2y = 5$
$y = -4$

$$\begin{aligned} x - 2y &= 5 \\ y &= -4 \end{aligned} \quad \rightarrow \quad \left[\begin{array}{cc:c} 1 & -2 & 5 \\ 0 & 1 & -4 \end{array}\right]$$

You can solve a system of equations by using an augmented matrix. By performing row operations, you can change the form of the matrix. The operations are the same as the ones used when working with equations.

KeyConcept Elementary Row Operations

The following operations can be performed on an augmented matrix.

- Interchange any two rows.
- Multiply all entries in a row by a nonzero constant.
- Replace one row with the sum of that row and a multiple of another row.

Row operations produce a matrix equivalent to the original system. **Row reduction** is the process of performing elementary row operations on an augmented matrix to solve a system.

The goal is to get the coefficients portion of the matrix to have the form $\begin{bmatrix} 1 & 0 \\ 0 & 1 \end{bmatrix}$, which is called the **identity matrix**. The first row will give you the solution for *x*, because the coefficient of *y* is 0. The second row will give you the solution for *y*, because the coefficient of *x* is 0.

Activity 2 Use Row Operations to Solve a System

Use an augmented matrix to solve the system of equations.

$-5x + 3y = 6$

$x - y = 4$

Step 1 Write the augmented matrix: $\left[\begin{array}{cc|c} -5 & 3 & 6 \\ 1 & -1 & 4 \end{array}\right]$.

Step 2 Notice that the first element in the second row is 1. Interchange the rows so 1 can be in the upper left-hand corner.

$$\left[\begin{array}{cc|c} -5 & 3 & 6 \\ 1 & -1 & 4 \end{array}\right] \xrightarrow{\text{Interchange } R_1 \text{ and } R_2.} \left[\begin{array}{cc|c} 1 & -1 & 4 \\ -5 & 3 & 6 \end{array}\right]$$

Step 3 To make the first element in the second row a 0, multiply the first row by 5 and add the result to row 2.

$$\left[\begin{array}{cc|c} 1 & -1 & 4 \\ -5 & 3 & 6 \end{array}\right] \xrightarrow{5R_1 + R_2} \left[\begin{array}{cc|c} 1 & -1 & 4 \\ 0 & -2 & 26 \end{array}\right]$$

$1(5) + (-5) = 0$; $-1(5) + 3 = -2$; $4(5) + 6 = 26$

Step 4 To make the second element in the second row a 1, multiply the second row by $-\frac{1}{2}$.

$$\left[\begin{array}{cc|c} 1 & -1 & 4 \\ 0 & -2 & 26 \end{array}\right] \xrightarrow{-\frac{1}{2}R_2} \left[\begin{array}{cc|c} 1 & -1 & 4 \\ 0 & 1 & -13 \end{array}\right]$$

$0\left(-\frac{1}{2}\right) = 0$; $-2\left(-\frac{1}{2}\right) = 1$; $26\left(-\frac{1}{2}\right) = -13$

Step 5 To make the second element in the second row a 0, add the rows together.

$$\left[\begin{array}{cc|c} 1 & -1 & 4 \\ 0 & 1 & -13 \end{array}\right] \xrightarrow{R_2 + R_1} \left[\begin{array}{cc|c} 1 & 0 & -9 \\ 0 & 1 & -13 \end{array}\right]$$

$1 + 0 = 1$; $-1 + 1 = 0$; $4 + (-13) = -9$

The solution is $(-9, -13)$.

Model and Analyze

Write an augmented matrix for each system of equations. Then solve the system. 1–6. See margin.

1. $x + y = -3$
   $x - y = 1$
2. $x - y = -2$
   $2x + 2y = 12$
3. $3x - 4y = -27$
   $x + 2y = 11$
4. $x + 4y = -6$
   $2x - 5y = 1$
5. $x - 3y = -2$
   $4x + y = 31$
6. $x + 2y = 3$
   $-3x + 3y = 27$

3 Assess

Formative Assessment

Use Exercises 1–6 to assess your students' knowledge of using matrices to solve systems of equations.

From Concrete to Abstract

Ask students to summarize their favorite methods for using row operations on matrices to solve systems of equations. Have them explain when and why they prefer to use certain row operations.

Tips for New Teachers

Alternate Method Row operations can be performed in different orders to arrive at the same result. In Activity 2, you could have started by multiplying the first row, R_1, by $-\frac{1}{5}$ instead of interchanging the rows.

Follow-up

Students have explored matrices and matrix operations.

Ask:

- What are the advantages of using matrices to solve problems? Sample answer: They provide a convenient way to organize data; they can be used to shorten notation.

Additional Answers

1. $\left[\begin{array}{cc|c} 1 & 1 & -3 \\ 1 & -1 & 1 \end{array}\right]$; $(-1, -2)$
2. $\left[\begin{array}{cc|c} 1 & -1 & -2 \\ 2 & 2 & 12 \end{array}\right]$; $(2, 4)$
3. $\left[\begin{array}{cc|c} 3 & -4 & -27 \\ 1 & 2 & 11 \end{array}\right]$; $(-1, 6)$
4. $\left[\begin{array}{cc|c} 1 & 4 & -6 \\ 2 & -5 & 1 \end{array}\right]$; $(-2, -1)$
5. $\left[\begin{array}{cc|c} 1 & -3 & -2 \\ 4 & 1 & 31 \end{array}\right]$; $(7, 3)$
6. $\left[\begin{array}{cc|c} 1 & 2 & 3 \\ -3 & 3 & 27 \end{array}\right]$; $(-5, 4)$

1 Focus

VerticalAlignment

Before Lesson 6-6 Graph and solve linear inequalities.

Lesson 6-6 Solve systems of linear inequalities by graphing.
Apply systems of linear inequalities.

After Lesson 6-6 Analyze situations and formulate systems of inequalities in two unknowns to solve problems.

2 Teach

Scaffolding Questions

Have students read the **Why?** section of the lesson.

Ask:

- According to the graph, what are three possible heart rates in the preferred range for Jacui? Sample answers: 110, 146, and 168
- What are three heart rates that fall outside the range? Sample answers: 100, 180, 195
- What happens to the range of preferred heart rates as Jacui becomes older? The lower and upper limits for the range decrease, and the overall range decreases.

LESSON 6-6 Systems of Inequalities

Then

- You graphed and solved linear inequalities.

Now

1. Solve systems of linear inequalities by graphing.
2. Apply systems of linear inequalities.

Why?

- Jacui is beginning an exercise program that involves an intense cardiovascular workout. Her trainer recommends that for a person her age, her heart rate should stay within the following range as she exercises.
  - It should be higher than 102 beats per minute.
  - It should not exceed 174 beats per minute.

The graph shows the maximum and minimum target heart rate for people ages 0 to 30 as they exercise. If the preferred range is in light green, how old do you think Jacui is?

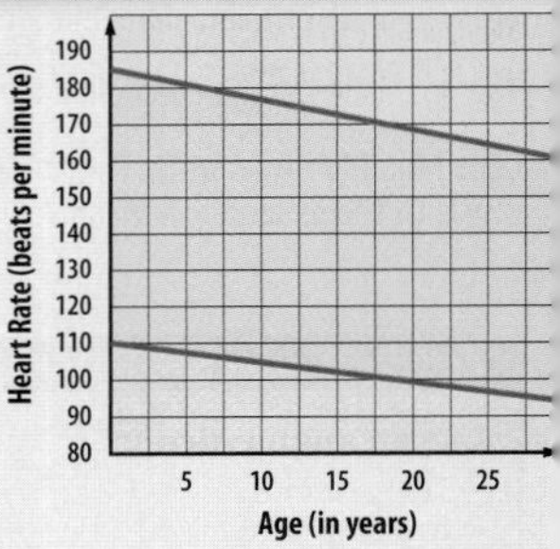

NewVocabulary
system of inequalities

Content Standards
A1.SEI.4

Process Standards
PS.6

1 Systems of Inequalities The graph above is a graph of two inequalities. A set of two or more inequalities with the same variables is called a **system of inequalities**.

The solution of a system of inequalities with two variables is the set of ordered pairs that satisfy all of the inequalities in the system. The solution set is represented by the overlap, or intersection, of the graphs of the inequalities.

Example 1 Solve by Graphing

Solve the system of inequalities by graphing.

$y > -2x + 1$
$y \leq x + 3$

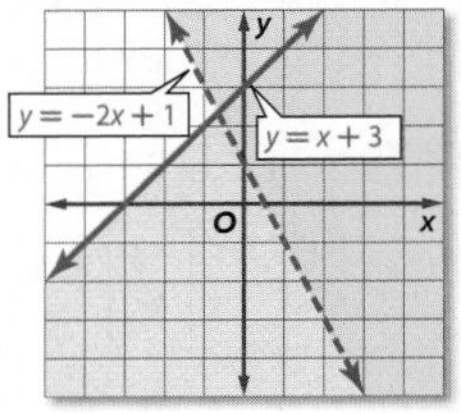

The graph of $y = -2x + 1$ is dashed and is not included in the graph of the solution. The graph of $y = x + 3$ is solid and is included in the graph of the solution.

The solution of the system is the set of ordered pairs in the intersection of the graphs of $y > -2x + 1$ and $y \leq x + 3$. This region is shaded in green.

When graphing more than one region, it is helpful to use two different colored pencils or two different patterns for each region. This will make it easier to see where the regions intersect and find possible solutions.

GuidedPractice **1A–1D. See Ch. 6 Answer Appendix.**

1A. $y \leq 3$
$x + y \geq 1$

1B. $2x + y \geq 2$
$2x + y < 4$

1C. $y \geq -4$
$3x + y \leq 2$

1D. $x + y > 2$
$-4x + 2y < 8$

Sometimes the regions never intersect. When this happens, there is no solution because there are no points in common.

Lesson 6-6 Resources

Resource	Approaching Level AL	On Level OL	Beyond Level BL	English Learners ELL
Teacher Edition	▪ Differentiated Instruction, p. 373	▪ Differentiated Instruction, pp. 373, 376	▪ Differentiated Instruction, p. 376	
Chapter Resource Masters	▪ Study Guide and Intervention, pp. 36–37 ▪ Skills Practice, p. 38 ▪ Practice, p. 39 ▪ Word Problem Practice, p. 40 ▪ Graphing Calculator Activity, p. 42 ▪ Spreadsheet Activity, p. 43	▪ Study Guide and Intervention, pp. 36–37 ▪ Skills Practice and Practice, pp. 38–39 ▪ Word Problem Practice, p. 40 ▪ Enrichment, p. 41 ▪ Graphing Calculator Activity, p. 42 ▪ Spreadsheet Activity, p. 43	▪ Practice, p. 39 ▪ Word Problem Practice, p. 40 ▪ Enrichment, p. 41 ▪ Graphing Calculator Activity, p. 42 ▪ Spreadsheet Activity, p. 43	▪ Study Guide and Intervention, pp. 36–37 ▪ Skills Practice, p. 38 ▪ Practice, p. 39 ▪ Word Problem Practice, p. 40 ▪ Graphing Calculator Activity, p. 42 ▪ Spreadsheet Activity, p. 43
Other	▪ 5-Minute Check 6-6 ▪ Study Notebook ▪ Teaching Algebra with Manipulatives	▪ 5-Minute Check 6-6 ▪ Study Notebook ▪ Teaching Algebra with Manipulatives	▪ 5-Minute Check 6-6 ▪ Study Notebook	▪ 5-Minute Check 6-6 ▪ Study Notebook ▪ Teaching Algebra with Manaipulatives

StudyTip

Parallel Boundaries A system of equations represented by parallel lines does not have a solution. However, a system of inequalities with parallel boundaries can have a solution. For example:

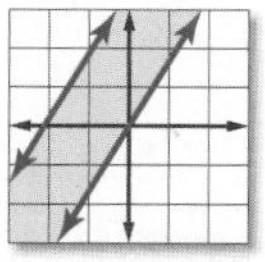

Example 2 No Solution

Solve the system of inequalities by graphing.

$3x - y \geq 2$
$3x - y < -5$

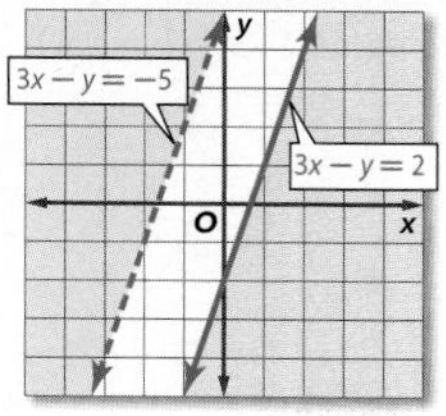

The graphs of $3x - y = 2$ and $3x - y = -5$ are parallel lines. The two regions do not intersect at any point, so the system has no solution.

GuidedPractice **2A–2B. See Ch. 6 Answer Appendix.**

2A. $y > 3$
$y < 1$

2B. $x + 6y \leq 2$
$y \geq -\frac{1}{6}x + 7$

2 Apply Systems of Inequalities

When using a system of inequalities to describe constraints on the possible combinations in a real-world problem, sometimes only whole-number solutions will make sense.

Real-WorldLink

Student government might be a good activity for you if you like to bring about change, plan events, and work with others.

Real-World Example 3 Whole-Number Solutions

ELECTIONS **Monifa is running for student council. The election rules say that for the election to be valid, at least 80% of the 900 students must vote. Monifa knows that she needs more than 330 votes to win.**

a. Define the variables, and write a system of inequalities to represent this situation. Then graph the system.

Let r = the number of votes required by the election rules; 80% of 900 students is 720 students. So $r \geq 720$.

Let v = the number of votes that Monifa needs to win. So $v > 330$.

The system of inequalities is $r \geq 720$ and $v > 330$.

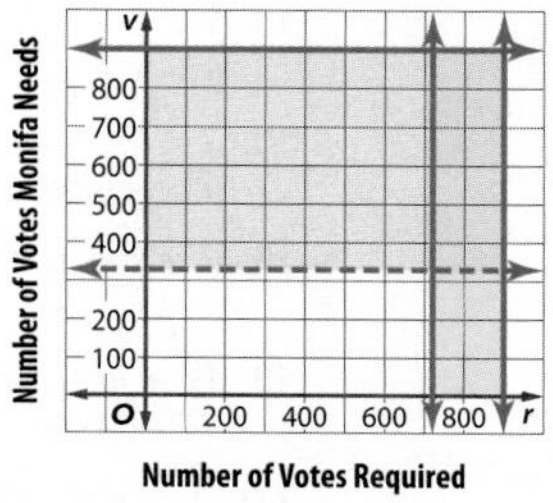

b. Name one viable option.

Only whole-number solutions make sense in this problem. One possible solution is (800, 400); 800 students voted and Monifa received 400 votes.

GuidedPractice

3. FUNDRAISING The Theater Club is selling shirts. They have only enough supplies to print 120 shirts. They will sell sweatshirts for \$22 and T-shirts for \$15, with a goal of at least \$2000 in sales.

A. Define the variables, and write a system of inequalities to represent this situation. **3A–3B. See Ch. 6 Answer Appendix.**

B. Then graph the system.

C. Name one possible solution. **Sample answer: 95 sweatshirts and 10 T-shirts**

D. Is (45, 30) a solution? Explain. **No, the point does not fall in the overlapping region.**

DifferentiatedInstruction AL OL

If students have difficulty graphing systems of inequalities,

Then suggest that they graph each inequality on a separate coordinate graph and then put the two graphs together on the same coordinate graph by copying them over or tracing them.

1 Systems of Inequalities

Example 1 shows how to solve a system of inequalities by graphing. **Example 2** shows how to determine that a system of inequalities has no solution.

Formative Assessment

Use the Guided Practice exercises after each Example to determine students' understanding of concepts.

Additional Examples

1 Solve the system of inequalities by graphing.

$y < 2x + 2$
$y \geq -x - 3$

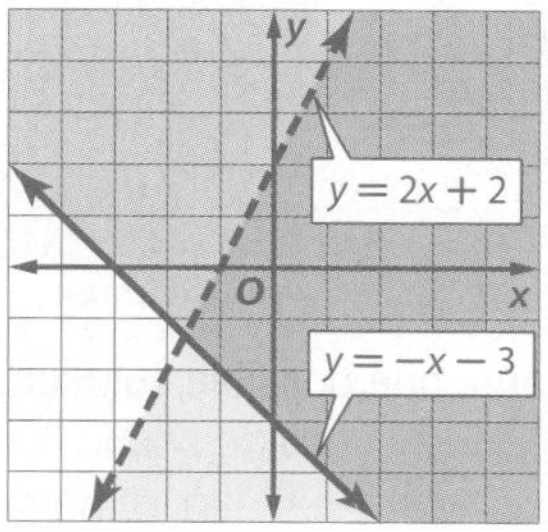

2 Solve the system of inequalities by graphing.

$y \geq -3x + 1$
$y \leq -3x - 2$ ∅

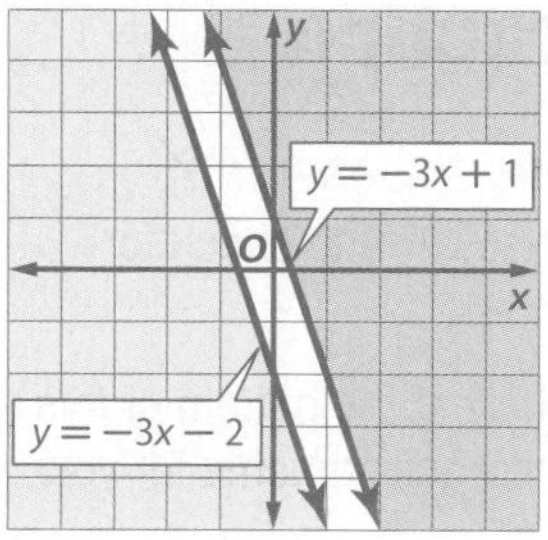

Additional Examples also in Interactive Classroom PowerPoint® Presentations

IWB Interactive White Board READY

2 Apply Systems of Inequalities

Example 3 shows how to use a system of inequalities to solve a real-world problem.

Additional Example

3 SERVICE A college service organization requires that its members maintain at least a 3.0 grade point average and volunteer at least 10 hours a week.

a. Define the variables and write a system of inequalities to represent this situation. Then graph the system.
Let g = grade point average; let v = the number of volunteer hours; $g \geq 3.0$, $v \geq 10$.

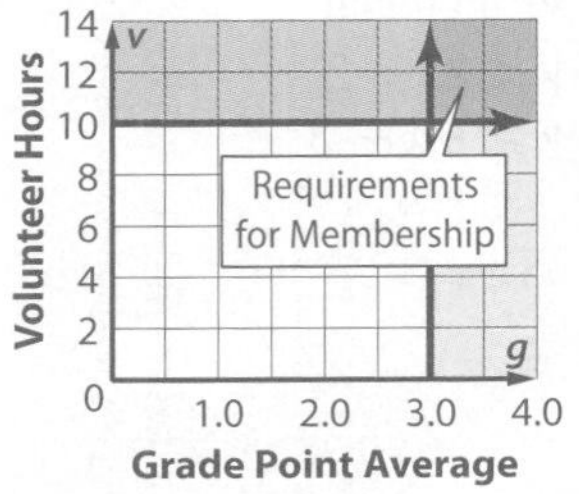

b. Name one possible solution.
(3.5, 12); a grade point average of 3.5 and 12 hours of volunteering

3 Practice

Formative Assessment

Use Exercises 1–9 to check for understanding.

Use the chart at the bottom of this page to customize assignments for your students.

Teaching the Process Standards

Modeling Mathematically proficient students apply mathematics to problems arising in the workplace. In Exercise 26, point out to students that they can first consider just the wages and then add the tips.

Precision Mathematically proficient students calculate accurately and efficiently. In Exercise 42, stress that a precise graph will allow for a more accurate estimate.

Check Your Understanding

◯ = Step-by-Step Solutions begin on page R13.

Examples 1–2 **Solve each system of inequalities by graphing.** **1–8. See Ch. 6 Answer Appendix.**

1. $x \geq 4$
$y \leq x - 3$

2. $y > -2$
$y \leq x + 9$

3. $y < 3x + 8$
$y \geq 4x$

4. $3x - y \geq -1$
$2x + y \geq 5$

5. $y \leq 2x - 7$
$y \geq 2x + 7$

6. $y > -2x + 5$
$y \geq -2x + 10$

7. $2x + y \leq 5$
$2x + y \leq 7$

8. $5x - y < -2$
$5x - y > 6$

Example 3

9. AUTO RACING At a racecar driving school there are safety requirements.

a. Define the variables, and write a system of inequalities to represent the height and weight requirements in this situation. Then graph the system. **See Ch. 6 Answer Appendix.**

b. Name one possible solution. **9b. Sample answer: 72 in. and 220 lb**

c. Is (50, 180) a solution? Explain.
Yes, the point falls in the overlapping region.

Practice and Problem Solving

Extra Practice is on page R6.

Examples 1–2 **Solve each system of inequalities by graphing.** **10–24. See Ch. 6 Answer Appendix.**

10. $y < 6$
$y > x + 3$

11. $y \geq 0$
$y \leq x - 5$

12. $y \leq x + 10$
$y > 6x + 2$

13. $y < 5x - 2$
$y > -6x + 2$

14. $2x - y \leq 6$
$x - y \geq -1$

15. $3x - y > -5$
$5x - y < 9$

16. $y \geq x + 10$
$y \leq x - 3$

17. $y < 5x - 5$
$y > 5x + 9$

18. $y \geq 3x - 5$
$3x - y > -4$

19. $4x + y > -1$
$y < -4x + 1$

20. $3x - y \geq -2$
$y < 3x + 4$

21. $y > 2x - 3$
$2x - y \geq 1$

22. $5x - y < -6$
$3x - y \geq 4$

23. $x - y \leq 8$
$y < 3x$

24. $4x + y < -2$
$y > -4x$

Example 3

25. ICE RINKS Ice resurfacers are used for rinks of at least 1000 square feet and up to 17,000 square feet. The price ranges from as little as $10,000 to as much as $150,000.

a. Define the variables, and write a system of inequalities to represent this situation. Then graph the system. **See Ch. 6 Answer Appendix.**

b. Name one possible solution.

25b. Sample answer: an ice resurfacer for a rink of 5000 ft^2 and a price of $20,000

c. Is (15,000, 30,000) a solution? Explain. **Yes; the point satisfies each inequality.**

26. MODELING Josefina works between 10 and 30 hours per week at a pizzeria. She earns $6.50 an hour, but can earn tips when she delivers pizzas.

a. Write a system of inequalities to represent the dollars d she could earn for working h hours in a week. $d \geq 6.50h$, $10 \leq h \leq 30$

b. Graph this system. **See Ch. 6 Answer Appendix.**

c. If Josefina received $17.50 in tips and earned a total of $180 for the week, how many hours did she work? **25 hours**

Differentiated Homework Options

Level	Assignment	Two-Day Option	
AL Basic	10–26, 39–41, 43–66	11–25 odd, 44–47	10–26 even, 39–41, 43, 48–58
OL Core	11–25 odd, 26, 27–35 odd, 36, 37, 39–41, 43–58	10–26, 44–47	27–35, 36, 37, 39–41, 43, 48–58
BL Advanced	27–55, (optional: 56–58)		

374 | Lesson 6-6 | Systems of Inequalities

B Solve each system of inequalities by graphing. **27–35. See Ch. 6 Answer Appendix.**

27. $x + y \geq 1$
$x + y \leq 2$

28. $3x - y < -2$
$3x - y < 1$

29. $2x - y \leq -11$
$3x - y \geq 12$

30. $y < 4x + 13$
$4x - y \geq 1$

31. $4x - y < -3$
$y \geq 4x - 6$

32. $y \leq 2x + 7$
$y < 2x - 3$

33. $y > -12x + 1$
$y \leq 9x + 2$

34. $2y \geq x$
$x - 3y > -6$

35. $x - 5y > -15$
$5y \geq x - 5$

36. CLASS PROJECT An economics class formed a company to sell school supplies. They would like to sell at least 20 notebooks and 50 pens per week, with a goal of earning at least $60 per week. **a–b. See Ch. 6 Answer Appendix.**

a. Define the variables, and write a system of inequalities to represent this situation.

b. Graph the system.

c. Name one possible solution. **Sample answer: 25 notebooks and 100 pens**

C **37 FINANCIAL LITERACY** Opal makes $15 per hour working for a photographer. She also coaches a competitive soccer team for $10 per hour. Opal needs to earn at least $90 per week, but she does not want to work more than 20 hours per week.

a. Define the variables, and write a system of inequalities to represent this situation. **37a. Let x = the hours worked for the photographer, let y = the hours coaching, $x + y \leq 20$, $15x + 10y \geq 90$.**

b. Graph this system. **See Ch. 6 Answer Appendix.**

c. Give two possible solutions to describe how Opal can meet her goals. **37c. Sample answer: 6 hours at the photographer, 10 hours of coaching; 8 hours at the photographer, 10 hours of coaching**

d. Is (2, 2) a solution? Explain. **37d. No; the point does not fall in the shaded region. She would not earn enough money.**

H.O.T. Problems Use Higher-Order Thinking Skills

38. CHALLENGE Create a system of inequalities equivalent to $|x| \leq 4$. **$x \leq 4$, $x \geq -4$**

39. REASONING State whether the following statement is *sometimes*, *always*, or *never* true. Explain your answer with an example or counterexample. **See Ch. 6 Answer Appendix.**

Systems of inequalities with parallel boundaries have no solutions.

40. REASONING Describe the graph of the solution of this system without graphing.
$6x - 3y \leq -5$
$6x - 3y \geq -5$ **It is the line $6x - 3y = -5$.**

41. OPEN ENDED One inequality in a system is $3x - y > 4$. Write a second inequality so that the system will have no solution. **Sample answer: $3x - y < -4$**

42. PRECISION Graph the system of inequalities. Estimate the area of the solution. **9 units^2; See Ch. 6 Answer Appendix for graph.**
$y \geq 1$
$y \leq x + 4$
$y \leq -x + 4$

43. WRITING IN MATH Refer to the beginning of the lesson. Explain what each colored region of the graph represents. Explain how shading in various colors can help to clearly show the solution set of a system of inequalities. **See Ch. 6 Answer Appendix.**

Teach with Tech

Wiki On your secure class wiki have students work in pairs to create a wiki page describing how to graph a system of inequalities. Describe how to decide whether to use a solid or dashed line and which side of the line to shade. Also, explain how to interpret the graph to determine the solutions of the system.

Enrichment
OL BL

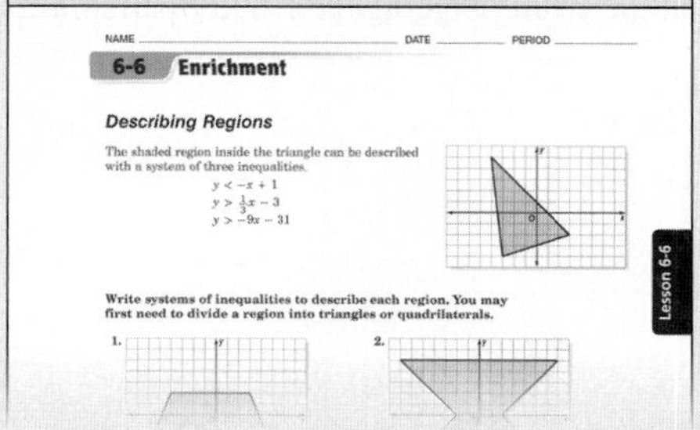
6-6 Enrichment

Describing Regions

The shaded region inside the triangle can be described with a system of three inequalities.
$y < -x + 1$
$y > \frac{1}{3}x - 3$
$y > -9x - 31$

Write systems of inequalities to describe each region. You may first need to divide a region into triangles or quadrilaterals.

Study Guide and Intervention
AL OL ELL

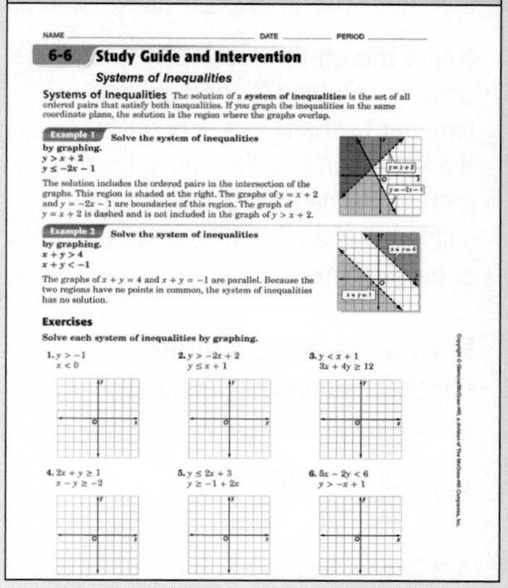
6-6 Study Guide and Intervention

Systems of Inequalities

Systems of Inequalities The solution of a system of inequalities is the set of all ordered pairs that satisfy both inequalities. If you graph the inequalities in the same coordinate plane, the solution is the region where the graphs overlap.

Example 1 Solve the system of inequalities by graphing.
$y > x + 2$
$y \leq -2x - 1$

Example 2 Solve the system of inequalities by graphing.
$x + y > 4$
$x + y < -1$

The graphs of $x + y = 4$ and $x + y = -1$ are parallel. Because the two regions have no points in common, the system of inequalities has no solution.

Exercises

Solve each system of inequalities by graphing.

Practice
AL OL BL ELL

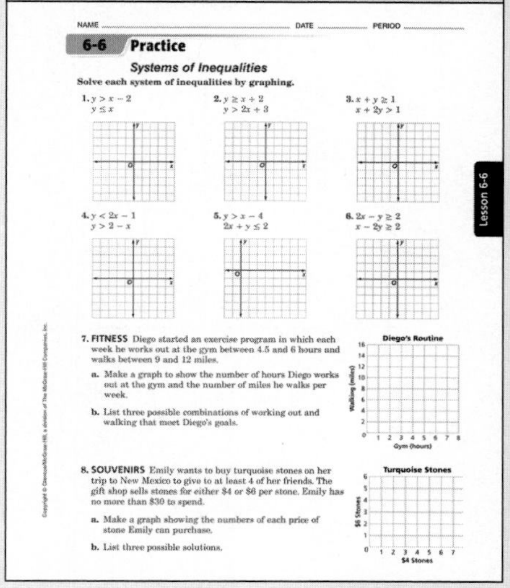
6-6 Practice

Systems of Inequalities

Solve each system of inequalities by graphing.

7. FITNESS

8. SOUVENIRS

Word Problem Practice
AL OL BL ELL

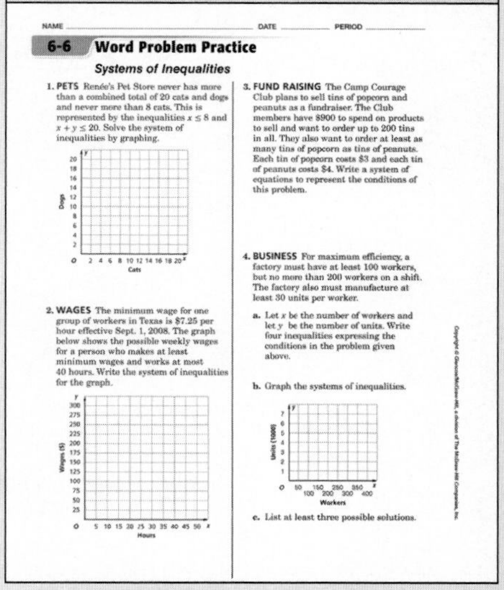
6-6 Word Problem Practice

Systems of Inequalities

1. PETS

2. WAGES

3. FUND RAISING

4. BUSINESS

4 Assess

Name the Math Have each student write the method for determining whether to shade above or below the line when graphing an inequality and how to determine the common solutions when graphing a system of inequalities.

Formative Assessment

Check for student understanding of concepts in Lesson 6-6.

Quiz 4, p. 48

Additional Answers

44a. $c \geq 20$ and $g \geq 3.75$
$c \geq 40$ and $g \geq 3.0$

44b. **Scholarship**

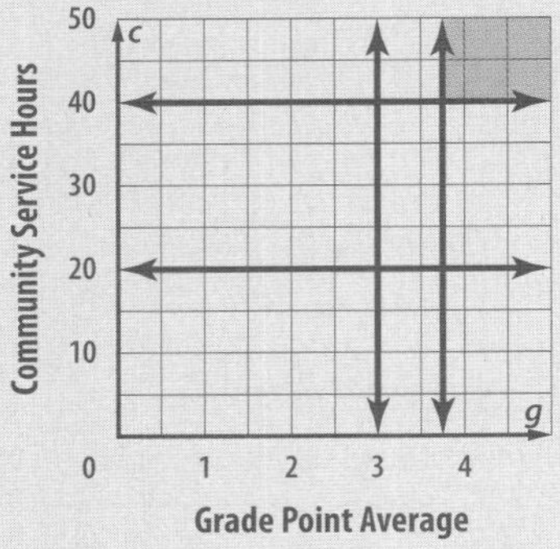

44c. Sample answer: 40 community service hours and a 3.75 grade points average

Standardized Test Practice

44. EXTENDED RESPONSE To apply for a scholarship, you must have a minimum of 20 hours of community service and a grade-point average of at least 3.75. Another scholarship requires at least 40 hours of community service and a minimum grade-point average of 3.0. **a–c. See margin.**

a. Write a system of inequalities to represent the credentials you must have to apply for both scholarships.

b. Graph the system of inequalities.

c. If you are eligible for both scholarships, give one possible solution.

45. GEOMETRY What is the measure of ∠1? **D**

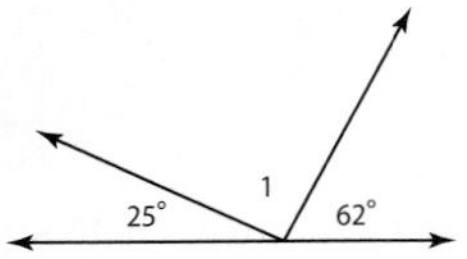

A 83°
B 87°
C 90°
D 93°

46. GEOMETRY What is the volume of the triangular prism? **H**

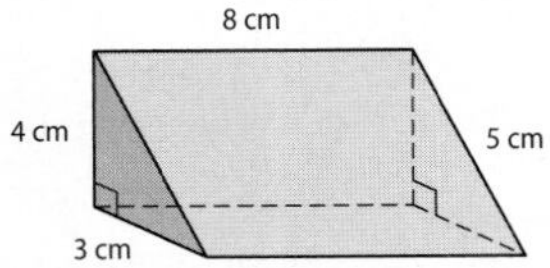

F 120 cm^3
G 96 cm^3
H 48 cm^3
J 30 cm^3

47. Ten pounds of fresh tomatoes make about 15 cups of cooked tomatoes. How many cups of cooked tomatoes does one pound of fresh tomatoes make? **A**

A $1\frac{1}{2}$ cups
B 3 cups
C 4 cups
D 5 cups

Spiral Review

48. CHEMISTRY Orion Labs needs to make 500 gallons of 34% acid solution. The only solutions available are a 25% acid solution and a 50% acid solution. Write and solve a system of equations to find the number of gallons of each solution that should be mixed to make the 34% solution. (Lesson 6-5) **$x + y = 500$, $0.25x + 0.5y = 170$; 320 gal of 25%; 180 gal of 50%**

Use elimination to solve each system of equations. (Lesson 6-4)

49. $x + y = 7$ **(4, 3)**
$2x + y = 11$

50. $a - b = 9$ **(2, −7)**
$7a + b = 7$

51. $q + 4r = -8$
$3q + 2r = 6$ **(4, −3)**

52. ENTERTAINMENT A group of 11 adults and children bought tickets for the baseball game. If the total cost was $156, how many of each type of ticket did they buy? (Lesson 6-4) **8 adult, 3 children**

Graph each inequality. (Lesson 5-6) **53–55. See Ch. 6 Answer Appendix.**

53. $4x - 2 \geq 2y$

54. $9x - 3y < 0$

55. $2y \leq -4x - 6$

Skills Review

Evaluate each expression.

56. 3^3 **27**

57. 2^4 **16**

58. $(-4)^3$ **−64**

Differentiated Instruction OL BL

Extension Have students graph $2 \leq x \leq 5$ and $1 \leq y \leq 4$ on the same coordinate plane. Have them describe what polygon is formed by their intersection. a square with vertices at (2, 4), (5, 4), (2, 1) and (5, 1)

6-6 Graphing Technology Lab
Systems of Inequalities

You can use TI-Nspire technology to explore systems of inequalities. To prepare your calculator, add a new **Graphs** page from the Home screen.

Content Standards
AI.SEI.4

Activity Graph Systems of Inequalities

Mr. Jackson owns a car washing and detailing business. It takes 20 minutes to wash a car and 60 minutes to detail a car. He works at most 8 hours per day and does at most 4 details per day. Write a system of linear inequalities to represent this situation.

First, write a linear inequality that represents the time it takes for car washing and car detailing. Let x represent the number of car washes, and let y represent the number of car details. Then $20x + 60y \le 480$.

To graph this using a graphing calculator, solve for y.

$20x + 60y \le 480$ Original inequality

$60y \le -20x + 480$ Subtract $20x$ from each side and simplify.

$y \le -\frac{1}{3}x + 8$ Divide each side by 60 and simplify.

Mr. Jackson does at most 4 details per day. This means that $y \le 4$.

Step 1 Adjust the viewing window and then graph $y \le 4$. Use the **Window Settings** option from the **Window/Zoom** menu to adjust the window to −4 to 30 for x and −2 to 10 for y. Keep the scales as **Auto**. Then enter **del** ≤ 4 **enter**.

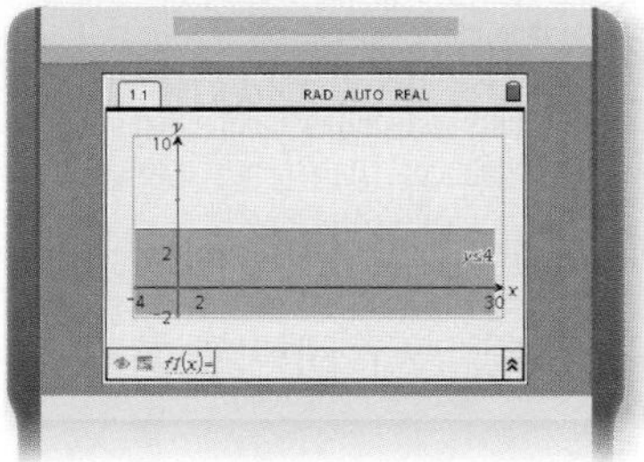

Step 2 Graph $y \le -\frac{1}{3}x + 8$. Press **tab del** ≤ and then enter $-\frac{1}{3}x + 8$.

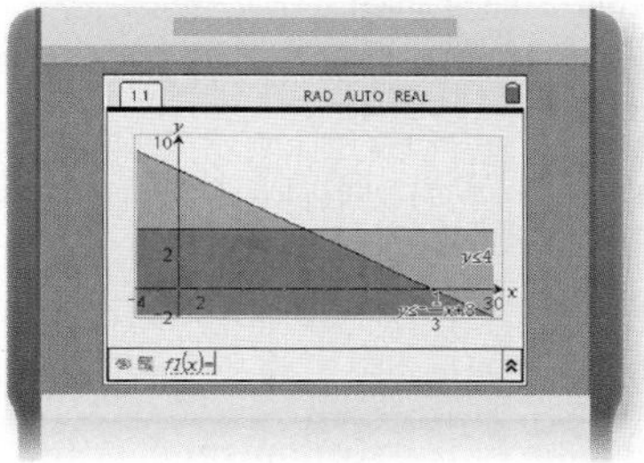

The darkest shaded region of the graph represents the solutions.

Analyze the Results

1. If Mr. Jackson charges \$75 for each car he details and \$25 for each car wash, what is the maximum amount of money he could earn in one day? **\$600**

2. What is the greatest number of car washes that Mr. Jackson could do in a day? Explain your reasoning. **24; It is the x-intercept of $y = -\frac{1}{3}x + 8$.**

1 Focus

Objective Use a graphing calculator to explore systems of inequalities.

Materials for Each Student

- TI-Nspire Technology

Teaching Tip

To start a new document, students can press **CTRL N** and then select **ADD GRAPHS.**

2 Teach

Working in Cooperative Groups

Have students work in groups of two or three, mixing abilities, to complete Steps 1 and 2 of the Activity.

- In Step 1, when changing the window settings, students should press **tab** or the down navigating arrow to move through the settings.
- If more or less contrast is needed to view the overlap of the graphs, press **CTRL +** for greater contrast and **CTRL −** for less contrast.

Practice Have students complete Exercises 1 and 2.

3 Assess

Formative Assessment

Use Exercise 1 to assess whether students can use a system of inequalities to solve a problem.

From Concrete to Abstract

Exercise 2 asks students to interpret the graph of a system of inequalities to determine a maximum value.

connectED.mcgraw-hill.com 377

Formative Assessment

KeyVocabulary The page references after each word denote where that term was first introduced. If students have difficulty answering questions 1–8, remind them that they can use these page references to refresh their memories about the vocabulary.

Summative Assessment

Vocabulary Test, p. 50

Vocabulary Review

Vocabulary Review provides students the opportunity to check their understanding of important concepts and terminology in an online game format.

FOLDABLES StudyOrganizer

Dinah Zike's Foldables®

Have students look through the chapter to make sure they have included examples in their Foldables. Suggest that students keep their Foldables handy while completing the Study Guide and Review pages. Point out that their Foldables can serve as a quick review tool when studying for the chapter test.

Additional Answers

9.

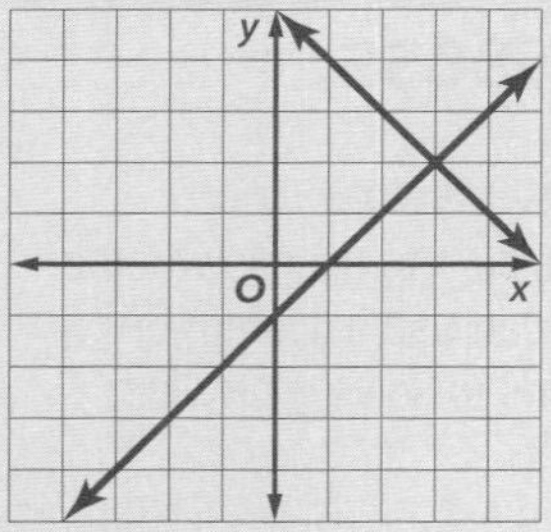

10.

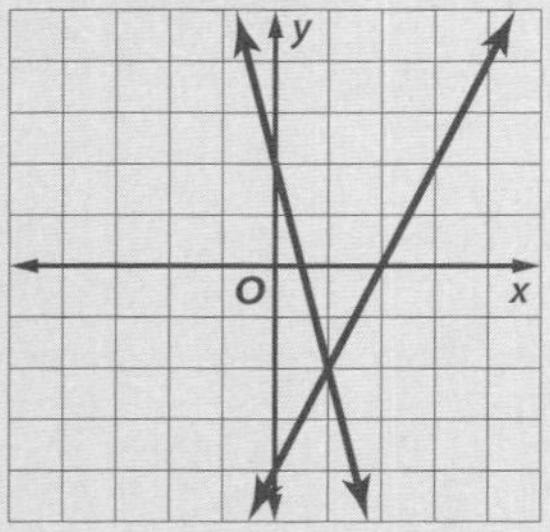

CHAPTER 6 Study Guide and Review

Study Guide

KeyConcepts

Systems of Equations (Lessons 6-1 through 6-5)

- A system with a graph of two intersecting lines has one solution and is *consistent and independent.*
- Graphing a system of equations can only provide approximate solutions. For exact solutions, you must use algebraic methods.
- In the substitution method, one equation is solved for a variable and the expression substituted into the second equation to find the value of another variable.
- In the elimination method, one variable is eliminated by adding or subtracting the equations.
- Sometimes multiplying one or both equations by a constant makes it easier to use the elimination method.
- The best method for solving a system of equations depends on the coefficients of the variables.

Systems of Inequalities (Lesson 6-6)

- A system of inequalities is a set of two or more inequalities with the same variables.
- The solution of a system of inequalities is the intersection of the graphs.

FOLDABLES StudyOrganizer

Be sure the Key Concepts are noted in your Foldable.

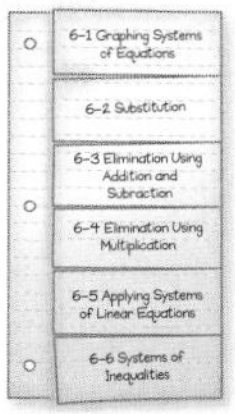

KeyVocabulary

augmented matrix (p. 370)	inconsistent (p. 335)
consistent (p. 335)	independent (p. 335)
dependent (p. 335)	matrix (p. 370)
dimension (p. 370)	substitution (p. 344)
element (p. 370)	system of equations (p. 335)
elimination (p. 350)	system of inequalities (p. 372)

VocabularyCheck

State whether each sentence is *true* or *false.* If *false,* replace the underlined term to make a true sentence.

1. If a system has at least one solution, it is said to be <u>consistent</u>. **true**
2. If a consistent system has exactly <u>two</u> solution(s), it is said to be independent. **false; one**
3. If a consistent system has an infinite number of solutions, it is said to be <u>inconsistent</u>. **false; dependent**
4. If a system has no solution, it is said to be <u>inconsistent</u>. **true**
5. <u>Substitution</u> involves substituting an expression from one equation for a variable in the other. **true**
6. In some cases, <u>dividing</u> two equations in a system together will eliminate one of the variables. This process is called elimination. **false; adding or subtracting**
7. A set of two or more inequalities with the same variables is called a <u>system of equations</u>. **false; system of inequalities**
8. When the graphs of the inequalities in a system of inequalities <u>do not intersect</u>, there are no solutions to the system. **true**

378 | Chapter 6 | Study Guide and Review

Lesson-by-Lesson Review

6-1 Graphing Systems of Equations

Graph each system and determine the number of solutions that it has. If it has one solution, name it. **9–14. See margin for graphs.**

9. $x - y = 1$
$x + y = 5$ **one; (3, 2)**

10. $y = 2x - 4$
$4x + y = 2$ **one; (1, −2)**

11. $2x - 3y = -6$
$y = -3x + 2$ **one; (0, 2)**

12. $-3x + y = -3$
$y = x - 3$ **one; (0, −3)**

13. $x + 2y = 6$
$3x + 6y = 8$ **no solution**

14. $3x + y = 5$
$6x = 10 - 2y$ **infinitely many solutions**

15. **MAGIC NUMBERS** Sean is trying to find two numbers with a sum of 14 and a difference of 4. Define two variables, write a system of equations, and solve by graphing. **See margin.**

Example 1

Graph the system and determine the number of solutions it has. If it has one solution, name it.

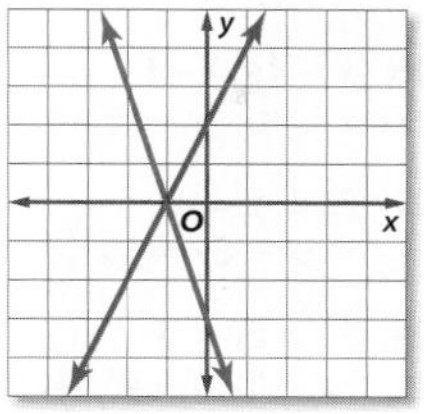

$y = 2x + 2$
$y = -3x - 3$

The lines appear to intersect at the point (−1, 0). You can check this by substituting −1 for x and 0 for y.

CHECK

$y = 2x + 2$	Original equation
$0 \stackrel{?}{=} 2(-1) + 2$	Substitution
$0 \stackrel{?}{=} -2 + 2$	Multiply.
$0 = 0$ ✓	
$y = -3x - 3$	Original equation
$0 \stackrel{?}{=} -3(-1) - 3$	Substitution
$0 \stackrel{?}{=} 3 - 3$	Multiply.
$0 = 0$ ✓	

The solution is (−1, 0).

6-2 Substitution

Use substitution to solve each system of equations.

16. $x + y = 3$
$x = 2y$ **(2, 1)**

17. $x + 3y = -28$
$y = -5x$ **(2, −10)**

18. $3x + 2y = 16$
$x = 3y - 2$ **(4, 2)**

19. $x - y = 8$
$y = -3x$ **(2, −6)**

20. $y = 5x - 3$
$x + 2y = 27$ **(3, 12)**

21. $x + 3y = 9$
$x + y = 1$ **(−3, 4)**

22. **GEOMETRY** The perimeter of a rectangle is 48 inches. The length is 6 inches greater than the width. Define the variables, and write equations to represent this situation. Solve the system by using substitution. **Sample answer: Let w be the width and let ℓ be the length; $2w + 2\ell = 48$, $\ell = w + 6$; 9 is the width and 15 is the length.**

Example 2

Use substitution to solve the system.

$3x - y = 18$
$y = x - 4$

$3x - y = 18$	First equation
$3x - (x - 4) = 18$	Substitute $x - 4$ for y.
$2x + 4 = 18$	Simplify.
$2x = 14$	Subtract 4 from each side.
$x = 7$	Divide each side by 2.

Use the value of x and either equation to find the value for y.

$y = x - 4$	Second equation
$= 7 - 4$ or 3	Substitute and simplify.

The solution is (7, 3).

Lesson-by-Lesson Review

Intervention If the given examples are not sufficient to review the topics covered by the questions, remind students that the lesson references tell them where to review that topic in their textbook.

Two-Day Option Have students complete the Lesson-by-Lesson Review. Then you can use McGraw-Hill eAssessment to customize another review worksheet that practices all the objectives of this chapter or only the objectives on which your students need more help.

Additional Answers

11.

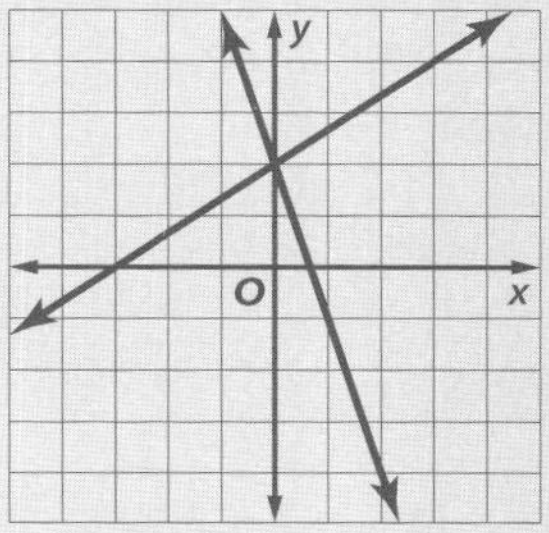

12.

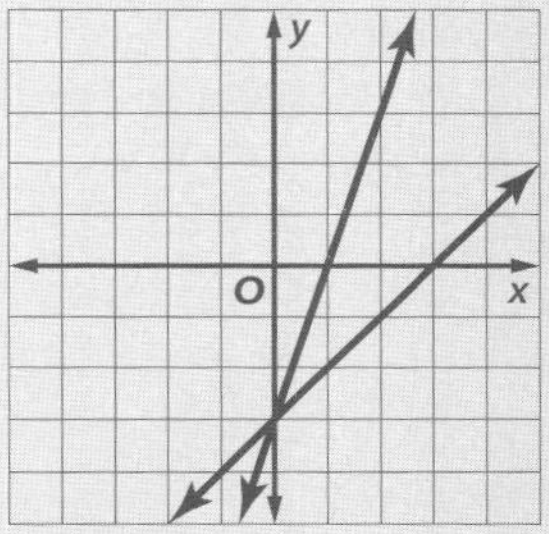

13.

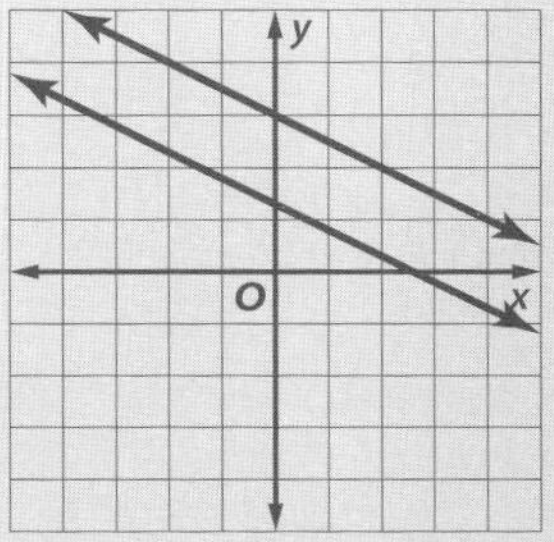

14.

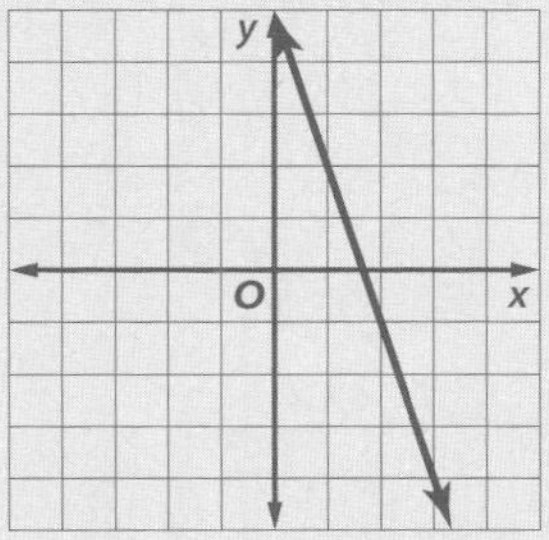

15. Sample answer: Let x be one number and y the other number; $x + y = 14$; $x - y = 4$; 9 and 5

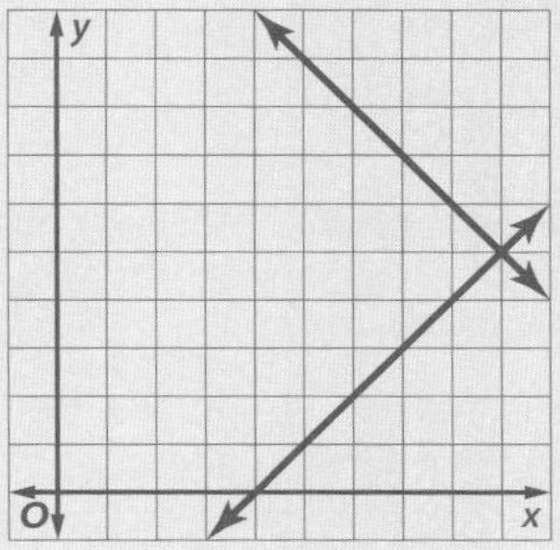

Additional Answers

31. Sample answer: Let f be the number of the first type of card, and let c be the number of the second type of card; $f + c = 24$, $f + 3c = 50$; 11 \$1 cards and 13 \$3 cards.

40. Sample answer: Let c represent the number of cakes, and let p represent the number of pies; $8c + 10p = 356$, $p + c = 40$; 22 cakes, 18 pies

CHAPTER 6 Study Guide and Review *Continued*

6-3 Elimination Using Addition and Subtraction

Use elimination to solve each system of equations.

23. $x + y = 13$, $x - y = 5$ **(9, 4)**

24. $-3x + 4y = 21$, $3x + 3y = 14$ $\left(-\frac{1}{3}, 5\right)$

25. $x + 4y = -4$, $x + 10y = -16$ **(4, −2)**

26. $2x + y = -5$, $x - y = 2$ **(−1, −3)**

27. $6x + y = 9$, $-6x + 3y = 15$ $\left(\frac{1}{2}, 6\right)$

28. $x - 4y = 2$, $3x + 4y = 38$ **(10, 2)**

29. $2x + 2y = 4$, $2x - 8y = -46$ **(−3, 5)**

30. $3x + 2y = 8$, $x + 2y = 2$ $\left(3, -\frac{1}{2}\right)$

31. BASEBALL CARDS Cristiano bought 24 baseball cards for \$50. One type cost \$1 per card, and the other cost \$3 per card. Define the variables, and write equations to find the number of each type of card he bought. Solve by using elimination. **See margin.**

Example 3

Use elimination to solve the system of equations.

$3x - 5y = 11$
$x + 5y = -3$

$$\begin{array}{rl} 3x - 5y = 11 & \\ (+)\ \ x + 5y = -3 & \\ \hline 4x \quad = 8 & \text{The variable } y \text{ is eliminated.} \\ x = 2 & \text{Divide each side by 4.} \end{array}$$

Now, substitute 2 for x in either equation to find the value of y.

$$\begin{array}{rl} 3x - 5y = 11 & \text{First equation} \\ 3(2) - 5y = 11 & \text{Substitute.} \\ 6 - 5y = 11 & \text{Multiply.} \\ -5y = 5 & \text{Subtract 6 from each side.} \\ y = -1 & \text{Divide each side by } -5. \end{array}$$

The solution is (2, −1).

6-4 Elimination Using Multiplication

Use elimination to solve each system of equations.

32. $x + y = 4$, $-2x + 3y = 7$ **(1, 3)**

33. $x - y = -2$, $2x + 4y = 38$ **(5, 7)**

34. $3x + 4y = 1$, $5x + 2y = 11$ **(3, −2)**

35. $-9x + 3y = -3$, $3x - 2y = -4$ **(2, 5)**

36. $8x - 3y = -35$, $3x + 4y = 33$ **(−1, 9)**

37. $2x + 9y = 3$, $5x + 4y = 26$ **(6, −1)**

38. $-7x + 3y = 12$, $2x - 8y = -32$ **(0, 4)**

39. $8x - 5y = 18$, $6x + 6y = -6$ **(1, −2)**

40. BAKE SALE On the first day, a total of 40 items were sold for \$356. Define the variables, and write a system of equations to find the number of cakes and pies sold. Solve by using elimination. **See margin.**

Example 4

Use elimination to solve the system of equations.

$3x + 6y = 6$
$2x + 3y = 5$

Notice that if you multiply the second equation by −2, the coefficients of the y-terms are additive inverses.

$3x + 6y = 6$
$2x + 3y = 5$ → Multiply by −2. →

$$\begin{array}{r} 3x + 6y = 6 \\ (+)\ -4x - 6y = -10 \\ \hline -x \quad = -4 \\ x = 4 \end{array}$$

Now, substitute 4 for x in either equation to find the value of y.

$$\begin{array}{rl} 2x + 3y = 5 & \text{Second equation} \\ 2(4) + 3y = 5 & \text{Substitution} \\ 8 + 3y = 5 & \text{Multiply.} \\ 3y = -3 & \text{Subtract 8 from both sides.} \\ y = -1 & \text{Divide each side by 3.} \end{array}$$

The solution is (4, −1).

6-5 Applying Systems of Linear Equations

Determine the best method to solve each system of equations. Then solve the system.

41. $y = x - 8$ **Subs.;** $y = -3x$ **(2, −6)**

42. $y = -x$ **Subs.;** $y = 2x$ **(0, 0)**

43. $x + 3y = 12$ **Subs.;** $x = -6y$ **(24, −4)**

44. $x + y = 10$ **Elim (+);** $x - y = 18$ **(14, −4)**

45. $3x + 2y = -4$; $5x + 2y = -8$

46. $6x + 5y = 9$ **Elim (×);** $-2x + 4y = 14$ **(−1, 3)**

47. $3x + 4y = 26$; $2x + 3y = 19$

48. $11x - 6y = 3$ **Elim (×);** $5x - 8y = -25$ **(3, 5)**

45. Elim (−); (−2, 1) **47. Elim (×); (2, 5)**

49. COINS Tionna has saved dimes and quarters in her piggy bank. Define the variables, and write a system of equations to determine the number of dimes and quarters. Then solve the system using the best method for the situation.

50. FAIR At a county fair, the cost for 4 slices of pizza and 2 orders of French fries is $21.00. The cost of 2 slices of pizza and 3 orders of French fries is $16.50. To find out how much a single slice of pizza and an order of French fries costs, define the variables and write a system of equations to represent the situation. Determine the best method to solve the system of equations. Then solve the system. (Lesson 6-5)

Example 5

Determine the best method to solve the system of equations. Then solve the system.

$3x + 5y = 4$
$4x + y = -6$

The coefficient of y is 1 in the second equation. So solving by substitution is a good method. Solve the second equation for y.

$4x + y = -6$	Second equation
$y = -6 - 4x$	Subtract $4x$ from each side.

Substitute $-6 - 4x$ for y in the first equation.

$3x + 5(-6 - 4x) = 4$	Substitute.
$3x - 30 - 20x = 4$	Distributive Property
$-17x - 30 = 4$	Simplify.
$-17x = 34$	Add 30 to each side.
$x = -2$	Divide by −17.

Last, substitute -2 for x in either equation to find y.

$4x + y = -6$	Second equation
$4(-2) + y = -6$	Substitute.
$-8 + y = -6$	Multiply.
$y = 2$	Add 8 to each side.

The solution is $(-2, 2)$.

49. Sample answer: Let d represent the dimes and q represent the quarters; $d + q = 25$; $0.10d + 0.25q = 4$; 15 dimes, 10 quarters.

50. Let p represent the cost of a slice of pizza and f represent the cost of an order of French fries; $4p + 2f = 21$, $2p + 3f = 16.5$; Sample answer: elimination; pizza $3.75; French fries $3.

connectED.mcgraw-hill.com 381

Anticipation Guide

Have students complete the Chapter 6 Anticipation Guide and discuss how their responses have changed now that they have completed Chapter 6.

Additional Answers

51.

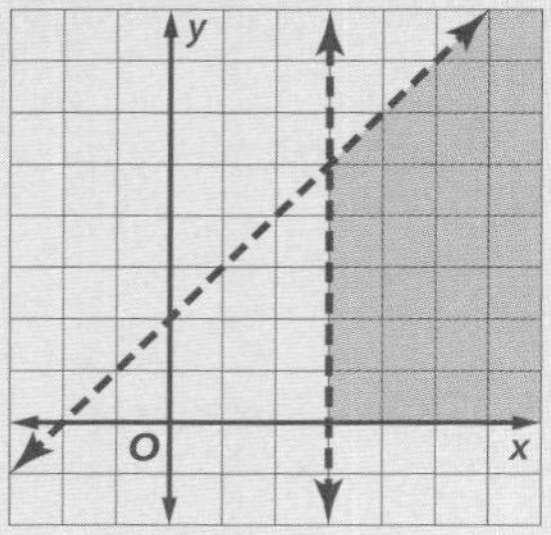

52.

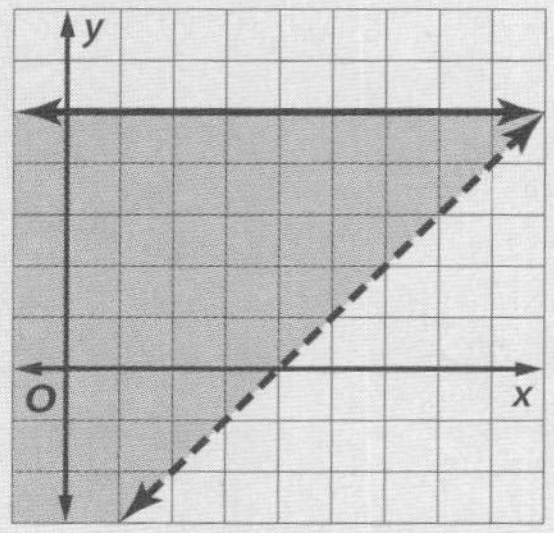

53.

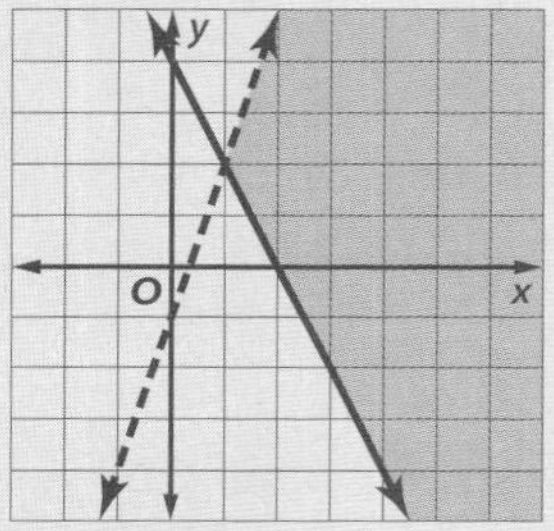

CHAPTER 6 Study Guide and Review *Continued*

6-6 Systems of Inequalities

Solve each system of inequalities by graphing.

51. $x > 3$
$y < x + 2$

52. $y \leq 5$
$y > x - 4$

53. $y < 3x - 1$
$y \geq -2x + 4$

54. $y \leq -x - 3$
$y \geq 3x - 2$

51–54. See margin.

55. JOBS Kishi makes $7 an hour working at the grocery store and $10 an hour delivering newspapers. She cannot work more than 20 hours per week. Graph two inequalities that Kishi can use to determine how many hours she needs to work at each job if she wants to earn at least $90 per week. **See margin.**

Example 6

Solve the system of inequalities by graphing.

$y < 3x + 1$
$y \geq -2x + 3$

The solution set of the system is the set of ordered pairs in the intersection of the two graphs. This portion is shaded in the graph below.

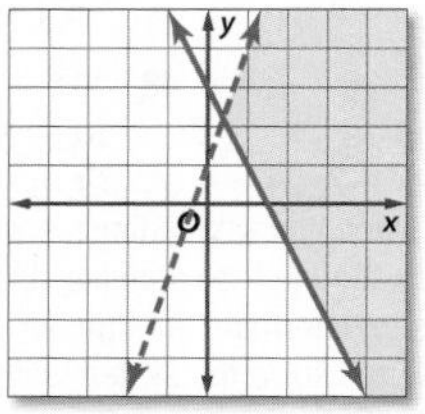

54.

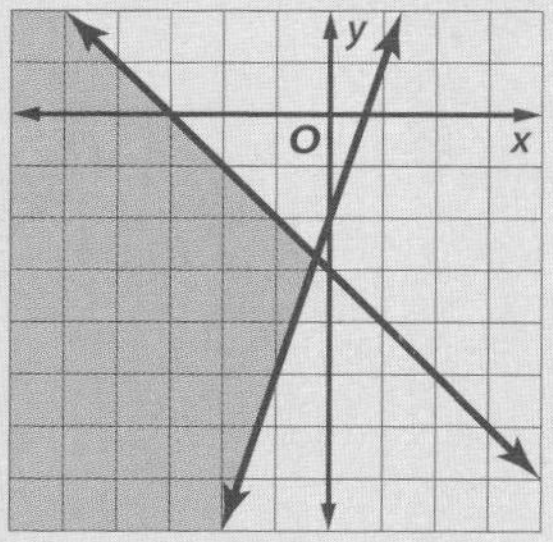

55.

Jobs

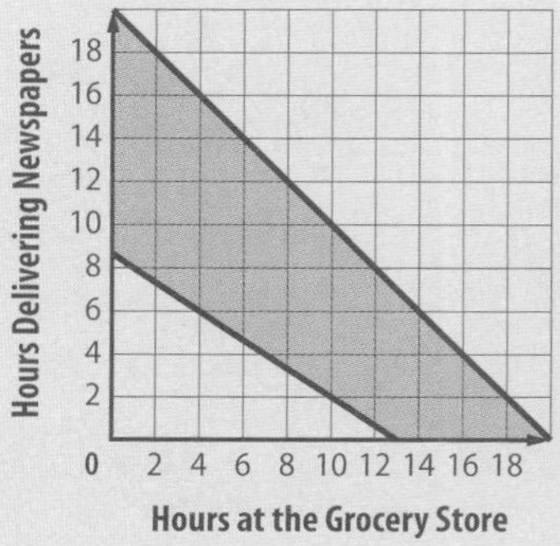

382 | Chapter 6 | Study Guide and Review

CHAPTER 6 Practice Test

Graph each system and determine the number of solutions that it has. If it has one solution, name it.

1. $y = 2x$
   $y = 6 - x$ one; (2, 4)
2. $y = x - 3$
   $y = -2x + 9$ one; (4, 1)
3. $x - y = 4$
   $x + y = 10$ one; (7, 3)
4. $2x + 3y = 4$
   $2x + 3y = -1$ no solution

1–4. See Ch. 6 Answer Appendix for graphs.

Use substitution to solve each system of equations.

5. $y = x + 8$
   $2x + y = -10$ (−6, 2)
6. $x = -4y - 3$
   $3x - 2y = 5$ (1, −1)
7. **GARDENING** Corey has 42 feet of fencing around his garden. The garden is rectangular in shape, and its length is equal to twice the width minus 3 feet. Define the variables, and write a system of equations to find the length and width of the garden. Solve the system by using substitution. See margin.

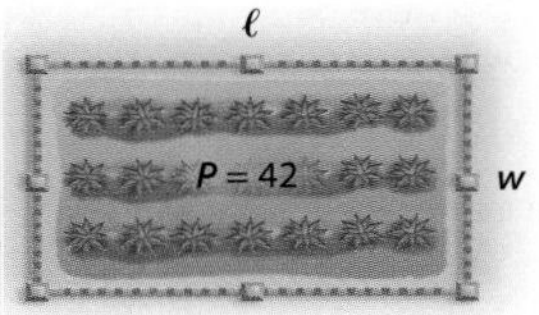

8. **MULTIPLE CHOICE** Use elimination to solve the system. B

$$6x - 4y = 6$$
$$-6x + 3y = 0$$

   A (5, 6)
   B (−3, −6)
   C (1, 0)
   D (4, −8)

9. **SHOPPING** Shelly has $175 to shop for jeans and sweaters. Each pair of jeans costs $25, each sweater costs $20, and she buys 8 items. Determine the number of pairs of jeans and sweaters Shelly bought. 3 jeans, 5 sweaters

Use elimination to solve each system of equations.

10. $x + y = 13$
    $x - y = 5$ (9, 4)
11. $3x + 7y = 2$
    $3x - 4y = 13$ (3, −1)
12. $x + y = 8$
    $x - 3y = -4$ (5, 3)
13. $2x + 6y = 18$
    $3x + 2y = 13$ (3, 2)
14. **MAGAZINES** Julie subscribes to a sports magazine and a fashion magazine. She received 24 issues this year. The number of fashion issues is 6 less than twice the number of sports issues. Define the variables, and write a system of equations to find the number of issues of each magazine. See margin.

Determine the best method to solve each system of equations. Then solve the system.

15. $y = 3x$
    $x + 2y = 21$ Subst.; (3, 9)
16. $x + y = 12$
    $y = x - 4$ Subst.;(8, 4)
17. $x + y = 15$
    $x - y = 9$ Elim. (+); (12, 3)
18. $3x + 5y = 7$
    $2x - 3y = 11$ Elim. (×); (4, −1)

19. $24p + 4c = 320$, $2p + c = 50$; Sample answer: subsitution; paper $7.50 per ream, inkjet cartridge, $35 each.

19. **OFFICE SUPPLIES** At a sale, Ricardo bought 24 reams of paper and 4 inkjet cartridges for $320. Britney bought 2 reams of paper and 1 inkjet cartridge for $50. The reams of paper were all the same price and the inkjet cartridges were all the same price. Write a system of equations to represent this situation. Determine the best method to solve the system of equations. Then solve the system.

20–23. See Ch. 6 Answer Appendix.

Solve each system of inequalities by graphing.

20. $x > 2$
    $y < 4$
21. $x + y \leq 5$
    $y \geq x + 2$
22. $3x - y > 9$
    $y > -2x$
23. $y \geq 2x + 3$
    $-4x - 3y > 12$

Summative Assessment

Use these alternate leveled chapter tests to differentiate assessment for your students.

Leveled Chapter 6 Tests

Form	Type	Level	Page(s)
1	MC	AL	51–52
2A	MC	OL	53–54
2B	MC	OL	55–56
2C	FR	OL	57–58
2D	FR	OL	59–60
3	FR	BL	61–62
Vocabulary Test			50
Extended-Response Test			63

MC = multiple-choice questions
FR = free-response questions

McGraw-Hill eAssessment Customize and create multiple versions of your chapter test and their answer keys. All of the questions from the leveled chapter tests in the *Chapter 6 Resource Masters* are also available on McGraw-Hill eAssessment.

Additional Answers

7. Sample answer: Let w be the width and let ℓ be the length; $2w + 2\ell = 42$, $\ell = 2w - 3$; $w = 8$ ft, $\ell = 13$ ft
14. Let f = the number of fashion magazines and s = the number of sports magazines. Then $f + s = 24$, and $f = 2s - 6$. So $s = 10$ and $f = 14$.

InterventionPlanner

TIER 1 On Level OL

If students miss about 25% of the exercises or less,

Then choose a resource:

SE Lessons 6-1 through 6-6
Skills Practice, pp. 7, 14, 20, 26, 32, and 38
TE Chapter Project
connectED.mcgraw-hill.com Self-Check Quiz

TIER 2 Strategic Intervention AL approaching grade level

If students miss about 50% of the exercises,

Then choose a resource:

Study Guide and Intervention, Chapter 6, pp. 5, 12, 18, 24, 30, and 36
Quick Review Math Handbook
connectED.mcgraw-hill.com Extra Examples, Personal Tutor, Homework Help

TIER 3 Intensive Intervention 2 or more grades below level

If students miss about 75% of the exercises,

Then use *Math Triumphs, Alg. 1*

connectED.mcgraw-hill.com Extra Examples, Personal Tutor, Homework Help, Review Vocabulary

1 Focus

Objective Use the strategy of guess and check to solve standardized test problems.

2 Teach

Scaffolding Questions

Ask:

- Have you ever used a guess to choose an answer on a test? If yes, why did you guess the answer? Answers will vary.
- Did you check the guess? If yes, how did you check it? Answers will vary.
- Why do you think it makes sense to check a guess? Sample answer: A guess could be wrong, so checking it could show that it is wrong and that you need to make another guess.

CHAPTER 6 Preparing for Standardized Tests

Guess and Check

It is very important to pace yourself and keep track of how much time you have when taking a standardized test. If time is running short, or if you are unsure how to solve a problem, the guess and check strategy may help you determine the correct answer quickly.

Strategies for Guessing and Checking

Step 1

Carefully look over each possible answer choice, and evaluate for reasonableness. Eliminate unreasonable answers.

Ask yourself:

- Are there any answer choices that are clearly incorrect?
- Are there any answer choices that are not in the proper format?
- Are there any answer choices that do not have the proper units for the correct answer?

Step 2

For the remaining answer choices, use the guess and check method.

- **Equations:** If you are solving an equation, substitute the answer choice for the variable and see if this results in a true number sentence.
- **Inequalities:** Likewise, you can substitute the answer choice for the variable and see if it satisfies the inequality.
- **System of Equations:** Find the answer choice that satisfies both equations of the system.

Step 3

Choose an answer choice and see if it satisfies the constraints of the problem statement. Identify the correct answer.

- If the answer choice you are testing does not satisfy the problem, move on to the next reasonable guess and check it.
- When you find the correct answer choice, stop. You do not have to check the other answer choices.

Standardized Test Example

Read the problem. Identify what you need to know. Then use the information in the problem to solve.

Solve $\begin{cases} 4x - 8y = 20 \\ -3x + 5y = -14 \end{cases}$.

A (5, 0)

B (4, −2)

C (3, −1)

D (−6, −5)

The solution of a system of equations is an ordered pair, (x, y). Since all four answer choices are of this form, they are all possible correct answers and must be checked. Begin with the first answer choice and substitute it in each equation. Continue until you find the ordered pair that satisfies both equations of the system.

	First Equation	Second Equation
Guess: (5, 0)	$4x - 8y = 20$ $4(5) - 8(0) = 20$ ✓	$-3x + 5y = -14$ $-3(5) + 5(0) \neq -14$ ✗

	First Equation	Second Equation
Guess: (4, −2)	$4x - 8y = 20$ $4(4) - 8(-2) \neq 20$ ✗	$-3x + 5y = -14$ $-3(4) + 5(-2) \neq -14$ ✗

	First Equation	Second Equation
Guess: (3, −1)	$4x - 8y = 20$ $4(3) - 8(-1) = 20$ ✓	$-3x + 5y = -14$ $-3(3) + 5(-1) = -14$ ✓

The ordered pair (3, −1) satisfies both equations of the system. So, the correct answer is C.

Exercises

Read each problem. Eliminate any unreasonable answers. Then use the information in the problem to solve.

1. Gina bought 5 hot dogs and 3 soft drinks at the ball game for $11.50. Renaldo bought 4 hot dogs and 2 soft drinks for $8.50. How much does a single hot dog and a single drink cost? B

A hot dogs: $1.25
soft drinks: $1.50

B hot dogs: $1.25
soft drinks: $1.75

C hot dogs: $1.50
soft drinks: $1.25

D hot dogs: $1.50
soft drinks: $1.75

2. The bookstore hopes to sell at least 30 binders and calculators each week. The store also hopes to have sales revenue of at least $200 in binders and calculators. How many binders and calculators could be sold to meet both of these sales goals? H

Store Prices	
Item	**Price**
binders	$3.65
calculators	$14.80

F 25 binders, 5 calculators

G 12 binders, 15 calculators

H 22 binders, 9 calculators

J 28 binders, 6 calculators

Additional Example

Solve $2x + 5y = -18$
$-4x + 3y = 10$ C

A (6, −6)

B (1, −4)

C (−4, −2)

D (−9, 0)

3 Assess

Use Exercises 1 and 2 to assess students' understanding.

connectED.mcgraw-hill.com 385

Diagnose Student Errors

Survey student responses for each item. Class trends may indicate common errors and misconceptions.

1. A misunderstood concept of possible solutions for a system of equations
B misunderstood concept of possible solutions for a system of equations
C misunderstood concept of possible solutions for a system of equations
D correct

2. F correct
G added x-terms and constants incorrectly
H added y-terms incorrectly
J added constant terms incorrectly

3. A transposed the results
B misunderstood how to solve a system of equations
C added equations and divided constant by coefficients
D correct

4. F correct
G guess or calculation error
H guess or calculation error
J guess or calculation error

5. A error in identifying quadrants
B misunderstood how to solve system of inequalities
C correct
D error in drawing quadrants

6. F did not choose the *best* answer
G correct
H confused one solution and infinite number of solutions
J misunderstood concept of possible solutions for a system of equations

7. A added x-terms incorrectly
B added y-terms incorrectly
C added x-terms and constants incorrectly
D correct

8. F solved for the first equation only
G solved for the second equation only
H guess
J correct

CHAPTER 6

Standardized Test Practice

Cumulative, Chapters 1 through 6

Multiple Choice

Read each question. Then fill in the correct answer on the answer document provided by your teacher or on a sheet of paper.

1. Which of the following terms *best* describes the system of equations shown in the graph? D

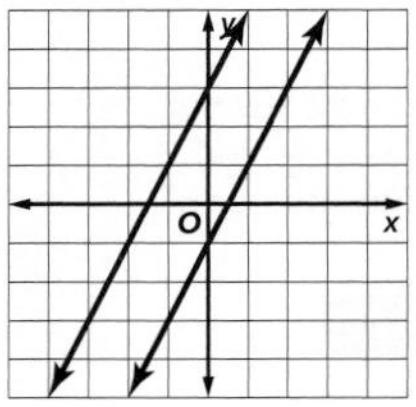

A consistent
B consistent and dependent
C consistent and independent
D inconsistent

2. Use substitution to solve the system of equations below. F

$$\begin{cases} y = 4x - 7 \\ 3x - 2y = -1 \end{cases}$$

F (3, 5)　　H (5, −2)
G (4, −1)　　J (−6, 2)

3. Which ordered pair is the solution of the system of linear equations shown below? D

$$\begin{cases} 3x - 8y = -50 \\ 3x - 5y = -38 \end{cases}$$

A $\left(\frac{5}{8}, \frac{3}{2}\right)$　　C $\left(-\frac{2}{7}, \frac{4}{9}\right)$
B (4, −9)　　D (−6, 4)

4. A home goods store received \$881 from the sale of 4 table saws and 9 electric drills. If the receipts from the saws exceeded the receipts from the drills by \$71, what is the price of an electric drill? F

F \$45　　H \$108
G \$59　　J \$119

5. A region is defined by this system. C

$$y > -\frac{1}{2}x - 1$$
$$y > -x + 3$$

In which quadrant(s) of the coordinate plane is the region located?

A I and IV only　　C I, II, and IV only
B III only　　D II and III only

6. Which of the following terms *best* describes the system of equations shown in the graph? G

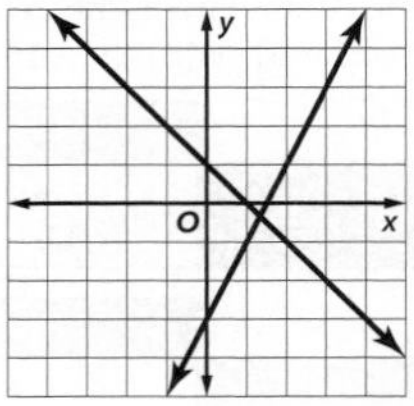

F consistent
G consistent and independent
H consistent and dependent
J inconsistent

7. Use elimination to solve the system of equations below. D

$$3x + 2y = -2$$
$$2x - 2y = -18$$

A (1, 3)　　C (−2, −3)
B (7, −4)　　D (−4, 5)

8. What is the solution of the following system of equations? J

$$\begin{cases} y = 6x - 1 \\ y = 6x + 1 \end{cases}$$

F (2, 11)　　H (7, 5)
G (−3, −14)　　J no solution

Test-Taking Tip

Question 8 You can subtract the second equation from the first equation to eliminate the x-variable. Then solve for y.

386 | Chapter 6 | Standardized Test Practice

Short Response/Gridded Response

Record your answers on the answer sheet provided by your teacher or on a sheet of paper.

9. **GRIDDED RESPONSE** Angie and her sister have \$15 to spend on pizza. A medium pizza costs \$11.50 plus \$0.75 per topping. What is the maximum number of toppings Angie and her sister can get on their pizza? **4**

10. Write an inequality for the graph below. $y > \frac{3}{4}x - 1$

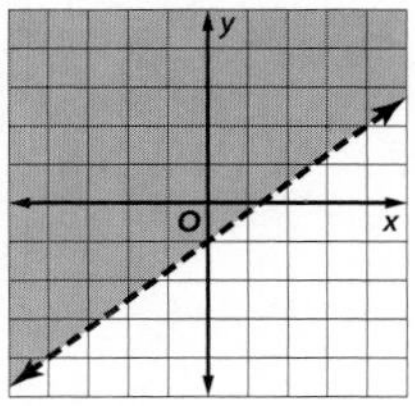

11. **GRIDDED RESPONSE** Christy is taking a road trip. After she drives 12 more miles, she will have driven at least half of the 108-mile trip. What is the least number of miles she has driven so far? **42**

12 Write an equation in slope-intercept form with a slope of $-\frac{2}{3}$ and a y-intercept of 6. $y = -\frac{2}{3}x + 6$

13. A rental company charges \$9.50 per hour for a scooter plus a \$15 fee. Write an equation in slope-intercept form for the total rental cost C of renting a scooter for h hours. $C = 9.5h + 15$

14. **GRIDDED RESPONSE** A computer supplies store is having a storewide sale this weekend. An inkjet printer that normally sells for \$179.00 is on sale for \$143.20. What is the percent discount of the sale price? **20**

15. In 1980, the population of Kentucky was about 3.66 million people. By 2000, this number had grown to about 4.04 million people. What was the annual rate of change in population from 1980 to 2000? **about 19,000 people per year**

16. Joseph's cell phone service charges him \$0.15 per text. Write an equation that represents the cost C of his cell phone service for t texts sent each month. $C = 0.15t$

17. A store is offering a \$15 mail-in-rebate on all printers. If Mark is looking at printers that range from \$45 to \$89, how much can he expect to pay? **\$30 to \$74**

Extended Response

Record your answers on a sheet of paper. Show your work.

18. The table shows how many canned goods were collected during the first day of a charity food drive.

Food Drive Day 1 Results	
Class	**Number Collected**
10th graders	78
11th graders	80
12th graders	92

a. Estimate how many canned goods will be collected during the 5-day food drive. Explain your answer. **a–b. See margin.**

b. Is this estimate a reasonable expectation? Explain.

Need ExtraHelp?

If you missed Question...	1	2	3	4	5	6	7	8	9	10	11	12	13	14	15	16	17	18
Go to Lesson...	6-1	6-2	6-3	6-3	6-6	6-1	6-3	6-3	5-3	5-6	5-3	4-2	4-2	2-7	2-7	3-4	5-4	1-4

Additional Answers

18a. 250 canned goods were collected on Day 1. So after 5 days 1,250 will be collected.

18b. Sample answer: No, because the number of canned goods will likely fluctuate from day-today.

Formative Assessment

You can use these pages to benchmark student progress.

Standardized Test Practice, pp. 64–66

Answer Sheet Practice

Have students simulate taking a standardized test by recording their answers on a practice recording sheet.

Student Recording Sheet

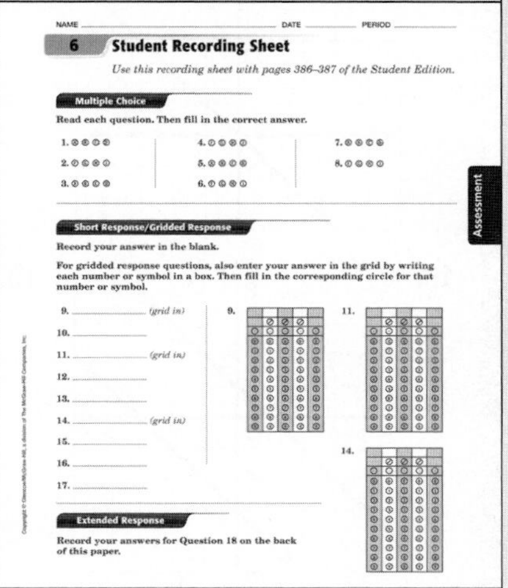
NAME DATE PERIOD

6 Student Recording Sheet

Use this recording sheet with pages 386–387 of the Student Edition.

Multiple Choice

Read each question. Then fill in the correct answer.

Short Response/Gridded Response

Record your answer in the blank.

For gridded response questions, also enter your answer in the grid by writing each number or symbol in a box. Then fill in the corresponding circle for that number or symbol.

Extended Response

Record your answers for Question 18 on the back of this paper.

McGraw-Hill eAssessment Create practice tests that align to your state standards, the Common Core State Standards, and other national standards such as TIMSS and NAEP.

Homework Option

Get Ready for Chapter 7 Assign students the exercises on p. 389 as homework to assess whether they possess the prerequisite skills needed for the next chapter.

Lesson 6-1 (Guided Practice)

2A.

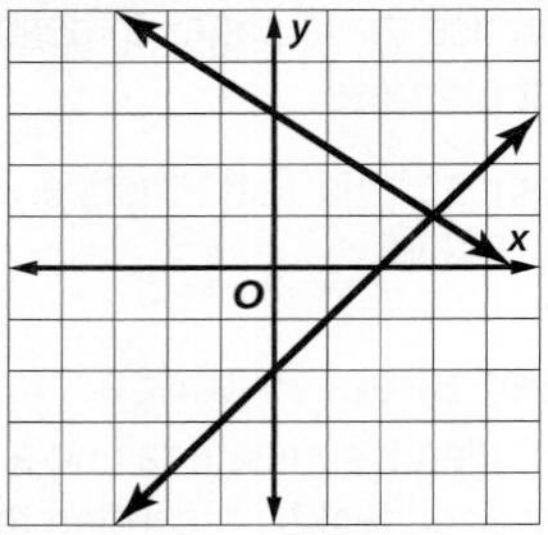

2B.

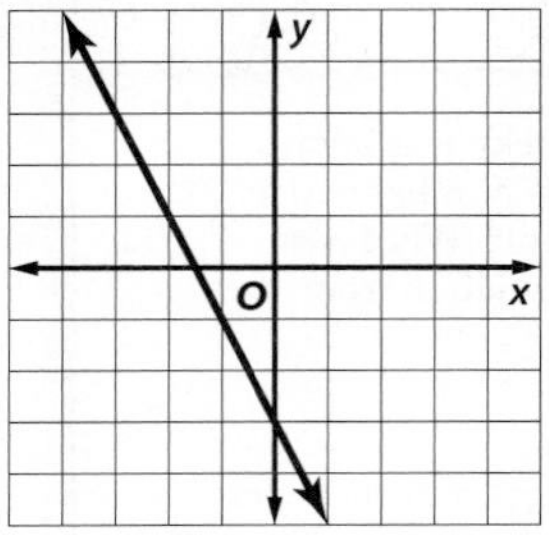

Lesson 6-1

16.

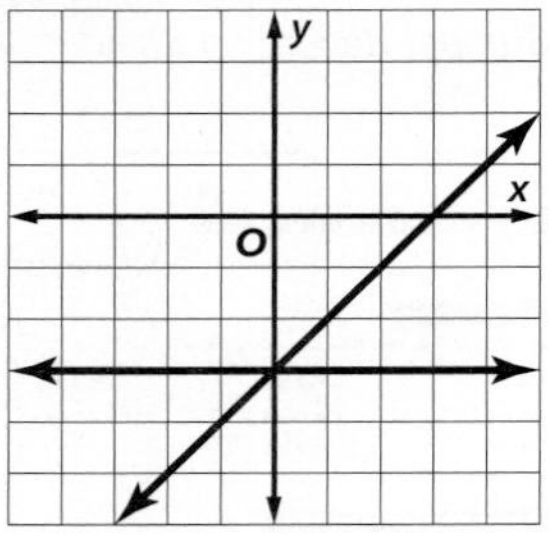

17.

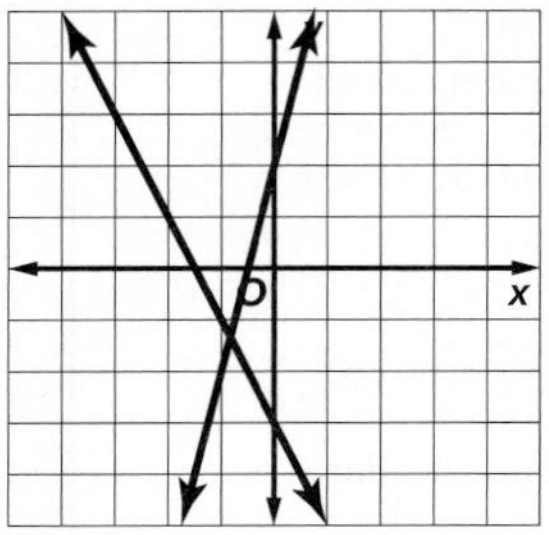

18.

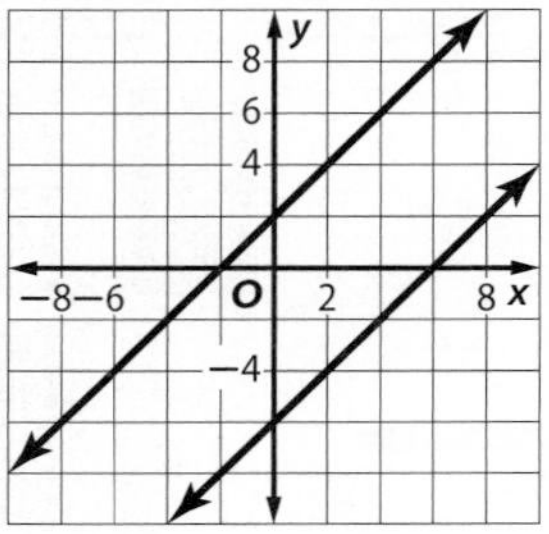

19.

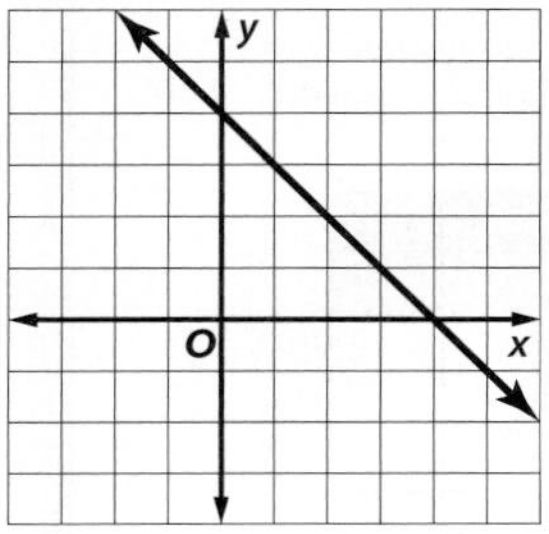

20.

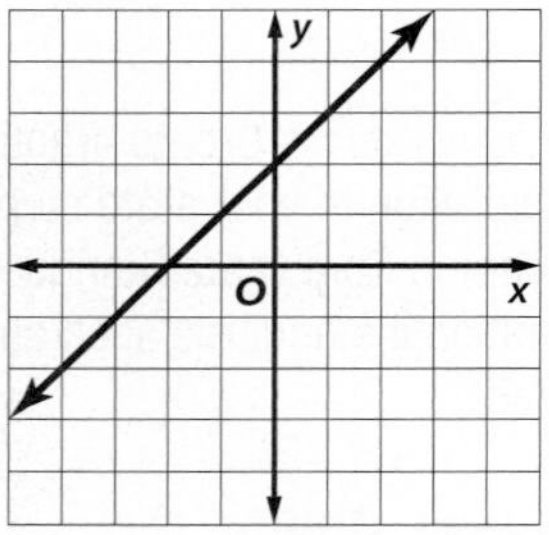

21.

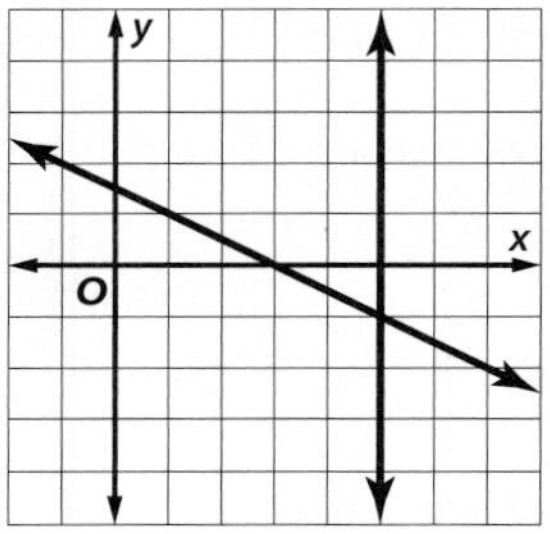

22.

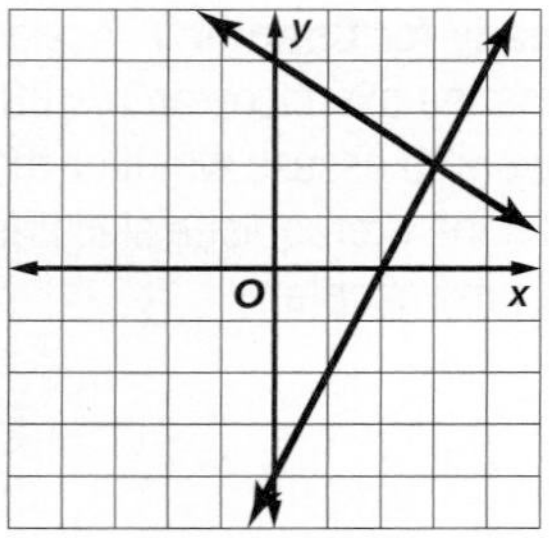

23.

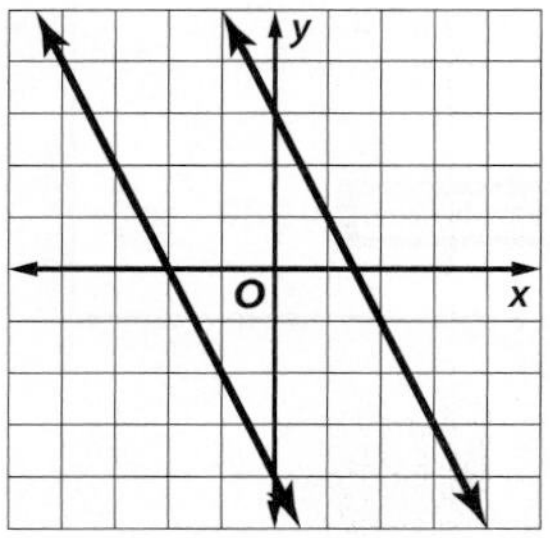

24.

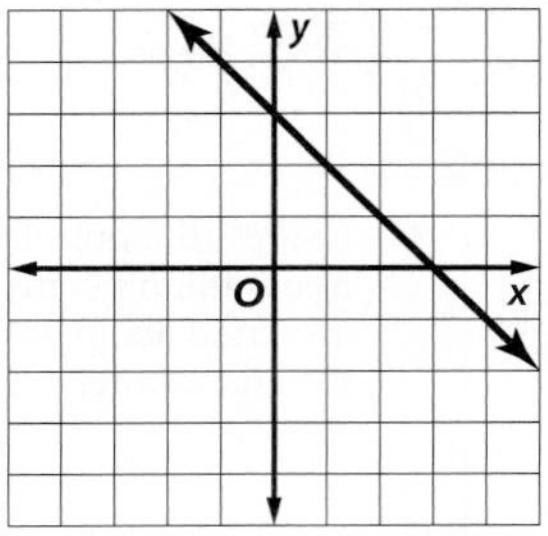

25b.

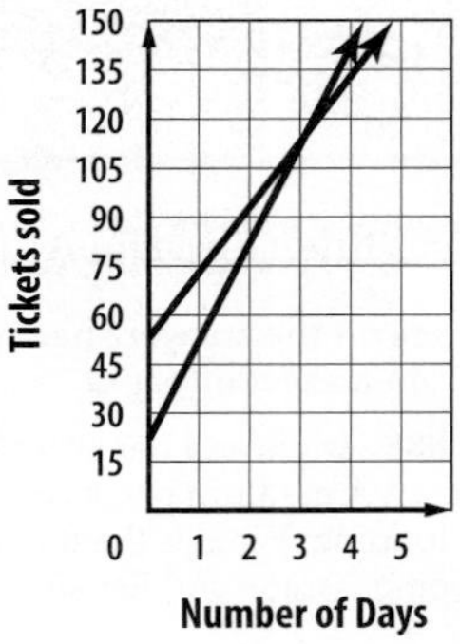

26a.

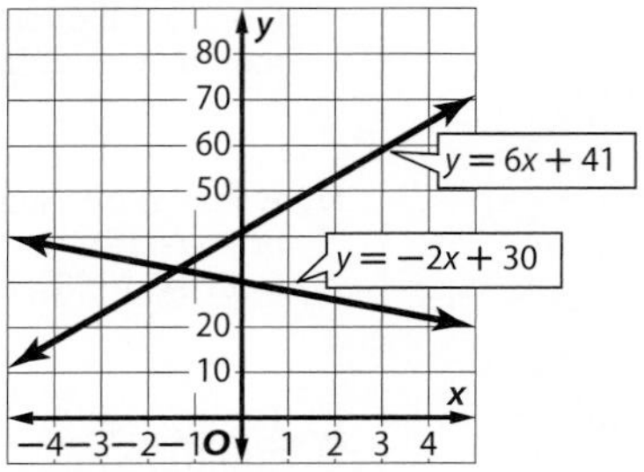

27.

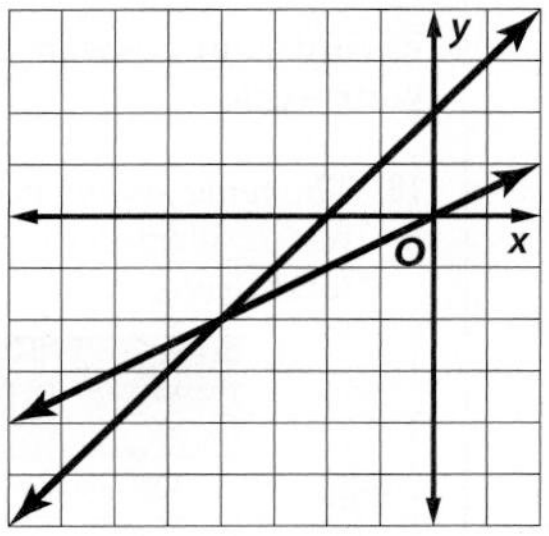

28.

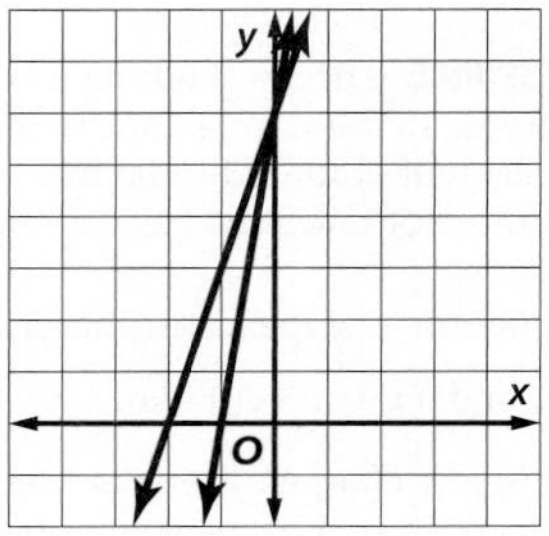

29.

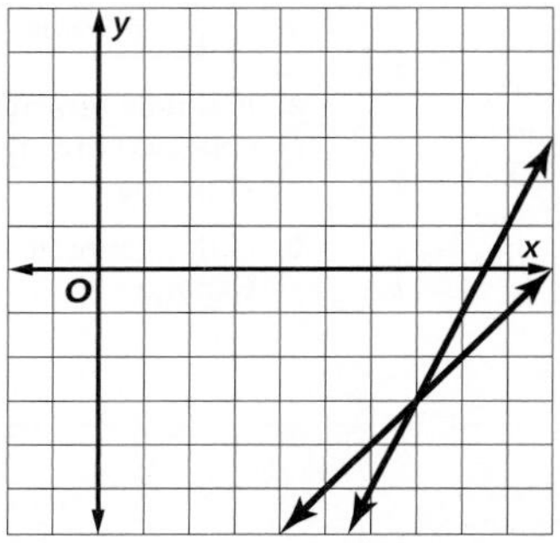

30.

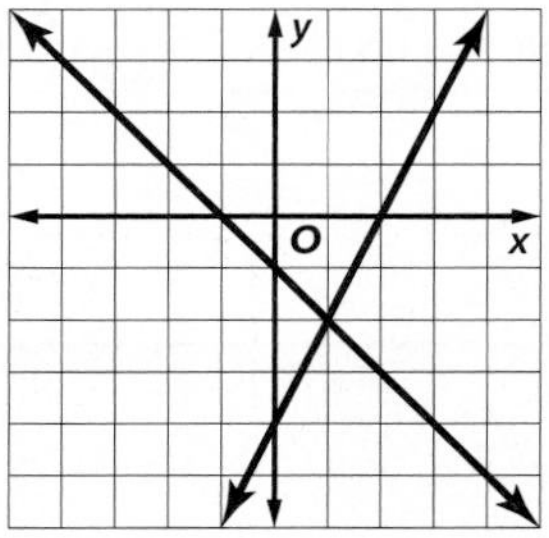

31.

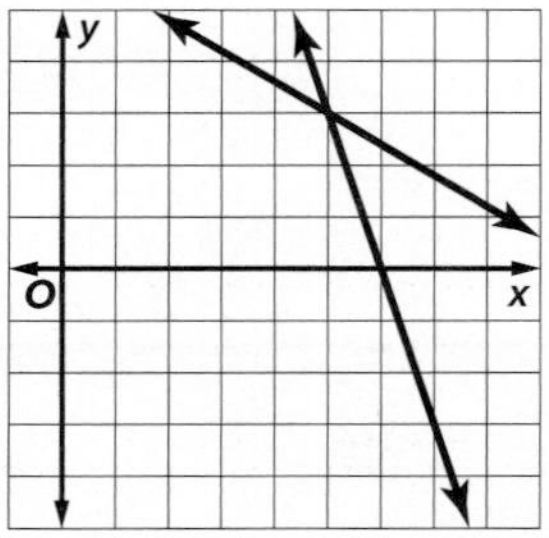

32.

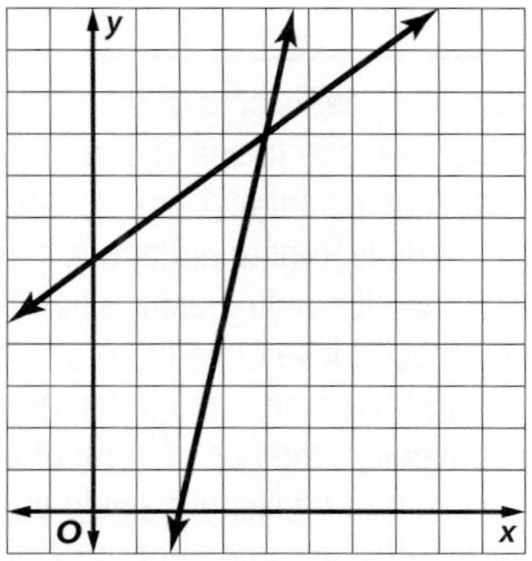

33.

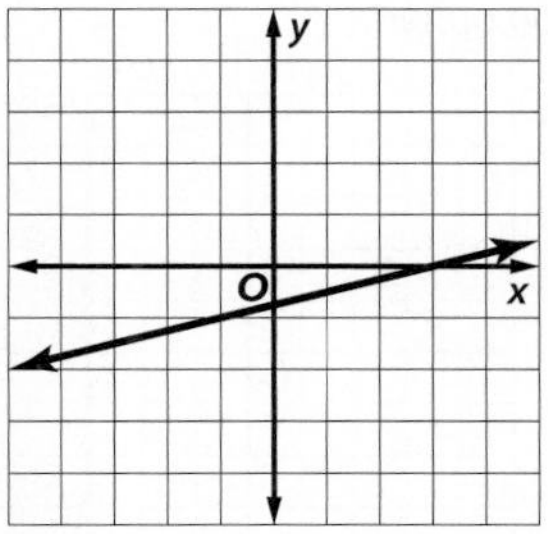

34.

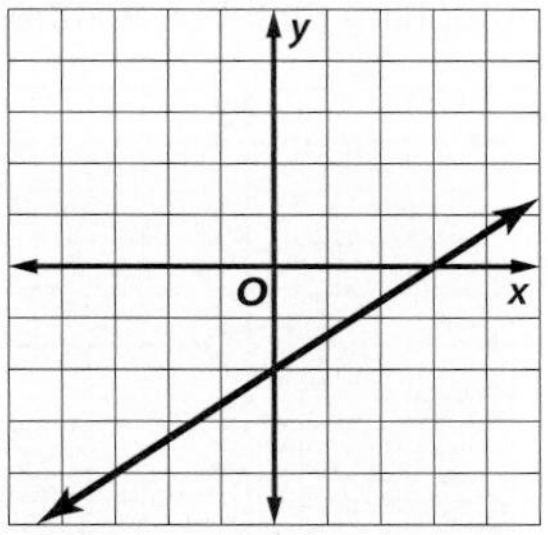

35.

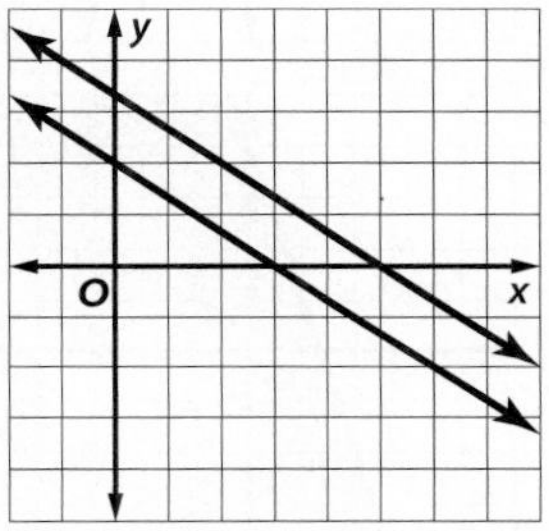

36.

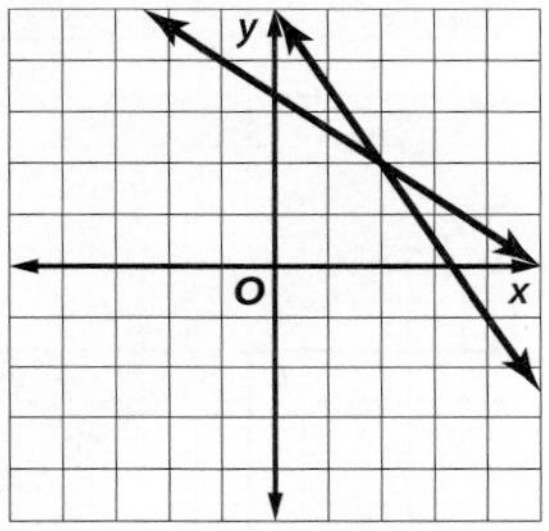

37.

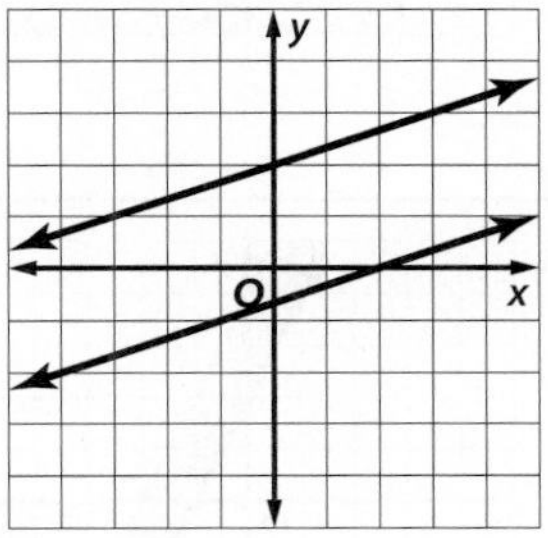

38.

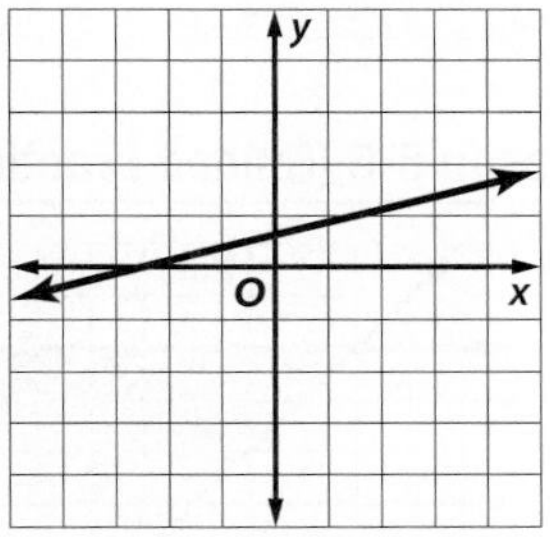

39.

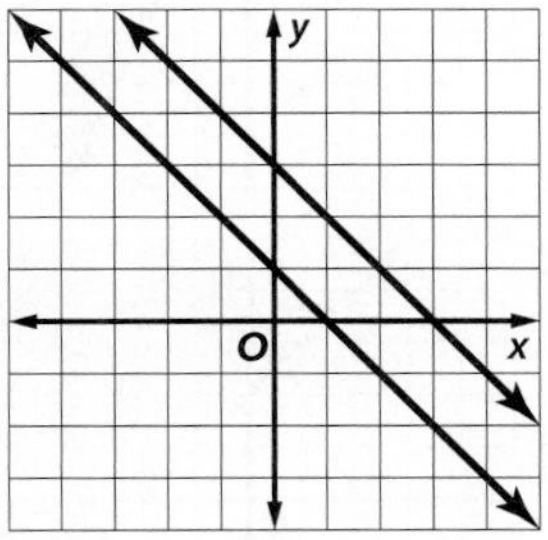

40.

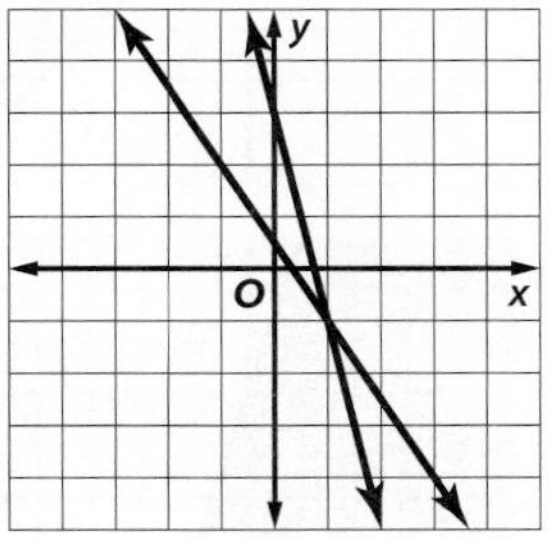

41.

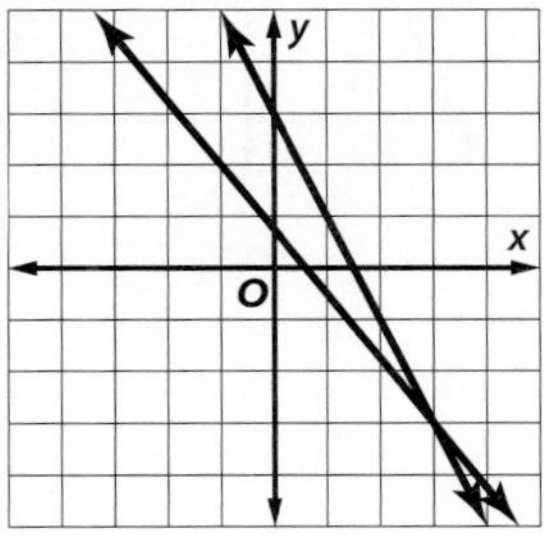

42a.

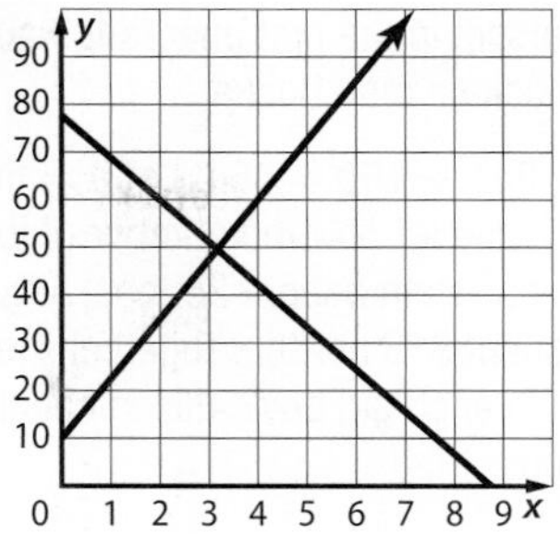

43.

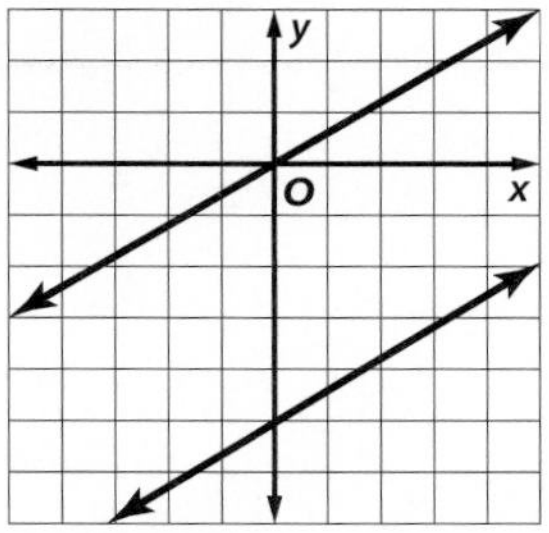

44.

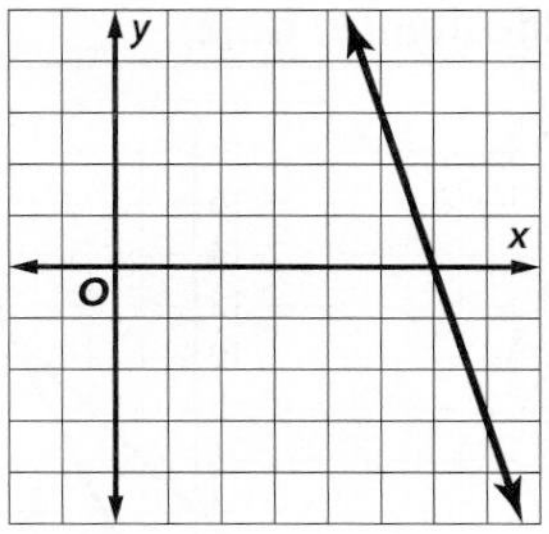

48.

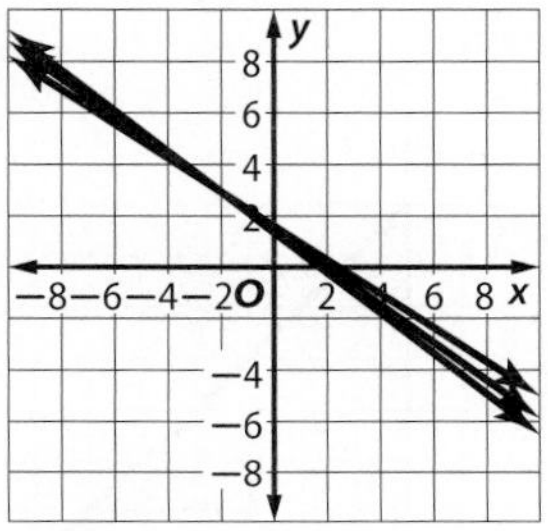

Lesson 6-2

26a. Let $x =$ number of tickets purchased and let $y =$ the cost; $y = 65x + 10$, $y = 69x + 13.60$.

26b.

Booker's Concert Tickets	
Number of Tickets	Cost($)
1	75
2	140
3	205
4	270
5	335

Paula's Concert Tickets	
Number of Tickets	Cost($)
1	82.60
2	151.60
3	220.60
4	289.60
5	358.60

26c.

Tickets

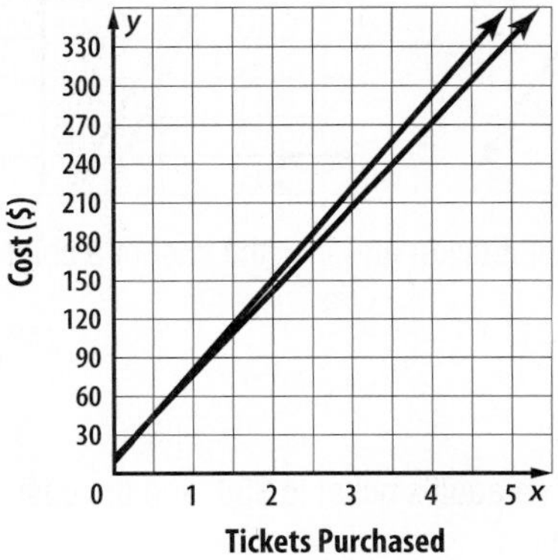

26d. Since the graphs do not intersect in the first quadrant, Paula is always paying more for the tickets than Booker.

30. Sample answer: $a + b = 25$, $24a + 16b = 464$; Let $a =$ the number of tops Allison bought, and let $b =$ the number of tops Beth bought; together, Allison and Beth bought 25 tops. Allison spent \$24 per top, and Beth spent \$16 per top. Together they spent \$464. How many tops did each girl buy? Allison bought 8 tops, and Beth bought 17 tops.

Mid-Chapter Quiz

3.

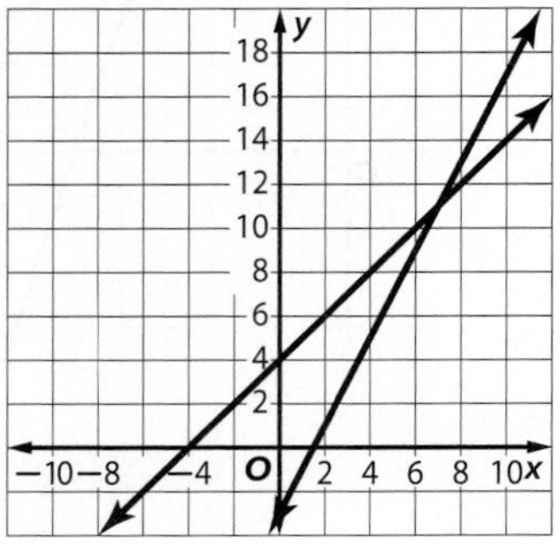

4.

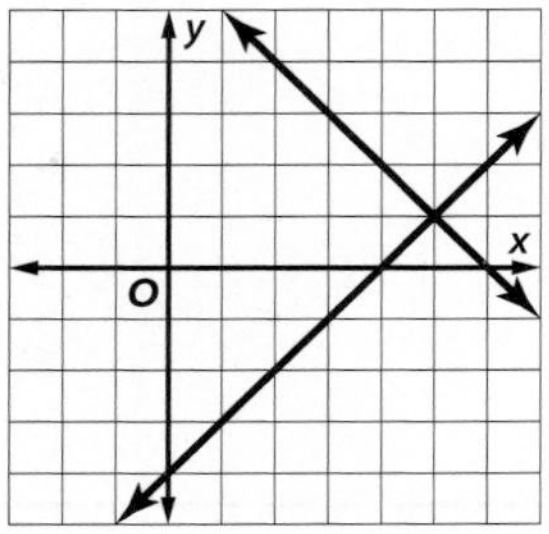

5.

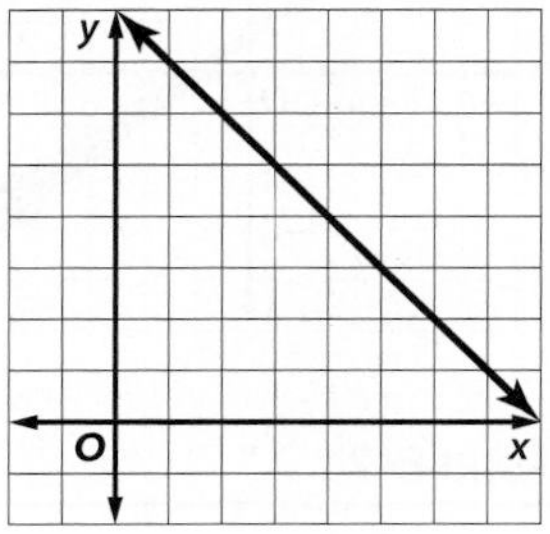

6.

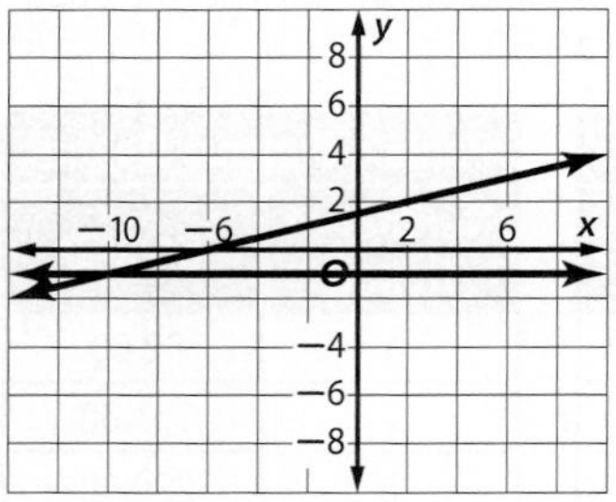

7.

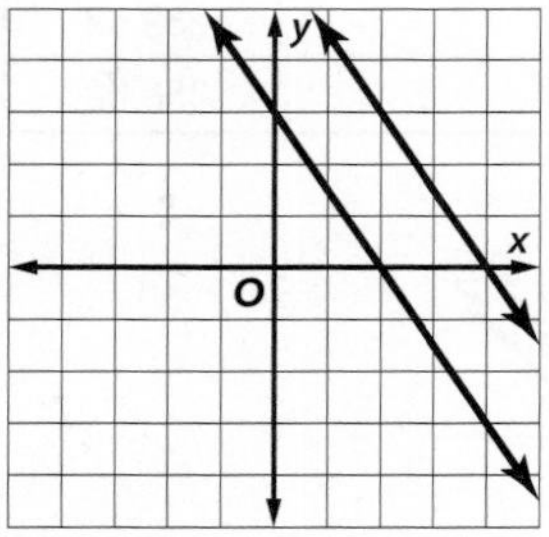

8.

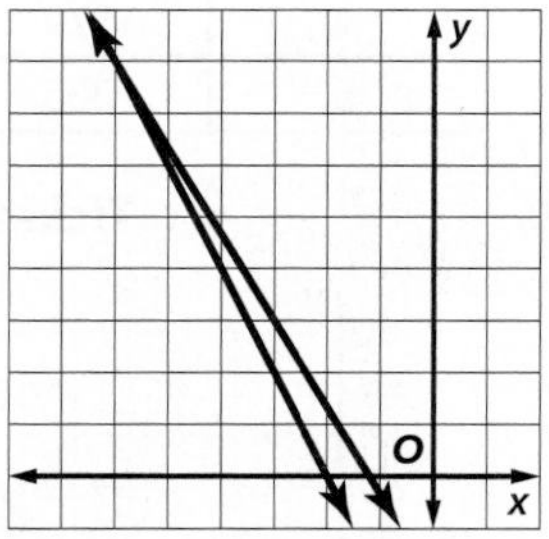

14a. Let $a =$ cost of an adult ticket and $c =$ the cost of a child ticket.

14b. $4a + 2c = 184$
$4a + 3c = 200$

14c. (38, 16); The cost of an adult's ticket is \$38, and the cost of a child's ticket is \$16.

Lesson 6-5

26. Sample answer: You can analyze the coefficients of the terms in each equation to determine which method to use. If one of the variables in either equation has a coefficient of 1 or −1, then substitution could be used. If a variable in both equations has coefficients that are opposites, then elimination using addition may be the most convenient method. If a variable in both equations has coefficients that are the same, elimination using subtraction may be the most convenient method. If none of these conditions are met, elimination using multiplication could be used. If both equations are written in slope-intercept form, graphing might be another solution option.

35.

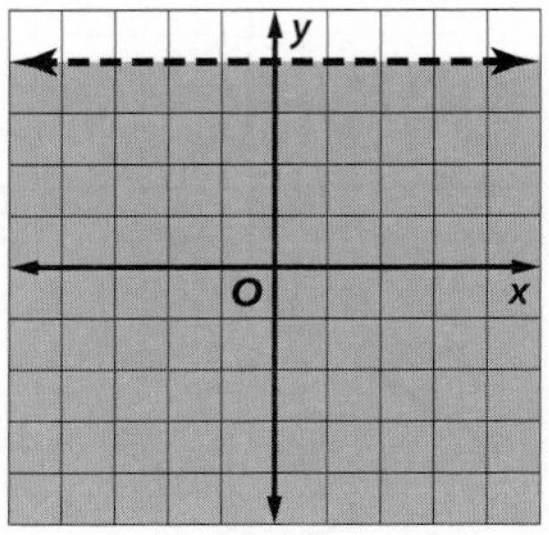

36.

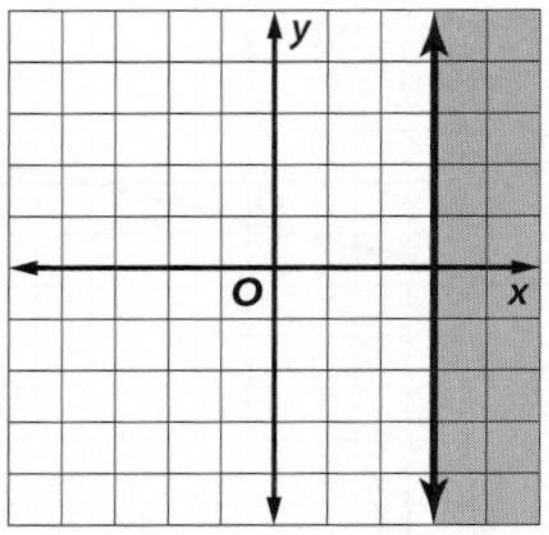

37.

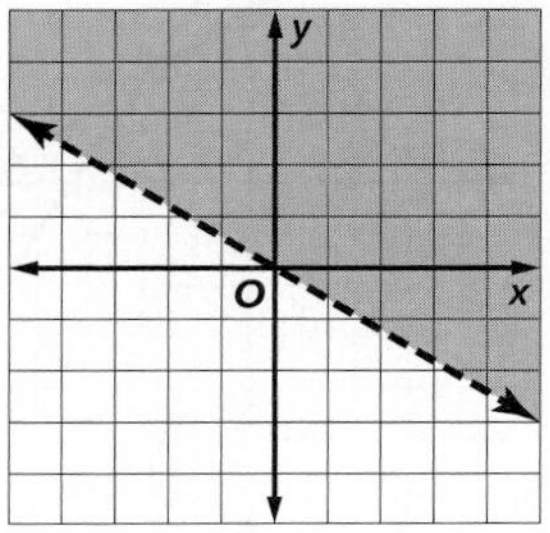

38.

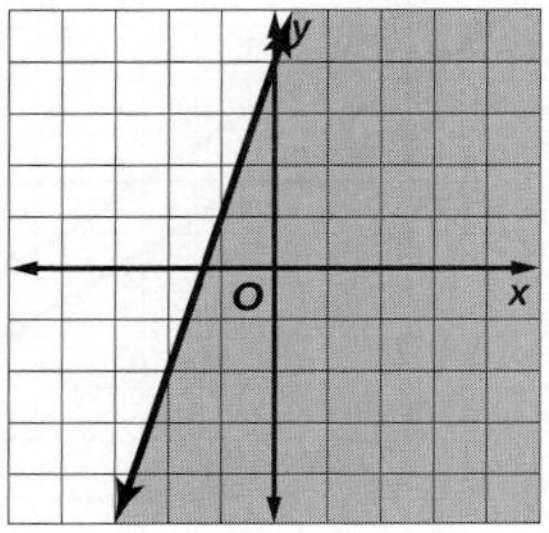

Lesson 6-6 (Guided Practice)

1A.

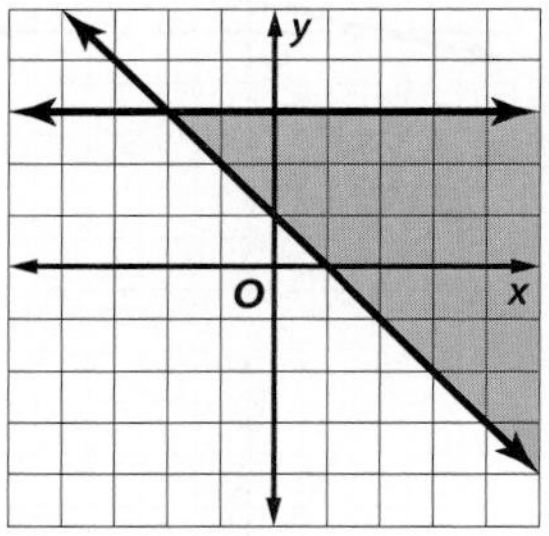

1B.

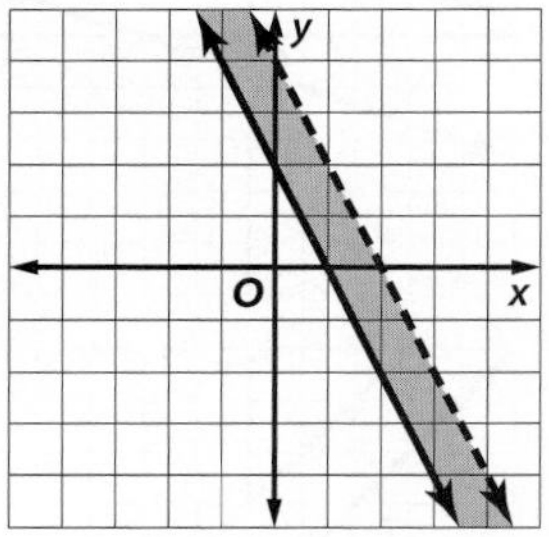

1C.

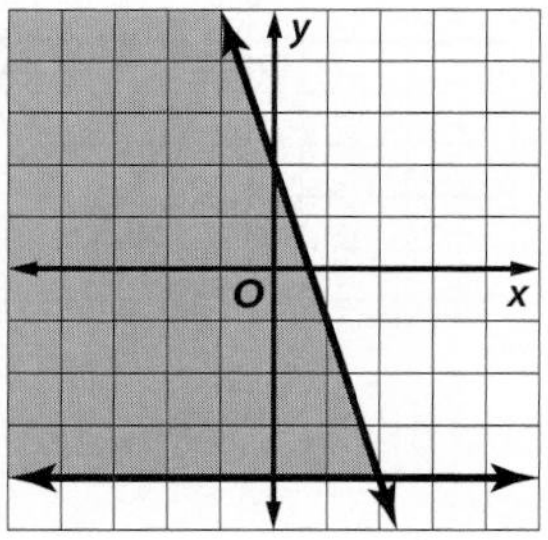

1D.

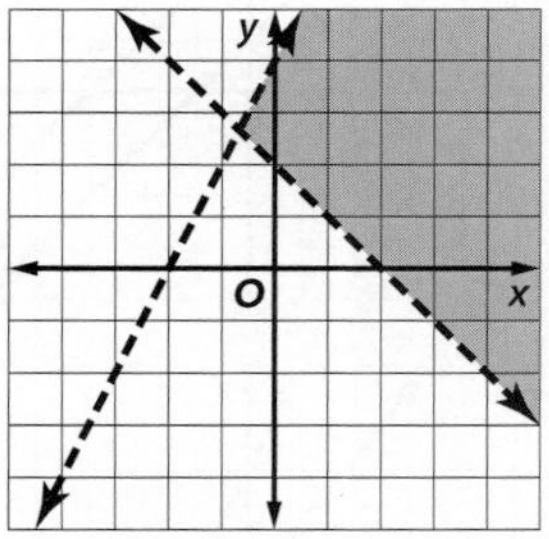

2A. no solution

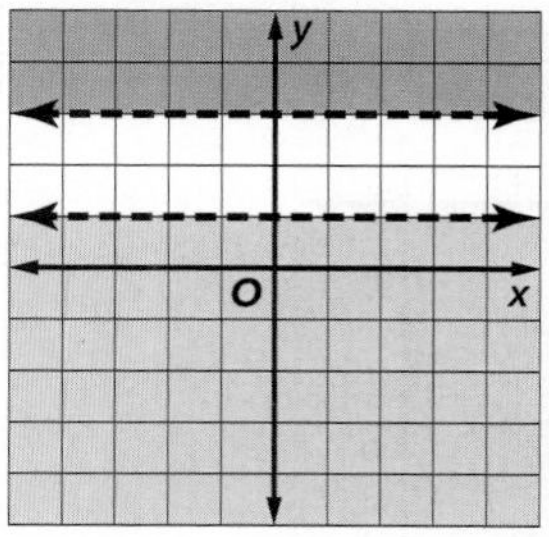

2B. no solution

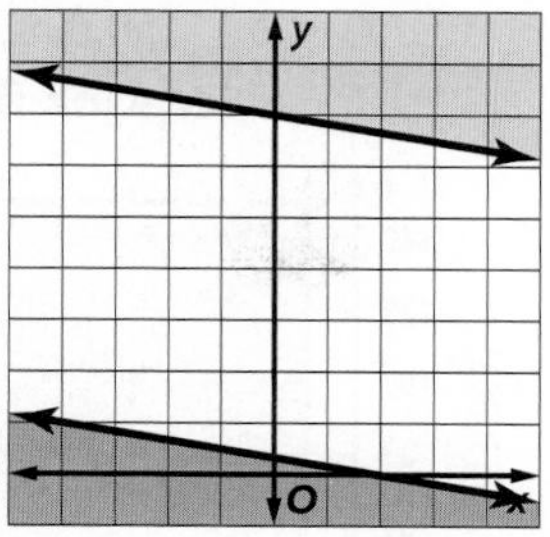

3A. Let $w =$ the number of sweatshirts and $t =$ the number of T-shirts; $w + t \leq 120$ and $22w + 15t \geq 2000$.

3B.

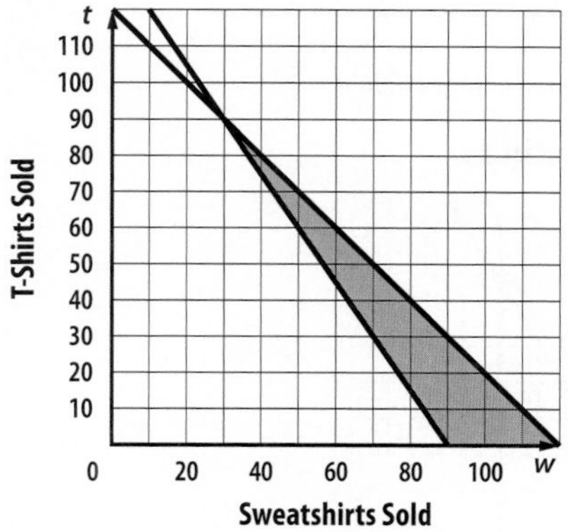

Lesson 6-6

1.

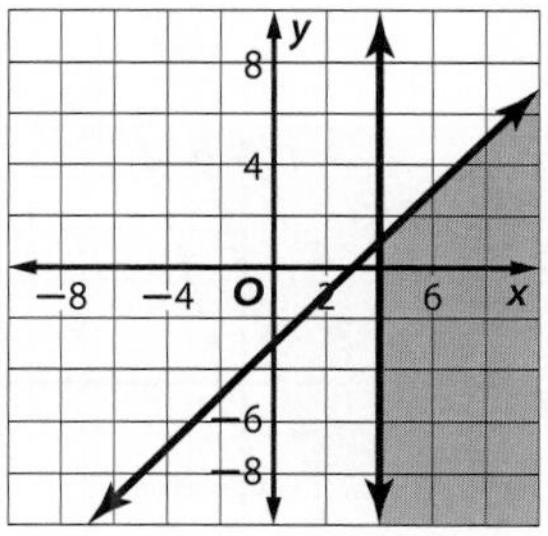

2.

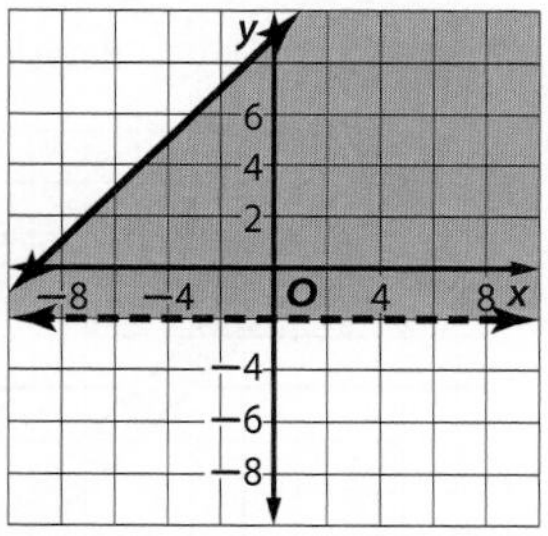

3.

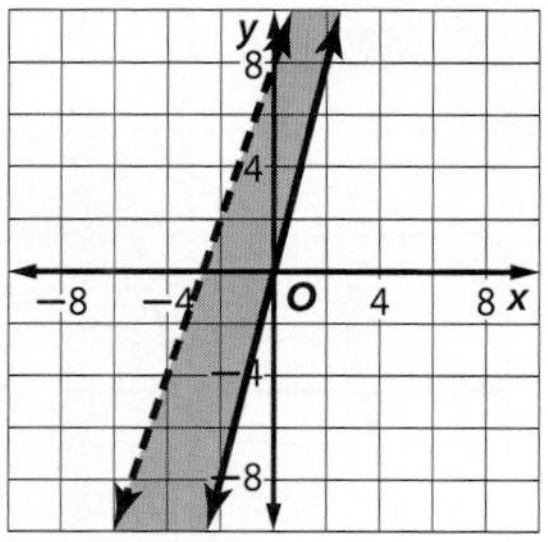

4.

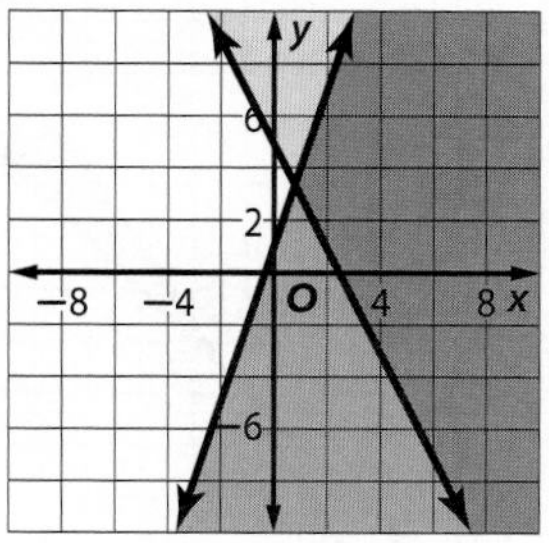

5. no solution

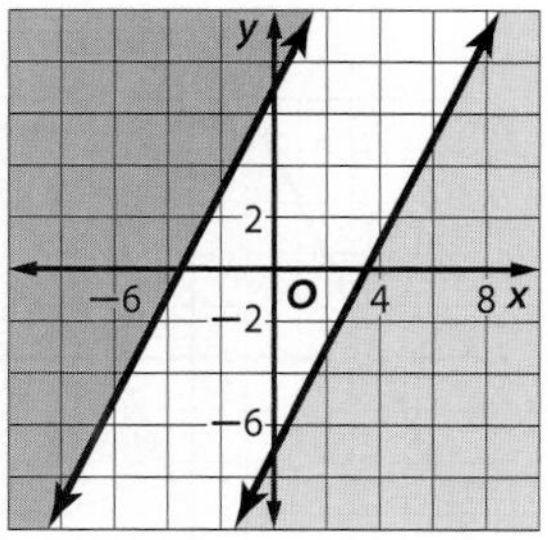

6.

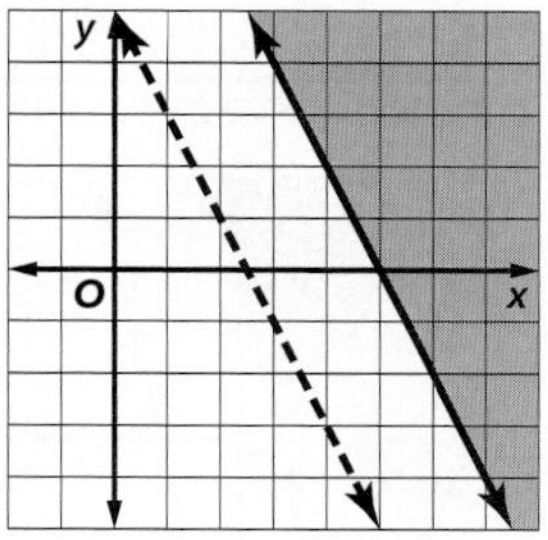

7.

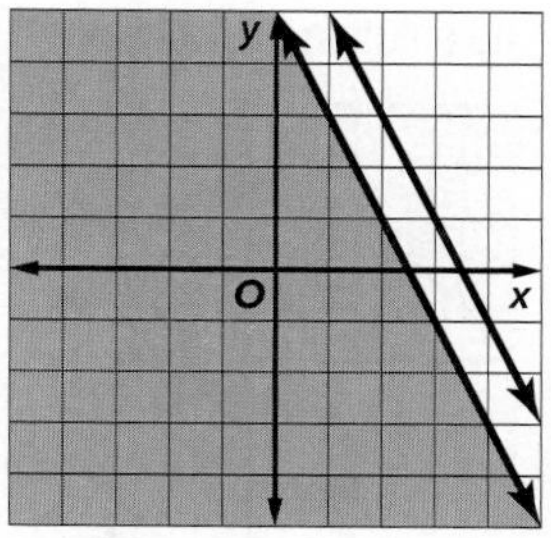

8. no solution

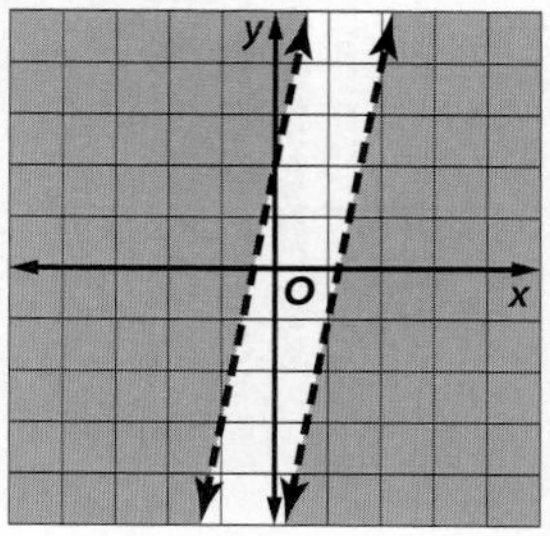

9a. Let $h =$ the height of the driver in inches and $w =$ the weight of the driver in pounds; $h < 79$ and $w < 295$.

Driving Requirements

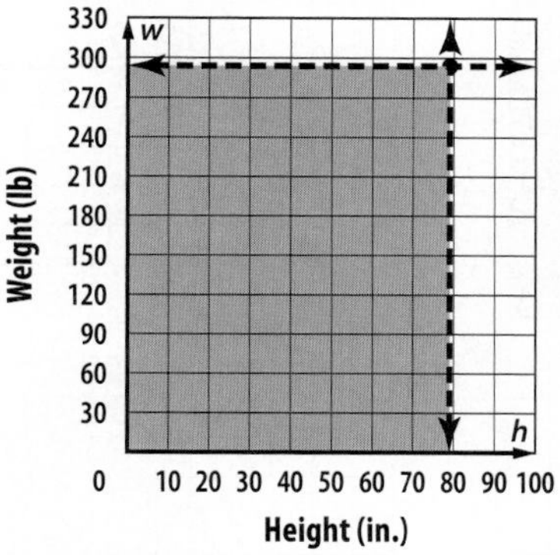

10.

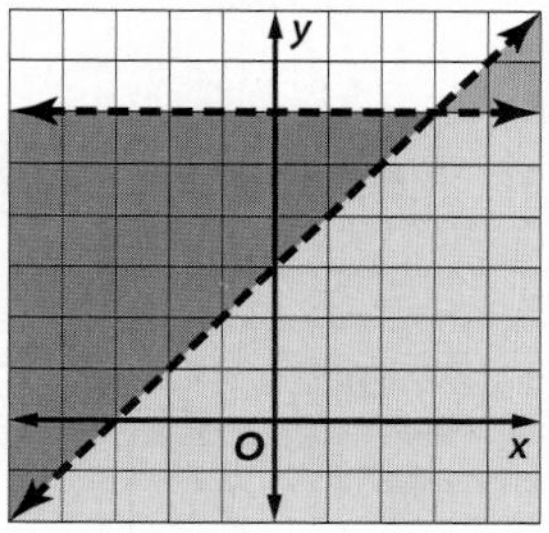

11.

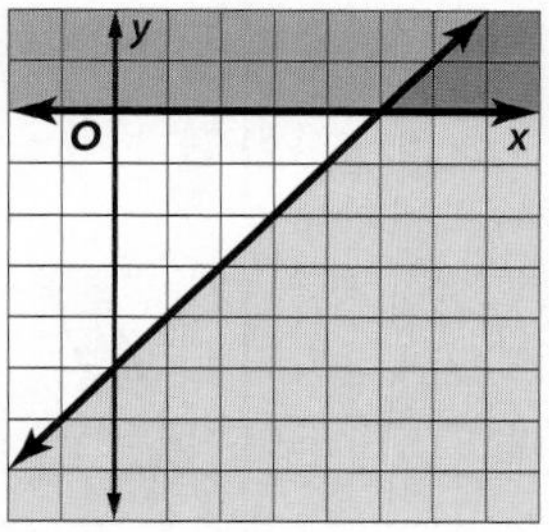

12.

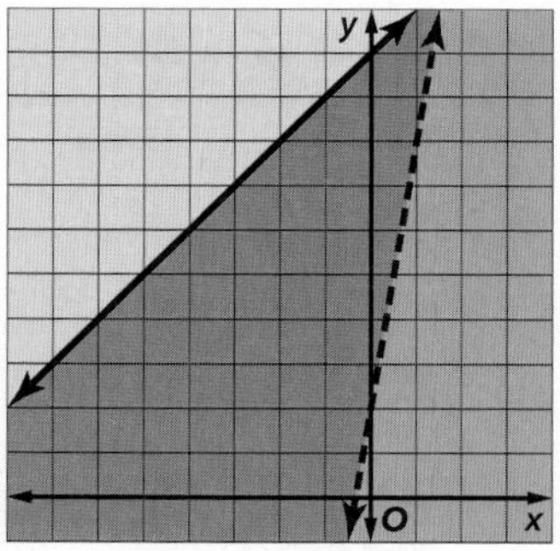

13.

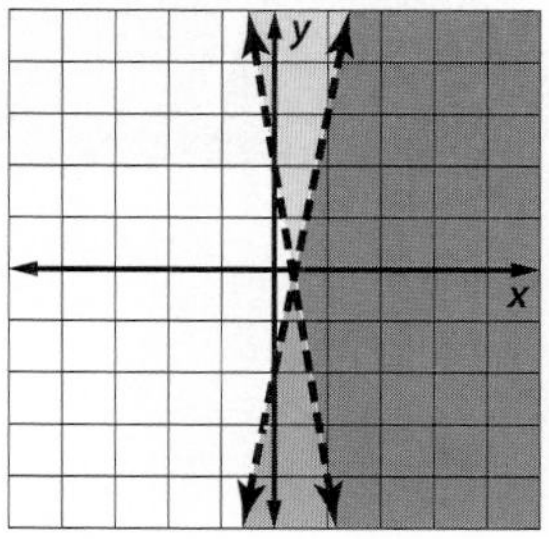

14.

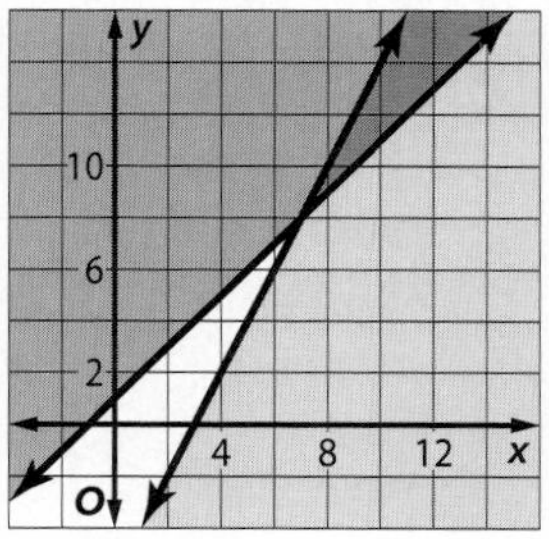

15.

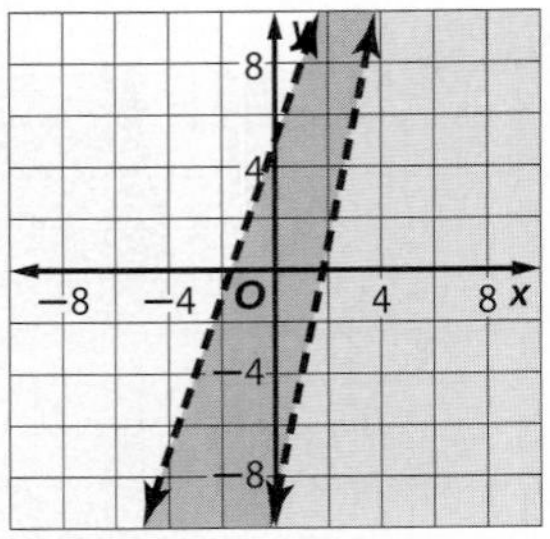

16. no solution

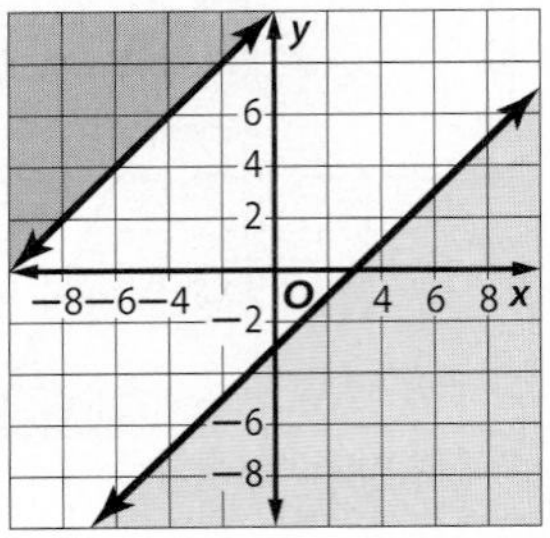

17. no solution

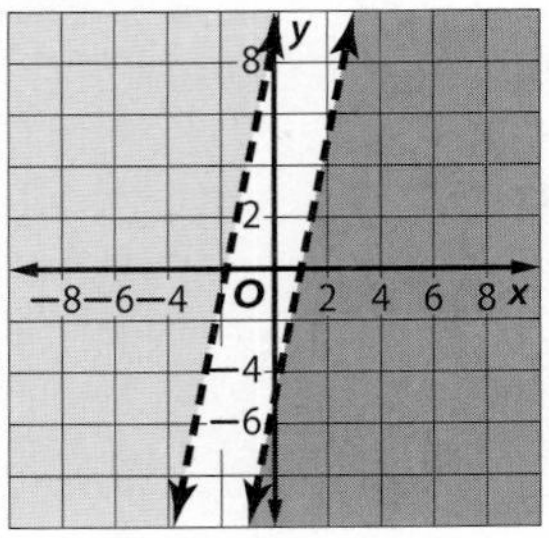

18.

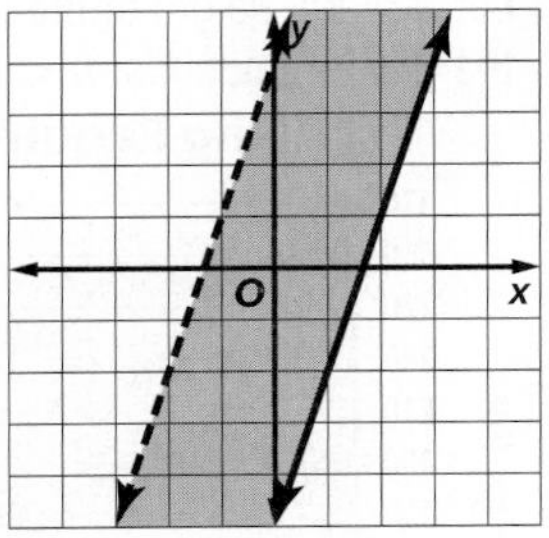

19.

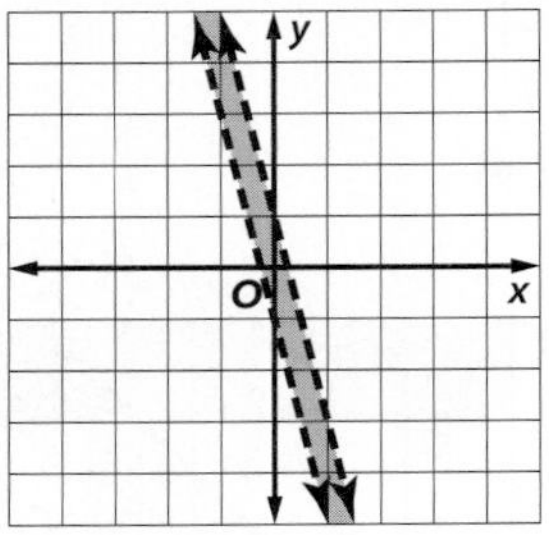

20.

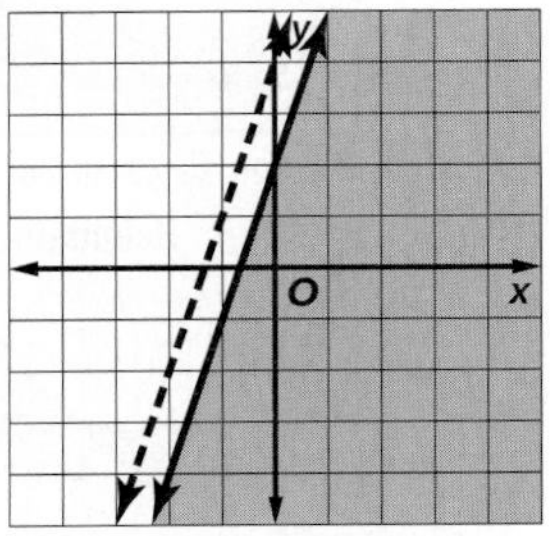

21.

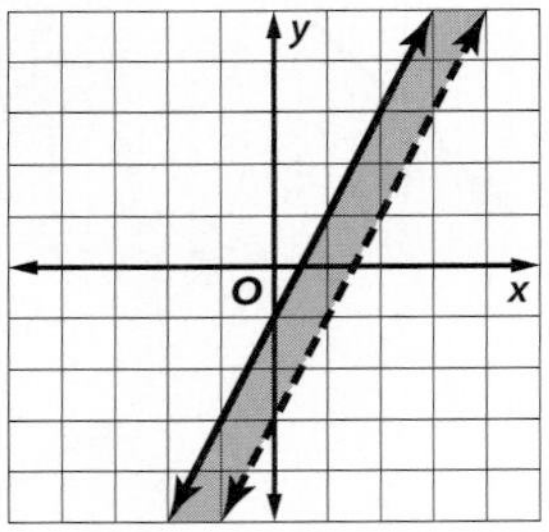

22.

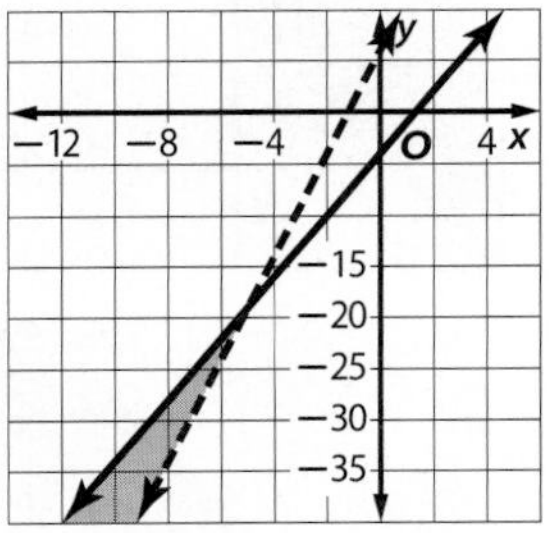

23.

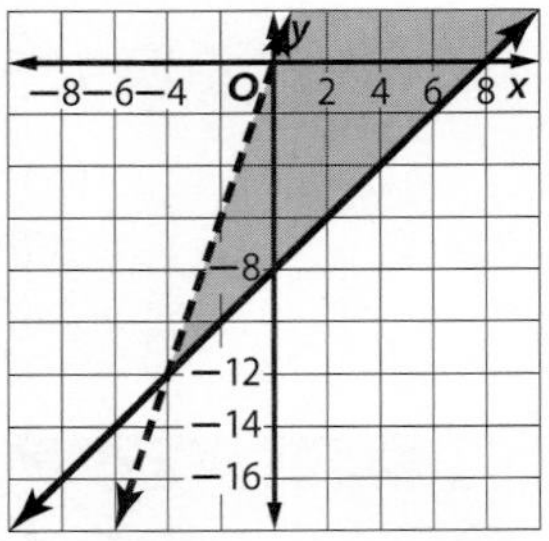

24. no solution

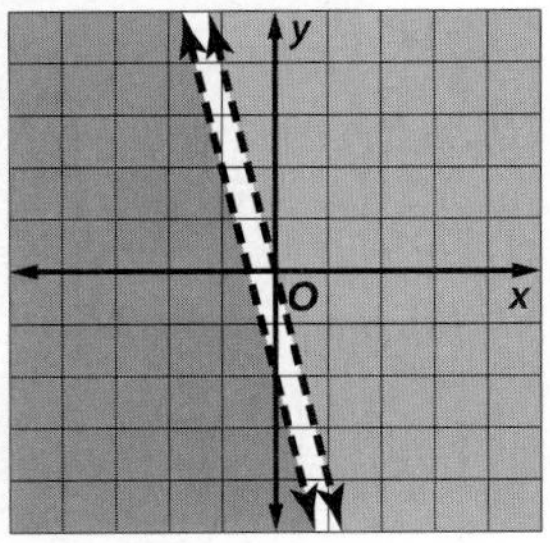

25a. Let f = square footage and p = price; $1000 \leq f \leq 17{,}000$ and $10{,}000 \leq p \leq 150{,}000$.

Ice Rink Resurfacers

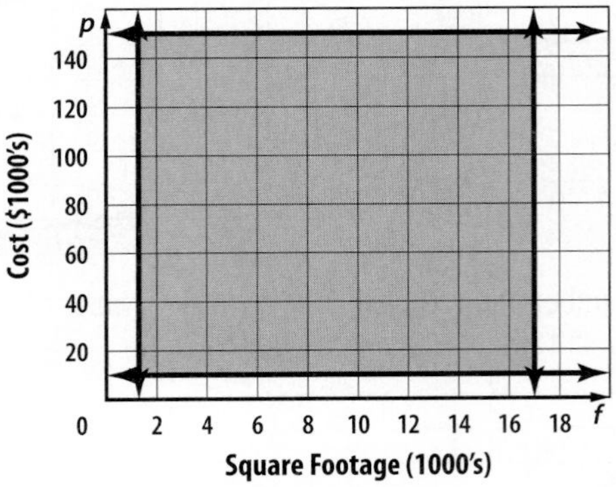

26b. **Earnings**

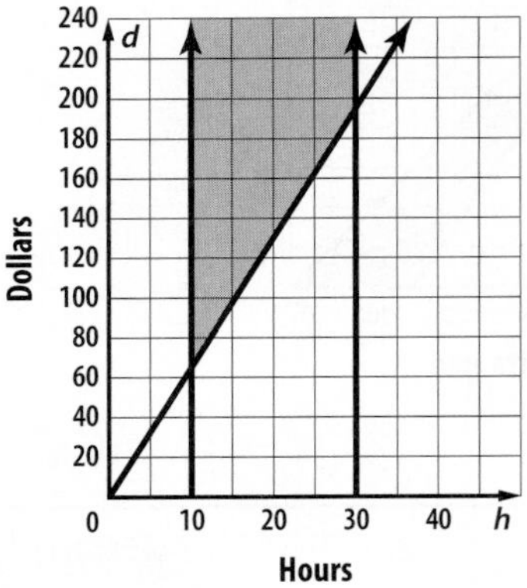

27.

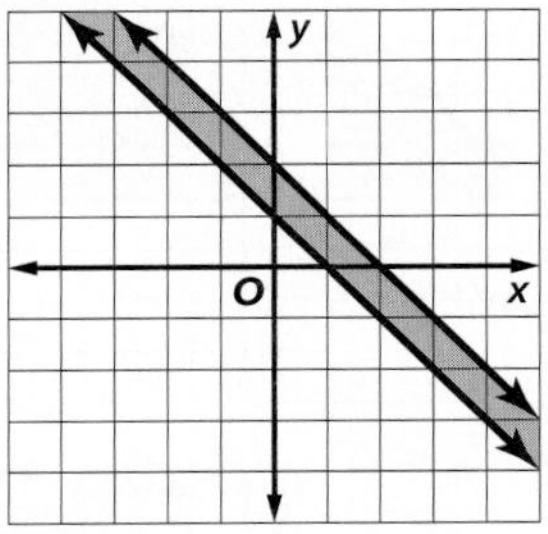

28.

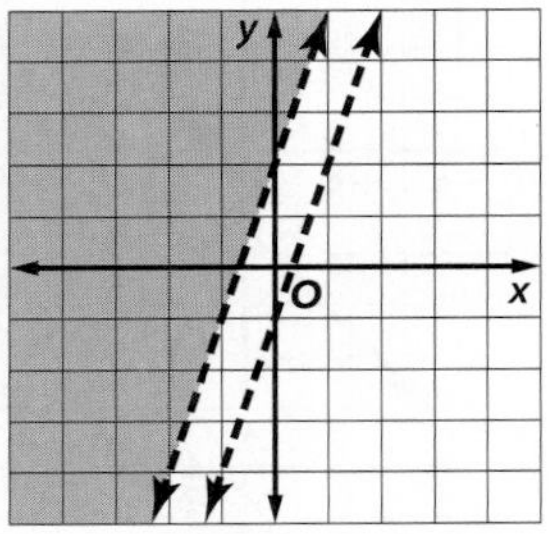

29.

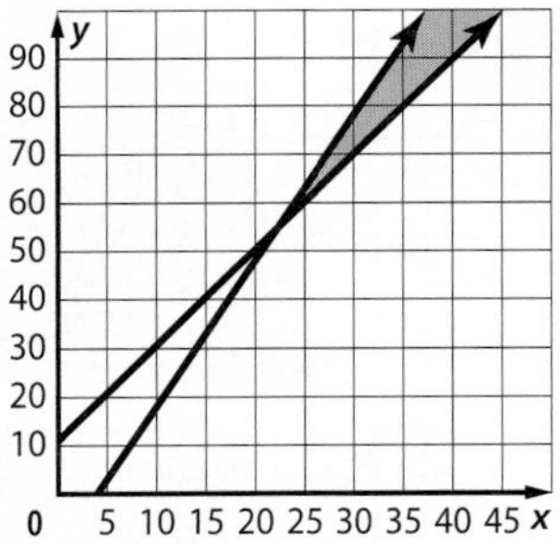

30.

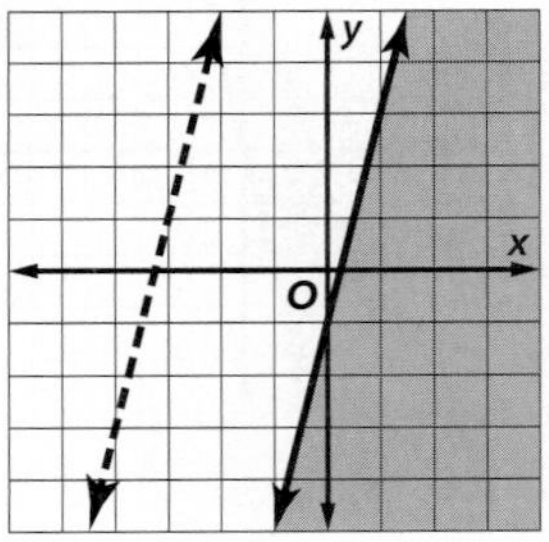

31.

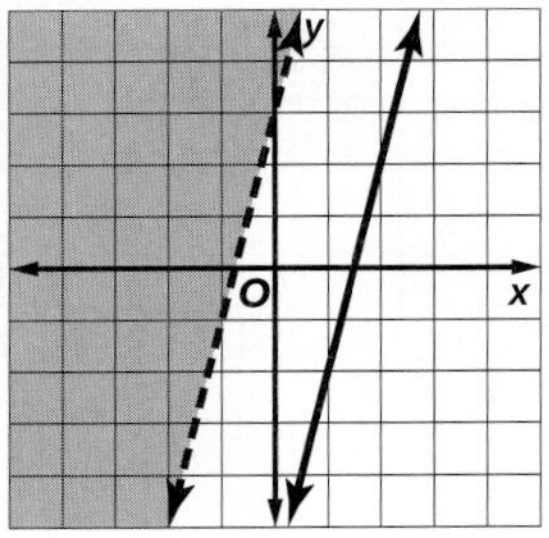

32.

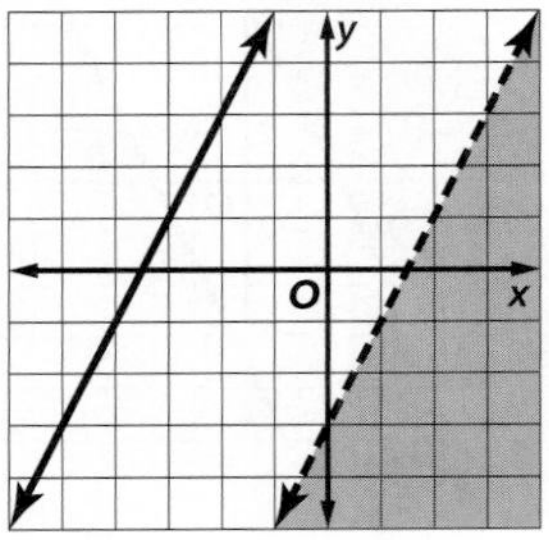

33. 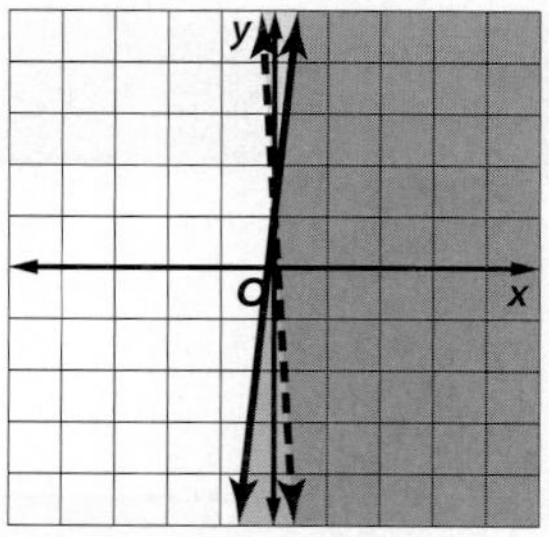

34. 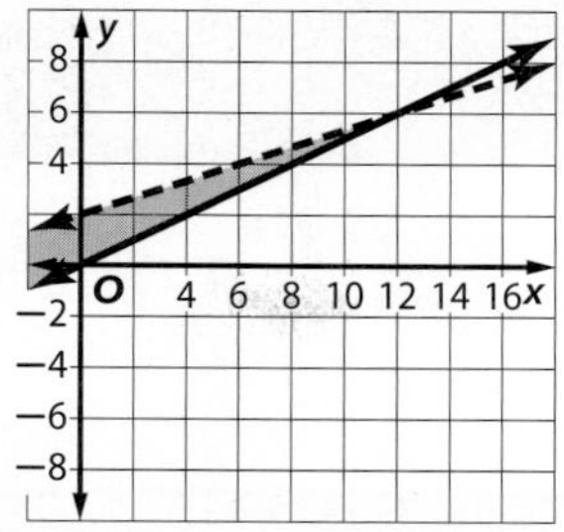

35. 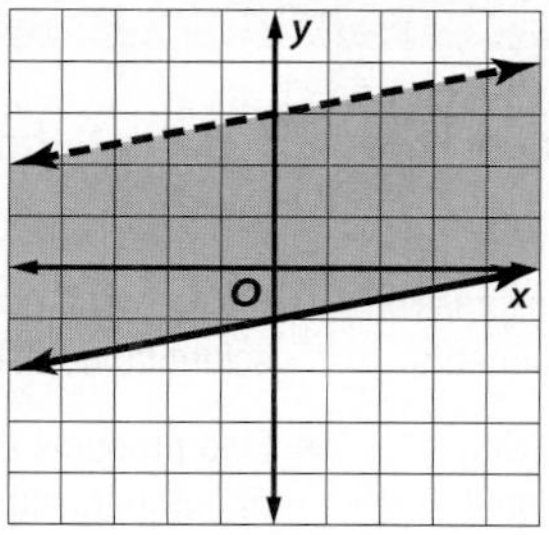

36a. Let $n =$ the number of notebooks and $p =$ the number of pens; $n \geq 20$, $p \geq 50$, $\$2.50n + \$1.25p \geq 60$.

36b.

Class Project

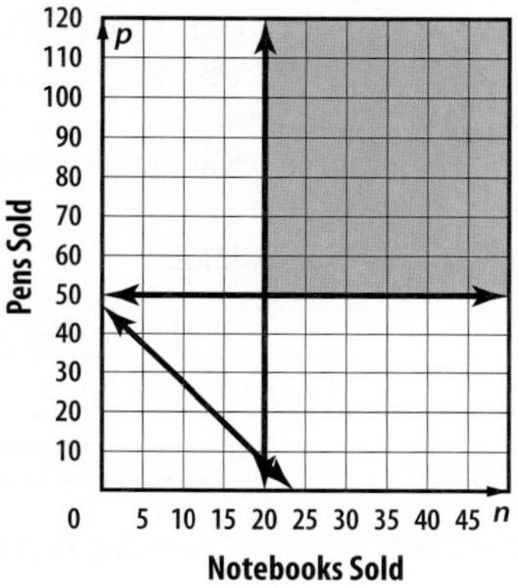

37b.

Earnings

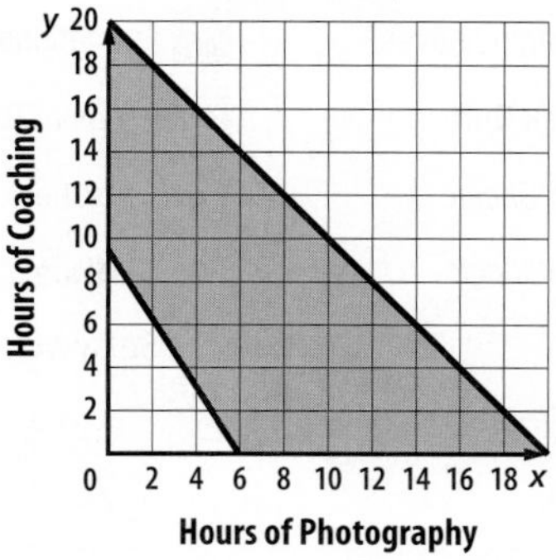

39. Sometimes; sample answer: $y > 3$, $y < -3$ will have no solution, but $y > -3$, $y < 3$ will have solutions.

42. 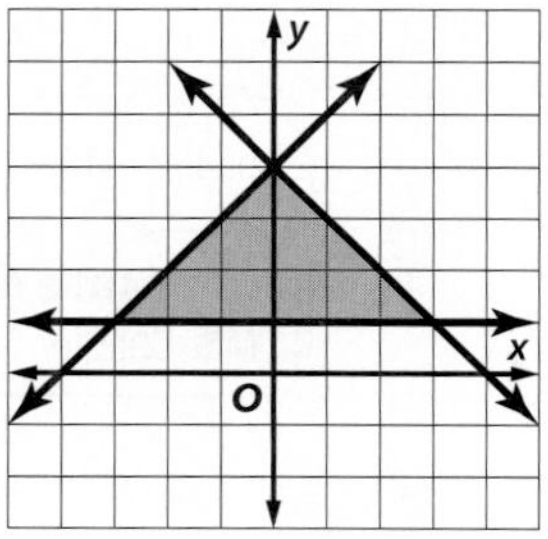

43. Sample answer: The yellow region represents the beats per minute below the target heart rate. The blue region represents the beats per minute above the target heart rate. The green region represents the beats per minute within the target heart rate. Shading in different colors clearly shows the overlapping solution set of the system of inequalities.

53. 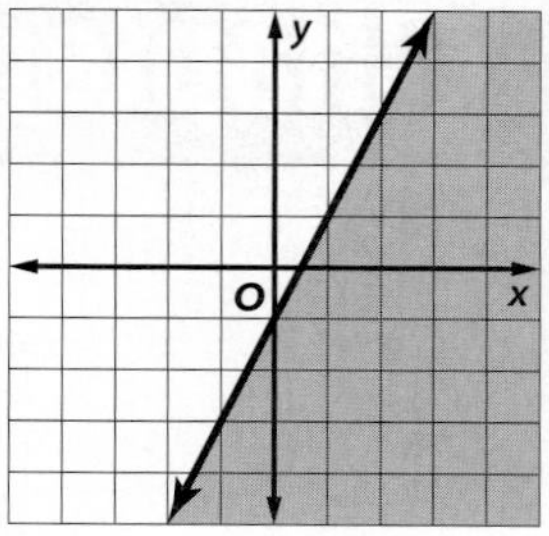

54. 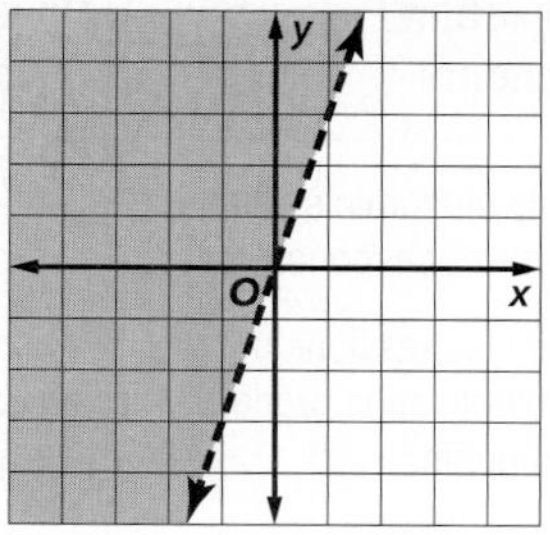

55. 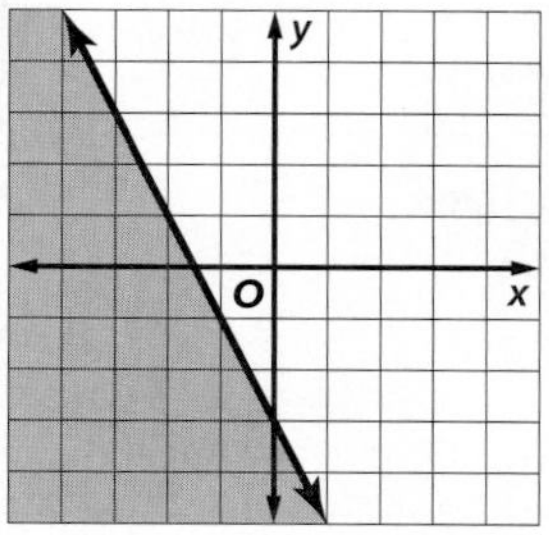

Practice Test

1. 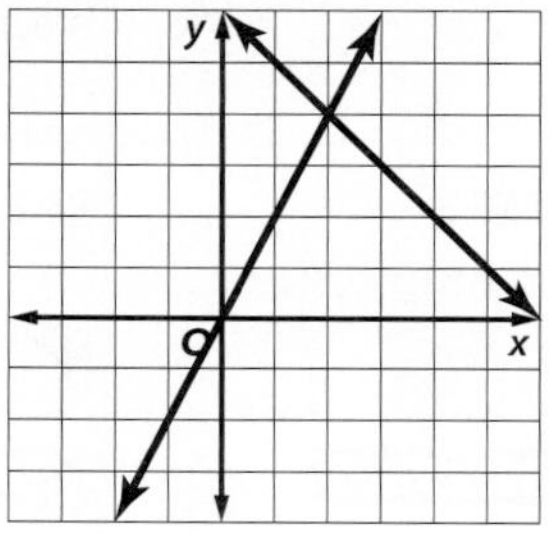

2. 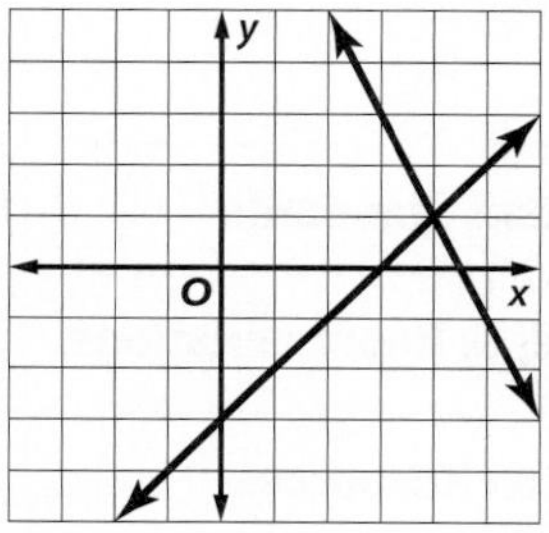

3. 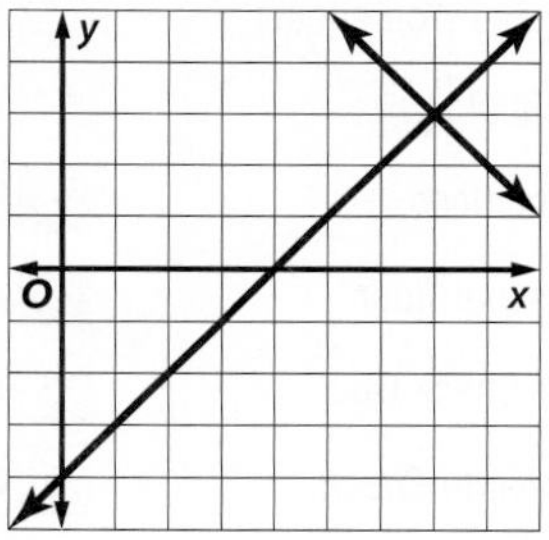

4. 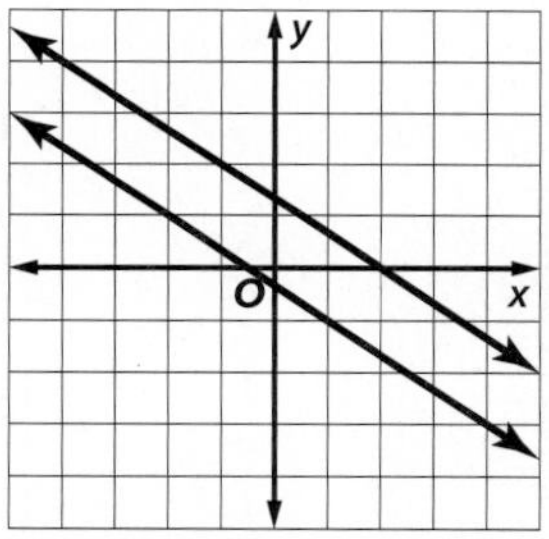

20. 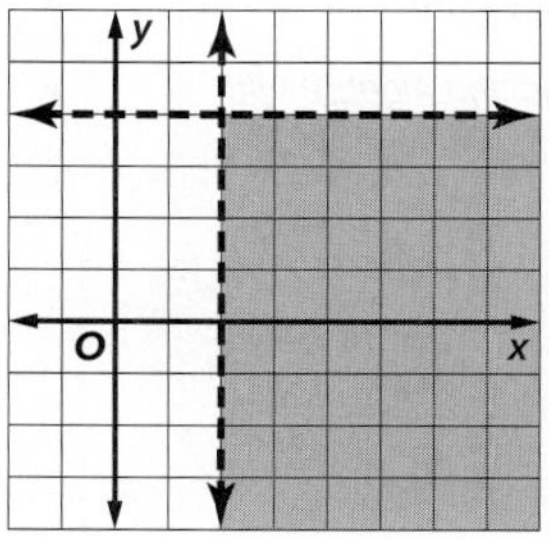

21. 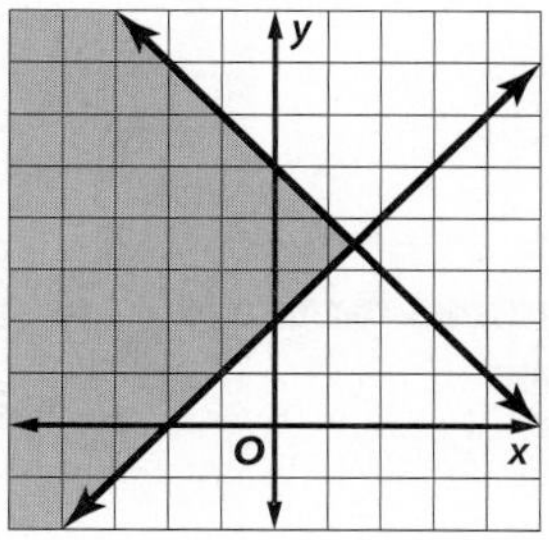

22. 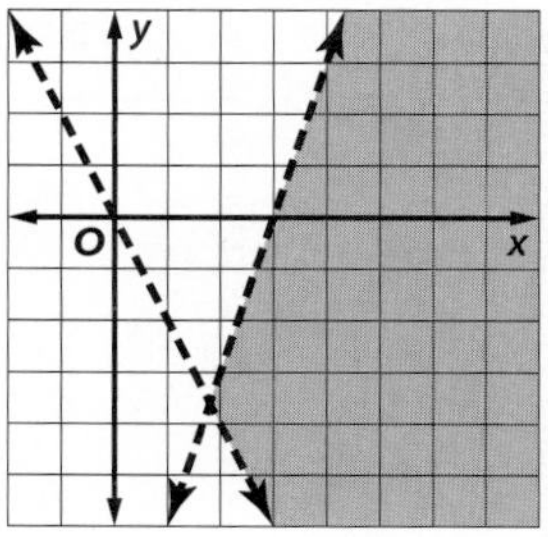

23. 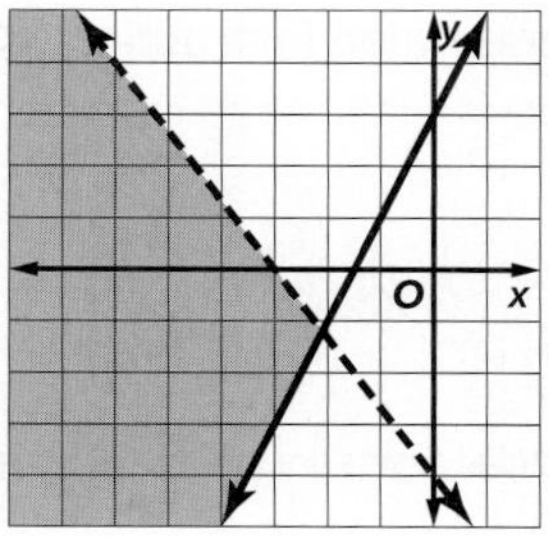

Chapter Planner

Diagnostic Assessment
Quick Check

	LESSON 7-1 (45 min: 1 day; 90 min: 0.5 day)	LESSON 7-2 (45 min: 1 day; 90 min: 0.5 day)	LESSON 7-3 (45 min: 1 day; 90 min: 0.5 day)	LESSON 7-4 (45 min: 1 day; 90 min: 0.5 day)
Title	**Multiplication Properties of Exponents**	**Division Properties of Exponents**	**Rational Exponents**	**Scientific Notation**
Objectives	▪ Multiply monomials using the properties of exponents. ▪ Simplify expressions using the multiplication properties of exponents.	▪ Divide monomials using the properties of exponents. ▪ Simplify expressions containing negative and zero exponents.	▪ Evaluate and rewrite expressions involving rational exponents. ▪ Solve equations involving expressions with rational exponents.	▪ Express numbers in scientific notation. ▪ Find products and quotients of numbers expressed in scientific notation.
Key Vocabulary	monomial constant	zero exponents negative exponent order of magnitude	rational exponent cube root *n*th root exponential equation	scientific notation
Content Standards	PS.8, AI.RNE.3	PS.2, AI.RNE.3	AI.RNE.3	PS.3, PS.6
Multiple Representations	✓	✓	✓	
Lesson Resources	connectED.mcgraw-hill.com Leveled Worksheets Vocabulary Animations Personal Tutor Self-Check Quiz ▪ *5-Minute Check* ▪ *Study Notebook* ▪ *Teaching Algebra with Manipulatives*	connectED.mcgraw-hill.com Leveled Worksheets Quiz 1 Vocabulary Animations Personal Tutor Self-Check Quiz ▪ *5-Minute Check* ▪ *Study Notebook*	connectED.mcgraw-hill.com Leveled Worksheets Personal Tutor Virtual Manipulatives Self-Check Quiz ▪ *5-Minute Check* ▪ *Study Notebook*	connectED.mcgraw-hill.com Leveled Worksheets Vocabulary Animations Personal Tutor Self-Check Quiz ▪ *5-Minute Check* ▪ *Study Notebook*
Resources for Every Lesson	IWB eStudent Edition IWB Interactive Classroom ▪ eTeacher Edition ▪ eSolutions Manual ▪ McGraw-Hill eAssessment			
Differentiated Instruction	pp. 393, 397	pp. 400, 405	pp. 408, 412	pp. 415, 418

Formative Assessment
Mid-Chapter Quiz

IWB All digital assets are Interactive Whiteboard ready.

Suggested Pacing			
Time Periods	Instruction	Review & Assess	Total
45-minute	10 days	2 days	12 days
90-minute	6 days	1 day	7 days

EXPLORE 7-5 (45 min: 0.5 day; 90 min: 0.5 day)	LESSON 7-5 (45 min: 1 day; 90 min: 0.5 day)	EXTEND 7-5 (45 min: 0.5 day; 90 min: 0.5 day)	LESSON 7-6 (45 min: 1 day; 90 min: 0.5 day)
Graphing Technology Lab: Family of Exponential Functions	**Exponential Functions**	**Graphing Technology Lab: Solving Exponential Equations and Inequalities**	**Growth and Decay**
▪ Use a graphing calculator to investigate families of exponential functions.	▪ Graph exponential functions. ▪ Identify data that display exponential behavior.	▪ Use a graphing calculator to solve exponential equations and inequalities.	▪ Solve problems involving exponential growth. ▪ Solve problems involving exponential decay.
	exponential function exponential growth function exponential decay function		compound interest
AI.QE.2, AI.QE.3	PS.1, AI.F.4, AI.QE.1, AI.QE.2, AI.QE.3	PS.4, PS.5	AI.QE.2
Personal Tutor **Materials:** TI-83/84 Plus or other graphing calculator	connectED.mcgraw-hill.com Leveled Worksheets Vocabulary Animations Personal Tutor Virtual Manipulatives Self-Check Quiz ▪ *5-Minute Check* ▪ *Study Notebook* ▪ *Teaching Algebra with Manipulatives*	Personal Tutor **Materials:** TI-Nspire Technology	connectED.mcgraw-hill.com Leveled Worksheets Quiz 3 Vocabulary Personal Tutor Self-Check Quiz ▪ *5-Minute Check* ▪ *Study Notebook*
IWB eStudent Edition IWB Interactive Classroom	▪ eTeacher Edition ▪ eSolutions Manual ▪ McGraw-Hill eAssessment		
	pp. 426, 429		p. 436

Chapter Planner

	EXTEND 7-6 (45 min: 0.5 day; 90 min: 0.5 day)	LESSON 7-7 (45 min: 1 day; 90 min: 0.5 day)	EXTEND 7-7 (45 min: 0.5 day; 90 min: 0.5 day)	LESSON 7-8 (45 min: 1 day; 90 min: 0.5 day)
Title	**Algebra Lab: Transforming Exponential Expressions**	**Geometric Sequences as Exponential Functions**	**Algebra Lab: Average Rate of Change of Exponential Functions**	**Recursive Formulas**
Objectives	▪ Use properties of rational exponents to transform expressions for exponential functions into equivalent forms to solve problems.	▪ Identify and generate geometric sequences. ▪ Relate geometric sequences to exponential functions.	▪ Calculate and interpret the average rate of change of an exponential function.	▪ Use a recursive formula to list the terms in a sequence. ▪ Write recursive formulas for arithmetic and geometric sequences.
Key Vocabulary		geometric sequence common ratio		recursive formula
Content Standards		PS.7	AI.QE.1	
Multiple Representations				
Lesson Resources	connectED.mcgraw-hill.com	connectED.mcgraw-hill.com Leveled Worksheets Vocabulary Animations Personal Tutor Self-Check Quiz ▪ *5-Minute Check* ▪ *Study Notebook*	connectED.mcgraw-hill.com **Materials:** grid paper	connectED.mcgraw-hill.com Leveled Worksheets Quiz 4 Animations Personal Tutor Virtual Manipulatives Self-Check Quiz ▪ *5-Minute Check* ▪ *Study Notebook*
Resources for Every Lesson	IWB eStudent Edition IWB Interactive Classroom	▪ eTeacher Edition ▪ eSolutions Manual ▪ McGraw-Hill eAssessment		
Differentiated Instruction		pp. 440, 443		pp. 445, 448

Summative Assessment
Study Guide and Review
Practice Test

IWB All digital assets are Interactive Whiteboard ready.

Quick Review Math Handbook*

is Glencoe's mathematical handbook for students and parents.

HotWords includes a glossary of terms.

HotTopics consists of two parts:

- explanations of key mathematical concepts
- exercises to check students' understanding

Lesson	Hot Topics Section
7-1	2.1, 6.2
7-2	3.4, 6.2
7-3	6.2
7-4	3.3

**Also available in Spanish*

What the Research says...

The Partnership for 21st Century Skills (2006) has identified Learning and Thinking Skills as one of the six key elements of 21st century learning.

Learning and thinking skills are comprised of:

- Critical-thinking and problem-solving skills
- Communication skills
- Creativity and innovation skills
- Collaboration skills
- Contextual learning skills
- Information and media literacy skills

Source: Partnership for 21st Century Skills (2006). *Results that Matter: 21st Century Skills and* High School Reform, Tucson, Arizona: Partnership for 21st Century Skills.

Project CRISS STUDY SKILL

Power notes can help students organize and outline a lesson or chapter. Students often benefit from making power notes as a cooperative activity.

In the outline at the right, Power 1 is the main idea, Power 2 provides details about the main idea, Power 3 provides details about Power 2, and so on.

You may have students copy the power notes at the right and complete them using the information in Chapter 7. Point out that more than one detail can be placed under each power.

1. Multiplication Properties of Exponents
    2. Multiply Monomials
        3. monomials are products, no addition, subtraction, or division of variables
        3. multiply powers; add the exponents
        3. raise a power to a power; multiply the exponents
        3. raise a product to a power, raise each factor to the power
    2. Simplify Expressions
        3. variables appear only once, no powers of powers, all fractions are simplified

Creating Independence through Student-owned Strategies

Assessment and Intervention

SE = Student Edition, **TE** = Teacher Edition, **CRM** = Chapter Resource Masters

	Diagnosis	Prescription
DIAGNOSTIC ASSESSMENT	**Beginning Chapter 7**	
	Get Ready for Chapter 7 **SE**	Response to Intervention **TE**
	Beginning Every Lesson	
	Then, Now, Why? **SE** 5-Minute Check	Chapter 0 **SE** *Quick Review Math Handbook*
FORMATIVE ASSESSMENT	**During/After Every Lesson**	
	Guided Practice **SE**, every example Check Your Understanding **SE** H.O.T. Problems **SE** Spiral Review **SE** Additional Examples **TE** Watch Out! **TE** Step 4, Assess **TE** Chapter 7 Quizzes **CRM**, pp. 57–58 Self-Check Quizzes connectED.mcgraw-hill.com	**TIER 1 Intervention** Skills Practice **CRM**, Ch. 1–7 connectED.mcgraw-hill.com **TIER 2 Intervention** Differentiated Instruction **TE** Study Guide and Intervention **CRM**, Ch. 1–7 *Quick Review Math Handbook* **TIER 3 Intervention** *Math Triumphs, Alg. 1*
	Mid-Chapter	
	Mid-Chapter Quiz **SE** Mid-Chapter Test **CRM**, p. 59 McGraw-Hill eAssessment	**TIER 1 Intervention** Skills Practice **CRM**, Ch. 1–7 connectED.mcgraw-hill.com **TIER 2 Intervention** Study Guide and Intervention **CRM**, Ch. 1–7; *Quick Review Math Handbook* **TIER 3 Intervention** *Math Triumphs, Alg. 1*
	Before Chapter Test	
	Chapter Study Guide and Review **SE** Practice Test **SE** Standardized Test Practice **SE** Chapter Test connectED.mcgraw-hill.com Standardized Test Practice connectED.mcgraw-hill.com Vocabulary Review connectED.mcgraw-hill.com McGraw-Hill eAssessment	**TIER 1 Intervention** Skills Practice **CRM**, Ch. 1–7 connectED.mcgraw-hill.com **TIER 2 Intervention** Study Guide and Intervention **CRM**, Ch. 1–7; *Quick Review Math Handbook* **TIER 3 Intervention** *Math Triumphs, Alg. 1*
SUMMATIVE ASSESSMENT	**After Chapter 7**	
	Multiple-Choice Tests, Forms 1, 2A, 2B **CRM**, pp. 61–66 Free-Response Tests, Forms 2C, 2D, 3 **CRM**, pp. 67–72 Vocabulary Test **CRM**, p. 60 Extended Response Test **CRM**, p. 73 Standardized Test Practice **CRM**, pp. 74–76 McGraw-Hill eAssessment	Study Guide and Intervention **CRM**, Ch. 1–7 *Quick Review Math Handbook* connectED.mcgraw-hill.com

Differentiated Instruction

Option 1 Reaching All Learners AL OL BL ELL

Auditory/Musical Music can be a powerful memory tool. Suggest that groups of students make up a song or poem to explain how to use the multiplication and division properties of exponents. Have the groups perform their songs or read their poems for the class.

Visual To help students remember the patterns in the multiplication and division properties of exponents, have students highlight the variables using two different colors. Students can make their own study cards and/or posters to hang in the classroom.

$$a^m \cdot a^p = a^{m+p}$$
$$(a^m)^p = a^{m \cdot p}$$
$$(ab)^m = a^m b^m$$
$$\frac{a^m}{a^p} = a^{m-p}$$
$$\left(\frac{a}{b}\right)^m = \frac{a^m}{b^m}$$
$$a^0 = 1$$
$$a^{-n} = \frac{1}{a^n}$$

Option 2 Approaching Level AL

Use a bent pipe cleaner and a coordinate grid on an overhead transparency to model the graph of an exponential function. Ask students to identify the y-intercept and to describe what happens to the y-values as the x-values increase. Repeat for the graphs of other exponential functions.

Option 3 English Learners ELL

Tell students that learning mathematics involves learning the language of mathematics.

On the board write several very large and very small numbers, such as 12,000,000,000,000,000 and 0.00000000067. Ask students to read these numbers using any language of their choice. Tell students that these numbers are written in standard notation, a type of math language.

Then ask students to use what they have learned to express these numbers in a shorter way using a different mathematical language. 1.2×10^{16}; 6.7×10^{-10}

Option 4 Beyond Level BL

Drop a tennis ball while standing in the front of the classroom. Ask students to describe how the bouncing ball can be modeled by a geometric sequence. Have students write an example of a sequence that might model the bouncing ball. Then, ask students to design their own physical models of a geometric sequence.

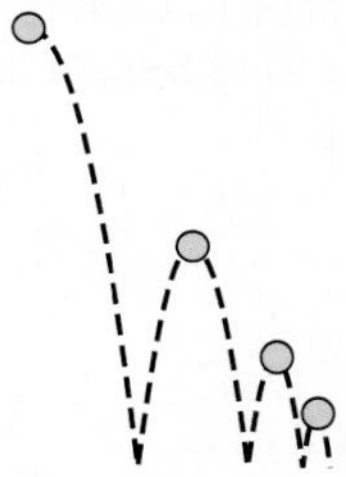

Focus on Mathematical Content

VerticalAlignment

Before Chapter 7

Related Topics before Grade 8

- make conjectures from patterns or sets of examples
- compare and order rational numbers including integers
- select appropriate operations to solve problems involving rational numbers

Previous Topics from Algebra 1

- use symbols to represent unknowns and variables

Chapter 7

- simplify polynomial expressions and apply the laws of exponents in problem-solving situations
- graph and analyze exponential functions
- analyze data and represent situations involving exponential growth and decay using tables, graphs, or algebraic methods
- relate geometric sequences to exponential functions, and write recursive formulas to represent sequences

After Chapter 7

Preparation for Algebra 2

- use the necessary algebraic skills required to simplify algebraic expressions and inequalities in problem-solving situations
- use properties of exponents to simplify expressions and to transform and solve exponential and logarithmic equations

Lesson-by-LessonPreview

7-1 Multiplication Properties of Exponents

A *monomial* is a number, a variable, or a product of a number and one or more variables. An expression involving negative integer exponents is not a monomial. Monomials that are real numbers are called *constants.* When multiplying monomials, use the Commutative and Associative Properties to group constants together and to group powers with the same base together.

- To multiply two powers that have the same base, add their exponents.
- To find the power of a power, multiply the exponents.
- To find the power of a product, find the power of each factor and multiply.

A monomial expression is simplified when

- each base appears exactly once,
- there are no powers of powers, and
- all fractions are in simplest form.

7-2 Division Properties of Exponents

Monomials may also be divided.

- To divide two powers that have the same base, subtract the exponents.
- To find the power of a quotient, find the power of the numerator and the power of the denominator.
- Any nonzero number raised to the zero power is equal to 1.

Expressions can also have negative exponents.

- A nonzero number raised to a negative integer power is the reciprocal of the same number with the opposite, or positive power.
- A fraction that has a negative exponent can be rewritten as its reciprocal with a positive power.

The order of magnitude of a quantity is the number rounded to the nearest power of 10.

7-3 Rational Exponents

Students have evaluated and simplified expressions involving exponents that are integers. Exponents can also be fractions.

- For any real numbers a and b, and any positive integer n, if $a^n = b$, then a is an nth root of b. If $a^n = b$, then $\sqrt[n]{b} = a$.
- For any positive real number b, and any integers m and n with $n > 1$, $b^{\frac{m}{n}} = \sqrt[n]{b^m}$.

7-4 Scientific Notation

A number is in *scientific notation* when it is written in the form $a \times 10^n$, where $1 \leq a < 10$ and n is an integer. To translate from standard form to scientific notation,

- move the decimal point until it is to the right of the first non-zero digit, then
- write the appropriate power of 10 to the right of the number. The direction the decimal point is moved indicates the sign of the power.
  To translate from scientific notation to standard form
- move the decimal point the number of places indicated by the exponent. A positive exponent is used to represent a number that is greater than or equal to 10 in standard form. A negative exponent represents a number that is less than 1 in standard form.

To multiply or divide numbers in scientific notation,

- multiply or divide the decimals;
- apply either the Product of Powers or the Quotient of Powers to simplify the powers of 10;
- rewrite the decimal in scientific notation and simplify the powers of 10. The result is in scientific notation, but it can also be presented in standard form if preferred.

7-5 Exponential Functions

Exponential functions are nonlinear and nonquadratic. An exponential function has a variable as an exponent and can be described by an equation of the form $y = ab^x$, where $a \neq 0$, $b > 0$, and $b \neq 1$.

- When $a > 0$ and $b > 1$, y-values change little for small values of x, but increase quickly as the values of x become greater. The graph rises from its left to its right.
- When $a > 0$ and $0 < b < 1$, y-values decrease as x increases. The graph falls as the x-values increase.

7-6 Growth and Decay

- Exponential growth can be modeled using the general equation $y = a(1 + r)^t$, where y is the final amount, a is the initial amount, r is the rate of change expressed as a decimal ($r > 0$), and t is time. An application of exponential growth is compound interest.
- Exponential decay can be modeled using the general equation $y = a(1 - r)^t$. An application of exponential decay is depreciation.

7-7 Geometric Sequences as Exponential Functions

In a geometric sequence, each term after the first is found by multiplying the previous term by the same nonzero constant r called the common ratio. Given several consecutive terms of a geometric sequence,

- r can be found by dividing any term by its previous term,
- successive terms can be found by multiplying the previous term by r, and
- the nth term, a_n, of a sequence, whose first term is a_1 ($a_1 \neq 0$) can be generated using the formula $a_n = a_1 \cdot r^{n-1}$, where n is any positive integer.

7-8 Recursive Formulas

Students have used *explicit formulas* for terms of sequences. These formulas define each term as a function of n. In a *recursive formula*, each term is defined in terms of one or more previous terms. To write a recursive formula, give the first term and a formula for the successive terms. For example, a recursive formula for the arithmetic sequence 2, 5, 8, 11, ... is $a_1 = 2$, $a_n = a_{n-1} + 3$. A recursive formula for the geometric sequence 3, 6, 12, 24, ... is $a_1 = 3$, $a_n = 2 \cdot a_{n-1}$.

McGraw Hill Professional Development

Targeted professional development has been articulated throughout Algebra 1. More quality, customized professional development is available from McGraw-Hill Professional Development. Visit connectED.mcgraw-hill.com for details on each product.

- Online Lessons emphasize the strategies and techniques used to teach Algebra 1. Includes streaming video, interactive pages, and online tools.
- Video Workshops allow mentors, coaches, or leadership personnel to facilitate on-site workshops on educational strategies in mathematics and mathematical concepts.
- MHPD Online (www.mhpdonline.com) offers online professional development with video clips of instructional strategies, links, student activities, and news and issues in education.
- Teaching Today (teachingtoday.glencoe.com) gives secondary teachers practical strategies and materials that inspire excellence and innovation in teaching.

Chapter Project

INTERE$T-ing Thing About Credit Cards…

Students use what they have learned about exponential functions to complete a project.

This chapter project addresses financial literacy, as well as several specific skills identified as being essential to student success by the Framework for 21st Century Learning.

Visit connectED.mcgraw-hill.com for student and teacher handouts.

KeyVocabulary Introduce the key vocabulary in the chapter using the routine below.

Define: A monomial is a number, a variable, or a product of a number and one or more variables.

Example: $\frac{1}{20}n^2$

Ask: Can you name another monomial?

Possible answers: $32ab$, 175, x, y

CHAPTER 7 Exponents and Exponential Functions

Then

- You evaluated expressions involving exponents.

Now

In this chapter, you will:

- Simplify and perform operations on expressions involving exponents.
- Extend the properties of integer exponents to rational exponents.
- Use scientific notation.
- Graph and use exponential functions.

Why?

SPACE The Very Large Array is an arrangement of 27 radio antennas in a Y pattern. The data the antennas collect is used by astronomers around the world to study the planets and stars. Astrophysicists use and apply properties of exponents to model the distance and orbit of celestial bodies.

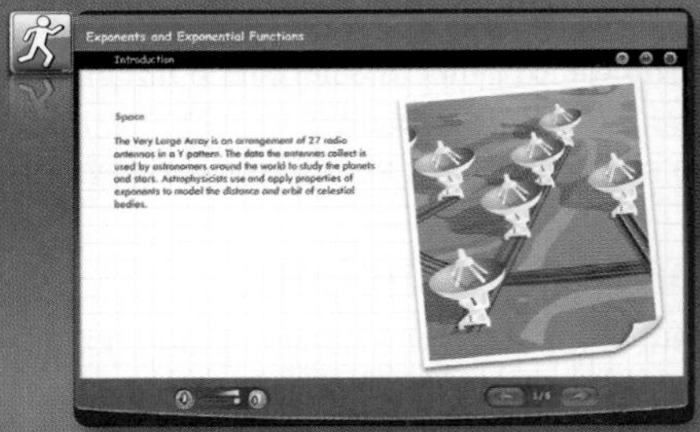

connectED.mcgraw-hill.com **Your Digital Math Portal**

Animation | Vocabulary | eGlossary | Personal Tutor | Virtual Manipulatives | Graphing Calculator | Audio | Foldables | Self-Check Practice | Worksheets

Content Standards
AI.RNE.3, AI.F.4, AI.QE.1, AI.QE.2, AI.QE.3

Process Standards
PS.1, PS.2, PS.3, PS.4, PS.5, PS.6, PS.7, PS.8

Get Ready for the Chapter

Diagnose Readiness | You have two options for checking prerequisite skills.

1 Textbook Option Take the Quick Check below. Refer to the Quick Review for help.

QuickCheck

Write each expression using exponents.

1. $4 \cdot 4 \cdot 4 \cdot 4 \cdot 4$ 4^5
2. $y \cdot y \cdot y$ y^3
3. $6 \cdot 6$ 6^2
4. $2 \cdot 2 \cdot 2 \cdot 2 \cdot 2 \cdot 2 \cdot 2 \cdot 2 \cdot 2$ 2^9
5. $b \cdot b \cdot b \cdot b \cdot b \cdot b$ b^6
6. $m \cdot m \cdot m \cdot p \cdot p \cdot p \cdot p \cdot p \cdot p$ m^3p^6
7. $\frac{1}{3} \cdot \frac{1}{3} \cdot \frac{1}{3} \cdot \frac{1}{3} \cdot \frac{1}{3} \cdot \frac{1}{3} \cdot \frac{1}{3} \cdot \frac{1}{3}$ $\left(\frac{1}{3}\right)^8$ or $\frac{1}{3^8}$
8. $\frac{x}{y} \cdot \frac{x}{y} \cdot \frac{x}{y} \cdot \frac{x}{y} \cdot \frac{w}{z} \cdot \frac{w}{z}$ $\frac{x^4w^3}{y^4z^2}$

Find the area or volume of each figure.

9. 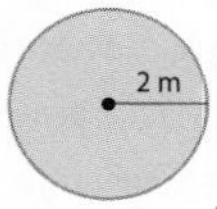

4π m^2

10. 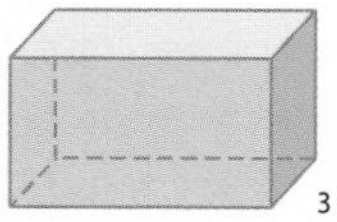

105 cm^3

11. **PHOTOGRAPHY** A photo is 4 inches by 6 inches. What is the area of the photo? 24 in^2

Evaluate each expression.

12. 2^3 8
13. $(-5)^2$ 25
14. 3^3 27
15. $(-4)^3$ -64
16. $\left(\frac{2}{3}\right)^2$ $\frac{4}{9}$
17. $\left(\frac{1}{2}\right)^4$ $\frac{1}{16}$
18. **SCHOOL** The probability of guessing correctly on 5 true-false questions is $\left(\frac{1}{2}\right)^5$. Express this probability as a fraction without exponents. $\frac{1}{32}$

QuickReview

Example 1 (Used in Lessons 7-1 and 7-2)

Write $5 \cdot 5 \cdot 5 \cdot 5 + x \cdot x \cdot x$ using exponents.

4 factors of 5 is 5^4.

3 factors of x is x^3.

So, $5 \cdot 5 \cdot 5 \cdot 5 + x \cdot x \cdot x = 5^4 + x^3$.

Example 2 (Used in Lessons 7-1 and 7-2)

Find the volume of the figure.

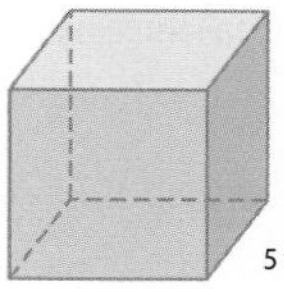

$V = \ell wh$ Volume of a rectangular prism

$= 5 \cdot 5 \cdot 5$ or 125 $\ell = 5$, $w = 5$, and $h = 5$

The volume is 125 cubic feet.

Example 3 (Used in Lessons 7-1 through 7-7)

Evaluate $\left(\frac{5}{7}\right)^2$.

$\left(\frac{5}{7}\right)^2 = \frac{5^2}{7^2}$ Power of a Quotient

$= \frac{25}{49}$ Simplify.

2 Online Option Take an online self-check Chapter Readiness Quiz at connectED.mcgraw-hill.com.

389

Essential Questions

- How can you make good decisions?
  Sample answer: Determine the available options, compare the advantages and disadvantages of each option, analyze the consequences, and choose the best option.
- What factors can affect good decision making?
  Sample answers: the amount of time that is available, the process used, the environment, the people that are involved, the available options

Get Ready for the Chapter

Response to Intervention (RtI)

Use the *Quick Check* results and the Intervention Planner chart to help you determine your Response to Intervention. The If-Then statements in the chart below help you decide the appropriate tier of RtI and suggest intervention resources for each tier.

InterventionPlanner

TIER 1 On Level OL

If students miss about 25% of the exercises or less,

Then choose a resource:

SE Lessons 1-1, 1-2, 0-8, and 0-9

Skills Practice, Chapter 1, pp. 7 and 13

connectED.mcgraw-hill.com Self-Check Quiz

TIER 2 Strategic Intervention AL approaching grade level

If students miss about 50% of the exercises,

Then choose a resource:

Study Guide and Intervention, Chapter 1, pp. 5 and 11

Quick Review Math Handbook

connectED.mcgraw-hill.com Extra Examples, Personal Tutor, Homework Help

TIER 3 Intensive Intervention 2 or more grades below level

If students miss about 75% of the exercises,

Then use *Math Triumphs, Alg. 1*

connectED.mcgraw-hill.com Extra Examples, Personal Tutor, Homework Help, Review Vocabulary

FOLDABLES StudyOrganizer

Dinah Zike's Foldables®

Focus Students create a tabbed book on which they organize information about polynomials.

Teach Have students make and label their Foldables as illustrated. Before beginning each lesson, ask students to think of one question that comes to mind as they skim through the lesson. Have them write the questions on the tabbed page of the corresponding lesson. As they read and work through the lesson, ask them to record the answers to their questions under the tabs.

When to Use It Encourage students to add to their Foldables as they work through the chapter and to use them to review for the chapter test.

Differentiated Instruction

Student-Built Glossary, pp. 1–2

Students should complete the chart by providing a definition of each term and an example as they progress through Chapter 7. This study tool can also be used to review for the chapter test.

Get Started on the Chapter

You will learn several new concepts, skills, and vocabulary terms as you study Chapter 7. To get ready, identify important terms and organize your resources. You may wish to refer to Chapter 0 to review prerequisite skills.

FOLDABLES StudyOrganizer

Exponents and Exponential Functions Make this Foldable to help you organize your Chapter 7 notes about exponents and exponential functions. Begin with nine sheets of notebook paper.

1 **Arrange** the paper into a stack.

2 **Staple** along the left side. Starting with the second sheet of paper, cut along the right side to form tabs.

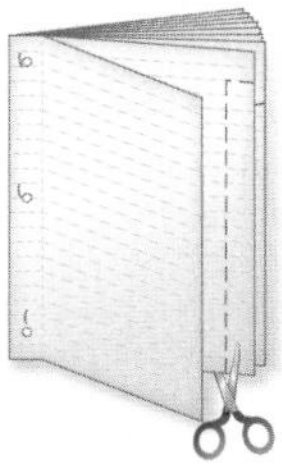

3 **Label** the cover sheet "Exponents and Exponential Functions" and label each tab with a lesson number.

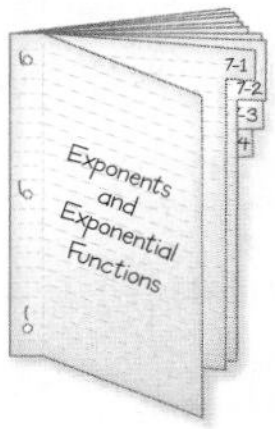

NewVocabulary

English		Español
monomial	p. 391	monomio
constant	p. 391	constante
zero exponent	p. 399	cero exponente
negative exponent	p. 400	exponente negativo
order of magnitude	p. 401	orden de magnitud
rational exponent	p. 406	exponent racional
cube root	p. 407	raíz cúbica
*n*th root	p. 407	raíz enésima
exponential equation	p. 409	ecuación exponencial
scientific notation	p. 414	notación científica
exponential function	p. 424	función exponencial
exponential growth	p. 424	crecimiento exponencial
exponential decay	p. 424	desintegración exponencial
compound interest	p. 433	interés es compuesta
geometric sequence	p. 438	secuencia geométrica
common ratio	p. 438	proporción común
recursive formula	p. 445	fórmula recursiva

ReviewVocabulary

base base In an expression of the form x^n, the base is x.

Distributive Property Propiedad distributiva
For any numbers a, b, and c, $a(b + c) = ab + ac$ and $a(b - c) = ab - ac$.

exponent exponente
In an expression of the form x^n, the exponent is n. It indicates the number of times x is used as a factor.

$$x^n = \underbrace{x \cdot x \cdot x \cdot x \cdot \ldots \cdot x}_{n \text{ times}}$$

(exponent: n; base: x)

Additional Answers (Guided Practice)

1A. No; the expression has addition and more than one term.

1B. Yes; this is a product of a number and variables.

1C. Yes; this is a product of variables, with a constant in the denominator.

1D. No; this expression has a variable in the denominator.

LESSON 7-1 Multiplication Properties of Exponents

Then

- You evaluated expressions with exponents.

Now

1. Multiply monomials using the properties of exponents.
2. Simplify expressions using the multiplication properties of exponents.

Why?

- Many formulas contain *monomials.* For example, the formula for the horsepower of a car is $H = w\left(\frac{v}{234}\right)^3$. *H* represents the horsepower produced by the engine, *w* equals the weight of the car with passengers, and *v* is the velocity of the car at the end of a quarter of a mile. As the velocity increases, the horsepower increases.

NewVocabulary
monomial
constant

Content Standards
AI.RNE.3

Process Standards
PS.8

1 Multiply Monomials

A **monomial** is a number, a variable, or the product of a number and one or more variables with nonnegative integer exponents. It has only one term. In the formula to calculate the horsepower of a car, the term $w\left(\frac{v}{234}\right)^3$ is a monomial.

An expression that involves division by a variable, like $\frac{ab}{c}$, is not a monomial.

A **constant** is a monomial that is a real number. The monomial $3x$ is an example of a *linear expression* since the exponent of x is 1. The monomial $2x^2$ is a *nonlinear expression* since the exponent is a positive number other than 1.

Example 1 Identify Monomials

Determine whether each expression is a monomial. Write *yes* or *no*. Explain your reasoning.

a. 10 — Yes; this is a constant, so it is a monomial.

b. $f + 24$ — No; this expression has addition, so it has more than one term.

c. h^2 — Yes; this expression is a product of variables.

d. j — Yes; single variables are monomials.

GuidedPractice

1A. $-x + 5$ **1A–1D. See margin.**

1B. $23abcd^2$

1C. $\frac{xyz^2}{2}$

1D. $\frac{mp}{n}$

Recall that an expression of the form x^n is called a *power* and represents the result of multiplying x by itself n times. x is the *base*, and n is the *exponent*. The word *power* is also used sometimes to refer to the exponent.

exponent (4), base (3), 4 factors:

$$3^4 = 3 \cdot 3 \cdot 3 \cdot 3 = 81$$

1 Focus

VerticalAlignment

Before Lesson 7-1 Evaluated expressions with exponents.

Lesson 7-1 Multiply monomials using the multiplication properties of exponents. Simplify expressions using the properties of exponents.

After Lesson 7-1 Find quotients of two monomials and simplify expressions containing negative exponents.

2 Teach

Scaffolding Questions

Have students read the **Why?** section of the lesson.

Ask:

- What two values do you need to know to be able to use the formula to find the horsepower of a car? weight of the car, *w*, with passengers; velocity of the car, *v*, at the end of a quarter of a mile
- Which values in the formula are raised to the third power? *v*, 234
- When would the horsepower of a car be equal to or greater than the weight of a car with passengers? when $v \geq 234$

Lesson 7-1 Resources

Resource	Approaching Level AL	On Level OL	Beyond Level BL	English Learners ELL
Teacher Edition		▪ Differentiated Instruction, pp. 393, 397	▪ Differentiated Instruction, pp. 393, 397	
Chapter Resource Masters	▪ Study Guide and Intervention, pp. 5–6 ▪ Skills Practice, p. 7 ▪ Practice, p. 8 ▪ Word Problem Practice, p. 9	▪ Study Guide and Intervention, pp. 5–6 ▪ Skills Practice, p. 7 ▪ Practice, p. 8 ▪ Word Problem Practice, p. 9 ▪ Enrichment, p. 10	▪ Practice, p. 8 ▪ Word Problem Practice, p. 9 ▪ Enrichment, p. 10	▪ Study Guide and Intervention, pp. 5–6 ▪ Skills Practice, p. 7 ▪ Practice, p. 8 ▪ Word Problem Practice, p. 9
Other	▪ 5-Minute Check 7-1 ▪ Study Notebook ▪ Teaching Algebra with Manipulatives	▪ 5-Minute Check 7-1 ▪ Study Notebook ▪ Teaching Algebra with Manipulatives	▪ 5-Minute Check 7-1 ▪ Study Notebook	▪ 5-Minute Check 7-1 ▪ Study Notebook ▪ Teaching Algebra with Manipulatives

1 Multiplying Monomials

Example 1 shows how to determine whether an expression is a monomial. **Example 2** shows how to find the product of powers. **Example 3** shows how to find the power of a power. **Example 4** shows how to find the power of a product.

Formative Assessment

Use the Guided Practice exercises after each Example to determine students' understanding of concepts.

Additional Examples

1 Determine whether each expression is a monomial. Write *yes* or *no*. Explain your reasoning.

a. $17 - c$ No; this expression involves subtraction, so it involves more than one term.

b. $8f^2g$ Yes; this expression is the product of a number and two variables.

c. $\frac{3}{4}$ Yes; The expression is a constant.

d. $\frac{5}{t}$ No; this expression has a variable in the denominator.

2 Simplify each expression.

a. $(r^4)(-12r^7)$ $-12r^{11}$

b. $(6cd^5)(5c^5d^2)$ $30c^6d^7$

Additional Examples also in Interactive Classroom PowerPoint® Presentations

IWB Interactive White Board READY

Teach with Tech

Video Recording Have students record themselves multiplying monomials and explaining their work. Share the videos with the class.

By applying the definition of a power, you can find the product of powers. Look for a pattern in the exponents.

$$2^2 \cdot 2^4 = \overbrace{2 \cdot 2}^{2\text{ factors}} \cdot \overbrace{2 \cdot 2 \cdot 2 \cdot 2}^{4\text{ factors}} \quad (2 + 4 = 6\text{ factors})$$

$$4^3 \cdot 4^2 = \overbrace{4 \cdot 4 \cdot 4}^{3\text{ factors}} \cdot \overbrace{4 \cdot 4}^{2\text{ factors}} \quad (3 + 2 = 5\text{ factors})$$

These examples demonstrate the property for the product of powers.

KeyConcept Product of Powers

Words	To multiply two powers that have the same base, add their exponents.
Symbols	For any real number a and any integers m and p, $a^m \cdot a^p = a^{m+p}$.
Examples	$b^3 \cdot b^5 = b^{3+5}$ or b^8 $g^4 \cdot g^6 = g^{4+6}$ or g^{10}

PT

Example 2 Product of Powers

Simplify each expression.

a. $(6n^3)(2n^7)$

$(6n^3)(2n^7) = (6 \cdot 2)(n^3 \cdot n^7)$ Group the coefficients and the variables.

$= (6 \cdot 2)(n^{3+7})$ Product of Powers

$= 12n^{10}$ Simplify.

b. $(3pt^3)(p^3t^4)$

$(3pt^3)(p^3t^4) = (3 \cdot 1)(p \cdot p^3)(t^3 \cdot t^4)$ Group the coefficients and the variables.

$= (3 \cdot 1)(p^{1+3})(t^{3+4})$ Product of Powers

$= 3p^4t^7$ Simplify.

StudyTip
Coefficients and Powers of 1 A variable with no exponent or coefficient shown can be assumed to have an exponent and coefficient of 1. For example, $x = 1x^1$.

GuidedPractice

2A. $(3y^4)(7y^5)$ $21y^9$

2B. $(-4rx^2t^3)(-6r^5x^2t)$ $24r^6x^4t^4$

We can use the Product of Powers Property to find the power of a power. In the following examples, look for a pattern in the exponents.

$$(3^2)^4 = \overbrace{(3^2)(3^2)(3^2)(3^2)}^{4\text{ factors}} = 3^{2+2+2+2} = 3^8$$

$$(r^4)^3 = \overbrace{(r^4)(r^4)(r^4)}^{3\text{ factors}} = r^{4+4+4} = r^{12}$$

These examples demonstrate the property for the power of a power.

KeyConcept Power of a Power

Words	To find the power of a power, multiply the exponents.
Symbols	For any real number a and any integers m and p, $(a^m)^p = a^{m \cdot p}$.
Examples	$(b^3)^5 = b^{3 \cdot 5}$ or b^{15} $(g^6)^7 = g^{6 \cdot 7}$ or g^{42}

Focus on Mathematical Content

Variables with No Exponents A variable without an exponent can be rewritten with an exponent of 1. For example, x can be written as x^1, and ab can be written as a^1b^1. In order for students to find the products of powers correctly, suggest that they rewrite variables without an exponent with an exponent of 1.

StudyTip

Regularity The power rules are general methods. If you are unsure about when to multiply the exponents and when to add the exponents, write the expression in expanded form.

Standardized Test Example 3 Power of a Power

Simplify $[(2^3)^2]^4$.

A 2^{24} **B** 2^{12} **C** 2^{10} **D** 2^9

Read the Test Item

You need to apply the power of a power rule.

Solve the Test Item

$[(2^3)^2]^4 = (2^{3 \cdot 2})^4$ Power of a Power

$= (2^6)^4$ Simplify.

$= 2^{6 \cdot 4}$ or 2^{24} Power of a Power

The correct choice is A.

GuidedPractice

3. Simplify $[(2^2)^2]^4$. **H**

F 2^8 **G** 2^{10} **H** 2^{16} **J** 2^{24}

We can use the Product of Powers Property and the Power of a Power Property to find the power of a product. Look for a pattern in the exponents below.

$$(tw)^3 = \overbrace{(tw)(tw)(tw)}^{\text{3 factors}} = (t \cdot t \cdot t)(w \cdot w \cdot w) = t^3w^3$$

$$(2yz^2)^3 = \overbrace{(2yz^2)(2yz^2)(2yz^2)}^{\text{3 factors}} = (2 \cdot 2 \cdot 2)(y \cdot y \cdot y)(z^2 \cdot z^2 \cdot z^2) = 2^3y^3z^6 \text{ or } 8y^3z^6$$

These examples demonstrate the property for the power of a product.

Math-HistoryLink

Albert Einstein

(1879–1955) Albert Einstein is perhaps the most well-known scientist of the 20th century. His formula $E = mc^2$, where E represents the energy, m is the mass of the material, and c is the speed of light, shows that if mass is accelerated enough, it could be converted into usable energy.

KeyConcept Power of a Product

Words	To find the power of a product, find the power of each factor and multiply.
Symbols	For any real numbers a and b and any integer m, $(ab)^m = a^mb^m$.
Example	$(-2xy^3)^5 = (-2)^5x^5y^{15}$ or $-32x^5y^{15}$

Example 4 Power of a Product

GEOMETRY Express the area of the circle as a monomial.

Area $= \pi r^2$ Formula for the area of a circle

$= \pi(2xy^2)^2$ Replace r with $2xy^2$.

$= \pi(2^2x^2y^4)$ Power of a Product

$= 4x^2y^4\pi$ Simplify.

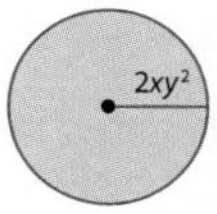

The area of the circle is $4x^2y^4\pi$ square units.

GuidedPractice

4A. Express the area of a square with sides of length $3xy^2$ as a monomial. $9x^2y^4$

4B. Express the area of a triangle with height $4a$ and base $5ab^2$ as a monomial. $10a^2b^2$

Additional Examples

3 STANDARDIZED TEST PRACTICE Simplify $[(2^3)^3]^2$. D

A 8^2

B 8^4

C 2^{11}

D 2^{18}

4 GEOMETRY Express the volume of a cube with side length $5xyz$ as a monomial. $(5xyz)^3 = 125x^3y^3z^3$

WatchOut!

Student Misconceptions Students may simplify an expression such as $\frac{4}{6}(x^2y^5)^3[2(xy)^7]$ into $\frac{8}{6}x^{13}y^{22}$, not realizing that the simplification is incomplete because the fraction is not in the simplest form.

Teaching the Process Standards

Regularity Mathematically proficient notice if calculations are repeated, and look both for general methods and for shortcuts. Work through examples to demonstrate each property in this lesson to help students see the repeated reasoning in the calculations.

DifferentiatedInstruction OL BL

Logical Learners Give students an expression such as $240x^{12}y^8$ and challenge them to write ten different monomial expressions that, when simplified, equal the given expression.

2 Simplify Expressions

Example 5 shows how to simplify expressions involving monomials by using the power and product rules.

Tips for New Teachers

Reasoning Remind students that there is often more than one strategy that can be used to simplify an expression. For example, in Example 5, the first step could be to simplify $(-2y)^2$ first and then raise the product to the third power.

Additional Example

5 Simplify $[(8g^3h^4)^2]^2(2gh^5)^4$.
$65{,}536g^{16}h^{36}$

3 Practice

Formative Assessment

Use Exercises 1–20 to check for understanding.

Use the chart at the bottom of this page to customize assignments for your students.

Additional Answers

1. Yes; constants are monomials.
2. No; there is subtraction and more than one term.
3. No; there is a variable in the denominator.
4. Yes; this is a product of a number and variables.
5. Yes; this is a product of a number and variables.
6. No; there is addition and more than one term.

2 Simplify Expressions

We can combine and use these properties to simplify expressions involving monomials.

KeyConcept Simplify Monomial Expressions

To simplify a monomial expression, write an equivalent expression in which:

- each variable base appears exactly once,
- there are no powers of powers, and
- all fractions are in simplest form.

StudyTip
Simplify When simplifying expressions with multiple grouping symbols, begin at the innermost expression and work outward.

Example 5 Simplify Expressions

Simplify $(3xy^4)^2[(-2y)^2]^3$.

$(3xy^4)^2[(-2y)^2]^3 = (3xy^4)^2(-2y)^6$	Power of a Power
$=(3)^2x^2(y^4)^2(-2)^6y^6$	Power of a Product
$= 9x^2y^8(64)y^6$	Power of a Power
$= 9(64)x^2 \cdot y^8 \cdot y^6$	Commutative
$= 576x^2y^{14}$	Product of Powers

GuidedPractice

5. Simplify $\left(\frac{1}{2}a^2b^2\right)^3[(-4b)^2]^2$. $32a^6b^{10}$

Check Your Understanding

◯ = Step-by-Step Solutions begin on page R13.

Example 1 Determine whether each expression is a monomial. Write *yes* or *no*. Explain your reasoning. 1–6. See margin.

1. 15
2. $2 - 3a$
3. $\frac{5c}{d}$
4. $-15g^2$
5. $\frac{r}{2}$
6. $7b + 9$

Examples 2–3 Simplify each expression.

7. $k(k^3)$ k^4
8. $m^4(m^2)$ m^6
9. $2q^2(9q^4)$ $18q^6$
10. $(5u^4v)(7u^4v^3)$ $35u^8v^4$
11. $[(3^2)^2]^2$ 3^8 or 6561
12. $(xy^4)^6$ x^6y^{24}
13. $(4a^4b^9c)^2$ $16a^8b^{18}c^2$
14. $(-2f^2g^3h^2)^3$ $-8f^6g^9h^6$
15. $(-3p^5t^6)^4$ $81p^{20}t^{24}$

Example 4

16. **GEOMETRY** The formula for the surface area of a cube is $SA = 6s^2$, where SA is the surface area and s is the length of any side.

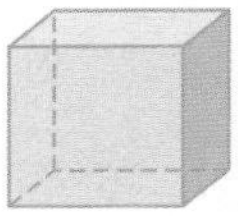
a^3b

a. Express the surface area of the cube as a monomial. $6a^6b^2$
b. What is the surface area of the cube if $a = 3$ and $b = 4$? 69,984 units^2

Example 5 Simplify each expression.

17. $(5x^2y)^2(2xy^3z)^3(4xyz)$ $800x^8y^{12}z^4$
18. $(-3d^2f^3g)^2[(-3d^2f)^3]^2$ $6561d^{16}f^{12}g^2$
19. $(-2g^3h)(-3gj^4)^2(-ghj)^2$ $-18g^7h^3j^{10}$
20. $(-7ab^4c)^3[(2a^2c)^2]^3$ $-21{,}952a^{15}b^{12}c^9$

394 | Lesson 7-1 | Multiplication Properties of Exponents

Practice and Problem Solving

Extra Practice is on page R7.

Example 1 Determine whether each expression is a monomial. Write *yes* or *no*. Explain your reasoning. **21–26. See margin.**

21. 122 **22.** $3a^4$ **23.** $2c + 2$

24. $\frac{-2g}{4h}$ **25.** $\frac{5k}{10}$ **26.** $6m + 3n$

Examples 2–3 Simplify each expression.

27. $(q^2)(2q^4)$ $2q^6$
28. $(-2u^2)(6u^6)$ $-12u^8$
29. $(9w^2x^8)(w^6x^4)$ $9w^8x^{12}$
30. $(y^6z^9)(6y^4z^2)$ $6y^{10}z^{11}$
31. $(b^8c^6d^5)(7b^6c^2d)$ $7b^{14}c^8d^6$
32. $(14fg^2h^2)(-3f^4g^2h^2)$ $-42f^5g^4h^4$
33. $(j^5k^7)^4$ $j^{20}k^{28}$
34. $(n^3p)^4$ $n^{12}p^4$
35. $[(2^2)^2]^2$ 2^8 or 256
36. $[(3^2)^2]^4$ 3^{16} or 43,046,721
37. $[(4r^2t)^3]^2$ $4096r^{12}t^6$
38. $[(-2xy^2)^3]^2$ $64x^6y^{12}$

Example 4 **GEOMETRY** Express the area of each triangle as a monomial.

39. $20c^5d^5$

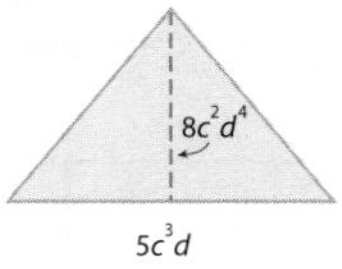

40. $3g^3h^6$

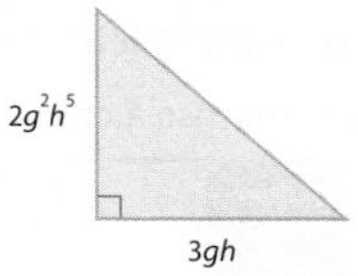

Example 5 Simplify each expression.

41. $(2a^3)^4(a^3)^3$ $16a^{21}$
42. $(c^3)^2(-3c^5)^2$ $9c^{16}$
43. $(2gh^4)^3[(-2g^4h)^3]^2$ $512g^{27}h^{18}$
44. $(5k^2m)^3[(4km^4)^2]^2$ $32{,}000k^{10}m^{19}$
45. $(p^5r^2)^4(-7p^3r^4)^2(6pr^3)$ $294p^{27}r^{19}$
46. $(5x^2y)^2(2xy^3z)^3(4xyz)$ $800x^8y^{12}z^4$
47. $(5a^2b^3c^4)(6a^3b^4c^2)$ $30a^5b^7c^6$
48. $(10xy^5z^3)(3x^4y^6z^3)$ $30x^5y^{11}z^6$
49. $(0.5x^3)^2$ $0.25x^6$
50. $(0.4h^5)^3$ $0.064h^{15}$
51. $\left(-\frac{3}{4}c\right)^3$ $-\frac{27}{64}c^3$
52. $\left(\frac{4}{5}a^2\right)^2$ $\frac{16}{25}a^4$
53. $(8y^3)(-3x^2y^2)\left(\frac{3}{8}xy^4\right)$ $-9x^3y^9$
54. $\left(\frac{4}{7}m\right)^2(49m)(17p)\left(\frac{1}{34}p^5\right)$ $8m^3p^6$
55. $(-3r^3w^4)^3(2rw)^2(-3r^2)^3(4rw^2)^3(2r^2w^3)^4$ $2{,}985{,}984r^{28}w^{32}$
56. $(3ab^2c)^2(-2a^2b^4)^2(a^4c^2)^3(a^2b^4c^5)^2(2a^3b^2c^4)^3$ $288a^{31}b^{26}c^{30}$

57. **FINANCIAL LITERACY** Cleavon has money in an account that earns 3% simple interest. The formula for computing simple interest is $I = Prt$, where I is the interest earned, P represents the principal that he put into the account, r is the interest rate (in decimal form), and t represents time in years.

a. Cleavon makes a deposit of \$$2c$ and leaves it for 2 years. Write a monomial that represents the interest earned. **$0.12c$**

b. If c represents a birthday gift of \$250, how much will Cleavon have in this account after 2 years? **\$280**

TOOLS Express the volume of each solid as a monomial.

58. $12x^4\pi$

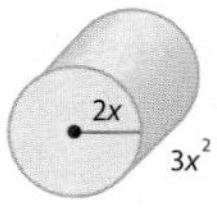

59. $15x^7$

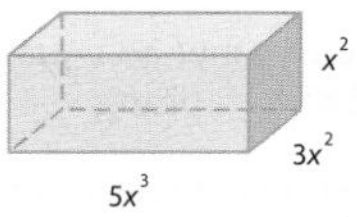

60. $16x^9$

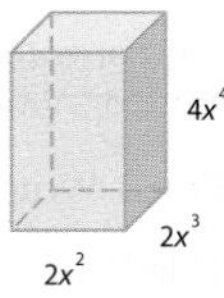

Exercise Alert

Formulas For Exercises 39, 40, and 58–60, students will need to know the formulas for area of a triangle and for volume of solids.

Teaching the Process Standards

Tools Mathematically proficient students are able to identify relevant external mathematical resources and use them to solve problems. In Exercises 58–60, point out that the volume formulas are listed inside the back cover of their book and can be found online.

Additional Answers

21. Yes; constants are monomials.

22. Yes; this is a product of a number and variables.

23. No; there is addition and more than one term.

24. No; there is a variable in the denominator.

25. Yes; this can be written as the product of a number and a variable.

26. No; there is addition and more than one term.

Differentiated Homework Options

Level	Assignment	Two-Day Option	
AL Basic	21–57, 65–84	21–57 odd, 68–71	22–56 even, 65–67, 72–84
OL Core	21–57 odd, 59, 61–63, 65–84	21–57, 68–71	58–63, 65–67, 72–84
BL Advanced	58–78, (optional: 79–84)		

Study Guide and Intervention

AL OL ELL

NAME ______________ DATE ________ PERIOD ________

7-1 Study Guide and Intervention

Multiplication Properties of Exponents

Multiply Monomials A **monomial** is a number, a variable, or the product of a number and one or more variables with nonnegative integer exponents. An expression of the form x^n is called a **power** and represents the product you obtain when x is used as a factor n times. To multiply two powers that have the same base, add the exponents.

Product of Powers	For any number a and all integers m and n, $a^m \cdot a^n = a^{m+n}$.

Example 1 Simplify $(3x^6)(5x^2)$.

$(3x^6)(5x^2) = (3)(5)(x^6 \cdot x^2)$ Group the coefficients and the variables
$= (3 \cdot 5)(x^{6+2})$ Product of Powers
$= 15x^8$ Simplify

The product is $15x^8$.

Example 2 Simplify $(-4a^3b)(3a^2b^5)$.

$(-4a^3b)(3a^2b^5) = (-4)(3)(a^3 \cdot a^2)(b \cdot b^5)$
$= -12(a^{3+2})(b^{1+5})$
$= -12a^5b^6$

The product is $-12a^5b^6$.

Lesson 7-1

Exercises

Simplify each expression.

1. $y(y^5)$
2. $n^2 \cdot n^7$
3. $(-7x^2)(x^4)$
4. $x(x^2)(x^4)$
5. $m \cdot m^5$
6. $(-x^3)(-x^4)$
7. $(2a^2)(8a)$
8. $(rn)(rn^3)(n^2)$
9. $(x^2y)(4xy^3)$
10. $\frac{1}{3}(2a^2b)(6b^3)$
11. $(-4x^3)(-5x^7)$
12. $(-3j^2k^4)(2jk^6)$
13. $(5a^2bc^3)\left(\frac{1}{5}abc^4\right)$
14. $(-5xy)(4x^2)(y^4)$
15. $(10x^3yz^2)(-2xy^5z)$

Practice

AL OL BL ELL

NAME ______________ DATE ________ PERIOD ________

7-1 Practice

Multiplication Properties of Exponents

Determine whether each expression is a monomial. Write *yes* or *no*. Explain your reasoning.

1. $\frac{21a^2}{7b}$
2. $\frac{b^3c^2}{2}$

Simplify each expression.

3. $(-5x^2y)(3x^4)$
4. $(2ab^2f^2)(4a^3b^2f^2)$
5. $(3ad^4)(-2a^2)$
6. $(4g^3h)(-2g^5)$
7. $(-15xy^4)\left(-\frac{1}{3}xy^3\right)$
8. $(-xy)^3(xz)$
9. $(-18m^2n)^2\left(-\frac{1}{6}mn^2\right)$
10. $(0.2a^2b^3)^2$
11. $\left(\frac{2}{3}p\right)^2$
12. $\left(\frac{1}{4}ad^3\right)^2$
13. $(0.4k^3)^3$
14. $[(4^2)^2]^2$

GEOMETRY Express the area of each figure as a monomial.

15. 16. 17.

GEOMETRY Express the volume of each solid as a monomial.

18. 19. 20.

21. **COUNTING** A panel of four light switches can be set in 2^4 ways. A panel of five light switches can set in twice this many ways. In how many ways can five light switches be set?

22. **HOBBIES** Tawa wants to increase her rock collection by a power of three this year and then increase it again by a power of two next year. If she has 2 rocks now, how many rocks will she have after the second year?

Word Problem Practice

AL OL BL ELL

NAME ______________ DATE ________ PERIOD ________

7-1 Word Problem Practice

Multiplication Properties of Exponents

1. **GRAVITY** An egg that has been falling for x seconds has dropped at an average speed of $16x$ feet per second. If the egg is dropped from the top of a building, its total distance traveled is the product of the average rate times the time. Write a simplified expression to show the distance the egg has traveled after x seconds.

2. **CIVIL ENGINEERING** A developer is planning a sidewalk for a new development. The sidewalk can be installed in rectangular sections that have a fixed width of 3 feet and a length that can vary. Assuming that each section is the same length, express the area of a 4-section sidewalk as a monomial.

3. **PROBABILITY** If you flip a coin 3 times in a row, there are 2^3 outcomes that can occur.

Outcomes	
HHH	TTT
HTT	THH
HTH	TTH
HHT	THT

If you then flip the coin two more times, there are $2^3 \times 2^2$ outcomes that can occur. How many outcomes can occur if you flip the coin as mentioned above four more times? Write your answer in the form 2^x.

4. **SPORTS** The volume of a sphere is given by the formula $V = \frac{4}{3}\pi r^3$, where r is the radius of the sphere. Find the volume of air in three different basketballs. Use $\pi = 3.14$. Round your answers to the nearest whole number.

Ball	Radius (in.)	Volume (in³)
Child's	4	
Women's	4.5	
Men's	4.8	

5. **ELECTRICITY** An electrician uses the formula $W = I^2R$, where W is the power in watts, I is the current in amperes, and R is the resistance in ohms.

a. Find the power in a household circuit that has 20 amperes of current and 5 ohms of resistance.

b. If the current is reduced by one half, what happens to the power?

Lesson 7-1

61. **PACKAGING** For a commercial art class, Aiko must design a new container for individually wrapped pieces of candy. The shape that she chose is a cylinder. The formula for the volume of a cylinder is $V = \pi r^2 h$.

a. The radius that Aiko would like to use is $2p^3$, and the height is $4p^3$. Write a monomial that represents the volume of her container. $16\pi p^9$

b. Make a table for five possible measures for the radius and height of a cylinder having the same volume.

c. What is the volume of Aiko's container if the height is doubled? $32\pi p^9$

62. **ENERGY** Albert Einstein's formula $E = mc^2$ shows that if mass is accelerated enough, it could be converted into usable energy. Energy E is measured in joules, mass m in kilograms, and the speed c of light is about 300 million meters per second.

a. Complete the calculations to convert 3 kilograms of gasoline completely into energy. 270,000,000,000,000,000 joules

b. What happens to the energy if the amount of gasoline is doubled? The energy is also doubled.

63. **MULTIPLE REPRESENTATIONS** In this problem, you will explore exponents.

a. **Tabular** Copy and use a calculator to complete the table.

Power	3^4	3^3	3^2	3^1	3^0	3^{-1}	3^{-2}	3^{-3}	3^{-4}
Value	81	27	9	3	1	$\frac{1}{3}$	$\frac{1}{9}$	$\frac{1}{27}$	$\frac{1}{81}$

b. **Analytical** What do you think the values of 5^0 and 5^{-1} are? Verify your conjecture using a calculator. 1 and $\frac{1}{5}$

c. **Analytical** Complete: For any nonzero number a and any integer n, $a^{-n} =$ ______. $\frac{1}{a^n}$

d. **Verbal** Describe the value of a nonzero number raised to the zero power. Any nonzero number raised to the zero power is 1.

61b. Sample answ

Radius	Heigh
$4p$	p^7
$4p^2$	p^5
$2p^3$	$4p^3$
$2p^4$	$4p$
$2p$	$4p^7$

H.O.T. Problems Use Higher-Order Thinking Skills

C 64. **PERSEVERANCE** For any nonzero real numbers a and b and any integers m and t, simplify the expression $\left(-\frac{a^m}{b^t}\right)^{2t}$ and describe each step.

64. Sample answer: First use the power of a power rule to simplify the expression to $\frac{a^{2tm}}{b^{2}t^{2}}$.

65. **REASONING** Copy the table below.

Equation	Related Expression	Power of x	Linear or Nonlinear
$y = x$	x	1	linear
$y = x^2$	x^2	2	nonlinear
$y = x^3$	x^3	3	nonlinear

a. For each equation, write the related expression and record the power of x. See chart above.

b. Graph each equation using a graphing calculator. See Ch. 7 Answer Appendix.

c. Classify each graph as *linear* or *nonlinear*. See chart above.

d. Explain how to determine whether an equation, or its related expression, is linear or nonlinear without graphing. See Ch. 7 Answer Appendix.

66. **OPEN ENDED** Write three different expressions that can be simplified to x^6. Sample answer: $x^4 \cdot x^2$; $x^5 \cdot x$; $(x^3)^2$

67. **WRITING IN MATH** Write two formulas that have monomial expressions in them. Explain how each is used in a real-world situation.

67. Sample answer: The area of a circle or $A = \pi r^2$, where the radius r can be used to find the area of any circle. The area of a rectangle or $A = w \cdot \ell$, where w is the width and ℓ is the length, can be used to find the area of any rectangle.

Enrichment

OL BL

NAME ______________ DATE ________ PERIOD ________

7-1 Enrichment

An Wang

An Wang (1920–1990) was an Asian-American who became one of the pioneers of the computer industry in the United States. He grew up in Shanghai, China, but came to the United States to further his studies in science. In 1948, he invented a magnetic pulse controlling device that vastly increased the storage capacity of computers. He later founded his own company, Wang Laboratories, and became a leader in the development of desktop calculators and word processing systems. In 1988, Wang was elected to the National Inventors Hall of Fame.

Digital computers store information as numbers. Because the electronic circuits of a computer can exist in only one of two states, open or closed, the numbers that are stored can consist of only two digits, 0 or 1. Numbers written using only these two digits are called **binary numbers**. To find the decimal value of a binary number, you use the digits to write *a polynomial in 2*. For instance, this is how to find the decimal value of the number 1001101_2. (The subscript 2 indicates that this is a binary number.)

$1001101_2 = 1 \times 2^6 + 0 \times 2^5 + 0 \times 2^4 + 1 \times 2^3 + 1 \times 2^2 + 0 \times 2^1 + 1 \times 2^0$
$= 1 \times 64 + 0 \times 32 + 0 \times 16 + 1 \times 8 + 1 \times 4 + 0 \times 2 + 1 \times 1$
$= 64 + 0 + 0 + 8 + 4 + 0 + 1$
$= 77$

Multiple Representations

In Exercise 63, students use a calculator, a table of values, and verbal analysis to relate the values of expressions involving positive and negative exponents.

Standardized Test Practice

68. Which of the following is not a monomial? **C**

A $-6xy$ C $-\frac{1}{2b^3}$

B $\frac{1}{2}a^2$ D $5gh^4$

69. GEOMETRY The accompanying diagram shows the transformation of $\triangle XYZ$ to $\triangle X'Y'Z'$. **F**

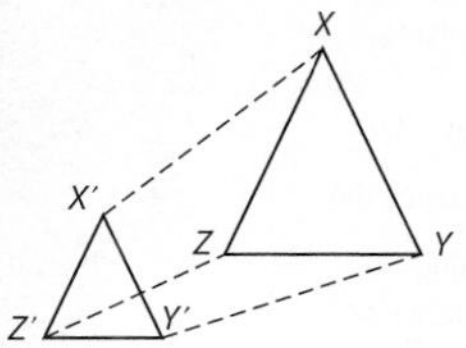

This transformation is an example of a

F dilation

G line reflection

H rotation

J translation

70. CARS In 2002, the average price of a new domestic car was \$19,126. In 2008, the average price was \$28,715. Based on a linear model, what is the predicted average price for 2014? **B**

A \$45,495 C \$35,906

B \$38,304 D \$26,317

71. SHORT RESPONSE If a line has a positive slope and a negative y-intercept, what happens to the x-intercept if the slope and the y-intercept are both doubled? **The x-intercept does not change.**

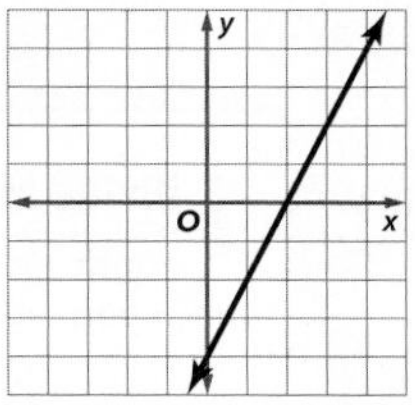

Spiral Review

Solve each system of inequalities by graphing. (Lesson 6-6) **72–75. See margin.**

72. $y < 4x$
$2x + 3y \geq -21$

73. $y \geq 2$
$2y + 2x \leq 4$

74. $y > -2x - 1$
$2y \leq 3x + 2$

75. $3x + 2y < 10$
$2x + 12y < -6$

76. SPORTS In the 2006 Winter Olympic Games, the total number of gold and silver medals won by the U.S. was 18. The total points scored for gold and silver medals was 45. Write and solve a system of equations to find how many gold and silver medals were won by the U.S. (Lesson 6-5) **$3g + 2v = 45$; $g + v = 18$; 9 gold, 9 silver**

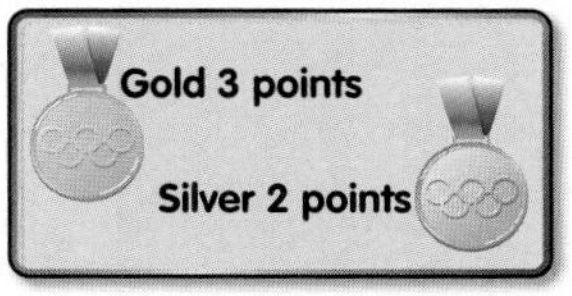

77. DRIVING Tires should be kept within 2 pounds per square inch (psi) of the manufacturer's recommended tire pressure. If the recommendation for a tire is 30 psi, what is the range of acceptable pressures? (Lesson 5-5) **$\{p \mid 28 \leq p \leq 32\}$**

78. BABYSITTING Alexis charges \$10 plus \$4 per hour to babysit. Alexis needs at least \$40 more to buy a television for which she is saving. Write an inequality for this situation. Will she be able to get her television if she babysits for 5 hours? (Lesson 5-6) **$10 + 4h \geq 40$; no**

Skills Review

Find each quotient.

79. $-64 \div (-8)$ **8**

80. $-78 \div 1.3$ **-60**

81. $42.3 \div (-6)$ **-7.05**

82. $-23.94 \div 10.5$ **-2.28**

83. $-32.5 \div (-2.5)$ **13**

84. $-98.44 \div 4.6$ **-21.4**

Differentiated Instruction OL BL

Extension Tell students that a sports car on a drag-racing strip can reach 100 miles per hour in a quarter mile. If s represents the speed in miles per hour, then the approximate number of feet that the driver must apply the brakes before stopping is $\frac{1}{20}s^2$. Calculate how far the car would travel on the drag strip, from start to stop, if the driver started braking when the car reached 100 miles per hour. A mile is 5280 feet. 1820 ft; the initial quarter mile (1320 ft) plus braking distance (500 ft)

Teaching the Process Standards

Perseverance Mathematically proficient students try simpler forms of the original problem in order to gain insight into its solution. In Exercise 64, advise students to substitute integers for a and b and simplify the expressions before generalizing.

4 Assess

Ticket Out the Door Make several copies each of five monomial expressions that need to be simplified. Give one expression to each student. As students leave the room, ask them to tell you the simplified versions of the expressions they possess.

Additional Answers

72.

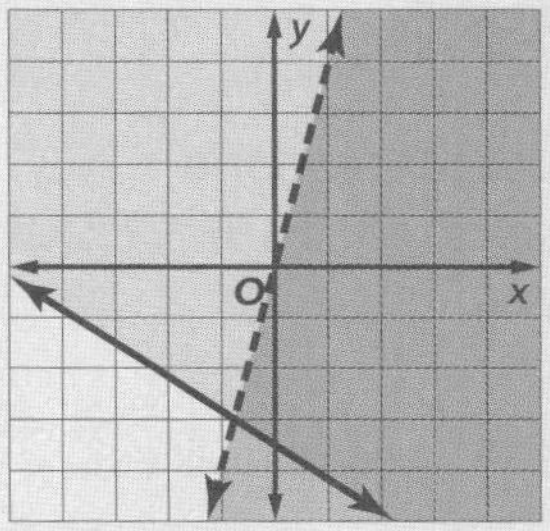

73.

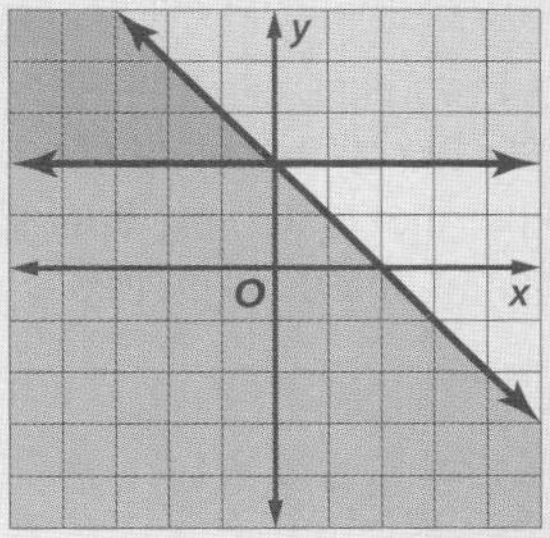

74.

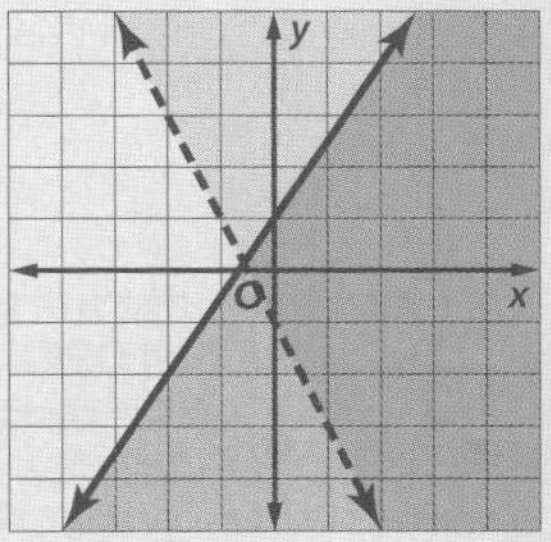

75.

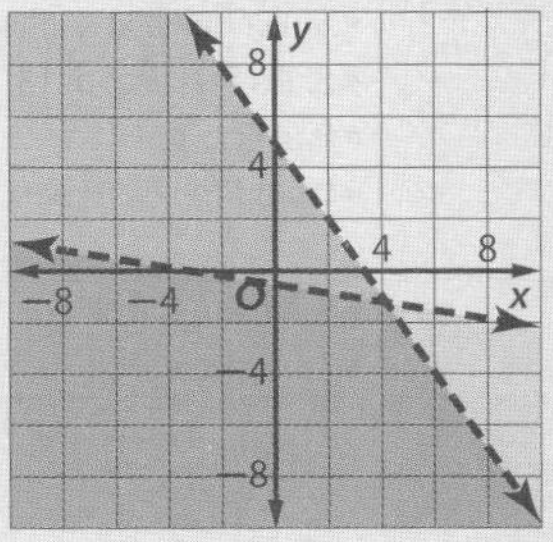

1 Focus

VerticalAlignment

Before Lesson 7-2 Multiply monomials using the properties of exponents.

Lesson 7-2 Divide monomials using the properties of exponents.
Simplify expressions containing negative and zero exponents.

After Lesson 7-2 Express numbers in scientific notation. Find products and quotients of numbers expressed in scientific notation.

2 Teach

Scaffolding Questions

Have students read the **Why?** section of the lesson.

Ask:

- What is 10^2 when simplified? 100
- What is 10^1 when simplified? 10
- How could you use exponents to write the ratio of the height of a skyscraper that is 900 meters tall to the height of the tallest tree? $\frac{10^3}{10^2}$ or 10^1

LESSON 7-2 Division Properties of Exponents

Then

- You multiplied monomials using the properties of exponents.

Now

1. Divide monomials using the properties of exponents.
2. Simplify expressions containing negative and zero exponents.

Why?

- The tallest redwood tree is 112 meters or about 10^2 meters tall. The average height of a redwood tree is 15 meters. The closest power of ten to 15 is 10^1, so an average redwood is about 10^1 meters tall. The ratio of the tallest tree's height to the average tree's height is $\frac{10^2}{10^1}$ or 10^1. This means the tallest redwood tree is approximately 10 times as tall as the average redwood tree.

NewVocabulary
zero exponent
negative exponent
order of magnitude

Content Standards
AI.RNE.3

Process Standards
PS.2

1 Divide Monomials

We can use the principles for reducing fractions to find quotients of monomials like $\frac{10^2}{10^1}$. In the following examples, look for a pattern in the exponents.

$$\frac{2^7}{2^4} = \frac{\overbrace{\cancel{2}\cdot\cancel{2}\cdot\cancel{2}\cdot\cancel{2}\cdot 2\cdot 2\cdot 2}^{7\text{ factors}}}{\underbrace{\cancel{2}\cdot\cancel{2}\cdot\cancel{2}\cdot\cancel{2}}_{4\text{ factors}}} = 2\cdot 2\cdot 2 \text{ or } 2^3 \qquad \frac{t^4}{t^3} = \frac{\overbrace{\cancel{t}\cdot\cancel{t}\cdot\cancel{t}\cdot t}^{4\text{ factors}}}{\underbrace{\cancel{t}\cdot\cancel{t}\cdot\cancel{t}}_{3\text{ factors}}} = t$$

These examples demonstrate the Quotient of Powers Rule.

KeyConcept Quotient of Powers

Words	To divide two powers with the same base, subtract the exponents.
Symbols	For any nonzero number a, and any integers m and p, $\frac{a^m}{a^p} = a^{m-p}$.
Examples	$\frac{c^{11}}{c^8} = c^{11-8}$ or c^3 $\frac{r^5}{r^2} = r^{5-2} = r^3$

Example 1 Quotient of Powers

Simplify $\frac{g^3h^5}{gh^2}$. Assume that no denominator equals zero.

$\frac{g^3h^5}{gh^2} = \left(\frac{g^3}{g}\right)\left(\frac{h^5}{h^2}\right)$ Group powers with the same base.

$= (g^{3-1})(h^{5-2})$ Quotient of Powers

$= g^2h^3$ Simplify.

GuidedPractice

Simplify each expression. Assume that no denominator equals zero.

1A. $\frac{x^3y^4}{x^2y}$ xy^3 **1B.** $\frac{k^7m^{10}p}{k^5m^3p}$ k^2m^7

398 | Lesson 7-2

Lesson 7-2 Resources

Resource	Approaching Level AL	On Level OL	Beyond Level BL	English Learners ELL
Teacher Edition	▪ Differentiated Instruction, p. 400	▪ Differentiated Instruction, pp. 400, 405	▪ Differentiated Instruction, p. 405	▪ Differentiated Instruction, p. 400
Chapter Resource Masters	▪ Study Guide and Intervention, pp. 11–12 ▪ Skills Practice, p. 13 ▪ Practice, p. 14 ▪ Word Problem Practice, p. 15	▪ Study Guide and Intervention, pp. 11–12 ▪ Skills Practice, p. 13 ▪ Practice, p. 14 ▪ Word Problem Practice, p. 15 ▪ Enrichment, p. 16	▪ Practice, p. 14 ▪ Word Problem Practice, p. 15 ▪ Enrichment, p. 16	▪ Study Guide and Intervention, pp. 11–12 ▪ Skills Practice, p. 13 ▪ Practice, p. 14 ▪ Word Problem Practice, p. 15
Other	▪ 5-Minute Check 7-2 ▪ Study Notebook	▪ 5-Minute Check 7-2 ▪ Study Notebook	▪ 5-Minute Check 7-2 ▪ Study Notebook	▪ 5-Minute Check 7-2 ▪ Study Notebook

We can use the Product of Powers Rule to find the powers of quotients for monomials. In the following example, look for a pattern in the exponents.

$$\left(\frac{3}{4}\right)^3 = \overbrace{\left(\frac{3}{4}\right)\left(\frac{3}{4}\right)\left(\frac{3}{4}\right)}^{\text{3 factors}} = \frac{\overbrace{3 \cdot 3 \cdot 3}^{\text{3 factors}}}{\underbrace{4 \cdot 4 \cdot 4}_{\text{3 factors}}} = \frac{3^3}{4^3}$$

$$\left(\frac{c}{d}\right)^2 = \overbrace{\left(\frac{c}{d}\right)\left(\frac{c}{d}\right)}^{\text{2 factors}} = \frac{\overbrace{c \cdot c}^{\text{2 factors}}}{\underbrace{d \cdot d}_{\text{2 factors}}} = \frac{c^2}{d^2}$$

StudyTip

Power Rules with Variables The power rules apply to variables as well as numbers. For example, $\left(\frac{3a}{4b}\right)^3 = \frac{(3a)^3}{(4b)^3}$ or $\frac{27a^3}{64b^3}$.

KeyConcept Power of a Quotient

Words To find the power of a quotient, find the power of the numerator and the power of the denominator.

Symbols For any real numbers a and $b \neq 0$, and any integer m, $\left(\frac{a}{b}\right)^m = \frac{a^m}{b^m}$.

Examples $\left(\frac{3}{5}\right)^4 = \frac{3^4}{5^4}$ $\quad \left(\frac{r}{t}\right)^5 = \frac{r^5}{t^5}$

Real-WorldCareer

Astronomer An astronomer studies the universe and analyzes space travel and satellite communications. To be a technician or research assistant, a bachelor's degree is required.

Example 2 Power of a Quotient

Simplify $\left(\frac{3p^3}{7}\right)^2$.

$\left(\frac{3p^3}{7}\right)^2 = \frac{(3p^3)^2}{7^2}$ Power of a Quotient

$= \frac{3^2(p^3)^2}{7^2}$ Power of a Product

$= \frac{9p^6}{49}$ Power of a Power

GuidedPractice

Simplify each expression.

2A. $\left(\frac{3x^4}{4}\right)^3$ $\frac{27x^{12}}{64}$ **2B.** $\left(\frac{5x^5y}{6}\right)^2$ $\frac{25x^{10}y^2}{36}$ **2C.** $\left(\frac{2y^2}{3z^3}\right)^2$ $\frac{4y^4}{9z^6}$ **2D.** $\left(\frac{4x^3}{5y^4}\right)^3$ $\frac{64x^9}{125y^{12}}$

A calculator can be used to explore expressions with 0 as the exponent. There are two methods to explain why a calculator gives a value of 1 for 3^0.

Method 1

$\frac{3^5}{3^5} = 3^{5-5}$ Quotient of Powers

$= 3^0$ Simplify.

Method 2

$\frac{3^5}{3^5} = \frac{\cancel{3} \cdot \cancel{3} \cdot \cancel{3} \cdot \cancel{3} \cdot \cancel{3}}{\cancel{3} \cdot \cancel{3} \cdot \cancel{3} \cdot \cancel{3} \cdot \cancel{3}}$ Definition of powers

$= 1$ Simplify.

Since $\frac{3^5}{3^5}$ can only have one value, we can conclude that $3^0 = 1$. A **zero exponent** is any nonzero number raised to the zero power.

Teach with Tech

Blog On your secure classroom blog have students create a blog entry explaining how to find the quotient of powers and the power of a quotient.

1 Divide Monomials

Example 1 shows how to find the quotient of powers. **Example 2** shows how to find the power of a quotient. **Example 3** shows how to simplify expressions involving zero exponents.

Formative Assessment

Use the Guided Practice exercises after each example to determine students' understanding of concepts.

Additional Examples

1 Simplify $\frac{x^7y^{12}}{x^6y^3}$. Assume that no denominator equals zero. xy^9

2 Simplify $\left(\frac{4c^3d^2}{5}\right)^3$. $\frac{64c^9d^6}{125}$

Additional Examples also in Interactive Classroom PowerPoint® Presentations

IWB Interactive White Board READY

WatchOut!

Preventing Errors Remind students to also find the powers of the constant terms of the monomials.

Tips for New Teachers

Properties Point out to students that the definition of the Quotient of Powers restricts a to being nonzero. Ask why must a be nonzero? If $a = 0$, we would be dividing by 0, which is undefined.

Focus on Mathematical Content

Powers of Negative Numbers Students may assume that the expression -6^3 means $(-6)(-6)(-6)$. Explain that -6^3 means $-(6^3)$. To express -6 to the third power, they must use parentheses, $(-6)^3$.

WatchOut!

Preventing Errors Ask students why the negative sign in Example 3 does not affect the outcome. Students should explain that any nonzero number raised to the zero power is 1, and a negative number is a nonzero number.

Additional Example

3 Simplify each expression. Assume that no denominator equals zero.

a. $\left(\frac{12m^8n^7}{8m^5n^{10}}\right)^0$ 1

b. $\frac{m^0n^3}{n^2}$ n

Tips for New Teachers

Zero to the Zero Power Ask students to write an expression involving division that will be equivalent to 0^0, for example, $\frac{0^6}{0^6}$. Show students that $\frac{0^6}{0^6} = \frac{0}{0}$ and remind them that division by zero is undefined.

2 Negative Exponents

Example 4 shows how to simplify expressions involving negative exponents. **Example 5** shows how to apply the properties of exponents in real-world situations.

KeyConcept Zero Exponent Property

Words	Any nonzero number raised to the zero power is equal to 1.
Symbols	For any nonzero number a, $a^0 = 1$.
Examples	$15^0 = 1$ $\left(\frac{b}{c}\right)^0 = 1$ $\left(\frac{2}{7}\right)^0 = 1$

PT

Example 3 Zero Exponent

Simplify each expression. Assume that no denominator equals zero.

a. $\left(-\frac{4n^2q^5r^2}{9n^3q^2r}\right)^0$

$\left(-\frac{4n^2q^5r^2}{9n^3q^2r}\right)^0 = 1$ $a^0 = 1$

b. $\frac{x^5y^0}{x^3}$

$\frac{x^5y^0}{x^3} = \frac{x^5(1)}{x^3}$ $a^0 = 1$

$= x^2$ Quotient of Powers

StudyTip

Zero Exponent Be careful of parentheses. The expression $(5x)^0$ is 1 but $5x^0 = 5$.

GuidedPractice

3A. $\frac{b^4c^2d^0}{b^2c}$ b^2c

3B. $\left(\frac{2f^4g^7h^3}{15f^3g^9h^6}\right)^0$ 1

2 Negative Exponents Any nonzero real number raised to a negative power is a **negative exponent**. To investigate the meaning of a negative exponent, we can simplify expressions like $\frac{c^2}{c^5}$ using two methods.

Method 1

$\frac{c^2}{c^5} = c^{2-5}$ Quotient of Powers

$= c^{-3}$ Simplify.

Method 2

$\frac{c^2}{c^5} = \frac{\cancel{c} \cdot \cancel{c}}{\cancel{c} \cdot \cancel{c} \cdot c \cdot c \cdot c}$ Definition of powers

$= \frac{1}{c^3}$ Simplify.

Since $\frac{c^2}{c^5}$ can only have one value, we can conclude that $c^{-3} = \frac{1}{c^3}$.

KeyConcept Negative Exponent Property

Words	For any nonzero number a and any integer n, a^{-n} is the reciprocal of a^n. Also, the reciprocal of a^{-n} is a^n.
Symbols	For any nonzero number a and any integer n, $a^{-n} = \frac{1}{a^n}$.
Examples	$2^{-4} = \frac{1}{2^4} = \frac{1}{16}$ $\frac{1}{j^{-4}} = j^4$

DifferentiatedInstruction AL OL ELL

If students have difficulty relating the Key Concepts in this lesson to expressions,

Then have students make flash cards to illustrate each Key Concept. Write an expression that is an example of a Key Concept on the board. Tell students to show their card that correlates to the example. Then ask a student to describe the process of simplifying the expression.

An expression is considered simplified when it contains only positive exponents, each base appears exactly once, there are no powers of powers, and all fractions are in simplest form.

Example 4 Negative Exponents

PT

Simplify each expression. Assume that no denominator equals zero.

a. $\dfrac{n^{-5}p^4}{r^{-2}}$

$\dfrac{n^{-5}p^4}{r^{-2}} = \left(\dfrac{n^{-5}}{1}\right)\left(\dfrac{p^4}{1}\right)\left(\dfrac{1}{r^{-2}}\right)$ Write as a product of fractions.

$= \left(\dfrac{1}{n^5}\right)\left(\dfrac{p^4}{1}\right)\left(\dfrac{r^2}{1}\right)$ $a^{-n} = \dfrac{1}{a^n}$ and $\dfrac{1}{a^{-n}} = a^n$

$= \dfrac{p^4r^2}{n^5}$ Multiply.

b. $\dfrac{5r^{-3}t^4}{-20r^2t^7u^{-5}}$

$\dfrac{5r^{-3}t^4}{-20r^2t^7u^{-5}} = \left(\dfrac{5}{-20}\right)\left(\dfrac{r^{-3}}{r^2}\right)\left(\dfrac{t^4}{t^7}\right)\left(\dfrac{1}{u^{-5}}\right)$ Group powers with the same base.

$= \left(-\dfrac{1}{4}\right)(r^{-3-2})(t^{4-7})(u^5)$ Quotient of Powers and Negative Exponents Property

$= -\dfrac{1}{4}r^{-5}t^{-3}u^5$ Simplify.

$= -\dfrac{1}{4}\left(\dfrac{1}{r^5}\right)\left(\dfrac{1}{t^3}\right)(u^5)$ Negative Exponent Property

$= -\dfrac{u^5}{4r^5t^3}$ Multiply.

c. $\dfrac{2a^2b^3c^{-5}}{10a^{-3}b^{-1}c^{-4}}$

$\dfrac{2a^2b^3c^{-5}}{10a^{-3}b^{-1}c^{-4}} = \left(\dfrac{2}{10}\right)\left(\dfrac{a^2}{a^{-3}}\right)\left(\dfrac{b^3}{b^{-1}}\right)\left(\dfrac{c^{-5}}{c^{-4}}\right)$ Group powers with the same base.

$= \left(\dfrac{1}{5}\right)(a^{2-(-3)})(b^{3-(-1)})(c^{-5-(-4)})$ Quotient of Powers and Negative Exponents Property

$= \dfrac{1}{5}a^5b^4c^{-1}$ Simplify.

$= \dfrac{1}{5}(a^5)(b^4)\left(\dfrac{1}{c}\right)$ Negative Exponent Property

$= \dfrac{a^5b^4}{5c}$ Multiply.

Guided Practice

Simplify each expression. Assume that no denominator equals zero.

4A. $\dfrac{v^{-3}wx^2}{wy^{-6}}$ $\dfrac{x^2y^6}{v^3}$ **4B.** $\dfrac{32a^{-8}b^3c^{-4}}{4a^3b^5c^{-2}}$ $\dfrac{8}{a^{11}b^2c^2}$ **4C.** $\dfrac{5j^{-3}k^2m^{-6}}{25k^{-4}m^{-2}}$ $\dfrac{k^6}{5j^3m^4}$

Order of magnitude is used to compare measures and to estimate and perform rough calculations. The **order of magnitude** of a quantity is the number rounded to the nearest power of 10. For example, the power of 10 closest to 95,000,000,000 is 10^{11}, or 100,000,000,000. So the order of magnitude of 95,000,000,000 is 10^{11}.

StudyTip

Negative Signs Be aware of where a negative sign is placed. $5^{-1} = \frac{1}{5}$, while $-5^1 \neq \frac{1}{5}$.

Real-WorldLink

An adult human weighs about 70 kilograms and an adult dairy cow weighs about 700 kilograms. Their weights differ by 1 order of magnitude.

WatchOut!

Preventing Errors Have students look at the first step of the solution of Example 4. Point out that rewriting an expression as a product of fractions makes applying the Negative Exponent Property easier. Fractions that have negative exponents can be rewritten as their reciprocals.

Additional Example

4 Simplify each expression. Assume that no denominator equals zero.

a. $\dfrac{x^{-4}y^9}{z^{-6}}$ $\dfrac{y^9z^6}{x^4}$

b. $\dfrac{75p^3m^{-5}}{15p^5m^{-4}r^{-8}}$ $\dfrac{5r^8}{p^2m}$

Tips for New Teachers

Monomials Point out to students that a variable with a negative exponent such as x^{-2} is not a monomial. A monomial does not involve division by variables and $x^{-2} = \dfrac{1}{x^2}$.

connectED.mcgraw-hill.com 401

Additional Example

5 **SAVINGS** Darin has \$123,456 in his savings account. Tabo has \$156 in his savings account. Determine the order of magnitude of Darin's account and Tabo's account. How many orders of magnitude as great is Darin's account as Tabo's account? Darin: 10^5, Tabo: 10^2; Darin's account is 3 orders of magnitude as great as Tabo's account.

3 Practice

Formative Assessment

Use Exercises 1–18 to check for understanding.

Use the chart at the bottom of the next page to customize assignments for your students.

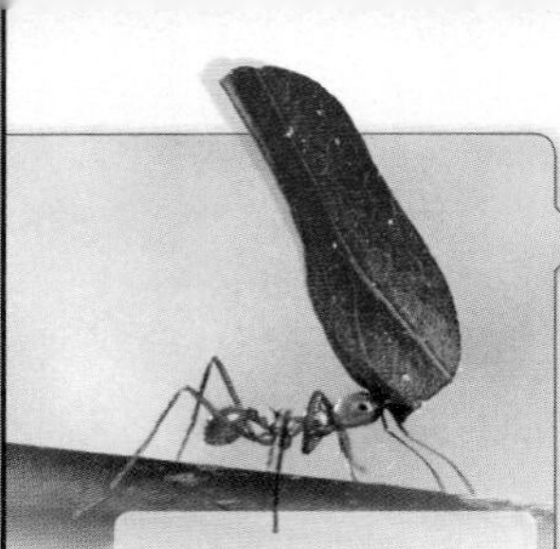

Real-WorldLink

There are over 14,000 species of ants living all over the world. Some ants can carry objects that are 50 times their own weight.

Source: Maine Animal Coalition

PT

Real-World Example 5 Apply Properties of Exponents

HEIGHT Suppose the average height of a man is about 1.7 meters, and the average height of an ant is 0.0008 meter. How many orders of magnitude as tall as an ant is a man?

Understand We must find the order of magnitude of the heights of the man and ant. Then find the ratio of the orders of magnitude of the man's height to that of the ant's height.

Plan Round each height to the nearest power of ten. Then find the ratio of the height of the man to the height of the ant.

Solve The average height of a man is close to 1 meter. So, the order of magnitude is 10^0 meter. The average height of an ant is about 0.001 meter. So, the order of magnitude is 10^{-3} meters.

The ratio of the height of a man to the height of an ant is about $\frac{10^0}{10^{-3}}$.

$\frac{10^0}{10^{-3}} = 10^{0-(-3)}$ Quotient of Powers

$= 10^3$ $0 - (-3) = 0 + 3$ or 3

$= 1000$ Simplify.

So, a man is approximately 1000 times as tall as an ant, or a man is 3 orders of magnitude as tall as an ant.

Check The ratio of the man's height to the ant's height is $\frac{1.7}{0.0008} = 2125$. The order of magnitude of 2125 is 10^3. ✓

GuidedPractice

5. ASTRONOMY The order of magnitude of the mass of Earth is about 10^{27}. The order of magnitude of the Milky Way galaxy is about 10^{44}. How many orders of magnitude as big is the Milky Way galaxy as Earth? 17

Check Your Understanding

◯ = Step-by-Step Solutions begin on page R13.

Examples 1–4 **Simplify each expression. Assume that no denominator equals zero.**

1. $\frac{t^5u^4}{t^2u}$ t^3u^3
2. $\frac{a^6b^4c^{10}}{a^3b^2c}$ $a^3b^2c^9$
3. $\frac{m^6r^5p^3}{m^5r^2p^3}$ mr^3
4. $\frac{b^4c^6f^8}{b^4c^3f^5}$ c^3f^3
5. $\frac{g^8h^2m}{hg^7}$ ghm
6. $\frac{r^4t^7v^2}{t^7v^2}$ r^4
7. $\frac{x^3y^2z^6}{z^5x^2y}$ xyz
8. $\frac{n^4q^4w^6}{q^2n^3w}$ nq^2w^5
9. $\left(\frac{2a^3b^5}{3}\right)^2$ $\frac{4a^6b^{10}}{9}$
10. $\frac{r^3v^{-2}}{t^{-7}}$ $\frac{r^3t^7}{v^2}$
11. $\left(\frac{2c^3d^5}{5g^2}\right)^5$ $\frac{32c^{15}d^{25}}{3125g^{10}}$
12. $\left(-\frac{3xy^4z^2}{x^3yz^4}\right)^0$ 1
13. $\left(\frac{3f^4gh^4}{32f^3g^4h}\right)^0$ 1
14. $\frac{4r^2v^0t^5}{2rt^3}$ $2rt^2$
15. $\frac{f^{-3}g^2}{h^{-4}}$ $\frac{g^2h^4}{f^3}$
16. $\frac{-8x^2y^8z^{-5}}{12x^4y^{-7}z^7}$ $\frac{-2y^{15}}{3x^2z^{12}}$
17. $\frac{2a^2b^{-7}c^{10}}{6a^{-3}b^2c^{-3}}$ $\frac{a^5c^{13}}{3b^9}$

Example 5

18. **FINANCIAL LITERACY** The gross domestic product (GDP) for the United States in 2008 was \$14.204 trillion, and the GDP per person was \$47,580. Use order of magnitude to approximate the population of the United States in 2008. 10^8 or 100,000,000

402 | Lesson 7-2 | Division Properties of Exponents

Practice and Problem Solving

Extra Practice is on page R7.

Examples 1–4 **Simplify each expression. Assume that no denominator equals zero.**

19. $\frac{m^4p^2}{m^2p}$ m^2p

20. $\frac{p^{12}t^3r}{p^2tr}$ $p^{10}t^2$

21. $\frac{3m^{-3}r^4p^2}{12t^4}$ $\frac{r^4p^2}{4m^3t^4}$

22. $\frac{c^4d^4f^3}{c^2d^4f^3}$ c^2

23. $\left(\frac{3xy^4}{5z^2}\right)^2$ $\frac{9x^2y^8}{25z^4}$

24. $\left(\frac{3t^6u^2v^5}{9tuv^{21}}\right)^0$ 1

25. $\left(\frac{p^2t^7}{10}\right)^3$ $\frac{p^6t^{21}}{1000}$

26. $\frac{x^{-4}y^9}{z^{-2}}$ $\frac{y^9z^2}{x^4}$

27. $\frac{a^7b^8c^8}{a^5bc^7}$ a^2b^7c

28. $\left(\frac{3np^3}{7q^2}\right)^2$ $\frac{9n^2p^6}{49q^4}$

29. $\left(\frac{2r^3t^6}{5u^9}\right)^4$ $\frac{16r^{12}t^{24}}{625u^{36}}$

30. $\left(\frac{3m^5r^3}{4p^8}\right)^4$ $\frac{81m^{20}r^{12}}{256p^{32}}$

31. $\left(-\frac{5f^9g^4h^2}{fg^2h^3}\right)^0$ 1

32. $\frac{p^{12}t^7r^2}{p^2t^7r}$ $p^{10}r$

33. $\frac{p^4t^{-3}}{r^{-2}}$ $\frac{p^4r^2}{t^3}$

34. $-\frac{5c^2d^5}{8cd^5f^0}$ $-\frac{5c}{8}$

35. $\frac{-2f^3g^2h^0}{8f^2g^2}$ $\frac{-f}{4}$

36. $\frac{12m^{-4}p^2}{-15m^3p^{-9}}$ $\frac{4p^{11}}{-5m^7}$

37. $\frac{k^4m^3p^2}{k^2m^2}$ k^2mp^2

38. $\frac{14f^{-3}g^2h^{-7}}{21k^3}$ $\frac{2g^2}{3f^3h^7k^3}$

39. $\frac{39t^4uv^{-2}}{13t^{-3}u^7}$ $\frac{3t^7}{u^6v^2}$

40. $\left(\frac{a^{-2}b^4c^5}{a^{-4}b^{-4}c^3}\right)^2$ $a^4b^{16}c^4$

41. $\frac{r^3t^{-1}x^{-5}}{tx^5}$ $\frac{r^3}{t^2x^{10}}$

42. $\frac{g^0h^7j^{-2}}{g^{-5}h^0j^{-2}}$ g^5h^7

43. 10^6; 10^8; about 10^2 or 100 times as many users as hosts

Example 5

43. **INTERNET** In a recent year, there were approximately 3.95 million Internet hosts. Suppose there were 208 million Internet users. Determine the order of magnitude for the Internet hosts and Internet users. Using the orders of magnitude, how many Internet users were there compared to Internet hosts?

B

44. **PROBABILITY** The probability of rolling a die and getting an even number is $\frac{1}{2}$. If you roll the die twice, the probability of getting an even number both times is $\left(\frac{1}{2}\right)\left(\frac{1}{2}\right)$ or $\left(\frac{1}{2}\right)^2$.
    a. What does $\left(\frac{1}{2}\right)^4$ represent? probability of all evens on 4 rolls
    b. Write an expression to represent the probability of rolling a die d times and getting an even number every time. Write the expression as a power of 2. $\left(\frac{1}{2}\right)^d$; 2^{-d}

Simplify each expression. Assume that no denominator equals zero.

45. $\frac{-4w^{12}}{12w^3}$ $-\frac{w^9}{3}$

46. $\frac{13r^7}{39r^4}$ $\frac{r^3}{3}$

47. $\frac{(4k^3m^2)^3}{(5k^2m^{-3})^{-2}}$ $1600k^{13}$

48. $\frac{3wy^{-2}}{(w^{-1}y)^3}$ $\frac{3w^4}{y^5}$

49. $\frac{20qr^{-2}t^{-5}}{4q^0r^4t^{-2}}$ $\frac{5q}{r^6t^3}$

50. $\frac{-12c^3d^0f^{-2}}{6c^5d^{-3}f^4}$ $\frac{-2d^3}{c^2f^6}$

51. $\frac{(2g^3h^{-2})^2}{(g^2h^0)^{-3}}$ $\frac{4g^{12}}{h^4}$

52. $\frac{(5pr^{-2})^{-2}}{(3p^{-1}r)^3}$ $\frac{pr}{675}$

53. $\left(\frac{-3x^{-6}y^{-1}z^{-2}}{6x^{-2}yz^{-5}}\right)^{-2}$ $\frac{4x^8y^4}{z^6}$

54. $\left(\frac{2a^{-2}b^4c^2}{-4a^{-2}b^{-5}c^{-7}}\right)^{-1}$ $\frac{-2}{b^9c^9}$

55. $\frac{(16x^2y^{-1})^0}{(4x^0y^{-4}z)^{-2}}$ $\frac{16z^2}{y^8}$

56. $\left(\frac{4^0c^2d^3f}{2c^{-4}d^{-5}}\right)^{-3}$ $\frac{8}{c^{18}d^{24}f^3}$

57. **SENSE-MAKING** The processing speed of an older desktop computer is about 10^8 instructions per second. A new computer can process about 10^{10} instructions per second. The newer computer is how many times as fast as the older one? 100

Tips for New Teachers

Checking Answers When simplifying expressions, students may wish to check their answers by choosing nonzero values for the variables and evaluating the original and simplified expressions. If the results are the same, the expressions are likely to be equivalent.

Teaching the Process Standards

Sense-Making Mathematically proficient students try simpler forms of the original problem in order to gain insight into its solution. In Exercise 57, encourage students to start by finding the number of instructions per second in a computer ten times as fast.

Differentiated Homework Options

Level	Assignment	Two-Day Option	
AL Basic	19–43, 61, 62, 64–89	19–43 odd, 66–69	20–42 even, 61, 62, 64, 65, 70–89
OL Core	19–43 odd, 44, 45–55 odd, 57–62, 64–89	19–43, 66–69	44–62, 64, 65, 70–89
BL Advanced	44–81, (optional: 82–89)		

Study Guide and Intervention

AL OL ELL

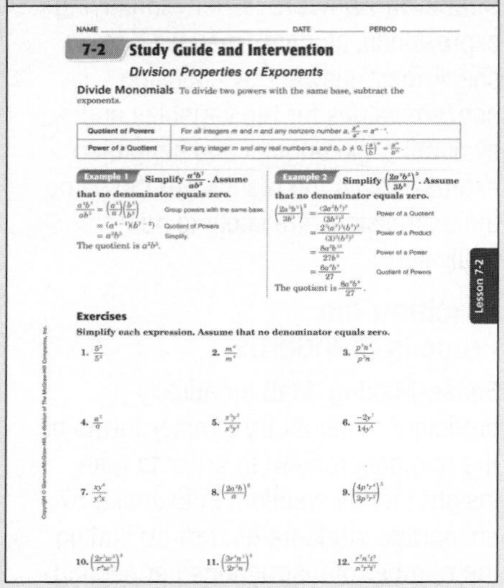
NAME ______ DATE ______ PERIOD ______

7-2 Study Guide and Intervention

Division Properties of Exponents

Divide Monomials To divide two powers with the same base, subtract the exponents.

Exercises

Simplify each expression. Assume that no denominator equals zero.

Practice

AL OL BL ELL

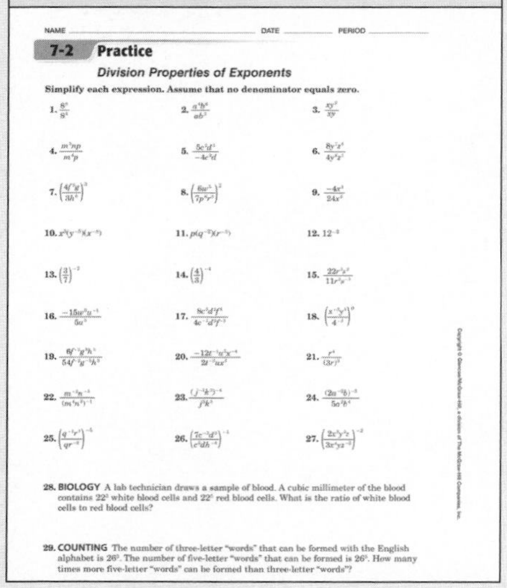
NAME ______ DATE ______ PERIOD ______

7-2 Practice

Division Properties of Exponents

Simplify each expression. Assume that no denominator equals zero.

28. BIOLOGY A lab technician draws a sample of blood. A cubic millimeter of the blood contains 22^3 white blood cells and 22^5 red blood cells. What is the ratio of white blood cells to red blood cells?

29. COUNTING The number of three-letter "words" that can be formed with the English alphabet is 26^3. The number of five-letter "words" that can be formed is 26^5. How many times more five-letter "words" can be formed than three-letter "words"?

Word Problem Practice

AL OL BL ELL

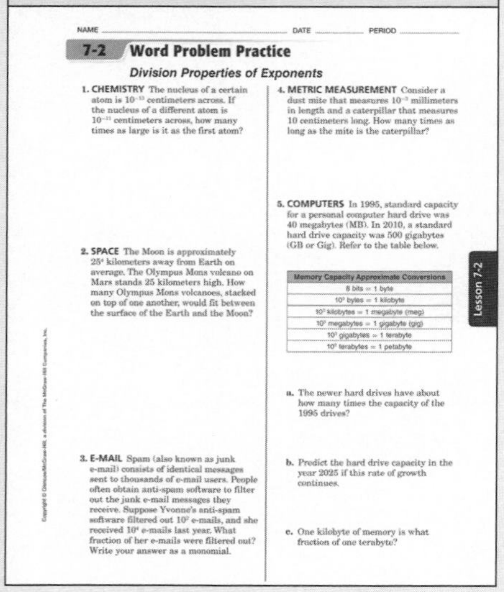
NAME ______ DATE ______ PERIOD ______

7-2 Word Problem Practice

Division Properties of Exponents

58. **ASTRONOMY** The brightness of a star is measured in magnitudes. The lower the magnitude, the brighter the star. A magnitude 9 star is 2.51 times as bright as a magnitude 10 star. A magnitude 8 star is 2.51 • 2.51 or 2.51^2 times as bright as a magnitude 10 star. **2.51^7 or 627.647857**

   a. How many times as bright is a magnitude 3 star as a magnitude 10 star?

   b. Write an expression to compare a magnitude m star to a magnitude 10 star. **2.51^{10-m}**

   c. A full moon is considered to be magnitude −13, approximately. Does your expression make sense for this magnitude? Explain.

59. **PROBABILITY** The probability of rolling a die and getting a 3 is $\frac{1}{6}$. If you roll the die twice, the probability of getting a 3 both times is $\frac{1}{6} \cdot \frac{1}{6}$ or $\left(\frac{1}{6}\right)^2$.

   a. Write an expression to represent the probability of rolling a die d times and getting a 3 each time. **$\left(\frac{1}{6}\right)^d$**

   b. Write the expression as a power of 6. **6^{-d}**

60. **MULTIPLE REPRESENTATIONS** To find the area of a circle, use $A = \pi r^2$. The formula for the area of a square is $A = s^2$.

   a. **Algebraic** Find the ratio of the area of the circle to the area of the square. **$\frac{\pi}{4}$**

   b. **Algebraic** If the radius of the circle and the length of each side of the square are doubled, find the ratio of the area of the circle to the square. **$\frac{\pi}{4}$**

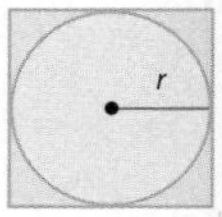

   c. **Tabular** Copy and complete the table.

Radius	Area of Circle	Area of Square	Ratio
r	πr^2	$4r^2$	$\frac{\pi}{4}$
$2r$	$\pi 4r^2$	$16r^2$	$\frac{\pi}{4}$
$3r$	$\pi 9r^2$	$36r^2$	$\frac{\pi}{4}$
$4r$	$\pi 16r^2$	$64r^2$	$\frac{\pi}{4}$
$5r$	$\pi 25r^2$	$100r^2$	$\frac{\pi}{4}$
$6r$	$\pi 36r^2$	$144r^2$	$\frac{\pi}{4}$

   d. **Analytical** What conclusion can be drawn from this? **The ratio of the area of the circle to the area of the square will always be $\frac{\pi}{4}$.**

58c. Sample answer: Yes; according to the expression, a full Moon would be $2.51^{10-m} = 2.51^{10-(-13)} = 2.51^{23}$ or 1,557,742,231 times as bright as a magnitude 10 star. Since we know that the lower the magnitude the brighter the object, it follows that a magnitude -13 object is significantly brighter than a magnitude 10 object.

61. Sometimes; sample answer: The equation is true when $x = 0$, $y = 2$, and $z = 3$, but it is false when $x = 1$, $y = 2$, and $z = 3$.

H.O.T. Problems Use Higher-Order Thinking Skills

61. **REASONING** Is $x^y \cdot x^z = x^{yz}$ *sometimes*, *always*, or *never* true? Explain.

62. **OPEN ENDED** Name two monomials with a quotient of $24a^2b^3$. **Sample answer: $24a^4b^6$ and a^2b^3**

63. **CHALLENGE** Use the Quotient of Powers Property to explain why $x^{-n} = \frac{1}{x^n}$. **$\frac{1}{x^n} = \frac{x^0}{x^n} = x^{0-n} = x^{-n}$**

64. **REGULARITY** Write a convincing argument to show why $3^0 = 1$. **See margin.**

65. **WRITING IN MATH** Explain how to use the Quotient of Powers property and the Power of a Quotient property. **See margin.**

Enrichment

OL BL

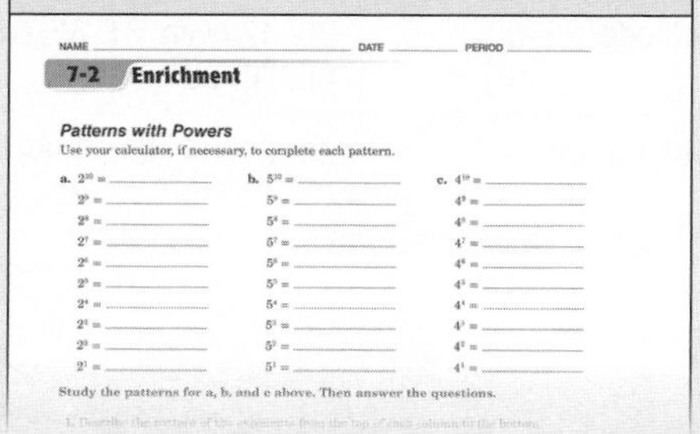
NAME ______ DATE ______ PERIOD ______

7-2 Enrichment

Patterns with Powers

Use your calculator, if necessary, to complete each pattern.

Study the patterns for a, b, and c above. Then answer the questions.

Multiple Representations

In Exercise 60, students use a geometric sketch, algebraic formulas, and a table of values to analyze the relation between a square and an inscribed circle.

Standardized Test Practice

66. What is the perimeter of the figure in meters? **B**

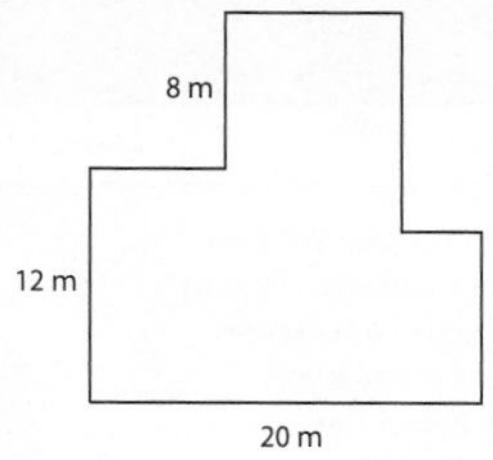

A 40 meters
B 80 meters
C 160 meters
D 400 meters

67. In researching her science project, Leigh learned that light travels at a constant rate and that it takes 500 seconds for light to travel the 93 million miles from the Sun to Earth. Mars is 142 million miles from the Sun. About how many seconds will it take for light to travel from the Sun to Mars? **J**

F 235 seconds
G 327 seconds
H 642 seconds
J 763 seconds

68. EXTENDED RESPONSE Jessie and Jonas are playing a game using the spinners below. Each spinner is equally likely to stop on any of the four numbers. In the game, a player spins both spinners and calculates the product of the two numbers on which the spinners have stopped.

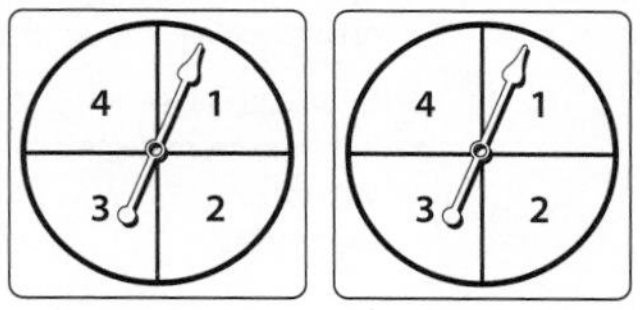

a. What product has the greatest probability of occurring? **4**

b. What is the probability of that product occurring? $\frac{3}{16}$

69. Simplify $(4^{-2} \cdot 5^0 \cdot 64)^3$. **B**

A $\frac{1}{64}$ C 320
B 64 D 1024

Spiral Review

70. GEOMETRY A rectangular prism has a width of $7x^3$ units, a length of $4x^2$ units, and a height of $3x$ units. What is the volume of the prism? (Lesson 7-1) **$84x^6$ units^3**

Solve each system of inequalities by graphing. (Lesson 6-6) **71–74. See Ch. 7 Answer Appendix.**

71. $y \geq 1$, $x < -1$
72. $y \geq -3$, $y - x < 1$
73. $y < 3x + 2$, $y \geq -2x + 4$
74. $y - 2x < 2$, $y - 2x > 4$

Solve each inequality. Check your solution. (Lesson 5-3)

75. $5(2h - 6) > 4h$ **$h > 5$**
76. $22 \geq 4(b - 8) + 10$ **$b \leq 11$**
77. $5(u - 8) \leq 3(u + 10)$ **$u \leq 35$**
78. $8 + t \leq 3(t + 4) + 2$ **$t \geq -3$**
79. $9n + 3(1 - 6n) \leq 21$ **$n \geq -2$**
80. $-6(b + 5) > 3(b - 5)$ **$b < -\frac{5}{3}$**

81. GRADES In a high school science class, a test is worth three times as much as a quiz. What is the student's average grade? (Lesson 2-9) **87**

Science Grades

Tests	Quizzes
85	82
92	75
	95

Skills Review

Evaluate each expression.

82. 9^2 **81**
83. 11^2 **121**
84. 10^6 **1,000,000**
85. 10^4 **10,000**
86. 3^5 **243**
87. 5^3 **125**
88. 12^3 **1728**
89. 4^6 **4096**

Differentiated Instruction (OL) (BL)

Extension Tell students that if you roll a color cube, the probability of getting red is $\frac{1}{2}$. If you throw the cube n times, the probability of getting red each time is $\left(\frac{1}{2}\right)^n$. Ask them to determine how many times the cube is rolled if the probability of getting red each time is $\frac{1}{512}$. $\frac{1}{512} = \left(\frac{1}{2}\right)^9$, $n = 9$, so 9 times

Exercise Alert

Grid Paper For Exercises 71–74, students will need grid paper.

Teaching the Process Standards

Regularity Mathematically proficient students notice if calculations are repeated. In Exercise 64, encourage students to examine the sequences $3^5, 3^4, 3^3, 3^2, \ldots$ and 243, 81, 27, 9, …

4 Assess

Yesterday's News Ask students to write two ways in which the concepts of multiplying monomials helped them to understand dividing monomials.

Formative Assessment

Check for student understanding of Lessons 7-1 and 7-2.

Quiz 1, p. 57

Additional Answers

64. We can use the Quotient of Powers Property to show that $3^0 = 1$.

$$3^5 = 243$$
$$\frac{3^5}{3^5} = \frac{243}{3^5}$$
$$3^{5-5} = \frac{243}{3^5}$$
$$3^0 = \frac{243}{243}$$
$$3^0 = 1$$

65. The Quotient of Powers Property is used when dividing two powers with the same base. The exponents are subtracted. The Power of a Quotient Property is used to find the power of a quotient. You find the power of the numerator and the power of the denominator.

1 Focus

Vertical Alignment

Before Lesson 7-3 Used the laws of exponents to find products and quotients of monomials.

Lesson 7-3 Evaluate and rewrite expressions involving rational exponents. Solve equations involving expressions with rational exponents.

After Lesson 7-3 Express numbers in scientific notation. Find products and quotients of numbers expressed in scientific notation.

2 Teach

Scaffolding Questions

Have students read the **Why?** section of the lesson.

Ask:

- How does $50f^{0.2}$ differ from other exponential expressions students have seen before? Sample answer: The exponent is not an integer.
- Does a higher SPF offer more or less protection from sun damage? more
- What SPF numbers have you seen on sunscreens in stores? Sample answer: 2, 4, 15, 30

LESSON 7-3 Rational Exponents

Then

- You used the laws of exponents to find products and quotients of monomials.

Now

1. Evaluate and rewrite expressions involving rational exponents.
2. Solve equations involving expressions with rational exponents.

Why?

- It's important to protect your skin with sunscreen to prevent damage. The sun protection factor (SPF) of a sunscreen indicates how well it protects you. Sunscreen with an SPF of f absorbs about p percent of the UV-B rays, where $p = 50f^{0.2}$.

New Vocabulary
rational exponent
cube root
nth root
exponential equation

Content Standards
AI.RNE.3

1 Rational Exponents

You know that an exponent represents the number of times that the base is used as a factor. But how do you evaluate an expression with an exponent that is not an integer like the one above? Let's investigate **rational exponents** by assuming that they behave like integer exponents.

$$\left(b^{\frac{1}{2}}\right)^2 = b^{\frac{1}{2}} \cdot b^{\frac{1}{2}} \quad \text{Write as a multiplication expression.}$$
$$= b^{\frac{1}{2}+\frac{1}{2}} \quad \text{Product of Powers}$$
$$= b^1 \text{ or } b \quad \text{Simplify.}$$

Thus, $b^{\frac{1}{2}}$ is a number with a square equal to b. So $b^{\frac{1}{2}} = \sqrt{b}$.

Key Concept $b^{\frac{1}{2}}$

Words	For any nonnegative real number b, $b^{\frac{1}{2}} = \sqrt{b}$.	
Examples	$16^{\frac{1}{2}} = \sqrt{16}$ or 4	$38^{\frac{1}{2}} = \sqrt{38}$

PT

Example 1 Radical and Exponential Forms

Write each expression in radical form, or write each radical in exponential form.

a. $25^{\frac{1}{2}}$

$25^{\frac{1}{2}} = \sqrt{25}$ Definition of $b^{\frac{1}{2}}$

$= 5$ Simplify.

b. $\sqrt{18}$

$\sqrt{18} = 18^{\frac{1}{2}}$ Definition of $b^{\frac{1}{2}}$

c. $5x^{\frac{1}{2}}$

$5x^{\frac{1}{2}} = 5\sqrt{x}$ Definition of $b^{\frac{1}{2}}$

d. $\sqrt{8p}$

$\sqrt{8p} = (8p)^{\frac{1}{2}}$ Definition of $b^{\frac{1}{2}}$

Guided Practice

1A. $a^{\frac{1}{2}}$ $\sqrt{a}$ **1B.** $\sqrt{22}$ $22^{\frac{1}{2}}$ **1C.** $(7w)^{\frac{1}{2}}$ $\sqrt{7w}$ **1D.** $2\sqrt{x}$ $2x^{\frac{1}{2}}$

Lesson 7-3 Resources

Resource	Approaching Level AL	On Level OL	Beyond Level BL	English Learners ELL
Teacher Edition	▪ Differentiated Instruction, p. 408	▪ Differentiated Instruction, p. 408	▪ Differentiated Instruction, pp. 408, 412	▪ Differentiated Instruction, p. 408
Chapter Resource Masters	▪ Study Guide and Intervention, pp. 17–18 ▪ Skills Practice, p. 19 ▪ Practice, p. 20 ▪ Word Problem Practice, p. 21	▪ Study Guide and Intervention, pp. 17–18 ▪ Skills Practice, p. 19 ▪ Practice, p. 20 ▪ Word Problem Practice, p. 21 ▪ Enrichment, p. 22	▪ Practice, p. 20 ▪ Word Problem Practice, p. 21 ▪ Enrichment, p. 22	▪ Study Guide and Intervention, pp. 17–18 ▪ Skills Practice, p. 19 ▪ Practice, p. 20 ▪ Word Problem Practice, p. 21
Other	▪ 5-Minute Check 7-3 ▪ Study Notebook	▪ 5-Minute Check 7-3 ▪ Study Notebook	▪ 5-Minute Check 7-3 ▪ Study Notebook	▪ 5-Minute Check 7-3 ▪ Study Notebook

You know that to find the square root of a number a you find a number with a square of a. In the same way, you can find other roots of numbers. If $a^3 = b$, then a is the **cube root** of b, and if $a^n = b$ for a positive integer n, then a is an **nth root** of b.

KeyConcept nth Root

Words	For any real numbers a and b and any positive integer n, if $a^n = b$, then a is an nth root of b.
Symbols	If $a^n = b$, then $\sqrt[n]{b} = a$.
Example	Because $2^4 = 16$, 2 is a fourth root of 16; $\sqrt[4]{16} = 2$.

StudyTip

Tools You can use a graphing calculator to find nth roots. Enter n, then press MATH and choose $\sqrt[x]{\ }$.

Since $3^2 = 9$ and $(-3)^2 = 9$, both 3 and -3 are square roots of 9. Similarly, since $2^4 = 16$ and $(-2)^4 = 16$, both 2 and -2 are fourth roots of 16. The positive roots are called *principal roots*. Radical symbols indicate principal roots, so $\sqrt[4]{16} = 2$.

Example 2 nth roots

Simplify.

a. $\sqrt[3]{27}$

$\sqrt[3]{27} = \sqrt[3]{3 \cdot 3 \cdot 3}$

$= 3$

b. $\sqrt[5]{32}$

$\sqrt[5]{32} = \sqrt[5]{2 \cdot 2 \cdot 2 \cdot 2 \cdot 2}$

$= 2$

GuidedPractice

2A. $\sqrt[3]{64}$ **4**

2B. $\sqrt[4]{10{,}000}$ **10**

Like square roots, nth roots can be represented by rational exponents.

$\left(b^{\frac{1}{n}}\right)^n = \underbrace{b^{\frac{1}{n}} \cdot b^{\frac{1}{n}} \cdot \ldots \cdot b^{\frac{1}{n}}}_{n \text{ factors}}$ Write as a multiplication expression.

$= b^{\frac{1}{n} + \frac{1}{n} + \ldots + \frac{1}{n}}$ Product of Powers

$= b^1$ or b Simplify.

Thus, $b^{\frac{1}{n}}$ is a number with an nth power equal to b. So $b^{\frac{1}{n}} = \sqrt[n]{b}$.

KeyConcept $b^{\frac{1}{n}}$

Words	For any positive real number b and any integer $n > 1$, $b^{\frac{1}{n}} = \sqrt[n]{b}$.
Example	$8^{\frac{1}{3}} = \sqrt[3]{8} = \sqrt[3]{2 \cdot 2 \cdot 2}$ or 2

1 Rational Exponents

Example 1 shows how to write an expression with a rational exponent in radical form and how to write an expression in radical form as an expression with a rational exponent. **Example 2** shows how to evaluate nth roots. **Example 3** shows how to evaluate expressions of the form $b^{\frac{1}{n}}$. **Example 4** shows how to evaluate expressions of the form $b^{\frac{m}{n}}$.

Formative Assessment

Use the Guided Practice exercises after each example to determine students' understanding of concepts.

Additional Examples

1 Write each expression in radical form, or write each radical in exponential form.

a. $81^{\frac{1}{2}}$ 9

b. $\sqrt{38}$ $38^{\frac{1}{2}}$

c. $12m^{\frac{1}{2}}$ $12\sqrt{m}$

d. $\sqrt{32w}$ $(32w)^{\frac{1}{2}}$

2 Simplify.

a. $\sqrt[4]{256}$ 4

b. $\sqrt[6]{15{,}625}$ 5

Additional Examples also in Interactive Classroom PowerPoint® Presentations

IWB Interactive White Board READY

Tips for New Teachers

Order of Operations Remind students to observe the order of operations with radical and exponential expressions. Emphasize that expressions like $5x^{\frac{1}{2}}$ and $(5x)^{\frac{1}{2}}$ are different.

Notation Emphasize that if there is no index on a radical symbol, it denotes a square root.

Teaching the Process Standards

Tools Mathematically proficient students are familiar with the tools appropriate for their course and make sound decisions about when each might be helpful. Encourage students to use mental math to verify answers they find with a calculator.

Additional Examples

3 Simplify.

a. $1331^{\frac{1}{3}}$ 11

b. $2401^{\frac{1}{4}}$ 7

4 Simplify.

a. $32^{\frac{2}{5}}$ 4

b. $81^{\frac{5}{2}}$ 59,049

Focus on Mathematical Content

Rational Exponents The meaning of a rational exponent follows from extending the properties of integer exponents to those values. This allows for a notation for radicals in terms of rational exponents. For example, we define $2^{\frac{1}{2}}$ to be the square root of 2 because we want $\left(2^{\frac{1}{2}}\right)^2 = 2^{\frac{1}{2} \cdot 2} = 2^1$ to hold, so $\left(2^{\frac{1}{2}}\right)^2$ must equal 2.

StudyTip

Rational Exponents on a Calculator Use parentheses to evaluate expressions involving rational exponents on a graphing calculator. For example to find $125^{\frac{1}{3}}$, press 125 [^] [(] 1 [÷] 3 [)] [ENTER].

Example 3 Evaluate $b^{\frac{1}{n}}$ Expressions

Simplify.

a. $125^{\frac{1}{3}}$

$125^{\frac{1}{3}} = \sqrt[3]{125}$ $b^{\frac{1}{n}} = \sqrt[n]{b}$

$= \sqrt[3]{5 \cdot 5 \cdot 5}$ $125 = 5^3$

$= 5$ Simplify.

b. $1296^{\frac{1}{4}}$

$1296^{\frac{1}{4}} = \sqrt[4]{1296}$ $b^{\frac{1}{n}} = \sqrt[n]{b}$

$= \sqrt[4]{6 \cdot 6 \cdot 6 \cdot 6}$ $1296 = 6^4$

$= 6$ Simplify.

GuidedPractice

3A. $27^{\frac{1}{3}}$ **3**

3B. $256^{\frac{1}{4}}$ **4**

The Power of a Power property allows us to extend the definition of $b^{\frac{1}{n}}$ to $b^{\frac{m}{n}}$.

$b^{\frac{m}{n}} = \left(b^{\frac{1}{n}}\right)^m$ Power of a Power

$= \left(\sqrt[n]{b}\right)^m$ or $\sqrt[n]{b^m}$ $b^{\frac{1}{n}} = \sqrt[n]{b}$

KeyConcept $b^{\frac{m}{n}}$

Words For any positive real number b and any integers m and $n > 1$,

$$b^{\frac{m}{n}} = \left(\sqrt[n]{b}\right)^m \text{ or } \sqrt[n]{b^m}.$$

Example $8^{\frac{2}{3}} = \left(\sqrt[3]{8}\right)^2 = 2^2$ or 4

Example 4 Evaluate $b^{\frac{m}{n}}$ Expressions

Simplify.

a. $64^{\frac{2}{3}}$

$64^{\frac{2}{3}} = \left(\sqrt[3]{64}\right)^2$ $b^{\frac{m}{n}} = \left(\sqrt[n]{b}\right)^m$

$= \left(\sqrt[3]{4 \cdot 4 \cdot 4}\right)^2$ $64 = 4^3$

$= 4^2$ or 16 Simplify.

b. $36^{\frac{3}{2}}$

$36^{\frac{3}{2}} = \left(\sqrt[2]{36}\right)^3$ $b^{\frac{m}{n}} = \left(\sqrt[n]{b}\right)^m$

$= 6^3$ $\sqrt{36} = 6$

$= 216$ Simplify.

GuidedPractice

4A. $27^{\frac{2}{3}}$ **9**

4B. $256^{\frac{5}{4}}$ **1024**

DifferentiatedInstruction AL OL BL ELL

Interpersonal Learners Divide the class into groups of two or three students. Have students discuss what they knew about exponents before starting the lesson and how it relates to rational exponents. For example, if an exponent tells you how many times to use the base as a factor, what does an exponent of $\frac{3}{2}$ represent?

2 Solve Exponential Equations

In an **exponential equation**, variables occur as exponents. The Power Property of Equality and the other properties of exponents can be used to solve exponential equations.

KeyConcept Power Property of Equality

Words	For any real number $b > 0$ and $b \neq 1$, $b^x = b^y$ if and only if $x = y$.
Examples	If $5^x = 5^3$, then $x = 3$. If $n = \frac{1}{2}$, then $4^n = 4^{\frac{1}{2}}$.

PT

Example 5 Solve Exponential Equations

Solve each equation.

a. $6^x = 216$

$6^x = 216$ Original equation

$6^x = 6^3$ Rewrite 216 as 6^3.

$x = 3$ Property of Equality

CHECK $6^x = 216$

$6^3 \stackrel{?}{=} 216$

$216 = 216$ ✓

b. $25^{x-1} = 5$

$25^{x-1} = 5$ Original equation

$(5^2)^{x-1} = 5$ Rewrite 25 as 5^2.

$5^{2x-2} = 5^1$ Power of a Power, Distributive Property

$2x - 2 = 1$ Power Property of Equality

$2x = 3$ Add 2 to each side.

$x = \frac{3}{2}$ Divide each side by 2.

CHECK $25^{x-1} = 5$

$25^{\frac{3}{2}-1} \stackrel{?}{=} 5$

$25^{\frac{1}{2}} = 5$ ✓

GuidedPractice

5A. $5^x = 125$ **3**

5B. $12^{2x+3} = 144$ $-\frac{1}{2}$

Real-WorldLink

Use extra caution near snow, water, and sand because they reflect the damaging rays of the Sun, which can increase your chance of sunburn.

Source: American Academy of Dermatology

PT

Real-World Example 6 Solve Exponential Equations

SUNSCREEN **Refer to the beginning of the lesson. Find the SPF that absorbs 100% of UV-B rays.**

$p = 50f^{0.2}$ Original equation

$100 = 50f^{0.2}$ $p = 100$

$2 = f^{0.2}$ Divide each side by 50.

$2 = f^{\frac{1}{5}}$ $0.2 = \frac{1}{5}$

$(2^5)^{\frac{1}{5}} = f^{\frac{1}{5}}$ $2 = 2^1 = (2^5)^{\frac{1}{5}}$

$2^5 = f$ Power Property of Equality

$32 = f$ Simplify.

GuidedPractice

6. CHEMISTRY The radius r of the nucleus of an atom of mass number A is $r = 1.2A^{\frac{1}{3}}$ femtometers. Find A if $r = 3.6$ femtometers. **27**

2 Exponential Equations

Example 5 shows how to solve an exponential equation by applying the Power Property of Equality. **Example 6** shows how to solve a real-world exponential equation.

Additional Examples

5 Solve each equation.

a. $9^x = 729$ 3

b. $16^{2x-1} = 8$ $\frac{7}{8}$

6 **BIOLOGY** The population p of a culture that begins with 40 bacteria and doubles every 8 hours can be modeled by $p = 40(2)^{\frac{t}{8}}$, where t is time in hours. Find t if $p = 20{,}480$. 72 hours

3 Practice

Formative Assessment

Use Exercises 1–16 to check for understanding.

Use the chart at the bottom of this page to customize assignments for your students.

Teaching the Process Standards

Tools Mathematically proficient students consider the available tools when solving a mathematical problem. In Exercise 16, discuss how a calculator could be used to solve and check the solution.

Modeling Mathematically proficient students can analyze relationships mathematically to draw conclusions. In Exercise 85, encourage students to use a calculator and substitute many whole number values of n to observe the relationship between n and f. Then they can use the results to check the reasonableness of their answers.

Check Your Understanding

● = Step-by-Step Solutions begin on page R13.

Example 1 Write each expression in radical form, or write each radical in exponential form.

1. $12^{\frac{1}{2}}$ **$\sqrt{12}$** **2.** $3x^{\frac{1}{2}}$ **$3\sqrt{x}$** **3.** $\sqrt{33}$ **$33^{\frac{1}{2}}$** **4.** $\sqrt{8n}$ **$(8n)^{\frac{1}{2}}$**

Examples 2–4 Simplify.

5. $\sqrt[3]{512}$ **8** **6.** $\sqrt[5]{243}$ **3** **7.** $343^{\frac{1}{3}}$ **7** **8.** $\left(\frac{1}{16}\right)^{\frac{1}{4}}$ **$\frac{1}{2}$**

9. $343^{\frac{2}{3}}$ **49** **10.** $81^{\frac{3}{4}}$ **27** **11.** $216^{\frac{4}{3}}$ **1296** **12.** $\left(\frac{1}{49}\right)^{\frac{3}{2}}$ **$\frac{1}{343}$**

Example 5 Solve each equation.

13. $8^x = 4096$ **4** **14.** $3^{3x+1} = 81$ **1** **15.** $4^{x-3} = 32$ **5.5**

Example 6 **16.** **TOOLS** A weir is used to measure water flow in a channel. For a rectangular broad crested weir, the flow Q in cubic feet per second is related to the weir length L in feet and height H of the water by $Q = 1.6LH^{\frac{3}{2}}$. Find the water height for a weir that is 3 feet long and has flow of 38.4 cubic feet per second. **4 ft**

Practice and Problem Solving

Extra Practice is on page R7.

Example 1 Write each expression in radical form, or write each radical in exponential form.

17. $15^{\frac{1}{2}}$ **$\sqrt{15}$** **18.** $24^{\frac{1}{2}}$ **$\sqrt{24}$** **19.** $4k^{\frac{1}{2}}$ **$4\sqrt{k}$** **20.** $(12y)^{\frac{1}{2}}$ **$\sqrt{12y}$**

21. $\sqrt{26}$ **$26^{\frac{1}{2}}$** **22.** $\sqrt{44}$ **$44^{\frac{1}{2}}$** **23.** $2\sqrt{ab}$ **$2(ab)^{\frac{1}{2}}$** **24.** $\sqrt{3xyz}$ **$(3xyz)^{\frac{1}{2}}$**

Examples 2–4 Simplify.

25. $\sqrt[3]{8}$ **2** **26.** $\sqrt[5]{1024}$ **4** **27.** $\sqrt[3]{216}$ **6** **28.** $\sqrt[4]{10{,}000}$ **10**

29. $\sqrt[3]{0.001}$ **0.1** **30.** $\sqrt[4]{\frac{16}{81}}$ **$\frac{2}{3}$** **31.** $1331^{\frac{1}{3}}$ **11** **32.** $64^{\frac{1}{6}}$ **2**

33. $3375^{\frac{1}{3}}$ **15** **34.** $512^{\frac{1}{9}}$ **2** **35.** $\left(\frac{1}{81}\right)^{\frac{1}{4}}$ **$\frac{1}{3}$** **36.** $\left(\frac{3125}{32}\right)^{\frac{1}{5}}$ **$\frac{5}{2}$**

37. $8^{\frac{2}{3}}$ **4** **38.** $625^{\frac{3}{4}}$ **125** **39.** $729^{\frac{5}{6}}$ **243** **40.** $256^{\frac{3}{8}}$ **8**

41. $125^{\frac{4}{3}}$ **625** **42.** $49^{\frac{5}{2}}$ **16,807** **43.** $\left(\frac{9}{100}\right)^{\frac{3}{2}}$ **$\frac{27}{1000}$** **44.** $\left(\frac{8}{125}\right)^{\frac{4}{3}}$ **$\frac{16}{625}$**

Differentiated Homework Options

Level	Assignment	Two-Day Option	
AL Basic	17–58, 89, 90, 92–114	18–58 even, 94–97	17–57 odd, 89, 90, 92, 93, 98–114
OL Core	17–83 odd, 85–90, 92–114	17–58, 94–97	59–90, 92, 93, 98–114
BL Advanced	59–97 (Optional: 98–114)		

Example 5 **Solve each equation.**

45. $3^x = 243$ **5** **46.** $12^x = 144$ **2** **47.** $16^x = 4$ $\frac{1}{2}$

48. $27^x = 3$ $\frac{1}{3}$ **49.** $9^x = 27$ $\frac{3}{2}$ **50.** $32^x = 4$ $\frac{2}{5}$

51. $2^{x-1} = 128$ **8** **52.** $4^{2x+1} = 1024$ **2** **53.** $6^{x-4} = 1296$ **8**

54. $9^{2x+3} = 2187$ $\frac{1}{4}$ **(55)** $4^{3x} = 512$ $\frac{3}{2}$ **56.** $128^{3x} = 8$ $\frac{1}{7}$

Example 6

57. CONSERVATION Water collected in a rain barrel can be used to water plants and reduce city water use. Water flowing from an open rain barrel has velocity $v = 8h^{\frac{1}{2}}$, where v is in feet per second and h is the height of the water in feet. Find the height of the water if it is flowing at 16 feet per second. **4 ft**

58. ELECTRICITY The radius r in millimeters of a platinum wire L centimeters long with resistance 0.1 ohm is $r = 0.059L^{\frac{1}{2}}$. How long is a wire with radius 0.236 millimeter? **16 cm**

B **Write each expression in radical form, or write each radical in exponential form.**

59. $17^{\frac{1}{3}}$ $\sqrt[3]{17}$ **60.** $q^{\frac{1}{4}}$ $\sqrt[4]{q}$ **61.** $7b^{\frac{1}{3}}$ $7\sqrt[3]{b}$ **62.** $m^{\frac{2}{3}}$ $\sqrt[3]{m^2}$

63. $\sqrt[3]{29}$ $29^{\frac{1}{3}}$ **64.** $\sqrt[5]{h}$ $h^{\frac{1}{5}}$ **65.** $2\sqrt[3]{a}$ $2a^{\frac{1}{3}}$ **66.** $\sqrt[3]{xy^2}$ $x^{\frac{1}{3}}y^{\frac{2}{3}}$

Simplify.

67. $\sqrt[3]{0.027}$ **0.3** **68.** $\sqrt[4]{\frac{n^4}{16}}$ $\frac{n}{2}$ **69.** $a^{\frac{1}{3}} \cdot a^{\frac{2}{3}}$ a **70.** $c^{\frac{1}{2}} \cdot c^{\frac{3}{2}}$ c^2

71. $(8^2)^{\frac{2}{3}}$ **16** **72.** $\left(y^{\frac{3}{4}}\right)^{\frac{1}{2}}$ $y^{\frac{3}{8}}$ **73.** $9^{-\frac{1}{2}}$ $\frac{1}{3}$ **74.** $16^{-\frac{3}{2}}$ $\frac{1}{64}$

75. $(3^2)^{-\frac{3}{2}}$ $\frac{1}{27}$ **76.** $\left(81^{\frac{1}{4}}\right)^{-2}$ $\frac{1}{9}$ **77.** $k^{-\frac{1}{2}}$ $\frac{1}{\sqrt{k}}$ **78.** $\left(d^{\frac{4}{3}}\right)^0$ **1**

Solve each equation.

79. $2^{5x} = 8^{2x-4}$ **12** **80.** $81^{2x-3} = 9^{x+3}$ **3** **81.** $2^{4x} = 32^{x+1}$ **−5**

82. $16^x = \frac{1}{2}$ $-\frac{1}{4}$ **83.** $25^x = \frac{1}{125}$ $-\frac{3}{2}$ **84.** $6^{8-x} = \frac{1}{216}$ **11**

85. MODELING The frequency f in hertz of the nth key on a piano is $f = 440\left(2^{\frac{1}{12}}\right)^{n-49}$.

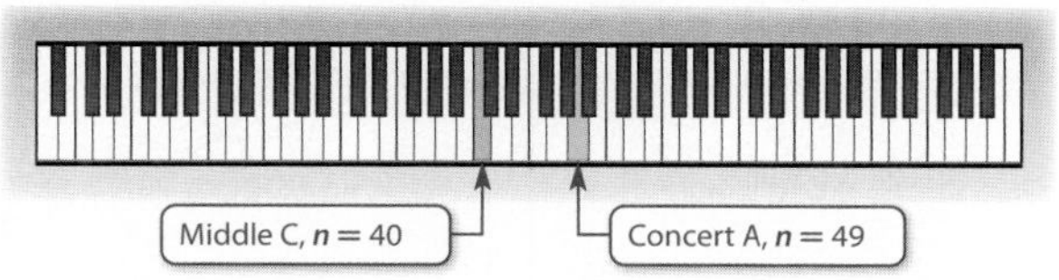

a. What is the frequency of Concert A? **440 Hz**

b. Which note has a frequency of 220 Hz? **the A below middle C, the 37th note**

Study Guide and Intervention

AL OL ELL

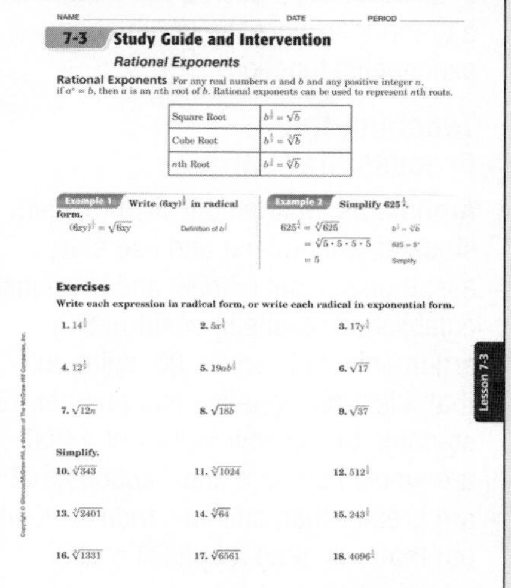

NAME ____ DATE ____ PERIOD ____

7-3 Study Guide and Intervention

Rational Exponents

Rational Exponents For any real numbers a and b and any positive integer n, if $a^n = b$, then a is an nth root of b. Rational exponents can be used to represent nth roots.

Square Root	$b^{\frac{1}{2}} = \sqrt{b}$
Cube Root	$b^{\frac{1}{3}} = \sqrt[3]{b}$
nth Root	$b^{\frac{1}{n}} = \sqrt[n]{b}$

Example 1 Write $(6xy)^{\frac{1}{2}}$ in radical form.

Example 2 Simplify $625^{\frac{1}{4}}$.

Exercises

Write each expression in radical form, or write each radical in exponential form.

Simplify.

Practice

AL OL BL ELL

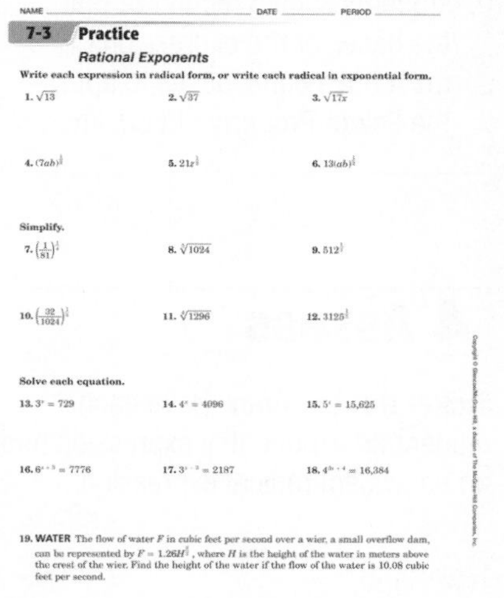

NAME ____ DATE ____ PERIOD ____

7-3 Practice

Rational Exponents

Write each expression in radical form, or write each radical in exponential form.

Simplify.

Solve each equation.

19. WATER The flow of water F in cubic feet per second over a wier, a small overflow dam, can be represented by $F = 1.26H^{\frac{3}{2}}$, where H is the height of the water in meters above the crest of the wier. Find the height of the water if the flow of the water is 10.08 cubic feet per second.

Word Problem Practice

AL OL BL ELL

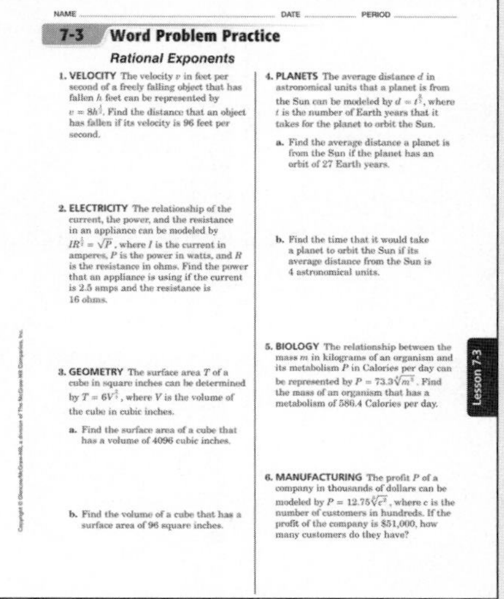

NAME ____ DATE ____ PERIOD ____

7-3 Word Problem Practice

Rational Exponents

1. VELOCITY The velocity v in feet per second of a freely falling object that has fallen h feet can be represented by $v = 8h^{\frac{1}{2}}$. Find the distance that an object has fallen if its velocity is 96 feet per second.

2. ELECTRICITY The relationship of the current, the power, and the resistance in an appliance can be modeled by $IR^{\frac{1}{2}} = \sqrt{P}$, where I is the current in amperes, P is the power in watts, and R is the resistance in ohms. Find the power that an appliance is using if the current is 2.5 amps and the resistance is 16 ohms.

3. GEOMETRY The surface area T of a cube in square inches can be determined by $T = 6V^{\frac{2}{3}}$, where V is the volume of the cube in cubic inches.

a. Find the surface area of a cube that has a volume of 4096 cubic inches.

b. Find the volume of a cube that has a surface area of 96 square inches.

4. PLANETS The average distance d in astronomical units that a planet is from the Sun can be modeled by $d = t^{\frac{2}{3}}$, where t is the number of Earth years that it takes for the planet to orbit the Sun.

a. Find the average distance a planet is from the Sun if the planet has an orbit of 27 Earth years.

b. Find the time that it would take a planet to orbit the Sun if its average distance from the Sun is 4 astronomical units.

5. BIOLOGY The relationship between the mass m in kilograms of an organism and its metabolism P in Calories per day can be represented by $P = 73.3\sqrt[4]{m^3}$. Find the mass of an organism that has a metabolism of 586.4 Calories per day.

6. MANUFACTURING The profit P of a company in thousands of dollars can be modeled by $P = 12.75\sqrt[4]{c^3}$, where c is the number of customers in hundreds. If the profit of the company is $51,000, how many customers do they have?

Enrichment

OL BL

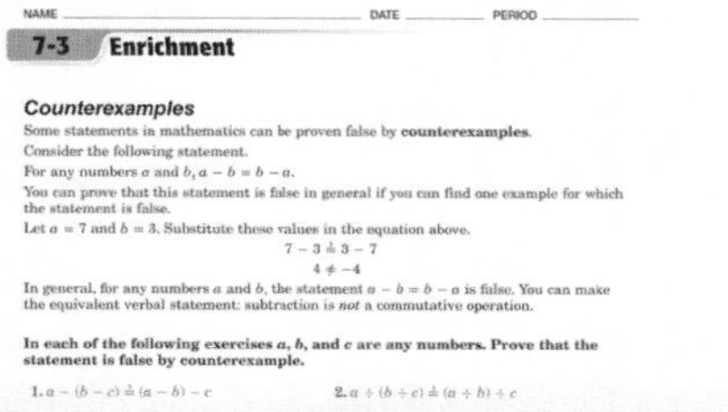

NAME ____ DATE ____ PERIOD ____

7-3 Enrichment

Counterexamples

Some statements in mathematics can be proven false by **counterexamples**. Consider the following statement.

For any numbers a and b, $a - b = b - a$.

You can prove that this statement is false in general if you can find one example for which the statement is false.

Let $a = 7$ and $b = 3$. Substitute these values in the equation above.

$7 - 3 \stackrel{?}{=} 3 - 7$

$4 \neq -4$

In general, for any numbers a and b, the statement $a - b = b - a$ is false. You can make the equivalent verbal statement: subtraction is *not* a commutative operation.

In each of the following exercises a, b, and c are any numbers. Prove that the statement is false by counterexample.

Multiple Representations

In Exercise 88, students use a table and a graph to explore the graph of an exponential function.

Teaching the Process Standards

Arguments Mathematically proficient students understand and use stated assumptions, definitions, and previously established results in constructing arguments. In Exercise 90, point out that x is a nonnegative real number. Tell students to consider values of x that are whole numbers and fractions that are greater than and less than 1. Point out that 1 is often a special case.

WatchOut!

Error Analysis In Exercise 92, students should recognize that the bases of the expressions must have equal bases to apply the Power Property of Equality.

4 Assess

Ticket Out the Door Have each student an exponential expression and an equivalent radical expression.

Additional Answers

88b.

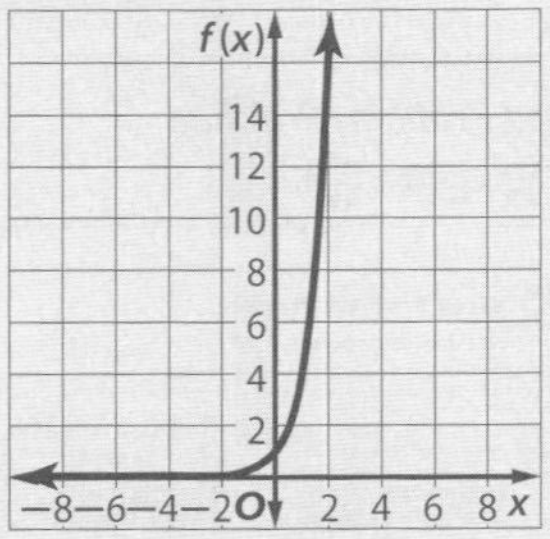

88c. The graph of $f(x) = 4^x$ is a curve. It has no x-intercept, a y-intercept of 1, the domain is all reals, the range is all positive reals, it is increasing over the entire domain, as x approaches infinity $f(x)$ approaches infinity, as x approaches negative infinity $f(x)$ approaches 0.

89. Sample answer: $2^{\frac{1}{2}}$ and $4^{\frac{1}{4}}$

C **86. RANDOM WALKS** Suppose you go on a walk where you choose the direction of each step at random. The path of a molecule in a liquid or a gas, the path of a foraging animal, and a fluctuating stock price are all modeled as random walks. The number of possible random walks w of n steps where you choose one of d directions at each step is $w = d^n$.

a. How many steps have been taken in a 2-direction random walk if there are 4096 possible walks? **12**

b. How many steps have been taken in a 4-direction random walk if there are 65,536 possible walks? **8**

c. If a walk of 7 steps has 2187 possible walks, how many directions could be taken at each step? **3**

87. SOCCER The radius r of a ball that holds V cubic units of air is modeled by $r = 0.62V^{\frac{1}{3}}$. What are the possible volumes of each size soccer ball? **Size 3, 204.0 to 230.2 in^3; Size 4, 268.5 to 299.9 in^3; Size 5, 333.6 to 382.4 in^3**

Soccer Ball Dimensions	
Size	**Diameter (in.)**
3	7.3–7.6
4	8.0–8.3
5	8.6–9.0

88. MULTIPLE REPRESENTATIONS In this problem, you will explore the graph of an exponential function.

a. **TABULAR** Copy and complete the table below.

x	-2	$-\frac{3}{2}$	-1	$-\frac{1}{2}$	0	$\frac{1}{2}$	1	$\frac{3}{2}$	2
$f(x) = 4^x$	$\frac{1}{16}$	$\frac{1}{8}$	$\frac{1}{4}$	$\frac{1}{2}$	1	2	4	8	16

b. **GRAPHICAL** Graph $f(x)$ by plotting the points and connecting them with a smooth curve. **b–c. See margin.**

c. **VERBAL** Describe the shape of the graph of $f(x)$. What are its key features? Is it linear?

H.O.T. Problems Use Higher-Order Thinking Skills

89. OPEN ENDED Write two different expressions with rational exponents equal to $\sqrt{2}$. **See margin.**

90. ARGUMENTS Determine whether each statement is *always, sometimes,* or *never* true. Assume that x is a nonnegative real number. Explain your reasoning. **a–f. See margin.**

a. $x^2 = x^{\frac{1}{2}}$ b. $x^{-2} = x^{\frac{1}{2}}$ c. $x^{\frac{1}{3}} = x^{\frac{1}{2}}$

d. $\sqrt{x} = x^{\frac{1}{2}}$ e. $\left(x^{\frac{1}{2}}\right)^2 = x$ f. $x^{\frac{1}{2}} \cdot x^2 = x$

91. CHALLENGE For what values of x is $x = x^{\frac{1}{3}}$? **−1, 0, 1**

92. ERROR ANALYSIS Anna and Jamal are solving $128^x = 4$. Is either of them correct? Explain your reasoning. **Anna; Jamal did not write the expressions with equal bases before applying the Power Property of Equality.**

Anna	Jamal
$128^x = 4$	$128^x = 4$
$(2^7)^x = 2^2$	$(2^7)^x = 4$
$2^{7x} = 2^2$	$2^{7x} = 4^1$
$7x = 2$	$7x = 1$
$x = \frac{2}{7}$	$x = \frac{1}{7}$

93. WRITING IN MATH Explain why 2 is the principal fourth root of 16. **Sample answer: 2 is the principal fourth root of 16 because 2 is positive and $2^4 = 16$.**

412 | Lesson 7-3 | Rational Exponents

Differentiated Instruction BL

Extension For Exercise 86, students found the numbers of random walks of a given length of steps. Have students investigate the applications of random walks.

Standardized Test Practice

94. What is the value of $16^{\frac{3}{4}} + 9^{\frac{3}{2}}$? **D**

A 5
B 11
C 25
D 35

95. At a movie theater, the costs for various numbers of popcorn and hot dogs are shown. **G**

Hot Dogs	Boxes of Popcorn	Total Cost
1	1	$8.50
2	4	$21.60

Which pair of equations can be used to find p, the cost of a box of popcorn, and h, the cost of a hot dog?

F $p + h = 8.5$
$p + 2h = 10.8$
G $p + h = 8.5$
$2h + 4p = 21.6$
H $p + h = 8.5$
$2p + 4h = 21.6$
J $p + h = 8.5$
$2p + 2h = 21.6$

96. SHORT RESPONSE Find the dimensions of the rectangle if its perimeter is 52 inches.
17.5 in. × 8.5 in.

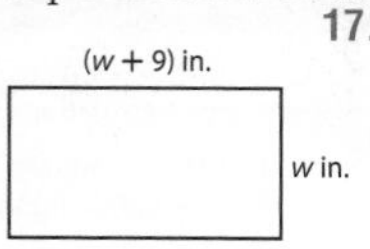

97. If $3^4 = 9^x$, then $x =$ **B**

A 1
B 2
C 4
D 5

Spiral Review

Simplify each expression. Assume that no denominator equals zero. (Lesson 7-2)

98. $\frac{a^3b^5}{ab^3}$ a^2b^2

99. $\frac{c^8d^{11}}{c^4d^5}$ c^4d^6

100. $\frac{4x^3y^3z^6}{xyz^5}$ $4x^2y^2z$

101. $\frac{a^5b^3c}{a^5bc}$ b^2

102. $\left(\frac{3m^4}{4p^2}\right)^2$ $\frac{9m^8}{16p^4}$

103. $\left(\frac{3df^2}{9d^2f}\right)^0$ 1

104. GARDENING Felipe is planting a flower garden that is shaped like a trapezoid as shown at the right. Use the formula $A = \frac{1}{2}h(b_1 + b_2)$ to find the area of the garden. (Lesson 7-1) $15a^2$

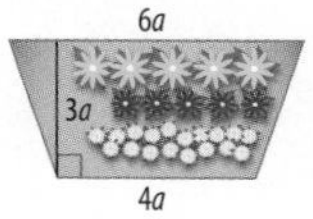

Write each equation in slope-intercept form. (Lesson 4-2)

105. $y - 2 = 3(x - 1)$ $y = 3x - 1$

106. $y - 5 = 6(x + 1)$ $y = 6x + 11$

107. $y + 2 = -2(x + 5)$ $y = -2x - 12$

108. $y + 3 = \frac{1}{2}(x + 4)$ $y = \frac{1}{2}x - 1$

109. $y - 1 = \frac{2}{3}(x + 9)$ $y = \frac{2}{3}x + 7$

110. $y + 3 = -\frac{1}{4}(x + 2)$ $y = -\frac{1}{4}x - \frac{7}{2}$

Skills Check

Find each power.

111. 10^3 1000

112. 10^5 100,000

113. 10^{-1} 0.1

114. 10^{-4} 0.0001

Additional Answers

90a. sometimes; true only when $x = 1$
90b. sometimes; true only when $x = 1$
90c sometimes; true only when $x = 1$
90d. always; by definition of $x^{\frac{1}{2}}$
90e. always; $\left(x^{\frac{1}{2}}\right)^2 = x^{\frac{1}{2} \cdot 2} = x^1$ or x
90f. sometimes; true only when $x = 1$

1 Focus

VerticalAlignment

Before Lesson 7-4 Use the laws of exponents to find products and quotients of monomials.

Lesson 7-4 Express numbers in scientific notation.
Find products and quotients of numbers expressed in scientific notation.

After Lesson 7-4 Graph exponential functions.

2 Teach

Scaffolding Questions

Have students read the **Why?** section of the lesson.

Ask:

- What would \$20 million look like when written out? \$20,000,000
- What would you have to multiply \$2 by to get \$20 million? 10,000,000
- How can you write 10,000,000 as a power of 10? 10^7
- What would you have to multiply 1.4 by to get 0.0000000014? 0.000000001
- How can you write 0.000000001 as a power of 10? 10^{-9}
- What is $\$2 \times 10^7$? 20,000,000
  What is 1.4×10^{-9}? 0.0000000014

LESSON 7-4 Scientific Notation

Then

- You used the laws of exponents to find products and quotients of monomials.

Now

1. Express numbers in scientific notation.
2. Find products and quotients of numbers expressed in scientific notation.

Why?

- Space tourism is a multibillion dollar industry. For a price of \$20 million, a civilian can travel on a rocket or shuttle and visit the International Space Station (ISS) for a week.

NewVocabulary
scientific notation

Process Standards
PS.3, PS.6

1 Scientific Notation

Very large and very small numbers such as \$20 million can be cumbersome to use in calculations. For this reason, numbers are often expressed in scientific notation. A number written in **scientific notation** is of the form $a \times 10^n$, where $1 \leq a < 10$ and n is an integer.

KeyConcept Standard Form to Scientific Notation

Step 1 Move the decimal point until it is to the right of the first nonzero digit. The result is a real number a.

Step 2 Note the number of places n and the direction that you moved the decimal point.

Step 3 If the decimal point is moved left, write the number as $a \times 10^n$.
If the decimal point is moved right, write the number as $a \times 10^{-n}$.

Step 4 Remove the unnecessary zeros.

Example 1 Standard Form to Scientific Notation

Express each number in scientific notation.

a. 201,000,000

Step 1 201,000,000 ⟶ 2.01000000 $a = 2.01000000$

Step 2 The decimal point moved 8 places to the left, so $n = 8$.

Step 3 $201{,}000{,}000 = 2.01000000 \times 10^8$

Step 4 2.01×10^8

b. 0.000051

Step 1 0.000051 ⟶ 00005.1 $a = 00005.1$

Step 2 The decimal point moved 5 places to the right, so $n = 5$.

Step 3 $0.000051 = 00005.1 \times 10^{-5}$

Step 4 5.1×10^{-5}

GuidedPractice

1A. 68,700,000,000 **6.87×10^{10}**

1B. 0.0000725 **7.25×10^{-5}**

414 | Lesson 7-4

Lesson 7-4 Resources

Resource	Approaching Level AL	On Level OL	Beyond Level BL	English Learners ELL
Teacher Edition	▪ Differentiated Instruction, p. 415	▪ Differentiated Instruction, p. 418	▪ Differentiated Instruction, p. 418	
Chapter Resource Masters	▪ Study Guide and Intervention, pp. 23–24 ▪ Skills Practice, p. 25 ▪ Practice, p. 26 ▪ Word Problem Practice, p. 27	▪ Study Guide and Intervention, pp. 23–24 ▪ Skills Practice, p. 25 ▪ Practice, p. 26 ▪ Word Problem Practice, p. 27 ▪ Enrichment, p. 28	▪ Practice, p. 20 ▪ Word Problem Practice, p. 27 ▪ Enrichment, p. 28	▪ Study Guide and Intervention, pp. 23–24 ▪ Skills Practice, p. 25 ▪ Practice, p. 26 ▪ Word Problem Practice, p. 27
Other	▪ 5-Minute Check 7-4 ▪ Study Notebook	▪ 5-Minute Check 7-4 ▪ Study Notebook	▪ 5-Minute Check 7-4 ▪ Study Notebook	▪ 5-Minute Check 7-4 ▪ Study Notebook

You can also rewrite numbers in scientific notation in standard form.

WatchOut!

Negative Signs Be careful about the placement of negative signs. A negative sign in the exponent means that the number is between 0 and 1. A negative sign before the number means that it is less than 0.

KeyConcept Scientific Notation to Standard Form

Step 1 In $a \times 10^n$, note whether $n > 0$ or $n < 0$.

Step 2 If $n > 0$, move the decimal point n places right.
If $n < 0$, move the decimal point $-n$ places left.

Step 3 Insert zeros, decimal point, and commas as needed for place value.

PT

Example 2 Scientific Notation to Standard Form

Express each number in standard form.

a. 6.32×10^9

Step 1 The exponent is 9, so $n = 9$.

Step 2 Since $n > 0$, move the decimal point 9 places to the right.
$6.32 \times 10^9 \longrightarrow 6320000000$

Step 3 $6.32 \times 10^9 = 6{,}320{,}000{,}000$ Rewrite; insert commas.

b. 4×10^{-7}

Step 1 The exponent is -7, so $n = -7$.

Step 2 Since $n < 0$, move the decimal point 7 places to the left.
$4 \times 10^{-7} \longrightarrow 0000004$

Step 3 $4 \times 10^{-7} = 0.0000004$ Rewrite; insert a 0 before the decimal point.

GuidedPractice

2A. 3.201×10^6 **3,201,000**

2B. 9.03×10^{-5} **0.0000903**

2 Product and Quotients in Scientific Notation

You can use scientific notation to simplify multiplying and dividing very large and very small numbers.

Problem-SolvingTip

Tools Estimating an answer before computing the solution can help you determine if your answer is reasonable.

PT

Example 3 Multiply with Scientific Notation

Evaluate $(3.5 \times 10^{-3})(7 \times 10^5)$. Express the result in both scientific notation and standard form.

$(3.5 \times 10^{-3})(7 \times 10^5)$ Original expression
$= (3.5 \times 7)(10^{-3} \times 10^5)$ Commutative and Associative Properties
$= 24.5 \times 10^2$ Product of Powers
$= (2.45 \times 10^1) \times 10^2$ $24.5 = 2.45 \times 10$
$= 2.45 \times 10^3$ or 2450 Product of Powers

GuidedPractice

Evaluate each product. Express the results in both scientific notation and standard form.

3A. $(6.5 \times 10^{12})(8.7 \times 10^{-15})$

3B. $(7.8 \times 10^{-4})^2$

3A. 5.655×10^{-2}; 0.05655
3B. 6.084×10^{-7}; 0.0000006084

DifferentiatedInstruction AL

If students have trouble keeping track of a moving decimal point,

Then have students write each digit in the number 201,000,000, for example, on an index card. Using an object such as a paper clip or penny as the decimal point, students can actually move the decimal point and count the number of places it moved. Repeat using other numbers from the examples, such as 0.000051.

1 Scientific Notation

Example 1 shows how to express a very large and a very small number in scientific notation. **Example 2** shows how to express a number written in scientific notation in standard form.

Formative Assessment

Use the Guided Practice exercises after each Example to determine students' understanding of concepts.

Additional Examples

1 Express each number in scientific notation.

a. 4,062,000,000,000 4.062×10^{12}

b. 0.000000823 8.23×10^{-7}

2 Express each number in standard form.

a. 6.49×10^5 649,000

b. 1.8×10^{-3} 0.0018

2 Products and Quotients in Scientific Notation

Example 3 shows how to multiply with scientific notation. **Example 4** shows how to divide with scientific notation. **Example 5** shows how to solve a real-world problem using scientific notation.

Additional Example

3 Evaluate $(5 \times 10^{-6})(2.3 \times 10^{12})$. Express the result in both scientific notation and standard form. 1.15×10^7; 11,500,000

Teaching the Process Standards

Tools Mathematically proficient detect possible errors by strategically using estimation and other mathematical knowledge. Model this behavior by verbalizing estimation as you solve example problems.

Additional Examples

4 Evaluate $\frac{4.5 \times 10^8}{1.5 \times 10^{10}}$. Express the result in both scientific notation and standard form. 3×10^{-2}; 0.03

5 **WATERCRAFT** Last year Afyu's state registered over 400 thousand watercraft. Boat sales in her state generated more than \$15.4 million in state sales taxes that same year.

a. Express the number of watercraft registered and the state sales tax generated from boat sales last year in Afyu's state in standard notation. Watercraft registered: 400,000; state sales tax generated: \$15,400,000

b. Write each number in scientific notation. 4×10^5; 1.54×10^7

c. How many watercraft have been registered in Afyu's state if 12 times the number registered last year have been registered in all? Write your answer in scientific notation and standard form. 4,800,000; 4.8×10^6

Additional Examples also in Interactive Classroom PowerPoint® Presentations

IWB Interactive White Board READY

Tips for New Teachers

E Notation On some calculators, the powers of 10 are written using E notation. For example, 3×10^{-6}, would be displayed as **3** E **−6**. The E means *times 10 to the given power.*

Teach with Tech

Interactive Whiteboard Write a number not in scientific notation on the board. Grab the decimal point and drag it to the left or right as you count the number of places you have moved it.

Example 4 Divide with Scientific Notation

Evaluate $\frac{3.066 \times 10^8}{7.3 \times 10^3}$. Express the result in both scientific notation and standard form.

$\frac{3.066 \times 10^8}{7.3 \times 10^3} = \left(\frac{3.066}{7.3}\right)\left(\frac{10^8}{10^3}\right)$	Product rule for fractions
$= 0.42 \times 10^5$	Quotient of Powers
$= 4.2 \times 10^{-1} \times 10^5$	$0.42 = 4.2 \times 10^{-1}$
$= 4.2 \times 10^4$	Product of Powers
$= 42{,}000$	Standard form

StudyTip

Quotient of Powers Recall that the Quotient of Powers Property is only valid for powers that have the same base. Since 10^8 and 10^3 have the same base, the property applies.

GuidedPractice

Evaluate each quotient. Express the results in both scientific notation and standard form.

4A. $\frac{2.3958 \times 10^3}{1.98 \times 10^8}$ 1.21×10^{-5}; 0.0000121 **4B.** $\frac{1.305 \times 10^3}{1.45 \times 10^{-4}}$ 9×10^6; 9,000,000

Real-WorldLink

The platinum award was created in 1976. In 2004, the criteria for the award was extended to digital sales. The top-selling artist of all time is the Beatles with 170 million units sold.

Source: Recording Industry Association of America

Real-World Example 5 Use Scientific Notation

MUSIC In the United States, a CD reaches gold status once 500 thousand copies are sold. A CD reaches platinum status once 1 million or more copies are sold.

a. Express the number of copies of CDs that need to be sold to reach each status in standard notation.

gold status: 500 thousand = 500,000; platinum status: 1 million = 1,000,000

b. Write each number in scientific notation.

gold status: $500{,}000 = 5 \times 10^5$; platinum status: $1{,}000{,}000 = 1 \times 10^6$

c. How many copies of a CD have sold if it has gone platinum 13 times? Write your answer in scientific notation and standard form.

A CD reaches platinum status once it sells 1 million records. Since the CD has gone platinum 13 times, we need to multiply by 13.

$(13)(1 \times 10^6)$	Original expression
$= (13 \times 1)(10^6)$	Associative Property
$= 13 \times 10^6$	$13 \times 1 = 13$
$= (1.3 \times 10^1) \times 10^6$	$13 = 1.3 \times 10$
$= 1.3 \times 10^7$	Product of Powers
$= 13{,}000{,}000$	Standard form

GuidedPractice

5. SATELLITE RADIO Suppose a satellite radio company earned \$125.4 million in one year.

A. Write this number in standard form. 125,400,000

B. Write this number in scientific notation. 1.254×10^8

C. If the following year the company earned 2.5 times the amount earned the previous year, determine the amount earned. Write your answer in scientific notation and standard form. 3.135×10^8; 313,500,000

Focus on Mathematical Content

Multiplying and Dividing with Scientific Notation If students think of numbers in scientific notation as monomials, then the procedures for multiplying and dividing are the same. For example, think of $(3 \times 10^{-2})(1.2 \times 10^5)$ as $(3x^{-2})(1.2x^5)$. In this case, you first multiply the constants and then the powers with the same bases. Similarly, with scientific notation, you multiply the constants, then the powers of 10.

Check Your Understanding

◯ = Step-by-Step Solutions begin on page R13.

Example 1 **Express each number in scientific notation.**

1. 185,000,000 1.85×10^8
2. 1,902,500,000 1.9025×10^9
3. 0.000564 5.64×10^{-4}
4. 0.00000804 8.04×10^{-6}

MONEY **Express each number in scientific notation.**

5. Teens spend \$13 billion annually on clothing. 1.3×10^{10}
6. Teens have an influence on their families' spending habit. They control about \$1.5 billion of discretionary income. 1.5×10^9

Example 2 **Express each number in standard form.**

7. 1.98×10^7 19,800,000
8. 4.052×10^6 4,052,000
9. 3.405×10^{-8} 0.00000003405
10. 6.8×10^{-5} 0.000068

Example 3 **Evaluate each product. Express the results in both scientific notation and standard form.** 11–14. See margin.

11. $(1.2 \times 10^3)(1.45 \times 10^{12})$
12. $(7.08 \times 10^{14})(5 \times 10^{-9})$
13. $(5.18 \times 10^2)(9.1 \times 10^{-5})$
14. $(2.18 \times 10^{-2})^2$

Example 4 **Evaluate each quotient. Express the results in both scientific notation and standard form.** 15–18. See margin.

15. $\frac{1.035 \times 10^8}{2.3 \times 10^4}$
16. $\frac{2.542 \times 10^5}{4.1 \times 10^{-10}}$
17. $\frac{1.445 \times 10^{-7}}{1.7 \times 10^5}$
18. $\frac{2.05 \times 10^{-8}}{4 \times 10^{-2}}$

Example 5 19. **PRECISION** Salvador bought an air purifier to help him deal with his allergies. The filter in the purifier will stop particles as small as one hundredth of a micron. A micron is one millionth of a millimeter.

a. Write one hundredth and one micron in standard form. 0.01, 0.000001

b. Write one hundredth and one micron in scientific notation. 1×10^{-2}, 1×10^{-6}

c. What is the smallest size particle in meters that the filter will stop? Write the result in both standard form and scientific notation. 0.00000000001; 1×10^{-11}

Practice and Problem Solving

Extra Practice is on page R7.

Example 1 **Express each number in scientific notation.**

20. 1,220,000 1.22×10^6
21. 58,600,000 5.86×10^7
22. 1,405,000,000,000 1.405×10^{12}
23. 0.0000013 1.3×10^{-6}
24. 0.000056 5.6×10^{-5}
25. 0.000000000709 7.09×10^{-10}

EMAIL **Express each number in scientific notation.**

26. Approximately 100 million emails sent to the President are put into the National Archives. 1×10^8
27. By 2015, the email security market will generate \$6.5 billion. 6.5×10^9

Example 2 **Express each number in standard form.** 28. 1,000,000,000,000

28. 1×10^{12}
29. 9.4×10^7 94,000,000
30. 8.1×10^{-3} 0.0081
31. 5×10^{-4} 0.0005
32. 8.73×10^{11} 873,000,000,000
33. 6.22×10^{-6} 0.00000622

Differentiated Homework Options

Level	Assignment	Two-Day Option	
AL Basic	20–54, 70, 71, 73–93	21–53 odd, 76–79	20–54 even, 70, 71, 73–75, 80–93
OL Core	21–61 odd, 63–71, 73–93	20–54, 76–79	55–71, 73–75, 80–93
BL Advanced	55–87, (optional: 88–93)		

Tips for New Teachers

Sense-Making Students may have encountered the use of scientific notation in their science classes, where they rounded numbers to two decimal places when converting from standard to scientific notation. Make sure that students do not automatically round numbers to two decimal places when they convert to scientific notation in this lesson.

3 Practice

Formative Assessment

Use Exercises 1–19 to check for understanding.

Use the chart at the bottom of this page to customize assignments for your students.

Teaching the Process Standards

Precision Mathematically proficient students express numerical answers with a degree of precision appropriate for the problem context. In Exercise 19, point out that in some scientific fields units of measure as small as microns or even smaller are commonly used.

Additional Answers

11. 1.74×10^{15}; 1,740,000,000,000,000
12. 3.54×10^6; 3,540,000
13. 4.7138×10^{-2}; 0.047138
14. 4.7524×10^{-4}; 0.00047524
15. 4.5×10^3; 4500
16. 6.2×10^{14}; 620,000,000,000,000
17. 8.5×10^{-13}; 0.00000000000085
18. 5.125×10^{-7}; 0.0000005215

Exercise Alert

Change in Units For Exercises 63–65, students are given the speed of light in meters per second but are asked to find results in kilometers per second.

Teaching the Process Standards

Modeling Mathematically proficient students are able to identify important quantities in a practical situation and map their relationships. In Exercise 66, the relationship may be clearer to students if they write the fraction using words for each quantity like $\frac{\text{Company B's data processed per second}}{\text{Company A's data processed per second}}$.

WatchOut!

Error Analysis For Exercise 71, help students see that everything is the same in the two methods except the exponent in the power of 10 in the last line. Ask students if the decimal point was moved to the left or right, and how the direction affects the power of 10.

Additional Answers

65.

Time	Kilometers Traveled
1 day	2.592×10^{10}
1 week	1.8144×10^{11}
1 month	7.776×10^{11}
1 year	9.4608×10^{12}

66. $\frac{1.41 \times 10^6}{7.95 \times 10^5} \approx 1.774$; The phone from company B is about 1.774 times as fast as the phone from company A.

75. Sample answer: Divide the numbers to the left of the × symbols. Then divide the powers of 10. If necessary, rewrite the results in scientific notation. To convert that to standard form, check to see if the exponent is positive or negative. If positive, move the decimal point to the right, and if negative, to the left. The number of places to move the decimal point is the absolute value of the exponent. Fill in with zeros as needed.

Example 2 **INTERNET** **Express each number in standard form.**

34. About 2.1×10^7 people aged 12 to 17 use the Internet. **21,000,000**

35. Approximately 1.1×10^7 teens go online daily. **11,000,000**

Examples 3–4 **Evaluate each product or quotient. Express the results in both scientific notation and standard form.**

36. $(3.807 \times 10^3)(5 \times 10^2)$ **1.9035×10^6; 1,903,500**

37. $\frac{9.6 \times 10^3}{1.2 \times 10^{-4}}$ **8×10^7; 80,000,000**

38. $\frac{2.88 \times 10^3}{1.2 \times 10^{-5}}$ **2.4×10^8; 240,000,000**

39. $(6.5 \times 10^7)(7.2 \times 10^{-2})$ **4.68×10^6; 4,680,000**

40. $(9.5 \times 10^{-18})(9 \times 10^9)$ **8.55×10^{-8}; 0.0000000855**

41. $\frac{8.8 \times 10^3}{4 \times 10^{-4}}$ **2.2×10^7; 22,000,000**

42. $\frac{9.15 \times 10^{-3}}{6.1 \times 10}$ **1.5×10^{-4}; 0.00015**

43. $(1.4 \times 10^6)^2$ **1.96×10^{12}; 1,960,000,000,000**

44. $(2.58 \times 10^2)(3.6 \times 10^6)$ **9.288×10^8; 928,800,000**

45. $\frac{5.6498 \times 10^{10}}{8.2 \times 10^4}$ **6.89×10^5; 689,000**

46. $\frac{1.363 \times 10^{16}}{2.9 \times 10^6}$ **4.7×10^9; 4,700,000,000**

47. $(5 \times 10^3)(1.8 \times 10^{-7})$ **9×10^{-4}; 0.0009**

48. $(2.3 \times 10^{-3})^2$ **5.29×10^{-6}; 0.00000529**

49. $\frac{6.25 \times 10^{-4}}{1.25 \times 10^2}$ **5×10^{-6}; 0.000005**

50. $\frac{3.75 \times 10^{-9}}{1.5 \times 10^{-4}}$ **2.5×10^{-5}; 0.000025**

51. $(7.2 \times 10^7)^2$ **5.184×10^{15}; 5,184,000,000,000,000**

52. $\frac{8.6 \times 10^4}{2 \times 10^{-6}}$ **4.3×10^{10}; 43,000,000,000**

53. $(6.3 \times 10^{-5})^2$ **3.969×10^{-9}; 0.000000003969**

Example 5

54. **ASTRONOMY** The distance between Earth and the Sun varies throughout the year. Earth is closest to the Sun in January when the distance is 91.4 million miles. In July, the distance is greatest at 94.4 million miles.

a. Write 91.4 million in both standard form and in scientific notation. **91,400,000; 9.14×10^7**

b. Write 94.4 million in both standard form and in scientific notation. **94,400,000; 9.44×10^7**

c. What is the percent increase in distance from January to July? Round to the nearest tenth of a percent. **3.3%**

B **Evaluate each product or quotient. Express the results in both scientific notation and standard form.**

55. $(4.65 \times 10^{-2})(5.91 \times 10^6)$ **2.74185×10^5; 274,815**

56. $\frac{2.548 \times 10^5}{2.8 \times 10^{-2}}$ **9.1×10^6; 9,100,000**

57. $\frac{2.135 \times 10^5}{3.5 \times 10^{12}}$ **6.1×10^{-8}; 0.000000061**

58. $(3.16 \times 10^{-2})^2$ **9.9856×10^{-4}; 0.00099856**

59. $(2.01 \times 10^{-4})(8.9 \times 10^{-3})$ **1.7889×10^{-6}; 0.0000017889**

60. $\frac{5.184 \times 10^{-5}}{7.2 \times 10^3}$ **7.2×10^{-9}; 0.0000000072**

61. $(9.04 \times 10^6)(5.2 \times 10^{-4})$ **4.7008×10^3; 4700.8**

62. $\frac{1.032 \times 10^{-4}}{8.6 \times 10^{-5}}$ **1.2×10^0; 1.2**

LIGHT **The speed of light is approximately 3×10^8 meters per second.**

63. Write an expression to represent the speed of light in kilometers per second. **3×10^5**

64. Write an expression to represent the speed of light in kilometers per hour. **1.08×10^9**

65. Make a table to show how many kilometers light travels in a day, a week, a 30-day month, and a 365-day year. Express your results in scientific notation. **See margin.**

66. **MODELING** A recent cell phone study showed that company A's phone processes up to 7.95×10^5 bits of data every second. Company B's phone processes up to 1.41×10^6 bits of data every second. Evaluate and interpret $\frac{1.41 \times 10^6}{7.95 \times 10^5}$. **See margin.**

418 | Lesson 7-4 | Scientific Notation

Differentiated Instruction OL BL

Extension Write the expression 0.00042 × 316,000,000 on the board. Ask students to write this expression using scientific notation. Then have students evaluate the product.
$4.2 \times 10^{-4} \times 3.16 \times 10^8$; 132,720

67. EARTH The population of Earth is about 6.623×10^9. The land surface of Earth is 1.483×10^8 square kilometers. What is the population density for the land surface area of Earth? **about 44.7 persons/km^2**

68. RIVERS A drainage basin separated from adjacent basins by a ridge, hill, or mountain is known as a watershed. The watershed of the Amazon River is 2,300,000 square miles. The watershed of the Mississippi River is 1,200,000 square miles.

a. Write each of these numbers in scientific notation. **2.3×10^6; 1.2×10^6**

b. How many times as large is the Amazon River watershed as the Mississippi River watershed? **about 1.9 times as large**

69. AGRICULTURE In a recent year, farmers planted approximately 92.9 million acres of corn. They also planted 64.1 million acres of soybeans and 11.1 million acres of cotton. **a. corn: 9.29×10^7, 92,900,000; soybeans: 6.41×10^7, 64,100,000; cotton: 1.11×10^7, 11,100,000**

a. Write each of these numbers in scientific notation and in standard form.

b. How many times as much corn was planted as soybeans? Write your results in standard form and in scientific notation. Round your answer to four decimal places. **about 1.4493×10^0; 1.4493**

c. How many times as much corn was planted as cotton? Write your results in standard form and in scientific notation. Round your answer to four decimal places. **about 8.3694×10^0; 8.3694**

70. 10^{100}; $100^{10} = (10^2)^{10}$ or 10^{20} and $10^{100} > 10^{20}$, so $10^{100} > 100^{10}$

71. Pete; Syreeta moved the decimal point in the wrong direction.

H.O.T. Problems Use Higher-Order Thinking Skills

C **70. REASONING** Which is greater, 100^{10} or 10^{100}? Explain your reasoning.

71. ERROR ANALYSIS Syreeta and Pete are solving a division problem with scientific notation. Is either of them correct? Explain your reasoning.

Syreeta

$$\frac{3.65 \times 10^{-12}}{5 \times 10^5} = 0.73 \times 10^{-17}$$
$$= 7.3 \times 10^{-16}$$

Pete

$$\frac{3.65 \times 10^{-12}}{5 \times 10^5} = 0.73 \times 10^{-17}$$
$$= 7.3 \times 10^{-18}$$

73. Sample answer: Always; if the numbers are $a \times 10^m$ and $b \times 10^n$ in scientific notation, then $1 \le a < 10$ and $1 \le b < 10$. So $1 \le ab < 100$.

74. Sample answer: product: 2.5×10^5, $5.2 \times 10{-9}$; quotient: 2.6×10^3, 2×10^6

72. CHALLENGE Order these numbers from least to greatest without converting them to standard form. **-4.65×10^5, -5.64×10^4, 4.56×10^{-4}, 5.46×10^{-3}, 6.54×10^3**

5.46×10^{-3}, 6.54×10^3, 4.56×10^{-4}, -5.64×10^4, -4.65×10^5

73. ARGUMENTS Determine whether the statement is *always, sometimes,* or *never* true. Give examples or a counterexample to verify your reasoning.

When multiplying two numbers written in scientific notation, the resulting number can have no more than two digits to the left of the decimal point.

74. OPEN ENDED Write two numbers in scientific notation with a product of 1.3×10^{-3}. Then name two numbers in scientific notation with a quotient of 1.3×10^{-3}.

75. WRITING IN MATH Write the steps that you would use to divide two numbers written in scientific notation. Then describe how you would write the results in standard form. Demonstrate by finding $\frac{a}{b}$ for $a = 2 \times 10^3$ and $b = 4 \times 10^5$. **See margin.**

Teaching the Process Standards

Arguments Mathematically proficient students can recognize and use counterexamples. In Exercise 73, stress that examples alone do not prove a conjecture but one counterexample disproves one.

Study Guide and Intervention

AL OL ELL

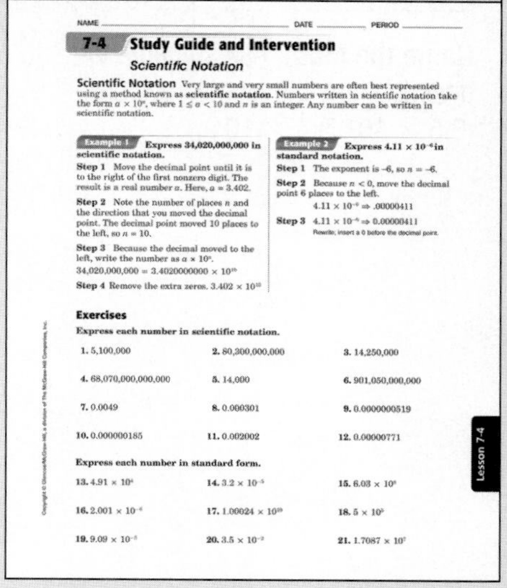
NAME ______ DATE ______ PERIOD ______

7-4 Study Guide and Intervention

Scientific Notation

Scientific Notation Very large and very small numbers are often best represented using a method known as **scientific notation**. Numbers written in scientific notation take the form $a \times 10^n$, where $1 \le a < 10$ and n is an integer. Any number can be written in scientific notation.

Example 1 Express 34,020,000,000 in scientific notation.

Step 1 Move the decimal point until it is to the right of the first nonzero digit. The result is a real number a. Here, $a = 3.402$.

Step 2 Note the number of places n and the direction that you moved the decimal point. The decimal point moved 10 places to the left, so $n = 10$.

Step 3 Because the decimal moved to the left, write the number as $a \times 10^n$.
$34{,}020{,}000{,}000 = 3.4020000000 \times 10^{10}$

Step 4 Remove the extra zeros. 3.402×10^{10}

Example 2 Express 4.11×10^{-6} in standard notation.

Step 1 The exponent is –6, so $n = -6$.

Step 2 Because $n < 0$, move the decimal point 6 places to the left.
$4.11 \times 10^{-6} \Rightarrow .00000411$

Step 3 $4.11 \times 10^{-6} \Rightarrow 0.00000411$
Rewrite; insert a 0 before the decimal point.

Exercises

Express each number in scientific notation.

1. 5,100,000
2. 80,300,000,000
3. 14,250,000
4. 68,070,000,000,000
5. 14,000
6. 901,050,000,000
7. 0.0049
8. 0.000301
9. 0.0000000519
10. 0.000000185
11. 0.002002
12. 0.00000771

Express each number in standard form.

13. 4.91×10^4
14. 3.2×10^{-5}
15. 6.03×10^8
16. 2.001×10^{-6}
17. 1.00024×10^{10}
18. 5×10^5
19. 9.09×10^{-5}
20. 3.5×10^{-2}
21. 1.7087×10^7

Lesson 7-4

Practice

AL OL BL ELL

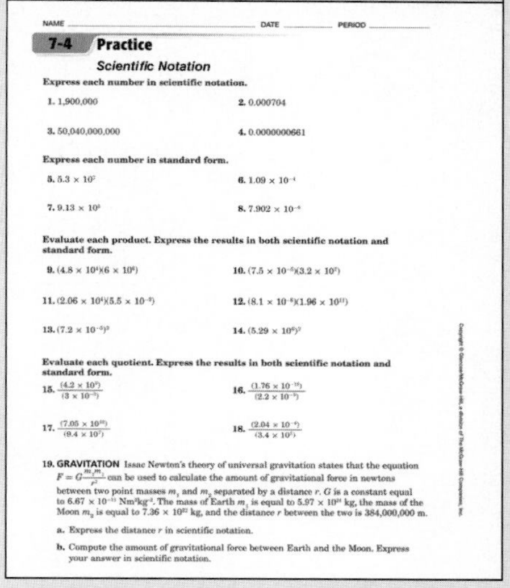
NAME ______ DATE ______ PERIOD ______

7-4 Practice

Scientific Notation

Express each number in scientific notation.

1. 1,900,000
2. 0.000704
3. 50,040,000,000
4. 0.0000000661

Express each number in standard form.

5. 5.3×10^2
6. 1.09×10^{-4}
7. 9.13×10^3
8. 7.902×10^{-6}

Evaluate each product. Express the results in both scientific notation and standard form.

9. $(4.8 \times 10^4)(6 \times 10^6)$
10. $(7.5 \times 10^{-6})(3.2 \times 10^7)$
11. $(2.06 \times 10^4)(5.5 \times 10^{-9})$
12. $(8.1 \times 10^{-8})(1.96 \times 10^{11})$
13. $(7.2 \times 10^{-5})^2$
14. $(5.29 \times 10^6)^2$

Evaluate each quotient. Express the results in both scientific notation and standard form.

15. $\frac{(4.2 \times 10^9)}{(3 \times 10^{-5})}$
16. $\frac{(1.76 \times 10^{-15})}{(2.2 \times 10^{-5})}$
17. $\frac{(7.05 \times 10^{10})}{(9.4 \times 10^7)}$
18. $\frac{(2.04 \times 10^{-4})}{(3.4 \times 10^3)}$

19. **GRAVITATION** Isaac Newton's theory of universal gravitation states that the equation $F = G\frac{m_1m_2}{r^2}$ can be used to calculate the amount of gravitational force in newtons between two point masses m_1 and m_2 separated by a distance r. G is a constant equal to 6.67×10^{-11} Nm^{2}kg^{-2}. The mass of Earth m_1 is equal to 5.97×10^{24} kg, the mass of the Moon m_2 is equal to 7.36×10^{22} kg, and the distance r between the two is 384,000,000 m.

a. Express the distance r in scientific notation.

b. Compute the amount of gravitational force between Earth and the Moon. Express your answer in scientific notation.

Word Problem Practice

AL OL BL ELL

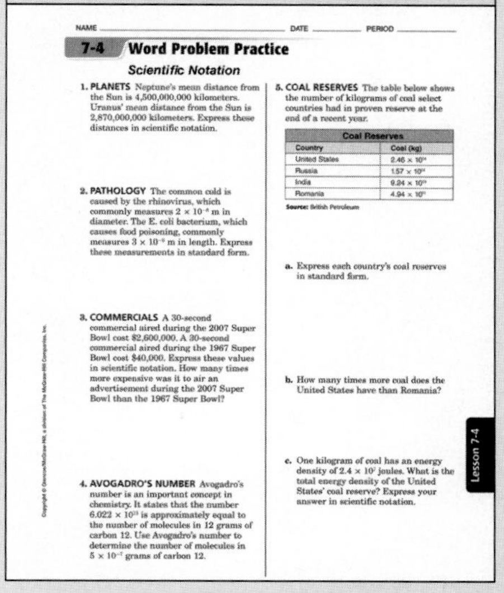
NAME ______ DATE ______ PERIOD ______

7-4 Word Problem Practice

Scientific Notation

1. **PLANETS** Neptune's mean distance from the Sun is 4,500,000,000 kilometers. Uranus' mean distance from the Sun is 2,870,000,000 kilometers. Express these distances in scientific notation.

2. **PATHOLOGY** The common cold is caused by the rhinovirus, which commonly measures 2×10^{-8} m in diameter. The E. coli bacterium, which causes food poisoning, commonly measures 3×10^{-6} m in length. Express these measurements in standard form.

3. **COMMERCIALS** A 30-second commercial aired during the 2007 Super Bowl cost $2,600,000. A 30-second commercial aired during the 1967 Super Bowl cost $40,000. Express these values in scientific notation. How many times more expensive was it to air an advertisement during the 2007 Super Bowl than the 1967 Super Bowl?

4. **AVOGADRO'S NUMBER** Avogadro's number is an important concept in chemistry. It states that the number 6.022×10^{23} is approximately equal to the number of molecules in 12 grams of carbon 12. Use Avogadro's number to determine the number of molecules in 5×10^{-7} grams of carbon 12.

5. **COAL RESERVES** The table below shows the number of kilograms of coal select countries had in proven reserve at the end of a recent year.

Coal Reserves

Country	Coal (kg)
United States	2.46×10^{14}
Russia	1.57×10^{14}
India	9.24×10^{13}
Romania	4.94×10^{12}

Source: British Petroleum

a. Express each country's coal reserves in standard form.

b. How many times more coal does the United States have than Romania?

c. One kilogram of coal has an energy density of 2.4×10^7 joules. What is the total energy density of the United States' coal reserve? Express your answer in scientific notation.

Lesson 7-4

Enrichment

OL BL

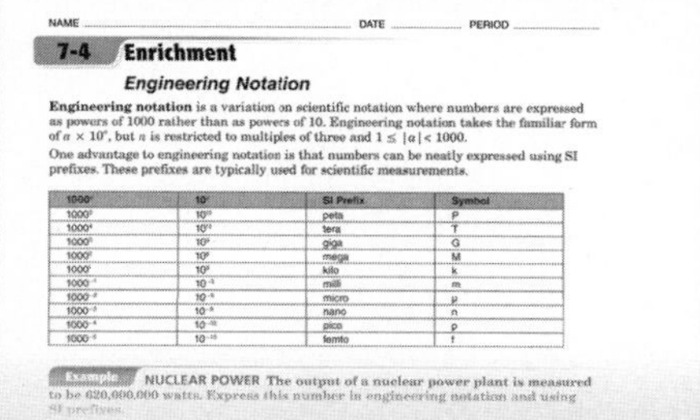
NAME ______ DATE ______ PERIOD ______

7-4 Enrichment

Engineering Notation

Engineering notation is a variation on scientific notation where numbers are expressed as powers of 1000 rather than as powers of 10. Engineering notation takes the familiar form of $a \times 10^n$, but n is restricted to multiples of three and $1 \le |a| < 1000$.

One advantage to engineering notation is that numbers can be neatly expressed using SI prefixes. These prefixes are typically used for scientific measurements.

1000^n	10^n	SI Prefix	Symbol
1000^5	10^{15}	peta	P
1000^4	10^{12}	tera	T
1000^3	10^9	giga	G
1000^2	10^6	mega	M
1000^1	10^3	kilo	k
1000^{-1}	10^{-3}	milli	m
1000^{-2}	10^{-6}	micro	μ
1000^{-3}	10^{-9}	nano	n
1000^{-4}	10^{-12}	pico	p
1000^{-5}	10^{-15}	femto	f

Example NUCLEAR POWER The output of a nuclear power plant is measured to be 620,000,000 watts. Express this number in engineering notation and using SI prefixes.

4 Assess

Name the Math Ask students to describe how they would evaluate $(3.5 \times 10^{-5})(4 \times 10^{2})$.

Standardized Test Practice

76. Which number represents 0.05604×10^8 written in standard form? **C**

A 0.0000000005604 C 5,604,000
B 560,400 D 50,604,000

77. Toni left school and rode her bike home. The graph below shows the relationship between her distance from the school and time.

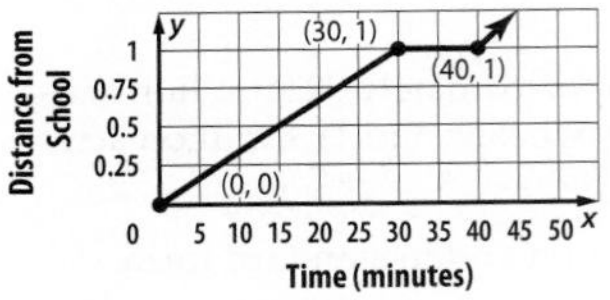

Which explanation could account for the section of the graph from $x = 30$ to $x = 40$? **H**

F Toni rode her bike down a hill.
G Toni ran all the way home.
H Toni stopped at a friend's house on her way home.
J Toni returned to school to get her mathematics book.

78. SHORT RESPONSE In his first four years of coaching football, Coach Delgato's team won 5 games the first year, 10 games the second year, 8 games the third year, and 7 games the fourth year. How many games does the team need to win during the fifth year to have an average of 8 wins per year? **10 games**

79. The table shows the relationship between Calories and grams of fat contained in an order of fried chicken from various restaurants.

Calories	305	410	320	500	510	440
Fat (g)	28	34	28	41	42	38

Assuming that the data can best be described by a linear model, about how many grams of fat would you expect to be in a 275-Calorie order of fried chicken? **B**

A 22
B 25
C 28
D 30

Spiral Review

80. HEALTH A ponderal index p is a measure of a person's body based on height h in centimeters and mass m in kilograms. One such formula is $p = 100m^{\frac{1}{3}}h^{-1}$. If a person who is 182 centimeters tall has a ponderal index of about 2.2, how much does the person weigh in kilograms? (Lesson 7-3) **64.2 kg**

Simplify. Assume that no denominator is equal to zero. (Lesson 7-2)

81. $\frac{8^9}{8^6}$ **8^3 or 512**

82. $\frac{6^5}{6^3}$ **6^2 or 36**

83. $\frac{r^8t^{12}}{r^2t^7}$ **r^6t^5**

84. $\left(\frac{3a^4b^4}{8c^2}\right)^4$ **$\frac{81a^{16}b^{16}}{4096c^8}$**

85. $\left(\frac{5d^3g^2}{3h^4}\right)^2$ **$\frac{25d^6g^4}{9h^8}$**

86. $\left(\frac{4n^2p^4}{8p^3}\right)^3$ **$\frac{n^6p^3}{8}$**

87. CHEMISTRY Lemon juice is 10^2 times as acidic as tomato juice. Tomato juice is 10^3 times as acidic as egg whites. How many times as acidic is lemon juice as egg whites? (Lesson 7-2) **10^5**

Skills Review

Evaluate $a(b^x)$ for each of the given values.

88. $a = 1, b = 2, x = 4$ **16**

89. $a = 4, b = 1, x = 7$ **4**

90. $a = 5, b = 3, x = 0$ **5**

91. $a = 0, b = 6, x = 8$ **0**

92. $a = -2, b = 3, x = 1$ **−6**

93. $a = -3, b = 5, x = 2$ **−75**

420 | Lesson 7-4 | Scientific Notation

CHAPTER 7

Mid-Chapter Quiz

Lessons 7-1 through 7-4

Simplify each expression. (Lesson 7-1)

1. $(x^3)(4x^5)$ **$4x^8$**

2. $(m^2p^5)^3$ **m^6p^{15}**

3. $[(2xy^3)^2]^3$ **$64x^6y^{18}$**

4. $(6ab^3c^4)(-3a^2b^3c)$ **$-18a^3b^6c^5$**

5. **MULTIPLE CHOICE** Express the volume of the solid as a monomial. (Lesson 7-1) **B**

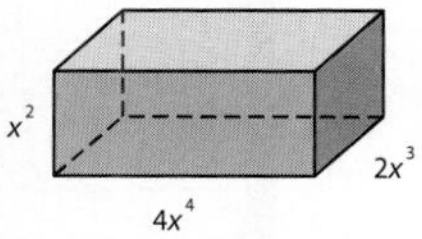

A $6x^9$

B $8x^9$

C $8x^{24}$

D $7x^{24}$

Simplify each expression. Assume that no denominator equals 0. (Lesson 7-2)

6. $\left(\frac{2a^4b^3}{c^6}\right)^3$ **$\frac{8a^{12}b^9}{c^{18}}$**

7. $\frac{2xy^0}{6x}$ **$\frac{1}{3}$**

8. $\frac{m^7n^4p}{m^3n^3p}$ **m^4n**

9. $\frac{p^4t^{-2}}{r^{-5}}$ **$\frac{p^4r^5}{t^2}$**

10. **ASTRONOMY** Physicists estimate that the number of stars in the universe has an order of magnitude of 10^{21}. The number of stars in the Milky Way galaxy is around 100 billion. Using orders of magnitude, how many times as many stars are there in the universe as the Milky Way? (Lesson 7-2) **10^{10}**

Write each expression in radical form, or write each radical in exponential form. (Lesson 7-3)

11. $42^{\frac{1}{2}}$ **$\sqrt{42}$**

12. $11x^{\frac{1}{2}}$ **$11\sqrt{x}$**

13. $(11g)^{\frac{1}{2}}$ **$\sqrt{11g}$**

14. $\sqrt{55}$ **$55^{\frac{1}{2}}$**

15. $\sqrt{5k}$ **$(5k)^{\frac{1}{2}}$**

16. $4\sqrt{p}$ **$4p^{\frac{1}{2}}$**

Simplify. (Lesson 7-3)

17. $\sqrt[3]{729}$ **9**

18. $\sqrt[4]{625}$ **5**

19. $1331^{\frac{1}{3}}$ **11**

20. $\left(\frac{16}{81}\right)^{\frac{1}{4}}$ **$\frac{2}{3}$**

21. $8^{\frac{2}{3}}$ **4**

22. $625^{\frac{3}{4}}$ **125**

23. $216^{\frac{5}{3}}$ **7776**

24. $\left(\frac{1}{4}\right)^{\frac{3}{2}}$ **$\frac{1}{8}$**

Solve each equation. (Lesson 7-3)

25. $4^x = 4096$ **6**

26. $5^{2x+1} = 125$ **1**

27. $4^{x-3} = 128$ **6.5**

Express each number in scientific notation. (Lesson 7-4)

28. 0.00000054 **5.4×10^{-7}**

29. 0.0042 **4.2×10^{-3}**

30. 234,000 **2.34×10^5**

31. 418,000,000 **4.18×10^8**

Express each number in standard form. (Lesson 7-4)

32. 4.1×10^{-3} **0.0041**

33. 2.74×10^5 **274,000**

34. 3×10^9 **3,000,000,000**

35. 9.1×10^{-5} **0.000091**

Evaluate each product or quotient. Express the results in scientific notation. (Lesson 7-4)

36. $(2.13 \times 10^2)(3 \times 10^5)$ **6.39×10^7**

37. $(7.5 \times 10^6)(2.5 \times 10^{-2})$ **1.875×10^5**

38. $\frac{7.5 \times 10^8}{2.5 \times 10^4}$ **3×10^4**

39. $\frac{6.6 \times 10^5}{2 \times 10^{-3}}$ **3.3×10^8**

40. **MAMMALS** A blue whale has been caught that was 4.2×10^5 pounds. The smallest mammal is a bumblebee bat, which is about 0.0044 pound. (Lesson 7-4)
   a. Write the whale's weight in standard form. **420,000 pounds**
   b. Write the bat's weight in scientific notation. **4.4×10^{-3} pounds**
   c. How many orders of magnitude as big as a blue whale is a bumblebee bat? **10^8**

Formative Assessment

Use the Mid-Chapter Quiz to assess students' progress in the first half of the chapter.

For problems answered incorrectly, have students review the lessons indicated in parentheses.

Summative Assessment

Mid-Chapter Test, p. 59

McGraw-Hill eAssessment Customize and create multiple versions of your Mid-Chapter Quiz and their answer keys.

FOLDABLES® StudyOrganizer

Dinah Zike's Foldables®

Before students complete the Mid-Chapter Quiz, encourage them to review the information for Lessons 7-1 through 7-4 in their Foldables.

InterventionPlanner

TIER 1 On Level OL	TIER 2 Strategic Intervention AL approaching grade level	TIER 3 Intensive Intervention 2 or more grades below level
If students miss about 25% of the exercises or less,	**If** students miss about 50% of the exercises,	**If** students miss about 75% of the exercises,
Then choose a resource: SE Lessons 7-1, 7-2, 7-3, and 7-4 Skills Practice, pp. 7, 13, 19, and 25 TE Chapter Project connectED.mcgraw-hill.com Self-Check Quiz	**Then** choose a resource: Study Guide and Intervention, Chapter 7, pp. 5, 11, 17, and 23 *Quick Review Math Handbook* connectED.mcgraw-hill.com Extra Examples, Personal Tutor, Homework Help	**Then** use *Math Triumphs, Alg. 1* connectED.mcgraw-hill.com Extra Examples, Personal Tutor, Homework Help, Review Vocabulary

1 Focus

Objective Use a graphing calculator to investigate families of exponential functions.

Materials

- TI-83/84 Plus or other graphing calculator

Teaching Tips

- Remind students that to set their viewing window to standard, use ZOOM 6. Otherwise, use the window settings shown.
- For Activity 2, remind students that to enter functions like $y = \left(\frac{1}{2}\right)^x$, they will need to type (1 ÷ 2) ^ X,T,θ,n ENTER in the Y= list.

2 Teach

Working in Cooperative Groups

Divide the class into pairs. Have one student work through Activity 1 and the other work through Activity 2. Ask students to describe to each other what they see on the calculator screens. Have them switch activities and see if they notice any other similarities or differences.

Then ask students to work with their partners to complete Activities 3 and 4.

Practice Have students complete Exercises 1 and 2.

EXPLORE 7-5

Graphing Technology Lab
Family of Exponential Functions

An **exponential function** is a function of the form $y = ab^x$, where $a \neq 0$, $b > 0$, and $b \neq 1$. You have studied the effects of changing parameters in linear functions. You can use a graphing calculator to analyze how changing the parameters a and b affects the graphs in the family of exponential functions.

Content Standards
AI.QE.2, AI.QE.3

Activity 1 b in $y = b^x$, $b > 1$

Graph the set of equations on the same screen.
Describe any similarities and differences among the graphs.

$y = 2^x$, $y = 3^x$, $y = 6^x$

Enter the equations in the Y= list and graph.

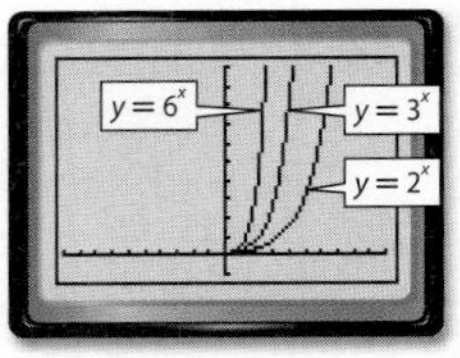

[−10, 10] scl: 1 by [−10, 100] scl: 10

There are many similarities in the graphs. The domain for each function is all real numbers, and the range is all positive real numbers. The functions are increasing over the entire domain. The graphs do not display any line symmetry.

Use the ZOOM feature to investigate the key features of the graphs.

Zooming in twice on a point near the origin allows closer inspection of the graphs. The y-intercept is 1 for all three graphs.

Tracing along the graphs reveals that there are no x-intercepts, no maxima and no minima.

The graphs are different in that the graphs for the equations in which b is greater are steeper.

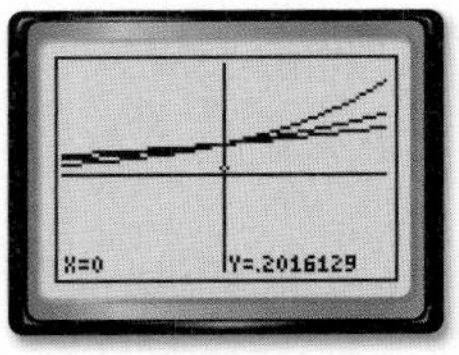

[−0.625, 0.625] scl: 1 by [−3.25..., 3.63...] scl: 10

The effect of b on the graph is different when $0 < b < 1$.

Activity 2 b in $y = b^x$, $0 < b < 1$

Graph the set of equations on the same screen.
Describe any similarities and differences among the graphs.

$y = \left(\frac{1}{2}\right)^x$, $y = \left(\frac{1}{3}\right)^x$, $y = \left(\frac{1}{6}\right)^x$

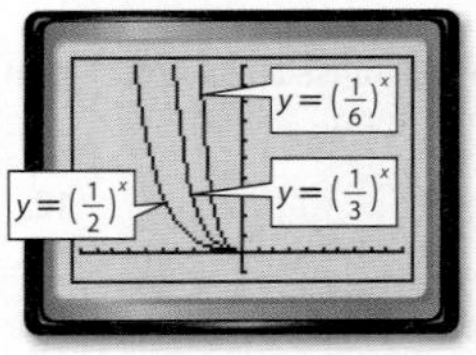

[−10, 10] scl: 1 by [−10, 100] scl: 10

The domain for each function is all real numbers, and the range is all positive real numbers. The function values are all positive and the functions are decreasing over the entire domain. The graphs display no line symmetry. There are no x-intercepts, and the y-intercept is 1 for all three graphs. There are no maxima or minima.

However, the graphs in which b is lesser are steeper.

WatchOut!

Common Misconceptions Be sure students do not confuse polynomial functions and exponential functions. While $y = x^2$ and $y = 2^x$ each have an exponent, $y = x^2$ is a polynomial function, and $y = 2^x$ is an exponential function.

Activity 3 a in $y = ab^x$, $a > 0$

Graph each set of equations on the same screen. Describe any similarities and differences among the graphs.

$y = 2^x$, $y = 3(2^x)$, $y = \frac{1}{6}(2^x)$

The domain for each function is all real numbers, and the range is all positive real numbers. The functions are increasing over the entire domain. The graphs do not display any line symmetry.

Use the ZOOM feature to investigate the key features of the graphs.

Zooming in twice on a point near the origin allows closer inspection of the graphs.

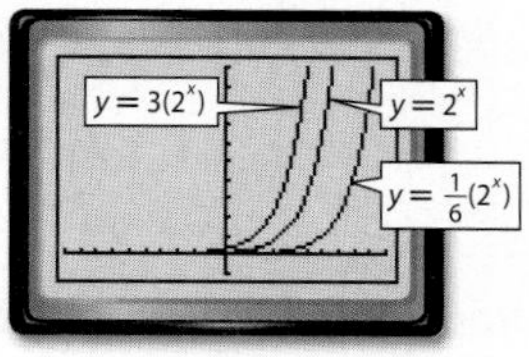

[−10, 10] scl: 1 by [−10, 100] scl: 10

Tracing along the graphs reveals that there are no x-intercepts, no maxima and no minima.

However, the graphs in which a is greater are steeper. The y-intercept is 1 in the graph of $y = 2^x$, 3 in $y = 3(2^x)$, and $\frac{1}{6}$ in $y = \frac{1}{6}(2^x)$.

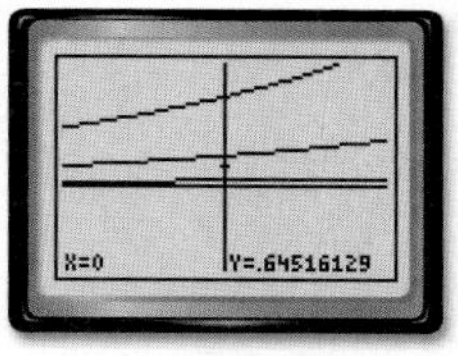

[−0.625, 0.625] scl: 1 by [−2.79..., 4.08...] scl: 10

Activity 4 a in $y = ab^x$, $a < 0$

Graph each set of equations on the same screen. Describe any similarities and differences among the graphs.

$y = -2^x$, $y = -3(2^x)$, $y = -\frac{1}{6}(2^x)$

The domain for each function is all real numbers, and the range is all negative real numbers. The functions are decreasing over the entire domain. The graphs do not display any line symmetry.

There are no x-intercepts, no maxima and no minima.

However, the graphs in which the absolute value of a is greater are steeper. The y-intercept is -1 in the graph of $y = -2^x$, -3 in $y = -3(2^x)$, and $-\frac{1}{6}$ in $y = -\frac{1}{6}(2^x)$.

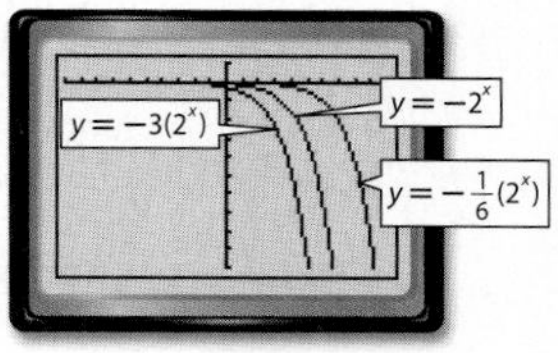

[−10, 10] scl: 1 by [−100, 10] scl: 10

Model and Analyze **1–3. See margin.**

1. How does b affect the graph of $y = ab^x$ when $b > 1$ and when $0 < b < 1$? Give examples.
2. How does a affect the graph of $y = ab^x$ when $a > 0$ and when $a < 0$? Give examples.
3. **REGULARITY** Make a conjecture about the relationship of the graphs of $y = 3^x$ and $y = \left(\frac{1}{3}\right)^x$. Verify your conjecture by graphing both functions.

3 Assess

Formative Assessment

Use Exercise 3 to assess each student's knowledge of graphing exponential functions.

From Concrete to Abstract

Ask students to summarize how to use technology to find the solutions to exponential equations and inequalities.

Additional Answers

1. The value of b affects the steepness of the graph. When $b > 1$, the greater the value of b the steeper the graph. When $0 < b < 1$, the lesser the value of b the steeper the graph. Sample answer: The graph of $y = 5^x$ is steeper than the graph of $y = 3^x$. The graph of $y = \left(\frac{1}{5}\right)^x$ is steeper than the graph of $y = \left(\frac{1}{3}\right)^x$.
2. The value of a affects the steepness and direction of opening of the graph. The greater the absolute value of a, the steeper the graph. When $a > 0$ the graph opens up, and when $a < 0$ the graph opens down. Sample answer: The graph of $y = 4(2^x)$ is steeper than the graph of $y = 3(2^x)$. The graph of $y = 4(2^x)$ opens up and the graph of $y = -4(2^x)$ opens down.
3. Sample answer: The graph of $y = \left(\frac{1}{3}\right)^x$ is the graph of $y = 3^x$ reflected over the y-axis.

Teaching the Process Standards

Regularity Mathematically proficient students look for and express regularity in repeated reasoning. In Exercise 3, guide students to look at the equations in Activity 2 to observe a pattern.

1 Focus

VerticalAlignment

Before Lesson 7-5 Evaluate numerical expressions involving exponents.

Lesson 7-5 Graph exponential functions. Identify data that display exponential behavior.

After Lesson 7-5 Solve problems involving exponential growth and decay.

2 Teach

Scaffolding Questions

Have students read the **Why?** section of the lesson.

Ask:

- How is this equation different from a linear equation? The independent variable x is an exponent.
- What is the value of y when $x = 0$? $y = 3$
- Can the value of y ever be 0? no

LESSON 7-5 Exponential Functions

Then

- You evaluated numerical expressions involving exponents.

Now

1. Graph exponential functions.
2. Identify data that display exponential behavior.

Why?

- Tarantulas can appear scary with their large hairy bodies and legs, but they are harmless to humans. The graph shows a tarantula spider population that increases over time. Notice that the graph is not linear.

The graph represents the function $y = 3(2)^x$. This is an example of an *exponential* function.

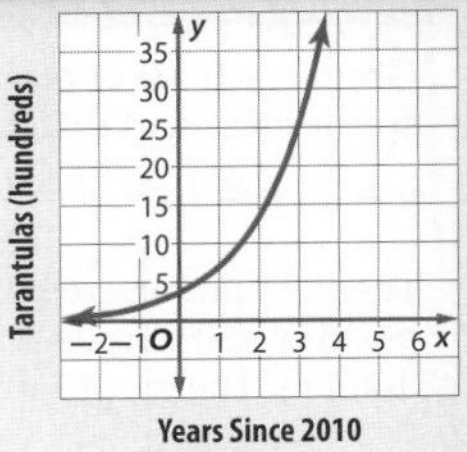

NewVocabulary
exponential function
exponential growth function
exponential decay function

Content Standards
AI.F.4, AI.QE.1, AI.QE.2, AI.QE.3

Process Standards
PS.1

1 Graph Exponential Functions

An **exponential function** is a function of the form $y = ab^x$, where $a \neq 0$, $b > 0$, and $b \neq 1$. Notice that the base is a constant and the exponent is a variable. Exponential functions are nonlinear.

KeyConcept Exponential Function

Words An exponential function is a function that can be described by an equation of the form $y = ab^x$, where $a \neq 0$, $b > 0$, and $b \neq 1$.

Examples $y = 2(3)^x$ $\quad y = 4^x \quad y = \left(\frac{1}{2}\right)^x$

Example 1 Graph with $a > 0$ and $b > 1$

Graph $y = 3^x$. Find the y-intercept, and state the domain and range.

The graph crosses the y-axis at 1, so the y-intercept is 1. The domain is all real numbers, and the range is all positive real numbers.

Notice that the graph approaches the x-axis but there is no x-intercept. The graph is increasing on the entire domain.

x	3^x	y
−2	3^{-2}	$\frac{1}{9}$
−1	3^{-1}	$\frac{1}{3}$
0	3^0	1
$\frac{1}{2}$	$3^{\frac{1}{2}}$	≈1.73
1	3^1	3
2	3^2	9

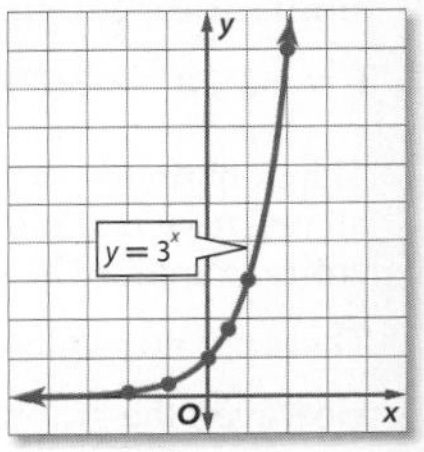

GuidedPractice

1. Graph $y = 7^x$. Find the y-intercept, and state the domain and range. See Ch. 7 Answer Appendix.

Functions of the form $y = ab^x$, where $a > 0$ and $b > 1$, are called **exponential growth functions** and all have the same shape as the graph in Example 1. Functions of the form $y = ab^x$, where $a > 0$ and $0 < b < 1$ are called **exponential decay functions** and also have the same general shape.

Lesson 7-5 Resources

Resource	Approaching Level AL	On Level OL	Beyond Level BL	English Learners ELL
Teacher Edition		▪ Differentiated Instruction, pp. 426, 429	▪ Differentiated Instruction, pp. 426, 429	
Chapter Resource Masters	▪ Study Guide and Intervention, pp. 29–30 ▪ Skills Practice, p. 31 ▪ Practice, p. 32 ▪ Word Problem Practice, p. 33	▪ Study Guide and Intervention, pp. 29–30 ▪ Skills Practice, p. 31 ▪ Practice, p. 32 ▪ Word Problem Practice, p. 33 ▪ Enrichment, p. 34	▪ Practice, p. 32 ▪ Word Problem Practice, p. 33 ▪ Enrichment, p. 34	▪ Study Guide and Intervention, pp. 29–30 ▪ Skills Practice, p. 31 ▪ Practice, p. 32 ▪ Word Problem Practice, p. 33
Other	▪ 5-Minute Check 7-5 ▪ Study Notebook ▪ Teaching Algebra with Manipulatives	▪ 5-Minute Check 7-5 ▪ Study Notebook ▪ Teaching Algebra with Manipulatives	▪ 5-Minute Check 7-5 ▪ Study Notebook	▪ 5-Minute Check 7-5 ▪ Study Notebook ▪ Teaching Algebra with Manipulatives

StudyTip

$a < 0$ If the value of a is less than 0, the graph will be reflected across the x-axis.

2.

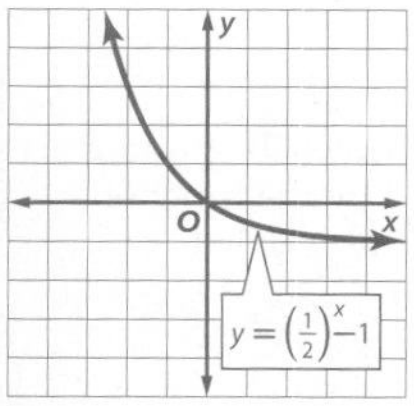

(0, 0); D = {all real numbers}; R = {y | y > −1}

Example 2 Graph with $a > 0$ and $0 < b < 1$

Graph $y = \left(\frac{1}{3}\right)^x$. Find the y-intercept, and state the domain and range.

The y-intercept is 1. The domain is all real numbers, and the range is all positive real numbers. Notice that as x increases, the y-values decrease less rapidly.

x	$\left(\frac{1}{3}\right)^x$	y
−2	$\left(\frac{1}{3}\right)^{-2}$	9
0	$\left(\frac{1}{3}\right)^{0}$	1
2	$\left(\frac{1}{3}\right)^{2}$	$\frac{1}{9}$

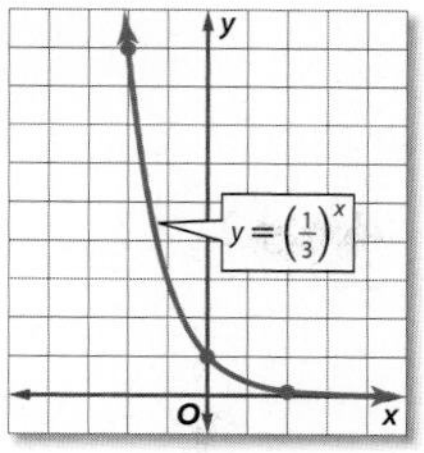

GuidedPractice

2. Graph $y = \left(\frac{1}{2}\right)^x - 1$. Find the y-intercept, and state the domain and range.

The key features of the graphs of exponential functions can be summarized as follows.

KeyConcept Graphs of Exponential Functions

Exponential Growth Functions

Equation: $f(x) = ab^x$, $a > 0$, $b > 1$

Domain, Range: all reals; all positive reals

Intercepts: one y-intercept, no x-intercepts

End behavior: as x increases, $f(x)$ increases; as x decreases, $f(x)$ approaches 0

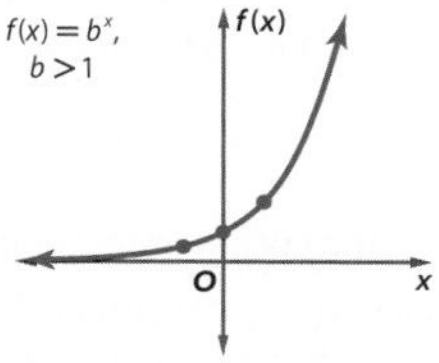

Exponential Decay Functions

Equation: $f(x) = ab^x$, $a > 0$, $0 < b < 1$

Domain, Range: all reals; all positive reals

Intercepts: one y-intercept, no x-intercepts

End behavior: as x increases, $f(x)$ approaches 0; as x decreases, $f(x)$ increases

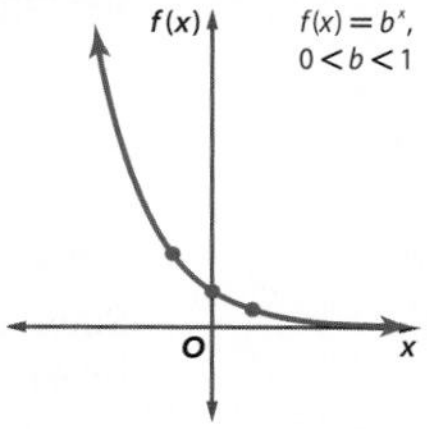

Exponential functions occur in many real world situations.

Real-WorldLink

The United States is the largest soda consumer in the world. In a recent year, the United States accounted for one third of the world's total soda consumption.

Source: Worldwatch Institute

Real-World Example 3 Use Exponential Functions to Solve Problems

SODA The function $C = 179(1.029)^t$ models the amount of soda consumed in the world, where C is the amount consumed in billions of liters and t is the number of years since 2000.

a. Graph the function. What values of C and t are meaningful in the context of the problem?

Since t represents time, $t > 0$. At $t = 0$, the consumption is 179 billion liters. Therefore, in the context of this problem, $C > 179$ is meaningful.

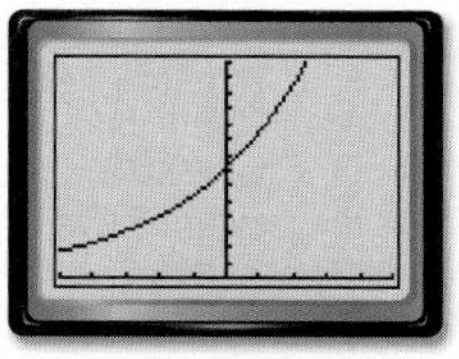

[−50, 50] scl: 10 by [0, 350] scl: 25

1 Graph Exponential Functions

Example 1 shows how to graph an exponential function when $a > 0$ and $b > 1$. **Example 2** shows how to graph an exponential function when $a > 0$ and $0 < b < 1$. **Example 3** shows how to use an exponential function to solve a real-world problem.

Formative Assessment

Use the Guided Practice exercises after each example to determine students' understanding of concepts.

Additional Examples

1 Graph $y = 4^x$. Find the y-intercept and state the domain and range. y-intercept: 1, D = {all real numbers}, R = {all positive numbers}

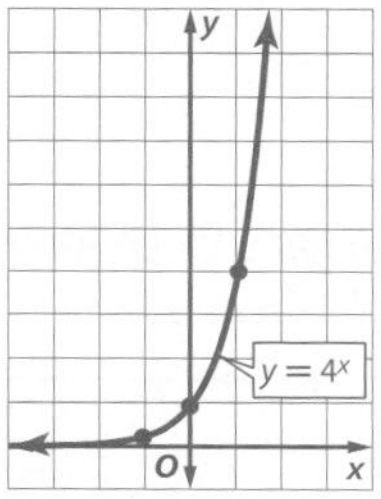

2 Graph $y = \left(\frac{1}{4}\right)^x$. Find the y-intercept and state the domain and range. y-intercept: 1, D = {all real numbers}, R = {all positive numbers}

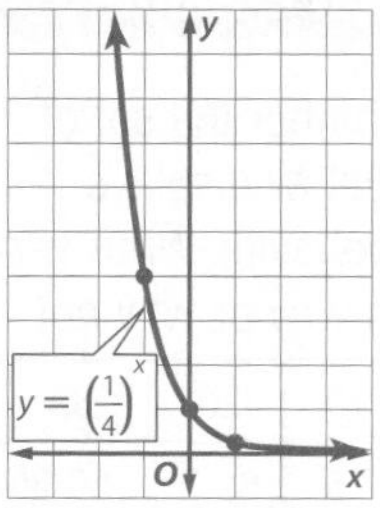

Additional Examples also in Interactive Classroom PowerPoint® Presentations

IWB Interactive White Board READY

Teach with Tech

Interactive Whiteboard Create a template for a table of values, and drag a coordinate grid onto the board. Write a function and have students complete the table of values. Then have students draw the graph of the function.

WatchOut!

Student Misconceptions Make sure students understand that the graphs of exponential functions never actually touch the x-axis. It is acceptable for hand-drawn graphs to show the graph just above and about parallel to the x-axis as long as students understand that the graph gets infinitely close to the axis without touching it.

Additional Example

3 **DEPRECIATION** Some people say that the value of a new car decreases as soon as it is driven off the lot. The function $V = 25{,}000 \cdot 0.82^t$ models the depreciation in the value of a new car that originally cost \$25,000. V represents the value of the car and t represents the time in years from the time of purchase.

a. Graph the function. What values of V and t are meaningful in the context of the problem?

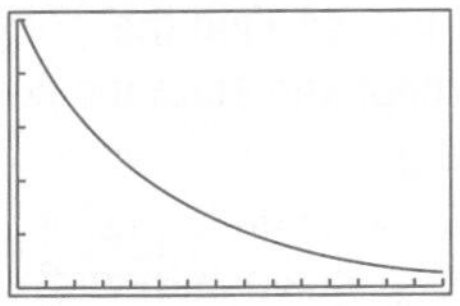

[0, 15] scl: 1 by [0, 25,000] scl: 500; Only values of $V \leq 25{,}000$ and $t \geq 0$ are meaningful.

b. What is the car's value after five years? about \$9270

2 Identify Exponential Behavior

Example 4 shows how to determine whether a set of data displays exponential behavior.

Additional Example

4 Determine whether the set of data shown below displays exponential behavior. Write *yes* or *no*. Explain why or why not.

x	0	10	20	30
y	10	25	62.5	156.25

The domain values are at regular intervals, and the range values have a common factor of 2.5, so the set is probably exponential. Also, the graph shows rapidly increasing values of y as x increases.

b. How much soda was consumed in 2005?

$C = 179(1.029)^t$ — Original equation

$= 179(1.029)^5$ — $t = 5$

≈ 206.5 — Use a calculator.

The world soda consumption in 2005 was approximately 206.5 billion liters.

Guided Practice

3. BIOLOGY A certain bacteria population doubles every 20 minutes. Beginning with 10 cells in a culture, the population can be represented by the function $B = 10(2)^t$, where B is the number of bacteria cells and t is the time in 20 minute increments. How many will there be after 2 hours? **640**

2 Identify Exponential Behavior

Recall from Lesson 3-3 that linear functions have a constant rate of change. Exponential functions do not have constant rates of change, but they do have constant ratios.

Problem-Solving Tip

Make an Organized List
Making an organized list of x-values and corresponding y-values is helpful in graphing the function. It can also help you identify patterns in the data.

Example 4 Identify Exponential Behavior

Determine whether the set of data shown below displays exponential behavior. Write *yes* or *no*. Explain why or why not.

x	0	5	10	15	20	25
y	64	32	16	8	4	2

Method 1 Look for a pattern.

The domain values are at regular intervals of 5. Look for a common factor among the range values.

$$64 \quad 32 \quad 16 \quad 8 \quad 4 \quad 2$$
$$\times\tfrac{1}{2} \quad \times\tfrac{1}{2} \quad \times\tfrac{1}{2} \quad \times\tfrac{1}{2} \quad \times\tfrac{1}{2}$$

The range values differ by the common factor of $\frac{1}{2}$.

Since the domain values are at regular intervals and the range values differ by a positive common factor, the data are probably exponential. Its equation may involve $\left(\frac{1}{2}\right)^x$.

Method 2 Graph the data.

Plot the points and connect them with a smooth curve. The graph shows a rapidly decreasing value of y as x increases. This is a characteristic of exponential behavior in which the base is between 0 and 1.

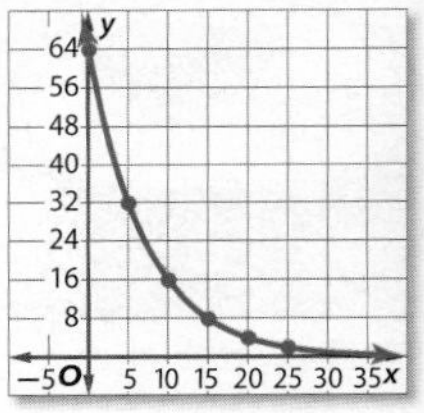

Guided Practice

4. Determine whether the set of data shown below displays exponential behavior. Write *yes* or *no*. Explain why or why not.

x	0	3	6	9	12	15
y	12	16	20	24	28	32

4. No; the domain values are at regular intervals, but the range values have a common difference of 4.

Differentiated Instruction OL BL

Logical Learners Ask students to write a comparison of an exponential function to a linear function.

Check Your Understanding

● = Step-by-Step Solutions begin on page R13.

Examples 1–2 **Graph each function. Find the y-intercept and state the domain and range.**

1. $y = 2^x$
2. $y = -5^x$
3. $y = -\left(\frac{1}{5}\right)^x$
4. $y = 3\left(\frac{1}{4}\right)^x$
5. $f(x) = 6^x + 3$
6. $f(x) = 2 - 2^x$

1–6. See Ch. 7 Answer Appendix.

Example 3

7. **BIOLOGY** The function $f(t) = 100(1.05)^t$ models the growth of a fruit fly population, where $f(t)$ is the number of flies and t is time in days.
   - **a.** What values for the domain and range are reasonable in the context of this situation? Explain. **$D = \{d \mid d \geq 0\}$, the number of days is greater than or equal to 0; $R = \{y \mid y \geq 100\}$, the number of fruit flies is greater than or equal to 100.**
   - **b.** After two weeks, approximately how many flies are in this population? **about 198 fruit flies**

Example 4 **Determine whether the set of data shown below displays exponential behavior. Write *yes* or *no*. Explain why or why not.** **8–9. See margin.**

8.

x	1	2	3	4	5	6
y	−4	−2	0	2	4	6

9.

x	2	4	6	8	10	12
y	1	4	16	64	256	1024

Practice and Problem Solving

Extra Practice is on page R7.

Examples 1–2 **Graph each function. Find the y-intercept and state the domain and range.** **10–19. See Ch. 7 Answer Appendix.**

10. $y = 2 \cdot 8^x$
11. $y = 2 \cdot \left(\frac{1}{6}\right)^x$
12. $y = \left(\frac{1}{12}\right)^x$
13. $y = -3 \cdot 9^x$
14. $y = -4 \cdot 10^x$
15. $y = 3 \cdot 11^x$
16. $y = 4^x + 3$
17. $y = \frac{1}{2}(2^x - 8)$
18. $y = 5(3^x) + 1$
19. $y = -2(3^x) + 5$

Example 3

20. **MODELING** A population of bacteria in a culture increases according to the model $p = 300(2.7)^{0.02t}$, where t is the number of hours and $t = 0$ corresponds to 9:00 A.M.
   - **a.** Use this model to estimate the number of bacteria at 11 A.M. **about 312**
   - **b.** Graph the function and name the p-intercept. Describe what the p-intercept represents, and describe a reasonable domain and range for this situation. **See Ch. 7 Answer Appendix.**

Example 4 **Determine whether the set of data shown below displays exponential behavior. Write *yes* or *no*. Explain why or why not.** **21–24. See margin.**

(21)

x	−4	0	4	8	12
y	2	−4	8	−16	32

22.

x	−6	−3	0	3
y	5	10	15	20

23.

x	−8	−6	−4	−2
y	0.25	0.5	1	2

24.

x	20	30	40	50	60
y	1	0.4	0.16	0.064	0.0256

B (25) **PHOTOGRAPHY** Jameka is enlarging a photograph to make a poster for school. She will enlarge the picture repeatedly at 150%. The function $P = 1.5^x$ models the new size of the picture being enlarged, where x is the number of enlargements. How many times as big is the picture after 4 enlargements? **about 506% bigger than the original**

Differentiated Homework Options

Level	Assignment	Two-Day Option	
AL Basic	10–24, 42–68	11–23 odd, 46–49	10–24 even, 42–45, 50–68
OL Core	11–39 odd, 26, 40, 42–68	10–24, 46–49	25–40, 42–45, 50–68
BL Advanced	25–62, (optional: 63–68)		

3 Practice

Formative Assessment

Use Exercises 1–9 to check for understanding.

Use the chart at the bottom of this page to customize assignments for your students.

Teaching the Process Standards

Modeling Mathematically proficient students can use a function to describe how one quantity of interest depends on another. In Exercise 20, ask students how time will affect the population.

Additional Answers

8. No; the domain values are at regular intervals, but the range values have a common difference of 2.
9. Yes; the domain values are at regular intervals, and the range values have a common factor of 4.
21. No; the domain values are at regular intervals, but the range values do not have a positive common factor.
22. No; the domain values are at regular intervals, but the range values have a common difference of 5.
23. Yes; the domain values are at regular intervals, and the range values have a common factor of 2.
24. Yes; the domain values are at regular intervals, and the range values have a common factor of 0.4.

Study Guide and Intervention

AL OL ELL

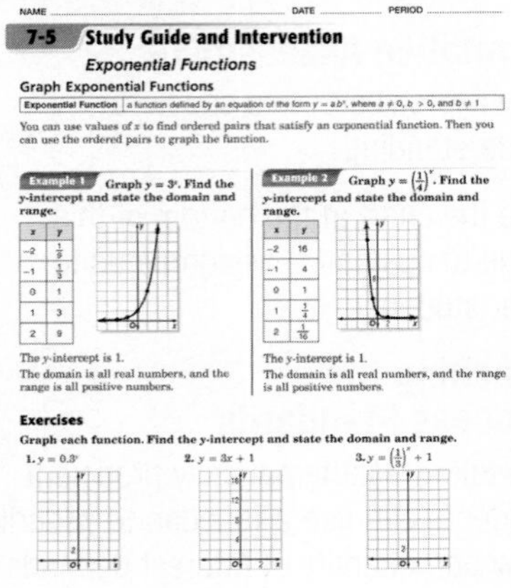

Practice

AL OL BL ELL

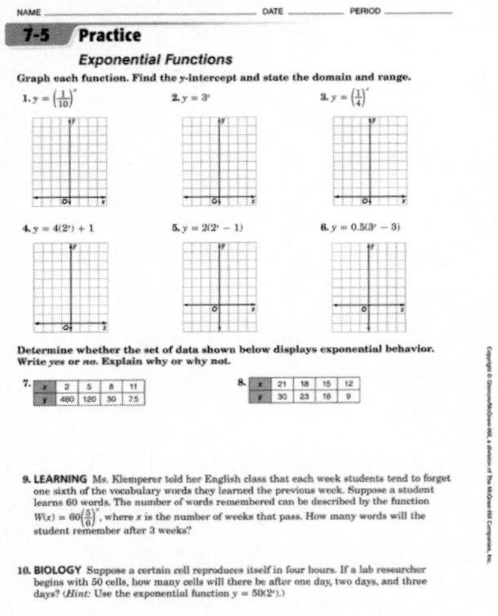

Word Problem Practice

AL OL BL ELL

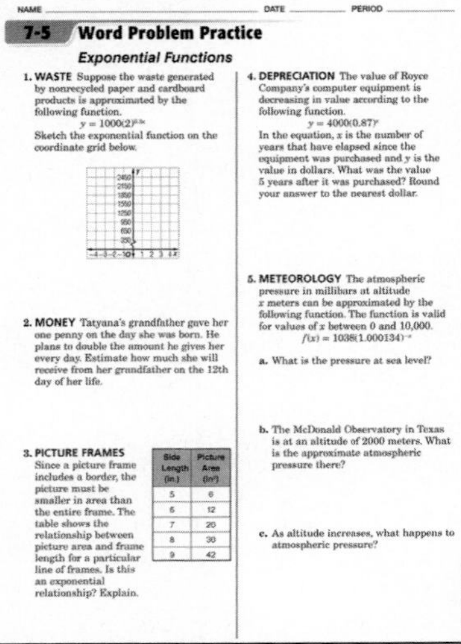

26. **FINANCIAL LITERACY** Daniel deposited \$500 into a savings account and after 8 years, his investment is worth \$807.07. The equation $A = d(1.005)^{12t}$ models the value of Daniel's investment A after t years with an initial deposit d.

a. What would the value of Daniel's investment be if he had deposited \$1000? **about \$1614.14**

b. What would the value of Daniel's investment be if he had deposited \$250? **about \$403.54**

c. Interpret $d(1.005)^{12t}$ to explain how the amount of the original deposit affects the value of Daniel's investment.

26c. Sample answer: Since Daniel's investment is the product of d and a factor not depending on d, it varies directly as the original deposit.

Identify each function as *linear*, *exponential*, or *neither*.

27.

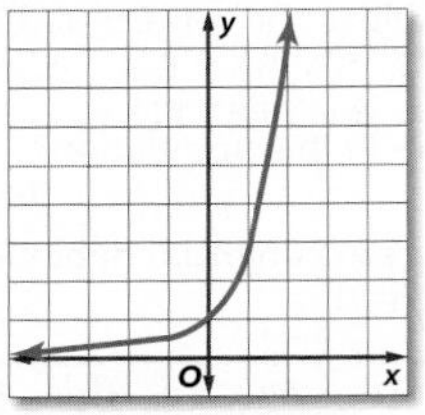

exponential

28.

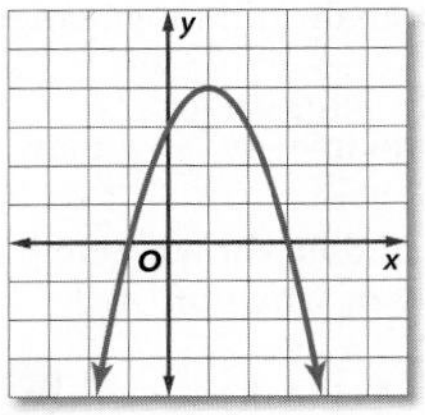

neither

29.

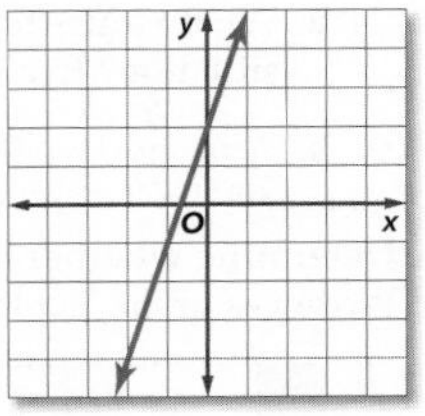

linear

30. $y = 4^x$ **exponential** **31.** $y = 2x(x - 1)$ **neither** **32.** $5x + y = 8$ **linear**

33. **GRADUATION** The number of graduates at a high school has increased by a factor of 1.055 every year since 2001. In 2001, 110 students graduated. The function $N = 110(1.055)^t$ models the number of students N expected to graduate t years after 2001. How many students will graduate in 2012? **about 198 students**

C **Describe the graph of each equation as a transformation of the graph of $y = 2^x$.**

34. $y = 2^x + 6$ **a translation 6 units up**

35. $y = 3(2)^x$ **a vertical stretch by a factor of 3**

36. $y = -\frac{1}{4}(2)^x$ **36. a reflection over the x-axis and a vertical compression**

37. $y = -3 + 2^x$ **a translation down 3 units**

38. $y = \left(\frac{1}{2}\right)^x$ **a reflection over the y-axis**

39. $y = -5(2)^x$ **39. a vertical stretch by a factor of 5 and a reflection over the x-axis.**

40. **DEER** The deer population at a national park doubles every year. In 2000, there were 25 deer in the park. The function $N = 25(2)^t$ models the number of deer N in the park t years after 2000. What will the deer population be in 2015? **819,200**

42. Never; the graph never crosses the x-axis because the powers of b are always positive and $a \neq 0$. Thus, ab^x is never 0.

H.O.T. Problems Use Higher-Order Thinking Skills

41. **PERSEVERANCE** Write an exponential function for which the graph passes through the points at (0, 3) and (1, 6). $f(x) = 3(2)^x$

42. **REASONING** Determine whether the graph of $y = ab^x$, where $a \neq 0$, $b > 0$, and $b \neq 1$, *sometimes*, *always*, or *never* has an x-intercept. Explain your reasoning.

43. **OPEN ENDED** Find an exponential function that represents a real-world situation, and graph the function. Analyze the graph, and explain why the situation is modeled by an exponential function rather than a linear function. **See margin.**

44. **REASONING** Use tables and graphs to compare and contrast an exponential function $f(x) = ab^x + c$, where $a \neq 0$, $b > 0$, and $b \neq 1$, and a linear function $g(x) = ax + c$. Include intercepts, intervals where the functions are increasing, decreasing, positive, or negative, relative maxima and minima, symmetry, and end behavior. **See Ch. 7 Answer Appendix.**

45. **WRITING IN MATH** Explain how to determine whether a set of data displays exponential behavior. **See margin.**

Enrichment

OL BL

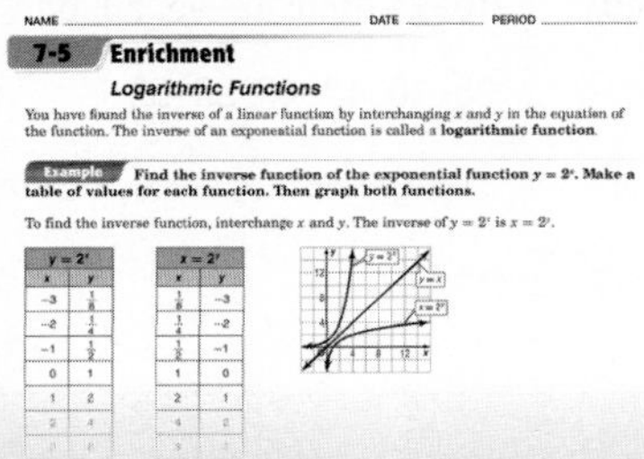

Follow-up

Students have explored modeling using exponential functions.

Ask:

- How can mathematical models help you make good decisions? Sample answer: Mathematical models can be used to compare different options that are available, as well as to predict the impact of an option if it is chosen.

Standardized Test Practice

46. SHORT RESPONSE What are the x-intercepts of the function graphed below? **2 and 4**

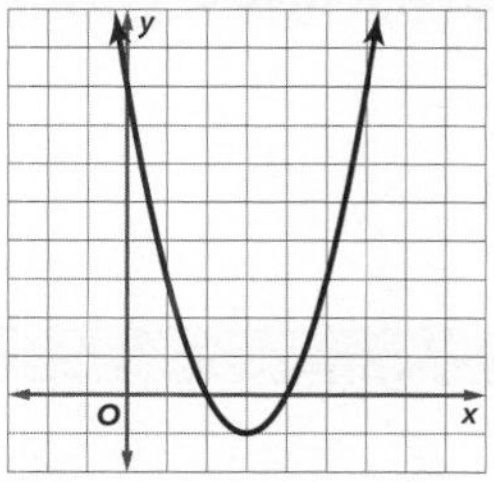

47. Hinto invested \$300 into a savings account. The equation $A = 300(1.005)^{12t}$ models the amount in Hinto's account A after t years. How much will be in Hinto's account after 7 years? **B**

A \$25,326   C \$385.01
B \$456.11   D \$301.52

48. GEOMETRY Ayana placed a circular piece of paper on a square picture as shown below. If the picture extends 4 inches beyond the circle on each side, what is the perimeter of the square picture? **J**

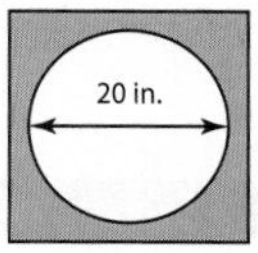

F 64 in.   H 94 in.
G 80 in.   J 112 in.

49. The points with coordinates $(0, -3)$ and $(2, 7)$ are on line ℓ. Line p contains $(3, -1)$ and is perpendicular to line ℓ. What is the x-coordinate of the point where ℓ and p intersect? **A**

A $\frac{1}{2}$ B $-\frac{2}{5}$
C $-\frac{1}{2}$ D -3

Spiral Review

Evaluate each product. Express the results in both scientific notation and standard form. (Lesson 7-4)

50. $(1.9 \times 10^2)(4.7 \times 10^6)$ **8.93×10^8, 893,000,000**

51. $(4.5 \times 10^{-3})(5.6 \times 10^4)$ **2.52×10^2, 252**

52. $(3.8 \times 10^{-4})(6.4 \times 10^{-8})$ **2.432×10^{-11}, 0.00000000002432**

Simplify. (Lesson 7-3)

53. $\sqrt[3]{343}$ **7**

54. $\sqrt[6]{729}$ **3**

55. $\left(\frac{1}{32}\right)^{\frac{1}{5}}$ **$\frac{1}{2}$**

56. $729^{\frac{5}{6}}$ **243**

57. $216^{\frac{5}{3}}$ **7776**

58. $\left(\frac{1}{81}\right)^{\frac{3}{2}}$ **$\frac{1}{729}$**

59. DEMOLITION DERBY When a car hits an object, the damage is measured by the collision impact. For a certain car the collision impact I is given by $I = 2v^2$, where v represents the speed in kilometers per minute. What is the collision impact if the speed of the car is 4 kilometers per minute? (Lesson 7-1) **32 km^2/min^2**

Use elimination to solve each system of equations. (Lesson 6-3)

60. $x + y = -3$, $x - y = 1$ **(−1, −2)**

61. $3a + b = 5$, $2a + b = 10$ **(−5, 20)**

62. $3x - 5y = 16$, $-3x + 2y = -10$ **(2, −2)**

Skills Review

Find the next three terms of each arithmetic sequence.

63. 1, 3, 5, 7, … **9, 11, 13**

64. −6, −4, −2, 0, … **2, 4, 6**

65. 6.5, 9, 11.5, 14, … **16.5, 19, 21.5**

66. 10, 3, −4, −11, … **−18, −25, −32**

67. $\frac{1}{2}, \frac{5}{4}, 2, \frac{11}{4}, \ldots$ **$\frac{7}{2}, \frac{17}{4}, 5$**

68. $1, \frac{3}{4}, \frac{1}{2}, \frac{1}{4}, \ldots$ **$0, -\frac{1}{4}, -\frac{1}{2}$**

Differentiated Instruction OL BL

Extension Give students this scenario: a wise man asked his ruler to provide rice for his people. The wise man asked the ruler to give him 2 grains of rice for the first square on a chess board, 4 grains for the second, and so on, doubling the amount of rice with each square of the board.

Ask:

- How many grains of rice will the wise man receive for the sixty-fourth square on the chessboard? 2^{64} or about 1.84×10^{19} grains
- If one pound of rice has approximately 24,000 grains, how many tons of rice will the wise man receive on the last day? (Hint: 1 ton = 2000 pounds) about 3.84×10^{11} tons

Teaching the Process Standards

Perseverance Mathematically proficient students analyze givens, constraints, relationships, and goals of a problem. In Exercise 41, students may struggle since they are given only two points. Suggest that they start with the general form of an exponential equation $y = ab^x$.

4 Assess

Crystal Ball Ask students to write how they think exponential functions will connect with the next lesson, which involves real-world growth and decay problems.

Additional Answers

43. Sample answer: The number of teams competing in a basketball tournament can be represented by $y = 2^x$, where the number of teams competing is y and the number of rounds is x.

The y-intercept of the graph is 1. The graph increases rapidly for $x > 0$. With an exponential model, each team that joins the tournament will play all of the other teams. If the scenario were modeled with a linear function, each team that joined would play a fixed number of teams.

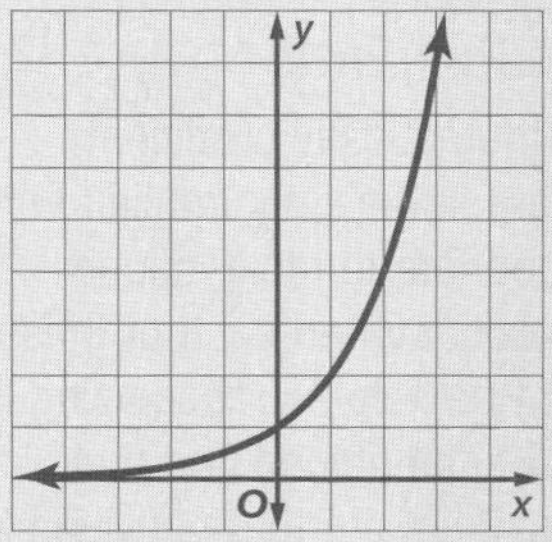

45. Sample answer: First, look for a pattern by making sure that the domain values are at regular intervals and the range values differ by a common factor.

1 Focus

Objective Use a graphing calculator to solve exponential equations and inequalities.

Materials

- TI-Nspire Technology

Teaching Tips

- For Activity 1, remind students that to enter $3^x + 4$, they will need to use the ^ key for the exponent and use the down arrow before entering the $+ 4$.
- When changing the windows settings, use the **tab** key to move from one field to another.
- In Activity 2, students will need to use the **tab** key to move the curser to the entry line to type **f2(*x*)**.

2 Teach

Working in Cooperative Groups

Divide the class into pairs. Work through Activity 1 and Activity 2 as a class. Then ask students to work with their partners to complete Exercises 1–9 and Activities 3 and 4.

Practice Have students complete Exercises 10–12.

Teaching the Process Standards

Tools Mathematically proficient students are sufficiently familiar with tools appropriate to make sound decisions about when each of these tools might be helpful, recognizing both the insight to be gained and their limitations. Point out that Activities 2, 3, and 4 offer various methods for solving equations and inequalities. Discuss when to use the methods and the technology tools available.

EXTEND 7-5 Graphing Technology Lab: Solving Exponential Equations and Inequalities

You can use TI-Nspire Technology to solve exponential equations and inequalities by graphing and by using tables.

Process Standards PS.5

Activity 1 Graph an Exponential Equation

Graph $y = 3^x + 4$ using a graphing calculator.

Step 1 Add a new **Graphs** page.

Step 2 Enter $3^x + 4$ as **f1(*x*)**.

Step 3 Use the **Window Settings** option from the **Window/Zoom** menu to adjust the window so that x is from -10 to 10 and y is from -100 to 100. Keep the scales as **Auto**.

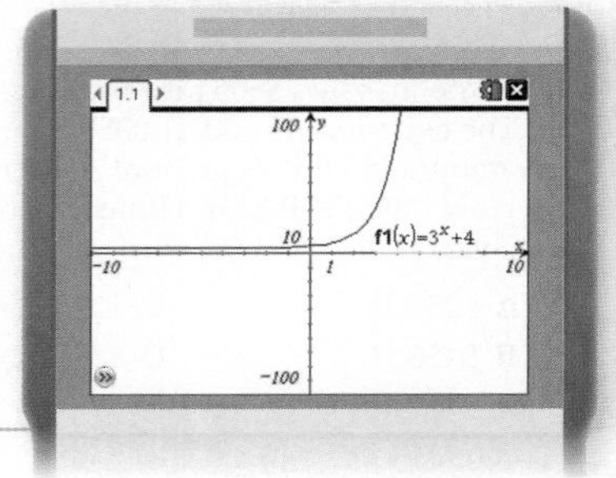

To solve an equation by graphing, graph both sides of the equation and locate the point(s) of intersection.

Activity 2 Solve an Exponential Equation by Graphing

Solve $2^{x-2} = \frac{3}{4}$.

Step 1 Add a new **Graphs** page.

Step 2 Enter 2^{x-2} as **f1(*x*)** and $\frac{3}{4}$ as **f2(*x*)**.

Step 3 Use the **Intersection Point(s)** tool from the **Points & Lines** menu to find the intersection of the two graphs. Select the graph of **f1(*x*) enter** and then the graph of **f2(*x*) enter**.

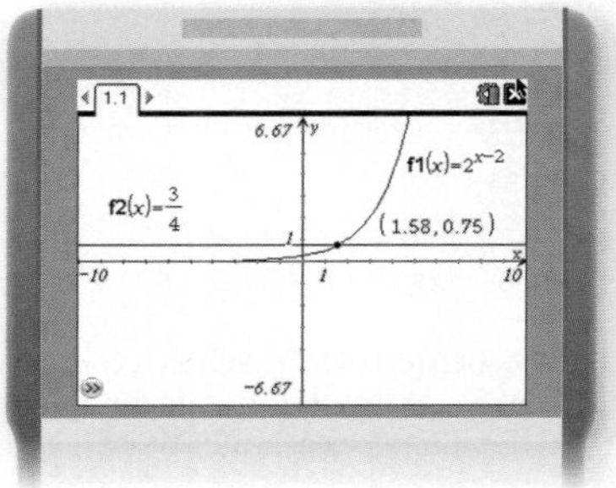

The graphs intersect at about (1.58, 0.75). Therefore, the solution of $2^{x-2} = \frac{3}{4}$ is 1.58.

Exercises

TOOLS Use a graphing calculator to solve each equation.

1. $\left(\frac{1}{3}\right)^{x-1} = \frac{3}{4}$ **≈1.26**
2. $2^{2x-1} = 2x$ **0.5, 1**
3. $\left(\frac{1}{2}\right)^{2x} = 2^{2x}$ **0**
4. $5^{\frac{1}{3}x+2} = -x$ **≈−3.61**
5. $\left(\frac{1}{8}\right)^{2x} = -2x + 1$ **0, ≈0.409**
6. $2^{\frac{1}{4}x-1} = 3^{x+1}$ **≈−1.94**
7. $2^{3x-1} = 4^x$ **1**
8. $4^{2x-3} = 5^{-x+1}$ **≈1.32**
9. $3^{2x-4} = 2^x + 1$ **3**

430 | Extend 7-5 | Graphing Technology Lab: Solving Exponential Equations and Inequalities

Activity 3 Solve an Exponential Equation by Using a Table

Solve $2\left(\frac{1}{2}\right)^{x+2} = \frac{1}{4}$ using a table.

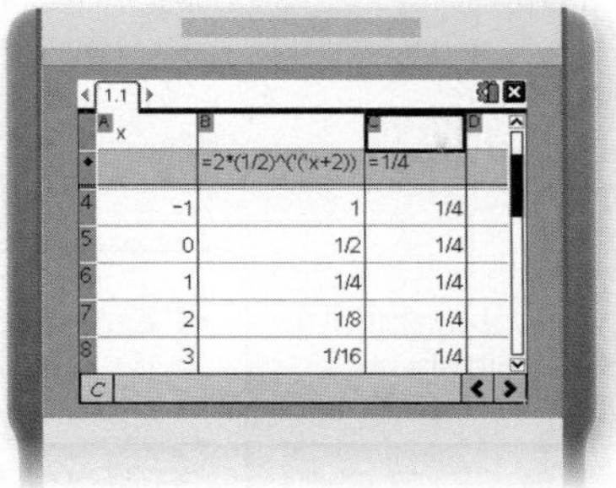

Step 1 Add a new **Lists & Spreadsheet** page.

Step 2 Label column A as x. Enter values from -4 to 4 in cells A1 to A9.

Step 3 In column B in the formula row, enter the left side of the rational equation. In column C of the formula row, enter $= \frac{1}{4}$. Specify **Variable Reference** when prompted.

Scroll until you see where the values in Columns B and C are equal. This occurs at $x = 1$. Therefore, the solution of $2\left(\frac{1}{2}\right)^{x+2} = \frac{1}{4}$ is 1.

You can also use a graphing calculator to solve exponential inequalities.

Activity 4 Solve an Exponential Inequality

Solve $4^{x-3} \leq \left(\frac{1}{4}\right)^{2x}$.

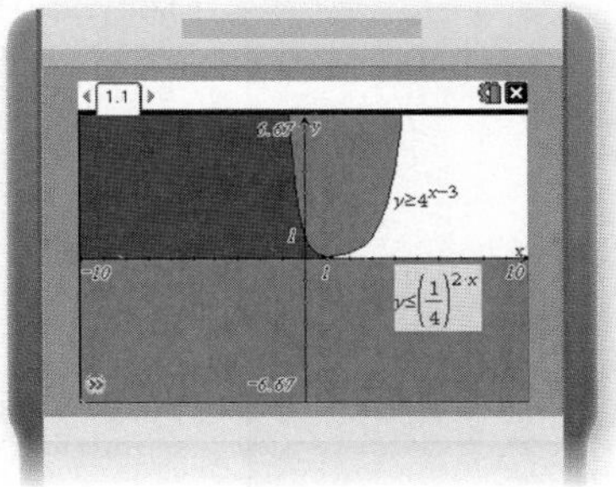

Step 1 Add a new **Graphs** page.

Step 2 Enter the left side of the inequality into **f1(*x*)**. Press **del**, select $\geq$, and enter 4^{x-3}. Enter the right side of the inequality into **f2(*x*)**. Press **tab del** $\leq$, and enter $\left(\frac{1}{4}\right)^{2x}$.

The x-values of the points in the region where the shading overlap is the solution set of the original inequality. Therefore the solution of $4^{x-3} \leq \left(\frac{1}{4}\right)^{2x}$ is $x \leq 1$.

Exercises

TOOLS Use a graphing calculator to solve each equation or inequality.

10. $\left(\frac{1}{3}\right)^{3x} = 3^x$ **0**

11. $\left(\frac{1}{6}\right)^{2x} = 4^x$ **0**

12. $3^{1-x} \leq 4^x$ $\mathbf{x \geq 0.442}$

13. $4^{3x} \leq 2x + 1$ $\mathbf{-0.409 \leq x \leq 0}$

14. $\left(\frac{1}{4}\right)^x > 2^{x+4}$ $\mathbf{x < -1.33}$

15. $\left(\frac{1}{3}\right)^{x-1} \geq 2^x$ $\mathbf{x \leq 0.613}$

3 Assess

Formative Assessment

Use Exercises 13–15 to assess each student's knowledge of solving exponential equations and inequalities.

From Concrete to Abstract

Ask students to summarize the use of technology to find the solutions to exponential equations and inequalities.

connectED.mcgraw-hill.com 431

1 Focus

VerticalAlignment

Before Lesson 7-6 Analyze exponential functions.

Lesson 7-6 Solve problems involving exponential growth. Solve problems involving exponential decay.

After Lesson 7-6 Relate geometric sequences to exponential functions.

2 Teach

Scaffolding Questions

Have students read the **Why?** section of the lesson.

Ask:

- Looking at the equation, how do you know the function is not linear? Time, represented as t, is an exponent so the function is not linear.
- Use the equation to predict the average number of blogs in millions in the 8th month. about 3 million Would you describe the average number of blogs per month as growing or decaying? growing

1 Exponential Growth

Example 1 shows how to solve a real-world problem involving exponential growth. **Example 2** shows how to solve a real-world problem involving compound interest.

LESSON 7-6 Growth and Decay

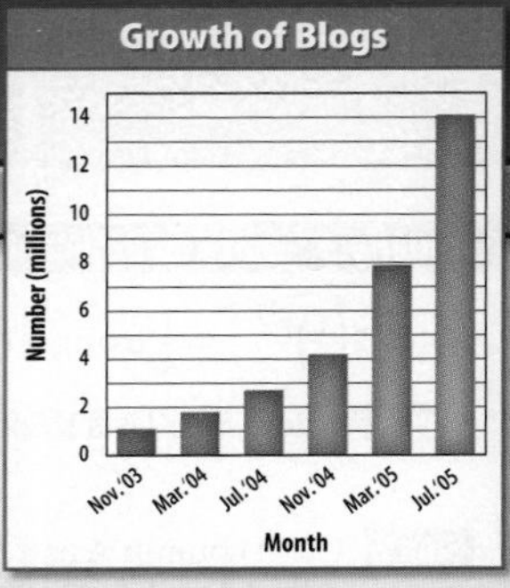

Then
- You analyzed exponential functions.

Now
1. Solve problems involving exponential growth.
2. Solve problems involving exponential decay.

Why?
- The number of Weblogs or blogs increased at a monthly rate of about 13.7% over 21 months. The average number of blogs per month can be modeled by $y = 1.1(1 + 0.137)^t$ or $y = 1.1(1.137)^t$, where y represents the total number of blogs in millions and t is the number of months since November 2003.

New Vocabulary
compound interest

Content Standards
AI.QE.2

Process Standards
PS.4

1 Exponential Growth

The equation for the number of blogs is in the form $y = a(1 + r)^t$. This is the general equation for exponential growth.

Key Concept Equation for Exponential Growth

$$y = a(1 + r)^t$$

- a is the initial amount.
- t is time.
- y is the final amount.
- r is the rate of change expressed as a decimal, $r > 0$.

Real-World Example 1 Exponential Growth

CONTEST **The prize for a radio station contest begins with a $100 gift card. Once a day, a name is announced. The person has 15 minutes to call or the prize increases by 2.5% for the next day.**

a. Write an equation to represent the amount of the gift card in dollars after t days with no winners.

$y = a(1 + r)^t$	Equation for exponential growth
$y = 100(1 + 0.025)^t$	$a = 100$ and $r = 2.5\%$ or 0.025
$y = 100(1.025)^t$	Simplify.

In the equation $y = 100(1.025)^t$, y is the amount of the gift card and t is the number of days since the contest began.

b. How much will the gift card be worth if no one wins after 10 days?

$y = 100(1.025)^t$	Equation for amount of gift card
$= 100(1.025)^{10}$	$t = 10$
≈ 128.01	Use a calculator.

In 10 days, the gift card will be worth $128.01.

Guided Practice

$y = 10{,}850(1.05)^t$; about $22,556.37

1. **TUITION** A college's tuition has risen 5% each year since 2000. If the tuition in 2000 was $10,850, write an equation for the amount of the tuition t years after 2000. Predict the cost of tuition for this college in 2015.

Lesson 7-6 Resources

Resource	Approaching Level AL	On Level OL	Beyond Level BL	English Learners ELL
Teacher Edition		▪ Differentiated Instruction, p. 436	▪ Differentiated Instruction, p. 436	
Chapter Resource Masters	▪ Study Guide and Intervention, pp. 35–36 ▪ Skills Practice, p. 37 ▪ Practice, p. 38 ▪ Word Problem Practice, p. 39	▪ Study Guide and Intervention, pp. 35–36 ▪ Skills Practice, p. 37 ▪ Practice, p. 38 ▪ Word Problem Practice, p. 39 ▪ Enrichment, p. 40 ▪ Spreadsheet Activity, p. 41	▪ Practice, p. 38 ▪ Word Problem Practice, p. 39 ▪ Enrichment, p. 40	▪ Study Guide and Intervention, pp. 35–36 ▪ Skills Practice, p. 37 ▪ Practice, p. 38 ▪ Word Problem Practice, p. 39
Other	▪ 5-Minute Check 7-6 ▪ Study Notebook	▪ 5-Minute Check 7-6 ▪ Study Notebook	▪ 5-Minute Check 7-6 ▪ Study Notebook	▪ 5-Minute Check 7-6 ▪ Study Notebook

Compound interest is interest earned or paid on both the initial investment and previously earned interest. It is an application of exponential growth.

KeyConcept Equation for Compound Interest

$$A = P\left(1 + \frac{r}{n}\right)^{nt}$$

- A is the current amount.
- n is the number of times the interest is compounded each year, and t is time in years.
- P is the principal or initial amount.
- r is the annual interest rate expressed as a decimal, $r > 0$.

Real-WorldCareer

Financial Advisor Financial advisors help people plan their financial futures. A good financial advisor has mathematical, problem-solving, and communication skills. A bachelor's degree is strongly preferred but not required.

Real-World Example 2 Compound Interest

PT

FINANCE **Maria's parents invested $14,000 at 6% per year compounded monthly. How much money will there be in the account after 10 years?**

$A = P\left(1 + \frac{r}{n}\right)^{nt}$	Compound interest equation
$= 14{,}000\left(1 + \frac{0.06}{12}\right)^{12(10)}$	$P = 14{,}000$, $r = 6\%$ or 0.06, $n = 12$, and $t = 10$
$= 14{,}000(1.005)^{120}$	Simplify.
$\approx 25{,}471.55$	Use a calculator.

There will be about $25,471.55 in 10 years.

GuidedPractice

2. FINANCE Determine the amount of an investment if $300 is invested at an interest rate of 3.5% compounded monthly for 22 years. **about $647.20**

2 Exponential Decay

In exponential decay, the original amount decreases by the same percent over a period of time. A variation of the growth equation can be used as the general equation for exponential decay.

StudyTip

Growth and Decay Since r is added to 1, the value inside the parentheses will be greater than 1 for exponential growth functions. For exponential decay functions, this value will be less than 1 since r is subtracted from 1.

KeyConcept Equation for Exponential Decay

$$y = a(1 - r)^t$$

- a is the initial amount.
- t is time.
- y is the final amount.
- r is the rate of decay expressed as a decimal, $0 < r < 1$.

Real-World Example 3 Exponential Decay

PT

SWIMMING **A fully inflated child's raft for a pool is losing 6.6% of its air every day. The raft originally contained 4500 cubic inches of air.**

a. Write an equation to represent the loss of air.

$y = a(1 - r)^t$	Equation for exponential decay
$= 4500(1 - 0.066)^t$	$a = 4500$ and $r = 6.6\%$ or 0.066
$= 4500(0.934)^t$	Simplify.

$y = 4500(0.934)^t$, where y is the air in the raft in cubic inches after t days.

Formative Assessment

Use the Guided Practice exercises after each example to determine students' understanding of concepts.

Additional Examples

1 **POPULATION** In 2008 the town of Flat Creek had a population of about 280,000 and a growth rate of 0.85% per year.

a. Write an equation to represent the population of Flat Creek since 2008. $y = 280{,}000\ (1.0085)^t$

b. According to the equation, what will be the population of Flat Creek in the year 2018? about 304,731

2 **COLLEGE** When Jing May was born, her grandparents invested $1000 in a fixed rate savings account at a rate of 7% compounded annually. Jing May will receive the money when she turns 18 to help with her college expenses. What amount of money will Jing May receive from the investment? She will receive about $3380.

Additional Examples also in Interactive Classroom PowerPoint® Presentations

IWB Interactive White Board READY

2 Exponential Decay

Example 3 shows how to solve a real-world problem involving exponential decay.

Focus on Mathematical Content

Compound Interest In contrast to simple interest, compound interest is applied to the original principal and any previously earned interest. There are four ways to increase the amount in a compound-interest account: the investor can increase the initial principal, increase the annual interest rate, increase the number of compoundings per year, or increase the time that the money is in the account.

WatchOut!

Student Misconceptions Remind students that in growth and decay equations, the amount inside the parentheses will be greater than 1 for growth and less than 1 for decay.

Additional Example

3 **CHARITY** During an economic recession, a charitable organization found that its donations dropped by 1.1% per year. Before the recession, its donations were $390,000.

a. Write an equation to represent the charity's donations since the beginning of the recession. $A = 390{,}000(0.989)^t$

b. Estimate the amount of the donations 5 years after the start of the recession. about $369,017

3 Practice

Formative Assessment

Use Exercises 1–3 to check for understanding.

Use the chart at the bottom of this page to customize assignments for your students.

Teach with Tech

Web Search Have students search the Web to find the half-life of different radioactive elements. Have them choose three elements, and ask them to calculate the amount of a 500 gram sample that remains after 3 years.

Exercise Alert

Grid Paper For Exercises 25–27 and 42–44, students will need grid paper.

Teaching the Process Standards

Precision Mathematically proficient students express answers with a degree of precision appropriate for the problem context. In Exercise 9, point out that an estimate is appropriate to answer the question. In Exercise 17, students can approximate by graphing on a graphing calculator or by guessing and checking on a scientific calculator.

b. Estimate the amount of air in the raft after 7 days.

$y = 4500(0.934)^t$ Equation for air loss

$= 4500(0.934)^7$ $t = 7$

≈ 2790 Use a calculator.

The amount of air in the raft after 7 days will be about 2790 cubic inches.

Guided Practice

3. **POPULATION** The population of Campbell County, Kentucky, has been decreasing at an average rate of about 0.3% per year. In 2000, its population was 88,647. Write an equation to represent the population since 2000. If the trend continues, predict the population in 2010. $y = 88{,}647(1 - 0.003)^t$; about 86,023

Check Your Understanding

◯ = Step-by-Step Solutions begin on page R13.

Example 1

1. **SALARY** Ms. Acosta received a job as a teacher with a starting salary of $34,000. According to her contract, she will receive a 1.5% increase in her salary every year. How much will Ms. Acosta earn in 7 years? **about $37,734.73**

Example 2

2. **MONEY** Paul invested $400 into an account with a 5.5% interest rate compounded monthly. How much will Paul's investment be worth in 8 years? **about $620.46**

Example 3

3. **ENROLLMENT** In 2000, 2200 students attended Polaris High School. The enrollment has been declining 2% annually.

a. Write an equation for the enrollment of Polaris High School t years after 2000. $y = 2200(0.98)^t$

b. If this trend continues, how many students will be enrolled in 2015? **about 1624**

Practice and Problem Solving

Extra Practice is on page R7.

Example 1

4. **MEMBERSHIPS** The Work-Out Gym sold 550 memberships in 2001. Since then the number of memberships sold has increased 3% annually.

a. Write an equation for the number of memberships sold at Work-Out Gym t years after 2001. $y = 550(1.03)^t$

b. If this trend continues, predict how many memberships the gym will sell in 2020. **about 964**

5. **COMPUTERS** The number of people who own computers has increased 23.2% annually since 1990. If half a million people owned a computer in 1990, predict how many people will own a computer in 2015. **about 92,095,349**

6. **COINS** Camilo purchased a rare coin from a dealer for $300. The value of the coin increases 5% each year. Determine the value of the coin in 5 years. **about $382.88**

Example 2

7. **INVESTMENTS** Theo invested $6600 at an interest rate of 4.5% compounded monthly. Determine the value of his investment in 4 years. **about $7898.97**

8. **COMPOUND INTEREST** Paige invested $1200 at an interest rate of 5.75% compounded quarterly. Determine the value of her investment in 7 years. **about $1789.54**

9. **PRECISION** Brooke is saving money for a trip to the Bahamas that costs $295.99. She puts $150 into a savings account that pays 7.25% interest compounded quarterly. Will she have enough money in the account after 4 years? Explain.

9. Sample answer: No; she will have about $199.94 in the account in 4 years.

Example 3

10. **INVESTMENTS** Jin's investment of $4500 has been losing its value at a rate of 2.5% each year. What will his investment be worth in 5 years? **about $3964.93**

Differentiated Homework Options

Level	Assignment	Two-Day Option	
AL Basic	4–12, 16, 18–44	5–11 odd, 21–24	4–12 even, 16, 18–20, 25–44
OL Core	5–11 odd, 13–16, 18–44	4–12, 21–24	13–16, 18–20, 25–44
BL Advanced	13–41, (optional: 42–44)		

11. **POPULATION** In the years from 2010 to 2015, the population of the District of Columbia is expected decrease about 0.9% annually. In 2010, the population was about 530,000. What is the population of the District of Columbia expected to be in 2015? **about 506,575**

12. **CARS** Leonardo purchases a car for \$18,995. The car depreciates at a rate of 18% annually. After 6 years, Manuel offers to buy the car for \$4500. Should Leonardo sell the car? Explain. **Sample answer: No; the car is worth about \$5774.61.**

B 13. **HOUSING** The median house price in the United States increased an average of 1.4% each year between 2005 and 2007. Assume that this pattern continues.

a. Write an equation for the median house price for t years after 2007. $l = 247{,}900(1.014)^t$

b. Predict the median house price in 2018. **about \$288,864**

Median House Price	
2005	\$240,900
2006	\$246,500
2007	\$247,900

Source: *Real Estate Journal*

C 14. **ELEMENTS** A radioactive element's half-life is the time it takes for one half of the element's quantity to decay. The half-life of Plutonium-241 is 14.4 years. The number of grams A of Plutonium-241 left after t years can be modeled by $A = p(0.5)^{\frac{t}{14.4}}$, where p is the original amount of the element.

a. How much of a 0.2-gram sample remains after 72 years? **0.00625 g**

b. How much of a 5.4-gram sample remains after 1095 days? **≈4.7 g**

15. **COMBINING FUNCTIONS** A swimming pool holds a maximum of 20,500 gallons of water. It evaporates at a rate of 0.5% per hour. The pool currently contains 19,000 gallons of water.

a. Write an exponential function $w(t)$ to express the amount of water remaining in the pool after time t where t is the number of hours after the pool has reached 19,000 gallons. $w(t) = 19{,}000(0.995)^t$

b. At this same time, a hose is turned on to refill the pool at a net rate of 300 gallons per hour. Write a function $p(t)$ where t is time in hours the hose is running to express the amount of water that is pumped into the pool. $p(t) = 300t$

c. Find $C(t) = p(t) + w(t)$. What does this new function represent? $C(t) = 300t + 19{,}000(0.995)^t$; **The function represents the number of gallons of water in the pool at any time after the hose is turned on.**

d. Use the graph of $C(t)$ to determine how long the hose must run to fill the pool to its maximun capacity. **about 7.3 hr**

H.O.T. Problems Use Higher-Order Thinking Skills

16. **REASONING** Determine the growth rate (as a percent) of a population that quadruples every year. Explain. **300%; Solving** $y = a(1 + r)^t$ **for** $y = 4$, $a = 1$, **and** $t = 1$ **gives** $r = 3$ **or 300%.**

17. **PRECISION** Santos invested \$1200 into an account with an interest rate of 8% compounded monthly. Use a calculator to approximate how long it will take for Santos's investment to reach \$2500. **about 9.2 yr**

18. **REASONING** The amount of water in a container doubles every minute. After 8 minutes, the container is full. After how many minutes was the container half full? Explain. **7; Sample answer: Since the amount of water doubles every minute, the container would be half full a minute before it was full.**

19. **WRITING IN MATH** What should you consider when using exponential models to make decisions? **See Ch. 7 Answer Appendix.**

20. **WRITING IN MATH** Compare and contrast the exponential growth formula and the exponential decay formula. **See Ch.7 Answer Appendix.**

Follow-up

Students have explored growth and decay.

Ask:

- How can being financially literate help you to make good decisions? Sample answer: If you are financially literate, you understand the vocabulary of financial terms and know how to analyze data and trends. Successfully applying these skills when considering your available options can help you to make good decisions in many real-world situations such as opening a bank account, applying for college loans, and buying a car.

Study Guide and Intervention

AL OL ELL

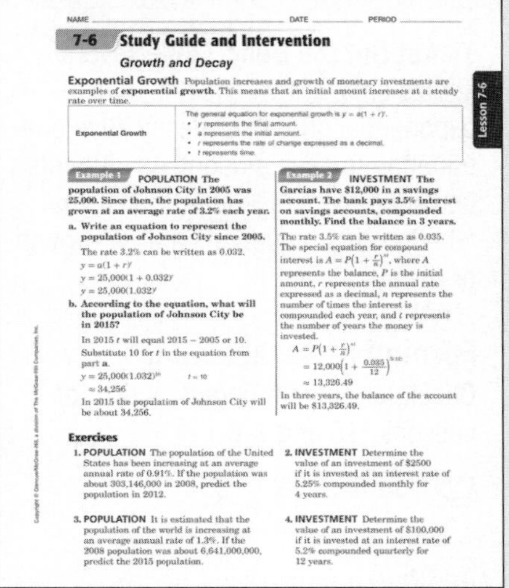
NAME ______ DATE ______ PERIOD ______

7-6 Study Guide and Intervention

Growth and Decay

Exponential Growth Population increases and growth of monetary investments are examples of **exponential growth**. This means that an initial amount increases at a steady rate over time.

Exponential Growth	The general equation for exponential growth is $y = a(1 + r)^t$. • y represents the final amount. • a represents the initial amount. • r represents the rate of change expressed as a decimal. • t represents time.

Example 1 **POPULATION The population of Johnson City in 2005 was 25,000. Since then, the population has grown at an average rate of 3.2% each year.**

a. Write an equation to represent the population of Johnson City since 2005.

The rate 3.2% can be written as 0.032.

$y = a(1 + r)^t$

$y = 25{,}000(1 + 0.032)^t$

$y = 25{,}000(1.032)^t$

b. According to the equation, what will the population of Johnson City be in 2015?

In 2015 t will equal 2015 − 2005 or 10. Substitute 10 for t in the equation from part **a**.

$y = 25{,}000(1.032)^{10}$ $t = 10$

$\approx 34{,}256$

In 2015 the population of Johnson City will be about 34,256.

Example 2 **INVESTMENT The Garcias have \$12,000 in a savings account. The bank pays 3.5% interest on savings accounts, compounded monthly. Find the balance in 3 years.**

The rate 3.5% can be written as 0.035. The special equation for compound interest is $A = P\left(1 + \frac{r}{n}\right)^{nt}$, where A represents the balance, P is the initial amount, r represents the annual rate expressed as a decimal, n represents the number of times the interest is compounded each year, and t represents the number of years the money is invested.

$A = P\left(1 + \frac{r}{n}\right)^{nt}$

$= 12{,}000\left(1 + \frac{0.035}{12}\right)^{36}$

$\approx 13{,}326.49$

In three years, the balance of the account will be \$13,326.49.

Exercises

1. **POPULATION** The population of the United States has been increasing at an average annual rate of 0.91%. If the population was about 303,146,000 in 2008, predict the population in 2012.

2. **INVESTMENT** Determine the value of an investment of \$2500 if it is invested at an interest rate of 5.25% compounded monthly for 4 years.

3. **POPULATION** It is estimated that the population of the world is increasing at an average annual rate of 1.3%. If the 2008 population was about 6,641,000,000, predict the 2015 population.

4. **INVESTMENT** Determine the value of an investment of \$100,000 if it is invested at an interest rate of 5.2% compounded quarterly for 12 years.

Lesson 7-6

Practice

AL OL BL ELL

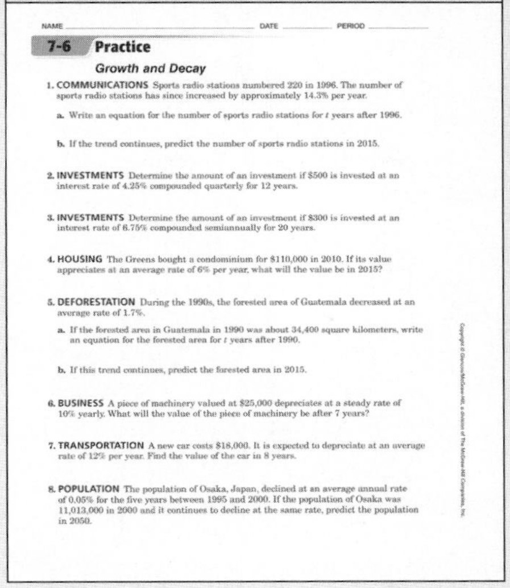
NAME ______ DATE ______ PERIOD ______

7-6 Practice

Growth and Decay

1. **COMMUNICATIONS** Sports radio stations numbered 220 in 1996. The number of sports radio stations has since increased by approximately 14.3% per year.

a. Write an equation for the number of sports radio stations for t years after 1996.

b. If the trend continues, predict the number of sports radio stations in 2015.

2. **INVESTMENTS** Determine the amount of an investment if \$500 is invested at an interest rate of 4.25% compounded quarterly for 12 years.

3. **INVESTMENTS** Determine the amount of an investment if \$300 is invested at an interest rate of 6.75% compounded semiannually for 20 years.

4. **HOUSING** The Greens bought a condominium for \$110,000 in 2010. If its value appreciates at an average rate of 6% per year, what will the value be in 2015?

5. **DEFORESTATION** During the 1990s, the forested area of Guatemala decreased at an average rate of 1.7%.

a. If the forested area in Guatemala in 1990 was about 34,400 square kilometers, write an equation for the forested area for t years after 1990.

b. If this trend continues, predict the forested area in 2015.

6. **BUSINESS** A piece of machinery valued at \$25,000 depreciates at a steady rate of 10% yearly. What will the value of the piece of machinery be after 7 years?

7. **TRANSPORTATION** A new car costs \$18,000. It is expected to depreciate at an average rate of 12% per year. Find the value of the car in 8 years.

8. **POPULATION** The population of Osaka, Japan, declined at an average annual rate of 0.05% for the five years between 1995 and 2000. If the population of Osaka was 11,013,000 in 2000 and it continues to decline at the same rate, predict the population in 2050.

Word Problem Practice

AL OL BL ELL

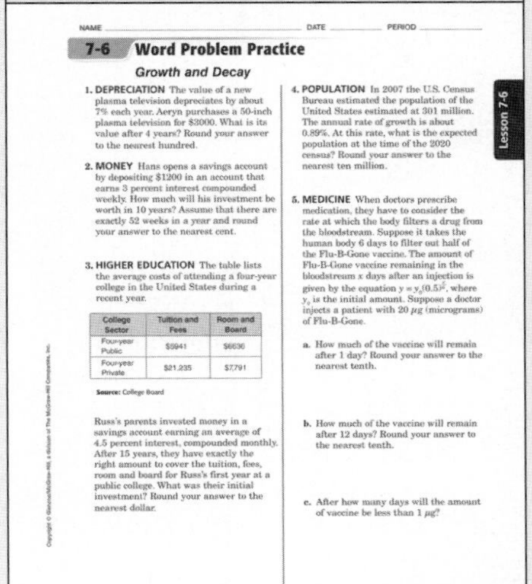
NAME ______ DATE ______ PERIOD ______

7-6 Word Problem Practice

Growth and Decay

1. **DEPRECIATION** The value of a new plasma television depreciates by about 7% each year. Aeryn purchases a 50-inch plasma television for \$3000. What is its value after 4 years? Round your answer to the nearest hundred.

2. **MONEY** Hans opens a savings account by depositing \$1200 in an account that earns 3 percent interest compounded weekly. How much will his investment be worth in 10 years? Assume that there are exactly 52 weeks in a year and round your answer to the nearest cent.

3. **HIGHER EDUCATION** The table lists the average costs of attending a four-year college in the United States during a recent year.

College Sector	Tuition and Fees	Room and Board
Four-year Public	\$5941	\$6636
Four-year Private	\$21,235	\$7,791

Source: College Board

Russ's parents invested money in a savings account earning an average of 4.5 percent interest, compounded monthly. After 15 years, they have exactly the right amount to cover the tuition, fees, room and board for Russ's first year at a public college. What was their initial investment? Round your answer to the nearest dollar.

4. **POPULATION** In 2007 the U.S. Census Bureau estimated the population of the United States estimated at 301 million. The annual rate of growth is about 0.89%. At this rate, what is the expected population at the time of the 2020 census? Round your answer to the nearest ten million.

5. **MEDICINE** When doctors prescribe medication, they have to consider the rate at which the body filters a drug from the bloodstream. Suppose it takes the human body 6 days to filter out half of the Flu-B-Gone vaccine. The amount of Flu-B-Gone vaccine remaining in the bloodstream x days after an injection is given by the equation $y = y_0(0.5)^{\frac{x}{6}}$, where y_0 is the initial amount. Suppose a doctor injects a patient with 20 μg (micrograms) of Flu-B-Gone.

a. How much of the vaccine will remain after 1 day? Round your answer to the nearest tenth.

b. How much of the vaccine will remain after 12 days? Round your answer to the nearest tenth.

c. After how many days will the amount of vaccine be less than 1 μg?

Lesson 7-6

Enrichment

OL BL

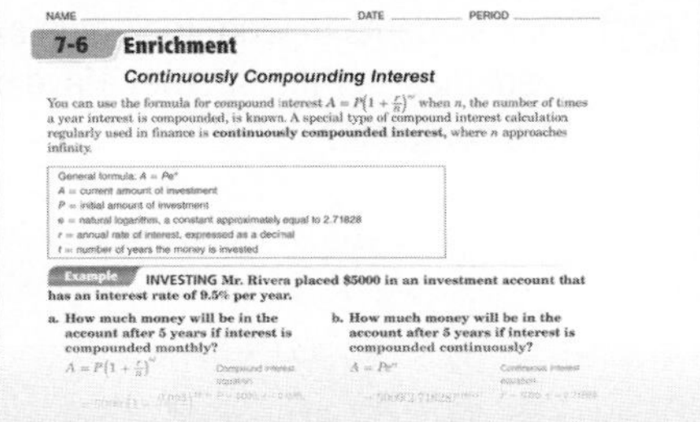
NAME ______ DATE ______ PERIOD ______

7-6 Enrichment

Continuously Compounding Interest

You can use the formula for compound interest $A = P\left(1 + \frac{r}{n}\right)^{nt}$ when n, the number of times a year interest is compounded, is known. A special type of compound interest calculation regularly used in finance is **continuously compounded interest**, where n approaches infinity.

General formula: $A = Pe^{rt}$

A = current amount of investment

P = initial amount of investment

e = natural logarithm, a constant approximately equal to 2.71828

r = annual rate of interest, expressed as a decimal

t = number of years the money is invested

Example **INVESTING Mr. Rivera placed \$5000 in an investment account that has an interest rate of 9.5% per year.**

a. How much money will be in the account after 5 years if interest is compounded monthly?

$A = P\left(1 + \frac{r}{n}\right)^{nt}$ Compound interest equation

b. How much money will be in the account after 5 years if interest is compounded continuously?

$A = Pe^{rt}$ Continuous interest equation

4 Assess

Ticket Out the Door Make several copies each of five equations for exponential growth or decay. Give one equation to each student. As students leave the room, ask them to tell you whether their equations are for growth or decay.

Formative Assessment

Check for student understanding of Lessons 7-5 and 7-6.

Quiz 3, p. 58

Additional Answers

25.

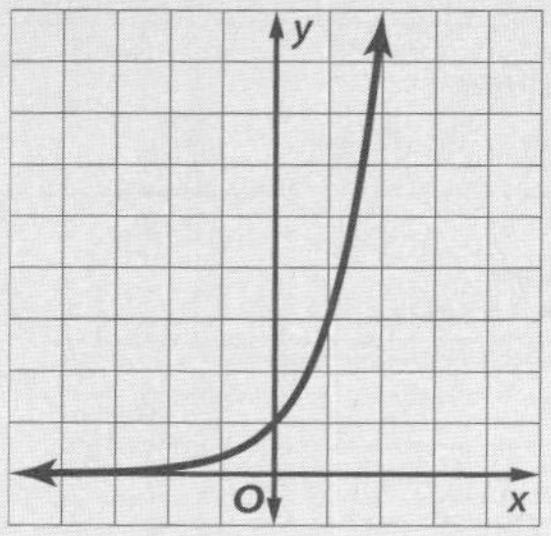

1; D = {all real numbers}; R = $\{y \mid y > 0\}$

26.

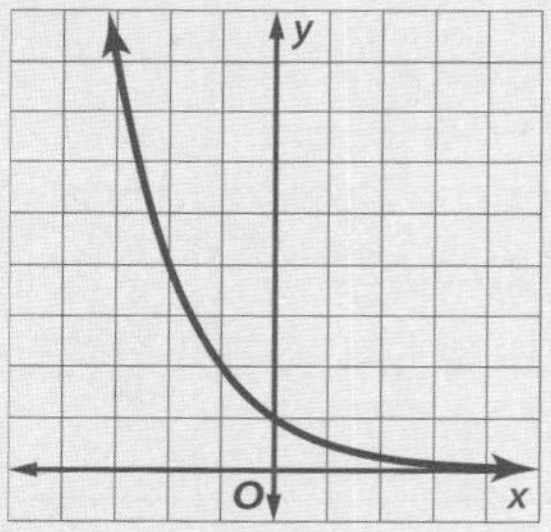

1; D = {all real numbers}; R = $\{y \mid y > 0\}$

27.

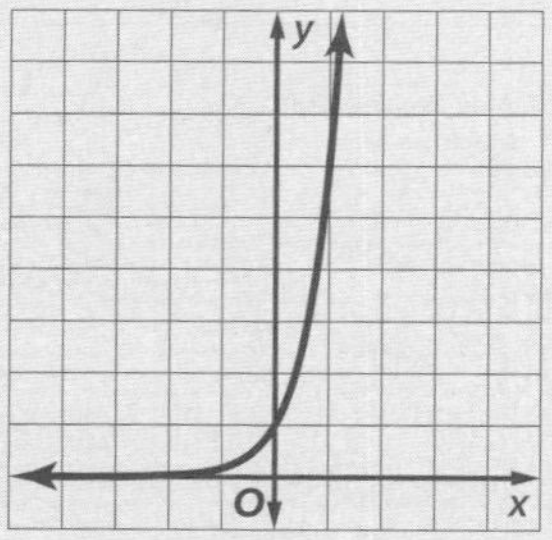

1; D = {all real numbers}; R = $\{y \mid y > 0\}$

Standardized Test Practice

21. GEOMETRY The parallelogram has an area of 35 square inches. Find the height h of the parallelogram. **C**

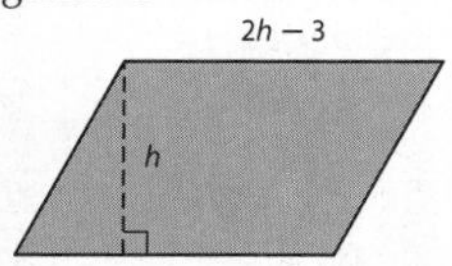

A 3.5 inches C 5 inches
B 4 inches D 7 inches

22. Which is greater than $64^{\frac{1}{3}}$? **H**

F 2^2 H $64^{\frac{1}{2}}$
G $64^{\frac{1}{6}}$ J 64^{-3}

23. Thi purchased a car for \$22,900. The car depreciated at an annual rate of 16%. Which of the following equations models the value of Thi's car after 5 years? **D**

A $A = 22{,}900(1.16)^5$
B $A = 22{,}900(0.16)^5$
C $A = 16(22{,}900)^5$
D $A = 22{,}900(0.84)^5$

24. GRIDDED RESPONSE A deck measures 12 feet by 18 feet. If a painter charges \$2.65 per square foot, including tax, how much will it cost in dollars to have the deck painted? **572.4**

Spiral Review

Graph each function. Find the y-intercept and state the domain and range. (Lesson 7-5) **25–27. See margin.**

25. $y = 3^x$ **26.** $y = \left(\frac{1}{2}\right)^x$ **27.** $y = 6^x$

Evaluate each product. Express the results in both scientific notation and standard form. (Lesson 7-4)

28. $(4.2 \times 10^3)(3.1 \times 10^{10})$ **1.302×10^{14}; 130,200,000,000,000**

29. $(6.02 \times 10^{23})(5 \times 10^{-14})$ **3.01×10^{10}; 30,100,000,000**

30. $(7 \times 10^5)^2$ **4.9×10^{11}; 490,000,000,000**

31. $(1.1 \times 10^{-2})^2$ **1.21×10^{-4}; 0.000121**

32. $(9.1 \times 10^{-2})(4.2 \times 10^{-7})$ **3.822×10^{-8}; 0.00000003822**

33. $(3.14 \times 10^2)(6.1 \times 10^{-3})$ **1.9154×10^0; 1.9154**

34. EVENT PLANNING A hall does not charge a rental fee as long as at least \$4000 is spent on food. For the prom, the hall charges \$28.95 per person for a buffet. How many people must attend the prom to avoid a rental fee for the hall? (Lesson 5-2) **at least 139 people**

Determine whether the graphs of each pair of equations are *parallel*, *perpendicular*, or *neither*. (Lesson 4-4)

35. $y = -2x + 11$, $y + 2x = 23$ **parallel**

36. $3y = 2x + 14$, $-3x - 2y = 2$ **perpendicular**

37. $y = -5x$, $y = 5x - 18$ **neither**

38. AGES The table shows equivalent ages for horses and humans. Write an equation that relates human age to horse age and find the equivalent horse age for a human who is 16 years old. (Lesson 3-4) **$y = 3x$; 5 yr 4 mo**

Horse age (x)	0	1	2	3	4	5
Human age (y)	0	3	6	9	12	15

Find the total price of each item. (Lesson 2-7)

39. umbrella: \$14.00, tax: 5.5% **\$14.77**

40. sandals: \$29.99, tax: 5.75% **\$31.71**

41. backpack: \$35.00, tax: 7% **\$37.45**

Skills Review

Graph each set of ordered pairs. **42–44. See Ch. 7 Answer Appendix.**

42. (3, 0), (0, 1), (−4, −6) **43.** (0, −2), (−1, −6), (3, 4) **44.** (2, 2), (−2, −3), (−3, −6)

Differentiated Instruction OL BL

If you think students need a challenge in this lesson,

Then ask students to write their own exponential growth or decay problems, using data from periodicals or the Internet. Have students share their problems with the class when they are complete.

EXTEND 7-6 Algebra Lab: Transforming Exponential Expressions

You can use the properties of rational exponents to transform exponential functions into other forms in order to solve real-world problems.

Activity Write Equivalent Exponential Expressions

Monique is trying to decide between two savings account plans. Plan A offers a monthly compounding interest rate of 0.25%, while Plan B offers 2.5% interest compounded annually. Which is the better plan? Explain.

In order to compare the plans, we must compare rates with the same compounding frequency. One way to do this is to compare the approximate monthly interest rates of each plan, also called the *effective* monthly interest rate. While you can use the compound interest formula to find this rate, you can also use the properties of exponents.

Write a function to represent the amount A Monique would earn after t years with Plan B. For convenience, let the initial amount of Monique's investment be $1.

$y = a(1 + r)^t$	Equation for exponential growth
$A(t) = 1(1 + 0.025)^t$	$y = A(t)$, $a = 1$, $r = 2.5\%$ or 0.025
$= 1.025^t$	Simplify.

Now write a function equivalent to $A(t)$ that represents 12 compoundings per year, with a power of $12t$, instead of 1 per year, with a power of $1t$.

$A(t) = 1.025^{1t}$	Original function
$= 1.025^{\left(\frac{1}{12} \cdot 12\right)t}$	$1 = \frac{1}{12} \cdot 12$
$= \left(1.025^{\frac{1}{12}}\right)^{12t}$	Power of a Power
$\approx 1.0021^{12t}$	$(1.025)^{\frac{1}{12}} = \sqrt[12]{1.025}$ or about 1.0021

From this equivalent function, we can determine that the effective monthly interest by Plan B is about 0.0021 or about 0.21% per month. This rate is less than the monthly interest rate of 0.25% per month offered by Plan A, so Plan A is the better plan.

Model and Analyze

1. Use the compound interest formula $A = P\left(1 + \frac{r}{n}\right)^{nt}$ to determine the effective monthly interest rate for Plan B. How does this rate compare to the rate calculated using the method in the Activity above? **About 0.21% per month; they are approximately the same.**
2. Write a function to represent the amount A Monique would earn after t months by Plan A. Then use the properties of exponents to write a function equivalent to $A(t)$ that represents the amount earned after t years. **$A(t) = (1.0025)^t$; $A(t) \approx (1.030)^{\frac{1}{12}t}$**
3. From the expression you wrote in Exercise 2, identify the effective annual interest rate by Plan A. Use this rate to explain why Plan A is the better plan. **See margin.**
4. Suppose Plan A offered a quarterly compounded interest rate of 1.5%. Use the properties of exponents to explain which is the better plan. **See margin.**

4. The function $A(t) = (1.025)^t$ gives the amount Plan B earned after t years.

$A(t) = (1.025)^{1t}$	Original function
$= (1.025)^{\left(\frac{1}{4} \cdot 4\right)t}$	$1 = \frac{1}{4} \cdot 4$
$= \left[(1.025)^{\frac{1}{4}}\right]^{4t}$	Power of a Power
$\approx (1.0062)^{4t}$	$(1.025)^{\frac{1}{4}} = \sqrt[4]{1.025}$ or about 1.0062

The effective quarterly interest rate is about 0.0062 or 0.62%, which is less than the quarterly interest rate of 1.5% offered by Plan A, so Plan A is the better plan.

1 Focus

Objective Use properties of rational exponents to transform expressions for exponential functions into equivalent forms to solve problems.

2 Teach

Working in Cooperative Groups

Organize students into groups of 2, mixing abilities. Then have groups complete the Activity and Exercises 1–3.

Teaching Tip

Point out to students that the annual interest formula is approximated as a monthly interest rate using $\frac{1}{12} \cdot 12$ because there are 12 months in a year.

Practice Have students complete Exercise 4.

3 Assess

Formative Assessment

Use Exercise 4 to assess whether students understand how to use the properties of exponents to write equivalent expressions in order to compare interest rates.

From Concrete to Abstract

Ask students to justify that $A = P\left(1 + \frac{r}{n}\right)^{nt}$ is approximately equivalent to $A = P\left[(1 + r)^{\frac{1}{n}}\right]^{nt}$ graphically by fixing the values for P, r and n. Depending on the values chosen, students should see that the graphs of the two functions nearly coincide for a large interval of their domain.

Additional Answers

3. About 3.0% per year; this rate is greater than the 2.5% per year offered by Plan B.

1 Focus

VerticalAlignment

Before Lesson 7-7 Relate arithmetic sequences to linear functions.

Lesson 7-7 Identify and generate geometric sequences. Relate geometric sequences to exponential functions.

After Lesson 7-7 Write recursive formulas for arithmetic and geometric sequences.

2 Teach

Scaffolding Questions

Have students read the **Why?** section of the lesson.

Ask:

- If one e-mail was sent in the first round, how many were sent in the second round? the third round? the fourth round? 5; 25; 125
- How do you determine the number of e-mails sent in each subsequent round of e-mails? Multiply the previous number by 5.
- What is the equation to find the number of e-mails y after x rounds? $y = 5^x$

LESSON 7-7 Geometric Sequences as Exponential Functions

Then

- You related arithmetic sequences to linear functions.

Now

1. Identify and generate geometric sequences.
2. Relate geometric sequences to exponential functions.

Why?

- You send a chain email to a friend who forwards the email to five more people. Each of these five people forwards the email to five more people. The number of new email generated forms a geometric sequence.

NewVocabulary
geometric sequence
common ratio

Process Standards
PS.7

1 Recognize Geometric Sequences

The first person generates 5 emails. If each of these people sends the email to 5 more people, 25 emails are generated. If each of the 25 people sends 5 emails, 125 emails are generated. The sequence of emails generated, 1, 5, 25, 125, … is an example of a **geometric sequence**.

In a geometric sequence, the first term is nonzero and each term after the first is found by multiplying the previous term by a nonzero constant r called the **common ratio**. The common ratio can be found by dividing any term by its previous term.

Example 1 Identify Geometric Sequences

Determine whether each sequence is *arithmetic*, *geometric*, or *neither*. Explain.

a. 256, 128, 64, 32, …

Find the ratios of consecutive terms.

256, 128, 64, 32

$\frac{128}{256} = \frac{1}{2}$ $\frac{64}{128} = \frac{1}{2}$ $\frac{32}{64} = \frac{1}{2}$

Since the ratios are constant, the sequence is geometric. The common ratio is $\frac{1}{2}$.

b. 4, 9, 12, 18, …

Find the ratios of consecutive terms.

4, 9, 12, 18

$\frac{9}{4} = 2\frac{1}{4}$ $\frac{12}{9} = 1\frac{1}{3}$ $\frac{18}{12} = 1\frac{1}{2}$

The ratios are not constant, so the sequence is not geometric.

Find the differences of consecutive terms.

4, 9, 12, 18

$9 - 4 = 5$ $12 - 9 = 3$ $18 - 12 = 6$

There is no common difference, so the sequence is not arithmetic. Thus, the sequence is neither geometric nor arithmetic.

GuidedPractice **1A–1C. See margin.**

1A. 1, 3, 9, 27, … **1B.** −20, −15, −10, −5, … **1C.** 2, 8, 14, 22, …

Lesson 7-7 Resources

Resource	Approaching Level AL	On Level OL	Beyond Level BL	English Learners ELL
Teacher Edition		▪ Differentiated Instruction, p. 443	▪ Differentiated Instruction, p. 443	▪ Differentiated Instruction, p. 440
Chapter Resource Masters	▪ Study Guide and Intervention, pp. 42–43 ▪ Skills Practice, p. 44 ▪ Practice, p. 45 ▪ Word Problem Practice, p. 46	▪ Study Guide and Intervention, pp. 42–43 ▪ Skills Practice, p. 44 ▪ Practice, p. 45 ▪ Word Problem Practice, p. 46 ▪ Enrichment, p. 47	▪ Practice, p. 45 ▪ Word Problem Practice, p. 46 ▪ Enrichment, p. 47	▪ Study Guide and Intervention, pp. 42–43 ▪ Skills Practice, p. 44 ▪ Practice, p. 45 ▪ Word Problem Practice, p. 46
Other	▪ 5-Minute Check 7-7 ▪ Study Notebook	▪ 5-Minute Check 7-7 ▪ Study Notebook	▪ 5-Minute Check 7-7 ▪ Study Notebook	▪ 5-Minute Check 7-7 ▪ Study Notebook

Once the common ratio is known, more terms of a sequence can be generated. The formula can be rewritten as $a_n = a_1 r^{n-1}$, where n is a counting number and r is the common ratio.

Example 2 Find Terms of Geometric Sequences

Find the next three terms in each geometric sequence.

a. 1, −4, 16, −64, ...

Step 1 Find the common ratio.

1 −4 16 −64

$\frac{-4}{1} = -4$ $\frac{16}{-4} = -4$ $\frac{-64}{16} = -4$

Step 2 Multiply each term by the common ratio to find the next three terms.

−64 256 −1024 4096

×(−4) ×(−4) ×(−4)

The next three terms are 256, −1024, and 4096.

b. $9, 3, 1, \frac{1}{3}$ ...

Step 1 Find the common ratio.

9 3 1 $\frac{1}{3}$

$\frac{3}{9} = \frac{1}{3}$ $\frac{1}{3} = \frac{1}{3}$ $\frac{\frac{1}{3}}{3} = \frac{1}{3}$

The value of r is $\frac{1}{3}$.

Step 2 Multiply each term by the common ratio to find the next three terms.

$\frac{1}{3}$ $\frac{1}{9}$ $\frac{1}{27}$ $\frac{1}{81}$

$\times\frac{1}{3}$ $\times\frac{1}{3}$ $\times\frac{1}{3}$

The next three terms are $\frac{1}{9}$, $\frac{1}{27}$, and $\frac{1}{81}$.

GuidedPractice

2A. −3, 15, −75, 375, ... **2A. −1875, 9375, −46,875**

2B. 24, 36, 54, 81, ... **2B. 121.5, 182.25, 273.375**

StudyTip

Structure If the terms of a geometric sequence alternate between positive and negative terms or vice versa, the common ratio is negative.

Math HistoryLink

Thomas Robert Malthus (1766–1834) Malthus studied populations and had pessimistic views about the future population of the world. In his work, he stated: "Population increases in a geometric ratio, while the means of subsistence increases in an arithmetic ratio."

2 Geometric Sequences and Functions

Finding the nth term of a geometric sequence would be tedious if we used the above method. The table below shows a rule for finding the nth term of a geometric sequence.

Position, n	1	2	3	4	...	n
Term, a_n	a_1	a_1r	a_1r^2	a_1r^3	...	a_1r^{n-1}

Notice that the common ratio between the terms is r. The table shows that to get the nth term, you multiply the first term by the common ratio r raised to the power $n - 1$. A geometric sequence can be defined by an exponential function in which n is the independent variable, a_n is the dependent variable, and r is the base. The domain is the counting numbers.

1 Recognize Geometric Sequences

Example 1 shows how to determine whether a sequence is arithmetic, geometric, or neither. **Example 2** shows how to find additional terms of a geometric sequence.

Formative Assessment

Use the Guided Practice exercises after each example to determine students' understanding of concepts.

Additional Examples

1 Determine whether each sequence is *arithmetic*, *geometric*, or *neither*. Explain.

a 0, 8, 16, 24, 32, ... Arithmetic; the common difference is 8.

b. 64, 48, 36, 27, ... Geometric; the common ratio is $\frac{3}{4}$.

2 Find the next three terms in each geometric sequence.

a. 1, −8, 64, −512, ... 4096; −32,768; 262,144

b. 40, 20, 10, 5, ... $\frac{5}{2}, \frac{5}{4}, \frac{5}{8}$

Additional Examples also in Interactive Classroom PowerPoint® Presentations

IWB Interactive White Board READY

2 Geometric Sequences and Functions

Example 3 shows how to find the nth term of a geometric sequence. **Example 4** shows how to use real-world data to draw a graph of a geometric sequence.

Teaching the Process Standards

Structure Mathematically proficient students look closely to discern a pattern or structure. Ask students to explain why the common difference is negative when the signs of the terms alternate.

Teach with Tech

Blog On your secure classroom blog have students write a blog entry describing how geometric sequences and exponential functions are related.

Additional Answers (Guided Practice)

1A. Geometric; the common ratio is 3.

1B. Arithmetic; the common difference is 5.

1C. Neither; there is no common ratio or common difference.

Focus on Mathematical Content

Common Ratio When finding the common ratio, it is important to set up the ratio in the correct order. For example, in Example 1, had the ratio been set up as $\frac{256}{128}$ instead of $\frac{128}{256}$, an incorrect ratio of 2 would have been found. It should be noted that when a geometric sequence is decreasing, the common ratio must be between 0 and 1.

Additional Examples

3 **a.** Write an equation for the nth term of the geometric sequence 1, −2, 4, −8, …
$a_n = 1 \cdot (-2)^{n-1}$

b. Find the 12th term of this sequence. −2048

4 **ART** A 50-pound ice sculpture is melting at a rate in which 80% of its weight remains each hour. Draw a graph to represent how many pounds of the sculpture is left at each hour.

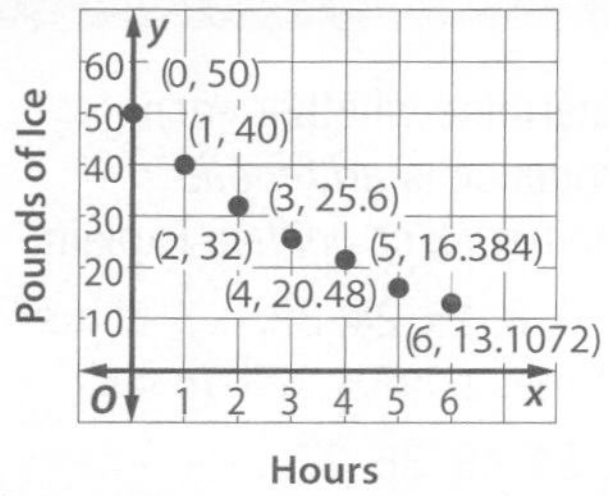

Tips for New Teachers

The Power of *r* Make sure students raise r to the power $(n - 1)$, in their equations for the nth term of a geometric sequence, instead of n.

Teaching the Process Standards

Reasoning Mathematically proficient students attend to the meaning of quantities, not just how to compute them. In Exercise 32, ask students why the common ratio is not 0.2. How does the common ratio relate to the meaning of the sequence?

Additional Answer (Guided Practice)

4. **Tennis Ball**

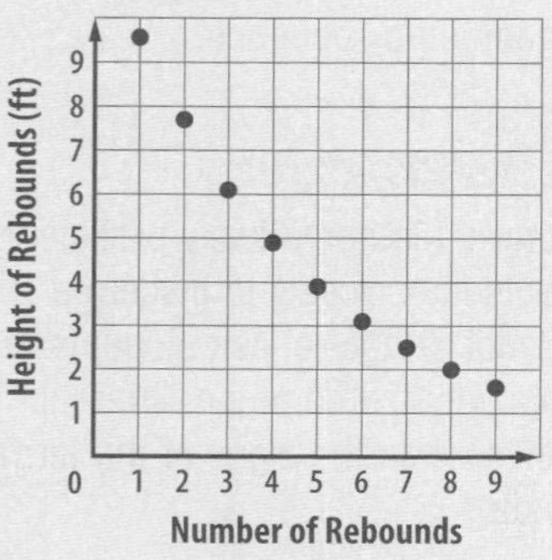

KeyConcept nth term of a Geometric Sequence

The nth term a_n of a geometric sequence with first term a_1 and common ratio r is given by the following formula, where n is any positive integer and $a_1, r \neq 0$.

$$a_n = a_1 r^{n-1}$$

Example 3 Find the nth Term of a Geometric Sequence

a. Write an equation for the nth term of the sequence −6, 12, −24, 48, … .

The first term of the sequence is −6. So, $a_1 = -6$. Now find the common ratio.

−6 → 12 → −24 → 48

$\frac{12}{-6} = -2$ $\quad \frac{-24}{12} = -2$ $\quad \frac{48}{-24} = -2$

The common ratio is −2.

$a_n = a_1 r^{n-1}$ — Formula for nth term

$a_n = -6(-2)^{n-1}$ — $a_1 = -6$ and $r = 2$

WatchOut! Negative Common Ratio If the common ratio is negative, as in Example 3, make sure to enclose the common ratio in parentheses. $(-2)^8 \neq -2^8$

b. Find the ninth term of this sequence.

$a_n = a_1 r^{n-1}$ — Formula for nth term

$a_9 = -6(-2)^{9-1}$ — For the nth term, $n = 9$.

$= -6(-2)^8$ — Simplify.

$= -6(256)$ — $(-2)^8 = 256$

$= -1536$

GuidedPractice **3.** $a_n = 96 \cdot \left(\frac{1}{2}\right)^{n-1}$; $\frac{3}{16}$

3. Write an equation for the nth term of the geometric sequence 96, 48, 24, 12, … . Then find the tenth term of the sequence.

Real-WorldLink

The first NCAA Division I women's basketball tournament was held in 1982. The University of Tennessee has won the most national titles with 8 titles as of 2012.

Source: NCAA Sports

Real-World Example 4 Graph a Geometric Sequence

BASKETBALL The NCAA women's basketball tournament begins with 64 teams. In each round, one half of the teams are left to compete, until only one team remains. Draw a graph to represent how many teams are left in each round.

Compared to the previous rounds, one half of the teams remain. So, $r = \frac{1}{2}$. Therefore, the geometric sequence that models this situation is 64, 32, 16, 8, 4, 2, 1. So in round two, 32 teams compete, in round three 16 teams compete and so forth. Use this information to draw a graph.

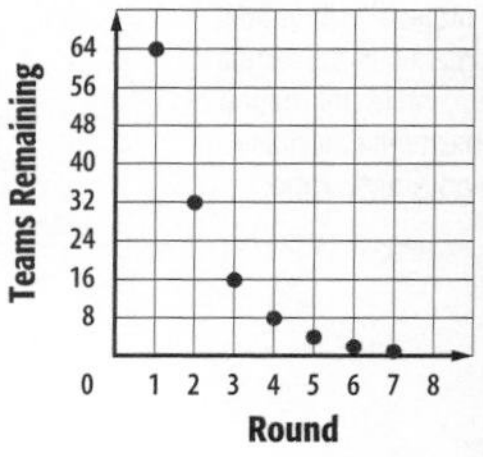

GuidedPractice

4. TENNIS A tennis ball is dropped from a height of 12 feet. Each time the ball bounces back to 80% of the height from which it fell. Draw a graph to represent the height of the ball after each bounce. **See margin.**

440 | Lesson 7-7 | Geometric Sequences as Exponential Functions

DifferentiatedInstruction ELL

Interpersonal Learners Put students into groups of mixed language and math abilities. Have groups discuss the differences between arithmetic and geometric sequences. Suggest they help each other organize clear, concise, and accurate notes about these and other concepts taught in this lesson.

Check Your Understanding

(circled number) = Step-by-Step Solutions begin on page R13.

Example 1 Determine whether each sequence is *arithmetic, geometric,* or *neither.* Explain.

1. 200, 40, 8, … **2.** 2, 4, 16, … **3.** −6, −3, 0, 3, … **4.** 1, −1, 1, −1, …

Example 2 Find the next three terms in each geometric sequence. **5–8. See margin.**

5. 10, 20, 40, 80, … **6.** 100, 50, 25, … **7.** 4, −1, $\frac{1}{4}$, … **8.** −7, 21, −63, …

Example 3 Write an equation for the *n*th term of each geometric sequence, and find the indicated term.

9. the fifth term of −6, −24, −96, … $a_n = -6 \cdot (4)^{n-1}$; **−1536**

10. the seventh term of −1, 5, −25, … $a_n = -1 \cdot (-5)^{n-1}$; **−15,625**

11. the tenth term of 72, 48, 32, … $a_n = 72 \cdot \left(\frac{2}{3}\right)^{n-1}$; $\frac{4096}{2187}$

12. the ninth term of 112, 84, 63, … $a_n = 112 \cdot \left(\frac{3}{4}\right)^{n-1}$; $\frac{45,927}{4096}$

Example 4 **13. EXPERIMENT** In a physics class experiment, Diana drops a ball from a height of 16 feet. Each bounce has 70% the height of the previous bounce. Draw a graph to represent the height of the ball after each bounce. **See margin.**

1. Geometric; the common ratio is $\frac{1}{5}$.

2. Neither; there is no common ratio or difference.

3. Arithmetic; the common difference is 3.

4. Geometric; the common ratio is −1.

Practice and Problem Solving

Extra Practice is on R7.

Example 1 Determine whether each sequence is *arithmetic, geometric,* or *neither.* Explain. **14–19. See margin.**

14. 4, 1, 2, … **15.** 10, 20, 30, 40, … **16.** 4, 20, 100, …

17. 212, 106, 53, … **18.** −10, −8, −6, −4, … **19.** 5, −10, 20, 40, …

Example 2 Find the next three terms in each geometric sequence. **20–25. See margin.**

20. 2, −10, 50, … **(21)** 36, 12, 4, … **22.** 4, 12, 36, …

23. 400, 100, 25, … **24.** −6, −42, −294, … **25.** 1024, −128, 16, …

Example 3 **26.** The first term of a geometric series is 1 and the common ratio is 9. What is the 8th term of the sequence? **4,782,969**

27. The first term of a geometric series is 2 and the common ratio is 4. What is the 14th term of the sequence? **134,217,728**

28. What is the 15th term of the geometric sequence −9, 27, −81, …? **−43,046,721**

29. What is the 10th term of the geometric sequence 6, −24, 96, …? **−1,572,864**

Example 4 **30. PENDULUM** The first swing of a pendulum is shown. On each swing after that, the arc length is 60% of the length of the previous swing. Draw a graph that represents the arc length after each swing. **See Ch. 7 Answer Appendix.**

31. Find the eighth term of a geometric sequence for which $a_3 = 81$ and $r = 3$. **19,683**

B **32. REASONING** At an online mapping site, Mr. Mosley notices that when he clicks a spot on the map, the map zooms in on that spot. The magnification increases by 20% each time. **a.** $a_n = 1.2^n$ **32b. 2.0736; The map will be magnified at approximately 207% of the original size after the fourth click.**

a. Write a formula for the *n*th term of the geometric sequence that represents the magnification of each zoom level. (*Hint:* The common ratio is not just 0.2.)

b. What is the fourth term of this sequence? What does it represent?

Differentiated Homework Options

Level	Assignment	Two-Day Option	
AL Basic	14–31, 39–69	15–31 odd, 43–46	14–30 even, 39–42, 47–69
OL Core	15–31 odd, 32–37, 39–69	14–31, 43–46	32–37, 39–42, 47–69
BL Advanced	32–63, (optional: 64–69)		

3 Practice

Formative Assessment

Use Exercises 1–13 to check for understanding.

Use the chart at the bottom of this page to customize assignments for your students.

Exercise Alert

Grid Paper For Exercises 13, 30, 37, and 53–55, students will need grid paper.

Additional Answers

5. 160, 320, 640

6. 12.5, 6.25, 3.125

7. $-\frac{1}{16}, \frac{1}{64}, -\frac{1}{256}$

8. 189, −567, 1701

13. **Experiment**

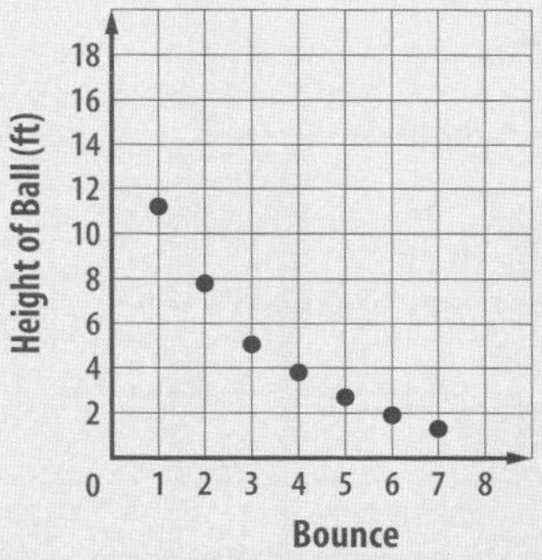

14. Neither; there is no common ratio or difference.

15. Arithmetic; the common difference is 10.

16. Geometric; the common ratio is 5.

17. Geometric; the common ratio is $\frac{1}{2}$.

18. Arithmetic; the common difference is 2.

19. Neither; there is no common ratio or difference.

20. −250, 1250, −6250

21. $\frac{4}{3}, \frac{4}{9}, \frac{4}{27}$

22. 108, 324, 972

23. $\frac{25}{4}, \frac{25}{16}, \frac{25}{64}$

24. −2058; −14,406; −100,842

25. $-2, \frac{1}{4}, -\frac{1}{32}$

Study Guide and Intervention

AL OL ELL

NAME ______ DATE ______ PERIOD ______

7-7 Study Guide and Intervention

Geometric Sequences as Exponential Functions

Recognize Geometric Sequences A geometric sequence is a sequence in which each term after the first is found by multiplying the previous term by a nonzero constant r called the **common ratio**. The common ratio can be found by dividing any term by its previous term.

Example 1 Determine whether the sequence is *arithmetic*, *geometric*, or *neither*: 21, 63, 189, 567, . . .

Find the ratios of the consecutive terms. If the ratios are constant, the sequence is geometric.

21, 63, 189, 567

$\frac{63}{21} = \frac{189}{63} = \frac{567}{189} = 3$

Because the ratios are constant, the sequence is geometric. The common ratio is 3.

Example 2 Find the next three terms in this geometric sequence: −1215, 405, −135, 45, . . .

Step 1 Find the common ratio.

−1215, 405, −135, 45

$\frac{405}{-1215} = \frac{-135}{405} = \frac{45}{-135} = -\frac{1}{3}$

The value of r is $-\frac{1}{3}$.

Step 2 Multiply each term by the common ratio to find the next three terms.

45, −15, 5, $-\frac{5}{3}$

$\times\left(-\frac{1}{3}\right)$ $\times\left(-\frac{1}{3}\right)$ $\times\left(-\frac{1}{3}\right)$

The next three terms of the sequence are −15, 5, and $-\frac{5}{3}$.

Exercises

Determine whether each sequence is *arithmetic*, *geometric*, or *neither*. Explain.

1. 1, 2, 4, 8, . . .
2. 9, 14, 6, 11, . . .
3. $\frac{2}{3}, \frac{1}{3}, \frac{1}{6}, \frac{1}{12}$, . . .
4. −2, 5, 12, 19, . . .

Find the next three terms in each geometric sequence.

5. 648, −216, 72, . . .
6. 25, −5, 1, . . .
7. $\frac{1}{16}, \frac{1}{2}, 4$, . . .
8. 72, 36, 18, . . .

Practice

AL OL BL ELL

NAME ______ DATE ______ PERIOD ______

7-7 Practice

Geometric Sequences as Exponential Functions

Determine whether each sequence is *arithmetic*, *geometric*, or *neither*. Explain.

1. 1, −5, −11, −17, . . .
2. 3, $\frac{3}{2}$, 1, $\frac{3}{4}$, . . .
3. 108, 36, 12, 4, . . .
4. −2, 4, −6, 8, . . .

Find the next three terms in each geometric sequence.

5. 64, 16, 4, . . .
6. 2, −12, 72, . . .
7. 3750, 750, 150, . . .
8. 4, 28, 196, . . .
9. Write an equation for the nth term of the geometric sequence 896, −448, 224, ... Find the eighth term of this sequence.
10. Write an equation for the nth term of the geometric sequence 3584, 896, 224, ... Find the sixth term of this sequence.
11. Find the sixth term of a geometric sequence for which $a_2 = 288$ and $r = \frac{1}{4}$.
12. Find the eighth term of a geometric sequence for which $a_3 = 35$ and $r = 7$.
13. **PENNIES** Thomas is saving pennies in a jar. The first day he saves 3 pennies, the second day 12 pennies, the third day 48 pennies, and so on. How many pennies does Thomas save on the eighth day?

Word Problem Practice

AL OL BL ELL

NAME ______ DATE ______ PERIOD ______

7-7 Word Problem Practice

Geometric Sequences as Exponential Functions

1. **WORLD POPULATION** The CIA estimates the world population is growing at a rate of 1.167% each year. The world population for 2007 was about 6.6 billion.
   a. Write an equation for the world population after n years. (*Hint:* The common ratio is not 0.01167.)
   b. What will the estimated world population be in 2017?
2. **MUSEUMS** The table shows the annual visitors to a museum in millions. Write an equation for the projected number of visitors after n years.

Year	Visitors (millions)
1	4
2	6
3	9
4	$13\frac{1}{2}$
n	?

3. **BANKING** Arnold has a bank account with a beginning balance of $5000. He spends one-fifth of the balance each month. How much money will be in the account after 6 months?
4. **POPULATION** The table shows the projected population of the United States through 2050. Does this table show an *arithmetic sequence*, a *geometric sequence* or neither? Explain.

Year	Projected Population
2000	282,125,000
2010	308,936,000
2020	335,805,000
2030	363,584,000
2040	391,946,000
2050	419,854,000

Source: U.S. Census Bureau

5. **SAVINGS ACCOUNTS** A bank offers a savings account with a 0.5% return each month.
   a. Write an equation for the balance of a savings account after n months. (*Hint:* The common ratio is not 0.005.)
   b. Given an initial deposit of $500, what will the account balance be after 15 months?

Enrichment

OL BL

NAME ______ DATE ______ PERIOD ______

7-7 Enrichment

Pay it Forward

The idea behind "pay it forward" is that on the first day, one person does a good deed for three different people. Then, on the second day, those three people will each perform good deeds for 3 more people, so that on Day 2, there are 3 × 3 or 9 good deeds being done. Continue this process to fill in the chart. A tree diagram will help you fill in the chart.

Day	# of Deeds
0	1
1	3
2	9
3	
4	
5	

Day 1 Day 2

Person 1 — New Person 1, New Person 2, New Person 3

1. Graph the data you found in the chart as ordered pairs and connect with a smooth curve.
2. What type of function is your graph from Exercise 1? Write an equation that can be used to determine the number of good deeds on any given day.

---

33. ALLOWANCE Danielle's parents have offered her two different options to earn her allowance for a 9-week period over the summer. She can either get paid $30 each week or $1 the first week, $2 for the second week, $4 for the third week, and so on. **a. Yes; the common ratio is 2.**

a. Does the second option form a geometric sequence? Explain.

b. Which option should Danielle choose? Explain.

33b. The second option; she would earn $511, which is much more than she would earn with the first option.

34. SIERPINSKI'S TRIANGLE Consider the inscribed equilateral triangles at the right. The perimeter of each triangle is one half of the perimeter of the next larger triangle. What is the perimeter of the smallest triangle? **7.5 cm**

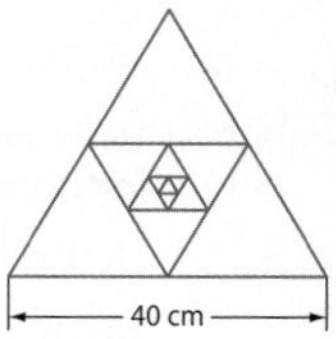

35. If the second term of a geometric sequence is 3 and the third term is 1, find the first and fourth terms of the sequence. **9; $\frac{1}{3}$**

36. If the third term of a geometric sequence is −12 and the fourth term is 24, find the first and fifth terms of the sequence. **−3; −48**

37. EARTHQUAKES The Richter scale is used to measure the force of an earthquake. The table shows the increase in magnitude for the values on the Richter scale.

Richter Number (x)	Increase in Magnitude (y)	Rate of Change (slope)
1	1	–
2	10	9
3	100	**90**
4	1000	**900**
5	10,000	**9000**

a. Copy and complete the table. Remember that the rate of change is the change in y divided by the change in x. **b–c. See Ch. 7 Answer Appendix.**

b. Plot the ordered pairs (Richter number, increase in magnitude).

c. Describe the graph that you made of the Richter scale data. Is the rate of change between any two points the same?

d. Write an exponential equation that represents the Richter scale. **$y = 1 \cdot (10)^{x-1}$**

H.O.T. Problems Use Higher-Order Thinking Skills

38. CHALLENGE Write a sequence that is both geometric and arithmetic. Explain your answer.

38. 1, 1, 1, 1, ...; The common ratio is 1 making it a geometric sequence, but the common difference is 0 making it an arithmetic sequence as well.

39. See Ch. 7 Answer Appendix.

39. CRITIQUE Haro and Matthew are finding the ninth term of the geometric sequence −5, 10, −20, ... Is either of them correct? Explain your reasoning.

Haro

$r = \frac{10}{-5}$ or -2

$a_9 = -5(-2)^{9-1}$

$= -5(512)$

$= -2560$

Matthew

$r = \frac{10}{-5}$ or -2

$a_9 = -5 \cdot (-2)^{9-1}$

$= -5 \cdot -256$

$= 1280$

40. REASONING Write a sequence of numbers that form a pattern but are neither arithmetic nor geometric. Explain the pattern.

40. Sample answer: 1, 4, 9, 16, 25, 36, ...; This is the sequence of squares of counting numbers.

41. WRITING IN MATH How are graphs of geometric sequences and exponential functions similar? different? **See Ch. 7 Answer Appendix.**

42. WRITING IN MATH Summarize how to find a specific term of a geometric sequence. **See Ch. 7 Answer Appendix.**

Teaching the Process Standards

Critique Mathematically proficient students can read the arguments of others and decide whether they make sense. In Exercise 39, advise students to start by comparing the arguments line by line to find the differences.

Standardized Test Practice

43. Find the eleventh term of the sequence 3, −6, 12, −24, … . **B**

A 6144 C 33
B 3072 D −6144

44. What is the total amount of the investment shown in the table below if interest is compounded monthly? **H**

Principal	\$500
Length of Investment	4 years
Annual Interest Rate	5.25%

F \$613.56 H \$616.56
G \$616.00 J \$718.75

45. SHORT RESPONSE Gloria has \$6.50 in quarters and dimes. If she has 35 coins in total, how many of each coin does she have? **15 dimes and 20 quarters**

46. What are the domain and range of the function $y = 4(3^x) - 2$? **A**

A D = {all real numbers}, R = $\{y \mid y > -2\}$
B D = {all real numbers}, R = $\{y \mid y > 0\}$
C D = {all integers}, R = $\{y \mid y > -2\}$
D D = {all integers}, R = $\{y \mid y > 0\}$

Spiral Review

Find the next three terms in each geometric sequence. (Lesson 7-6) **47–52. See margin.**

47. 2, 6, 18, 54, … **48.** −5, −10, −20, −40, … **49.** $1, -\frac{1}{2}, \frac{1}{4}, -\frac{1}{8}, \ldots$

50. −3, 1.5, −0.75, 0.375, … **51.** 1, 0.6, 0.36, 0.216, … **52.** 4, 6, 9, 13.5, …

Graph each function. Find the *y*-intercept and state the domain and range. (Lesson 7-5) **53–55. See margin.**

53. $y = \left(\frac{1}{4}\right)^x - 5$ **54.** $y = 2(4)^x$ **55.** $y = \frac{1}{2}(3^x)$

56. LANDSCAPING A blue spruce grows an average of 6 inches per year. A hemlock grows an average of 4 inches per year. If a blue spruce is 4 feet tall and a hemlock is 6 feet tall, write a system of equations to represent their growth. Find and interpret the solution in the context of the situation. (Lesson 6-2) **See Ch. 7 Answer Appendix.**

57. MONEY City Bank requires a minimum balance of \$1500 to maintain free checking services. If Mr. Hayashi is going to write checks for the amounts listed in the table, how much money should he start with in order to have free checking? (Lesson 5-1) **at least \$3747**

Check	Amount
750	\$1300
751	\$947

Write an equation in slope-intercept form of the line with the given slope and *y*-intercept. (Lesson 4-2) **58–63. See Ch. 7 Answer Appendix.**

58. slope: 4, *y*-intercept: 2 **59.** slope: −3, *y*-intercept: $-\frac{2}{3}$

60. slope: $-\frac{1}{4}$, *y*-intercept: −5 **61.** slope: $\frac{1}{2}$, *y*-intercept: −9

62. slope: $-\frac{2}{5}$, *y*-intercept: $\frac{3}{4}$ **63.** slope: −6, *y*-intercept: −7

Skills Review

Simplify each expression. If not possible, write *simplified*.

64. $3u + 10u$ **$13u$** **65.** $5a - 2 + 6a$ **$11a - 2$** **66.** $6m^2 - 8m$ **simplified**

67. $4w^2 + w + 15w^2$ **$19w^2 + w$** **68.** $13(5 + 4a)$ **$65 + 52a$** **69.** $(4t - 6)16$ **$64t - 96$**

Differentiated Instruction OL BL

Extension Often sequences of numbers do not appear, on first calculations, to have a pattern. Sometimes the differences between terms themselves create a sequence that can be used to determine the next term in the original sequence. Ask students to determine the 6th term in the sequence 4, 7, 14, 25, 40, …. Have them also explain how they found the term.

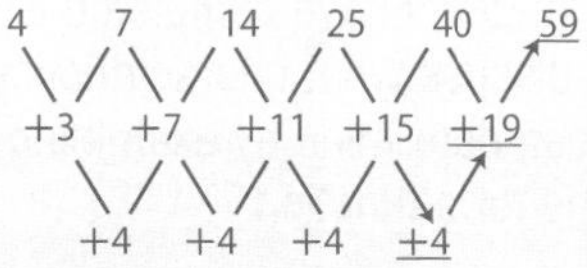

4 Assess

Name the Math Give each student one of five different geometric sequences. Ask students to explain how to find the common ratio for their sequence.

Additional Answers

47. 162, 486, 1458

48. −80, −160, −320

49. $\frac{1}{16}, -\frac{1}{32}, \frac{1}{64}$

50. −0.1875, 0.09375, −0.046875

51. 0.1296, 0.07776, 0.046656

52. 20.25, 30.375, 45.5625

53.

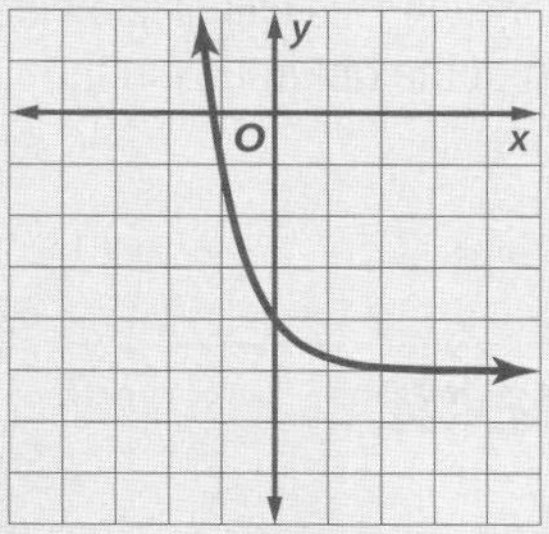

−4; D = {all real numbers}; R = $\{y \mid y > -5\}$

54.

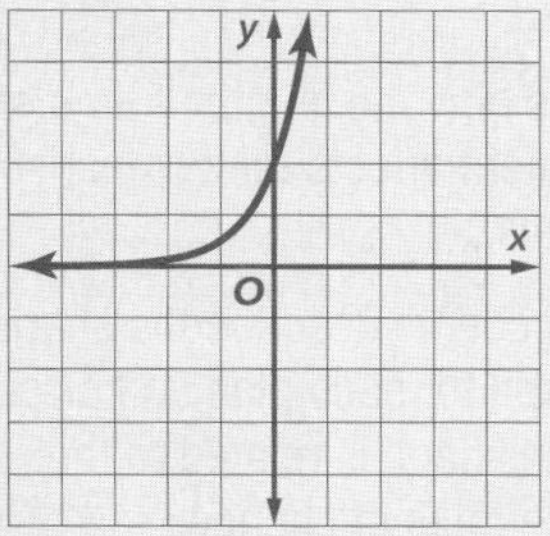

2; D = {all real numbers}; R = $\{y \mid y > 0\}$

55.

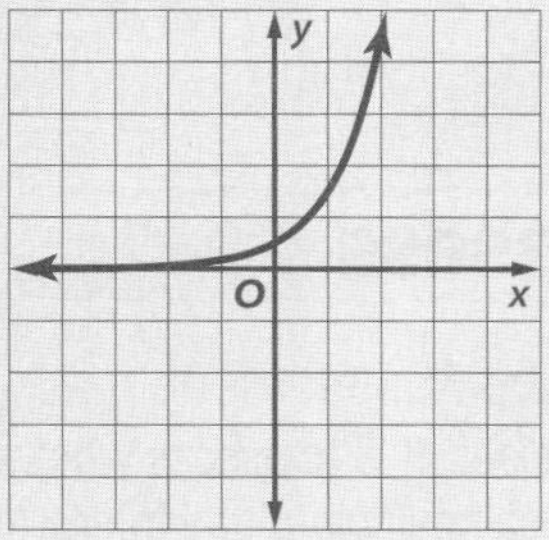

$\frac{1}{2}$; D = {all real numbers}; R = $\{y \mid y > 0\}$

1 Focus

Objective Calculate and interpret the average rate of change of an exponential function.

Materials for Each Student

- grid paper

Easy to Make Manipulatives

Teaching Algebra with Manipulatives
Template for grid paper, p. 1

Teaching Tip

Have students use increments of 25 on the vertical axis. This will give a clearer illustration of the difference in the two graphs.

2 Teach

Working in Cooperative Groups

Put students in groups of two or three, mixing abilities. Have groups complete the activity.

- Discuss how the length of time of the investment affects the comparison of the plans.
- Have students describe the shape of the graph for each plan and discuss how the shape is related to the average rates of change.

Practice Have students complete Exercises 1–4.

3 Assess

Formative Assessment

Use Exercises 1–3 to assess whether students can calculate and interpret an average rate of change.

EXTEND 7-7

Algebra Lab

Average Rate of Change of Exponential Functions

You know that the rate of change of a linear function is the same for any two points on the graph. The rate of change of an exponential function is not constant.

Content Standards
AI.QE.1

Activity Evaluating Investment Plans

John has $2000 to invest in one of two plans. Plan 1 offers to increase his principal by $75 each year, while Plan 2 offers to pay 3.6% interest compounded monthly. The dollar value of each investment after t years is given by $A_1 = 2000 + 75t$ and $A_2 = 2000(1.003)^{12t}$, respectively. Use the function values, the average rate of change, and the graphs of the equations to interpret and compare the plans.

Step 1 Copy and complete the table below by finding the missing values for A_1 and A_2.

t	0	1	2	3	4	5
A_1	2000	2075	2150	2225	2300	2375
A_2	2000	2073.2	2149.08	2227.74	2309.27	2393.79

Step 2 Find the average rate of change for each plan from $t = 0$ to 1, $t = 3$ to 4, and $t = 0$ to 5.

Plan 1: $\frac{2075 - 2000}{1 - 0}$ or 75 $\frac{2300 - 2225}{4 - 3}$ or 75 $\frac{2375 - 2000}{5 - 0}$ or 75

Plan 2: $\frac{2073.2 - 2000}{1 - 0}$ or 73.2 $\frac{2309.27 - 2227.74}{4 - 3}$ or about 82 $\frac{2393.79 - 2000}{5 - 0}$ or about 79

Step 3 Graph the ordered pairs for each function. Connect each set of points with a smooth curve.

Step 4 Use the graph and the rates of change to compare the plans. Both graphs have a rate of change for the first year of about $75 per year. From year 3 to 4, Plan 1 continues to increase at $75 per year, but Plan 2 grows at a rate of more than $81 per year. The average rate of change over the first five years for Plan 1 is $75 per year and for Plan 2 is over $78 per year. This indicates that as the number of years increases, the investment in Plan 2 grows at an increasingly faster pace. This is supported by the widening gap between their graphs.

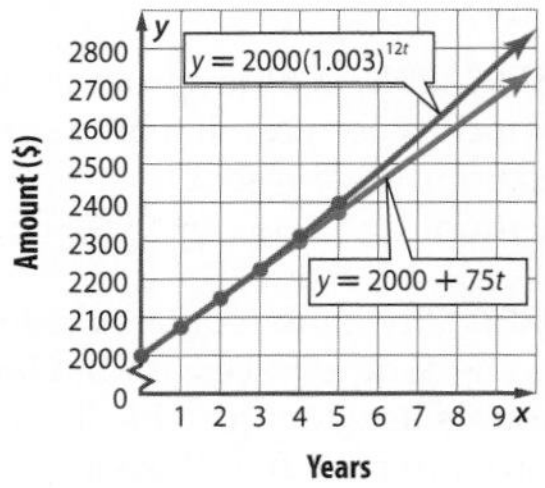

3. Sample answer: The value of the equipment decreases at a slower rate as the number of years increases.

Exercises

The value of a company's piece of equipment decreases over time due to depreciation. The function $y = 16{,}000(0.985)^{2t}$ represents the value after t years.

1. What is the average rate of change over the first five years? **−$448.86 per year**
2. What is the average rate of change of the value from year 5 to year 10? **−$386 per year**
3. What conclusion about the value can we make based on these average rates of change?
4. **REGULARITY** Copy and complete the table for $y = x^4$.

x	−3	−2	−1	0	1	2	3
y	81	16	1	0	1	16	81

Compare and interpret the average rate of change for $x = -3$ to 0 and for $x = 0$ to 3.

4. Sample answer: The average rate of change for $x = -3$ to 0 is −27 while the average rate of change for $x = 0$ to 3 is 27. This would indicate that the graph of the function was going down and then changed to going up.

From Concrete to Abstract

After students have completed Exercise 4, have them discuss what characteristics of a graph they can determine by examining the rate of change for a function.

Teaching the Process Standards

Regularity Mathematically proficient students notice if calculations are repeated, and look both for general methods and for shortcuts. In Exercise 4, advise students to look for and use regularity in their calculations.

LESSON 7-8 Recursive Formulas

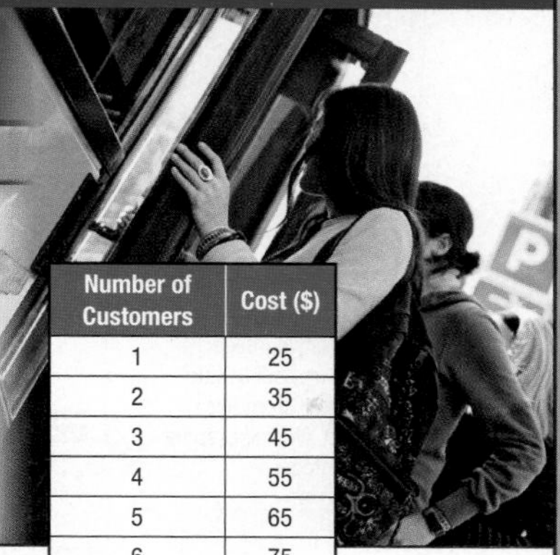

Then

- You wrote explicit formulas to represent arithmetic and geometric sequences.

Now

1. Use a recursive formula to list terms in a sequence.
2. Write recursive formulas for arithmetic and geometric sequences.

Why?

- Clients of a shuttle service get picked up from their homes and driven to premium outlet stores for shopping. The total cost of the service depends on the total number of customers. The costs for the first six customers are shown.

Number of Customers	Cost ($)
1	25
2	35
3	45
4	55
5	65
6	75

NewVocabulary
recursive formula

1 Using Recursive Formulas

An explicit formula allows you to find any term a_n of a sequence by using a formula written in terms of n. For example, $a_n = 2n$ can be used to find the fifth term of the sequence 2, 4, 6, 8, …: $a_5 = 2(5)$ or 10.

A **recursive formula** allows you to find the nth term of a sequence by performing operations to one or more of the preceding terms. Since each term in the sequence above is 2 greater than the term that preceded it, we can add 2 to the fourth term to find that the fifth term is 8 + 2 or 10. We can then write a recursive formula for a_n.

$$\begin{aligned} a_1 &= & &= 2 \\ a_2 &= a_1 + 2 \text{ or } 2 + 2 & &= 4 \\ a_3 &= a_2 + 2 \text{ or } 4 + 2 & &= 6 \\ a_4 &= a_3 + 2 \text{ or } 6 + 2 & &= 8 \\ &\vdots & & \\ a_n &= a_{n-1} + 2 & & \end{aligned}$$

A recursive formula for the sequence above is $a_1 = 2$, $a_n = a_{n-1} + 2$, for $n \geq 2$ where n is an integer. The term denoted a_{n-1} represents the term immediately before a_n. Notice that the first term a_1 is given, along with the domain for n.

Example 1 Use a Recursive Formula

PT

Find the first five terms of the sequence in which $a_1 = 7$ and $a_n = 3a_{n-1} - 12$, if $n \geq 2$.

Use $a_1 = 7$ and the recursive formula to find the next four terms.

$$\begin{aligned} a_2 &= 3a_{2-1} - 12 & & n = 2 \\ &= 3a_1 - 12 & & \text{Simplify.} \\ &= 3(7) - 12 \text{ or } 9 & & a_1 = 7 \end{aligned}$$

$$\begin{aligned} a_3 &= 3a_{3-1} - 12 & & n = 3 \\ &= 3a_2 - 12 & & \text{Simplify.} \\ &= 3(9) - 12 \text{ or } 15 & & a_2 = 9 \end{aligned}$$

$$\begin{aligned} a_4 &= 3a_{4-1} - 12 & & n = 4 \\ &= 3a_3 - 12 & & \text{Simplify.} \\ &= 3(15) - 12 \text{ or } 33 & & a_3 = 15 \end{aligned}$$

$$\begin{aligned} a_5 &= 3a_{5-1} - 12 & & n = 5 \\ &= 3a_4 - 12 & & \text{Simplify.} \\ &= 3(33) - 12 \text{ or } 87 & & a_4 = 33 \end{aligned}$$

The first five terms are 7, 9, 15, 33, and 87.

GuidedPractice

1. Find the first five terms of the sequence in which $a_1 = -2$ and $a_n = (-3)a_{n-1} + 4$, if $n \geq 2$. **−2, 10, −26, 82, −242**

1 Focus

VerticalAlignment

Before Lesson 7-8 Wrote explicit formulas to represent arithmetic and geometric sequences.

Lesson 7-8 Use a recursive formula to list terms in a sequence. Write recursive formulas for arithmetic and geometric sequences.

After Lesson 7-8 Identify linear, quadratic, and exponential functions from given data.

2 Teach

Scaffolding Questions

Have students read the **Why?** section of the lesson.

Ask:

- How does the total cost of the shuttle service change as a customer is added? Sample answer: The total cost increases by $10.
- Is this sequence *arithmetic*, *geometric*, or neither? arithmetic
- How much would it cost for 9 customers? $105

Lesson 7-8 Resources

Resource	Approaching Level AL	On Level OL	Beyond Level BL	English Learners ELL
Teacher Edition	▪ Differentiated Instruction, p. 445	▪ Differentiated Instruction, p. 445	▪ Differentiated Instruction, p. 448	
Chapter Resource Masters	▪ Study Guide and Intervention, pp. 48–49 ▪ Skills Practice, p. 50 ▪ Practice, p. 51 ▪ Word Problem Practice, p. 52	▪ Study Guide and Intervention, pp. 48–49 ▪ Skills Practice, p. 50 ▪ Practice, p. 51 ▪ Word Problem Practice, p. 52 ▪ Enrichment, p. 53	▪ Practice, p. 51 ▪ Word Problem Practice, p. 52 ▪ Enrichment, p. 53	▪ Study Guide and Intervention, pp. 48–49 ▪ Skills Practice, p. 50 ▪ Practice, p. 51 ▪ Word Problem Practice, p. 52
Other	▪ 5-Minute Check 7-8 ▪ Study Notebook	▪ 5-Minute Check 7-8 ▪ Study Notebook	▪ 5-Minute Check 7-8 ▪ Study Notebook	▪ 5-Minute Check 7-8 ▪ Study Notebook

1 Using Recursive Formulas

Example 1 shows how to find the first five terms of a sequence using a recursive formula.

Formative Assessment

Use the Guided Practice exercises after each example to determine students' understanding of concepts.

Additional Example

1 Find the first five terms of the sequence in which $a_1 = -8$ and $a_n = -2a_{n-1} + 5$, if $n \geq 2$. $-8, 21, -37, 79, -153$

Additional Examples also in Interactive Classroom PowerPoint® Presentations

IWB Interactive White Board READY

2 Writing Recursive Formulas

Example 2 shows how to write a recursive formula for a sequence. **Example 3** shows how to write recursive and explicit formulas for a sequence. **Example 4** shows how to translate between recursive and explicit formulas.

Additional Example

2 Write a recursive formula for each sequence.

a. 23, 29, 35, 41, ... $a_1 = 23$, $a_n = a_{n-1} + 6, n \geq 2$

b. 7, −21, 63, −189, ... $a_1 = 7$, $a_n = -3a_{n-1}, n \geq 2$

---

2 Writing Recursive Formulas

To write a recursive formula for an arithmetic or geometric sequence, complete the following steps.

StudyTip

Defining *n* For the *n*th term of a sequence, the value of *n* must be a positive integer. Although we must still state the domain of *n*, from this point forward, we will assume that *n* is an integer.

KeyConcept Writing Recursive Formulas

Step 1 Determine if the sequence is arithmetic or geometric by finding a common difference or a common ratio.

Step 2 Write a recursive formula.

Arithmetic Sequences $a_n = a_{n-1} + d$, where d is the common difference

Geometric Sequences $a_n = r \cdot a_{n-1}$, where r is the common ratio

Step 3 State the first term and domain for n.

Example 2 Write Recursive Formulas

Write a recursive formula for each sequence.

a. 17, 13, 9, 5, ...

Step 1 First subtract each term from the term that follows it.

$13 - 17 = -4$ $\quad 9 - 13 = -4$ $\quad 5 - 9 = -4$

There is a common difference of −4. The sequence is arithmetic.

Step 2 Use the formula for an arithmetic sequence.

$a_n = a_{n-1} + d$ Recursive formula for arithmetic sequence

$a_n = a_{n-1} + (-4)$ $d = -4$

Step 3 The first term a_1 is 17, and $n \geq 2$.

A recursive formula for the sequence is $a_1 = 17, a_n = a_{n-1} - 4, n \geq 2$.

StudyTip

Domain The domain for *n* is decided by the given terms. Since the first term is already given, it makes sense that the first term to which the formula would apply is the 2nd term of the sequence, or when $n = 2$.

b. 6, 24, 96, 384, ...

Step 1 First subtract each term from the term that follows it.

$24 - 6 = 18$ $\quad 96 - 24 = 72$ $\quad 384 - 96 = 288$

There is no common difference. Check for a common ratio by dividing each term by the term that precedes it.

$\frac{24}{6} = 4$ $\quad \frac{96}{24} = 4$ $\quad \frac{384}{96} = 4$

There is a common ratio of 4. The sequence is geometric.

Step 2 Use the formula for a geometric sequence.

$a_n = r \cdot a_{n-1}$ Recursive formula for geometric sequence

$a_n = 4a_{n-1}$ $r = 4$

Step 3 The first term a_1 is 6, and $n \geq 2$.

A recursive formula for the sequence is $a_1 = 6, a_n = 4a_{n-1}, n \geq 2$.

GuidedPractice

2A. 4, 10, 25, 62.5, ... $a_1 = 4, a_n = 2.5a_{n-1}, n \geq 2.$

2B. 9, 36, 63, 90, ... $a_1 = 9, a_n = a_{n-1} + 27, n \geq 2.$

Tips for New Teachers

Notation Recursive formulas are occasionally defined for a_{n+1} and written in terms of a_n. For part **a** of Example 2, the recursive formula can be written as $a_1 = 17, a_{n+1} = a_n - 4, n \geq 1$.

A sequence can be represented by both an explicit formula and a recursive formula.

Real-WorldCareer

Transportation The number of jobs in the transportation industry is expected to grow by an estimated 1.1 million between 2004 and 2014. The specific fields dictate the educational requirements, which include a high school diploma and some form of specialized training.

Source: United States Department of Labor

Example 3 Write Recursive and Explicit Formulas

COST Refer to the beginning of the lesson. Let n be the number of customers.

a. Write a recursive formula for the sequence.

Steps 1 and 2 First subtract each term from the term that follows it.

$35 - 25 = 10 \qquad 45 - 35 = 10 \qquad 55 - 45 = 10$

There is a common difference of 10. The sequence is arithmetic.

Step 3 Use the formula for an arithmetic sequence.

$a_n = a_{n-1} + d$ Recursive formula for arithmetic sequence

$a_n = a_{n-1} + 10$ $d = 10$

Step 4 The first term a_1 is 25, and $n \geq 2$.

A recursive formula for the sequence is $a_1 = 25$, $a_n = a_{n-1} + 10$, $n \geq 2$.

b. Write an explicit formula for the sequence.

Step 1 The common difference is 10.

Step 2 Use the formula for the nth term of an arithmetic sequence.

$a_n = a_1 + (n - 1)d$ Formula for the nth term

$= 25 + (n - 1)10$ $a_1 = 25$ and $d = 10$

$= 25 + 10n - 10$ Distributive Property

$= 10n + 15$ Simplify.

An explicit formula for the sequence is $a_n = 10n + 15$.

GuidedPractice

3. SAVINGS The money that Ronald has in his savings account earns interest each year. He does not make any withdrawals or additional deposits. The account balance at the beginning of each year is \$10,000, \$10,300, \$10,609, \$10,927.27, and so on. Write a recursive formula and an explicit formula for the sequence. $a_1 = 10{,}000$, $a_n = 1.03a_{n-1}$, $n \geq 2$; $a_n = 10{,}000(1.03)^{n-1}$

If several successive terms of a sequence are needed, a recursive formula may be useful, whereas if just the nth term of a sequence is needed, an explicit formula may be useful. Thus, it is sometimes beneficial to translate between the two forms.

Example 4 Translate between Recursive and Explicit Formulas

a. Write a recursive formula for $a_n = 6n + 3$.

$a_n = 6n + 3$ is an explicit formula for an arithmetic sequence with $d = 6$ and $a_1 = 6(1) + 3$ or 9. Therefore, a recursive formula for a_n is $a_1 = 9$, $a_n = a_{n-1} + 6$, $n \geq 2$.

b. Write an explicit formula for $a_1 = 120$, $a_n = 0.8a_{n-1}$, $n \geq 2$.

$a_n = 0.8a_{n-1}$ is a recursive formula for a geometric sequence with $a_1 = 120$ and $r = 0.8$. Therefore, an explicit formula for a_n is $a_n = 120(0.8)^{n-1}$.

StudyTip

Geometric Sequence Recall that the formula for the nth term of a geometric sequence is $a_n = a_1r^{n-1}$.

GuidedPractice

4A. Write a recursive formula for $a_n = 4(3)^{n-1}$. $a_1 = 4$, $a_n = 3a_{n-1}$, $n \geq 2$.

4B. Write an explicit formula for $a_1 = -16$, $a_n = a_{n-1} - 7$, $n \geq 2$. $a_n = -7n - 9$.

Additional Examples

3 CARS The price of a car depreciates at the end of each year.

Year	Price ($)
1	12,000
2	7200
3	4320
4	2592

a. Write a recursive formula for the sequence. $a_1 = 12{,}000$, $a_n = 0.6a_{n-1}$

b. Write an explicit formula for the sequence. $a_n = 12{,}000(0.6)^{n-1}$

4 a. Write a recursive formula for $a_n = 2n - 4$. $a_1 = -2$, $a_n = a_{n-1} + 2$, $n \geq 2$

b. Write an explicit formula for $a_1 = 84$, $a_n = 1.5a_{n-1}$, $n \geq 2$. $a_n = 84(1.5)^{n-1}$

Tips for New Teachers

Terms The first term of a sequence is occasionally denoted as a_0.

DifferentiatedInstruction AL OL

Interpersonal Learners Divide the class into groups of two or three students. Have each student write a sequence on one note card and the recursive formula for the sequence on another note card. Repeat the process for 10 sequences. Then, have the students lay the cards face down. Each student should take turns flipping over two cards, attempting to find a match between a sequence and its recursive formula.

3 Practice

Formative Assessment

Use Exercises 1–9 to check for understanding.

Use the chart at the bottom of this page to customize assignments for your students.

Teaching the Process Standards

Modeling Mathematically proficient students use tools such as diagrams to map the relationships of important quantities in a practical situation. In Exercise 22, tell students that they can sketch the patio to help them see the pattern.

Arguments Mathematically proficient students can recognize and use counterexamples. In Exercise 33, tell students that they can start with a sequence for which they know a recursive formula and see if they can write another recursive formula that fits the sequence to see if they can find a counterexample to the statement.

WatchOut!

Error Analysis In Exercise 31, students should recognize that the sequence is geometric with a common ratio of −1. Therefore, the sequence can be represented as both an explicit formula and a recursive formula.

Additional Answer

31. Both; sample answer: The sequence can be written as the recursive formula $a_1 = 2$, $a_n = (-1)a_{n-1}$, $n \geq 2$. The sequence can also be written as the explicit formula $a_n = 2(-1)^{n-1}$.

Check Your Understanding

= Step-by-Step Solutions begin on page R13.

Example 1 **Find the first five terms of each sequence.**

1. $a_1 = 16, a_n = a_{n-1} - 3, n \geq 2$
16, 13, 10, 7, 4

2. $a_1 = -5, a_n = 4a_{n-1} + 10, n \geq 2$
−5, −10, −30, −110, −430

Example 2 **Write a recursive formula for each sequence.**

3. 1, 6, 11, 16, …
$a_1 = 1,\ a_n = a_{n-1} + 5,\ n \geq 2$

4. 4, 12, 36, 108, …
$a_1 = 4,\ a_n = 3a_{n-1},\ n \geq 2$

Example 3

5. BALL A ball is dropped from an initial height of 10 feet. The maximum heights the ball reaches on the first three bounces are shown.

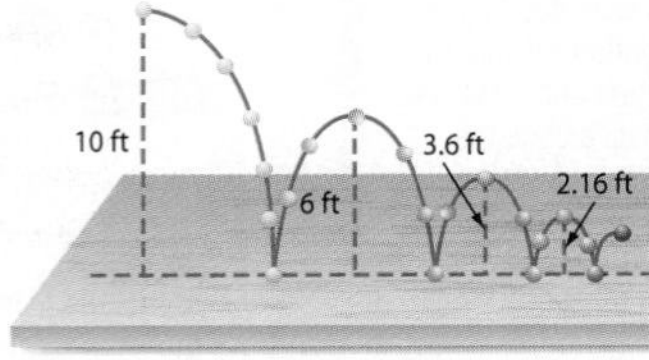

a. Write a recursive formula for the sequence.

b. Write an explicit formula for the sequence.

5a. $a_1 = 10,\ a_n = 0.6a_{n-1},\ n \geq 2$
5b. $a_n = 10(0.6)^{n-1}$

Example 4 **For each recursive formula, write an explicit formula. For each explicit formula, write a recursive formula.**

6. $a_1 = 4, a_n = a_{n-1} + 16, n \geq 2$
$a_n = 16n - 12$

7. $a_n = 5n + 8$
$a_1 = 13,\ a_n = a_{n-1} + 5,\ n \geq 2$

8. $a_n = 15(2)^{n-1}$
$a_1 = 15,\ a_n = 2a_{n-1},\ n \geq 2$

9. $a_1 = 22, a_n = 4a_{n-1}, n \geq 2$
$a_n = 22(4)^{n-1}$

Practice and Problem Solving

Extra Practice is on page R7.

Example 1 **Find the first five terms of each sequence.**

10. $a_1 = 23, a_n = a_{n-1} + 7, n \geq 2$
23, 30, 37, 44, 51

11. $a_1 = 48, a_n = -0.5a_{n-1} + 8, n \geq 2$
48, −16, 16, 0, 8

12. $a_1 = 8, a_n = 2.5a_{n-1}, n \geq 2$
8, 20, 50, 125, 312.5

13. $a_1 = 12, a_n = 3a_{n-1} - 21, n \geq 2$
12, 15, 24, 51, 132

14. $a_1 = 13, a_n = -2a_{n-1} - 3, n \geq 2$
13, −29, 55, −113, 223

15. $a_1 = \frac{1}{2}, a_n = a_{n-1} + \frac{3}{2}, n \geq 2$
$\frac{1}{2}, 2, \frac{7}{2}, 5, \frac{13}{2}$

Example 2 **Write a recursive formula for each sequence.**

16. 12, −1, −14, −27, …
$a_1 = 12,\ a_n = a_{n-1} - 13,\ n \geq 2$

17. 27, 41, 55, 69, …
$a_1 = 27,\ a_n = a_{n-1} + 14,\ n \geq 2$

18. 2, 11, 20, 29, …
$a_1 = 2,\ a_n = a_{n-1} + 9,\ n \geq 2$

19. 100, 80, 64, 51.2, …
$a_1 = 100,\ a_n = 0.8a_{n-1},\ n \geq 2$

20. 40, −60, 90, −135, …
$a_1 = 40,\ a_n = -1.5a_{n-1},\ n \geq 2$

21. 81, 27, 9, 3, …
$a_1 = 81,\ a_n = \frac{1}{3}a_{n-1},\ n \geq 2$

Example 3

22. MODELING A landscaper is building a brick patio. Part of the patio includes a pattern constructed from triangles. The first four rows of the pattern are shown. **22a.** $a_1 = 15,\ a_n = a_{n-1} - 2,\ n \geq 2$

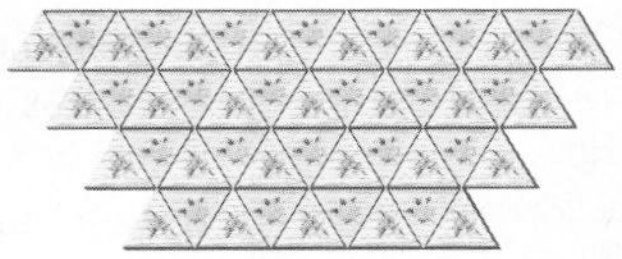

a. Write a recursive formula for the sequence.

b. Write an explicit formula for the sequence. $a_n = 17 - 2n$

Example 4 **For each recursive formula, write an explicit formula. For each explicit formula, write a recursive formula.**

23. $a_n = 3(4)^{n-1}$
$a_1 = 3,\ a_n = 4a_{n-1},\ n \geq 2$

24. $a_1 = -2, a_n = a_{n-1} - 12, n \geq 2$ $a_n = -12n + 10$

25. $a_1 = 38, a_n = \frac{1}{2}a_{n-1}, n \geq 2$
$a_n = 38\left(\frac{1}{2}\right)^{n-1}$

26. $a_n = -7n + 52$ $a_1 = 45,\ a_n = a_{n-1} - 7,\ n \geq 2$

Differentiated Homework Options

Level	Assignment	Two-Day Option	
AL Basic	10–26, 31, 33–59	11–25 odd, 36–39	10–26 even, 31, 33–35, 40–59
OL Core	11–25 odd, 27–31, 33–59	10–26, 36–39	27–31, 33–35, 40–59
BL Advanced	27–53, (optional: 54–59)		

B 27. **TEXTING** Barbara received a chain text that she forwarded to five of her friends. Each of her friends forwarded the text to five more friends, and so on.

a. Find the first five terms of the sequence representing the number of people who receive the text in the nth round. **1, 5, 25, 125, 625**

b. Write a recursive formula for the sequence. $a_1 = 1, a_n = 5a_{n-1}, n \geq 2$

c. If Barbara represents a_1, find a_8. **78,125**

28. **GEOMETRY** Consider the pattern below. The number of blue boxes increases according to a specific pattern.

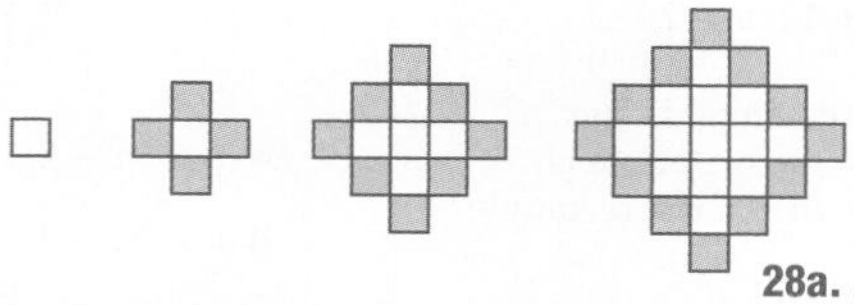

28a. $a_1 = 0, a_n = a_{n-1} + 4, n \geq 2$

a. Write a recursive formula for the sequence of the number of blue boxes in each figure.

b. If the first box represents a_1, find the number of blue boxes in a_8. **28**

29. **TREE** The growth of a certain type of tree slows as the tree continues to age. The heights of the tree over the past four years are shown.

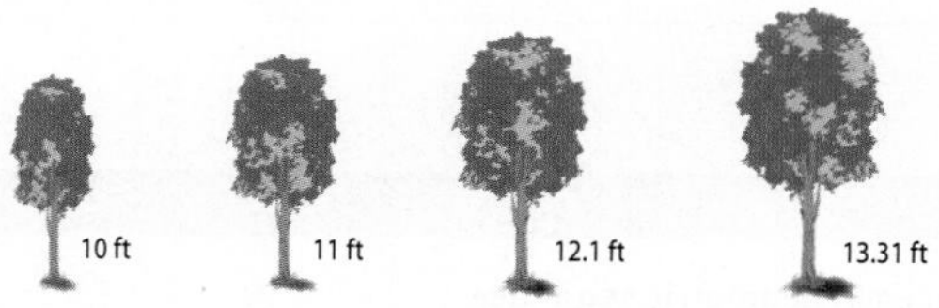

a. Write a recursive formula for the height of the tree. $a_1 = 10, a_n = 1.1a_{n-1}, n \geq 2$

b. If the pattern continues, how tall will the tree be in two more years? Round your answer to the nearest tenth of a foot. **16.1 ft**

30a. Sample answer: The first two terms are 1. Starting with the third term, the two previous terms are added together to get the next term; 13, 21, 34, 55, 89.

C 30. **MULTIPLE REPRESENTATIONS** The Fibonacci sequence is neither arithmetic nor geometric and can be defined by a recursive formula. The first terms are 1, 1, 2, 3, 5, 8, ...

a. **Logical** Determine the relationship between the terms of the sequence. What are the next five terms in the sequence? 30b. $a_1 = 1, a_2 = 1, a_n = a_{n-2} + a_{n-1}, n \geq 3$

b. **Algebraic** Write a formula for the nth term if $a_1 = 1, a_2 = 1$, and $n \geq 3$.

c. **Algebraic** Find the 15th term. **610**

d. **Analytical** Explain why the Fibonacci sequence is not an arithmetic sequence. **Sample answer: There is no common difference.**

alse; le answer: ursive formula for equence 1, 2, 3, ... e written as 1, $a_n = a_{n-1} + 1$, or as 1, $a_2 = 2$, $a_{n-2} + 2, n \geq 3$.

H.O.T. Problems Use Higher-Order Thinking Skills

31. **ERROR ANALYSIS** Patrick and Lynda are working on a math problem that involves the sequence 2, −2, 2, −2, 2, ... Patrick thinks that the sequence can be written as a recursive formula. Lynda believes that the sequence can be written as an explicit formula. Is either of them correct? Explain. **See margin.**

32. **CHALLENGE** Find a_1 for the sequence in which $a_4 = 1104$ and $a_n = 4a_{n-1} + 16$. **12**

33. **ARGUMENTS** Determine whether the following statement is *true* or *false*. Justify your reasoning.

There is only one recursive formula for every sequence.

34. **CHALLENGE** Find a recursive formula for 4, 9, 19, 39, 79, ... $a_1 = 4, a_n = 2a_{n-1} + 1, n \geq 2$

35. **WRITING IN MATH** Explain the difference between an explicit formula and a recursive formula.

ample answer: explicit ula, the nth a_n is given as a ion of n. In a sive formula, th term a_n is d by performing ations to one or of the terms recede it.

Multiple Representations

In Exercise 30, students use logic, analysis, and algebra to explore the Fibonacci sequence and find terms as needed.

Study Guide and Intervention

AL OL ELL

7-8 Study Guide and Intervention

Recursive Formulas

Using Recursive Formulas A **recursive formula** allows you to find the nth term of a sequence by performing operations on one or more of the terms that precede it.

The first five terms are 5, 4, 6, 2, and 10.

Exercises

Find the first five terms of each sequence.

Practice

AL OL BL ELL

7-8 Practice

Recursive Formulas

Find the first five terms of each sequence.

Write a recursive formula for each sequence.

13. PIZZA The total costs for ordering one to five cheese pizzas from Luigi's Pizza Palace are shown.

Total Number of Pizzas Ordered	Cost
1	$7.00
2	$12.50
3	$18.00
4	$23.50
5	$29.00

a. Write a recursive formula for the sequence.

b. Write an explicit formula for the sequence.

Word Problem Practice

AL OL BL ELL

7-8 Word Problem Practice

Recursive Formulas

Enrichment

OL BL

7-8 Enrichment

Arithmetic Series

4 Assess

Ticket Out the Door Have each student create a sequence by writing the first five terms. Then have them write an explicit formula and a recursive formula for the sequence.

Formative Assessment

Check for student understanding of concepts in Lessons 7-7 and 7-8.

Quiz 4, p. 58

Standardized Test Practice

36. Find a recursive formula for the sequence 12, 24, 36, 48, … . **C**

A $a_1 = 12, a_n = 2a_{n-1}, n \geq 2.$

B $a_1 = 12, a_n = 4a_{n-1} - 24, n \geq 2.$

C $a_1 = 12, a_n = a_{n-1} + 12, n \geq 2.$

D $a_1 = 12, a_n = 12a_{n-1} + 12, n \geq 2.$

37. GEOMETRY The area of a rectangle is $36m^4n^6$ square feet. The length of the rectangle is $6m^3n^3$ feet. What is the width of the rectangle? **G**

F $216m^7n^9$ ft

G $6mn^3$ ft

H $42m^7n^3$ ft

J $30mn^3$ ft

38. Find an inequality for the graph shown. **C**

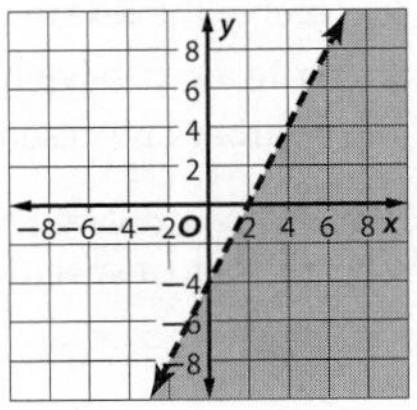

A $y > 2x - 4$

B $y \geq 2x - 4$

C $y < 2x - 4$

D $y \leq 2x - 4$

39. Write an equation of the line that passes through (−2, −20) and (4, 58). **F**

F $y = 13x + 6$

G $y = 19x - 18$

H $y = 19x + 18$

J $y = 13x - 6$

Spiral Review

Find the next three terms in each geometric sequence. (Lesson 7-7)

40. 675, 225, 75, … **$25, \frac{25}{3}, \frac{25}{9}$**

41. 16, −24, 36, … **−54, 81, −121.5**

42. 6, 18, 54, … **162, 486, 1458**

43. 512, −256, 128, … **−64, 32, −16**

44. 125, 25, 5, … **$1, \frac{1}{5}, \frac{1}{25}$**

45. 12, 60, 300, … **1500; 7500; 37,500**

46. INVESTMENT Nicholas invested $2000 with a 5.75% interest rate compounded monthly. How much money will Nicholas have after 5 years? (Lesson 7-6) **$2664.35**

47. TOURS The Snider family and the Rollins family are traveling together on a trip to visit a candy factory. The number of people in each family and the total cost are shown in the table below. Find the adult and children's admission prices. (Lesson 6-3) **adults: $14; children: $10**

Family	Number of Adults	Number of Children	Total Cost
Snider	2	3	$58
Rollins	2	1	$38

Write each equation in standard form. (Lesson 4-3)

48. $y + 6 = -3(x + 2)$ **$3x + y = -12$**

49. $y - 12 = 4(x - 7)$ **$4x - y = 16$**

50. $y + 9 = 5(x - 3)$ **$5x - y = 24$**

51. $y - 1 = \frac{1}{3}(x + 15)$ **$x - 3y = -18$**

52. $y + 10 = \frac{2}{5}(x - 6)$ **$2x - 5y = 62$**

53. $y - 4 = -\frac{2}{7}(x + 1)$ **$2x + 7y = 26$**

Skills Review

Simplify each expression. If not possible, write *simplified*.

54. $8x + 3y^2 + 7x - 2y$ **$3y^2 + 15x - 2y$**

55. $4(x - 16) + 6x$ **$10x - 64$**

56. $4n - 3m + 9m - n$ **$3n + 6m$**

57. $6r^2 + 7r$ **simplified**

58. $-2(4g - 5h) - 6g$ **$-14g + 10h$**

59. $9x^2 - 7x + 16y^2$ **simplified**

Differentiated Instruction BL

Extension For Exercise 30, students wrote a recursive formula for the Fibonacci sequence, which is neither arithmetic nor geometric. Have students write a recursive formula for another sequence that is neither arithmetic nor geometric.

CHAPTER 7 Study Guide and Review

Study Guide

KeyConcepts

Multiplication and Division Properties of Exponents (Lessons 7-1 and 7-2)

For any nonzero real numbers a and b and any integers m, n, and p, the following are true.

- Product of Powers: $a^m \cdot a^n = a^{m+n}$
- Power of a Power: $(a^m)^n = a^{m \cdot n}$
- Power of a Product: $(ab)^m = a^m b^m$
- Quotient of Powers: $\frac{a^m}{a^p} = a^{m-p}$
- Power of a Quotient: $\left(\frac{a}{b}\right)^m = \frac{a^m}{b^m}$
- Zero Exponent: $a^0 = 1$
- Negative Exponent: $a^{-n} = \frac{1}{a^n}$ and $\frac{1}{a^{-n}} = a^n$

Rational Exponents (Lesson 7-3)

For any positive real number b and any integers m and $n > 1$, the following are true.

$b^{\frac{1}{2}} = \sqrt{b}$ $\qquad b^{\frac{1}{n}} = \sqrt[n]{b}$ $\qquad b^{\frac{m}{n}} = \left(\sqrt[n]{b}\right)^m$ or $\sqrt[n]{b^m}$

Scientific Notation (Lesson 7-4)

- A number is in scientific notation if it is in the form $a \times 10^n$, where $1 \le a < 10$.
- To write in standard form:
  - If $n > 0$, move the decimal n places right.
  - If $n < 0$, move the decimal n places left.

Exponential Functions (Lessons 7-5 and 7-6)

- The equation for exponential growth is $y = a(1 + r)^t$, where $r > 0$. The equation for exponential decay is $y = a(1 - r)^t$, where $0 < r < 1$. y is the final amount, a is the initial amount, r is the rate of change, and t is the time in years.

FOLDABLES StudyOrganizer

Be sure the Key Concepts are noted in your Foldable.

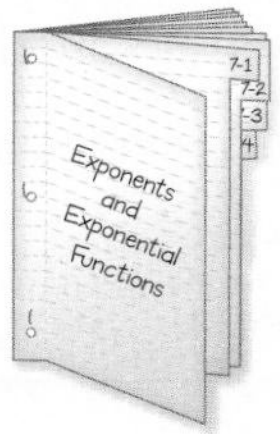

KeyVocabulary

common ratio (p. 438)	monomial (p. 391)
compound interest (p. 433)	negative exponent (p. 400)
constant (p. 391)	nth root (p. 407)
cube root (p. 407)	order of magnitude (p. 401)
exponential decay (p. 424)	rational exponent (p. 406)
exponential equation (p. 409)	recursive formula (p. 445)
exponential function (p. 424)	scientific notation (p. 414)
exponential growth (p. 424)	zero exponent (p. 399)
geometric sequence (p. 438)	

VocabularyCheck

Choose the word or term that best completes each sentence.

1. $7xy^4$ is an example of a(n) ________. **monomial**
2. The ________ of 95,234 is 10^5. **order of magnitude**
3. 2 is a(n) ________ of 8. **cube root**
4. The rules for operations with exponents can be extended to apply to expressions with a(n) ________ such as $7^{\frac{2}{3}}$. **rational exponent**
5. A number written in ________ is of the form $a \times 10^n$, where $1 \le a < 10$ and n is an integer. **scientific notation**
6. $f(x) = 3^x$ is an example of a(n) ________. **exponential function**
7. $a_1 = 4$ and $a_n = 3a_{n-1} - 12$, if $n \ge 2$, is a(n) ________ for the sequence 4, −8, −20, −32, …. **recursive formula**
8. $2^{3x-1} = 16$ is an example of a(n) ________. **exponential equation**
9. The equation for ________ is $y = C(1 - r)^t$. **exponential decay**
10. If $a^n = b$ for a positive integer n, then a is a(n) ________ of b. **nth root**

Formative Assessment

KeyVocabulary The page reference after each word denotes where that term was first introduced. If students have difficulty answering questions 1–10, remind them that they can use these page references to refresh their memories about the vocabulary terms.

Summative Assessment

Vocabulary Test, p. 60

Vocabulary Review

Vocabulary Review provides students the opportunity to check their understanding of important concepts and terminology in an online game format.

FOLDABLES StudyOrganizer

Dinah Zike's Foldables®

Have students look through the chapter to make sure they have included examples in their Foldables for each lesson of the chapter. Suggest that students keep their Foldables handy while completing the Study Guide and Review pages. Point out that their Foldables can serve as a quick review when studying for the chapter test.

Lesson-by-Lesson Review

Intervention If the given examples are not sufficient to review the topics covered by the questions, remind students that the lesson references tell them where to review that topic in their textbook.

Two-Day Option Have students complete the Lesson-by-Lesson Review. Then you can use McGraw-Hill eAssessment to customize another review worksheet that practices all the objectives of this chapter or only the objectives on which your students need more help.

CHAPTER 7 Study Guide and Review *Continued*

Lesson-by-Lesson Review

7-1 Multiplication Properties of Exponents

Simplify each expression.

11. $x \cdot x^3 \cdot x^5$ x^9
12. $(2xy)(-3x^2y^5)$ $-6x^3y^6$
13. $(-4ab^4)(-5a^5b^2)$ $20a^6b^6$
14. $(6x^3y^2)^2$ $36x^6y^4$
15. $\left[(2r^3t)^3\right]^2$ $64r^{18}t^6$
16. $(-2u^3)(5u)$ $-10u^4$
17. $(2x^2)^3(x^3)^3$ $8x^{15}$
18. $\frac{1}{2}(2x^3)^3$ $4x^9$
19. **GEOMETRY** Use the formula $V = \pi r^2 h$ to find the volume of the cylinder. $45\pi x^4$

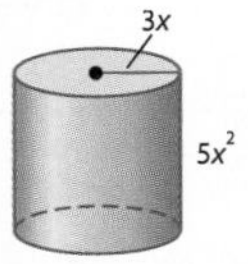

Example 1

Simplify $(5x^2y^3)(2x^4y)$.

$(5x^2y^3)(2x^4y)$

$= (5 \cdot 2)(x^2 \cdot x^4)(y^3 \cdot y)$ Commutative Property

$= 10x^6y^4$ Product of Powers

Example 2

Simplify $(3a^2b^4)^3$.

$(3a^2b^4)^3 = 3^3(a^2)^3(b^4)^3$ Power of a Product

$= 27a^6b^{12}$ Simplify.

7-2 Division Properties of Exponents

Simplify each expression. Assume that no denominator equals zero.

20. $\frac{(3x)^0}{2a}$ $\frac{1}{2a}$
21. $\left(\frac{3xy^3}{2z}\right)^3$ $\frac{27x^3y^9}{8z^3}$
22. $\frac{12y^{-4}}{3y^{-5}}$ $4y$
23. $a^{-3}b^0c^6$ $\frac{c^6}{a^3}$
24. $\frac{-15x^7y^8z^4}{-45x^3y^5z^3}$ $\frac{x^4y^3z}{3}$
25. $\frac{(3x^{-1})^{-2}}{(3x^2)^{-2}}$ x^6
26. $\left(\frac{6xy^{11}z^9}{48x^6yz^{-7}}\right)^0$ 1
27. $\left(\frac{12}{2}\right)\left(\frac{x}{y^5}\right)\left(\frac{y^4}{x^4}\right)$ $\frac{6}{yx^3}$
28. **GEOMETRY** The area of a rectangle is $25x^2y^4$ square feet. The width of the rectangle is $5xy$ feet. What is the length of the rectangle? $5xy^3$ ft

Example 3

Simplify $\frac{2k^4m^3}{4k^2m}$. Assume that no denominator equals zero.

$\frac{2k^4m^3}{4k^2m} = \left(\frac{2}{4}\right)\left(\frac{k^4}{k^2}\right)\left(\frac{m^3}{m}\right)$ Group powers with the same base.

$= \left(\frac{1}{2}\right)k^{4-2}m^{3-1}$ Quotient of Powers

$= \frac{k^2m^2}{2}$ Simplify.

Example 4

Simplify $\frac{t^4uv^{-2}}{t^{-3}u^7}$. Assume that no denominator equals zero.

$\frac{t^4uv^{-2}}{t^{-3}u^7} = \left(\frac{t^4}{t^{-3}}\right)\left(\frac{u}{u^7}\right)(v^{-2})$ Group the powers with the same base.

$= (t^{4+3})(u^{1-7})(v^{-2})$ Quotient of Powers

$= t^7u^{-6}v^{-2}$ Simplify.

$= \frac{t^7}{u^6v^2}$ Simplify.

7-3 Rational Exponents

Simplify.

29. $\sqrt[3]{343}$ **7**

30. $\sqrt[6]{729}$ **3**

31. $625^{\frac{1}{4}}$ **5**

32. $\left(\frac{8}{27}\right)^{\frac{1}{3}}$ $\frac{2}{3}$

33. $256^{\frac{3}{4}}$ **64**

34. $32^{\frac{2}{5}}$ **4**

35. $343^{\frac{4}{3}}$ **2401**

36. $\left(\frac{4}{49}\right)^{\frac{3}{2}}$ $\frac{8}{343}$

Solve each equation.

37. $6^x = 7776$ **5**

38. $4^{4x-1} = 32$ $\frac{7}{8}$

Example 5

Simplify $125^{\frac{2}{3}}$.

$125^{\frac{2}{3}} = (\sqrt[3]{125})^2$ — $b^{\frac{m}{n}} = (\sqrt[n]{b})^m$

$= (\sqrt[3]{5 \cdot 5 \cdot 5})^2$ — $125 = 5^3$

$= 5^2$ or 25 — Simplify.

Example 6

Solve $9^{x-1} = 729$.

$9^{x-1} = 729$ — Original equation

$9^{x-1} = 9^3$ — Rewrite 729 as 9^3.

$x - 1 = 3$ — Power Property of Equality

$x = 4$ — Add 1 to each side.

7-4 Scientific Notation

Express each number in scientific notation.

39. 2,300,000 **2.3×10^6**

40. 0.0000543 **5.43×10^{-5}**

41. ASTRONOMY Earth has a diameter of about 8000 miles. Jupiter has a diameter of about 88,000 miles. Write in scientific notation the ratio of Earth's diameter to Jupiter's diameter. **about 9.1×10^{-2}**

Example 7

Express 300,000,000 in scientific notation.

Step 1 300,000,000 ⟶ 3.00000000

Step 2 The decimal point moved 8 places to the left, so $n = 8$.

Step 3 $300{,}000{,}000 = 3 \times 10^8$

7-5 Exponential Functions

Graph each function. Find the y-intercept, and state the domain and range. **42–45. See margin.**

42. $y = 2^x$

43. $y = 3^x + 1$

44. $y = 4^x + 2$

45. $y = 2^x - 3$

46. BIOLOGY The population of bacteria in a petri dish increases according to the model $p = 550(2.7)^{0.008t}$, where t is the number of hours and $t = 0$ corresponds to 1:00 P.M. Use this model to estimate the number of bacteria in the dish at 5:00 P.M. **about 568**

Example 8

Graph $y = 3^x + 6$. Find the y-intercept, and state the domain and range.

x	$3^x + 6$	y
−3	$3^{-3} + 6$	6.04
−2	$3^{-2} + 6$	6.11
−1	$3^{-1} + 6$	6.33
0	$3^0 + 6$	7
1	$3^1 + 6$	9

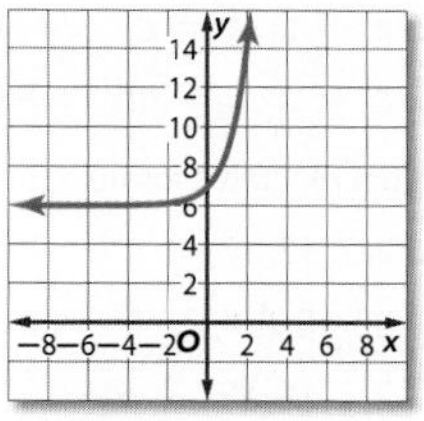

The y-intercept is (0, 7). The domain is all real numbers, and the range is all real numbers greater than 6.

Additional Answers

42. y-intercept 1; D = {all real numbers}; R = $\{y \mid y > 0\}$

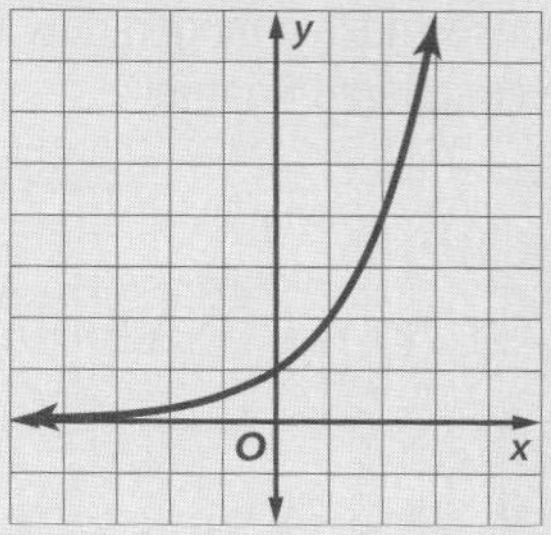

43. y-intercept 2; D = {all real numbers}; R = $\{y \mid y > 1\}$

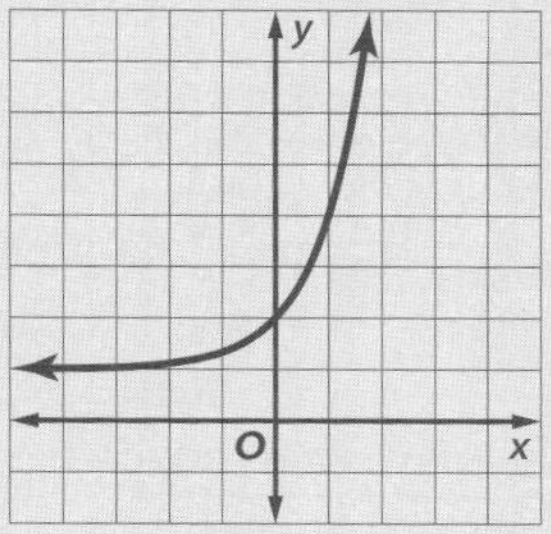

44. y-intercept 3; D = {all real numbers}; R = $\{y \mid y > 2\}$

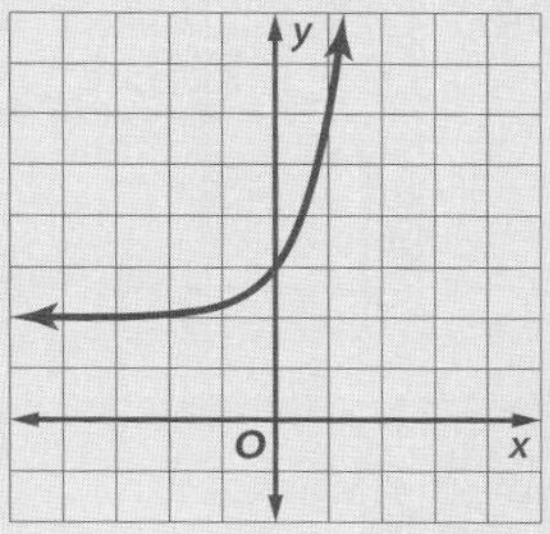

45. y-intercept −2; D = {all real numbers}; R = $\{y \mid y > -3\}$

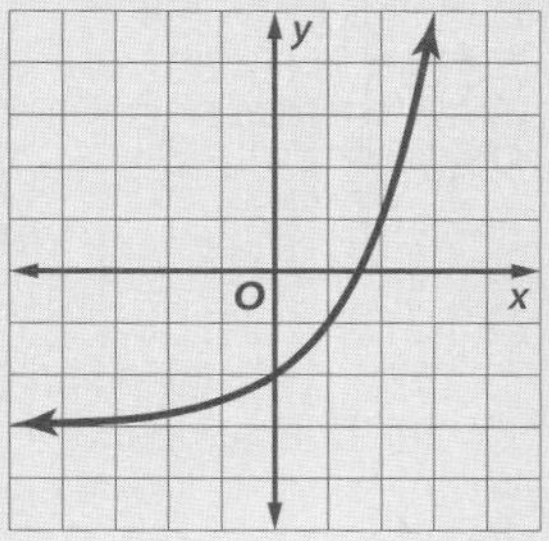

Anticipation Guide

Have students complete the Chapter 7 Anticipation Guide and discuss how their responses have changed now that they have completed Chapter 7.

Additional Answer

55. **Basketball Rebound**

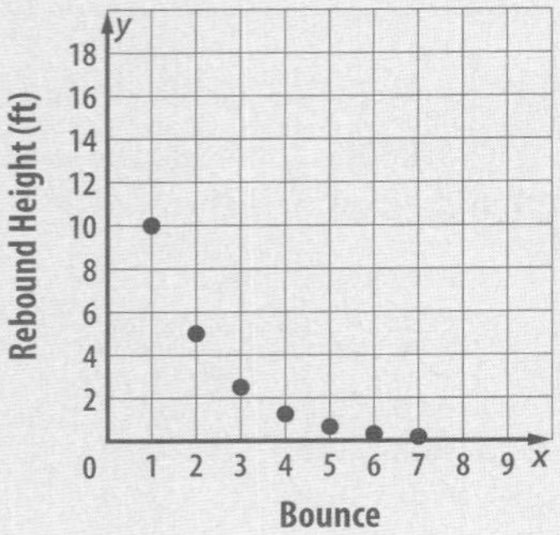

Additional Answers (Practice Test)

25.

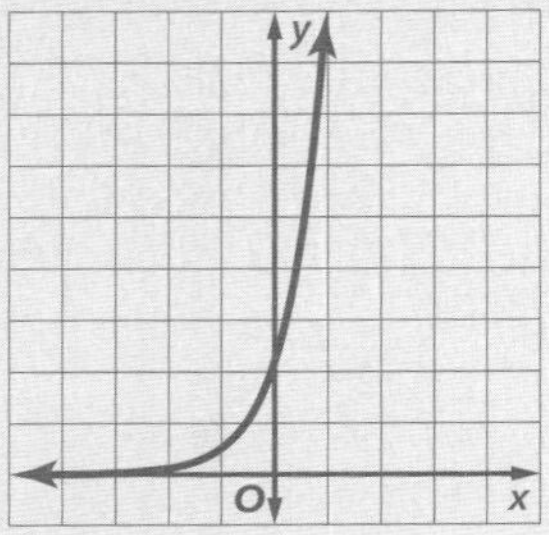

2; D = {all real numbers}, R = $\{y \mid y > 0\}$

26.

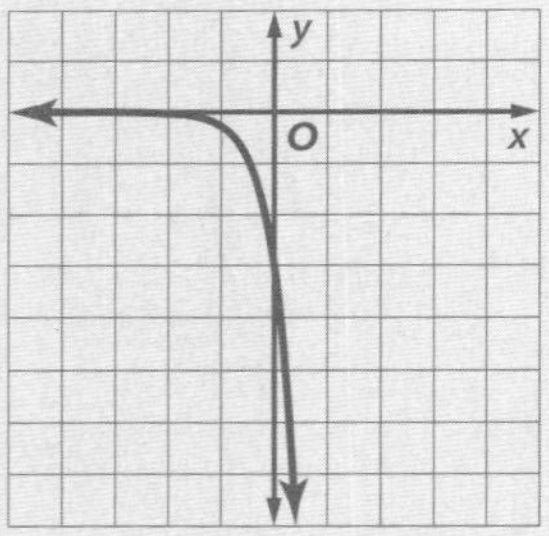

−3; D = {all real numbers}, R = $\{y \mid y < 0\}$

27.

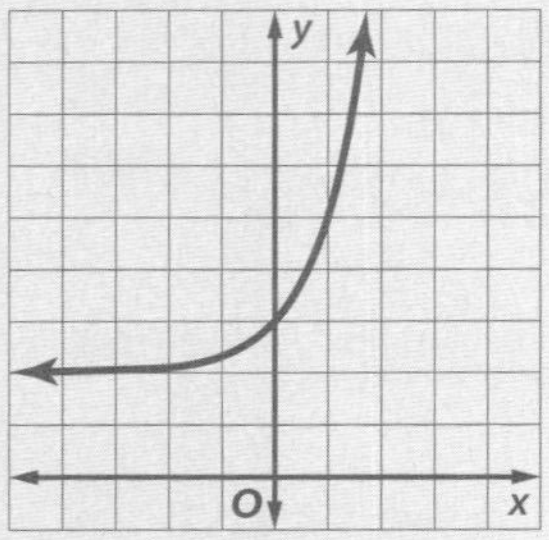

3; D = {all real numbers}, R = $\{y \mid y > 2\}$

CHAPTER 7 Study Guide and Review *Continued*

7-6 Growth and Decay

47. Find the final value of \$2500 invested at an interest rate of 2% compounded monthly for 10 years. **\$3053.00**

48. **COMPUTERS** Zita's computer is depreciating at a rate of 3% per year. She bought the computer for \$1200.

a. Write an equation to represent this situation.

b. What will the computer's value be after 5 years? **\$1030.48**

48a. $y = 1200(1 - 0.03)^t$

Example 9

Find the final value of \$2000 invested at an interest rate of 3% compounded quarterly for 8 years.

$A = P\left(1 + \frac{r}{n}\right)^{nt}$ — Compound interest equation

$= 2000\left(1 + \frac{0.03}{4}\right)^{4(8)}$ — $P = 2000$, $r = 0.03$, $n = 4$, and $t = 8$

$\approx \$2540.22$ — Use a calculator.

7-7 Geometric Sequences as Exponential Functions

Find the next three terms in each geometric sequence.

49. −1, 1, −1, 1, ... **−1, 1, −1**

50. 3, 9, 27, ... **81, 243, 729**

51. 256, 128, 64, ... **32, 16, 8**

Write the equation for the *n*th term of each geometric sequence.

52. −1, 1, −1, 1, ... $a_n = -1(-1)^{n-1}$

53. 3, 9, 27, ... $a_n = 3(3)^{n-1}$

54. 256, 128, 64, ... $a_n = 256\left(\frac{1}{2}\right)^{n-1}$

55. **SPORTS** A basketball is dropped from a height of 20 feet. It bounces to $\frac{1}{2}$ its height after each bounce. Draw a graph to represent the situation. **See margin.**

Example 10

Find the next three terms in the geometric sequence 2, 6, 18, ...

Step 1 Find the common ratio. Each number is 3 times the previous number, so $r = 3$.

Step 2 Multiply each term by the common ratio to find the next three terms.

$18 \times 3 = 54$, $54 \times 3 = 162$, $162 \times 3 = 486$

The next three terms are 54, 162, and 486.

Example 11

Write the equation for the *n*th term of the geometric sequence −3, 12, −48, ...

The common ratio is −4. So $r = -4$.

$a_n = a_1 r^{n-1}$ — Formula for the *n*th term

$a_n = -3(-4)^{n-1}$ — $a_1 = -3$ and $r = -4$

7-8 Recursive Formulas

Find the first five terms of each sequence.

56. $a_1 = 11$, $a_n = a_{n-1} - 4$, $n \geq 2$ **11, 7, 3, −1, −5**

57. $a_1 = 3$, $a_n = 2a_{n-1} + 6$, $n \geq 2$ **3, 12, 30, 66, 138**

Write a recursive formula for each sequence.

58. 2, 7, 12, 17, ... $a_1 = 2$, $a_n = a_{n-1} + 5$, $n \geq 2$

59. 32, 16, 8, 4, ... $a_1 = 32$, $a_n = 0.5a_{n-1}$, $n \geq 2$

60. 2, 5, 11, 23, ... $a_1 = 2$, $a_n = 2a_{n-1} + 1$, $n \geq 2$

Example 12

Write a recursive formula for 3, 1, −1, −3, ...

Step 1 First subtract each term from the term that follows it.

$1 - 3 = -2$, $-1 - 1 = -2$, $-3 - (-1) = -2$

There is a common difference of −2. The sequence is arithmetic.

Step 2 Use the formula for an arithmetic sequence.

$a_n = a_{n-1} + d$ — Recursive formula

$a_n = a_{n-1} + (-2)$ — $d = -2$

Step 3 The first term a_1 is 3, and $n \geq 2$.

A recursive formula is $a_1 = 3$, $a_n = a_{n-1} - 2$, $n \geq 2$.

454 | Chapter 7 | Study Guide and Review

CHAPTER 7 Practice Test

Simplify each expression.

1. $(x^2)(7x^8)$ **$7x^{10}$**
2. $(5a^7bc^2)(-6a^2bc^5)$ **$-30a^9b^2c^7$**
3. **MULTIPLE CHOICE** Express the volume of the solid as a monomial. **A**

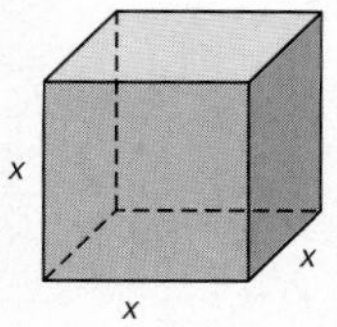

A x^3 | C $6x^3$

B $6x$ | D x^6

Simplify each expression. Assume that no denominator equals 0.

4. $\frac{x^6y^8}{x^2}$ **x^4y^8**
5. $\left(\frac{2a^4b^3}{c^6}\right)^0$ **1**
6. $\frac{2xy^{-7}}{8x}$ **$\frac{1}{4y^7}$**

Simplify.

7. $\sqrt[3]{1000}$ **10**
8. $\sqrt[5]{3125}$ **5**
9. $1728^{\frac{1}{3}}$ **12**
10. $\left(\frac{16}{81}\right)^{\frac{1}{2}}$ **$\frac{4}{9}$**
11. $27^{\frac{2}{3}}$ **9**
12. $10{,}000^{\frac{3}{4}}$ **1000**
13. $27^{\frac{5}{3}}$ **243**
14. $\left(\frac{1}{121}\right)^{\frac{3}{2}}$ **$\frac{1}{1331}$**

Solve each equation.

15. $12^x = 1728$ **3**
16. $7^{x-1} = 2401$ **5**
17. $9^{x-3} = 729$ **6**

Express each number in scientific notation.

18. 0.00021 **2.1×10^{-4}**
19. 58,000 **5.8×10^4**

Express each number in standard form.

20. 2.9×10^{-5} **0.000029**
21. 9.1×10^6 **9,100,000**

Evaluate each product or quotient. Express the results in scientific notation.

22. $(2.5 \times 10^3)(3 \times 10^4)$ **7.5×10^7**
23. $\frac{8.8 \times 10^2}{4 \times 10^{-4}}$ **2.2×10^6**
24. **ASTRONOMY** The average distance from Mercury to the Sun is 35,980,000 miles. Express this distance in scientific notation. **3.598×10^7**

Graph each function. Find the y-intercept, and state the domain and range.

25–27. See margin.

25. $y = 2(5)^x$
26. $y = -3(11)^x$
27. $y = 3^x + 2$

Find the next three terms in each geometric sequence.

28. 2, −6, 18, … **−54, 162, −486**
29. 1000, 500, 250, … **125, 62.5, 31.25**
30. 32, 8, 2, … **$\frac{1}{2}, \frac{1}{8}, \frac{1}{32}$**
31. **MULTIPLE CHOICE** Lynne invested $500 into an account with a 6.5% interest rate compounded monthly. How much will Lynne's investment be worth in 10 years? **H**

F $600.00

G $938.57

H $956.09

J $957.02

32. **INVESTMENTS** Shelly's investment of $3000 has been losing value at a rate of 3% each year. What will her investment be worth in 6 years? **$2498.92**

Find the first five terms of each sequence.

33. $a_1 = 18, a_n = a_{n-1} - 4, n \geq 2$ **18, 14, 10, 6, 2**
34. $a_1 = -2, a_n = 4a_{n-1} + 5, n \geq 2$ **−2, −3, −7, −23, −87**

Summative Assessment

Use these alternate leveled chapter tests to differentiate assessment for your students.

Leveled Chapter 7 Tests

Form	Type	Level	Page(s)
1	MC	AL	61–62
2A	MC	OL	63–64
2B	MC	OL	65–66
2C	FR	OL	67–68
2D	FR	OL	69–70
3	FR	BL	71–72
Vocabulary Test			60
Extended-Response Test			73

MC = multiple-choice questions
FR = free-response questions

McGraw-Hill eAssessment Customize and create multiple versions of your chapter tests and their answer keys. All of the questions from the leveled chapter tests in the *Chapter 7 Resource Masters* are also available on McGraw-Hill eAssessment.

InterventionPlanner

Tier 1 On Level OL

If students miss about 25% of the exercises or less,

Then choose a resource:

SE Lessons 7-1, 7-2, 7-3, 7-4, 7-5, 7-6, 7-7, and 7-8

Skills Practice, pp. 7, 13, 19, 25, 31, 37, 44, and 50

TE Chapter Project

connectED.mcgraw-hill.com Self-Check Quiz

Tier 2 Strategic Intervention AL
approaching grade level

If students miss about 50% of the exercises,

Then choose a resource:

Study Guide and Intervention, Chapter 7, pp. 5, 11, 17, 23, 29, 35, 42, and 48

connectED.mcgraw-hill.com Extra Examples, Personal Tutor, Homework Help

Tier 3 Intensive Intervention
2 or more grades below level

If students miss about 75% of the exercises,

Then use *Math Triumphs, Alg. 1*

connectED.mcgraw-hill.com Extra Examples, Personal Tutor, Homework Help, Review Vocabulary

1 Focus

Objective Use the strategy of using a scientific calculator to solve standardized test problems.

2 Teach

Scaffolding Questions

Ask:

- For which types of math problems have you used a scientific calculator? Answers will vary.
- Are there any types of math problems in which you find that it is faster or easier to *not* use a scientific calculator? Answers will vary.
- Are you more likely or less likely to make calculation errors when using a scientific calculator? Explain. Sample answer: You are less likely to make a calculation error, but you could still make errors if you enter the numbers incorrectly, or use formulas incorrectly, or round incorrectly.

CHAPTER 7 Preparing for Standardized Tests

Using a Scientific or Graphing Calculator

Scientific and graphing calculators are powerful problem-solving tools. There are times when a calculator can be used to make computations faster and easier, such as computations with very large numbers. However, there are times when using a calculator is necessary, like the estimation of irrational numbers.

Strategies for Using a Scientific or Graphing Calculator

Step 1

Familiarize yourself with the various functions of a scientific or graphing calculator as well as when they should be used:

- **Exponents** scientific notation, calculating with large or small numbers
- **Pi** solving circle problems, like circumference and area
- **Square roots** distance on a coordinate plane, Pythagorean theorem
- **Graphs** analyzing paired data in a scatter plot, graphing functions, finding roots of equations

Step 2

Use your scientific or graphing calculator to solve the problem.

- Remember to work as efficiently as possible. Some steps may be done mentally or by hand, while others should be completed using your calculator.
- If time permits, check your answer.

Standardized Test Example

Read the problem. Identify what you need to know. Then use the information in the problem to solve.

The distance from the Sun to Jupiter is approximately 7.786×10^{11} meters. If the speed of light is about 3×10^{8} meters per second, how long does it take for light from the Sun to reach Jupiter? Round to the nearest minute.

A about 43 minutes
B about 51 minutes
C about 1876 minutes
D about 2595 minutes

456 | Chapter 7 | Preparing for Standardized Tests

Read the problem carefully. You are given the approximate distance from the Sun to Jupiter as well as the speed of light. Both quantities are given in scientific notation. You are asked to find how many minutes it takes for light from the Sun to reach Jupiter. Use the relationship distance = rate × time to find the amount of time.

$d = r \times t$

$\frac{d}{r} = t$

To find the amount of time, divide the distance by the rate. Notice, however, that the units for time will be seconds.

$\frac{7.786 \times 10^{11} \text{ m}}{3 \times 10^{8} \text{ m/s}} = t$ seconds

Use a scientific calculator to quickly find the quotient. On most scientific calculators, the EE key is used to enter numbers in scientific notation.

KEYSTROKES: [( ] 7.786 [2nd] [EE] 11 [ )] [÷] [( ] 3 [2nd] [EE] 8 [ )] [ENTER]

The result is 2595.33333333 seconds. To convert this number to minutes, use your calculator to divide the result by 60. This gives an answer of about 43.2555 minutes. The answer is A.

Exercises

Read each problem. Identify what you need to know. Then use the information in the problem to solve.

1. Since its creation 5 years ago, approximately 2.504×10^7 items have been sold or traded on a popular online website. What is the average daily number of items sold or traded over the 5-year period? B

   A about 9640 items per day

   B about 13,720 items per day

   C about 1,025,000 items per day

   D about 5,008,000 items per day

2. Evaluate $\sqrt{ab}$ if $a = 121$ and $b = 23$. J

   F about 5.26

   G about 9.90

   H about 12

   J about 52.75

3. The population of the United States is about 3.034×10^8 people. The land area of the country is about 3.54×10^6 square miles. What is the average *population density* (number of people per square mile) of the United States? D

   A about 136.3 people per square mile

   B about 112.5 people per square mile

   C about 94.3 people per square mile

   D about 85.7 people per square mile

4. Eleece is making a cover for the marching band's bass drum. The drum has a diameter of 20 inches. Estimate the area of the face of the bass drum. J

   F 31.41 square inches

   G 62.83 square inches

   H 78.54 square inches

   J 314.16 square inches

Additional Example

Light travels at about 9.46×10^{12} kilometers per year. The star Altair is about 1.5136×10^{14} kilometers from Earth. About many months would it take light to travel from Earth to Altair? B

A about 1920 months

B about 192 months

C about 160 months

D about 16 months

3 Assess

Use Exercise 1–4 to assess students' understanding.

Diagnose Student Errors

Survey student responses for each item. Class trends may indicate common errors and misconceptions.

1. A forgot to multiply by $\frac{1}{2}$
B forgot to multiply by $\frac{1}{2}$ and multiplied instead of added exponents
C multiplied instead of added exponents
D correct

2. F forgot to raise $\frac{2}{3}$ to the power of 3 and added instead of multiplied exponents
G correct
H added instead of multiplied exponents
J forgot to raise $\frac{2}{3}$ to the power of 3

3. A correct
B slope is opposite, but not opposite reciprocal
C slope is reciprocal, but not opposite sign
D same slope, this is a parallel line

4. F wrote an explicit formula
G wrote a formula for a geometric sequence
H correct
J guess

5. A correct
B not written in scientific notation
C added instead of multiplied 4.2 and 5.7
D multiplied instead of added 6 and 8

6. F boundary has wrong intercept
G boundary has wrong slope and intercept
H correct
J boundary has wrong slope

CHAPTER 7

Standardized Test Practice

Cumulative, Chapters 1 through 7

Multiple Choice

Read each question. Then fill in the correct answer on the answer document provided by your teacher or on a sheet of paper.

1. Express the area of the triangle below as a monomial. D

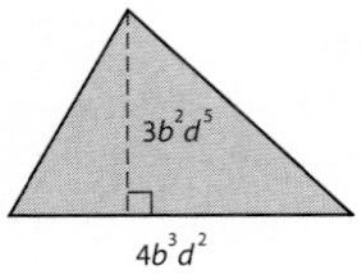

A $12b^5d^7$

B $12b^6d^{10}$

C $6b^6d^{10}$

D $6b^5d^7$

2. Simplify the following expression. G

$$\left(\frac{2w^2z^5}{3y^4}\right)^3$$

F $\frac{2w^5z^8}{3y^7}$

G $\frac{8w^6z^{15}}{27y^{12}}$

H $\frac{8w^5z^8}{27y^7}$

J $\frac{2w^6z^{15}}{3y^{12}}$

3. Which equation of a line is perpendicular to $y = \frac{3}{5}x - 3$? A

A $y = -\frac{5}{3}x + 2$

B $y = -\frac{3}{5}x + 2$

C $y = \frac{5}{3}x - 2$

D $y = \frac{3}{5}x - 2$

Test-Taking Tip

Question 2 Use the laws of exponents to simplify the expression. Remember, to find the power of a power, multiply the exponents.

4. Write a recursive formula for the sequence of the number of squares in each figure. H

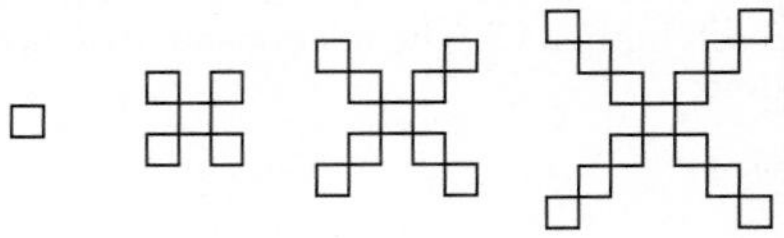

F $a_1 = 1, a_n = 4a_{n-1} - 3, n \geq 1$

G $a_1 = 1, a_n = 4a_{n-1}, n \geq 2$

H $a_1 = 1, a_n = a_{n-1} + 4, n \geq 2$

J $a_1 = 1, a_n = 4a_{n-1} + 4, n \geq 2$

5. Evaluate $(4.2 \times 10^6)(5.7 \times 10^8)$. A

A 2.394×10^{15}

B 23.94×10^{14}

C 9.9×10^{14}

D 2.394×10^{48}

6. Which inequality is shown in the graph? H

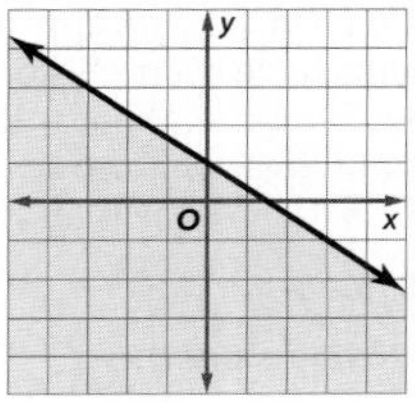

F $y \leq -\frac{2}{3}x - 1$

G $y \leq -\frac{3}{4}x - 1$

H $y \leq -\frac{2}{3}x + 1$

J $y \leq -\frac{3}{4}x + 1$

Short Response/Gridded Response

7. Jaden created a Web site for the Science Olympiad team. The total number of hits the site has received is shown.

Day	Total Hits	Day	Total Hits
3	5	17	27
6	7	21	33
10	12	26	40
13	17	34	55

$y = 1.67x - 2.64$

a. Find an equation for the regression line.

b. Predict the number of total hits that the Web site will have received on day 46. **about 74**

8. Find the value of x so that the figures have the same area. **4**

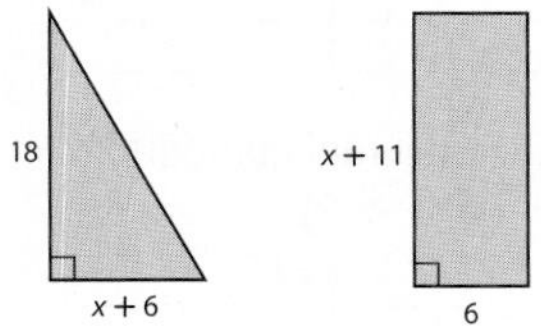

9. What is the solution to the following system of equations? Show your work. **no solution**

$$\begin{cases} y = 6x - 1 \\ y = 6x + 4 \end{cases}$$

10. GRIDDED RESPONSE At a family fun center, the Wilson and Sanchez families each bought video game tokens and batting cage tokens as shown in the table.

Family	Wilson	Sanchez
Number of Video Game Tokens	25	30
Number of Batting Cage Tokens	8	6
Total Cost	$26.50	$25.50

What is the cost in dollars of a batting cage token at the family fun center? **1.75**

Extended Response

Record your answers on a sheet of paper. Show your work.

11. The table below shows the distances from the Sun to Mercury, Earth, Mars, and Saturn. Use the data to answer each question.

Planet	Distance from Sun (km)
Mercury	5.79×10^7
Earth	1.50×10^8
Mars	2.28×10^8
Saturn	1.43×10^9

a. Of the planets listed, which one is the closest to the Sun? **Mercury**

b. About how many times as far from the Sun is Mars as Earth? **about 1.52 times farther**

Need ExtraHelp?

If you missed Question...	1	2	3	4	5	6	7	8	9	10	11
Go to Lesson...	7-1	7-2	4-4	6-6	7-3	5-6	4-6	2-4	6-2	6-4	7-4

Formative Assessment

You can use these pages to benchmark student progress.

Standardized Test Practice, pp. 74–76

Answer Sheet Practice

Have students simulate taking a standardized test by recording their answers on a practice recording sheet.

Student Recording Sheet

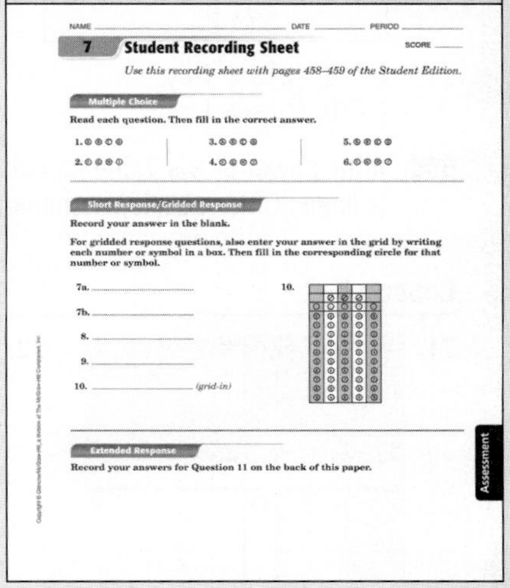

McGraw-Hill eAssessment Create practice tests that align to your state standards, the Common Core State Standards, and other national standards such as TIMSS and NAEP.

Homework Option

Get Ready for Chapter 8 Assign students the exercises on p. 461 as homework to assess whether they possess the prerequisite skills needed for the next chapter.

Lesson 7-1

65b.

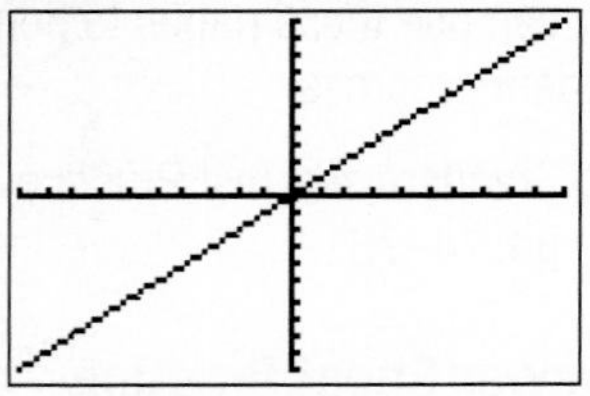

[−10, 10] scl: 1 by
[−10, 10] scl: 1

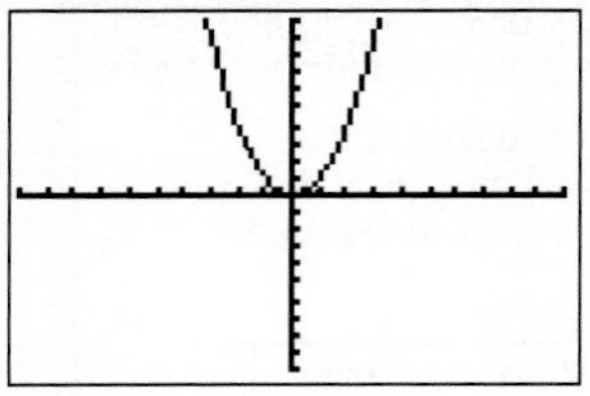

[−10, 10] scl: 1 by
[−10, 10] scl: 1

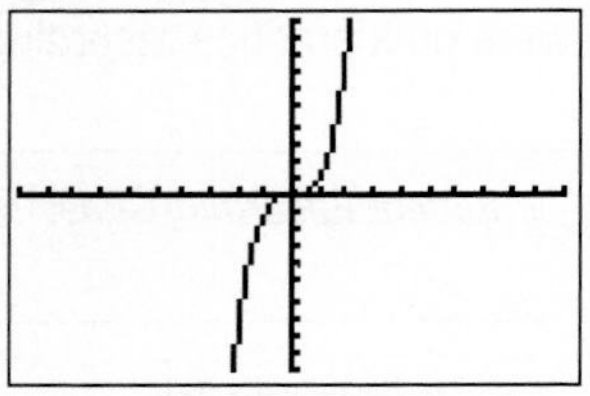

[−10, 10] scl: 1 by
[−10, 10] scl: 1

65d. If the power of x is 1, the equation or its related expression is linear. Otherwise, it is nonlinear.

Lesson 7-2

71.

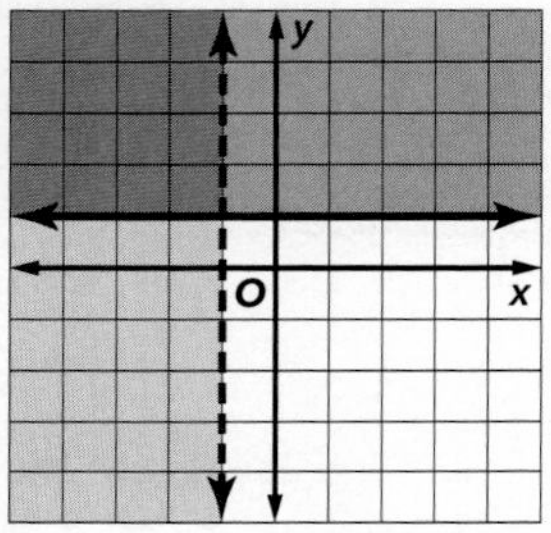

72.

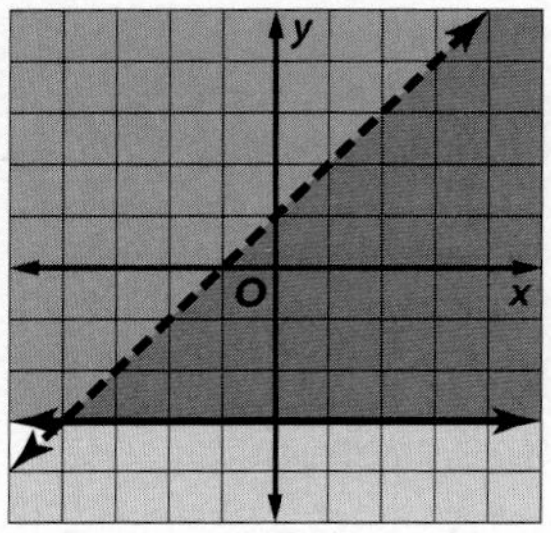

73.

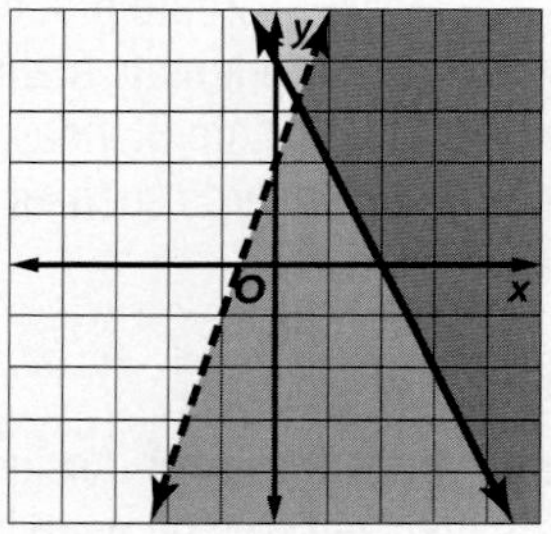

74.

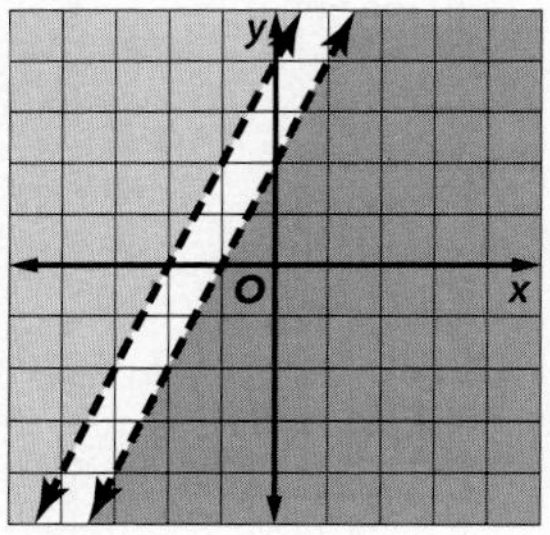

no solution

Lesson 7-5 (Guided Practice)

1.

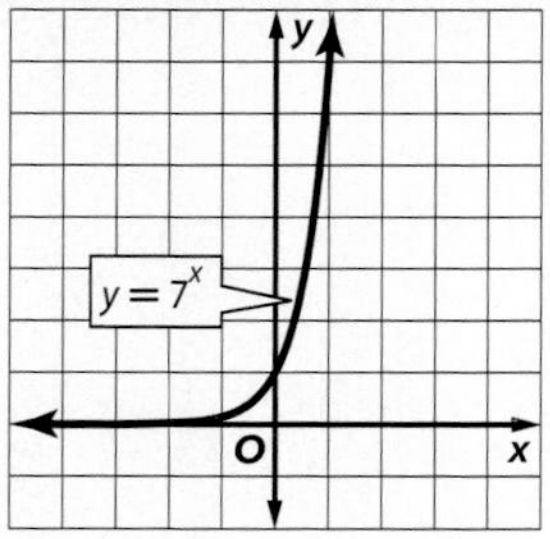

(0, 1); D = {all real numbers}
R = $\{y \mid y > 0\}$

Lesson 7-5

1. 1; D = {all real numbers};
R = $\{y \mid y > 0\}$

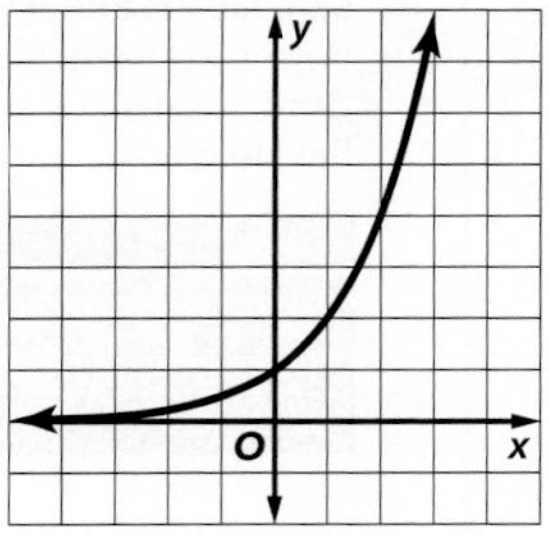

2. −1; D = {all real numbers};
R = $\{y \mid y < 0\}$

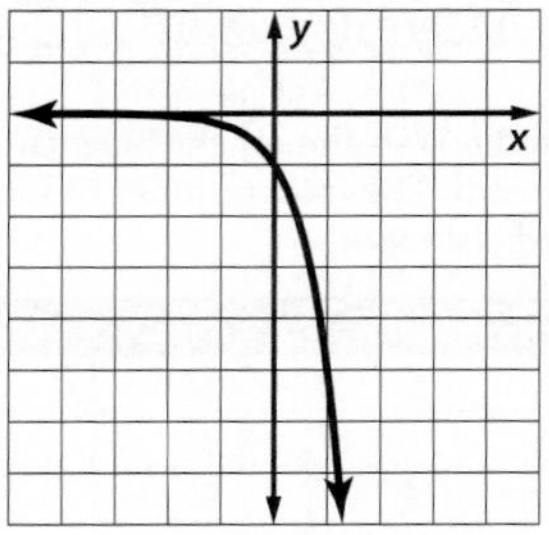

3. −1; D = {all real numbers};
R = $\{y \mid y < 0\}$

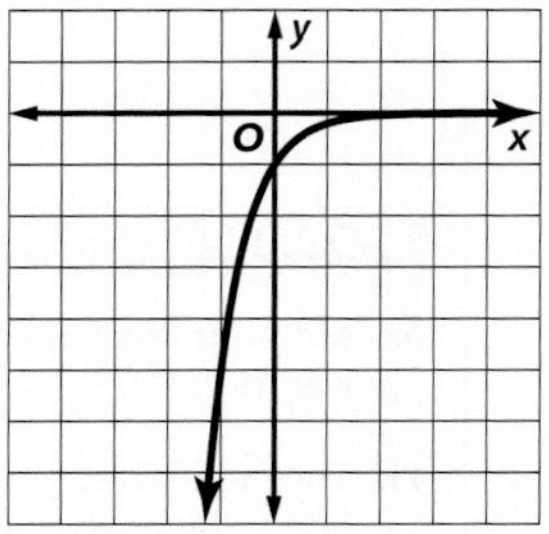

4. 3; D = {all real numbers};
R = $\{y \mid y > 0\}$

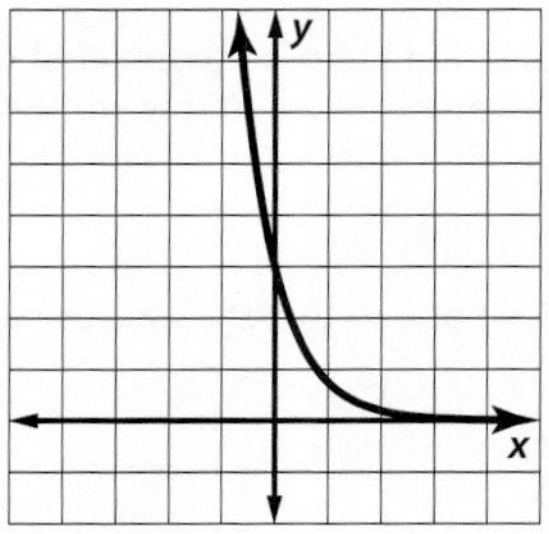

5. 4; D = {all real numbers};
R = $\{y \mid y > 3\}$

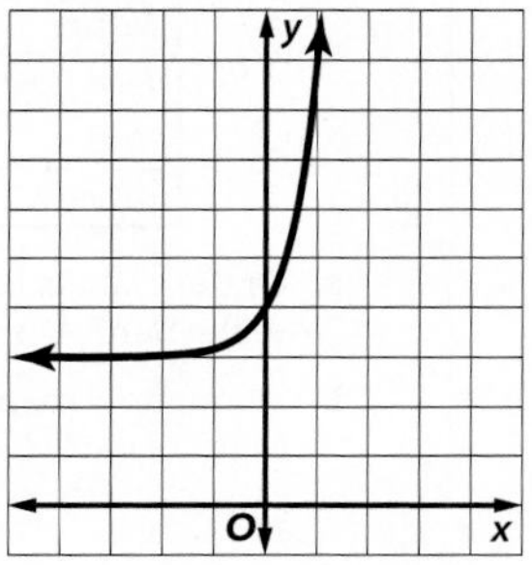

6. 1; D = {all real numbers};
R = $\{y \mid y < 2\}$

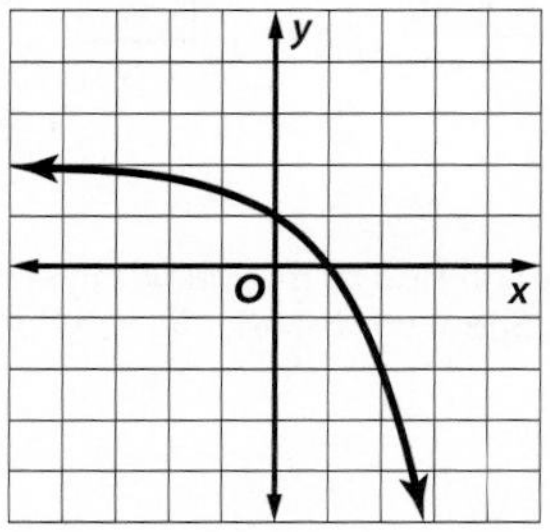

10. 2; D = {all real numbers};
R = $\{y \mid y > 0\}$

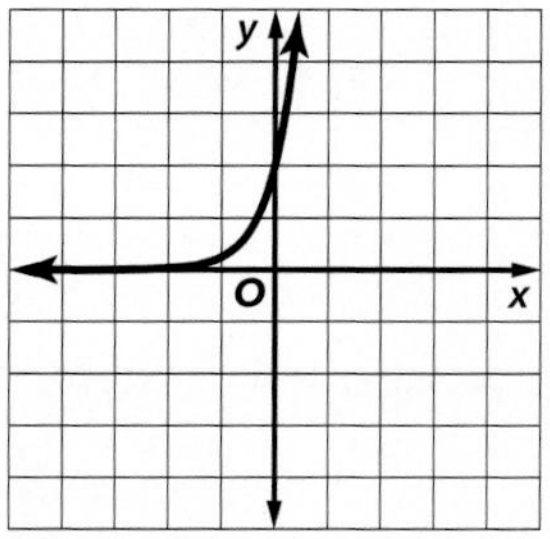

11. 2; D = {all real numbers};
R = $\{y \mid y > 0\}$

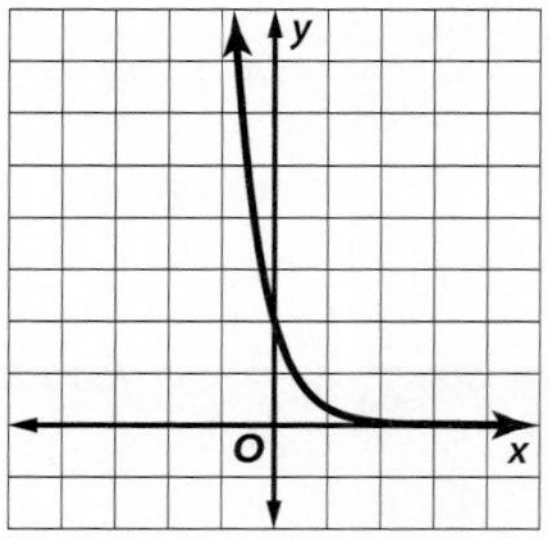

12. 1; D = {all real numbers}; R = $\{y \mid y > 0\}$

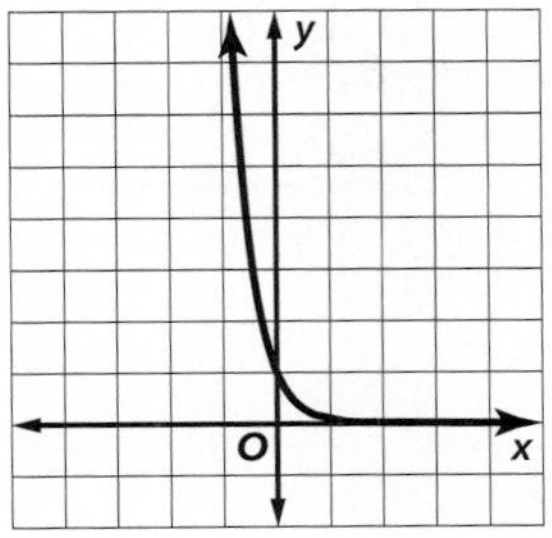

13. −3; D = {all real numbers}; R = $\{y \mid y < 0\}$

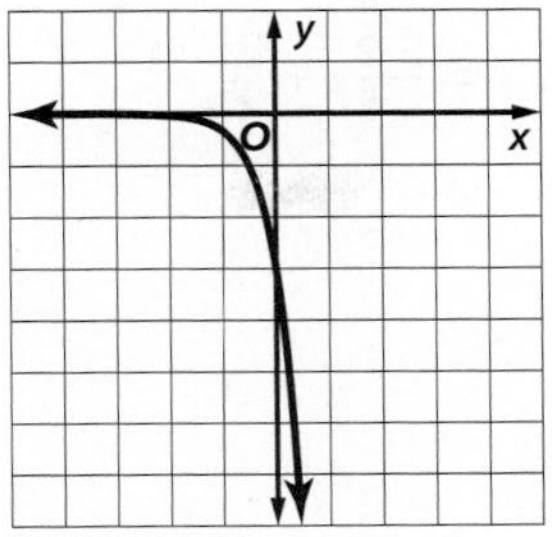

14. −4; D = {all real numbers}; R = $\{y \mid y < 0\}$

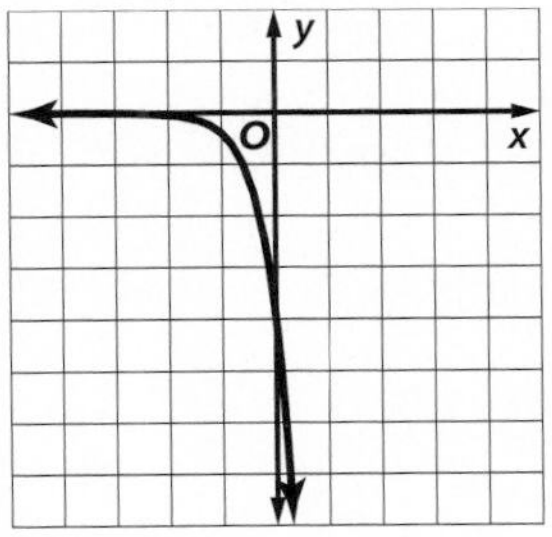

15. 3; D = {all real numbers}; R = $\{y \mid y > 0\}$

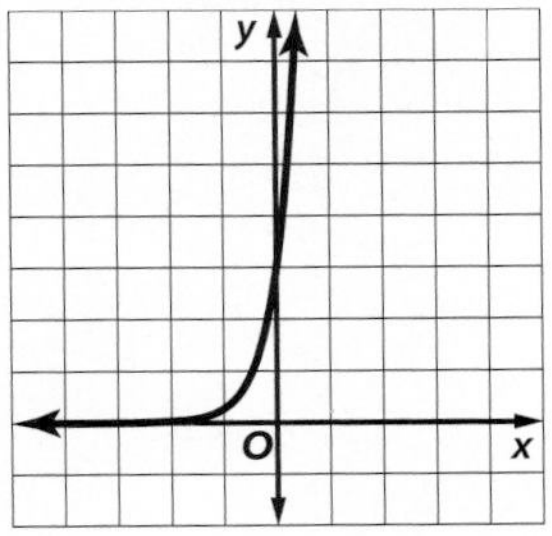

16. 4; D = {all real numbers} R = $\{y \mid y > 3\}$

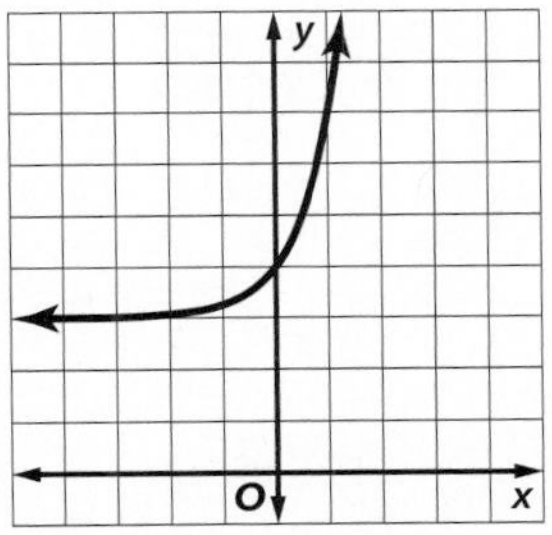

17. −3.5; D = {all real numbers} R = $\{y \mid y > -4\}$

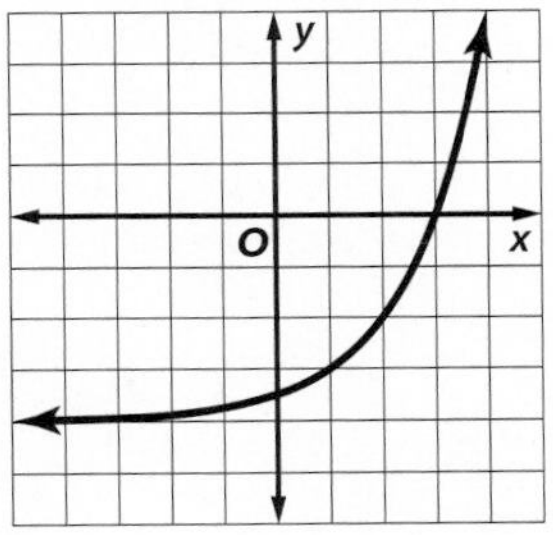

18. 6; D = {all real numbers} R = $\{y \mid y > 1\}$

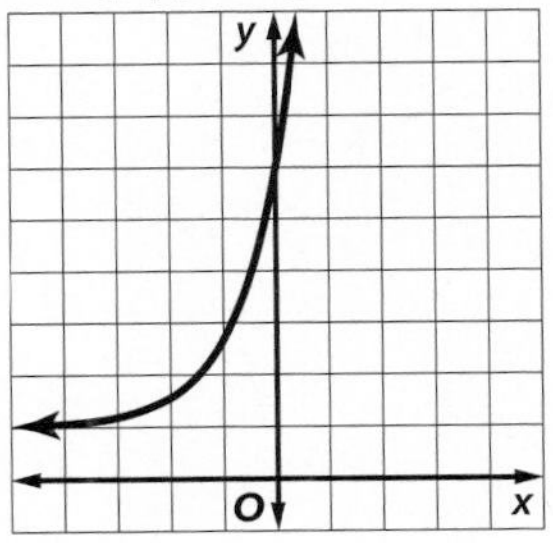

19. 3; D = {all real numbers}; R = $\{y \mid y < 5\}$

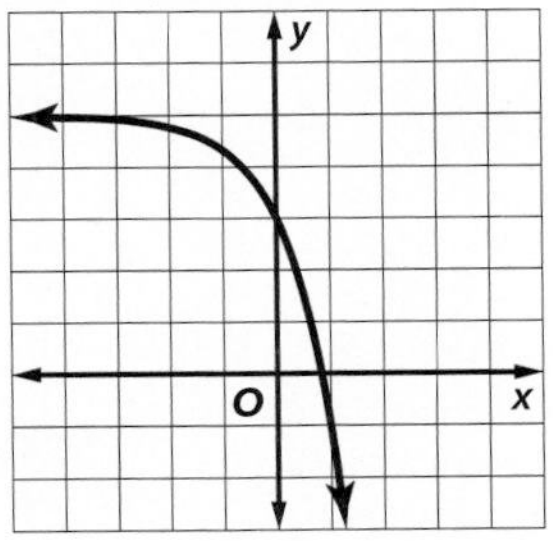

20b.

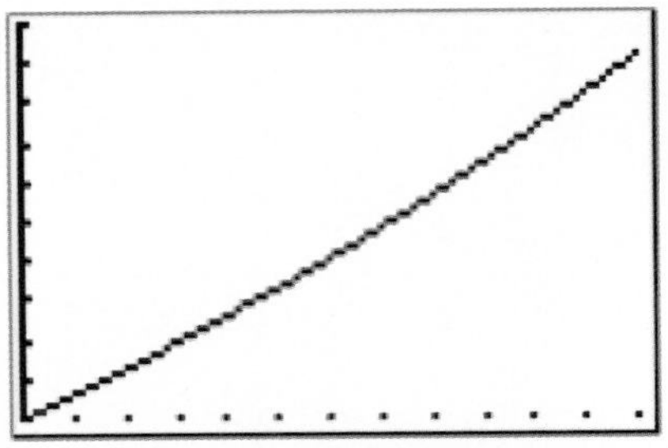

[0, 24] scl: 2 by [300, 500] scl: 20

The p-intercept is 300; there are 300 bacteria at 9:00 A.M.; D = $\{t \mid t \geq 0\}$; R = $\{p \mid p \geq 300\}$.

44. Sample answer: Let $a = 3$, $b = 2$ and $c = 1$.

x	$f(x) = 3 \times 2^x + 1$	$g(x) = 3x + 1$
−5	1.09375	−14
−4	1.1875	−11
−3	1.375	−8
−2	1.75	−5
−1	2.5	−2
0	4	1
1	7	4
2	13	7
3	25	10
4	49	13
5	97	16

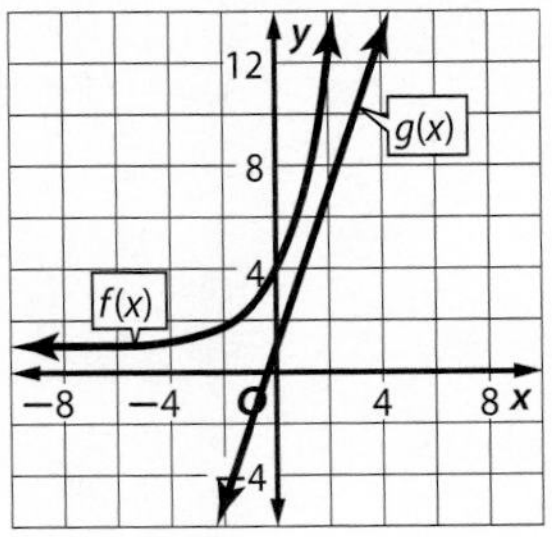

The y-intercept of $f(x)$ is 4 and the y-intercept of $g(x)$ is 1. Both $f(x)$ and $g(x)$ increase as x increases. All function values for $f(x)$ are positive, while $g(x)$ has both positive and negative values. Neither $f(x)$ nor $g(x)$ have maximum or minimum points, and neither has symmetry.

Lesson 7-6

19. Sample answer: Exponential models can grow without bound, which is usually not the case of the situation that is being modeled. For instance, a population cannot grow without bound due to space and food constraints. Therefore, when using a model, the situation that is being modeled should be carefully considered when used to make decisions.

20. The exponential growth formula is $y = a(1 + r)^t$, where a is the initial amount, t is time, y is the final amount, and r is the rate of change expressed as a decimal. The exponential decay formula is basically the same except the rate is subtracted from 1 and r represents the rate of decay.

42.

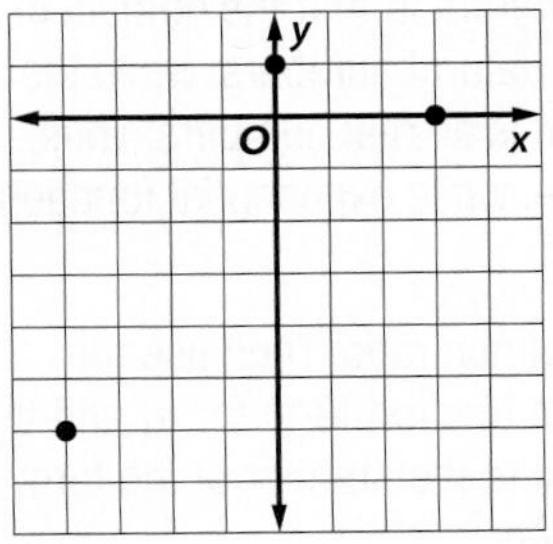

43.

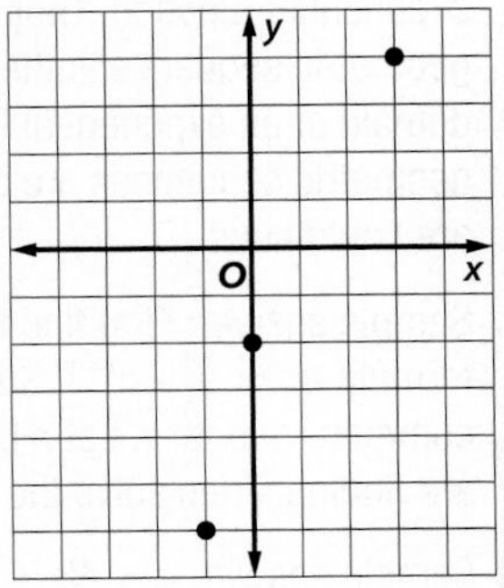

44.

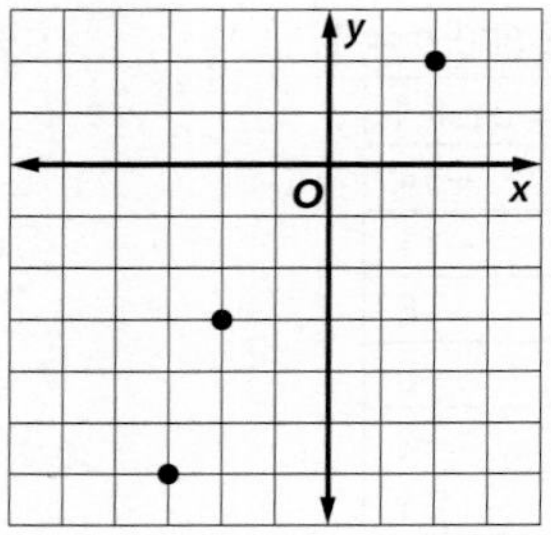

Lesson 7-7

30.

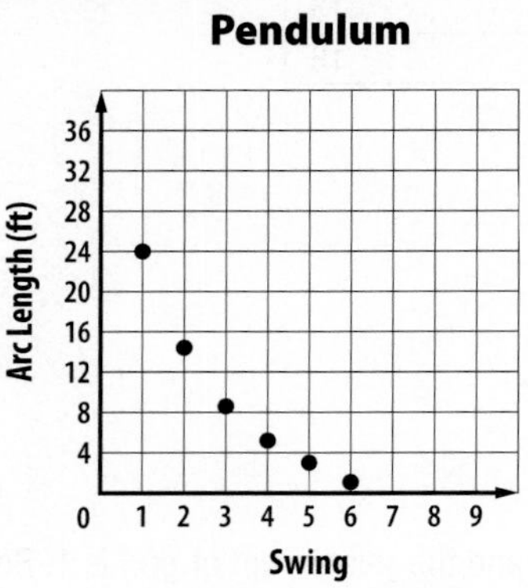

37b.

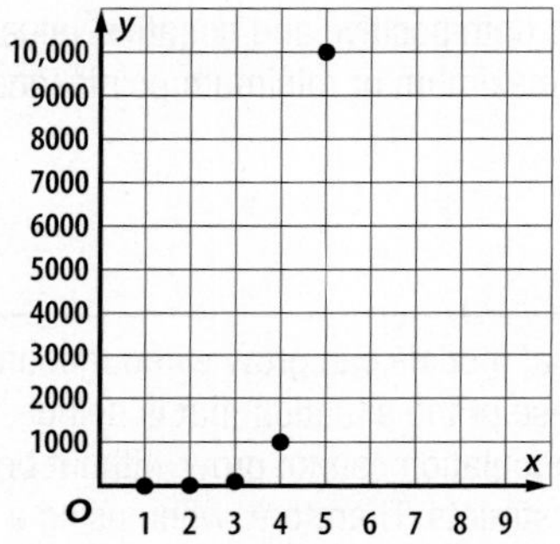

37c. The graph appears to be exponential. The rate of change between any two points does not match any others.

39. Neither; Haro calculated the exponent incorrectly. Matthew did not calculate $(-2)^8$ correctly.

41. Sample answer: When graphed, the terms of a geometric sequence lie on a curve that can be represented by an exponential function. They are different in that the domain of a geometric sequence is the set of natural numbers, while the domain of an exponential function is all real numbers. Thus, geometric sequences are discrete, while exponential functions are continuous.

42. Sample answer: First find the common ratio. Then use the formula $a_n = a_1 \cdot r^{n-1}$. Substitute the first term for a_1 and the common ratio for r. Let n be equal to the number of the term you are finding. Then solve the equation.

56. Sample answer. $y = 48 + 6x$, $y = 72 + 4x$; (12, 120) means that in 12 years the trees will be the same height, 120 inches or 10 feet.

58. $y = 4x + 2$

59. $y = -3x - \frac{2}{3}$

60. $y = -\frac{1}{4}x - 5$

61. $y = \frac{1}{2}x - 9$

62. $y = -\frac{2}{5}x + \frac{3}{4}$

63. $y = -6x - 7$

NOTES

Chapter Planner

	Diagnostic Assessment Quick Check EXPLORE 8-1 45 min: 0.5 day 90 min: 0.5 day	LESSON 8-1 45 min: 1.5 days 90 min: 0.5 day	LESSON 8-2 45 min: 1 day 90 min: 0.5 day
Title	**Algebra Lab: Adding and Subtracting Polynomials**	**Adding and Subtracting Polynomials**	**Multiplying a Polynomial by a Monomial**
Objectives	▪ Use algebra tiles to add and subtract polynomials.	▪ Write polynomials in standard form. ▪ Add and subtract polynomials.	▪ Multiply a polynomial by a monomial. ▪ Solve equations involving the products of monomials and polynomials.
Key Vocabulary		polynomial, binomial, trinomial, degree of a monomial, degree of a polynomial, leading coefficient	
Content Standards	AI.RNE.7	PS.3, AI.RNE.7	PS.5, AI.RNE.7
Multiple Representations			
Lesson Resources	connectED.mcgraw-hill.com Animations Virtual Manipulatives ▪ *Teaching Algebra with Manipulatives* **Materials:** ▪ algebra tiles	connectED.mcgraw-hill.com Vocabulary Leveled Worksheets Personal Tutor Animations Virtual Manipulatives Self-Check Quiz ▪ *5-Minute Check* ▪ *Study Notebook* ▪ *Teaching Algebra with Manipulatives*	connectED.mcgraw-hill.com Leveled Worksheets Quiz 1 Personal Tutor Self-Check Quiz ▪ *5-Minute Check* ▪ *Study Notebook* ▪ *Teaching Algebra with Manipulatives*
Resources for Every Lesson	IWB eStudent Edition IWB Interactive Classroom	▪ eTeacher Edition ▪ eSolutions Manual ▪ McGraw-Hill eAssessment	
Differentiated Instruction		pp. 469, 471	pp. 474, 476

IWB All digital assets are Interactive Whiteboard ready.

Suggested Pacing			
Time Periods	Instruction	Review & Assess	Total
45-minute	14 days	2 days	16 days
90-minute	8 days	1 day	9 days

EXPLORE 8-3 (45 min: 0.5 day; 90 min: 0.5 day)	LESSON 8-3 (45 min: 1.5 days; 90 min: 1 day)	LESSON 8-4 (45 min: 1 day; 90 min: 1 day)
Algebra Lab: Multiplying Polynomials	**Multiplying Polynomials**	**Special Products**
▪ Use algebra tiles to multiply polynomials.	▪ Multiply binomials by using the FOIL method. ▪ Multiply polynomials by using the Distributive Property.	▪ Find squares of sums and differences. ▪ Find the product of a sum and a difference.
	FOIL method quadratic expression	
AI.RNE.7	AI.RNE.7	PS.8, AI.RNE.7
connectED.mcgraw-hill.com Animations Virtual Manipulatives ▪ *Teaching Algebra with Manipulatives* **Materials:** ▪ algebra tiles ▪ product mat	connectED.mcgraw-hill.com Leveled Worksheets Vocabulary Animations Personal Tutor Virtual Manipulatives Self-Check Quiz ▪ *5-Minute Check* ▪ *Study Notebook* ▪ *Teaching Algebra with Manipulatives*	connectED.mcgraw-hill.com Leveled Worksheets Animations Personal Tutor Virtual Manipulatives Self-Check Quiz ▪ *5-Minute Check* ▪ *Study Notebook* ▪ *Teaching Algebra with Manipulatives*

IWB eStudent Edition
IWB Interactive Classroom
- eTeacher Edition
- eSolutions Manual
- McGraw-Hill eAssessment

	pp. 481, 485	pp. 488, 491

Formative Assessment
Mid-Chapter Quiz

Chapter Planner

	EXPLORE 8-5 (45 min: 0.5 day; 90 min: 0.25 day)	LESSON 8-5 (45 min: 1.5 days; 90 min: 0.75 day)	EXPLORE 8-6 (45 min: 0.5 day; 90 min: 0.25 day)
Title	**Algebra Lab: Factoring Using the Distributive Property**	**Using the Distributive Property**	**Algebra Lab: Factoring Trinomials**
Objectives	■ Use algebra tiles to model using the Distributive Property to factor binomials.	■ Use the Distributive Property to factor polynomials. ■ Solve quadratic equations of the form $ax^2 + bx = 0$.	■ Use algebra tiles to model factoring trinomials.
Key Vocabulary		factoring factoring by grouping Zero Product Property	
Content Standards		PS.2, AI.RNE.6, AI.QE.4, AI.QE.5	AI.RNE.6
Multiple Representations			
Lesson Resources	connectED.mcgraw-hill.com Animations Virtual Manipulatives ■ *Teaching Algebra with Manipulatives* **Materials:** ■ algebra tiles ■ product mats	connectED.mcgraw-hill.com Leveled Worksheets Quiz 2 Vocabulary Animations Personal Tutor Virtual Manipulatives Self-Check Quiz ■ *5-Minute Check* ■ *Study Notebook* ■ *Teaching Algebra with Manipulatives*	connectED.mcgraw-hill.com Animations Virtual Manipulatives ■ *Teaching Algebra with Manipulatives* **Materials:** ■ algebra tiles ■ product mats
Resources for Every Lesson	IWB eStudent Edition IWB Interactive Classroom	■ eTeacher Edition ■ eSolutions Manual ■ McGraw-Hill eAssessment	
Differentiated Instruction		pp. 496, 500	

IWB All digital assets are Interactive Whiteboard ready.

LESSON 8-6 (45 min: 1.5 days; 90 min: 0.75 day)	LESSON 8-7 (45 min: 2 days; 90 min: 1 day)	LESSON 8-8 (45 min: 1 day; 90 min: 0.5 day)	LESSON 8-9 (45 min: 1 day; 90 min: 0.5 day)
Solving $x^2 + bx + c = 0$	**Solving $ax^2 + bx + c = 0$**	**Differences of Squares**	**Perfect Squares**
▪ Factor trinomials of the form $x^2 + bx + c$. ▪ Solve equations of the form $x^2 + bx + c = 0$.	▪ Factor trinomials of the form $ax^2 + bx + c$. ▪ Solve equations of the form $ax^2 + bx + c = 0$.	▪ Factor binomials that are the difference of squares. ▪ Use the difference of squares to solve equations.	▪ Factor perfect square trinomials. ▪ Solve equations involving perfect squares.
quadratic equation	prime polynomial	difference of two squares	perfect square trinomial
PS.7, AI.RNE.6, AI.QE.4, AI.QE.5	PS.4, AI.RNE.6, AI.QE.4, AI.QE.5	PS.1, AI.RNE.6, AI.QE.4, AI.QE.5	PS.6, AI.RNE.6, AI.QE.4, AI.QE.5
connectED.mcgraw-hill.com Leveled Worksheets Vocabulary Personal Tutor Virtual Manipulatives Self-Check Quiz ▪ *5-Minute Check* ▪ *Study Notebook*	connectED.mcgraw-hill.com Leveled Worksheets Quiz 3 Vocabulary Personal Tutor Self-Check Quiz ▪ *5-Minute Check* ▪ *Study Notebook* ▪ *Teaching Algebra with Manipulatives*	connectED.mcgraw-hill.com Leveled Worksheets Vocabulary Animations Personal Tutor Self-Check Quiz ▪ *5-Minute Check* ▪ *Study Notebook* ▪ *Teaching Algebra with Manipulatives*	connectED.mcgraw-hill.com Leveled Worksheets Quiz 4 Vocabulary Animations Personal Tutor Self-Check Quiz ▪ *5-Minute Check* ▪ *Study Notebook* ▪ *Teaching Algebra with Manipulatives*
IWB eStudent Edition IWB Interactive Classroom	▪ eTeacher Edition ▪ eSolutions Manual ▪ McGraw-Hill eAssessment		
pp. 504, 506	pp. 511, 515	pp. 518, 521	p. 529

Summative Assessment
Study Guide and Review
Practice Test

Assessment and Intervention

SE = Student Edition, **TE** = Teacher Edition, **CRM** = Chapter Resource Masters

	Diagnosis	Prescription
DIAGNOSTIC ASSESSMENT	**Beginning Chapter 8**	
	Get Ready for Chapter 8 **SE**	Response to Intervention **TE**
	Beginning Every Lesson	
	Then, Now, Why? **SE** 5-Minute Check	Chapter 0 **SE** *Quick Review Math Handbook*
FORMATIVE ASSESSMENT	**During/After Every Lesson**	
	Guided Practice **SE**, every example Check Your Understanding **SE** H.O.T. Problems **SE** Spiral Review **SE** Additional Examples **TE** Watch Out! **TE** Step 4, Assess **TE** Chapter 8 Quizzes **CRM**, pp. 65–66 Self-Check Quizzes connectED.mcgraw-hill.com	TIER 1 Intervention Skills Practice **CRM**, Ch. 1–8 connectED.mcgraw-hill.com TIER 2 Intervention Differentiated Instruction **TE** Differentiated Homework Options **TE** Study Guide and Intervention **CRM**, Ch. 1–8 *Quick Review Math Handbook* TIER 3 Intervention *Math Triumphs, Alg. 1*
	Mid-Chapter	
	Mid-Chapter Quiz **SE** Mid-Chapter Test **CRM**, p. 67 McGraw-Hill eAssessment	TIER 1 Intervention Skills Practice **CRM**, Ch. 1–8 connectED.mcgraw-hill.com TIER 2 Intervention Study Guide and Intervention **CRM**, Ch. 1–8; *Quick Review Math Handbook* TIER 3 Intervention *Math Triumphs, Alg. 1*
	Before Chapter Test	
	Chapter Study Guide and Review **SE** Practice Test **SE** Standardized Test Practice **SE** Chapter Test connectED.mcgraw-hill.com Standardized Test Practice connectED.mcgraw-hill.com Vocabulary Review connectED.mcgraw-hill.com McGraw-Hill eAssessment	TIER 1 Intervention Skills Practice **CRM**, Ch. 1–8 connectED.mcgraw-hill.com TIER 2 Intervention Study Guide and Intervention **CRM**, Ch. 1–8; *Quick Review Math Handbook* TIER 3 Intervention *Math Triumphs, Alg. 1*
SUMMATIVE ASSESSMENT	**After Chapter 8**	
	Multiple-Choice Tests, Forms 1, 2A, 2B **CRM**, pp. 69–74 Free-Response Tests, Forms 2C, 2D, 3 **CRM**, pp. 75–80 Vocabulary Test **CRM**, p. 68 Extended Response Test **CRM**, p. 81 Standardized Test Practice **CRM**, pp. 82–84 McGraw-Hill eAssessment	Study Guide and Intervention **CRM**, Ch. 1–8 *Quick Review Math Handbook* connectED.mcgraw-hill.com

Differentiated Instruction

Option 1 Reaching All Learners AL OL BL ELL

Visual/Spatial As students learn the rules for factoring trinomials, encourage them to use algebra tiles to confirm their results. Students should soon realize that the greater the values of b and c in the trinomials, the more cumbersome the algebra tiles become, which should then reinforce the importance of learning to factor using the methods in the text.

Auditory Ask groups to create a mnemonic device that will help them remember how to factor one of the types of trinomials studied in this chapter. Then write an example of a trinomial on the board and have a volunteer say his or her mnemonic device as he or she factors the trinomial.

Option 2 Approaching Level AL

In large print, write a number and each step of its prime factorization (using the factor tree-method) on sticky notes. Each number in the steps should be on a separate note. On other notes draw some arrows. Stick the notes randomly on the board. Ask volunteers to arrange the factor and arrow notes so that they show the prime factorization of the number.

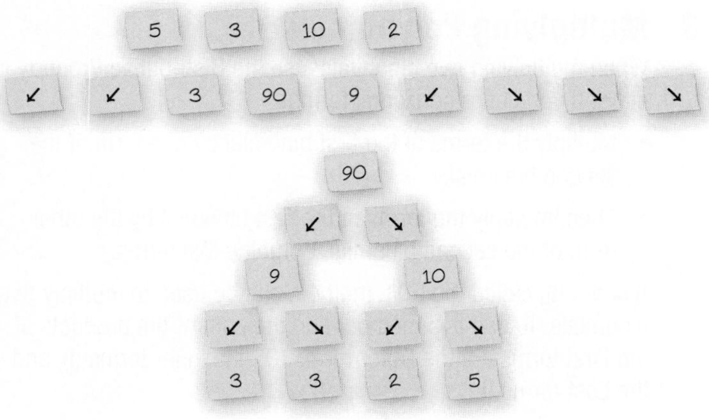

Make a set of "problem" cards showing a monomial times a polynomial, such as $-3x(5x^2 - 2x + 3)$. Make a set of "simplification" cards showing the simplification of the problems on the "problem" cards. Make enough cards so that students from half the class gets one card from the "problem" set and the other students get cards from the "simplification" set. Ask each student holding a card from the "problem" set to find the classmate holding the "simplification" card that corresponds to his or her problem.

Option 3 English Learners ELL

Factoring integers is a very visual skill, whether it is done by writing out factors in a line or by using a factor tree. Have students describe one of the methods of factoring in their own words, without actually writing out the factors as an example. Alternatively, have students write a description of how to factor, using an example as a guide.

Option 4 Beyond Level BL

Tell students that some polynomials are prime when considering the set of integers, but can be factored when the set of real numbers is considered. For example, $x^2 - 7$ is a prime polynomial. However, it can be factored if the set of real numbers is considered. That is, $x^2 - 7 = (x + \sqrt{7})(x - \sqrt{7})$. Ask students to factor other prime polynomials such as $3x^2 - 2$ when the set of real numbers is considered. $(x\sqrt{3} + \sqrt{2})(x\sqrt{3} - \sqrt{2})$

Challenge students to a competition. Have pairs go to the board. Have one student multiply two 2-digit numbers using the FOIL method while the other student multiplies the same numbers using the multiplication algorithm. Repeat with other numbers. Which method appears to be faster? Then, extend the competition to include a mixed number times a mixed number.

CHAPTER 8 Quadratic Expressions and Equations

Focus on Mathematical Content

VerticalAlignment

Before Chapter 8

Related Topics before Grade 8

- write prime factorizations using exponents
- identify the greatest common factor of a set of positive integers

Previous Topics from Algebra 1

- use the Distributive Property to simplify algebraic expressions

Chapter 8

Related Topics from Algebra 1

- add, subtract, and multiply polynomials
- factor as necessary in problem situations
- solve quadratic equations using concrete models, tables, graphs, and algebraic methods

After Chapter 8

Preparation for Algebra 2

- use tools including factoring to simplify expressions and to transform and solve equations
- determine reasonable domain and range values of quadratic functions
- analyze situations involving quadratic functions and formulate quadratic equations to solve problems
- solve quadratic equations using graphs, tables, and algebraic methods

Lesson-by-Lesson Preview

8-1 Adding and Subtracting Polynomials

A *polynomial* is a monomial or a sum or difference of monomials. Polynomials can be added or subtracted.

- To add polynomials, add the coefficients of like terms using the rules for adding real numbers.
- To subtract polynomials, first replace each term of the polynomial being subtracted with its additive inverse. Then combine the like terms.

To aid in adding and subtracting polynomials, like terms can be grouped using a horizontal or vertical format.

8-2 Multiplying a Polynomial by a Monomial

The Distributive Property can be used to find the product of a polynomial and a monomial.

- Each term of the polynomial is multiplied by the monomial using the rules for monomial multiplication.
- Apply the rules for multiplying real numbers if the monomial is negative.
- Simplify the product by combining like terms.

Equations often contain polynomials that must be added, subtracted, or multiplied before they can be solved. To solve such equations, first simplify each side. Then apply the rules for solving multi-step equations and equations with variables on each side.

8-3 Multiplying Polynomials

When multiplying two binomials, use the Distributive Property in either a vertical or horizontal format.

- Multiply the terms of the first binomial by one term of the second binomial.
- Then, multiply the terms of the first binomial by the other term of the second binomial. Combine like terms.

A shortcut, called the FOIL method, can be used to multiply two binomials. To use this method, find the sum of the products of the First terms (F), the Outer terms (O), the Inner terms (I), and the Last terms (L).

F L I O

Product of First terms; Product of Outer terms; Product of Inner terms; Product of Last terms

$$(x + 3)(x - 2) = (x)(x) + (-2)(x) + (3)(x) + (3)(-2)$$
$$= x^2 - 2x + 3x - 6$$
$$= x^2 + x - 6$$

The Distributive Property can be used to multiply any two polynomials. Products are not in simplest form until all like terms have been combined.

8-4 Special Products

Some binomials have products that follow a specific pattern. Some patterns are the

- *square of a sum or a difference:* $(a + b)^2 = a^2 + 2ab + b^2$ or $(a - b)^2 = a^2 - 2ab + b^2$
- *product of a sum and a difference* of the same two terms: $(a + b)(a - b) = a^2 - b^2$

Being able to identify and use these patterns can make it easier to simplify these special products.

8-5 Using the Distributive Property

The Distributive Property is used to find the product of a monomial and a polynomial. Reverse the process to factor a polynomial whose terms have a GCF. To factor a polynomial,

- First, find the GCF of all its terms.
- Then, rewrite each term as the product of the GCF and its remaining factors.
- Finally, use the Distributive Property to factor out the GCF.

Or, use factoring by grouping if the polynomial has four or more terms.

Factoring can be used to solve some equations containing polynomials. According to the Zero Product Property, if the product of two factors is 0, then at least one of the factors must be 0. The Zero Product Property can be used to solve equations that can be written in the form $ab = 0$. Each factor is set equal to 0 and the resulting equations are solved.

8-6 Solving $x^2 + bx + c = 0$

Some trinomials of the form $x^2 + bx + c$ can be factored into two binomials.

- To factor a trinomial of the form $x^2 + bx + c$, find two integers, m and p, whose sum is b and whose product is c. The factors of the trinomial are the two binomials $(x + m)$ and $(x + p)$, when $b = m + p$ and $c = mp$.
- Determining whether m and p are positive or negative depends on b and c. If b is negative and c is negative, then m and p must have different signs.
- First, factor the trinomial. Then set each factor equal to 0. Solve the resulting equations.

8-7 Solving $ax^2 + bx + c = 0$

In this lesson the trinomials are of the form $ax^2 + bx + c$ with $a \neq 1$. To factor $ax^2 + bx + c$,

- first factor out the GCF of the terms,
- then, if the new trinomial has $a = 1$, use the method learned in Lesson 8-6 to complete the factorization.
- If, in the new trinomial, a still does not equal 1, then find two factors, m and p, such that $ac = mp$ and $b = m + p$. Rewrite the trinomial, replacing bx with $mx + px$, forming the polynomial $ax^2 + mx + px + c$. In this form, the grouping technique used in Lesson 8-5 can be used to factor the polynomial into two binomial factors.
- Any polynomial that cannot be factored is prime.
- Equations of the form $ax^2 + bx + c = 0$ can be solved by using the method above to factor the trinomial and then applying the Zero Product Property.

8-8 Differences of Squares

To factor the difference of squares, find a (the square root of the first term) and b (the square root of the last term). The two binomial factors are the sum of the square roots and difference of the square roots. In the factored form, $a^2 - b^2 = (a + b)(a - b)$.

If the terms of the original expression have a GCF, factor it out before applying any other factoring technique.

8-9 Perfect Squares

Products that result from squaring a binomial, $a^2 + 2ab + b^2$ or $a^2 - 2ab + b^2$, are known as *perfect square trinomials.*

Three conditions must be satisfied for a trinomial to be a perfect square trinomial.

- The first term must be a perfect square.
- The last term must be a perfect square.
- The middle term must be twice the product of the square roots of the first and last terms.

To factor a perfect square trinomial with a plus sign before the middle term, use the pattern $a^2 + 2ab + b^2 = (a + b)^2$.

To factor a perfect square trinomial with a minus sign before the middle term, use the pattern $a^2 - 2ab + b^2 = (a - b)^2$.

The Square Root Property can be used to solve any equation that is in the form $x^2 = n$, where $n \geq 0$, or that can be written in that form. This property lets you take the square root of each side of the equation as long as both $\sqrt{n}$ and $-\sqrt{n}$ are considered.

Chapter Project

Greens Going Green

Students use what they have learned about factoring quadratic equations to complete a project.

This chapter project addresses environmental literacy, as well as several specific skills identified as being essential to student success by the Framework for 21st Century Learning.

Visit connectED.mcgraw-hill.com for student and teacher handouts.

KeyVocabulary Introduce the key vocabulary in the chapter using the routine below.

Define: Writing an integer or polynomial in factored form is writing the integer or a polynomial as a product of its prime factors.

Example: The factored form of 12 is $2^2 \cdot 3$. The factored form of $x^2 + 5x + 6$ is $(x + 2)(x + 3)$.

Ask: What is the factored form of 48? $2^4 \cdot 3$

CHAPTER 8 Quadratic Expressions and Equations

Then

You applied the laws of exponents and explored exponential functions.

Now

In this chapter, you will:

- Add, subtract, and multiply polynomials.
- Factor trinomials.
- Factor differences of squares.
- Graph quadratic functions.
- Solve quadratic equations.

Why?

ARCHITECTURE Quadratic equations can be used to model the shape of architectural structures.

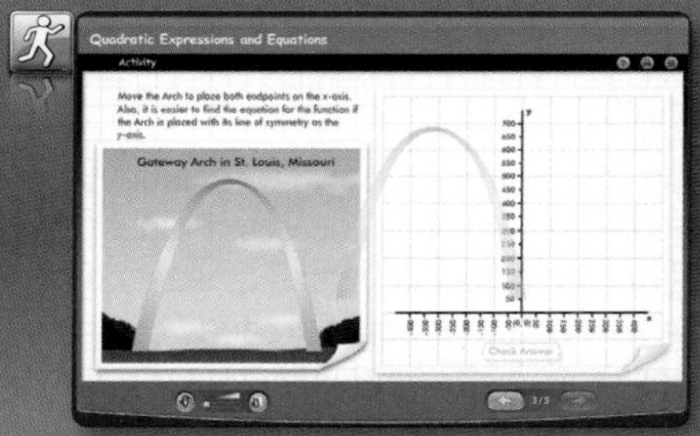

connectED.mcgraw-hill.com **Your Digital Math Portal**

Animation | Vocabulary | eGlossary | Personal Tutor | Virtual Manipulatives | Graphing Calculator | Audio | Foldables | Self-Check Practice | Worksheets

Content Standards
AI.RNE.6, AI.RNE.7, AI.QE.4, AI.QE.5

Process Standards
PS.1, PS.2, PS.3, PS.4, PS.5, PS.6, PS.7, PS.8

Get Ready for the Chapter

Diagnose Readiness | You have two options for checking prerequisite skills.

1 Textbook Option Take the Quick Check below. Refer to the Quick Review for help.

QuickCheck

Rewrite each expression using the Distributive Property. Then simplify.

1. $a(a+5)$ $a(a)+a(5);\ a^2+5a$
2. $2(3+x)$ $2(3)+2(x);\ 6+2x$
3. $n(n-3n^2+2)$ $n(n)+n(-3n^2)+n(2);\ n^2-3n^3+2n$
4. $-6(x^2-5x+6)$ $-6(x^2)+(-6)(-5x)+(-6)(6);\ -6x^2+30x-36$
5. **FINANCIAL LITERACY** Five friends will pay \$9 per ticket, \$3 per drink, and \$6 per popcorn at the movies. Write an expression that could be used to determine the cost for them to go to the movies. $5(9+3+6)$; \$90

Simplify each expression. If not possible, write *simplified.*

6. $3u+10u$ $13u$
7. $5a-2+6a$ $11a-2$
8. $6m^2-8m$ simplified
9. $4w^2+w+15w^2$ $19w^2+w$
10. $2x^2+5-11x^2$ $-9x^2+5$
11. $8v^3-27$ simplified
12. $4k^2+2k-2k+1$ $4k^2+1$
13. $a^2-4a-4a+16$ $a^2-8a+16$
14. $6y^2+2y-3y-1$ $6y^2-y-1$
15. $9g^2-3g-6g+2$ $9g^2-9g+2$

Simplify.

16. $b(b^6)$ b^7
17. $4n^3(n^2)$ $4n^5$
18. $8m(4m^2)$ $32m^3$
19. $-5z^4(3z^5)$ $-15z^9$
20. $5xy(4x^3y)$ $20x^4y^2$
21. $(-2a^4c^5)(7ac^4)$ $-14a^5c^9$
22. **GEOMETRY** A square is $6x^3$ inches on each side. What is the area of the square? $36x^6$

QuickReview

Example 1 (Used in Lessons 8-2 through 8-9)

Rewrite $6x(-3x-5x-5x^2+x^3)$ using the Distributive Property. Then simplify.

$6x(-3x-5x-5x^2+x^3)$
$= 6x(-3x)+6x(-5x)+6x(-5x^2)+6x(x^3)$
$= -18x^2-30x^2-30x^3+6x^4$
$= -48x^2-30x^3+6x^4$

Example 2 (Used in Lessons 8-1 through 8-4)

Simplify $8c+6-4c+2c^2$.

$8c+6-4c+2c^2 = 2c^2+8c-4c+6$
$= 2c^2+(8-4)c+6$
$= 2c^2+4c+6$

Example 3 (Used in Lessons 8-2 through 8-4)

Simplify $(-2y^3)(9y^4)$.

$(9y^3)(-2y^4) = (-2\cdot 9)(y^3\cdot y^4)$
$= (-2\cdot 9)(y^{3+4})$
$= -18y^7$

2 Online Option Take an online self-check Chapter Readiness Quiz at connectED.mcgraw-hill.com.

Essential Question

- When could a nonlinear function be used to model a real-world situation? Sample answer: When the relationship that is modeled has a rate of change that is not constant, and thus, is nonlinear.

Get Ready for the Chapter

Response to Intervention (RtI)

Use the *Quick Check* results and the Intervention Planner chart to help you determine your Response to Intervention. The If-Then statements in the chart below help you decide the appropriate tier of RtI and suggest intervention resources for each tier.

InterventionPlanner

TIER 1 On Level OL

If students miss about 25% of the exercises or less,

Then choose a resource:

SE Lessons 1-4 and 7-1

Skills Practice, Chapter 1, p. 26, Chapter 7, p. 7

connectED.mcgraw-hill.com Self-Check Quiz

TIER 2 Strategic Intervention AL approaching grade level

If students miss about 50% of the exercises,

Then choose a resource:

Study Guide and Intervention, Chapter 1, p. 24, Chapter 7, p. 5

Quick Review Math Handbook

connectED.mcgraw-hill.com Extra Examples, Personal Tutor, Homework Help

TIER 3 Intensive Intervention 2 or more grades below level

If students miss about 75% of the exercises,

Then use *Math Triumphs, Alg. 1*

connectED.mcgraw-hill.com Extra Examples, Personal Tutor, Homework Help, Review Vocabulary

FOLDABLES® StudyOrganizer

Dinah Zike's Foldables®

Focus Students write about factoring and quadratic equations as these concepts are presented in the lessons of this chapter.

Teach Have students make and label their Foldables as illustrated. Suggest that students use their Foldables to take notes, record concepts, and define terms. They can also use them to record the direction and progress of learning, to describe positive and negative experiences during learning, to write about personal associations and experiences, and to list examples of ways in which this new knowledge has been or will be used in their daily lives.

When to Use It Encourage students to add to their Foldables as they work through the chapter and to use them to review for the chapter test.

Differentiated Instruction

Student-Built Glossary, pp. 1–2

Students should complete the chart by providing a definition of each term and an example as they progress through Chapter 8. This study tool can also be used to review for the chapter test.

Get Started on the Chapter

You will learn several new concepts, skills, and vocabulary terms as you study Chapter 8. To get ready, identify important terms and organize your resources. You may wish to refer to Chapter 0 to review prerequisite skills.

FOLDABLES StudyOrganizer

Quadratic Expressions and Equations Make this Foldable to help you organize your Chapter 8 notes about quadratic expressions and equations. Begin with five sheets of grid paper.

1 **Fold** in half along the width. On the first three sheets, cut 5 centimeters along the fold at the ends. On the second two sheets cut in the center, stopping 5 centimeters from the ends.

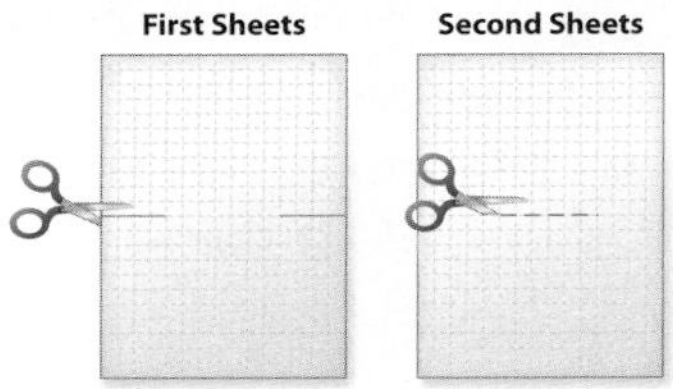

2 **Insert** the first sheets through the second sheets and align the folds. Label the front Chapter 8, Quadratic Expressions and Equations. Label the pages with lesson numbers and the last page with vocabulary.

NewVocabulary

English		Español
polynomial	p. 465	polinomio
binomial	p. 465	binomio
trinomial	p. 465	trinomio
degree of a monomial	p. 465	grado de un monomio
degree of a polynomial	p. 465	grado de un polinomio
standard form of a polynomial	p. 466	forma estándar de polinomio
leading coefficient	p. 466	coeficiente lider
FOIL method	p. 481	método foil
quadratic expression	p. 481	expression cuadrática
factoring	p. 494	factorización
factoring by grouping	p. 495	factorización por agrupamiento
Zero Product Property	p. 496	propiedad del producto de cero
quadratic equation	p. 506	ecuación cuadrática
prime polynomial	p. 512	polinomio primo
difference of two squares	p. 516	diferencia de cuadrados
perfect square trinomial	p. 522	trinomio cuadrado perfecto
Square Root Property	p. 525	Propiedad de la raíz cuadrada

ReviewVocabulary

absolute value valor absoluto the absolute value of any number n is the distance the number is from zero on a number line and is written $|n|$

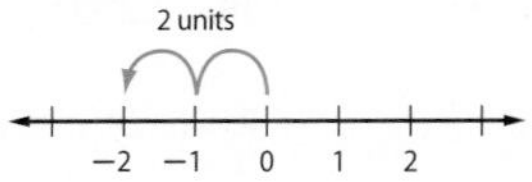

The absolute value of −2 is 2 because it is 2 units from 0.

perfect square cuadrado perfecto a number with a square root that is a rational number

462 | Chapter 8 | Quadratic Expressions and Equations

EXPLORE 8-1

Algebra Lab: Adding and Subtracting Polynomials

Algebra tiles can be used to model polynomials. A polynomial is a monomial or the sum of monomials. The diagram below shows the models.

Content Standards
AI.RNE.7

Polynomial Models

- Polynomials are modeled using three types of tiles.
- Each tile has an opposite.

Activity 1 Model Polynomials

Use algebra tiles to model each polynomial.

- $5x$

  To model this polynomial, you will need 5 green x-tiles.

- $-2x^2 + x + 3$

  To model this polynomial, you will need 2 red $-x^2$-tiles, 1 green x-tile, and 3 yellow 1-tiles.

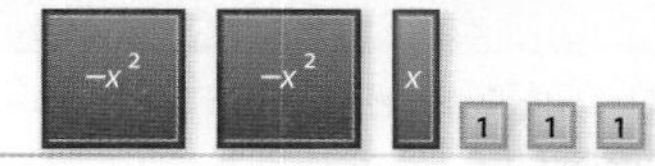

Monomials such as $3x$ and $-2x$ are called *like terms* because they have the same variable to the same power.

Polynomial Models

- Like terms are represented by tiles that have the same shape and size.
- A *zero pair* may be formed by pairing one tile with its opposite. You can remove or add zero pairs without changing the polynomial.

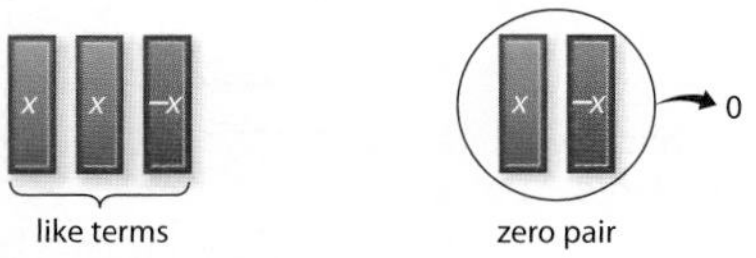

Activity 2 Add Polynomials

Use algebra tiles to find $(2x^2 - 3x + 5) + (x^2 + 6x - 4)$.

Step 1

Model each polynomial.

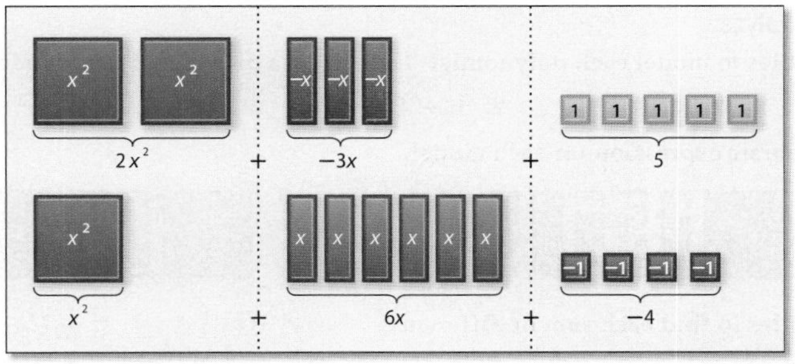

(continued on the next page)

1 Focus

Objective Use algebra tiles to add and subtract polynomials.

Materials for Each Student

- algebra tiles

Easy-to-Make Manipulatives

Teaching Algebra with Manipulatives
Template for algebra tiles, pp. 10–11

Tips for New Teachers

Zero Pairs Prior to Activities 2 and 3, discuss the concept of a zero pair. Have students form zero pairs using 1-tiles, x-tiles, and x^2-tiles and their opposites.

2 Teach

Working in Cooperative Groups

Put students in groups of two or three, mixing abilities. Have groups complete Activity 1 and Exercises 1–3.

- Make sure students understand that the number of x-tiles and x^2-tiles represent the coefficients of x and x^2, respectively. The number of 1-tiles represents the constant in the expression.
- Tell students to be careful to use the tiles with the correct colors. It is easy to incorrectly substitute an x-tile for a $-x$-tile.
- Talk about like terms in the context of the tiles. Tiles with the same shape and size represent like terms.
- For Activity 2, tell students that it is easier to model the polynomials if they arrange the tiles in the same order as the monomials within each polynomial. In this case, the monomials are arranged in descending order of degree. Therefore, students should arrange the tiles in descending order from left to right.

- After groups have completed Activity 2, write the addition of the two polynomials vertically so students can see that the coefficients of like terms are added.
- For Activity 3, explain that adding a zero pair to the polynomial does not change its value because the zero pair is equal to zero.
- After groups complete Activity 3, write the difference vertically so students can see that coefficients of like terms are subtracted.

Practice Have students complete Exercises 6 and 7.

3 Assess

Formative Assessment

Use Exercise 8 to assess whether students can use models to compare polynomials.

From Concrete to Abstract

Write a polynomial addition or subtraction problem on the board. Have students determine the sum or difference without using tiles. If they answer incorrectly, have them use their tiles to help them find their errors.

Algebra Lab

Adding and Subtracting Polynomials *Continued*

Step 2 Combine like terms and remove zero pairs.

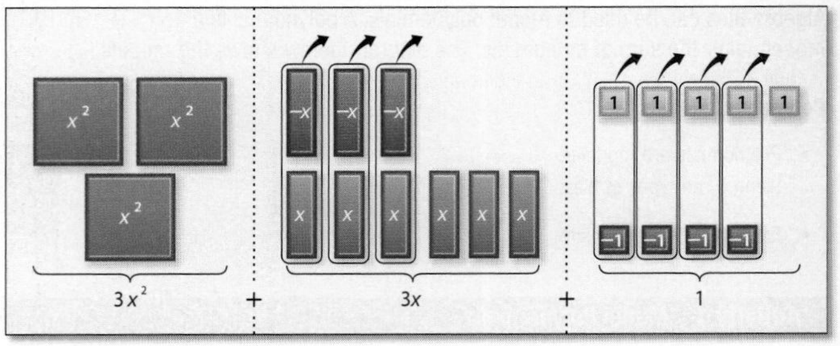

Step 3 Write the polynomial. $(2x^2 - 3x + 5) + (x^2 + 6x - 4) = 3x^2 + 3x + 1$

Activity 3 Subtract Polynomials

Use algebra tiles to find $(4x + 5) - (-3x + 1)$.

Step 1 Model the polynomial $4x + 5$.

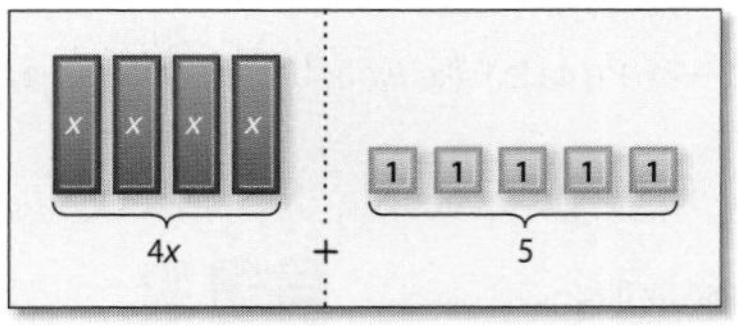

Step 2 To subtract $-3x + 1$, remove 3 red $-x$-tiles and 1 yellow 1-tile. You can remove the 1-tile, but there are no $-x$-tiles. Add 3 zero pairs of x-tiles. Then remove the 3 red $-x$-tiles.

Step 3 Write the polynomial.
$(4x + 5) - (-3x + 1) = 7x + 4$

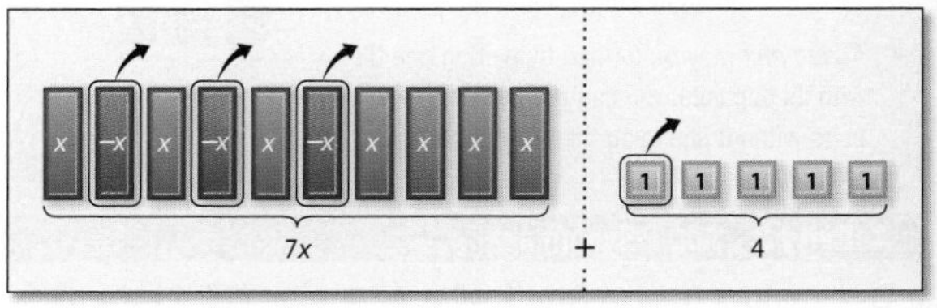

Model and Analyze

Use algebra tiles to model each polynomial. Then draw a diagram of your model. **1–3. See margin.**

1. $-2x^2$
2. $5x - 4$
3. $x^2 - 4x$

Write an algebraic expression for each model.

4. 

$2x^2 - 5x$

5. 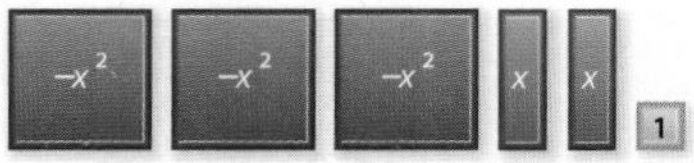

$-3x^2 + 2x + 1$

Use algebra tiles to find each sum or difference. **6. $4x^2 + 3x + 4$ 7. $x^2 + 12x + 3$ 8. $-5x^2 - 4x$**

6. $(x^2 + 5x - 2) + (3x^2 - 2x + 6)$
7. $(2x^2 + 8x + 1) - (x^2 - 4x - 2)$
8. $(-4x^2 + x) - (x^2 + 5x)$

Additional Answers

1. 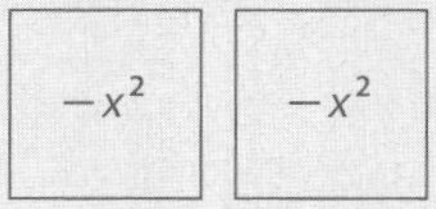

3. 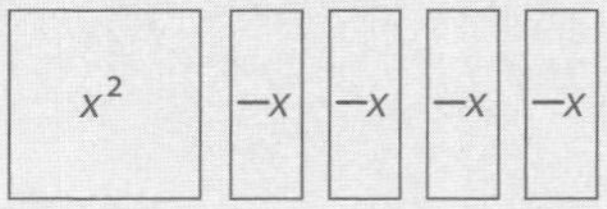

2. 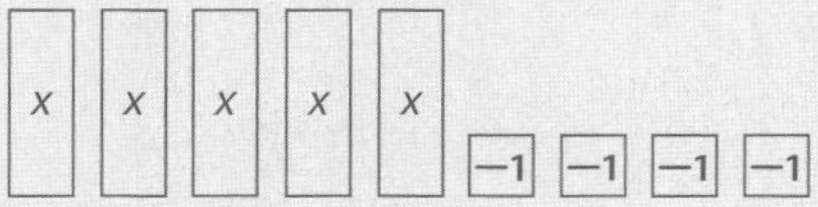

LESSON 8-1 Adding and Subtracting Polynomials

Then
- You identified monomials and their characteristics.

Now
1. Write polynomials in standard form.
2. Add and subtract polynomials.

Why?
- In 2017, sales of digital audio players are expected to reach record numbers. The sales data can be modeled by the equation $U = -2.7t^2 + 49.4t + 128.7$, where U is the number of units shipped in millions and t is the number of years since 2005.

The expression $-2.7t^2 + 49.4t + 128.7$ is an example of a polynomial. Polynomials can be used to model situations.

NewVocabulary
polynomial
binomial
trinomial
degree of a monomial
degree of a polynomial
standard form of a polynomial
leading coefficient

Content Standards
AI.RNE.7

Process Standards
PS.3

1 Polynomials in Standard Form

A **polynomial** is a monomial or the sum of monomials, each called a *term* of the polynomial. Some polynomials have special names. A **binomial** is the sum of *two* monomials, and a **trinomial** is the sum of *three* monomials.

Monomial	Binomial	Trinomial
$5x$	$2x^2 + 7$	$x^3 - 10x + 1$

The **degree of a monomial** is the sum of the exponents of all its variables. A nonzero constant term has degree 0, and zero has no degree.

The **degree of a polynomial** is the greatest degree of any term in the polynomial. You can find the degree of a polynomial by finding the degree of each term. Polynomials are named based on their degree.

Degree	Name
0	constant
1	linear
2	quadratic
3	cubic
4	quartic
5	quintic
6 or more	6th degree, 7th degree, and so on

PT

Example 1 Identify Polynomials

Determine whether each expression is a polynomial. If it is a polynomial, find the degree and determine whether it is a *monomial, binomial,* or *trinomial.*

Expression	Is it a polynomial?	Degree	Monomial, binomial, or trinomial?
a. $4y - 5xz$	Yes; $4y - 5xz$ is the sum of $4y$ and $-5xz$.	2	binomial
b. -6.5	Yes; -6.5 is a real number.	0	monomial
c. $7a^{-3} + 9b$	No; $7a^{-3} = \frac{7}{a^3}$, which is not a monomial.	—	——
d. $6x^3 + 4x + x + 3$	Yes; $6x^3 + 4x + x + 3 = 6x^3 + 5x + 3$, the sum of three monomials.	3	trinomial

GuidedPractice

1A. x yes; 1; monomial

1B. $-3y^2 - 2y + 4y - 1$ yes; 2; trinomial

1C. $5rx + 7tuv$ yes; 3; binomial

1D. $10x^{-4} - 8x^a$

1D. No; $10x^{-4} = \frac{10}{x^4}$, which is not a monomial, and $8x^a$ has a variable exponent.

1 Focus

VerticalAlignment

Before Lesson 8-1 Identify monomials and their characteristics.

Lesson 8-1 Find the degree of a polynomial. Write polynomials in standard form. Add and subtract polynomials.

After Lesson 8-1 Simplify the product of a polynomial by a monomial.

2 Teach

Scaffolding Questions

Have students read the **Why?** section of the lesson.

Ask:
- What is the value of t for the year 2007? 2
- What would be the value of t for the year 2010? 5
- Using the equation, find the value of U for the year 2007. 216.7
- How many monomials make up the expression that equals U? 3
- What are they? $-2.7t^2$; $49.4t$; 128.7

Lesson 8-1 Resources

Resource	Approaching Level AL	On Level OL	Beyond Level BL	English Learners ELL
Teacher Edition	▪ Differentiated Instruction, p. 468	▪ Differentiated Instruction, pp. 468, 471	▪ Differentiated Instruction, p. 471	▪ Differentiated Instruction, p. 468
Chapter Resource Masters	▪ Study Guide and Intervention, pp. 5–6 ▪ Skills Practice, p. 7 ▪ Practice, p. 8 ▪ Word Problem Practice, p. 9	▪ Study Guide and Intervention, pp. 5–6 ▪ Skills Practice, p. 7 ▪ Practice, p. 8 ▪ Word Problem Practice, p. 9 ▪ Enrichment, p. 10 ▪ Graphing Calculator Activity, p. 11	▪ Practice, p. 8 ▪ Word Problem Practice, p. 9 ▪ Enrichment, p. 10	▪ Study Guide and Intervention, pp. 5–6 ▪ Skills Practice, p. 7 ▪ Practice, p. 8 ▪ Word Problem Practice, p. 9
Other	▪ 5-Minute Check 8-1 ▪ Study Notebook	▪ 5-Minute Check 8-1 ▪ Study Notebook	▪ 5-Minute Check 8-1 ▪ Study Notebook	▪ 5-Minute Check 8-1 ▪ Study Notebook

1 Degree of a Polynomial

Example 1 shows how to determine whether an expression is a polynomial and how to find the degree of a polynomial. **Example 2** shows how to write a polynomial in standard form and identify the leading coefficient.

Formative Assessment

Use the Guided Practice exercises after each example to determine students' understanding of concepts.

Additional Examples

1 Determine whether each expression is a polynomial. If it is a polynomial, find the degree and determine whether it is a *monomial*, *binomial*, or *trinomial*.

a. $6x - 4$ yes; 1; binomial

b. $x^2 + 2xy - 7$ yes; 2; trinomial

c. $\frac{14d + 19e^3}{5d^4}$ no

d. $26b^2$ yes; 2; monomial

2 Write each polynomial in standard form. Identify the leading coefficient.

a. $9x^2 + 3x^6 - 4x$
$3x^6 + 9x^2 - 4x$; 3

b. $12 + 5y + 6xy + 8xy^2$
$8xy^2 + 6xy + 5y + 12$; 8

Additional Examples also in Interactive Classroom PowerPoint® Presentations

IWB Interactive White Board READY

2 Add and Subtract Polynomials

Example 3 shows how to add polynomials by grouping like terms. **Example 4** shows how to subtract a polynomial by adding its additive inverse. **Example 5** shows how to use addition or subtraction of polynomials to model a real-world situation.

The terms of a polynomial can be written in any order. However, polynomials in one variable are usually written in standard form. The **standard form of a polynomial** has the terms in order from greatest to least degree. In this form, the coefficient of the first term is called the **leading coefficient**.

Standard form: $4x^3 - 5x^2 + 2x + 7$ (leading coefficient: 4; greatest degree: 3)

Example 2 Standard Form of a Polynomial

Write each polynomial in standard form. Identify the leading coefficient.

a. $3x^2 + 4x^5 - 7x$

Find the degree of each term.

Degree: 2, 5, 1

Polynomial: $3x^2 + 4x^5 - 7x$

The greatest degree is 5. Therefore, the polynomial can be rewritten as $4x^5 + 3x^2 - 7x$, with a leading coefficient of 4.

b. $5y - 9 - 2y^4 - 6y^3$

Find the degree of each term.

Degree: 1, 0, 4, 3

Polynomial: $5y - 9 - 2y^4 - 6y^3$

The greatest degree is 4. Therefore, the polynomial can be rewritten as $-2y^4 - 6y^3 + 5y - 9$, with a leading coefficient of -2.

Guided Practice **2A.** $4x^4 - 2x^2 - 3x + 8$; 4 **2B.** $-7y^6 + 5y^3 - 2y^2 + y + 10$; -7

2A. $8 - 2x^2 + 4x^4 - 3x$ **2B.** $y + 5y^3 - 2y^2 - 7y^6 + 10$

2 Add and Subtract Polynomials

Adding polynomials involves adding like terms. You can group like terms by using a horizontal or vertical format.

Example 3 Add Polynomials

Find each sum.

a. $(2x^2 + 5x - 7) + (3 - 4x^2 + 6x)$

Horizontal Method

Group and combine like terms.

$(2x^2 + 5x - 7) + (3 - 4x^2 + 6x)$

$= [2x^2 + (-4x^2)] + [5x + 6x] + [-7 + 3]$ Group like terms.

$= -2x^2 + 11x - 4$ Combine like terms.

b. $(3y + y^3 - 5) + (4y^2 - 4y + 2y^3 + 8)$

Vertical Method

Align like terms in columns and combine.

$y^3 + 0y^2 + 3y - 5$ Insert a placeholder to help align the terms.

$(+)\ 2y^3 + 4y^2 - 4y + 8$ Align and combine like terms.

$3y^3 + 4y^2 - y + 3$

Study Tip

Vertical Method Notice that the polynomials are written in standard form with like terms aligned. Since there is no y^2-term in the first polynomial, $0y^2$ is used as a placeholder.

Guided Practice

3A. $(5x^2 - 3x + 4) + (6x - 3x^2 - 3)$ $2x^2 + 3x + 1$

3B. $(y^4 - 3y + 7) + (2y^3 + 2y - 2y^4 - 11)$ $-y^4 + 2y^3 - y - 4$

Teach with Tech

Interactive Whiteboard Write numbers 1 through 10 on the board. Then write several polynomials on the board. For each polynomial, ask students to identify the degree of the polynomial. Grab the correct number and drag it underneath that polynomial.

Focus on Mathematical Content

Degree of a Polynomial The degree of a polynomial should not be confused with the number of terms. For example, $x^3 + 1$ is a binomial, but the degree is 3, not 2, because the greatest degree of any of the terms is 3.

StudyTip

Additive Inverse When finding the additive inverse of a polynomial, you are multiplying every term by −1.

You can subtract a polynomial by adding its additive inverse. To find the additive inverse of a polynomial, write the opposite of each term, as shown.

$$-(3x^2 + 2x - 6) = \underbrace{-3x^2 - 2x + 6}_{\text{Additive Inverse}}$$

Example 4 Subtract Polynomials

Find each difference.

a. $(3 - 2x + 2x^2) - (4x - 5 + 3x^2)$

Horizontal Method

Subtract $4x - 5 + 3x^2$ by adding its additive inverse.

$(3 - 2x + 2x^2) - (4x - 5 + 3x^2)$

$= (3 - 2x + 2x^2) + (-4x + 5 - 3x^2)$ — The additive inverse of $4x - 5 + 3x^2$ is $-4x + 5 - 3x^2$.

$= [2x^2 + (-3x^2)] + [(-2x) + (-4x)] + [3 + 5]$ — Group like terms.

$= -x^2 - 6x + 8$ — Combine like terms.

b. $(7p + 4p^3 - 8) - (3p^2 + 2 - 9p)$

Vertical Method

Align like terms in columns and subtract by adding the additive inverse.

$$\begin{array}{r} 4p^3 + 0p^2 + 7p - 8 \\ (-) \quad\quad 3p^2 - 9p + 2 \\ \hline \end{array} \quad \text{Add the opposite.} \quad \begin{array}{r} 4p^3 + 0p^2 + 7p - 8 \\ (+) \quad -3p^2 + 9p - 2 \\ \hline 4p^3 - 3p^2 + 16p - 10 \end{array}$$

GuidedPractice

4A. $(4x^3 - 3x^2 + 6x - 4) - (-2x^3 + x^2 - 2)$ $6x^3 - 4x^2 + 6x - 2$

4B. $(8y - 10 + 5y^2) - (7 - y^3 + 12y)$ $y^3 + 5y^2 - 4y - 17$

Adding or subtracting integers results in an integer, so the set of integers is closed under addition and subtraction. Similarly, adding or subtracting polynomials results in a polynomial, so the set of polynomials is closed under addition and subtraction.

Real-WorldLink

Sales of digital cameras recently increased by 42% in one year. Sales are expected to increase by at least 15% each year as consumers upgrade their cameras.

Source: Big Planet Marketing Company

Real-World Example 5 Add and Subtract Polynomials

ELECTRONICS The equations $P = 7m + 137$ and $C = 4m + 78$ represent the number of cell phones P and digital cameras C sold in m months at an electronics store. Write an equation for the total monthly sales T of phones and cameras. Then predict the number of phones and cameras sold in 10 months.

To write an equation that represents the total sales T, add the equations that represent the number of cell phones P and digital cameras C.

$T = 7m + 137 + 4m + 78$

$= 11m + 215$

Substitute 10 for m to predict the number of phones and cameras sold in 10 months.

$T = 11(10) + 215$

$= 110 + 215$ or 325

Therefore, a total of 325 cell phones and digital cameras will be sold in 10 months.

GuidedPractice

$D(m) = 3m - 59$; 13

5. Use the information above to write an equation that represents the difference in the monthly sales of cell phones and the monthly sales of digital cameras. Use the equation to predict the difference in monthly sales in 24 months.

Additional Examples

3 Find each sum.

a. $(7y^2 + 2y - 3) + (2 - 4y + 5y^2)$ $12y^2 - 2y - 1$

b. $(4x^2 - 2x + 7) + (3x - 7x^2 - 9)$ $-3x^2 + x - 2$

4 Find each difference.

a. $(6y^2 + 8y^4 - 5y) - (9y^4 - 7y + 2y^2)$ $-y^4 + 4y^2 + 2y$

b. $(6n^2 + 11n^3 + 2n) - (4n - 3 + 5n^2)$ $11n^3 + n^2 - 2n + 3$

WatchOut!

Preventing Errors Some students may find it helpful to mark through like terms as they mentally combine them. This saves time spent on rewriting to group like terms.

Focus on Mathematical Content

Number of Terms When adding or subtracting polynomials, the number of terms in the sum or difference may or may not be the same number as in the polynomials being added or subtracted. Students may assume that having more or fewer terms in the sum or difference must be the sign of an error or an unsimplified answer. Use an example to explain why this is faulty thinking.

Additional Example

5 VIDEO GAMES The total amount of toy sales T (in billions of dollars) consists of two groups: sales of video games V and sales of traditional toys R. In recent years, the sales of traditional toys and total sales could be represented by the following equations, where n is the number of years since 2000.

$R = 0.46n^3 - 1.9n^2 + 3n + 19$

$T = 0.45n^3 - 1.85n^2 + 4.4n + 22.6$

a. Write an equation that represents the sales of video games V. $V = -0.01n^3 + 0.05n^2 + 1.4n + 3.6$

b. Use the equation to predict the amount of video game sales in the year 2012. 10.32 billion dollars

Check Your Understanding

= Step-by-Step Solutions begin on page R13.

Example 1 **Determine whether each expression is a polynomial. If it is a polynomial, find the degree and determine whether it is a *monomial, binomial,* or *trinomial.***

1. $7ab + 6b^2 - 2a^3$ yes; 3; trinomial
2. $2y - 5 + 3y^2$ yes; 2; trinomial
3. $3x^2$ yes; 2; monomial
4. $\frac{4m}{3p}$ No; a monomial cannot have a variable in the denominator.
5. $5m^2p^3 + 6$ yes; 5; binomial
6. $5q^{-4} + 6q$ No; $5q^{-4} = \frac{5}{q^4}$, and a monomial cannot have a variable in the denominator.

Example 2 **Write each polynomial in standard form. Identify the leading coefficient.**

7. $2x^5 - 12 + 3x$ $2x^5 + 3x - 12$; 2
8. $-4d^4 + 1 - d^2$ $-4d^4 - d^2 + 1$; -4
9. $4z - 2z^2 - 5z^4$ $-5z^4 - 2z^2 + 4z$; -5
10. $2a + 4a^3 - 5a^2 - 1$ $4a^3 - 5a^2 + 2a - 1$; 4

Examples 3–4 **Find each sum or difference.** 13. $-a^2 + 6a - 3$ 15. $-8z^3 - 3z^2 - 2z + 13$ 16. $-2d^2 + 6d - 2$

11. $(6x^3 - 4) + (-2x^3 + 9)$ $4x^3 + 5$
12. $(g^3 - 2g^2 + 5g + 6) - (g^2 + 2g)$ $g^3 - 3g^2 + 3g + 6$
13. $(4 + 2a^2 - 2a) - (3a^2 - 8a + 7)$
14. $(8y - 4y^2) + (3y - 9y^2)$ $-13y^2 + 11y$
15. $(-4z^3 - 2z + 8) - (4z^3 + 3z^2 - 5)$
16. $(-3d^2 - 8 + 2d) + (4d - 12 + d^2)$
17. $(y + 5) + (2y + 4y^2 - 2)$ $4y^2 + 3y + 3$
18. $(3n^3 - 5n + n^2) - (-8n^2 + 3n^3)$ $9n^2 - 5n$

Example 5 **19. SENSE-MAKING** The total number of students T who traveled for spring break consists of two groups: students who flew to their destinations F and students who drove to their destination D. The number (in thousands) of students who flew and the total number of students who flew or drove can be modeled by the following equations, where n is the number of years since 1995.

$$T = 14n + 21 \qquad F = 8n + 7$$

a. Write an equation that models the number of students who drove to their destination for this time period. $D(n) = 6n + 14$

b. Predict the number of students who will drive to their destination in 2012. 116,000 students

c. How many students will drive or fly to their destination in 2015? 301,000 students

Practice and Problem Solving

Extra Practice is on page R8.

Example 1 **Determine whether each expression is a polynomial. If it is a polynomial, find the degree and determine whether it is a *monomial, binomial,* or *trinomial.***

20. $\frac{5y^3}{x^2} + 4x$ 20. No; a monomial cannot have a variable in the denominator.
21. 21 yes; 0; monomial
22. $c^4 - 2c^2 + 1$ yes; 4; trinomial
23. $d + 3d^c$ No; the exponent is a variable.
24. $a - a^2$ yes; 2; binomial
25. $5n^3 + nq^3$ yes; 4; binomial

Example 2 **Write each polynomial in standard form. Identify the leading coefficient.**

26. $5x^2 - 2 + 3x$ $5x^2 + 3x - 2$; 5
27. $8y + 7y^3$ $7y^3 + 8y$; 7
28. $4 - 3c - 5c^2$ $-5c^2 - 3c + 4$; -5
29. $-y^3 + 3y - 3y^2 + 2$ $-y^3 - 3y^2 + 3y + 2$; -1
30. $11t + 2t^2 - 3 + t^5$ $t^5 + 2t^2 + 11t - 3$; 1
31. $2 + r - r^3$ $-r^3 + r + 2$; -1
32. $\frac{1}{2}x - 3x^4 + 7$ $-3x^4 + \frac{1}{2}x + 7$; -3
33. $-9b^2 + 10b - b^6$ $-b^6 - 9b^2 + 10b$; -1

3 Practice

Formative Assessment

Use Exercises 1–19 to check for understanding.

Use the chart at the bottom of the next page to customize assignments for your students.

Teach with Tech

Interactive Whiteboard Write an expression on the board to add or subtract two polynomials. Drag the like terms to group them together. Then combine like terms and simplify the expression.

Differentiated Instruction AL OL ELL

Interpersonal Learners Have students work in pairs to find the sums and differences in Exercises 11–18. Then compare answers and steps used to get their answers. When they differ, pairs should consult with another pair of students. Students should offer constructive reinforcement to each other.

Examples 3–4 **Find each sum or difference.**

34. $(2c^2 + 6c + 4) + (5c^2 - 7)$ $7c^2 + 6c - 3$

35. $(2x + 3x^2) - (7 - 8x^2)$ $11x^2 + 2x - 7$

36. $(3c^3 - c + 11) - (c^2 + 2c + 8)$ $3c^3 - c^2 - 3c + 3$

37. $(z^2 + z) + (z^2 - 11)$ $2z^2 + z - 11$

38. $(2x - 2y + 1) - (3y + 4x)$ $-2x - 5y + 1$

39. $(4a - 5b^2 + 3) + (6 - 2a + 3b^2)$ $-2b^2 + 2a + 9$

40. $(x^2y - 3x^2 + y) + (3y - 2x^2y)$ $-x^2y - 3x^2 + 4y$

41. $(-8xy + 3x^2 - 5y) + (4x^2 - 2y + 6xy)$ $7x^2 - 2xy - 7y$

42. $(5n - 2p^2 + 2np) - (4p^2 + 4n)$ $-6p^2 + 2np + n$

43. $(4rxt - 8r^2x + x^2) - (6rx^2 + 5rxt - 2x^2)$ $3x^2 - rxt - 8r^2x - 6rx^2$

Example 5

44. **PETS** From 1999 through 2009, the number of dogs D and the number of cats C (in hundreds) adopted from animal shelters in the United States are modeled by the equations $D = 2n + 3$ and $C = n + 4$, where n is the number of years since 1999.

a. Write a function that models the total number T of dogs and cats adopted in hundreds for this time period. $T(n) = 3n + 7$

b. If this trend continues, how many dogs and cats will be adopted in 2013? 4900 dogs and cats

B **Classify each polynomial according to its degree and number of terms.**

45. $4x - 3x^2 + 5$ quadratic trinomial

46. $11z^3$ cubic monomial

47. $9 + y^4$ quartic binomial

48. $3x^3 - 7$ cubic binomial

49. $-2x^5 - x^2 + 5x - 8$ quintic polynomial

50. $10t - 4t^2 + 6t^3$ cubic trinomial

51. **ENROLLMENT** In a rapidly growing school system, the numbers (in hundreds) of total students is represented by N and the number of students in Kindergarten through 5th grade is represented by P. The equations $N = 1.25t^2 - t + 7.5$ and $P = 0.7t^2 - 0.95t + 3.8$, models the number of students enrolled from 2000 to 2009, where t is the number of years since 2000.

a. Write an equation modeling the number of students S in grades 6 through 12 enrolled for this time period. $S = 0.55t^2 + 0.05t + 3.7$

b. How many students were enrolled in grades 6 through 12 in the school system in 2007? 3030 students

52. **REASONING** The perimeter of the triangle can be represented by the expression $3x^2 - 7x + 2$. Write a polynomial that represents the measure of the third side. $4x$

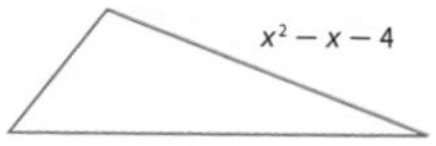

53. **GEOMETRY** Consider the rectangle.

a. What does $(4x^2 + 2x - 1)(2x^2 - x + 3)$ represent?

b. What does $2(4x^2 + 2x - 1) + 2(2x^2 - x + 3)$ represent?

53a. the area of the rectangle 53b. the perimeter of the rectangle

Find each sum or difference.

54. $(4x + 2y - 6z) + (5y - 2z + 7x) + (-9z - 2x - 3y)$ $9x + 4y - 17z$

55. $(5a^2 - 4) + (a^2 - 2a + 12) + (4a^2 - 6a + 8)$ $10a^2 - 8a + 16$

56. $(3c^2 - 7) + (4c + 7) - (c^2 + 5c - 8)$ $2c^2 - c + 8$

57. $(3n^3 + 3n - 10) - (4n^2 - 5n) + (4n^3 - 3n^2 - 9n + 4)$ $7n^3 - 7n^2 - n - 6$

58. **FOOTBALL** The National Football League is divided into two conferences, the American A and the National N. From 2002 through 2009, the total attendance T (in thousands) for both conferences and for the American Conference games can be modeled by the following equations, where x is the number of years since 2002.

$T = -0.69x^3 + 55.83x^2 + 643.31x + 10{,}538$ $\quad A = -3.78x^3 + 58.96x^2 + 265.96x + 5257$

Estimate how many people attended National Conference football games in 2009. 8,829,000 people

Teaching the Process Standards

Sense-Making Mathematically proficient students start by explaining to themselves the meaning of a problem. In Exercise 19, ask students to explain how the given polynomials relate to the number of students who drove.

Reasoning Mathematically proficient students abstract a given situation and represent it symbolically and manipulate the representing symbols. In Exercise 52, tell students to start by writing an equation for perimeter.

Differentiated Homework Options

Level	Assignment	Two-Day Option	
AL Basic	20–44, 60–62, 65–91	21–43 odd, 60, 66–69	20–44 even, 61, 62, 65, 70–91
OL Core	21–49 odd, 58–69	20–33, 66–69	34–44, 58–65, 70–91
BL Advanced	44–83, (optional: 84–91)		

Study Guide and Intervention

AL OL ELL

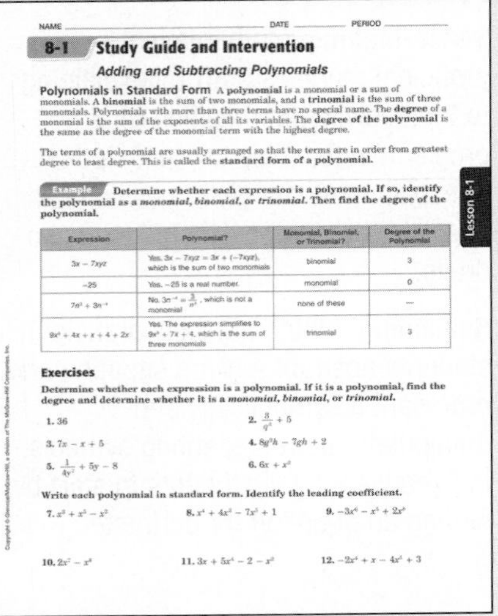
8-1 Study Guide and Intervention

Adding and Subtracting Polynomials

Practice

AL OL BL ELL

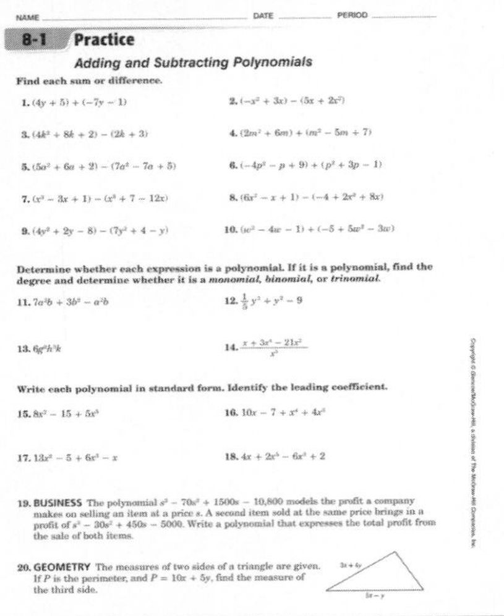
8-1 Practice

Adding and Subtracting Polynomials

Word Problem Practice

AL OL BL ELL

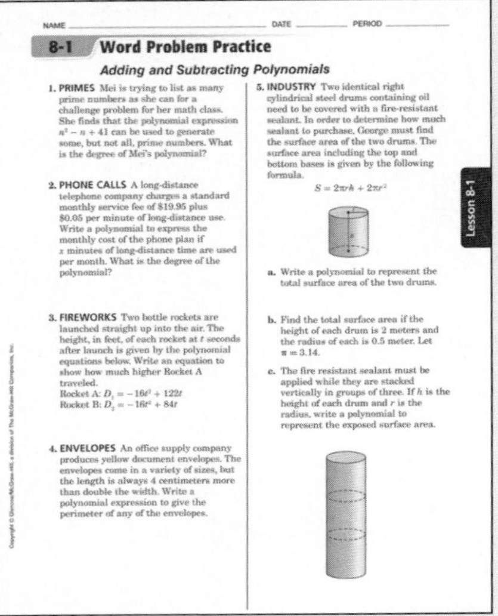
8-1 Word Problem Practice

Adding and Subtracting Polynomials

C 59. **CAR RENTAL** The cost to rent a car for a day is \$15 plus \$0.15 for each mile driven.

a. Write a polynomial that represents the cost of renting a car for m miles. **$15 + 0.15m$**

b. If a car is driven 145 miles, how much would it cost to rent? **\$36.75**

c. If a car is driven 105 miles each day for four days, how much would it cost to rent a car? **\$123**

d. If a car is driven 220 miles each day for seven days, how much would it cost to rent a car? **\$336**

60. **MULTIPLE REPRESENTATIONS** In this problem, you will explore perimeter and area. **See Ch. 8 Answer Appendix.**

a. **Geometric** Draw three rectangles that each have a perimeter of 400 feet.

b. **Tabular** Record the width and length of each rectangle in a table like the one shown below. Find the area of each rectangle.

Rectangle	Length	Width	Area
1	100 ft	**100 ft**	**10,000 ft²**
2	50 ft	**150 ft**	**7500 ft²**
3	75 ft	**125 ft**	**9375 ft²**
4	x ft	**$(200 - x)$ ft**	**$x(200 - x)$ ft²**

See Ch. 8 Answer Appendix.

c. **Graphical** On a coordinate system, graph the area of rectangle 4 in terms of the length, x. Use the graph to determine the largest area possible.

d. **Analytical** Determine the length and width that produce the largest area. **The length and width of the rectangle must be 100 feet each to have the largest area.**

H.O.T. Problems Use Higher-Order Thinking Skills

61. **CRITIQUE** Cheyenne and Sebastian are finding $(2x^2 - x) - (3x + 3x^2 - 2)$. Is either of them correct? Explain your reasoning.

Neither; neither of them found additive inverse correctly. All terms should have been multiplied by –1.

Cheyenne	Sebastian
$(2x^2 - x) - (3x + 3x^2 - 2)$	$(2x^2 - x) - (3x + 3x^2 - 2)$
$= (2x^2 - x) + (-3x + 3x^2 - 2)$	$= (2x^2 - x) + (-3x - 3x^2 - 2)$
$= 5x^2 - 4x - 2$	$= -x^2 - 4x - 2$

62. **REASONING** Determine whether each of the following statements is *true* or *false*. Explain your reasoning.

a. A binomial can have a degree of zero. **62a. False; sample answer: a binomial must have at least one monomial term with degree greater than zero**

b. The order in which polynomials are subtracted does not matter. **False; sample answer: $(2x - 3) - (4x - 3) = -2x$, but $(4x - 3) - (2x - 3) = 2x$.**

63. **CHALLENGE** Write a polynomial that represents the sum of an odd integer $2n + 1$ and the next two consecutive odd integers. **$6n + 9$**

64. **WRITING IN MATH** Why would you add or subtract equations that represent real-world situations? Explain.

64. Sample answer: When you add or subtract two or more polynomial equations, like terms are combined, which reduces the number of terms in the resulting equation. This could help minimize the number of operations performed when using the equations.

65. **WRITING IN MATH** Describe how to add and subtract polynomials using both the vertical and horizontal formats. **See margin.**

Enrichment

OL BL

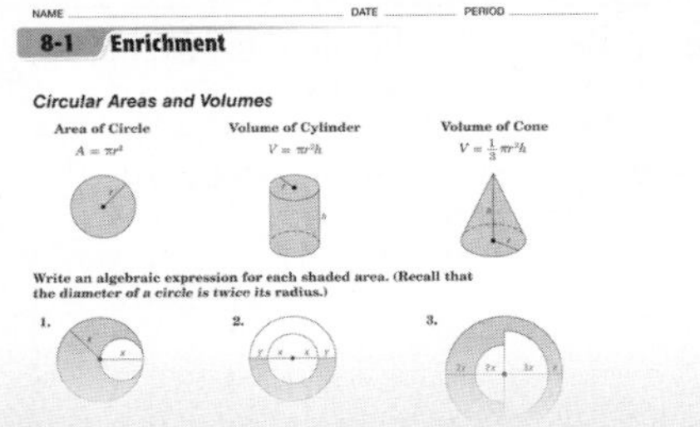
8-1 Enrichment

Circular Areas and Volumes

Multiple Representations

In Exercise 60, students explore perimeter and area of rectangles graphically and analyze their results to determine the length and width that produces the largest area possible.

Standardized Test Practice

66. Three consecutive integers can be represented by x, $x + 1$, and $x + 2$. What is the sum of these three integers? **C**

A $x(x + 1)(x + 2)$ C $3x + 3$

B $x^3 + 3$ D $x + 3$

67. SHORT RESPONSE What is the perimeter of a square with sides that measure $2x + 3$ units? **$8x + 12$ units**

68. Jim cuts a board in the shape of a regular hexagon and pounds in a nail at each vertex, as shown. How many rubber bands will he need to stretch a rubber band across every possible pair of nails? **F**

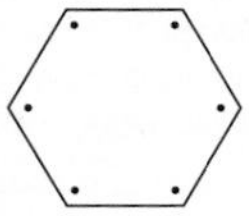

F 15 G 14 H 12 J 9

69. Which ordered pair is in the solution set of the system of inequalities shown in the graph? **C**

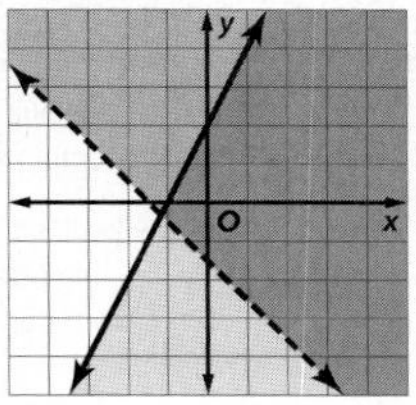

A $(-3, 0)$ C $(5, 0)$

B $(0, -3)$ D $(0, 5)$

Spiral Review

70. COMPUTERS A computer technician charges by the hour to fix and repair computer equipment. The total cost of the technician for one hour is \$75, for two hours is \$125, for three hours is \$175, for four hours is \$225, and so on. Write a recursive formula for the sequence. (Lesson 7-8) **$a_1 = 75$, $a_n = a_{n-1} + 50$, $n \geq 2$**

Determine whether each sequence is *arithmetic, geometric,* or *neither.* Explain. (Lesson 7-7) **71–76. See margin.**

71. 8, −32, 128, −512, … **72.** 25, 8, −9, −26, … **73.** $1, \frac{1}{2}, \frac{1}{3}, \frac{1}{4}, \ldots$

74. 43, 52, 61, 70, … **75.** −27, −16, −5, 6, … **76.** 200, 100, 50, 25, …

77. JOBS Kimi received an offer for a new job. She wants to compare the offer with her current job. What is total amount of sales that Kimi must get each month to make the same income at either job? (Lesson 6-2) **\$80,000**

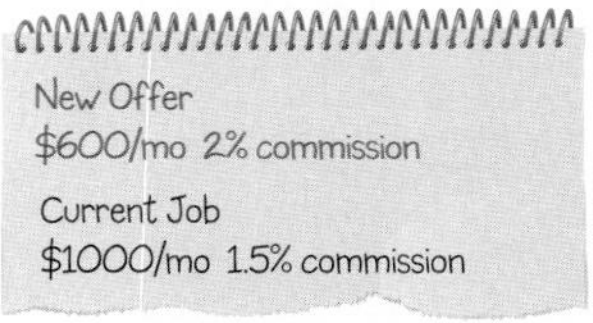

Determine whether each sequence is an arithmetic sequence. If it is, state the common difference. (Lesson 3-5)

78. 24, 16, 8, 0, … **yes; −8** **79.** $3\frac{1}{4}, 6\frac{1}{2}, 13, 26, \ldots$ **no** **80.** 7, 6, 5, 4, … **yes; −1**

81. 10, 12, 15, 18, … **no** **82.** −15, −11, −7, −3, … **yes; 4** **83.** −0.3, 0.2, 0.7, 1.2, … **yes; 0.5**

Skills Review

Simplify.

84. $t(t^5)(t^7)$ **t^{13}** **85.** $n^3(n^2)(-2n^3)$ **$-2n^8$** **86.** $(5t^5v^2)(10t^3v^4)$ **$50t^8v^6$** **87.** $(-8u^4z^5)(5uz^4)$ **$-40u^5z^9$**

88. $[(3)^2]^3$ **729** **89.** $[(2)^3]^2$ **64** **90.** $(2m^4k^3)^2(-3mk^2)^3$ **$-108m^{11}k^{12}$** **91.** $(6xy^2)^2(2x^2y^2z^2)^3$ **$288x^8y^{10}z^6$**

Differentiated Instruction OL BL

Extension Tell students the equations for the monthly unit sales of CDs C and DVDs D are $C = 7m + 87$ and $D = 9m + 152$, where m represents time in months since a store opened. Suppose the total monthly sales of CDs, DVDs, and videos is represented by $T = 15m + 248$. Write an equation that can be used to calculate monthly video sales V. How many videos did the store sell in the sixth month when $m = 5$? $V = (-1)m + 9$; 4

Teaching the Process Standards

Critique Mathematically proficient students distinguish correct logic or reasoning from that which is flawed, and explain any flaws in an argument. In Exercise 61, have students check each step of each solution. Remind students that both need to add the additive inverse of each term in the polynomial being subtracted.

4 Assess

Ticket Out the Door Make several copies each of five polynomial expressions. Give one expression to each student. As the students leave the room, ask them to tell you the degree of their expressions.

Additional Answers

65. Sample answer: To add polynomials in a horizontal format, you combine like terms. For the vertical format, you write the polynomials in standard form, align like terms in columns, and combine like terms. To subtract polynomials in a horizontal format you find the additive inverse of the polynomial you are subtracting, and then combine like terms. For the vertical format you write the polynomials in standard form, align like terms in columns, and subtract by adding the additive inverse.

71. Geometric; the common ratio is −4.

72. Arithmetic; the common difference is −17.

73. Neither; there is no common ratio or difference.

74. Arithmetic; the common difference is 9.

75. Arithmetic; the common difference is 11.

76. Geometric; the common ratio is $\frac{1}{2}$.

1 Focus

Vertical Alignment

Before Lesson 8-2 Multiply monomials.

Lesson 8-2 Multiply a polynomial by a monomial.
Solve equations involving the products of monomials and polynomials.

After Lesson 8-2 Multiply binomials and polynomials.

2 Teach

Scaffolding Questions

Have students read the **Why?** section of the lesson.

Ask:

- What is the formula for finding the area of a rectangle? $A = \ell w$, where ℓ is the length and w is the width.
- What are ℓ and w for the expression shown? ℓ is $(3w + 8)$ and w is w.
- Which of the dimensions is a monomial? w
- Describe how you would find the area of the room if the width is 20 feet. $20(3 \cdot 20 + 8) = 20(60 + 8) = 1200 + 160 = 1360$ ft^2

LESSON 8-2 Multiplying a Polynomial by a Monomial

Then

- You multiplied monomials.

Now

1. Multiply a polynomial by a monomial.
2. Solve equations involving the products of monomials and polynomials.

Why?

- Charmaine Brooks is opening a fitness club. She tells the contractor that the length of the fitness room should be three times the width plus 8 feet.

To cover the floor with mats for exercise classes, Ms. Brooks needs to know the area of the floor. So she multiplies the width times the length, $w(3w + 8)$.

Content Standards
AI.RNE.7

Process Standards
PS.5

1 Polynomial Multiplied by Monomial

To find the product of a polynomial and a monomial, you can use the Distributive Property.

Example 1 Multiply a Polynomial by a Monomial

Find $-3x^2(7x^2 - x + 4)$.

Horizontal Method

$-3x^2(7x^2 - x + 4)$	Original expression
$= -3x^2(7x^2) - (-3x^2)(x) + (-3x^2)(4)$	Distributive Property
$= -21x^4 - (-3x^3) + (-12x^2)$	Multiply.
$= -21x^4 + 3x^3 - 12x^2$	Simplify.

Vertical Method

$$\begin{array}{r} 7x^2 - x + 4 \\ (\times) \qquad -3x^2 \\ \hline -21x^4 + 3x^3 - 12x^2 \end{array}$$

Distributive Property

Multiply.

Guided Practice

Find each product.

1A. $5a^2(-4a^2 + 2a - 7)$ $-20a^4 + 10a^3 - 35a^2$

1B. $-6d^3(3d^4 - 2d^3 - d + 9)$ $-18d^7 + 12d^6 + 6d^4 - 54d^3$

We can use this same method more than once to simplify large expressions.

Example 2 Simplify Expressions

Simplify $2p(-4p^2 + 5p) - 5(2p^2 + 20)$.

$2p(-4p^2 + 5p) - 5(2p^2 + 20)$	Original expression
$= (2p)(-4p^2) + (2p)(5p) + (-5)(2p^2) + (-5)(20)$	Distributive Property
$= -8p^3 + 10p^2 - 10p^2 - 100$	Multiply.
$= -8p^3 + (10p^2 - 10p^2) - 100$	Commutative and Associative Properties
$= -8p^3 - 100$	Combine like terms.

472 | Lesson 8-2

Lesson 8-2 Resources

Resource	Approaching Level AL	On Level OL	Beyond Level BL	English Learners ELL
Teacher Edition	▪ Differentiated Instruction, p. 474	▪ Differentiated Instruction, pp. 474, 477	▪ Differentiated Instruction, p. 477	
Chapter Resource Masters	▪ Study Guide and Intervention, pp. 12–13 ▪ Skills Practice, p. 14 ▪ Practice, p. 15 ▪ Word Problem Practice, p. 16	▪ Study Guide and Intervention, pp. 12–13 ▪ Skills Practice, p. 14 ▪ Practice, p. 15 ▪ Word Problem Practice, p. 16 ▪ Enrichment, p. 17	▪ Practice, p. 15 ▪ Word Problem Practice, p. 16 ▪ Enrichment, p. 17	▪ Study Guide and Intervention, pp. 12–13 ▪ Skills Practice, p. 14 ▪ Practice, p. 15 ▪ Word Problem Practice, p. 16 ▪ Word Problem Practice, p. 33
Other	▪ 5-Minute Check 8-2 ▪ Study Notebook ▪ Teaching Algebra with Manipulatives	▪ 5-Minute Check 8-2 ▪ Study Notebook ▪ Teaching Algebra with Manipulatives	▪ 5-Minute Check 8-2 ▪ Study Notebook	▪ 5-Minute Check 8-2 ▪ Study Notebook ▪ Teaching Algebra with Manipulatives

GuidedPractice

Simplify each expression.

2A. $3(5x^2 + 2x - 4) - x(7x^2 + 2x - 3)$

2B. $15t(10y^3t^5 + 5y^2t) - 2y(yt^2 + 4y^2)$

2A. $-7x^3 + 13x^2 + 9x - 12$
2B. $150y^3t^6 + 73y^2t^2 - 8y^3$

We can use the Distributive Property to multiply monomials by polynomials and solve real world problems.

Standardized Test Example 3 Write and Evaluate a Polynomial Expression

PT

GRIDDED RESPONSE The theme for a school dance is "Solid Gold." For one decoration, Kana is covering a trapezoid-shaped piece of poster board with metallic gold paper to look like a bar of gold. If the height of the poster board is 18 inches, how much metallic paper will Kana need in square inches?

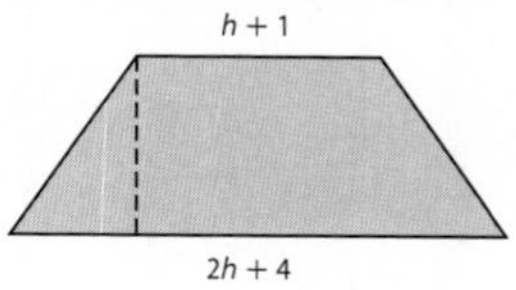

Test-TakingTip

Tools Many standardized tests provide formula sheets with commonly used formulas. If you are unsure of the correct formula, check the sheet before beginning to solve the problem.

Read the Test Item

The question is asking you to find the area of the trapezoid with a height of h and bases of $h + 1$ and $2h + 4$.

Solve the Test Item

Write an equation to represent the area of the trapezoid.
Let $b_1 = h + 1$, let $b_2 = 2h + 4$ and let h = height of the trapezoid.

$A = \frac{1}{2}h(b_1 + b_2)$	Area of a trapezoid
$= \frac{1}{2}h[(h + 1) + (2h + 4)]$	$b_1 = h + 1$ and $b_2 = 2h + 4$
$= \frac{1}{2}h(3h + 5)$	Add and simplify.
$= \frac{3}{2}h^2 + \frac{5}{2}h$	Distributive Property
$= \frac{3}{2}(18)^2 + \frac{5}{2}(18)$	$h = 18$
$= 531$	Simplify.

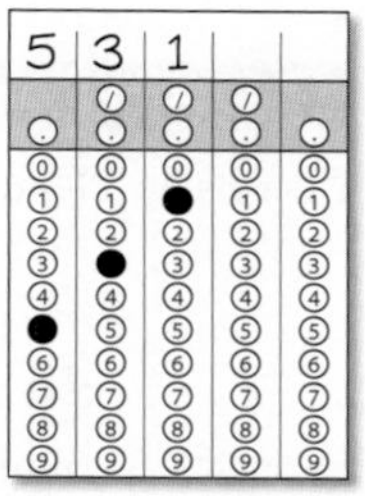

Kana will need 531 square inches of metallic paper. Grid in your response of 531.

Real-WorldLink

In a recent year, the pet supply business hit an estimated \$7.05 billion in sales. This business ranges from gourmet food to rhinestone tiaras, pearl collars, and cashmere coats.

Source: *Entrepreneur Magazine*

GuidedPractice

3. SHORT RESPONSE Kachima is making triangular bandanas for the dogs and cats in her pet club. The base of the bandana is the length of the collar with 4 inches added to each end to tie it on. The height is $\frac{1}{2}$ of the collar length.

A. If Kachima's dog has a collar length of 12 inches, how much fabric does she need in square inches? **60**

B. If Kachima makes a bandana for her friend's cat with a 6-inch collar, how much fabric does Kachima need in square inches? **21**

1 Polynomial Multiplied by Monomial

Example 1 shows how the Distributive Property can be used to multiply a polynomial by a monomial. **Example 2** shows how to use the Distributive Property more than once to simplify large expressions. **Example 3** shows how to write and evaluate a polynomial expression for a real-world problem.

Formative Assessment

Use the Guided Practice exercises after each example to determine students' understanding of concepts.

Additional Examples

1 Find $6y(4y^2 - 9y - 7)$. $24y^3 - 54y^2 - 42y$

2 Simplify $3(2t^2 - 4t - 15) + 6t(5t + 2)$. $36t^2 - 45$

3 **GRIDDED RESPONSE** Admission to the Super Fun Amusement Park is \$10. Once in the park, super rides are an additional \$3 each, and regular rides are an additional \$2. Wyome goes to the park and rides 15 rides, of which s of those 15 are super rides. Find the cost in dollars if Wyome rode 9 super rides. 49

Additional Examples also in Interactive Classroom PowerPoint® Presentations

IWB Interactive White Board READY

Teach with Tech

Document Camera Display a square photograph. Label each side as p. Discuss how to find the area of the photo. Then add a portion of a frame to the top of the photo. Discuss the new length of the photo and frame, and how to find the new area of the view.

Teaching the Process Standards

Tools Mathematically proficient are able to use relevant external mathematical resources. Point out that there are different ways to represent the same formula, and formula sheets may show a different representation than one they learned. For example, the area of a trapezoid may also be shown as

$A = \frac{h}{2}(b_1 + b_2)$ or $A = h\left(\frac{b_1 + b_2}{2}\right)$.

Focus on Mathematical Content

Order of Operations When simplifying expressions involving products of monomials and polynomials, the order of operations must be followed. Multiplication precedes addition, unless parentheses indicate otherwise.

2 Solve Equations with Polynomial Expressions

Example 4 shows how to solve equations that contain polynomials on both sides.

Additional Example

4 Solve $b(12 + b) - 7 = 2b + b(-4 + b)$. $\frac{1}{2}$

3 Practice

Formative Assessment

Use Exercises 1–17 to check for understanding.

Use the chart at the bottom of the next page to customize assignments for your students.

Tips for New Teachers

Multiplying by a Negative Monomial If students are having difficulty multiplying by a monomial with a negative sign, you may want to have them apply the negative first (by multiplying all terms by (−1) and then multiply by the rest of the monomial.

2 Solve Equations with Polynomial Expressions

We can use the Distributive Property to solve equations that involve the products of monomials and polynomials.

StudyTip

Combining Like Terms When simplifying a long expression, it may be helpful to put a circle around one set of like terms, a rectangle around another set, a triangle around another set, and so on.

PT

Example 4 Equations with Polynomials on Both Sides

Solve $2a(5a - 2) + 3a(2a + 6) + 8 = a(4a + 1) + 2a(6a - 4) + 50$.

$2a(5a - 2) + 3a(2a + 6) + 8 = a(4a + 1) + 2a(6a - 4) + 50$	Original equation
$10a^2 - 4a + 6a^2 + 18a + 8 = 4a^2 + a + 12a^2 - 8a + 50$	Distributive Property
$16a^2 + 14a + 8 = 16a^2 - 7a + 50$	Combine like terms.
$14a + 8 = -7a + 50$	Subtract $16a^2$ from each side.
$21a + 8 = 50$	Add $7a$ to each side.
$21a = 42$	Subtract 8 from each side.
$a = 2$	Divide each side by 21.

CHECK

$2a(5a - 2) + 3a(2a + 6) + 8 = a(4a + 1) + 2a(6a - 4) + 50$	
$2(2)[5(2) - 2] + 3(2)[2(2) + 6] + 8 \stackrel{?}{=} 2[4(2) + 1] + 2(2)[6(2) - 4] + 50$	
$4(8) + 6(10) + 8 \stackrel{?}{=} 2(9) + 4(8) + 50$	Simplify.
$32 + 60 + 8 \stackrel{?}{=} 18 + 32 + 50$	Multiply.
$100 = 100$ ✓	Add and subtract.

GuidedPractice

Solve each equation.

4A. $2x(x + 4) + 7 = (x + 8) + 2x(x + 1) + 12$ $2\frac{3}{5}$

4B. $d(d + 3) - d(d - 4) = 9d - 16$ 8

1. $-15w^3 + 10w^2 - 20w$ 2. $18g^5 + 24g^4 + 60g^3 - 6g^2$ 3. $32k^2m^4 + 8k^3m^3 + 20k^2m^2$

Check Your Understanding

● = Step-by-Step Solutions begin on page R13.

Example 1 **Find each product.** 5. $14a^5b^3 + 2a^6b^2 - 4a^2b$

1. $5w(-3w^2 + 2w - 4)$

2. $6g^2(3g^3 + 4g^2 + 10g - 1)$

3. $4km^2(8km^2 + 2k^2m + 5k)$

4. $-3p^4r^3(2p^2r^4 - 6p^6r^3 - 5)$ $-6p^6r^7 + 18p^{10}r^6 + 15p^4$

(5) $2ab(7a^4b^2 + a^5b - 2a)$

6. $c^2d^3(5cd^7 - 3c^3d^2 - 4d^3)$ $5c^3d^{10} - 3c^5d^5 - 4c^2d^6$

Example 2 **Simplify each expression.** 7. $4t^3 + 15t^2 - 8t + 4$

7. $t(4t^2 + 15t + 4) - 4(3t - 1)$

8. $x(3x^2 + 4) + 2(7x - 3)$ $3x^3 + 18x - 6$

9. $-2d(d^3c^2 - 4dc^2 + 2d^2c) + c^2(dc^2 - 3d^4)$ $-5d^4c^2 + 8d^2c^2 - 4d^3c + dc^4$

10. $-5w^2(8w^2x - 11wx^2) + 6x(9wx^4 - 4w - 3x^2)$ $-40w^4x + 55w^3x^2 + 54wx^5 - 24wx - 18x^3$

Example 3 **11. GRIDDED RESPONSE** Marlene is buying a new plasma television. The height of the screen of the television is one half the width plus 5 inches. The width is 30 inches. Find the height of the screen in inches. 20

Example 4 **Solve each equation.**

12. $-6(11 - 2c) = 7(-2 - 2c)$ 2

13. $t(2t + 3) + 20 = 2t(t - 3)$ $-\frac{20}{9}$

14. $-2(w + 1) + w = 7 - 4w$ 3

15. $3(y - 2) + 2y = 4y + 14$ 20

16. $a(a + 3) + a(a - 6) + 35 = a(a - 5) + a(a + 7)$ 7

17. $n(n - 4) + n(n + 8) = n(n - 13) + n(n + 1) + 16$ 1

DifferentiatedInstruction AL OL

Visual/Spatial Learners Have students group algebra tiles to form a rectangle with a width of $2x$ and a length of $x + 3$ using 2 blue x^2-tiles and 6 green x-tiles. Ask students to use their models to write an expression for the area of the rectangle. Then ask students to use the formula for area to calculate the area. $2x^2 + 6x$; $2x(x + 3) = 2x^2 + 6x$

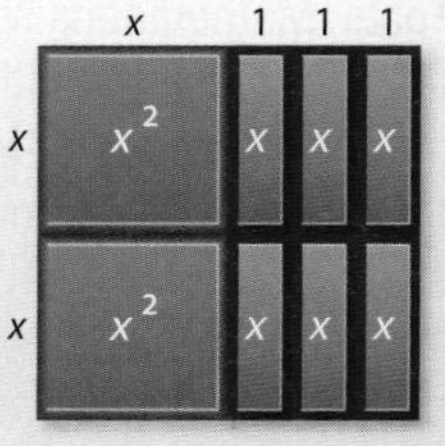

Practice and Problem Solving

Extra Practice is on page R8.

Example 1 **Find each product.** 18–23. See margin.

18. $b(b^2 - 12b + 1)$

19. $f(f^2 + 2f + 25)$

20. $-3m^3(2m^3 - 12m^2 + 2m + 25)$

21. $2j^2(5j^3 - 15j^2 + 2j + 2)$

22. $2pr^2(2pr + 5p^2r - 15p)$

23. $4t^3u(2t^2u^2 - 10tu^4 + 2)$

Example 2 **Simplify each expression.** 24. $-13x^2 - 9x - 27$ 26. $-20d^3 + 55d + 35$

24. $-3(5x^2 + 2x + 9) + x(2x - 3)$

25. $a(-8a^2 + 2a + 4) + 3(6a^2 - 4)$ $-8a^3 + 20a^2 + 4a - 12$

26. $-4d(5d^2 - 12) + 7(d + 5)$

27. $-9g(-2g + g^2) + 3(g^2 + 4)$ $-9g^3 + 21g^2 + 12$

28. $2j(7j^2k^2 + jk^2 + 5k) - 9k(-2j^2k^2 + 2k^2 + 3j)$ $14j^3k^2 + 2j^2k^2 - 17jk + 18j^2k^3 - 18k^3$

29. $4n(2n^3p^2 - 3np^2 + 5n) + 4p(6n^2p - 2np^2 + 3p)$
$8n^4p^2 + 12n^2p^2 + 20n^2 - 8np^3 + 12p^2$

Example 3 **30. DAMS** A new dam being built has the shape of a trapezoid. The length of the base at the bottom of the dam is 2 times the height. The length of the base at the top of the dam is $\frac{1}{5}$ times the height minus 30 feet.

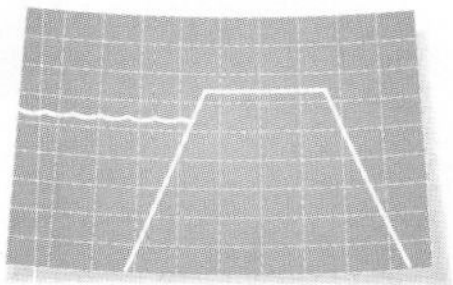

a. Write an expression to find the area of the trapezoidal cross section of the dam. $\frac{11}{10}h^2 - 15h$

b. If the height of the dam is 180 feet, find the area of this cross section. 32,940 ft^2

Example 4 **Solve each equation.**

31. $7(t^2 + 5t - 9) + t = t(7t - 2) + 13$ 2

32. $w(4w + 6) + 2w = 2(2w^2 + 7w - 3)$ 1

33. $5(4z + 6) - 2(z - 4) = 7z(z + 4) - z(7z - 2) - 48$ $\frac{43}{6}$

34. $9c(c - 11) + 10(5c - 3) = 3c(c + 5) + c(6c - 3) - 30$ 0

35. $2f(5f - 2) - 10(f^2 - 3f + 6) = -8f(f + 4) + 4(2f^2 - 7f)$ $\frac{30}{43}$

36. $2k(-3k + 4) + 6(k^2 + 10) = k(4k + 8) - 2k(2k + 5)$ -6

B **Simplify each expression.** 37. $20np^4 + 6n^3p^3 - 8np^2$ 38. $6r^5t + 3r^3t^4 + 9r^2t^3$

37. $\frac{2}{3}np^2(30p^2 + 9n^2p - 12)$

38. $\frac{3}{5}r^2t(10r^3 + 5rt^3 + 15t^2)$

39. $-5q^2w^3(4q + 7w) + 4qw^2(7q^2w + 2q) - 3qw(3q^2w^2 + 9)$ 39. $-q^3w^3 - 35q^2w^4 + 8q^2w^2 - 27qw$

40. $-x^2z(2z^2 + 4xz^3) + xz^2(xz + 5x^3z) + x^2z^3(3x^2z + 4xz)$ $-x^2z^3 + 5x^4z^3 + 3x^4z^4$

41. PARKING A parking garage charges \$30 per month plus \$0.50 per daytime hour and \$0.25 per hour during nights and weekends. Suppose Trent parks in the garage for 47 hours in January and h of those are night and weekend hours.

a. Find an expression for Trent's January bill. $53.50 - 0.25h$

b. Find the cost if Trent had 12 hours of night and weekend hours. \$50.50

42. MODELING Che is building a dog house for his new puppy. The upper face of the dog house is a trapezoid. If the height of the trapezoid is 12 inches, find the area of the face of this piece of the dog house. 318 in^2

Tips for New Teachers

Multiplication Facts In Exercises 18 through 29, some students may prefer using the horizontal method for multiplying a polynomial by a monomial. Others may prefer the vertical method. Since these two methods are equivalent, either may be used.

Exercise Alert

Formula For Exercises 30 and 42, suggest students refer to Example 3 to help them with the formula for the area of a trapezoid.

Teaching the Process Standards

Modeling Mathematically proficient students routinely interpret their mathematical results in the context of the situation. In Exercise 41, ask students what their result means and why it might be useful to Che.

Additional Answers

18. $b^3 - 12b^2 + b$

19. $f^3 + 2f^2 + 25f$

20. $-6m^6 + 36m^5 - 6m^4 - 75m^3$

21. $10j^5 - 30j^4 + 4j^3 + 4j^2$

22. $4p^2r^3 + 10p^3r^3 - 30p^2r^2$

23. $8t^5u^3 - 40t^4u^5 + 8t^3u$

Differentiated Homework Options

Level	Assignment	Two-Day Option	
AL Basic	18–36, 45, 48–75	19–35 odd, 51–54	18–36 even, 45, 48–50, 55–75
OL Core	19–39 odd, 41–45, 48–75	18–36, 51–54	37–45, 48–50, 55–75
BL Advanced	37–69, (optional: 70–75)		

Study Guide and Intervention

AL OL ELL

8-2 Study Guide and Intervention

Multiplying a Polynomial by a Monomial

Practice

AL OL BL ELL

8-2 Practice

Multiplying a Polynomial by a Monomial

Word Problem Practice

AL OL BL ELL

8-2 Word Problem Practice

Multiplying a Polynomial by a Monomial

43. TENNIS The tennis club is building a new tennis court with a path around it.

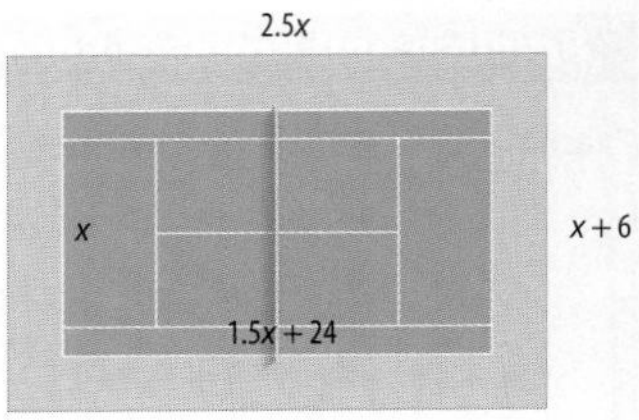

a. Write an expression for the area of the tennis court. **$1.5x^2 + 24x$**

b. Write an expression for the area of the path. **$x^2 - 9x$**

c. If $x = 36$ feet, what is the perimeter of the outside of the path? **264 ft**

C **44. MULTIPLE REPRESENTATIONS** In this problem, you will investigate the degree of the product of a monomial and a polynomial.

a. Tabular Write three monomials of different degrees and three polynomials of different degrees. Determine the degree of each monomial and polynomial. Multiply the monomials by the polynomials. Determine the degree of each product. Record your results in a table like the one shown below.

Monomial	Degree	Polynomial	Degree	Product of Monomial and Polynomial	Degree
$2x$	1	$x^2 - 1$	2	$2x^3 - 2x$	3
$3x^2$	2	$x^5 + 1$	5	$3x^7 + 3x^2$	7
$4x^3$	3	$x^6 + 1$	6	$4x^9 + 4x^3$	9

b. Verbal Make a conjecture about the degree of the product of a monomial and a polynomial. What is the degree of the product of a monomial of degree a and a polynomial of degree b? **The degree of the product is the sum of the degree of the monomial and the degree of the polynomial; $a + b$.**

H.O.T. Problems Use Higher-Order Thinking Skills

45. ERROR ANALYSIS Pearl and Ted both worked on this problem. Is either of them correct? Explain your reasoning. **Ted; Pearl used the Distributive Property incorrectly.**

Pearl	Ted
$2x^2(3x^2 + 4x + 2)$	$2x^2(3x^2 + 4x + 2)$
$6x^4 + 8x^2 + 4x^2$	$6x^4 + 8x^3 + 4x^2$
$6x^4 + 12x^2$	

50. Sample answer: To multiply a polynomial by a monomial, use the Distributive Property. Multiply each term of the polynomial by the monomial. Then simplify by multiplying the coefficients together and using the Product of Powers Property for the variables.

46. PERSEVERANCE Find p such that $3x^p(4x^{2p+3} + 2x^{3p-2}) = 12x^{12} + 6x^{10}$. **3**

47. CHALLENGE Simplify $4x^{-3}y^2(2x^5y^{-4} + 6x^{-7}y^6 - 4x^0y^{-2})$. **$8x^2y^{-2} + 24x^{-10}y^8 - 16x^{-3}$**

48. REASONING Is there a value for x that makes the statement $(x + 2)^2 = x^2 + 2^2$ true? If so, find a value for x. Explain your reasoning. **Yes; 0; when 0 is substituted in for x in the equation, both sides are 2^2 or 4, which makes the equation true.**

49. OPEN ENDED Write a monomial and a polynomial using n as the variable. Find their product. **Sample answer: $3n$, $4n + 1$; $12n^2 + 3n$**

50. WRITING IN MATH Describe the steps to multiply a polynomial by a monomial.

Enrichment

OL BL

8-2 Enrichment

Figurate Numbers

Multiple Representations

In Exercise 44, students use algebraic expressions and a table of values to show the degree of a product of a monomial and a polynomial.

Standardized Test Practice

51. Every week a store sells j jeans and t T-shirts. The store makes \$8 for each T-shirt and \$12 for each pair of jeans. Which of the following expressions represents the total amount of money, in dollars, the store makes every week? **B**

A $8j + 12t$ C $20(j + t)$
B $12j + 8t$ D $96jt$

52. If $a = 5x + 7y$ and $b = 2y - 3x$, what is $a + b$? **H**

F $2x - 9y$ H $2x + 9y$
G $3y + 4x$ J $2x - 5y$

53. **GEOMETRY** A triangle has sides of length 5 inches and 8.5 inches. Which of the following cannot be the length of the third side? **A**

A 3.5 inches
B 4 inches
C 5.5 inches
D 12 inches

54. **SHORT RESPONSE** Write an equation in which x varies directly as the cube of y and inversely as the square of z. **Sample answer:** $x = \frac{y^3}{z^2}$

Spiral Review

Find each sum or difference. (Lesson 8-1)

55. $(2x^2 - 7) + (8 - 5x^2)$ $-3x^2 + 1$
56. $(3z^2 + 2z - 1) + (z^2 - 6)$ $4z^2 + 2z - 7$
57. $(2a - 4a^2 + 1) - (5a^2 - 2a - 6)$ $-9a^2 + 4a + 7$
58. $(a^3 - 3a^2 + 4) - (4a^2 + 7)$ $a^3 - 7a^2 - 3$
59. $(2ab - 3a + 4b) + (5a + 4ab)$ $6ab + 2a + 4b$
60. $(8c^3 - 3c^2 + c - 2) - (3c^3 + 9)$ $5c^3 - 3c^2 + c - 11$

Write a recursive formula for each sequence. (Lesson 7-8) **61–66. See margin.**

61. 16, 2, −12, −26, …
62. −5, 3, 11, 19, …
63. 27, 43, 59, 75, …
64. 80, −200, 500, −1250, …
65. 100, 60, 36, 21.6, …
66. $\frac{1}{16}, \frac{1}{4}, 1, 4, \ldots$

67. **TRAVEL** In 2003, about 9.5 million people took cruises. Between 2003 and 2008, the number increased by about 740,000 each year. Write the point-slope form of an equation to find the total number of people y taking a cruise for any year x. Estimate the number of people who took a cruise in 2010. (Lesson 4-3) $y - 9{,}500{,}000 = 740{,}000(x - 2003)$; 14,680,000 people

Write an equation in function notation for each relation. (Lesson 3-6)

68. 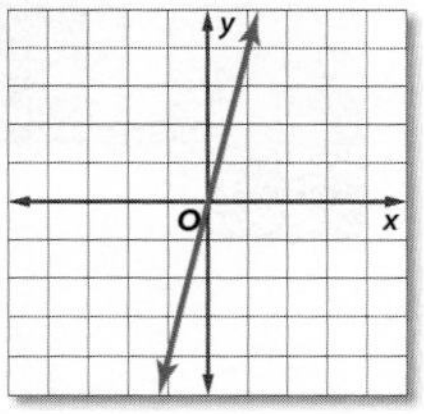

$f(x) = 4x$

69. 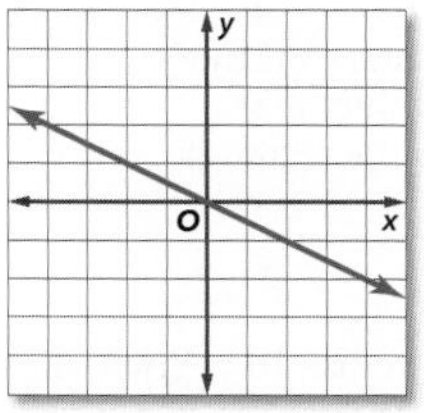

$f(x) = -0.5x$

Skills Review

Simplify.

70. $b(b^2)(b^3)$ b^6
71. $2y(3y^2)$ $6y^3$
72. $-y^4(-2y^3)$ $2y^7$
73. $-3z^3(-5z^4 + 2z)$ $15z^7 - 6z^4$
74. $2m(-4m^4) - 3(-5m^3)$ $-8m^5 + 15m^3$
75. $4p^2(-2p^3) + 2p^4(5p^6)$ $-8p^5 + 10p^{10}$

Differentiated Instruction OL BL

Extension Give students this problem: Nate multiplied a polynomial by a monomial and got $6x^8 - 3x^4 + 9x^2$. If the polynomial factor was $2x^6 - x^2 + 3$, what was the monomial factor? $3x^2$

WatchOut!

Error Analysis For Exercise 45, point out to students that Pearl's method should draw a critical eye because her final polynomial has only two terms. When a monomial is multiplied by a polynomial with three different degree terms, the result will be a polynomial with three terms.

Teaching the Process Standards

Perseverance Mathematically proficient students consider analogous problems. In Exercise 46, students may be intimidated by the variables in the exponents. Encourage them to think of how they treat numbers as exponents.

4 Assess

Crystal Ball Ask students to write a sentence predicting how learning to multiply a polynomial by a monomial will help them to learn to multiply polynomials by other polynomials in the next lesson.

Formative Assessment

Check for student understanding of Lessons 8-1 and 8-2.

Quiz 1, p. 65

Additional Answers

61. $a_1 = 16, a_n = a_{n-1} - 14, n \geq 2$
62. $a_1 = -5, a_n = a_{n-1} + 8, n \geq 2$
63. $a_1 = 27, a_n = a_{n-1} + 16, n \geq 2$
64. $a_1 = 80, a_n = -2.5a_{n-1}, n \geq 2$
65. $a_1 = 100, a_n = 0.6a_{n-1}, n \geq 2$
66. $a_1 = \frac{1}{16}, a_n = 4a_{n-1}, n \geq 2$

1 Focus

Objective Use algebra tiles to multiply polynomials.

Materials for Each Student

- algebra tiles
- product mat

Easy to Make Manipulatives

Teaching Algebra with Manipulatives
Template for:

- algebra tiles, pp. 10–11
- product mat , p. 17

Teaching Tip

Some students may benefit from laying tiles along the top and side of the product mat to model each expression. Have them remove the two factors before determining their final product.

2 Teach

Working in Cooperative Groups

Put students in groups of two or three, mixing abilities. Have groups complete Activities 1–3 and Exercise 1.

- For Activity 1, make sure groups mark the dimensions properly on the product mat. Since x-tiles are rectangular, remind students that the long side is the correct side to use to mark a value of x on the mat.
- When students are filling in the mats with the tiles, remind them to look carefully at the horizontal and vertical dimensions of each tile on the product mat. If both dimensions have a value of x, then use an x^2-tile. If one dimension is x and the other is 1, then use an x-tile. If both dimensions are 1, then use a 1-tile.

EXPLORE 8-3 Algebra Lab
Multiplying Polynomials

You can use algebra tiles to find the product of two binomials.

Content Standards
AI.RNE.7

Activity 1 Multiply Binomials

Use algebra tiles to find $(x + 3)(x + 4)$.

The rectangle will have a width of $x + 3$ and a length of $x + 4$. Use algebra tiles to mark off the dimensions on a product mat. Then complete the rectangle with algebra tiles.

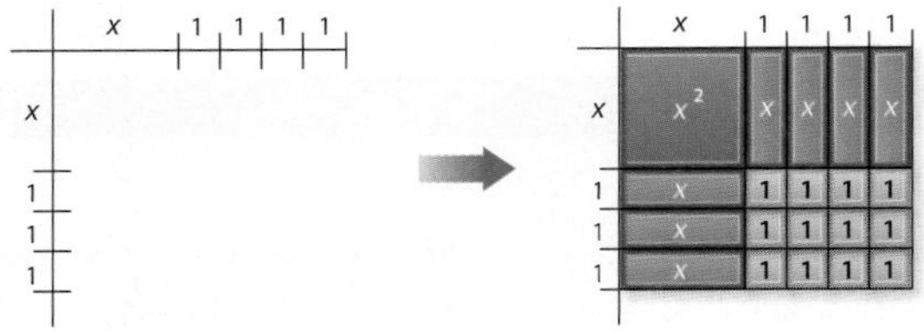

The rectangle consists of 1 blue x^2-tile, 7 green x-tiles, and 12 yellow 1-tiles. The area of the rectangle is $x^2 + 7x + 12$. So, $(x + 3)(x + 4) = x^2 + 7x + 12$.

Activity 2 Multiply Binomials

Use algebra tiles to find $(x - 2)(x - 5)$.

Step 1 The rectangle will have a width of $x - 2$ and a length of $x - 5$. Use algebra tiles to mark off the dimensions on a product mat. Then begin to make the rectangle with algebra tiles.

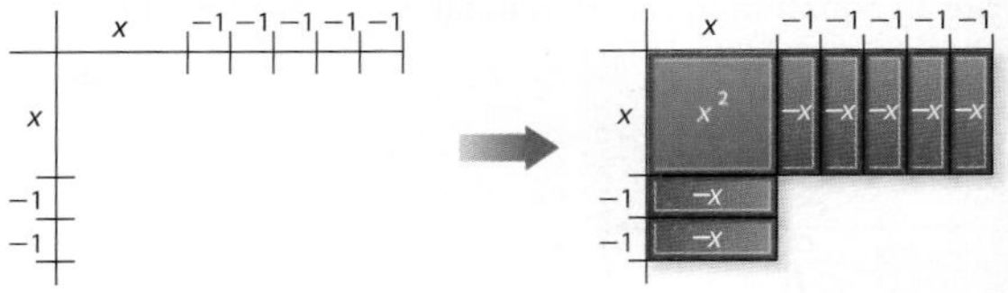

Step 2 Determine whether to use 10 yellow 1-tiles or 10 red -1-tiles to complete the rectangle. The area of each yellow tile is the product of -1 and -1. Fill in the space with 10 yellow 1-tiles to complete the rectangle.

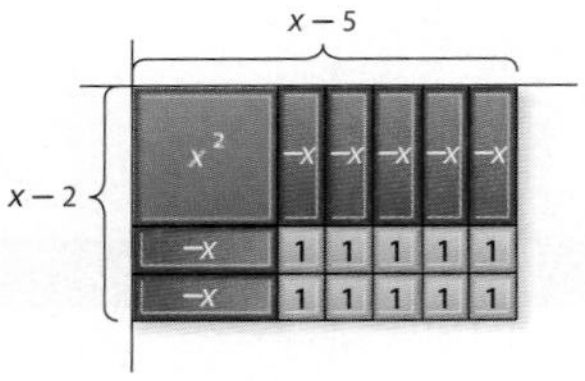

The rectangle consists of 1 blue x^2-tile, 7 red $-x$-tiles, and 10 yellow 1-tiles. The area of the rectangle is $x^2 - 7x + 10$. So, $(x - 2)(x - 5) = x^2 - 7x + 10$.

478 | Explore 8-3 | Algebra Lab: Multiplying Polynomials

Activity 3 Multiply Binomials

Use algebra tiles to find $(x - 4)(2x + 3)$.

Step 1 The rectangle will have a width of $x - 4$ and a length of $2x + 3$. Use algebra tiles to mark off the dimensions on a product mat. Then begin to make the rectangle with algebra tiles.

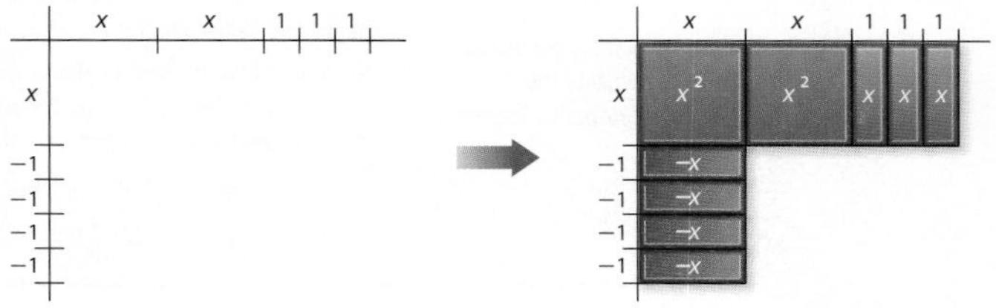

Step 2 Determine what color x-tiles and what color 1-tiles to use to complete the rectangle. The area of each red x-tile is the product of x and -1. The area of each red -1-tile is represented by $1(-1)$ or -1.

Complete the rectangle with 4 red x-tiles and 12 red -1-tiles.

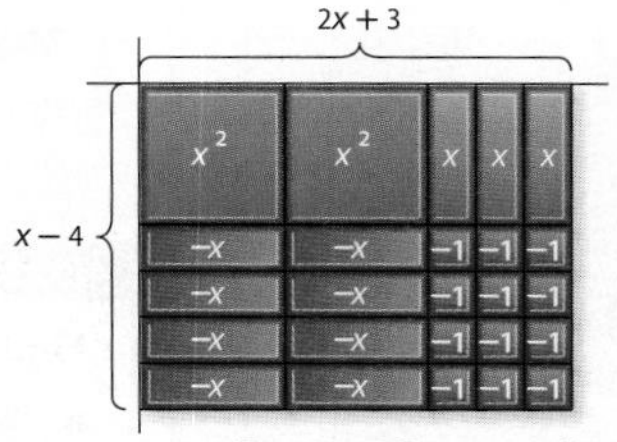

Step 3 Rearrange the tiles to simplify the polynomial you have formed. Notice that a 3 zero pair are formed by three positive and three negative x-tiles.

There are 2 blue x^2-tiles, 5 red $-x$-tiles, and 12 red -1-tiles left. In simplest form, $(x - 4)(2x + 3) = 2x^2 - 5x - 12$.

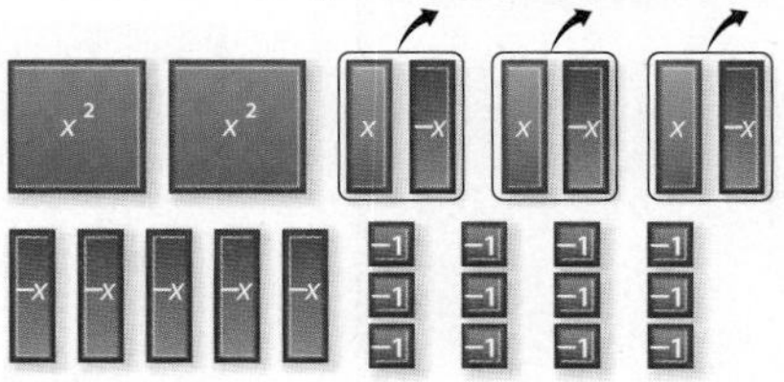

Model and Analyze

Use algebra tiles to find each product.

1. $(x + 1)(x + 4)$ $x^2 + 5x + 4$
2. $(x - 3)(x - 2)$ $x^2 - 5x + 6$
3. $(x + 5)(x - 1)$ $x^2 + 4x - 5$
4. $(x + 2)(2x + 3)$ $2x^2 + 7x + 6$
5. $(x - 1)(2x - 1)$ $2x^2 - 3x + 1$
6. $(x + 4)(2x - 5)$ $2x^2 + 3x - 20$

7–8. See margin for drawings.

Is each statement *true* or *false*? Justify your answer with a drawing of algebra tiles.

7. $(x - 4)(x - 2) = x^2 - 6x + 8$ **true**
8. $(x + 3)(x + 5) = x^2 + 15$ **false**

9. **WRITING IN MATH** You can also use the Distributive Property to find the product of two binomials. The figure at the right shows the model for $(x + 4)(x + 5)$ separated into four parts. Write a sentence or two explaining how this model shows the use of the Distributive Property.
By the Distributive Property, $(x + 4)(x + 5) = x(x + 5) + 4(x + 5)$. The top row represents $x(x + 5)$ or $x^2 + 5x$. The bottom row represents $4(x + 5)$ or $4x + 20$.

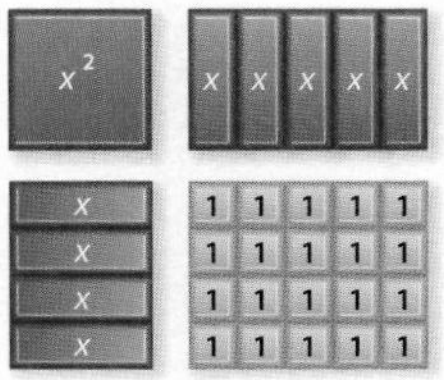

- For Activity 2, Step 2, have students pay close attention to whether the dimensions for each tile are positive or negative, as this affects which tile to use. If both dimensions are positive, then the tile is positive. If one is positive and the other is negative, the tile is negative. If both are negative, then the tile is positive.
- For Activity 3, as an alternative to removing zero pairs, have students write the expression based on the tiles without removing zero pairs. They can then simplify the expression by combining like terms.

Practice Have students complete Exercises 2–9.

3 Assess

Formative Assessment

Use Exercise 9 to assess whether students can model a product correctly.

From Concrete to Abstract

After students have completed Exercise 9, help them to see that when using the Distributive Property to multiply polynomials, each term from the first polynomial is multiplied by each term from the second polynomial.

Extending the Concept

Ask students to model $(x - 3)(x + 2)$ using algebra tiles. Then ask students to write the expression based on the tiles without removing zero pairs.
$x^2 + 2x - 3x - 6$

Finally, ask students to find the sum of the product of the two first terms, outer terms, inner terms, and last terms of $(x - 3)(x + 2)$ and then compare the results to the expression they wrote.
The two expressions are the same.

Additional Answers

7.

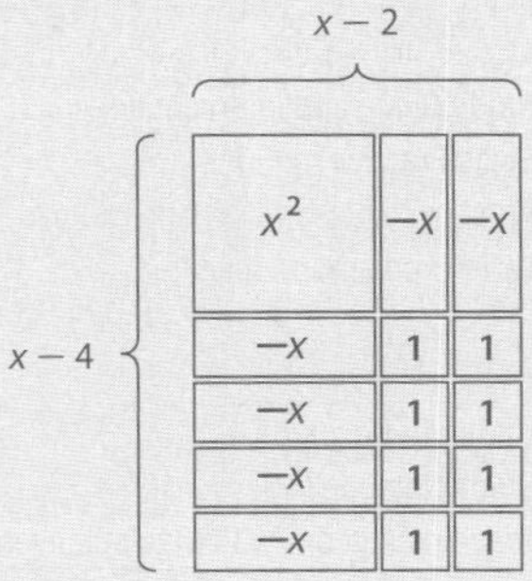

8.

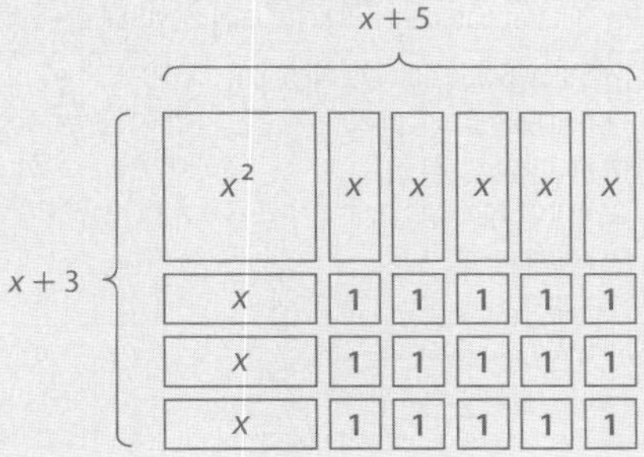

1 Focus

VerticalAlignment

Before Lesson 8-3 Multiply polynomials by monomials.

Lesson 8-3 Multiply binomials by using the FOIL method. Multiply polynomials by using the Distributive Property.

After Lesson 8-3 Find squares of binomials involving sums and differences.

2 Teach

Scaffolding Questions

Have students read the **Why?** section of the lesson.

Ask:

- What expression would you get if you multiplied the first term in $(h - 32)$ times $\left(\frac{1}{2}h + 11\right)$? $\frac{1}{2}h^2 + 11h$
- What expression would you get if you multiplied the second term in $(h - 32)$ by $\left(\frac{1}{2}h + 11\right)$? $-16h - 352$
- What expression do you get when you add these two answers together? $\frac{1}{2}h^2 - 5h - 352$

LESSON 8-3 Multiplying Polynomials

Then

- You multiplied polynomials by monomials.

Now

1. Multiply binomials by using the FOIL method.
2. Multiply polynomials by using the Distributive Property.

Why?

- Bodyboards, which are used to ride waves, are made of foam and are more rectangular than surfboards. A bodyboard's dimensions are determined by the height and skill level of the user.

  The length of Ann's bodyboard should be Ann's height h minus 32 inches or $h - 32$. The board's width should be half of Ann's height plus 11 inches or $\frac{1}{2}h + 11$. To approximate the area of the bodyboard, you need to find $(h - 32)\left(\frac{1}{2}h + 11\right)$.

NewVocabulary
FOIL method
quadratic expression

Content Standards
AI.RNE.7

1 Multiply Binomials

To multiply two binomials such as $h - 32$ and $\frac{1}{2}h + 11$, the Distributive Property is used. Binomials can be multiplied horizontally or vertically.

Example 1 The Distributive Property

Find each product.

a. $(2x + 3)(x + 5)$

Vertical Method

Multiply by 5.

$$\begin{array}{r} 2x + 3 \\ (\times)\ x + 5 \\ \hline 10x + 15 \end{array}$$

$5(2x + 3) = 10x + 15$

Multiply by x.

$$\begin{array}{r} 2x + 3 \\ (\times)\ x + 5 \\ \hline 10x + 15 \\ 2x^2 + 3x \quad\quad \\ \hline \end{array}$$

$x(2x + 3) = 2x^2 + 3x$

Combine like terms.

$$\begin{array}{r} 2x + 3 \\ (\times)\ x + 5 \\ \hline 10x + 15 \\ 2x^2 + 3x \quad\quad \\ \hline 2x^2 + 13x + 15 \end{array}$$

Horizontal Method

$$\begin{aligned} (2x + 3)(x + 5) &= 2x(x + 5) + 3(x + 5) && \text{Rewrite as the sum of two products.} \\ &= 2x^2 + 10x + 3x + 15 && \text{Distributive Property} \\ &= 2x^2 + 13x + 15 && \text{Combine like terms.} \end{aligned}$$

b. $(x - 2)(3x + 4)$

Vertical Method

Multiply by 4.

$$\begin{array}{r} x - 2 \\ (\times)\ 3x + 4 \\ \hline 4x - 8 \end{array}$$

$4(x - 2) = 4x - 8$

Multiply by $3x$.

$$\begin{array}{r} x - 2 \\ (\times)\ 3x + 4 \\ \hline 4x - 8 \\ 3x^2 - 6x \quad\quad \\ \hline \end{array}$$

$3x(x - 2) = 3x^2 - 6x$

Combine like terms.

$$\begin{array}{r} x - 2 \\ (\times)\ 3x + 4 \\ \hline 4x - 8 \\ 3x^2 - 6x \quad\quad \\ \hline 3x^2 - 2x - 8 \end{array}$$

Horizontal Method

$$\begin{aligned} (x - 2)(3x + 4) &= x(3x + 4) - 2(3x + 4) && \text{Rewrite as the difference of two products.} \\ &= 3x^2 + 4x - 6x - 8 && \text{Distributive Property} \\ &= 3x^2 - 2x - 8 && \text{Combine like terms.} \end{aligned}$$

Lesson 8-3 Resources

Resource	Approaching Level AL	On Level OL	Beyond Level BL	English Learners ELL
Teacher Edition	▪ Differentiated Instruction, p. 481	▪ Differentiated Instruction, pp. 481, 485	▪ Differentiated Instruction, p. 485	
Chapter Resource Masters	▪ Study Guide and Intervention, pp. 18–19 ▪ Skills Practice, p. 20 ▪ Practice, p. 21 ▪ Word Problem Practice, p. 22	▪ Study Guide and Intervention, pp. 18–19 ▪ Skills Practice, p. 20 ▪ Practice, p. 21 ▪ Word Problem Practice, p. 22 ▪ Enrichment, p. 23 ▪ Spreadsheet Activity, p. 24	▪ Practice, p. 21 ▪ Word Problem Practice, p. 22 ▪ Enrichment, p. 23	▪ Study Guide and Intervention, pp. 18–19 ▪ Skills Practice, p. 20 ▪ Practice, p. 21 ▪ Word Problem Practice, p. 22
Other	▪ 5-Minute Check 8-3 ▪ Study Notebook ▪ Teaching Algebra with Manipulatives	▪ 5-Minute Check 8-3 ▪ Study Notebook ▪ Teaching Algebra with Manipulatives	▪ 5-Minute Check 8-3 ▪ Study Notebook	▪ 5-Minute Check 8-3 ▪ Study Notebook ▪ Teaching Algebra with Manipulatives

GuidedPractice

1A. $(3m + 4)(m + 5)$ $3m^2 + 19m + 20$ **1B.** $(5y - 2)(y + 8)$ $5y^2 + 38y - 16$

A shortcut version of the Distributive Property for multiplying binomials is called the **FOIL method**.

KeyConcept FOIL Method

Words To multiply two binomials, find the sum of the products of *F* the *First* terms, *O* the *Outer* terms, *I* the *Inner* terms, *L* and the *Last* terms.

Example

	Product of First Terms		Product of Outer Terms		Product of Inner Terms		Product of Last Terms
$(x + 4)(x - 2) =$	$(x)(x)$	+	$(x)(-2)$	+	$(4)(x)$	+	$(4)(-2)$

$= x^2 - 2x + 4x - 8$

$= x^2 + 2x - 8$

ReadingMath

Polynomials as Factors The expression $(x + 4)(x - 2)$ is read *the quantity x plus 4 times the quantity x minus 2.*

Example 2 FOIL Method

Find each product.

a. $(2y - 7)(3y + 5)$

$(2y - 7)(3y + 5) = (2y)(3y) + (2y)(5) + (-7)(3y) + (-7)(5)$ FOIL method

$= 6y^2 + 10y - 21y - 35$ Multiply.

$= 6y^2 - 11y - 35$ Combine like terms.

b. $(4a - 5)(2a - 9)$

$(4a - 5)(2a - 9)$

$= (4a)(2a) + (4a)(-9) + (-5)(2a) + (-5)(-9)$ FOIL method

$= 8a^2 - 36a - 10a + 45$ Multiply.

$= 8a^2 - 46a + 45$ Combine like terms.

GuidedPractice

2A. $(x + 3)(x - 4)$ $x^2 - x - 12$ **2B.** $(4b - 5)(3b + 2)$ $12b^2 - 7b - 10$

2C. $(2y - 5)(y - 6)$ $2y^2 - 17y + 30$ **2D.** $(5a + 2)(3a - 4)$ $15a^2 - 14a - 8$

Notice that when two linear expressions are multiplied, the result is a quadratic expression. A **quadratic expression** is an expression in one variable with a degree of 2. When three linear expressions are multiplied, the result has a degree of 3.

The FOIL method can be used to find an expression that represents the area of a rectangular object when the lengths of the sides are given as binomials.

DifferentiatedInstruction OL BL

If students are less familiar with the Distributive Property,

Then they may wish to use the vertical method for multiplying binomials because it is similar to multiplying two-digit numbers. Suggest that students use the method with which they are most comfortable.

1 Multiply Binomials

Example 1 shows how to multiply two binomials using the Distributive Property. **Example 2** shows how to multiply two binomials using a shortcut of the Distributive Property called the FOIL method. **Example 3** shows how to use the FOIL method to solve a real-world problem.

Formative Assessment

Use the Guided Practice exercises after each example to determine students' understanding of concepts.

Additional Examples

1 Find each product.

a. $(y + 8)(y - 4)$
$y^2 + 4y - 32$

b. $(2x + 1)(x + 6)$
$2x^2 + 13x + 6$

2 Find each product.

a. $(z - 6)(z - 12)$
$z^2 - 18z + 72$

b. $(5x - 4)(2x + 8)$
$10x^2 + 32x - 32$

Additional Examples also in Interactive Classroom PowerPoint® Presentations

IWB Interactive White Board READY

Focus on Mathematical Content

Multiplying Other Polynomials The FOIL method only works for multiplying two binomials. To multiply any other polynomials, the Distributive Property must be used.

Tips for New Teachers

FOIL Point out that FOIL is a memory tool. The order in which the terms are multiplied is not important, as long as all four products are found.

Additional Example

3 **PATIO** A patio in the shape of the triangle shown below is being built in Lavali's backyard. The dimensions given are in feet. The area A of the triangle is one half the height h times the base b. Write an expression for the area of the patio.

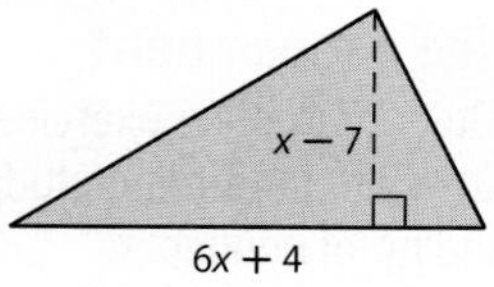

$(3x^2 - 19x - 14)$ ft^2

2 Multiply Polynomials

Example 4 shows how the Distributive Property can be used to multiply any two polynomials.

Additional Example

4 Find each product.

a. $(3a + 4)(a^2 - 12a + 1)$
$3a^3 - 32a^2 - 45a + 4$

b. $(2b^2 + 7b + 9)(b^2 + 3b - 1)$
$2b^4 + 13b^3 + 28b^2 + 20b - 9$

Teach with Tech

Interactive Whiteboard Work through an example multiplying two binomials. Write the example on the board and use a different color for each of the four terms. Then create a table with four columns, one for each of the four parts of FOIL. In each column, write the expression for the two terms to be multiplied using the color coding from the original expression.

Real-WorldLink

The cost of a swimming pool depends on many factors, including the size of the pool, whether the pool is an above-ground or an in-ground pool, and the material used.

Source: American Dream Homes

Real-World Example 3 FOIL Method

SWIMMING POOL A contractor is building a deck around a rectangular swimming pool. The deck is x feet from every side of the pool. Write an expression for the total area of the pool and deck.

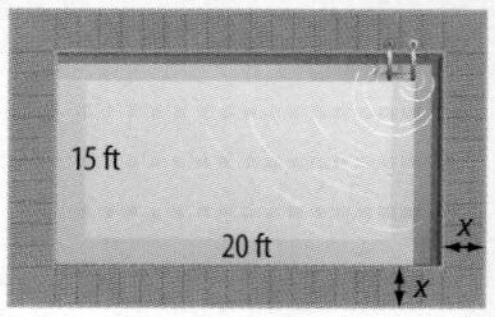

Understand We need to find an expression for the total area of the pool and deck.

Plan Find the product of the length and width of the pool with the deck.

Solve Since the deck is the same distance from every side of the pool, the length and width of the pool are $2x$ longer. So, the length can be represented by $2x + 20$ and the width can be represented by $2x + 15$.

Area = length • width	Area of a rectangle
$= (2x + 20)(2x + 15)$	Substitution
$= (2x)(2x) + (2x)(15) + (20)(2x) + (20)(15)$	FOIL Method
$= 4x^2 + 30x + 40x + 300$	Multiply.
$= 4x^2 + 70x + 300$	Combine like terms.

So, the total area of the deck and pool is $4x^2 + 70x + 300$.

Check Choose a value for x. Substitute this value into $(2x + 20)(2x + 15)$ and $4x^2 + 70x + 300$. The result should be the same for both expressions.

GuidedPractice $4x^2 + 90x + 500$

3. If the pool is 25 feet long and 20 feet wide, find the area of the pool and deck.

2 Multiply Polynomials

The Distributive Property can also be used to multiply any two polynomials.

Example 4 The Distributive Property

Find each product.

a. $(6x + 5)(2x^2 - 3x - 5)$

$(6x + 5)(2x^2 - 3x - 5)$	
$= 6x(2x^2 - 3x - 5) + 5(2x^2 - 3x - 5)$	Distributive Property
$= 12x^3 - 18x^2 - 30x + 10x^2 - 15x - 25$	Multiply.
$= 12x^3 - 8x^2 - 45x - 25$	Combine like terms.

b. $(2y^2 + 3y - 1)(3y^2 - 5y + 2)$

$(2y^2 + 3y - 1)(3y^2 - 5y + 2)$	
$= 2y^2(3y^2 - 5y + 2) + 3y(3y^2 - 5y + 2) - 1(3y^2 - 5y + 2)$	Distributive Property
$= 6y^4 - 10y^3 + 4y^2 + 9y^3 - 15y^2 + 6y - 3y^2 + 5y - 2$	Multiply.
$= 6y^4 - y^3 - 14y^2 + 11y - 2$	Combine like terms.

StudyTip

Multiplying Polynomials If a polynomial with c terms and a polynomial with d terms are multiplied together, there will be $c \cdot d$ terms before simplifying. In Example 4a, there are $2 \cdot 3$ or 6 terms before simplifying.

GuidedPractice

4A. $(3x - 5)(2x^2 + 7x - 8)$ $6x^3 + 11x^2 - 59x + 40$

4B. $(m^2 + 2m - 3)(4m^2 - 7m + 5)$ $4m^4 + m^3 - 21m^2 + 31m - 15$

Check Your Understanding

= Step-by-Step Solutions begin on page R13.

Examples 1–2 Find each product.

1. $(x + 5)(x + 2)$ $x^2 + 7x + 10$
2. $(y - 2)(y + 4)$ $y^2 + 2y - 8$
3. $(b - 7)(b + 3)$ $b^2 - 4b - 21$
4. $(4n + 3)(n + 9)$ $4n^2 + 39n + 27$
5. $(8h - 1)(2h - 3)$ $16h^2 - 26h + 3$
6. $(2a + 9)(5a - 6)$ $10a^2 + 33a - 54$

Example 3

7. **FRAME** Hugo is designing a frame as shown at the right. The frame has a width of x inches all the way around. Write an expression that represents the total area of the picture and frame. $4x^2 + 72x + 320$

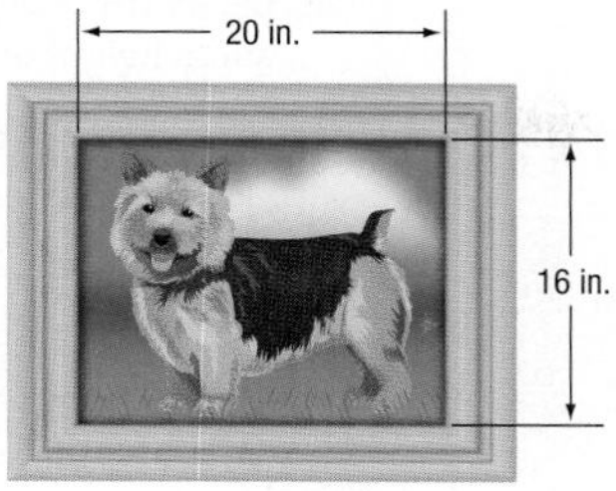

Example 4 Find each product.

8. $(2a - 9)(3a^2 + 4a - 4)$ $6a^3 - 19a^2 - 44a + 36$
9. $(4y^2 - 3)(4y^2 + 7y + 2)$ $16y^4 + 28y^3 - 4y^2 - 21y - 6$
10. $(x^2 - 4x + 5)(5x^2 + 3x - 4)$ $5x^4 - 17x^3 + 9x^2 + 31x - 20$
11. $(2n^2 + 3n - 6)(5n^2 - 2n - 8)$ $10n^4 + 11n^3 - 52n^2 - 12n + 48$

16. $15y^2 - 17y + 4$
17. $24d^2 - 62d + 35$
18. $6m^2 + 19m + 15$
19. $49n^2 - 84n + 36$

Practice and Problem Solving

Extra Practice is on page R8.

Examples 1–2 Find each product. 12. $3c^2 + 4c - 15$ 13. $2g^2 + 15g - 50$ 15. $24x^2 + 18x + 3$

12. $(3c - 5)(c + 3)$
13. $(g + 10)(2g - 5)$
14. $(6a + 5)(5a + 3)$ $30a^2 + 43a + 15$
15. $(4x + 1)(6x + 3)$
16. $(5y - 4)(3y - 1)$
17. $(6d - 5)(4d - 7)$
18. $(3m + 5)(2m + 3)$
19. $(7n - 6)(7n - 6)$
20. $(12t - 5)(12t + 5)$ $144t^2 - 25$
21. $(5r + 7)(5r - 7)$ $25r^2 - 49$
22. $(8w + 4x)(5w - 6x)$ $40w^2 - 28wx - 24x^2$
23. $(11z - 5y)(3z + 2y)$ $33z^2 + 7yz - 10y^2$

Example 3

24. **GARDEN** A walkway surrounds a rectangular garden. The width of the garden is 8 feet, and the length is 6 feet. The width x of the walkway around the garden is the same on every side. Write an expression that represents the total area of the garden and walkway. $4x^2 + 28x + 48$

Example 4 Find each product. **25–30. See margin.**

25. $(2y - 11)(y^2 - 3y + 2)$
26. $(4a + 7)(9a^2 + 2a - 7)$
27. $(m^2 - 5m + 4)(m^2 + 7m - 3)$
28. $(x^2 + 5x - 1)(5x^2 - 6x + 1)$
29. $(3b^3 - 4b - 7)(2b^2 - b - 9)$
30. $(6z^2 - 5z - 2)(3z^3 - 2z - 4)$

B Simplify.

31. $(m + 2)[(m^2 + 3m - 6) + (m^2 - 2m + 4)]$ $2m^3 + 5m^2 - 4$
32. $[(t^2 + 3t - 8) - (t^2 - 2t + 6)](t - 4)$ $5t^2 - 34t + 56$

STRUCTURE Find an expression to represent the area of each shaded region.

33.

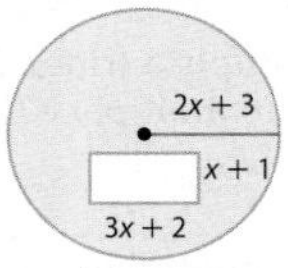

$4\pi x^2 + 12\pi x + 9\pi - 3x^2 - 5x - 2$

34.

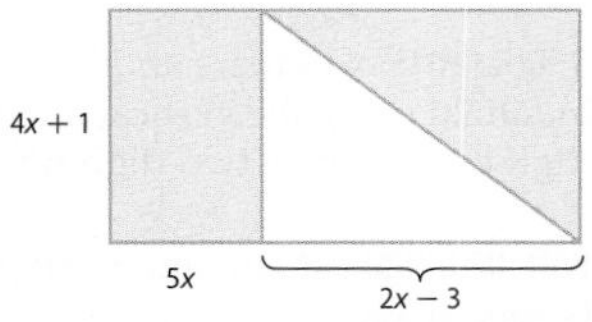

$24x^2 - \frac{3}{2}$

3 Practice

Formative Assessment

Use Exercises 1–11 to check for understanding.

Use the chart at the bottom of this page to customize assignments for your students.

WatchOut!

Common Errors When students multiply polynomials horizontally, they often try to combine terms that are not like terms. For students who are having difficulty finding the product in Exercises 12–23, suggest that they try multiplying the polynomials in vertical form, aligning like terms.

Exercise Alert

Formula For Exercise 33, students will need to know the formula for the area of a circle, $A = \pi r^2$.

Teaching the Process Standards

Structure Mathematically proficient students can see complicated things as single objects or as being composed of several objects. In Exercises 33 and 34, ask students what shapes they see in each diagram, and how the area of each shape can be represented.

Additional Answers

25. $2y^3 - 17y^2 + 37y - 22$
26. $36a^3 + 71a^2 - 14a - 49$
27. $m^4 + 2m^3 - 34m^2 + 43m - 12$
28. $5x^4 + 19x^3 - 34x^2 + 11x - 1$
29. $6b^5 - 3b^4 - 35b^3 - 10b^2 + 43b + 63$
30. $18z^5 - 15z^4 - 18z^3 - 14z^2 + 24z + 8$

Differentiated Homework Options

Level	Assignment	Two-Day Option	
AL Basic	12–30, 45, 47–66	13–29 odd, 50–53	12–30 even, 45, 47–49, 54–66
OL Core	13–33 odd, 35, 36, 37–41 odd, 43–45, 47–66	12–30, 50–53	31–45, 47–49, 54–66
BL Advanced	31–62, (optional: 63–66)		

Study Guide and Intervention

AL OL ELL

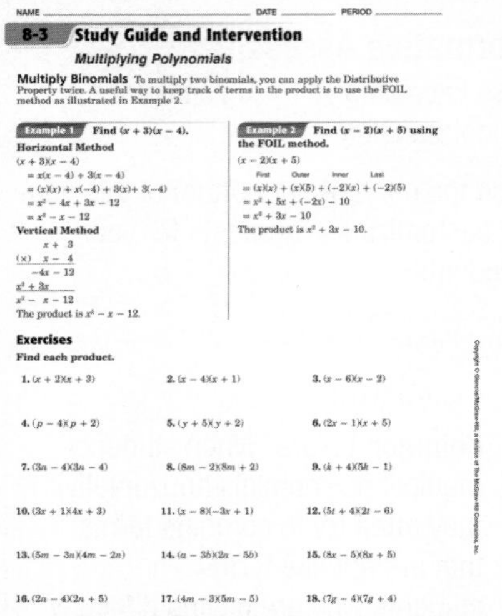
NAME ____ DATE ____ PERIOD ____

8-3 Study Guide and Intervention

Multiplying Polynomials

Multiply Binomials To multiply two binomials, you can apply the Distributive Property twice. A useful way to keep track of terms in the product is to use the FOIL method as illustrated in Example 2.

Example 1 Find $(x + 3)(x - 4)$.

Horizontal Method

$(x + 3)(x - 4)$
$= x(x - 4) + 3(x - 4)$
$= (x)(x) + x(-4) + 3(x) + 3(-4)$
$= x^2 - 4x + 3x - 12$
$= x^2 - x - 12$

Vertical Method

The product is $x^2 - x - 12$.

Example 2 Find $(x - 2)(x + 5)$ using the FOIL method.

$(x - 2)(x + 5)$
$= (x)(x) + (x)(5) + (-2)(x) + (-2)(5)$
$= x^2 + 5x + (-2x) - 10$
$= x^2 + 3x - 10$

The product is $x^2 + 3x - 10$.

Exercises

Find each product.

1. $(x + 2)(x + 3)$
2. $(x - 4)(x + 1)$
3. $(x - 6)(x - 2)$
4. $(p - 4)(p + 2)$
5. $(y + 5)(y + 2)$
6. $(2x - 1)(x + 5)$
7. $(3n - 4)(3n - 4)$
8. $(8m - 2)(8m + 2)$
9. $(k + 4)(5k - 1)$
10. $(3x + 1)(4x + 3)$
11. $(x - 8)(-3x + 1)$
12. $(5t + 4)(2t - 6)$
13. $(5m - 3n)(4m - 2n)$
14. $(a - 3b)(2a - 5b)$
15. $(8x - 5)(8x + 5)$
16. $(2n - 4)(2n + 5)$
17. $(4m - 3)(5m - 5)$
18. $(7g - 4)(7g + 4)$

Practice

AL OL BL ELL

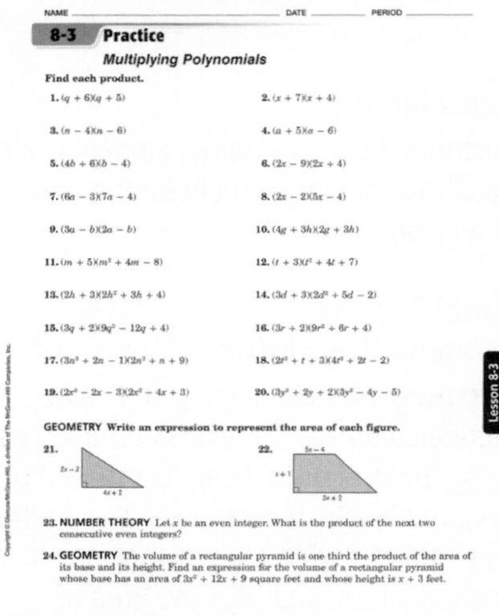
NAME ____ DATE ____ PERIOD ____

8-3 Practice

Multiplying Polynomials

Find each product.

1. $(q + 6)(q + 5)$
2. $(x + 7)(x + 4)$
3. $(n - 4)(n - 6)$
4. $(a + 5)(a - 6)$
5. $(4b + 6)(b - 4)$
6. $(2x - 9)(2x + 4)$
7. $(6a - 3)(7a - 4)$
8. $(2x - 2)(5x - 4)$
9. $(3a - b)(2a - b)$
10. $(4g + 3h)(2g + 3h)$
11. $(m + 5)(m^2 + 4m - 8)$
12. $(t + 3)(t^2 + 4t + 7)$
13. $(2h + 3)(2h^2 + 3h + 4)$
14. $(3d + 3)(2d^2 + 5d - 2)$
15. $(3q + 2)(9q^2 - 12q + 4)$
16. $(3r + 2)(9r^2 + 6r + 4)$
17. $(3n^2 + 2n - 1)(2n^2 + n + 9)$
18. $(2t^2 + t + 3)(4t^2 + 2t - 2)$
19. $(2x^2 - 2x - 3)(2x^2 - 4x + 3)$
20. $(3y^2 + 2y + 2)(3y^2 - 4y - 5)$

GEOMETRY Write an expression to represent the area of each figure.

21.
22.

23. NUMBER THEORY Let x be an even integer. What is the product of the next two consecutive even integers?

24. GEOMETRY The volume of a rectangular pyramid is one third the product of the area of its base and its height. Find an expression for the volume of a rectangular pyramid whose base has an area of $3x^2 + 12x + 9$ square feet and whose height is $x + 3$ feet.

Word Problem Practice

AL OL BL ELL

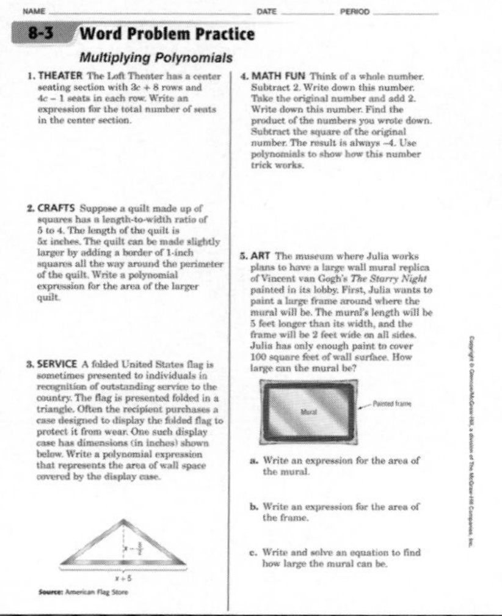
NAME ____ DATE ____ PERIOD ____

8-3 Word Problem Practice

Multiplying Polynomials

1. THEATER The Loft Theater has a center seating section with $3c + 8$ rows and $4c - 1$ seats in each row. Write an expression for the total number of seats in the center section.

2. CRAFTS Suppose a quilt made up of squares has a length-to-width ratio of 5 to 4. The length of the quilt is 5x inches. The quilt can be made slightly larger by adding a border of 1-inch squares all the way around the perimeter of the quilt. Write a polynomial expression for the area of the larger quilt.

3. SERVICE A folded United States flag is sometimes presented to individuals in recognition of outstanding service to the country. The flag is presented folded in a triangle. Often the recipient purchases a case designed to display the folded flag to protect it from wear. One such display case has dimensions (in inches) shown below. Write a polynomial expression that represents the area of wall space covered by the display case.

Source: American Flag Store

4. MATH FUN Think of a whole number. Subtract 2. Write down this number. Take the original number and add 2. Write down this number. Find the product of the numbers you wrote down. Subtract the square of the original number. The result is always −4. Use polynomials to show how this number trick works.

5. ART The museum where Julia works plans to have a large wall mural replica of Vincent van Gogh's *The Starry Night* painted in its lobby. First, Julia wants to paint a large frame around where the mural will be. The mural's length will be 5 feet longer than its width, and the frame will be 2 feet wide on all sides. Julia has only enough paint to cover 100 square feet of wall surface. How large can the mural be?

a. Write an expression for the area of the mural.

b. Write an expression for the area of the frame.

c. Write and solve an equation to find how large the mural can be.

35. **VOLLEYBALL** The dimensions of a sand volleyball court are represented by a width of $6y - 5$ feet and a length of $3y + 4$ feet.

a. Write an expression that represents the area of the court. $18y^2 + 9y - 20$

b. The length of a sand volleyball court is 31 feet. Find the area of the court. 1519 ft^2

36. **GEOMETRY** Write an expression for the area of a triangle with a base of $2x + 3$ and a height of $3x - 1$. $3x^2 + \frac{7}{2}x - \frac{3}{2}$

Find each product. 37–42. See margin.

37. $(a - 2b)^2$	38. $(3c + 4d)^2$	39. $(x - 5y)^2$
40. $(2r - 3t)^3$	41. $(5g + 2h)^3$	42. $(4y + 3z)(4y - 3z)^2$

43. **CONSTRUCTION** A sandbox kit allows you to build a square sandbox or a rectangular sandbox as shown.

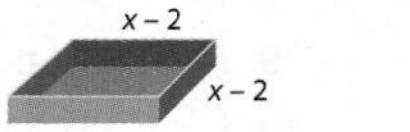

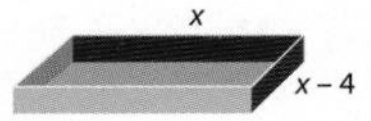

a. What are the possible values of x? Explain. See margin.

b. Which shape has the greater area? square

c. What is the difference in areas between the two? 4 ft^2

C **44.** **MULTIPLE REPRESENTATIONS** In this problem, you will investigate the square of a sum.

a. **Tabular** Copy and complete the table for each sum.

Expression	(Expression)^2
$x + 5$	$x^2 + 10x + 25$
$3y + 1$	$9y^2 + 6y + 1$
$z + q$	$z^2 + 2zq + q^2$

b. **Verbal** Make a conjecture about the terms of the square of a sum. See margin.

c. **Symbolic** For a sum of the form $a + b$, write an expression for the square of the sum. $a^2 + 2ab + b^2$

45. Always; by grouping two adjacent terms a trinomial can be written as a binomial a sum of two quantities, and apply the FOIL method. For example, $(2x + 3)(x^2 + 5x + 7) = (2x + 3)[x^2 + (5x + 7)] = 2x(x^2) + 2x(5x + 7) + 3(x^2) + 3(5x + 7)$. Then use the Distributive Property and simplify.

H.O.T. Problems Use Higher-Order Thinking Skills

45. **REASONING** Determine if the following statement is *sometimes*, *always*, or *never* true. Explain your reasoning.

The FOIL method can be used to multiply a binomial and a trinomial.

46. **CHALLENGE** Find $(x^m + x^p)(x^{m-1} - x^{1-p} + x^p)$.
$x^{2m-1} - x^{m-p+1} + x^{m+p} + x^{m+p-1} - x + x^{2p}$

47. **OPEN ENDED** Write a binomial and a trinomial involving a single variable. Then find their product. Sample answer: $x - 1$, $x^2 - x - 1$; $(x - 1)(x^2 - x - 1) = x^3 - 2x^2 + 1$

48. **REGULARITY** Compare and contrast the procedure used to multiply a trinomial by a binomial using the vertical method with the procedure used to multiply a three-digit number by a two-digit number. See Ch. 8 Answer Appendix.

49. **WRITING IN MATH** Summarize the methods that can be used to multiply polynomials. See Ch. 8 Answer Appendix.

Enrichment

OL BL

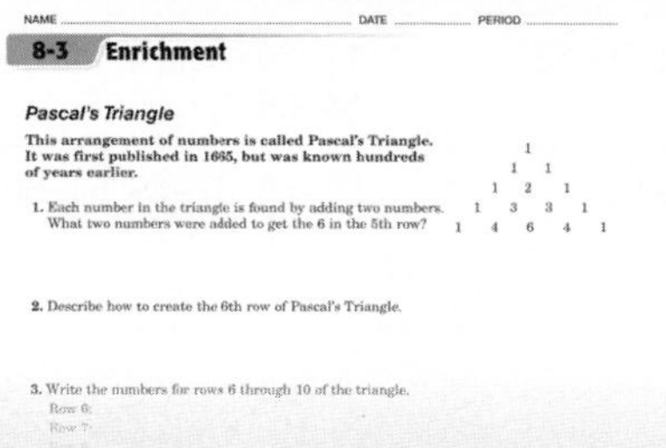
NAME ____ DATE ____ PERIOD ____

8-3 Enrichment

Pascal's Triangle

This arrangement of numbers is called Pascal's Triangle. It was first published in 1665, but was known hundreds of years earlier.

1
1 1
1 2 1
1 3 3 1
1 4 6 4 1

1. Each number in the triangle is found by adding two numbers. What two numbers were added to get the 6 in the 5th row?

2. Describe how to create the 6th row of Pascal's Triangle.

3. Write the numbers for rows 6 through 10 of the triangle.

Multiple Representations

In Exercise 44, students use a table of values and analysis to express the results of squaring a sum of the form $(a + b)$.

Standardized Test Practice

50. What is the product of $2x - 5$ and $3x + 4$? **B**

A $5x - 1$

B $6x^2 - 7x - 20$

C $6x^2 - 20$

D $6x^2 + 7x - 20$

51. Which statement is correct about the symmetry of this design? **F**

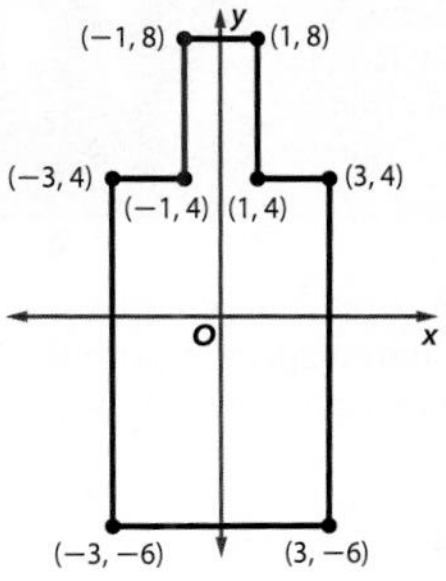

F The design is symmetrical only about the y-axis.

G The design is symmetrical only about the x-axis.

H The design is symmetrical about both the y- and the x-axes.

J The design has no symmetry.

52. Which point on the number line represents a number that, when cubed, will result in a number greater than itself? **D**

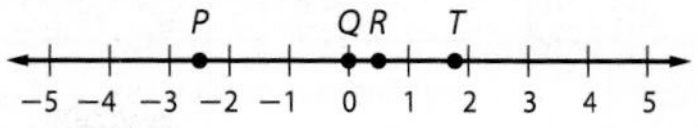

A P C R

B Q D T

53. SHORT RESPONSE For a science project, Jodi selected three bean plants of equal height. Then, for five days, she measured their heights in centimeters and plotted the values on the graph below.

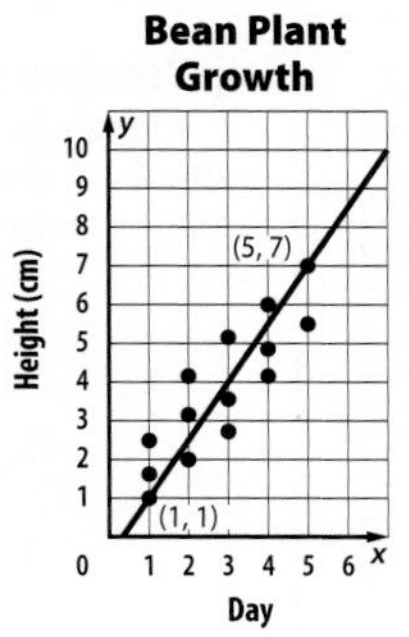

She drew a line of best fit on the graph. What is the slope of the line that she drew? $\frac{3}{2}$

Spiral Review

54. SAVINGS Carrie has \$6000 to invest. She puts x dollars of this money into a savings account that earns 2% interest per year. She uses the rest of the money to purchase a certificate of deposit that earns 4% interest. Write an equation for the amount of money that Carrie will have in one year. (Lesson 8-2) $T = 1.02x + 1.04(6000 - x)$

Find each sum or difference. (Lesson 8-1) **57.** $3n^3 - 6n^2 + 10$

55. $(7a^2 - 5) + (-3a^2 + 10)$ $4a^2 + 5$

56. $(8n - 2n^2) + (4n - 6n^2)$ $12n - 8n^2$

57. $(4 + n^3 + 3n^2) + (2n^3 - 9n^2 + 6)$

58. $(-4u^2 - 9 + 2u) + (6u + 14 + 2u^2)$ $-2u^2 + 8u + 5$

59. $(b + 4) + (c + 3b - 2)$ $4b + c + 2$

60. $(3a^3 - 6a) - (3a^3 + 5a)$ $-11a$

61. $(-4m^3 - m + 10) - (3m^3 + 3m^2 - 7)$ $-7m^3 - 3m^2 - m + 17$

62. $(3a + 4ab + 3b) - (2b + 5a + 8ab)$ $-2a - 4ab + b$

Skills Review

Simplify.

63. $(-2t^4)^3 - 3(-2t^3)^4$ $-56t^{12}$

64. $(-3h^2)^3 - 2(-h^3)^2$ $-29h^6$

65. $2(-5y^3)^2 + (-3y^3)^3$ $50y^6 - 27y^9$

66. $3(-6n^4)^2 + (-2n^2)^2$ $108n^8 + 4n^4$

Teaching the Process Standards

Regularity Mathematically proficient students look both for general methods and for shortcuts. In Exercise 48, tell students to start by multiplying a three-digit number and a two-digit number to analyze the procedure.

4 Assess

Name the Math Ask students to name the mathematical procedures they use when multiplying two binomials with the FOIL method.

Additional Answers

37. $a^2 - 4ab + 4b^2$

38. $9c^2 + 24cd + 16d^2$

39. $x^2 - 10xy + 25y^2$

40. $8r^3 - 36r^2t + 54rt^2 - 27t^3$

41. $125g^3 + 150g^2h + 60gh^2 + 8h^3$

42. $64y^3 - 48y^2z - 36yz^2 + 27z^3$

43a. $x > 4$; If $x = 4$ the width of the rectangular sandbox would be zero and if $x < 4$ the width of the rectangular sandbox would be negative.

44b. The first term of the square of a sum is the first term of the sum squared. The middle term of the sum is two times the first term of the sum multiplied by the last term of the sum. The third term of the square of the sum is the last term of the sum squared.

Differentiated Instruction OL BL

Extension Tell students that one way to multiply 25 and 18 mentally is to multiply $(20 + 5)$ by $(20 - 2)$. Have them show how the FOIL method can be used to find each product.

a. 35(19) $35(19) = (30 + 5)(10 + 9) = (30)(10) + (30)(9) + 5(10) + 5(9) = 300 + 270 + 50 + 45 = 665$

b. 67(102) $67(102) = (60 + 7)(100 + 2) = (60)(100) + (60)(2) + 7(100) + 7(2) = 6000 + 120 + 700 + 14 = 6834$

1 Focus

VerticalAlignment

Before Lesson 8-4 Multiply binomials by using the FOIL method.

Lesson 8-4 Find squares of sums and differences.
Find the product of a sum and a difference.

After Lesson 8-4 Factor a polynomial using the Distributive Property.

2 Teach

Scaffolding Questions

Have students read the **Why?** section of the lesson.

Ask:

- What two factors equal $(2r + 24)^2$ when multiplied? $(2r + 24)(2r + 24)$
- Use the FOIL method to find $(2r + 24)^2$. $4r^2 + 96r + 576$
- If $2r = a$ and $24 = b$, does $(2r + 24)^2$ equal $a^2 + 2ab + b^2$? Explain. Yes; $(2r + 24)^3 = (2r)^2 + 2(2r)(24) + 24^2 = 4r^2 + 96r + 576$.

LESSON 8-4 Special Products

Then	Now	Why?
You multiplied binomials by using the FOIL method.	1 Find squares of sums and differences. 2 Find the product of a sum and a difference.	Colby wants to attach a dartboard to a square piece of corkboard. If the radius of the dartboard is $r + 12$, how large does the square corkboard need to be? Colby knows that the diameter of the dartboard is $2(r + 12)$ or $2r + 24$. Each side of the square also measures $2r + 24$. To find how much corkboard is needed, Colby must find the area of the square: $A = (2r + 24)^2$.

Content Standards
AI.RNE.7

Process Standards
PS.8

1 Squares of Sums and Differences Some pairs of binomials, such as squares like $(2r + 24)^2$, have products that follow a specific pattern. Using the pattern can make multiplying easier. The square of a sum, $(a + b)^2$ or $(a + b)(a + b)$, is one of those products.

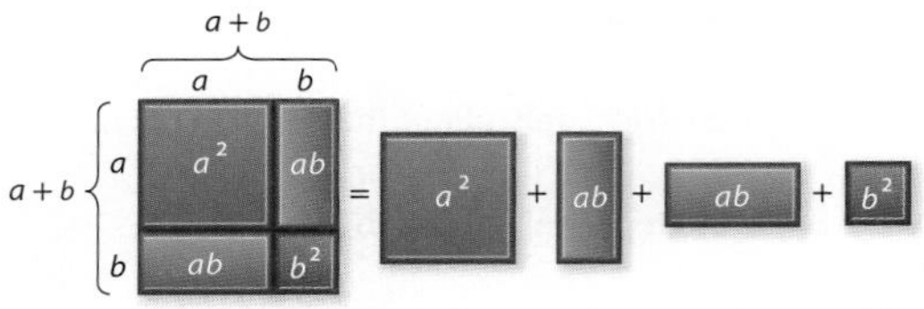

$(a + b)^2 = a^2 + ab + ab + b^2$

KeyConcept Square of a Sum

Words The square of $a + b$ is the square of a plus twice the product of a and b plus the square of b.

Symbols $(a + b)^2 = (a + b)(a + b)$
$= a^2 + 2ab + b^2$

Example $(x + 4)^2 = (x + 4)(x + 4)$
$= x^2 + 8x + 16$

Example 1 Square of a Sum

Find $(3x + 5)^2$.

$(a + b)^2 = a^2 + 2ab + b^2$ — Square of a sum

$(3x + 5)^2 = (3x)^2 + 2(3x)(5) + 5^2$ — $a = 3x$, $b = 5$

$= 9x^2 + 30x + 25$ — Simplify. Use FOIL to check your solution.

GuidedPractice

Find each product.

1A. $(8c + 3d)^2$ $64c^2 + 48cd + 9d^2$

1B. $(3x + 4y)^2$ $9x^2 + 24xy + 16y^2$

486 | Lesson 8-4

Lesson 8-4 Resources

Resource	Approaching Level AL	On Level OL	Beyond Level BL	English Learners ELL
Teacher Edition	▪ Differentiated Instruction, p. 488	▪ Differentiated Instruction, p. 491	▪ Differentiated Instruction, p. 491	▪ Differentiated Instruction, p. 488
Chapter Resource Masters	▪ Study Guide and Intervention, pp. 25–26 ▪ Skills Practice, p. 27 ▪ Practice, p. 28 ▪ Word Problem Practice, p. 29	▪ Study Guide and Intervention, pp. 25–26 ▪ Skills Practice, p. 27 ▪ Practice, p. 28 ▪ Word Problem Practice, p. 29 ▪ Enrichment, p. 30	▪ Practice, p. 28 ▪ Word Problem Practice, p. 29 ▪ Enrichment, p. 30	▪ Study Guide and Intervention, pp. 25–26 ▪ Skills Practice, p. 27 ▪ Practice, p. 28 ▪ World Problem Practice, p. 29
Other	▪ 5-Minute Check 8-4 ▪ Study Notebook ▪ Teaching Algebra with Manipulatives	▪ 5-Minute Check 8-4 ▪ Study Notebook ▪ Teaching Algebra with Manipulatives	▪ 5-Minute Check 8-4 ▪ Study Notebook	▪ 5-Minute Check 8-4 ▪ Study Notebook ▪ Teaching Algebra with Manipulatives

There is also a pattern for the *square of a difference*. Write $a - b$ as $a + (-b)$ and square it using the square of a sum pattern.

$$\begin{aligned}(a-b)^2 &= [a + (-b)]^2 \\ &= a^2 + 2(a)(-b) + (-b)^2 && \text{Square of a sum} \\ &= a^2 - 2ab + b^2 && \text{Simplify.}\end{aligned}$$

KeyConcept Square of a Difference

Words The square of $a - b$ is the square of a minus twice the product of a and b plus the square of b.

Symbols $(a - b)^2 = (a - b)(a - b) = a^2 - 2ab + b^2$ **Example** $(x - 3)^2 = (x - 3)(x - 3) = x^2 - 6x + 9$

WatchOut!

Regularity Remember that $(x - 7)^2$ does not equal $x^2 - 7^2$, or $x^2 - 49$.

$(x - 7)^2$
$= (x - 7)(x - 7)$
$= x^2 - 14x + 49$

Example 2 Square of a Difference

Find $(2x - 5y)^2$.

$$\begin{aligned}(a-b)^2 &= a^2 - 2ab + b^2 && \text{Square of a difference} \\ (2x - 5y)^2 &= (2x)^2 - 2(2x)(5y) + (5y)^2 && a = 2x \text{ and } b = 5y \\ &= 4x^2 - 20xy + 25y^2 && \text{Simplify.}\end{aligned}$$

GuidedPractice

Find each product.

2A. $(6p - 1)^2$ **$36p^2 - 12p + 1$**

2B. $(a - 2b)^2$ **$a^2 - 4ab + 4b^2$**

The product of the square of a sum or the square of a difference is called a *perfect square trinomial*. We can use these to find patterns to solve real-world problems.

Real-World Example 3 Square of a Difference

PHYSICAL SCIENCE **Each edge of a cube of aluminum is 4 centimeters less than each edge of a cube of copper. Write an equation to model the surface area of the aluminum cube.**

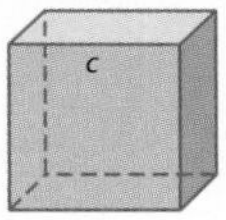

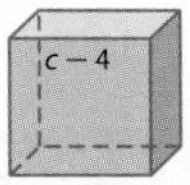

Let c = the length of each edge of the cube of copper. So, each edge of the cube of aluminum is $c - 4$.

$$\begin{aligned}SA &= 6s^2 && \text{Formula for surface area of a cube} \\ SA &= 6(c - 4)^2 && \text{Replace } s \text{ with } c - 4. \\ SA &= 6[c^2 - 2(4)(c) + 4^2] && \text{Square of a difference} \\ SA &= 6(c^2 - 8c + 16) && \text{Simplify.}\end{aligned}$$

GuidedPractice

3. **GARDENING** Alano has a garden that is g feet long and g feet wide. He wants to add 3 feet to the length and the width.

A. Show how the new area of the garden can be modeled by the square of a binomial. **$(g + 3)^2$**

B. Find the square of this binomial. **$g^2 + 6g + 9$**

1 Squares of Sums and Differences

Example 1 shows how to follow a specific pattern to find the square of a sum. **Example 2** shows how to find the square of a difference. **Example 3** shows how to use the square of a difference to write an expression that models a real–world situation.

Formative Assessment

Use the Guided Practice exercises after each example to determine students' understanding of concepts.

Additional Examples

1 Find $(7z + 2)^2$.
$49z^2 + 28z + 4$

2 Find $(3c - 4)^2$.
$9c^2 - 24c + 16$

3 **GEOMETRY** Write an expression that represents the area of a square that has a side length of $3x + 12$ units.
$(9x^2 + 72x + 144)$ units^2

Additional Examples also in Interactive Classroom PowerPoint® Presentations

IWB Interactive White Board READY

Tips for New Teachers

Alternative Method Even though it is important to learn the special products, point out to students that they can always find these products using methods from previous lessons in the chapter.

Teaching the Process Standards

Regularity Mathematically proficient students notice if calculations are repeated, and look both for general methods and for shortcuts. Encourage students to look for patterns in the Examples and step through finding each pattern before you present the formulas in the Key Concepts.

Focus on Mathematical Content

Squares of Sums and Differences Since the square of a sum and the square of a difference are the same except for the sign of the middle term, the risk of making a careless mistake when finding the sum or difference of a square is high. Tell students to pay close attention to the signs when finding squares of sums or differences.

Teach with Tech

Wiki On your secure classroom wiki have students write a real world situation that uses their choice of the square of sums, the square of differences, or the product of a sum and difference. These situations can be used as a review for a chapter test.

2 Product of a Sum and a Difference

Example 4 shows how to use the pattern for the product of the sum and difference of the same two terms.

Additional Example

4 Find $(9d + 4)(9d - 4)$. $81d^2 - 16$

Focus on Mathematical Content

Difference of Squares The product of a sum and difference of the same two terms, $(a + b)(a - b)$, is $a^2 - b^2$. This resulting product has a special name, the *difference of squares.*

3 Practice

Formative Assessment

Use Exercises 1–11 to check for understanding.

Use the chart at the bottom of the next page to customize assignments for your students.

---

2 Product of a Sum and a Difference

Now we will see what the result is when we multiply a sum and a difference, or $(a + b)(a - b)$. Recall that $a - b$ can be written as $a + (-b)$.

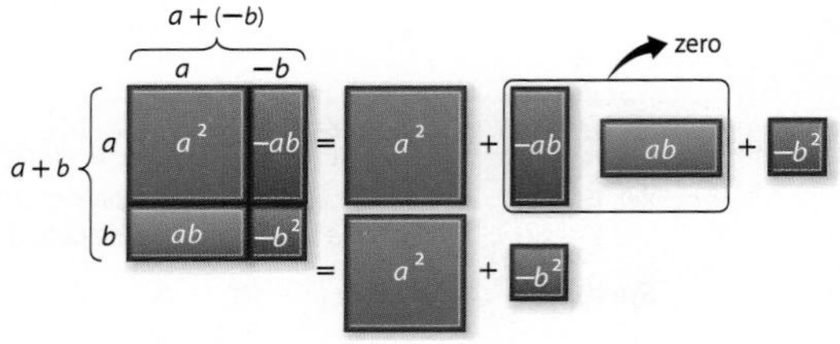

Notice that the middle terms are opposites and add to a zero pair.
So $(a + b)(a - b) = a^2 - ab + ab - b^2 = a^2 - b^2$.

StudyTip

Patterns When using any of these patterns, *a* and *b* can be numbers, variables, or expressions with numbers and variables.

KeyConcept Product of a Sum and a Difference

Words The product of $a + b$ and $a - b$ is the square of a minus the square of b.

Symbols $(a + b)(a - b) = (a - b)(a + b)$
$= a^2 - b^2$

Example 4 Product of a Sum and a Difference

Find $(2x^2 + 3)(2x^2 - 3)$.

$(a + b)(a - b)$	$= a^2 - b^2$	Product of a sum and a difference
$(2x^2 + 3)(2x^2 - 3)$	$= (2x^2)^2 - (3)^2$	$a = 2x^2$ and $b = 3$
	$= 4x^4 - 9$	Simplify.

GuidedPractice

Find each product.

4A. $(3n + 2)(3n - 2)$ $9n^2 - 4$

4B. $(4c - 7d)(4c + 7d)$ $16c^2 - 49d^2$

Check Your Understanding

◯ = Step-by-Step Solutions begin on page R13.

Examples 1–2 **Find each product.**

1. $(x + 5)^2$ $x^2 + 10x + 25$

2. $(11 - a)^2$ $121 - 22a + a^2$

3. $(2x + 7y)^2$ $4x^2 + 28xy + 49y^2$

4. $(3m - 4)(3m - 4)$ $9m^2 - 24m + 16$

5. $(g - 4h)(g - 4h)$ $g^2 - 8gh + 16h^2$

6. $(3c + 6d)^2$ $9c^2 + 36cd + 36d^2$

Example 3

7. GENETICS The color of a Labrador retriever's fur is genetic. Dark genes *D* are dominant over yellow genes *y*. A dog with genes *DD* or *Dy* will have dark fur. A dog with genes *yy* will have yellow fur. Pepper's genes for fur color are *Dy*, and Ramiro's are *yy*.

	D	y
D	DD	Dy
y	Dy	yy

a. Write an expression for the possible fur colors of Pepper's and Ramiro's puppies. $0.5Dy + 0.5y^2$

b. What is the probability that a puppy will have yellow fur? 50%

DifferentiatedInstruction AL ELL

If students have trouble remembering the pattern for special products studied in this lesson,

Then have them write the symbols for and examples of each Key Concept in this lesson on separate index cards. They can use their note cards for a quick reminder on how to proceed when they are finding products of squares of sums or differences or the product of a sum and a difference.

Example 4 Find each product.

8. $(a-3)(a+3)$ a^2-9
9. $(x+5)(x-5)$ x^2-25
10. $(6y-7)(6y+7)$ $36y^2-49$
11. $(9t+6)(9t-6)$ $81t^2-36$

Practice and Problem Solving

Extra Practice is on page R8.

Examples 1–2 Find each product.

12. $(a+10)(a+10)$ $a^2+20a+100$
13. $(b-6)(b-6)$ $b^2-12b+36$
14. $(h+7)^2$ $h^2+14h+49$
15. $(x+6)^2$ $x^2+12x+36$
16. $(8-m)^2$ $64-16m+m^2$
17. $(9-2y)^2$ $81-36y+4y^2$
18. $(2b+3)^2$ $4b^2+12b+9$
19. $(5t-2)^2$ $25t^2-20t+4$
20. $(8h-4n)^2$ $64h^2-64hn+16n^2$

Example 3

21. **GENETICS** The ability to roll your tongue is inherited genetically from parents if either parent has the dominant trait *T*. Children of two parents without the trait will not be able to roll their tongues.

	T	*t*
T	*TT*	*Tt*
t	*Tt*	*tt*

   a. Show how the combinations can be modeled by the square of a sum. $(T+t)^2=T^2+2Tt+t^2$

   b. Predict the percent of children that will have both dominant genes, one dominant gene, and both recessive genes. *TT*: 25%; *Tt*: 50%; *tt*: 25%

Example 4 Find each product. **22–44. See margin.**

22. $(u+3)(u-3)$
23. $(b+7)(b-7)$
24. $(2+x)(2-x)$
25. $(4-x)(4+x)$
26. $(2q+5r)(2q-5r)$
27. $(3a^2+7b)(3a^2-7b)$
28. $(5y+7)^2$
29. $(8-10a)^2$
30. $(10x-2)(10x+2)$
31. $(3t+12)(3t-12)$
32. $(a+4b)^2$
33. $(3q-5r)^2$
34. $(2c-9d)^2$
35. $(g+5h)^2$
36. $(6y-13)(6y+13)$
37. $(3a^4-b)(3a^4+b)$
38. $(5x^2-y^2)^2$
39. $(8a^2-9b^3)(8a^2+9b^3)$
40. $\left(\frac{3}{4}k+8\right)^2$
41. $\left(\frac{2}{5}y-4\right)^2$
42. $(7z^2+5y^2)(7z^2-5y^2)$
43. $(2m+3)(2m-3)(m+4)$
44. $(r+2)(r-5)(r-2)(r+5)$

45. **SENSE-MAKING** Write a polynomial that represents the area of the figure at the right. $2x^2+2x+5$

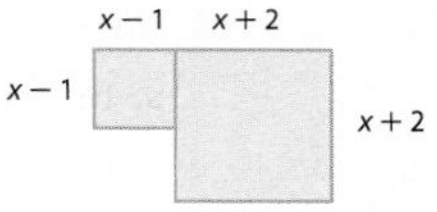

46. **FLYING DISKS** A flying disk shaped like a circle has a radius of $x+3$ inches.

   a. Write an expression representing the area of the flying disk. $\pi x^2+6\pi x+9\pi$

   b. A hole with a radius of $x-1$ inches is cut in the center of the disk. Write an expression for the remaining area. $8\pi x+8\pi$

GEOMETRY Find the area of each shaded region.

47. $6x+3$

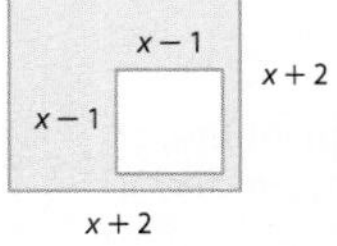

48. $x^2+11x-6$

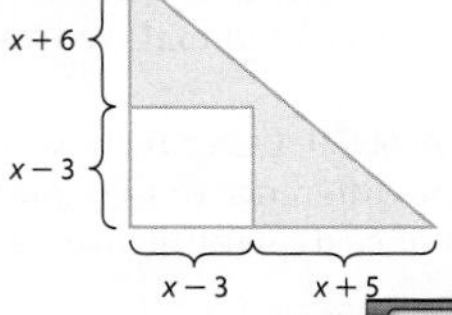

Teaching the Process Standards

Sense-Making Mathematically proficient students can explain the correspondences between equations, verbal descriptions, and diagrams. In Exercise 45, ask students to explain how to write and simplify the polynomial based on the diagram.

Exercise Alert

Formula For Exercises 46 and 55, students will need to know the formula for the area of a circle, $A=\pi r^2$.

Additional Answers

22. u^2-9
23. b^2-49
24. $4-x^2$
25. $16-x^2$
26. $4q^2-25r^2$
27. $9a^4-49b^2$
28. $25y^2+70y+49$
29. $64-160a+100a^2$
30. $100x^2-4$
31. $9t^2-144$
32. $a^2+8ab+16b^2$
33. $9q^2-30qr+25r^2$
34. $4c^2-36cd+81d^2$
35. $g^2+10gh+25h^2$
36. $36y^2-169$
37. $9a^8-b^2$
38. $25x^4-10x^2y^2+y^4$
39. $64a^4-81b^6$
40. $\frac{9}{16}k^2+12k+64$
41. $\frac{4}{25}y^2-\frac{16}{5}y+16$
42. $49z^4-25y^4$
43. $4m^3+16m^2-9m-36$
44. r^4-29r^2+100

Differentiated Homework Options

Level	Assignment	Two-Day Option	
AL Basic	12–28, 56, 57, 59–88	13–27 odd, 62–65	12–28 even, 56, 57, 59–61, 66–88
OL Core	13–53 odd, 55–57, 59–88	12–45, 62–65	46–57, 59–61, 66–88
BL Advanced	46–85, (optional: 84–88)		

Study Guide and Intervention
AL OL ELL

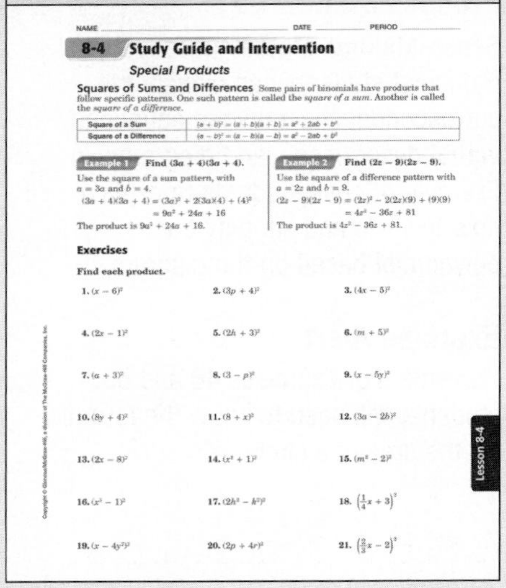

Practice
AL OL BL ELL

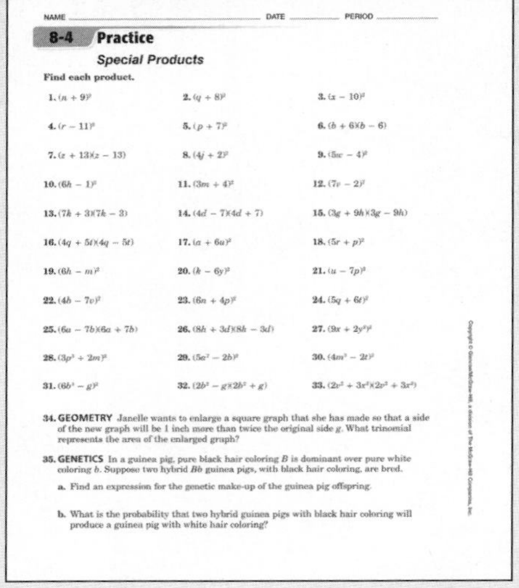

Word Problem Practice
AL OL BL ELL

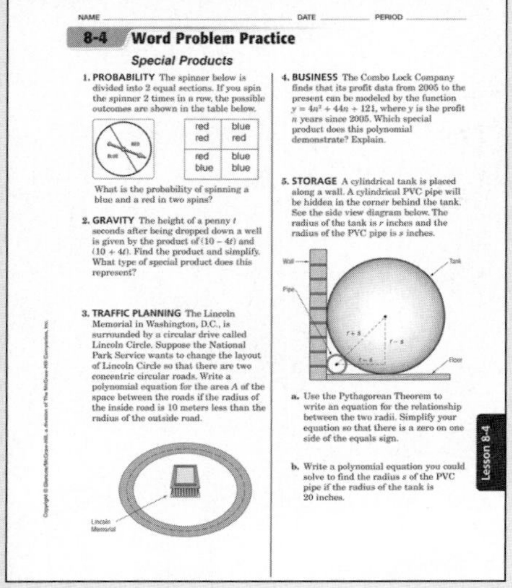

Find each product. **49.** $c^3 + 3c^2d + 3cd^2 + d^3$ **50.** $8a^3 - 12a^2b + 6ab^2 - b^3$

49. $(c + d)(c + d)(c + d)$ **50.** $(2a - b)^3$ **51.** $(f + g)(f - g)(f + g)$ $f^3 + f^2g - fg^2 - g^3$

52. $(k - m)(k + m)(k - m)$ $k^3 - k^2m - km^2 + m^3$ **53.** $(n - p)^2(n + p)$ $n^3 - n^2p - np^2 + p^3$ **54.** $(q + r)^2(q - r)$ $q^3 + q^2r - qr^2 - r^3$

55a. about $(3.14r^2 + 56.52r + 254.34)$ ft²

55. **WRESTLING** A high school wrestling mat must be a square with 38-foot sides and contain two circles as shown. Suppose the inner circle has a radius of r feet, and the radius of the outer circle is nine feet longer than the inner circle.

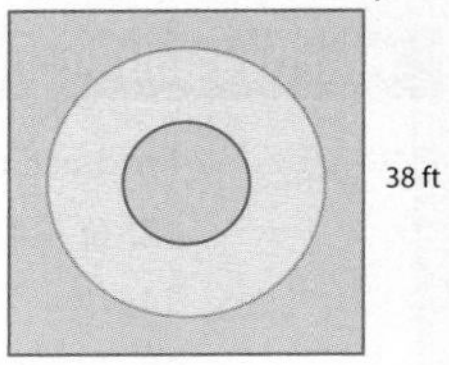

a. Write an expression for the area of the larger circle.

b. Write an expression for the area of the portion of the square outside the larger circle.
about $(1189.66 - 3.14r^2 - 56.52r)$ ft²

C **56.** **MULTIPLE REPRESENTATIONS** In this problem, you will investigate a pattern. Begin with a square piece of construction paper. Label each edge of the paper a. In any of the corners, draw a smaller square and label the edges b.

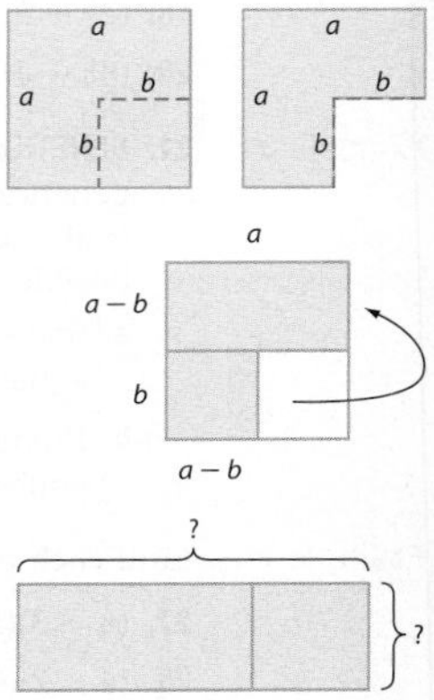

a. Numerical Find the area of each of the squares. See margin.

b. Concrete Cut the smaller square out of the corner. What is the area of the shape? $a^2 - b^2$

c. Analytical Remove the smaller rectangle on the bottom. Turn it and slide it next to the top rectangle. What is the length of the new arrangement? What is the width? What is the area? $a + b$, $a - b$, $(a + b)(a - b)$

d. Analytical What pattern does this verify?
$(a + b)(a - b) = a^2 - b^2$

H.O.T. Problems Use Higher-Order Thinking Skills

57. **WHICH ONE DOESN'T BELONG?** Which expression does not belong? Explain. See margin.

$(2c - d)(2c - d)$	$(2c + d)(2c - d)$	$(2c + d)(2c + d)$	$(c + d)(c + d)$

58. **STRUCTURE** Does a pattern exist for the cube of a sum $(a + b)^3$?

a. Investigate this question by finding the product $(a + b)(a + b)(a + b)$. $a^3 + 3a^2b + 3ab^2 + b^3$

b. Use the pattern you discovered in part **a** to find $(x + 2)^3$. $x^3 + 6x^2 + 12x + 8$

c. Draw a diagram of a geometric model for $(a + b)^3$.

d. What is the pattern for the cube of a difference, $(a - b)^3$? $a^3 - 3a^2b + 3ab^2 - b^3$

59. **REASONING** Find c that makes $25x^2 - 90x + c$ a perfect square trinomial. 81

58c. Sample answer:

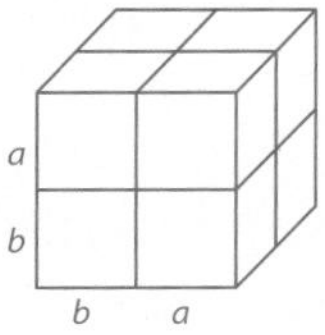

60. **OPEN ENDED** Write two binomials with a product that is a binomial. Then write two binomials with a product that is not a binomial.
Sample answer: $(x - 2)(x + 2) = x^2 - 4$ and $(x - 2)(x - 2) = x^2 - 4x + 4$

61. **WRITING IN MATH** Describe how to square the sum of two quantities, square the difference of two quantities, and how to find the product of a sum of two quantities and a difference of two quantities.
See margin.

Enrichment
OL BL

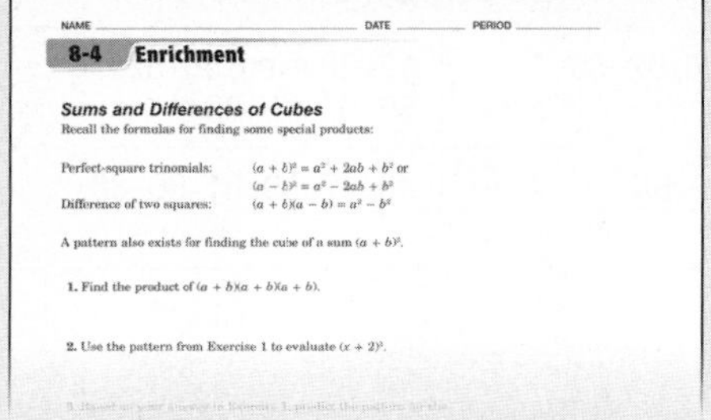

Multiple Representations
In Exercise 56, students use algebra and a physical model to represent the difference of two squares.

Standardized Test Practice

62. **GRIDDED RESPONSE** In the right triangle, $\overline{DB}$ bisects $\angle B$. What is the measure of $\angle ADB$ in degrees? **85**

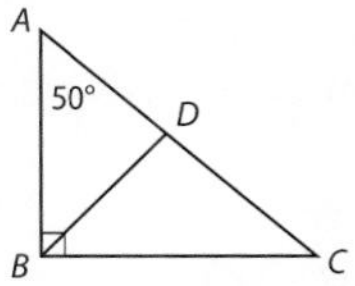

63. What is the product of $(2a - 3)$ and $(2a - 3)$? **D**

A $4a^2 + 12a + 9$
B $4a^2 + 9$
C $4a^2 - 12a - 9$
D $4a^2 - 12a + 9$

64. Myron can drive 4 miles in m minutes. At this rate, how many minutes will it take him to drive 19 miles? **G**

F $76m$
G $\frac{19m}{4}$
H $\frac{4m}{19}$
J $\frac{4}{19m}$

65. What property is illustrated by the equation $2x + 0 = 2x$? **C**

A Commutative Property of Addition
B Additive Inverse Property
C Additive Identity Property
D Associative Property of Addition

Spiral Review

Find each product. (Lesson 8-3)

66. $(y - 4)(y - 2)$ $\mathbf{y^2 - 6y + 8}$
67. $(2c - 1)(c + 3)$ $\mathbf{2c^2 + 5c - 3}$
68. $(d - 9)(d + 5)$ $\mathbf{d^2 - 4d - 45}$
69. $(4h - 3)(2h - 7)$ $\mathbf{8h^2 - 34h + 21}$
70. $(3x + 5)(2x + 3)$ $\mathbf{6x^2 + 19x + 15}$
71. $(5m + 4)(8m + 3)$ $\mathbf{40m^2 + 47m + 12}$

Simplify. (Lesson 8-2)

72. $x(2x - 7) + 5x$ $\mathbf{2x^2 - 2x}$
73. $c(c - 8) + 2c(c + 3)$ $\mathbf{3c^2 - 2c}$
74. $8y(-3y + 7) - 11y^2$ $\mathbf{-35y^2 + 56y}$
75. $-2d(5d) - 3d(d + 6)$ $\mathbf{-13d^2 - 18d}$
76. $5m(2m^3 + m^2 + 8) + 4m$ $\mathbf{10m^4 + 5m^3 + 44m}$
77. $3p(6p - 4) + 2\left(\frac{1}{2}p^2 - 3p\right)$ $\mathbf{19p^2 - 18p}$

Use substitution to solve each system of equations. (Lesson 6-2)

78. $4c = 3d + 3$, $c = d - 1$ **(6, 7)**
79. $c - 5d = 2$, $2c + d = 4$ **(2, 0)**
80. $5r - t = 5$, $-4r + 5t = 17$ **(2, 5)**

81. **BIOLOGY** Each type of fish thrives in a specific range of temperatures. The best temperatures for sharks range from 18°C to 22°C, inclusive. Write a compound inequality to represent temperatures where sharks will not thrive. (Lesson 5-4) $\mathbf{t < 18}$ **or** $\mathbf{t > 22}$

Write an equation of the line that passes through each pair of points. (Lesson 4-2)

82. (1, 1), (7, 4) $\mathbf{y = \frac{1}{2}x + \frac{1}{2}}$
83. (5, 7), (0, 6) $\mathbf{y = \frac{1}{5}x + 6}$
84. (5, 1), (8, −2) $\mathbf{y = -x + 6}$

85. **COFFEE** A coffee store wants to create a mix using two coffees. How many pounds of coffee A should be mixed with 9 pounds of coffee B to get a mixture that can sell for $6.95 per pound? (Lesson 2-9) **15 lb**

86. $\mathbf{-x^4 + 2x^2 + x - 8; -1}$ **87.** $\mathbf{2p^5 - 5p^4 + p^2 + 12; 2}$ **88.** $\mathbf{a^3 + 6a^2 - a - 10; 1}$

Skills Review

Write each polynomial in standard form. Identify the leading coefficient.

86. $2x^2 - x^4 - 8 + x$
87. $-5p^4 + p^2 + 12 + 2p^5$
88. $-10 + a^3 - a + 6a^2$

Differentiated Instruction OL BL

Extension A diagram of the Gwennap Pit is shown here. Tell students the historical Gwennap Pit, an outdoor amphitheater in southern England, consists of a circular stage surrounded by circular levels used for seating. Each seating level is about 1 meter wide. Suppose the radius of the stage is s meters.

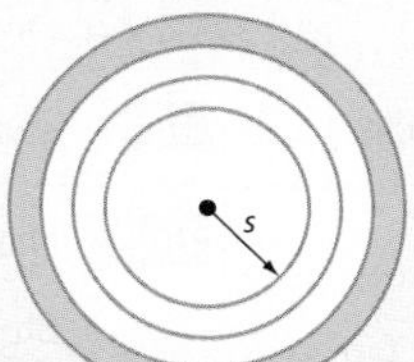

a. Find binomial representations for the radii of the second and third seating levels. $s + 2, s + 3$

b. Find the area of the shaded region representing the third seating level. about $(6.3s + 15.7)$ m^2

Exercise Alerts

Construction Paper For Exercise 56, students will need a square piece of construction paper.

Isometric Dot Paper For Exercise 58, students may want to use isometric dot paper to draw their models for the cube of a sum.

Teaching the Process Standards

Structure Mathematically proficient students look closely to discern a pattern or structure. In Exercise 58a, point out that $(a + b)(a + b)(a + b)$ can be rewritten as $(a + b)(a^2 + 2ab + b^2)$.

4 Assess

Ticket Out the Door Make several copies each of five squares of sums that need to be multiplied. Give one expression to each student. As the students leave the room, ask them to tell you the products of the expressions.

Additional Answers

56a. The area of the larger square is a^2. The area of the smaller square is b^2.

57. Sample answer: $(2c + d) \cdot (2c - d)$; The product of these binomials is a difference of two squares and does not have a middle term. The other three do.

61. Sample answer: To find the square of a sum, apply the FOIL method or apply the pattern. The square of the sum of two quantities is the first quantity squared plus two times the product of the two quantities plus the second quantity squared. The square of the difference of two quantities is the first quantity squared minus two times the product of the two quantities plus the second quantity squared. The product of the sum and difference of two quantities is the square of the first quantity minus the square of the second quantity.

Formative Assessment

Use the Mid-Chapter Quiz to assess students' progress in the first half of the chapter.

For problems answered incorrectly, have students review the lessons indicated in parentheses.

Summative Assessment

Mid-Chapter Test, p. 65

McGraw-Hill eAssessment Customize and create multiple versions of your Mid-Chapter Quiz and their answer keys.

FOLDABLES® StudyOrganizer

Dinah Zike's Foldables®

Before students complete the Mid-Chapter Quiz, encourage them to review the information for Lessons 8-1 through 8-4 in their Foldables.

Additional Answer

7c. 30.07 people/mi^2; Since 2020 is 90 years after 1930, substitute 90 for y in the equation.; 38.3 people/mi^2; Since 2030 is 100 years after 1930, substitute 100 for y in the equation.

CHAPTER 8 Mid-Chapter Quiz

Lessons 8-1 through 8-4

Determine whether each expression is a polynomial. If it is a polynomial, find the degree and determine whether it is a *monomial*, *binomial*, or *trinomial*. (Lesson 8-1)

1. $3y^2 - 2$ **yes; 2; binomial**
2. $4t^5 + 3t^2 + t$ **yes; 5; trinomial**
3. $\frac{3x}{5y}$ **not a polynomial**
4. ax^{-3} **not a polynomial**
5. $3b^2$ **yes; 2; monomial**
6. $2x^{-3} - 4x + 1$ **not a polynomial**

7. **POPULATION** The table shows the population density for Nevada for various years. (Lesson 8-1)

Year	Years Since 1930	People/ Square Mile
1930	0	0.8
1960	30	2.6
1980	50	7.3
1990	60	10.9
2000	70	18.2

a. The population density d of Nevada from 1930 to 2000 can be modeled by $d = 0.005n^2 - 0.127n + 1$, where n represents the number of years since 1930. Identify the type of polynomial for $0.005n^2 - 0.127n + 1$. **quadratic trinomial**

b. What is the degree of the polynomial? **2**

c. Predict the population density of Nevada for 2020 and for 2030. Explain your method. **See margin.**

Find each sum or difference. (Lesson 8-1)

8. $(y^2 + 2y + 3) + (y^2 + 3y - 1)$ $\mathbf{2y^2 + 5y + 2}$
9. $(3n^3 - 2n + 7) - (n^2 - 2n + 8)$ $\mathbf{3n^3 - n^2 - 1}$
10. $(5d + d^2) - (4 - 4d^2)$ $\mathbf{5d^2 + 5d - 4}$
11. $(x + 4) + (3x + 2x^2 - 7)$ $\mathbf{2x^2 + 4x - 3}$
12. $(3a - 3b + 2) - (4a + 5b)$ $\mathbf{-a - 8b + 2}$
13. $(8x - y^2 + 3) + (9 - 3x + 2y^2)$ $\mathbf{5x + y^2 + 12}$

Find each product. (Lesson 8-2)

14. $6y(y^2 + 3y + 1)$ $\mathbf{6y^3 + 18y^2 + 6y}$
15. $3n(n^2 - 5n + 2)$ $\mathbf{3n^3 - 15n^2 + 6n}$
16. $d^2(-4 - 3d + 2d^2)$ $\mathbf{-4d^2 - 3d^3 + 2d^4}$
17. $-2xy(3x^2 + 2xy - 4y^2)$ $\mathbf{-6x^3y - 4x^2y^2 + 8xy^3}$
18. $ab^2(12a + 5b - ab)$ $\mathbf{12a^2b^2 + 5ab^3 - a^2b^3}$
19. $x^2y^4(3xy^2 - x + 2y^2)$ $\mathbf{3x^3y^6 - x^3y^4 + 2x^2y^6}$

20. **MULTIPLE CHOICE** Simplify $x(4x + 5) + 3(2x^2 - 4x + 1)$. (Lesson 8-2) **B**

A $10x^2 + 17x + 3$
B $10x^2 - 7x + 3$
C $2x^2 - 7x + 3$
D $2x^2 + 17x + 3$

Find each product. (Lesson 8-3)

21. $(x + 2)(x + 5)$ $\mathbf{x^2 + 7x + 10}$
22. $(3b - 2)(b - 4)$ $\mathbf{3b^2 - 14b + 8}$
23. $(n - 5)(n + 3)$ $\mathbf{n^2 - 2n - 15}$
24. $(4c - 2)(c + 2)$ $\mathbf{4c^2 + 6c - 4}$
25. $(k - 1)(k - 3k^2)$ $\mathbf{-3k^3 + 4k^2 - k}$
26. $(8d - 3)(2d^2 + d + 1)$ $\mathbf{16d^3 + 2d^2 + 5d - 3}$

27. **MANUFACTURING** A company is designing a box for dry pasta in the shape of a rectangular prism. The length is 2 inches more than twice the width, and the height is 3 inches more than the length. Write an expression, in terms of the width, for the volume of the box. (Lesson 8-3) $\mathbf{4w^3 + 14w^2 + 10w}$

Find each product. (Lesson 8-4)

28. $(x + 2)^2$ $\mathbf{x^2 + 4x + 4}$
29. $(n - 11)^2$ $\mathbf{n^2 - 22n + 121}$
30. $(4b - 2)^2$ $\mathbf{16b^2 - 16b + 4}$
31. $(6c + 3)^2$ $\mathbf{36c^2 + 36c + 9}$
32. $(5d - 3)(5d + 3)$ $\mathbf{25d^2 - 9}$
33. $(9k + 1)(9k - 1)$ $\mathbf{81k^2 - 1}$

34a. $\boldsymbol{\pi(x + 3.25)^2}$ **in^2, $(\pi x^2 + 6.5\pi x + 10.5625\pi)$ in^2**

34. **DISC GOLF** The discs approved for use in disc golf vary in size. (Lesson 8-4)

Smallest disc   Largest disc

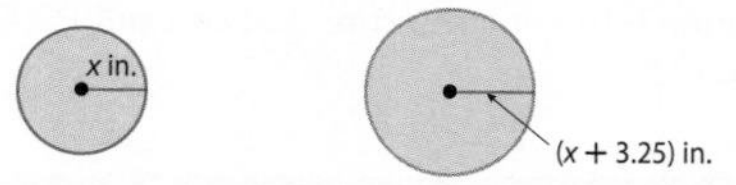

a. Write two different expressions for the area of the largest disc.

b. If x is 10.5, what are the areas of the smallest and largest discs? **346.4 in^2; 594.0 in^2**

InterventionPlanner

TIER 1 On Level OL	TIER 2 Strategic Intervention AL approaching grade level	TIER 3 Intensive Intervention 2 or more grades below level
If students miss about 25% of the exercises or less,	**If** students miss about 50% of the exercises,	**If** students miss about 75% of the exercises,
Then choose a resource: **SE** Lessons 8-1, 8-2, 8-3, and 8-4 Skills Practice, pp. 7, 14, 20, and 27 **TE** Chapter Project connectED.mcgraw-hill.com Self-Check Quiz	**Then** choose a resource: Study Guide and Intervention, Chapter 8, pp. 5, 12, 18, and 25 *Quick Review Math Handbook* connectED.mcgraw-hill.com Extra Examples, Personal Tutor, Homework Help	**Then** use *Math Triumphs, Alg. 1* connectED.mcgraw-hill.com Extra Examples, Personal Tutor, Homework Help, Review Vocabulary

EXPLORE 8-5

Algebra Lab
Factoring Using the Distributive Property

When two or more numbers are multiplied, these numbers are *factors* of the product. Sometimes you know the product of binomials and are asked to find the factors. This is called factoring. You can use algebra tiles and a product mat to factor binomials.

Activity 1 Use Algebra Tiles to Factor $2x - 8$

Step 1 Model $2x - 8$.

Step 2 Arrange the tiles into a rectangle. The total area of the rectangle represents the product, and its length and width represent the factors.

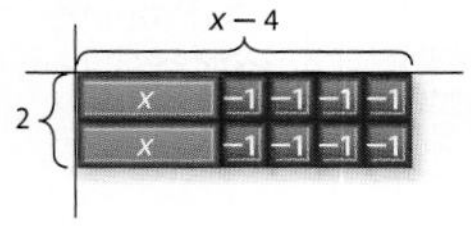

The rectangle has a width of 2 and a length of $x - 4$. Therefore, $2x - 8 = 2(x - 4)$.

Activity 2 Use Algebra Tiles to Factor $x^2 + 3x$

Step 1 Model $x^2 + 3x$.

Step 2 Arrange the tiles into a rectangle.

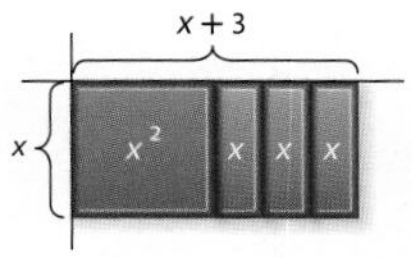

The rectangle has a width of x and a length of $x + 3$. Therefore, $x^2 + 3x = x(x + 3)$.

Model and Analyze

Use algebra tiles to factor each binomial.

1. $4x + 12$ $4(x + 3)$

2. $4x - 6$ $2(2x - 3)$

3. $3x^2 + 4x$ $x(3x + 4)$

4. $10 - 2x$ $2(5 - x)$

Determine whether each binomial can be factored. Justify your answer with a drawing.

5. $6x - 9$ yes

6. $5x - 4$ no

7. $4x^2 + 7$ no

8. $x^2 + 3x$ yes

5–8. See Ch. 8 Answer Appendix for drawings.

9. WRITING IN MATH Write a paragraph that explains how you can use algebra tiles to determine whether a binomial can be factored. Include an example of one binomial that can be factored and one that cannot.

9. Sample answer: Binomials can be factored if they can be represented by a rectangle. Examples: $3x + 3$ can be factored and $3x + 2$ cannot be factored.

1 Focus

Objective Use algebra tiles to model using the Distributive Property to factor binomials.

Materials for Each Student

- algebra tiles and product mats

Easy to Make Manipulatives

Teaching Algebra with Manipulatives
Templates for:

- algebra tiles, pp. 10–11
- product mat, p. 17

2 Teach

Working in Cooperative Groups

Put students in groups of two or three, mixing abilities. Have groups complete Activities 1 and 2 and Exercises 1–4.

- For Exercises 1–4, students should recognize that they must arrange the tiles into a rectangle with a width greater than 1 in order to find the factors of the polynomial.
- Point out that the area of the rectangle represents the polynomial, and the length and width represent the factors of the polynomial.

Practice Have students complete Exercises 5–9.

- For Exercises 5–9, emphasize that if a binomial can only be modeled with a width of 1, it cannot be factored.

3 Assess

Formative Assessment

Use Exercise 3 to assess whether students can use algebra tiles to factor a binomial.

From Concrete to Abstract

Write $x^2 + 5x$ on the board. Have students factor the binomial without using tiles. If they answer incorrectly, have them use their tiles to help them find their errors.

1 Focus

Vertical Alignment

Before Lesson 8-5 Use the Distributive Property to evaluate expressions.

Lesson 8-5 Use the Distributive Property to factor polynomials. Solve quadratic equations of the form $ax^2 + bx = 0$.

After Lesson 8-5 Solve equations of the form $ax^2 + bx + c = 0$.

2 Teach

Scaffolding Questions

Have students read the **Why?** section of the lesson.

Ask:

- What is the formula for the area of a rectangle? $A = \ell \times w$
- What do you multiply w by to get $1.6w^2 + 6w$? $1.6w + 6$
- What is the area for Mr. Cole's store expressed as a monomial times a polynomial? $w(1.6w + 6)$
- What is the area when $w = 50$? 4300 ft^2

LESSON 8-5 Using the Distributive Property

Then

- Used the Distributive Property to evaluate expressions.

Now

1. Use the Distributive Property to factor polynomials.
2. Solve equations of the form $ax^2 + bx = 0$.

Why?

- The cost of rent for Mr. Cole's store is determined by the square footage of the space. The area of the store can be modeled by the equation $A = 1.6w^2 + 6w$, where w is the width of the store in feet. We can use factoring and the Zero Product Property to find possible dimensions of the store.

New Vocabulary

factoring
factoring by grouping
Zero Product Property

Content Standards
AI.RNE.6, AI.QE.4, AI.QE.5

Process Standards
PS.2

1 Use the Distributive Property to Factor

You have used the Distributive Property to multiply a monomial by a polynomial. You can work backward to express a polynomial as the product of a monomial factor and a polynomial factor.

$$1.6w^2 + 6w = 1.6w(w) + 6(w)$$
$$= w(1.6w + 6)$$

So, $w(1.6w + 6)$ is the *factored form* of $1.6w^2 + 6w$. **Factoring** a polynomial involves finding the *completely* factored form.

Example 1 Use the Distributive Property

Use the Distributive Property to factor each polynomial.

a. $27y^2 + 18y$

Find the GCF of each term.

$27y^2 = ③ \cdot ③ \cdot 3 \cdot (y) \cdot y$ — Factor each term.

$18y = 2 \cdot ③ \cdot ③ \cdot (y)$ — Circle common factors.

$\text{GCF} = 3 \cdot 3 \cdot y$ or $9y$

Write each term as the product of the GCF and the remaining factors. Use the Distributive Property to *factor out* the GCF.

$27y^2 + 18y = 9y(3y) + 9y(2)$ — Rewrite each term using the GCF.

$= 9y(3y + 2)$ — Distributive Property

b. $-4a^2b - 8ab^2 + 2ab$

$-4a^2b = -1 \cdot ② \cdot 2 \cdot (a) \cdot a \cdot (b)$ — Factor each term.

$-8ab^2 = -1 \cdot ② \cdot 2 \cdot 2 \cdot (a) \cdot (b) \cdot b$ — Circle common factors.

$2ab = ② \cdot (a) \cdot (b)$

$\text{GCF} = 2 \cdot a \cdot b$ or $2ab$

$-4a^2b - 8ab^2 + 2ab = 2ab(-2a) - 2ab(4b) + 2ab(1)$ — Rewrite each term using the GCF.

$= 2ab(-2a - 4b + 1)$ — Distributive Property

Guided Practice

1A. $15w - 3v$ $3(5w - v)$

1B. $7u^2t^2 + 21ut^2 - ut$ $ut(7ut + 21t - 1)$

Lesson 8-5 Resources

Resource	Approaching Level AL	On Level OL	Beyond Level BL	English Learners ELL
Teacher Edition	▪ Differentiated Instruction, p. 496	▪ Differentiated Instruction, p. 496	▪ Differentiated Instruction, p. 500	
Chapter Resource Masters	▪ Study Guide and Intervention, pp. 31–32 ▪ Skills Practice, p. 33 ▪ Practice, p. 34 ▪ Word Problem Practice, p. 35	▪ Study Guide and Intervention, pp. 31–32 ▪ Skills Practice, p. 33 ▪ Practice, p. 34 ▪ Word Problem Practice, p. 35 ▪ Enrichment, p. 36	▪ Practice, p. 34 ▪ Word Problem Practice, p. 35 ▪ Enrichment, p. 36	▪ Study Guide and Intervention, pp. 31–32 ▪ Skills Practice, p. 33 ▪ Practice, p. 34 ▪ Word Problem Practice, p. 35
Other	▪ 5-Minute Check 8-5 ▪ Study Notebook ▪ Teaching Algebra with Manipulatives	▪ 5-Minute Check 8-5 ▪ Study Notebook ▪ Teaching Algebra with Manipulatives	▪ 5-Minute Check 8-5 ▪ Study Notebook	▪ 5-Minute Check 8-5 ▪ Study Notebook ▪ Teaching Algebra with Manipulatives

Using the Distributive Property to factor polynomials with four or more terms is called **factoring by grouping** because terms are put into groups and then factored. The Distributive Property is then applied to a common binomial factor.

KeyConcept Factoring by Grouping

Words A polynomial can be factored by grouping only if all of the following conditions exist.

- There are four or more terms.
- Terms have common factors that can be grouped together.
- There are two common factors that are identical or additive inverses of each other.

Symbols

$$\begin{aligned} ax + bx + ay + by &= (ax + bx) + (ay + by) \\ &= x(a + b) + y(a + b) \\ &= (x + y)(a + b) \end{aligned}$$

PT

Example 2 Factor by Grouping

Factor $4qr + 8r + 3q + 6$.

$4qr + 8r + 3q + 6$	Original expression
$= (4qr + 8r) + (3q + 6)$	Group terms with common factors.
$= 4r(q + 2) + 3(q + 2)$	Factor the GCF from each group.

Notice that $(q + 2)$ is common in both groups, so it becomes the GCF.

$= (4r + 3)(q + 2)$ Distributive Property

GuidedPractice

Factor each polynomial.

2A. $rn + 5n - r - 5$ $(r + 5)(n - 1)$ **2B.** $3np + 15p - 4n - 20$ $(n + 5)(3p - 4)$

It can be helpful to recognize when binomials are additive inverses of each other. For example $6 - a = -1(a - 6)$.

StudyTip

Check To check your factored answers, multiply your factors out. You should get your original expression as a result.

PT

Example 3 Factor by Grouping with Additive Inverses

Factor $2mk - 12m + 42 - 7k$.

$2mk - 12m + 42 - 7k$	
$= (2mk - 12m) + (42 - 7k)$	Group terms with common factors.
$= 2m(k - 6) + 7(6 - k)$	Factor the GCF from each group.
$= 2m(k - 6) + 7[(-1)(k - 6)]$	$6 - k = -1(k - 6)$
$= 2m(k - 6) - 7(k - 6)$	Associative Property
$= (2m - 7)(k - 6)$	Distributive Property

GuidedPractice

Factor each polynomial.

3A. $c - 2cd + 8d - 4$ **3B.** $3p - 2p^2 - 18p + 27$

3A. $(-c + 4)(2d - 1)$ or $(c - 4)(1 - 2d)$
3B. $(p + 9)(3 - 2p)$ or $(-p - 9)(2p - 3)$

1 Use the Distributive Property to Factor

Example 1 shows how to use the Distributive Property to factor a polynomial. **Example 2** shows how to use grouping to factor a polynomial. **Example 3** shows how to use grouping with additive inverses to factor a polynomial.

Formative Assessment

Use the Guided Practice exercises after each Example to determine students' understanding of concepts.

Additional Examples

1 Use the Distributive Property to factor each polynomial.

a. $15x + 25x^2$ $5x(3 + 5x)$

b. $12xy + 24xy^2 - 30x^2y^4$ $6xy(2 + 4y - 5xy^3)$

2 Factor $2xy + 7x - 2y - 7$. $(x - 1)(2y + 7)$

3 Factor $15a - 3ab + 4b - 20$. $(-3a + 4)(b - 5)$ or $(3a - 4)(5 - b)$

Additional Examples also in Interactive Classroom PowerPoint® Presentations

IWB Interactive White Board READY

Focus on Mathematical Content

Greatest Common Factor

Factoring using the Distributive Property requires expressing a polynomial as the product of the greatest common monomial factor of the polynomial's terms and a polynomial factor. To find the nonmonomial factor, each term of the polynomial is divided by the common monomial factor.

Tips for New Teachers

Reasoning Sometimes students find the monomial that is the GCF of the terms of the polynomial but do not know how to get the other polynomial factor. One way to find the remaining factor is to divide each term of the polynomial by the GCF. Tell students to check their answers by multiplying their factors using the Distributive Property.

Teach with Tech

Video Recording Separate the class into groups and have each group create a video showing how to factor by grouping. Assign a different expression to each group, and share each group's video with the class.

2 Solve Equations by Factoring

Example 4 shows how to solve two different quadratic equations—one in factored form and one that must be factored. **Example 5** shows how to solve a real-world problem using the Zero Product Property.

Additional Example

4 Solve each equation. Check your solutions.

a. $(x - 2)(4x - 1) = 0$ $2, \frac{1}{4}$

b. $4y = 12y^2$ $0, \frac{1}{3}$

Focus on Mathematical Content

Zero Product Property Quadratic equations can be solved by using the Zero Product Property: If the product of two factors is zero, then one of the factors is zero. To solve equations using this property, write the equation with the terms in factored form on one side of the equation and zero on the other side. Each factor is then set equal to zero, and the resulting equations are solved to arrive at the solutions.

2 Solve Equations by Factoring

Some equations can be solved by factoring. Consider the following.

$3(0) = 0$ $\quad 0(2 - 2) = 0$ $\quad -312(0) = 0$ $\quad 0(0.25) = 0$

Notice that in each case, at least one of the factors is 0. These examples are demonstrations of the **Zero Product Property**.

KeyConcept Zero Product Property

Words	If the product of two factors is 0, then at least one of the factors must be 0.
Symbols	For any real numbers a and b, if $ab = 0$, then $a = 0$, $b = 0$, or both a and b equal zero.

Recall that a solution or root of an equation is any value that makes the equation true.

WatchOut!

Unknown Value It may be tempting to solve an equation by dividing each side by the variable. However, the variable has an unknown value, so you may be dividing by 0, which is undefined.

Example 4 Solve Equations

Solve each equation. Check your solutions.

a. $(2d + 6)(3d - 15) = 0$

$(2d + 6)(3d - 15) = 0$	Original equation
$2d + 6 = 0$ or $3d - 15 = 0$	Zero Product Property
$2d = -6$ $\quad 3d = 15$	Solve each equation.
$d = -3$ $\quad d = 5$	Divide.

The roots are −3 and 5.

CHECK Substitute −3 and 5 for d in the original equation.

$(2d + 6)(3d - 15) = 0$	$(2d + 6)(3d - 15) = 0$
$[2(-3) + 6][3(-3) - 15] \stackrel{?}{=} 0$	$[2(5) + 6][3(5) - 15] \stackrel{?}{=} 0$
$(-6 + 6)(-9 - 15) \stackrel{?}{=} 0$	$(10 + 6)(15 - 15) \stackrel{?}{=} 0$
$(0)(-24) \stackrel{?}{=} 0$	$16(0) \stackrel{?}{=} 0$
$0 = 0$ ✓	$0 = 0$ ✓

b. $c^2 = 3c$

$c^2 = 3c$	Original equation
$c^2 - 3c = 0$	Subtract $3c$ from each side to get 0 on one side of the equation.
$c(c - 3) = 0$	Factor by using the GCF to get the form $ab = 0$.
$c = 0$ or $c - 3 = 0$	Zero Product Property
$c = 3$	Solve each equation.
The roots are 0 and 3.	Check by substituting 0 and 3 for c.

GuidedPractice

4A. $3n(n + 2) = 0$ **0, −2** **4B.** $8b^2 - 40b = 0$ **0, 5** **4C.** $x^2 = -10x$ **0, −10**

DifferentiatedInstruction AL OL

If students have trouble solving quadratic equations like Example 4b,

Then you may wish to allow students to use algebra tiles. They can use the methods from Explore 8-5 to factor the quadratic to solve the equation.

Real-WorldLink

Dog agility tests a person's skills as a trainer and handler. Competitors race through an obstacle course that includes hurdles, tunnels, a see-saw, and line poles.

Source: United States Dog Agility Association

Real-World Example 5 Use Factoring

AGILITY **Penny is a Fox Terrier who competes with her trainer in the agility course. Within the course, Penny must leap over a hurdle. Penny's jump can be modeled by the equation $h = -16t^2 + 20t$, where h is the height of the leap in inches at t seconds. Find the values of t when $h = 0$.**

$h = -16t^2 + 20t$	Original equation
$0 = -16t^2 + 20t$	Substitution, $h = 0$
$0 = 4t(-4t + 5)$	Factor by using the GCF.
$4t = 0$ or $-4t + 5 = 0$	Zero Product Property
$t = 0$ $\quad -4t = -5$	Solve each equation.
$t = \frac{5}{4}$ or 1.25	Divide each side by −4.

Penny's height is 0 inches at 0 seconds and 1.25 seconds into the jump.

GuidedPractice

5. **KANGAROOS** The hop of a kangaroo can be modeled by $h = 24t - 16t^2$ where h represents the height of the hop in meters and t is the time in seconds. Find the values of t when $h = 0$. **0, 1.5**

Additional Example

5 **FOOTBALL** A football is kicked into the air. The height of the football can be modeled by the equation $h = -16x^2 + 16x$, where h is the height reached by the ball after x seconds. Find the values of x when $h = 0$.
0 seconds, 1 second

Check Your Understanding

= Step-by-Step Solutions begin on page R13.

Example 1 **Use the Distributive Property to factor each polynomial.**

1. $21b - 15a$ **$3(7b - 5a)$**
2. $14c^2 + 2c$ **$2c(7c + 1)$**
3. $10g^2h^2 + 9gh^2 - g^2h$ **$gh(10gh + 9h - g)$**
4. $12jk^2 + 6j^2k + 2j^2k^2$ **$2jk(6k + 3j + jk)$**

Examples 2–3 **Factor each polynomial.**

5. $np + 2n + 8p + 16$ **$(n + 8)(p + 2)$**
6. $xy - 7x + 7y - 49$ **$(x + 7)(y - 7)$**
7. $3bc - 2b - 10 + 15c$ **$(b + 5)(3c - 2)$**
8. $9fg - 45f - 7g + 35$ **$(9f - 7)(g - 5)$**

Example 4 **Solve each equation. Check your solutions.**

9. $3k(k + 10) = 0$ **0, −10**
10. $(4m + 2)(3m - 9) = 0$ **$-\frac{1}{2}$, 3**
11. $20p^2 - 15p = 0$ **0, $\frac{3}{4}$**
12. $r^2 = 14r$ **0, 14**

Example 5

13. **SPIDERS** Jumping spiders can commonly be found in homes and barns throughout the United States. A jumping spider's jump can be modeled by the equation $h = 33.3t - 16t^2$, where t represents the time in seconds and h is the height in feet.
    a. When is the spider's height at 0 feet? **0 s and 2.08125 s**
    b. What is the spider's height after 1 second? after 2 seconds? **17.3 ft, 2.6 ft**

14. **REASONING** At a Fourth of July celebration, a rocket is launched straight up with an initial velocity of 125 feet per second. The height h of the rocket in feet above sea level is modeled by the formula $h = 125t - 16t^2$, where t is the time in seconds after the rocket is launched.
    a. What is the height of the rocket when it returns to the ground? **0 ft**
    b. Let $h = 0$ in the equation and solve for t. **0, 7.8125**
    c. How many seconds will it take for the rocket to return to the ground? **about 7.8 s**

3 Practice

Formative Assessment

Use Exercises 1–14 to check for understanding.

Use the chart at the bottom of the next page to customize assignments for your students.

Teaching the Process Standards

Reasoning Mathematically proficient attend to the meaning of quantities, not just how to compute them. In Exercise 14, tell students that the path of a projectile or other body moving through space is called a trajectory. Quadratic functions are always used to represent motion of a trajectory.

Follow-up

Students have explored modeling using quadratic functions.

Ask:

- What are the advantages of using quadratic functions for modeling? Sample answer: They have well-known and understood properties; they can be used to model situations that have both increasing and decreasing behavior; the computation that is done to make predictions is relatively easy to perform.

Teaching the Process Standards

Sense-Making Mathematically proficient students check their answers to problems using a different method. In Exercise 45, have students check their answers by substituting values for *a* and *b* and finding the areas directly and by using their expressions.

Exercise Alert

Grid Paper For Exercise 47, students will need grid paper.

Multiple Representations

In Exercise 51, students use a diagram and analysis to factor an algebraic expression.

Additional Answers

47a.

x	0	1	2	3	4
y	0	9	12	9	0

47b.

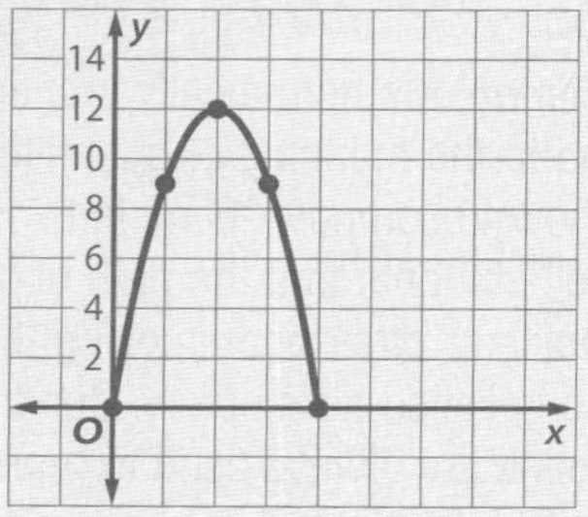

51b.

x^2	$+3x$
$-2x$	-6

51c.

	x	$+3$
x	x^2	$+3x$
-2	$-2x$	-6

$(x + 3)(x - 2)$

53. Since the solutions are $-\frac{b}{a}$ and $\frac{b}{a}$, $a \neq 0$ and b is any real number.

56. Rewrite the equation to have zero on one side of the equals sign. Then factor the other side. Set each factor equal to zero, and then solve each equation.

Practice and Problem Solving

Extra Practice is on page R8.

Example 1 **Use the Distributive Property to factor each polynomial.**

15. $16t - 40y$ **$8(2t - 5y)$**

16. $30v + 50x$ **$10(3v + 5x)$**

17. $2k^2 + 4k$ **$2k(k + 2)$**

18. $5z^2 + 10z$ **$5z(z + 2)$**

19. $4a^2b^2 + 2a^2b - 10ab^2$ **$2ab(2ab + a - 5b)$**

20. $5c^2v - 15c^2v^2 + 5c^2v^3$ **$5c^2v(1 - 3v + v^2)$**

Examples 2–3 **Factor each polynomial.** **25. $(9q - 10)(5p - 3)$ 35. $3cd(9d - 6cd + 1)$ 37. $2(8u - 15)(3t + 2)$**

21. $fg - 5g + 4f - 20$ **$(g + 4)(f - 5)$**

22. $a^2 - 4a - 24 + 6a$ **$(a - 4)(a + 6)$**

23. $hj - 2h + 5j - 10$ **$(h + 5)(j - 2)$**

24. $xy - 2x - 2 + y$ **$(x + 1)(y - 2)$**

25. $45pq - 27q - 50p + 30$

26. $24ty - 18t + 4y - 3$ **$(6t + 1)(4y - 3)$**

27. $3dt - 21d + 35 - 5t$ **$(3d - 5)(t - 7)$**

28. $8r^2 + 12r$ **$4r(2r + 3)$**

29. $21th - 3t - 35h + 5$ **$(3t - 5)(7h - 1)$**

30. $vp + 12v + 8p + 96$ **$(v + 8)(p + 12)$**

31. $5br - 25b + 2r - 10$ **$(r - 5)(5b + 2)$**

32. $2nu - 8u + 3n - 12$ **$(2u + 3)(n - 4)$**

33. $5gf^2 + g^2f + 15gf$ **$gf(5f + g + 15)$**

34. $rp - 9r + 9p - 81$ **$(r + 9)(p - 9)$**

35. $27cd^2 - 18c^2d^2 + 3cd$

36. $18r^3t^2 + 12r^2t^2 - 6r^2t$ **$6r^2t(3rt + 2t - 1)$**

37. $48tu - 90t + 32u - 60$

38. $16gh + 24g - 2h - 3$ **$(8g - 1)(2h + 3)$**

Example 4 **Solve each equation. Check your solutions.**

39. $3b(9b - 27) = 0$ **0, 3**

40. $2n(3n + 3) = 0$ **0, −1**

41. $(8z + 4)(5z + 10) = 0$ **$-\frac{1}{2}, -2$**

42. $(7x + 3)(2x - 6) = 0$ **$-\frac{3}{7}, 3$**

43. $b^2 = -3b$ **0, −3**

44. $a^2 = 4a$ **0, 4**

Example 5

45. SENSE-MAKING Use the drawing at the right.

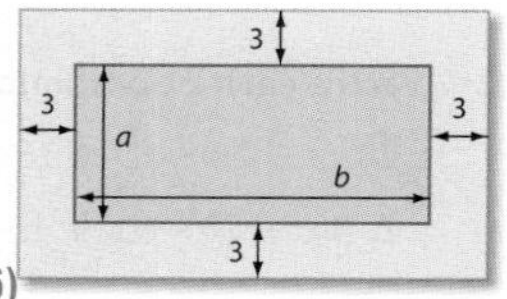

a. Write an expression in factored form to represent the area of the blue section. ***ab***

b. Write an expression in factored form to represent the area of the region formed by the outer edge. **$(a + 6)(b + 6)$**

c. Write an expression in factored form to represent the yellow region. **$6(a + b + 6)$**

B **46. FIREWORKS** A ten-inch fireworks shell is fired from ground level. The height of the shell in feet is given by the formula $h = 263t - 16t^2$, where t is the time in seconds after launch.

a. Write the expression that represents the height in factored form. **$t(263 - 16t)$**

b. At what time will the height be 0? Is this answer practical? Explain.

c. What is the height of the shell 8 seconds and 10 seconds after being fired? **1080 ft; 1030 ft**

d. At 10 seconds, is the shell rising or falling? **The shell has begun to fall.**

46b. 0 and 16.4375 seconds; Yes, the shell starts at ground level and is in the air for 16.4375 seconds before landing on the ground again.

47. ARCHITECTURE The frame of a doorway is an arch that can be modeled by the graph of the equation $y = -3x^2 + 12x$, where x and y are measured in feet. On a coordinate plane, the floor is represented by the x-axis. **a–b. See margin.**

a. Make a table of values for the height of the arch if $x = 0, 1, 2, 3,$ and 4 feet.

b. Plot the points from the table on a coordinate plane and connect the points to form a smooth curve to represent the arch.

c. How high is the doorway? **12 ft**

Differentiated Homework Options

Level	Assignment	Two-Day Option	
AL Basic	15–45, 52, 54–86	15–45 odd, 57–60	16–44 even, 52, 54–56, 61–86
OL Core	15–45 odd, 46–52, 54–86	15–45, 57–60	46–52, 54–56, 61–86
BL Advanced	46–80, (optional: 81–86)		

48. **RIDES** Suppose the height of a rider after being dropped can be modeled by $h = -16t^2 - 96t + 160$, where h is the height in feet and t is time in seconds.

a. Write an expression to represent the height in factored form. **$16(-t^2 - 6t + 10)$**

b. From what height is the rider initially dropped? **160 ft**

c. At what height will the rider be after 3 seconds of falling? Is this possible? Explain. **-272 ft; No, the rider cannot be a negative number of feet in the air.**

C 49. **ARCHERY** The height h in feet of an arrow can be modeled by the equation $h = 64t - 16t^2$, where t is time in seconds. Ignoring the height of the archer, how long after the arrow is released does it hit the ground? **4 s**

50. **TENNIS** A tennis player hits a tennis ball upward with an initial velocity of 80 feet per second. The height h in feet of the tennis ball can be modeled by the equation $h = 80t - 16t^2$, where t is time in seconds. Ignoring the height of the tennis player, how long does it take the ball to hit the ground? **5 s**

51. **MULTIPLE REPRESENTATIONS** In this problem, you will explore the *box method* of factoring. To factor $x^2 + x - 6$, write the first term in the top left-hand corner of the box, and then write the last term in the lower right-hand corner.

	?	?
?	x^2	?
?	?	-6

a. **Analytical** Determine which two factors have a product of -6 and a sum of 1. **3 and -2**

b. **Symbolic** Write each factor in an empty square in the box. Include the positive or negative sign and variable. **See margin.**

c. **Analytical** Find the factor for each row and column of the box. What are the factors of $x^2 + x - 6$? **See margin.**

d. **Verbal** Describe how you would use the box method to factor $x^2 - 3x - 40$.

51d. Sample answer: Place x^2 in the top left-hand corner and place -40 in the lower right-hand corner. Then determine which two factors have a product of -40 and a sum of -3. Then place these factors in the box. Then find the factor of each row and column. The factors will be listed on the very top and far left of the box.

H.O.T. Problems Use Higher-Order Thinking Skills

52. **CRITIQUE** Hernando and Rachel are solving $2m^2 = 4m$. Is either of them correct? Explain your reasoning. **Rachel; the equation first must have 0 on one side.**

Hernando

$2m^2 = 4m$

$\frac{2m^2}{m} = \frac{4m^2}{2m}$

$2m = 2$

$m = 1$

Rachel

$2m^2 = 4m$

$2m^2 - 4m = 0$

$2m(m - 2) = 0$

$2m = 0$ or $m - 2 = 0$

$m = 0$ or 2

53. **CHALLENGE** Given the equation $(ax + b)(ax - b) = 0$, solve for x. What do we know about the values of a and b? **See margin.**

54. **OPEN ENDED** Write a four-term polynomial that can be factored by grouping. Then factor the polynomial. **Sample answers: $x^2 + 2xy + 3x + 6y$, $(x + 3)(x + 2y)$**

55. **REASONING** Given the equation $c = a^2 - ab$, for what values of a and b does $c = 0$? **Sample answer: $a = 0$ or $a = b$ for any real values of a and b.**

56. **WRITING IN MATH** Explain how to solve a quadratic equation by using the Zero Product Property. **See margin.**

Teaching the Process Standards

Critique Mathematically proficient students compare the effectiveness of two plausible arguments. In Exercise 52, remind students that the quickest way to check a solution is to substitute the value back into the original equation.

Study Guide and Intervention

AL OL ELL

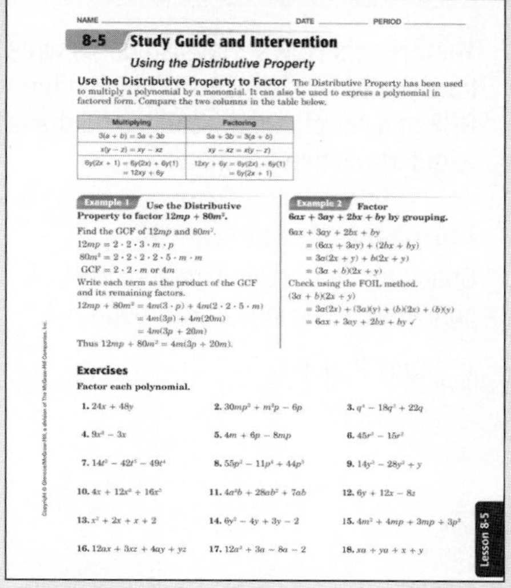

8-5 Study Guide and Intervention

Using the Distributive Property

Practice

AL OL BL ELL

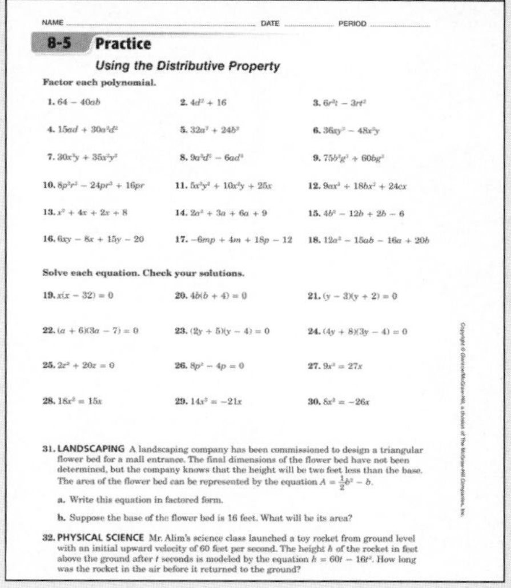

8-5 Practice

Using the Distributive Property

Enrichment

OL BL

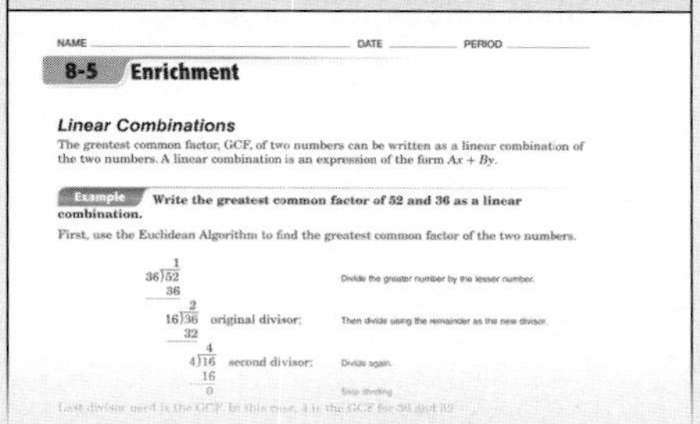

8-5 Enrichment

Linear Combinations

Word Problem Practice

AL OL BL ELL

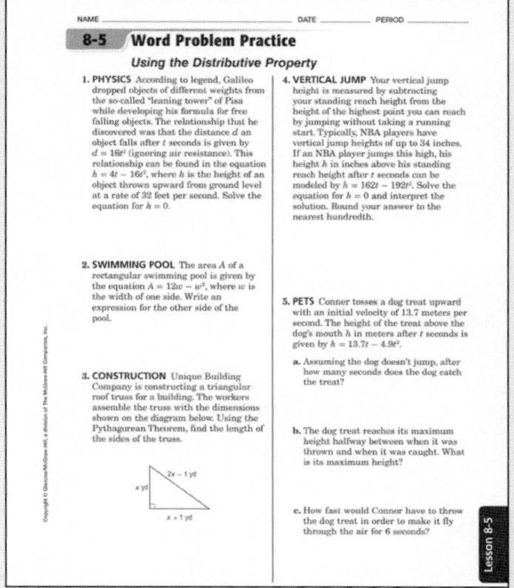

8-5 Word Problem Practice

Using the Distributive Property

4 Assess

Yesterday's News Have students write how yesterday's concept of finding the GCF of a set of monomials helped them with today's new material.

Formative Assessment

Check for student understanding of concepts in Lessons 8-3 through 8-5.

Quiz 2, p. 65

Standardized Test Practice

57. Which is a factor of $6z^2 - 3z - 2 + 4z$? **D**

A $2z + 1$ C $z + 2$
B $3z - 2$ D $2z - 1$

58. PROBABILITY Hailey has 10 blocks: 2 red, 4 blue, 3 yellow, and 1 green. What is the probability that a randomly chosen block will be either red or yellow? **H**

F $\frac{3}{10}$ H $\frac{1}{2}$
G $\frac{1}{5}$ J $\frac{7}{10}$

59. GRIDDED RESPONSE Cho is making a 140-inch by 160-inch quilt with quilt squares that measure 8 inches on each side. How many will be needed to make the quilt? **350**

60. GEOMETRY The area of the right triangle shown below is $5h$ square centimeters. What is the height of the triangle? **D**

A 2 cm
B 5 cm
C 8 cm
D 10 cm

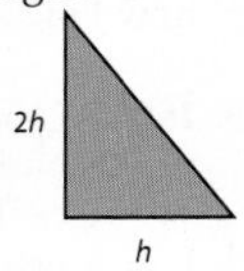

Spiral Review

61. GENETICS Brown genes B are dominant over blue genes b. A person with genes BB or Bb has brown eyes. Someone with genes bb has blue eyes. Elisa has brown eyes with Bb genes, and Bob has blue eyes. Write an expression for the possible eye coloring of Elisa and Bob's children. Determine the probability that their child would have blue eyes. (Lesson 8-4) $0.5Bb + 0.5b^2$; $\frac{1}{2}$

Find each product. (Lesson 8-2)

62. $n(n^2 - 4n + 3)$ $n^3 - 4n^2 + 3n$

63. $2b(b^2 + b - 5)$ $2b^3 + 2b^2 - 10b$

64. $-c(4c^2 + 2c - 2)$ $-4c^3 - 2c^2 + 2c$

65. $-4x(x^3 + x^2 + 2x - 1)$ $-4x^4 - 4x^3 - 8x^2 + 4x$

66. $2ab(4a^2b + 2ab - 2b^2)$ $8a^3b^2 + 4a^2b^2 - 4ab^3$

67. $-3xy(x^2 + xy + 2y^2)$ $-3x^3y - 3x^2y^2 - 6xy^3$

Simplify. (Lesson 7-1)

68. $(ab^4)(ab^2)$ a^2b^6

69. $(p^5r^4)(p^2r)$ p^7r^5

70. $(-7c^3d^4)(4cd^3)$ $-28c^4d^7$

71. $(9xy^7)^2$ $81x^2y^{14}$

72. $[(3^2)^4]^2$ 43,046,721

73. $[(4^2)^3]^2$ 16,777,216

74. BASKETBALL In basketball, a free throw is 1 point and a field goal is either 2 or 3 points. In a season, Tim Duncan of the San Antonio Spurs scored a total of 1342 points. The total number of 2-point field goals and 3-point field goals was 517, and he made 305 of the 455 free throws that he attempted. Find the number of 2-point field goals and 3-point field goals Duncan made that season. (Lesson 6-4) **514 2-point field goals; 3 3-point field goals**

Solve each inequality. Check your solution. (Lesson 5-3)

75. $3y - 4 > -37$ $\{y \mid y > -11\}$

76. $-5q + 9 > 24$ $\{q \mid q < -3\}$

77. $-2k + 12 < 30$ $\{k \mid k > -9\}$

78. $5q + 7 \leq 3(q + 1)$ $\{q \mid q \leq -2\}$

79. $\frac{z}{4} + 7 \geq -5$ $\{z \mid z \geq -48\}$

80. $8c - (c - 5) > c + 17$ $\{c \mid c > 2\}$

Skills Review

Find each product.

81. $(a + 2)(a + 5)$ $a^2 + 7a + 10$

82. $(d + 4)(d + 10)$ $d^2 + 14d + 40$

83. $(z - 1)(z - 8)$ $z^2 - 9z + 8$

84. $(c + 9)(c - 3)$ $c^2 + 6c - 27$

85. $(x - 7)(x - 6)$ $x^2 - 13x + 42$

86. $(g - 2)(g + 11)$ $g^2 + 9g - 22$

Differentiated Instruction BL

Extension Write the following polynomial on the board: $c^2xy - c^3 - x^2y + cx$. Ask students to factor it by grouping.
$(c^2 - x)(xy - c)$, or $(x - c^2)(c - xy)$

EXPLORE 8-6 Algebra Lab
Factoring Trinomials

You can use algebra tiles to factor trinomials. If a polynomial represents the area of a rectangle formed by algebra tiles, then the rectangle's length and width are *factors* of the area. If a rectangle cannot be formed to represent the trinomial, then the trinomial is not factorable.

Content Standards
AI.RNE.6

Activity 1 Factor $x^2 + bx + c$

Use algebra tiles to factor $x^2 + 4x + 3$.

Step 1 Model $x^2 + 4x + 3$.

Step 2 Place the x^2-tile at the corner of the product mat. Arrange the 1-tiles into a rectangular array. Because 3 is prime, the 3 tiles can be arranged in a rectangle in one way, a 1-by-3 rectangle.

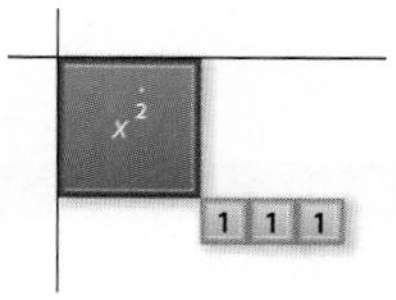

Step 3 Complete the rectangle with the x-tiles.

The rectangle has a width of $x + 1$ and a length of $x + 3$.

Therefore, $x^2 + 4x + 3 = (x + 1)(x + 3)$.

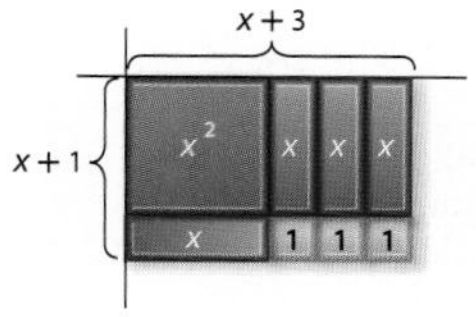

Activity 2 Factor $x^2 + bx + c$

Use algebra tiles to factor $x^2 + 8x + 12$.

Step 1 Model $x^2 + 8x + 12$.

Step 2 Place the x^2-tile at the corner of the product mat. Arrange the 1-tiles into a rectangular array. Since $12 = 3 \times 4$, try a 3-by-4 rectangle. Try to complete the rectangle. Notice that there is an extra x-tile.

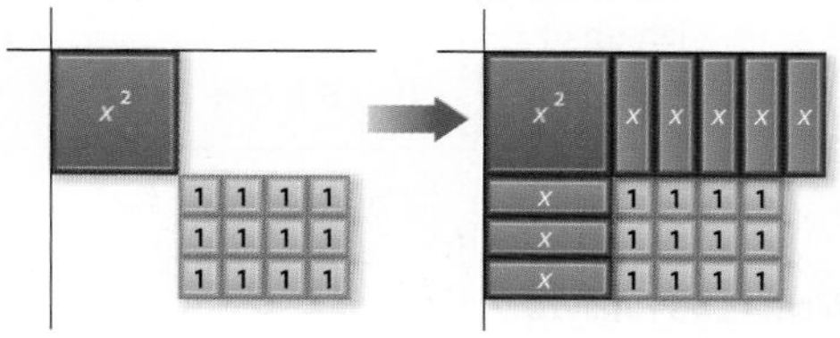

Step 3 Arrange the 1-tiles into a 2-by-6 rectangular array. This time you can complete the rectangle with the x-tiles.

The rectangle has a width of $x + 2$ and a length of $x + 6$.

Therefore, $x^2 + 8x + 12 = (x + 2)(x + 6)$.

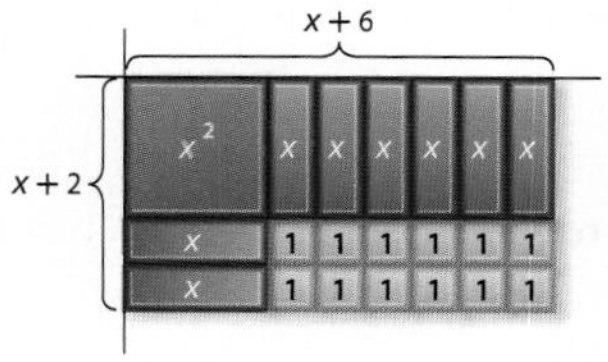

1 Focus

Objective Use algebra tiles to model factoring trinomials.

Materials for Each Group

- algebra tiles
- product mat

Easy to Make Manipulatives

Teaching Algebra with Manipulatives
Templates for:

- algebra tiles, pp. 10–11
- product mat, p. 17

Teaching Tip

You may want to remind students that the area of the rectangle represents the polynomial, and the length and width of the rectangle represent the factors of the polynomial.

2 Teach

Working in Cooperative Groups

Place students in groups of two or three, mixing abilities. Have groups complete Activities 1–4.

- Ask students to name the shape they must form with the tiles in order to factor a polynomial. rectangle
- In Activity 1, remind students to read the width of the tiles along the edge of the rectangle. The x^2-tiles have a width of x and the x-tiles have a width of one.
- For Activity 2, encourage students to try several different arrangements until they can form a rectangle. While the x^2-tile should be in the corner, there is more than one correct way to arrange the tiles into a rectangle.

- As students work through Activity 3, remind them to pay close attention to the sign of each tile.
- As students work through Activity 4, remind them to be careful to add one *x*-tile and one −*x*-tile when they add a zero pair.

Practice Have students complete Exercises 5–13.

3 Assess

Formative Assessment

Use Exercises 7 and 8 to assess whether students can use algebra tiles to factor trinomials.

From Concrete to Abstract

After students complete Exercises 1–8, ask them whether they noticed a correlation between the need to use zero pairs to factor the trinomial and the appearance of the resulting factors.
Sample answer: When zero pairs are used, the signs of the constant terms of the factors are opposite. When zero pairs are not used, the signs of the constant terms of factors are the same.

Extending the Concept

Ask students what they notice about the sum of the constant terms in the factors of the trinomials in Exercises 1–8.
Sample answer: Their sum equals the coefficient of the middle term of the trinomial.

Additional Answers

1. $(x + 1)(x + 2)$
2. $(x + 2)(x + 4)$
3. $(x - 1)(x + 4)$
4. $(x - 3)(x - 4)$
5. $(x + 2)(x + 5)$
6. $(x - 1)(x - 1)$
7. $(x + 4)(x - 3)$
8. $(x - 3)(x - 5)$

Algebra Lab

Factoring Trinomials *Continued*

Activity 3 Factor $x^2 - bx + c$

Use algebra tiles to factor $x^2 - 5x + 6$.

Step 1 Model $x^2 - 5x + 6$.

Step 2 Place the x^2-tile at the corner of the product mat. Arrange the 1-tiles into a 2-by-3 rectangular array as shown.

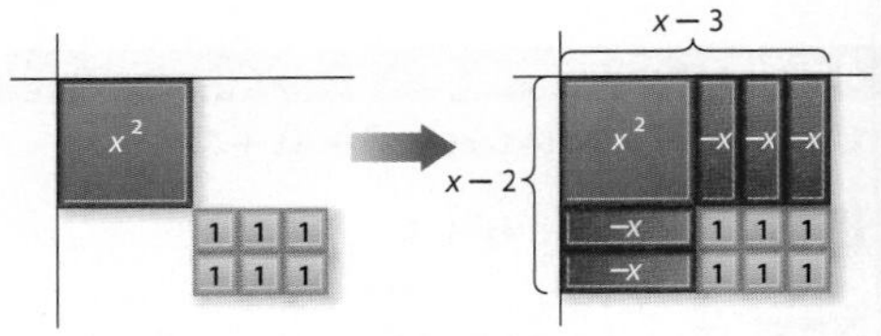

Step 3 Complete the rectangle with the *x*-tiles. The rectangle has a width of $x - 2$ and a length of $x - 3$.

Therefore, $x^2 - 5x + 6 = (x - 2)(x - 3)$.

Activity 4 Factor $x^2 - bx - c$

Use algebra tiles to factor $x^2 - 4x - 5$.

Step 1 Model $x^2 - 4x - 5$.

Step 2 Place the x^2-tile at the corner of the product mat. Arrange the 1-tiles into a 1-by-5 rectangular array as shown.

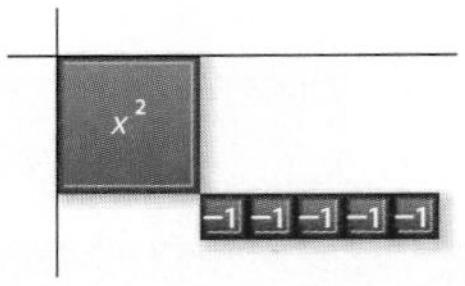

Step 3 Place the *x*-tile as shown. Recall that you can add zero pairs without changing the value of the polynomial. In this case, add a zero pair of *x*-tiles.

The rectangle has a width of $x + 1$ and a length of $x - 5$.

Therefore, $x^2 - 4x - 5 = (x + 1)(x - 5)$.

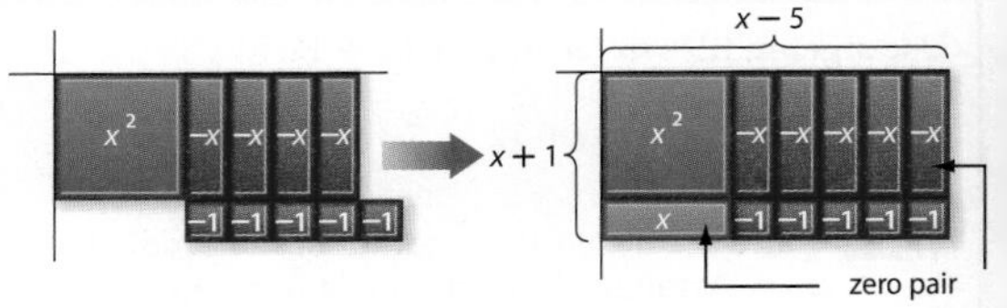

Model and Analyze

Use algebra tiles to factor each trinomial. **1–8. See margin.**

1. $x^2 + 3x + 2$	**2.** $x^2 + 6x + 8$	**3.** $x^2 + 3x - 4$	**4.** $x^2 - 7x + 12$
5. $x^2 + 7x + 10$	**6.** $x^2 - 2x + 1$	**7.** $x^2 + x - 12$	**8.** $x^2 - 8x + 15$

Tell whether each trinomial can be factored. Justify your answer with a drawing.

9. $x^2 + 3x + 6$ **no**	**10.** $x^2 - 5x - 6$ **yes**	**11.** $x^2 - x - 4$ **no**	**12.** $x^2 - 4$ **yes**

9–12. See Ch. 8 Answer Appendix for drawings.

13. WRITING IN MATH How can you use algebra tiles to determine whether a trinomial can be factored?

13. Trinomials can be factored if they can be represented by a rectangle. Sample answers: $x^2 + 4x + 4$ can be factored, and $x^2 + 6x + 4$ cannot be factored.

Teaching the Process Standards

Tools Mathematically proficient students consider the available tools when solving a mathematical problem. Encourage students to use algebra tiles as they progress in the chapter. Provide tiles or paper tiles that they can keep in their notebooks so they are always available.

LESSON 8-6 Solving $x^2 + bx + c = 0$

Then

- You multiplied binomials by using the FOIL method.

Now

1. Factor trinomials of the form $x^2 + bx + c$.
2. Solve equations of the form $x^2 + bx + c = 0$.

Why?

- Diana is having a rectangular in-ground swimming pool installed and she wants to include a 24-foot fence around the pool. The pool requires a space of 36 square feet. What dimensions should the pool have?

To solve this problem, the landscape architect needs to find two numbers that have a product of 36 and a sum of 12, half the perimeter of the pool.

NewVocabulary
quadratic equation

Content Standards
AI.RNE.6, AI.QE.4, AI.QE.5

Process Standards
PS.7

1 Factor $x^2 + bx + c$

You have learned how to multiply two binomials using the FOIL method. Each of the binomials was a factor of the product. The pattern for multiplying two binomials can be used to factor certain types of trinomials.

$$(x + 3)(x + 4) = x^2 + 4x + 3x + 3 \cdot 4 \quad \text{Use the FOIL method.}$$
$$= x^2 + (4 + 3)x + 3 \cdot 4 \quad \text{Distributive Property}$$
$$= x^2 + 7x + 12 \quad \text{Simplify.}$$

Notice that the coefficient of the middle term, $7x$, is the sum of 3 and 4, and the last term, 12, is the product of 3 and 4.

Observe the following pattern in this multiplication.

$$(x + 3)(x + 4) = x^2 + (4 + 3)x + (3 \cdot 4)$$
$$(x + m)(x + p) = x^2 + (p + m)x + mp \quad \text{Let } 3 = m \text{ and } 4 = p.$$
$$= x^2 + \underbrace{(m + p)}_{bx}x + \underbrace{mp}_{c} \quad \text{Commutative (+)}$$
$$x^2 + bx + c \quad b = m + p \text{ and } c = mp$$

Notice that the coefficient of the middle term is the sum of m and p, and the last term is the product of m and p. This pattern can be used to factor trinomials of the form $x^2 + bx + c$.

KeyConcept Factoring $x^2 + bx + c$

Words	To factor trinomials in the form $x^2 + bx + c$, find two integers, m and p, with a sum of b and a product of c. Then write $x^2 + bx + c$ as $(x + m)(x + p)$.
Symbols	$x^2 + bx + c = (x + m)(x + p)$ when $m + p = b$ and $mp = c$.
Example	$x^2 + 6x + 8 = (x + 2)(x + 4)$, because $2 + 4 = 6$ and $2 \cdot 4 = 8$.

When c is positive, its factors have the same signs. Both of the factors are positive or negative based upon the sign of b. If b is positive, the factors are positive. If b is negative, the factors are negative.

1 Focus

VerticalAlignment

Before Lesson 8-6 Multiply binomials by using the FOIL method.

Lesson 8-6 Factor trinomials of the form $x^2 + bx + c$. Solve equations of the form $x^2 + bx + c = 0$.

After Lesson 8-6 Factor trinomials into two binomials.

2 Teach

Scaffolding Questions

Have students read the **Why?** section of the lesson.

Ask:

- Why do you need to find two numbers that have a product of 36 to find the dimensions of the pool? The pool is a rectangle, so the area is equal to the length times the width. Since the pool's area is 36 ft^2, the length and width must be two numbers with a product of 36.
- What pairs of integers have a product of 36? 1 and 36; 2 and 18; 3 and 12; 4 and 9; 6 and 6
- Which pair has a sum of 12? 6 and 6
- What are the dimensions of the pool? 6 ft by 6 ft

Lesson 8-6 Resources

Resource	Approaching Level AL	On Level OL	Beyond Level BL	English Learners ELL
Teacher Edition	▪ Differentiated Instruction, p. 504	▪ Differentiated Instruction, pp. 504, 506	▪ Differentiated Instruction, p. 506	
Chapter Resource Masters	▪ Study Guide and Intervention, pp. 37–38 ▪ Skills Practice, p. 39 ▪ Practice, p. 40 ▪ Word Problem Practice, p. 41	▪ Study Guide and Intervention, pp. 37–38 ▪ Skills Practice, p. 39 ▪ Practice, p. 40 ▪ Word Problem Practice, p. 41 ▪ Enrichment, p. 42	▪ Practice, p. 40 ▪ Word Problem Practice, p. 41 ▪ Enrichment, p. 42	▪ Study Guide and Intervention, pp. 37–38 ▪ Skills Practice, p. 39 ▪ Practice, p. 40 ▪ Word Problem Practice, p. 41
Other	▪ 5-Minute Check 8-6 ▪ Study Notebook	▪ 5-Minute Check 8-6 ▪ Study Notebook	▪ 5-Minute Check 8-6 ▪ Study Notebook	▪ 5-Minute Check 8-6 ▪ Study Notebook

1 Factor $x^2 + bx + c$

Examples 1–3 show how to factor trinomials of the form $x^2 + bx + c$, when b and c are positive, when b is negative and c is positive, and when c is negative.

Formative Assessment

Use the Guided Practice exercises after each example to determine students' understanding of concepts.

Additional Examples

1 Factor $x^2 + 7x + 12$.
$(x + 3)(x + 4)$

2 Factor $x^2 - 12x + 27$.
$(x - 3)(x - 9)$

Additional Examples also in Interactive Classroom PowerPoint® Presentations

IWB Interactive White Board READY

WatchOut!

Preventing Errors If students use a graphing calculator to check their factoring, make sure they clear all other functions from the [Y=] list and clear all other drawings from the draw menu. Caution students that while two graphs may appear to coincide in the standard viewing window, they may not. Suggest that students use the [TABLE] feature to verify identical y-values.

Tips for New Teachers

Calculators Have students change the line type on the graph of the second equation so they can see it as it is graphed on the first graph.

Problem-SolvingTip

Guess and Check When factoring a trinomial, make an educated guess, check for reasonableness, and then adjust the guess until the correct answer is found.

Example 1 b and c are Positive

Factor $x^2 + 9x + 20$.

In this trinomial, $b = 9$ and $c = 20$. Since c is positive and b is positive, you need to find two positive factors with a sum of 9 and a product of 20. Make an organized list of the factors of 20, and look for the pair of factors with a sum of 9.

Factors of 20	Sum of Factors
1, 20	21
2, 10	12
4, 5	9

The correct factors are 4 and 5.

$x^2 + 9x + 20 = (x + m)(x + p)$ — Write the pattern.
$= (x + 4)(x + 5)$ — $m = 4$ and $p = 5$

CHECK You can check this result by multiplying the two factors. The product should be equal to the original expression.

$(x + 4)(x + 5) = x^2 + 5x + 4x + 20$ — FOIL Method
$= x^2 + 9x + 20$ ✓ — Simplify.

GuidedPractice

Factor each polynomial.

1A. $d^2 + 11d + 24$ **$(d + 3)(d + 8)$**

1B. $9 + 10t + t^2$ **$(t + 9)(t + 1)$**

When factoring a trinomial in which b is negative and c is positive, use what you know about the product of binomials to narrow the list of possible factors.

Example 2 b is Negative and c is Positive

Factor $x^2 - 8x + 12$. Confirm your answer using a graphing calculator.

In this trinomial, $b = -8$ and $c = 12$. Since c is positive and b is negative, you need to find two negative factors with a sum of -8 and a product of 12.

Factors of 12	Sum of Factors
−1, −12	−13
−2, −6	−8
−3, −4	−7

The correct factors are −2 and −6.

$x^2 - 8x + 12 = (x + m)(x + p)$ — Write the pattern.
$= (x - 2)(x - 6)$ — $m = -2$ and $p = -6$

StudyTip

Regularity Once the correct factors are found, it is not necessary to test any other factors. In Example 2, −2 and −6 are the correct factors, so −3 and −4 do not need to be tested.

CHECK Graph $y = x^2 - 8x + 12$ and $y = (x - 2)(x - 6)$ on the same screen. Since only one graph appears, the two graphs must coincide. Therefore, the trinomial has been factored correctly. ✓

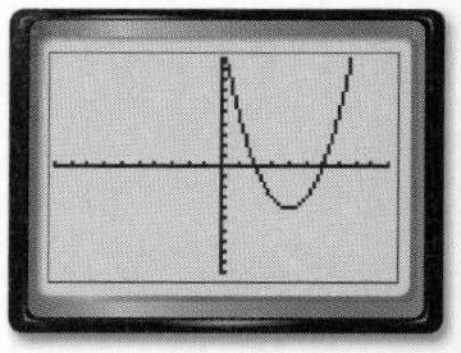

[−10, 10] scl: 1 by [−10, 10] scl: 1

GuidedPractice

Factor each polynomial.

2A. $21 - 22m + m^2$ **$(m - 1)(m - 21)$**

2B. $w^2 - 11w + 28$ **$(w - 7)(w - 4)$**

DifferentiatedInstruction AL OL

If the concept of factoring trinomials seems somewhat abstract to some students,

Then whenever you introduce abstract concepts, it is a good idea to reinforce them with concrete examples. After introducing factoring trinomials, refer students to the lesson-opener problem. Ask students to describe any similarities they notice between finding the dimensions of the pool and factoring a trinomial. Some students may benefit from modeling some problems using algebra tiles. They can then use this method to solve quadratic equations.

504 | Lesson 8-6 | Solving $x^2 + bx + c = 0$

ReviewVocabulary

absolute value the distance a number is from zero on a number line, written $|n|$

When c is negative, its factors have opposite signs. To determine which factor is positive and which is negative, look at the sign of b. The factor with the greater absolute value has the same sign as b.

Example 3 c is Negative

Factor each polynomial. Confirm your answers using a graphing calculator.

a. $x^2 + 2x - 15$

In this trinomial, $b = 2$ and $c = -15$. Since c is negative, the factors m and p have opposite signs. So either m or p is negative, but not both. Since b is positive, the factor with the greater absolute value is also positive.

List the factors of -15, where one factor of each pair is negative. Look for the pair of factors with a sum of 2.

Factors of -15	Sum of Factors
$-1, 15$	14
$-3, 5$	2

The correct factors are -3 and 5.

$x^2 + 2x - 15 = (x + m)(x + p)$ Write the pattern.

$= (x - 3)(x + 5)$ $m = -3$ and $p = 5$

CHECK $(x - 3)(x + 5) = x^2 + 5x - 3x - 15$ FOIL Method

$= x^2 + 2x - 15$ ✓ Simplify.

b. $x^2 - 7x - 18$

In this trinomial, $b = -7$ and $c = -18$. Either m or p is negative, but not both. Since b is negative, the factor with the greater absolute value is also negative.

List the factors of -18, where one factor of each pair is negative. Look for the pair of factors with a sum of -7.

Factors of -18	Sum of Factors
$1, -18$	-17
$2, -9$	-7
$3, -6$	-3

The correct factors are 2 and -9.

$x^2 - 7x - 18 = (x + m)(x + p)$ Write the pattern.

$= (x + 2)(x - 9)$ $m = 2$ and $p = -9$

CHECK Graph $y = x^2 - 7x - 18$ and $y = (x + 2)(x - 9)$ on the same screen.

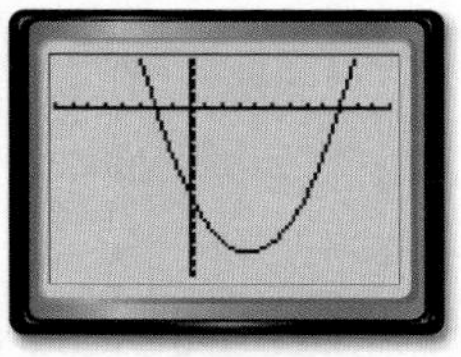

[−10, 15] scl: 1 by [−40, 20] scl: 1

The graphs coincide. Therefore, the trinomial has been factored correctly. ✓

GuidedPractice

3A. $y^2 + 13y - 48$ **$(y - 3)(y + 16)$** **3B.** $r^2 - 2r - 24$ **$(r + 4)(r - 6)$**

Additional Example

3 Factor each polynomial.

a. $x^2 + 3x - 18$
$(x + 6)(x - 3)$

b. $x^2 - x - 20$
$(x - 5)(x + 4)$

Focus on Mathematical Content

Factoring Trinomials A trinomial of the form $x^2 + bx + c$ may or may not be factorable into binomial factors. If the trinomial is factorable, then the factors of c must be two integers, m and p, such that $m + p = b$ and $mp = c$.

Teach with Tech

Web Page Develop a class Web page about how to factor different types of trinomials. Update the page with information from the most recent lesson, such as notes from class, video clips, and additional resources.

Teaching the Process Standards

Regularity Mathematically proficient students maintain oversight of the process, while attending to the details of solving a problem. Stress that exactly one pair of factors correctly factors a trinomial of the form $x^2 + bx + c$ that can be factored.

2 Solve Equations by Factoring

Example 4 shows how to solve an equation of the form $x^2 + bx + c = 0$ by factoring. **Example 5** shows how to solve a real-world problem by factoring.

Additional Examples

4 Solve $x^2 + 2x = 15$. Check your solutions. $-5, 3$

5 **ARCHITECTURE** Marion wants to build a new art studio that has three times the area of her old studio by increasing the length and width of the old studio by the same amount. What should be the dimensions of the new studio?

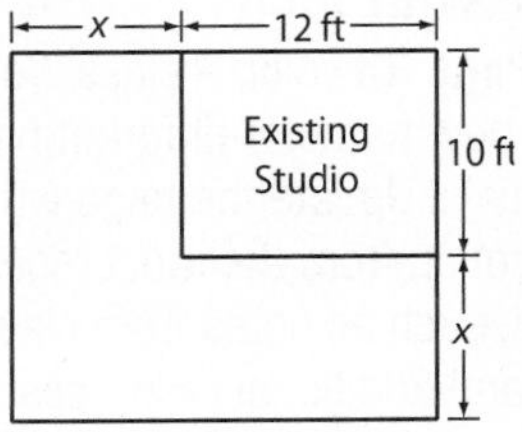

The dimensions of the new studio should be 18 ft by 20 ft.

WatchOut!

Common Errors Students often are not careful when rewriting equations so that one side equals zero. Remind them that they must perform the same operation on both sides of the equation and pay attention to the signs in the resulting equation.

2 Solve Equations by Factoring

A **quadratic equation** can be written in the standard form $ax^2 + bx + c = 0$, where $a \neq 0$. Some equations of the form $x^2 + bx + c = 0$ can be solved by factoring and then using the Zero Product Property.

Example 4 Solve an Equation by Factoring

Solve $x^2 + 6x = 27$. Check your solutions.

$x^2 + 6x = 27$	Original equation
$x^2 + 6x - 27 = 0$	Subtract 27 from each side.
$(x - 3)(x + 9) = 0$	Factor.
$x - 3 = 0$ or $x + 9 = 0$	Zero Product Property
$x = 3$ $\quad x = -9$	Solve each equation.

The roots are 3 and −9.

CHECK Substitute 3 and −9 for x in the original equation.

$$x^2 + 6x = 27 \qquad x^2 + 6x = 27$$
$$(3)^2 + 6(3) \stackrel{?}{=} 27 \qquad (-9)^2 + 6(-9) \stackrel{?}{=} 27$$
$$9 + 18 \stackrel{?}{=} 27 \qquad 81 - 54 \stackrel{?}{=} 27$$
$$27 = 27 \checkmark \qquad 27 = 27 \checkmark$$

StudyTip

Solving an Equation By Factoring Remember to get 0 on one side of the equation before factoring.

GuidedPractice

Solve each equation. Check your solutions.

4A. $z^2 - 3z = 70$ $-7, 10$

4B. $x^2 + 3x - 18 = 0$ $3, -6$

Factoring can be useful when solving real-world problems.

Real-WorldLink

A company that produces event signs recommends foamcore boards for event signs that will be used only once. For signs used more than once, use a stronger type of foamcore board.

Source: MegaPrint Inc.

Real-World Example 5 Solve a Problem by Factoring

DESIGN Ling is designing a poster. The top of the poster is 4 inches long and the rest of the poster is 2 inches longer than the width. If the poster requires 616 square inches of poster board, find the width w of the poster.

Understand You want to find the width of the poster.

Plan Since the poster is a rectangle, width • length = area.

Solve Let w = the width of the poster. The length is $w + 2 + 4$ or $w + 6$.

$w(w + 6) = 616$	Write the equation.
$w^2 + 6w = 616$	Multiply.
$w^2 + 6w - 616 = 0$	Subtract 616 from each side.
$(w + 28)(w - 22) = 0$	Factor.
$w + 28 = 0$ or $w - 22 = 0$	Zero Product Property
$w = -28$ $\quad w = 22$	Solve each equation.

Since dimensions cannot be negative, the width is 22 inches.

Check If the width is 22 inches, then the area of the poster is $22 \cdot (22 + 6)$ or 616 square inches, which is the amount the poster requires. ✓

GuidedPractice

5. **GEOMETRY** The height of a parallelogram is 18 centimeters less than its base. If the area is 175 square centimeters, what is its height? **7 cm**

DifferentiatedInstruction OL BL

Extension Write the trinomials $x^2 + x - 6$ and $x^2 - x - 6$ on the board. Ask students to compare the two trinomials. How are the trinomials related? How are their factors related? The trinomials are the same except for the sign of the middle term. When factored, $x^2 + x - 6$ is $(x + 3)(x - 2)$, while $x^2 - x - 6$ is $(x - 3)(x + 2)$. The factors have opposite signs in the constant term.

Check Your Understanding

◯ = Step-by-Step Solutions begin on page R13.

Examples 1–3 Factor each polynomial. Confirm your answers using a graphing calculator.

1. $x^2 + 14x + 24$ $(x + 2)(x + 12)$

2. $y^2 - 7y - 30$ $(y - 10)(y + 3)$

3. $n^2 + 4n - 21$ $(n + 7)(n - 3)$

4. $m^2 - 15m + 50$ $(m - 5)(m - 10)$

Example 4 Solve each equation. Check your solutions.

5. $x^2 - 4x - 21 = 0$ $-3, 7$

6. $n^2 - 3n + 2 = 0$ $1, 2$

7. $x^2 - 15x + 54 = 0$ $6, 9$

8. $x^2 + 12x = -32$ $-4, -8$

9. $x^2 - x - 72 = 0$ $-8, 9$

10. $x^2 - 10x = -24$ $4, 6$

Example 5

11. **FRAMING** Tina bought a frame for a photo, but the photo is too big for the frame. Tina needs to reduce the width and length of the photo by the same amount. The area of the photo should be reduced to half the original area. If the original photo is 12 inches by 16 inches, what will be the dimensions of the smaller photo? 8 in. by 12 in.

Practice and Problem Solving

Extra Practice is on page R8.

Examples 1–3 Factor each polynomial. Confirm your answers using a graphing calculator.

12. $x^2 + 17x + 42$ $(x + 3)(x + 14)$

13. $y^2 - 17y + 72$ $(y - 9)(y - 8)$

14. $a^2 + 8a - 48$ $(a - 4)(a + 12)$

15. $n^2 - 2n - 35$ $(n - 7)(n + 5)$

16. $44 + 15h + h^2$ $(h + 4)(h + 11)$

17. $40 - 22x + x^2$ $(x - 2)(x - 20)$

18. $-24 - 10x + x^2$ $(x + 2)(x - 12)$

19. $-42 - m + m^2$ $(m + 6)(m - 7)$

Example 4 Solve each equation. Check your solutions.

20. $x^2 - 7x + 12 = 0$ $3, 4$

(21) $y^2 + y = 20$ $4, -5$

22. $x^2 - 6x = 27$ $-3, 9$

23. $a^2 + 11a = -18$ $-2, -9$

24. $c^2 + 10c + 9 = 0$ $-1, -9$

25. $x^2 - 18x = -32$ $2, 16$

26. $n^2 - 120 = 7n$ $-8, 15$

27. $d^2 + 56 = -18d$ $-4, -14$

28. $y^2 - 90 = 13y$ $-5, 18$

29. $h^2 + 48 = 16h$ $4, 12$

Example 5

30. **GEOMETRY** A triangle has an area of 36 square feet. If the height of the triangle is 6 feet more than its base, what are its height and base? 12 ft, 6 ft

31. **GEOMETRY** A rectangle has an area represented by $x^2 - 4x - 12$ square feet. If the length is $x + 2$ feet, what is the width of the rectangle? $(x - 6)$ ft

32a. Let ℓ = length, A = area of the field, $\ell(\ell - 45) = A$.

B **32.** **SOCCER** The width of a high school soccer field is 45 yards shorter than its length.

a. Define a variable, and write an expression for the area of the field.

b. The area of the field is 9000 square yards. Find the dimensions. 75 yd by 120 yd

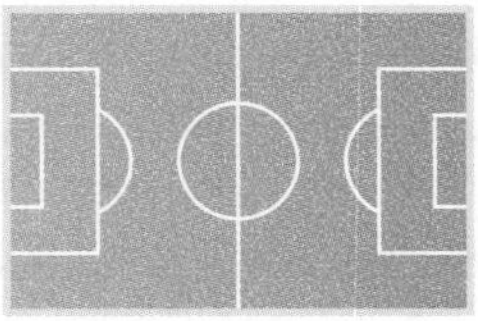

STRUCTURE Factor each polynomial.

33. $q^2 + 11qr + 18r^2$ $(q + 2r)(q + 9r)$

34. $x^2 - 14xy - 51y^2$ $(x + 3y)(x - 17y)$

35. $x^2 - 6xy + 5y^2$ $(x - y)(x - 5y)$

36. $a^2 + 10ab - 39b^2$ $(a + 13b)(a - 3b)$

3 Practice

Formative Assessment

Use Exercises 1–11 to check for understanding.

Use the chart at the bottom of this page to customize assignments for your students.

WatchOut!

Student Misconceptions For Exercises 1–4, students may need to be reminded that the order in which they record the factors does not matter. So, $(x + m)(x + p)$ and $(x + p)(x + m)$ are both correct.

Exercise Alert

Formula For Exercise 30, students will need to know that the formula for the area of a triangle is $A = \frac{1}{2}bh$.

Teaching the Process Standards

Structure Mathematically proficient students look closely to discern a pattern or structure. In Exercises 33–36, point out that the same patterns that apply to polynomials that contain numbers apply to variables.

Differentiated Homework Options

Level	Assignment	Two-Day Option	
AL Basic	12–31, 41, 46, 47, 49–68	13–31 odd, 50–53	12–30 even, 41, 46, 47, 49, 54–68
OL Core	13–31 odd, 32, 33, 35, 37, 39–41, 46, 47, 49–68	12–31, 50–53	32–41, 46, 47, 49, 54–68
BL Advanced	32–65, (optional: 66–68)		

37c. The solution of 15 means that the width is 15 ft. The solution −35 does not make sense because length cannot be negative.

37. SWIMMING The length of a rectangular swimming pool is 20 feet greater than its width. The area of the pool is 525 square feet.

a. Define a variable and write an equation for the area of the pool. **Sample answer: Let w = width; $(w + 20)w = 525$.**

b. Solve the equation. **−35, 15**

c. Interpret the solutions. Do both solutions make sense? Explain.

GEOMETRY **Find an expression for the perimeter of a rectangle with the given area.**

38. $A = x^2 + 24x - 81$ **$4x + 48$**

39. $A = x^2 + 13x - 90$ **$4x + 26$**

40. MULTIPLE REPRESENTATIONS In this problem, you will explore factoring when the leading coefficient is not 1.

a. **Tabular** Copy and complete the table below.

Product of Two Binomials	$ax^2 + mx + px + c$	$ax^2 + bx + c$	$m \times p$	$a \times c$
$(2x + 3)(x + 4)$	$2x^2 + 8x + 3x + 12$	$2x^2 + 11x + 12$	24	24
$(x + 1)(3x + 5)$	$3x^2 + 5x + 3x + 5$	$3x^2 + 8x + 5$	15	15
$(2x - 1)(4x + 1)$	$8x^2 + 2x - 4x - 1$	$8x^2 - 2x - 1$	−8	−8
$(3x + 5)(4x - 2)$	$12x^2 - 6x + 20x - 10$	$12x^2 + 14x - 10$	−120	−120

b. **Analytical** How are m and p related to a and c? **$mp = ac$**

c. **Analytical** How are m and p related to b? **$m + p = b$**

d. **Verbal** Describe a process you can use for factoring a polynomial of the form $ax^2 + bx + c$. **Look for two integers, m and p, for which $mp = ac$ and $m + p = b$.**

41. Charles; Jerome's answer once multiplied is $x^2 - 6x - 16$. The middle term should be positive.

H.O.T. Problems Use Higher-Order Thinking Skills

41. ERROR ANALYSIS Jerome and Charles have factored $x^2 + 6x - 16$. Is either of them correct? Explain your reasoning.

Jerome	Charles
$x^2 + 6x - 16 = (x + 2)(x - 8)$	$x^2 + 6x - 16 = (x - 2)(x + 8)$

48. $(4y - 5)^2 + 3(4y - 5) - 70 = [(4y - 5) + 10] \cdot [(4y - 5) - 7] = (4y + 5)(4y - 12) = 4(4y + 5)(y - 3)$

ARGUMENTS **Find all values of k so that each polynomial can be factored using integers.**

42. $x^2 + kx - 19$ **−18, 18**

43. $x^2 + kx + 14$ **−15, −9, 9, 15**

44. $x^2 - 8x + k, k > 0$ **7, 12, 15, 16**

45. $x^2 - 5x + k, k > 0$ **4, 6**

46. REASONING For any factorable trinomial, $x^2 + bx + c$, will the absolute value of b *sometimes*, *always*, or *never* be less than the absolute value of c? Explain. **See margin.**

47. OPEN ENDED Give an example of a trinomial that can be factored using the factoring techniques presented in this lesson. Then factor the trinomial. **Sample answer: $x^2 + 19x - 20$; $(x - 1)(x + 20)$**

48. CHALLENGE Factor $(4y - 5)^2 + 3(4y - 5) - 70$.

49. WRITING IN MATH Explain how to factor trinomials of the form $x^2 + bx + c$ and how to determine the signs of the factors of c. **See margin.**

Study Guide and Intervention

AL OL ELL

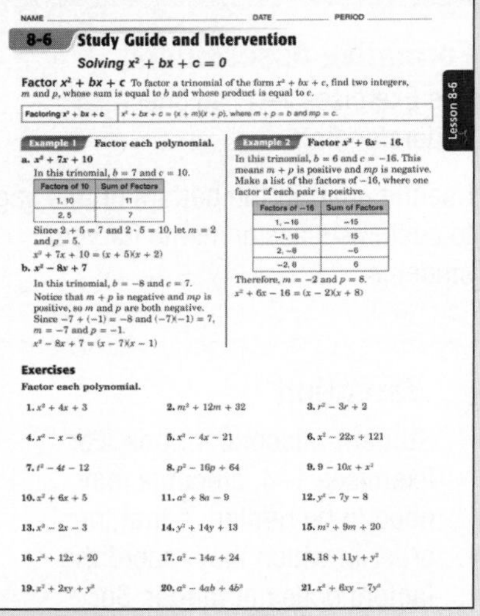
8-6 Study Guide and Intervention

Solving $x^2 + bx + c = 0$

Practice

AL OL BL ELL

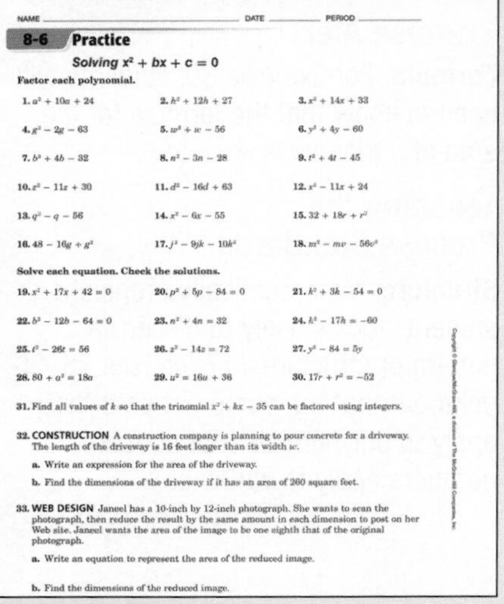
8-6 Practice

Solving $x^2 + bx + c = 0$

Word Problem Practice

AL OL BL ELL

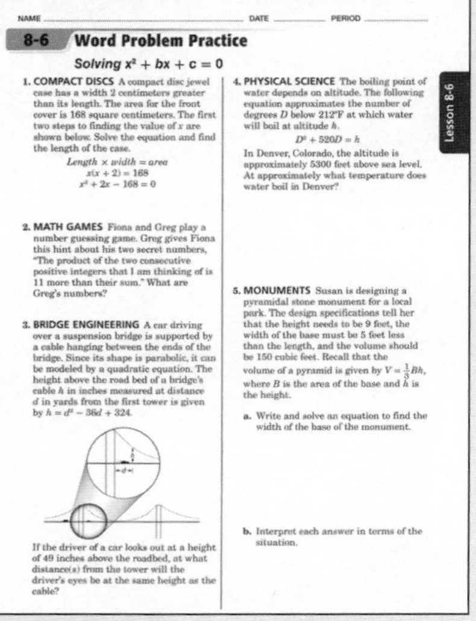
8-6 Word Problem Practice

Solving $x^2 + bx + c = 0$

Enrichment

OL BL

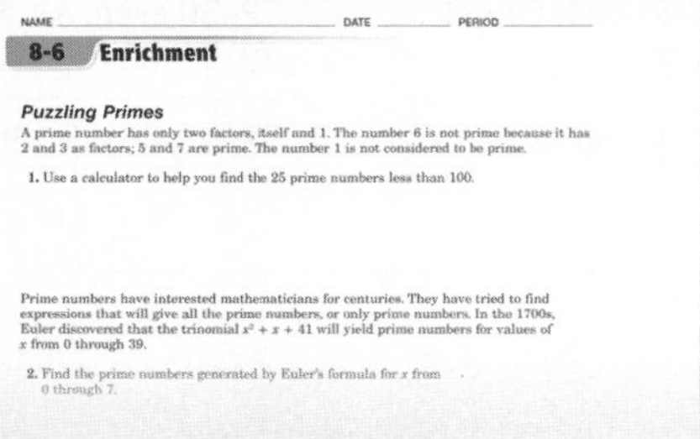
8-6 Enrichment

Puzzling Primes

Multiple Representations

In Exercise 40, students use information organized in a table and algebra to factor polynomials.

Standardized Test Practice

50. Which inequality is shown in the graph below? **C**

A $y \leq -\frac{3}{4}x + 3$

B $y < -\frac{3}{4}x + 3$

C $y > -\frac{3}{4}x + 3$

D $y \geq -\frac{3}{4}x + 3$

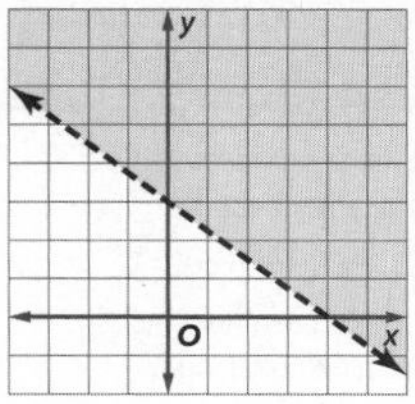

51. SHORT RESPONSE Olivia must earn more than \$254 from selling candy bars in order to go on a trip with the National Honor Society. If each candy bar is sold for \$1.25, what is the fewest candy bars she must sell? **204**

52. GEOMETRY Which expression represents the length of the rectangle? **H**

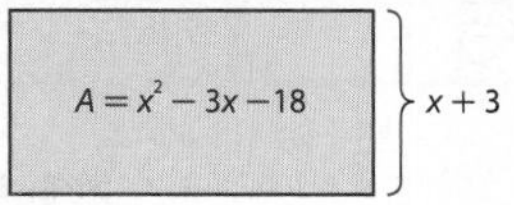

F $x + 5$

G $x + 6$

H $x - 6$

J $x - 5$

53. The difference of 21 and a number n is 6. Which equation shows the relationship? **A**

A $21 - n = 6$

B $21 + n = 6$

C $21n = 6$

D $6n = -21$

Spiral Review

Factor each polynomial. (Lesson 8-5)

54. $10a^2 + 40a$ **$10a(a + 4)$**

55. $11x + 44x^2y$ **$11x(1 + 4xy)$**

56. $2m^3p^2 - 16mp^2 + 8mp$ **$2mp(m^2p - 8p + 4)$**

57. $2ax + 6xc + ba + 3bc$ **$(2x + b)(a + 3c)$**

58. $8ac - 2ad + 4bc - bd$ **$(2a + b)(4c - d)$**

59. $x^2 - xy - xy + y^2$ **$(x - y)(x - y)$**

60. Write a polynomial that represents the area of the shaded region in the figure at the right. (Lesson 8-4) **$8d + 16$**

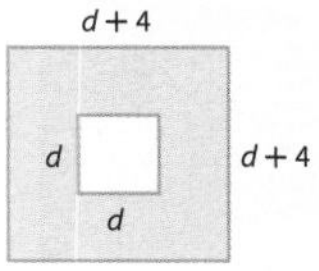

Use elimination to solve each system of equations. (Lesson 6-3)

61. $-x + y = 9$ **(4, 13)**
$x + 2y = 30$

62. $5a + 2b = 4$ **(2, −3)**
$-5a - b = -7$

63. $2c + d = 12$ **(3, 6)**
$c - d = -3$

64. $6x + 2y = 14$ **(2, 1)**
$5x - 2y = 8$

65. LANDSCAPING Kendrick is planning a circular flower garden with a low fence around the border. He has 38 feet of fence. What is the radius of the largest garden he can make? (*Hint:* $C = 2\pi r$) (Lesson 5-2) **about 6 ft**

Skills Review

Factor each polynomial. **66. $(2m + r)(3x - 2)$** **67. $(3x - 4)(a - 2b)$** **68. $2(d^2 + f)(g + 2h)$**

66. $6mx - 4m + 3rx - 2r$

67. $3ax - 6bx + 8b - 4a$

68. $2d^2g + 2fg + 4d^2h + 4fh$

WatchOut!

Error Analysis For Exercise 41, remind students that they can check the correctness of the factors by multiplying them to see if the result is the original polynomial. They could also use their graphing calculators for the procedure in Example 2.

Teaching the Process Standards

Arguments Mathematically proficient students make conjectures and build a logical progression of statements to explore the truth of their conjectures. In Exercises 42–45, tell students to start by thinking about how they would factor each polynomial if k is given. How is k related to the other constants in the polynomial?

4 Assess

Crystal Ball Tell students that the next lesson they will study is titled *Quadratic Equations*: $ax^2 + bx + c = 0$. Ask them to write how they think what they learned today will connect with the next lesson.

Additional Answers

46. Sometimes; Sample answer: The trinomial $x^2 + 10x + 9 = (x + 1)(x + 9)$ and $10 > 9$. The trinomial $x^2 + 7x + 10 = (x + 2)(x + 5)$ and $7 < 10$.

49. Sample answer: Find factors m and n such that $m + n = b$ and $mn = c$. If b and c are positive, then m and n are positive. If b is negative and c is positive, then m and n are negative. When c is negative, m and n have different signs and the factor with the greatest absolute value has the same sign as b.

1 Focus

Vertical Alignment

Before Lesson 8-7 Factor trinomials of the form $x^2 + bx + c$.

Lesson 8-7 Factor trinomials of the form $ax^2 + bx + c$. Solve equations of the form $ax^2 + bx + c = 0$.

After Lesson 8-7 Factor binomials that are the difference of squares.

2 Teach

Scaffolding Questions

Have students read the **Why?** section of the lesson.

Ask:

- How is the trinomial $16t^2 - 5t + 120$ different from those you learned how to factor in Lesson 8-6? The coefficient of the t^2 term of the trinomial is an integer greater than 1, while the coefficients of the x^2 terms of the trinomials in Lesson 8-6 were always 1.
- What trinomial does the product of $(3x + 1)(2x + 5)$ give? $6x^2 + 17x + 5$
- How does the coefficient of the x^2 term relate to the coefficients of the x term in each factor? The coefficient of the x^2 term equals their product. $3 \times 2 = 6$

LESSON 8-7 Solving $ax^2 + bx + c = 0$

Then

- You factored trinomials of the form $x^2 + bx + c$.

Now

1. Factor trinomials of the form $ax^2 + bx + c$.
2. Solve equations of the form $ax^2 + bx + c = 0$.

Why?

- The path of a rider on the amusement park ride shown at the right can be modeled by $16t^2 - 5t + 120$.

  Factoring this expression can help the ride operators determine how long a rider rides on the initial swing.

New Vocabulary
prime polynomial

Content Standards
AI.RNE.6, AI.QE.4, AI.QE.5

Process Standards
PS.4

1 Factor $ax^2 + bx + c$

In the last lesson, you factored quadratic expressions of the form $ax^2 + bx + c$, where $a = 1$. In this lesson, you will apply the factoring methods to quadratic expressions in which a is not 1.

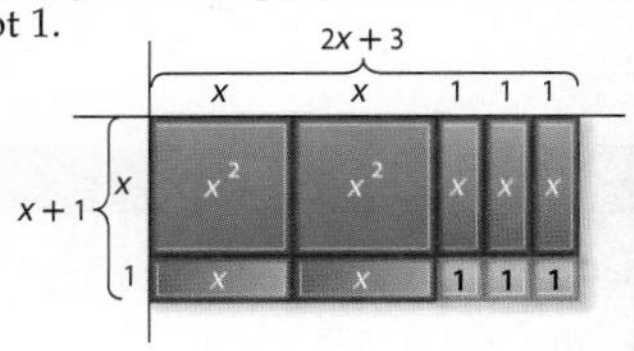

The dimensions of the rectangle formed by the algebra tiles are the factors of $2x^2 + 5x + 3$. The factors of $2x^2 + 5x + 3$ are $x + 1$ and $2x + 3$.

You can also use the method of factoring by grouping to solve this expression.

Step 1 Apply the pattern: $2x^2 + 5x + 3 = 2x^2 + mx + px + 3$.

Step 2 Find two numbers that have a product of $2 \cdot 3$ or 6 and a sum of 5.

Factors of 6	Sum of Factors
1, 6	7
2, 3	5

Step 3 Use grouping to find the factors.

$$\begin{aligned}2x^2 + 5x + 3 &= 2x^2 + mx + px + 3 && \text{Write the pattern.}\\ &= 2x^2 + 2x + 3x + 3 && m = 2 \text{ and } p = 3\\ &= (2x^2 + 2x) + (3x + 3) && \text{Group terms with common factors.}\\ &= 2x(x + 1) + 3(x + 1) && \text{Factor the GCF.}\\ &= (2x + 3)(x + 1) && x + 1 \text{ is the common factor.}\end{aligned}$$

Therefore, $2x^2 + 5x + 3 = (2x + 3)(x + 1)$.

Key Concept Factoring $ax^2 + bx + c$

Words To factor trinomials of the form $ax^2 + bx + c$, find two integers, m and p, with a sum of b and a product of ac. Then write $ax^2 + bx + c$ as $ax^2 + mx + px + c$, and factor by grouping.

Example

$$\begin{aligned}5x^2 - 13x + 6 &= 5x^2 - 10x - 3x + 6 && m = -10 \text{ and } p = -3\\ &= 5x(x - 2) + (-3)(x - 2)\\ &= (5x - 3)(x - 2)\end{aligned}$$

510 | Lesson 8-7

Lesson 8-7 Resources

Resource	Approaching Level AL	On Level OL	Beyond Level BL	English Learners ELL
Teacher Edition	▪ Differentiated Instruction, p. 511	▪ Differentiated Instruction, p. 515	▪ Differentiated Instruction, p. 515	
Chapter Resource Masters	▪ Study Guide and Intervention, pp. 43–44 ▪ Skills Practice, p. 45 ▪ Practice, p. 46 ▪ Word Problem Practice, p. 47 ▪ Graphing Calculator Activity, p. 49	▪ Study Guide and Intervention, pp. 43–44 ▪ Skills Practice, p. 45 ▪ Practice, p. 46 ▪ Word Problem Practice, p. 47 ▪ Enrichment, p. 48 ▪ Graphing Calculator Activity, p. 49	▪ Practice, p. 46 ▪ Word Problem Practice, p. 47 ▪ Enrichment, p. 48 ▪ Graphing Calculator Activity, p. 49	▪ Study Guide and Intervention, pp. 43–44 ▪ Skills Practice, p. 45 ▪ Practice, p. 46 ▪ Word Problem Practice, p. 47 ▪ Graphing Calculator Activity, p. 49
Other	▪ 5-Minute Check 8-7 ▪ Study Notebook ▪ Teaching Algebra with Manipulatives	▪ 5-Minute Check 8-7 ▪ Study Notebook ▪ Teaching Algebra with Manipulatives	▪ 5-Minute Check 8-7 ▪ Study Notebook	▪ 5-Minute Check 8-7 ▪ Study Notebook ▪ Teaching Algebra with Manipulatives

Example 1 Factor $ax^2 + bx + c$

Factor each trinomial.

a. $7x^2 + 29x + 4$

In this trinomial, $a = 7$, $b = 29$, and $c = 4$. You need to find two numbers with a sum of 29 and a product of $7 \cdot 4$ or 28. Make a list of the factors of 28 and look for the pair of factors with the sum of 29.

Factors of 28	Sum of Factors
1, 28	29

The correct factors are 1 and 28.

$7x^2 + 29x + 4 = 7x^2 + mx + px + 4$ — Write the pattern.
$= 7x^2 + 1x + 28x + 4$ — $m = 1$ and $p = 28$
$= (7x^2 + 1x) + (28x + 4)$ — Group terms with common factors.
$= x(7x + 1) + 4(7x + 1)$ — Factor the GCF.
$= (x + 4)(7x + 1)$ — $7x + 1$ is the common factor.

b. $3x^2 + 15x + 18$

The GCF of the terms $3x^2$, $15x$, and 18 is 3. Factor this first.

$3x^2 + 15x + 18 = 3(x^2 + 5x + 6)$ — Distributive Property
$= 3(x + 3)(x + 2)$ — Find two factors of 6 with a sum of 5.

Guided Practice

1A. $5x^2 + 13x + 6$ **$(5x + 3)(x + 2)$** **1B.** $6x^2 + 22x - 8$ **$2(3x - 1)(x + 4)$**

StudyTip
Greatest Common Factor Always look for a GCF of the terms of a polynomial before you factor.

Sometimes the coefficient of the x-term is negative.

Example 2 Factor $ax^2 - bx + c$

Factor $3x^2 - 17x + 20$.

In this trinomial, $a = 3$, $b = -17$, and $c = 20$. Since b is negative, $m + p$ will be negative. Since c is positive, mp will be positive.

To determine m and p, list the negative factors of ac or 60. The sum of m and p should be -17.

Factors of 60	Sum of Factors
−2, −30	−32
−3, −20	−23
−4, −15	−19
−5, −12	−17

The correct factors are −5 and −12.

$3x^2 - 17x + 20 = 3x^2 - 12x - 5x + 20$ — $m = -12$ and $p = -5$
$= (3x^2 - 12x) + (-5x + 20)$ — Group terms with common factors.
$= 3x(x - 4) + (-5)(x - 4)$ — Factor the GCF.
$= (3x - 5)(x - 4)$ — Distributive Property

Guided Practice

2A. $2n^2 - n - 1$ **$(n - 1)(2n + 1)$** **2B.** $10y^2 - 35y + 30$ **$5(2y - 3)(y - 2)$**

Real-WorldCareer
Urban Planner Urban planners design the layout of an area. They take into consideration the available land and geographical and environmental factors to design an area that benefits the community the most. City planners have a bachelor's degree in planning and almost half have a master's degree.

1 Factor $ax^2 + bx + c$

Example 1 shows how to factor a trinomial of the form $ax^2 + bx + c$. **Example 2** shows how to factor a trinomial of the form $ax^2 - bx + c$. **Example 3** shows how to determine whether a polynomial is prime.

Formative Assessment

Use the Guided Practice exercises after each example to determine students' understanding of concepts.

Additional Examples

1 Factor each trinomial.

a. $5x^2 + 27x + 10$
$(5x + 2)(x + 5)$

b. $4x^2 + 24x + 32$
$4(x + 2)(x + 4)$

2 Factor $24x^2 - 22x + 3$.
$(4x - 3)(6x - 1)$

Additional Examples also in Interactive Classroom PowerPoint® Presentations

IWB Interactive White Board READY

WatchOut!
Preventing Errors Many students forget to include the GCF that they factored from the trinomial. Remind students to put the GCF in front of the other two factors.

DifferentiatedInstruction AL

If some students have trouble factoring polynomials,

Then place students in groups to factor polynomials such as those in Example 1. Depending on the number of factors and number of students in each group, have each student find one or two factors for mp. By dividing the labor, students should be able to find the factors for mp that sum to $m + p$ quickly. Once they have found the factors, have students complete the factoring as a group.

WatchOut!

Preventing Errors Make sure students list all possible factors of *mp*, including both positive and negative factors, before they decide the polynomial is prime.

Additional Example

3 Factor $3x^2 + 7x - 5$. If the polynomial cannot be factored using integers, write *prime*. prime

2 Solve Equations by Factoring

Example 4 shows how to solve a real-world problem by writing an equation of the form $ax^2 + bx + c = 0$ and then solving it.

Additional Example

4 **MODEL ROCKETS** Mr. Nguyen's science class built a model rocket. They launched the rocket outside. It cleared the top of a 60-foot high pole and then landed in a nearby tree. If the launch pad was 2 feet above the ground, the initial velocity of the rocket was 64 feet per second, and the rocket landed 30 feet above the ground, how long was the rocket in flight? Use the equation $h = -16t^2 + vt + h_0$. about 3.5 seconds

Teach with Tech

Interactive Whiteboard Create a template that shows the multiplication of two binomials, such as (□±□)(□±□). Demonstrate finding the factors of a quadratic expression. Drag each factor into the spaces until the correct one is found.

A polynomial that cannot be written as a product of two polynomials with integral coefficients is called a **prime polynomial**.

Example 3 Determine Whether a Polynomial is Prime

Factor $4x^2 - 3x + 5$, if possible. If the polynomial cannot be factored using integers, write *prime*.

In this trinomial, $a = 4$, $b = -3$, and $c = 5$. Since b is negative, $m + p$ is negative. Since c is positive, mp is positive. So, m and p are both negative. Next, list the factors of 20. Look for the pair with a sum of -3.

Factors of 20	Sum of Factors
−20, −1	−21
−4, −5	−9
−2, −10	−12

There are no factors with a sum of -3. So the quadratic expression cannot be factored using integers. Therefore, $4x^2 - 3x + 5$ is prime.

GuidedPractice

Factor each polynomial, if possible. If the polynomial cannot be factored using integers, write *prime*.

3A. $4r^2 - r + 7$ prime

3B. $2x^2 + 3x - 5$ $(2x + 5)(x - 1)$

2 Solve Equations by Factoring

A model for the height of a projectile is given by $h = -16t^2 + vt + h_0$, where h is the height in feet, t is the time in seconds, v is the initial upward velocity in feet per second, and h_0 is the initial height in feet. Equations of the form $ax^2 + bx + c = 0$ can be solved by factoring and by using the Zero Product Property.

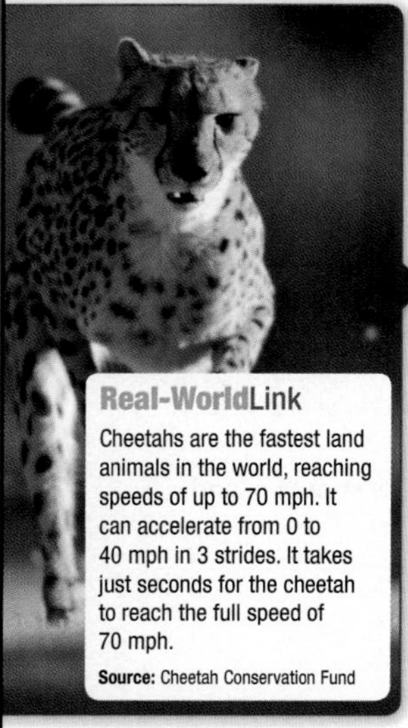

Real-WorldLink

Cheetahs are the fastest land animals in the world, reaching speeds of up to 70 mph. It can accelerate from 0 to 40 mph in 3 strides. It takes just seconds for the cheetah to reach the full speed of 70 mph.

Source: Cheetah Conservation Fund

Real-World Example 4 Solve Equations by Factoring

WILDLIFE **Suppose a cheetah pouncing on an antelope leaps with an initial upward velocity of 19 feet per second. How long is the cheetah in the air if it lands on the antelope's hind quarter, 3 feet from the ground?**

$h = -16t^2 + vt + h_0$	Equation for height
$3 = -16t^2 + 19t + 0$	$h = 3$, $v = 19$, and $h_0 = 0$
$0 = -16t^2 + 19t - 3$	Subtract 3 from each side.
$0 = 16t^2 - 19t + 3$	Multiply each side by −1.
$0 = (16t - 3)(t - 1)$	Factor $16t^2 - 19t + 3$.
$16t - 3 = 0$ or $t - 1 = 0$	Zero Product Property
$16t = 3$ $\quad t = 1$	Solve each equation.
$t = \frac{3}{16}$	

The solutions are $\frac{3}{16}$ and 1 seconds. It takes the cheetah $\frac{3}{16}$ second to reach a height of 3 feet on his way up. It takes the cheetah 1 second to reach a height of 3 feet on his way down. So, the cheetah is in the air 1 second before he catches the antelope.

WatchOut!

Keep the −1 Do not forget to carry the −1 that was factored out through the rest of the steps or multiply both sides by −1.

GuidedPractice

4. **PHYSICAL SCIENCE** A person throws a ball upward from a 506-foot tall building. The ball's height h in feet after t seconds is given by the equation $h = -16t^2 + 48t + 506$. The ball lands on a balcony that is 218 feet above the ground. How many seconds was it in the air? 6 s

Focus on Mathematical Content

Factoring $ax^2 + bx + c$ To factor trinomials by grouping where x^2 has a coefficient other than 1, express the trinomial as four terms, $ax^2 + mx + px + c$, where $m + p = b$ and $mp = ac$. Make a table of possible factors for mp and the sum of these factors for b. Replace a, m, p, and c with their values. Group terms with common factors. Factor out the GCF from each grouping, then factor using the Distributive Property.

512 | Lesson 8-7 | Solving $ax^2 + bx + c = 0$

Check Your Understanding

= Step-by-Step Solutions begin on page R13.

Examples 1–3 Factor each polynomial, if possible. If the polynomial cannot be factored using integers, write *prime*.

1. $3x^2 + 17x + 10$ **$(3x + 2)(x + 5)$**
2. $2x^2 + 22x + 56$ **$2(x + 4)(x + 7)$**
3. $5x^2 - 3x + 4$ **prime**
4. $3x^2 - 11x - 20$ **$(3x + 4)(x - 5)$**

Example 4 Solve each equation. Confirm your answers using a graphing calculator.

5. $2x^2 + 9x + 9 = 0$ **$-\frac{3}{2}, -3$**
6. $3x^2 + 17x + 20 = 0$ **$-\frac{5}{3}, -4$**
7. $3x^2 - 10x + 8 = 0$ **$\frac{4}{3}, 2$**
8. $2x^2 - 17x + 30 = 0$ **$\frac{5}{2}, 6$**

9. **MODELING** Ken throws the discus at a school meet.
   a. What is the initial height of the discus? **5 ft**
   b. After how many seconds does the discus hit the ground? **2.5 seconds**

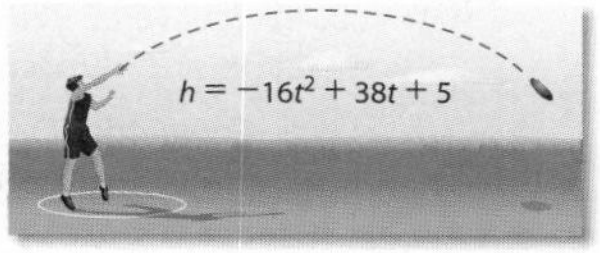

10. $(5x + 4)(x + 6)$ 11. $(2x + 3)(x + 8)$ 13. $2(2x + 5)(x + 7)$ 14. $(2x + 3)(x - 3)$

Practice and Problem Solving

Extra Practice is on page R8.

Examples 1–3 Factor each polynomial, if possible. If the polynomial cannot be factored using integers, write *prime*.

10. $5x^2 + 34x + 24$
11. $2x^2 + 19x + 24$
12. $4x^2 + 22x + 10$ **$2(2x + 1)(x + 5)$**
13. $4x^2 + 38x + 70$
14. $2x^2 - 3x - 9$
15. $4x^2 - 13x + 10$ **$(4x - 5)(x - 2)$**
16. $2x^2 + 3x + 6$ **prime**
17. $5x^2 + 3x + 4$ **prime**
18. $12x^2 + 69x + 45$ **$3(4x + 3)(x + 5)$**
19. $4x^2 - 5x + 7$ **prime**
20. $5x^2 + 23x + 24$ **$(5x + 8)(x + 3)$**
21. $3x^2 - 8x + 15$ **prime**

Example 4

22. **SHOT PUT** An athlete throws a shot put with an initial upward velocity of 29 feet per second and from an initial height of 6 feet.
    a. Write an equation that models the height of the shot put in feet with respect to time in seconds. **$h = -16t^2 + 29t + 6$**
    b. After how many seconds will the shot put hit the ground? **2 seconds**

Solve each equation. Confirm your answers using a graphing calculator.

23. $2x^2 + 9x - 18 = 0$ **$\frac{3}{2}, -6$**
24. $4x^2 + 17x + 15 = 0$ **$-\frac{5}{4}, -3$**
25. $-3x^2 + 26x = 16$ **$\frac{2}{3}, 8$**
26. $-2x^2 + 13x = 15$ **$\frac{3}{2}, 5$**
27. $-3x^2 + 5x = -2$ **$-\frac{1}{3}, 2$**
28. $-4x^2 + 19x = -30$ **$-\frac{5}{4}, 6$**

B

29. **BASKETBALL** When Jerald shoots a free throw, the ball is 6 feet from the floor and has an initial upward velocity of 20 feet per second. The hoop is 10 feet from the floor.
    a. Use the vertical motion model to determine an equation that models Jerald's free throw. **$10 = -16t^2 + 20t + 6$**
    b. How long is the basketball in the air before it reaches the hoop? **1 second**
    c. Raymond shoots a free throw that is 5 foot 9 inches from the floor with the same initial upward velocity. Will the ball be in the air more or less time? Explain. **Less; sample answer: It starts closer to the ground so the shot will not have as far to fall.**
30. **DIVING** Ben dives from a 36-foot platform. The equation $h = -16t^2 + 14t + 36$ models the dive. How long will it take Ben to reach the water? **2 seconds**

3 Practice

Formative Assessment

Use Exercises 1–9 to check for understanding.

Use the chart at the bottom of this page to customize assignments for your students.

Exercise Alert

Scissors For Exercise 39, students will need a pair of scissors.

Multiple Representations

In Exercise 39, students use a concrete model and algebraic reasoning to represent the difference of two squares.

4 Assess

Yesterday's News Have students write how yesterday's lesson on quadratic equations helped them with today's lesson on quadratic equations.

Formative Assessment

Check for student understanding of concepts in Lessons 8-6 and 8-7.

Quiz 3, p. 66

Teaching the Process Standards

Modeling Mathematically proficient students can apply the mathematics they know to solve problems arising in everyday life. In Exercise 9, point out that the equation for the height of a projectile applies. Tell students that this is used frequently and encourage them to learn the equation given before Example 4.

Differentiated Homework Options

Level	Assignment	Two-Day Option	
AL Basic	10–28, 40, 41, 43–74	11–27 odd, 45–48	10–28 even, 40, 41, 43, 44, 49–74
OL Core	11–27 odd, 29–31, 33–37 odd, 39–41, 43–74	10–28, 45–48	29–41, 43, 44, 49–74
BL Advanced	29–68, (optional: 69–74)		

Study Guide and Intervention

AL OL ELL

NAME ______ DATE ______ PERIOD ______

8-7 Study Guide and Intervention

Solving $ax^2 + bx + c = 0$

Factor $ax^2 + bx + c$ To factor a trinomial of the form $ax^2 + bx + c$, find two integers, m and p whose product is equal to ac and whose sum is equal to b. If there are no integers that satisfy these requirements, the polynomial is called a **prime polynomial**.

Example 1 Factor $2x^2 + 15x + 18$.

In this example, $a = 2$, $b = 15$, and $c = 18$. You need to find two numbers that have a sum of 15 and a product of $2 \cdot 18$ or 36. Make a list of the factors of 36 and look for the pair of factors with a sum of 15.

Factors of 36	Sum of Factors
1, 36	37
2, 18	20
3, 12	15

Use the pattern $ax^2 + mx + px + c$, with $a = 2$, $m = 3$, $p = 12$, and $c = 18$.

$2x^2 + 15x + 18 = 2x^2 + 3x + 12x + 18$
$= (2x^2 + 3x) + (12x + 18)$
$= x(2x + 3) + 6(2x + 3)$
$= (x + 6)(2x + 3)$

Therefore, $2x^2 + 15x + 18 = (x + 6)(2x + 3)$.

Example 2 Factor $3x^2 - 3x - 18$.

Note that the GCF of the terms $3x^2$, $3x$, and 18 is 3. First factor out this GCF.

$3x^2 - 3x - 18 = 3(x^2 - x - 6)$.

Now factor $x^2 - x - 6$. Since $a = 1$, find the two factors of -6 with a sum of -1.

Factors of −6	Sum of Factors
1, −6	−5
−1, 6	5
−2, 3	1
2, −3	−1

Now use the pattern $(x + m)(x + p)$ with $m = 2$ and $p = -3$.

$x^2 - x - 6 = (x + 2)(x - 3)$

The complete factorization is $3x^2 - 3x - 18 = 3(x + 2)(x - 3)$.

Exercises

Factor each polynomial, if possible. If the polynomial cannot be factored using integers, write *prime*.

1. $2x^2 - 3x - 2$
2. $3m^2 - 8m - 3$
3. $16r^2 - 8r + 1$
4. $6x^2 + 5x - 6$
5. $3x^2 + 2x - 8$
6. $18x^2 - 27x - 5$
7. $2a^2 + 5a + 3$
8. $18y^2 + 9y - 5$
9. $-4t^2 + 19t - 21$
10. $8x^2 - 4x - 24$
11. $28p^2 + 60p - 25$
12. $48x^2 + 22x - 15$
13. $3y^2 - 6y - 24$
14. $4x^2 + 26x - 48$
15. $8m^2 - 44m + 48$
16. $6x^2 - 7x + 18$
17. $2a^2 - 14a + 18$
18. $18 + 11y + 2y^2$

Lesson 8-7

Practice

AL OL BL ELL

NAME ______ DATE ______ PERIOD ______

8-7 Practice

Solving $ax^2 + bx + c = 0$

Factor each polynomial, if possible. If the polynomial cannot be factored using integers, write *prime*.

1. $2b^2 + 10b + 12$
2. $3g^2 + 8g + 4$
3. $4x^2 + 4x - 3$
4. $8b^2 - 5b - 10$
5. $6m^2 + 7m - 3$
6. $10d^2 + 17d - 20$
7. $6a^2 - 17a + 12$
8. $8w^2 - 18w + 9$
9. $10x^2 - 9x + 6$
10. $15n^2 - n - 28$
11. $10x^2 + 21x - 10$
12. $9r^2 + 15r + 6$
13. $12y^2 - 4y - 5$
14. $14k^2 - 9k - 18$
15. $8z^2 + 20z - 48$
16. $12q^2 + 34q - 28$
17. $18h^2 + 15h - 18$
18. $12p^2 - 22p - 20$

Solve each equation. Check the solutions.

19. $3h^2 + 2h - 16 = 0$
20. $15n^2 - n = 2$
21. $8q^2 - 10q + 3 = 0$
22. $6b^2 - 5b = 4$
23. $10r^2 - 21r = -4r + 6$
24. $10g^2 + 10 = 29g$
25. $6y^2 = -7y - 2$
26. $9z^2 = -6z + 15$
27. $12k^2 + 15k = 16k + 20$
28. $12x^2 - 1 = -x$
29. $8a^2 - 16a = 6a - 12$
30. $18a^2 + 10a = -11a + 4$

31. **DIVING** Lauren dove into a swimming pool from a 15-foot-high diving board with an initial upward velocity of 8 feet per second. Find the time t in seconds it took Lauren to enter the water. Use the model for vertical motion given by the equation $h = -16t^2 + vt + s$, where h is height in feet, t is time in seconds, v is the initial upward velocity in feet per second, and s is the initial height in feet. (*Hint:* Let $h = 0$ represent the surface of the pool.)

32. **BASEBALL** Brad tossed a baseball in the air from a height of 6 feet with an initial upward velocity of 14 feet per second. Enrique caught the ball on its way down at a point 4 feet above the ground. How long was the ball in the air before Enrique caught it? Use the model of vertical motion from Exercise 31.

Word Problem Practice

AL OL BL ELL

NAME ______ DATE ______ PERIOD ______

8-7 Word Problem Practice

Solving $ax^2 + bx + c = 0$

1. **BREAK EVEN** Breaking even occurs when the revenues for a business equal the cost. A local children's museum studied their costs and revenues from paid admission. They found that their break-even time is given by the equation $2h^2 - 2h - 24 = 0$, where h is the number of hours the museum is open per day. How many hours must the museum be open per day to reach the break even point?

2. **CARPENTRY** Miko wants to build a toy box for her sister. It is to be 2 feet high, and the width is to be 3 feet less than its length. If it needs to hold a volume of 80 cubic feet, find the length and width of the box.

3. **FURNITURE** The student council wants to purchase a table for the school lobby. The table comes in a variety of dimensions, but for every table, the length is 1 meter greater than twice the width. The student council has budgeted for a table top with an area of exactly 3 square meters.

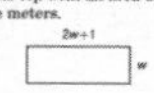

Find the width and length of the table they can purchase.

4. **LADDERS** A ladder is resting against a wall. The top of the ladder touches the wall at a height of 15 feet, and the length of the ladder is one foot more than twice its distance from the wall. Find the distance from the wall to the bottom of the ladder. (*Hint:* Use the Pythagorean Theorem to solve the problem.)

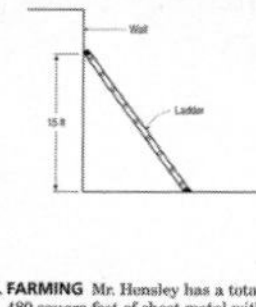

5. **FARMING** Mr. Hensley has a total of 480 square feet of sheet metal with which he would like to construct a cylindrical tank for storing grain. The local zoning law limits the height of the tank to 13.5 feet. Recall that a formula for the surface area of a bottomless cylinder with radius r and height h is $A = \pi r^2 + 2\pi rh$.

a. Write a quadratic equation to represent the information.

b. Using 3 as an approximation for π, solve the equation for r.

c. What radius should Mr. Hensley use for his tank?

Lesson 8-7

31. **NUMBER THEORY** Six times the square of a number x plus 11 times the number equals 2. What are possible values of x? -2 **or** $\frac{1}{6}$

Factor each polynomial, if possible. If the polynomial cannot be factored using integers, write *prime*.

32. $-6x^2 - 23x - 20$ **$-(2x + 5)(3x + 4)$**
33. $-4x^2 - 15x - 14$ **$-(x + 2)(4x + 7)$**
34. $-5x^2 + 18x + 8$ **$-(x - 4)(5x + 2)$**
35. $-6x^2 + 31x - 35$ **$-(2x - 7)(3x - 5)$**
36. $-4x^2 + 5x - 12$ **prime**
37. $-12x^2 + x + 20$ **$-(3x - 4)(4x + 5)$**

38. **URBAN PLANNING** The city has commissioned the building of a rectangular park. The area of the park can be expressed as $660x^2 + 524x + 85$. Factor this expression to find binomials with integer coefficients that represent possible dimensions of the park. If $x = 8$, what is a possible perimeter of the park? **$(22x + 5)(30x + 17)$; 876 units**

C 39. **MULTIPLE REPRESENTATIONS** In this problem, you will explore factoring a special type of polynomial.

a. **Geometric** Draw a square and label the sides a. Within this square, draw a smaller square that shares a vertex with the first square. Label the sides b. What are the areas of the two squares? **a^2 and b^2**

b. **Geometric** Cut and remove the small square. What is the area of the remaining region? **$a^2 - b^2$**

c. **Analytical** Draw a diagonal line between the inside corner and outside corner of the figure, and cut along this line to make two congruent pieces. Then rearrange the two pieces to form a rectangle. What are the dimensions? **width: $a - b$, length: $a + b$**

d. **Analytical** Write the area of the rectangle as the product of two binomials. **$(a - b)(a + b)$**

e. **Verbal** Complete this statement: $a^2 - b^2 = \ldots$ Why is this statement true? **$(a - b)(a + b)$; the figure with area $a^2 - b^2$ and the rectangle with area $(a - b)(a + b)$ have the same area, so $a^2 - b^2 = (a - b)(a + b)$.**

H.O.T. Problems Use Higher-Order Thinking Skills

40. **CRITIQUE** Zachary and Samantha are solving $6x^2 - x = 12$. Is either of them correct? Explain your reasoning.

Zachary

$6x^2 - x = 12$

$x(6x - 1) = 12$

$x = 12$ or $6x - 1 = 12$

$6x = 13$

$x = \frac{13}{6}$

Samantha

$6x^2 - x = 12$

$6x^2 - x - 12 = 0$

$(2x - 3)(3x + 4) = 0$

$2x - 3 = 0$ or $3x + 4 = 0$

$x = \frac{3}{2}$ $\quad x = -\frac{4}{3}$

40. Samantha; sample answer: She rewrote the equation to have zero on one side. Then she factored and used the Zero Product Property.

44. Sample answer: Find two numbers, m and p, with a product of ac and a sum of b.

41. **REASONING** A square has an area of $9x^2 + 30xy + 25y^2$ square inches. The dimensions are binomials with positive integer coefficients. What is the perimeter of the square? Explain. **See margin.**

42. **CHALLENGE** Find all values of k so that $2x^2 + kx + 12$ can be factored as two binomials using integers. **±25, ±14, ±11, ±10**

43. **WRITING IN MATH** What should you consider when solving a quadratic equation that models a real-world situation? **See margin.**

44. **WRITING IN MATH** Explain how to determine which values should be chosen for m and p when factoring a polynomial of the form $ax^2 + bx + c$.

Enrichment

OL BL

NAME ______ DATE ______ PERIOD ______

8-7 Enrichment

Area Models for Quadratic Trinomials

After you have factored a quadratic trinomial, you can use the factors to draw geometric models of the trinomial.

$x^2 + 5x - 6 = (x - 1)(x + 6)$

To draw a rectangular model, the value 2 was used for x so that the shorter side would have a length of 1. Then the drawing was done in centimeters. So, the area of the rectangle is $x^2 + 5x - 6$.

To draw a right triangle model, recall that the area of a triangle is one-half the base times the height. So, one of the sides must be twice as long as the shorter side of the rectangular model.

$x^2 + 5x - 6 = (x - 1)(x + 6)$
$= \frac{1}{2}(2x - 2)(x + 6)$

The area of the right triangle is also $x^2 + 5x - 6$.

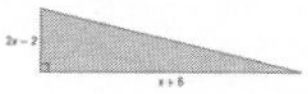

Factor each trinomial. Then follow the directions to draw each model of the trinomial.

Teaching the Process Standards

Critique Mathematically proficient students respond to the arguments of others. For Exercise 40, tell students to think about the first step in solving an equation by factoring: *write the equation in standard form.* You might also remind them that while at least one factor in a zero product must be 0, no such principle holds for any other number.

Standardized Test Practice

45. Gridded Response Savannah has two sisters. One sister is 8 years older than her and the other sister is 2 years younger than her. The product of Savannah's sisters' ages is 56. How old is Savannah? **6**

46. What is the product of $\frac{2}{3}a^3b^5$ and $\frac{3}{5}a^5b^2$? **A**

A $\frac{2}{5}a^8b^7$

B $\frac{2}{5}a^2b^3$

C $\frac{2}{5}a^8b^3$

D $\frac{2}{5}a^2b^7$

47. What is the solution set of $x^2 + 2x - 24 = 0$? **J**

F {−4, 6} H {−3, 8}

G {3, −8} J {4, −6}

48. Which is the solution set of $x \geq -2$? **C**

A 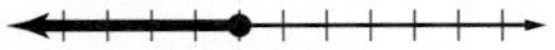

B 

C 

D 

Spiral Review

Factor each polynomial. (Lesson 8-6)

49. $x^2 - 9x + 14$ **$(x - 2)(x - 7)$**

50. $n^2 - 8n + 15$ **$(n - 3)(n - 5)$**

51. $x^2 - 5x - 24$ **$(x + 3)(x - 8)$**

52. $z^2 + 15z + 36$ **$(z + 12)(z + 3)$**

53. $r^2 + 3r - 40$ **$(r + 8)(r - 5)$**

54. $v^2 + 16v + 63$ **$(v + 9)(v + 7)$**

Solve each equation. Check your solutions. (Lesson 8-5)

55. $a(a - 9) = 0$ **0, 9**

56. $(2y + 6)(y - 1) = 0$ **−3, 1**

57. $10x^2 - 20x = 0$ **0, 2**

58. $8b^2 - 12b = 0$ **0, 1.5**

59. $15a^2 = 60a$ **0, 4**

60. $33x^2 = -22x$ **$-\frac{2}{3}$, 0**

61. ART A painter has 32 units of yellow dye and 54 units of blue dye to make two shades of green. The units needed to make a gallon of light green and a gallon of dark green are shown. Make a graph showing the numbers of gallons of the two greens she can make, and list three possible solutions. (Lesson 6-6) **See margin.**

Color	Units of Yellow Dye	Units of Blue Dye
light green	4	1
dark green	1	6

Solve each compound inequality. Then graph the solution set. (Lesson 5-4) **62–67. See margin.**

62. $k + 2 > 12$ and $k + 2 \leq 18$

63. $d - 4 > 3$ or $d - 4 \leq 1$

64. $3 < 2x - 3 < 15$

65. $3t - 7 \geq 5$ and $2t + 6 \leq 12$

66. $h - 10 < -21$ or $h + 3 < 2$

67. $4 < 2y - 2 < 10$

68. FINANCIAL LITERACY A home security company provides security systems for $5 per week, plus an installation fee. The total cost for installation and 12 weeks of service is $210. Write the point-slope form of an equation to find the total fee y for any number of weeks x. What is the installation fee? (Lesson 4-3) **$y - 210 = 5(x - 12)$; $150**

Skills Review

Find the principal square root of each number.

69. 16 **4**

70. 36 **6**

71. 64 **8**

72. 81 **9**

73. 121 **11**

74. 100 **10**

Additional Answers

41. $(12x + 20y)$ in.; The area of the square equals $(3x + 5y) \cdot (3x + 5y)$ in^2, so the length of one side is $(3x + 5y)$ in. The perimeter is $4(3x + 5y)$ or $(12x + 20y)$ in.

43. Sample answer: A quadratic equation may have zero, one, or two solutions. If there are two solutions, you must consider the context of the situation to determine whether one or both solutions answer the given question.

61.

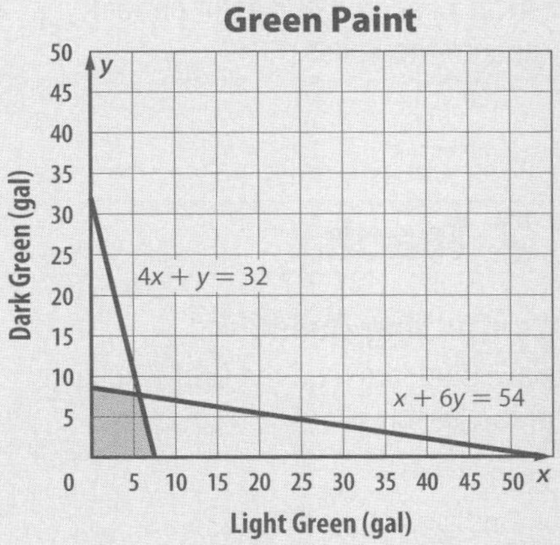

Sample answers: 2 light, 8 dark; 6 light, 8 dark; 7 light, 4 dark

62. $\{k \mid 10 < k \leq 16\}$

63. $\{d \mid d \leq 5$ or $d > 7\}$

64. $\{x \mid 3 < x < 9\}$

65. $\varnothing$

66. $\{h \mid h < -1\}$

67. $\{y \mid 3 < y < 6\}$

Differentiated Instruction OL BL

Extension Have students write a quadratic equation in the form $ax^2 + bx + c = 0$. Tell them that a, b, and c must be integers, and the solutions to the equation must be $\frac{1}{2}$ and 4. Sample answer: $2x^2 - 9x + 4 = 0$

1 Focus

Vertical Alignment

Before Lesson 8-8 Factor trinomials into two binomials.

Lesson 8-8 Factor binomials that are the difference of squares. Use the difference of squares to solve equations.

After Lesson 8-8 Factor perfect square trinomials.

2 Teach

Scaffolding Questions

Have students read the **Why?** section of the lesson.

Ask:

- Find $(x + 3)(x - 3)$. $x^2 - 9$
- Find $(x - 6)(x + 6)$. $x^2 - 36$
- Find $(a - b)(a + b)$. $a^2 - b^2$

Teach with Tech

Interactive Whiteboard Use the template from the previous lesson to demonstrate why the difference of squares is factorable, but the difference of sums is not.

LESSON 8-8 Differences of Squares

Then

- You factored trinomials into two binomials.

Now

1. Factor binomials that are the difference of squares.
2. Use the difference of squares to solve equations.

Why?

- Computer graphics designers use a combination of art and mathematics skills to design images and videos. They use equations to form shapes and lines on computers. Factoring can help to determine the dimensions and shapes of the figures.

New Vocabulary
difference of two squares

Content Standards
AI.RNE.6, AI.QE.4, AI.QE.5

Process Standards
PS.1

1 Factor Differences of Squares

You have previously learned about the product of the sum and difference of two quantities. This resulting product is referred to as the **difference of two squares**. So, the factored form of the difference of squares is called the product of the sum and difference of the two quantities.

Key Concept Factoring Differences of Squares

Symbols $a^2 - b^2 = (a + b)(a - b)$ or $(a - b)(a + b)$

Examples $x^2 - 25 = (x + 5)(x - 5)$ or $(x - 5)(x + 5)$

$t^2 - 64 = (t + 8)(t - 8)$ or $(t - 8)(t + 8)$

PT

Example 1 Factor Differences of Squares

Factor each polynomial.

a. $16h^2 - 9a^2$

$16h^2 - 9a^2 = (4h)^2 - (3a)^2$ Write in the form of $a^2 - b^2$.

$= (4h + 3a)(4h - 3a)$ Factor the difference of squares.

b. $121 - 4b^2$

$121 - 4b^2 = (11)^2 - (2b)^2$ Write in the form of $a^2 - b^2$.

$= (11 - 2b)(11 + 2b)$ Factor the difference of squares.

c. $27g^3 - 3g$

Because the terms have a common factor, factor out the GCF first. Then proceed with other factoring techniques.

$27g^3 - 3g = 3g(9g^2 - 1)$ Factor out the GCF of $3g$.

$= 3g[(3g)^2 - (1)^2]$ Write in the form $a^2 - b^2$.

$= 3g(3g - 1)(3g + 1)$ Factor the difference of squares.

Guided Practice

1A. $81 - c^2$ $(9 + c)(9 - c)$

1B. $64g^2 - h^2$ $(8g + h)(8g - h)$

1C. $9x^3 - 4x$ $x(3x + 2)(3x - 2)$

1D. $-4y^3 + 9y$ $-y(2y + 3)(2y - 3)$

516 | Lesson 8-8

Lesson 8-8 Resources

Resource	Approaching Level AL	On Level OL	Beyond Level BL	English Learners ELL
Teacher Edition		▪ Differentiated Instruction, pp. 518, 521	▪ Differentiated Instruction, pp. 518, 521	
Chapter Resource Masters	▪ Study Guide and Intervention, pp. 50–51 ▪ Skills Practice, p. 52 ▪ Practice, p. 53 ▪ Word Problem Practice, p. 54 ▪ Spreadsheet Activity, p. 56	▪ Study Guide and Intervention, pp. 50–51 ▪ Skills Practice, p. 52 ▪ Practice, p. 53 ▪ Word Problem Practice, p. 54 ▪ Enrichment, p. 55 ▪ Spreadsheet Activity, p. 56	▪ Practice, p. 53 ▪ Word Problem Practice, p. 54 ▪ Enrichment, p. 55 ▪ Spreadsheet Activity, p. 56	▪ Study Guide and Intervention, pp. 50–51 ▪ Skills Practice, p. 52 ▪ Practice, p. 53 ▪ Spreadsheet Activity, p. 56 ▪ Word Problem Practice, p. 28
Other	▪ 5-Minute Check 8-8 ▪ Study Notebook ▪ Teaching Algebra with Manipulatives	▪ 5-Minute Check 8-8 ▪ Study Notebook ▪ Teaching Algebra with Manipulatives	▪ 5-Minute Check 8-8 ▪ Study Notebook	▪ 5-Minute Check 8-8 ▪ Study Notebook ▪ Teaching Algebra with Manipulatives

To factor a polynomial completely, a technique may need to be applied more than once. This also applies to the difference of squares pattern.

Example 2 Apply a Technique More than Once

Factor each polynomial.

a. $b^4 - 16$

$b^4 - 16 = (b^2)^2 - (4)^2$ — Write $b^4 - 16$ in $a^2 - b^2$ form.

$= (b^2 + 4)(b^2 - 4)$ — Factor the difference of squares.

$= (b^2 + 4)(b^2 - 2^2)$ — $b^2 - 4$ is also a difference of squares.

$= (b^2 + 4)(b + 2)(b - 2)$ — Factor the difference of squares.

b. $625 - x^4$

$625 - x^4 = (25)^2 - (x^2)^2$ — Write $625 - x^4$ in $a^2 - b^2$ form.

$= (25 + x^2)(25 - x^2)$ — Factor the difference of squares.

$= (25 + x^2)(5^2 - x^2)$ — Write $25 - x^2$ in $a^2 - b^2$ form.

$= (25 + x^2)(5 - x)(5 + x)$ — Factor the difference of squares.

WatchOut!

Sum of Squares The sum of squares, $a^2 + b^2$, does not factor into $(a + b)(a + b)$. The sum of squares is a prime polynomial and cannot be factored.

GuidedPractice

2A. $y^4 - 1$ $(y^2 + 1)(y + 1)(y - 1)$

2B. $4a^4 - b^4$ $(2a^2 + b^2)(2a^2 - b^2)$

2C. $81 - x^4$ $(3 - x)(3 + x)(9 + x^2)$

2D. $16y^4 - 1$ $(4y^2 + 1)(2y - 1)(2y + 1)$

Sometimes more than one factoring technique needs to be applied to ensure that a polynomial is factored completely.

Example 3 Apply Different Techniques

Factor each polynomial.

a. $5x^5 - 45x$

$5x^5 - 45x = 5x(x^4 - 9)$ — Factor out GCF.

$= 5x[(x^2)^2 - (3)^2]$ — Write $x^4 - 9$ in the form $a^2 - b^2$.

$= 5x(x^2 - 3)(x^2 + 3)$ — Factor the difference of squares.

$x^2 - 3$ is not a difference of squares because 3 is not a perfect square.

b. $7x^3 + 21x^2 - 7x - 21$

$7x^3 + 21x^2 - 7x - 21$ — Original expression

$= 7(x^3 + 3x^2 - x - 3)$ — Factor out GCF.

$= 7[(x^3 + 3x^2) - (x + 3)]$ — Group terms with common factors.

$= 7[x^2(x + 3) - 1(x + 3)]$ — Factor each grouping.

$= 7(x + 3)(x^2 - 1)$ — $x + 3$ is the common factor.

$= 7(x + 3)(x + 1)(x - 1)$ — Factor the difference of squares.

GuidedPractice

3A. $2y^4 - 50$ $2(y^2 - 5)(y^2 + 5)$

3B. $6x^4 - 96$ $6(x - 2)(x + 2)(x^2 + 4)$

3C. $2m^3 + m^2 - 50m - 25$ $(2m + 1)(m + 5)(m - 5)$

3D. $r^3 + 6r^2 + 11r + 66$ $(r^2 + 11)(r + 6)$

1 Factor Differences of Squares

Example 1 shows how to factor the differences of squares. **Examples 2** and **3** show how to apply a factoring technique more than once to factor a polynomial completely.

Formative Assessment

Use the Guided Practice exercises after each example to determine students' understanding of concepts.

Additional Examples

1 Factor each polynomial.

a. $m^2 - 64$ $(m + 8)(m - 8)$

b. $16y^2 - 81z^2$ $(4y + 9z)(4y - 9z)$

c. $3b^3 - 27b$ $3b(b + 3)(b - 3)$

2 Factor each polynomial.

a. $y^4 - 625$ $(y^2 + 25)(y + 5)(y - 5)$

b. $256 - n^4$ $(16 + n^2)(4 - n)(4 + n)$

3 Factor each polynomial.

a. $9x^5 - 36x$ $9x(x^2 - 2)(x^2 + 2)$

b. $6x^3 + 30x^2 - 24x - 120$ $6(x + 2)(x - 2)(x + 5)$

Additional Examples also in Interactive Classroom PowerPoint® Presentations

IWB Interactive White Board READY

WatchOut!

Preventing Errors Students should always check their factoring by multiplying the factors using the FOIL method.

The Math Forum

Have your students refer to the Math Forum's Ask Dr. Math to learn more about the difference of two squares. They can start their search at connectED.mcgraw-hill.com.

Focus on Mathematical Content

Factoring Differences of Squares The binomial $a^2 - b^2$ is the difference of two squares, a^2 and b^2. One of the binomial factors, $(a + b)$, is the sum of the principal square roots of a^2 and b^2, and the other binomial factor, $(a - b)$, is the difference of their principal square roots.

WatchOut!

Preventing Errors Students should notice that after the GCF has been factored out and the difference of squares factoring technique has been applied once, one of the factors should be prime.

2 Solve Equations by Factoring

Example 4 shows how to answer a multiple-choice test item on solving equations by factoring.

Additional Example

4 STANDARDIZED TEST PRACTICE
In the equation $y = q^2 - \frac{4}{25}$, which is a value of q when $y = 0$? D

A $\frac{2}{25}$ C 0
B $\frac{4}{25}$ D $-\frac{2}{5}$

Tips for New Teachers

Sense-Making Students may not be used to thinking of fractions as perfect squares. Remind them that if both the numerator and denominator are perfect squares, then the fraction is a perfect square.

Teaching the Process Standards

Sense-Making Mathematically proficient students check their answers to problems using a different method. Point out that substituting the choices in a multiple choice question is sometimes a faster solution method.

2 Solve Equations by Factoring

After factoring, you can apply the Zero Product Property to an equation that is written as the product of factors set equal to 0.

PT

Standardized Test Example 4 Solve an Equation by Factoring

In the equation $y = x^2 - \frac{9}{16}$, which is a value of x when $y = 0$?

A $-\frac{9}{4}$ B 0 C $\frac{3}{4}$ D $\frac{9}{4}$

Test-TakingTip
Sense-Making
Another method that can be used to solve this equation is to substitute each answer choice into the equation.

Read the Test Item

Replace y with 0 and then solve.

Solve the Test Item

$y = x^2 - \frac{9}{16}$ Original equation

$0 = x^2 - \frac{9}{16}$ Replace y with 0.

$0 = x^2 - \left(\frac{3}{4}\right)^2$ Write in the form $a^2 - b^2$.

$0 = \left(x + \frac{3}{4}\right)\left(x - \frac{3}{4}\right)$ Factor the difference of squares.

$0 = x + \frac{3}{4}$ or $0 = x - \frac{3}{4}$ Zero Product Property

$x = -\frac{3}{4}$ $x = \frac{3}{4}$ The correct answer is C.

GuidedPractice

4. Which are the solutions of $18x^3 = 50x$? H

F $0, \frac{5}{3}$ G $-\frac{5}{3}, \frac{5}{3}$ H $-\frac{5}{3}, \frac{5}{3}, 0$ J $-\frac{5}{3}, \frac{5}{3}, 1$

Check Your Understanding

= Step-by-Step Solutions begin on page R13.

Examples 1–3 Factor each polynomial. 9. $(c + 1)(c - 1)(2c + 3)$ 11. $(t + 4)(t - 4)(3t + 2)$

1. $x^2 - 9$ $(x + 3)(x - 3)$
2. $4a^2 - 25$ $(2a + 5)(2a - 5)$
3. $9m^2 - 144$ $9(m + 4)(m - 4)$
4. $2p^3 - 162p$ $2p(p + 9)(p - 9)$
5. $u^4 - 81$ $(u + 3)(u - 3)(u^2 + 9)$
6. $2d^4 - 32f^4$ $2(d^2 + 4f^2)(d + 2f)(d - 2f)$
7. $20r^4 - 45n^4$ $5(2r^2 - 3n^2)(2r^2 + 3n^2)$
8. $256n^4 - c^4$ $(16n^2 + c^2)(4n + c)(4n - c)$
9. $2c^3 + 3c^2 - 2c - 3$
10. $f^3 - 4f^2 - 9f + 36$ $(f + 3)(f - 3)(f - 4)$
11. $3t^3 + 2t^2 - 48t - 32$
12. $w^3 - 3w^2 - 9w + 27$ $(w - 3)(w + 3)(w - 3)$

Example 4 **EXTENDED RESPONSE** **During an accident, skid marks may result from sudden breaking. The formula $\frac{1}{24}s^2 = d$ approximates a vehicle's speed s in miles per hour given the length d in feet of the skid marks on dry concrete.**

13. If skid marks on dry concrete are 54 feet long, how fast was the car traveling when the brakes were applied? **36 mph**
14. If the skid marks on dry concrete are 150 feet long, how fast was the car traveling when the brakes were applied? **60 mph**

DifferentiatedInstruction OL BL

Visual/Spatial Learners Draw the geometric model shown below on the board. Ask students to use their own paper square and scissors to make the model for a^2 when the b^2 square is removed. Then ask students to explain how their models show that $(a - b)(a + b) = a^2 - b^2$.

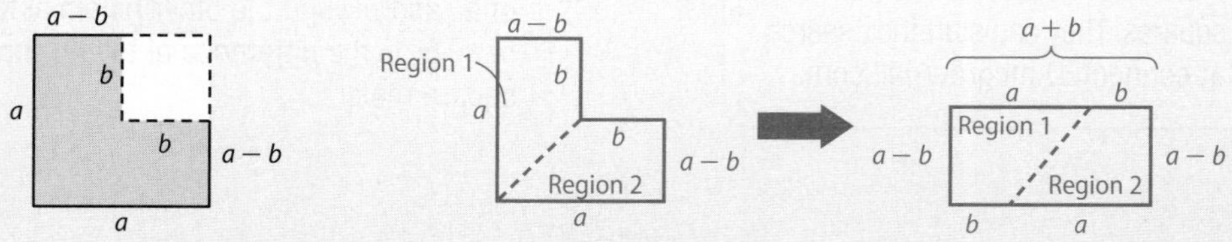

Practice and Problem Solving

Extra Practice is on page R8.

Examples 1–3 Factor each polynomial. **25–43. See margin.**

15. $q^2 - 121$ **$(q + 11)(q - 11)$**
16. $r^4 - k^4$ **$(r^2 + k^2)(r + k)(r - k)$**
17. $6n^4 - 6$ **$6(n^2 + 1)(n + 1)(n - 1)$**
18. $w^4 - 625$ **$(w^2 + 25)(w + 5)(w - 5)$**
19. $r^2 - 9t^2$ **$(r + 3t)(r - 3t)$**
20. $2c^2 - 32d^2$ **$2(c + 4d)(c - 4d)$**
21. $h^3 - 100h$ **$h(h + 10)(h - 10)$**
22. $h^4 - 256$ **$(h^2 + 16)(h + 4)(h - 4)$**
23. $2x^3 - x^2 - 162x + 81$ **$(x + 9)(x - 9)(2x - 1)$**
24. $x^2 - 4y^2$ **$(x + 2y)(x - 2y)$**
25. $7h^4 - 7p^4$
26. $3c^3 + 2c^2 - 147c - 98$
27. $6k^2h^4 - 54k^4$
28. $5a^3 - 20a$
29. $f^3 + 2f^2 - 64f - 128$
30. $3r^3 - 192r$
31. $10q^3 - 1210q$
32. $3xn^4 - 27x^3$
33. $p^3r^5 - p^3r$
34. $8c^3 - 8c$
35. $r^3 - 5r^2 - 100r + 500$
36. $3t^3 - 7t^2 - 3t + 7$
37. $a^2 - 49$
38. $4m^3 + 9m^2 - 36m - 81$
39. $3m^4 + 243$
40. $3x^3 + x^2 - 75x - 25$
41. $12a^3 + 2a^2 - 192a - 32$
42. $x^4 + 6x^3 - 36x^2 - 216x$
43. $15m^3 + 12m^2 - 375m - 300$

Example 4

44. **GEOMETRY** The drawing at the right is a square with a square cut out of it.

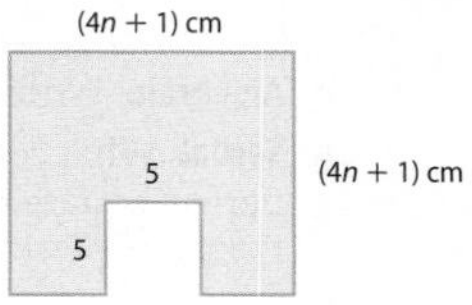

   a. Write an expression that represents the area of the shaded region. **$(4n + 1)^2 - 5^2$**
   b. Find the dimensions of a rectangle with the same area as the shaded region in the drawing. Assume that the dimensions of the rectangle must be represented by binomials with integral coefficients. **$(4n + 6)$ by $(4n - 4)$**

B

45. **DECORATIONS** An arch decorated with balloons was used to decorate the gym for the spring dance. The shape of the arch can be modeled by the equation $y = -0.5x^2 + 4.5x$, where x and y are measured in feet and the x-axis represents the floor.
   a. Write the expression that represents the height of the arch in factored form. **$-0.5x(x - 9)$**
   b. How far apart are the two points where the arch touches the floor? **9 ft**
   c. Graph this equation on your calculator. What is the highest point of the arch? **10.125 ft**

46. **SENSE-MAKING** Zelda is building a deck in her backyard. The plans for the deck show that it is to be 24 feet by 24 feet. Zelda wants to reduce one dimension by a number of feet and increase the other dimension by the same number of feet. If the area of the reduced deck is 512 square feet, what are the dimensions of the deck? **16 ft by 32 ft**

47. **SALES** The sales of a particular CD can be modeled by the equation $S = -25m^2 + 125m$, where S is the number of CDs sold in thousands, and m is the number of months that it is on the market.
   a. In what month should the music store expect the CD to stop selling? **5**
   b. In what month will CD sales peak? **2.5**
   c. How many copies will the CD sell at its peak? **156,250**

Differentiated Homework Options

Level	Assignment	Two-Day Option	
AL Basic	15–44, 57, 60–87	15–43 odd, 64–67	16–44 even, 57, 60–63, 68–87
OL Core	15–43 odd, 44–47, 49–55 odd, 56–57, 60–87	15–44, 64–67	45–57, 60–63, 68–87
BL Advanced	45–81, (optional: 82–87)		

3 Practice

Formative Assessment

Use Exercises 1–14 to check for understanding.

Use the chart at the bottom of this page to customize assignments for your students.

Exercise Alert

Graphing Calculator For Exercise 45, students will need a graphing calculator.

Teaching the Process Standards

Sense-Making Mathematically proficient students draw diagrams of important features and relationships. In Exercise 46, point out that a diagram can help students visualize the situation.

Additional Answers

25. $7(h^2 + p^2)(h + p)(h - p)$
26. $(c + 7)(c - 7)(3c + 2)$
27. $6k^2(h^2 + 3k)(h^2 - 3k)$
28. $5a(a + 2)(a - 2)$
29. $(f + 8)(f - 8)(f + 2)$
30. $3r(r + 8)(r - 8)$
31. $10q(q + 11)(q - 11)$
32. $3x(n^2 + 3x)(n^2 - 3x)$
33. $p^3r(r + 1)(r - 1)(r^2 + 1)$
34. $8c(c + 1)(c - 1)$
35. $(r + 10)(r - 10)(r - 5)$
36. $(t + 1)(t - 1)(3t - 7)$
37. $(a + 7)(a - 7)$
38. $(m + 3)(m - 3)(4m + 9)$
39. $3(m^4 + 81)$
40. $(x + 5)(x - 5)(3x + 1)$
41. $2(a + 4)(a - 4)(6a + 1)$
42. $x(x + 6)(x - 6)(x + 6)$
43. $3(m + 5)(m - 5)(5m + 4)$

Study Guide and Intervention

AL OL ELL

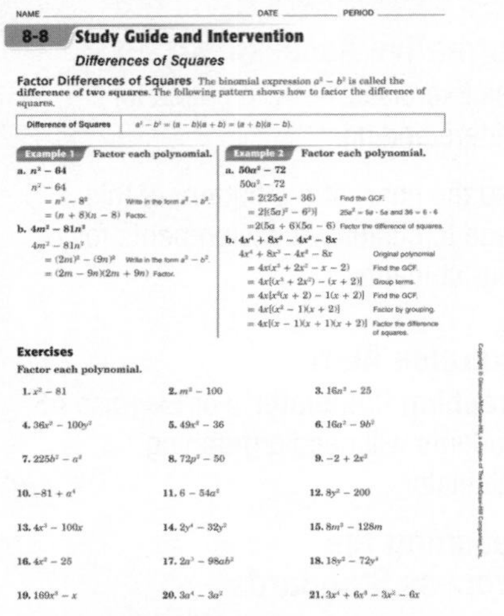
NAME ______ DATE ______ PERIOD ______

8-8 Study Guide and Intervention

Differences of Squares

Factor Differences of Squares The binomial expression $a^2 - b^2$ is called the difference of two squares. The following pattern shows how to factor the difference of squares.

Difference of Squares	$a^2 - b^2 = (a - b)(a + b) = (a + b)(a - b)$

Example 1 Factor each polynomial.

a. $n^2 - 64$

$n^2 - 64 = n^2 - 8^2$ Write in the form $a^2 - b^2$.

$= (n + 8)(n - 8)$ Factor.

b. $4m^2 - 81n^2$

$4m^2 - 81n^2 = (2m)^2 - (9n)^2$ Write in the form $a^2 - b^2$.

$= (2m - 9n)(2m + 9n)$ Factor.

Example 2 Factor each polynomial.

a. $50a^2 - 72$

$50a^2 - 72 = 2(25a^2 - 36)$ Find the GCF.

$= 2[(5a)^2 - 6^2]$ $25a^2 = 5a \cdot 5a$ and $36 = 6 \cdot 6$

$= 2(5a + 6)(5a - 6)$ Factor the difference of squares.

b. $4x^4 + 8x^3 - 4x^2 - 8x$

$4x^4 + 8x^3 - 4x^2 - 8x$ Original polynomial

$= 4x(x^3 + 2x^2 - x - 2)$ Find the GCF.

$= 4x[(x^3 + 2x^2) - (x + 2)]$ Group terms.

$= 4x[x^2(x + 2) - 1(x + 2)]$ Find the GCF.

$= 4x[(x^2 - 1)(x + 2)]$ Factor by grouping.

$= 4x[(x - 1)(x + 1)(x + 2)]$ Factor the difference of squares.

Exercises

Factor each polynomial.

1. $x^2 - 81$ 2. $m^2 - 100$ 3. $16n^2 - 25$
4. $36x^2 - 100y^2$ 5. $49x^2 - 36$ 6. $16a^2 - 9b^2$
7. $225b^2 - a^2$ 8. $72p^2 - 50$ 9. $-2 + 2x^2$
10. $-81 + a^4$ 11. $6 - 54a^2$ 12. $8y^2 - 200$
13. $4x^3 - 100x$ 14. $2y^4 - 32y^2$ 15. $8m^3 - 128m$
16. $4x^2 - 25$ 17. $2a^3 - 98ab^2$ 18. $18y^2 - 72y^4$
19. $169x^3 - x$ 20. $3a^4 - 3a^2$ 21. $3x^4 + 6x^3 - 3x^2 - 6x$

Practice

AL OL BL ELL

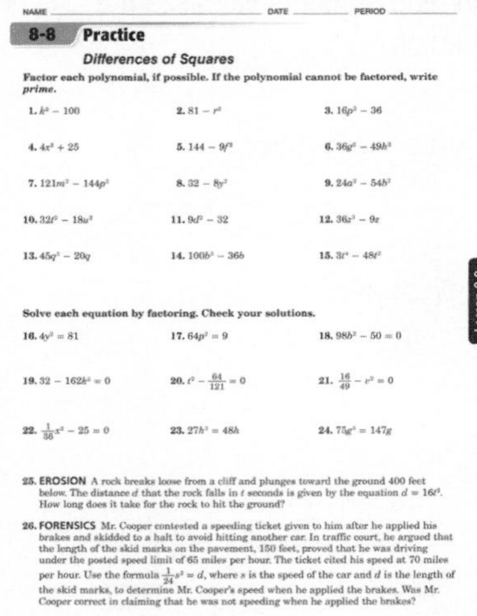
NAME ______ DATE ______ PERIOD ______

8-8 Practice

Differences of Squares

Factor each polynomial, if possible. If the polynomial cannot be factored, write *prime*.

1. $k^2 - 100$ 2. $81 - r^2$ 3. $16p^2 - 36$
4. $4x^2 + 25$ 5. $144 - 9f^2$ 6. $36g^2 - 49h^2$
7. $121m^2 - 144p^2$ 8. $32 - 8y^2$ 9. $24a^2 - 54b^2$
10. $32t^2 - 18u^2$ 11. $9d^2 - 32$ 12. $36z^2 - 9r$
13. $45q^2 - 20g$ 14. $100b^2 - 36b$ 15. $3t^4 - 48t^2$

Solve each equation by factoring. Check your solutions.

16. $4y^2 = 81$ 17. $64p^2 = 9$ 18. $98b^2 - 50 = 0$
19. $32 - 162k^2 = 0$ 20. $t^2 - \frac{64}{121} = 0$ 21. $\frac{16}{49} - v^2 = 0$
22. $\frac{1}{36}x^2 - 25 = 0$ 23. $27h^2 = 48h$ 24. $75g^2 = 147g$

25. **EROSION** A rock breaks loose from a cliff and plunges toward the ground 400 feet below. The distance d that the rock falls in t seconds is given by the equation $d = 16t^2$. How long does it take for the rock to hit the ground?

26. **FORENSICS** Mr. Cooper contested a speeding ticket given to him after he applied his brakes and skidded to a halt to avoid hitting another car. In traffic court, he argued that the length of the skid marks on the pavement, 150 feet, proved that he was driving under the posted speed limit of 65 miles per hour. The ticket cited his speed at 70 miles per hour. Use the formula $\frac{1}{24}s^2 = d$, where s is the speed of the car and d is the length of the skid marks, to determine Mr. Cooper's speed when he applied the brakes. Was Mr. Cooper correct in claiming that he was not speeding when he applied the brakes?

Word Problem Practice

AL OL BL ELL

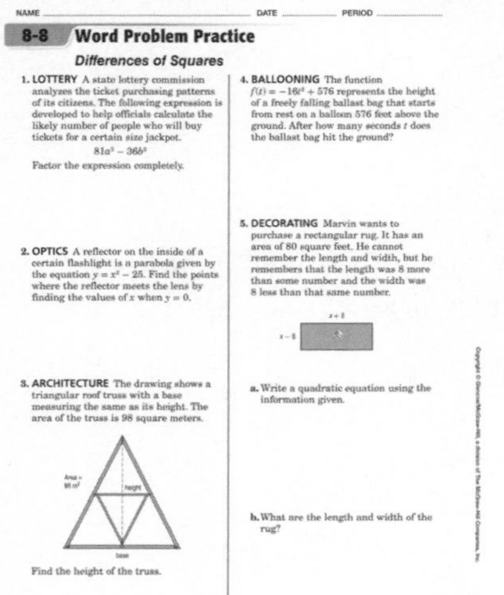
NAME ______ DATE ______ PERIOD ______

8-8 Word Problem Practice

Differences of Squares

1. **LOTTERY** A state lottery commission analyzes the ticket purchasing patterns of its citizens. The following expression is developed to help officials calculate the likely number of people who will buy tickets for a certain size jackpot.

$81a^2 - 36b^2$

Factor the expression completely.

2. **OPTICS** A reflector on the inside of a certain flashlight is a parabola given by the equation $y = x^2 - 25$. Find the points where the reflector meets the lens by finding the values of x when $y = 0$.

3. **ARCHITECTURE** The drawing shows a triangular roof truss with a base measuring the same as its height. The area of the truss is 98 square meters.

Find the height of the truss.

4. **BALLOONING** The function $f(t) = -16t^2 + 576$ represents the height of a freely falling ballast bag that starts from rest on a balloon 576 feet above the ground. After how many seconds t does the ballast bag hit the ground?

5. **DECORATING** Marvin wants to purchase a rectangular rug. It has an area of 80 square feet. He cannot remember the length and width, but he remembers that the length was 8 more than some number and the width was 8 less than that same number.

a. Write a quadratic equation using the information given.

b. What are the length and width of the rug?

Solve each equation by factoring. Confirm your answers using a graphing calculator.

48. $36w^2 = 121$ $\frac{11}{6}, -\frac{11}{6}$

49 $100 = 25x^2$ **2, −2**

50. $64x^2 - 1 = 0$ $\frac{1}{8}, -\frac{1}{8}$

51. $4y^2 - \frac{9}{16} = 0$ $\frac{3}{8}, -\frac{3}{8}$

52. $\frac{1}{4}b^2 = 16$ **−8, 8**

53. $81 - \frac{1}{25}x^2 = 0$ **−45, 45**

54. $9d^2 - 81 = 0$ **3, −3**

55. $4a^2 = \frac{9}{64}$ $\frac{3}{16}, -\frac{3}{16}$

C **56.** **MULTIPLE REPRESENTATIONS** In this problem, you will investigate perfect square trinomials. **56c.** $(a + b)(a + b) = a^2 + 2ab + b^2$ **and** $(a - b)(a - b) = a^2 - 2ab + b^2$

a. **Tabular** Copy and complete the table below by factoring each polynomial. Then write the first and last terms of the given polynomials as perfect squares.

b. **Analytical** Write the middle term of each polynomial using the square roots of the perfect squares of the first and last terms. **See table.**

Polynomial	Factored Polynomial	First Term	Last Term	Middle Term
$4x^2 + 12x + 9$	$(2x + 3)(2x + 3)$	$4x^2 = (2x)^2$	$9 = 3^2$	$12x = 2 \cdot 2x \cdot 3$
$9x^2 - 24x + 16$	$(3x - 4)(3x - 4)$	$9x^2 = (3x)^2$	$16 = 4^2$	$-24x = -2 \cdot 3x \cdot 4$
$4x^2 - 20x + 25$	$(2x - 5)(2x - 5)$	$4x^2 = (2x)^2$	$25 = 5^2$	$-20x = -2 \cdot 2x \cdot 5$
$16x^2 + 24x + 9$	$(4x + 3)(4x + 3)$	$16x^2 = (4x)^2$	$9 = 3^2$	$24x = 2 \cdot 4x \cdot 3$
$25x^2 + 20x + 4$	$(5x + 2)(5x + 2)$	$25x^2 = (5x)^2$	$4 = 2^2$	$20x = 2 \cdot 5x \cdot 2$

c. **Algebraic** Write the pattern for a perfect square trinomial.

d. **Verbal** What conditions must be met for a trinomial to be classified as a perfect square trinomial? **The first and last terms must be perfect squares and the middle term must be 2 times the square roots of the first and last terms.**

H.O.T. Problems Use Higher-Order Thinking Skills

57. **ERROR ANALYSIS** Elizabeth and Lorenzo are factoring an expression. Is either of them correct? Explain your reasoning.

57. Lorenzo; sample answer: Checking Elizabeth's answer gives us $16x^2 - 25y^2$. The exponent on x in the final product should be 4.

Elizabeth	Lorenzo
$16x^4 - 25y^2 =$	$16x^4 - 25y^2 =$
$(4x - 5y)(4x + 5y)$	$(4x^2 - 5y)(4x^2 + 5y)$

63. When the difference of squares pattern is multiplied together using the FOIL method, the outer and inner terms are opposites of each other. When these terms are added together, the sum is zero.

58. **CHALLENGE** Factor and simplify $9 - (k + 3)^2$, a difference of squares. $[3 + (k + 3)][3 - (k + 3)] = (k + 6)(-k) = -k^2 - 6k$

59. **PERSEVERANCE** Factor $x^{16} - 81$. $(x^4 - 3)(x^4 + 3)(x^8 + 9)$

60. **REASONING** Write and factor a binomial that is the difference of two perfect squares and that has a greatest common factor of $5mk$. **Sample answer:** $5mka^2 - 5mkb^2 = 5mk(a^2 - b^2) = 5mk(a - b)(a + b)$

61. **REASONING** Determine whether the following statement is *true* or *false*. Give an example or counterexample to justify your answer. **false;** $a^2 + b^2$

All binomials that have a perfect square in each of the two terms can be factored.

62. **OPEN ENDED** Write a binomial in which the difference of squares pattern must be repeated to factor it completely. Then factor the binomial. **Sample answer:** $x^4 - 16$; $(x - 2)(x + 2)(x^2 + 4)$

63. **WRITING IN MATH** Describe why the difference of squares pattern has no middle term with a variable.

Enrichment

OL BL

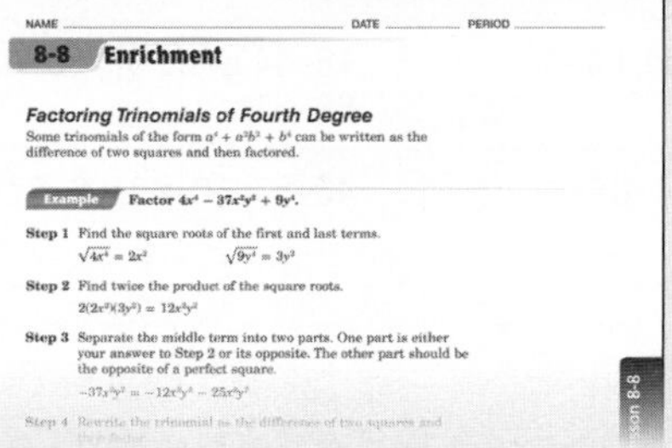
NAME ______ DATE ______ PERIOD ______

8-8 Enrichment

Factoring Trinomials of Fourth Degree

Some trinomials of the form $a^4 + a^2b^2 + b^4$ can be written as the difference of two squares and then factored.

Example Factor $4x^4 - 37x^2y^2 + 9y^4$.

Step 1 Find the square roots of the first and last terms. $\sqrt{4x^4} = 2x^2$ $\sqrt{9y^4} = 3y^2$

Step 2 Find twice the product of the square roots. $2(2x^2)(3y^2) = 12x^2y^2$

Step 3 Separate the middle term into two parts. One part is either your answer to Step 2 or its opposite. The other part should be the opposite of a perfect square. $-37x^2y^2 = -12x^2y^2 - 25x^2y^2$

Step 4 Rewrite the trinomial as the difference of two squares and then factor.

Multiple Representations

In Exercise 56, students use algebra and information organized in a table to explore the format of a perfect-square trinomial.

Standardized Test Practice

64. One of the roots of $2x^2 + 13x = 24$ is -8. What is the other root? **D**

A $-\frac{3}{2}$ C $\frac{2}{3}$

B $-\frac{2}{3}$ D $\frac{3}{2}$

65. Which of the following is the sum of both solutions of the equation $x^2 + 3x = 54$? **G**

F -21 H 3

G -3 J 21

66. What are the x-intercepts of the graph of $y = -3x^2 + 7x + 20$? **C**

A $\frac{5}{3}, -4$ C $-\frac{5}{3}, 4$

B $-\frac{5}{3}, -4$ D $\frac{5}{3}, 4$

67. EXTENDED RESPONSE Two cars leave Cleveland at the same time from different parts of the city and both drive to Cincinnati. The distance in miles of the cars from the center of Cleveland can be represented by the two equations below, where t represents the time in hours.

Car A: $65t + 15$ Car B: $60t + 25$

a. Which car is faster? Explain. **a. Car A, because it is traveling at 65 mph, and Car B is traveling at 60 mph.**

b. Find an expression that models the distance between the two cars. **$5t - 10$**

c. How far apart are the cars after $2\frac{1}{2}$ hours? **2.5 mi**

Spiral Review

Factor each trinomial, if possible. If the trinomial cannot be factored using integers, write *prime*. (Lesson 8-7)

68. $5x^2 - 17x + 14$ **$(5x - 7)(x - 2)$**

69. $5a^2 - 3a + 15$ **prime**

70. $10x^2 - 20xy + 10y^2$ **$10(x - y)(x - y)$**

Solve each equation. Check your solutions. (Lesson 8-6)

71. $n^2 - 9n = -18$ **{3, 6}**

72. $10 + a^2 = -7a$ **{−5, −2}**

73. $22x - x^2 = 96$ **{6, 16}**

74. SAVINGS Victoria and Trey each want to buy a scooter. In how many weeks will Victoria and Trey have saved the same amount of money, and how much will each of them have saved? (Lesson 6-2) **3 wk; $40**

Solve each inequality. Graph the solution set on a number line. (Lesson 5-1) **75–80. See margin.**

75. $t + 14 \geq 18$

76. $d + 5 \leq 7$

77. $-5 + k > -1$

78. $5 < 3 + g$

79. $2 \leq -1 + m$

80. $2y > -8 + y$

81. FITNESS Silvia is beginning an exercise program that calls for 20 minutes of walking each day for the first week. Each week thereafter, she has to increase her daily walking for a week by 7 minutes. In which week will she first walk over an hour a day? (Lesson 3-5) **the seventh week**

Skills Review

Find each product.

82. $(x - 6)^2$ **$x^2 - 12x + 36$**

83. $(x - 2)(x - 2)$ **$x^2 - 4x + 4$**

84. $(x + 3)(x + 3)$ **$x^2 + 6x + 9$**

85. $(2x - 5)^2$ **$4x^2 - 20x + 25$**

86. $(6x - 1)^2$ **$36x^2 - 12x + 1$**

87. $(4x + 5)(4x + 5)$ **$16x^2 + 40x + 25$**

DifferentiatedInstruction OL BL

Extension Have students solve the equation $x^3 - 4x = 12 - 3x^2$ by factoring. Ask them to check their solutions. $-3, -2, 2$

WatchOut!

Error Analysis For Exercise 57, make sure students can explain what Elizabeth did wrong. Stress that her error is a common one. Ask students what they can do to avoid making the same mistake themselves.

Teaching the Process Standards

Perseverance Mathematically proficient students analyze givens, constraints, relationships, and goals. In Exercise 59, tell students to make sure their final polynomial is completely factored.

4 Assess

Ticket Out the Door Have students write the factors of $18x^2 - 50$. $2(3x + 5)(3x - 5)$

Additional Answers

75. $\{t \mid t \geq 4\}$

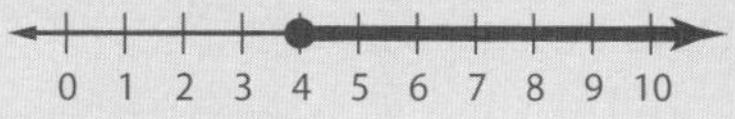

76. $\{d \mid d \leq 2\}$

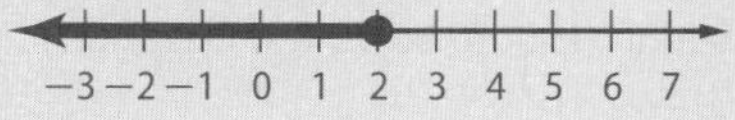

77. $\{k \mid k > 4\}$

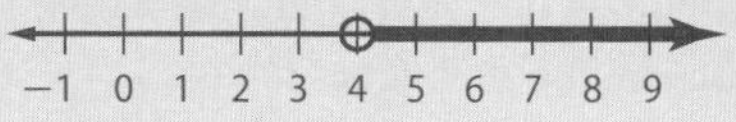

78. $\{g \mid g > 2\}$

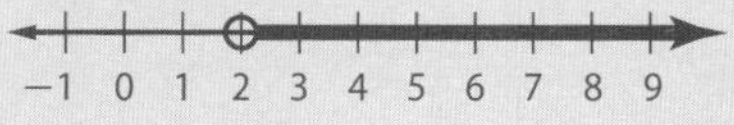

79. $\{m \mid m \geq 3\}$

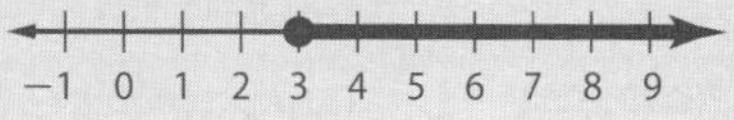

80. $\{y \mid y > -8\}$

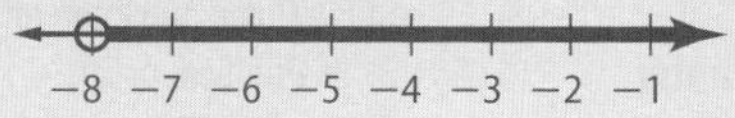

1 Focus

VerticalAlignment

Before Lesson 8-9 Find the product of the sum and difference of two quantities.

Lesson 8-9 Factor perfect square trinomials. Solve equations involving perfect squares.

After Lesson 8-9 Solve quadratic equations by using the quadratic formula.

2 Teach

Scaffolding Questions

Have students read the **Why?** section of the lesson.

Ask:

- If the initial height is 64 feet, what equation would you write to determine how long it takes an object to hit the ground? $0 = -16t^2 + 64$
- Solve the equation for t. $-16(t - 2)(t + 2) = 0$; 2 seconds
- How could you use the definition of square root to solve the equation? $0 = -16t^2 + 64$; $-64 = -16t^2$; $4 = t^2$; $t = \pm\sqrt{4}$ or ± 2; Since a negative answer is not reasonable in this situation, the solution is $t = 2$.

LESSON 8-9 Perfect Squares

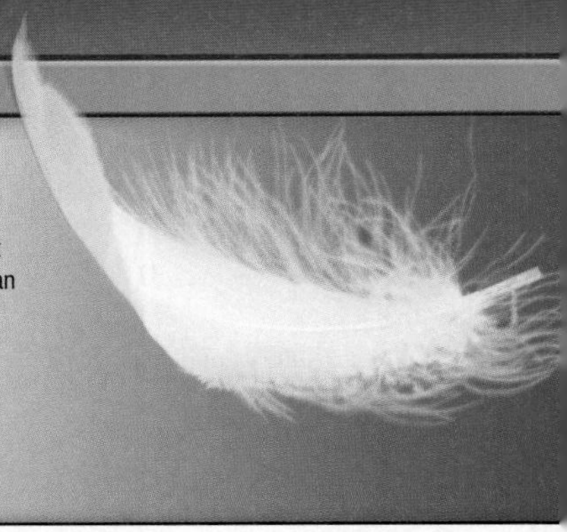

Then

- You found the product of a sum and difference.

Now

- **1** Factor perfect square trinomials.
- **2** Solve equations involving perfect squares.

Why?

- In a vacuum, a feather and a piano would fall at the same speed, or velocity. To find about how long it takes an object to hit the ground if it is dropped from an initial height of h_0 feet above ground, you would need to solve the equation $0 = -16t^2 + h_0$, where t is time in seconds after the object is dropped.

NewVocabulary
perfect square trinomial

Content Standards
AI.RNE.6, AI.QE.4, AI.QE.5

Process Standards
PS.6

1 Factor Perfect Square Trinomials

You have learned the patterns for the products of the binomials $(a + b)^2$ and $(a - b)^2$. Recall that these are special products that follow specific patterns.

$$(a + b)^2 = (a + b)(a + b) \qquad (a - b)^2 = (a - b)(a - b)$$
$$= a^2 + ab + ab + b^2 \qquad = a^2 - ab - ab + b^2$$
$$= a^2 + 2ab + b^2 \qquad = a^2 - 2ab + b^2$$

These products are called **perfect square trinomials**, because they are the squares of binomials. The above patterns can help you factor perfect square trinomials.

For a trinomial to be factorable as a perfect square, the first and last terms must be perfect squares and the middle term must be two times the square roots of the first and last terms.

The trinomial $16x^2 + 24x + 9$ is a perfect square trinomial, as illustrated below.

$$16x^2 + 24x + 9$$

- Is the first term a perfect square? Yes, because $16x^2 = (4x)^2$.
- Is the middle term twice the product of the square roots of the first and last terms? Yes, because $24x = 2(4x)(3)$.
- Is the last term a perfect square? Yes, because $9 = 3^2$.

KeyConcept Factoring Perfect Square Trinomials

Symbols
$a^2 + 2ab + b^2 = (a + b)(a + b) = (a + b)^2$
$a^2 - 2ab + b^2 = (a - b)(a - b) = (a - b)^2$

Examples
$x^2 + 8x + 16 = (x + 4)(x + 4)$ or $(x + 4)^2$
$x^2 - 6x + 9 = (x - 3)(x - 3)$ or $(x - 3)^2$

Lesson 8-9 Resources

Resource	Approaching Level AL	On Level OL	Beyond Level BL	English Learners ELL
Teacher Edition		▪ Differentiated Instruction, p. 529	▪ Differentiated Instruction, p. 529	
Chapter Resource Masters	▪ Study Guide and Intervention, pp. 57–58 ▪ Skills Practice, p. 59 ▪ Practice, p. 60 ▪ Word Problem Practice, p. 61	▪ Study Guide and Intervention, pp. 57–58 ▪ Skills Practice, p. 59 ▪ Practice, p. 60 ▪ Word Problem Practice, p. 61 ▪ Enrichment, p. 62	▪ Practice, p. 60 ▪ Word Problem Practice, p. 61 ▪ Enrichment, p. 62	▪ Study Guide and Intervention, pp. 57–58 ▪ Skills Practice, p. 59 ▪ Practice, p. 60 ▪ Word Problem Practice, p. 35
Other	▪ 5-Minute Check 8-9 ▪ Study Notebook ▪ Teaching Algebra with Manipulatives	▪ 5-Minute Check 8-9 ▪ Study Notebook ▪ Teaching Algebra with Manipulatives	▪ 5-Minute Check 8-9 ▪ Study Notebook	▪ 5-Minute Check 8-9 ▪ Study Notebook ▪ Teaching Algebra with Manipulatives

StudyTip

Recognizing Perfect Square Trinomials If the constant term of the trinomial is negative, the trinomial is not a perfect square trinomial, so it is not necessary to check the other conditions.

Example 1 Recognize and Factor Perfect Square Trinomials

Determine whether each trinomial is a perfect square trinomial. Write *yes* or *no*. If so, factor it.

a. $4y^2 + 12y + 9$

1. Is the first term a perfect square? Yes, $4y^2 = (2y)^2$.
2. Is the last term a perfect square? Yes, $9 = 3^2$.
3. Is the middle term equal to $2(2y)(3)$? Yes, $12y = 2(2y)(3)$

Since all three conditions are satisfied, $4y^2 + 12y + 9$ is a perfect square trinomial.

$4y^2 + 12y + 9 = (2y)^2 + 2(2y)(3) + 3^2$ Write as $a^2 + 2ab + b^2$.

$= (2y + 3)^2$ Factor using the pattern.

b. $9x^2 - 6x + 4$

1. Is the first term a perfect square? Yes, $9x^2 = (3x)^2$.
2. Is the last term a perfect square? Yes, $4 = 2^2$.
3. Is the middle term equal to $-2(3x)(2)$? No, $-6x \neq -2(3x)(2)$.

Since the middle term does not satisfy the required condition, $9x^2 - 6x + 4$ is not a perfect square trinomial.

GuidedPractice

1A. $9y^2 + 24y + 16$ **yes; $(3y + 4)(3y + 4)$** **1B.** $2a^2 + 10a + 25$ **no**

A polynomial is completely factored when it is written as a product of prime polynomials. More than one method might be needed to factor a polynomial completely. When completely factoring a polynomial, the Concept Summary can help you decide where to start.

Remember, if the polynomial does not fit any pattern or cannot be factored, the polynomial is prime.

ConceptSummary Factoring Methods

Steps	Number of Terms	Examples
Step 1 Factor out the GCF.	any	$4x^3 + 2x^2 - 6x = 2x(2x^2 + x - 3)$
Step 2 Check for a difference of squares or a perfect square trinomial.	2 or 3	$9x^2 - 16 = (3x + 4)(3x - 4)$ $16x^2 + 24x + 9 = (4x + 3)^2$
Step 3 Apply the factoring patterns for $x^2 + bx + c$ or $ax^2 + bx + c$ (general trinomials), or factor by grouping.	3 or 4	$x^2 - 8x + 12 = (x - 2)(x - 6)$ $2x^2 + 13x + 6 = (2x + 1)(x + 6)$ $12y^2 + 9y + 8y + 6$ $= (12y^2 + 9y) + (8y + 6)$ $= 3y(4y + 3) + 2(4y + 3)$ $= (4y + 3)(3y + 2)$

1 Factor Perfect Square Trinomials

Example 1 shows how to determine whether a trinomial is a perfect square trinomial and, if it is, how to factor it. **Example 2** shows how to use various factoring methods to factor a polynomial completely.

Formative Assessment

Use the Guided Practice exercises after each example to determine students' understanding of concepts.

Additional Example

1 Determine whether each trinomial is a perfect square trinomial. Write *yes* or *no*. If it is a perfect square, factor it.

a. $25x^2 - 30x + 9$ yes; $(5x - 3)^2$

b. $49y^2 + 42y + 36$ no

Additional Examples also in Interactive Classroom PowerPoint® Presentations

IWB Interactive White Board READY

WatchOut!

Preventing Errors Students should be reminded to look closely at the coefficient of the second term of a perfect square trinomial. Its sign determines whether the factors are in the form $(a + b)$ or $(a - b)$.

Teach with Tech

Blog On your secure classroom blog have students create a blog entry explaining the inverse relationship between squaring a binomial and factoring a perfect square trinomial.

WatchOut!

Common Errors Students often fail to factor polynomials completely. Point out that $4x^2 - 36$ is a difference of squares and can be factored as $(2x - 6)(2x + 6)$, but remind students that a polynomial is not considered completely factored if the terms of any of its factors have a GCF greater than 1.

Student Misconceptions Students have been taught that second-degree equations will have two solutions, so they may be confused when an equation involving a perfect square trinomial has only one solution. Explain that perfect square trinomials have a repeated factor, so that both solutions are the same number. Thus, only one solution is listed.

Additional Example

2 Factor each polynomial if possible. If the polynomial cannot be factored, write *prime*.

a. $6x^2 - 96$ $6(x + 4)(x - 4)$

b. $16y^2 + 8y - 15$ $(4y + 5)(4y - 3)$

2 Solve Equations with Perfect Squares

Example 3 shows how to solve equations with repeated factors. **Examples 4** and **5** show how to solve equations using the Square Root Property.

Additional Example

3 Solve $4x^2 + 36x = -81$. $-\frac{9}{2}$

PT

Example 2 Factor Completely

Factor each polynomial, if possible. If the polynomial cannot be factored, write *prime*.

a. $5x^2 - 80$

Step 1 The GCF of $5x^2$ and -80 is 5, so factor it out.

Step 2 Since there are two terms, check for a difference of squares.

$5x^2 - 80 = 5(x^2 - 16)$	5 is the GCF of the terms.
$= 5(x^2 - 4^2)$	$x^2 = x \cdot x$ and $16 = 4 \cdot 4$
$= 5(x - 4)(x + 4)$	Factor the difference of squares.

b. $9x^2 - 6x - 35$

Step 1 The GCF of $9x^2$, $-6x$, and -35 is 1.

Step 2 Since 35 is not a perfect square, this is not a perfect square trinomial.

Step 3 Factor using the pattern $ax^2 + bx + c$. Are there two numbers with a product of $9(-35)$ or -315 and a sum of -6? Yes, the product of 15 and -21 is -315, and the sum is -6.

$9x^2 - 6x - 35 = 9x^2 + mx + px - 35$	Write the pattern.
$= 9x^2 + 15x - 21x - 35$	$m = 15$ and $n = -21$
$= (9x^2 + 15x) + (-21x - 35)$	Group terms with common factors.
$= 3x(3x + 5) - 7(3x + 5)$	Factor out the GCF from each grouping.
$= (3x + 5)(3x - 7)$	$3x + 5$ is the common factor.

StudyTip

Check Your Answer You can check your answer by:

- Using the FOIL method.
- Using the Distributive Property.
- Graphing the original expression and factored expression and comparing the graphs.

If the product of the factors does not match the original expression exactly, the answer is incorrect.

GuidedPractice

2A. $2x^2 - 32$ $2(x - 4)(x + 4)$

2B. $12x^2 + 5x - 25$ $(4x - 5)(3x + 5)$

2 Solve Equations with Perfect Squares

When solving equations involving repeated factors, it is only necessary to set one of the repeated factors equal to zero.

PT

Example 3 Solve Equations with Repeated Factors

Solve $9x^2 - 48x = -64$.

$9x^2 - 48x = -64$	Original equation
$9x^2 - 48x + 64 = 0$	Add 64 to each side.
$(3x)^2 - 2(3x)(8) + (8)^2 = 0$	Recognize $9x^2 - 48x + 64$ as a perfect square trinomial.
$(3x - 8)^2 = 0$	Factor the perfect square trinomial.
$(3x - 8)(3x - 8) = 0$	Write $(3x - 8)^2$ as two factors.
$3x - 8 = 0$	Set the repeated factor equal to zero.
$3x = 8$	Add 8 to each side.
$x = \frac{8}{3}$	Divide each side by 3.

GuidedPractice

Solve each equation. Check your solutions.

3A. $a^2 + 12a + 36 = 0$ -6

3B. $y^2 - \frac{4}{3}y + \frac{4}{9} = 0$ $\frac{2}{3}$

Focus on Mathematical Content

Factor Perfect Square Trinomials Once a trinomial has been determined to be a perfect square trinomial, it can be factored into two identical binomials or expressed as a binomial squared. The binomial factors are the sum or difference, depending on the sign of the middle term of the trinomial, of the principal square roots of the first term and last term of the trinomial.

You have solved equations like $x^2 - 16 = 0$ by factoring. You can also use the definition of a square root to solve the equation.

ReadingMath
Square Root Solutions
$\pm\sqrt{16}$ is read as plus or minus the square root of 16.

$x^2 - 16 = 0$	Original equation
$x^2 = 16$	Add 16 to each side.
$x = \pm\sqrt{16}$	Take the square root of each side.

Remember that there are two square roots of 16, namely 4 and −4. Therefore, the solution set is {−4, 4}. You can express this as {±4}.

KeyConcept Square Root Property

Words To solve a quadratic equation in the form $x^2 = n$, take the square root of each side.

Symbols For any number $n \geq 0$, if $x^2 = n$, then $x = \pm\sqrt{n}$.

Example $x^2 = 25$
$x = \pm\sqrt{25}$ or ± 5

In the equation $x^2 = n$, if n is not a perfect square, you need to approximate the square root. Use a calculator to find an approximation. If n is a perfect square, you will have an exact answer.

Example 4 Use the Square Root Property

StudyTip
Solving by Inspection
Equations involving square roots can often be solved mentally. For $x^2 = n$, think: *The square of what number is n?* When n is a perfect square, x is rational. Otherwise, x is irrational.

Solve each equation. Check your solutions.

a. $(y - 6)^2 = 81$

$(y - 6)^2 = 81$	Original equation
$y - 6 = \pm\sqrt{81}$	Square Root Property
$y - 6 = \pm 9$	$81 = 9 \cdot 9$
$y = 6 \pm 9$	Add 6 to each side.
$y = 6 + 9$ or $y = 6 - 9$	Separate into two equations.
$= 15$ $\quad = -3$	Simplify.
The roots are 15 and −3.	Check in the original equation.

b. $(x + 6)^2 = 12$

$(x + 6)^2 = 12$	Original equation
$x + 6 = \pm\sqrt{12}$	Square Root Property
$x = -6 \pm \sqrt{12}$	Subtract 6 from each side.

The roots are $-6 \pm \sqrt{12}$ or $-6 + \sqrt{12}$ and $-6 - \sqrt{12}$.

Using a calculator, $-6 + \sqrt{12} \approx -2.54$ and $-6 - \sqrt{12} \approx -9.46$.

GuidedPractice

4A. $(a - 10)^2 = 121$ **21, −1**

4B. $(z + 3)^2 = 26$ **$-3 \pm\sqrt{26}$ or about 2.1 and −8.1**

Additional Example

4 Solve each equation. Check the solutions.

a. $(b - 7)^2 = 36$ 1, 13

b. $(x + 9)^2 = 8$ $-9 \pm 2\sqrt{2}$

Tips for New Teachers

Solutions to Second-Degree Equations If students do not understand how a second-degree equation can have only one solution, suggest that they graph a perfect square trinomial on a graphing calculator. The graph will immediately reveal how this is possible. The vertex of the graph of a perfect square trinomial equation lies on the x-axis, and therefore the equation has only one solution.

Additional Example

5 **PHYSICAL SCIENCE** A book falls from a shelf that is 5 feet above the floor. A model for the height h in feet if an object dropped from an initial height of h_0 feet is $h = -16t^2 + h_0$, where t is the time in seconds after the object is dropped. Use this model to determine approximately how long it took for the book to reach the ground. 0.56 s

Tips for New Teachers

Formulas Students are naturally curious about *why* certain formulas work. Encourage this curiosity and ask students to develop a way to test the formula $h = -16t^2 + h_0$ from Example 5. What assumptions must be made for the formula to hold true?

3 Practice

Formative Assessment

Use Exercises 1–11 to check for understanding.

Use the chart at the bottom of this page to customize assignments for your students.

WatchOut!

Factoring Remind students that any of the factoring methods they have studied thus far can be used in the exercises.

Teaching the Process Standards

Reasoning Mathematically proficient students make sense of quantities and their relationships in problem situations. In Exercise 11, ask students how to represent the height of the paintbrush when it hits the floor.

Math HistoryLink

Galileo Galilei **(1564–1642)** Galileo was the first person to prove that objects of different weights fall at the same velocity by dropping two objects of different weights from the top of the Leaning Tower of Pisa in 1589.

PT

Real-World Example 5 Solve an Equation

PHYSICAL SCIENCE **During an experiment, a ball is dropped from a height of 205 feet. The formula $h = -16t^2 + h_0$ can be used to approximate the number of seconds t it takes for the ball to reach height h from an initial height of h_0 in feet. Find the time it takes the ball to reach the ground.**

At ground level, $h = 0$ and the initial height is 205, so $h_0 = 205$.

$h = -16t^2 + h_0$ Original Formula

$0 = -16t^2 + 205$ Replace h with 0 and h_0 with 205.

$-205 = -16t^2$ Subtract 205 from each side.

$12.8125 = t^2$ Divide each side by -16.

$\pm 3.6 \approx t$ Use the Square Root Property.

Since a negative number does not make sense in this situation, the solution is 3.6. It takes about 3.6 seconds for the ball to reach the ground.

GuidedPractice

5. Find the time it takes a ball to reach the ground if it is dropped from a bridge that is half as high as the one described above. about 2.5 seconds

Check Your Understanding

◯ = Step-by-Step Solutions begin on page R13.

Example 1 **Determine whether each trinomial is a perfect square trinomial. Write *yes* or *no*. If so, factor it.**

1. $25x^2 + 60x + 36$ yes; $(5x + 6)^2$

2. $6x^2 + 30x + 36$ no

Example 2 **Factor each polynomial, if possible. If the polynomial cannot be factored, write *prime*.**

3. $2x^2 - x - 28$ $(x - 4)(2x + 7)$

4. $6x^2 - 34x + 48$ $2(x - 3)(3x - 8)$

5. $4x^2 + 64$ $4(x^2 + 16)$

6. $4x^2 + 9x - 16$ prime

Examples 3–4 **Solve each equation. Confirm your answers using a graphing calculator.**

7. $4x^2 = 36$ ± 3

8. $25a^2 - 40a = -16$ $\frac{4}{5}$

9. $64y^2 - 48y + 18 = 9$ $\frac{3}{8}$

10. $(z + 5)^2 = 47$ $-5 \pm \sqrt{47}$ or about -11.86 and 1.86

Example 5 **11.** **REASONING** While painting his bedroom, Nick drops his paintbrush off his ladder from a height of 6 feet. Use the formula $h = -16t^2 + h_0$ to approximate the number of seconds it takes for the paintbrush to hit the floor. 0.6 second

Practice and Problem Solving

Extra Practice is on page R8.

Example 1 **Determine whether each trinomial is a perfect square trinomial. Write *yes* or *no*. If so, factor it.**

12. $4x^2 - 42x + 110$ no

13. $16x^2 - 56x + 49$ yes; $(4x - 7)^2$

14. $81x^2 - 90x + 25$ yes; $(9x - 5)^2$

15 $x^2 + 26x + 168$ no

Differentiated Homework Options

Level	Assignment	Two-Day Option	
AL Basic	12–47, 53, 55–85	13–47 odd, 61–64	12–46 even, 53, 55–60, 65–85
OL Core	13–47 odd, 48–53, 55–85	12–47, 61–64	48–53, 55–60, 65–85
BL Advanced	48–79, (optional: 80–85)		

Example 2 **Factor each polynomial, if possible. If the polynomial cannot be factored, write *prime*.** **28.** $(x + 2y)(x - 2)(x + 2)$ **30.** $(r - 6)(r + 6)(2r - 1)$ **32.** $2cd(c^2 + d^2)(2c - 5)$

16. $24d^2 + 39d - 18$ $3(8d - 3)(d + 2)$

17. $8x^2 + 10x - 21$ prime

18. $2b^2 + 12b - 24$ $2(b^2 + 6b - 12)$

19. $8y^2 - 200z^2$ $8(y - 5z)(y + 5z)$

20. $16a^2 - 121b^2$ $(4a - 11b)(4a + 11b)$

21. $12m^3 - 22m^2 - 70m$ $2m(2m - 7)(3m + 5)$

22. $8c^2 - 88c + 242$ $2(2c - 11)^2$

23. $12x^2 - 84x + 147$ $3(2x - 7)^2$

24. $w^4 - w^2$ $w^2(w - 1)(w + 1)$

25. $12p^3 - 3p$ $3p(2p + 1)(2p - 1)$

26. $16q^3 - 48q^2 + 36q$ $4q(2q - 3)^2$

27. $4t^3 + 10t^2 - 84t$ $2t(t + 6)(2t - 7)$

28. $x^3 + 2x^2y - 4x - 8y$

29. $2a^2b^2 - 2a^2 - 2ab^3 + 2ab$ $2a(a - b)(b + 1)(b - 1)$

30. $2r^3 - r^2 - 72r + 36$

31. $3k^3 - 24k^2 + 48k$ $3k(k - 4)(k - 4)$

32. $4c^4d - 10c^3d + 4c^2d^3 - 10cd^3$

33. $g^2 + 2g - 3h^2 + 4h$ prime

Examples 3–4 **Solve each equation. Confirm your answers using a graphing calculator.**

34. $4m^2 - 24m + 36 = 0$ 3

35. $(y - 4)^2 = 7$ $4 \pm \sqrt{7}$

36. $a^2 + \frac{10}{7}a + \frac{25}{49} = 0$ $-\frac{5}{7}$

37. $x^2 - \frac{3}{2}x + \frac{9}{16} = 0$ $\frac{3}{4}$

38. $x^2 + 8x + 16 = 25$ $1, -9$

39. $5x^2 - 60x = -180$ 6

40. $4x^2 = 80x - 400$ 10

41. $9 - 54x = -81x^2$ $\frac{1}{3}$

42. $4c^2 + 4c + 1 = 15$ $\frac{-1 \pm \sqrt{15}}{2}$

43. $x^2 - 16x + 64 = 6$ $8 \pm \sqrt{6}$

44. PHYSICAL SCIENCE For an experiment in physics class, a water balloon is dropped from the window of the school building. The window is 40 feet high. How long does it take until the balloon hits the ground? Round to the nearest hundredth. **1.58 seconds**

45. SCREENS The area A in square feet of a projected picture on a movie screen can be modeled by the equation $A = 0.25d^2$, where d represents the distance from a projector to a movie screen. At what distance will the projected picture have an area of 100 square feet? **20 ft**

Example 5

46. GEOMETRY The area of a square is represented by $9x^2 - 42x + 49$. Find the length of each side. $|3x - 7|$

47. GEOMETRY The area of a square is represented by $16x^2 + 40x + 25$. Find the length of each side. $|4x + 5|$

B **48. GEOMETRY** The volume of a rectangular prism is represented by the expression $8y^3 + 40y^2 + 50y$. Find the possible dimensions of the prism if the dimensions are represented by polynomials with integer coefficients. **Sample answer: $2y$, $2y + 5$, $2y + 5$**

49. POOLS Ichiro wants to buy an above-ground swimming pool for his yard. Model A is 42 inches deep and holds 1750 cubic feet of water. The length of the rectangular pool is 5 feet more than the width.

a. What is the surface area of the water? **500 ft²**

b. What are the dimensions of the pool? **20 ft by 25 ft by 42 in.**

c. Model B pool holds twice as much water as Model A. What are some possible dimensions for this pool? **Sample answer: 20 ft by 50 ft by 42 in.**

d. Model C has length and width that are both twice as long as Model A, but the height is the same. What is the ratio of the volume of Model A to Model C? **1:4**

Teaching the Process Standards

Precision Mathematically proficient students are careful about specifying units of measure. In Exercise 49, make sure students remember that volume is measured in cubic units and length is in linear units.

Study Guide and Intervention

AL BL ELL

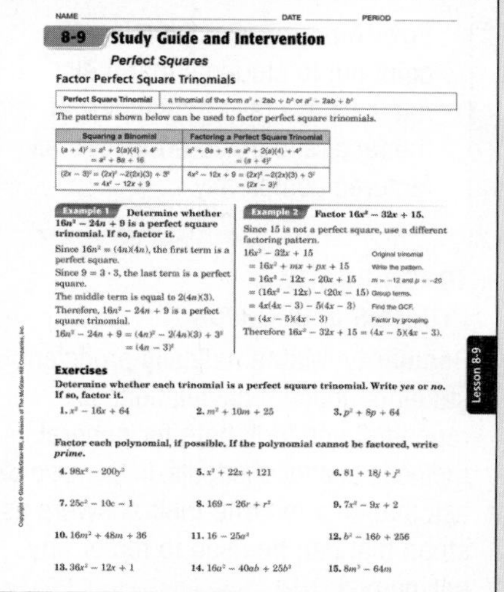
8-9 Study Guide and Intervention

Perfect Squares

Factor Perfect Square Trinomials

Practice

AL OL BL ELL

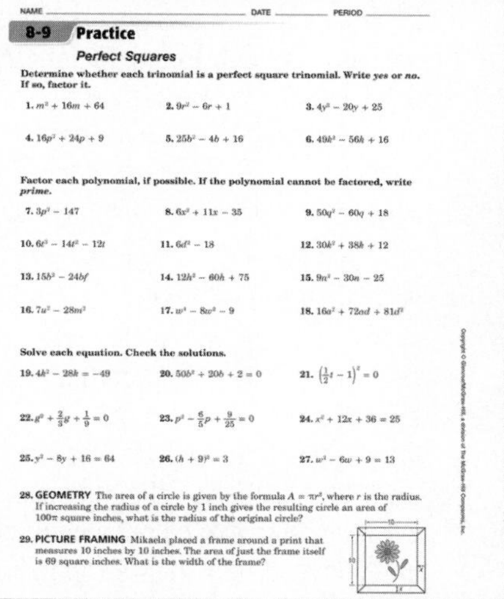
8-9 Practice

Perfect Squares

Word Problem Practice

AL OL BL ELL

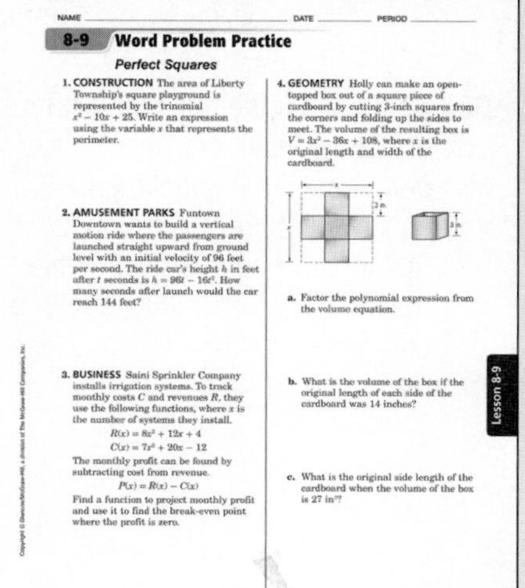
8-9 Word Problem Practice

Perfect Squares

Enrichment

OL BL

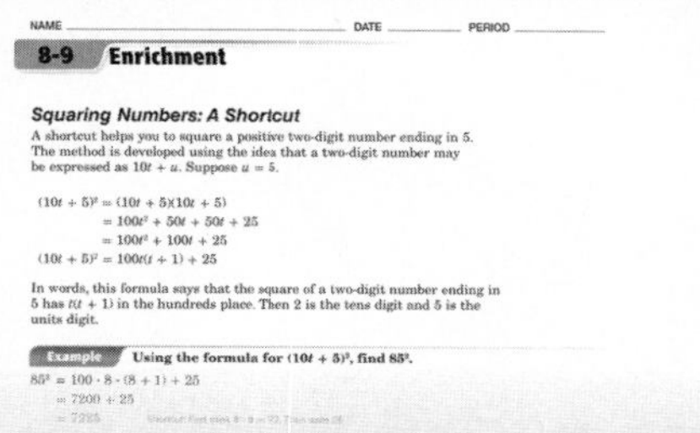
8-9 Enrichment

Squaring Numbers: A Shortcut

WatchOut!

Error Analysis For Exercise 53, point out to students that they must always take a final look at the factors to be sure they are all factored completely.

Teaching the Process Standards

Regularity Mathematically proficient students notice if calculations are repeated, and look both for general methods and for shortcuts. In Exercise 57, ask students to write their answers as steps that can be used to factor any polynomial.

Additional Answers

56. Sample answer: The equation $x^3 + x^2 + x + 1 = 0$ only has one solution. The polynomial factors to $(x^2 + 1)(x + 1)$ and setting those factors equal to zero gives us only one solution $x = -1$ since $x^2 + 1 = 0$ has no real solutions.

57. First look for a GCF in all the terms and factor the GCF out of all the terms. Then, if the polynomial has two terms, check if the terms are the differences of squares and factor if so. If the polynomial has three terms, check if the trinomial will factor into two binomial factors or if it is a perfect square trinomial and factor if so. If the polynomial has four or more terms, factor by grouping. If the polynomial does not have a GCF and cannot be factored, the polynomial is a prime polynomial.

60. Determine if the first and last terms are perfect squares. Then determine if the middle term is equal to ± 2 times the product of the principal square roots of the first and last terms. If these three criteria are met, the trinomial is a perfect square trinomial.

50. GEOMETRY Use the rectangular prism at the right.

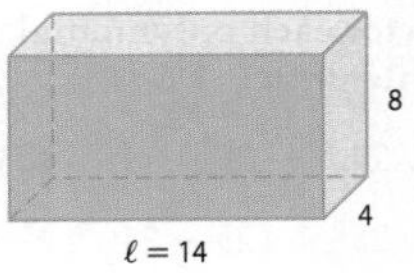

a. Write an expression for the height and width of the prism in terms of the length, ℓ. **height $= \ell - 6$; width $= \ell - 10$**

b. Write a polynomial for the volume of the prism in terms of the length. **$V = \ell^3 - 16\ell^2 + 60\ell$**

51. PRECISION A zoo has an aquarium shaped like a rectangular prism. It has a volume of 180 cubic feet. The height of the aquarium is 9 feet taller than the width, and the length is 4 feet shorter than the width. What are the dimensions of the aquarium? **6 feet wide by 2 feet long by 15 feet high**

C **52 ELECTION** For the student council elections, Franco is building the voting box shown with a volume of 96 cubic inches. What are the dimensions of the voting box? **4 in. high by 12 in. long by 2 in. wide**

H.O.T. Problems Use Higher-Order Thinking Skills

53. ERROR ANALYSIS Debbie and Adriano are factoring the expression $x^8 - x^4$ completely. Is either of them correct? Explain your reasoning.

Debbie	Adriano
$x^8 - x^4 = x^4(x^2 + 1)(x^2 - 1)$	$x^8 - x^4 = x^4(x^2 + 1)(x - 1)(x + 1)$

Adriano; Debbie did not factor the expression completely.

54. CHALLENGE Factor $x^{n+6} + x^{n+2} + x^n$ completely. **$x^n(x^6 + x^2 + 1)$**

55. OPEN ENDED Write a perfect square trinomial equation in which the coefficient of the middle term is negative and the last term is a fraction. Solve the equation. **Sample answer: $x^2 - 3x + \frac{9}{4} = 0; \left\{\frac{3}{2}\right\}$**

56. REASONING A counterexample is a specific case in which a statement is false. Find a counterexample to the following statement. **See margin.**

A polynomial equation of degree three always has three real solutions.

57. REGULARITY Explain how to factor a polynomial completely. **See margin.**

58. WHICH ONE DOESN'T BELONG? Identify the trinomial that does not belong. Explain.

$4x^2 - 36x + 81$	$25x^2 + 10x + 1$	$4x^2 + 10x + 4$	$9x^2 - 24x + 16$

$4x^2 + 10x + 4$ because it is the only expression that is not a perfect square trinomial.

59. OPEN ENDED Write a binomial that can be factored using the difference of two squares twice. Set your binomial equal to zero and solve the equation. **Sample answer: $x^4 - 1$; 1, −1**

60. WRITING IN MATH Explain how to determine whether a trinomial is a perfect square trinomial. **See margin.**

528 | Lesson 8-9 | Perfect Squares

Standardized Test Practice

61. What is the solution set for the equation $(x - 3)^2 = 25$? **B**

A $\{-8, 2\}$　　C $\{4, 14\}$
B $\{-2, 8\}$　　D $\{-4, 14\}$

62. SHORT RESPONSE Write an equation in slope-intercept form for the graph shown below. $y = -2x - 4$

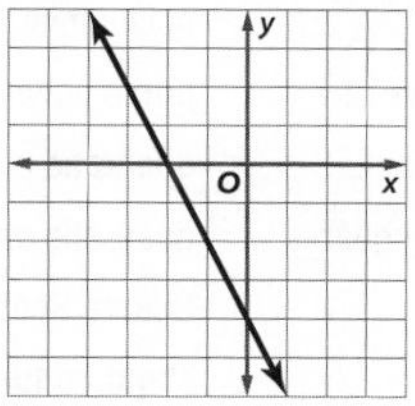

63. At an amphitheater, the price of 2 lawn seats and 2 pavilion seats is \$120. The price of 3 lawn seats and 4 pavilion seats is \$225. How much do lawn and pavilion seats cost? **H**

F \$20 and \$41.25
G \$10 and \$50
H \$15 and \$45
J \$30 and \$30

64. GEOMETRY The circumference of a circle is $\frac{6\pi}{5}$ units. What is the area of the circle? **A**

A $\frac{9\pi}{25}$ units^2　　B $\frac{3\pi}{5}$ units^2
C $\frac{6\pi}{5}$ units^2　　D $\frac{12\pi}{5}$ units^2

Spiral Review

Factor each polynomial, if possible. If the polynomial cannot be factored, write *prime*. (Lesson 8-8)

65. $x^2 - 16$ $(x - 4)(x + 4)$
66. $4x^2 - 81y^2$ $(2x - 9y)(2x + 9y)$
67. $1 - 100p^2$ $(1 - 10p)(1 + 10p)$
68. $3a^2 - 20$ prime
69. $25n^2 - 1$ $(5n - 1)(5n + 1)$
70. $36 - 9c^2$ $9(2 - c)(2 + c)$

Solve each equation. Confirm your answers using a graphing calculator. (Lesson 8-7)

71. $4x^2 - 8x - 32 = 0$ $\{-2, 4\}$
72. $6x^2 - 48x + 90 = 0$ $\{3, 5\}$
73. $14x^2 + 14x = 28$ $\{-2, 1\}$
74. $2x^2 - 10x = 48$ $\{-3, 8\}$
75. $5x^2 - 25x = -30$ $\{2, 3\}$
76. $8x^2 - 16x = 192$ $\{-4, 6\}$

SOUND The intensity of sound can be measured in watts per square meter. The table gives the watts per square meter for some common sounds. (Lesson 7-2)

Watts Per Square Meter	Common Sounds
10^{-11}	rustling leaves
10^{-10}	whisper
10^{-6}	normal conversation
10^{-5}	busy street traffic
10^{-4}	vacuum cleaner
10^{-1}	front rows of rock concert
10^{1}	threshold of pain
10^{2}	military jet takeoff

77. How many times more intense is the sound from busy street traffic than sound from normal conversation? 10^1 or 10

78. Which sound is 10,000 times as loud as a busy street traffic? front rows of rock concert

79. How does the intensity of a whisper compare to that of normal conversation? $\frac{1}{10,000}$

Skills Review

Find the slope of the line that passes through each pair of points.

80. $(5, 7), (-2, -3)$ $\frac{10}{7}$
81. $(2, -1), (5, -3)$ $-\frac{2}{3}$
82. $(-4, -1), (-3, -3)$ -2
83. $(-3, -4), (5, -1)$ $\frac{3}{8}$
84. $(-2, 3), (8, 3)$ 0
85. $(-5, 4), (-5, -1)$ undefined

Differentiated Instruction OL BL

Extension Write the following polynomial on the board for students to factor completely: $(m - p)m^2 - 2m(m - p) + (m - p)$
$(m - p)(m - 1)(m - 1)$ or $(m - p)(m - 1)^2$

4 Assess

Name the Math Have each student tell a partner or write how to determine if a trinomial is a perfect square trinomial.

Formative Assessment

Check for student understanding of concepts in Lessons 8-8 and 8-9.

Quiz 4, p. 66

Follow-up

Students have explored factoring.

Ask:

- What are the limitations of mathematical modeling? Sample answer: Not all situations can be modeled. For those that can, the domain of the model may need to be limited. For example, with a model that represents the height of an object over time, height and time cannot be negative. Also, model may only produce approximate answers. Therefore, after a model is created, it should be carefully analyzed before it is used to make predictions/decisions.

Formative Assessment

KeyVocabulary The page references after each word denote where that term was first introduced. If students have difficulty answering questions 1–10, remind them that they can use these page references to refresh their memories about the vocabulary.

Summative Assessment

Vocabulary Test, p. 68

Vocabulary Review

Vocabulary Review provides students the opportunity to check their understanding of important concepts and terminology in an online game format.

FOLDABLES StudyOrganizer

Dinah Zike's Foldables®

Have students look through the chapter to make sure they have included examples in their Foldables for each lesson of the chapter. Suggest that students keep their Foldables handy while completing the Study Guide and Review pages. Point out that their Foldables can serve as a quick review when studying for the chapter test.

CHAPTER 8 Study Guide and Review

Study Guide

KeyConcepts

Operations with Polynomials (Lessons 8-1 through 8-4)

- To add or subtract polynomials, add or subtract like terms.
- To multiply polynomials, use the Distributive Property.
- Special products: $(a + b)^2 = a^2 + 2ab + b^2$
  $(a - b)^2 = a^2 - 2ab + b^2$
  $(a + b)(a - b) = a^2 - b^2$

Factoring Using the Distributive Property (Lesson 8-5)

- Using the Distributive Property to factor polynomials with four or more terms is called factoring by grouping.
  $ax + bx + ay + by = x(a + b) + y(a + b)$
  $= (a + b)(x + y)$

Solving Quadratic Equations by Factoring (Lessons 8-6 through 8-8)

- To factor $x^2 + bx + c$, find m and p with a sum of b and a product of c. Then write $x^2 + bx + c$ as $(x + m)(x + p)$.
- To factor $ax^2 + bx + c$, find m and p with a sum of b and a product of ac. Then write as $ax^2 + mx + px + c$ and factor by grouping.
- $a^2 - b^2 = (a - b)(a + b)$

Perfect Squares and Factoring (Lesson 8-9)

- For a trinomial to be a perfect square, the first and last terms must be perfect squares, and the middle term must be twice the product of the square roots of the first and last terms.
- For any number $n \geq 0$, if $x^2 = n$, then $x = \pm\sqrt{n}$.

FOLDABLES StudyOrganizer

Be sure the Key Concepts are noted in your Foldable.

KeyVocabulary

binomial (p. 465)
degree of a monomial (p. 465)
degree of a polynomial (p. 465)
difference of two squares (p. 516)
factoring (p. 494)
factoring by grouping (p. 495)
FOIL method (p. 481)
leading coefficient (p. 466)
perfect square trinomial (p. 522)
polynomial (p. 465)
prime polynomial (p. 512)
quadratic equation (p. 506)
quadratic expression (p. 481)
Square Root Property (p. 525)
standard form of a polynomial (p. 466)
trinomial (p. 465)
Zero Product Property (p. 496)

VocabularyCheck

State whether each sentence is *true* or *false*. If *false*, replace the underlined phrase or expression to make a true sentence.

1. $\underline{x^2 + 5x + 6}$ is an example of a prime polynomial. **false; sample answer: $x^2 + 5x + 7$**
2. $\underline{(x + 5)(x - 5)}$ is the factorization of a difference of squares. **true**
3. $4x^2 - 2x + 7$ is a polynomial of degree $\underline{2}$. **true**
4. $\underline{(x + 5)(x - 2)}$ is the factored form of $x^2 - 3x - 10$. **false; $(x - 5)(x + 2)$**
5. Expressions with four or more unlike terms can sometimes be <u>factored by grouping</u>. **true**
6. The Zero Product Property states that if <u>$ab = 1$, then a or b is 1</u>. **false; $ab = 0$, then a or b is 0, or both a and b are 0.**
7. $x^2 - 12x + 36$ is an example of a <u>perfect square trinomial</u>. **true**
8. The leading coefficient of $1 + 6a + 9a^2$ is $\underline{1}$. **false; 9**
9. $x^2 - 16$ is an example of a <u>perfect square trinomial</u>. **false; difference of squares**
10. The FOIL method is used to multiply two <u>trinomials</u>. **false; binomials**

530 | Chapter 8 | Study Guide and Review

Lesson-by-Lesson Review

8-1 Adding and Subtracting Polynomials

Write each polynomial in standard form. **11.** $3x^2 + x + 2$

11. $x + 2 + 3x^2$

12. $1 - x^4$ $-x^4 + 1$

13. $2 + 3x + x^2$ $x^2 + 3x + 2$

14. $3x^5 - 2 + 6x - 2x^2 + x^3$ $3x^5 + x^3 - 2x^2 + 6x - 2$

Find each sum or difference.

15. $(x^3 + 2) + (-3x^3 - 5)$ $-2x^3 - 3$

16. $a^2 + 5a - 3 - (2a^2 - 4a + 3)$ $-a^2 + 9a - 6$

17. $(4x - 3x^2 + 5) + (2x^2 - 5x + 1)$ $-x^2 - x + 6$

18. **PICTURE FRAMES** Jean is framing a painting that is a rectangle. What is the perimeter of the frame? $4x^2 + 4x + 8$

Example 1

Write $3 - x^2 + 4x$ in standard form.

Step 1 Find the degree of each term.

3: degree 0

$-x^2$: degree 2

$4x$: degree 1

Step 2 Write the terms in descending order of degree.

$3 - x^2 + 4x = -x^2 + 4x + 3$

Example 2

Find $(8r^2 + 3r) - (10r^2 - 5)$.

$(8r^2 + 3r) - (10r^2 - 5)$

$= (8r^2 + 3r) + (-10r^2 + 5)$ Use the additive inverse.

$= (8r^2 - 10r^2) + 3r + 5$ Group like terms.

$= -2r^2 + 3r + 5$ Add like terms.

8-2 Multiplying a Polynomial by a Monomial

Solve each equation.

19. $x^2(x + 2) = x(x^2 + 2x + 1)$ 0

20. $2x(x + 3) = 2(x^2 + 3)$ 1

21. $2(4w + w^2) - 6 = 2w(w - 4) + 10$ 1

22. **GEOMETRY** Find the area of the rectangle. $3x^3 + 3x^2 - 21x$

Example 3

Solve $m(2m - 5) + m = 2m(m - 6) + 16$.

$m(2m - 5) + m = 2m(m - 6) + 16$

$2m^2 - 5m + m = 2m^2 - 12m + 16$

$2m^2 - 4m = 2m^2 - 12m + 16$

$-4m = -12m + 16$

$8m = 16$

$m = 2$

8-3 Multiplying Polynomials

Find each product. **23.** $x^2 + 4x - 21$ **24.** $18a^2 + 3a - 10$

23. $(x - 3)(x + 7)$

24. $(3a - 2)(6a + 5)$

25. $(3r - 7t)(2r + 5t)$ $6r^2 + rt - 35t^2$

26. $(2x + 5)(5x + 2)$ $10x^2 + 29x + 10$

27. **PARKING LOT** The parking lot shown is to be paved. What is the area to be paved? $10x^2 + 7x - 12$

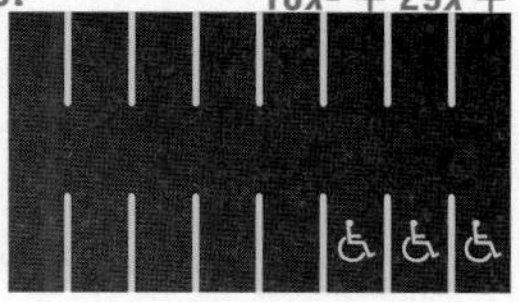

Example 4

Find $(6x - 5)(x + 4)$.

$(6x - 5)(x + 4)$

F O I L

$= (6x)(x) + (6x)(4) + (-5)(x) + (-5)(4)$

$= 6x^2 + 24x - 5x - 20$ Multiply.

$= 6x^2 + 19x - 20$ Combine like terms.

Lesson-by-Lesson Review

Intervention If the given examples are not sufficient to review the topics covered by the questions, remind students that the lesson references tell them where to review that topic in their textbooks.

Two-Day Option Have students complete the Lesson-by-Lesson Review. Then you can use McGraw-Hill eAssessment to customize another review worksheet that practices all the objectives of this chapter or only the objectives on which your students need more help.

CHAPTER 8 Study Guide and Review *Continued*

8-4 Special Products

Find each product.

28. $(x + 5)(x - 5)$ **$x^2 - 25$**
29. $(3x - 2)^2$ **$9x^2 - 12x + 4$**
30. $(5x + 4)^2$ **$25x^2 + 40x + 16$**
31. $(2x - 3)(2x + 3)$ **$4x^2 - 9$**
32. $(2r + 5t)^2$ **$4r^2 + 20rt + 25t^2$**
33. $(3m - 2)(3m + 2)$ **$9m^2 - 4$**
34. **GEOMETRY** Write an expression to represent the area of the shaded region. **$3x^2 - 21$**

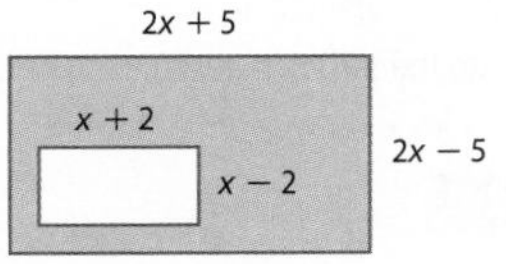

Example 5

Find $(x - 7)^2$.

$(a - b)^2 = a^2 - 2ab + b^2$ — Square of a Difference

$(x - 7)^2 = x^2 - 2(x)(7) + (-7)^2$ — $a = x$ and $b = 7$

$= x^2 - 14x + 49$ — Simplify.

Example 6

Find $(5a - 4)(5a + 4)$.

$(a + b)(a - b) = a^2 - b^2$ — Product of a Sum and Difference

$(5a - 4)(5a + 4) = (5a)^2 - (4)^2$ — $a = 5a$ and $b = 4$

$= 25a^2 - 16$ — Simplify.

8-5 Using the Distributive Property

Use the Distributive Property to factor each polynomial.

35. $12x + 24y$ **$12(x + 2y)$**
36. $14x^2y - 21xy + 35xy^2$ **$7xy(2x - 3 + 5y)$**
37. $8xy - 16x^3y + 10y$ **$2y(4x - 8x^3 + 5)$**
38. $a^2 - 4ac + ab - 4bc$ **$(a + b)(a - 4c)$**
39. $2x^2 - 3xz - 2xy + 3yz$ **$(2x - 3z)(x - y)$**
40. $24am - 9an + 40bm - 15bn$ **$(3a + 5b)(8m - 3n)$**

Solve each equation. Check your solutions.

41. $x(3x - 6) = 0$ **0, 2**
42. $6x^2 = 12x$ **0, 2**
43. $x^2 = 3x$ **0, 3**
44. $3x^2 = 5x$ **$0, \frac{5}{3}$**
45. **GEOMETRY** The area of the rectangle shown is $x^3 - 2x^2 + 5x$ square units. What is the length? **$x^2 - 2x + 5$**

Example 7

Factor $12y^2 + 9y + 8y + 6$.

$12y^2 + 9y + 8y + 6$

$= (12y^2 + 9y) + (8y + 6)$ — Group terms with common factors.

$= 3y(4y + 3) + 2(4y + 3)$ — Factor the GCF from each group.

$= (4y + 3)(3y + 2)$ — Distributive Property

Example 8

Solve $x^2 - 6x = 0$. Check your solutions.

Write the equation so that it is of the form $ab = 0$.

$x^2 - 6x = 0$ — Original equation

$x(x - 6) = 0$ — Factor by using the GCF.

$x = 0$ or $x - 6 = 0$ — Zero Product Property

$x = 6$ — Solve.

The roots are 0 and 6. Check by substituting 0 and 6 for x in the original equation.

8-6 Solving $x^2 + bx + c = 0$

Factor each trinomial. Confirm your answers using a graphing calculator.

46. $x^2 - 8x + 15$ **47.** $x^2 + 9x + 20$

48. $x^2 - 5x - 6$ **49.** $x^2 + 3x - 18$

Solve each equation. Check your solutions.

50. $x^2 + 5x - 50 = 0$ $-10, 5$

51. $x^2 - 6x + 8 = 0$ $2, 4$

52. $x^2 + 12x + 32 = 0$ $-8, -4$

53. $x^2 - 2x - 48 = 0$ $-6, 8$

54. $x^2 + 11x + 10 = 0$ $-10, -1$

46. $(x - 5)(x - 3)$
47. $(x + 5)(x + 4)$
48. $(x - 6)(x + 1)$
49. $(x + 6)(x - 3)$

55. **ART** An artist is working on a painting that is 3 inches longer than it is wide. The area of the painting is 154 square inches. What is the length of the painting? 14 in.

Example 9

Factor $x^2 + 10x + 21$

$b = 10$ and $c = 21$, so $m + p$ is positive and mp is positive. Therefore, m and p must both be positive. List the positive factors of 21, and look for the pair of factors with a sum of 10.

Factors of 21	Sum of 10
1, 21	22
3, 7	10

The correct factors are 3 and 7.

$x^2 + 10x + 21 = (x + m)(x + p)$ Write the pattern.

$= (x + 3)(x + 7)$ $m = 3$ and $p = 7$

8-7 Solving $ax^2 + bx + c = 0$

Factor each trinomial, if possible. If the trinomial cannot be factored, write *prime*.

56. $12x^2 + 22x - 14$ $2(2x - 1)(3x + 7)$

57. $2y^2 - 9y + 3$ prime

58. $3x^2 - 6x - 45$ $3(x - 5)(x + 3)$

59. $2a^2 + 13a - 24$ $(2a - 3)(a + 8)$

Solve each equation. Confirm your answers using a graphing calculator.

60. $40x^2 + 2x = 24$ $\frac{3}{4}, -\frac{4}{5}$

61. $2x^2 - 3x - 20 = 0$ $4, -\frac{5}{2}$

62. $-16t^2 + 36t - 8 = 0$ $2, \frac{1}{4}$

63. $6x^2 - 7x - 5 = 0$ $\frac{5}{3}, -\frac{1}{2}$

64. **GEOMETRY** The area of the rectangle shown is $6x^2 + 11x - 7$ square units. What is the width of the rectangle? $3x + 7$

$2x - 1$

Example 10

Factor $12a^2 + 17a + 6$

$a = 12$, $b = 17$, and $c = 6$. Since b is positive, $m + p$ is positive. Since c is positive, mp is positive. So, m and p are both positive. List the factors of 12(6) or 72, where both factors are positive.

Factors of 72	Sum of 17
1, 72	73
2, 36	38
3, 24	27
4, 18	22
6, 12	18
8, 9	17

The correct factors are 8 and 9.

$$\begin{aligned} 12a^2 + 17a + 6 &= 12a^2 + ma + pa + 6 \\ &= 12a^2 + 8a + 9a + 6 \\ &= (12a^2 + 8a) + (9a + 6) \\ &= 4a(3a + 2) + 3(3a + 2) \\ &= (3a + 2)(4a + 3) \end{aligned}$$

So, $12a^2 + 17a + 6 = (3a + 2)(4a + 3)$.

connectED.mcgraw-hill.com 533

Anticipation Guide

Have students complete the Chapter 8 Anticipation Guide and discuss how their responses have changed now that they have completed Chapter 8.

CHAPTER 8 Study Guide and Review *Continued*

8-8 Differences of Squares

Factor each polynomial.

65. $y^2 - 81$ **$(y + 9)(y - 9)$**

66. $64 - 25x^2$ **$(8 + 5x)(8 - 5x)$**

67. $16a^2 - 21b^2$ **prime**

68. $3x^2 - 3$ **$3(x + 1)(x - 1)$**

Solve each equation by factoring. Confirm your answers using a graphing calculator.

69. $a^2 - 25 = 0$ **5, −5**

70. $9x^2 - 25 = 0$ **$\frac{5}{3}, -\frac{5}{3}$**

71. $81 - y^2 = 0$ **−9, 9**

72. $x^2 - 5 = 20$ **−5, 5**

73. **EROSION** A boulder falls down a mountain into water 64 feet below. The distance d that the boulder falls in t seconds is given by the equation $d = 16t^2$. How long does it take the boulder to hit the water? **2 seconds**

Example 11

Solve $x^2 - 4 = 12$ by factoring.

$x^2 - 4 = 12$	Original equation
$x^2 - 16 = 0$	Subtract 12 from each side.
$x^2 - (4)^2 = 0$	$16 = 4^2$
$(x + 4)(x - 4) = 0$	Factor the difference of squares.
$x + 4 = 0$ or $x - 4 = 0$	Zero Product Property
$x = -4$ $\quad$ $x = 4$	Solve each equation.

The solutions are −4 and 4.

8-9 Perfect Squares

Factor each polynomial, if possible. If the polynomial cannot be factored write *prime*.

74. $x^2 + 12x + 36$ **$(x + 6)^2$**

75. $x^2 + 5x + 25$ **prime**

76. $9y^2 - 12y + 4$ **$(3y - 2)^2$**

77. $4 - 28a + 49a^2$ **$(2 - 7a)^2$**

78. $x^4 - 1$ **$(x^2 + 1)(x + 1)(x - 1)$**

79. $x^4 - 16x^2$ **$x^2(x + 4)(x - 4)$**

Solve each equation. Confirm your answers using a graphing calculator.

80. $(x - 5)^2 = 121$ **16, −6**

81. $4c^2 + 4c + 1 = 9$ **1, −2**

82. $4y^2 = 64$ **−4, 4**

83. $16d^2 + 40d + 25 = 9$ **$-2, -\frac{1}{2}$**

84. **LANDSCAPING** A sidewalk of equal width is being built around a square yard. What is the width of the sidewalk? **2.5 ft**

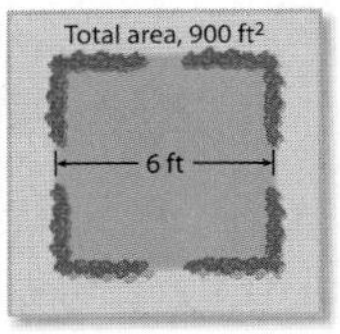

Example 12

Solve $(x - 9)^2 = 144$.

$(x - 9)^2 = 144$	Original equation
$x - 9 = \pm\sqrt{144}$	Square Root Property
$x - 9 = \pm 12$	$144 = 12 \cdot 12$
$x = 9 \pm 12$	Add 9 to each side.
$x = 9 + 12$ or $x = 9 - 12$	Zero Product Property
$x = 21$ $\quad$ $x = -3$	Solve.

CHECK

$(x - 9)^2 = 144$	$(x - 9)^2 = 144$
$(21 - 9)^2 \stackrel{?}{=} 144$	$(-3 - 9)^2 \stackrel{?}{=} 144$
$(12)^2 \stackrel{?}{=} 144$	$(-12)^2 \stackrel{?}{=} 144$
$144 = 144$ ✓	$144 = 144$ ✓

CHAPTER 8 Practice Test

Find each sum or difference. 2. $3m - 6n^2 + 6n$

1. $(x + 5) + (x^2 - 3x + 7)$ $x^2 - 2x + 12$

2. $(7m - 8n^2 + 3n) - (-2n^2 + 4m - 3n)$

3. MULTIPLE CHOICE Antonia is carpeting two of the rooms in her house. The dimensions are shown. Which expression represents the total area to be carpeted? B

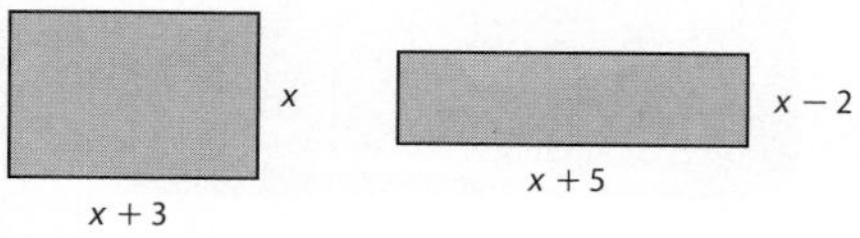

A $x^2 + 3x$

B $2x^2 + 6x - 10$

C $x^2 + 3x - 5$

D $8x + 12$

Find each product.

4. $a(a^2 + 2a - 10)$ $a^3 + 2a^2 - 10a$

5. $(2a - 5)(3a + 5)$ $6a^2 - 5a - 25$

6. $(x - 3)(x^2 + 5x - 6)$ $x^3 + 2x^2 - 21x + 18$

7. $(x + 3)^2$ $x^2 + 6x + 9$

8. $(2b - 5)(2b + 5)$ $4b^2 - 25$

9. FINANCIAL LITERACY Suppose you invest \$4000 in a 2-year certificate of deposit (CD).

a. If the interest rate is 5% per year, the expression $4000(1 + 0.05)^2$ can be evaluated to find the total amount of money after two years. Explain the numbers in this expression. See margin.

b. Find the amount at the end of two years. \$4410

c. Suppose you invest \$10,000 in a CD for 4 years at an annual rate of 6.25%. What is the total amount of money you will have after 4 years? about \$12,744

10. MULTIPLE CHOICE The area of the rectangle shown below is $2x^2 - x - 15$ square units. What is the width of the rectangle? H

F $x - 5$

G $x + 3$

H $x - 3$

J $2x - 3$

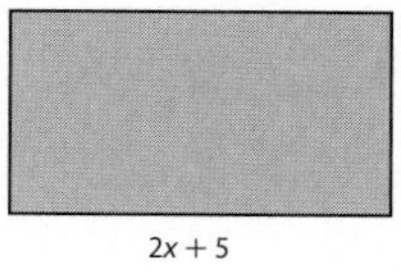

Solve each equation.

11. $5(t^2 - 3t + 2) = t(5t - 2)$ $\frac{10}{13}$

12. $3x(x + 2) = 3(x^2 - 2)$ -1

Factor each polynomial.

13. $5xy - 10x$ $5x(y - 2)$

14. $7ab + 14ab^2 + 21a^2b$ $7ab(1 + 2b + 3a)$

15. $4x^2 + 8x + x + 2$ $(4x + 1)(x + 2)$

16. $10a^2 - 50a - a + 5$ $(10a - 1)(a - 5)$

Solve each equation. Confirm your answers using a graphing calculator.

17. $y(y - 14) = 0$ $0, 14$

18. $3x(x + 6) = 0$ $0, -6$

19. $a^2 = 12a$ $0, 12$

20. MULTIPLE CHOICE Chantel is carpeting a room that has an area of $x^2 - 100$ square feet. If the width of the room is $x - 10$ feet, what is the length of the room? B

A $x - 10$ ft

B $x + 10$ ft

C $x - 100$ ft

D 10 ft

Factor each trinomial.

21. $x^2 + 7x + 6$ $(x + 6)(x + 1)$

22. $x^2 - 3x - 28$ $(x - 7)(x + 4)$

23. $10x^2 - x - 3$ $(5x - 3)(2x + 1)$

24. $15x^2 + 7x - 2$ $(3x + 2)(5x - 1)$

25. $x^2 - 25$ $(x + 5)(x - 5)$

26. $4x^2 - 81$ $(2x + 9)(2x - 9)$

27. $9x^2 - 12x + 4$ $(3x - 2)(3x - 2)$

28. $16x^2 + 40x + 25$ $(4x + 5)(4x + 5)$

Solve each equation. Confirm your answers using a graphing calculator.

29. $x^2 - 4x = 21$ $-3, 7$

30. $x^2 - 2x - 24 = 0$ $-4, 6$

31. $6x^2 - 5x - 6 = 0$ $-\frac{2}{3}, \frac{3}{2}$

32. $2x^2 - 13x + 20 = 0$ $4, \frac{5}{2}$

33. MULTIPLE CHOICE Which choice is a factor of $x^4 - 1$ when it is factored completely? G

F $x^2 - 1$

G $x - 1$

H x

J 1

Summative Assessment

Use these alternate leveled chapter tests to differentiate assessment for your students.

Leveled Chapter 8 Tests

Form	Type	Level	Page(s)
1	MC	AL	67–68
2A	MC	OL	69–70
2B	MC	OL	71–72
2C	FR	OL	73–74
2D	FR	OL	75–76
3	FR	BL	77–78
Vocabulary Test			66
Extended-Response Test			79

MC = multiple-choice questions
FR = free-response questions

McGraw-Hill eAssessment Customize and create multiple versions of your chapter test and their answer keys. All of the questions from the leveled chapter tests in the *Chapter 8 Resource Masters* are also available on McGraw-Hill eAssessment.

Additional Answer

9a. \$4000 is the amount of the investment, 1 will add the amount of the investment to the interest, 0.05 is the interest rate as a decimal, and 2 is the number of the years of the investment.

InterventionPlanner

TIER 1 On Level OL

If students miss about 25% of the exercises or less,

Then choose a resource:

SE Lessons 8-1, 8-2, 8-3, 8-4, 8-5, 8-6, 8-7, 8-8, and 8-9

Skills Practice, pp. 7, 14, 20, 27, 33, 39, 45, 52, and 59

TE Chapter Project

connectED.mcgraw-hill.com Self-Check Quiz

TIER 2 Strategic Intervention AL
approaching grade level

If students miss about 50% of the exercises,

Then choose a resource:

Study Guide and Intervention, Chapter 8, pp. 5, 12, 18, 25, 31, 37, 43, 50, and 57

Quick Review Math Handbook

connectED.mcgraw-hill.com Extra Examples, Personal Tutor, Homework Help

TIER 3 Intensive Intervention
2 or more grades below level

If students miss about 75% of the exercises,

Then use *Math Triumphs, Alg. 1*

connectED.mcgraw-hill.com Extra Examples, Personal Tutor, Homework Help, Review Vocabulary

1 Focus

Objective Use strategies for solving multi-step standardized test problems.

2 Teach

Scaffolding Questions

Ask:

- Have you ever had to write a research paper or complete some other school project? Answers will vary.
- Did you write the entire paper or complete the project in one session? Or did you use a number of steps to complete the job? Answers will vary.
- Could you have completed the steps in a different order? Could you have used a different set of steps? Answers will vary.

CHAPTER 8 Preparing for Standardized Tests

Solve Multi-Step Problems

Some problems that you will encounter on standardized tests require you to solve multiple parts in order to come up with the final solution. Use this lesson to practice these types of problems.

Strategies for Solving Multi-Step Problems

Step 1

Read the problem statement carefully.

Ask yourself:

- What am I being asked to solve? What information is given?
- Are there any intermediate steps that need to be completed before I can solve the problem?

Step 2

Organize your approach.

- List the steps you will need to complete in order to solve the problem.
- Remember that there may be more than one possible way to solve the problem.

Step 3

Solve and check.

- Work as efficiently as possible to complete each step and solve.
- If time permits, check your answer.

Standardized Test Example

Read the problem. Identify what you need to know. Then use the information in the problem to solve.

A florist has 80 roses, 50 tulips, and 20 lilies that he wants to use to create bouquets. He wants to create the maximum number of bouquets possible and use all of the flowers. Each bouquet should have the same number of each type of flower. How many roses will be in each bouquet?

A 4 roses
B 8 roses
C 10 roses
D 15 roses

Read the problem carefully. You are given the number of roses, tulips, and lilies and told that bouquets will be made using the same number of flowers in each. You need to find the number of roses that will be in each bouquet.

Step 1 Find the GCF of the number of roses, tulips, and lilies.

Step 2 Use the GCF to determine how many bouquets will be made.

Step 3 Divide the total number of roses by the number of bouquets.

Step 1 Write the prime factorization of each number of flowers to find the GCF.

$80 = \mathbf{2} \cdot 2 \cdot 2 \cdot 2 \cdot \mathbf{5}$

$50 = \mathbf{2} \cdot \mathbf{5} \cdot 5$

$20 = \mathbf{2} \cdot 2 \cdot \mathbf{5}$

$\text{GCF} = 2 \cdot 5 = 10$

Step 2 The GCF of the number of roses, tulips, and lilies tells you how many bouquets can be made because each bouquet will contain the same number of flowers. So, the florist can make a total of 10 bouquets.

Step 3 Divide the number of roses by the number of bouquets to find the number of roses in each bouquet.

$\frac{80}{10} = 8$

So, there will be 8 roses in each bouquet. The answer is B.

Exercises

Read each problem. Identify what you need to know. Then use the information in the problem to solve.

1. Which of the following values is not a solution to $x^3 - 3x^2 - 25x + 75 = 0$? C

A $x = 5$ C $x = -3$

B $x = 3$ D $x = -5$

2. There are 12 teachers, 90 students, and 36 parent volunteers going on a field trip. Mrs. Bartholomew wants to divide everyone into equal groups with the same number of teachers, students, and parents in each group. If she makes as many groups as possible, how many students will be in each group? J

F 6 H 12

G 9 J 15

3. What is the area of the square? D

A $x^2 + 16$

B $4x - 16$

C $x^2 - 8x - 16$

D $x^2 - 8x + 16$

4. Students are selling magazines to raise money for a field trip. They make \$2.75 for each magazine they sell. If they want to raise \$600, what is the least amount of magazines they need to sell? J

F 121 H 202

G 177 J 219

Additional Example

A geologist is preparing rock boxes for students. She has 90 igneous, 75 metamorphic, and 120 sedimentary rocks. She wants to make the maximum number of boxes possible and use all of the rocks. Each box should have the same number of each type of rock. How many metamorphic rocks will be in each box? A

A 5 metamorphic rocks

B 6 metamorphic rocks

C 8 metamorphic rocks

D 15 metamorphic rocks

3 Assess

Use Exercises 1–4 to assess students' understanding.

Diagnose Student Errors

Survey student responses for each item. Class trends may indicate common errors and misconceptions.

1. A found players remaining after first round
B found players remaining after second round
C found players remaining after fourth round
D correct

2. F guess
G correct
H incorrectly simplified $5^6 - 5^5$ as 5
J incorrectly simplified $5^6 - 5^5$ as 5^2 or 25

3. A guess
B transposed *m* and *n*
C transposed 3 and 5
D correct

4. F correct
G error in sign: should be 8 instead of −8
H calculation error or guess
J calculation error or guess

5. A can be factored: $(5x + 4)(x + 6)$
B can be factored: $2(2x + 1)(x + 5)$
C can be factored: $2(2x + 5)(x + 7)$
D correct

6. F chose a factor
G chose a factor
H correct
J chose a factor

7. A correct
B chose one of the dimensions
C chose one of the dimensions
D chose one of the dimensions

8. F chose factors that would give y^2 and 20, but $-12y$ instead of $-9y$
G correct
H chose factors that would give $-9y$, but 14 instead of 20
J guess

9. A confused negative exponent with negative number
B misunderstood concept of scientific notation
C misunderstood concept of scientific notation
D correct

CHAPTER 8 Standardized Test Practice

Cumulative, Chapters 1 through 8

Multiple Choice

Read each question. Then fill in the correct answer on the answer document provided by your teacher or on a sheet of paper.

1. Each year a local country club sponsors a tennis tournament. Play starts with 256 participants. During each round, half of the players are eliminated. How many players remain after 6 rounds? **D**

A 128

B 64

C 16

D 4

2. Evaluate $\frac{5^6 - 5^5}{4}$. **G**

F 5^6

G 5^5

H $\frac{5}{4}$

J $\frac{25}{4}$

3. Factor $mn + 5m - 3n - 15$. **D**

A $(mn - 3)(5)$

B $(n - 3)(m + 5)$

C $(m - 5)(n + 3)$

D $(m - 3)(n + 5)$

4. Which of the following is a solution to $x^2 + 6x - 112 = 0$? **F**

F −14

G −8

H 6

J 12

5. Which of the following polynomials is prime? **D**

A $5x^2 + 34x + 24$

B $4x^2 + 22x + 10$

C $4x^2 + 38x + 70$

D $5x^2 + 3x + 4$

6. Which of the following is not a factor of the polynomial $45a^2 - 80b^2$? **H**

F 5

G $3a - 4b$

H $2a - 5b$

J $3a + 4b$

7. A rectangular gift box has dimensions that can be represented as shown in the figure. The volume of the box is $56w$ cubic inches. Which of the following is *not* a dimension of the box? **A**

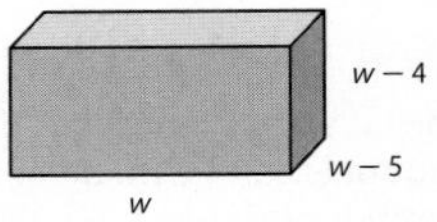

A 6 in.

B 7 in.

C 8 in.

D 12 in.

8. Factor the polynomial $y^2 - 9y + 20$. **G**

F $(y - 2)(y - 10)$

G $(y - 4)(y - 5)$

H $(y - 2)(y - 7)$

J $(y - 5)(y + 2)$

9. Which of the following numbers is less than zero? **D**

A 1.03×10^{-21}

B 7.5×10^2

C 8.21543×10^{10}

D none of the above

Test-TakingTip

Question 4 If time permits, be sure to check your answer. Substitute it into the equation to see if you get a true number sentence.

Short Response/Gridded Response

Record your answers on the answer sheet provided by your teacher or on a sheet of paper.

10. GRIDDED RESPONSE Mr. Branson bought a total of 9 tickets to the zoo. He bought children tickets at the rate of \$6.50 and adult tickets for \$9.25 each. If he spent \$69.50 altogether, how many adult tickets did Mr. Branson purchase? **4**

11. What is the domain of the following relation? $\{(2, -1), (4, 3), (7, 6)\}$ **{2, 4, 7}**

12. Ken just added 15 more songs to his digital media player, making the total number of songs more than 84. Draw a number line that represents the original number of songs he had on his digital media player. **See margin.**

13. Carlos bought a rare painting in 1995 for \$14,200. By 2003, the painting was worth \$17,120. Assuming that a linear relationship exists, write an equation in slope-intercept form that represents the value V of the painting after t years. $V(t) = 365t + 14{,}200$

14. The equation $h = -16t^2 + 40t + 3$ models the height h in feet of a soccer ball after t seconds. What is the height of the ball after 2 seconds? **19 ft**

15. Marcel spent \$24.50 on peanuts and walnuts for a party. He bought 1.5 pounds more peanuts than walnuts. How many pounds of peanuts and walnuts did he buy?

Product	Price per pound
Peanuts p	\$3.80
Cashews c	\$6.90
Walnuts w	\$5.60

3.5 lbs of peanuts and 2 lbs of walnuts

16. GRIDDED RESPONSE The amount of money that Humberto earns varies directly as the number of hours that he works as shown in the graph. How much money will he earn for working 40 hours next week? Express your answer in dollars. **600**

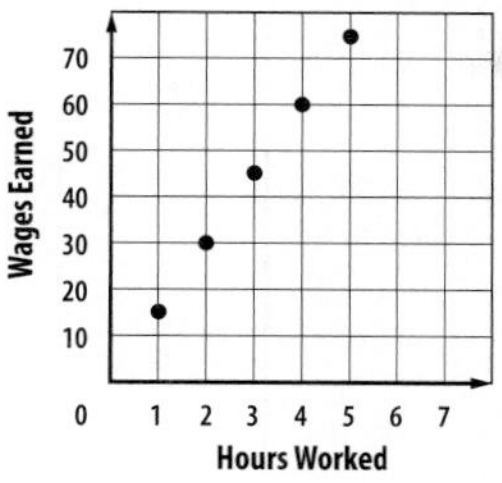

Extended Response

Record your answers on a sheet of paper. Show your work.

17. The height in feet of a model rocket t seconds after being launched into the air is given by the function $h(t) = -16t^2 + 200t$.

a. Write the expression that shows the height of the rocket in factored form. $h(t) = t(-16t + 200)$

b. At what time(s) is the height of the rocket equal to zero feet above the ground? Describe the real world meaning of your answer. **See margin.**

c. What is the greatest height reached by the model rocket? When does this occur? **625 ft; at $t = 6.25$ seconds**

Need ExtraHelp?

If you missed Question...	1	2	3	4	5	6	7	8	9	10	11	12	13	14	15	16	17
Go to Lesson...	7-7	7-2	8-5	8-6	8-3	8-7	8-9	8-6	7-4	6-5	1-6	5-1	4-2	8-7	2-9	3-4	8-5

Additional Answers

12.

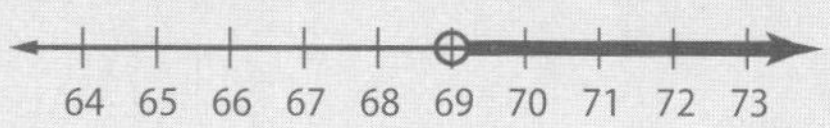

17b. $t = 0$, 12.5 seconds; Sample answer: The rocket is on the ground at launch and takes 12.5 seconds to land again after its flight.

Formative Assessment

You can use these pages to benchmark student progress.

Standardized Test Practice, pp. 82–84

Answer Sheet Practice

Have students simulate taking a standardized test by recording their answers on a practice recording sheet.

Student Recording Sheet

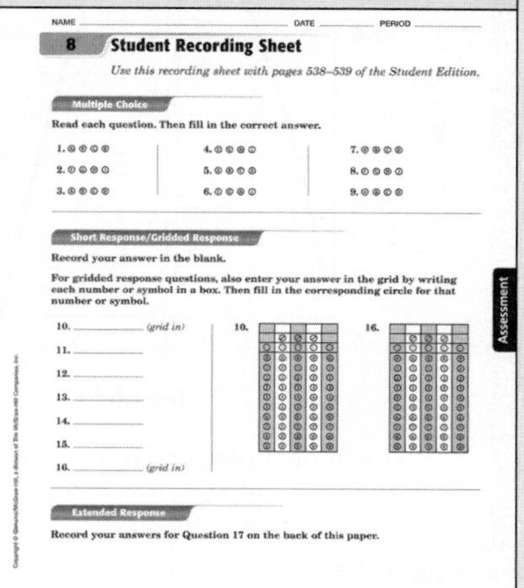

McGraw-Hill eAssessment Create practice tests that align to your state standards, the Common Core State Standards, and other national standards such as TIMSS and NAEP.

Homework Option

Get Ready for Chapter 9 Assign students the exercises on p. 541 as homework to assess whether they possess the prerequisite skills needed for the next chapter.

Lesson 8-1

60a. Sample answer:

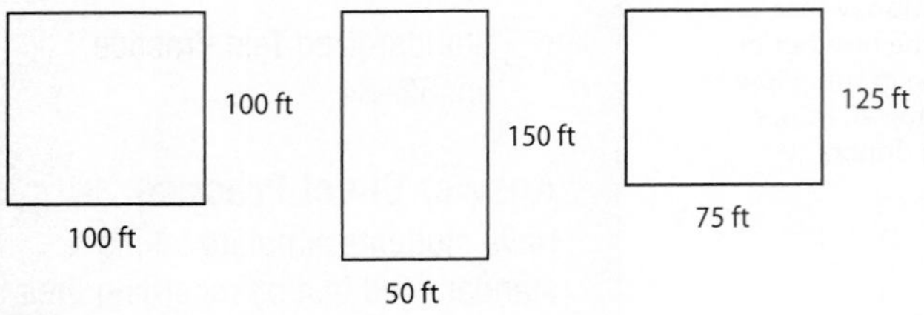

60c.

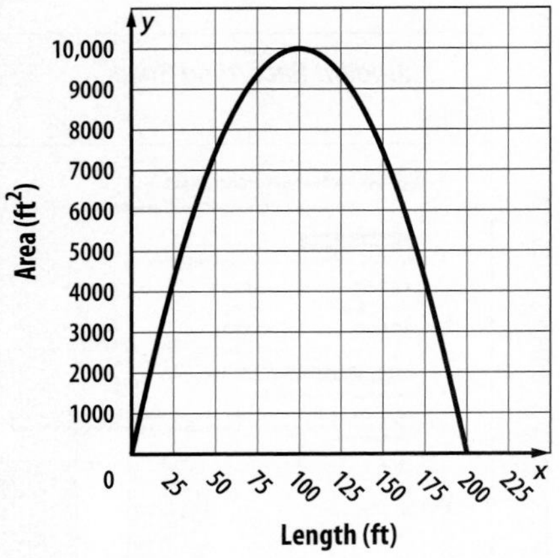

The largest possible area is 10,000 square feet.

Lesson 8-3

48. The three monomials that make up the trinomial are similar to the three digits that make up the 3-digit number. The single monomial is similar to a 1-digit number. With each procedure you perform 3 multiplications. The difference is that polynomial multiplication involves variables and the resulting product is often the sum of two or more monomials, while numerical multiplication results in a single number.

49. The Distributive Property can be used with a vertical or horizontal format by distributing, multiplying, and combining like terms. The FOIL method is used with a horizontal format. You multiply the first, outer, inner, and last terms of the binomials and then combine like terms. A rectangular method can also be used by writing the terms of the polynomials along the top and left side of a rectangle and then multiplying the terms and combining like terms.

Explore 8-5

5.

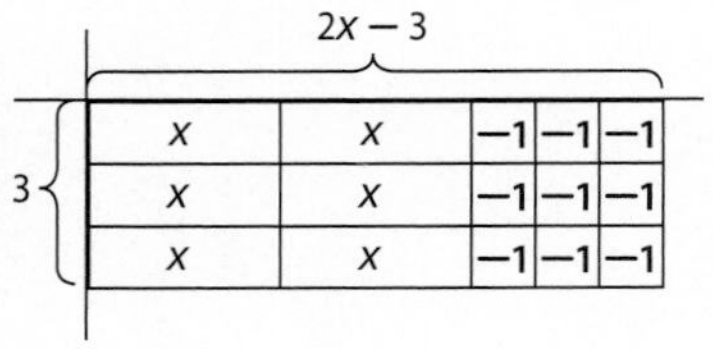

6.

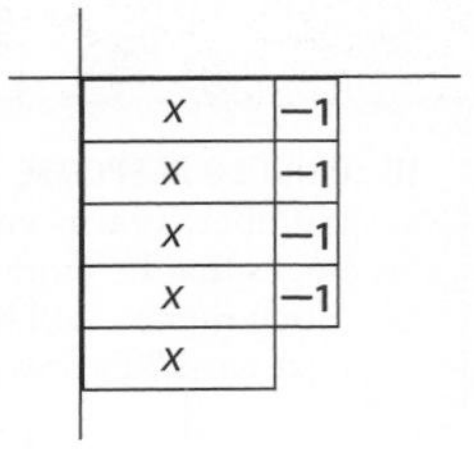

7.

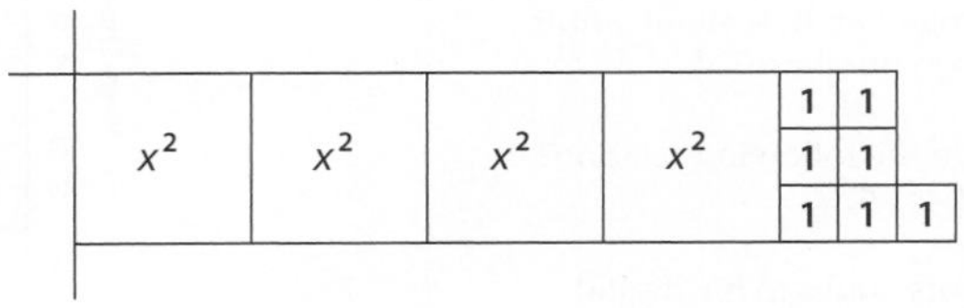

8.

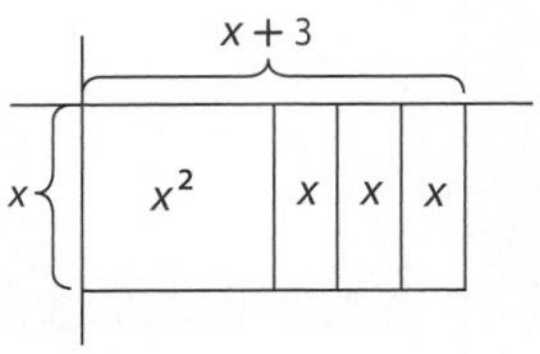

Explore 8-6

9.

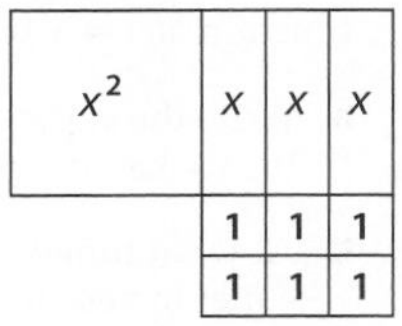

10.

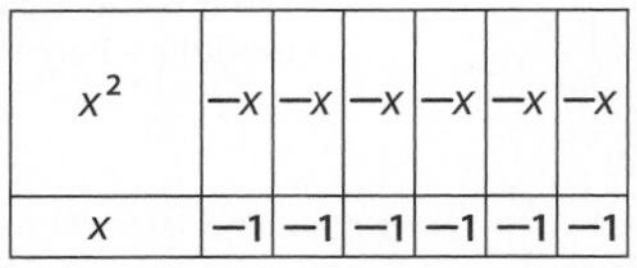

11.

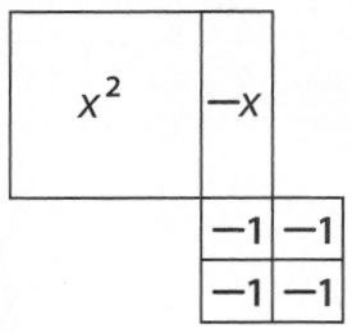

12.

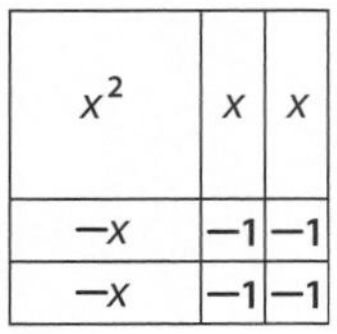

NOTES

Chapter 8 Answer Appendix

Chapter Planner

	Diagnostic Assessment Quick Check LESSON 9-1 (45 min: 1.5 days; 90 min: 1 day)	EXTEND 9-1 (45 min: 0.5 day; 90 min: 0.5 day)	LESSON 9-2 (45 min: 1 day; 90 min: 0.5 day)
Title	**Graphing Quadratic Functions**	**Algebra Lab: Rate of Change of a Quadratic Function**	**Solving Quadratic Equations by Graphing**
Objectives	▪ Analyze the characteristics of the graphs of quadratic functions. ▪ Graph quadratic functions.	▪ Use a given quadratic function to investigate the rate of change of a quadratic function.	▪ Solve quadratic equations by graphing. ▪ Estimate solutions of quadratic equations by graphing.
Key Vocabulary	quadratic function standard form parabola axis of symmetry vertex minimum maximum		double root
Content Standards	PS.2, AI.F.4, AI.QE.3, AI.QE.5		PS.3, AI.QE.3, AI.QE.4, AI.QE.5, AI.QE.6, AI.QE.7
Multiple Representations	✓		✓
Lesson Resources	connectED.mcgraw-hill.com Leveled Worksheets Vocabulary Animations Personal Tutor Virtual Manipulatives Self-Check Quiz ▪ *5-Minute Check* ▪ *Study Notebook* ▪ *Teaching Algebra with Manipulatives*	connectED.mcgraw-hill.com Animations Virtual Manipulatives ▪ *Teaching Algebra with Manipulatives* **Materials:** ▪ grid paper	connectED.mcgraw-hill.com Leveled Worksheets Vocabulary Animations Personal Tutor Virtual Manipulatives Self-Check Quiz ▪ *5-Minute Check* ▪ *Study Notebook*
Resources for Every Lesson	IWB eStudent Edition IWB Interactive Classroom	▪ eTeacher Edition ▪ eSolutions Manual ▪ McGraw-Hill eAssessment	
Differentiated Instruction	pp. 547, 553		pp. 556, 560

IWB All digital assets are Interactive Whiteboard ready.

Suggested Pacing			
Time Periods	Instruction	Review & Assess	Total
45-minute	13 days	2 days	15 days
90-minute	8 days	1 day	9 days

EXTEND 9-2 (45 min: 0.5 day; 90 min: 0.5 day)	EXPLORE 9-3 (45 min: 0.5 day; 90 min: 0.5 day)	LESSON 9-3 (45 min: 1.5 days; 90 min: 0.5 day)	EXTEND 9-3 (45 min: 0.5 day; 90 min: 0.5 day)
Graphing Technology Lab: Quadratic Inequalities	**Graphing Technology Lab: Family of Quadratic Functions**	**Transformations of Quadratic Functions**	**Graphing Technology Lab: Systems of Linear and Quadratic Equations**
■ Use a graphing calculator to investigate quadratic inequalities.	■ Use a graphing calculator to investigate families of quadratic functions.	■ Apply translations of quadratic functions. ■ Apply dilations and reflections to quadratic functions.	■ Use a graphing calculator to solve a system of one linear and one quadratic equation.
		transformation translation dilation reflection vertex form	
		PS.1, PS.8, AI.QE.6, AI.QE.7	
connectED.mcgraw-hill.com Personal Tutor **Materials:** ■ TI-83/84 Plus or other graphing calculator	Personal Tutor **Materials:** ■ TI-83/84 Plus or other graphing calculator	connectED.mcgraw-hill.com Leveled Worksheets Quiz 1 Vocabulary Animations Personal Tutor Virtual Manipulatives Self-Check Quiz ■ *5-Minute Check* ■ *Study Notebook*	connectED.mcgraw-hill.com Personal Tutor **Materials:** ■ TI-83/84 Plus or other graphing calculator
IWB eStudent Edition IWB Interactive Classroom	■ eTeacher Edition ■ eSolutions Manual ■ McGraw-Hill eAssessment		
		pp. 566, 571	

Chapter Planner

	LESSON 9-4 (45 min: 1 day; 90 min: 0.75 day)	EXTEND 9-4 (45 min: 0.5 day; 90 min: 0.25 day)	LESSON 9-5 (45 min: 1.5 days; 90 min: 1 day)
Title	**Solving Quadratic Equations by Completing the Square**	**Algebra Lab: Finding the Maximum or Minimum Value**	**Solving Quadratic Equations by Using the Quadratic Formula**
Objectives	▪ Complete the square to write perfect square trinomials. ▪ Solve quadratic equations by completing the square.	▪ Complete the square in a quadratic expression to find the maximum or minimum value of the related function.	▪ Solve quadratic equations by using the Quadratic Formula. ▪ Use the discriminant to determine the number of solutions to a quadratic equation.
Key Vocabulary	completing the square		Quadratic Formula discriminant
Content Standards	AI.QE.4, AI.QE.5, AI.QE.6, AI.QE.7	AI.QE.6, AI.QE.7	PS.6, AI.QE.4, AI.QE.5
Multiple Representations	✓		✓
Lesson Resources	connectED.mcgraw-hill.com Leveled Worksheets Vocabulary Animations Personal Tutor Virtual Manipulatives Self-Check Quiz ▪ *5-Minute Check* ▪ *Study Notebook* ▪ *Teaching Algebra with Manipulatives*		connectED.mcgraw-hill.com Leveled Worksheets Quiz 2 Vocabulary Personal Tutor Virtual Manipulatives Self-Check Quiz ▪ *5-Minute Check* ▪ *Study Notebook*
Resources for Every Lesson	IWB eStudent Edition IWB Interactive Classroom	▪ eTeacher Edition ▪ eSolutions Manual ▪ McGraw-Hill eAssessment	
Differentiated Instruction	pp. 574, 577		pp. 586, 589

Formative Assessment
Mid-Chapter Quiz

IWB All digital assets are Interactive Whiteboard ready.

LESSON 9-6 (45 min: 1 day; 90 min: 0.5 day)	EXTEND 9-6 (45 min: 1 day; 90 min: 0.5 day)	LESSON 9-7 (45 min: 1.5 days; 90 min: 0.75 days)	EXTEND 9-7 (45 min: 0.5 day; 90 min: 0.25 day)
Analyzing Functions with Successive Differences	**Graphing Technology Lab: Curve Fitting**	**Special Functions**	**Graphing Technology Lab: Piecewise-Linear Functions**
▪ Identify linear, quadratic, and exponential functions from given data. ▪ Write equations that model data.	▪ Use a graphing calculator to find an appropriate regression equation for a set of data.	▪ Identify and graph step functions. ▪ Identify and graph absolute value and piecewise-defined functions.	▪ Use a graphing calculator to investigate piecewise-linear functions.
	coefficient of determination	step function piecewise-linear function greatest integer function absolute value function piecewise-defined function	
PS.7, AI.QE.1	PS.5, AI.QE.1, AI.DS.2	PS.4, AI.L.10	
connectED.mcgraw-hill.com Leveled Worksheets Quiz 3 Personal Tutor Virtual Manipulatives Self-Check Quiz ▪ *5-Minute Check* ▪ *Study Notebook*	connectED.mcgraw-hill.com Vocabulary Personal Tutor **Materials:** ▪ TI-83/84 Plus or other graphing calculator	connectED.mcgraw-hill.com Leveled Worksheets Quiz 4 Vocabulary Personal Tutor Virtual Manipulatives Self-Check Quiz ▪ *5-Minute Check* ▪ *Study Notebook*	connectED.mcgraw-hill.com Animations Personal Tutor **Materials:** ▪ TI-83/84 Plus or other graphing calculator
IWB eStudent Edition IWB Interactive Classroom	▪ eTeacher Edition ▪ eSolutions Manual ▪ McGraw-Hill eAssessment		
pp. 592, 595		pp. 602, 603	

Summative Assessment
Study Guide and Review
Practice Test

Assessment and Intervention

SE = Student Edition, **TE** = Teacher Edition, **CRM** = Chapter Resource Masters

	Diagnosis	Prescription
DIAGNOSTIC ASSESSMENT	**Beginning Chapter 9**	
	Get Ready for Chapter 9 **SE**	Response to Intervention **TE**
	Beginning Every Lesson	
	Then, Now, Why? **SE** 5-Minute Check	Chapter 0 **SE** *Quick Review Math Handbook*
FORMATIVE ASSESSMENT	**During/After Every Lesson**	
	Guided Practice **SE**, every example Check Your Understanding **SE** H.O.T. Problems **SE** Spiral Review **SE** Additional Examples **TE** Watch Out! **TE** Step 4, Assess **TE** Chapter 9 Quizzes **CRM**, pp. 49–50 Self-Check Quizzes connectED.mcgraw-hill.com	TIER 1 Intervention Skills Practice **CRM**, Ch. 1–9 connectED.mcgraw-hill.com TIER 2 Intervention Differentiated Instruction **TE** Study Guide and Intervention **CRM**, Ch. 1–9 *Quick Review Math Handbook* TIER 3 Intervention *Math Triumphs, Alg. 1*
	Mid-Chapter	
	Mid-Chapter Quiz **SE** Mid-Chapter Test **CRM**, p. 51 McGraw-Hill eAssessment	TIER 1 Intervention Skills Practice **CRM**, Ch. 1–9 connectED.mcgraw-hill.com TIER 2 Intervention Study Guide and Intervention **CRM**, Ch. 1–9; *Quick Review Math Handbook* TIER 3 Intervention *Math Triumphs, Alg. 1*
	Before Chapter Test	
	Chapter Study Guide and Review **SE** Practice Test **SE** Standardized Test Practice **SE** Chapter Test connectED.mcgraw-hill.com Standardized Test Practice connectED.mcgraw-hill.com Vocabulary Review connectED.mcgraw-hill.com McGraw-Hill eAssessment	TIER 1 Intervention Skills Practice **CRM**, Ch. 1–9 connectED.mcgraw-hill.com TIER 2 Intervention Study Guide and Intervention **CRM**, Ch. 1–9; *Quick Review Math Handbook* TIER 3 Intervention *Math Triumphs, Alg. 1*
SUMMATIVE ASSESSMENT	**After Chapter 9**	
	Multiple-Choice Tests, Forms 1, 2A, 2B **CRM**, pp. 53–58 Free-Response Tests, Forms 2C, 2D, 3 **CRM**, pp. 59–64 Vocabulary Test **CRM**, p. 52 Extended Response Test **CRM**, p. 65 Standardized Test Practice **CRM**, pp. 66–68 McGraw-Hill eAssessment	Study Guide and Intervention **CRM**, Ch. 1–9 *Quick Review Math Handbook* connectED.mcgraw-hill.com

Differentiated Instruction

Option 1 Reaching All Learners AL OL BL ELL

Interpersonal Place students in small groups. Since there are several tasks involved in graphing quadratic functions, have the group members decide which tasks they should each complete in order to graph a given function. For example, one member can be responsible for finding the equation for the axis of symmetry, another can substitute values in order to determine points on the graph, and a third member can graph the points and draw the curve of the parabola.

Option 2 Approaching Level AL

Make three large columns on the chalkboard. Label the columns: "Two Real Roots," "One Real Root," and "No Real Roots." Ask volunteers to write a quadratic equation for each of the columns. Ask the class to use the discriminant to check whether the volunteers were correct. Then, use the quadratic formula to find the roots of those equations that have real roots.

Option 3 English Learners ELL

Have students describe how to solve a quadratic equation by graphing, as if they were teaching the procedure. Make sure students include any tips or hints that they use when they solve by graphing.

Option 4 Beyond Level BL

Toss a tennis ball while standing in the front of the classroom. Ask students to describe how the path of the ball can be modeled by a quadratic function. If video equipment is available, set up a grid on a wall and have groups of students record the path of a tossed ball thrown in front of the wall. Have the students write the equation of a function that models the path of the ball. Each group should analyze the function and compare the results to the actual path of the ball.

Focus on Mathematical Content

VerticalAlignment

Vertical Alignment

Related Topics before Grade 8

- approximate the value of irrational numbers as they arise from problem situations

Previous Topics from Algebra 1

- find specific function values
- simplify polynomial expressions and factor as necessary in problem situations
- analyze graphs of linear and exponential functions and draw conclusions

Chapter 9

Related Topics from Algebra 1

- identify and sketch the general forms of quadratic parent functions
- analyze graphs of quadratic functions and draw conclusions
- make connections among the solutions (roots) of quadratic equations, the zeros of their related functions, and the horizontal intercepts of the graph of the function
- solve quadratic equations using concrete models, tables, graphs, and algebraic methods
- use characteristics of the quadratic parent function to sketch the related graphs
- analyze functions with successive differences and ratios
- identify and graph special functions.

After Chapter 9

Preparation for Algebra 2

- relate representations of quadratic functions, such as algebraic, tabular, graphical, and verbal descriptions
- determine a quadratic function from its roots or a graph
- determine solutions of exponential equations using graphs, tables, and algebraic methods

Lesson-by-Lesson Preview

9-1 Graphing Quadratic Functions

The standard form of a quadratic function is $y = ax^2 + bx + c$, where $a \neq 0$.

- If a is positive, the parabola opens upward and the vertex is the minimum of the function.
- If a is negative, the parabola opens downward and the vertex is the maximum of the function.

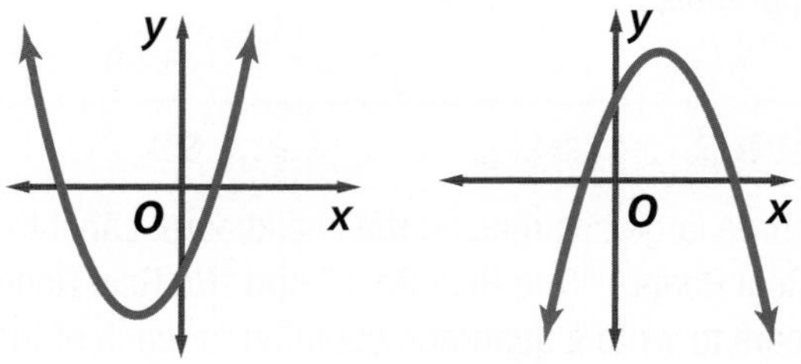

The line that divides a parabola into two congruent halves is called the *axis of symmetry*. The equation for the axis of symmetry for the graph of $y = ax^2 + bx + c$ is $x = \frac{-b}{2a}$.

9-2 Solving Quadratic Equations by Graphing

The solutions of a quadratic equation are called *roots*. All quadratic equations have two roots. The roots are as follows:

- two real roots–when the parabola crosses the x-axis at two distinct points,
- a double real root–when the vertex of the parabola is on the x-axis, or
- two imaginary roots–when the parabola does not intersect the x-axis.

9-3 Transformations of Quadratic Functions

A family of functions is a group of functions with graphs that share the same basic characteristics. The parent graph, which is the graph of the *parent function*, is the simplest of the graphs in a family. All other functions in the family are *transformations* of the graph of the parent function.

Three types of transformations performed on the graph of the parent function of the family of quadratics, $f(x) = x^2$, are

- *translation*–moves the parent graph up, down, left, or right,
- *vertical stretches*–shrinks or enlarges a parent graph proportionally,
- *reflection*–flips a graph over a line.

9-4 Solving Quadratic Equations by Completing the Square

If the quadratic expression on one side of the equation, in the form $ax^2 + bx + c = n$, is a perfect square and $n \geq 0$, the equation can be solved by taking the square root of each side. However, since few quadratic expressions are perfect squares, a method called *completing the square* may be used.

To solve an equation of the form $x^2 + bx + c = 0$ by completing the square, isolate the x^2 and bx terms on one side of the equation. Find half of b and square it. Then add this amount to each side of the equation. Solve by factoring and taking the square root of each side, if the right side is a nonnegative number. If the coefficient of x^2 is not 1, divide each term by the coefficient before completing the square.

9-5 Solving Quadratic Equations by Using the Quadratic Formula

A quadratic equation in the standard form $ax^2 + bx + c = 0$, where $a \neq 0$, can be solved using the Quadratic Formula. The coefficients a and b and the constant c are substituted in the formula $x = \frac{-b \pm \sqrt{b^2 - 4ac}}{2a}$. The expression is then simplified to find the solutions. The expression under the radical sign, $b^2 - 4ac$, is called the *discriminant*. The discriminant can be used to determine the number of real solutions of a quadratic equation.

9-6 Analyzing Functions with Successive Differences

Linear, quadratic, and exponential functions can be used to model data. To determine which of these three types of functions (if any) represents a set of data,

- observe a pattern in the graph of a set of data,
- observe one of these patterns in the data: *linear function*: the first differences of the y-values are all equal; *quadratic function*: the first differences are not all equal, but the second differences are; and *exponential function*: the ratios of successive y-values are all equal.

9-7 Special Functions

Other functions closely related to linear functions are the piecewise functions. These include the following functions.

Piecewise-defined function

- These functions are defined by two or more equations. For example,
  $f(x) = \begin{cases} x + 1 \text{ if } x > -1 \\ x + 3 \text{ if } x \leq -1 \end{cases}$

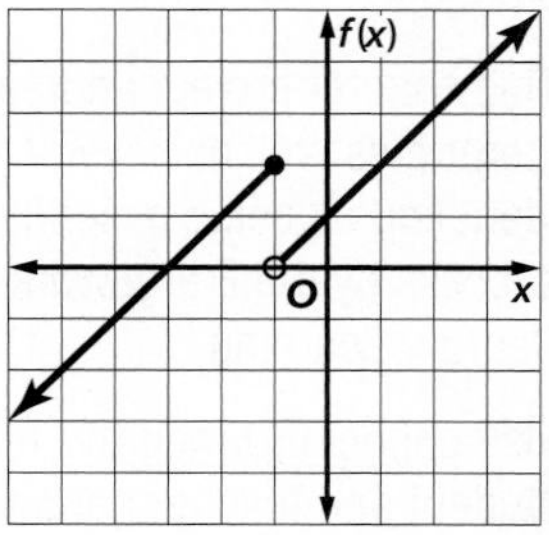

Greatest integer function (step function)

- $f(x) = [\![x]\!]$ means the greatest integer less than or equal to x. For example, $[\![3.25]\!] = 3$. The graph is made up of line segments that look like a set of steps.

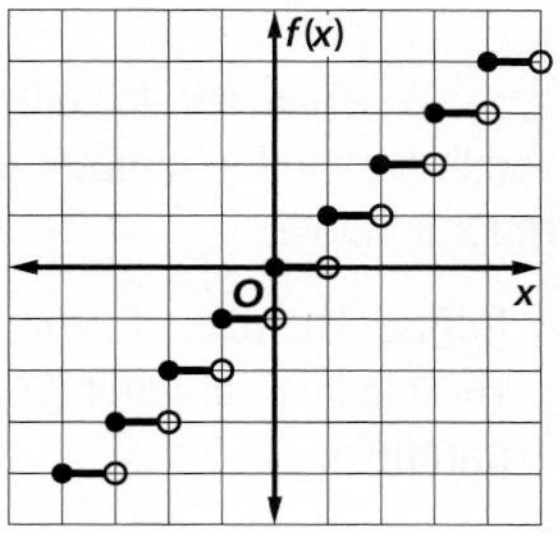

Absolute value function

- $f(x) = |x|$ means that when $x \geq 0$, the graph of the function is like $y = x$, but when finding $x < 0$, the graph of the function is like $y = -x$. The graph has a V-shape.

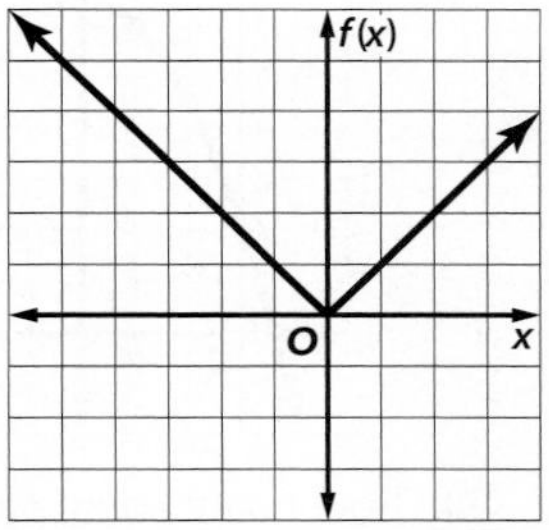

Chapter Project

3...2...1...Blast Off!

Students use what they have learned about quadratic equations to complete a project.

This chapter project addresses business literacy, as well as several specific skills identified as being essential to student success by the Framework for 21st Century Learning.

Visit connectED.mcgraw-hill.com for student and teacher handouts.

KeyVocabulary Introduce the key vocabulary in the chapter using the routine below.

Define: The axis of symmetry is the vertical line containing the vertex of a parabola.

Example:

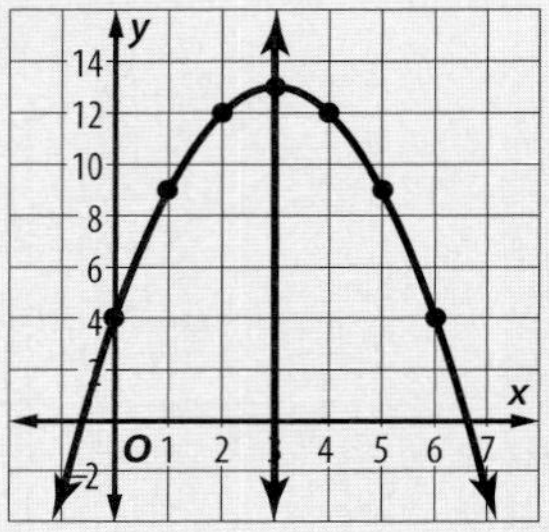

Ask: How many equal parts of a parabola does an axis of symmetry create? two

CHAPTER 9 Quadratic Functions and Equations

Then

You solved quadratic equations by factoring and by using the Square Root Property.

Now

In this chapter, you will:

- Solve quadratic equations by graphing, completing the square, and using the Quadratic Formula.
- Analyze functions with successive differences and ratios.
- Identify and graph special functions.

Why?

FINANCE The value of a certain company's stock can be modeled by the function $f(x) = x^2 - 12x + 75$. By graphing this quadratic function, we can make an educated guess as to how the stock will perform in the near future.

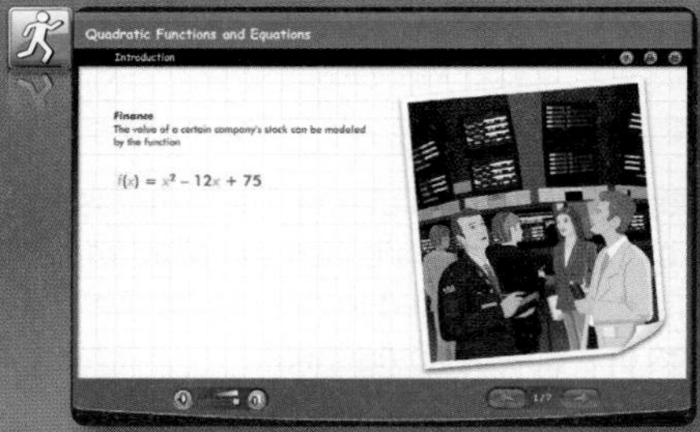

connectED.mcgraw-hill.com Your Digital Math Portal

Animation | Vocabulary | eGlossary | Personal Tutor | Virtual Manipulatives | Graphing Calculator | Audio | Foldables | Self-Check Practice | Worksheets

Content Standards
AI.F.4, AI.L.10, AI.QE.1, AI.QE.3, AI.QE.4, AI.QE.5, AI.QE.6, AI.QE.7, AI.DS.2

Process Standards
PS.1, PS.2, PS.3, PS.4, PS.5, PS.6, PS.7, PS.8

Get Ready for the Chapter

Diagnose Readiness | You have two options for checking prerequisite skills.

1 Textbook Option Take the Quick Check below. Refer to the Quick Review for help.

QuickCheck

Use a table of values to graph each equation. 1–7. See Ch. 9 Answer Appendix.

1. $y = x + 3$
2. $y = 2x + 2$
3. $y = -2x - 3$
4. $y = 0.5x - 1$
5. $4x - 3y = 12$
6. $3y = 6 + 9x$
7. **SAVINGS** Jack has \$100 to buy a game system. He plans to save \$10 each week. Graph an equation to show the total amount T Jack will have in w weeks.

Determine whether each trinomial is a perfect square trinomial. Write *yes* or *no*. If so, factor it.

8. $a^2 + 12a + 36$ yes; $(a + 6)^2$
9. $x^2 + 5x + 25$ no
10. $x^2 - 12x + 32$ no
11. $x^2 + 20x + 100$ yes; $(x + 10)^2$
12. $4x^2 + 28x + 49$ yes; $(2x + 7)^2$
13. $k^2 - 16k + 64$ yes; $(k - 8)^2$
14. $a^2 - 22a + 121$ yes; $(a - 11)^2$
15. $5t^2 - 12t + 25$ no

Evaluate each expression if $a = -2$, $b = -1$, $c = 0$, and $d = 2.5$.

16. $|a - 3|$ 5
17. $|2a + 1|$ 3
18. $|4 - b|$ 5
19. $\left|\frac{1}{2}b - 2\right|$ $2\frac{1}{2}$
20. $|12 - 4c|$ 12
21. $|2c - 3| + 1$ 4
22. $|4d - 6|$ 4
23. $|3d - 2| - 8$ −2.5

QuickReview

Example 1 (Used in Lesson 9-1)

Use a table of values to graph $y = 3x + 1$.

x	$y = 3x + 1$	y
−1	3(−1) + 1	−2
0	3(0) + 1	1
1	3(1) + 1	4
2	3(2) + 1	7

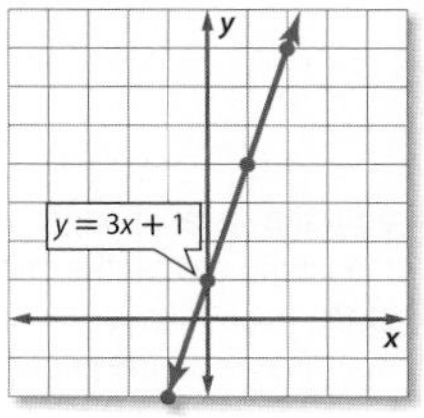

Example 2 (Used in Lesson 9-4)

Determine whether $x^2 - 10x + 25$ is a perfect square trinomial. Write *yes* or *no*. If so, factor it.

1. Is the first term a perfect square? yes
2. Is the last term a perfect square? yes
3. Is the middle term equal to $-2(1x)(5)$? yes

$x^2 - 10x + 25 = (x - 5)^2$

Example 3 (Used in Lesson 9-7)

Evaluate $|2x + 1| - 7$ if $x = -1$.

$|2x + 1| - 7 = |2(-1) + 1| - 7$ $x = -1$
$= |-2 + 1| - 7$ Multiply.
$= |-1| - 7$ Add.
$= 1 - 7$ $|-1| = 1$
$= -6$ Subtract.

2 Online Option Take an online self-check Chapter Readiness Quiz at connectED.mcgraw-hill.com.

Essential Question

- Why do we use different methods to solve math problems? Depending on the information given, one method may be easier to use than another. It also depends on whether you need an approximate or exact answer. For example, you could approximate the answer using a graph or mental math; you could find an exact answer using algebraic techniques.

Get Ready for the Chapter

Response to Intervention (RtI)

Use the *Quick Check* results and the Intervention Planner chart to help you determine your Response to Intervention. The If-Then statements in the chart below help you decide the appropriate tier of RtI and suggest intervention resources for each tier.

InterventionPlanner

TIER 1 On Level OL

If students miss about 25% of the exercises or less,

Then choose a resource:

SE Lessons 2-5, 3-1, and 8-9

TE Chapter Project

Skills Practice, Chapter 2, p. 32, Chapter 3, p. 32, Chapter 8, p. 59

connectED.mcgraw-hill.com Self-Check Quiz

TIER 2 Strategic Intervention AL approaching grade level

If students miss about 50% of the exercises,

Then choose a resource:

Study Guide and Intervention, Chapter 2, p. 30, Chapter 3, p. 30, Chapter 8, p. 57

Quick Review Math Handbook

connectED.mcgraw-hill.com Extra Examples, Personal Tutor, Homework Help

TIER 3 Intensive Intervention 2 or more grades below level

If students miss about 75% of the exercises,

Then use *Math Triumphs, Alg. 1*

connectED.mcgraw-hill.com Extra Examples, Personal Tutor, Homework Help, Review Vocabulary

FOLDABLES StudyOrganizer

Dinah Zike's Foldables®

Focus Students write about the characteristics of quadratic functions as they are presented in the lessons of this chapter.

Teach Have students make and label their Foldables as illustrated. Students should use the appropriate section to fill in examples of each characteristic listed. Under each example have students write a brief explanation as to how that characteristic relates to the other three concepts in the Foldable.

When to Use It Encourage students to add to their Foldables as they work through the chapter and to use them to review for the chapter test.

Differentiated Instruction

Student-Built Glossary, pp. 1–2

Students should complete the chart by providing a definition of each term and an example as they progress through Chapter 9. This study tool can also be used to review for the chapter test.

Get Started on the Chapter

You will learn several new concepts, skills, and vocabulary terms as you study Chapter 9. To get ready, identify important terms and organize your resources. You may wish to refer to Chapter 0 to review prerequisite skills.

FOLDABLES StudyOrganizer

Quadratic Functions and Equations Make this Foldable to help you organize your Chapter 9 notes about quadratic functions. Begin with a sheet of notebook paper.

1 **Fold** the sheet of paper along the length so that the edge of the paper aligns with the margin rule on the paper.

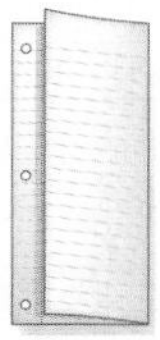

2 **Fold** the sheet twice widthwise to form four sections.

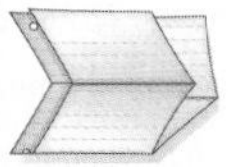

3 **Unfold** the sheet, and cut along the folds on the front flap only.

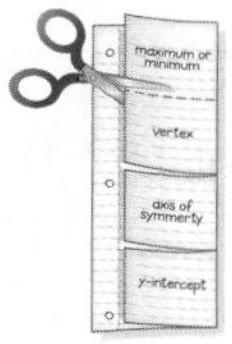

4 **Label** each section as shown.

NewVocabulary

English		Español
quadratic function	p. 543	función cuadrática
parabola	p. 543	parábola
axis of symmetry	p. 543	eje de simetría
vertex	p. 543	vértice
minimum	p. 543	mínimo
maximum	p. 543	máximo
double root	p. 556	doble raíz
transformation	p. 564	transformación
completing the square	p. 574	completar el cuadrado
Quadratic Formula	p. 583	Formula cuadrática
discriminant	p. 586	discriminante
step function	p. 598	función etapa
greatest integer function	p. 598	función del máximo entero
absolute value function	p. 599	función del valor absoluto

ReviewVocabulary

domain dominio all the possible values of the independent variable, x

leading coefficient coeficiente delantero the coefficient of the first term of a polynomial written in standard form

range rango all the possible values of the dependent variable, y

In the function represented by the table, the domain is {0, 2, 4, 6}, and the range is {3, 5, 7, 9}.

x	y
0	3
2	5
4	7
6	9

Additional Answer (Guided Practice)

1.

x	y
−2	7
−1	4
0	3
1	4
2	7

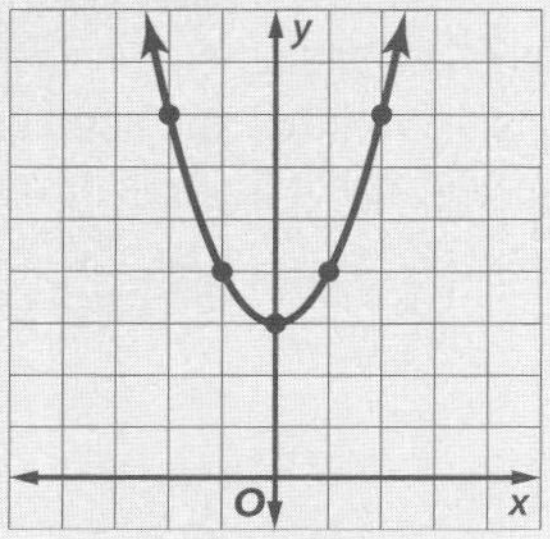

D = {all real numbers},
R = $\{y \mid y \geq 3\}$

LESSON 9-1 Graphing Quadratic Functions

Then
- You graphed linear and exponential functions.

Now
1. Analyze the characteristics of graphs of quadratic functions.
2. Graph quadratic functions.

Why?
- The Innovention Fountain in Epcot's Futureworld in Orlando, Florida, is an elaborate display of water, light, and music. The sprayers shoot water in shapes that can be modeled by quadratic equations. You can use graphs of these equations to show the path of the water.

NewVocabulary
quadratic function
standard form
parabola
axis of symmetry
vertex
minimum
maximum

Content Standards
AI.F.4, AI.QE.3, AI.QE.5

Process Standards
PS.2

1 Characteristics of Quadratic Functions

Quadratic functions are nonlinear and can be written in the form $f(x) = ax^2 + bx + c$, where $a \neq 0$. This form is called the **standard form** of a quadratic function.

The shape of the graph of a quadratic function is called a **parabola**. Parabolas are symmetric about a central line called the **axis of symmetry**. The axis of symmetry intersects a parabola at only one point, called the **vertex**.

KeyConcept Quadratic Functions

Parent Function:	$f(x) = x^2$
Standard Form:	$f(x) = ax^2 + bx + c$
Type of Graph:	parabola
Axis of Symmetry:	$x = -\frac{b}{2a}$
y-intercept:	c

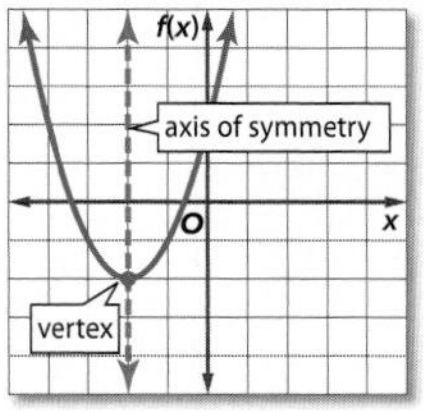

When $a > 0$, the graph of $y = ax^2 + bx + c$ opens upward. The lowest point on the graph is the **minimum**. When $a < 0$, the graph opens downward. The highest point is the **maximum**. The maximum or minimum is the vertex.

Example 1 Graph a Parabola

Use a table of values to graph $y = 3x^2 + 6x - 4$. State the domain and range.

x	y
1	5
0	−4
−1	−7
−2	−4
−3	5

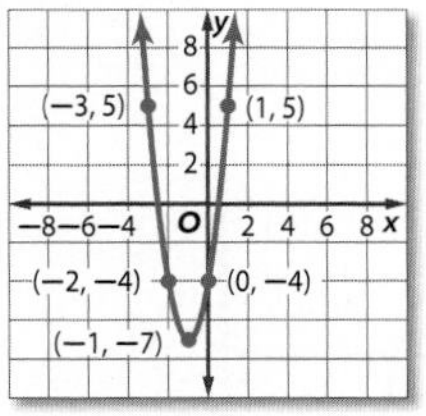

Graph the ordered pairs, and connect them to create a smooth curve. The parabola extends to infinity. The domain is all real numbers. The range is $\{y \mid y \geq -7\}$, because −7 is the minimum.

GuidedPractice

1. Use a table of values to graph $y = x^2 + 3$. State the domain and range. See margin.

1 Focus

VerticalAlignment

Before Lesson 9-1 Graph linear functions.

Lesson 9-1 Analyze the characteristics of graphs of quadratic functions. Graph quadratic functions.

After Lesson 9-1 Apply translations, dilations, and reflections to quadratic functions.

2 Teach

Scaffolding Questions

Have students read the **Why?** section of the lesson.

Ask:
- The shape of the water's path can be modeled by $y = -8x^2 - 49x - 75$. Is this a linear equation? Explain. No; it has an x^2-term.
- Is the path of the water a line? No.
- How would you describe the shape the water makes when it is shot from the sprayer? Sample answer: a symmetrical curve called a parabola

Teach with Tech

Interactive Whiteboard Drag a coordinate grid on the board. Use this throughout the lesson as you work through examples graphing quadratic functions.

Lesson 9-1 Resources

Resource	Approaching Level AL	On Level OL	Beyond Level BL	English Learners ELL
Teacher Edition	▪ Differentiated Instruction, p. 547	▪ Differentiated Instruction, pp. 547, 553	▪ Differentiated Instruction, p. 553	
Chapter Resource Masters	▪ Study Guide and Intervention, pp. 5–6 ▪ Skills Practice, p. 7 ▪ Practice, p. 8 ▪ Word Problem Practice, p. 9	▪ Study Guide and Intervention, pp. 5–6 ▪ Skills Practice, p. 7 ▪ Practice, p. 8 ▪ Word Problem Practice, p. 9 ▪ Enrichment, p. 10	▪ Practice, p. 8 ▪ Word Problem Practice, p. 9 ▪ Enrichment, p. 10	▪ Study Guide and Intervention, pp. 5–6 ▪ Skills Practice, p. 7 ▪ Practice, p. 8 ▪ Word Problem Practice, p. 9
Other	▪ 5-Minute Check 9-1 ▪ Study Notebook ▪ Teaching Algebra with Manipulatives	▪ 5-Minute Check 9-1 ▪ Study Notebook ▪ Teaching Algebra with Manipulatives	▪ 5-Minute Check 9-1 ▪ Study Notebook	▪ 5-Minute Check 9-1 ▪ Study Notebook ▪ Teaching Algebra with Manipulatives

1 Characteristics of Quadratic Functions

Example 1 shows how to use a table of values to graph a quadratic function. **Example 2** shows how to find the vertex, an equation for the axis of symmetry, and the y-intercept of a parabola from a graph. **Example 3** shows how to find the vertex, the equation of the axis of symmetry, and the y-intercept from an equation. **Example 4** shows how to determine whether the function has a maximum or minimum value, and how to find these values.

Formative Assessment

Use the Guided Practice exercises after each example to determine students' understanding of concepts.

Additional Example

1 Use a table of values to graph $y = x^2 - x - 2$. State the domain and range.

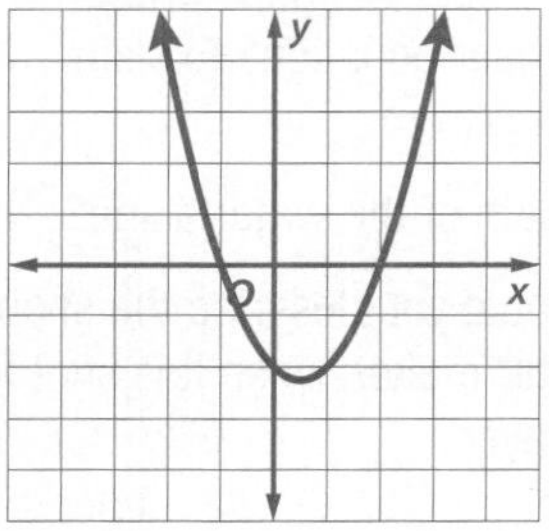

domain: all real numbers; range $\left\{y \middle| y \geq -2\frac{1}{4}\right\}$

Additional Examples also in Interactive Classroom PowerPoint® Presentations

IWB Interactive White Board READY

Recall that figures with symmetry are those in which each half of the figure matches exactly.

A parabola is symmetric about the axis of symmetry. Every point on the parabola to the left of the axis of symmetry has a corresponding point on the other half. The function is increasing on one side of the axis of symmetry and decreasing on the other side.

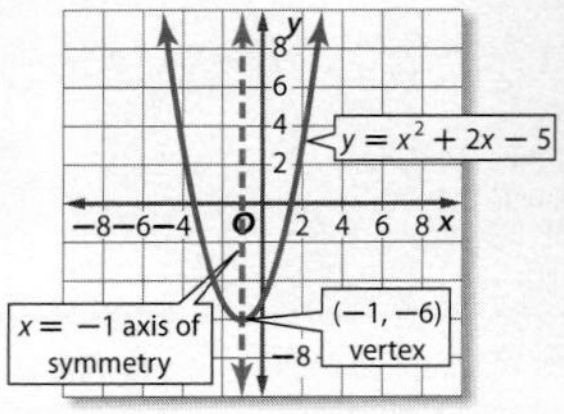

When identifying characteristics from a graph, it is often easiest to locate the vertex first. It is either the maximum or minimum point of the graph.

Example 2 Identify Characteristics from Graphs

Find the vertex, the equation of the axis of symmetry, and the y-intercept of each graph.

a.

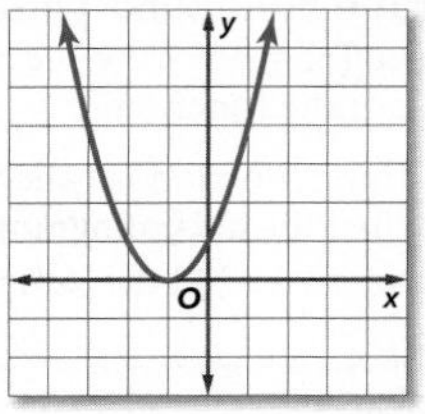

Step 1 Find the vertex.
Because the parabola opens upward, the vertex is located at the minimum point of the parabola. It is located at $(-1, 0)$.

Step 2 Find the axis of symmetry.
The axis of symmetry is the line that goes through the vertex and divides the parabola into congruent halves. It is located at $x = -1$.

Step 3 Find the y-intercept.
The y-intercept is the point where the graph intersects the y-axis. It is located at $(0, 1)$, so the y-intercept is 1.

b.

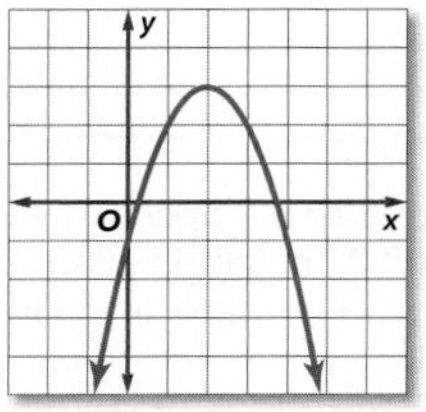

Step 1 Find the vertex.
The parabola opens downward, so the vertex is located at its maximum point, $(2, 3)$.

Step 2 Find the axis of symmetry.
The axis of symmetry is located at $x = 2$.

Step 3 Find the y-intercept.
The y-intercept is where the parabola crosses the y-axis. It is located at $(0, -1)$, so the y-intercept is -1.

Guided Practice

2A.

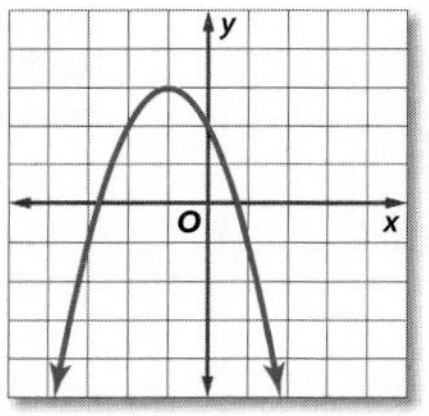

2B.

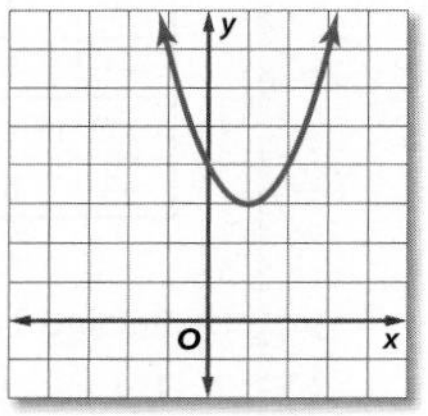

2A. vertex $(-1, 3)$, axis of symmetry $x = -1$, y-intercept 2
2B. vertex $(1, 3)$, axis of symmetry $x = 1$, y-intercept 4

StudyTip

Function Characteristics When identifying characteristics of a function, it is often easiest to locate the axis of symmetry first.

Example 3 Identify Characteristics from Functions

Find the vertex, the equation of the axis of symmetry, and the y-intercept of each function.

a. $y = 2x^2 + 4x - 3$

$x = -\frac{b}{2a}$ Formula for the equation of the axis of symmetry

$x = -\frac{4}{2 \cdot 2}$ $a = 2$ and $b = 4$

$x = -1$ Simplify.

The equation for the axis of symmetry is $x = -1$.

To find the vertex, use the value you found for the axis of symmetry as the x-coordinate of the vertex. Find the y-coordinate using the original equation.

$y = 2x^2 + 4x - 3$ Original equation

$= 2(-1)^2 + 4(-1) - 3$ $x = -1$

$= -5$ Simplify.

The vertex is at $(-1, -5)$.

The y-intercept always occurs at $(0, c)$. So, the y-intercept is -3.

b. $y = -x^2 + 6x + 4$

$x = -\frac{b}{2a}$ Formula for the equation of the axis of symmetry

$x = -\frac{6}{2(-1)}$ $a = -1$ and $b = 6$

$x = 3$ Simplify.

The equation of the axis of symmetry is $x = 3$.

$y = -x^2 + 6x + 4$ Original equation

$= -(3)^2 + 6(3) + 4$ $x = 3$

$= 13$ Simplify.

The vertex is at $(3, 13)$.

The y-intercept is 4.

StudyTip

y-intercept The y-coordinate of the y-intercept is also the constant term (c) of the quadratic function in standard form.

GuidedPractice

3A. $y = -3x^2 + 6x - 5$ **3B.** $y = 2x^2 + 2x + 2$

3A. vertex $(1, -2)$, axis of symmetry $x = 1$, y-intercept -5

3B. vertex $\left(-\frac{1}{2}, \frac{3}{2}\right)$, axis of symmetry $x = -\frac{1}{2}$, y-intercept 2

Next you will learn how to identify whether the vertex is a maximum or a minimum.

KeyConcept Maximum and Minimum Values

Words The graph of $f(x) = ax^2 + bx + c$, where $a \neq 0$:

- opens upward and has a minimum value when $a > 0$, and
- opens downward and has a maximum value when $a < 0$.
- The range of a quadratic function is all real numbers greater than or equal to the minimum, or all real numbers less than or equal to the maximum.

Examples a is positive.

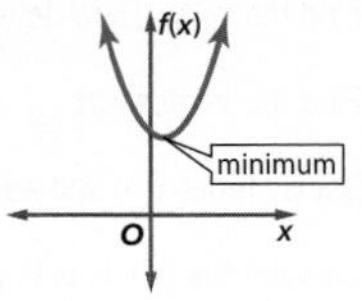

a is negative.

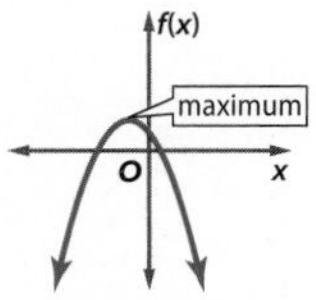

Additional Examples

2 Find the vertex, the equation of the axis of symmetry, and y-intercept.

a.

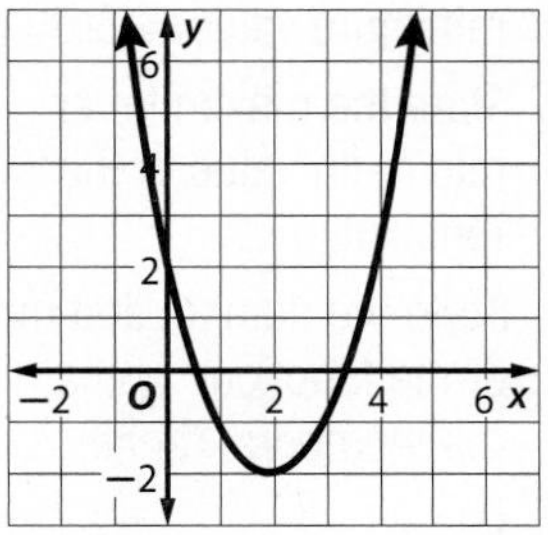

vertex: $(2, -2)$; axis of symmetry: $x = 2$; y-intercept: 2

b.

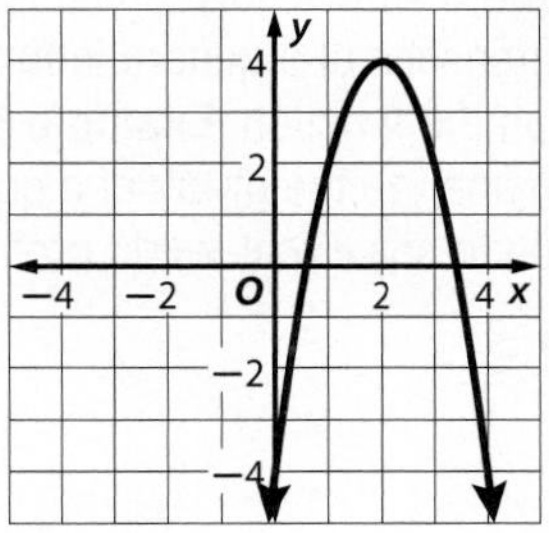

vertex: $(2, 4)$; axis of symmetry: $x = 2$; y-intercept: -4

3 Find the vertex, the equation of the axis of symmetry, and y-intercept.

a. $y = -2x^2 - 8x - 2$ $(-2, 6)$, $x = -2$, -2

b. $y = 3x^2 + 6x - 2$ $(-1, -5)$, $x = -1$, -2

connectED.mcgraw-hill.com 545

Additional Example

4 Consider $f(x) = -x^2 - 2x - 2$.

a. Determine whether the function has a maximum or a minimum value. maximum

b. State the maximum or minimum value of the function. -1

c. State the domain and range of the function. domain: all real numbers; range: $\{y|y \le -1\}$

2 Graph Quadratic Functions

Example 5 shows how to use the characteristics of a quadratic function to graph the function. **Example 6** shows how to analyze the graph of a quadratic function to solve real-world problems.

WatchOut!

Minimum and Maximum Values Don't forget to find both coordinates of the vertex (x, y). The minimum or maximum value is the y-coordinate.

ReviewVocabulary

Domain and Range The domain is the set of all of the possible values of the independent variable x. The range is the set of all of the possible values of the dependent variable y.

Example 4 Maximum and Minimum Values

Consider $f(x) = -2x^2 - 4x + 6$.

a. Determine whether the function has a *maximum* or *minimum* value.

For $f(x) = -2x^2 - 4x + 6$, $a = -2$, $b = -4$, and $c = 6$.

Because a is negative the graph opens down, so the function has a maximum value.

b. State the maximum or minimum value of the function.

The maximum value is the y-coordinate of the vertex.

The x-coordinate of the vertex is $\frac{-b}{2a}$ or $\frac{4}{2(-2)}$ or -1.

$f(x) = -2x^2 - 4x + 6$	Original function
$f(-1) = -2(-1)^2 - 4(-1) + 6$	$x = -1$
$f(-1) = 8$	Simplify.

The maximum value is 8.

c. State the domain and range of the function.

The domain is all real numbers. The range is all real numbers less than or equal to the maximum value, or $\{y \mid y \le 8\}$.

GuidedPractice

Consider $g(x) = 2x^2 - 4x - 1$.

4A. Determine whether the function has a *maximum* or *minimum* value. **minimum**

4B. State the maximum or minimum value. **-3**

4C. State the domain and range of the function.

4C. D = all real numbers, R = $\{y|y \ge -3\}$

2 Graph Quadratic Functions

You have learned how to find several important characteristics of quadratic functions.

KeyConcept Graph Quadratic Functions

Step 1 Find the equation of the axis of symmetry.

Step 2 Find the vertex, and determine whether it is a maximum or minimum.

Step 3 Find the y-intercept.

Step 4 Use symmetry to find additional points on the graph, if necessary.

Step 5 Connect the points with a smooth curve.

Focus on Mathematical Content

Vertex The maximum or minimum point of a parabola is called the *vertex*. When a quadratic function is written in standard form $y = ax^2 + bx + c$, and a is positive, the parabola opens upward, and the vertex is a minimum. When a is negative, the parabola opens downward, and the vertex is a maximum.

StudyTip

Symmetry and Points When locating points that are on opposite sides of the axis of symmetry, not only are the points equidistant from the axis of symmetry, they are also equidistant from the vertex.

Example 5 Graph Quadratic Functions

Graph $f(x) = x^2 + 4x + 3$.

Step 1 Find the equation of the axis of symmetry.

$x = \frac{-b}{2a}$ Formula for the equation of the axis of symmetry

$x = \frac{-4}{2 \cdot 1}$ or -2 $a = 1$ and $b = 4$

Step 2 Find the vertex, and determine whether it is a maximum or minimum.

$f(x) = x^2 + 4x + 3$ Original equation

$= (-2)^2 + 4(-2) + 3$ $x = -2$

$= -1$ Simplify.

The vertex lies at $(-2, -1)$. Because a is positive the graph opens up, and the vertex is a minimum.

Step 3 Find the y-intercept.

$f(x) = x^2 + 4x + 3$ Original equation

$= (0)^2 + 4(0) + 3$ $x = 0$

$= 3$ The y-intercept is 3.

Step 4 The axis of symmetry divides the parabola into two equal parts. So if there is a point on one side, there is a corresponding point on the other side that is the same distance from the axis of symmetry and has the same y-value.

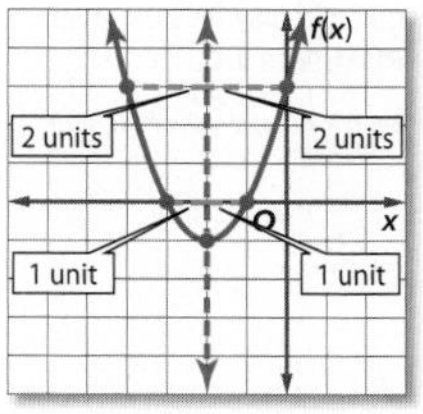

Step 5 Connect the points with a smooth curve.

GuidedPractice **Graph each function.**

5A. $f(x) = -2x^2 + 2x - 1$ **5B.** $f(x) = 3x^2 - 6x + 2$

5A.

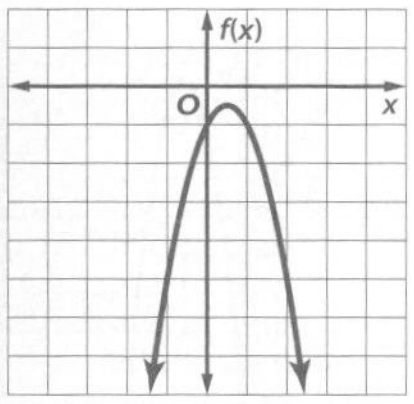

5B.

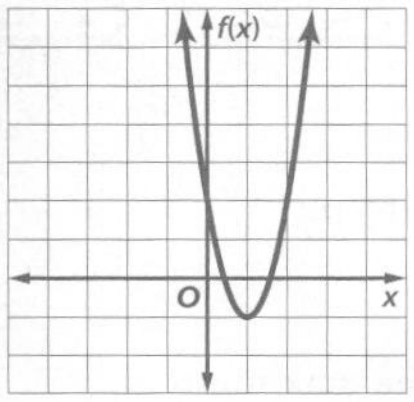

There are general differences between linear, exponential, and quadratic functions.

	Linear Functions	Exponential Functions	Quadratic Functions
Equation	$y = mx + b$	$y = ab^x, a \neq 0, b > 0, b \neq 1$	$y = ax^2 + bx + c, a \neq 0$
Degree	1	x	2
Graph	line	curve	parabola
Increasing / Decreasing	$m > 0$: y is increasing on the entire domain. $m < 0$: y is decreasing on the entire domain.	$a > 0, b > 1$ or $a < 0, 0 < b < 1$: y is increasing on the entire domain. $a > 0, 0 < b < 1$ or $a < 0, b > 1$: y is decreasing on the entire domain.	$a > 0$: y is decreasing to the left of the axis of symmetry and increasing on the right. $a < 0$: y is increasing to the left of the axis of symmetry and decreasing on the right.
End Behavior	$m > 0$: as x increases, y increases; as x decreases, y decreases $m < 0$: as x increases, y decreases; as x decreases, y increases	$b > 1$: as x decreases, y approaches 0; $a > 0$, as x increases, y increases; $a < 0$, as x increases, y decreases. $0 < b < 1$: as x increases, y approaches 0; $a > 0$, as x decreases, y increases; $a < 0$, as x decreases, y decreases.	$a > 0$: as x increases, y increases; as x decreases, y increases. $a < 0$: as x increases, y decreases; as x decreases, y decreases

WatchOut!

Preventing Errors Tell students that their sketches of parabolas do not have to be perfect. However, students should not "connect the dots" with straight lines. The important thing is for the curve to pass through the graphed ordered pairs.

Symmetry and Graphing

When students use symmetry to graph parabolas, they only need to find a few points and then reflect those points across the line of symmetry. You may want to suggest that students occasionally check their reflected points by substituting them into the original equation.

Additional Example

5 Graph $f(x) = -x^2 + 5x - 2$.

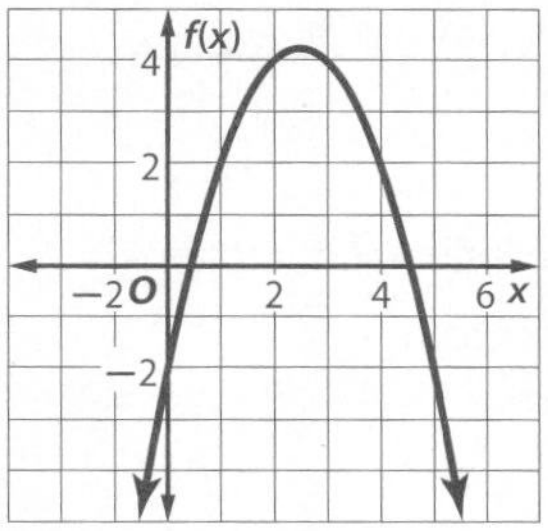

DifferentiatedInstruction AL OL

If students need a visual to understand the concept of a vertex and an axis of symmetry,

Then ask students to make a table of values and graph $y = x^2 + 6x + 8$ on grid paper. Have students hold their paper up to the light and fold their parabola in half so that the two sides match exactly. Have students use the crease on their unfolded paper to locate the vertex, axis of symmetry, and minimum value. $(-3, -1)$; $x = -3$; -1

Additional Example

6 ARCHERY Ben shoots an arrow. The height of the arrow can be modeled by $y = -16x^2 + 100x + 4$, where y represents the height in feet of the arrow x seconds after it is shot into the air.

a. Graph the height of the arrow.

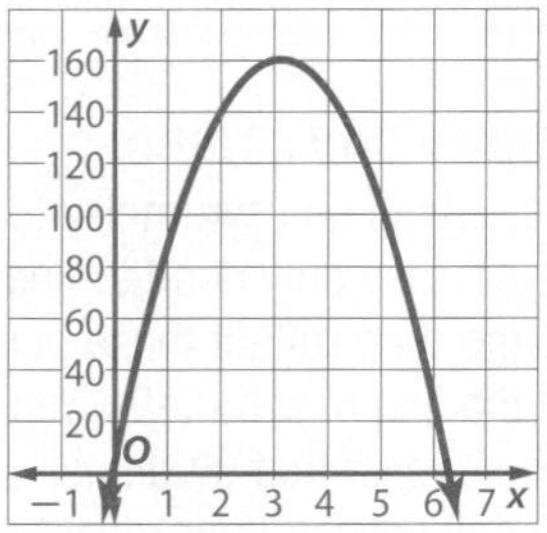

b. At what height was the arrow shot? 4 feet

c. What is the maximum height of the arrow? $160\frac{1}{4}$ feet

Additional Answers

13a. maximum

13b. 1

13c. D = {all real numbers}; R = $\{y \mid y \leq 1\}$

14a. maximum

14b. 3

14c. D = {all real numbers}; R = $\{y \mid y \leq 3\}$

15a. maximum

15b. 6

15c. D = {all real numbers}; R = $\{y \mid y \leq 6\}$

16a. maximum

16b. 2

16c. D = {all real numbers}; R = $\{y \mid y \leq 2\}$

17.

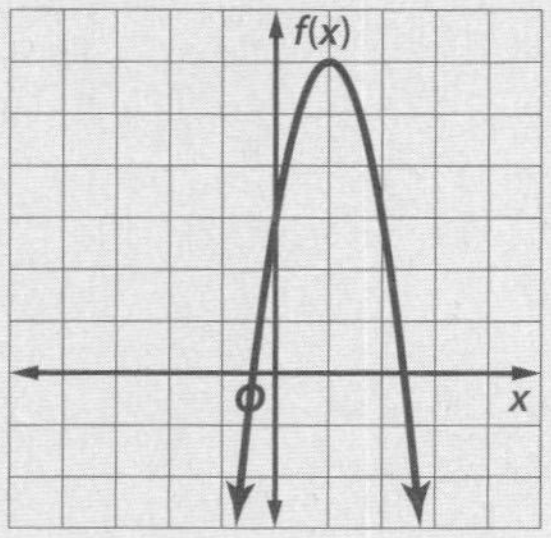

18.

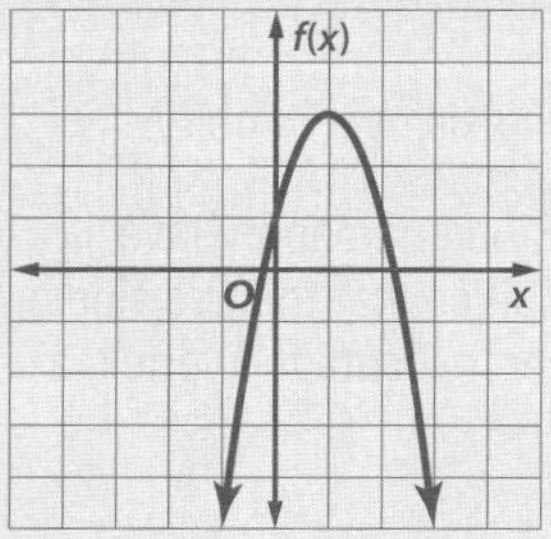

19.

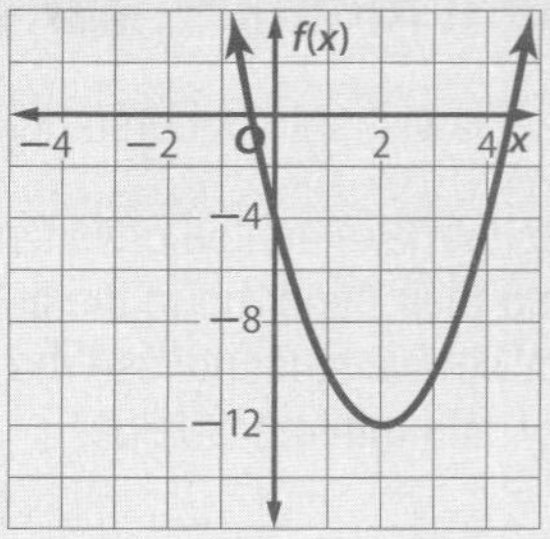

You have used what you know about quadratic functions, parabolas, and symmetry to create graphs. You can analyze these graphs to solve real-world problems.

Real-WorldLink

About 1 in 17 high school seniors playing football will go on to play football at an NCAA school.

Source: National Collegiate Athletic Association

Real-World Example 6 Use a Graph of a Quadratic Function

SCHOOL SPIRIT The cheerleaders at Lake High School launch T-shirts into the crowd every time the Lakers score a touchdown. The height of the T-shirt can be modeled by the function $h(x) = -16x^2 + 48x + 6$, where $h(x)$ represents the height in feet of the T-shirt after x seconds.

a. Graph the function.

$x = -\frac{b}{2a}$ — Equation of the axis of symmetry

$x = -\frac{48}{2(-16)}$ or $\frac{3}{2}$ — $a = -16$ and $b = 48$

The equation of the axis of symmetry is $x = \frac{3}{2}$. Thus, the x-coordinate for the vertex is $\frac{3}{2}$.

$y = -16x^2 + 48x + 6$ — Original equation

$= -16\left(\frac{3}{2}\right)^2 + 48\left(\frac{3}{2}\right) + 6$ — $x = \frac{3}{2}$

$= -16\left(\frac{9}{4}\right) + 48\left(\frac{3}{2}\right) + 6$ — $\left(\frac{3}{2}\right)^2 = \frac{9}{4}$

$= -36 + 72 + 6$ or 42 — Simplify.

The vertex is at $\left(\frac{3}{2}, 42\right)$.

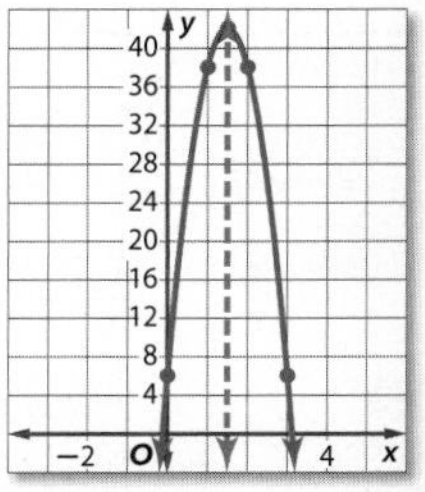

Let's find another point. Choose an x-value of 0 and substitute. Our new point is at (0, 6). The point paired with it on the other side of the axis of symmetry is (3, 6).

Repeat this and choose an x-value of 1 to get (1, 38) and its corresponding point (2, 38). Connect these points and create a smooth curve.

b. At what height was the T-shirt launched?

The T-shirt is launched when time equals 0, or at the y-intercept.

So, the T-shirt was launched 6 feet from the ground.

c. What is the maximum height of the T-shirt? When was the maximum height reached?

The maximum height of the T-shirt occurs at the vertex.

So the T-shirt reaches a maximum height of 42 feet. The time was $\frac{3}{2}$ or 1.5 seconds after launch.

6A.

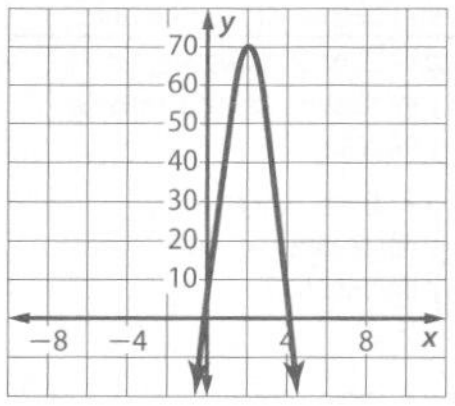

GuidedPractice

6. TRACK Emilio is competing in the javelin throw. The height of the javelin can be modeled by the equation $y = -16x^2 + 64x + 6$, where y represents the height in feet of the javelin after x seconds.

A. Graph the path of the javelin.

B. At what height is the javelin thrown? **6 ft**

C. What is the maximum height of the javelin? **70 ft**

Check Your Understanding

= Step-by-Step Solutions begin on page R13.

Example 1 Use a table of values to graph each equation. State the domain and range. **1–4. See Ch. 9 Answer Appendix.**

1. $y = 2x^2 + 4x - 6$ **2.** $y = x^2 + 2x - 1$

3. $y = x^2 - 6x - 3$ **4.** $y = 3x^2 - 6x - 5$

Example 2 Find the vertex, the equation of the axis of symmetry, and the y-intercept of each graph.

5.

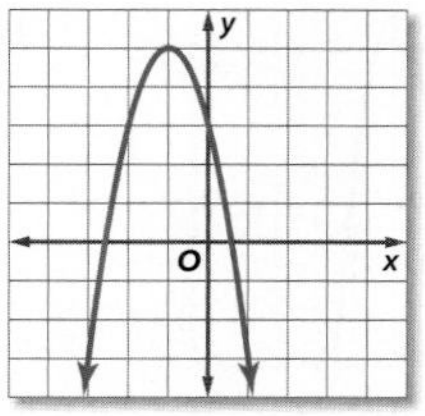

6.

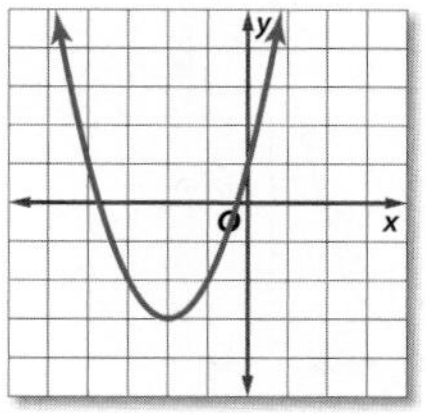

7.

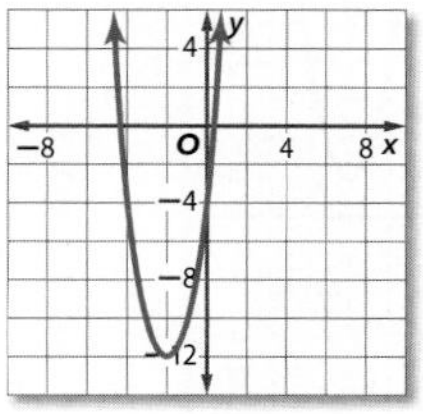

8.

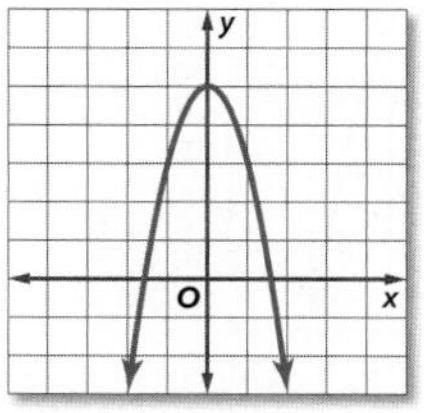

5. vertex $(-1, 5)$, axis of symmetry $x = -1$, y-intercept 3
6. vertex $(-2, -3)$, axis of symmetry $x = -2$, y-intercept 1
7. vertex $(-2, -12)$, axis of symmetry $x = -2$, y-intercept -4
8. vertex $(0, 5)$, axis of symmetry $x = 0$, y-intercept 5
9. vertex $(1, 2)$, axis of symmetry $x = 1$, y-intercept -1
10. vertex $(1, 2)$, axis of symmetry $x = 1$, y-intercept 1
11. vertex $(2, 1)$, axis of symmetry $x = 1$, y-intercept 5

Example 3 Find the vertex, the equation of the axis of symmetry, and the y-intercept of the graph of each function.

9. $y = -3x^2 + 6x - 1$ **10.** $y = -x^2 + 2x + 1$

11. $y = x^2 - 4x + 5$ **12.** $y = 4x^2 - 8x + 9$ **vertex (1, 5), axis of symmetry $x = 1$, y-intercept 9**

Example 4 Consider each function. **13–16. See margin.**

a. Determine whether the function has *maximum* or *minimum* value.

b. State the maximum or minimum value.

c. What are the domain and range of the function?

13 $y = -x^2 + 4x - 3$ **14.** $y = -x^2 - 2x + 2$

15. $y = -3x^2 + 6x + 3$ **16.** $y = -2x^2 + 8x - 6$

Example 5 Graph each function. **17–20. See margin.**

17. $f(x) = -3x^2 + 6x + 3$ **18.** $f(x) = -2x^2 + 4x + 1$

19. $f(x) = 2x^2 - 8x - 4$ **20.** $f(x) = 3x^2 - 6x - 1$

Example 6 **21. REASONING** A juggler is tossing a ball into the air. The height of the ball in feet can be modeled by the equation $y = -16x^2 + 16x + 5$, where y represents the height of the ball at x seconds.

a. Graph this equation. **See margin.**

b. At what height is the ball thrown? **5 ft**

c. What is the maximum height of the ball? **9 ft**

3 Practice

Formative Assessment

Use Exercises 1–21 to check for understanding.

Use the chart at the bottom of this page to customize assignments for your students.

Exercise Alert

Grid Paper For Exercises 1–4, 17–27, 52–58, 63, and 68 students will need grid paper.

Teaching the Process Standards

Reasoning Mathematically proficient students make sense of quantities and their relationships in problem situations. In Exercise 21, discuss with students why the coefficient of x^2 is negative.

Additional Answers

20.

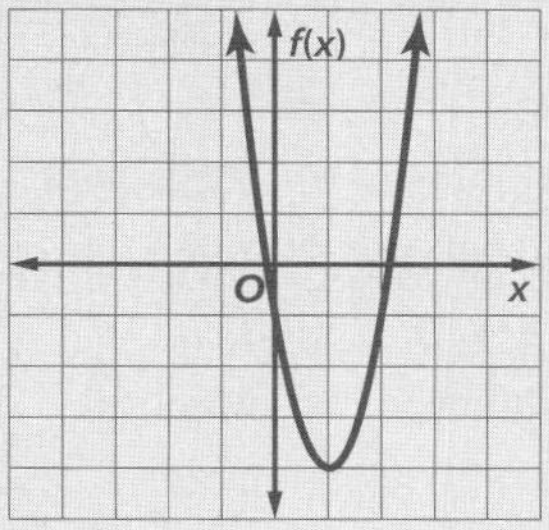

21a.

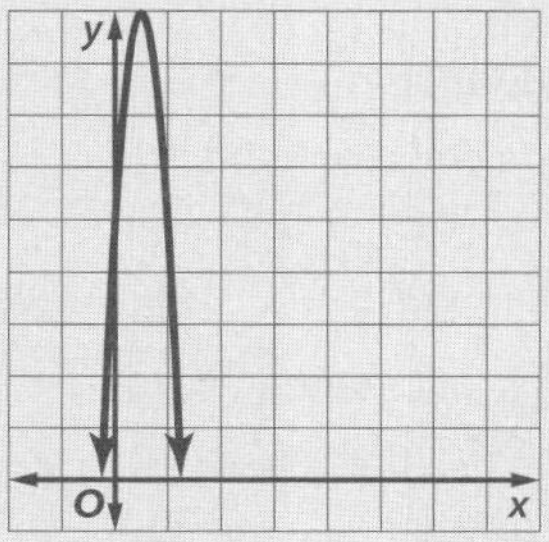

Differentiated Homework Options

Level	Assignment	Two-Day Option	
AL Basic	22–58, 68, 69, 71–95	23–57 odd, 75–78	22–58 even, 68, 69, 71–74, 79–95
OL Core	23–63 odd, 64–69, 71–95	22–58, 75–78	59–69, 71–74, 79–95
BL Advanced	59–92, (optional: 93–95)		

Practice and Problem Solving

Extra Practice is on page R9.

22–27. See Ch. 9 Answer Appendix.

Example 1 Use a table of values to graph each equation. State the domain and range.

22. $y = x^2 + 4x + 6$ **23.** $y = 2x^2 + 4x + 7$ **24.** $y = 2x^2 - 8x - 5$

25. $y = 3x^2 + 12x + 5$ **26.** $y = 3x^2 - 6x - 2$ **27.** $y = x^2 - 2x - 1$

Example 2 Find the vertex, the equation of the axis of symmetry, and the y-intercept of each graph.

28.

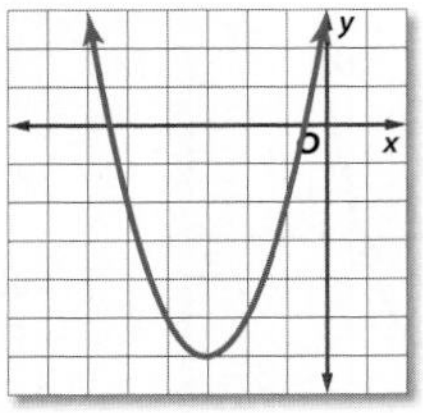

29.

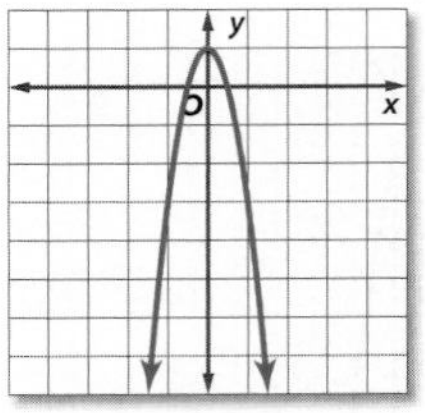

30.

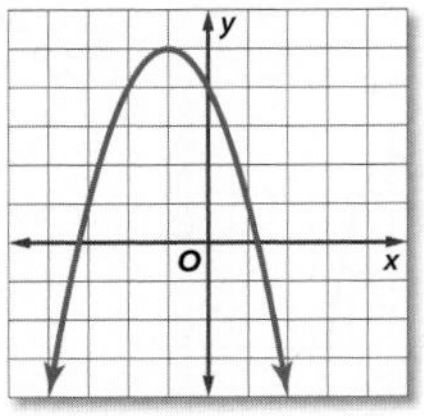

31.

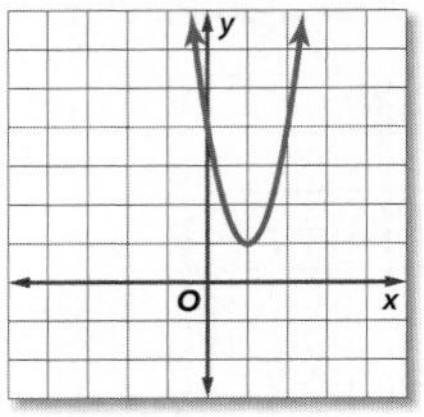

32.

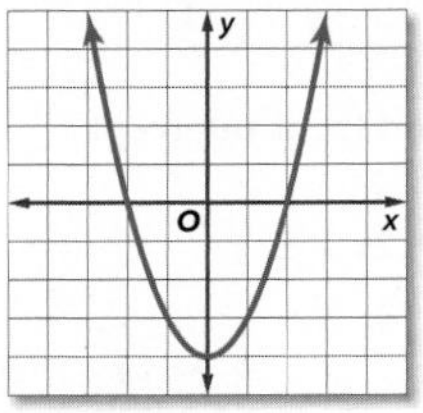

33.

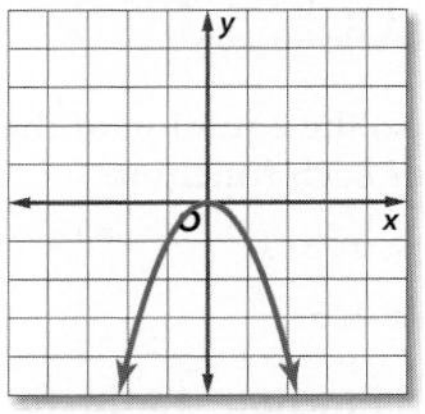

28. vertex (−3, −6), axis of symmetry $x = -3$, y-intercept 3
29. vertex (0, 1), axis of symmetry $x = 0$, y-intercept 1
30. vertex (−1, 5), axis of symmetry $x = -1$, y-intercept 4
31. vertex (1, 1), axis of symmetry $x = 1$, y-intercept 4
32. vertex (0, −4), axis of symmetry $x = 0$, y-intercept −4
33. vertex (0, 0), axis of symmetry $x = 0$, y-intercept 0

Example 3 Find the vertex, the equation of the axis of symmetry, and the y-intercept of each function. 34–42. See margin.

34. $y = x^2 + 8x + 10$ **35.** $y = 2x^2 + 12x + 10$ **36.** $y = -3x^2 - 6x + 7$

37. $y = -x^2 - 6x - 5$ **38.** $y = 5x^2 + 20x + 10$ **39.** $y = 7x^2 - 28x + 14$

40. $y = 2x^2 - 12x + 6$ **41.** $y = -3x^2 + 6x - 18$ **42.** $y = -x^2 + 10x - 13$

Example 4 Consider each function. 43–51. See margin.

a. Determine whether the function has a *maximum* or *minimum* value.

b. State the maximum or minimum value.

c. What are the domain and range of the function?

43. $y = -2x^2 - 8x + 1$ **44.** $y = x^2 + 4x - 5$ **45.** $y = 3x^2 + 18x - 21$

46. $y = -2x^2 - 16x + 18$ **47.** $y = -x^2 - 14x - 16$ **48.** $y = 4x^2 + 40x + 44$

49. $y = -x^2 - 6x - 5$ **50.** $y = 2x^2 + 4x + 6$ **51.** $y = -3x^2 - 12x - 9$

Example 5 Graph each function. 52–57. See Ch. 9 Answer Appendix.

52. $y = -3x^2 + 6x - 4$ **53.** $y = -2x^2 - 4x - 3$ **54.** $y = -2x^2 - 8x + 2$

55. $y = x^2 + 6x - 6$ **56.** $y = x^2 - 2x + 2$ **57.** $y = 3x^2 - 12x + 5$

Additional Answers

34. vertex (−4, −6), axis of symmetry $x = -4$, y-intercept 10
35. vertex (−3, −8), axis of symmetry $x = -3$, y-intercept 10
36. vertex (−1, 10), axis of symmetry $x = -1$, y-intercept 7
37. vertex (−3, 4), axis of symmetry $x = -3$, y-intercept −5
38. vertex (−2, −10), axis of symmetry $x = -2$, y-intercept 10
39. vertex (2, −14), axis of symmetry $x = 2$, y-intercept 14
40. vertex (3, −12), axis of symmetry $x = 3$, y-intercept 6
41. vertex (1, −15), axis of symmetry $x = 1$, y-intercept −18
42. vertex (5, 12), axis of symmetry $x = 5$, y-intercept −13

43a. maximum **43b.** 9
43c. D = {all real numbers}, R = $\{y \mid y \leq 9\}$
44a. minimum **44b.** −9
44c. D = {all real numbers}, R = $\{y \mid y \geq -9\}$
45a. minimum **45b.** −48
45c. D = {all real numbers}, R = $\{y \mid y \geq -48\}$
46a. maximum **46b.** 50
46c. D = {all real numbers}, R = $\{y \mid y \leq 50\}$
47a. maximum **47b.** 33
47c. D = {all real numbers}, R = $\{y \mid y \leq 33\}$
48a. minimum **48b.** −56
48c. D = {all real numbers}, R = $\{y \mid y \geq -56\}$
49a. maximum **49b.** 4
49c. D = {all real numbers}, R = $\{y \mid y \leq 4\}$
50a. minimum **50b.** 4
50c. D = {all real numbers}, R = $\{y \mid y \geq 4\}$
51a. maximum **51b.** 3
51c. D = {all real numbers}, R = $\{y \mid y \leq 3\}$

58a.

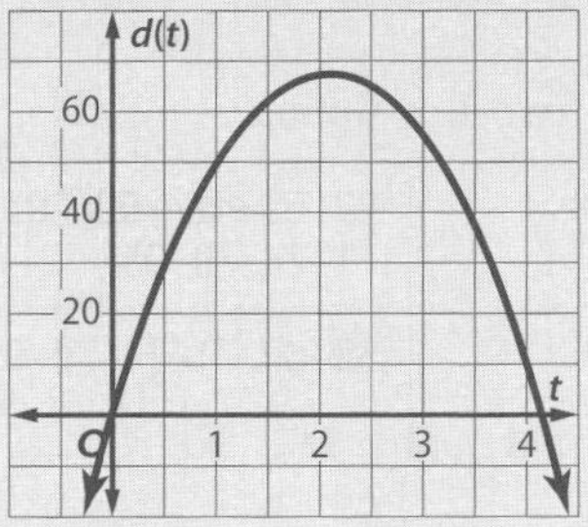

63a.

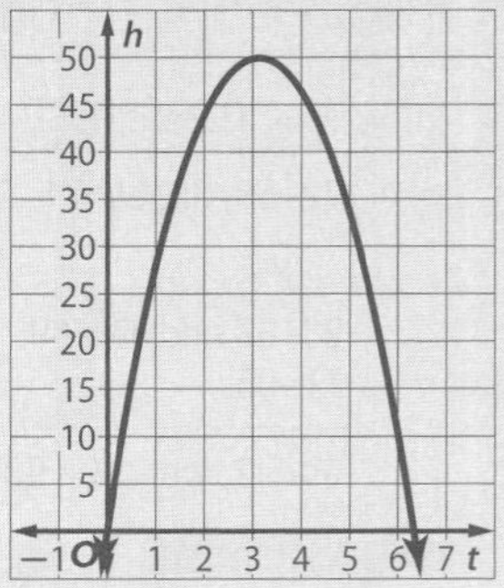

Where $h > 0$, the ball is above the ground. The height of the ball decreases as more time passes.

Example 6

58. BOATING Miranda has her boat docked on the west side of Casper Point. She is boating over to Casper Marina, which is located strictly east of where her boat is docked. The equation $d = -16t^2 + 66t$ models the distance she travels north of her starting point, where d is the number of feet and t is the time traveled in minutes.

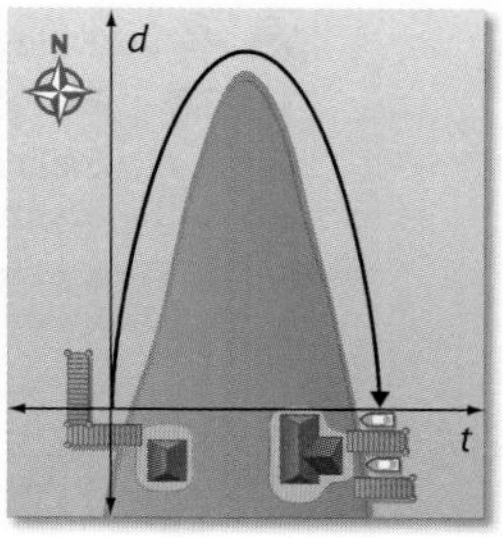

a. Graph this equation. **See margin.**

b. What is the maximum number of feet north that she traveled? **about 68 ft**

c. How long did it take her to reach Casper Marina? **about 4 min**

B **GRAPHING CALCULATOR** **Graph each equation. Use the TRACE feature to find the vertex on the graph. Round to the nearest thousandth if necessary.** **59–62. See Ch. 9 Answer Appendix for graphs.**

59. $y = 4x^2 + 10x + 6$ **(−1.25, −0.25)**

60. $y = 8x^2 - 8x + 8$ **(0.5, 6)**

61. $y = -5x^2 - 3x - 8$ **(−0.3, −7.55)**

62. $y = -7x^2 + 12x - 10$ **(0.857, −4.857)**

63. GOLF The average amateur golfer can hit a ball with an initial upward velocity of 31.3 meters per second. The height can be modeled by the equation $h = -4.9t^2 + 31.3t$, where h is the height of the ball, in meters, after t seconds.

a. Graph this equation. What do the portions of the graph where $h > 0$ represent in the context of the situation? What does the end behavior of the graph represent? **See margin.**

b. At what height is the ball hit? **0 m**

c. What is the maximum height of the ball? **about 50.0 m**

d. How long did it take for the ball to hit the ground? **about 6.4 s**

e. State a reasonable range and domain for this situation. $D = \{t \mid 0 \leq t \leq 6.4\}$; $R = \{h \mid 0 \leq h \leq 50.0\}$

64. FUNDRAISING The marching band is selling poinsettias to buy new uniforms. Last year the band charged \$5 each, and they sold 150. They want to increase the price this year, and they expect to lose 10 sales for each \$1 increase. The sales revenue R, in dollars, generated by selling the poinsettias is predicted by the function $R = (5 + p)(150 - 10p)$, where p is the number of \$1 price increases.

a. Write the function in standard form. $R = -10p^2 + 100p + 750$

b. Find the maximum value of the function. **1000**

c. At what price should the poinsettias be sold to generate the most sales revenue? Explain your reasoning. **\$10; Sample answer: The maximum revenue is generated by five \$1 increases. The original price was \$5, so the new price should be \$10.**

65. FOOTBALL A football is kicked up from ground level at an initial upward velocity of 90 feet per second. The equation $h = -16t^2 + 90t$ gives the height h of the football after t seconds.

a. What is the height of the ball after one second? **74 ft**

b. When is the ball 126 feet high? **2.625 seconds and 3 seconds**

c. When is the height of the ball 0 feet? What do these points represent in the context of the situation? $t = 0$, $t = 5.625$; **before the ball is kicked, and when the ball hits the ground after the kick**

C **66. STRUCTURE** Let $f(x) = x^2 - 9$.

a. What is the domain of $f(x)$? **{all real numbers}**

b. What is the range of $f(x)$? $\{f(x) \mid f(x) \geq -9\}$

c. For what values of x is $f(x)$ negative? $\{x \mid -3 < x < 3\}$

d. When x is a real number, what are the domain and range of $f(x) = \sqrt{x^2 - 9}$?

66d. $D = \{x \mid x \leq -3 \text{ or } x \geq 3\}$, $R = \{y \mid y \geq 0\}$

Teaching the Process Standards

Structure Mathematically proficient students can step back for an overview and shift perspective. In Exercise 66, ask students how the square and square root functions are related.

Study Guide and Intervention

AL OL BL

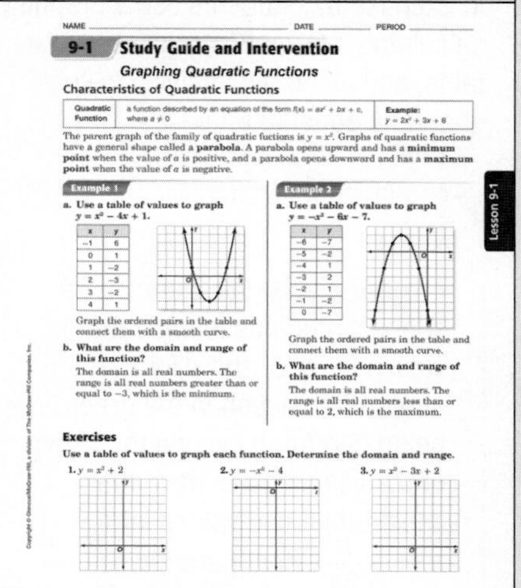
9-1 Study Guide and Intervention
Graphing Quadratic Functions
Characteristics of Quadratic Functions

Practice

AL OL BL ELL

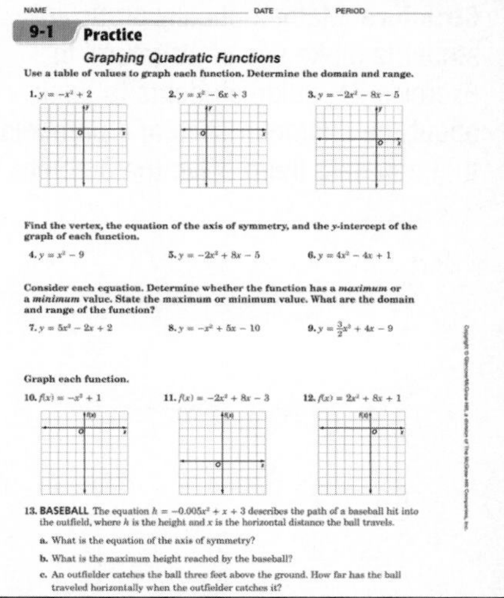
9-1 Practice
Graphing Quadratic Functions

Word Problem Practice

AL OL BL ELL

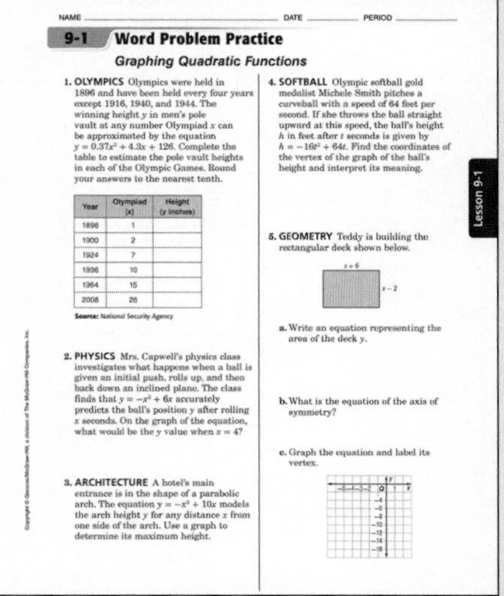
9-1 Word Problem Practice
Graphing Quadratic Functions

Enrichment

OL BL

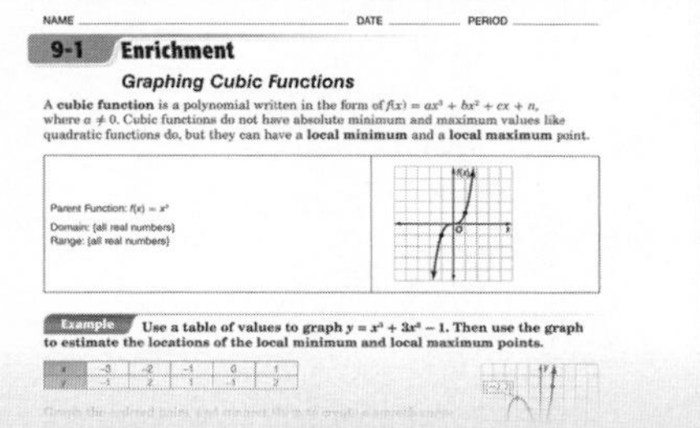
9-1 Enrichment
Graphing Cubic Functions

Multiple Representations

In Exercise 67, students use a graphing calculator, information organized in a table, and algebraic analysis to solve quadratic equations.

WatchOut!

Error Analysis For Exercise 69, suggest students identify the values for a, b, and c for the quadratic function in the graph, being careful to include the signs of the values. Then have them substitute those values into $x = -\frac{b}{2a}$, using parentheses as necessary.

Teaching the Process Standards

Structure Mathematically proficient students make use of structure. In Exercise 71, guide students to think about the characteristics of a parabola that can help them solve the problem.

67. **MULTIPLE REPRESENTATIONS** In this problem, you will investigate solving quadratic equations using tables.

a. **Algebraic** Determine the related function for each equation. Copy and complete the first two columns of the table below.

Equation	Related Function	Zeros	y-Values
$x^2 - x = 12$	$y = x^2 - x - 12$	−3, 4	−3; 8, −6; 4; −6, 8
$x^2 + 8x = 9$	$y = x^2 + 8x - 9$	−9, 1	−9; 11, −9; 1; −9, 11
$x^2 = 14x - 24$	$y = x^2 - 14x + 24$	2, 12	2; 11, −9; 12; −9. 11
$x^2 + 16x = -28$	$y = x^2 + 16x + 28$	−14, −2	−14; 13, −11; −2; −11, 13

b. **Graphical** Graph each related function with a graphing calculator. **See margin.**

c. **Analytical** The number of zeros is equal to the degree of the related function. Use the table feature on your calculator to determine the zeros of each related function. Record the zeros in the table above. Also record the values of the function one unit less than and one unit more than each zero. **See table.**

d. **Verbal** Examine the function values for x-values just before and just after a zero. What happens to the sign of the function value before and after a zero? **The function values have opposite signs just before and just after a zero.**

H.O.T. Problems Use Higher-Order Thinking Skills

68. **OPEN ENDED** Write a quadratic function for which the graph has an axis of symmetry of $x = -\frac{3}{8}$. Summarize your steps. **See margin.**

69. **ERROR ANALYSIS** Jade thinks that the parabolas represented by the graph and the description have the same axis of symmetry. Chase disagrees. Who is correct? Explain your reasoning.
Chase; the lines of symmetry are $x = 2$ and $x = 1.5$.

a parabola that opens downward, passing through (0, 6) and having a vertex at (2, 2)

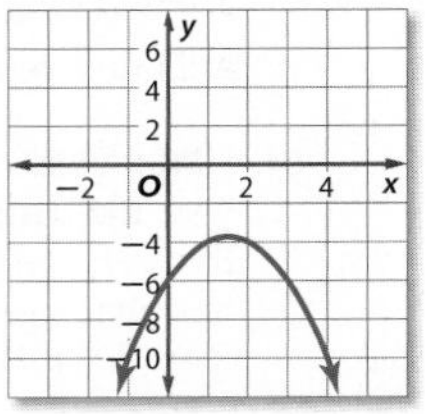

70. **CHALLENGE** Using the axis of symmetry, the y-intercept, and one x-intercept, write an equation for the graph shown.
$y = -x^2 + 6x + 16$

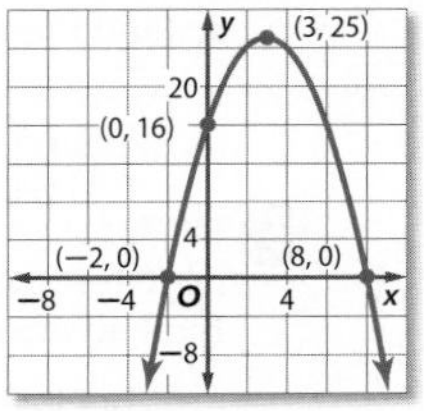

71. **STRUCTURE** The graph of a quadratic function has a vertex at (2, 0). One point on the graph is (5, 9). Find another point on the graph. Explain how you found it. **See margin.**

72. **OPEN ENDED** Describe a real-world situation that involves a quadratic equation. Explain what the vertex represents. **Sample answer: A football is kicked during a game. The vertex gives the maximum height of the ball.**

73. **REASONING** Provide a counterexample that is a specific case to show that the following statement is false. *The vertex of a parabola is always the minimum of the graph.*
Sample answer: The function $y = -x^2 - 4$ has a vertex at (0, −4), but it is a maximum.

74. **WRITING IN MATH** Use tables and graphs to compare and contrast an exponential function $f(x) = ab^x + c$, where $a \neq 0$, $b > 0$, and $b \neq 1$, a quadratic function $g(x) = ax^2 + c$, and a linear function $h(x) = ax + c$. Include intercepts, portions of the graph where the functions are increasing, decreasing, positive, or negative, relative maxima and minima, symmetries, and end behavior. Which function eventually exceeds the others? **See Ch. 9 Answer Appendix.**

Additional Answers

67b.

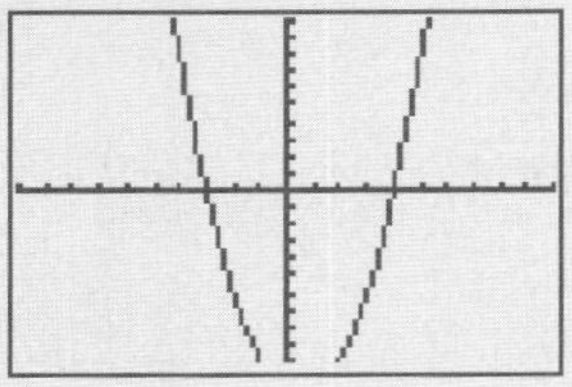

[−10, 10] scl: 1 by [−10, 10] scl: 1

$y = x^2 - x - 12$

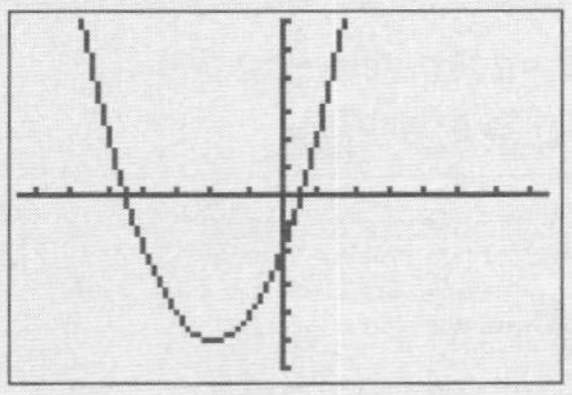

[−15, 15] scl: 2 by [−30, 30] scl: 5

$y = x^2 + 8x - 9$

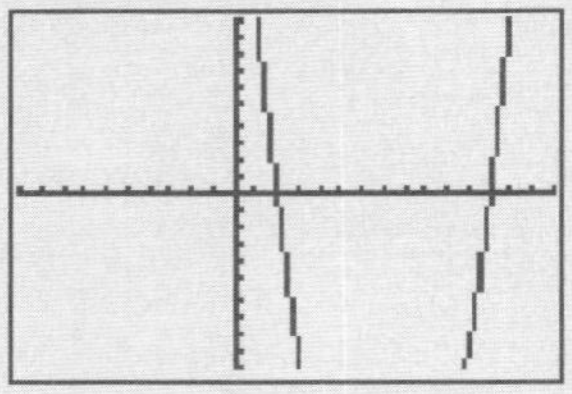

[−10, 15] scl: 1 by [−10, 10] scl: 1

$y = x^2 - 14x + 24$

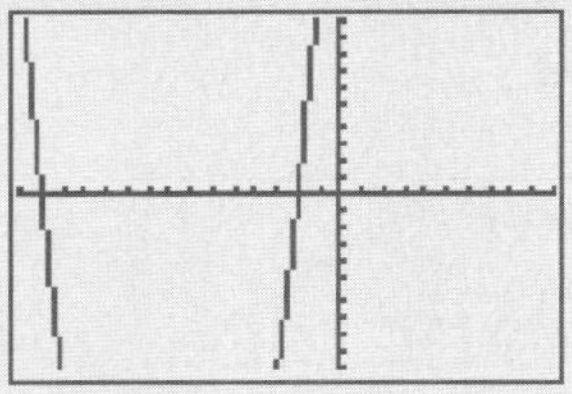

[−15, 10] scl: 1 by [−10, 10] scl: 1

$y = x^2 + 16x + 28$

552 | Lesson 9-1 | Graphing Quadratic Functions

Standardized Test Practice

75. Which of the following is an equation for the line that passes through (2, −5) and is perpendicular to $2x + 4y = 8$? **C**

A $y = 2x + 10$

B $y = -\frac{1}{2}x - 4$

C $y = 2x - 9$

D $y = -2x - 1$

76. GEOMETRY The area of the circle is 36π square units. If the radius is doubled, what is the area of the new circle? **G**

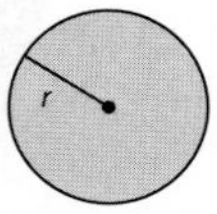

$A = 36\pi$

F 1296π units^2

G 144π units^2

H 72π units^2

J 9π units^2

77. What is the range of the function $f(x) = -4x^2 - \frac{1}{2}$? **D**

A $\left\{\text{all integers less than or equal to } \frac{1}{2}\right\}$

B {all nonnegative integers}

C {all real numbers}

D $\left\{\text{all real numbers less than or equal to } -\frac{1}{2}\right\}$

78. SHORT RESPONSE Dylan delivers newspapers for extra money. He starts delivering the newspapers at 3:15 P.M. and finishes at 5:05 P.M. How long does it take Dylan to complete his route? **1 hour 50 min**

Spiral Review

Determine whether each trinomial is a perfect square trinomial. Write *yes* or *no*. If so, factor it. (Lesson 8-9)

79. $4x^2 + 4x + 1$ **yes; $(2x + 1)^2$**

80. $4x^2 - 20x + 25$ **yes; $(2x - 5)^2$**

81. $9x^2 + 8x + 16$ **no**

Factor each polynomial if possible. If the polynomial cannot be factored, write *prime*. (Lesson 8-8)

82. $n^2 - 16$ **$(n - 4)(n + 4)$**

83. $x^2 + 25$ **prime**

84. $9 - 4a^2$ **$(3 - 2a)(3 + 2a)$**

Find each product. (Lesson 8-3)

85. $(b - 7)(b + 3)$ **$b^2 - 4b - 21$**

86. $(c - 6)(c - 5)$ **$c^2 - 11c + 30$**

87. $(2x - 1)(x + 9)$ **$2x^2 + 17x - 9$**

88. MULTIPLE BIRTHS The number of quadruplet births Q in the United States in recent years can be modeled by $Q = -0.5t^3 + 11.7t^2 - 21.5t + 218.6$, where t represents the number of years since 2002. What is the expected number of quadruplet births in the United States in 2017? (Lesson 8-1) **about 841**

Use elimination to solve each system of equations. (Lesson 6-4)

89. $2x + y = 5$, $3x - 2y = 4$ **(2, 1)**

90. $4x - 3y = 12$, $x + 2y = 14$ **(6, 4)**

91. $2x - 3y = 2$, $5x + 4y = 28$ **(4, 2)**

92. HEALTH About 20% of the time you sleep is spent in rapid eye movement (REM), which is associated with dreaming. If an adult sleeps 7 to 8 hours, how much time is spent in REM sleep? (Lesson 5-4) **between 1.4 and 1.6 hours, inclusive**

Skills Review

Find the *x*-intercept of the graph of each equation.

93. $x + 2y = 10$ **10**

94. $2x - 3y = 12$ **6**

95. $3x - y = -18$ **−6**

Differentiated Instruction OL BL

Extension Tell students that a fireworks rocket is designed to explode at its highest point. The height is given by the equation $h = -4.9t^2 + 34.2t + 1.6$, where h is the rocket's height in meters after t seconds. At what time and height will the rocket explode? The rocket will explode after about 3.5 seconds at a height of approximately 61 meters.

4 Assess

Ticket Out the Door Make several copies each of the five graphs of quadratic functions. Give one graph to each student. As the students leave the room, ask them to tell you the coordinates of the parabolas' vertices and to identify them as maximums or minimums.

Additional Answers

68. Sample answer: $y = 4x^2 + 3x + 5$; Write the equation of the axis of symmetry, $x = -\frac{b}{2a}$. From the equation, $b = 3$ and $2a = 8$, so $a = 4$. Substitute these values for a and b into the equation $y = ax^2 + bx + c$.

71. $(-1, 9)$; Sample answer: I graphed the points given, and sketched the parabola that goes through them. I counted the spaces over and up from the vertex and did the same on the opposite side of the line $x = 2$.

1 Focus

Objective Use a given quadratic function to investigate the rate of change of a quadratic function.

Materials for Each Student

- grid paper

Teaching Tip

Students will need to make a table with 19 columns for Step 1 of the Activity.

2 Teach

Working in Cooperative Groups

Put students in groups of two or three, mixing abilities. Have groups complete the Activity.

Ask:

- What maximum and minimum x- and y-axis values do you need when drawing the coordinate system for the function in the Activity? x: 0 to 9, y: 0 to 324
- How does the rate of change of a quadratic function differ from the rate of change of a linear function? A linear function has a constant rate of change, so it never changes sign. The rate of change of a quadratic function is positive on some intervals and negative on others.

Practice Have students complete Exercises 1–4.

EXTEND 9-1

Algebra Lab

Rate of Change of a Quadratic Function

A model rocket is launched from the ground with an upward velocity of 144 feet per second. The function $y = -16x^2 + 144x$ models the height y of the rocket in feet after x seconds. Using this function, we can investigate the rate of change of a quadratic function.

Activity

Step 1 Copy the table below.

x	0	0.5	1.0	1.5	…	9.0
y	0					
Rate of Change	–					

(0.5, 68), (1, 128), (1.5, 180), (2, 224), (2.5, 260), (3, 288), (3.5, 308), (4, 320), (4.5, 324), (5, 320), (5.5, 308), (6, 288), (6.5, 260), (7, 224), (7.5, 180), (8, 128), (8.5, 68), (9, 0)

Step 2 Find the value of y for each value of x from 0 through 9.

Step 3 Graph the ordered pairs (x, y) on grid paper. Connect the points with a smooth curve. Notice that the function *increases* when $0 < x < 4.5$ and *decreases* when $4.5 < x < 9$.

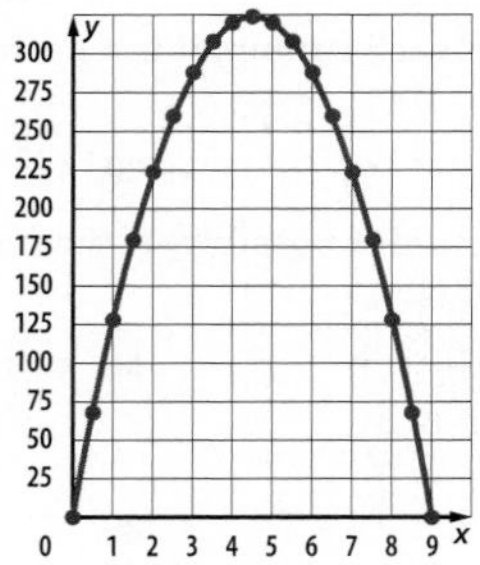

Step 4 Recall that the *rate of change* is the change in y divided by the change in x. Find the rate of change for each half second interval of x and y. 136, 120, 104, 88, 72, 56, 40, 24, 8, −8, −24, −40, −56, −72, −88, −104, −120, −136

Exercises

Use the quadratic function $y = x^2$. 1–4. See Ch. 9 Answer Appendix.

1. Make a table, similar to the one in the Activity, for the function using $x = -4, -3, -2, -1, 0, 1, 2, 3,$ and 4. Find the values of y for each x-value.
2. Graph the ordered pairs on grid paper. Connect the points with a smooth curve. Describe where the function is increasing and where it is decreasing.
3. Find the rate of change for each column starting with $x = -3$. Compare the rates of change when the function is increasing and when it is decreasing.
4. **CHALLENGE** If an object is dropped from 100 feet in the air and air resistance is ignored, the object will fall at a rate that can be modeled by the function $f(x) = -16x^2 + 100$, where $f(x)$ represents the object's height in feet after x seconds. Make a table like that in Exercise 1, selecting appropriate values for x. Fill in the x-values, the y-values, and rates of change. Compare the rates of change. Describe any patterns that you see.

3 Assess

Formative Assessment

Use Exercises 1–3 to assess whether students understand the rate of change in a quadratic function.

From Concrete to Abstract

Have students examine the situation in the Activity. Ask students how the equation and its rate of change will be affected if the model rocket is launched from the ground with an upward velocity of 44 meters per second. The equation (with rounded coefficients) will be $h = -5t^2 + 44t$. Since a meter is about 3.3 times as long as a foot, the coefficients in the equation for feet per second are divided by 3.3. The variables are not affected. The rates of change will change accordingly.

LESSON 9-2 Solving Quadratic Equations by Graphing

Then

- You solved quadratic equations by factoring.

Now

1. Solve quadratic equations by graphing.
2. Estimate solutions of quadratic equations by graphing.

Why?

- Dorton Arena at the state fairgrounds in Raleigh, North Carolina, has a shape created by two intersecting parabolas. The shape of one of the parabolas can be modeled by $y = -x^2 + 127x$, where x is the width of the parabola in feet, and y is the length of the parabola in feet. The x-intercepts of the graph of this function can be used to find the distance between the points where the parabola meets the ground.

NewVocabulary
double root

Content Standards
AI.QE.3, AI.QE.4, AI.QE.5, AI.QE.6, AI.QE.7

Process Standards
PS.3

1 Solve by Graphing

A quadratic equation can be written in the standard form $ax^2 + bx + c = 0$, where $a \neq 0$. To write a quadratic function as an equation, replace y or $f(x)$ with 0. Recall that the solutions or roots of an equation can be identified by finding the x-intercepts of the related graph. Quadratic equations may have two, one, or no real solutions.

KeyConcept Solutions of Quadratic Equations

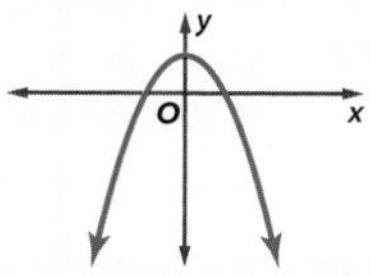

two unique real solutions

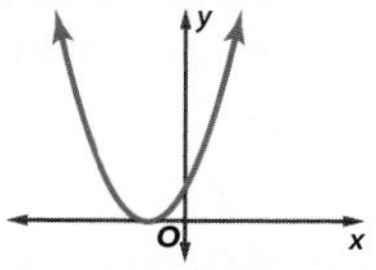

one unique real solution

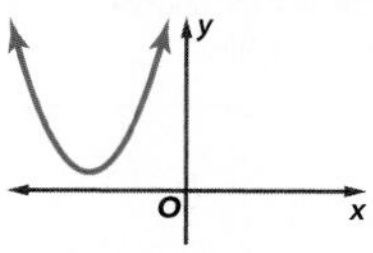

no real solutions

Example 1 Two Roots

Solve $x^2 - 2x - 8 = 0$ by graphing.

Graph the related function $f(x) = x^2 - 2x - 8$.

The x-intercepts of the graph appear to be at -2 and 4, so the solutions are -2 and 4.

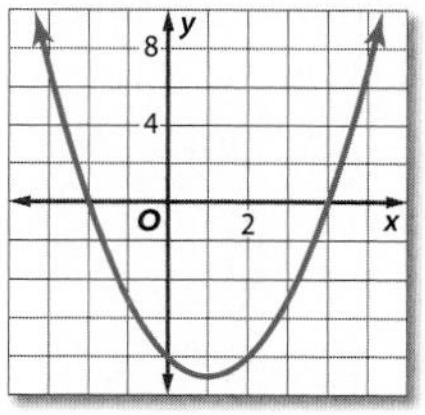

CHECK Check each solution in the original equation.

$x^2 - 2x - 8 = 0$	Original equation	$x^2 - 2x - 8 = 0$
$(-2)^2 - 2(-2) - 8 \stackrel{?}{=} 0$	$x = -2$ or $x = 4$	$(4)^2 - 2(4) - 8 \stackrel{?}{=} 0$
$0 = 0$ ✓	Simplify.	$0 = 0$ ✓

1A–1B. See Ch. 9 Answer Appendix for graphs.

GuidedPractice Solve each equation by graphing.

1A. $-x^2 - 3x + 18 = 0$ **3, −6**

1B. $x^2 - 4x + 3 = 0$ **1, 3**

1 Focus

VerticalAlignment

Before Lesson 9-2 Solve quadratic equations by factoring.

Lesson 9-2 Solve quadratic equations by graphing. Estimate solutions of quadratic equations by graphing.

After Lesson 9-2 Identify quadratic functions from given data.

2 Teach

Scaffolding Questions

Have students read the **Why?** section of the lesson.

Ask:

- If the x-intercepts represent where the parabola meets the ground, what represents the ground? the x-axis
- What are the x-intercepts of the graph of the equation? 0, 127
- What is the equation of the axis of symmetry? $x = 63.5$
- What is the distance between the points where the parabola meets the ground? 127 feet

Lesson 9-2 Resources

Resource	Approaching Level AL	On Level OL	Beyond Level BL	English Learners ELL
Teacher Edition	▪ Differentiated Instruction, p. 556	▪ Differentiated Instruction, p. 556	▪ Differentiated Instruction, p. 560	
Chapter Resource Masters	▪ Study Guide and Intervention, pp. 11–12 ▪ Skills Practice, p. 13 ▪ Practice, p. 14 ▪ Word Problem Practice, p. 15	▪ Study Guide and Intervention, pp. 11–12 ▪ Skills Practice, p. 13 ▪ Practice, p. 14 ▪ Word Problem Practice, p. 15 ▪ Enrichment, p. 16	▪ Practice, p. 14 ▪ Word Problem Practice, p. 15 ▪ Enrichment, p. 16	▪ Study Guide and Intervention, pp. 11–12 ▪ Skills Practice, p. 13 ▪ Practice, p. 14 ▪ Word Problem Practice, p. 15
Other	▪ 5-Minute Check 9-2 ▪ Study Notebook	▪ 5-Minute Check 9-2 ▪ Study Notebook	▪ 5-Minute Check 9-2 ▪ Study Notebook	▪ 5-Minute Check 9-2 ▪ Study Notebook

1 Solve By Graphing

Example 1 shows how to use a graph to find the two roots of a quadratic equation. **Example 2** shows how to use graphing to find the double root of a quadratic equation. **Example 3** shows how to use a graph to identify a quadratic equation that has no real number solutions.

Formative Assessment

Use the Guided Practice exercises after each example to determine students' understanding of concepts.

Additional Examples

1 Solve $x^2 - 3x - 10 = 0$ by graphing. $-2, 5$

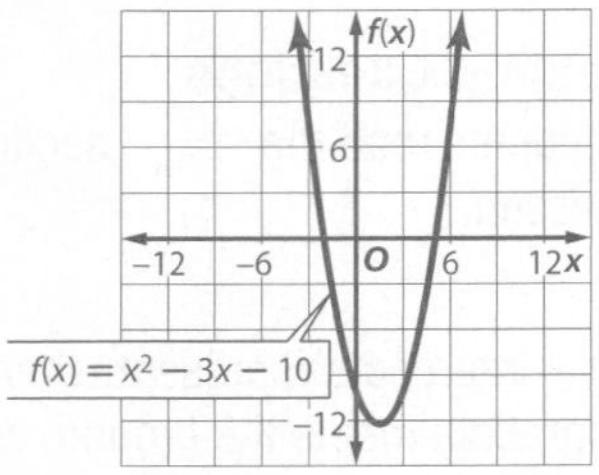

2 Solve $x^2 + 8x = -16$ by graphing. -4

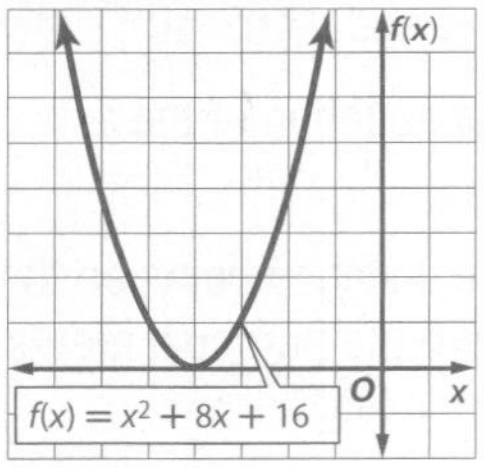

3 Solve $x^2 + 2x + 3 = 0$ by graphing. $\varnothing$

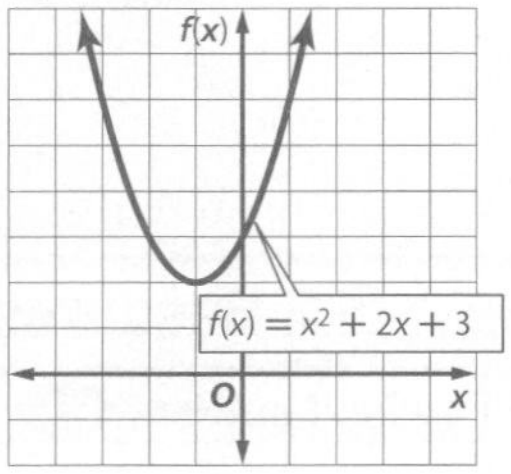

Additional Examples also in Interactive Classroom PowerPoint® Presentations

IWB Interactive White Board READY

The solutions in Example 1 were two distinct numbers. Sometimes the two roots are the same number, called a **double root**.

Example 2 Double Root

Solve $x^2 - 6x = -9$ by graphing.

Step 1 Rewrite the equation in standard form.

$x^2 - 6x = -9$ Original equation

$x^2 - 6x + 9 = 0$ Add 9 to each side.

Step 2 Graph the related function $f(x) = x^2 - 6x + 9$.

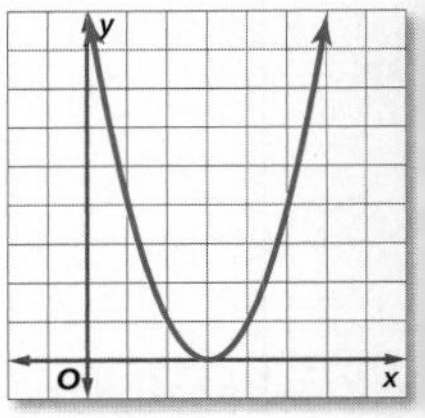

Step 3 Locate the x-intercepts of the graph. Notice that the vertex of the parabola is the only x-intercept. Therefore, there is only one solution, 3.

CHECK Solve by factoring.

$x^2 - 6x + 9 = 0$ Original equation

$(x - 3)(x - 3) = 0$ Factor.

$x - 3 = 0$ or $x - 3 = 0$ Zero Product Property

$x = 3$ $\quad x = 3$ Add 3 to each side.

The only solution is 3.

WatchOut!
Precision Solutions found from the graph of an equation may appear to be exact. Check them in the original equation to be sure.

GuidedPractice

Solve each equation by graphing. **2A–2B. See Ch. 9 Answer Appendix for graphs.**

2A. $x^2 + 25 = 10x$ **5** **2B.** $x^2 = -8x - 16$ **−4**

Sometimes the roots are not real numbers. Quadratic equations with solutions that are not real numbers lead us to extend the number system to allow for solutions of these equations. These numbers are called *complex numbers*. You will study complex numbers in Algebra 2.

Example 3 No Real Roots

Solve $2x^2 - 3x + 5 = 0$ by graphing.

Step 1 Rewrite the equation in standard form. This equation is written in standard form.

Step 2 Graph the related function $f(x) = 2x^2 - 3x + 5$.

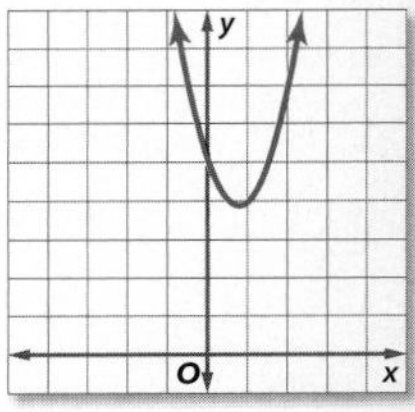

Step 3 Locate the x-intercepts of the graph. This graph has no x-intercepts. Therefore, this equation has no real number solutions. The solution set is $\varnothing$.

GuidedPractice

Solve each equation by graphing. **3A–3B. See Ch. 9 Answer Appendix for graphs.**

3A. $-x^2 - 3x = 5$ $\varnothing$ **3B.** $-2x^2 - 8 = 6x$ $\varnothing$

DifferentiatedInstruction AL OL

If students assume that the vertex of a parabola always has coordinates that are integers,

Then point out that in Example 3, the y-value for the vertex of the graph is greater than 3 and somewhat less than 4.

2 Estimate Solutions

Estimate Solutions The real roots found thus far have been integers. However, the roots of quadratic equations are usually not integers. In these cases, use estimation to approximate the roots of the equation.

Example 4 Approximate Roots with a Table

StudyTip
Location of Zeros
Since quadratic functions are continuous, there must be a zero between two x-values for which the corresponding y-values have opposite signs.

Solve $x^2 + 6x + 6 = 0$ by graphing. If integral roots cannot be found, estimate the roots to the nearest tenth.

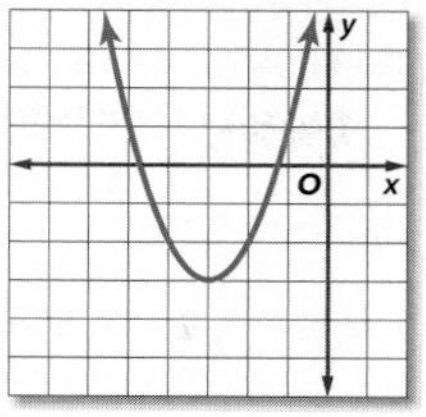

Graph the related function $f(x) = x^2 + 6x + 6$.

The x-intercepts are located between −5 and −4 and between −2 and −1.

Make a table using an increment of 0.1 for the x-values located between −5 and −4 and between −2 and −1.

Look for a change in the signs of the function values. The function value that is closest to zero is the best approximation for a zero of the function.

x	−4.9	−4.8	−4.7	−4.6	−4.5	−4.4	−4.3	−4.2	−4.1
y	0.61	0.24	−0.11	−0.44	−0.75	−1.04	−1.31	−1.56	−1.79

x	−1.9	−1.8	−1.7	−1.6	−1.5	−1.4	−1.3	−1.2	−1.1
y	−1.79	−1.56	−1.31	−1.04	−0.75	−0.44	−0.11	0.24	0.61

For each table, the function value that is closest to zero when the sign changes is −0.11. Thus, the roots are approximately −4.7 and −1.3.

GuidedPractice

4. Solve $2x^2 + 6x - 3 = 0$ by graphing. If integral roots cannot be found, estimate the roots to the nearest tenth. **0.4, −3.4**

Real-WorldLink
The game of soccer, called "football" outside of North America, began in 1863 in Britain when the Football Association was founded. Soccer is played on every continent of the world.

Source: Sports Know How

Approximating the x-intercepts of graphs is helpful for real-world applications.

Real-World Example 5 Approximate Roots with a Calculator

SOCCER A goalie kicks a soccer ball with an upward velocity of 65 feet per second, and her foot meets the ball 1 foot off the ground. The quadratic function $h = -16t^2 + 65t + 1$ represents the height of the ball h in feet after t seconds. Approximately how long is the ball in the air?

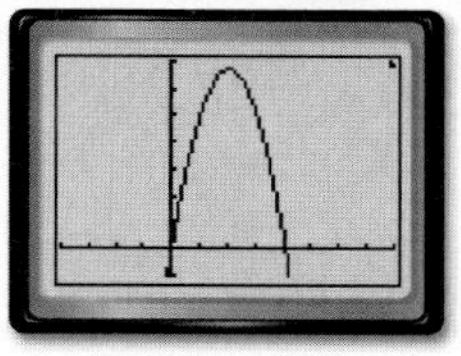

[−4, 7] scl: 1 by [−10, 70] scl: 10

You need to find the roots of the equation $-16t^2 + 65t + 1 = 0$. Use a graphing calculator to graph the related function $f(x) = -16t^2 + 65t + 1$.

The positive x-intercept of the graph is approximately 4. Therefore, the ball is in the air for approximately 4 seconds.

GuidedPractice

5. If the goalie kicks the soccer ball with an upward velocity of 55 feet per second and his foot meets the ball 2 feet off the ground, approximately how long is the ball in the air? **3.5 seconds**

2 Estimate Solutions

Example 4 shows how to use graphing and a table of values to estimate roots of a quadratic equation when integral roots cannot be found. **Example 5** shows how to estimate a solution to a real-world problem involving quadratic equations.

Additional Examples

4 Solve $x^2 - 4x + 2 = 0$ by graphing. If integral roots cannot be found, estimate the roots to the nearest tenth. 0.6, 3.4

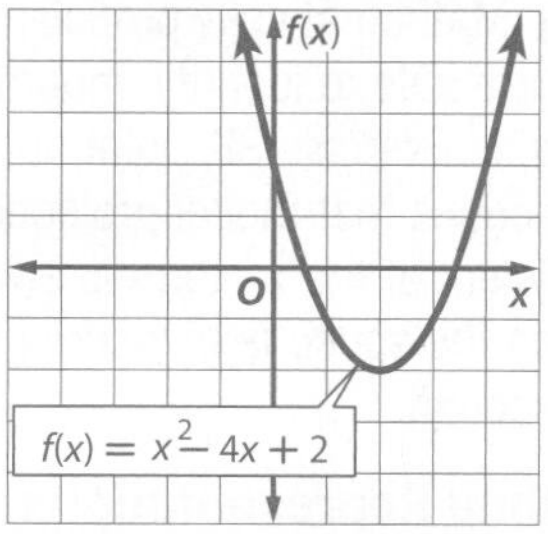

5 **MODEL ROCKETS** Consuela built a model rocket for her science project. The equation $h = -16t^2 + 250t$ models the flight of the rocket launched from ground level at a velocity of 250 feet per second, where h is the height of the rocket in feet after t seconds. Approximately how long was Consuela's rocket in the air? 15.6 seconds

Teach with Tech

Portable Media Player Load images of graphs of quadratic functions onto your class web page for students to download to their portable media players. For each graph, have students find the zeros of the function.

Teaching the Process Standards

Precision Mathematically proficient students calculate accurately and efficiently. Discuss with students why a graph may not give an exact answer.

Focus on Mathematical Content

No Real Roots Creating a table of values before graphing a function helps to reveal whether a function has no x-intercepts. If all y-values of a function are positive, first decreasing then increasing, or if all are negative, first increasing then decreasing, the graph of the function does not cross the x-axis, and there are no real roots. In Algebra 2, students will learn that when quadratic equations have no real solutions the number system must be extended so that solutions exist, similar to the way whole numbers are extended to the negative numbers to allow $x + 1 = 0$ to have a solution.

Double Root When there are two identical factors for the trinomial in a quadratic equation, there is only one root, called a *double root*. If either the greatest or least y-value in the range is 0, then the vertex is on the x-axis and the solution is a double root.

3 Practice

Formative Assessment

Use Exercises 1–9 to check for understanding.

Use the chart at the bottom of this page to customize assignments for students.

Exercise Alert

Grid Paper For Exercises 1–8, 10–27, 38, 51–56, and 71–76, students will need grid paper.

Teaching the Process Standards

Modeling Mathematically proficient students are able to identify important quantities. In Exercise 36, point out that in the functions that model projectiles the coefficient of the x^2-term is always -16 when the speed is measured in feet per second.

Multiple Representations

In Exercise 38, students use graphing and analysis to compare related quadratic functions.

Additional Answers

41. Iku; sample answer: The zeros of a quadratic function are the x-intercepts of the graph. Since the graph does not intersect the x-axis, there are no x-intercepts and no real zeros.

42. Sample answer: A tennis ball being hit in the air; an equation is $h = -16t^2 + 25t + 2$. The ball is in the air for about 1.6 seconds.

43. Sometimes; for (1, 3), the y-value is greater than 2, but for (1, −1), it is less than 2.

45. 1.5 and −1.5; Sample answer: Make a table of values for x from −2.0 to 2.0. Use increments of 0.1.

46. First graph the related function. Then determine between which two integers the graph crosses the x-axis. Make a table going by tenths of the values between the integers. Locate where the function value changes signs. The x-value for which the function value is closest to zero is the best approximation of the root of the equation.

Check Your Understanding

= Step-by-Step Solutions begin on page R13.

Examples 1–3 Solve each equation by graphing. **1–4. See Ch. 9 Answer Appendix for graphs.**

1. $x^2 + 3x - 10 = 0$ **2, −5**

2. $2x^2 - 8x = 0$ **0, 4**

3. $x^2 + 4x = -4$ **−2**

4. $x^2 + 12 = -8x$ **−6, −2**

Example 4 Solve each equation by graphing. If integral roots cannot be found, estimate the roots to the nearest tenth. **5–8. See Ch. 9 Answer Appendix for graphs.**

5. $-x^2 - 5x + 1 = 0$ **−5.2, 0.2**

6. $-9 = x^2$ **no solutions**

7. $x^2 = 25$ **5, −5**

8. $x^2 - 8x = -9$ **6.6, 1.4**

Example 5

9. SCIENCE FAIR Ricky built a model rocket. Its flight can be modeled by the equation shown, where h is the height of the rocket in feet after t seconds. About how long was Ricky's rocket in the air? **about 8.4 seconds**

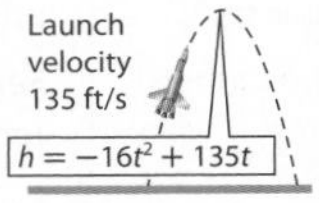

Practice and Problem Solving

Extra Practice is on page R9.

Examples 1–3 Solve each equation by graphing. **10–21. See Ch. 9 Answer Appendix for graphs.**

10. $x^2 + 7x + 14 = 0$ **∅**

11. $x^2 + 2x - 24 = 0$ **4, −6**

12. $x^2 - 16x + 64 = 0$ **8**

13. $x^2 - 5x + 12 = 0$ **∅**

14. $x^2 + 14x = -49$ **−7**

15. $x^2 = 2x - 1$ **1**

16. $x^2 - 10x = -16$ **2, 8**

17. $-2x^2 - 8x = 13$ **∅**

18. $2x^2 - 16x = -30$ **3, 5**

19. $2x^2 = -24x - 72$ **−6**

20. $-3x^2 + 2x = 15$ **∅**

21. $x^2 = -2x + 80$ **8, −10**

Example 4 Solve each equation by graphing. If integral roots cannot be found, estimate the roots to the nearest tenth. **22–27. See Ch. 9 Answer Appendix for graphs.**

22. $x^2 + 2x - 9 = 0$ **2.2, −4.2**

23. $x^2 - 4x = 20$ **6.9, −2.9**

24. $x^2 + 3x = 18$ **3, −6**

25. $2x^2 - 9x = -8$ **3.3, 1.2**

26. $3x^2 = -2x + 7$ **1.2, −1.9**

27. $5x = 25 - x^2$ **3.1, −8.1**

Example 5

28. SOFTBALL The equation $h = -16t^2 + 47t + 3$ models the height h, in feet, of a ball that Sofia hits after t seconds. How long is the ball in the air? **3 seconds**

B

29. RIDES The Terror Tower launches riders straight up and returns straight down. The equation $h = -16t^2 + 122t$ models the height h, in feet, of the riders from their starting position after t seconds. How long is it until the riders return to the bottom? **about 7.6 seconds**

Use factoring to determine how many times the graph of each function intersects the x-axis. Identify each zero.

30. $y = x^2 - 8x + 16$ **1; 4**

31. $y = x^2 + 4x + 4$ **1; −2**

32. $y = x^2 + 2x - 24$ **2; −6, 4**

33. $y = x^2 + 12x + 32$ **2; −4, −8**

34. NUMBER THEORY Use a quadratic equation to find two numbers that have a sum of 9 and a product of 20. **4, 5**

35. NUMBER THEORY Use a quadratic equation to find two numbers that have a sum of 1 and a product of −12. **−3, 4**

36. MODELING The height of a golf ball in the air can be modeled by the equation $h = -16t^2 + 76t$, where h is the height in feet of the ball after t seconds.

a. How long was the ball in the air? **about 4.5 seconds**

b. What is the ball's maximum height? **about 81 ft**

c. When will the ball reach its maximum height? **about 2.2 seconds**

Differentiated Homework Options

Level	Assignment	Two-Day Option	
AL Basic	10–28, 41–43, 46–76	11–27 odd, 47–50	10–28 even, 41–43, 46, 51–76
OL Core	11–33 odd, 34–43, 46–76	10–28, 47–50	29–43, 46, 51–76
BL Advanced	29–70, (optional: 71–76)		

37. **SKIING** Stefanie is in a freestyle aerial competition. The equation $h = -16t^2 + 30t + 10$ models Stefanie's height h, in feet, t seconds after leaving the ramp.

a. How long is Stefanie in the air? **about 2.2 seconds**

b. When will Stefanie reach a height of 15 feet? **about 1.7 seconds and 0.2 seconds**

c. To earn bonus points in the competition, you must reach a height of 20 feet. Will Stefanie earn bonus points? **Yes; Stefanie's maximum height is about 24 ft.**

38. **MULTIPLE REPRESENTATIONS** In this problem, you will explore how to further interpret the relationship between quadratic functions and graphs.

a. **Graphical** Graph $y = x^2$. **a, c. See Ch. 9 Answer Appendix.**

b. **Analytical** Name the vertex and two other points on the graph. **(0, 0); Sample answers: (1, 1), (−1, 1)**

c. **Graphical** Graph $y = x^2 + 2$, $y = x^2 + 4$, and $y = x^2 + 6$ on the same coordinate plane as the previous graph.

d. **Analytical** Name the vertex and two points from each of these graphs that have the same x-coordinates as the first graph.

e. **Analytical** What conclusion can you draw from this?

38d. $y = x^2 + 2$: **(0, 2), (1, 3), (−1, 3);** $y = x^2 + 4$: **(0, 4), (1, 5), (−1, 5);** $y = x^2 + 6$: **(0, 6), (1, 7), (−1, 7)**

GRAPHING CALCULATOR Solve each equation by graphing.

39. $x^3 - 3x^2 - 6x + 8 = 0$ **−2, 1, 4**

40. $x^3 - 8x^2 + 15x = 0$ **0, 3, 5**

38e. Sample answer: The graphs of $y = x^2 + 2$, $y = x^2 + 4$, and $y = x^2 + 6$ can be obtained by moving the graph of $y = x^2$ straight up 2 units, 4 units, and 6 units, respectively.

H.O.T. Problems Use Higher-Order Thinking Skills

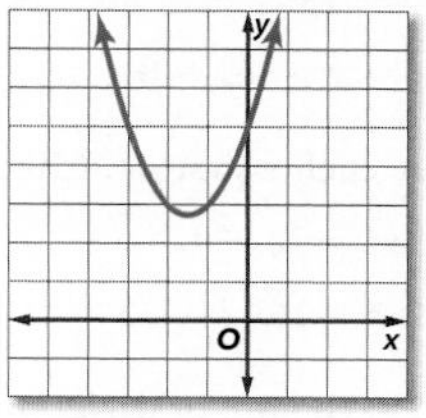

41. **CRITIQUE** Iku and Zachary are finding the number of real zeros of the function graphed at the right. Iku says that the function has no real zeros because there are no x-intercepts. Zachary says that the function has one real zero because the graph has a y-intercept. Is either of them correct? Explain your reasoning. **See margin.**

42. **OPEN ENDED** Describe a real-world situation in which a thrown object travels in the air. Write an equation that models the height of the object with respect to time, and determine how long the object travels in the air. **See margin.**

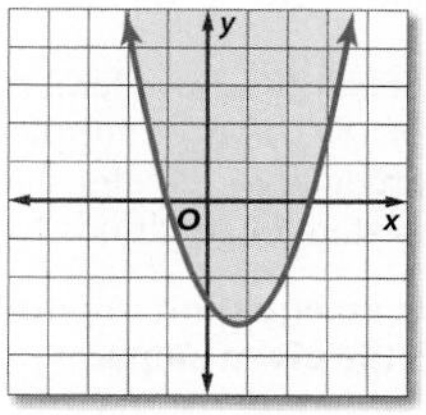

43. **REASONING** The graph shown is that of a *quadratic inequality*. Analyze the graph, and determine whether the y-value of a solution of the inequality is *sometimes*, *always*, or *never* greater than 2. Explain. **See margin.**

44. **CHALLENGE** Write a quadratic equation that has the roots described.

a. one double root **Sample answer: $x^2 + 8x + 16 = 0$**

b. one rational (nonintegral) root and one integral root

c. two distinct integral roots that are additive opposites. **Sample answer: $x^2 - 4 = 0$**

44b. Sample answer: $2x^2 - 23x + 45 = 0$

45. **CHALLENGE** Find the roots of $x^2 = 2.25$ without using a calculator. Explain your strategy. **See margin.**

46. **WRITING IN MATH** Explain how to approximate the roots of a quadratic equation when the roots are not integers. **See margin.**

Study Guide and Intervention

AL OL ELL

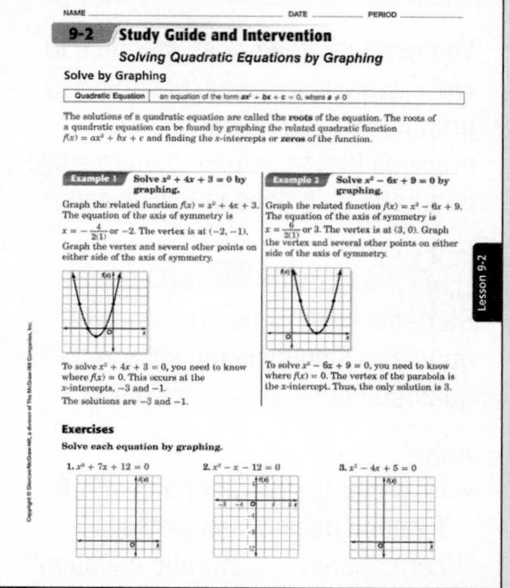
9-2 Study Guide and Intervention
Solving Quadratic Equations by Graphing

Practice

AL OL BL ELL

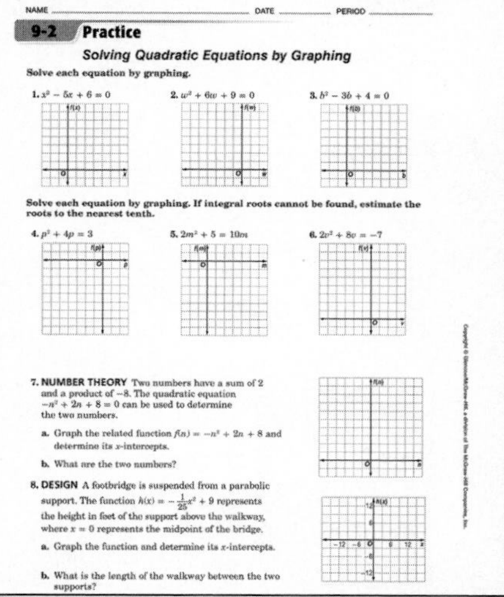
9-2 Practice
Solving Quadratic Equations by Graphing

Word Problem Practice

AL OL BL ELL

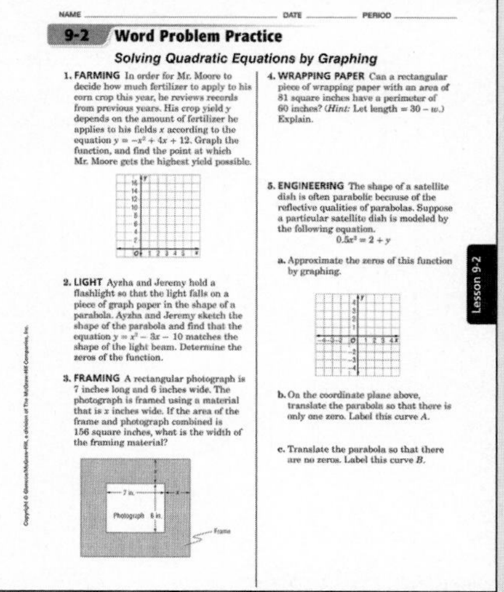
9-2 Word Problem Practice
Solving Quadratic Equations by Graphing

Teaching the Process Standards

Critique Mathematically proficient students can read the arguments of others and decide whether they make sense. In Exercise 41, ask students to recall that the solutions or roots of an equation can be identified by finding the x-intercepts or zeros of the related function.

Enrichment

OL BL

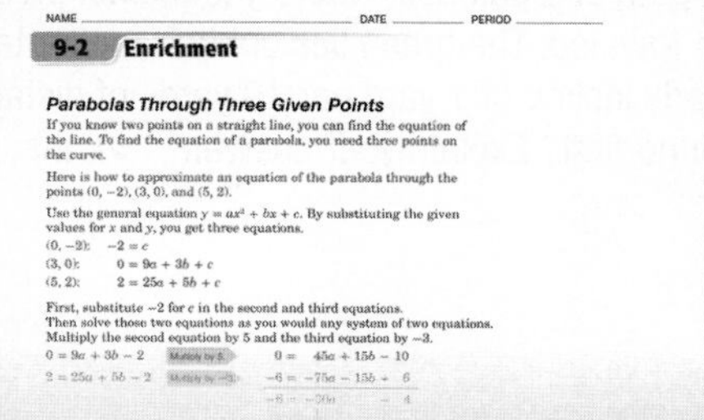
9-2 Enrichment
Parabolas Through Three Given Points

4 Assess

Yesterday's News Ask students to write two ways in which learning to graph quadratic functions in the previous lesson helped them to solve quadratic equations in this lesson.

Essential Question

Students have explored graphs of quadratic functions and solving quadratic equations by graphing.

Ask:

- How can the graph of a quadratic function help you solve the corresponding quadratic equation? Sample answer: From the placement of the graph, you can see whether there are 0, 1, or 2 real solutions. The symmetry of the graph helps you identify a second solution when one solution is found.

Additional Answer

49.

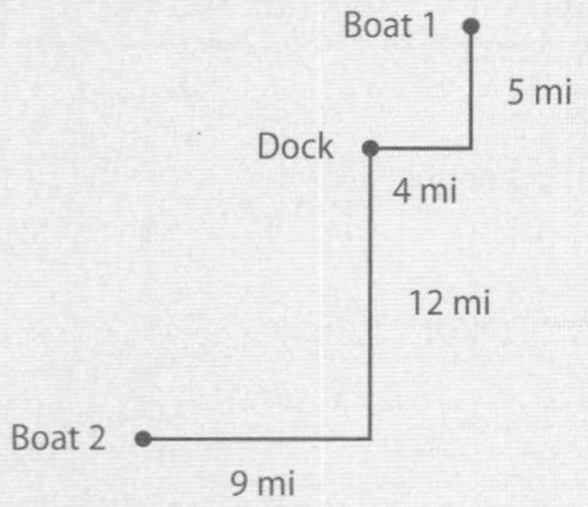

about 21.4 mi

Standardized Test Practice

47. Adrahan earned 50 out of 80 points on a test. What percentage did Adrahan score on the test? **A**

A 62.5% B 16% C 6.25% D 1.6%

48. Ernesto needs to loosen a bolt. He needs a wrench that is smaller than a $\frac{7}{8}$-inch wrench, but larger than a $\frac{3}{4}$-inch wrench. Which of the following sizes should Ernesto use? **H**

F $\frac{3}{8}$ inch G $\frac{5}{8}$ inch H $\frac{13}{16}$ inch J $\frac{15}{16}$ inch

49. EXTENDED RESPONSE Two boats leave a dock. One boat travels 4 miles east and then 5 miles north. The second boat travels 12 miles south and 9 miles west. Draw a diagram that represents the paths traveled by the boats. How far apart are the boats in miles? **See margin.**

50. The formula $s = \frac{1}{2}at^2$ represents the distance s in meters that a free-falling object will fall on a planet or moon in a given time t in seconds. Solve the formula for a, the acceleration due to gravity. **D**

A $a = \frac{1}{2}t^2 - s$ B $a = 2s - t^2$ C $a = s - \frac{1}{2}t^2$ D $a = \frac{2s}{t^2}$

Spiral Review

Write the equation of the axis of symmetry, and find the coordinates of the vertex of the graph of each function. Identify the vertex as a maximum or minimum. Then graph the function. (Lesson 9-1) **51–56. See Ch. 9 Answer Appendix.**

51. $y = 3x^2$ **52.** $y = -4x^2 - 5$ **53.** $y = -x^2 + 4x - 7$

54. $y = x^2 - 6x - 8$ **55.** $y = 3x^2 + 2x + 1$ **56.** $y = -4x^2 - 8x + 5$

Solve each equation. Check the solutions. (Lesson 8-9)

57. $2x^2 = 32$ **−4, 4** **58.** $(x - 4)^2 = 25$ **−1, 9** **59.** $4x^2 - 4x + 1 = 16$ $-\frac{3}{2}, \frac{5}{2}$

60. $2x^2 + 16x = -32$ **−4** **61.** $(x + 3)^2 = 5$ $-3 \pm \sqrt{5}$ **62.** $4x^2 - 12x = -9$ $\frac{3}{2}$

Find each sum or difference. (Lesson 8-1) **65.** $-3b^4 + 2b^3 - 9b^2 + 13$ **66.** $6h^4 + 2h^3 + h^2 + 5$

63. $(3n^2 - 3) + (4 + 4n^2)$ $7n^2 + 1$ **64.** $(2d^2 - 7d - 3) - (4d^2 + 7)$ $-2d^2 - 7d - 10$

65. $(2b^3 - 4b^2 + 4) - (3b^4 + 5b^2 - 9)$ **66.** $(8 - 4h^2 + 6h^4) + (5h^2 - 3 + 2h^3)$

67. GEOMETRY Supplementary angles are two angles with measures that have a sum of 180°. For the supplementary angles in the figure, the measure of the larger angle is 24° greater than the measure of the smaller angle. Write and solve a system of equations to find these measures. (Lesson 6-5) $x + y = 180$; $x = y + 24$; 102°, 78°

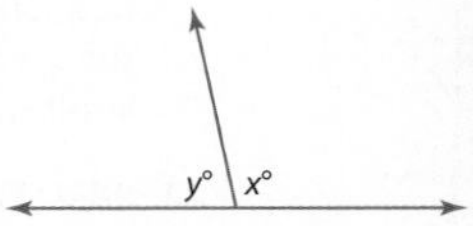

Write an equation in point-slope form for the line that passes through each point with the given slope. (Lesson 4-3)

68. $(2, 5), m = 3$ $y - 5 = 3(x - 2)$ **69.** $(-3, 6), m = -7$ $y - 6 = -7(x + 3)$ **70.** $(-1, -2), m = -\frac{1}{2}$ $y + 2 = -\frac{1}{2}(x + 1)$

Skills Review

Graph each function. **71–76. See Ch. 9 Answer Appendix.**

71. $y = x^2 + 5$ **72.** $y = x^2 - 8$ **73.** $y = 2x^2 - 7$

74. $y = -x^2 + 2$ **75.** $y = -0.5x^2 - 3$ **76.** $y = (-x)^2 + 1$

Differentiated Instruction BL

Extension Tell students that in a computer golf game, the function $y = -0.002x^2 + 0.22x$ models the path of a golf ball, where y is the height of the ball and x is the horizontal distance in yards the ball has traveled. The green lies uphill from the tee, 90 yards away horizontally, atop a hill that has a steady incline of 1 yard per 10 yards of distance. Ask, "Will the ball reach the green without hitting the ground first? Explain your answer." No; the ball will land on the slope when it is 60 yards horizontally from the tee.

EXTEND 9-2 Graphing Technology Lab: Quadratic Inequalities

Recall that the graph of a linear inequality consists of the boundary and the shaded half plane. The solution set of the inequality lies in the shaded region of the graph. Graphing quadratic inequalities is similar to graphing linear inequalities.

Activity 1 Shade Inside a Parabola

Graph $y \geq x^2 - 5x + 4$ in a standard viewing window.

First, clear all functions from the Y= list.

To graph $y \geq x^2 - 5x + 4$, enter the equation in the Y= list. Then use the left arrow to select =. Press [ENTER] until shading above the line is selected.

KEYSTROKES: [◄] [◄] [ENTER] [ENTER] [►] [►] [X,T,θ,n] [x^2] [−] 5 [X,T,θ,n] [+] 4 [ZOOM] 6

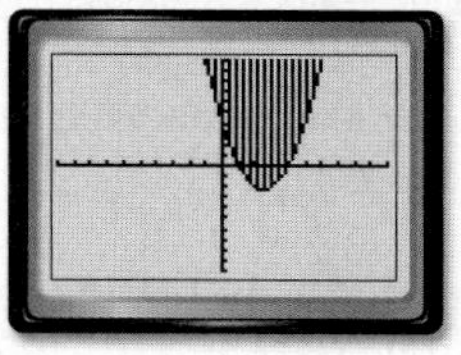

[−10, 10] scl: 1 by [−10, 10] scl: 1

All ordered pairs for which y is *greater than or equal* to $x^2 - 5x + 4$ lie *above or on* the line and are solutions.

A similar procedure will be used to graph an inequality in which the shading is outside of the parabola.

Activity 2 Shade Outside a Parabola

Graph $y - 4 \leq x^2 - 5x$ in a standard viewing window.

First, clear the graph that is displayed.

KEYSTROKES: [Y=] [CLEAR]

Then rewrite $y - 4 \leq x^2 - 5x$ as $y \leq x^2 - 5x + 4$, and graph it.

KEYSTROKES: [◄] [◄] [ENTER] [ENTER] [ENTER] [►] [►] [X,T,θ,n] [x^2] [−] 5 [X,T,θ,n] [+] 4 [GRAPH]

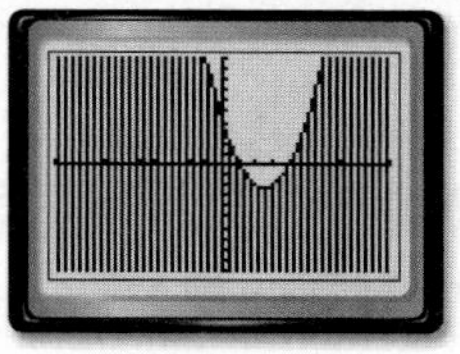

[−10, 10] scl: 1 by [−10, 10] scl: 1

All ordered pairs for which y is *less than or equal* to $x^2 - 5x + 4$ lie *below or on* the line and are solutions.

Exercises

1. Compare and contrast the two graphs shown above.
2. Graph $y - 2x + 6 \geq 5x^2$ in the standard viewing window. Name three solutions of the inequality. **(0, −6), (1, 1), (2, 18)**
3. Graph $y - 6x \leq -x^2 - 3$ in the standard viewing window. Name three solutions of the inequality. **(0, −3), (1, 2), (2, 5)**

1. The graph of $y \geq x^2 - 5x + 4$ is a parabola with the inside shaded. The graph of $y \leq x^2 - 5x + 4$ is a parabola with the outside shaded.

1 Focus

Objective Use a graphing calculator to investigate quadratic inequalities.

Materials for Each Student

- TI-83/84 Plus or other graphing calculator

Teaching Tip

Remind students that the [x^2] key squares the quantity but does not enter x^2 into an equation. To enter $5x^2$, press 5 [X,T,θ,n] [x^2].

2 Teach

Working in Cooperative Groups

Put students in groups of two or three, mixing abilities. Have groups complete the Activities and Exercise 1.

Ask:

- Where are the solutions for the inequalities? all ordered pairs in the shaded area of the graph, including the graph of the related function itself
- How many solutions does each inequality have? infinite number
- Are any of the solutions to the first graph the same as for the second graph? yes, the solutions that lie on the graph of the function itself

Practice Have students complete Exercises 2 and 3.

3 Assess

Formative Assessment

Use Exercise 3 to assess whether students understand how to use a graphing calculator to solve an inequality.

From Concrete to Abstract

Have students examine the graph they made for the inequality in Activity 1. Then have them explain how the solution set to this inequality is the same as, or different from, the solution set for $y > x^2 - 5x + 4$. The solution set for $y > x^2 - 5x + 4$ does not include the values on the graph of the related function, while the solution set for $y \geq x^2 - 5x + 4$ does.

1 Focus

Objective Use a graphing calculator to investigate families of quadratic functions.

Materials

- TI-83/84 Plus or other graphing calculator

Teaching Tips

- Encourage students to compare the key characteristics of quadratic functions to those of linear and exponential functions.
- Remind students to use ZOOM 6 to show graphs in the standard viewing window.
- In Activities 2 and 3, students will need to clear the **Y=** lists. To do this, they can use CLEAR.
- Use TRACE and ▲ or ▼ to display the equation for a graph.

2 Teach

Working in Cooperative Groups

Divide the class into pairs. Work through Activities 1–3. Then ask students to work with their partners to complete Exercises 1–3.

Practice Have students complete Exercises 4–11.

EXPLORE 9-3

Graphing Technology Lab
Family of Quadratic Functions

You have studied the effects of changing parameters in the equations of linear and exponential functions. You can use a graphing calculator to analyze how changing the parameters of the equation of a quadratic function affects the graphs in the family of quadratic functions.

Activity 1 Change k in $y = a(x - h)^2 + k$

Graph the set of equations on the same screen in the standard viewing window. Describe any similarities and differences among the graphs.

$y = x^2$, $y = x^2 + 2$, $y = x^2 - 4$

Enter the equations in the **Y =** list and graph in the standard viewing window. Use the **ZOOM** feature to investigate the key features of the graphs.

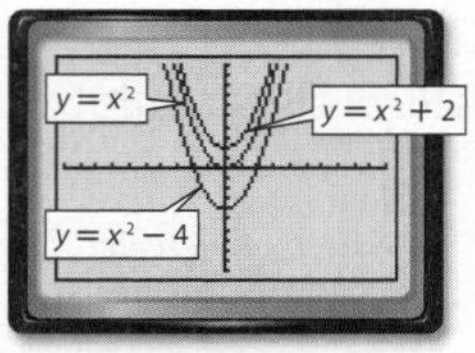

[−10, 10] scl: 1 by [−10, 10] scl: 1

The graphs have the same shape, and all open up. The vertex of each graph is on the y-axis, which is the axis of symmetry.

However, the graphs have different vertical positions. The graph of $y = x^2 + 2$ is shifted up 2 units. The graph of $y = x^2 - 4$ is shifted down 4 units.

Changing the value of h in $y = a(x - h)^2 + k$ affects the graphs in a different way than changing k.

Activity 2 Change h in $y = a(x - h)^2 + k$

Graph the set of equations on the same screen in the standard viewing window. Describe any similarities and differences among the graphs.

$y = x^2$, $y = (x + 2)^2$, $y = (x - 4)^2$

The graphs have the same shape, and all open up. The vertex of each graph is on the x-axis.

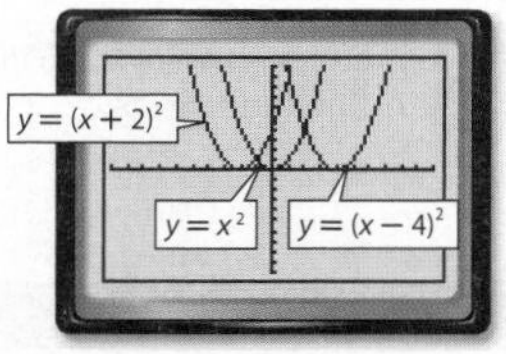

[−10, 10] scl: 1 by [−10, 10] scl: 1

However, the graphs have different horizontal positions. Each has a different axis of symmetry. The graph of $y = (x + 2)^2$ is shifted to the left 2 units. The graph of $y = (x - 4)^2$ is shifted to the right 4 units.

It appears that changing the values of h and k in $y = a(x - h)^2 + k$ moves the graph vertically or horizontally. How does changing the value of a affect the graphs?

562 | Explore 9-3 | Graphing Technology Lab: Family of Quadratic Functions

Activity 3 Change a in $y = a(x - h)^2 + k$

Graph each set of equations on the same screen in the standard viewing window. Describe any similarities and differences among the graphs.

a. $y = x^2$, $y = 2x^2$, $y = \frac{1}{3}x^2$

The graphs have the same vertex, they have the same axis of symmetry, and all open up.

However, the graphs have different widths. The graph of $y = 2x^2$ is narrower than the graph of $y = x^2$. The graph of $y = \frac{1}{3}x^2$ is wider than the graph of $y = x^2$.

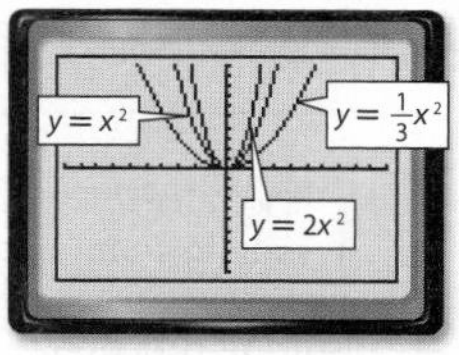

[−10, 10] scl: 1 by [−10, 10] scl: 1

b. $y = x^2$, $y = -\frac{1}{3}x^2$, $y = -2x^2$

The graphs have the same vertex and the same axis of symmetry.

However, the graphs of $y = -\frac{1}{3}x^2$ and $y = -2x^2$ open down. Also the graph of $y = -2x^2$ is narrower than the graph of $y = x^2$. The graph of $y = -\frac{1}{3}x^2$ is wider than the graph of $y = x^2$.

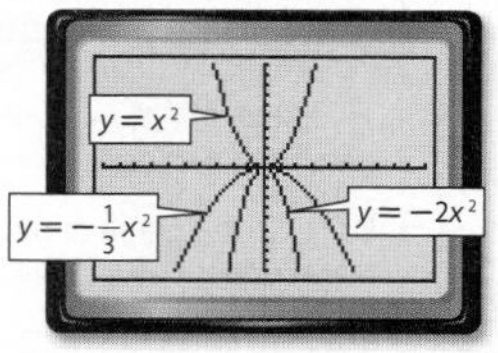

[−10, 10] scl: 1 by [−10, 10] scl: 1

Model and Analyze

How does each parameter affect the graph of $y = a(x - h)^2 + k$? Give examples. **1–3. See margin.**

1. k **2.** h **3.** a

Examine each pair of equations and predict the similarities and differences in their graphs. Use a graphing calculator to confirm your predictions. Write a sentence or two comparing the two graphs. **4–11. See Ch. 9 Answer Appendix.**

4. $y = x^2$, $y = x^2 + 3$

5. $y = \frac{1}{2}x^2$, $y = 3x^2$

6. $y = x^2$, $y = (x - 5)^2$

7. $y = 3x^2$, $y = -3x^2$

8. $y = x^2$, $y = -4x^2$

9. $y = x^2 - 1$, $y = x^2 + 2$

10. $y = \frac{1}{2}x^2 + 3$, $y = -2x^2$

11. $y = x^2 - 4$, $y = (x - 4)^2$

3 Assess

Formative Assessment

Use Exercise 11 to assess each student's ability to predict similarities and differences in quadratic functions.

From Concrete to Abstract

Ask students to summarize using technology to investigate families of quadratic functions.

Additional Answers

1. The value of k affects the vertical position of the graph. Sample answer: The graph of $y = x^2 + 5$ is 5 units above the x-axis.
2. The value of h affects the horizontal position of the graph. Sample answer: The graph of $y = (x + 5)^2$ is 5 units to the left of the y-axis.
3. The value of a affects the width and direction of opening of the graph. If a is positive the graph opens up and if a is negative the graph opens down. Sample answer: The graph of $y = -2x^2$ is narrower than the graph of $y = x^2$; the graph of $y = -\frac{1}{2}x^2$ is wider than the graph of $y = x^2$; the graph of $y = x^2$ opens up and the graphs of $y = -x^2$, $y = -2x^2$, and $y = -\frac{1}{2}x^2$ open down.

1 Focus

VerticalAlignment

Before Lesson 9-3 Graph quadratic functions by using the vertex and axis of symmetry.

Lesson 9-3 Apply translations to quadratic functions. Apply dilations and reflections to quadratic functions.

After Lesson 9-3 Write equations that model data.

2 Teach

Scaffolding Questions

Have students read the **Why?** section of the lesson.

Ask:

- What is the vertex of each parabola? blue: (0, 1); red: (0, 4)
- What do we know about the coefficient of the x^2 term for the equations of these graphs? They are both positive.
- What is the axis of symmetry for these two graphs? the y-axis
- What do we know about the b value in the equations for these graphs? Since $-\frac{b}{2a} = 0$, we know then that b must equal 0 for both.

LESSON 9-3 Transformations of Quadratic Functions

Then	Now	Why?
You graphed quadratic functions by using the vertex and axis of symmetry.	1 Apply translations to quadratic functions. 2 Apply dilations and reflections to quadratic functions.	The graphs of the parabolas shown at the right are the same size and shape, but notice that the vertex of the red parabola is higher on the y-axis than the vertex of the blue parabola. Shifting a parabola up and down is an example of a transformation.

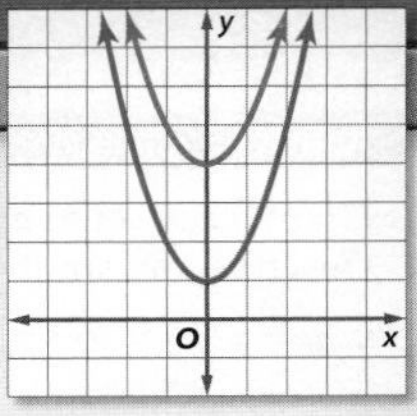

NewVocabulary
transformation
translation
dilation
reflection
vertex form

Content Standards
AI.QE.6, AI.QE.7

Process Standards
PS.1, PS.8

1 Translations

A **transformation** changes the position or size of a figure. One transformation, a **translation**, moves a figure up, down, left, or right. When a constant k is added to or subtracted from the parent function, the graph of the resulting function $f(x) \pm k$ is the graph of the parent function translated up or down.

The parent function of the family of quadratics is $f(x) = x^2$. All other quadratic functions have graphs that are transformations of the graph of $f(x) = x^2$.

KeyConcept Vertical Translations

The graph of $f(x) = x^2 + k$ is the graph of $f(x) = x^2$ translated vertically.

If $k > 0$, the graph of $f(x) = x^2$ is translated $|k|$ units **up**.

If $k < 0$, the graph of $f(x) = x^2$ is translated $|k|$ units **down**.

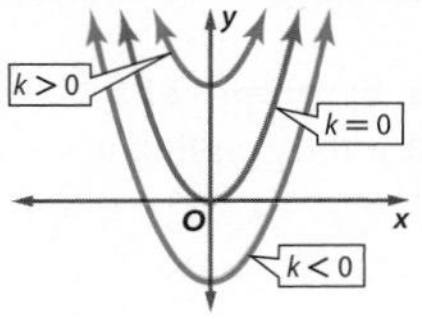

Example 1 Describe and Graph Translations

Describe how the graph of each function is related to the graph of $f(x) = x^2$.

a. $h(x) = x^2 + 3$

$k = 3$ and $3 > 0$
$h(x)$ is a translation of the graph of $f(x) = x^2$ up 3 units.

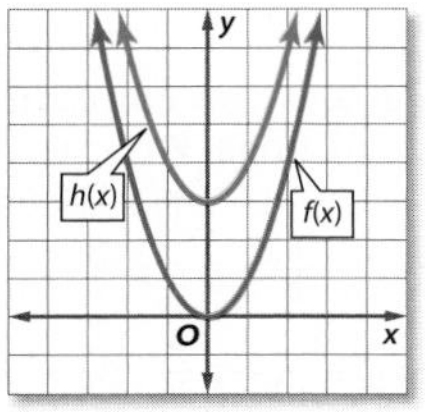

b. $g(x) = x^2 - 4$

$k = -4$ and $-4 < 0$
$g(x)$ is a translation of the graph of $f(x) = x^2$ down 4 units.

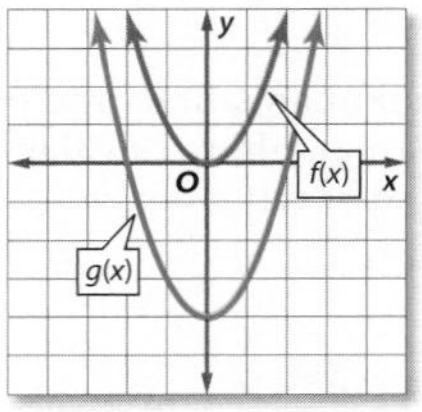

GuidedPractice

1A. $f(x) = x^2 - 7$ translated down 7
1B. $g(x) = 5 + x^2$ translated up 5
1C. $h(x) = -5 + x^2$ translated down 5
1D. $f(x) = x^2 + 1$ translated up 1

Lesson 9-3 Resources

Resource	Approaching Level AL	On Level OL	Beyond Level BL	English Learners ELL
Teacher Edition	• Differentiated Instruction, p. 566	• Differentiated Instruction, pp. 566, 571	• Differentiated Instruction, p. 571	
Chapter Resource Masters	• Study Guide and Intervention, pp. 17–18 • Skills Practice, p. 19 • Practice, p. 20 • Word Problem Practice, p. 21	• Study Guide and Intervention, pp. 17–18 • Skills Practice, p. 19 • Practice, p. 20 • Word Problem Practice, p. 21 • Enrichment, p. 10	• Practice, p. 20 • Word Problem Practice, p. 21 • Enrichment, p. 22	• Study Guide and Intervention, pp. 17–18 • Skills Practice, p. 19 • Practice, p. 20 • Word Problem Practice, p. 21
Other	• 5-Minute Check 9-3 • Study Notebook	• 5-Minute Check 9-3 • Study Notebook	• 5-Minute Check 9-3 • Study Notebook	• 5-Minute Check 9-3 • Study Notebook

A quadratic graph can be translated horizontally by subtracting an h term from x.

KeyConcept Horizontal Translations

The graph of $g(x) = (x - h)^2$ is the graph of $f(x) = x^2$ translated horizontally.

If $h > 0$, the graph of $f(x) = x^2$ is translated h units to the **right**.

If $h < 0$, the graph of $f(x) = x^2$ is translated $|h|$ units to the **left**.

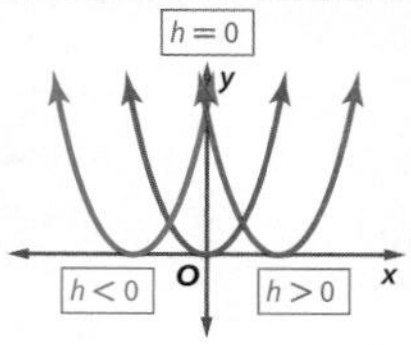

Example 2 Horizontal Translations

Describe how the graph of each function is related to the graph of $f(x) = x^2$.

a. $g(x) = (x - 2)^2$

$k = 0, h = 2$ and $2 > 0$

$g(x)$ is a translation of the graph of $f(x) = x^2$ to the right 2 units.

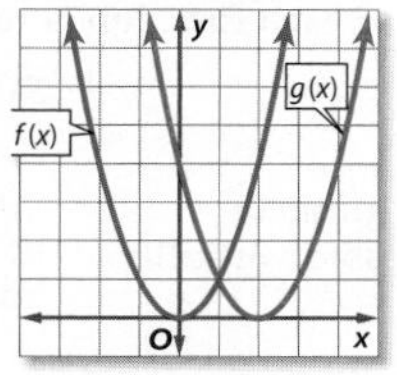

b. $g(x) = (x + 1)^2$

$k = 0, h = -1$ and $-1 < 0$

$g(x)$ is a translation of the graph of $f(x) = x^2$ to the left 1 unit.

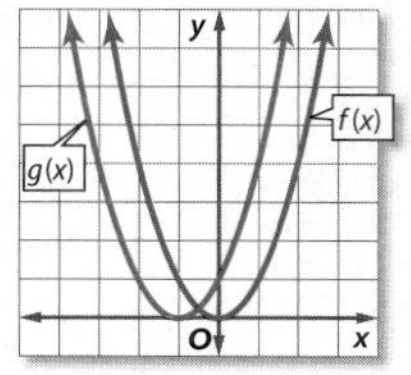

GuidedPractice

2A. $g(x) = (x - 3)^2$ **translated right 3**

2B. $g(x) = (x + 2)^2$ **translated left 2**

A quadratic graph can be translated both horizontally and vertically.

Example 3 Horizontal and Vertical Translations

Describe how the graph of each function is related to the graph of $f(x) = x^2$.

a. $g(x) = (x - 3)^2 + 2$

$k = 2, h = 3$ and $3 > 0$

$g(x)$ is a translation of the graph of $f(x) = x^2$ to the right 3 units and up 2 units.

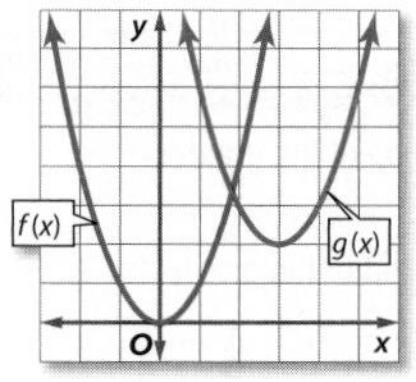

b. $g(x) = (x + 3)^2 - 1$

$k = -1, h = -3$ and $-3 < 0$

$g(x)$ is a translation of the graph of $f(x) = x^2$ to the left 3 units and down 1 unit.

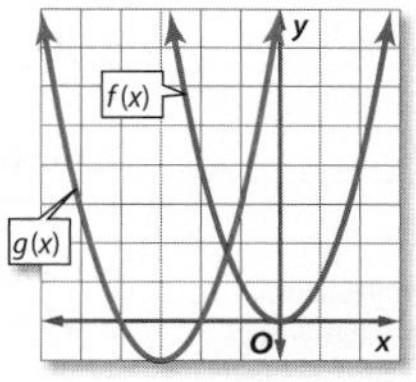

GuidedPractice

3A. $g(x) = (x + 2)^2 + 3$

3B. $g(x) = (x - 4)^2 - 4$

3A. translated left 2 and up 3

3B. translated down 4 and left 4

1 Translations

Example 1 shows how to describe the graph of a quadratic function of the form $f(x) = x^2 + c$ based on its relationship to the parent function $f(x) = x^2$. **Example 2** shows how to describe the graph of a quadratic function of the form $f(x) = (x - h)^2$ based on its relationship to the parent function of $f(x) = x^2$. **Example 3** shows combined vertical and horizontal translations.

Formative Assessment

Use the Guided Practice exercises after each example to determine students' understanding of concepts.

Additional Examples

1 Describe how the graph of each function is related to the graph of $f(x) = x^2$.

a. $g(x) = 10 + x^2$ translated up 10 units

b. $g(x) = x^2 - 8$ translated down 8 units

2 Describe how the graph of each function is related to the graph of $f(x) = x^2$.

a. $g(x) = (x + 1)^2$ translated to left 1 unit

b. $g(x) = (x - 4)^2$ translated to right 4 units

3 Describe how the graph of each function is related to the graph of $f(x) = x^2$.

a. $g(x) = (x + 1)^2 + 1$ translated to left 1 unit and up 1 unit

b. $g(x) = (x - 2)^2 + 6$ translated right 2 units and up 6 units

Additional Examples also in Interactive Classroom PowerPoint® Presentations

IWB Interactive White Board READY

2 Dilations and Reflections

Example 4 shows how to describe the graph of a quadratic function of the form $f(x) = ax^2$ based on its relationship to the parent function $f(x) = x^2$. **Example 5** shows how to describe the graph of a quadratic function of the form $f(x) = -ax^2 + k$ based on its relationship to the parent function $f(x) = x^2$. **Example 6** shows how to choose the equation that correlates to a function shown in a graph. **Example 7** shows how transformations are used in real-world situations.

Additional Example

4 Describe how the graph of each function is related to the graph of $f(x) = x^2$.

a. $d(x) = \frac{1}{3}x^2$ The graph of $y = \frac{1}{3}x^2$ is a vertical compression of the graph of $f(x) = x^2$.

b. $m(x) = 2x^2 + 1$ The graph of $y = 2x^2 + 1$ is stretched vertically and then translated up 1 unit.

Teaching the Process Standards

Sense-Making Mathematically proficient students can explain correspondences. Point out that students may have studied transformations of figures in previous math courses. Stress that the dilations of graphs in this lesson are with respect to the y-axis, not with respect to a point as in dilations with respect to the origin.

2 Dilations and Reflections

Another type of transformation is a dilation. A **dilation** makes the graph narrower than the parent graph or wider than the parent graph. When the parent function $f(x) = x^2$ is multiplied by a constant a, the graph of the resulting function $f(x) = ax^2$ is either stretched or compressed vertically.

KeyConcept Dilations

The graph of $g(x) = ax^2$ is the graph of $f(x) = x^2$ stretched or compressed vertically.

If $|a| > 1$, the graph of $f(x) = x^2$ is stretched vertically.

If $0 < |a| < 1$, the graph of $f(x) = x^2$ is compressed vertically.

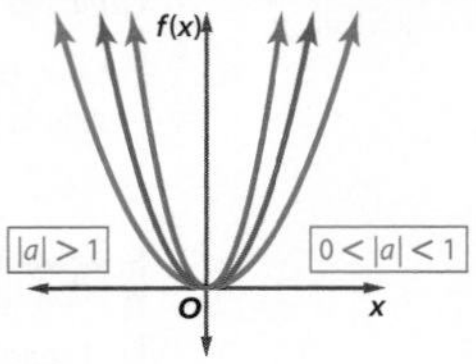

StudyTip

Sense-Making When the graph of a quadratic function is stretched vertically, the shape of the graph is narrower than that of the parent function. When it is compressed vertically, the graph is wider than the parent function.

Example 4 Describe and Graph Dilations

Describe how the graph of each function is related to the graph of $f(x) = x^2$.

a. $h(x) = \frac{1}{2}x^2$

$a = \frac{1}{2}$ and $0 < \frac{1}{2} < 1$

$h(x)$ is a dilation of the graph of $f(x) = x^2$ that is compressed vertically.

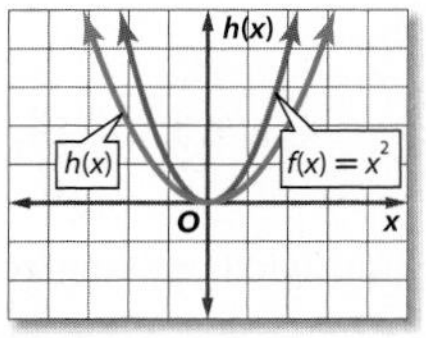

b. $g(x) = 3x^2 + 2$

$a = 3$ and $3 > 1$, $k = 2$ and $2 > 0$

$g(x)$ is a dilation of the graph of $f(x) = x^2$ that is stretched vertically and translated up 2 units.

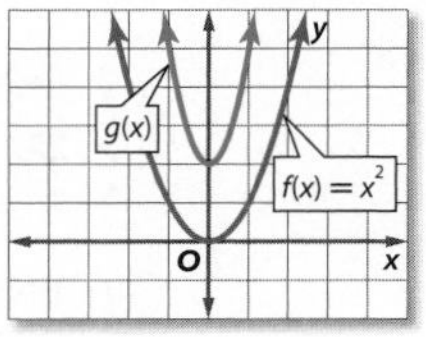

GuidedPractice

4A. $j(x) = 2x^2$ **4B.** $h(x) = 5x^2 - 2$ **4C.** $g(x) = \frac{1}{3}x^2 + 2$

4A. stretched vertically
4B. stretched vertically and translated down
4C. compressed vertically and translated up

A **reflection** flips a figure across a line.

KeyConcept Reflections

The graph of $-f(x)$ is the reflection of the graph of $f(x) = x^2$ across the x-axis.

The graph of $f(-x)$ is the reflection of the graph of $f(x) = x^2$ across the y-axis.

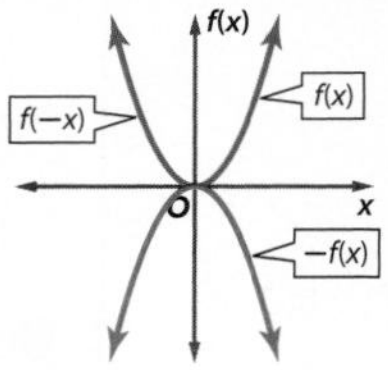

StudyTip

Reflection A reflection of $f(x) = x^2$ across the y-axis results in the same function, because $f(-x) = (-x)^2 = x^2$.

DifferentiatedInstruction AL OL

If students need help comparing and contrasting a function's graph and its parent function's graph,

Then have students write and graph three different functions on the same coordinate plane. Using a red pencil, on this same coordinate plane, have students graph the parent function $f(x) = x^2$. Finally, have students create observation notebooks in which to record their thoughts on how each function's graph is similar to or different from the parent function's graph.

WatchOut!

Transformations The graph of $f(x) = -ax^2$ can result in two transformations of the graph of $f(x) = x^2$: a reflection across the x-axis if $a > 0$ and either a compression or expansion depending on the absolute value of a.

Example 5 Describe and Graph Reflections

Describe how the graph of each function is related to the graph of $f(x) = x^2$.

a. $g(x) = -2x^2 - 3$

- $a = -2$, $-2 < 0$, and $|-2| > 1$, so there is a reflection across the x-axis and the graph is vertically stretched.
- $k = -3$ and $-3 < 0$, so there is a translation down 3 units.

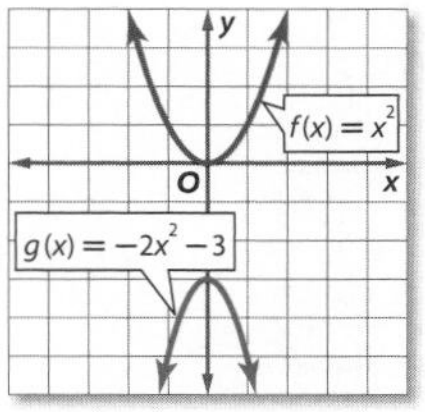

b. $h(x) = -4(x + 2)^2 + 1$

- $a = -4$, $-4 < 0$, and $|-4| > 1$, so there is a reflection across the x-axis and the graph is vertically stretched.
- $h = -2$ and $-2 < 0$, so there is a translation 2 units to the left.
- $k = 1$ and $1 > 0$, so there is a translation up 1 unit.

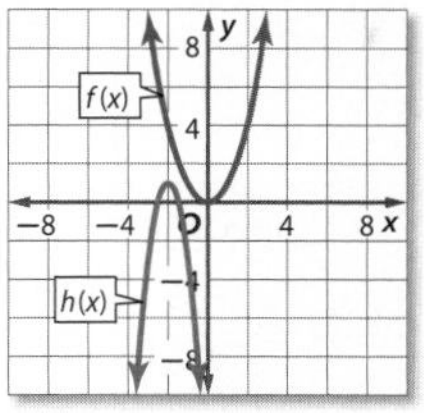

GuidedPractice

5A. $h(x) = 2(-x)^2 - 9$ **5B.** $g(x) = \frac{1}{5}x^2 + 3$ **5C.** $j(x) = -2(x - 1)^2 - 2$

5A. translated down 9 units and stretched vertically
5B. translated up 3 units and compressed vertically
5C. reflected over x-axis, translated down 2 units and 1 unit right and stretched vertically

You can use what you know about the characteristics of graphs of quadratic equations to match an equation with a graph.

Standardized Test Example 6 Identify an Equation for a Graph

Which is an equation for the function shown in the graph?

A $y = \frac{1}{2}x^2 - 5$ **C** $y = -\frac{1}{2}x^2 + 5$

B $y = -2x^2 - 5$ **D** $y = 2x^2 + 5$

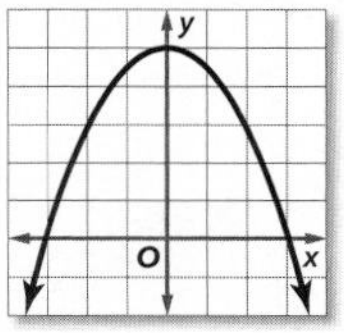

Read the Test Item

You are given a graph. You need to find its equation.

Solve the Test Item

The graph opens downward, so the graph of $y = x^2$ has been reflected across the x-axis. The leading coefficient should be negative, so eliminate choices A and D.

The parabola is translated up 5 units, so $k = 5$. Look at the equations. Only choices C and D have $k = 5$. The answer is C.

GuidedPractice

6. Which is the graph of $y = -3x^2 + 1$? H

F

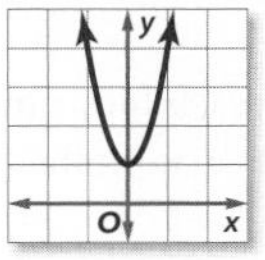

G

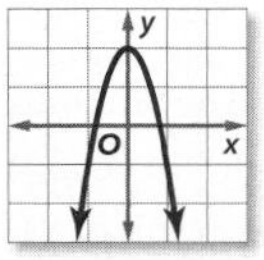

H

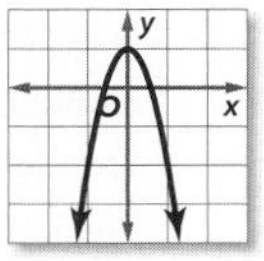

J

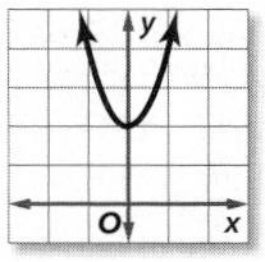

Additional Examples

5 Describe how the graph of each function is related to the graph of $f(x) = x^2$.

a. $g(x) = -3x^2 + 1$ The graph of $g(x) = -3x^2 + 1$ is reflected across the x-axis, stretched vertically, and translated up 1 unit.

b. $g(x) = \frac{1}{5}x^2 - 7$ The graph of $g(x) = \frac{1}{5}x^2 - 7$ is compressed vertically and translated down 7 units.

6 **STANDARDIZED TEST PRACTICE** Which is an equation for the function shown in the graph? A

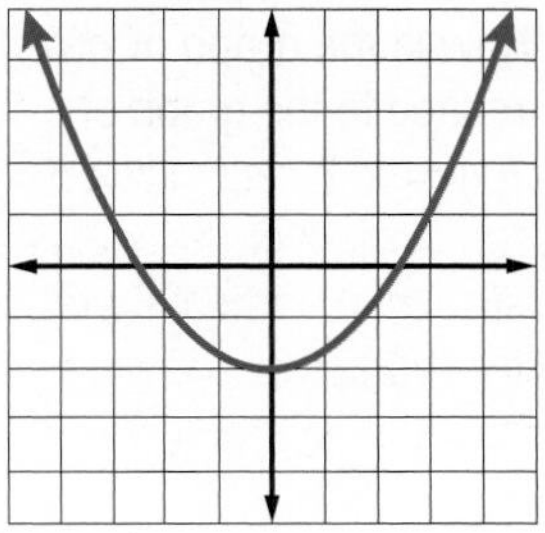

A $y = \frac{1}{3}x^2 - 2$

B $y = 3x^2 + 2$

C $y = -\frac{1}{3}x^2 + 2$

D $y = -3x^2 - 2$

Focus on Mathematical Content

Quadratic Functions Each constant in the quadratic function $f(x) = a(x - h)^2 + k$ has meaning when compared to its parent function $f(x) = x^2$. The value of $|a|$ in the function either compresses or expands (dilates) the graph of the parent function. When the value of a is negative, the graph of the parent function is flipped (reflected) over the x-axis. The value of k in the function moves (translates) the graph of the parent function $|k|$ units up or down. The value of h moves the graph $|h|$ units left or right.

Teach with Tech

Interactive Whiteboard Drag a coordinate grid onto the board. Sketch the graph of a quadratic function on the board and give students the equation of the graph. Drag the parabola to another location on the board and have students find the new equation. Discuss similarities and differences.

Additional Example

7 CANNON During a 4th of July celebration, a cannon is fired. The flight of the cannon ball can be modeled by $d(t) = -4(x - 5)^2 + 100$, where t is time in seconds and $d(t)$ is distance in meters.

a. Graph the function.

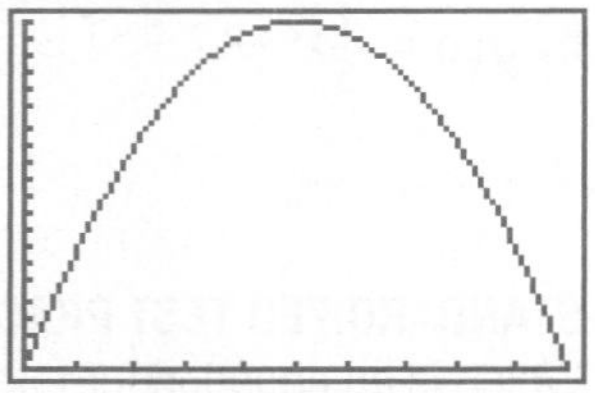

[0, 10] scl: 1 by [0, 100] scl: 10

b. How is the graph of $d(t)$ related to the graph of $f(x) = x^2$? The graph is reflected over the x-axis, stretched vertically, vertically translated up 100, and horizontally translated right 5.

Tips for New Teachers

Width of the Parabola Students often mistake a greater value for $|a|$ to imply a wider parabola. Suggest that students think of the value of a in $y = ax^2 + k$ the same way they thought of the value of the slope m in $y = mx + b$. A greater value for m means a steeper line. A greater value for $|a|$ means that the sides of the parabola are steeper.

A quadratic function written in the form $f(x) = a(x - h)^2 + k$ is said to be in **vertex form**. Transformations of the parent graph are easily found from an equation in vertex form.

Concept Summary Transformations of Quadratic Functions

$f(x) = a(x - h)^2 + k$

h, Horizontal Translation
h units to the right if h is positive
$|h|$ units to the left if h is negative

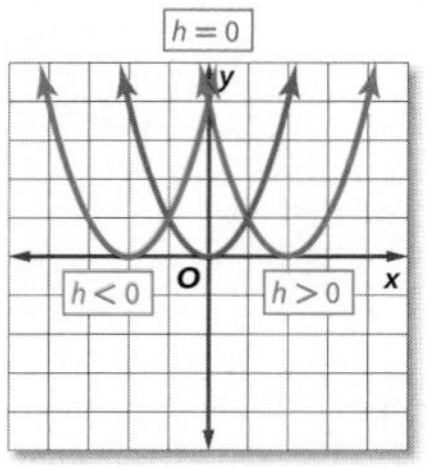

k, Vertical Translation
k units up if k is positive
$|k|$ units down if k is negative

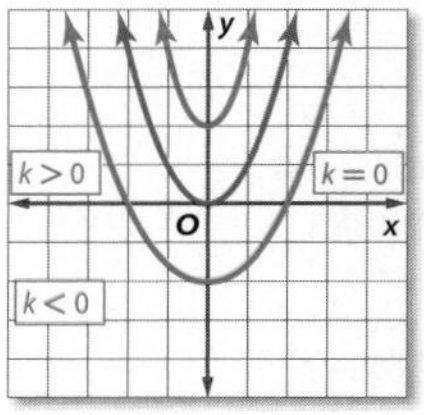

a, Reflection
If $a > 0$, the graph opens up.
If $a < 0$, the graph opens down.

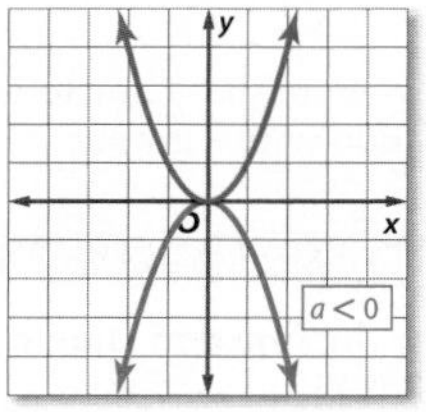

a, Dilation
If $|a| > 1$, the graph is stretched vertically. If $0 < |a| < 1$, the graph is compressed vertically.

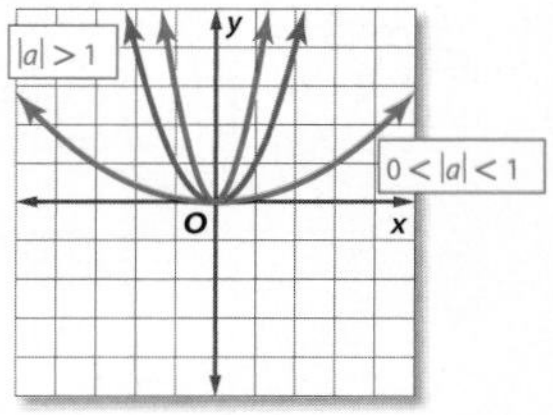

Real-World Example 7 Transformations with a Calculator

FIREWORKS During a firework show, the height h in meters of a specific rocket after t seconds can be modeled by $h(t) = -4.6(t - 3)^2 + 75$. Graph the function. How is it related to the graph of $f(x) = x^2$?

Four separate transformations are occurring.

The negative sign of the coefficient of x^2 causes a reflection across the x-axis. A dilation occurs, which stretches the graph vertically.
There are also translations up 75 units and to the right 3 units.

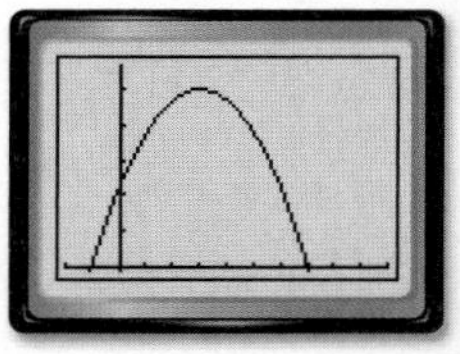

[−2, 10] scl: 1 by [−2, 85] scl: 15

Guided Practice

7. MONUMENTS The St. Louis Arch resembles a quadratic and can be modeled by $h(x) = -\frac{2}{315}x^2 + 630$. Graph the function. How is it related to the graph of $f(x) = x^2$?

7.

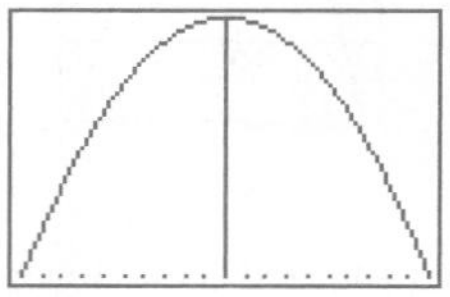

[−10, 10] scl: 1 by [629, 630] scl: 1

Three separate transformations are occurring.
The negative sign of the coefficient of x^2 causes a reflection across the x-axis. Then a dilation occurs which compresses the graph vertically. Finally, there is a vertical translation of 630 units up.

Check Your Understanding

● = Step-by-Step Solutions begin on page R13.

Examples 1–5, 7

Describe how the graph of each function is related to the graph of $f(x) = x^2$. **1–6. See margin.**

1. $g(x) = x^2 - 11$
2. $h(x) = \frac{1}{2}(x - 2)^2$
3. $h(x) = -x^2 + 8$
4. $g(x) = x^2 + 6$
5. $g(x) = -4(x + 3)^2$
6. $h(x) = -x^2 - 2$

Example 6

7. **MULTIPLE CHOICE** Which is an equation for the function shown in the graph? **C**

   A $g(x) = \frac{1}{5}x^2 + 2$ C $g(x) = \frac{1}{5}x^2 - 2$

   B $g(x) = -5x^2 - 2$ D $g(x) = -\frac{1}{5}x^2 - 2$

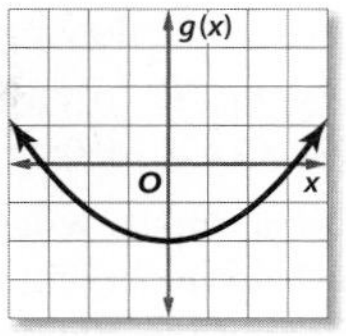

Practice and Problem Solving

Extra Practice is on page R9.

Examples 1–5, 7

Describe how the graph of each function is related to the graph of $f(x) = x^2$. **8–17. See margin.**

8. $g(x) = -10 + x^2$
9. $h(x) = -7 - x^2$
10. $g(x) = 2(x - 3)^2 + 8$
11. $h(x) = 6 + \frac{2}{3}x^2$
12. $g(x) = -5 - \frac{4}{3}x^2$
13. $h(x) = 3 + \frac{5}{2}x^2$
14. $g(x) = 0.25x^2 - 1.1$
15. $h(x) = 1.35(x + 1)^2 + 2.6$
16. $g(x) = \frac{3}{4}x^2 + \frac{5}{6}$
17. $h(x) = 1.01x^2 - 6.5$

Example 6

Match each equation to its graph.

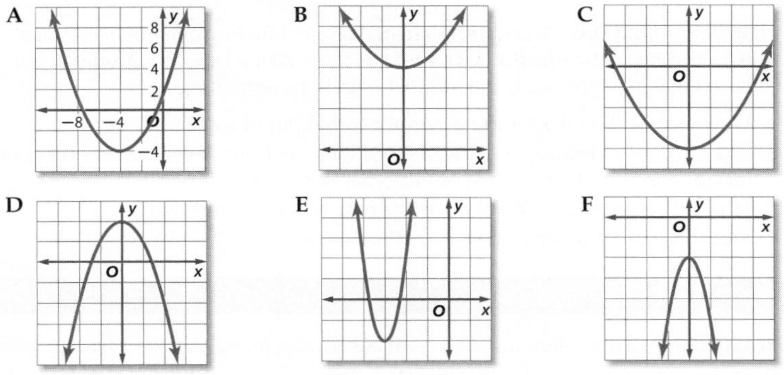

18. $y = \frac{1}{3}x^2 - 4$ **C**
19. $y = \frac{1}{3}(x + 4)^2 - 4$ **A**
20. $y = \frac{1}{3}x^2 + 4$ **B**
21. $y = -3x^2 - 2$ **F**
22. $y = -x^2 + 2$ **D**
23. $y = (2x + 6)^2 + 2$ **E**

B 24. **SQUIRRELS** A squirrel 12 feet above the ground drops an acorn from a tree. The function $h = -16t^2 + 12$ models the height of the acorn above the ground in feet after t seconds. Graph the function, and compare this graph to the graph of its parent function. **The graph is stretched vertically, reflected across the x-axis, and translated up. See Ch. 9 Answer Appendix for graph.**

REGULARITY List the functions in order from the most stretched vertically to the least stretched vertically graph. **27. $h(x)$, $g(x)$, $f(x)$ 28. $f(x)$, $h(x)$, $g(x)$**

25. $g(x) = 2x^2$, $h(x) = \frac{1}{2}x^2$ **$g(x)$, $h(x)$**
26. $g(x) = -3x^2$, $h(x) = \frac{2}{3}x^2$ **$g(x)$, $h(x)$**
27. $g(x) = -4x^2$, $h(x) = 6x^2$, $f(x) = 0.3x^2$
28. $g(x) = -x^2$, $h(x) = \frac{5}{3}x^2$, $f(x) = -4.5x^2$

Differentiated Homework Options

Level	Assignment	Two-Day Option	
AL Basic	8–23, 36, 38–63	9–23 odd, 41–44	8–22 even, 36, 38–40, 45–63
OL Core	9–33 odd, 30, 34, 35, 37–63	8–23, 41–44	25–36, 38–40, 45–63
BL Advanced	25–57, (optional: 58–63)		

3 Practice

Formative Assessment

Use Exercises 1–7 to check for understanding.

Use the chart at the bottom of this page to customize assignments for your students.

Exercise Alert

Grid Paper For Exercise 24, students will need grid paper.

Teaching the Process Standards

Regularity Mathematically proficient students look for general methods and for shortcuts. In Exercises 25–28, point out that the only differences in the functions are the coefficients of the x^2-terms.

Additional Answers

1. translated down 11 units
2. translated right 2 units and compressed vertically
3. reflected across the x-axis, translated up 8 units
4. translated up 6 units
5. reflected across the x-axis, translated left 3 units and stretched vertically
6. reflected across the x-axis, translated down 2 units
8. translated down 10 units
9. reflected across the x-axis, translated down 7 units
10. translated right 3 units and up 8 units and stretched vertically
11. compressed vertically, translated up 6 units
12. reflected across the x-axis, stretched vertically, translated down 5 units
13. stretched vertically, translated up 3 units
14. compressed vertically, translated down 1.1 unit
15. translated left 1 unit and up 2.6 units and stretched vertically
16. compressed vertically, translated up $\frac{5}{6}$ unit
17. stretched vertically, translated down 6.5 units

connectED.mcgraw-hill.com

Study Guide and Intervention

AL OL ELL

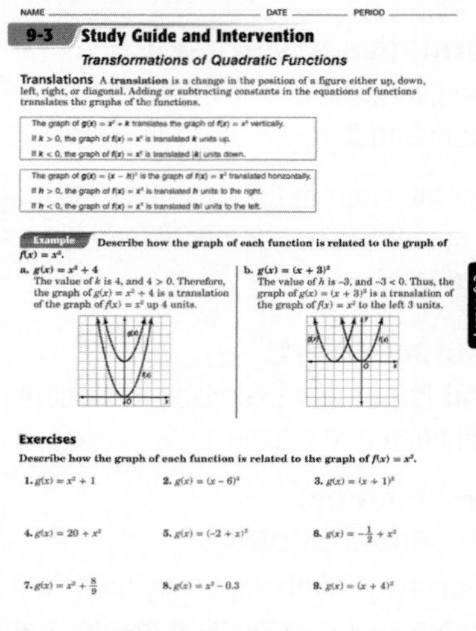
9-3 Study Guide and Intervention

Transformations of Quadratic Functions

Practice

AL OL BL ELL

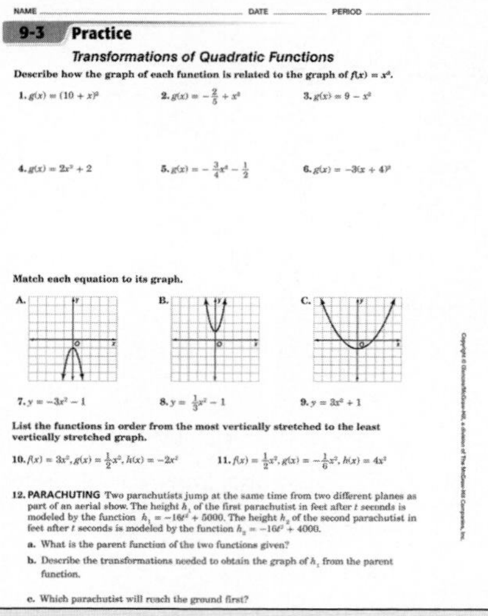
9-3 Practice

Transformations of Quadratic Functions

Word Problem Practice

AL OL BL ELL

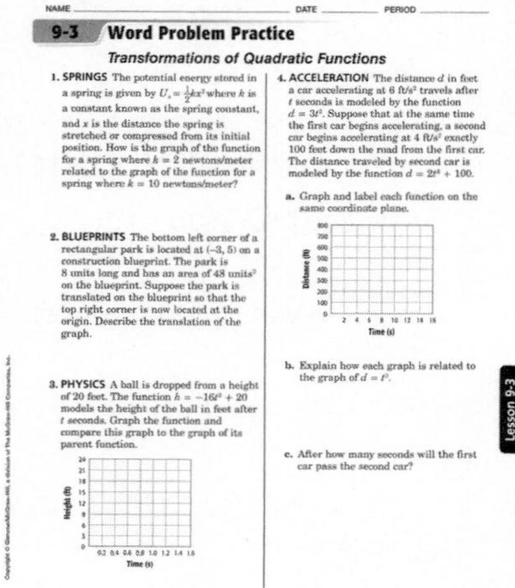
9-3 Word Problem Practice

Transformations of Quadratic Functions

29. **ROCKS** A rock falls from a cliff 300 feet above the ground. At the same time, another rock falls from a cliff 700 feet above the ground. **a. $h = -16t^2 + 300$ and $h = -16t^2 + 700$**

a. Write functions that model the height h of each rock after t seconds.

b. If the rocks fall at the same time, how much sooner will the first rock reach the ground? **b. about 2.3 seconds**

30. **SPRINKLERS** The path of water from a sprinkler can be modeled by quadratic functions. The following functions model paths for three different sprinklers.

Sprinkler A: $y = -0.35x^2 + 3.5$ Sprinkler B: $y = -0.21x^2 + 1.7$
Sprinkler C: $y = -0.08x^2 + 2.4$

a. Which sprinkler will send water the farthest? Explain. **a. Sprinkler C because the graph is compressed vertically the most.**

b. Which sprinkler will send water the highest? Explain. **Sprinkler A because it is translated up the most.**

c. Which sprinkler will produce the narrowest path? Explain. **Sprinkler A because it is expanded the least.**

31a. The graph of $g(x)$ is the graph of $f(x)$ translated 200 yards right, compressed vertically, reflected in the x-axis, and translated up 20 yards.

31. **GOLF** The path of a drive can be modeled by a quadratic function where $g(x)$ is the vertical distance in yards of the ball from the ground and x is the horizontal distance in yards.

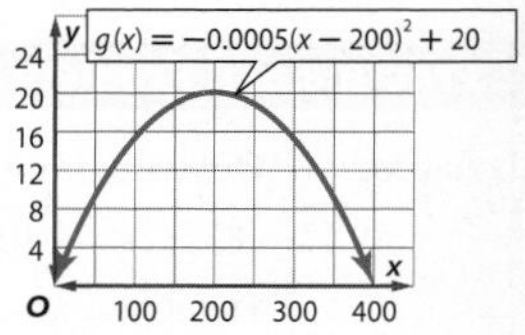

a. How can you obtain $g(x)$ from the graph of $f(x) = x^2$.

b. A second golfer hits a ball from the red tee, which is 30 yards closer to the hole. What function $h(x)$ can be used to describe the second golfer's shot? **$h(x) = 0.0005(x - 230)^2 + 20$**

Describe the transformations to obtain the graph of $g(x)$ from the graph of $f(x)$.

32. $f(x) = x^2 + 3$; $g(x) = x^2 - 2$ **32. Translate the graph of $f(x)$ down 5 units.**

33. $f(x) = x^2 - 4$; $g(x) = (x - 2)^2 + 7$ **33. Translate the graph of $f(x)$ up 11 units and to the right 2 units.**

34. $f(x) = -6x^2$; $g(x) = -3x^2$ **Compress vertically the graph of $f(x)$.**

C **35.** **COMBINING FUNCTIONS** An engineer created a self-refueling generator that burns fuel according to the function $g(t) = -t^2 + 10t + 200$, where t represents the time in hours and $g(t)$ represents the number of gallons remaining.

a. How long will it take for the generator to run out of fuel? **20 h**

b. The engine self-refuels at a rate of 40 gallons per hour. Write a linear function $h(t)$ to represent the refueling of the generator. **$h(t) = 40t$**

c. Find $T(t) = g(t) + h(t)$. What does this new function represent? **35c. $T(t) = -t^2 + 50t + 200$; the fuel in the tank after t hours with refueling**

d. Will the generator run out of fuel? If so, when? **Yes; after about 53 hours 43 minutes.**

H.O.T. Problems Use Higher-Order Thinking Skills

36. **REASONING** Are the following statements *sometimes*, *always*, or *never* true? Explain. **See margin.**

a. The graph of $y = x^2 + k$ has its vertex at the origin.

b. The graphs of $y = ax^2$ and its reflection over the x-axis are the same width.

c. The graph of $y = x^2 + k$, where $k \geq 0$, and the graph of a quadratic with vertex at $(0, -3)$ have the same maximum or minimum point.

37. **CHALLENGE** Write a function of the form $y = ax^2 + k$ with a graph that passes through the points $(-2, 3)$ and $(4, 15)$. **$y = x^2 - 1$**

38. **ARGUMENTS** Determine whether all quadratic functions that are reflected across the y-axis produce the same graph. Explain your answer. **See margin.**

39. **OPEN ENDED** Write a quadratic function that opens downward and is wider than the parent graph. **Sample answer: $f(x) = -\frac{1}{2}x^2$**

40. **WRITING IN MATH** Describe how the values of a and k affect the graphical and tabular representations for the functions $y = ax^2$, $y = x^2 + k$, and $y = ax^2 + k$. **See margin.**

Enrichment

OL BL

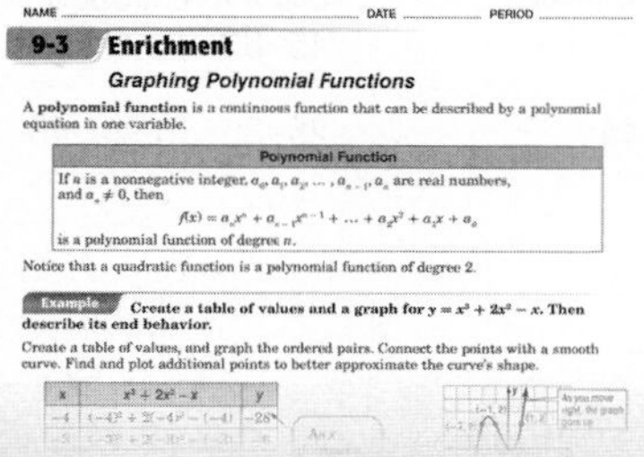
9-3 Enrichment

Graphing Polynomial Functions

Teaching the Process Standards

Arguments Mathematically proficient students are able to analyze situations by breaking them into cases. In Exercise 38, suggest that students look back at the graphs that appear throughout the lesson to see various types of graphs.

Standardized Test Practice

41. SHORT RESPONSE A tutor charges a flat fee of \$55 and \$30 for each hour of work. Write a function that represents the total charge C, in terms of the number of hours h worked. **$C = 55 + 30h$**

42. Which *best* describes the graph of $y = 2x^2$? **D**

A a line with a y-intercept of 2 and an x-intercept at the origin

B a parabola with a minimum point at (0, 0) and that is wider than the graph of $y = x^2$

C a parabola with a maximum point at (0, 0) and that is narrower than the graph of $y = x^2$

D a parabola with a minimum point at (0, 0) and that is narrower than the graph of $y = x^2$

43. Candace is 5 feet tall. If 1 inch is about 2.54 centimeters, how tall is Candace to the nearest centimeter? **J**

F 13 cm H 123 cm
G 26 cm J 152 cm

44. While in England, Imani spent 49.60 British pounds on a pair of jeans. If this is equivalent to \$100 in U.S. currency, how many British pounds would Imani have spent on a sweater that cost \$60? **B**

A 2976 pounds
B 29.76 pounds
C 19.84 pounds
D 8.26 pounds

Spiral Review

Solve each equation by graphing. (Lesson 9-2) **45–50. See Ch. 9 Answer Appendix for graphs.**

45. $x^2 + 6 = 0$ **∅** **46.** $x^2 - 10x = -24$ **4, 6** **47.** $x^2 + 5x + 4 = 0$ **4, −1**

48. $2x^2 - x = 3$ **$-1, \frac{3}{2}$** **49.** $2x^2 - x = 15$ **$-\frac{5}{2}, 3$** **50.** $12x^2 = -11x + 15$ **$-\frac{5}{3}, \frac{3}{4}$**

Find the vertex, the equation of the axis of symmetry, and the y-intercept of each graph. (Lesson 9-1)

51.
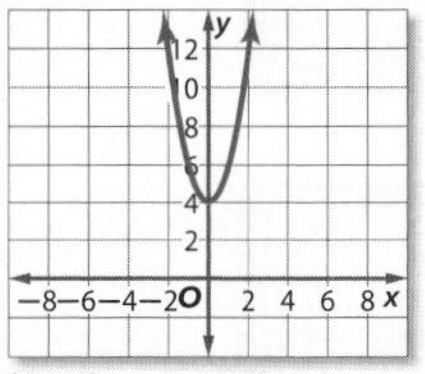

(0, 4); $x = 0$; 4

52.
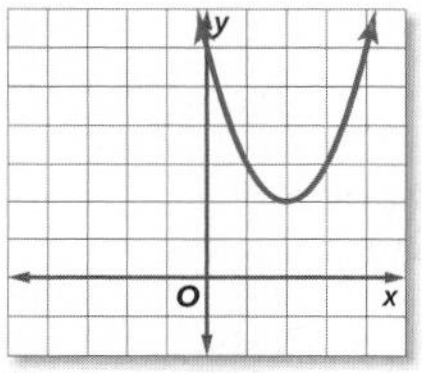

(2, 2); $x = 2$; 6

53.
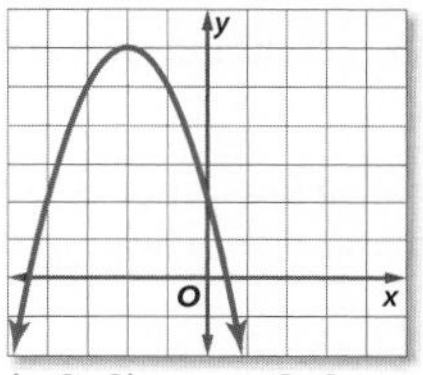

(−2, 6); $x = -2$; 2

54. CLASS TRIP Mr. Wong's American History class will take taxis from their hotel in Washington, D.C., to the Lincoln Memorial. The fare is \$2.75 for the first mile and \$1.25 for each additional mile. If the distance is m miles and t taxis are needed, write an expression for the cost to transport the group. (Lesson 8-2) **$2.75t + 1.25t(m - 1)$**

Solve each inequality. Check your solution. (Lesson 5-3)

55. $-3t + 6 \leq -3$ **$\{t \mid t \geq 3\}$** **56.** $59 > -5 - 8f$ **$\{f \mid f > -8\}$** **57.** $-2 - \frac{d}{5} < 23$ **$\{d \mid d > -125\}$**

Skills Review

Determine whether each trinomial is a perfect square trinomial. If so, factor it.

58. $16x^2 - 24x + 9$ **$(4x - 3)^2$** **59.** $9x^2 + 6x + 1$ **$(3x + 1)^2$** **60.** $25x^2 - 60x + 36$ **$(5x - 6)^2$**

61. $x^2 - 8x + 81$ **no** **62.** $36x^2 - 84x + 49$ **$(6x - 7)^2$** **63.** $4x^2 - 3x + 9$ **no**

Differentiated Instruction OL BL

Extension All of the functions graphed and analyzed in this lesson had their vertex located on the y-axis. Ask students to graph $y = (x - 3)^2 + 2$ and then tell how the graph is related to the graph of $y = x^2$. It is a parabola that is moved 3 units to the right and 2 units up.

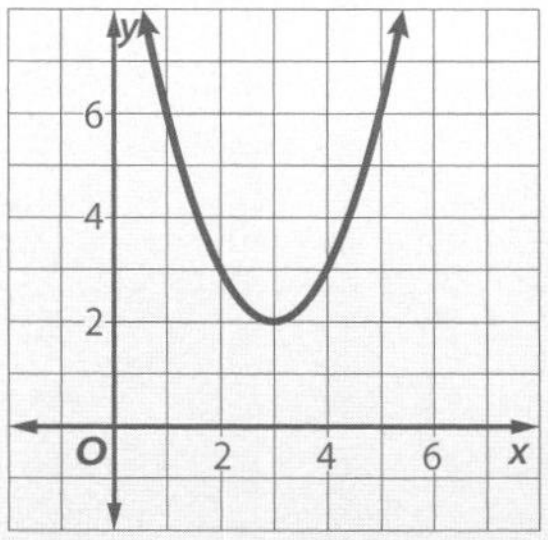

4 Assess

Ticket Out the Door Write five different quadratic functions of the form $f(x) = ax^2 + k$ on pieces of paper. Give each student one. Have students tell you how the graph of each function is related to the graph of $y = x^2$ as they walk out the door.

Formative Assessment

Check for student understanding of Lessons 9-1 and 9-3.

Additional Answers

36a. Sometimes; this only occurs if $k = 0$. For any other value, the graph will be translated up or down.

36b. Always; the reflection does not affect the width. Both graphs are dilated by a factor of a.

36c. Never; if the graph with a vertex at (0, −3) opens upward, it will have a lower minimum. If it opens downward, it will have a maximum. The first graph has a minimum.

38. Sample answer: Not all reflections over the y-axis produce the same graph. If the vertex of the original graph is not on the y-axis, the graph will not have the y-axis as its axis of symmetry and its reflection across the y-axis will be a different parabola.

40. Sample answer: For $y = ax^2$, the parent graph is stretched vertically if $a > 1$ or compressed vertically if $0 < a < 1$. The y-values in the table will all be multiplied by a factor of a. For $y = x^2 + k$, the parent graph is translated up if k is positive and moved down if k is negative. The y-values in the table will all have the constant k added to them or subtracted from them. For $y = ax^2 + k$, the graph will either be stretched vertically or compressed vertically based upon the value of a and then will be translated up or down depending on the value of k. The y-values in the table will be multiplied by a factor of a and the constant k added to them.

1 Focus

Objective Use a graphing calculator to solve a system of one linear and one quadratic equation.

Materials for Each Group

- TI-83/84 Plus or other graphing calculator

Teaching Tip

Remind students that a solution to a system of equations is an ordered pair that satisfies both equations. Ask them how that looks on a graph of a system. Lead them through discussion to an understanding that a system involving a quadratic equation and a linear equation could have 2, 1, or no solutions.

2 Teach

Working in Cooperative Groups

Pair students with different abilities. Have students work through Activities 1–3 and Exercises 1–5.

Activity 1

Ask:

- Where can you find the solutions for $y = x - 3$? They all lie on the line.
- Where can you find the solutions for $y = x^2 - x - 6$? They all lie on the parabola.
- Where can you find the solutions for the system of equations: $y = x^2 - x - 6$ and $y = x - 3$? They are found where the two graphs intersect.
- How many times does the graph of the line intersect the graph of the parabola? two
- How many solutions are there to the system? two

EXTEND 9-3 Graphing Technology Lab: Systems of Linear and Quadratic Equations

You can use a graphing calculator to solve systems involving linear and quadratic equations.

Activity 1 Solve a System of Equations Graphically

Use a graphing calculator to solve the system of equations.

$y = x^2 - x - 6$
$y = x - 3$

Step 1 Enter each equation in the **Y=** list.

KEYSTROKES: [X,T,θ,n] [x^2] [−] [X,T,θ,n] [−] 6 [ENTER] [X,T,θ,n] [−] 3

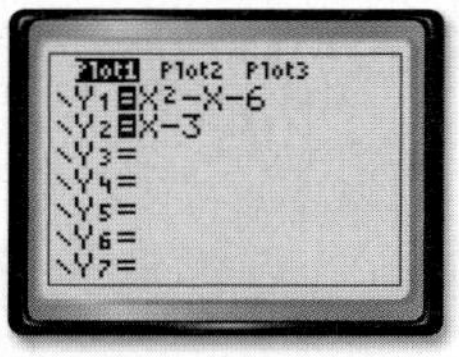

Step 2 Graph the system. KEYSTROKES: [GRAPH]

The graphs intersect at two points. So, there are two solutions.

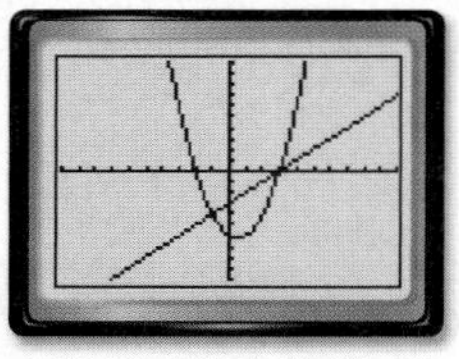

[−10, 10] scl: 1 by [−10, 10] scl: 1

Step 3 Find the intersection on the left by using the **CALC** menu.

KEYSTROKES: [2nd] [CALC] 5 [ENTER] [ENTER]

Use the arrow keys to move the cursor close to the intersection on the left. Press [ENTER] again.

The graphs intersect at $(-1, -4)$.

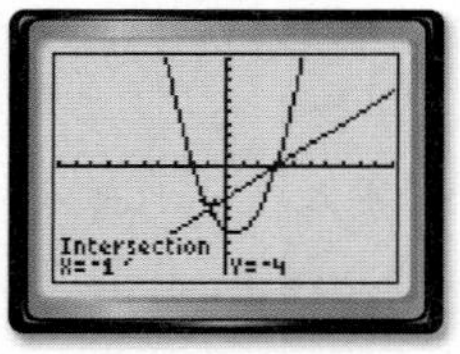

[−10, 10] scl: 1 by [−10, 10] scl: 1

Step 4 Repeat Step 3 but move the cursor to the other intersection. The graphs intersect at $(3, 0)$.

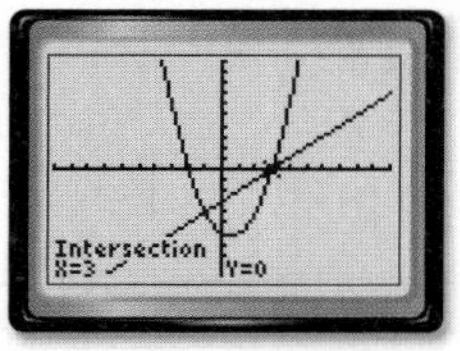

[−10, 10] scl: 1 by [−10, 10] scl: 1

You can use a graphing calculator to verify solutions of systems found algebraically.

Activity 2 Check Solutions Graphically

Solve the system of equations algebraically. Use a graphing calculator to check your solutions.

$y = 2x - 6$
$y = x^2 - 8x + 19$

Step 1 Set the expressions equal to each other, and solve for x.

$x^2 - 8x + 19 = 2x - 6$	Substitute $x^2 - 8x + 19$ for y.
$x^2 - 10x + 25 = 0$	Simplify.
$(x - 5)^2 = 0$	Factor.
$x = 5$	Solve for x.

572 | Extend 9-3 | Graphing Technology Lab: Systems of Linear and Quadratic Equations

Step 2 Substitute the x-value into either equation to find the y-value: $y = 2(5) - 6$ or 4.

Step 3 Graph the system and find the point(s) of intersection as in Activity 1.

The graphs intersect at (5, 4). Thus, the solution of the system of equations is (5, 4).

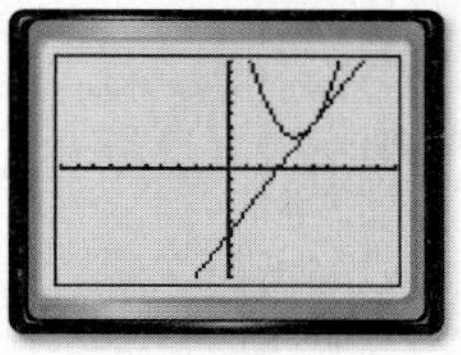

[−10, 10] scl: 1 by [−10, 10] scl: 1

You can solve a quadratic equation graphically by writing each side of the equation as a separate function. The x-coordinate of the point(s) of intersection will be the solution of the equation, since at that point(s) the original equations are true.

Activity 3 Use a System to Solve an Equation

Use a system of equations to solve $x^2 - 3x + 1 = \frac{11}{4}x - 6$.

Step 1 Write as a system of equations. $y = x^2 - 3x + 1$
$y = \frac{11}{4}x - 6$

Step 2 Enter the equations into the graphing calculator, and graph them.

Step 3 Use the **[CALC]** menu to find the two points of intersection.

The graphs intersect at (1.75, −1.1875) and (4, 5). Thus, the solutions of $x^2 - 3x + 1 = \frac{11}{4}x - 6$ are 1.75 and 4.

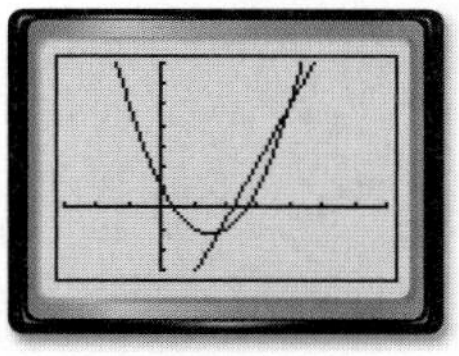

[−3, 7] scl: 1 by [−3, 7] scl: 1

Exercises

Use a graphing calculator to solve each system of equations.

1. $y = x^2$ (0, 0), (2, 4)
   $y = 2x$
2. $y = -2x^2 + 7x - 2$ $\left(\frac{1}{2}, 1\right)$, (5, −17)
   $y = 3 - 4x$
3. $y = -x^2 + 4$ no solution
   $y = \frac{1}{2}x + 5$

Solve each system of equations algebraically. Use a graphing calculator to check your solutions.

4. $y = x^2 + 7x + 12$
   $y = 2x + 8$ (−1, 6), (−4, 0)
5. $y = x^2 - x - 20$
   $y = 3x + 12$ (−4, 0), (8, 36)
6. $y = 3x^2 - x - 2$
   $y = -2x + 2$ (1, 0), $\left(-1\frac{1}{3}, 4\frac{2}{3}\right)$

Use a system of equations to solve each equation.

7. $x^2 = -2x - 1$ −1
8. $\frac{1}{2}x^2 - 4 = 3x + 4$ −2, 8
9. $x^2 + 5x + 5 = -x - 8$ no solution

CHALLENGE Use a graphing calculator to solve other types of systems.

10. $y = x^2 + 3x - 5$
    $y = -x^2$ (−2.5, −6.25), (1, −1)
11. $y = \frac{3}{4}x$ (0.8, 0.6), (−0.8, −0.6)
    $x^2 + y^2 = 1$ (*Hint:* Enter as two functions, $y = \sqrt{1 - x^2}$ and $y = -\sqrt{1 - x^2}$.)

Extending the Concept

Ask students how many solutions are possible for a system that includes a quadratic equation and two linear equations that are not dependent. One solution or none is possible since there is, at most, one solution to a system of non-dependent linear equations.

Activity 2

Ask:

- How many times does the graph of the line intersect the graph of the parabola? one
- How many solutions are there to the system? one

Activity 3

Ask:

- How many times does the graph of the line intersect the graph of the parabola? twice
- How many solutions are there to the system? two
- At how many points could the graph of a line intersect the graph of a parabola? 0, 1, or 2
- How many solutions are there to a system of a linear and a quadratic equation if their graphs do not intersect? none

Practice Have students complete Exercises 6–11 independently.

3 Assess

Formative Assessment

Use Exercises 6–10 to assess whether students are able to solve systems of equations using a graphing calculator.

From Concrete to Abstract

In Exercises 10 and 11, students find the solutions for a system of two quadratic equations and a system of a circle and a linear equation.

Ask:

- How many times can the graphs of two quadratic equations intersect? 0, 1, or 2
- What figure was obtained by graphing $y = \sqrt{1 - x^2}$ and $y = -\sqrt{1 - x^2}$? a circle

The circle in Exercise 11 is known as a unit circle. The solutions of the system are points on this circle, most with fractional coordinates. Students will explore the unit circle in depth in later courses when they study trigonometry.

1 Focus

VerticalAlignment

Before Lesson 9-4 Solve quadratic equations by using the square root property.

Lesson 9-4 Complete the square to write perfect square trinomials. Solve quadratic equations by competing the square.

After Lesson 9-4 Solve quadratic equations using the Quadratic Formula.

2 Teach

Scaffolding Questions

Have students read the **Why?** section of the lesson.

Ask:

- Look at the equation. Is 25 a perfect square? yes
- Is $-16t^2 + 20t + 12$ a perfect square? no
- Can you solve the equation by taking the square root of each side of the equation? no

Teach with Tech

Interactive Whiteboard As you teach students to complete the square, save each example as a notes page. Then send your notes to students.

LESSON 9-4 Solving Quadratic Equations by Completing the Square

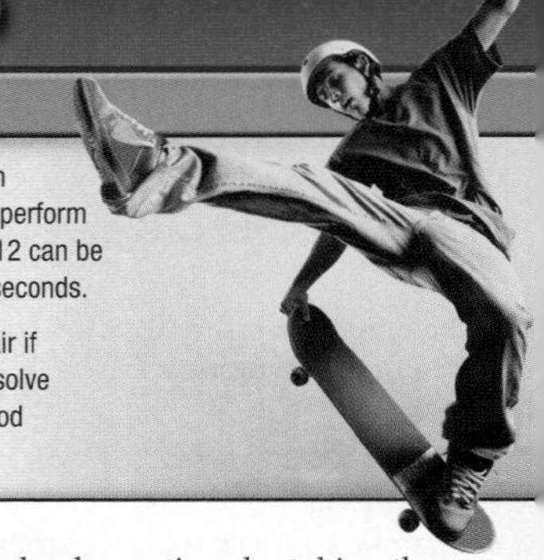

Then

- You solved quadratic equations by using the square root property.

Now

1. Complete the square to write perfect square trinomials.
2. Solve quadratic equations by completing the square.

Why?

- In competitions, skateboarders may launch themselves from a half pipe into the air to perform tricks. The equation $h = -16t^2 + 20t + 12$ can be used to model their height, in feet, after t seconds.

To find how long a skateboarder is in the air if he is 25 feet above the half pipe, you can solve $25 = -16t^2 + 20t + 12$ by using a method called completing the square.

NewVocabulary
completing the square

Content Standards
AI.QE.4, AI.QE.5, AI.QE.6, AI.QE.7

1 Complete the Square

You have previously solved equations by taking the square root of each side. This method worked only because the expression on the left-hand side was a perfect square. In perfect square trinomials in which the leading coefficient is 1, there is a relationship between the coefficient of the x-term and the constant term.

$$(x + 5)^2 = x^2 + 2(5)(x) + 5^2$$
$$= x^2 + 10x + 25$$

Notice that $\left(\frac{10}{2}\right)^2 = 25$. To get the constant term, divide the coefficient of the x-term by 2 and square the result. Any quadratic expression in the form $x^2 + bx$ can be made into a perfect square by using a method called **completing the square**.

KeyConcept Completing the Square

Words To complete the square for any quadratic expression of the form $x^2 + bx$, follow the steps below.

Step 1 Find one half of b, the coefficient of x.

Step 2 Square the result in Step 1.

Step 3 Add the result of Step 2 to $x^2 + bx$.

Symbols $x^2 + bx + \left(\frac{b}{2}\right)^2 = \left(x + \frac{b}{2}\right)^2$

Example 1 Complete the Square

Find the value of c that makes $x^2 + 4x + c$ a perfect square trinomial.

Method 1 Use algebra tiles.

Lesson 9-4 Resources

Resource	Approaching Level AL	On Level OL	Beyond Level BL	English Learners ELL
Teacher Edition	▪ Differentiated Instruction, p. 576	▪ Differentiated Instruction, p. 576	▪ Differentiated Instruction, p. 579	
Chapter Resource Masters	▪ Study Guide and Intervention, pp. 23–24 ▪ Skills Practice, p. 25 ▪ Practice, p. 26 ▪ Word Problem Practice, p. 27	▪ Study Guide and Intervention, pp. 23–24 ▪ Skills Practice, p. 25 ▪ Practice, p. 26 ▪ Word Problem Practice, p. 27 ▪ Enrichment, p. 28	▪ Practice, p. 26 ▪ Word Problem Practice, p. 27 ▪ Enrichment, p. 28	▪ Study Guide and Intervention, pp. 23–24 ▪ Skills Practice, p. 25 ▪ Practice, p. 26 ▪ Word Problem Practice, p. 27
Other	▪ 5-Minute Check 9-4 ▪ Study Notebook ▪ Teaching Algebra with Manipulatives	▪ 5-Minute Check 9-4 ▪ Study Notebook ▪ Teaching Algebra with Manipulatives	▪ 5-Minute Check 9-4 ▪ Study Notebook	▪ 5-Minute Check 9-4 ▪ Study Notebook ▪ Teaching Algebra with Manipulatives

StudyTip
Algorithms An algorithm is a series of steps for carrying out a procedure or solving a problem.

Method 2 Use complete the square algorithm.

Step 1 Find $\frac{1}{2}$ of 4. $\frac{4}{2} = 2$

Step 2 Square the result in Step 1. $2^2 = 4$

Step 3 Add the result of Step 2 to $x^2 + 4x$. $x^2 + 4x + 4$

Thus, $c = 4$. Notice that $x^2 + 4x + 4 = (x + 2)^2$.

GuidedPractice

1. Find the value of c that makes $r^2 - 8r + c$ a perfect square trinomial. **16**

2 Solve Equations by Completing the Square

You can complete the square to solve quadratic equations. First, you must isolate the x^2- and bx-terms.

PT

Example 2 Solve an Equation by Completing the Square

Solve $x^2 - 6x + 12 = 19$ by completing the square.

$x^2 - 6x + 12 = 19$	Original equation
$x^2 - 6x = 7$	Subtract 12 from each side.
$x^2 - 6x + 9 = 7 + 9$	Since $\left(\frac{-6}{2}\right)^2 = 9$, add 9 to each side.
$(x - 3)^2 = 16$	Factor $x^2 - 6x + 9$.
$x - 3 = \pm 4$	Take the square root of each side.
$x = 3 \pm 4$	Add 3 to each side.
$x = 3 + 4$ or $x = 3 - 4$	Separate the solutions.
$= 7$ $\quad = -1$	The solutions are 7 and -1.

GuidedPractice

2. Solve $x^2 - 12x + 3 = 8$ by completing the square. **about −0.4, 12.4**

To solve a quadratic equation in which the leading coefficient is not 1, divide each term by the coefficient. Then isolate the x^2- and x-terms and complete the square.

PT

Example 3 Equation with $a \neq 1$

WatchOut!
Leading Coefficient
Remember that the leading coefficient has to be 1 before you can complete the square.

Solve $-2x^2 + 8x - 18 = 0$ by completing the square.

$-2x^2 + 8x - 18 = 0$	Original equation
$\frac{-2x^2 + 8x - 18}{-2} = \frac{0}{-2}$	Divide each side by -2.
$x^2 - 4x + 9 = 0$	Simplify.
$x^2 - 4x = -9$	Subtract 9 from each side.
$x^2 - 4x + 4 = -9 + 4$	Since $\left(\frac{-4}{2}\right)^2 = 4$, add 4 to each side.
$(x - 2)^2 = -5$	Factor $x^2 - 4x + 4$.

No real number has a negative square. So, this equation has no real solutions.

GuidedPractice

3. Solve $3x^2 - 9x - 3 = 21$ by completing the square. **about −1.7, 4.7**

1 Complete the Square

Example 1 shows how to make any binomial of the form $x^2 + bx$ a perfect square by completing the square.

Formative Assessment

Use Guided Practice exercises after each example to determine students' understanding of concepts.

Additional Example

1 Find the value of c that makes $x^2 - 12x + c$ a perfect square trinomial. 36

Additional Examples also in Interactive Classroom PowerPoint® Presentations

IWB **Interactive White Board READY**

2 Solve by Completing the Square

Example 2 shows how to solve a quadratic equation by completing the square. **Example 3** shows how to solve a quadratic equation in which a does not equal 1. **Example 4** shows how to use completing the square to solve real-world problems.

Tips for New Teachers

Reasoning Students should always check their solutions by graphing the related function or by substituting the solutions into the original equation. For instance, tell students that in Example 2, substituting 7 and −1 into $x^2 - 6x + 12$ should produce 19.

Additional Examples

2 Solve $x^2 + 6x + 5 = 12$ by completing the square. −7, 1

3 Solve $-2x^2 + 36x - 10 = 24$ by completing the square. 17, 1

Additional Example

4 CANOEING Suppose the rate of flow of an 80-foot-wide river is given by the equation $r = -0.01x^2 + 0.8x$, where r is the rate in miles per hour and x is the distance from the shore in feet. Joacquim does not want to paddle his canoe against a current that is faster than 5 miles per hour. At what distance from the river bank must he paddle in order to avoid a current of 5 miles per hour? up to 7 ft from either bank **Note:** The solutions of the equation are about 7 feet and about 73 feet. Since the river is 80 feet wide, $80 - 73 = 7$. Both ranges are within 7 feet of one bank or the other.

Tips for New Teachers

Student Misconceptions Tell students not to throw out negative solutions to real-world problems. Remind them that they must first examine the problem to see if the solution fits the situation.

3 Practice

Formative Assessment

Use Exercises 1–9 to check for understanding.

Use the chart on the bottom of the next page to customize assignments for your students.

Teaching the Process Standards

Modeling Mathematically proficient students can analyze relationships mathematically. In Exercise 9, suggest that students draw a diagram to represent the situation.

Real-WorldLink

The oldest public high school rivalry takes place between Wellesley High School and Needham Heights High School in Massachusetts. The first football game between them took place on Thanksgiving morning in 1882 in Needham.

Source: USA Football

Real-World Example 4 Solve a Problem by Completing the Square

JERSEYS The senior class at Bay High School buys jerseys to wear to the football games. The cost of the jerseys can be modeled by the equation $C = 0.1x^2 + 2.4x + 25$, where C is the amount it costs to buy x jerseys. How many jerseys can they purchase for $430?

The seniors have $430, so set the equation equal to 430 and complete the square.

$0.1x^2 + 2.4x + 25 = 430$	Original equation
$\frac{0.1x^2 + 2.4x + 25}{0.1} = \frac{430}{0.1}$	Divide each side by 0.1.
$x^2 + 24x + 250 = 4300$	Simplify.
$x^2 + 24x + 250 - 250 = 4300 - 250$	Subtract 250 from each side.
$x^2 + 24x = 4050$	Simplify.
$x^2 + 24x + 144 = 4050 + 144$	Since $\left(\frac{24}{2}\right)^2 = 144$, add 144 to each side.
$x^2 + 24x + 144 = 4194$	Simplify.
$(x + 12)^2 = 4194$	Factor $x^2 + 24x + 144$.
$x + 12 = \pm\sqrt{4194}$	Take the square root of each side.
$x = -12 \pm \sqrt{4194}$	Subtract 12 from each side.

Use a calculator to approximate each value of x.

$x = -12 + \sqrt{4194}$	or	$x = -12 - \sqrt{4194}$	Separate the solutions.
≈ 52.8		≈ -76.8	Evaluate.

Since you cannot buy a negative number of jerseys, the negative solution is not reasonable. The seniors can afford to buy 52 jerseys.

GuidedPractice

4. If the senior class were able to raise $620, how many jerseys could they buy? **66 jerseys**

Check Your Understanding

◯ = Step-by-Step Solutions begin on page R13.

Example 1 **Find the value of c that makes each trinomial a perfect square.**

1. $x^2 - 18x + c$ **81**

2. $x^2 + 22x + c$ **121**

3. $x^2 + 9x + c$ $\frac{81}{4}$

4. $x^2 - 7x + c$ $\frac{49}{4}$

Examples 2–3 **Solve each equation by completing the square. Round to the nearest tenth if necessary.**

5. $x^2 + 4x = 6$ **−5.2, 1.2**

6. $x^2 - 8x = -9$ **1.4, 6.6**

7. $4x^2 + 9x - 1 = 0$ **−2.4, 0.1**

8. $-2x^2 + 10x + 22 = 4$ **−1.4, 6.4**

Example 4 **9. MODELING** Collin is building a deck on the back of his family's house. He has enough lumber for the deck to be 144 square feet. The length should be 10 feet more than its width. What should the dimensions of the deck be? **8 ft by 18 ft**

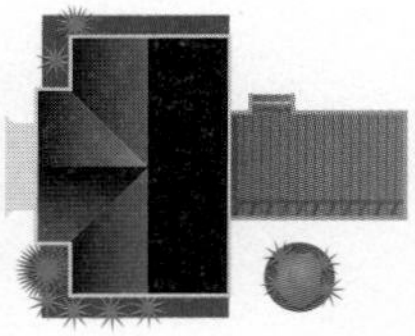

DifferentiatedInstruction AL OL

Kinesthetic Learners Some students may benefit from using algebra tiles to complete the square when solving quadratic equations like those in Examples 2 and 3. Have students use an equation mat. Remind them to add or remove the same number of tiles to or from each side of the mat.

Practice and Problem Solving

Extra Practice is on page R9.

Example 1 **Find the value of c that makes each trinomial a perfect square.**

10. $x^2 + 26x + c$ **169** **11.** $x^2 - 24x + c$ **144** **12.** $x^2 - 19x + c$ $\frac{361}{4}$

13. $x^2 + 17x + c$ $\frac{289}{4}$ **14.** $x^2 + 5x + c$ $\frac{25}{4}$ **15.** $x^2 - 13x + c$ $\frac{169}{4}$

16. $x^2 - 22x + c$ **121** **17.** $x^2 - 15x + c$ $\frac{225}{4}$ **18.** $x^2 + 24x + c$ **144**

Examples 2–3 **Solve each equation by completing the square. Round to the nearest tenth if necessary.**

19. $x^2 + 6x - 16 = 0$ **−8, 2**

20. $x^2 - 2x - 14 = 0$ **−2.9, 4.9**

21. $x^2 - 8x - 1 = 8$ **−1, 9**

22. $x^2 + 3x + 21 = 22$ **−3.3, 0.3**

23. $x^2 - 11x + 3 = 5$ **−0.2, 11.2**

24. $5x^2 - 10x = 23$ **−1.4, 3.4**

25. $2x^2 - 2x + 7 = 5$ **∅**

26. $3x^2 + 12x + 81 = 15$ **∅**

27. $4x^2 + 6x = 12$ **−2.6, 1.1**

28. $4x^2 + 5 = 10x$ **0.7, 1.8**

29. $-2x^2 + 10x = -14$ **−1.1, 6.1**

30. $-3x^2 - 12 = 14x$ **−3.5, −1.1**

Example 4 **31.** **FINANCIAL LITERACY** The price p in dollars for a particular stock can be modeled by the quadratic equation $p = 3.5t - 0.05t^2$, where t represents the number of days after the stock is purchased. When is the stock worth $60? **on the 30th and 40th day after purchase**

GEOMETRY **Find the value of x for each figure. Round to the nearest tenth if necessary.**

32. $A = 45$ in^2 **6.3**

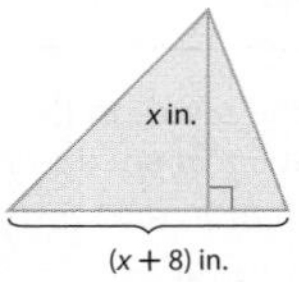

33. $A = 110$ ft^2 **5.3**

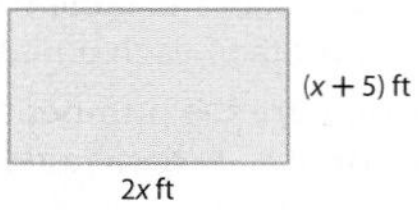

34. **NUMBER THEORY** The product of two consecutive even integers is 224. Find the integers. **14 and 16; −14 and −16**

35. **PRECISION** The product of two consecutive negative odd integers is 483. Find the integers. **−21 and −23**

36. **GEOMETRY** Find the area of the triangle below. **216 m^2**

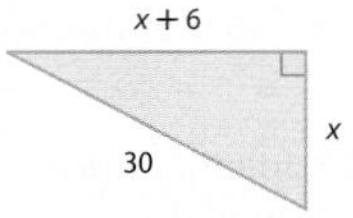

B **Solve each equation by completing the square. Round to the nearest tenth if necessary.**

37. $0.2x^2 - 0.2x - 0.4 = 0$ **−1, 2**

38. $0.5x^2 = 2x - 0.3$ **0.2, 3.8**

39. $2x^2 - \frac{11}{5}x = -\frac{3}{10}$ **0.2, 0.9**

40. $\frac{2}{3}x^2 - \frac{4}{3}x = \frac{5}{6}$ **−0.5, 2.5**

41. $\frac{1}{4}x^2 + 2x = \frac{3}{8}$ **−8.2, 0.2**

42. $\frac{2}{5}x^2 + 2x = \frac{1}{5}$ **−5.1, 0.1**

WatchOut!

Preventing Errors For Exercises 19–30, remind students that the amount that they add to one side of the equation to complete the square must also be added to the other side of the equation.

Formula For Exercises 32 and 36, students will need to know the formula for the area of a triangle, $A = \frac{1}{2}bh$.

Focus on Mathematical Content

Irrational Solutions Completing the square to solve a quadratic equation does not mean that the solutions will be integers. If the equation already has a nonzero constant term, it is likely that after completing the square, the constant will not be a perfect square, and the solutions will be irrational.

Teaching the Process Standards

Precision Mathematically proficient students attend to precision. In Exercise 35, tell students to make sure that their answer fits the criteria of the problem.

Differentiated Homework Options

Level	Assignment	Two-Day Option	
AL Basic	10–36, 49–81	11–35 odd, 53–56	10–36 even, 49–52, 57–81
OL Core	11–43 odd, 44–47, 49–81	10–36, 53–56	37–47, 49–52, 57–81
BL Advanced	37–75, (optional: 76–81)		

Study Guide and Intervention
AL OL ELL

NAME ____________ DATE ________ PERIOD ______

9-4 Study Guide and Intervention

Solving Quadratic Equations by Completing the Square

Complete the Square Perfect square trinomials can be solved quickly by taking the square root of both sides of the equation. A quadratic equation that is not in perfect square form can be made into a perfect square by a method called **completing the square**.

Completing the Square
To complete the square for any quadratic equation of the form $x^2 + bx$:
Step 1 Find one-half of b, the coefficient of x.
Step 2 Square the result in Step 1.
Step 3 Add the result of Step 2 to $x^2 + bx$.
$x^2 + bx + \left(\frac{b}{2}\right)^2 = \left(x + \frac{b}{2}\right)^2$

Example Find the value of c that makes $x^2 + 2x + c$ a perfect square trinomial.

Step 1 Find $\frac{1}{2}$ of 2. $\frac{2}{2} = 1$
Step 2 Square the result of Step 1. $1^2 = 1$
Step 3 Add the result of Step 2 to $x^2 + 2x$. $x^2 + 2x + 1$
Thus, $c = 1$. Notice that $x^2 + 2x + 1$ equals $(x + 1)^2$.

Exercises
Find the value of c that makes each trinomial a perfect square.

1. $x^2 + 10x + c$ 2. $x^2 + 14x + c$
3. $x^2 - 4x + c$ 4. $x^2 - 8x + c$
5. $x^2 + 5x + c$ 6. $x^2 + 9x + c$
7. $x^2 - 3x + c$ 8. $x^2 - 15x + c$
9. $x^2 + 28x + c$ 10. $x^2 + 22x + c$

Lesson 9-4

Practice
AL OL BL ELL

NAME ____________ DATE ________ PERIOD ______

9-4 Practice

Solving Quadratic Equations by Completing the Square

Find the value of c that makes each trinomial a perfect square.

1. $x^2 - 24x + c$ 2. $x^2 + 28x + c$ 3. $x^2 + 40x + c$
4. $x^2 + 3x + c$ 5. $x^2 - 9x + c$ 6. $x^2 - x + c$

Solve each equation by completing the square. Round to the nearest tenth if necessary.

7. $x^2 - 14x + 24 = 0$ 8. $x^2 + 12x = 13$ 9. $x^2 - 30x + 56 = -25$
10. $x^2 + 8x + 9 = 0$ 11. $x^2 - 10x + 6 = -7$ 12. $x^2 + 18x + 50 = 9$
13. $3x^2 + 15x - 3 = 0$ 14. $4x^2 - 72 = 24x$ 15. $0.9x^2 + 5.4x - 4 = 0$
16. $0.4x^2 + 0.8x = 0.2$ 17. $\frac{1}{2}x^2 - x - 10 = 0$ 18. $\frac{1}{4}x^2 + x - 2 = 0$

19. **NUMBER THEORY** The product of two consecutive even integers is 728. Find the integers.

20. **BUSINESS** Jaime owns a business making decorative boxes to store jewelry, mementos, and other valuables. The function $y = x^2 + 50x + 1800$ models the profit y that Jaime has made in month x for the first two years of his business.

a. Write an equation representing the month in which Jaime's profit is $2400.

b. Use completing the square to find out in which month Jaime's profit is $2400.

21. **PHYSICS** From a height of 256 feet above a lake on a cliff, Mikaela throws a rock out over the lake. The height H of the rock t seconds after Mikaela throws it is represented by the equation $H = -16t^2 + 32t + 256$. To the nearest tenth of a second, how long does it take the rock to reach the lake below? (*Hint:* Replace H with 0.)

Word Problem Practice
AL OL BL ELL

NAME ____________ DATE ________ PERIOD ______

9-4 Word Problem Practice

Solving Quadratic Equations by Completing the Square

1. **INTERIOR DESIGN** Modular carpeting is installed in small pieces rather than as a large roll so that only a few pieces need to be replaced if a small area is damaged. Suppose the room shown in the diagram below is being fitted with modular carpeting. Complete the square to determine the number of 1 foot by 1 foot squares of carpeting needed to finish the room. Fill in the missing terms in the corresponding equation below.

$x^2 + 10x +$ ____ $= (x +$ ____$)^2$

2. **FALLING OBJECTS** Keisha throws a rock down an old well. The distance d in feet the rock falls after t seconds can be represented by $d = 16t^2 + 64t$. If the water in the well is 80 feet below ground, how many seconds will it take for the rock to hit the water?

3. **MARS** On Mars, the gravity acting on an object is less than that on Earth. On Earth, a golf ball hit with an initial upward velocity of 26 meters per second will hit the ground in about 5.4 seconds. The height h of an object on Mars that leaves the ground with an initial velocity of 26 meters per second is given by the equation $h = -1.9t^2 + 26t$. How much longer will it take for the golf ball hit on Mars to reach the ground? Round your answer to the nearest tenth.

4. **FROGS** A frog sitting on a stump 3 feet high hops off and lands on the ground. During its leap, its height h in feet is given by $h = -0.5d^2 + 2d + 3$, where d is the distance from the base of the stump. How far is the frog from the base of the stump when it landed on the ground?

5. **GARDENING** Peg is planning a rectangular vegetable garden using 200 feet of fencing material. She only needs to fence three sides of the garden since one side borders an existing fence.

a. Let x = the width of the rectangle. Write an equation to represent the area A of the garden if Peg uses all the fencing material.

b. For what widths would the area of Peg's garden equal 4800 square feet if she uses all the fencing material?

Lesson 9-4

43 **ASTRONOMY** The height of an object t seconds after it is dropped is given by the equation $h = -\frac{1}{2}gt^2 + h_0$, where h_0 is the initial height and g is the acceleration due to gravity. The acceleration due to gravity near the surface of Mars is $3.73\ m/s^2$, while on Earth it is $9.8\ m/s^2$. Suppose an object is dropped from an initial height of 120 meters above the surface of each planet.

a. On which planet would the object reach the ground first? **Earth**

b. How long would it take the object to reach the ground on each planet? Round each answer to the nearest tenth. **Earth: 4.9 seconds, Mars: 8.0 seconds**

c. Do the times that it takes the object to reach the ground seem reasonable? Explain your reasoning.

43c. Sample answer: Yes; the acceleration due to gravity is much greater on Earth than on Mars, so the time to reach the ground should be much less.

44. Find all values of c that make $x^2 + cx + 100$ a perfect square trinomial. **−20 and 20**

45. Find all values of c that make $x^2 + cx + 225$ a perfect square trinomial. **−30 and 30**

46. **PAINTING** Before she begins painting a picture, Donna stretches her canvas over a wood frame. The frame has a length of 60 inches and a width of 4 inches. She has enough canvas to cover 480 square inches. Donna decides to increase the dimensions of the frame. If the increase in the length is 10 times the increase in the width, what will the dimensions of the frame be? **6 in. by 80 in.**

C 47. **MULTIPLE REPRESENTATIONS** In this problem, you will investigate a property of quadratic equations.

a. **Tabular** Copy the table shown and complete the second column.

b. **Algebraic** Set each trinomial equal to zero, and solve the equation by completing the square. Complete the last column of the table with the number of roots of each equation.

Trinomial	$b^2 - 4ac$	Number of Roots
$x^2 - 8x + 16$	0	1
$2x^2 - 11x + 3$	97	2
$3x^2 + 6x + 9$	−72	0
$x^2 - 2x + 7$	−24	0
$x^2 + 10x + 25$	0	1
$x^2 + 3x - 12$	57	2

c. **Verbal** Compare the number of roots of each equation to the result in the $b^2 - 4ac$ column. Is there a relationship between these values? If so, describe it.

d. **Analytical** Predict how many solutions $2x^2 - 9x + 15 = 0$ will have. Verify your prediction by solving the equation. **0 because $b^2 - 4ac$ is negative. The equation has no real solutions because taking the square root of a negative number does not produce a real number.**

47c. If $b^2 - 4ac$ is negative, the equation has no real solutions. If $b^2 - 4ac$ is zero, the equation has one solution. If $b^2 - 4ac$ is positive, the equation has 2 solutions.

H.O.T. Problems Use Higher-Order Thinking Skills

48. **PERSEVERANCE** Given $y = ax^2 + bx + c$ with $a \neq 0$, derive the equation for the axis of symmetry by completing the square and rewriting the equation in the form $y = a(x - h)^2 + k$. **48–52. See margin.**

49. **REASONING** Determine the number of solutions $x^2 + bx = c$ has if $c < -\left(\frac{b}{2}\right)^2$. Explain.

50. **WHICH ONE DOESN'T BELONG?** Identify the expression that does not belong with the other three. Explain your reasoning.

$n^2 - n + \frac{1}{4}$	$n^2 + n + \frac{1}{4}$	$n^2 - \frac{2}{3}n + \frac{1}{9}$	$n^2 + \frac{1}{3}n + \frac{1}{9}$

51. **OPEN ENDED** Write a quadratic equation for which the only solution is 4.

52. **WRITING IN MATH** Compare and contrast the following strategies for solving $x^2 - 5x - 7 = 0$: completing the square, graphing, and factoring.

578 | Lesson 9-4 | Solving Quadratic Equations by Completing the Square

Enrichment
OL BL

NAME ____________ DATE ________ PERIOD ______

9-4 Enrichment

Factoring Quartic Polynomials

Completing the square is a useful tool for factoring quadratic expressions. You can utilize a similar technique to factor simple **quartic polynomials** of the form $x^4 + c$.

Example Factor the quartic polynomial $x^4 + 64$.

Step 1 Find the value of the middle term needed to complete the square. This value is $(2\sqrt{64})(x^2)$, or $16x^2$.
Step 2 Rewrite the original polynomial in factorable form. $\left(x^4 + 16x^2 + \left(\frac{16}{2}\right)^2\right) - 16x^2$
Step 3 Factor the polynomials. $(x^2 + 8)^2 - (4x)^2$
Step 4 Rewrite using the difference of two squares. $(x^2 + 8 + 4x)(x^2 + 8 - 4x)$

The factored form of $x^4 + 64$ is $(x^2 + 4x + 8)(x^2 - 4x + 8)$. This could then be factored further, if needed, to find the solutions to a quartic equation.

Exercises
Factor each quartic polynomial.

Multiple Representations

In Exercise 47, students use information organized in a table, algebraic equations, and analysis to relate the value of the discriminant in a quadratic equation with the number of real roots of the equation.

Standardized Test Practice

53. The length of a rectangle is 3 times its width. The area of the rectangle is 75 square feet. Find the length of the rectangle in feet. **B**

A 25 B 15 C 10 D 5

54. PROBABILITY At a festival, winners of a game draw a token for a prize. There is one token for each prize. The prizes include 9 movie passes, 8 stuffed animals, 5 hats, 10 jump ropes, and 4 glow necklaces. What is the probability that the first person to draw a token will win a movie pass? **J**

F $\frac{1}{36}$ G $\frac{1}{9}$ H $\frac{9}{61}$ J $\frac{1}{4}$

55. GRIDDED RESPONSE The population of a town can be modeled by $P = 22{,}000 + 125t$, where P represents the population and t represents the number of years from 2000. How many years after 2000 will the population be 26,000? **32**

56. Percy delivers pizzas for Pizza King. He is paid \$6 an hour plus \$2.50 for each pizza he delivers. Percy earned \$280 last week. If he worked a total of 30 hours, how many pizzas did he deliver? **C**

A 250 pizzas
B 184 pizzas
C 40 pizzas
D 34 pizzas

Spiral Review

Describe how the graph of each function is related to the graph of $f(x) = x^2$. **57–62. See Ch. 9 Answer Appendix.** (Lesson 9-3)

57. $g(x) = -12 + x^2$ **58.** $h(x) = (x + 2)^2$ **59.** $g(x) = 2x^2 + 5$

60. $h(x) = \frac{2}{3}(x - 6)^2$ **61.** $g(x) = 6 + \frac{4}{3}x^2$ **62.** $h(x) = -1 - \frac{3}{2}x^2$

63. RIDES A popular amusement park ride whisks riders to the top of a 250-foot tower and drops them. A function for the height of a rider is $h = -16t^2 + 250$, where h is the height and t is the time in seconds. The ride stops the descent of the rider 40 feet above the ground. Write an equation that models the drop of the rider. How long does it take to fall from 250 feet to 40 feet? (Lesson 9-2) **$40 = -16t^2 + 250$; about 3.6 s**

Simplify. Assume that no denominator is equal to zero. (Lesson 7-2)

64. $\frac{a^6}{a^3}$ **a^3** **65.** $\frac{4^7}{4^5}$ **16** **66.** $\frac{c^3d^4}{cd^7}$ **$\frac{c^2}{d^3}$**

67. $\left(\frac{4h^{-2}g}{2g^5}\right)^0$ **1** **68.** $\frac{5q^{-2}t^6}{10q^2t^{-4}}$ **$\frac{t^{10}}{2q^4}$** **69.** $b^3(m^{-3})(b^{-6})$ **$\frac{1}{m^3b^3}$**

Solve each open sentence. (Lesson 5-5)

70. $|y - 2| > 7$ **$\{y \mid y > 9$ or $y < -5\}$** **71.** $|z + 5| < 3$ **$\{z \mid -8 < z < -2\}$** **72.** $|2b + 7| \leq -6$ **$\varnothing$**

73. $|3 - 2y| \geq 8$ **$\{y \mid y \geq 5.5$ or $y \leq -2.5\}$** **74.** $|9 - 4m| < -1$ **$\varnothing$** **75.** $|5c - 2| \leq 13$ **$\{c \mid -2.2 \leq c \leq 3\}$**

Skills Review

Evaluate $\sqrt{b^2 - 4ac}$ for each set of values. Round to the nearest tenth if necessary.

76. $a = 2, b = -5, c = 2$ **±3** **77.** $a = 1, b = 12, c = 11$ **±10** **78.** $a = -9, b = 10, c = -1$ **±8**

79. $a = 1, b = 7, c = -3$ **±7.8** **80.** $a = 2, b = -4, c = -6$ **±8** **81.** $a = 3, b = 1, c = 2$ **not a real number**

Differentiated Instruction BL

Extension Have students solve $\frac{1}{3}x^2 - \frac{7}{6}x + \frac{1}{2} = 0$ by completing the square. Ask them how this strategy compares to factoring and graphing. $\frac{1}{2}$, 3; the equation can be solved more easily by factoring. Graphing may not produce an exact answer.

4 Assess

Name the Math Ask students what mathematical procedures they would use to solve a quadratic equation by completing the square.

Additional Answers

48. $y = ax^2 + bx + c$

$y = a\left(x^2 + \frac{b}{a}x\right) + c$

$y = a\left[x^2 + \frac{b}{a}x + \left(\frac{b}{2a}\right)^2\right] + c - a\left(\frac{b}{2a}\right)^2$

$y = a\left[x - \left(-\frac{b}{2a}\right)\right]^2 + \frac{4ac - b^2}{4a}$

If $h = -\frac{b}{2a}$ and $k = \frac{4ac - b^2}{4a}$ then $y = a(x - h)^2 + k$. The axis of symmetry is $x = -\frac{b}{2a}$ or $x = h$.

49. None; sample answer: If you add $\left(\frac{b}{2}\right)^2$ to each side of the equation and each side of the inequality, you get $x^2 + bx + \left(\frac{b}{2}\right)^2 = c + \left(\frac{b}{2}\right)^2$ and $c + \left(\frac{b}{2}\right)^2 < 0$. Since the left side of the last equation is a perfect square, it cannot equal the negative number $c + \left(\frac{b}{2}\right)^2$. So, there are no real solutions.

50. $n^2 + \frac{1}{3}n + \frac{1}{9}$; It is the trinomial that is not a perfect square.

51. Sample answer: $x^2 - 8x + 16 = 0$

52. Sample answer: Because the leading coefficient is 1, completing the square is simpler. Graphing the related function may be done with a graphing calculator and using the zero option. However, this is only good for estimation. Factoring is not possible.

1 Focus

Objective

- Complete the square in a quadratic expression to find the maximum or minimum value of the related function.

2 Teach

Working in Cooperative Groups

Divide the class into pairs. Work through Activity 1 as a class. Then ask students to work with their partners to complete Activities 2 and 3.

Practice Have students complete Exercises 1–8 and 11.

EXTEND 9-4 Algebra Lab
Finding the Maximum or Minimum Value

In Lesson 9-3, we learned about the vertex form of the equation of a quadratic function. You will now learn how to write equations in vertex form and use them to identify key characteristics of the graphs of quadratic functions.

Content Standards
AI.QE.6, AI.QE.7

Activity 1 Find a Minimum

Write $y = x^2 + 4x - 10$ in vertex form. Identify the axis of symmetry, extrema, and zeros. Then graph the function.

Step 1 Complete the square to write the function in vertex form.

$y = x^2 + 4x - 10$	Original function
$y + 10 = x^2 + 4x$	Add 10 to each side.
$y + 10 + 4 = x^2 + 4x + 4$	Since $\left(\frac{4}{2}\right)^2 = 4$, add 4 to each side.
$y + 14 = (x + 2)^2$	Factor $x^2 + 4x + 4$.
$y = (x + 2)^2 - 14$	Subtract 14 from each side to write in vertex form.

Step 2 Identify the axis of symmetry and extrema based on the equation in vertex form. The vertex is at (h, k) or $(-2, -14)$. Since there is no negative sign before the x^2-term, the parabola opens up and has a minimum at $(-2, -14)$. The equation of the axis of symmetry is $x = -2$.

Step 3 Solve for x to find the zeros.

$(x + 2)^2 - 14 = 0$	Vertex form, $y = 0$
$(x + 2)^2 = 14$	Add 14 to each side.
$x + 2 = \pm\sqrt{14}$	Take square root of each side.
$x \approx -5.74$ or 1.74	Subtract 2 from each side.

The zeros are approximately -5.74 and 1.74.

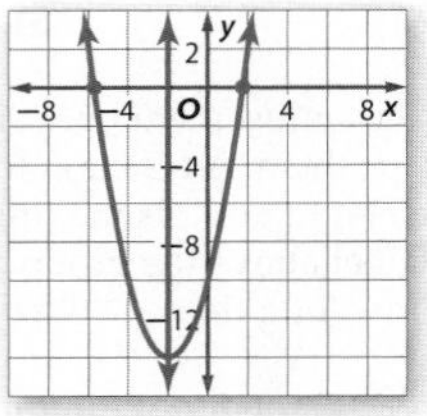

Step 4 Use the key features to graph the function.

There may be a negative coefficient before the quadratic term. When this is the case, the parabola will open down and have a maximum.

Activity 2 Find a Maximum

Write $y = -x^2 + 6x - 5$ in vertex form. Identify the axis of symmetry, extrema, and zeros. Then graph the function.

Step 1 Complete the square to write the equation of the function in vertex form.

$y = -x^2 + 6x - 5$	Original function
$y + 5 = -x^2 + 6x$	Add 5 to each side.
$y + 5 = -(x^2 - 6x)$	Factor out −1.
$y + 5 - 9 = -(x^2 - 6x + 9)$	Since $\left(\frac{6}{2}\right)^2 = 9$, add −9 to each side.
$y - 4 = -(x - 3)^2$	Factor $x^2 - 6x + 9$.
$y = -(x - 3)^2 + 4$	Add 4 to each side to write in vertex form.

Step 2 Identify the axis of symmetry and extrema based on the equation in vertex form. The vertex is at (h, k) or $(3, 4)$. Since there is a negative sign before the x^2-term, the parabola opens down and has a maximum at $(3, 4)$. The equation of the axis of symmetry is $x = 3$.

Step 3 Solve for x to find the zeros.

$0 = -(x - 3)^2 + 4$	Vertex form, $y = 0$
$(x - 3)^2 = 4$	Add $(x - 3)^2$ to each side.
$x - 3 = \pm 2$	Take the square root of each side.
$x = 5$ or 1	Add 3 to each.

Step 4 Use the key features to graph the function.

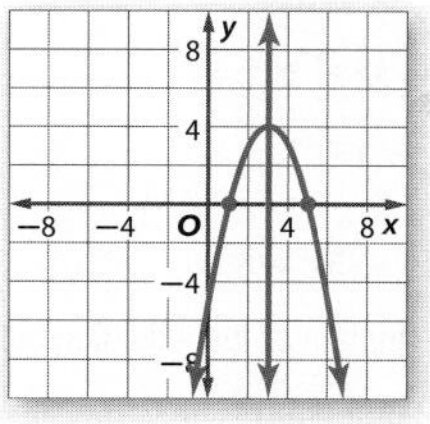

Analyze the Results

1. Why do you need to complete the square to write the equation of a quadratic function in vertex form? **See margin.**

Write each function in vertex form. Identify the axis of symmetry, extrema, and zeros. Then graph the function. **2–10. See Ch. 9 Answer Appendix.**

2. $y = x^2 + 6x$
3. $y = x^2 - 8x + 6$
4. $y = x^2 + 2x - 12$
5. $y = x^2 + 6x + 8$
6. $y = x^2 - 4x + 3$
7. $y = x^2 - 2.4x - 2.2$
8. $y = -4x^2 + 16x - 11$
9. $y = 3x^2 - 12x + 5$
10. $y = -x^2 + 6x - 5$

Activity 3 Use Extrema in the Real World

DIVING **Alexis jumps from a diving platform upward and outward before diving into the pool. The function $h = -9.8t^2 + 4.9t + 10$, where h is the height of the diver in meters above the pool after t seconds approximates Alexis's dive. Graph the function, then find the maximum height that she reaches and the equation of the axis of symmetry.**

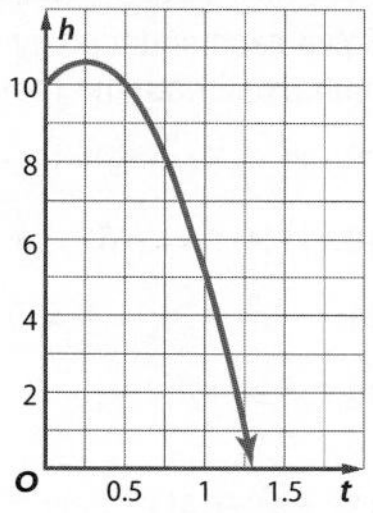

Step 1 Graph the function.

Step 2 Complete the square to write the eqution of the function in vertex form.
$h = -9.8t^2 + 4.9t + 10$
$h = -9.8(t - 0.25)^2 + 10.6125$

Step 3 The vertex is at $(0.25, 10.6125)$, so the maximum height is 10.6125 meters. The equation of the axis of symmetry is $x = 0.25$.

Exercise

11. **SOFTBALL** Jenna throws a ball in the air. The function $h = -16t^2 + 40t + 5$, where h is the height in feet and t represents the time in seconds, approximates Jenna's throw. Graph the function, then find the maximum height of the ball and the equation of the axis of symmetry. When does the ball hit the ground? **See margin.**

3 Assess

Formative Assessment

Use Exercises 9 and 10 to assess each student's knowledge of vertex form and finding zeros, the line of symmetry, and extrema.

From Concrete to Abstract

Ask students to summarize how to write an equation in vertex form and find the zeros, the line of symmetry, and extrema.

Additional Answers

1. Sample answer: In vertex form, the x only appears once. You must use completing the square to create a perfect square trinomial, so that it can be factored and reduce the x-terms to one.

11.

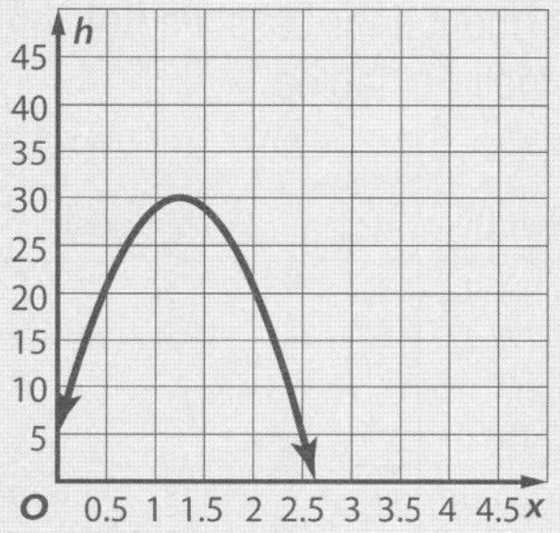

30 ft; $t \approx 1.25$; 2.62 seconds

connectED.mcgraw-hill.com 581

Formative Assessment

Use the Mid-Chapter Quiz to assess students' progress in the first half of the chapter.

For problems answered incorrectly, have students review the lessons indicated in parentheses.

Summative Assessment

Mid-Chapter Test, p. 52

McGraw-Hill eAssessment Customize and create multiple versions of your Mid-Chapter Quiz and their answer keys.

FOLDABLES StudyOrganizer

Dinah Zike's Foldables®

Before students complete the Mid-Chapter Quiz, encourage them to review the information for Lessons 9-1 through 9-4 in their Foldables.

Additional Answer

7.

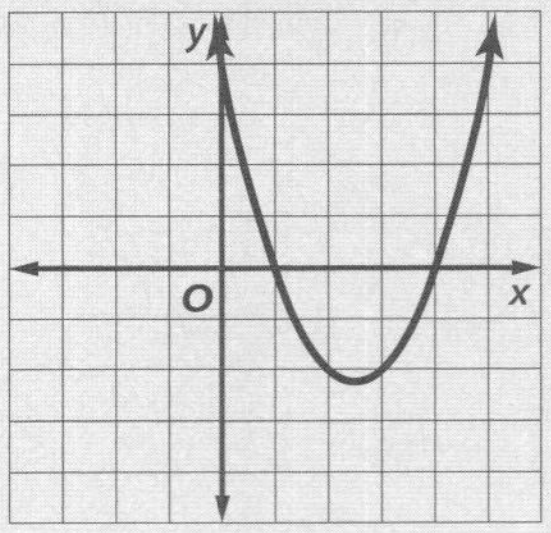

CHAPTER 9 Mid-Chapter Quiz

Lessons 9-1 through 9-4

Use a table of values to graph each equation. State the domain and range. (Lesson 9-1) **1–4. See Ch. 9 Answer Appendix.**

1. $y = x^2 + 3x + 1$
2. $y = 2x^2 - 4x + 3$
3. $y = -x^2 - 3x - 3$
4. $y = -3x^2 - x + 1$

Consider $y = x^2 - 5x + 4$. (Lesson 9-1)

5. Write the equation of the axis of symmetry. **$x = 2.5$**
6. Find the coordinates of the vertex. Is it a maximum or minimum point? **(2.5, −2.25); minimum**
7. Graph the function. **See margin.**
8. **SOCCER** A soccer ball is kicked from ground level with an initial upward velocity of 90 feet per second. The equation $h = -16t^2 + 90t$ gives the height h of the ball after t seconds. (Lesson 9-1)
   a. What is the height of the ball after one second? **74 ft**
   b. How many seconds will it take for the ball to reach its maximum height? **2.8125 s**
   c. When is the height of the ball 0 feet? What do these points represent in this situation? **8c. $t = 0$, $t = 5.625$; Before the ball is kicked, and when the ball hits the ground after the kick.**

Solve each equation by graphing. If integral roots cannot be found, estimate the roots to the nearest tenth. (Lesson 9-2)

9. $x^2 + 5x + 6 = 0$ **−3, −2**
10. $x^2 + 8 = -6x$ **−4, −2**
11. $-x^2 + 3x - 1 = 0$ **0.4, 2.6**
12. $x^2 = 12$ **−3.5, 3.5**
13. **BASEBALL** Juan hits a baseball. The equation $h = -16t^2 + 120t$ models the height h, in feet, of the ball after t seconds. How long is the ball in the air? (Lesson 9-2) **7.5 s**
14. **CONSTRUCTION** Christopher is repairing the roof on a shed. He accidentally dropped a box of nails from a height of 14 feet. This is represented by the equation $h = -16t^2 + 14$, where h is the height in feet and t is the time in seconds. Describe how the graph is related to $h = t^2$. (Lesson 9-3) **compressed vertically and shifted up 14 units**
15. **PARTIES** Della's parents are throwing a Sweet 16 party for her. At 10:00, a ball will slide 25 feet down a pole and light up. A function that models the drop is $h = -t^2 + 5t + 25$, where h is height in feet of the ball after t seconds. How many seconds will it take for the ball to reach the bottom of the pole? (Lesson 9-2) **≈8.1 s**

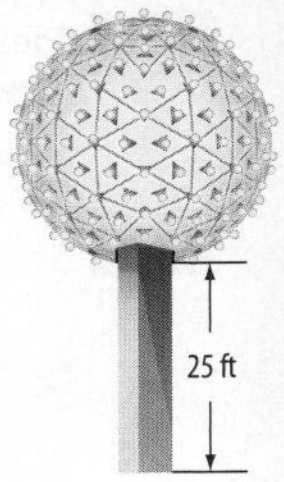

Describe how the graph of each function is related to the graph of $f(x) = x^2$. (Lesson 9-3)

16. $g(x) = x^2 + 3$ **translated up 3 units**
17. $h(x) = 2x^2$ **stretched vertically**
18. $g(x) = x^2 - 6$ **translated down 6 units**
19. $h(x) = \frac{1}{5}x^2$ **compressed vertically**
20. $g(x) = -x^2 + 1$ **reflected over x-axis and translated up 1 unit**
21. $h(x) = -\frac{5}{8}x^2$ **reflected over x-axis and compressed vertically**
22. **MULTIPLE CHOICE** Which is an equation for the function shown in the graph? (Lesson 9-3) **D**

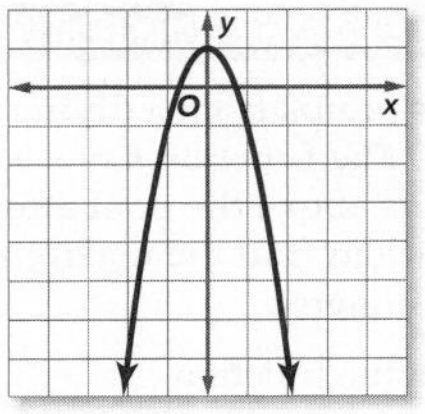

A $y = -2x^2$
B $y = 2x^2 + 1$
C $y = x^2 - 1$
D $y = -2x^2 + 1$

Solve each equation by completing the square. Round to the nearest tenth. (Lesson 9-4)

23. $x^2 + 4x + 2 = 0$ **−3.4, −0.6**
24. $x^2 - 2x - 10 = 0$ **−2.3, 4.3**
25. $2x^2 + 4x - 5 = 7$ **−3.6, 1.6**

InterventionPlanner

TIER 1 On Level OL	TIER 2 Strategic Intervention AL approaching grade level	TIER 3 Intensive Intervention 2 or more grades below level
If students miss about 25% of the exercises or less,	**If** students miss about 50% of the exercises,	**If** students miss about 75% of the exercises,
Then choose a resource: SE Lessons 9-1, 9-2, 9-3, and 9-4 Skills Practice, pp. 7, 13, 19, and 25 TE Chapter Project connectED.mcgraw-hill.com Self-Check Quiz	**Then** choose a resource: Study Guide and Intervention, Chapter 9, pp. 5, 11, 17, and 23 *Quick Review Math Handbook* connectED.mcgraw-hill.com Extra Examples, Personal Tutor, Homework Help	**Then** use *Math Triumphs, Alg. 1* connectED.mcgraw-hill.com Extra Examples, Personal Tutor, Homework Help, Review Vocabulary

LESSON 9-5 Solving Quadratic Equations by Using the Quadratic Formula

:: Then	:: Now	:: Why?
You solved quadratic equations by completing the square.	1 Solve quadratic equations by using the Quadratic Formula. 2 Use the discriminant to determine the number of solutions of a quadratic equation.	For adult women, the normal systolic blood pressure P in millimeters of mercury (mm Hg) can be modeled by $P = 0.01a^2 + 0.05a + 107$, where a is age in years. This equation can be used to approximate the age of a woman with a certain systolic blood pressure. However, it would be difficult to solve by factoring, graphing, or completing the square.

NewVocabulary
Quadratic Formula
discriminant

Content Standards
AI.QE.4, AI.QE.5

Process Standards
PS.6

1 Quadratic Formula

Completing the square of the quadratic equation $ax^2 + bx + c = 0$ produces a formula that allows you to find the solutions of *any* quadratic equation. This formula is called the **Quadratic Formula**.

KeyConcept The Quadratic Formula

The solutions of a quadratic equation $ax^2 + bx + c = 0$, where $a \neq 0$, are given by the Quadratic Formula.

$$x = \frac{-b \pm \sqrt{b^2 - 4ac}}{2a}$$

You will derive this formula in Lesson 10-2.

Example 1 Use the Quadratic Formula

Solve $x^2 - 12x = -20$ by using the Quadratic Formula.

Step 1 Rewrite the equation in standard form.

$x^2 - 12x = -20$ Original equation

$x^2 - 12x + 20 = 0$ Add 20 to each side.

Step 2 Apply the Quadratic Formula.

$x = \frac{-b \pm \sqrt{b^2 - 4ac}}{2a}$ Quadratic Formula

$= \frac{-(-12) \pm \sqrt{(-12)^2 - 4(1)(20)}}{2(1)}$ $a = 1$, $b = -12$, and $c = 20$

$= \frac{12 \pm \sqrt{144 - 80}}{2}$ Multiply.

$= \frac{12 \pm \sqrt{64}}{2}$ or $\frac{12 \pm 8}{2}$ Subtract and take the square root.

$x = \frac{12 - 8}{2}$ or $x = \frac{12 + 8}{2}$ Separate the solutions.

$= 2$ $= 10$ The solutions are 2 and 10.

GuidedPractice

1. Solve $2x^2 + 9x = 18$ by using the Quadratic Formula. **$-6, \frac{3}{2}$**

connectED.mcgraw-hill.com 583

1 Focus

VerticalAlignment

Before Lesson 9-5 Solve quadratic equations by completing the square.

Lesson 9-5 Solve quadratic equations by using the Quadratic Formula. Use the discriminant to determine the number of solutions of a quadratic equation.

After Lesson 9-5 Use the Quotient Property of Square Roots to derive the Quadratic Formula.

2 Teach

Scaffolding Questions

Have students read the **Why?** section of the lesson.

Ask:

- What equation would you need to solve to find the age of a woman whose systolic blood pressure is 120? $120 = 0.01a^2 + 0.05a + 107$
- Write this equation in standard form. $0 = 0.01a^2 + 0.05a - 13$
- What are the values for a, b, and c? $a = 0.01$, $b = 0.05$, $c = -13$

(continued on the next page)

Lesson 9-5 Resources

Resource	Approaching Level AL	On Level OL	Beyond Level BL	English Learners ELL
Teacher Edition	▪ Differentiated Instruction, p. 586	▪ Differentiated Instruction, pp. 586, 589	▪ Differentiated Instruction, pp. 586, 589	▪ Differentiated Instruction, p. 586
Chapter Resource Masters	▪ Study Guide and Intervention, pp. 29–30 ▪ Skills Practice, p. 31 ▪ Practice, p. 32 ▪ Word Problem Practice, p. 33	▪ Study Guide and Intervention, pp. 29–30 ▪ Skills Practice, p. 31 ▪ Practice, p. 32 ▪ Word Problem Practice, p. 33 ▪ Enrichment, p. 34	▪ Practice, p. 32 ▪ Word Problem Practice, p. 33 ▪ Enrichment, p. 34	▪ Study Guide and Intervention, pp. 29–30 ▪ Skills Practice, p. 31 ▪ Practice, p. 32 ▪ Word Problem Practice, p. 33
Other	▪ 5-Minute Check 9-5 ▪ Study Notebook	▪ 5-Minute Check 9-5 ▪ Study Notebook	▪ 5-Minute Check 9-5 ▪ Study Notebook	▪ 5-Minute Check 9-5 ▪ Study Notebook

- Why would the equation be difficult to solve using factoring or completing the square? The decimal values of the coefficients may make using the methods difficult, if not impossible.

1 Quadratic Formula

Examples 1 and 2 show how to use the Quadratic Formula to solve quadratic equations with integral and non-integral roots. **Example 3** shows how to solve a quadratic equation using four different methods.

Formative Assessment

Use the Guided Practice exercises after each example to determine students' understanding of concepts.

Additional Examples

1 Solve $x^2 - 2x = 35$ by using the Quadratic Formula. $-5, 7$

2 Solve each equation by using the Quadratic Formula. Round to the nearest tenth if necessary.

a. $2x^2 - 2x - 5 = 0$
$2.2, -1.2$

b. $5x^2 - 8x = 4$
$2, -0.4$

Additional Examples also in Interactive Classroom PowerPoint® Presentations

IWB Interactive White Board READY

WatchOut!

Preventing Errors Some students may notice that the trinomial in Example 1 can be factored. Explain that an equation that could be factored was used to demonstrate that the Quadratic Formula produces the correct solutions. Tell students that if they see an easier way (such as factoring) to solve a quadratic equation, they should use the easier method.

The solutions of quadratic equations are not always integers.

Example 2 Use the Quadratic Formula

Solve each equation by using the Quadratic Formula. Round to the nearest tenth if necessary.

a. $3x^2 + 5x - 12 = 0$

For this equation, $a = 3$, $b = 5$, and $c = -12$.

$x = \dfrac{-b \pm \sqrt{b^2 - 4ac}}{2a}$ — Quadratic Formula

$= \dfrac{-(5) \pm \sqrt{(5)^2 - 4(3)(-12)}}{2(3)}$ — $a = 3$, $b = 5$, and $c = -12$

$= \dfrac{-5 \pm \sqrt{25 + 144}}{6}$ — Multiply.

$= \dfrac{-5 \pm \sqrt{169}}{6}$ or $\dfrac{-5 \pm 13}{6}$ — Add and simplify.

$x = \dfrac{-5 - 13}{6}$ or $x = \dfrac{-5 + 13}{6}$ — Separate the solutions.

$= -3 \qquad = \dfrac{4}{3}$ — Simplify.

The solutions are -3 and $\frac{4}{3}$.

b. $10x^2 - 5x = 25$

Step 1 Rewrite the equation in standard form.

$10x^2 - 5x = 25$ — Original equation

$10x^2 - 5x - 25 = 0$ — Subtract 25 from each side.

Step 2 Apply the Quadratic Formula.

$x = \dfrac{-b \pm \sqrt{b^2 - 4ac}}{2a}$ — Quadratic Formula

$= \dfrac{-(-5) \pm \sqrt{(-5)^2 - 4(10)(-25)}}{2(10)}$ — $a = 10$, $b = -5$, and $c = -25$

$= \dfrac{5 \pm \sqrt{25 + 1000}}{20}$ — Multiply.

$= \dfrac{5 \pm \sqrt{1025}}{20}$ — Add.

$= \dfrac{5 - \sqrt{1025}}{20}$ or $\dfrac{5 + \sqrt{1025}}{20}$ — Separate the solutions.

$\approx -1.4 \qquad \approx 1.9$ — Simplify.

The solutions are about -1.4 and 1.9.

StudyTip

Precision In Example 2, the number $\sqrt{1025}$ is irrational, so the calculator can only give you an approximation of its value. So, the exact answer in Example 2 is $\frac{5 \pm \sqrt{1025}}{20}$. The numbers -1.4 and 1.9 are approximations.

GuidedPractice

2A. $4x^2 - 24x + 35 = 0$ $\frac{7}{2}, \frac{5}{2}$

2B. $3x^2 - 2x - 9 = 0$ **2.1, −1.4**

You can solve quadratic equations by using one of many equivalent methods. No one way is always best.

Teaching the Process Standards

Precision Mathematically proficient students express numerical answers with a degree of precision appropriate for the problem context. Discuss with students how to know when an exact answer is required.

Teach with Tech

Video Recording On your favorite video sharing site, have students search for a rap or song to help them remember the Quadratic Formula. One such song can be sung to the tune of "Pop Goes the Weasel."

x equals negative *b*
Plus or minus the square root
Of *b* squared minus 4*ac*
All over 2*a*.

584 | Lesson 9-5 | Solving Quadratic Equations by Using the Quadratic Formula

WatchOut!

Solutions Remember that the methods of factoring, completing the square, or using the quadractic formula to solve quadratic equations are equivalent. Each method should produce the same solution.

Example 3 Solve Quadratic Equations Using Different Methods

Solve $x^2 - 4x = 12$.

Method 1 Graphing

Rewrite the equation in standard form.

$x^2 - 4x = 12$ — Original equation

$x^2 - 4x - 12 = 0$ — Subtract 12 from each side.

Graph the related function $f(x) = x^2 - 4x - 12$. Locate the x-intercepts of the graph.

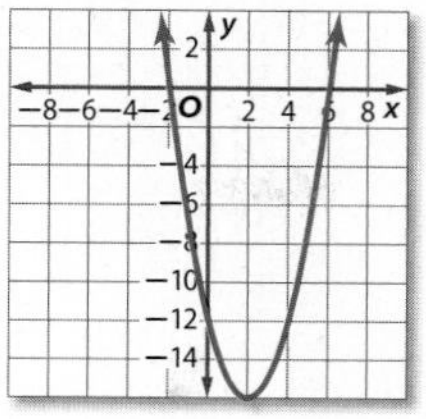

The solutions are −2 and 6.

Method 2 Factoring

$x^2 - 4x = 12$	Original equation
$x^2 - 4x - 12 = 0$	Subtract 12 from each side.
$(x - 6)(x + 2) = 0$	Factor.
$x - 6 = 0$ or $x + 2 = 0$	Zero Product Property
$x = 6$ $\quad x = -2$	Solve for x.

Method 3 Completing the Square

The equation is in the correct form to complete the square, since the leading coefficient is 1 and the x^2 and x terms are isolated.

$x^2 - 4x = 12$	Original equation
$x^2 - 4x + 4 = 12 + 4$	Since $\left(\frac{-4}{2}\right)^2 = 4$, add 4 to each side.
$(x - 2)^2 = 16$	Factor $x^2 - 4x + 4$.
$x - 2 = \pm 4$	Take the square root of each side.
$x = 2 \pm 4$	Add 2 to each side.
$x = 2 + 4$ or $x = 2 - 4$	Separate the solutions.
$= 6 \quad = -2$	Simplify.

Method 4 Quadratic Formula

From Method 1, the standard form of the equation is $x^2 - 4x - 12 = 0$.

$x = \frac{-b \pm \sqrt{b^2 - 4ac}}{2a}$	Quadratic Formula
$= \frac{-(-4) \pm \sqrt{(-4)^2 - 4(1)(-12)}}{2(1)}$	$a = 1$, $b = -4$, and $c = -12$
$= \frac{4 \pm \sqrt{16 + 48}}{2}$	Multiply.
$= \frac{4 \pm \sqrt{64}}{2}$ or $\frac{4 \pm 8}{2}$	Add and simplify.
$x = \frac{4 - 8}{2}$ or $x = \frac{4 + 8}{2}$	Separate the solutions.
$= -2 \quad = 6$	Simplify.

Guided Practice

Solve each equation.

3A. $2x^2 - 17x + 8 = 0$ **8, $\frac{1}{2}$**

3B. $4x^2 - 4x - 11 = 0$ **about 2.2, −1.2**

Focus on Mathematical Content

The Quadratic Formula Even though the Quadratic Formula may not be the easiest way to solve some quadratic equations, it always works. To derive the formula, solve $ax^2 + bx + c = 0$ by completing the square. Students derive the formula when they learn about simplifying radical expressions.

Tips for New Teachers

Using the Quadratic Formula Tell students that when they use the Quadratic Formula, it is best to simplify one step at a time. For example, students should first simplify under the radical sign, then find the square root, then simplify the numerator and denominator, and finally perform the division. Skipping steps may introduce errors.

Additional Example

3 Solve $3x^2 - 5x = 12$. $3, -\frac{4}{3}$

Tips for New Teachers

Sense-Making While the chart on this page offers suggestions for when to use each method, do not hold students to using all methods. Some students do not yet have the mathematical maturity to analyze each equation and determine the best method to use to save time.

2 The Discriminant

Example 4 shows how to use the discriminant to determine the number of real solutions for a quadratic equation.

Additional Example

4 State the value of the discriminant of $3x^2 + 10x = 12$. Then determine the number of real solutions of the equation.
244; 2 real solutions

WatchOut!

Preventing Errors Remind students to be careful to include any negative signs when finding the discriminant. One missed negative sign can turn the discriminant from positive to negative and yield an incorrect result.

ConceptSummary Solving Quadratic Equations

Method	When to Use
Factoring	Use when the constant term is 0 or if the factors are easily determined. Not all equations are factorable.
Graphing	Use when an approximate solution is sufficient.
Using Square Roots	Use when an equation can be written in the form $x^2 = n$. Can only be used if the equation has no x-term.
Completing the Square	Can be used for any equation $ax^2 + bx + c = 0$, but is simplest to apply when b is even and $a = 1$.
Quadratic Formula	Can be used for any equation $ax^2 + bx + c = 0$.

2 The Discriminant

In the Quadratic Formula, the expression under the radical sign, $b^2 - 4ac$, is called the **discriminant**. The discriminant can be used to determine the number of real solutions of a quadratic equation.

StudyTip

Discriminant Recall that when the left side of the standard form of an equation is a perfect square trinomial, there is only one solution. Therefore, the discriminant of a perfect square trinomial will always be zero.

KeyConcept Using the Discriminant

Equation	$x^2 + 2x + 5 = 0$	$x^2 + 10x + 25 = 0$	$2x^2 - 7x + 2 = 0$
Discriminant	$b^2 - 4ac = -16$ negative	$b^2 - 4ac = 0$ zero	$b^2 - 4ac = 33$ positive
Graph of Related Function	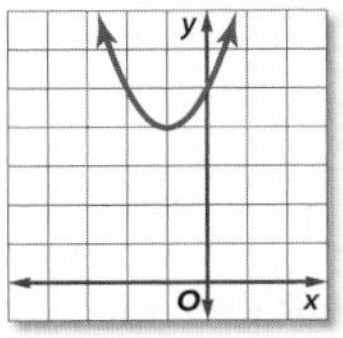 0 x-intercepts	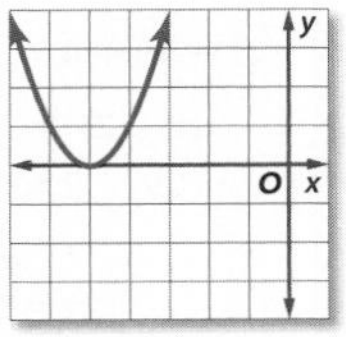 1 x-intercept	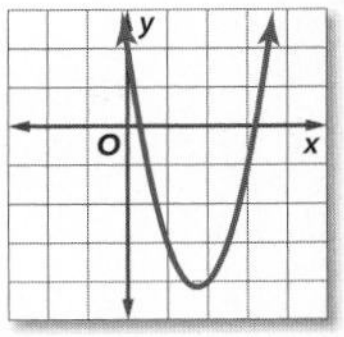 2 x-intercepts
Real Solutions	0	1	2

Example 4 Use the Discriminant

State the value of the discriminant of $4x^2 + 5x = -3$. Then determine the number of real solutions of the equation.

Step 1 Rewrite in standard form. $4x^2 - 5x = -3 \rightarrow 4x^2 - 5x + 3 = 0$

Step 2 Find the discriminant.

$b^2 - 4ac = (-5)^2 - 4(4)(3)$ $a = 4, b = -5$, and $c = 3$

$= -23$ Simplify.

Since the discriminant is negative, the equation has no real solutions.

GuidedPractice **4A.** 1; two real solutions **4B.** 0; one real solution

4A. $2x^2 + 11x + 15 = 0$ **4B.** $9x^2 - 30x + 25 = 0$

DifferentiatedInstruction AL OL BL ELL

If you think students would benefit from being creative in this lesson,

Then have students come up with a riddle, poem, or some other mnemonic device to help them remember the Quadratic Formula and how to use the discriminant to determine the number of real solutions. Ask students to share with the class.

586 | Lesson 9-5 | Solving Quadratic Equations by Using the Quadratic Formula

Check Your Understanding

= Step-by-Step Solutions begin on page R13.

Examples 1–2 **Solve each equation by using the Quadratic Formula. Round to the nearest tenth if necessary.**

1. $x^2 - 2x - 15 = 0$ −3, 5
2. $x^2 - 10x + 16 = 0$ 2, 8
3. $x^2 - 8x = -10$ 6.4, 1.6
4. $x^2 + 3x = 12$ 2.3, −5.3
5. $10x^2 - 31x + 15 = 0$ 0.6, 2.5
6. $5x^2 + 5 = -13x$ −0.5, −2.1

Example 3 **Solve each equation. State which method you used.** See student work for method.

7. $2x^2 + 11x - 6 = 0$ $-6, \frac{1}{2}$
8. $2x^2 - 3x - 6 = 0$ 2.6, −1.1
9. $9x^2 = 25$ $\pm\frac{5}{3}$
10. $x^2 - 9x = -19$ 5.6, 3.4

Example 4 **State the value of the discriminant for each equation. Then determine the number of real solutions of the equation.**

11. $x^2 - 9x + 21 = 0$ −3; no real solutions
12. $2x^2 - 11x + 10 = 0$ 12. 41; two real solutions
13. $9x^2 + 24x = -16$ 0; one real solution
14. $3x^2 - x = 8$ 97; two real solutions
15. **TRAMPOLINE** Eva springs from a trampoline to dunk a basketball. Her height h in feet can be modeled by the equation $h = -16t^2 + 22.3t + 2$, where t is time in seconds. Use the discriminant to determine if Eva will reach a height of 10 feet. Explain. The discriminant is −14.91, so the equation has no real solution. Thus, Eva will not reach a height of 10 feet.

Practice and Problem Solving

Extra Practice is on page R9.

Examples 1–2 **Solve each equation by using the Quadratic Formula. Round to the nearest tenth if necessary.**

16. $4x^2 + 5x - 6 = 0$ $-2, \frac{3}{4}$
17. $x^2 + 16 = 0$ ∅
18. $6x^2 - 12x + 1 = 0$ 1.9,0.1
19. $5x^2 - 8x = 6$ 2.2, −0.6
20. $2x^2 - 5x = -7$ ∅
21. $5x^2 + 21x = -18$ $-3, -\frac{6}{5}$
22. $81x^2 = 9$ $\pm\frac{1}{3}$
23. $8x^2 + 12x = 8$ 0.5, −2
24. $4x^2 = -16x - 16$ −2
25. $10x^2 = -7x + 6$ 0.5, −1.2
26. $-3x^2 = 8x - 12$ 1.1, −3.7
27. $2x^2 = 12x - 18$ 3
28. **AMUSEMENT PARKS** The Demon Drop at Cedar Point in Ohio takes riders to the top of a tower and drops them 60 feet. A function that approximates this ride is $h = -16t^2 + 64t - 60$, where h is the height in feet and t is the time in seconds. About how many seconds does it take for riders to drop 60 feet? about 2.5 seconds

Example 3 **Solve each equation. State which method you used.** See student work for method.

29. $2x^2 - 8x = 12$ −1.2, 5.2
30. $3x^2 - 24x = -36$ 2, 6
31. $x^2 - 3x = 10$ −2, 5
32. $4x^2 + 100 = 0$ ∅
33. $x^2 = -7x - 5$ −6.2, −0.8
34. $12 - 12x = -3x^2$ 2

Example 4 **State the value of the discriminant for each equation. Then determine the number of real solutions of the equation.** 35–40. See margin.

35. $0.2x^2 - 1.5x + 2.9 = 0$
36. $2x^2 - 5x + 20 = 0$
37. $x^2 - \frac{4}{5}x = 3$
38. $0.5x^2 - 2x = -2$
39. $2.25x^2 - 3x = -1$
40. $2x^2 = \frac{5}{2}x + \frac{3}{2}$
41. **MODELING** The percent of U.S. households with high-speed Internet h can be estimated by $h = -0.2n^2 + 7.2n + 1.5$, where n is the number of years since 1990.
    a. Use the Quadratic Formula to determine when 20% of the population will have high-speed Internet. in 1993 and 2023
    b. Is a quadratic equation a good model for this information? Explain. See margin.

Differentiated Homework Options

Level	Assignment	Two-Day Option	
AL Basic	16–41, 52–77	17–41 odd, 59–62	16–40 even, 52–58, 63–77
OL Core	17–41 odd, 42, 43–49 odd, 52–77	16–41, 59–62	42–50, 52–58, 63–77
BL Advanced	42–71, (optional: 72–77)		

3 Practice

Formative Assessment

Use Exercises 1–15 to check for understanding.

Use the chart at the bottom of this page to customize assignments for students.

Follow-up

Students have explored solving quadratic equations.

Ask:

- How do you know what method to use when solving a quadratic equation? Sample answer: If the equation has terms that you know are easily factorable, you could solve by factoring. If the equation has more complex terms, you could solve by using the Quadratic Formula or by graphing. You could also use one method to solve and a second method to check your answer.

Teaching the Process Standards

Modeling Mathematically proficient students interpret their mathematical results in the context of the situation and reflect on whether the results make sense. In Exercise 41, explain that sometimes a mathematical model can fit data for part, but not all, of the domain.

Additional Answers

35. −0.07; no real solution
36. −135; no real solutions
37. 12.64; two real solutions
38. 0; one real solution
39. 0; one real solution
40. 18.25; two real solutions

41b. Sample answer: No; the parabola has a maximum at about 66, meaning only 66% of the population would ever have high-speed Internet.

Study Guide and Intervention

AL OL ELL

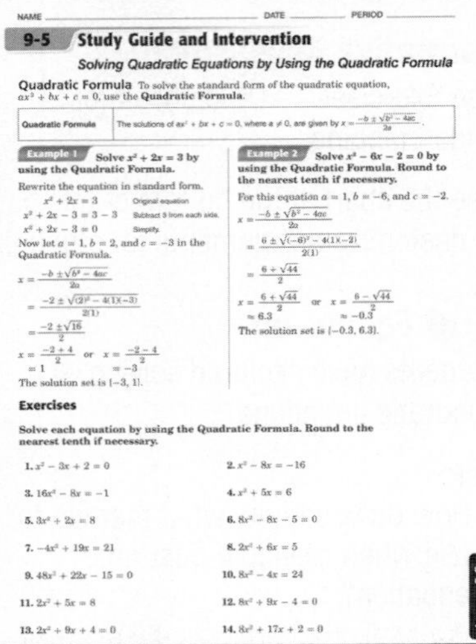
9-5 Study Guide and Intervention

Solving Quadratic Equations by Using the Quadratic Formula

Quadratic Formula To solve the standard form of the quadratic equation, $ax^2 + bx + c = 0$, use the Quadratic Formula.

Exercises

Solve each equation by using the Quadratic Formula. Round to the nearest tenth if necessary.

1. $x^2 - 3x + 2 = 0$
2. $x^2 - 8x = -16$
3. $16x^2 - 8x = -1$
4. $x^2 + 5x = 6$
5. $3x^2 + 2x = 8$
6. $8x^2 - 8x - 5 = 0$
7. $-4x^2 + 19x = 21$
8. $2x^2 + 6x = 5$
9. $48x^2 + 22x - 15 = 0$
10. $8x^2 - 4x = 24$
11. $2x^2 + 5x = 8$
12. $8x^2 + 9x - 4 = 0$
13. $2x^2 + 9x + 4 = 0$
14. $8x^2 + 17x + 2 = 0$

Practice

AL OL BL ELL

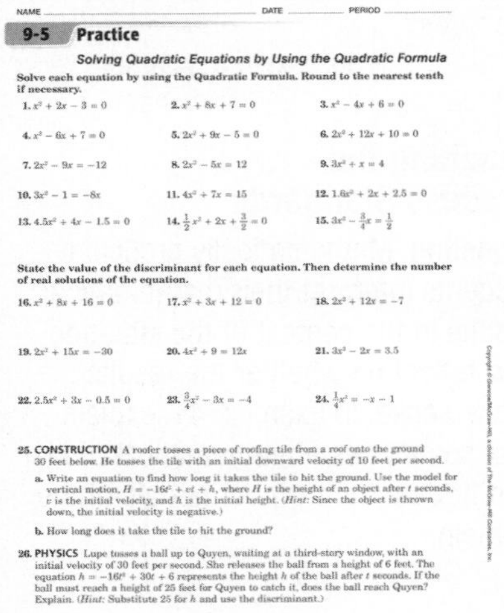
9-5 Practice

Solving Quadratic Equations by Using the Quadratic Formula

Word Problem Practice

AL OL BL ELL

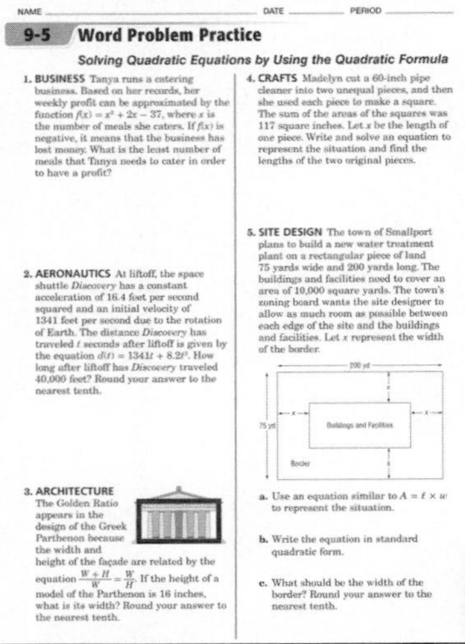
9-5 Word Problem Practice

Solving Quadratic Equations by Using the Quadratic Formula

B **42. TRAFFIC** The equation $d = 0.05v^2 + 1.1v$ models the distance d in feet it takes a car traveling at a speed of v miles per hour to come to a complete stop. If Hannah's car stopped after 250 feet on a highway with a speed limit of 65 miles per hour, was she speeding? Explain your reasoning. **See margin.**

Without graphing, determine the number of x-intercepts of the graph of the related function for each equation.

43. $4.25x + 3 = -3x^2$ **0**

44. $x^2 + \frac{2}{25} = \frac{3}{5}x$ **2**

45. $0.25x^2 + x = -1$ **1**

Solve each equation by using the Quadratic Formula. Round to the nearest tenth if necessary.

46. $-2x^2 - 7x = -1.5$ **46. −3.7, 0.2**

47. $2.3x^2 - 1.4x = 6.8$ **47. −1.4, 2.1**

48. $x^2 - 2x = 5$ **3.4, −1.4**

49 POSTER Bartolo is making a poster for the dance. He wants to cover three fourths of the area with text.

a. Write an equation for the area of the section with text. **(20 − 2x)(25 − 7x) = 375**

b. Solve the equation by using the Quadratic Formula. **about 12.9, 0.7**

c. What should be the margins of the poster? **about 0.7 in. on the sides, 2.8 in. on the top, and 2.1 in. on the bottom**

C **50. MULTIPLE REPRESENTATIONS** In this problem, you will investigate writing a quadratic equation with given roots. If p is a root of $0 = ax^2 + bx + c$, then $(x - p)$ is a factor of $ax^2 + bx + c$.

a. **Tabular** Copy and complete the first two columns of the table.

b. **Algebraic** Multiply the factors to write each equation with integral coefficients. Use the equations to complete the last column of the table. Write each equation.

c. **Analytical** How could you write an equation with three roots? Test your conjecture by writing an equation with roots 1, 2, and 3. Is the equation quadratic? Explain. **See margin.**

Roots	Factors	Equation
2, 5	$(x - 2), (x - 5)$	$(x - 2)(x - 5) = 0$ $x^2 - 7x + 10 = 0$
1, 9	$(x - 1), (x - 9)$	$x^2 - 10x + 9 = 0$
−1, 3	$(x + 1), (x - 3)$	$x^2 - 2x - 3 = 0$
0, 6	$x, (x - 6)$	$x^2 - 6x = 0$
$\frac{1}{2}$, 7	$\left(x - \frac{1}{2}\right), (x - 7)$	$2x^2 - 15x + 7 = 0$
$-\frac{2}{3}$, 4	$\left(x + \frac{2}{3}\right), (x - 4)$	$3x^2 - 10x - 8 = 0$

H.O.T. Problems Use Higher-Order Thinking Skills

51. CHALLENGE Find all values of k such that $2x^2 - 3x + 5k = 0$ has two solutions. $k < \frac{9}{40}$

52. REASONING Use factoring techniques to determine the number of real zeros of $f(x) = x^2 - 8x + 16$. Compare this method to using the discriminant. **See Ch. 9 Answer Appendix.**

STRUCTURE Determine whether there are *two*, *one*, or *no* real solutions of each equation.

53. The graph of the related quadratic function does not have an x-intercept. **none**

54. The graph of the related quadratic function touches but does not cross the x-axis. **one**

55. The graph of the related quadratic function intersects the x-axis twice. **two**

56. Both a and b are greater than 0 and c is less than 0 in a quadratic equation. **two**

57. WRITING IN MATH Why can the discriminant be used to confirm the number of real solutions of a quadratic equation? **See margin.**

58. WRITING IN MATH Describe the advantages and disadvantages of each method of solving quadratic equations. Why are the methods equivalent? Which method do you prefer, and why? **See Ch. 9 Answer Appendix.**

Enrichment

OL BL

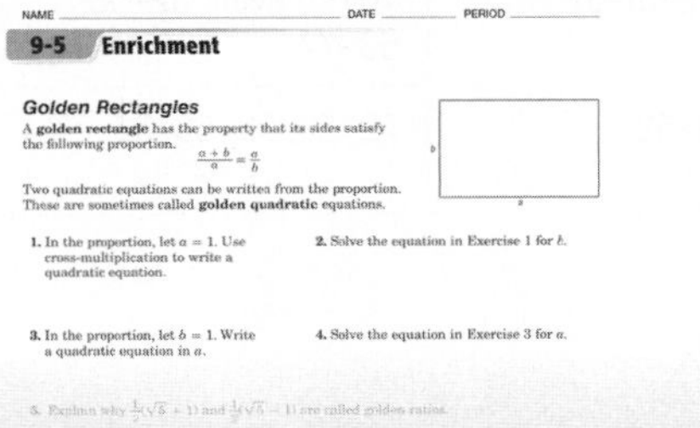
9-5 Enrichment

Golden Rectangles

Additional Answers

42. No; sample answer: Hannah was traveling at about 61 mph, so she was not speeding.

50c. Sample answer: Multiply three factors written from the roots.
$(x - 1)(x - 2)(x - 3) = 0$
$x^3 - 6x^2 + 11x - 6 = 0$
The equation is not quadratic because its degree is 3 not 2.

Standardized Test Practice

59. If n is an even integer, which expression represents the product of three consecutive even integers? D

A $n(n + 1)(n + 2)$
B $(n + 1)(n + 2)(n + 3)$
C $3n + 2$
D $n(n + 2)(n + 4)$

60. SHORT RESPONSE The triangle shown is an isosceles triangle. What is the value of x? 58 or 64

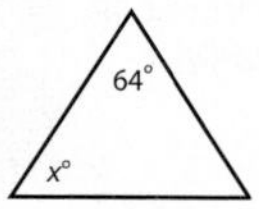

61. Which statement best describes the graph of $x = 5$? G

F It is parallel to the x-axis.
G It is parallel to the y-axis.
H It passes through the point (2, 5).
J It has a y-intercept of 5.

62. What are the solutions of the quadratic equation $6h^2 + 6h = 72$? A

A 3 or −4
B −3 or 4
C no solution
D 12 or −48

Spiral Review

Solve each equation by completing the square. Round to the nearest tenth if necessary. (Lesson 9-4)

63. $6x^2 - 17x + 12 = 0$ $\frac{4}{3}, \frac{3}{2}$

64. $x^2 - 9x = -12$ 1.6, 7.4

65. $4x^2 = 20x - 25$ $\frac{5}{2}$

Describe the transformations needed to obtain the graph of $g(x)$ from the graph of $f(x)$. (Lesson 9-3)

66. $f(x) = 4x^2$, $g(x) = 2x^2$ Compress vertically.

67. $f(x) = x^2 + 5$, $g(x) = x^2 - 1$ Translate down 6 units.

68. $f(x) = x^2 - 6$, $g(x) = x^2 + 3$ Translate up 9 units.

Determine whether each graph shows a *positive*, a *negative*, or *no* correlation. If there is a positive or negative correlation, describe its meaning in the situation. (Lesson 4-5)

69. Electronic Tax Returns

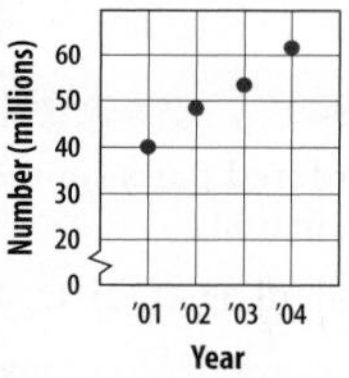

Positive; as time goes on, more people use electronic tax returns.

70. Atlantic Hurricanes

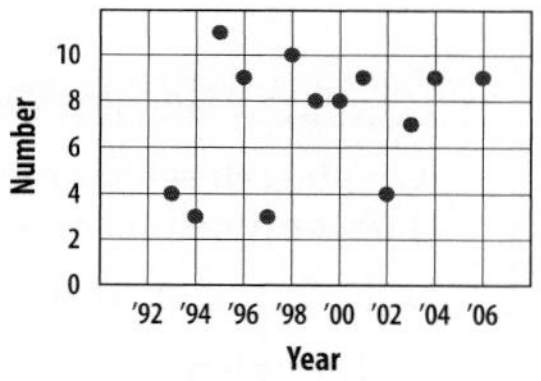

no correlation

71. ENTERTAINMENT Coach Washington wants to take her softball team out for pizza and soft drinks after the last game of the season. A large pizza costs \$12 and a pitcher of a soft drink costs \$3. She does not want to spend more than \$60. Write an inequality that represents this situation and graph the solution set. (Lesson 5-6) $12x + 3y \leq 60$; See margin for graph.

Skills Review

Determine whether each sequence is *arithmetic*, *geometric*, or *neither*. Explain. 72–77. See margin.

72. 20, 25, 30, …

73. 1000, 950, 900, …

74. 200, 350, 650, …

75. 6, 18, 54, …

76. 2, 4, 16, …

77. 8, −4, 2 …

Differentiated Instruction OL BL

Extension Since students are much more likely to retain a concept that they have researched and explained, ask them to research the derivation of the Quadratic Formula and to write short paragraphs showing and explaining the derivation.

Multiple Representations

In Exercise 50, students use a table to write quadratic equations with given roots.

4 Assess

Ticket Out the Door Make several copies each of five quadratic equations. Give one equation to each student. As students leave the room, ask each of them to tell you the discriminant of the equation and the number of real solutions.

Formative Assessment

Check for student understanding of Lessons 9-4 and 9-5.

Quiz 2, p. 50

Additional Answers

57. Sample answer: If the discriminant is positive, the Quadratic Formula will result in two real solutions because you are adding and subtracting the square root of a positive number in the numerator of the expression. If the discriminant is zero, there will be one real solution because you are adding and subtracting the square root of zero. If the discriminant is negative, there will be no real solutions because you are adding and subtracting the square root of a negative number in the numerator of the expression.

71.

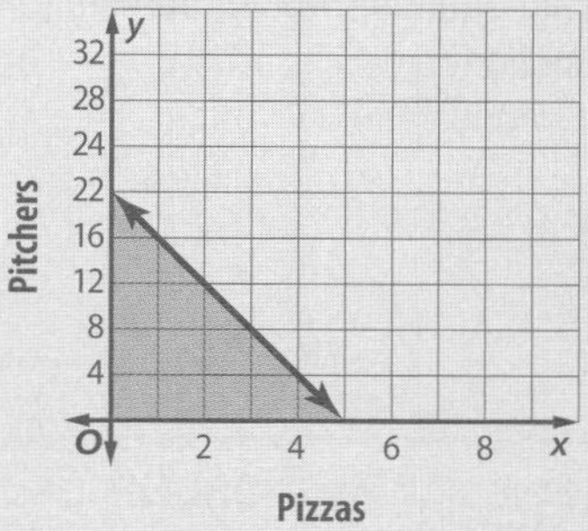

72. Arithmetic; the common difference is 5.

73. Arithmetic; the common difference is −50.

74. Neither; there is no common difference or common ratio.

75. Geometric; the common ratio is 3.

76. Neither; there is no common difference or common ratio.

77. Geometric; the common ratio is $-\frac{1}{2}$.

1 Focus

VerticalAlignment

Before Lesson 9-6 Graph linear, quadratic, and exponential functions.

Lesson 9-6 Identify linear, quadratic, and exponential functions from given data. Write equations that model that data.

After Lesson 9-6 Graph and solve direct variation equations.

2 Teach

Scaffolding Questions

Have students read the **Why?** section of the lesson.

Ask:

- If the data for the cost of 1–4 pounds of candy sold results in the following data, is this a geometric sequence? no

pounds	1	2	3	4
price (in $)	4	8	12	16

- What is the common difference for this sequence? 4
- What equation would represent this function? $y = 4x$, where x = number of pounds and y = price

LESSON 9-6 Analyzing Functions with Successive Differences

Then	Now	Why?
You graphed linear, quadratic, and exponential functions.	**1** Identify linear, quadratic, and exponential functions from given data. **2** Write equations that model data.	Every year the golf team sells candy to raise money for charity. By knowing what type of function models the sales of the candy, they can determine the best price of the candy.

Content Standards
AI.QE.1

Process Standards
PS.7

1 Identify Functions You can use linear functions, quadratic functions, and exponential functions to model data. The general forms of the equations and a graph of each function type are listed below.

ConceptSummary Linear and Nonlinear Functions

Linear Function	Quadratic Function	Exponential Function
$y = mx + b$	$y = ax^2 + bx + c$	$y = ab^x$, when $b > 0$

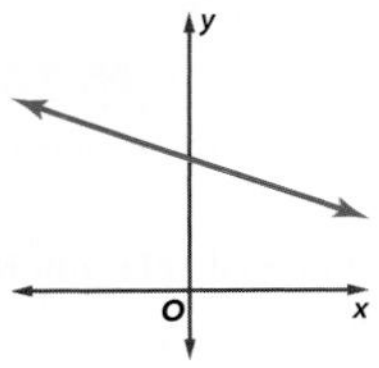

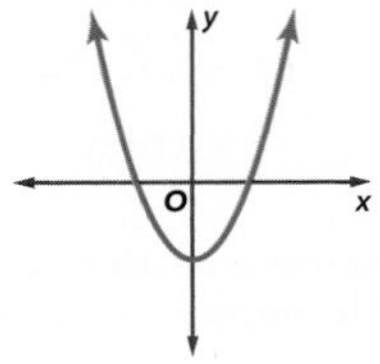

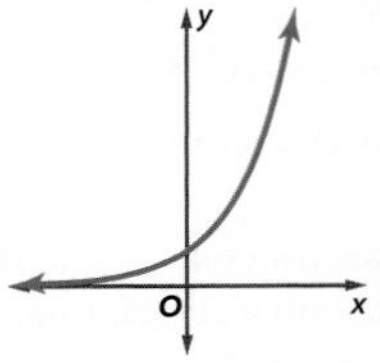

Example 1 Choose a Model Using Graphs

Graph each set of ordered pairs. Determine whether the ordered pairs represent a *linear* function, a *quadratic* function, or an *exponential* function.

a. $\{(-2, 5), (-1, 2), (0, 1), (1, 2), (2, 5)\}$

The ordered pairs appear to represent a quadratic function.

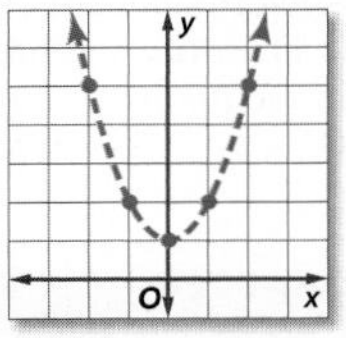

b. $\left\{\left(-2, \frac{1}{4}\right), \left(-1, \frac{1}{2}\right), (0, 1), (1, 2), (2, 4)\right\}$

The ordered pairs appear to represent an exponential function.

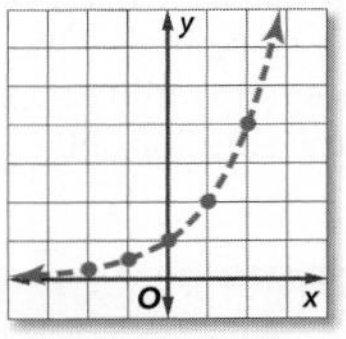

GuidedPractice

1A. $(-2, -3), (-1, -1), (0, 1), (1, 3)$ linear

1B. $(-1, 0.25), (0, 1), (1, 4), (2, 16)$ exponential

Lesson 9-6 Resources

Resource	Approaching Level AL	On Level OL	Beyond Level BL	English Learners ELL
Teacher Edition		▪ Differentiated Instruction, p. 595	▪ Differentiated Instruction, p. 595	▪ Differentiated Instruction, p. 592
Chapter Resource Masters	▪ Study Guide and Intervention, pp. 35–36 ▪ Skills Practice, p. 37 ▪ Practice, p. 38 ▪ Word Problem Practice, p. 39	▪ Study Guide and Intervention, pp. 35–36 ▪ Skills Practice, p. 37 ▪ Practice, p. 38 ▪ Word Problem Practice, p. 39 ▪ Enrichment, p. 40	▪ Practice, p. 38 ▪ Word Problem Practice, p. 39 ▪ Enrichment, p. 40	▪ Study Guide and Intervention, pp. 35–36 ▪ Skills Practice, p. 37 ▪ Practice, p. 38 ▪ Word Problem Practice, p. 39
Other	▪ 5-Minute Check 9-6 ▪ Study Notebook	▪ 5-Minute Check 9-6 ▪ Study Notebook	▪ 5-Minute Check 9-6 ▪ Study Notebook	▪ 5-Minute Check 9-6 ▪ Study Notebook

Another way to determine which model best describes data is to use patterns. The differences of successive y-values are called *first differences*. The differences of successive first differences are called *second differences*.

- If the differences of successive y-values are all equal, the data represent a linear function.
- If the second differences are all equal, but the first differences are not equal, the data represent a quadratic function.
- If the ratios of successive y-values are all equal and $r \neq 1$, the data represent an exponential function.

WatchOut!

x-Values Before you check for successive differences or ratios, make sure the x-values are increasing by the same amount.

Example 2 Choose a Model Using Differences or Ratios

Look for a pattern in each table of values to determine which kind of model best describes the data.

a.

x	−2	−1	0	1	2
y	−8	−3	2	7	12

First differences: −8 −3 2 7 12 → 5 5 5 5

Since the first differences are all equal, the table of values represents a linear function.

b.

x	−1	0	1	2	3
y	8	4	2	1	0.5

First differences: 8 4 2 1 0.5 → −4 −2 −1 −0.5

The first differences are not all equal. So, the table of values does not represent a linear function. Find the second differences and compare.

First differences: −4 −2 −1 −0.5

Second differences: 2 1 0.5

The second differences are not all equal. So, the table of values does not represent a quadratic function. Find the ratios of the y-values and compare.

8 4 2 1 0.5

Ratios: $\frac{4}{8} = \frac{1}{2}$ $\frac{2}{4} = \frac{1}{2}$ $\frac{1}{2}$ $\frac{0.5}{1} = \frac{1}{2}$

The ratios of successive y-values are equal. Therefore, the table of values can be modeled by an exponential function.

GuidedPractice

2A.

x	−3	−2	−1	0	1
y	−3	−7	−9	−9	−7

quadratic

2B.

x	−2	−1	0	1	2
y	−18	−13	−8	−3	2

linear

2 Write Equations Once you find the model that best describes the data, you can write an equation for the function. For a quadratic function in this lesson, the equation will have the form $y = ax^2$.

Focus on Mathematical Content

Patterns in Data For the table of values to be useful in determining which model best describes a set of data, the x-values must increase or decrease by a constant amount. If they do not, then the methods shown on this page cannot be used.

Teach with Tech

Video Recording Create a short video introduction to show at the beginning of class, and then work through additional examples with the class.

1 Identify Functions

Example 1 shows how to use a graph of a set of ordered pairs to determine whether the data represents a linear, quadratic, or exponential function. **Example 2** shows how to look for a pattern in a table of values to determine whether the data represents a linear, quadratic, or exponential function.

Formative Assessment

Use the Guided Practice exercises after each example to determine students' understanding of concepts.

Additional Example

1 Graph each set of ordered pairs. Determine whether the ordered pairs represent a *linear*, *quadratic*, or *exponential* function.

a. (1, 2), (2, 5), (3, 6), (4, 5), (5, 2) quadratic

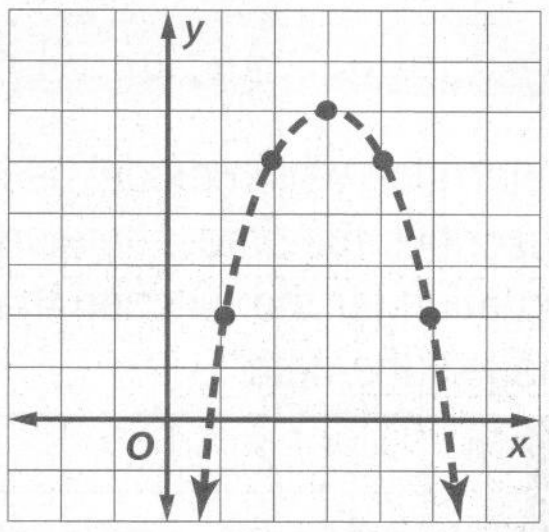

b. (−1, 6), (0, 2), $\left(1, \frac{2}{3}\right)$, $\left(2, \frac{2}{9}\right)$ exponential

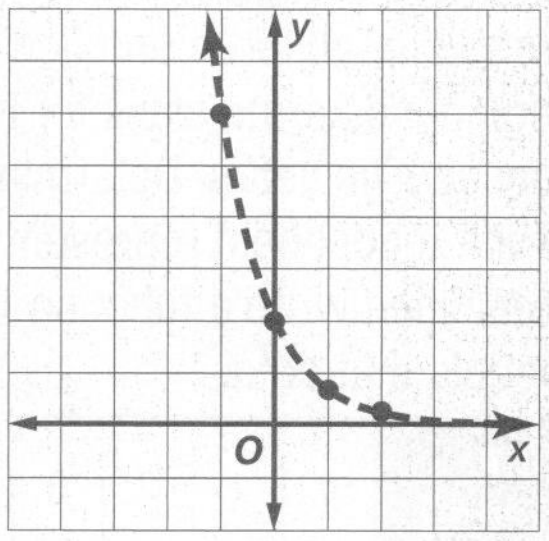

Additional Examples also in Interactive Classroom PowerPoint® Presentations

IWB Interactive White Board READY

Additional Example

2 Look for a pattern in each table of values to determine which kind of model best describes the data.

a.

x	−2	−1	0	1	2
y	−1	1	3	5	7

linear

b.

x	−2	−1	0	1	2
y	36	12	4	$\frac{4}{3}$	$\frac{4}{9}$

exponential

2 Write Equations

Example 3 shows how to write an equation for a function modeled by a set of data. **Example 4** shows how to write a function that models real-world data.

Additional Examples

3 Determine which model best describes the data. Then write an equation for the function that models the data.

x	0	1	2	3	4
y	−1	−8	−64	−512	−4096

exponential, $y = -(8)^x$

4 **KARATE** The table shows the number of children enrolled in a beginner's karate class for four consecutive years. Determine which model best represents the data. Then write a function that models that data.

Time (years)	0	1	2	3	4
Number enrolled	8	11	14	17	20

linear, $y = 3x + 8$

Tips for New Teachers

Checking the Equation Encourage students to verify that the ordered pairs satisfy the written equation.

Example 3 Write an Equation

Determine which kind of model best describes the data. Then write an equation for the function that models the data.

x	−4	−3	−2	−1	0
y	32	18	8	2	0

Step 1 Determine which model fits the data.

32 18 8 2 0

First differences: −14 −10 −6 −2

Second differences: 4 4 4

Since the second differences are equal, a quadratic function models the data.

Step 2 Write an equation for the function that models the data.

The equation has the form $y = ax^2$. Find the value of a by choosing one of the ordered pairs from the table of values. Let's use $(-1, 2)$.

$y = ax^2$ Equation for quadratic function

$2 = a(-1)^2$ $x = -1$ and $y = 2$

$2 = a$ An equation that models the data is $y = 2x^2$.

WatchOut!

Finding *a* In Example 3, the point (0, 0) cannot be used to find the value of a. You will have to divide each side by 0, giving you an undefined value for a.

GuidedPractice

3A. linear; $y = -4x + 3$

x	−2	−1	0	1	2
y	11	7	3	−1	−5

3B. exponential; $y = 3(2)^x$

x	−3	−2	−1	0	1
y	0.375	0.75	1.5	3	6

Real-WorldLink

A poll by the National Education Association found that 87% of all teens polled found reading relaxing, 85% viewed reading as rewarding, and 79% found reading exciting.

Source: *American Demographics*

Real-World Example 4 Write an Equation for a Real-World Situation

BOOK CLUB The table shows the number of book club members for four consecutive years. Determine which model best represents the data. Then write a function that models the data.

Time (years)	0	1	2	3	4
Members	5	10	20	40	80

Understand We need to find a model for the data, and then write a function.

Plan Find a pattern using successive differences or ratios. Then use the general form of the equation to write a function.

Solve The constant ratio is 2. This is the value of the base. An exponential function of the form $y = ab^x$ models the data.

$y = ab^x$ Equation for exponential function

$5 = a(2)^0$ $x = 0$, $y = 5$, and $b = 2$

$5 = a$ The equation that models the data is $y = 5 \cdot 2^x$.

Check You used (0, 5) to write the function. Verify that every other ordered pair satisfies the equation.

GuidedPractice

4. ADVERTISING The table shows the cost of placing an ad in a newspaper. Determine a model that best represents the data and write a function that models the data. linear; $C = 2.1n + 4$

No. of Lines	5	6	7	8
Total Cost ($)	14.50	16.60	18.70	20.80

DifferentiatedInstruction ELL

Verbal/Linguistic Learners Have students write a list of tips to help someone determine which model best describes a set of data and to write an equation for the function.

Check Your Understanding

= Step-by-Step Solutions begin on page R13.

Example 1 Graph each set of ordered pairs. Determine whether the ordered pairs represent a *linear* function, a *quadratic* function, or an *exponential* function. **1–4. See margin.**

1. (−2, 8), (−1, 5), (0, 2), (1, −1)
2. (−3, 7), (−2, 3), (−1, 1), (0, 1), (1, 3)
3. (−3, 8), (−2, 4), (−1, 2), (0, 1), (1, 0.5)
4. (0, 2), (1, 2.5), (2, 3), (3, 3.5)

Example 2 Look for a pattern in each table of values to determine which kind of model best describes the data.

5.

x	0	1	2	3	4
y	5	8	17	32	53

quadratic

6.

x	−3	−2	−1	0
y	−6.75	−7.5	−8.25	−9

linear

7.

x	−1	0	1	2	3
y	3	6	12	24	48

exponential

8.

x	3	4	5	6	7
y	−1.5	0	2.5	6	10.5

quadratic

Example 3 Determine which kind of model best describes the data. Then write an equation for the function that models the data.

9.

x	−1	0	1	2	3
y	1	3	9	27	81

exponential; $y = 3 \cdot 3^x$

10.

x	−5	−4	−3	−2	−1
y	125	80	45	20	5

quadratic; $y = 5x^2$

11.

x	−3	−2	−1	0	1
y	1	1.5	2	2.5	3

linear; $y = \frac{1}{2}x + \frac{5}{2}$

12.

x	−1	0	1	2
y	−1.25	−1	−0.75	−0.5

linear; $y = \frac{1}{4}x - 1$

Example 4 13. **PLANTS** The table shows the height of a plant for four consecutive weeks. Determine which kind of function best models the height. Then write a function that models the data. **linear; $y = 0.5x + 3$**

Week	0	1	2	3	4
Height (in.)	3	3.5	4	4.5	5

Practice and Problem Solving

Extra Practice is on page R9.

Example 1 Graph each set of ordered pairs. Determine whether the ordered pairs represent a *linear* function, a *quadratic* function, or an *exponential* function.

14–19. See Ch. 9 Answer Appendix.

14. (−1, 1), (0, −2), (1, −3), (2, −2), (3, 1)
15. (1, 2.75), (2, 2.5), (3, 2.25), (4, 2)
16. (−3, 0.25), (−2, 0.5), (−1, 1), (0, 2)
17. (−3, −11), (−2, −5), (−1, −3), (0, −5)
18. (−2, 6), (−1, 1), (0, −4), (1, −9)
19. (−1, 8), (0, 2), (1, 0.5), (2, 0.125)

Examples 2–3 Look for a pattern in each table of values to determine which kind of model best describes the data. Then write an equation for the function that models the data.

20.

x	−3	−2	−1	0
y	−8.8	−8.6	−8.4	−8.2

linear; $y = 0.2x - 8.2$

21.

x	−2	−1	0	1	2
y	10	2.5	0	2.5	10

quadratic; $y = 2.5x^2$

22.

x	−1	0	1	2	3
y	0.75	3	12	48	192

exponential; $y = 3 \cdot 4^x$

23.

x	−2	−1	0	1	2
y	0.008	0.04	0.2	1	5

exponential; $y = 0.2 \cdot 5^x$

24.

x	0	1	2	3	4
y	0	4.2	16.8	37.8	67.2

quadratic; $y = 4.2x^2$

25.

x	−3	−2	−1	0	1
y	14.75	9.75	4.75	−0.25	−5.25

linear; $y = -5x - 0.25$

Differentiated Homework Options

Level	Assignment	Two-Day Option	
AL Basic	14–26, 32–65	15–25 odd, 36–39	14–26 even, 32–35, 40–65
OL Core	15–25 odd, 27–30, 32–65	14–26, 36–39	27–30, 32–35, 40–65
BL Advanced	27–59, (optional: 60–65)		

3 Practice

Formative Assessment

Use Exercises 1–13 to check for understanding.

Use the chart at the bottom of this page to customize assignments for your students.

Exercise Alert

Grid Paper For Exercises 1–4, 14–19, and 27, students will need grid paper.

Additional Answers

1.

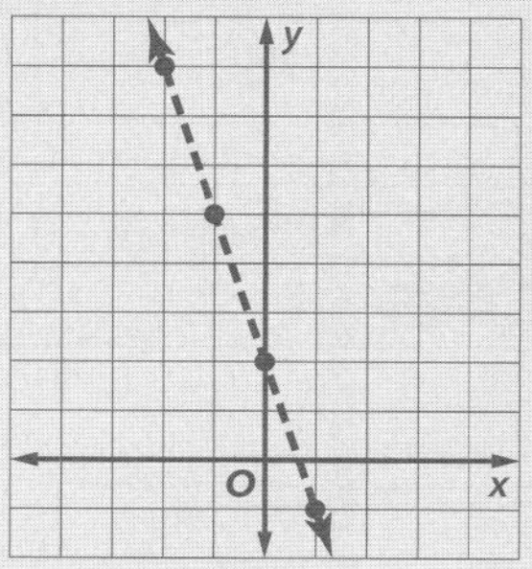

linear

2.

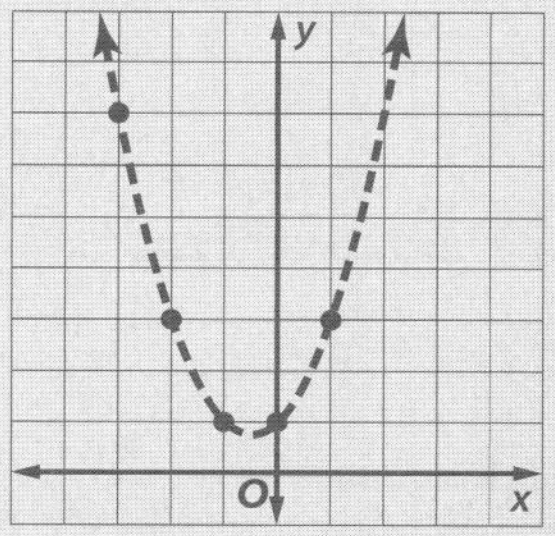

quadratic

3.

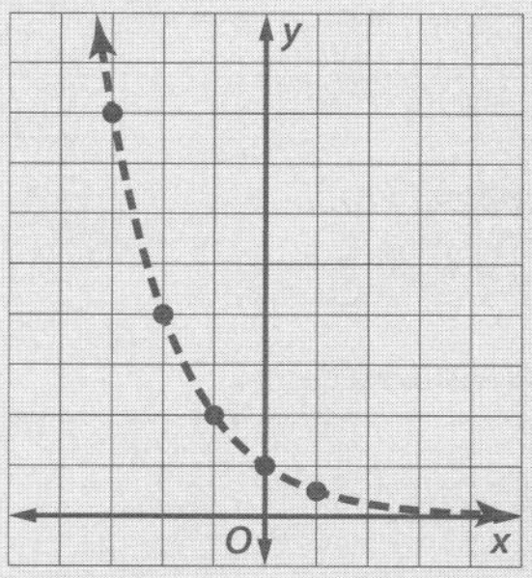

exponential

4.

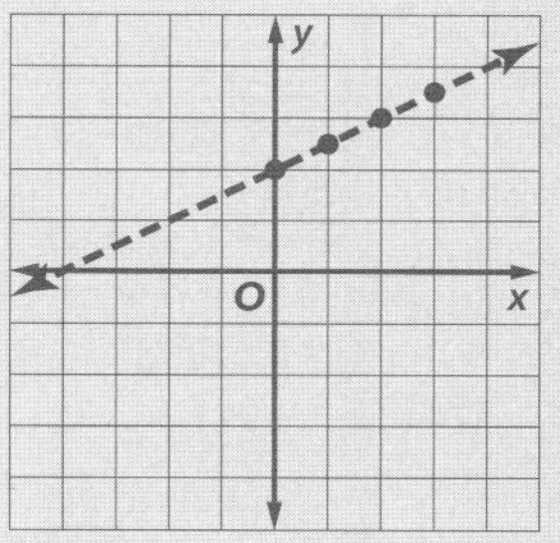

linear

Example 4 **26. WEB SITES** A company tracked the number of visitors to its Web site over 4 days. Determine which kind of model best represents the number of visitors to the Web site with respect to time. Then write a function that models the data. **quadratic; $y = 0.9x^2$**

Day	0	1	2	3	4
Visitors (in thousands)	0	0.9	3.6	8.1	14.4

B **27. CALLING** The cost of an international call depends on the length of the call. The table shows the cost for up to 6 minutes.

Length of call (min)	1	2	3	4	5	6
Cost ($)	0.12	0.24	0.36	0.48	0.60	0.72

a. Graph the data and determine which kind of function best models the data. **See margin for graph; linear.**

b. Write an equation for the function that models the data. **$y = 0.12x$**

c. Use your equation to determine how much a 10-minute call would cost. **$1.20**

28. DEPRECIATION The value of a car depreciates over time. The table shows the value of a car over a period of time.

Year	0	1	2	3	4
Value ($)	18,500	15,910	13,682.60	11,767.04	10,119.65

a. Determine which kind of function best models the data. **exponential**

b. Write an equation for the function that models the data. **$v = 18{,}500 \cdot (0.86)^t$**

c. Use your equation to determine how much the car is worth after 7 years. **$6436.66**

C **29. BACTERIA** A scientist estimates that a bacteria culture with an initial population of 12 will triple every hour.

a. Make a table to show the bacteria population for the first 4 hours. **See Ch.9 Answer Appendix.**

b. Which kind of model best represents the data? **exponential**

c. Write a function that models the data. **$b = 12 \cdot 3^t$**

d. How many bacteria will there be after 8 hours? **78,732**

30. PRINTING A printing company charges the fees shown to print flyers. Write a function that models the total cost of the flyers, and determine how much 30 flyers would cost. **$c = 0.15f + 25$; $29.50**

Quick 2 U Printing
Set Up Fee $25
15¢ each flyer

32. Linear functions have a constant first difference and quadratic functions have a constant second difference, so cubic equations would have a constant third difference.

H.O.T. Problems Use Higher-Order Thinking Skills

31. CHALLENGE Write a function that has constant second differences, first differences that are not constant, a y-intercept of -5, and contains the point (2, 3). **Sample answer: $y = 2x^2 - 5$**

32. ARGUMENTS What type of function will have constant third differences but not constant second differences? Explain.

33. OPEN ENDED Write a linear function that has a constant first difference of 4. **$y = 4x + 1$**

34. PROOF Write a paragraph proof to show that linear functions grow by equal differences over equal intervals, and exponential functions grow by equal factors over equal intervals. (*Hint:* Let $y = ax$ represent a linear function and let $y = a^x$ represent an exponential function.) **See margin.**

35. WRITING IN MATH How can you determine whether a given set of data should be modeled by a *linear* function, a *quadratic* function, or an *exponential* function? **See margin.**

594 | Lesson 9-6 | Analyzing Functions with Successive Differences

Study Guide and Intervention
AL OL ELL

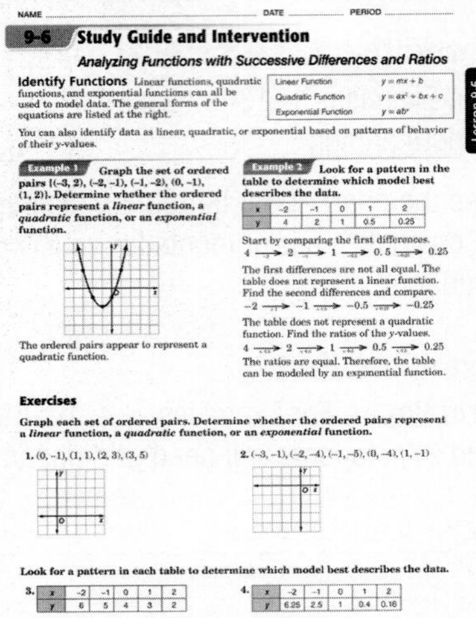
9-6 Study Guide and Intervention
Analyzing Functions with Successive Differences and Ratios

Practice
AL OL BL ELL

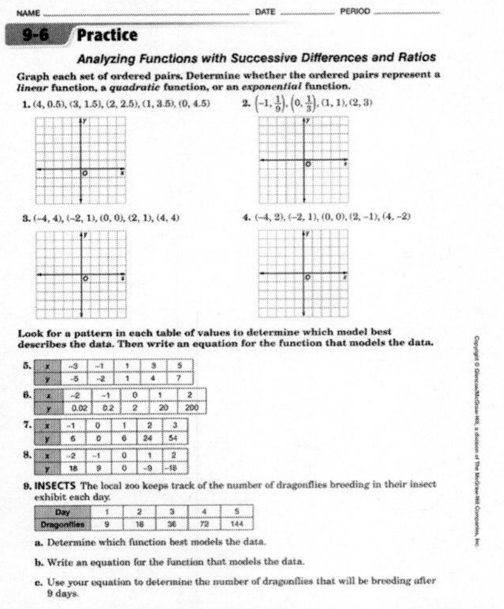
9-6 Practice
Analyzing Functions with Successive Differences and Ratios

Word Problem Practice
AL OL BL ELL

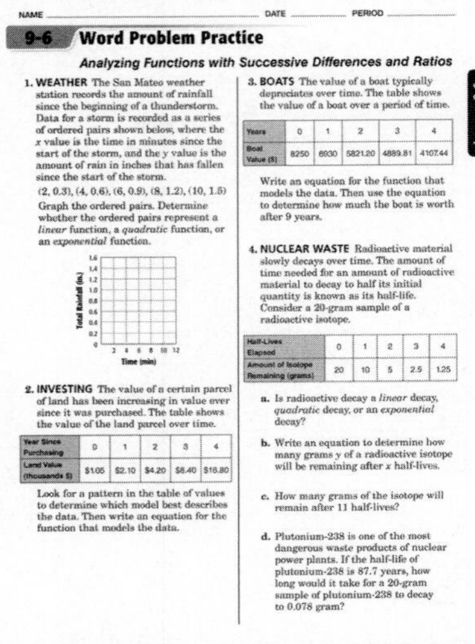
9-6 Word Problem Practice
Analyzing Functions with Successive Differences and Ratios

Enrichment
OL BL

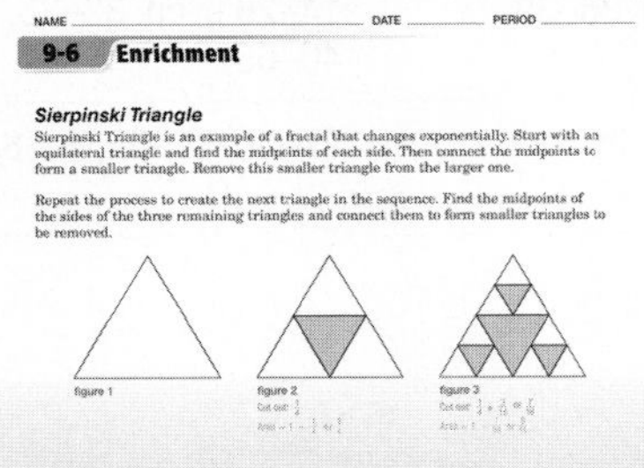
9-6 Enrichment
Sierpinski Triangle

Teaching the Process Standards

Arguments Mathematically proficient students reason inductively. In Exercise 32, tell students to look for a pattern.

Standardized Test Practice

36. **SHORT RESPONSE** Write an equation that models the data in the table. $y = 3 \cdot 2^x$

x	0	1	2	3	4
y	3	6	12	24	48

37. What is the equation of the line below? **A**

A $y = \frac{2}{5}x + 2$

B $y = \frac{2}{5}x - 2$

C $y = \frac{5}{2}x + 2$

D $y = \frac{5}{2}x - 2$

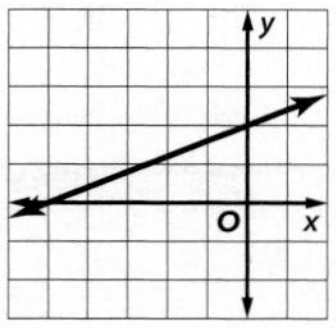

38. The point $(r, -4)$ lies on a line with an equation of $2x + 3y = -8$. Find the value of r. **H**

F -10 H 2

G 0 J 8

39. **GEOMETRY** The rectangle has an area of 220 square feet. Find the length ℓ. **B**

A 8 feet

B 10 feet

C 22 feet

D 34 feet

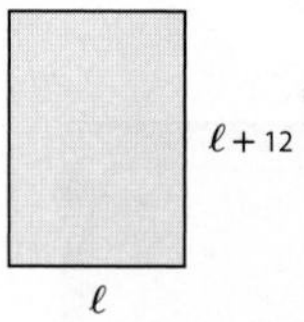

Spiral Review

Solve each equation by using the Quadratic Formula. Round to the nearest tenth if necessary. (Lesson 9-5)

40. $6x^2 - 3x - 30 = 0$ **−2, 2.5**

41. $4x^2 + 18x = 10$ **−5, 0.5**

42. $2x^2 + 6x = 7$ **−3.9, 0.9**

Solve each equation by taking the square root of each side. Round to the nearest tenth if necessary. (Lesson 9-4)

43. $x^2 = 25$ **±5**

44. $x^2 + 6x + 9 = 16$ **−7, 1**

45. $x^2 - 14x + 49 = 15$ **3.1, 10.9**

46. **INVESTMENTS** Joey's investment of $2500 has been decreasing in value at a rate of 1.5% each year. What will his investment be worth in 5 years? (Lesson 7-7) **$2318.04**

Write an equation for the nth term of each geometric sequence, and find the seventh term of each sequence. (Lesson 7-6)

47. 1, 2, 4, 8, … $a_n = 1(2)^{n-1}$; 64

48. −20, −10, −5, … $a_n = -20(0.5)^{n-1}$; −0.3125

49. 4, −12, 36, … $a_n = 4(-3)^{n-1}$; 2916

50. 99, −33, 11, … $a_n = 99\left(\frac{-1}{3}\right)^{n-1}$; $\frac{11}{81}$

51. 22, 44, 88, … $a_n = 22(2)^{n-1}$; 1408

52. $\frac{2}{3}, \frac{1}{3}, \frac{1}{6}, \ldots$ $a_n = \frac{2}{3}\left(\frac{1}{2}\right)^{n-1}$; $\frac{1}{96}$

53. **CANOE RENTAL** To rent a canoe, you must pay a daily rate plus $10 per hour. Ilia and her friends rented a canoe for 3 hours and paid $45. Write a linear equation for the cost C of renting the canoe for h hours, and determine how much it cost to rent the canoe for 8 hours. (Lesson 4-2) **$C = 10h + 15$; $95**

Determine whether each equation is a linear equation. If so, write the equation in standard form. (Lesson 3-1)

54. $3x = 5y$ **yes; $3x - 5y = 0$**

55. $6 - y = 2x$ **yes; $2x + y = 6$**

56. $6xy + 3x = 4$ **no**

57. $y + 5 = 0$ **yes; $y = -5$**

58. $7y = 2x + 5x$ **yes; $x - y = 0$**

59. $y = 4x^2 - 1$ **no**

Skills Review

Evaluate each expression if $x = -3$, $y = -1$, and $z = 4$.

60. $|x - 4|$ **7**

61. $|2y + 1|$ **1**

62. $|4 - z|$ **0**

63. $\left|\frac{1}{2}x + 2\right|$ **$\frac{1}{2}$**

64. $|12 - 4z|$ **4**

65. $|2y - 3| - 6$ **−1**

Differentiated Instruction OL BL

Extension Ask students to make a table of values for $y = \sqrt{x}$ and then graph it. Be sure students do not include any negative values for x, because the square root of a negative number is not a real number.

x	0	1	4	9	16	25
y	0	1	2	3	4	5

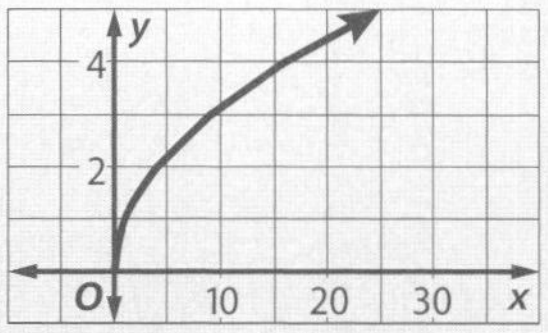

4 Assess

Yesterdays News Ask students to write how yesterday's lesson on quadratic equations helped them with today's lesson.

Formative Assessment

Check for student understanding of Lesson 9-6.

Quiz 3, p. 50

Additional Answer

27a.

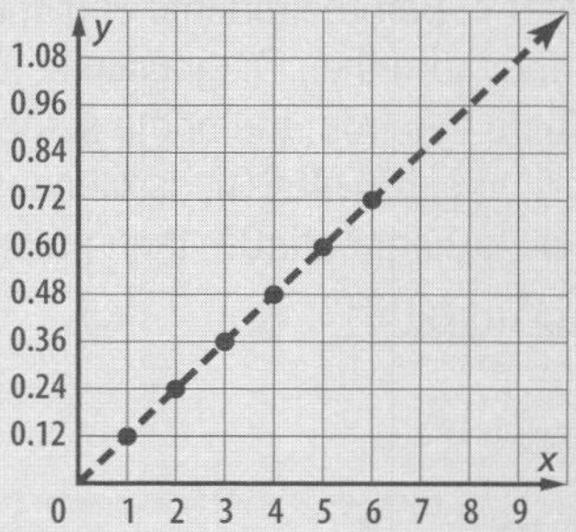

34. If one linear term is ax, the next term is $a(x + 1)$, and the difference between the terms is $a(x + 1) - ax = ax + a - ax$ or a. If one exponential term is a^x, the next term is a^{x+1}, and the ratio of the terms is $\frac{a^{x+1}}{a^x}$ or a.

35. Sample answer: The data can be graphed to determine which function best models the data. You can also find the differences in ratios of the y-values. If the first differences are constant, the data can be modeled by a linear function. If the second differences are constant but the first differences are not, the data can be modeled by a quadratic function. If the ratios are constant, then the data can be modeled by an exponential function.

1 Focus

Objective Use a graphing calculator to find an appropriate regression equation for a set of data.

Materials for Each Group

- TI-83/84 Plus or other graphing calculator

Teaching Tip

Remind students that they learned about regression and median fit lines in Chapter 4. Before students begin, make sure they turn their Diagnostic setting on. To do this from the home screen, press [2nd] **[CATALOG]**, scroll down and click **DiagnosticOn**, then press [ENTER] [ENTER].

2 Teach

Working in Cooperative Groups

Put students in groups of two or three, mixing abilities. Have groups complete the Activity and Exercises 1–4.

- In Step 1 of the Activity, make sure students clear previous lists before entering the data. Students should enter years after 2000 in **L1** and the number of flights in **L2**.
- In Step 2 of the Activity, point out that the R^2 value, 0.9998751467 is the coefficient of determination. Generally, the closer this is to 1, the better the model.
- For Step 3 of the Activity, tell students that they must copy the quadratic regression exactly to the **Y=** LIST in order to get the proper graph.

Practice Have students complete Exercise 5.

EXTEND 9-6 Graphing Technology Lab: Curve Fitting

If there is a constant increase or decrease in data values, there is a linear trend. If the values are increasing or decreasing more and more rapidly, there may be a quadratic or exponential trend.

Content Standards
AI.QE.1, AI.DS.2

Process Standards
PS.5

Linear Trend

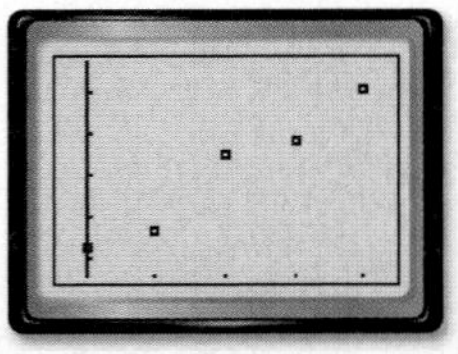

[0, 5] scl: 1 by [0, 6] scl: 1

Quadratic Trend

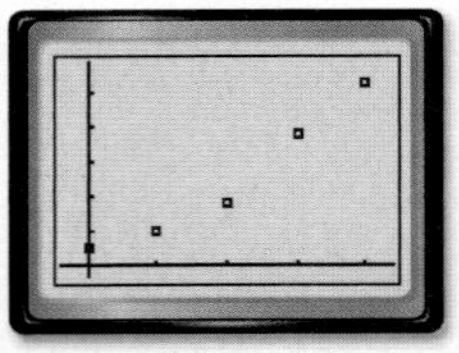

[0, 5] scl: 1 by [0, 6] scl: 1

Exponential Trend

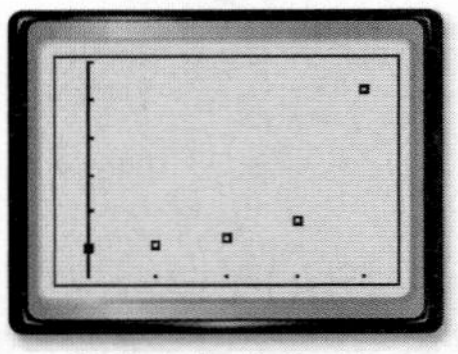

[0, 5] scl: 1 by [0, 6] scl: 1

With a graphing calculator, you can find the appropriate regression equation.

Activity

CHARTER AIRLINE The table shows the average monthly number of flights made each year by a charter airline that was founded in 2000.

Year	2000	2001	2002	2003	2004	2005	2006	2007
Flights	17	20	24	28	33	38	44	50

Step 1 Make a scatter plot.

- Enter the number of years since 2000 in **L1** and the number of flights in **L2**.

KEYSTROKES: *Review entering a list on page 255.*

- Use **STAT PLOT** to graph the scatter plot.

KEYSTROKES: *Review statistical plots on page 256.*

Use [ZOOM] 9 to graph.

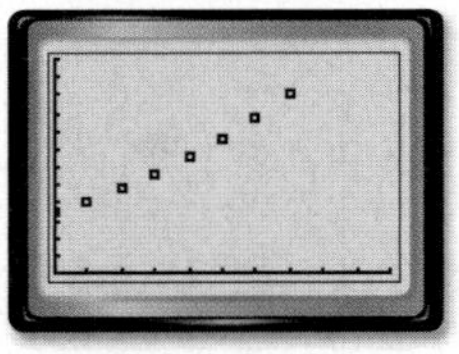

[0, 10] scl: 1 by [0, 60] scl: 5

From the scatter plot we can see that the data may have either a quadratic trend or an exponential trend.

Step 2 Find the regression equation.

We will check both trends by examining their regression equations.

- Select **DiagnosticOn** from the **CATALOG**.
- Select **QuadReg** on the **STAT** menu.

KEYSTROKES: [STAT] [▶] 5 [ENTER] [ENTER]

The equation is in the form $y = ax^2 + bx + c$.

The equation is about $y = 0.25x^2 + 3x + 17$.

R^2 is the **coefficient of determination**. The closer R^2 is to 1, the better the model. To acquire the exponential equation select **ExpReg** on the **STAT** menu. To choose a quadratic or exponential model, fit both and use the one with the R^2 value closer to 1.

596 | Extend 9-6 | Graphing Technology Lab: Curve Fitting

Step 3 Graph the quadratic regression equation.

- Copy the equation to the **Y=** list and graph.

KEYSTROKES: [Y=] [VARS] 5 [▶] [▶] 1 [ZOOM] 9

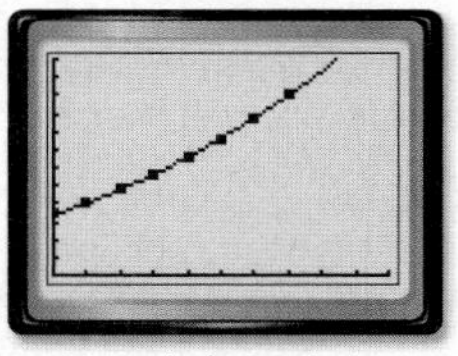

[0, 10] scl: 1 by [0, 60] scl: 5

Step 4 Predict using the equation.

If this trend continues, we can use the graph of our equation to predict the monthly number of flights the airline will make in a specific year. Let's check the year 2020. First adjust the window.

KEYSTROKES: [2nd] [CALC] 1 At $x =$ enter 20 [ENTER].

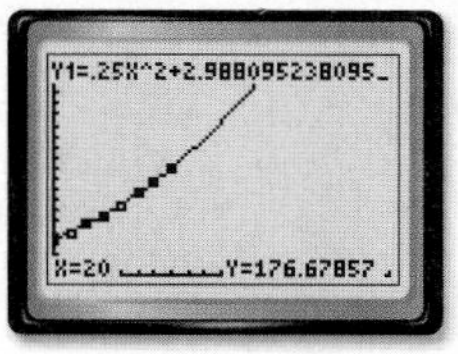

[0, 25] scl: 1 by [0, 200] scl: 5

There will be approximately 177 flights per month if this trend continues.

Exercises

Plot each set of data points. Determine whether to use a *linear*, *quadratic* or *exponential* regression equation. State the coefficient of determination.

1. quadratic; $R^2 \approx 0.969$

x	y
1	30
2	40
3	50
4	55
5	50
6	40

2. quadratic; $R^2 \approx 0.964$

x	y
0.0	12.1
0.1	9.6
0.2	6.3
0.3	5.5
0.4	4.8
0.5	1.9

3. quadratic; $R^2 \approx 0.980$

x	y
0	1.1
2	3.3
4	2.9
6	5.6
8	11.9
10	19.8

4. quadratic; $R^2 \approx 0.840$

x	y
1	1.67
5	2.59
9	4.37
13	6.12
17	5.48
21	3.12

5c. $y = (306)(0.96^x)$; $R^2 = 0.957$; D = $\{x \mid x > 0\}$; R = $\{y \mid y > 0\}$

5. BAKING **Alyssa baked a cake and is waiting for it to cool so she can ice it. The table shows the temperature of the cake every 5 minutes after Alyssa took it out of the oven.**

Time (min)	Temperature (°F)
0	350
5	244
10	178
15	137
20	112
25	96
30	89

a. Make a scatter plot of the data. **See margin.**

b. Which regression equation has an R^2 value closest to 1? Is this the equation that best fits the context of the problem? Explain your reasoning. **See margin.**

c. Find an appropriate regression equation, and state the coefficient of determination. What is the domain and range?

d. Alyssa will ice the cake when it reaches room temperature (70°F). Use the regression equation to predict when she can ice her cake. **36 min**

Additional Answers

5a.

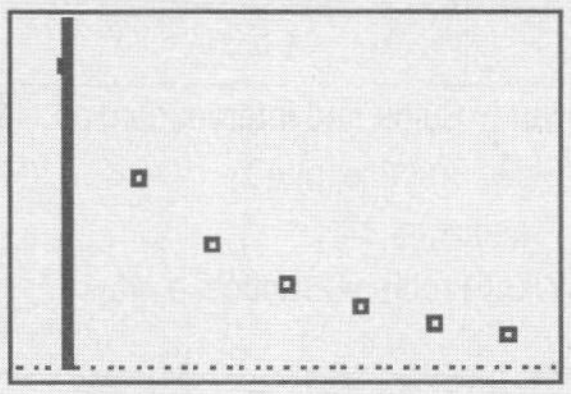

[−5, 35] scl:1 by [0, 400] scl:1

5b. The quadratic equation has an R^2 value closest to 1. However in a quadratic trend, the cake would cool and then heat up again. The exponential regression best fits the context of the problem.

3 Assess

Formative Assessment

In Step 4 of the Activity, the quadratic regression estimated that during the 7th month the most passengers flew, about 59 million. Ask students to explain why the estimated number of passengers that flew in the 7th month may not be completely accurate. Sample answer: The quadratic regression equation is a best fit to data points that do not fall on an actual graphed function. There will be differences between actual data points and points that fall on the regression function.

From Concrete to Abstract

Ask: How do you determine whether to use a linear, quadratic, or exponential regression equation for your data? Sample answer: Make a scatter plot of your data points. If it looks close to a straight line, use a linear regression equation. If the data points follow a curve, fit a quadratic regression equation and an exponential regression equation to your points. The model with the coefficient of determination closest to 1 is the model to use.

1 Focus

VerticalAlignment

Before Lesson 9-7 Identify and graph linear, exponential, and quadratic functions.

Lesson 9-7 Identify and graph step functions, absolute value functions, and piecewise-defined functions.

After Lesson 9-7 Identify and graph radical and rational functions.

2 Teach

Scaffolding Questions

Have students read the **Why?** section of the lesson.

Ask:

- For what order values will you pay \$3 for shipping? all values greater than \$0 and less than \$10
- If x is the cost of an order that is less than \$10 and y is the cost of the shipping, name three ordered pairs on the graph that represent this situation. Sample answer: (5, 3), (6, 3), (9, 3)
- How much would it cost to ship a \$10 item? \$5

LESSON 9-7 Special Functions

Then

- You identified and graphed linear, exponential, and quadratic functions.

Now

1. Identify and graph step functions.
2. Identify and graph absolute value and piecewise-defined functions.

Why?

- Kim is ordering books online. The site charges for shipping based on the amount of the order. If the order is less than \$10, shipping costs \$3. If the order is at least \$10 but less than \$20, it will cost \$5 to ship it.

NewVocabulary

step function
piecewise-linear function
greatest integer function
absolute value function
piecewise-defined function

Content Standards
AI.L.10

Process Standards
PS.4

1 Step Functions

The graph of a **step function** is a series of line segments. Because each part of a step function is linear, this type of function is called a **piecewise-linear function**. One example of a step function is the **greatest integer function**, written as $f(x) = [\![x]\!]$, where $f(x)$ is the greatest integer not greater than x. For example, $[\![6.8]\!] = 6$ because 6 is the greatest integer that is not greater than 6.8.

KeyConcept Greatest Integer Function

Parent function:	$f(x) = [\![x]\!]$
Type of graph:	disjointed line segments
Domain:	all real numbers
Range:	all integers

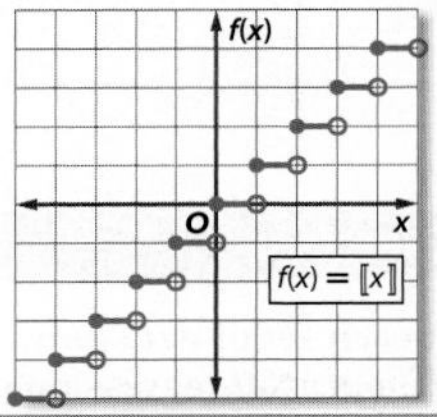

Example 1 Greatest Integer Function

Graph $f(x) = [\![x + 2]\!]$. State the domain and range.

First, make a table. Select a few values between integers. On the graph, dots represent included points. Circles represent points not included.

x	$x + 2$	$[\![x + 2]\!]$
0	2	2
0.25	2.25	2
0.5	2.5	2
1	3	3
1.25	3.25	3
1.5	3.5	3
2	4	4
2.25	4.25	4

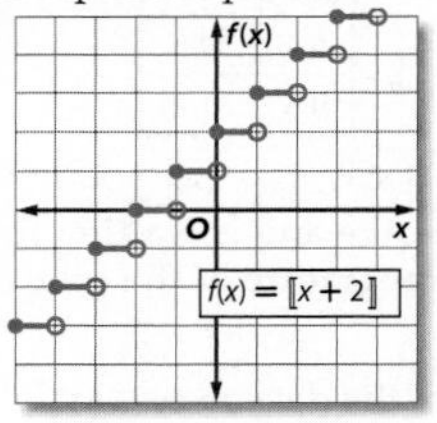

Note that this is the graph of $f(x) = [\![x]\!]$ shifted 2 units to the left.

Because the dots and circles overlap, the domain is all real numbers. The range is all integers. Notice that the graph has no symmetry and no maximum or minimum values. As x increases, $f(x)$ increases, and as x decreases, $f(x)$ decreases.

GuidedPractice

1. Graph $g(x) = 2[\![x]\!]$. State the domain and range. **See Ch. 9 Answer Appendix.**

598 | Lesson 9-7

Lesson 9-7 Resources

Resource	Approaching Level AL	On Level OL	Beyond Level BL	English Learners ELL
Teacher Edition	▪ Differentiated Instruction, p. 602	▪ Differentiated Instruction, pp. 602, 603	▪ Differentiated Instruction, p. 603	
Chapter Resource Masters	▪ Study Guide and Intervention, pp. 41–42 ▪ Skills Practice, p. 43 ▪ Practice, p. 44 ▪ Word Problem Practice, p. 45	▪ Study Guide and Intervention, pp. 41–42 ▪ Skills Practice, p. 43 ▪ Practice, p. 44 ▪ Word Problem Practice, p. 45 ▪ Enrichment, p. 46	▪ Practice, p. 44 ▪ Word Problem Practice, p. 45 ▪ Enrichment, p. 46	▪ Study Guide and Intervention, pp. 41–42 ▪ Skills Practice, p. 43 ▪ Practice, p. 44 ▪ Word Problem Practice, p. 45
Other	▪ 5-Minute Check 9-7 ▪ Study Notebook	▪ 5-Minute Check 9-7 ▪ Study Notebook	▪ 5-Minute Check 9-7 ▪ Study Notebook	▪ 5-Minute Check 9-7 ▪ Study Notebook

Step functions can be used to represent many real-world situations involving money.

Real-WorldLink
North Americans are the most likely to have cell phones with 93.2% of the population owning phones.
Source: IT Facts

Real-World Example 2 Step Function

CELL PHONE PLANS Cell phone companies charge by the minute, not by the second. A cell phone company charges $0.45 per minute or any fraction thereof for exceeding the number of minutes allotted on each plan. Draw a graph that represents this situation.

The total cost for the extra minutes will be a multiple of $0.45, and the graph will be a step function. If the time is greater than 0 but less than or equal to 1 minute, the charge will be $0.45. If the time is greater than 2 but is less than or equal to 3 minutes, you will be charged for 3 minutes or $1.35.

x	$f(x)$
$0 < x \leq 1$	0.45
$1 < x \leq 2$	0.90
$2 < x \leq 3$	1.35
$3 < x \leq 4$	1.80
$4 < x \leq 5$	2.25
$5 < x \leq 6$	2.70
$6 < x \leq 7$	3.15

Cell Phone Overage

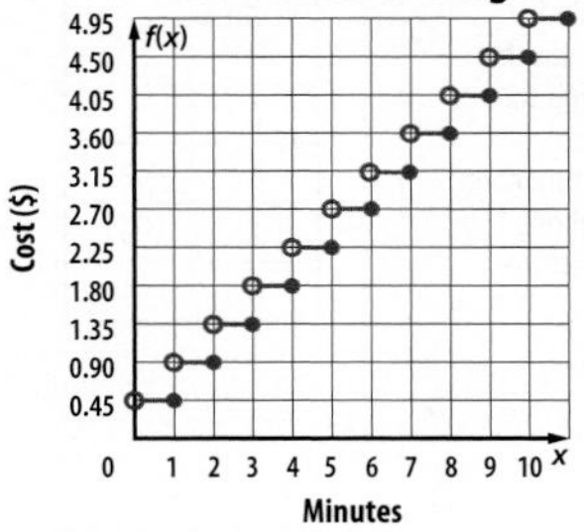

GuidedPractice

2. **PARKING** A garage charges $4 for the first hour and $1 for each additional hour. Draw a graph that represents this situation. **See Ch. 9 Answer Appendix.**

ReviewVocabulary
absolute value the distance a number is from zero on a number line; written $|n|$

2 Absolute Value Functions

Another type of piecewise-linear function is the **absolute value function**. Recall that the absolute value of a number is always nonnegative. So in the absolute value parent function, written as $f(x) = |x|$, all of the values of the range are nonnegative.

KeyConcept Absolute Value Function

Parent function: $f(x) = |x|$, defined as

$$f(x) = \begin{cases} x \text{ if } x > 0 \\ 0 \text{ if } x = 0 \\ -x \text{ if } x < 0 \end{cases}$$

Type of graph: V-shaped

Domain: all real numbers

Range: all nonnegative real numbers

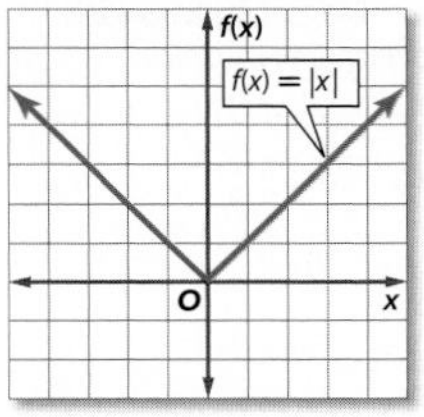

The absolute value function is called a **piecewise-defined function** because it is defined using two or more expressions.

1 Step Functions

Example 1 shows how to state the domain and range and draw the graph of a greatest integer function. **Example 2** shows how to represent a real-world situation with a step function graph.

Formative Assessment

Use the Guided Practice exercises after each Example to determine students' understanding of concepts.

Additional Examples

1 Graph $f(x) = [\![x - 2]\!]$. State the domain and range. D = all real numbers; R = all integers

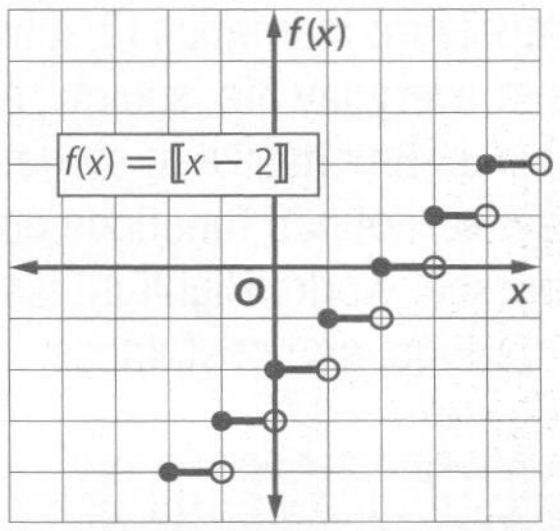

2 **TAXI** A taxi company charges a fee for waiting at a rate of $0.75 per minute or any fraction thereof. Draw a graph that represents this situation.

Taxi Waiting Fee

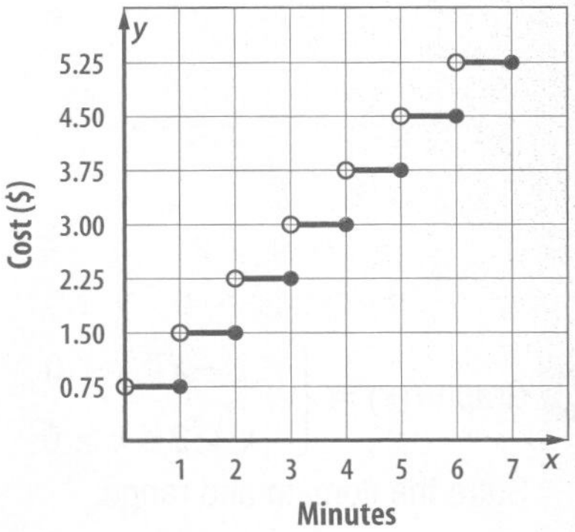

Additional Examples also in Interactive Classroom PowerPoint® Presentations

IWB Interactive White Board READY

Focus on Mathematical Content

Functions The vertical line test can be used to verify that an absolute value function, a greatest-integer function, and a piecewise-defined function are actually functions. Graph the functions and then draw vertical lines anywhere on the graph. If any of the lines intersect the graph in more than one point, it is not a graph of a function. A vertical line drawn on a step function at the end of one step and the beginning of the next would appear to intersect at two points, however the circle on one end of a step in the graph represents a point not included on the graph.

2 Absolute Value Function

Example 3 shows how to graph an absolute value function and determine the domain and range of the function. **Example 4** shows how to graph a piecewise-defined function that is not an absolute value function, and determine its domain and range.

Tips for New Teachers

Table of Values Students having difficulty with the absolute value function may benefit from making a table of values for the parent function $f(x) = |x|$ and then graphing it.

Teaching the Process Standards

Modeling Mathematically proficient students apply mathematics to solve problems in everyday life, society, and the workplace. Emphasize to students that piecewise-defined functions occur often in the real world. Highlight issues of domain, range, and usefulness.

Additional Examples

3 Graph $f(x) = |2x + 2|$. State the domain and range.

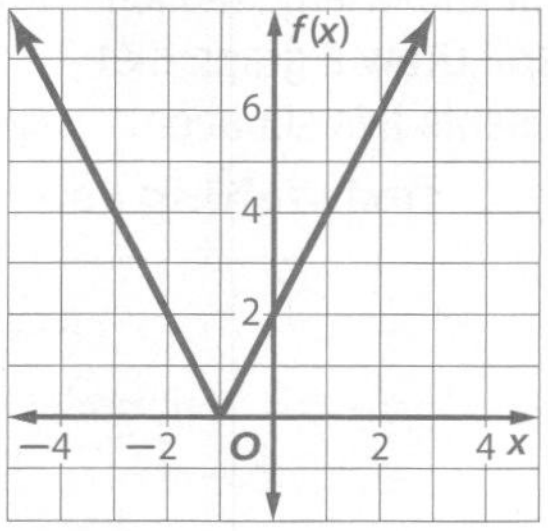

D = all real numbers;
R = all nonnegative numbers

4 Graph $f(x) = \begin{cases} -x \text{ if } x < 0 \\ -x + 2 \text{ if } x \geq 0 \end{cases}$.
State the domain and range.

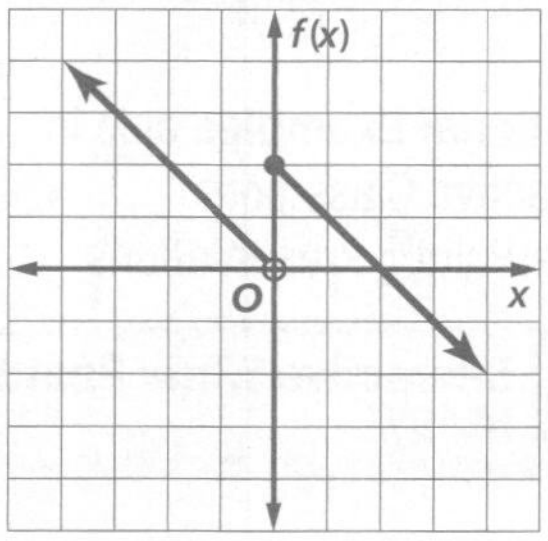

D = all real numbers;
R = all real numbers

Math HistoryLink

Florence Nightingale David (1909–1993) A renowned statistician born in Ivington, England, Florence Nightingale David received the first Elizabeth L. Scott Award for her "efforts in opening the door to women in statistics; … for research contributions to … statistical methods …; and her spirit as a lecturer and as a role model."

Example 3 Absolute Value Function

Graph $f(x) = |x - 4|$. State the domain and range.

Since $f(x)$ cannot be negative, the minimum point of the graph is where $f(x) = 0$.

$f(x) = |x - 4|$ Original function
$0 = x - 4$ Replace $f(x)$ with 0 and $|x - 4|$ with $x - 4$.
$4 = x$ Add 4 to each side.

Next make a table of values. Include values for $x > 4$ and $x < 4$.

$f(x) = \|x - 4\|$	
x	$f(x)$
−2	6
0	4
2	2
4	0
5	1
6	2
7	3
8	4

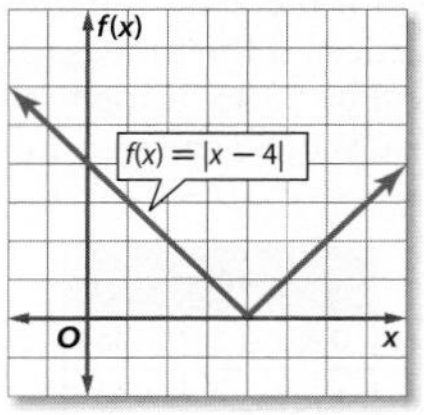

The domain is all real numbers. The range is all real numbers greater than or equal to 0. Note that this is the graph of $f(x) = |x|$ shifted 4 units to the right. Notice that the graph is symmetric about the line $x = 4$, and the minimum value of the function is 0 at $x = 4$. As x increases, $f(x)$ increases, and as x decreases, $f(x)$ increases.

Guided Practice

3. Graph $f(x) = |2x + 1|$. State the domain and range. **See margin for graph; D = all real numbers, R = $f(x) > 0$.**

Not all piecewise-defined functions are absolute value functions. Step functions are also piecewise-defined functions. In fact, all piecewise-linear functions are piecewise-defined.

StudyTip

Piecewise Functions To graph a piecewise-defined function, graph each "piece" separately. There should be a dot or line that contains each member of the domain.

Example 4 Piecewise-Defined Function

Graph $f(x) = \begin{cases} -2x \text{ if } x > 1 \\ x + 3 \text{ if } x \leq 1 \end{cases}$. State the domain and range.

Graph the first expression. Create a table of values for when $x > 1$, $f(x) = -2x$ and draw the graph. Since x is not equal to 1, place a circle at $(1, -2)$.

Next, graph the second expression. Create a table of values for when $x \leq 1$, $f(x) = x + 3$ and draw the graph. If $x = 1$, then $f(x) = 4$; place a dot at $(1, 4)$.

The domain is all real numbers. The range is $y \leq 4$.

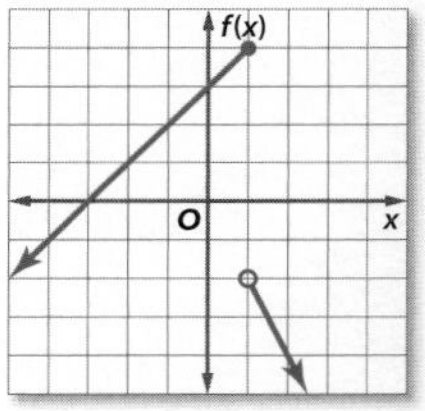

Guided Practice

4. Graph $f(x) = \begin{cases} 2x + 1 \text{ if } x > 0 \\ 3 \text{ if } x \leq 0 \end{cases}$. State the domain and range. **See margin for graph; D = all real numbers, R = $f(x) > 1$.**

600 | Lesson 9-7 | Special Functions

Teach with Tech

Blog On your secure classroom blog give students a picture file of a graph of the greatest integer function. Have students write a blog entry explaining how to interpret the function and its graph.

Additional Answers (Guided Practice)

3.

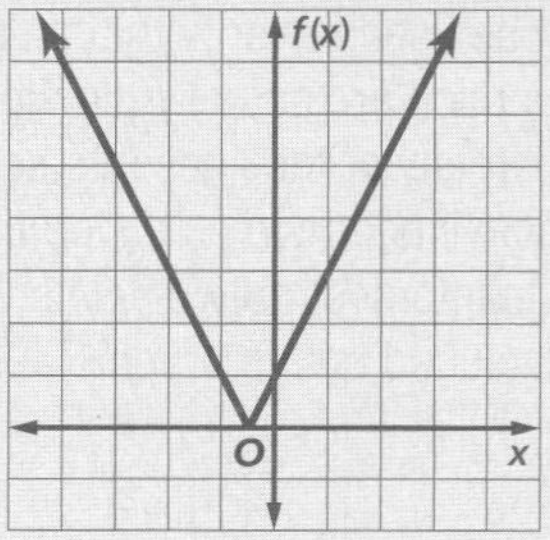

4.

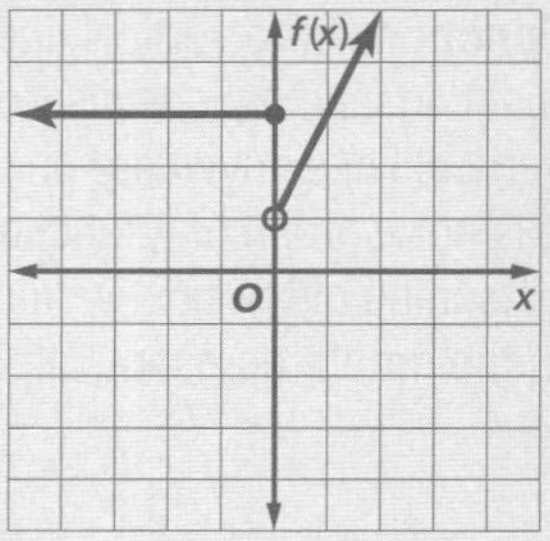

StudyTip

Nonlinear Functions Like exponential and quadratic functions, the greatest integer function, absolute value function, and piecewise-defined functions are nonlinear functions.

ConceptSummary Special Functions

Step Function	Absolute Value Function	Piecewise-Defined Function
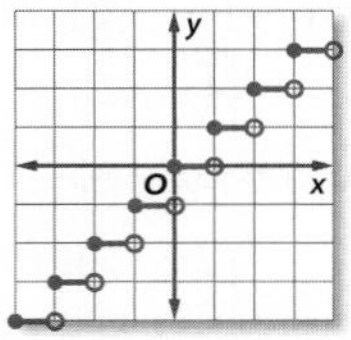	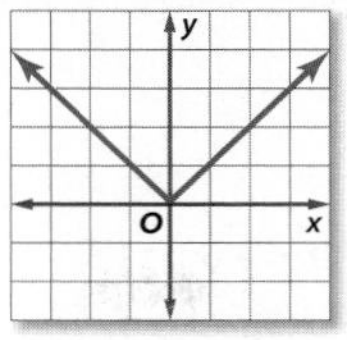	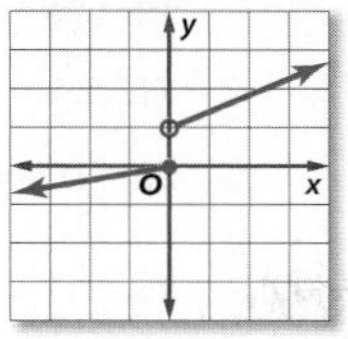

Check Your Understanding

= Step-by-Step Solutions begin on page R13.

Example 1 Graph each function. State the domain and range.

1. $f(x) = \frac{1}{2}[\![x]\!]$ **1–3. See margin.**
2. $g(x) = -[\![x]\!]$
3. $h(x) = [\![2x]\!]$

Example 2

4. **SHIPPING** Elan is ordering a gift for his dad online. The table shows the shipping rates. Graph the step function. **See margin.**

Order Total ($)	Shipping Cost ($)
0–15	3.99
15.01–30	5.99
30.01–50	6.99
50.01–75	7.99
75.01–100	8.99
Over $100	9.99

Examples 3–4 Graph each function. State the domain and range. **5–8. See Ch. 9 Answer Appendix.**

5. $f(x) = |x - 3|$
6. $g(x) = |2x + 4|$
7. $f(x) = \begin{cases} 2x - 1 \text{ if } x > -1 \\ -x \text{ if } x \leq -1 \end{cases}$
8. $g(x) = \begin{cases} -3x - 2 \text{ if } x > -2 \\ -x + 1 \text{ if } x \leq -2 \end{cases}$

Practice and Problem Solving

Extra Practice is on page R9.

Example 1 Graph each function. State the domain and range. **9–14. See Ch. 9 Answer Appendix.**

9. $f(x) = 3[\![x]\!]$
10. $f(x) = [\![-x]\!]$
11. $g(x) = -2[\![x]\!]$
12. $g(x) = [\![x]\!] + 3$
13. $h(x) = [\![x]\!] - 1$
14. $h(x) = \frac{1}{2}[\![x]\!] + 1$

Example 2

15. **CAB FARES** Lauren wants to take a taxi from a hotel to a friend's house. The rate is $3 plus $1.50 per mile after the first mile. Every fraction of a mile is rounded up to the next mile.
    a. Draw a graph to represent the cost of using a taxi cab. **See Ch. 9 Answer Appendix.**
    b. What is the cost if the trip is 8.5 miles long? **$15**

16. **MODELING** The United States Postal Service increases the rate of postage periodically. The table shows the cost to mail a letter weighing 1 ounce or less from 1995 through 2009. Draw a step graph to represent the data. **See Ch. 9 Answer Appendix.**

Year	1995	1999	2001	2002	2006	2007	2008	2009
Cost ($)	0.32	0.33	0.34	0.37	0.39	0.41	0.42	0.44

Differentiated Homework Options

Level	Assignment	Two-Day Option	
AL Basic	9–30, 55, 59, 61–79	9–29 odd, 61–64	10–30 even, 55, 59, 65–79
OL Core	9–35 odd, 37–47, 49, 51, 53–55, 59, 61–79	9–30, 61–64	31–55, 59, 65–79
BL Advanced	31–73, (optional: 74–79)		

3 Practice

Formative Assessment

Use Exercises 1–8 to check for understanding.

Use the chart at the bottom of this page to customize assignments for your students.

Additional Answers

1. 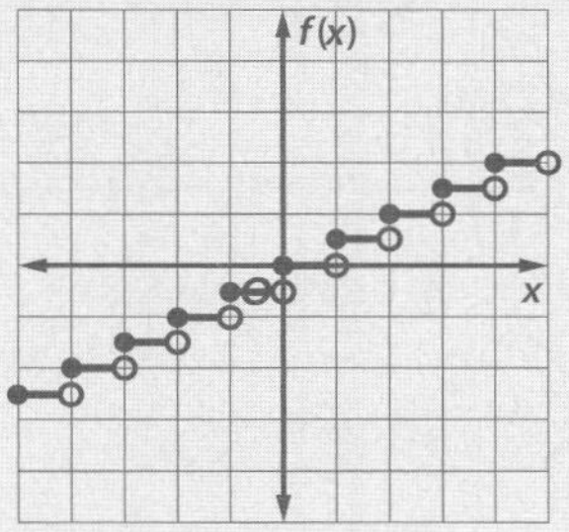

D = all real numbers;
R = all integer multiples of 0.5

2. 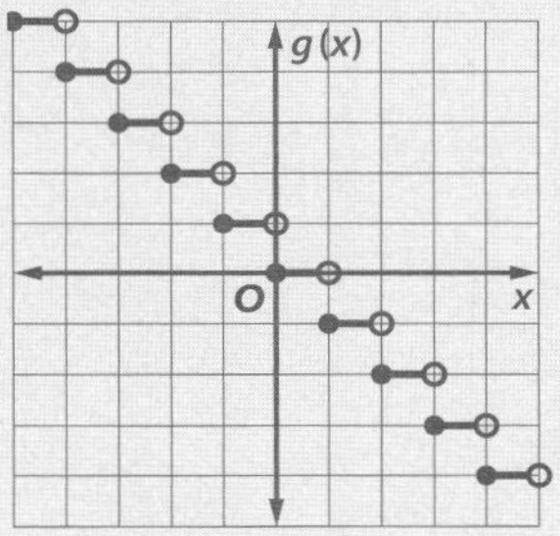

D = all real numbers;
R = all integers

3. 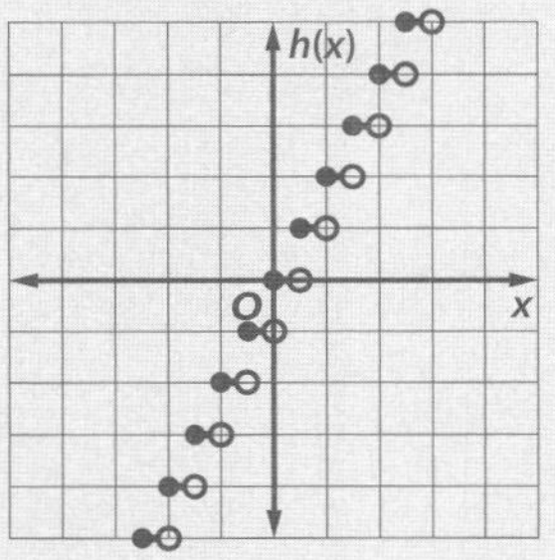

D = all real numbers;
R = all integers

4. 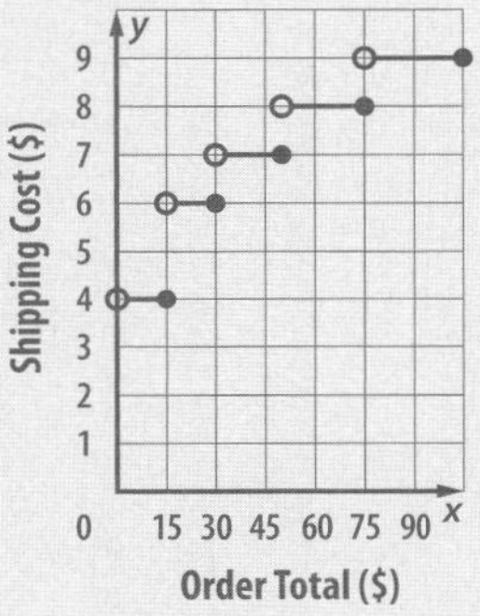

Exercise Alert

Grid Paper For Exercises 1–30, 37, 42–54, and 60, students will need grid paper.

Additional Answer

37. 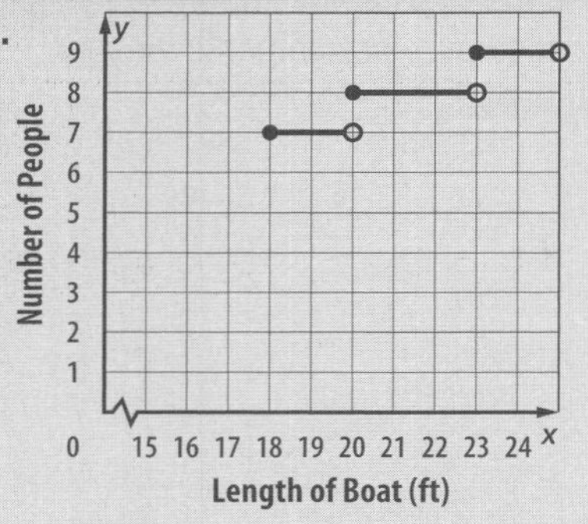

Examples 3–4 **Graph each function. State the domain and range.** 17–30. See Ch. 9 Answer Appendix.

17. $f(x) = |2x - 1|$

18. $f(x) = |x + 5|$

19. $g(x) = |-3x - 5|$

20. $g(x) = |-x - 3|$

21. $f(x) = \left|\frac{1}{2}x - 2\right|$

22. $f(x) = \left|\frac{1}{3}x + 2\right|$

23. $g(x) = |x + 2| + 3$

24. $g(x) = |2x - 3| + 1$

25. $f(x) = \begin{cases} \frac{1}{2}x - 1 \text{ if } x > 3 \\ -2x + 3 \text{ if } x \leq 3 \end{cases}$

26. $f(x) = \begin{cases} 2x - 5 \text{ if } x > 1 \\ 4x - 3 \text{ if } x \leq 1 \end{cases}$

27. $f(x) = \begin{cases} 2x + 3 \text{ if } x \geq -3 \\ -\frac{1}{3}x + 1 \text{ if } x < -3 \end{cases}$

28. $f(x) = \begin{cases} 3x + 4 \text{ if } x \geq 1 \\ x + 3 \text{ if } x < 1 \end{cases}$

29. $f(x) = \begin{cases} 3x + 2 \text{ if } x > -1 \\ -\frac{1}{2}x - 3 \text{ if } x \leq -1 \end{cases}$

30. $f(x) = \begin{cases} 2x + 1 \text{ if } x < -2 \\ -3x - 1 \text{ if } x \geq -2 \end{cases}$

B **Determine the domain and range of each function.**

31. 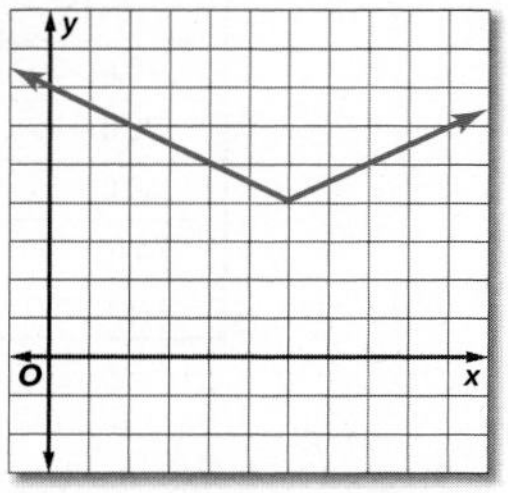

D = all real numbers; R = $y \geq 4$

32. 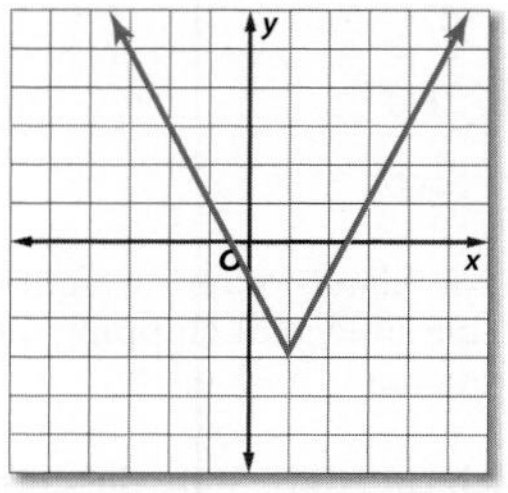

D = all real numbers; R = $y \geq -3$

33. 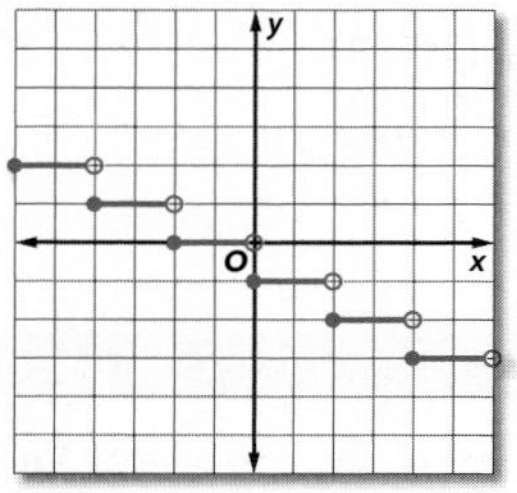

D = all real numbers; R = all integers

34. 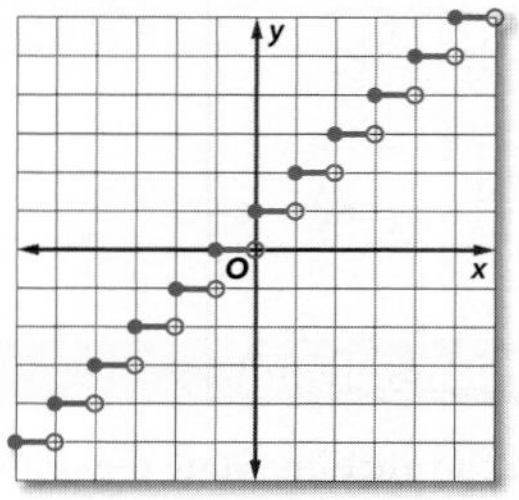

D = all real numbers; R = all integers

35. 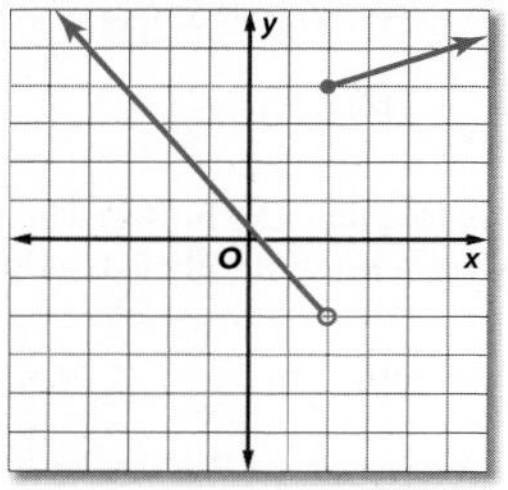

D = all real numbers; R = $y > -2$

36. 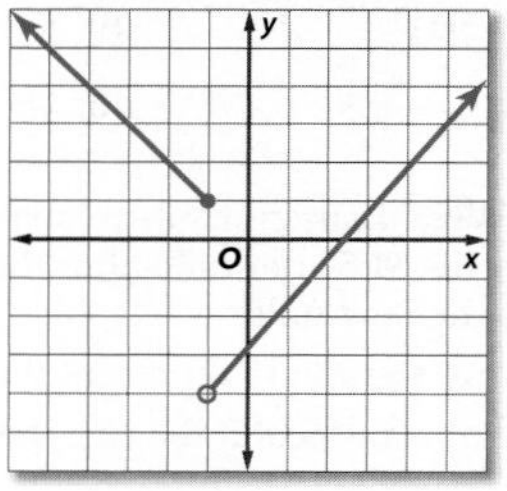

D = all real numbers; R = $y > -4$

37. BOATING According to Boat Minnesota, the maximum number of people that can safely ride in a boat is determined by the boat's length and width. The table shows some guidelines for the length of a boat that is 6 feet wide. Graph this relation. See margin.

Length of Boat (ft)	18–19	20–22	23–24
Number of People	7	8	9

Differentiated Instruction AL OL

If students have trouble picturing the graphs of special functions,

Then have students draw a large coordinate grid on three sheets of inch-grid paper. Students should use scissors, tape or glue, and straws to model the general shape of a step function, an absolute value function, and a piecewise-defined function. Have students label each type of graph.

For Exercises 38–41, match each graph to one of the following equations.

A	B	C	D
$y = 2x - 1$	$y = [\![2x]\!] - 1$	$y = \lvert 2x \rvert - 1$	$y = \begin{cases} 2x + 1 \text{ if } x > 0 \\ -2x + 1 \text{ if } x \leq 0 \end{cases}$

38. 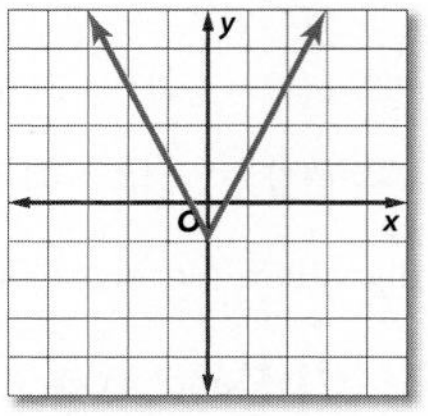 C

39. 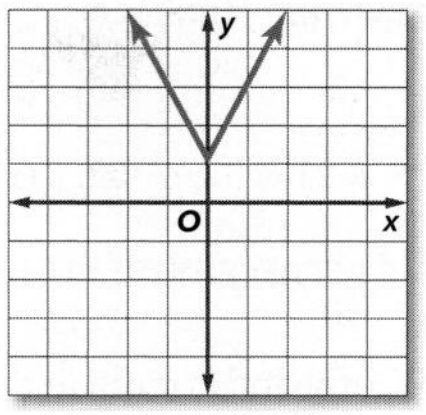 D

40. 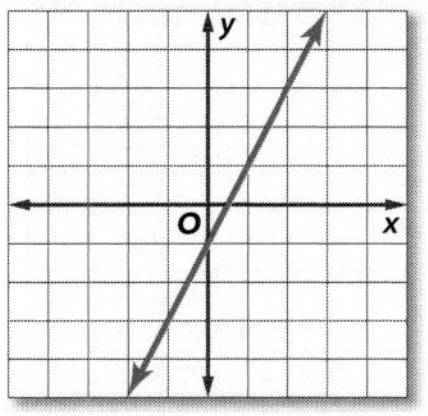 A

41. 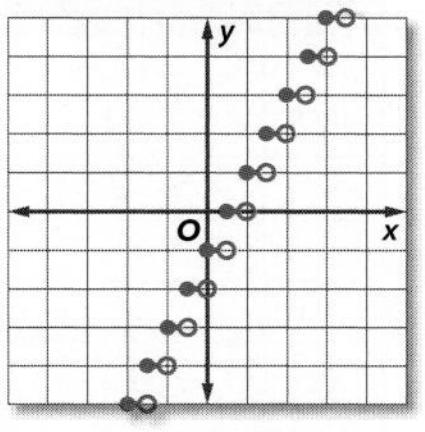 B

42. **CAR LEASE** As part of Marcus' leasing agreement, he will be charged \$0.20 per mile for each mile over 12,000. Any fraction of a mile is rounded up to the next mile. Make a step graph to represent the cost of going over the mileage. See margin.

43 **BASEBALL** A baseball team is ordering T-shirts with the team logo on the front and the players' names on the back. For an order of 10 shirts or less, a graphic design store charges \$10 to set up the artwork plus \$10 per shirt, \$4 each for the team logo, and \$2 to print the last name for an order of 10 shirts or less. For orders of 11–20 shirts, a 5% discount is given. For orders of more than 20 shirts, a 10% discount is given.

a. Organize the information into a table. Include a column showing the total order price for each size order. See Ch. 9 Answer Appendix.

b. Write an equation representing the total price for an order of x shirts.

c. Graph the piecewise relation. See Ch. 9 Answer Appendix.

44. Consider the function $f(x) = \lvert 2x + 3 \rvert$. a–c. See Ch. 9 Answer Appendix.

a. Make a table of values where x is all integers from -5 to 5, inclusive.

b. Plot the points on a coordinate grid.

c. Graph the function.

43b. $y = \begin{cases} 10 + 16x \text{ if } 1 \leq x \leq 10 \\ 9.50 + 15.20x \text{ if } 10 < x \leq 20 \\ 9 + 14.40x \text{ if } x > 20 \end{cases}$

45. Consider the function $f(x) = \lvert 2x \rvert + 3$. a–d. See Ch. 9 Answer Appendix.

a. Make a table of values where x is all integers from -5 to 5, inclusive.

b. Plot the points on a coordinate grid.

c. Graph the function.

d. Describe how this graph is different from the graph in Exercise 44.

Additional Answer

42.

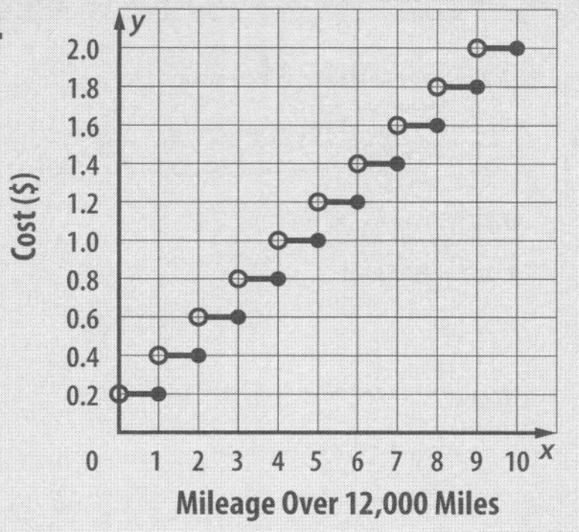

Differentiated Instruction OL BL

Extension Ask students to compare the graph of $f(x) = x$ to the graph of $f(x) = [\![x]\!]$ and the graph of $f(x) = \lvert x \rvert$ to the graph of $f(x) = \lvert [\![x]\!] \rvert$.

$f(x) = x$:

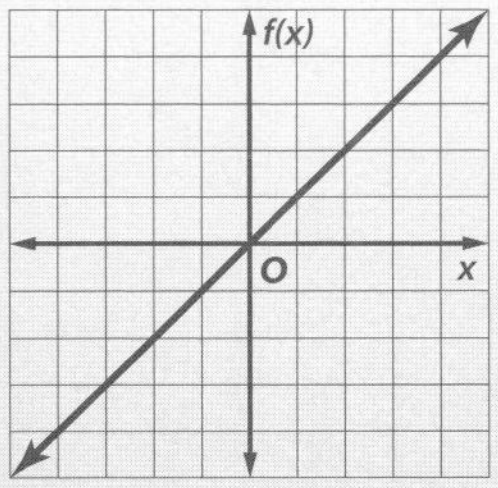

$f(x) = [\![x]\!]$:

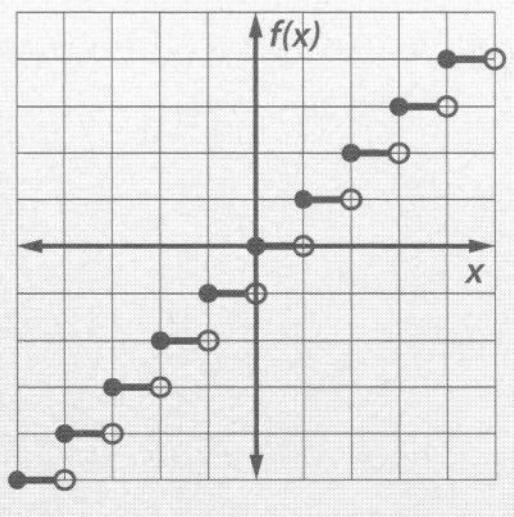

$f(x) = \lvert x \rvert$:

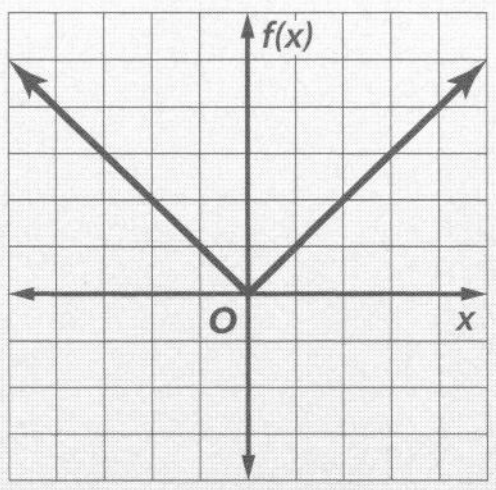

$f(x) = \lvert [\![x]\!] \rvert$:

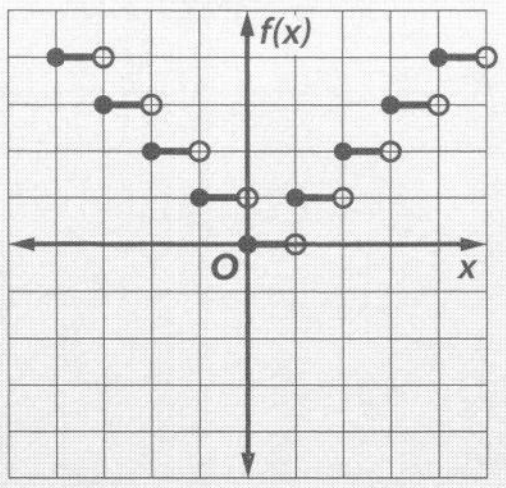

Study Guide and Intervention

AL OL ELL

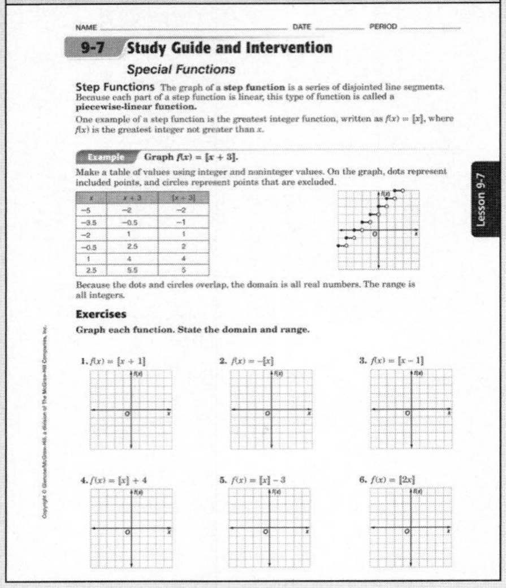
NAME ______ DATE ______ PERIOD ______

9-7 Study Guide and Intervention

Special Functions

Step Functions The graph of a **step function** is a series of disjointed line segments. Because each part of a step function is linear, this type of function is called a **piecewise-linear function**.

One example of a step function is the greatest integer function, written as $f(x) = [\![x]\!]$, where $f(x)$ is the greatest integer not greater than x.

Example Graph $f(x) = [\![x + 3]\!]$.

Make a table of values using integer and noninteger values. On the graph, dots represent included points, and circles represent points that are excluded.

x	$x + 3$	$[\![x + 3]\!]$
−5	−2	−2
−3.5	−0.5	−1
−2	1	1
−0.5	2.5	2
1	4	4
2.5	5.5	5

Because the dots and circles overlap, the domain is all real numbers. The range is all integers.

Exercises

Graph each function. State the domain and range.

1. $f(x) = [\![x + 1]\!]$ 2. $f(x) = -[\![x]\!]$ 3. $f(x) = [\![x - 1]\!]$

4. $f(x) = [\![x]\!] + 4$ 5. $f(x) = [\![x]\!] - 3$ 6. $f(x) = [\![2x]\!]$

Lesson 9-7

Practice

AL OL BL ELL

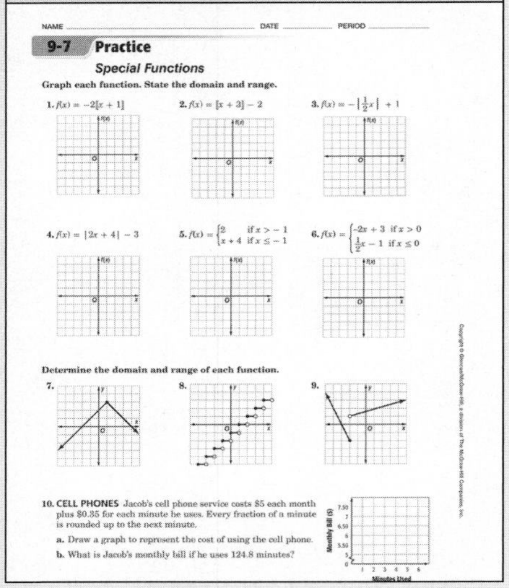
NAME ______ DATE ______ PERIOD ______

9-7 Practice

Special Functions

Graph each function. State the domain and range.

1. $f(x) = -2[\![x + 1]\!]$ 2. $f(x) = [\![x + 3]\!] - 2$ 3. $f(x) = -\left|\frac{1}{2}x\right| + 1$

4. $f(x) = |2x + 4| - 3$ 5. $f(x) = \begin{cases} 2 & \text{if } x > -1 \\ x + 4 & \text{if } x \le -1 \end{cases}$ 6. $f(x) = \begin{cases} -2x + 3 & \text{if } x > 0 \\ \frac{1}{2}x - 1 & \text{if } x \le 0 \end{cases}$

Determine the domain and range of each function.

7. 8. 9.

10. **CELL PHONES** Jacob's cell phone service costs $5 each month plus $0.35 for each minute he uses. Every fraction of a minute is rounded up to the next minute.

a. Draw a graph to represent the cost of using the cell phone.

b. What is Jacob's monthly bill if he uses 124.8 minutes?

Word Problem Practice

AL OL BL ELL

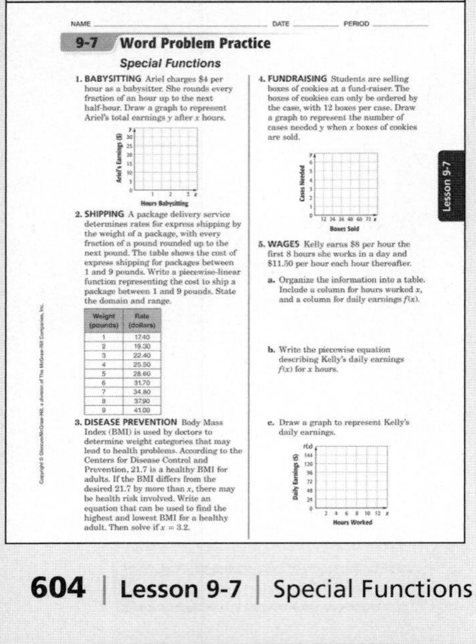
NAME ______ DATE ______ PERIOD ______

9-7 Word Problem Practice

Special Functions

1. **BABYSITTING** Ariel charges $4 per hour as a babysitter. She rounds every fraction of an hour up to the next half-hour. Draw a graph to represent Ariel's total earnings y after x hours.

2. **SHIPPING** A package delivery service determines rates for express shipping by the weight of a package, with every fraction of a pound rounded up to the next pound. The table shows the cost of express shipping for packages between 1 and 9 pounds. Write a piecewise-linear function representing the cost to ship a package between 1 and 9 pounds. State the domain and range.

Weight (pounds)	Rate (dollars)
1	17.40
2	19.30
3	22.40
4	25.50
5	28.60
6	31.70
7	34.80
8	37.90
9	41.00

3. **DISEASE PREVENTION** Body Mass Index (BMI) is used by doctors to determine weight categories that may lead to health problems. According to the Centers for Disease Control and Prevention, 21.7 is a healthy BMI for adults. If the BMI differs from the desired 21.7 by more than x, there may be health risk involved. Write an equation that can be used to find the highest and lowest BMI for a healthy adult. Then solve if $x = 3.2$.

4. **FUNDRAISING** Students are selling boxes of cookies at a fund-raiser. The boxes of cookies can only be ordered by the case, with 12 boxes per case. Draw a graph to represent the number of cases needed y when x boxes of cookies are sold.

5. **WAGES** Kelly earns $8 per hour the first 8 hours she works in a day and $11.50 per hour each hour thereafter.

a. Organize the information into a table. Include a column for hours worked x, and a column for daily earnings $f(x)$.

b. Write the piecewise equation describing Kelly's daily earnings $f(x)$ for x hours.

c. Draw a graph to represent Kelly's daily earnings.

Lesson 9-7

46. **DANCE** A local studio owner will teach up to four students by herself. Her instructors can teach up to 5 students each. Draw a step function graph that best describes the number of instructors needed for the different numbers of students. **See margin.**

47. **THEATERS** A community theater will only perform a show if there are at least 250 pre-sale ticket requests. Additional performances will be added for each 250 requests after that. Draw a step function graph that best describes this situation. **See margin.**

C **Graph each function.** **48–53. See Ch. 9 Answer Appendix.**

48. $f(x) = \frac{1}{2}|x| + 2$ 49. $g(x) = \frac{1}{3}|x| + 4$ 50. $h(x) = -2|x - 3| + 2$

51. $f(x) = -4|x + 2| - 3$ 52. $g(x) = -\frac{2}{3}|x + 6| - 1$ 53. $h(x) = -\frac{3}{4}|x - 8| + 1$

54. **MULTIPLE REPRESENTATIONS** In this problem, you will explore piecewise linear functions.

a. **Tabular** Copy and complete the table of values for $f(x) = |[\![x]\!]|$ and $g(x) = [\![|x|]\!]$.

x	$[\![x]\!]$	$f(x) = \lvert[\![x]\!]\rvert$	$\lvert x\rvert$	$g(x) = [\![\lvert x\rvert]\!]$
−3	−3	3	3	3
−2.5	**−3**	**3**	**2.5**	**2**
−2	**−2**	**2**	**2**	**2**
0	**0**	**0**	**0**	**0**
0.5	**0**	**0**	**0.5**	**0**
1	**1**	**1**	**1**	**1**
1.5	**1**	**1**	**1.5**	**1**

54c. When x is nonnegative, the graphs have the same y-values. The graphs have different y-values for the negative x-values.

b. **Graphical** Graph each function on a coordinate plane. **See Ch. 9 Answer Appendix.**

c. **Analytical** Compare and contrast the graphs of $f(x)$ and $g(x)$.

H.O.T. Problems Use Higher-Order Thinking Skills

55. **REASONING** Does the piecewise relation $y = \begin{cases} -2x + 4 \text{ if } x \ge 2 \\ -\frac{1}{2}x - 1 \text{ if } x \le 4 \end{cases}$ represent a function? Why or why not? **See margin.**

SENSE-MAKING Refer to the graph.

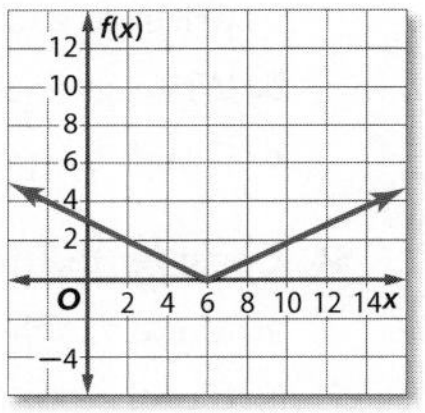

56. Write an absolute value function that represents the graph. $f(x) = \left|\frac{1}{2}x - 3\right|$

57. Write a piecewise function to represent the graph. **57.** $f(x) = \begin{cases} \frac{1}{2}x - 3 \text{ if } x > 6 \\ -\frac{1}{2}x + 3 \text{ if } x \le 6 \end{cases}$

58. What are the domain and range? **58. D = all real numbers; R = $f(x) \ge 0$**

59. **WRITING IN MATH** Compare and contrast the graphs of absolute value, step, and piecewise-defined functions with the graphs of quadratic and exponential functions. Discuss the domains, ranges, maxima, minima, and symmetry. **See margin.**

60. **CHALLENGE** A bicyclist travels up and down a hill with a vertical cross section that can be modeled by $y = -\frac{1}{4}|x - 400| + 100$, where x and y are measured in feet.

a. If $0 \le x \le 800$, find the slope for the uphill portion of the trip and downhill portion of the trip. **$\frac{1}{4}$ going up; $-\frac{1}{4}$ going down**

b. Graph this function. What are the domain and range?
See Ch. 9 Answer Appendix for graph; D = $0 \le x \le 800$; R = $0 \le y \le 100$

Enrichment

OL BL

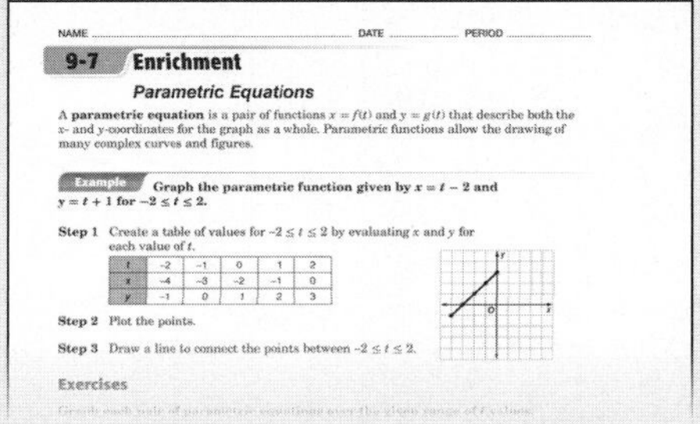
NAME ______ DATE ______ PERIOD ______

9-7 Enrichment

Parametric Equations

A **parametric equation** is a pair of functions $x = f(t)$ and $y = g(t)$ that describe both the x- and y-coordinates for the graph as a whole. Parametric functions allow the drawing of many complex curves and figures.

Example Graph the parametric function given by $x = t - 2$ and $y = t + 1$ for $-2 \le t \le 2$.

Step 1 Create a table of values for $-2 \le t \le 2$ by evaluating x and y for each value of t.

t	−2	−1	0	1	2
x	−4	−3	−2	−1	0
y	−1	0	1	2	3

Step 2 Plot the points.

Step 3 Draw a line to connect the points between $-2 \le t \le 2$.

Exercises

Multiple Representations

In Exercise 54, students use a table of values and a graph in the coordinate plane to compare and contrast the graphs of two piecewise functions.

Standardized Test Practice

61. Which equation represents a line that is perpendicular to the graph and passes through the point at (2, 0)? **C**

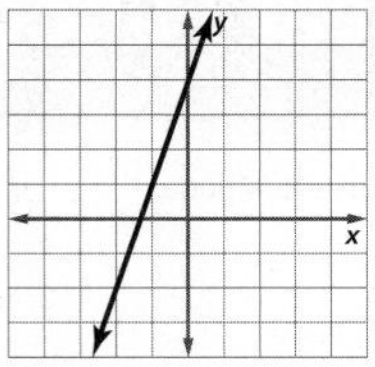

A $y = 3x - 6$

B $y = -3x + 6$

C $y = -\frac{1}{3}x + \frac{2}{3}$

D $y = \frac{1}{3}x - \frac{2}{3}$

62. A giant tortoise travels at a rate of 0.17 mile per hour. Which equation models the time t it would take the giant tortoise to travel 0.8 mile? **F**

F $t = \frac{0.8}{0.17}$

H $t = \frac{0.17}{0.8}$

G $t = (0.17)(0.8)$

J $0.8 = \frac{0.17}{t}$

63. GEOMETRY If $\triangle JKL$ is similar to $\triangle JNM$ what is the value a? **B**

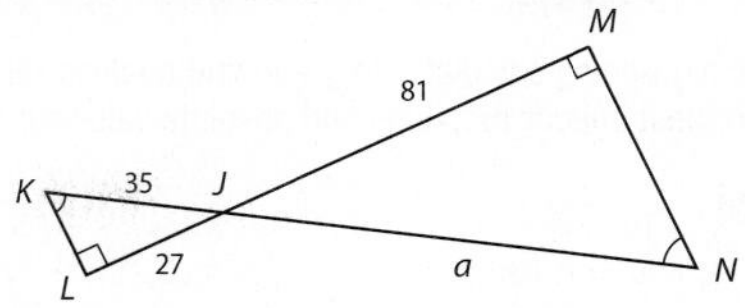

A 62.5

B 105

C 125

D 155.5

64. GRIDDED RESPONSE What is the difference in the value of $2.1(x + 3.2)$, when $x = 5$ and when $x = 3$? **4.2**

Spiral Review

Look for a pattern in each table of values to determine which model best describes the data. (Lesson 9-6)

65. linear

x	0	1	2	3	4
y	1	3	5	7	9

66. quadratic

x	−2	−1	0	1	2
y	5	2	1	2	5

67. exponential

x	−1	0	1	2	3
y	1	2	4	8	16

68. quadratic

x	5	6	7	8	9
y	−2.5	−1.5	1.5	6.5	13.5

69. TESTS Determine whether the graph at the right shows a *positive*, *negative*, or *no* correlation. If there is a correlation, describe its meaning. (Lesson 4-5) **See margin.**

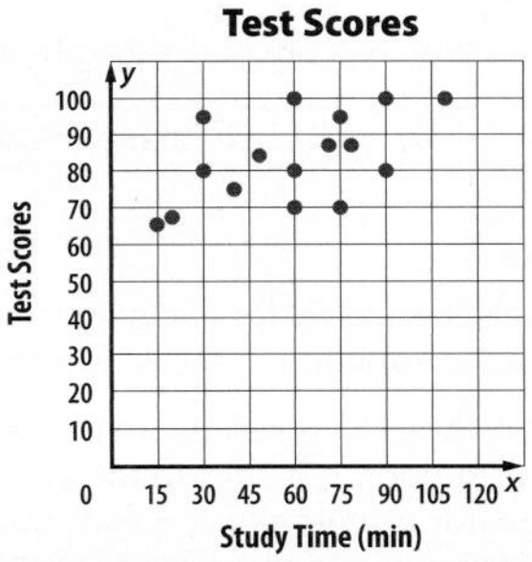

Suppose y varies directly as x. (Lesson 3-4)

70. If $y = 2.5$ when $x = 0.5$, find y when $x = 20$. **100**

71. If $y = -6.6$ when $x = 9.9$, find y when $x = 6.6$. **−4.4**

72. If $y = 2.6$ when $x = 0.25$, find y when $x = 1.125$. **11.7**

73. If $y = 6$ when $x = 0.6$, find x when $y = 12$. **1.2**

Skills Review

Evaluate each expression. If necessary, round to the nearest hundredth.

74. $\sqrt{9}$ **3**

75. $\sqrt{12}$ **3.46**

76. $\sqrt{4.5}$ **2.12**

77. $3\sqrt{16}$ **12**

78. $2\sqrt{10}$ **6.32**

79. $\sqrt{5} - 2$ **0.24**

4 Assess

Ticket Out the Door Write the function $f(x) = 25[\![x]\!]$ on the board. As the students leave the room, ask them to tell you a real-world situation that could be described by the function. For example, a piano tuner charges $25 for every hour or fraction of an hour.

Formative Assessment

Check for student understanding of Lesson 9-7.

Quiz 4, p. 50

Additional Answers

46.

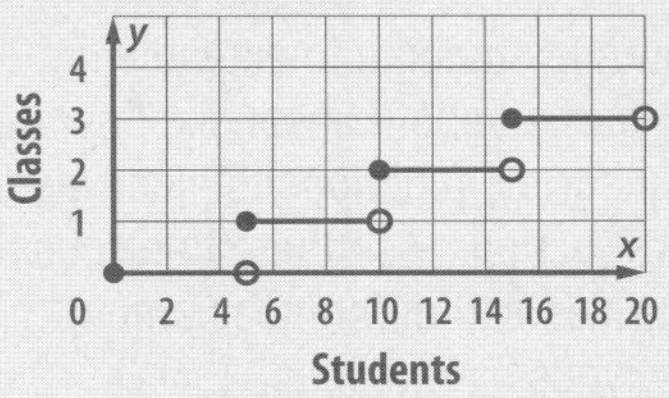

47.

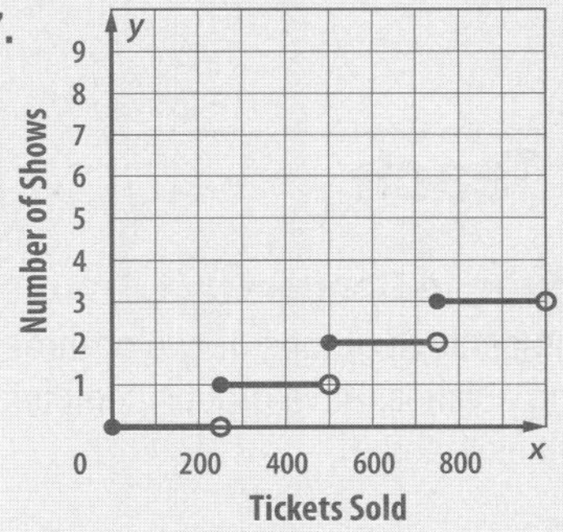

55. No; the pieces of the graph overlap vertically, so the graph fails the vertical line test.

59. Sample answer: The domain of absolute value, step, quadratic, and exponential functions is all real numbers, while some piecewise functions may not be defined for all real numbers. The range of absolute value, step, quadratic, and exponential functions is limited to a portion of the real numbers, but the range of a piecewise-defined function can be all real numbers. The graphs of absolute value and quadratic functions have either one maximum and no minima or one minimum and no maxima, and both have symmetry with respect to a vertical line through the point where this maximum or minimum occurs. The graphs of absolute value, quadratic, and exponential functions have no breaks or jumps, while graphs of step functions always do and graphs of piecewise-defined functions sometimes do.

69. Positive; it means the more you study, the better your test score.

1 Focus

Objective Use a graphing calculator to investigate piecewise-linear functions.

Materials for Each Student

- T1–83/84 Plus or other graphing calculator

Teaching Tips

Students may be unfamiliar with how to select the dot mode and the correct viewing window for their calculators. Demonstrate the steps needed as students follow along on their own calculators.

Encourage students to extend what they have learned about linear, exponential, and quadratic functions to piecewise-linear functions. Ask them to discuss similarities and differences among these types of functions.

2 Teach

Working in Cooperative Groups

Put students in groups of two or three, mixing abilities. Have groups complete Activities 1 and 2.

Ask:

- What viewing window setting do you need for Activities 1 and 2? [−10, 10] scl: 1 by [−10, 10] scl:1
- In Activity 2, how does the y-intercept of the graph of a function in the form $y = |x| \pm k$ relate to the constant in each function? The y-intercept of a function's graph is the same as the value of k in each function.

Practice Have students complete Exercises 1–5.

3 Assess

Formative Assessment

Use Activity 1 to assess whether students understand the difference between a piecewise-linear function and a linear function.

EXTEND 9-7

Graphing Technology Lab
Piecewise-Linear Functions

You can use a graphing calculator to graph and analyze various piecewise functions, including greatest integer functions and absolute value functions.

1A. The graph of $f(x) = x$ is a line that passes through the left endpoints of the segments that comprise the graph of $f(x) = [\![x]\!]$.

Activity 1 Greatest Integer Functions

Graph $f(x) = [\![x]\!]$ in the standard viewing window.

The calculator may need to be changed to dot mode for the function to graph correctly. Press MODE then use the arrow and ENTER keys to select **DOT**.

Enter the equation in the **Y=** list. Then graph the equation.

KEYSTROKES: Y= MATH ▶ 5 X,T,θ,n) ZOOM 6

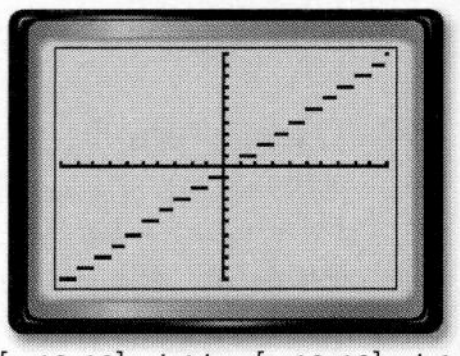

[−10, 10] scl: 1 by [−10, 10] scl: 1

1A. How does the graph of $f(x) = [\![x]\!]$ compare to the graph of $f(x) = x$?

1B. What are the domain and range of the function $f(x) = [\![x]\!]$? Explain. **D = all real numbers; R = all integers**

The graphs of piecewise functions are affected by changes in parameters.

2A. The graph of $y = |x| - 3$ is the graph of $y = |x|$, shifted 3 units down. The graph of $y = |x| + 1$ is the graph of $y = |x|$, shifted 1 unit up.

Activity 2 Absolute Value Functions

Graph $y = |x| - 3$ and $y = |x| + 1$ in the standard viewing window.

Enter the equations in the **Y=** list. Then graph.

KEYSTROKES: Y= MATH ▶ 1 X,T,θ,n) − 3 ENTER MATH ▶ 1 X,T,θ,n) + 1 ZOOM 6

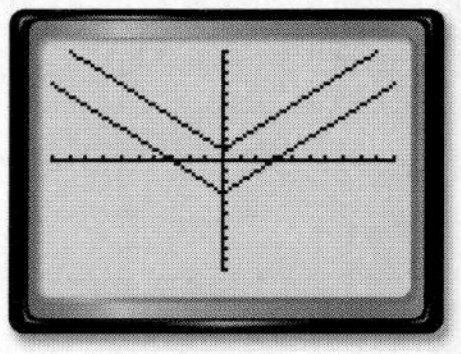

[−10, 10] scl: 1 by [−10, 10] scl: 1

2A. Compare and contrast the graphs to the graph of $y = |x|$.

2B. How does the value of k affect the graph of $y = |x| + k$?

2B. Sample answer: The value of k shifts the graph up k units if $k > 0$ and down $|k|$ units if $k < 0$.

Analyze the Results

1. A parking garage charges $4 for every hour or fraction of an hour. Is this situation modeled by a *linear* function or a *step* function? Explain your reasoning. **1. Step; the garage charges $4 for a portion of an hour.**
2. A maintenance technician is testing an elevator system. The technician starts the elevator at the fifth floor. It is sent to the ground floor, then back to the fifth floor. Assume the elevator travels at a constant rate. Should the height of the elevator be modeled by a step function or an absolute value function? Explain. **See margin.**

Because the points on a graph are solutions of its equation, the x-coordinates of points where $y = f(x)$ and $y = g(x)$ intersect are solutions of $f(x) = g(x)$. For example, the solution of $5x - 2 = |x|$ is the intersection of the graphs of $y = 5x - 2$ and $y = |x|$. Write each equation as a system of equations, and then use a graph or a table to solve it.

3. $5x - 2 = |x|$ **0.5**
4. $2|x - 2| = x - 1$ **$\frac{4}{3}$, 3**
5. $|4x + 2| = -|x| + 3$ **-1, $\frac{1}{5}$**

606 | Lesson 9-7 | Graphing Technology Lab: Piecewise-Linear Functions

From Concrete to Abstract

Have students write and graph an equation that would represent Exercise 1. Ask students how the equation would change if the parking garage charged $8 for every hour or fraction of an hour. The equations would be $f(x) = -4[\![-x]\!]$ and $g(x) = -8[\![-x]\!]$.

Additional Answer

2. This situation is modeled by an absolute value function because the graph will consist of segments joined at their endpoints.

9 Study Guide and Review

Study Guide

KeyConcepts

Graphing Quadratic Functions (Lesson 9-1)

- A quadratic function can be described by an equation of the form $y = ax^2 + bx + c$, where $a \neq 0$.
- The axis of symmetry for the graph of $y = ax^2 + bx + c$, where $a \neq 0$, is $x = -\frac{b}{2a}$.

Solving Quadratic Equations (Lessons 9-2, 9-4, and 9-5)

- Quadratic equations can be solved by graphing. The solutions are the x-intercepts or zeros of the related quadratic function.
- Quadratic equations can be solved by completing the square. To complete the square for $x^2 + bx$, find $\frac{1}{2}$ of b, square this result, and then add the result to $x^2 + bx$.
- Quadratic equations can be solved by using the Quadratic Formula, $x = \frac{-b \pm \sqrt{b^2 - 4ac}}{2a}$.

Transformations of Quadratic Functions (Lesson 9-3)

- $f(x) = x^2 + c$ translates the graph up or down.
- $f(x) = ax^2$ compresses or expands the graph vertically.

Special Functions (Lesson 9-7)

- The greatest integer function is written as $f(x) = [\![x]\!]$, where $f(x)$ is the greatest integer not greater than x.
- The absolute value function is written as $f(x) = |x|$, where $f(x)$ is the distance from x to 0 on a number line.

FOLDABLES StudyOrganizer

Be sure the Key Concepts are noted in your Foldable.

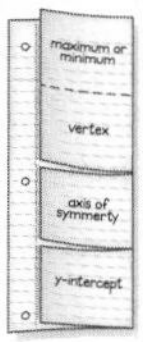

KeyVocabulary

absolute value function (p. 599)
axis of symmetry (p. 543)
completing the square (p. 574)
dilation (p. 566)
discriminant (p. 586)
double root (p. 556)
greatest integer function (p. 598)
maximum (p. 543)
minimum (p. 543)
parabola (p. 543)
piecewise-defined function (p. 599)
piecewise-linear function (p. 598)
Quadratic Formula (p. 583)
quadratic function (p. 543)
reflection (p. 566)
standard form (p. 543)
step function (p. 598)
transformation (p. 564)
translation (p. 564)
vertex (p. 543)

VocabularyCheck

State whether each sentence is ***true*** or ***false***. If *false*, replace the underlined term to make a true sentence.

1. The <u>axis of symmetry</u> of a quadratic function can be found by using the equation $x = -\frac{b}{2a}$. **true**
2. The <u>vertex</u> is the maximum or minimum point of a parabola. **true**
3. The graph of a quadratic function is a <u>straight line</u>. **false; parabola**
4. The graph of a quadratic function has a <u>maximum</u> if the coefficient of the x^2-term is positive. **false; minimum**
5. A quadratic equation with a graph that has two x-intercepts has <u>one</u> real root. **false; two**
6. The expression $b^2 - 4ac$ is called the <u>discriminant</u>. **true**
7. A function that is defined differently for different parts of its domain is called a <u>piecewise-defined function</u>. **true**
8. The <u>range</u> of the greatest integer function is the set of all real numbers. **false; domain**
9. The solutions of a quadratic equation are called <u>roots</u>. **true**
10. The graph of the parent function is <u>translated down</u> to form the graph of $f(x) = x^2 + 5$. **false; translated up 5 units**

Formative Assessment

KeyVocabulary The page reference after each word denotes where that term was first introduced. If students have difficulty answering questions 1–10, remind them that they can use these page references to refresh their memories about the vocabulary terms.

Summative Assessment

Vocabulary Test, p. 52

Vocabulary Review

Vocabulary Review provides students the opportunity to check their understanding of important concepts and terminology in an online game format.

FOLDABLES StudyOrganizer

Dinah Zike's Foldables®

Have students look through the chapter to make sure they have included examples in their Foldables for each lesson of the chapter. Suggest that students keep their Foldables handy while completing the Study Guide and Review pages. Point out that their Foldables can serve as a quick review when studying for the chapter test.

connectED.mcgraw-hill.com 607

Lesson-by-Lesson Review

Intervention If the given examples are not sufficient to review the topics covered by the questions, remind students that the lesson references tell them where to review that topic in their textbook.

Two-Day Option Have students complete the Lesson-by-Lesson Review. Then you can use McGraw-Hill eAssessment to customize another review worksheet that practices all the objectives of this chapter or only the objectives on which your students need more help.

Additional Answers

11a. minimum
11b. 0
11c. D = {all real numbers}; R = $\{y \mid y \geq 0\}$
12a. maximum
12b. 2.25
12c. D = {all real numbers}; R = $\{y \mid y \leq 2.25\}$
13a. minimum
13b. −4
13c. D = {all real numbers}; R = $\{y \mid y \geq -4\}$
14a. maximum
14b. 2
14c. D = {all real numbers}; R = $\{y \mid y \leq 2\}$

CHAPTER 9 Study Guide and Review *Continued*

Lesson-by-Lesson Review

9-1 Graphing Quadratic Functions

Consider each equation.

a. Determine whether the function has a *maximum* or *minimum* value.

b. State the maximum or minimum value.

c. What are the domain and range of the function?

11. $y = x^2 - 4x + 4$ **11–14. See margin.**

12. $y = -x^2 + 3x$

13. $y = x^2 - 2x - 3$

14. $y = -x^2 + 2$.

15. ROCKET A toy rocket is launched with an upward velocity of 32 feet per second. The equation $h = -16t^2 + 32t$ gives the height of the ball t seconds after it is launched.

a. Determine whether the function has a *maximum* or *minimum* value. **maximum**

b. State the maximum or minimum value. **16**

c. State a reasonable domain and range for this situation. **D = $\{t \mid 0 \leq t \leq 2\}$; R = $\{h \mid 0 \leq h \leq 16\}$**

Example 1

Consider $f(x) = x^2 + 6x + 5$.

a. Determine whether the function has a *maximum* or *minimum* value.

For $f(x) = x^2 + 6x + 5$, $a = 1$, $b = 6$, and $c = 5$.

Because a is positive, the graph opens up, so the function has a minimum value.

b. State the *maximum* or *minimum* value of the function.

The minimum value is the y-coordinate of the vertex.

The x-coordinate of the vertex is $\frac{-b}{2a}$ or $\frac{-6}{2(1)}$ or -3.

$f(x) = x^2 + 6x + 5$ Original function

$f(-3) = (-3)^2 + 6(-3) + 5$ $x = -3$

$f(-3) = -4$ Simplify.

The minimum value is −4.

c. State the domain and range of the function.

The domain is all real numbers. The range is all real numbers greater than or equal to the minimum value, or $\{y \mid y \geq -4\}$.

9-2 Solving Quadratic Equations by Graphing

Solve each equation by graphing. If integral roots cannot be found, estimate the roots to the nearest tenth.

16. $x^2 - 3x - 4 = 0$ **−1, 4**

17. $-x^2 + 6x - 9 = 0$ **3**

18. $x^2 - x - 12 = 0$ **−3, 4**

19. $x^2 + 4x - 3 = 0$ **−4.6, 0.6**

20. $x^2 - 10x = -21$ **3, 7**

21. $6x^2 - 13x = 15$ **−0.8, 3**

22. NUMBER THEORY Find two numbers that have a sum of 2 and a product of −15. **−3 and 5**

Example 2

Solve $x^2 - x - 6 = 0$ by graphing.

Graph the related function $f(x) = x^2 - x - 6$.

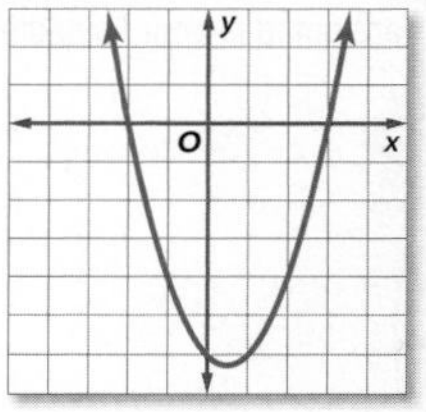

The x-intercepts of the graph appear to be at −2 and 3, so the solutions are −2 and 3.

608 | Chapter 9 | Study Guide and Review

9-3 Transformations of Quadratic Functions

Describe how the graph of each function is related to the graph of $f(x) = x^2$. 23–28. See margin.

23. $f(x) = x^2 + 8$

24. $f(x) = x^2 - 3$

25. $f(x) = 2x^2$

26. $f(x) = 4x^2 - 18$

27. $f(x) = \frac{1}{3}x^2$

28. $f(x) = \frac{1}{4}x^2$

29. Write an equation for the function shown in the graph. $y = 2x^2 - 3$

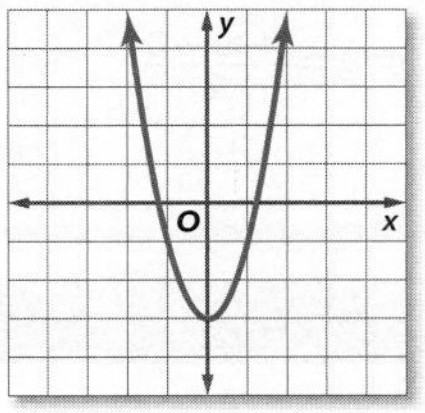

30. **PHYSICS** A ball is dropped off a cliff that is 100 feet high. The function $h = -16t^2 + 100$ models the height h of the ball after t seconds. Compare the graph of this function to the graph of $h = t^2$. See margin.

Example 3

Describe how the graph of $f(x) = x^2 - 2$ is related to the graph of $f(x) = x^2$.

The graph of $f(x) = x^2 + c$ represents a translation up or down of the parent graph.

Since $c = -2$, the translation is down.

So, the graph is translated down 2 units from the parent function.

Example 4

Write an equation for the function shown in the graph.

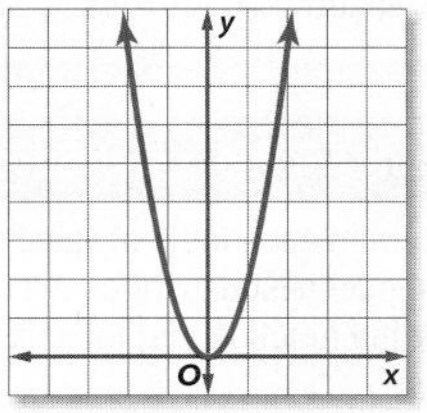

Since the graph opens upward, the leading coefficient must be positive. The parabola has not been translated up or down, so $c = 0$. Since the graph is stretched vertically, it must be of the form of $f(x) = ax^2$ where $a > 1$. The equation for the function is $y = 2x^2$.

9-4 Solving Quadratic Equations by Completing the Square

Solve each equation by completing the square. Round to the nearest tenth if necessary.

31. $x^2 + 6x + 9 = 16$ 1, −7

32. $-a^2 - 10a + 25 = 25$ 0, −10

33. $y^2 - 8y + 16 = 36$ 10, −2

34. $y^2 - 6y + 2 = 0$ 5.6, 0.4

35. $n^2 - 7n = 5$ −0.7, 7.7

36. $-3x^2 + 4 = 0$ −1.2, 1.2

37. **NUMBER THEORY** Find two numbers that have a sum of −2 and a product of −48. −8, 6

Example 5

Solve $x^2 - 16x + 32 = 0$ by completing the square. Round to the nearest tenth if necessary.

Isolate the x^2- and x-terms. Then complete the square and solve.

$x^2 - 16x + 32 = 0$	Original equation
$x^2 - 16x = -32$	Isolate the x^2- and x-terms.
$x^2 - 16x + 64 = -32 + 64$	Complete the square.
$(x - 8)^2 = 32$	Factor.
$x - 8 = \pm\sqrt{32}$	Take the square root.
$x = 8 \pm \sqrt{32}$	Add 8 to each side.
$x = 8 \pm 4\sqrt{2}$	Simplify.

The solutions are about 2.3 and 13.7.

Additional Answers

23. shifted up 8 units

24. shifted down 3 units

25. vertical stretch

26. vertical stretch and shifted down 18 units

27. vertical compression

28. vertical compression

30. reflected across the x-axis, vertically stretched and shifted up 100 units

connectED.mcgraw-hill.com 609

Anticipation Guide

Have students complete the Chapter 9 Anticipation Guide and discuss how their responses have changed now that they have completed Chapter 9.

Additional Answers

48. D = all real numbers; R = all integers

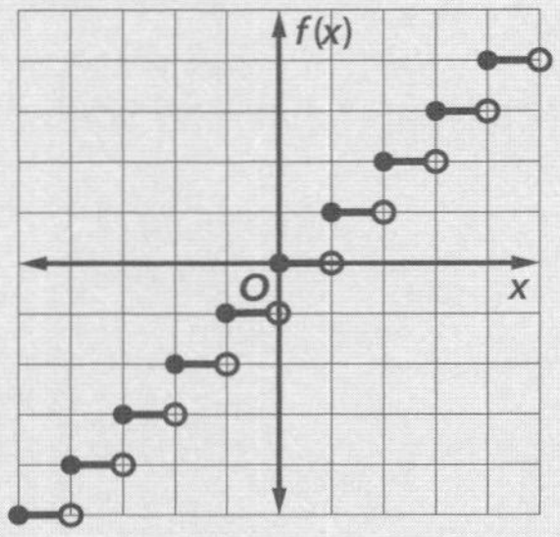

49. D = all real numbers; R = all integers

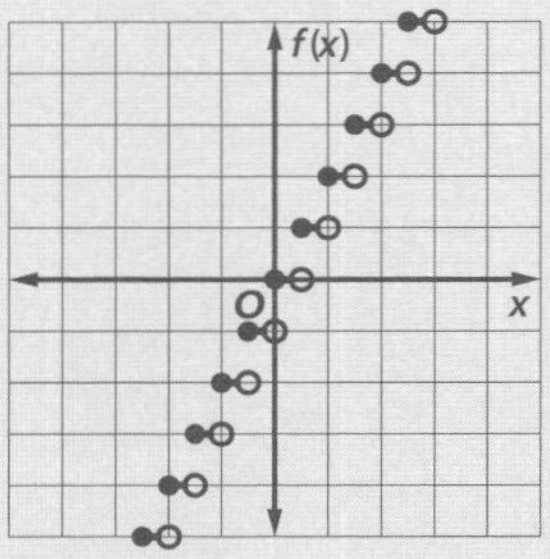

50. D = all real numbers; R = $f(x) \geq 0$

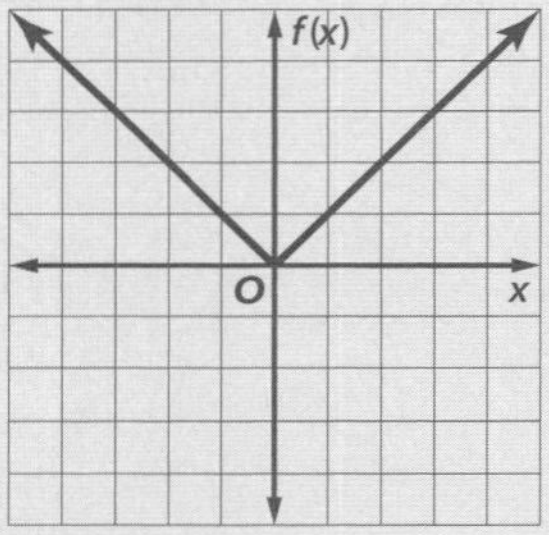

CHAPTER 9 Study Guide and Review *Continued*

9-5 Solving Quadratic Equations by Using the Quadratic Formula

Solve each equation by using the Quadratic Formula. Round to the nearest tenth if necessary.

38. $x^2 - 8x = 20$ **−2, 10**

39. $21x^2 + 5x - 7 = 0$ **−0.7, 0.5**

40. $d^2 - 5d + 6 = 0$ **2, 3**

41. $2f^2 + 7f - 15 = 0$ **−5, 1.5**

42. $2h^2 + 8h + 3 = 3$ **−4, 0**

43. $4x^2 + 4x = 15$ **−2.5, 1.5**

44. **GEOMETRY** The area of a square can be quadrupled by increasing the side length and width by 4 inches. What is the side length? **4 in.**

Example 6

Solve $x^2 + 10x + 9 = 0$ by using the Quadratic Formula.

$x = \frac{-b \pm \sqrt{b^2 - 4ac}}{2a}$ Quadratic Formula

$= \frac{-10 \pm \sqrt{10^2 - 4(1)(9)}}{2(1)}$ $a = 1, b = 10, c = 9$

$= \frac{-10 \pm \sqrt{64}}{2}$ Simplify.

$x = \frac{-10 + 8}{2}$ or $x = \frac{-10 - 8}{2}$ Separate the solutions.

$= -1$ $= -9$ Simplify.

9-6 Analyzing Functions with Successive Differences

Look for a pattern in each table of values to determine which kind of model best describes the data. Then write an equation for the function that models the data.

45. **quadratic; $y = 3x^2$**

x	0	1	2	3	4
y	0	3	12	27	48

46. **exponential; $y = 2^x$**

x	0	1	2	3	4
y	1	2	4	8	16

47. **quadratic; $y = -x^2$**

x	0	1	2	3	4
y	0	−1	−4	−9	−16

Example 7

Determine the model that best describes the data. Then write an equation for the function that models the data.

x	0	1	2	3	4
y	3	4	5	6	7

Step 1 First differences: 3 4 5 6 7 → 1 1 1 1

A linear function models the data.

Step 2 The slope is 1 and the y-intercept is 3, so the equation is $y = x + 3$.

9-7 Special Functions

Graph each function. State the domain and range. **48–53. See margin.**

48. $f(x) = [\![x]\!]$

49. $f(x) = [\![2x]\!]$

50. $f(x) = |x|$

51. $f(x) = |2x - 2|$

52. $f(x) = \begin{cases} x - 2 \text{ if } x < 1 \\ 3x \text{ if } x \geq 1 \end{cases}$

53. $f(x) = \begin{cases} 2x - 3 \text{ if } x \leq 2 \\ x + 1 \text{ if } x > 2 \end{cases}$

Example 8

Graph $f(x) = |x + 3|$. State the domain and range.

x	f(x)
−5	2
−4	1
−3	0
−2	1
−1	2

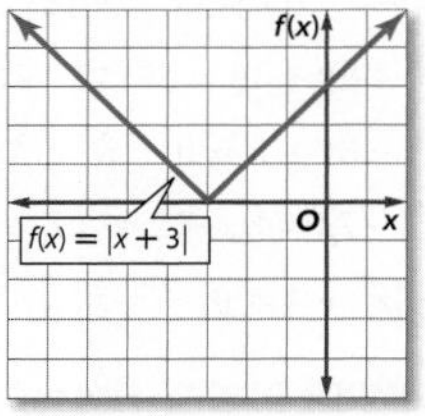

The domain is all real numbers, and the range is $f(x) \geq 0$.

51. D = all real numbers; R = $f(x) \geq 0$

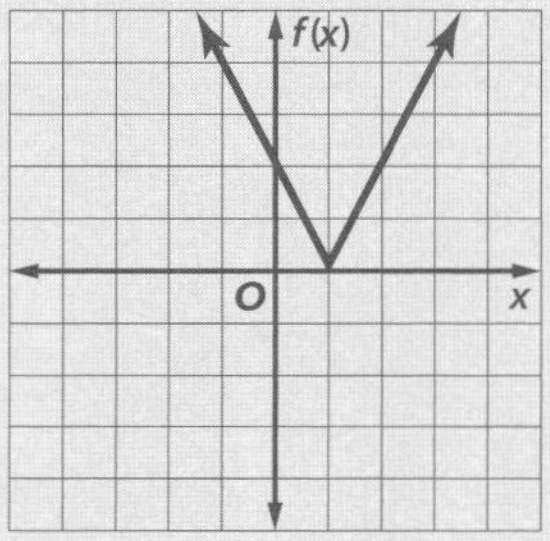

52. D = all real numbers; R = $f(x) < -1$ or $f(x) \geq 3$

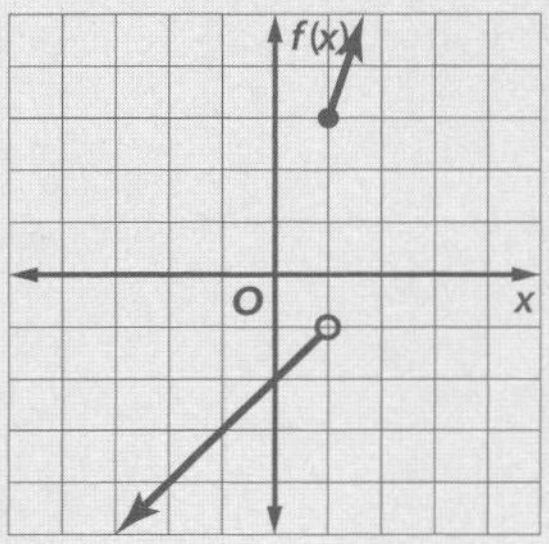

53. D = all real numbers; R = $f(x) \leq -1$ or $f(x) > 3$

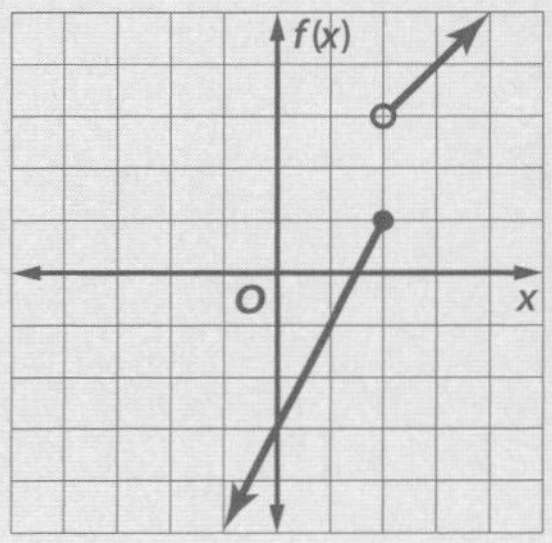

610 | Chapter 9 | Study Guide and Review

CHAPTER 9 Practice Test

Use a table of values to graph the following functions. State the domain and range.

1. $y = x^2 + 2x + 5$ **1–2. See Ch. 9 Answer Appendix.**
2. $y = 2x^2 - 3x + 1$

Consider $y = x^2 - 7x + 6$.

3. Determine whether the function has a *maximum* or *minimum* value. **minimum**
4. State the maximum or minimum value. **−6.25**
5. What are the domain and range? **D = {all real numbers}; R = {y| y ≥ −6.25}**

Solve each equation by graphing. If integral roots cannot be found, estimate the roots to the nearest tenth.

6. $x^2 + 7x + 10 = 0$ **−5, −2**
7. $x^2 - 5 = -3x$ **−4.2, 1.2**

Describe how the graph of each function is related to the graph of $f(x) = x^2$.

8. $g(x) = x^2 - 5$ **translated down 5 units**
9. $g(x) = -3x^2$ **reflected across the x-axis, stretched vertically**
10. $h(x) = \frac{1}{2}x^2 + 4$ **compressed vertically and translated 4 units up**
11. **MULTIPLE CHOICE** Which is an equation for the function shown in the graph? **D**

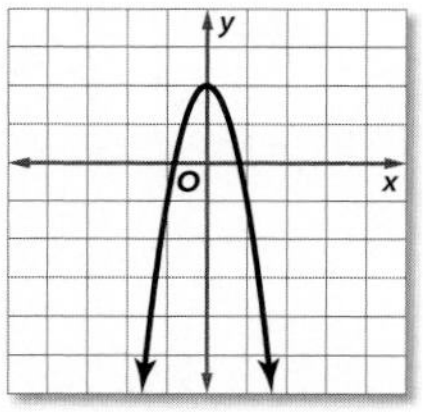

A $y = -3x^2$

B $y = 3x^2 + 1$

C $y = x^2 + 2$

D $y = -3x^2 + 2$

Solve each equation by completing the square.

12. $x^2 + 2x + 5 = 0$ **no real solution**
13. $x^2 - x - 6 = 0$ **−2, 3**
14. $2x^2 - 36 = -6x$ **−6, 3**

Solve each equation by using the Quadratic Formula. Round to the nearest tenth if necessary.

15. $x^2 - x - 30 = 0$ **−5, 6**
16. $x^2 - 10x = -15$ **1.8, 8.2**
17. $2x^2 + x - 15 = 0$ **2.5, −3**
18. **BASEBALL** Elias hits a baseball into the air. The equation $h = -16t^2 + 60t + 3$ models the height h in feet of the ball after t seconds. How long is the ball in the air? **about 3.8 seconds**
19. Graph {(−2, 4), (−1, 1), (0, 0), (1, 1), (2, 4)}. Determine whether the ordered pairs represent a *linear function*, a *quadratic function*, or an *exponential function*. **See margin.**
20. Look for a pattern in the table to determine which kind of model best describes the data. **linear**

x	0	1	2	3	4
y	1	3	5	7	9

21. **CAR CLUB** The table shows the number of car club members for four consecutive years after it began.

Time (years)	0	1	2	3	4
Members	10	20	40	80	160

a. Determine which model best represents the data. **exponential**

b. Write a function that models the data. **$y = (10)2^x$**

c. Predict the number of car club members after 6 years. **640**

Graph each function. **22–25. See Ch. 9 Answer Appendix.**

22. $f(x) = |x - 1|$
23. $f(x) = -|2x|$
24. $f(x) = [\![x]\!]$
25. $f(x) = \begin{cases} 2x - 1 \text{ if } x < 2 \\ x - 3 \text{ if } x \geq 2 \end{cases}$
26. Determine the domain and range of the function graphed below.

D = all real numbers; R = y ≥ −2

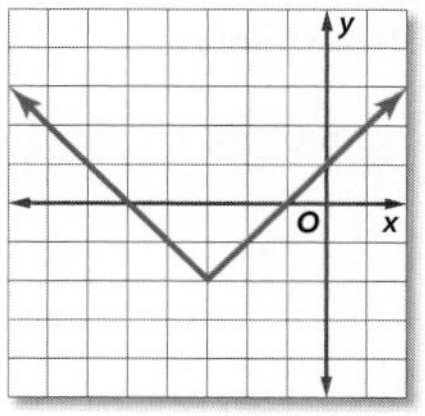

Summative Assessment

Use these alternate leveled chapter tests to differentiate assessment for your students.

Leveled Chapter 9 Tests

Form	Type	Level	Page(s)
1	MC	AL	53–54
2A	MC	OL	55–56
2B	MC	OL	57–58
2C	FR	OL	59–60
2D	FR	OL	61–62
3	FR	BL	63–64
Vocabulary Test			52
Extended-Response Test			65

MC = multiple-choice questions
FR = free-response questions

McGraw-Hill eAssessment Customize and create multiple versions of your chapter tests and their answer keys. All of the questions from the leveled chapter tests in the *Chapter 9 Resource Masters* are also available on McGraw-Hill eAssessment.

Additional Answer

19.

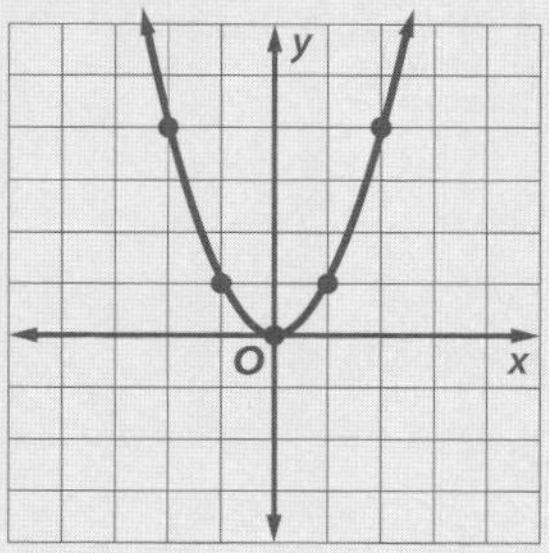

quadratic

InterventionPlanner

Tier 1 On Level OL

If students miss about 25% of the exercises or less,

Then choose a resource:

- SE Lessons 9-1, 9-2, 9-3, 9-4, 9-5, 9-6, and 9-7
- Skills Practice, pp. 7, 13, 19, 25, 31, 37, and 43
- TE Chapter Project
- connectED.mcgraw-hill.com Self-Check Quiz

Tier 2 Strategic Intervention AL approaching grade level

If students miss about 50% of the exercises,

Then choose a resource:

- Study Guide and Intervention, Chapter 9, pp. 5, 11, 17, 23, 29, 35, and 41
- *Quick Review Math Handbook*
- connectED.mcgraw-hill.com Extra Examples, Personal Tutor, Homework Help

Tier 3 Intensive Intervention 2 or more grades below level

If students miss about 75% of the exercises,

Then use *Math Triumphs, Alg. 1*

connectED.mcgraw-hill.com Extra Examples, Personal Tutor, Homework Help, Review Vocabulary

1 Focus

Objective Use the strategy of using a formula to solve standardized test problems.

2 Teach

Scaffolding Questions

Ask:

- What formulas do you already know? Answers will vary. What formulas do you think it would be useful to know? Answers will vary.
- Do you think it would be possible to solve a problem that uses a formula if you do not know the formula? Explain. Sample answer: If the problem involves something such as perimeter or the volume of a rectangular prism, you could probably solve the problem without the formula, but if the problem involves the Quadratic Formula, you would need to know the formula.

CHAPTER 9 Preparing for Standardized Tests

Use a Formula

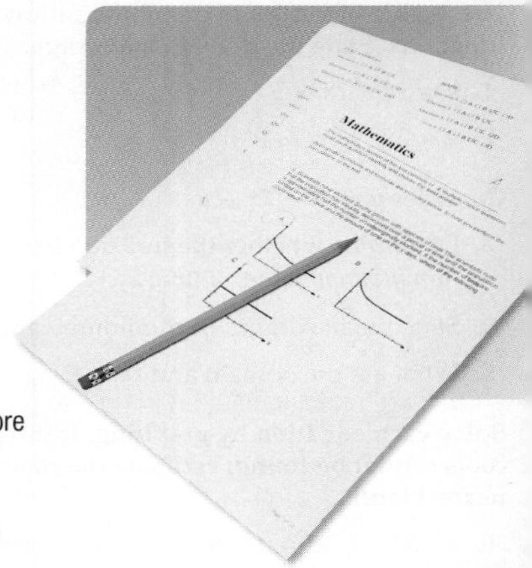

A *formula* is an equation that shows a relationship among certain quantities. Many standardized test problems will require using a formula to solve them.

Strategies for Using a Formula

Step 1

Become familiar with common formulas and their uses. You may or may not be given access to a formula sheet to use during the test.

- **If given a formula sheet,** be sure to practice with the formulas on it before taking the test so you know how to apply them.
- **If not given a formula sheet,** study and practice with common formulas such as perimeter, area, and volume formulas, the Distance Formula, the Pythagorean Theorem, the Midpoint Formula, the Quadratic Formula, and others.

Step 2

Choose a formula and solve.

- **Ask Yourself:** What quantities are given in the problem statement?
- **Ask Yourself:** What quantities am I looking for?
- **Ask Yourself:** Is there a formula I know that relates these quantities?
- **Write:** Write the formula out that you have chosen each time.
- **Solve:** Substitute known quantities into the formula and solve for the unknown quantity.
- **Check:** Check your answer if time permits.

Standardized Test Example

Read the problem. Identify what you need to know. Then use the information in the problem to solve.

Find the exact roots of the quadratic equation $-2x^2 + 6x + 5 = 0$.

A $\frac{3 \pm \sqrt{17}}{4}$ C $\frac{3 \pm \sqrt{19}}{2}$

B $\frac{4 \pm \sqrt{17}}{3}$ D $\frac{3 \pm \sqrt{19}}{4}$

Read the problem carefully. You are given a quadratic equation and asked to find the exact roots of the equation. Use the **Quadratic Formula** to find the roots.

$-2x^2 + 6x + 5 = 0$	Original equation
$a = -2, b = 6, c = 5$	Identify the coefficients of the equation.
$x = \frac{-b \pm \sqrt{b^2 - 4ac}}{2a}$	Quadratic Formula
$= \frac{-(6) \pm \sqrt{(6)^2 - 4(-2)(5)}}{2(-2)}$	$a = -2$, $b = 6$, and $c = 5$
$= \frac{-6 \pm \sqrt{36 - (-40)}}{-4}$	Simplify.
$= \frac{-6 \pm \sqrt{76}}{-4}$	Subtract.
$= \frac{-6 \pm 2\sqrt{19}}{-4}$	$\sqrt{76} = \sqrt{4 \cdot 19}$ or $2\sqrt{19}$.
$= \frac{-2(3 \pm \sqrt{19})}{-2(2)}$	Factor out −2 from the numerator and denominator.
$= \frac{3 \pm \sqrt{19}}{2}$	Simplify.

The roots of the equation are $\frac{3 + \sqrt{19}}{2}$ and $\frac{3 - \sqrt{19}}{2}$. The correct answer is C.

Exercises

Read each problem. Identify what you need to know. Then use the information in the problem to solve.

1. Find the exact roots of the quadratic equation $x^2 + 5x - 12 = 0$. A

A $\frac{-5 \pm \sqrt{73}}{2}$

B $\frac{4 \pm \sqrt{61}}{3}$

C $\frac{-3 \pm \sqrt{73}}{4}$

D $\frac{-1 \pm \sqrt{61}}{2}$

2. The area of a triangle in which the length of the base is 4 centimeters greater than twice the height is 80 square centimeters. What is the length of the base of the triangle? J

F −10

G 8

H 16

J 20

3. Find the volume of the figure below. D

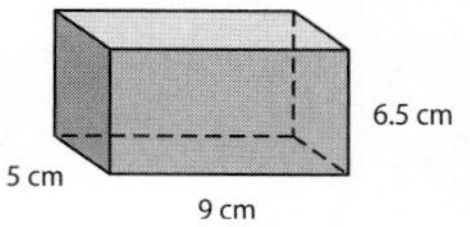

A 18.5 cm^3

B 91 cm^3

C 272 cm^3

D 292.5 cm^3

4. Myron is traveling 263.5 miles at an average rate of 62 miles per hour. How long will it take Myron to complete his trip? G

F 4 h 10 min

G 4 h 15 min

H 5 h 10 min

J 5 h 25 min

Additional Example

Find the exact roots of the quadratic equation $2x^2 + 5x - 5 = 0$. C

A $\frac{5 \pm \sqrt{65}}{4}$

B $\frac{5 \pm \sqrt{15}}{4}$

C $\frac{-5 \pm \sqrt{65}}{4}$

D $\frac{-5 \pm \sqrt{15}}{4}$

3 Assess

Use Exercises 1–4 to assess students' understanding.

connectED.mcgraw-hill.com 613

Diagnose Student Errors

Survey student responses for each item. Class trends may indicate common errors and misconceptions.

1. A switched coordinates of y-intercept
B coordinates of y-intercept instead of vertex
C switched x-and y-coordinates
D correct

2. F switched slope and y-intercept
G correct
H incorrectly chose negative instead of positive y-intercept
J switched slope and y-intercept and incorrectly chose negative instead of positive y-intercept

3. A correct
B error in simplifying radical and did not factor 2 out of denominator
C error in using quadratic formula or guess
D guess

4. F forgot to multiply $-3bc$ by $5bc^2$
G correct
H forgot to multiply coefficients
J multiplied instead of added exponents

5. A incorrectly graphed quadratic equation
B correct
C switched x- and y-coordinates
D incorrectly graphed equation and/or used negative instead of positive coefficient for x^2

6. F calculation error for minimum points
G correct
H guess
J calculation error for maximum points

CHAPTER 9 Standardized Test Practice

Cumulative, Chapters 1 through 9

Multiple Choice

Read each question. Then fill in the correct answer on the answer document provided by your teacher or on a sheet of paper.

1. What is the vertex of the parabola graphed below? D

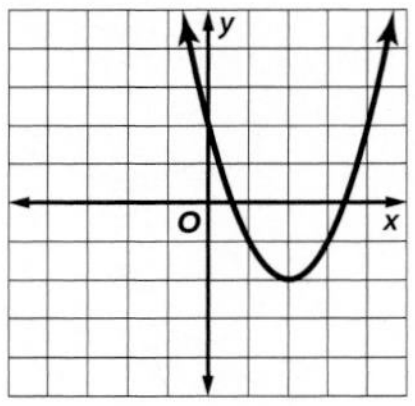

A (2, 0)
B (0, 2)
C (−2, 2)
D (2, −2)

2. Write an equation in slope-intercept form with a slope of $\frac{9}{10}$ and y-intercept of 3. G

F $y = 3x + \frac{9}{10}$
G $y = \frac{9}{10}x + 3$
H $y = \frac{9}{10}x - 3$
J $y = 3x - \frac{9}{10}$

3. Use the Quadratic Formula to find the exact solutions of the equation $2x^2 - 6x + 3 = 0$. A

A $\frac{3 \pm \sqrt{3}}{2}$
B $\frac{3 \pm \sqrt{2}}{4}$
C $\frac{2 \pm \sqrt{5}}{3}$
D $\frac{5 \pm \sqrt{2}}{2}$

4. Write an expression for the area of the rectangle below. G

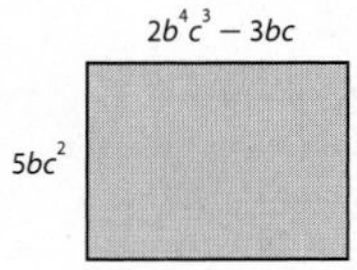

F $10b^5c^5 - 3bc$
G $10b^5c^5 - 15b^2c^3$
H $2b^5c^5 - 3b^2c^3$
J $10b^4c^6 - 15bc^2$

5. Solve the quadratic equation below by graphing. B

$$x^2 - 2x - 15 = 0$$

A −1, 4
B −3, 5
C 3, −5
D ∅

6. Jason is playing games at a family fun center. So far he has won 38 prize tickets. How many more tickets would he need to win to place him in the gold prize category? G

Number of Tickets	Prize Category
1–20	bronze
21–40	silver
41–60	gold
61–80	platinum

F $2 \leq t \leq 22$
G $3 \leq t \leq 22$
H $1 \leq t \leq 20$
J $3 \leq t \leq 20$

Test-TakingTip
Question 5 If permitted, you can use a graphing calculator to quickly graph an equation and find its roots.

Short Response/Gridded Response

Record your answers on the answer sheet provided by your teacher or on a sheet of paper.

7. GRIDDED RESPONSE Misty purchased a car several years ago for $21,459. The value of the car depreciated at a rate of 15% annually. What was the value of the car after 5 years? Round your answer to the nearest whole dollar. **9521**

8. Use the graph of the quadratic equation shown below to answer each question.

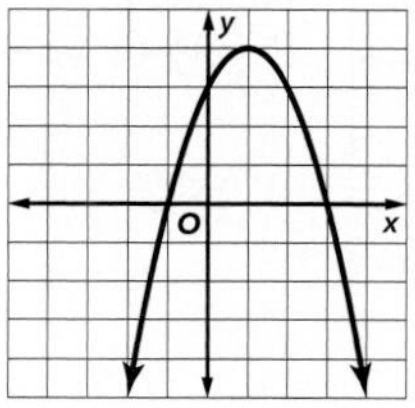

a. What is the vertex? **(1, 4)**

b. What is the y-intercept? **(0, 3)**

c. What is the axis of symmetry? $x = 1$

d. What are the roots of the corresponding quadratic equation? **−1, 3**

9. The cost of 5 notebooks and 3 pens is $9.75. The cost of 4 notebooks and 6 pens is $10.50.

a. Write a system of equations to model the situation. **See margin.**

b. Solve the system of equations. How much does each item cost?
pen: $0.75, notebook: $1.50

10. The table shows the total cost of renting a canoe for n hours.

Number of Hours (n)	Rental Cost (C)
1	$15
2	$20
3	$25
4	$30

a. Write a function to represent the situation. $C(n) = 5n + 10$

b. How much would it cost to rent the canoe for 7 hours? **$45**

Extended Response

Record your answers on a sheet of paper. Show your work.

11. Use the equation and its graph to answer each question.

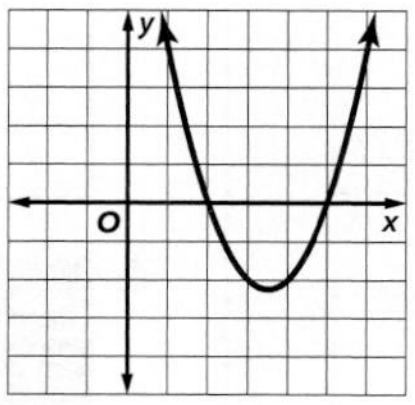

a. Factor $x^2 - 7x + 10$. $(x - 2)(x - 5)$

b. What are the solutions of $x^2 - 7x + 10 = 0$? $x = 2, 5$

c. What do you notice about the graph of the quadratic equation and where it crosses the x-axis? How do these values compare to the solutions of $x^2 - 7x + 10 = 0$? Explain.
See margin.

Need ExtraHelp?

If you missed Question...	1	2	3	4	5	6	7	8	9	10	11
Go to Lesson...	9-1	4-2	9-5	8-2	9-2	5-1	7-6	9-1	6-4	3-5	8-6

Additional Answers

9a. $5n + 3p = 9.75$
$4n + 6p = 10.50$

11c. Sample answer: the graph crosses the x-axis at $x = 2$ and $x = 5$. These are the solutions to the equation. On the graph they show what values of x result in $y = 0$.

Formative Assessment

You can use these pages to benchmark student progress.

Standardized Test Practice, pp. 66–68

Answer Sheet Practice

Have students simulate taking a standardized test by recording their answers on a practice recording sheet.

Student Recording Sheet

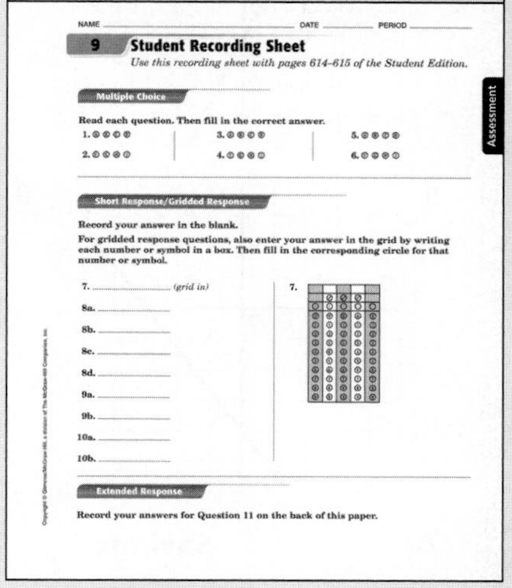
9 Student Recording Sheet
Use this recording sheet with pages 614–615 of the Student Edition.

Multiple Choice

Read each question. Then fill in the correct answer.

Short Response/Gridded Response

Record your answer in the blank.

For gridded response questions, also enter your answer in the grid by writing each number or symbol in a box. Then fill in the corresponding circle for that number or symbol.

7. (grid in) 8a. 8b. 8c. 8d. 9a. 9b. 10a. 10b.

Extended Response

Record your answers for Question 11 on the back of this paper.

McGraw-Hill eAssessment Create practice tests that align to your state standards, the Common Core State Standards, and other national standards such as TIMSS and NAEP.

Homework Option

Get Ready for Chapter 10 Assign students the exercises on p. 617 as homework to assess whether they possess the prerequisite skills needed for the next chapter.

Get Ready for Chapter 9

1. 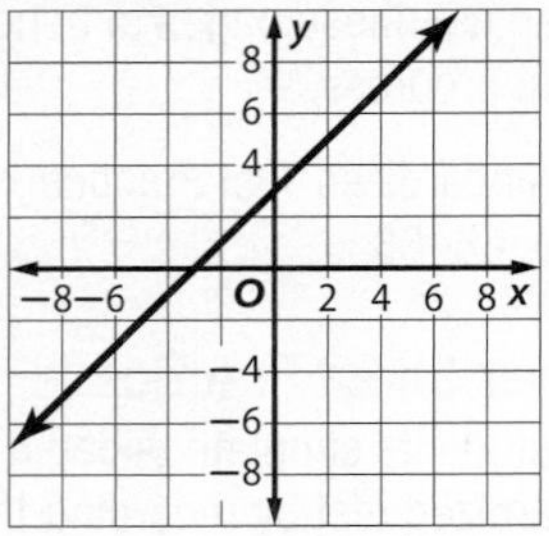

2. 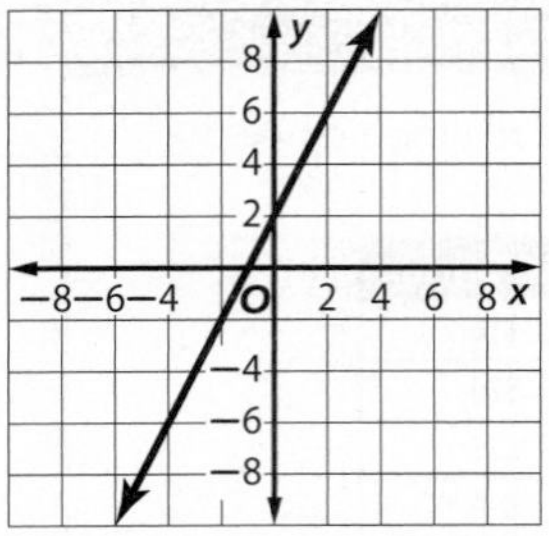

3. 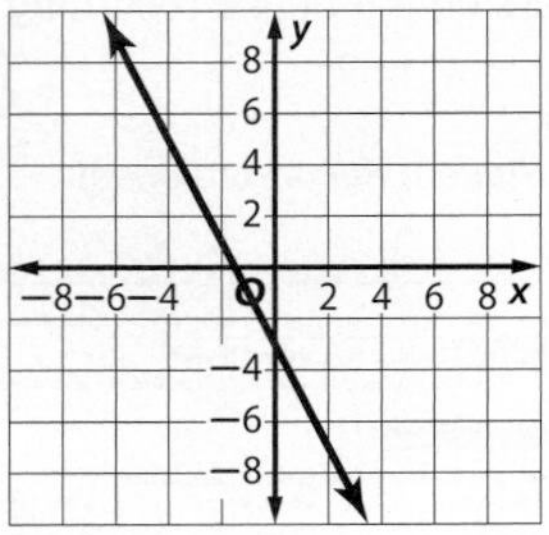

4. 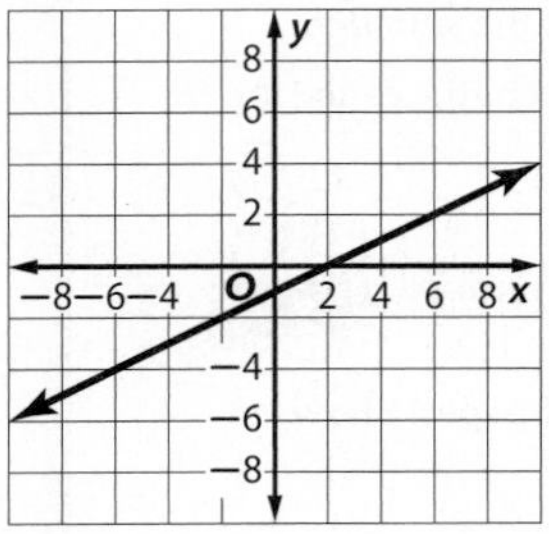

5. 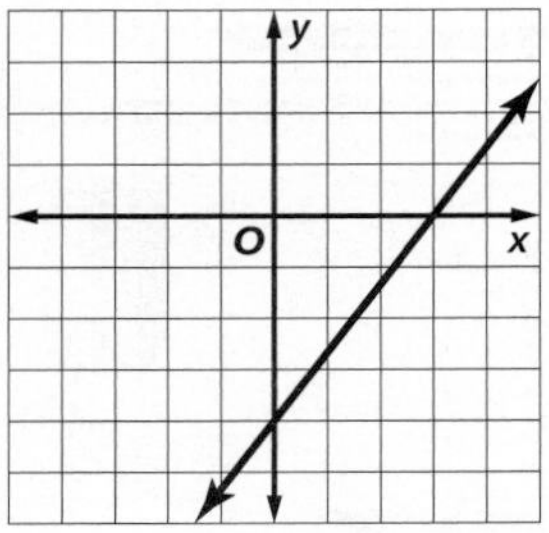

6. 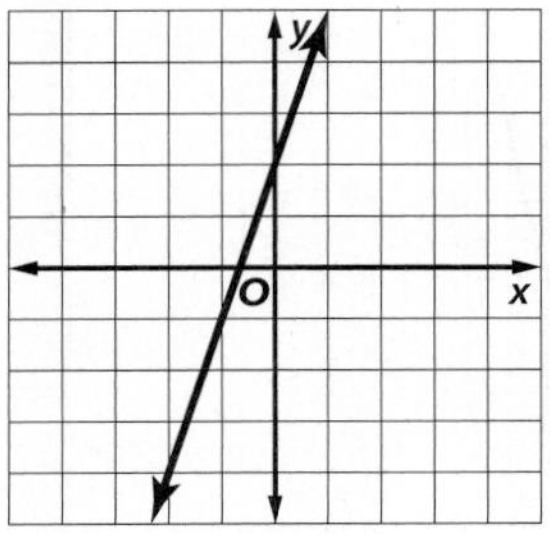

7. 

Lesson 9-1

1.

x	−3	−2	−1	0	1	2
y	0	−6	−8	−6	0	10

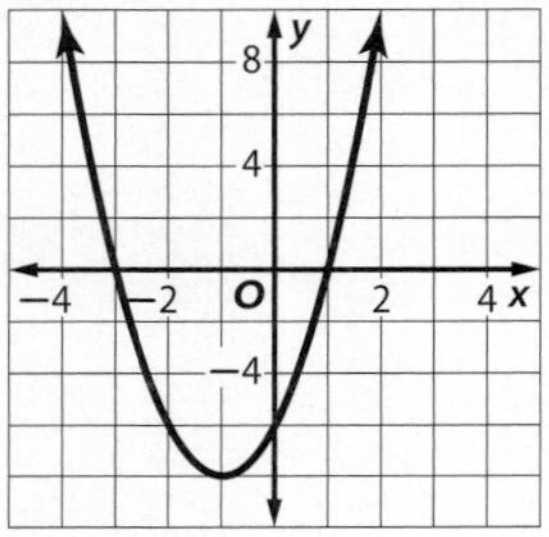

D = {all real numbers};
R = {y | y ≥ −8}

2.

x	−3	−2	−1	0	1	2
y	2	−1	−2	−1	2	7

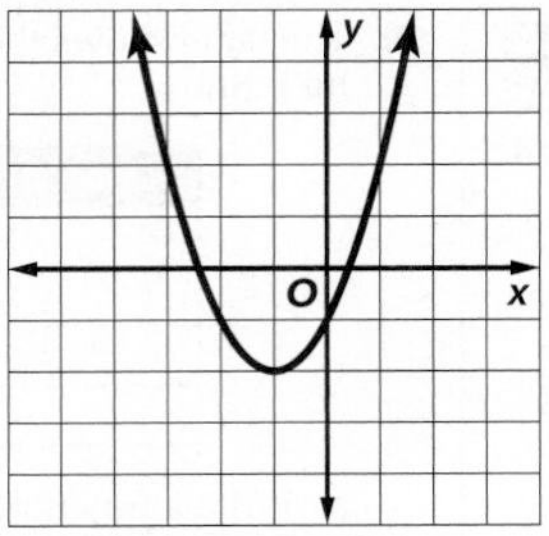

D = {all real numbers};
R = {y | y ≥ −2}

3.

x	y
−1	4
0	−3
1	−8
2	−11
3	−12
4	−11
5	−8
6	−3
7	4

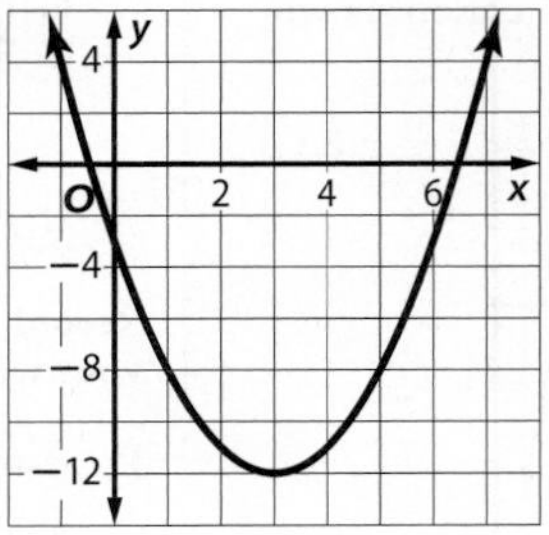

D = {all real numbers};
R = {y | y ≥ −12}

4.

x	−2	−1	0	1	2	3
y	19	4	−5	−8	−5	4

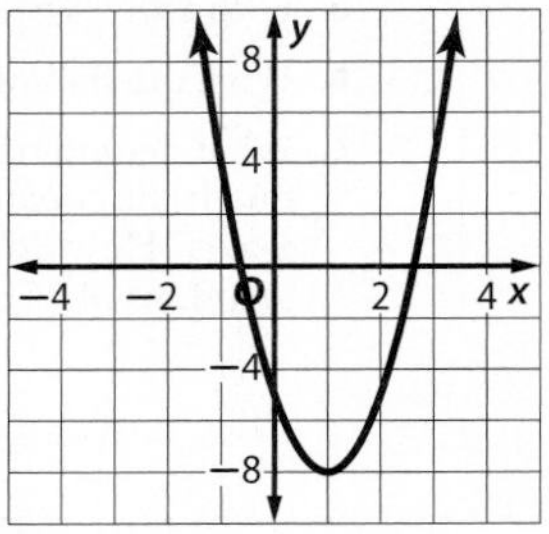

D = {all real numbers};
R = {y | y ≥ −8}

22.

x	−4	−3	−2	−1	0
y	6	3	2	3	6

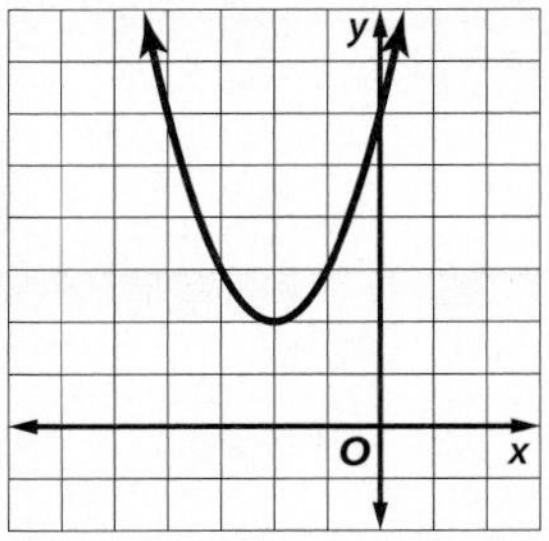

D = {all real numbers};
R = {y | y ≥ 2}

23.

x	−3	−2	−1	0	1
y	13	7	5	7	13

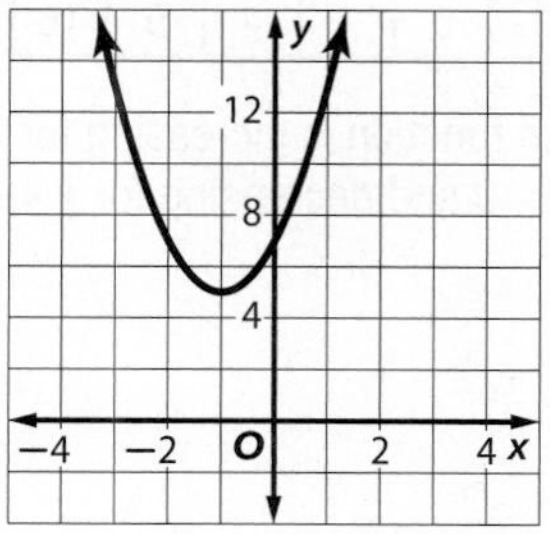

D = {all real numbers};
R = {y | y ≥ 5}

24.

x	4	3	2	1	0
y	−5	−11	−13	−11	−5

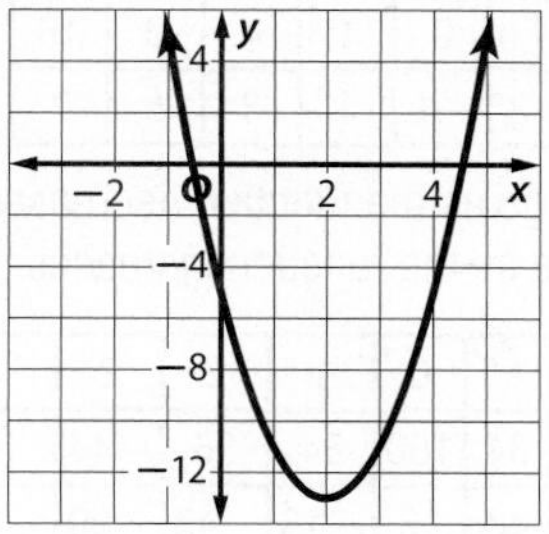

D = {all real numbers};
R = {y | y ≥ −13}

25.

x	0	−1	−2	−3	−4
y	5	−4	−7	−4	5

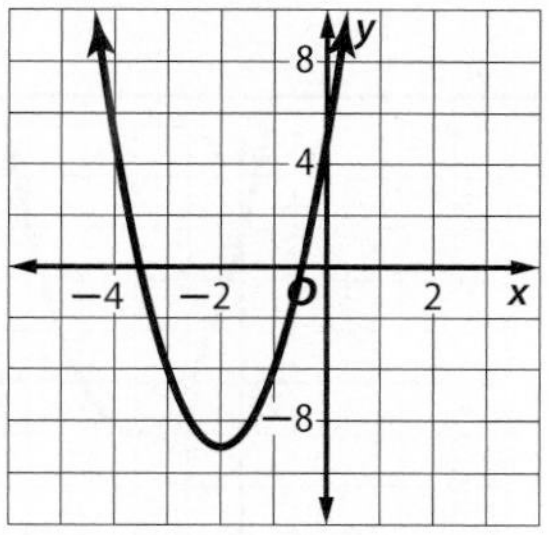

D = {all real numbers};
R = {y | y ≥ −7}

26.

x	3	2	1	0	−1
y	7	−2	−5	−2	7

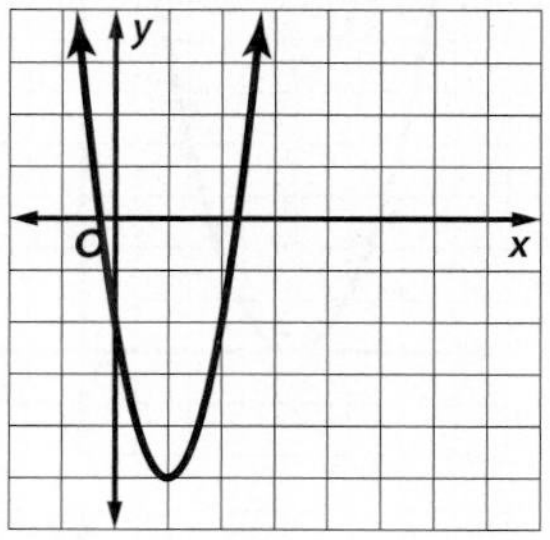

D = {all real numbers};
R = {y | y ≥ −5}

27.

x	3	2	1	0	−1
y	2	−1	−2	−1	2

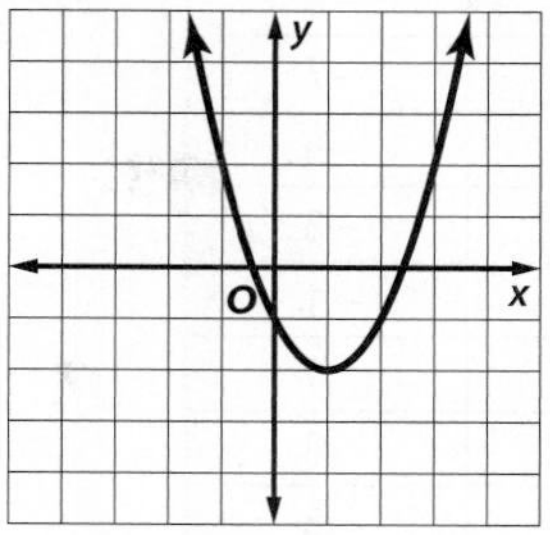

D = {all real numbers};
R = {y | y ≥ −2}

52.

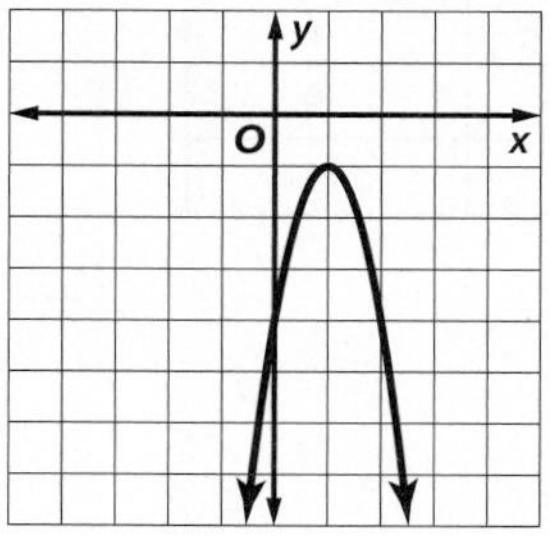

53.

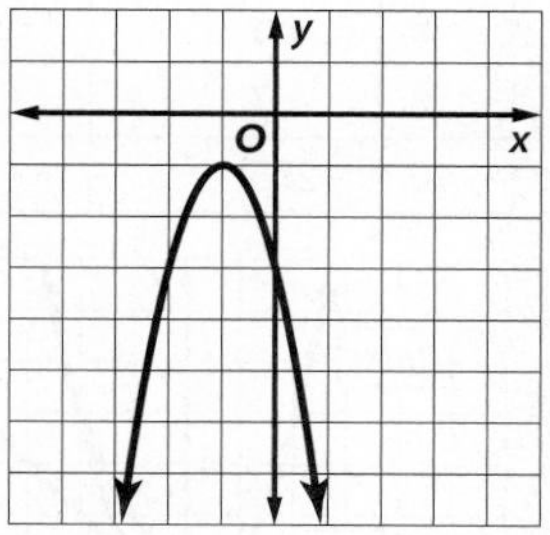

54.

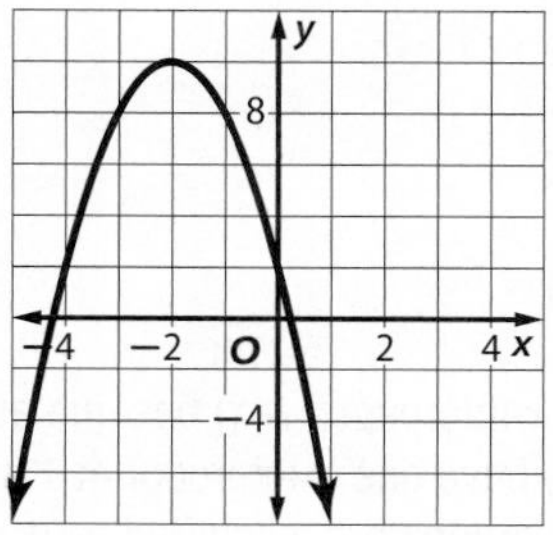

55.

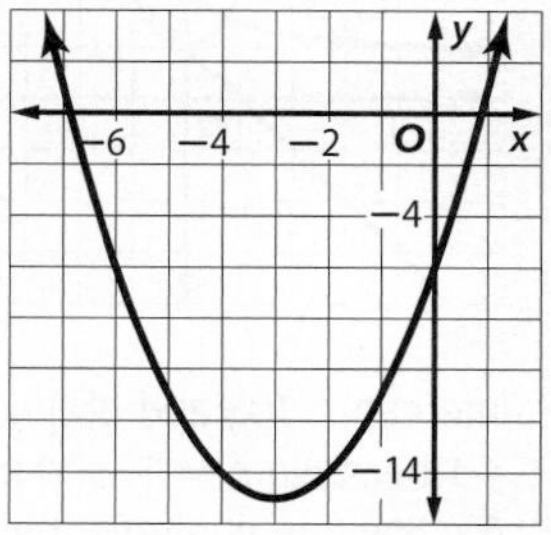

56.

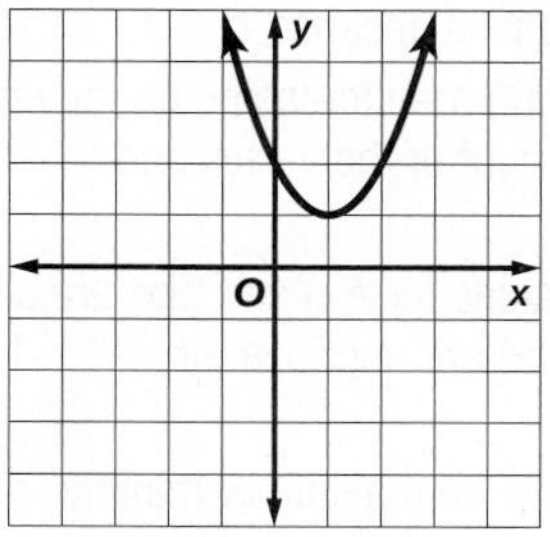

57.

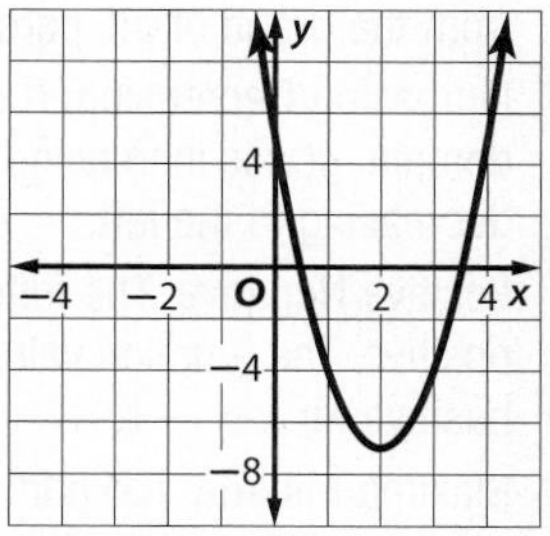

59.

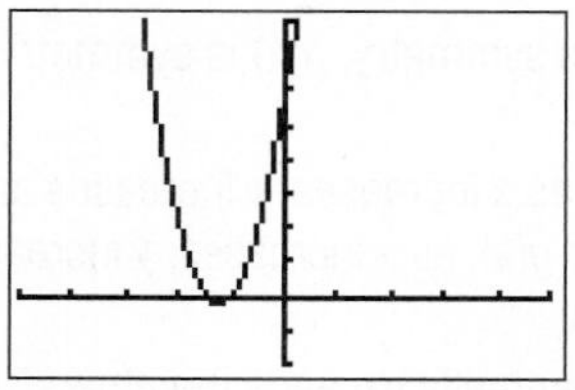

[−5, 5] scl:1 by [−5, 5] scl:1

60.

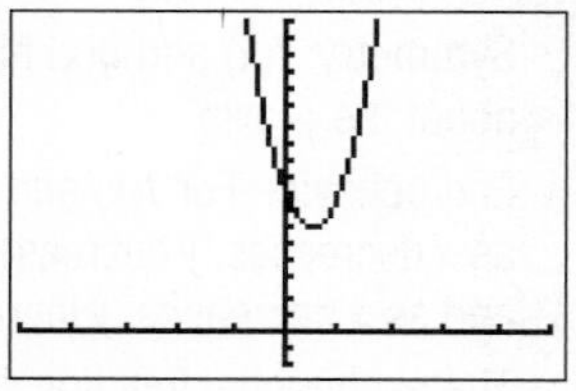

[−5, 5] scl: 1 by [−2, 18] scl: 2

61.

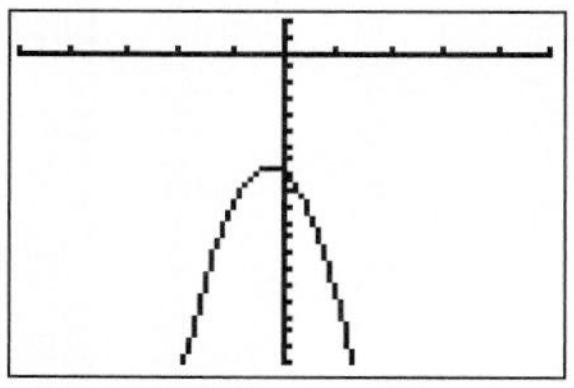

[−5, 5] scl: 1 by [−20, 2] scl: 2

62.

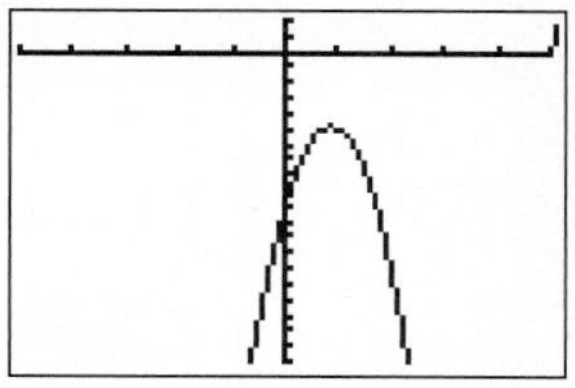

[−5, 5] scl: 1 by [−20, 2] scl: 2

74. Sample answer: Suppose $a = 1$, $b = 2$, and $c = 1$.

x	$f(x) = 2^x + 1$	$g(x) = x^2 + 1$	$h(x) = x + 1$
−10	1.00098	101	−9
−8	1.00391	65	−7
−6	1.01563	37	−5
−4	1.0625	17	−3
−2	1.25	5	−1
0	2	1	1
2	5	5	3
4	17	17	5
6	65	37	7
8	257	65	9
10	1205	101	11

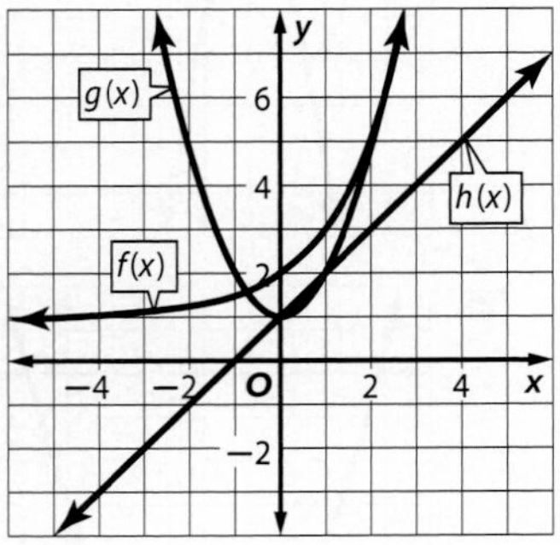

Intercepts: $f(x)$ and $g(x)$ have no x-intercepts, $h(x)$ has one at -1 because $c = 1$. $g(x)$ and $h(x)$ have one y-intercept at 1 and $f(x)$ has one y-intercept at 2. The graphs are all shifted up 1 unit from the graph of the parent functions because $c = 1$.

Increasing/Decreasing: $f(x)$ and $h(x)$ are increasing on the entire domain. $g(x)$ is increasing to the right of the vertex and decreasing to the left.

Positive/Negative: The function values for $f(x)$ and $g(x)$ are all positive. The function values of $h(x)$ are negative for $x < -1$ and positive for $x > -1$.

Maxima/Minima: $f(x)$ and $h(x)$ have no maxima or minima. $g(x)$ has a minimum at (0, 1).

Symmetry: $f(x)$ and $g(x)$ have no symmetry. $g(x)$ is symmetric about the y-axis.

End behavior: For $f(x)$ and $h(x)$, as x increases, y increases and as x decreases, y decreases. For $g(x)$, as x increases, y increases and as x decreases, y increases.

The exponential function $f(x)$ eventually exceeds the others.

Extend 9-1

1.

x	−4	−3	−2	−1	0	1	2	3	4
y	16	9	4	1	0	1	4	9	16

2.

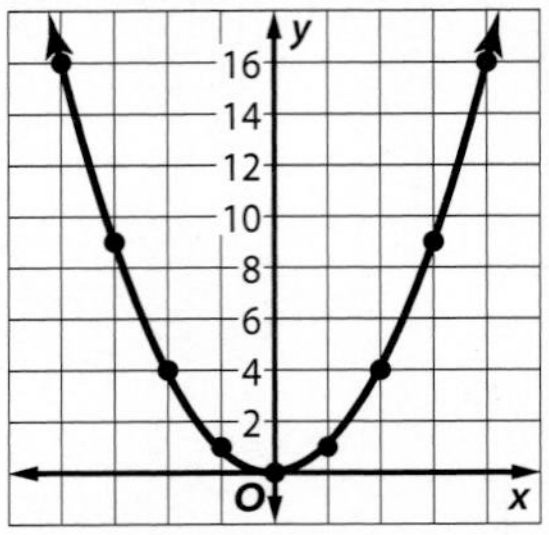

The function is increasing for $x > 0$ and decreasing for $x < 0$.

3.

x	−4	−3	−2	−1	0	1	2	3	4
y	16	9	4	1	0	1	4	9	16
Rate of Change	--	−7	−5	−3	−1	1	3	5	7

Sample answer: The rate of change as the function decreases is the opposite of the rate of change as the function increases.

4.

x	−4	−3	−2	−1	0	1	2	3	4
y	−156	−44	36	84	100	84	36	−44	156
Rate of Change	--	112	80	48	16	−16	−48	−80	−112

Sample answer: The rate of change as the function increases has the same absolute value as when the function decreases.

Lesson 9-2 (Guided Practice)

1A.

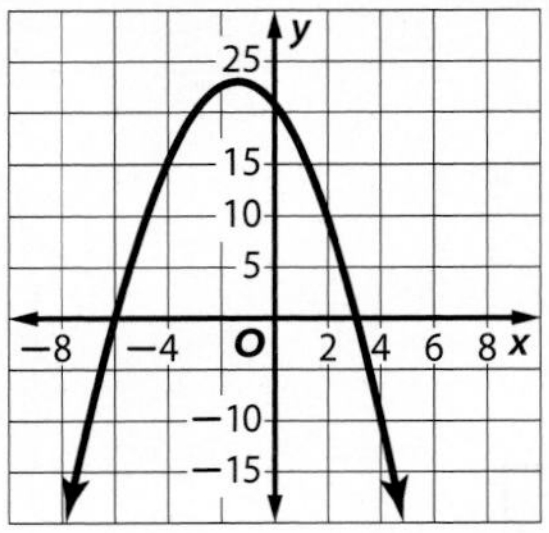

1B.

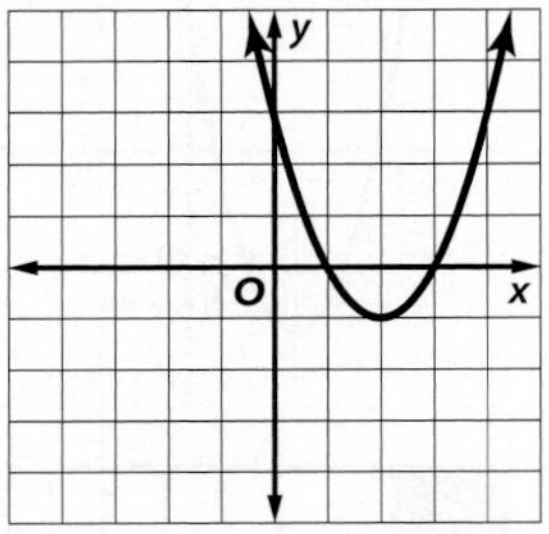

2A.

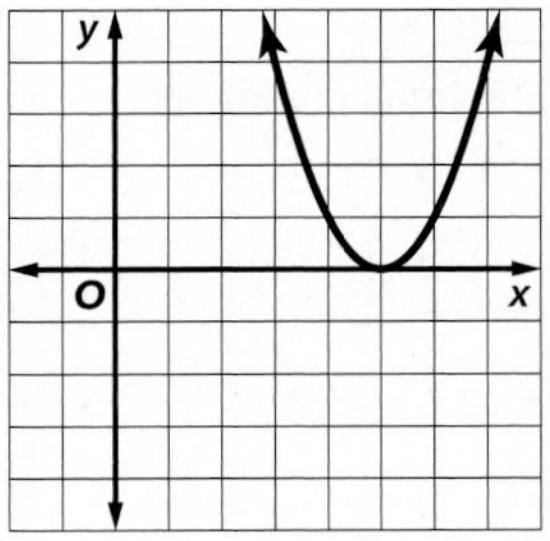

2B.

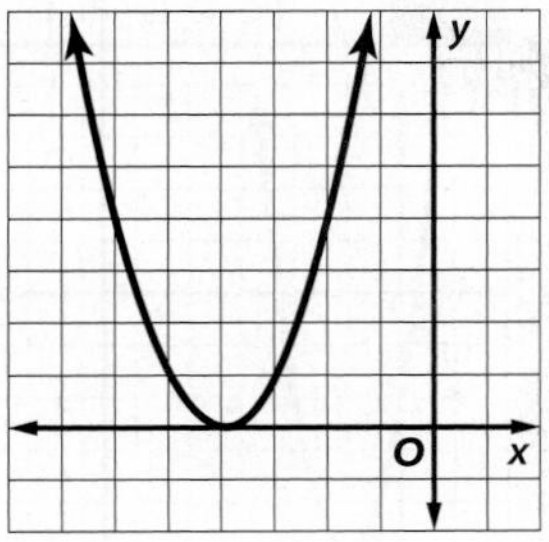

3A.

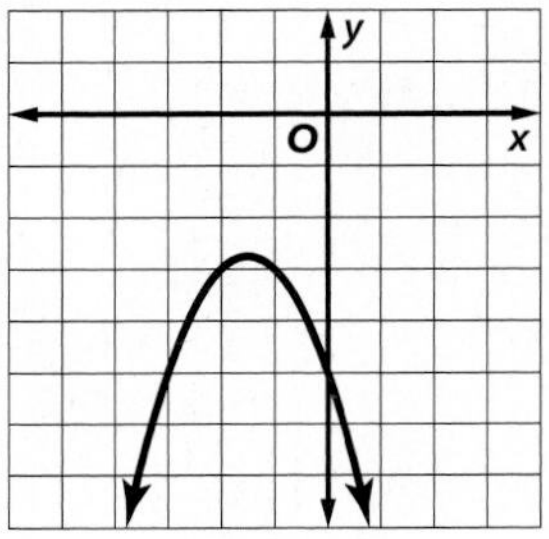

3B.

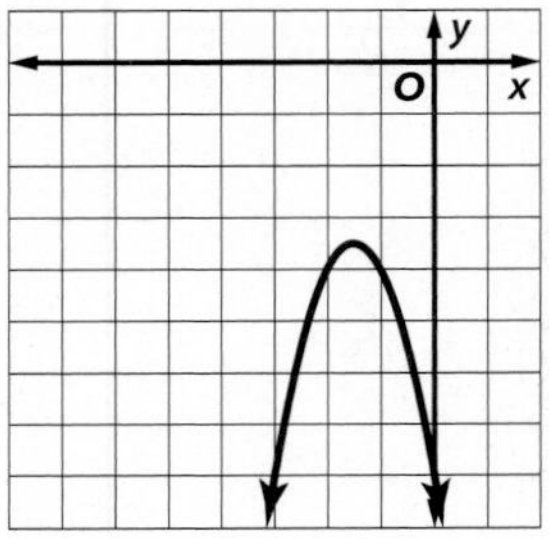

Lesson 9-2

1.
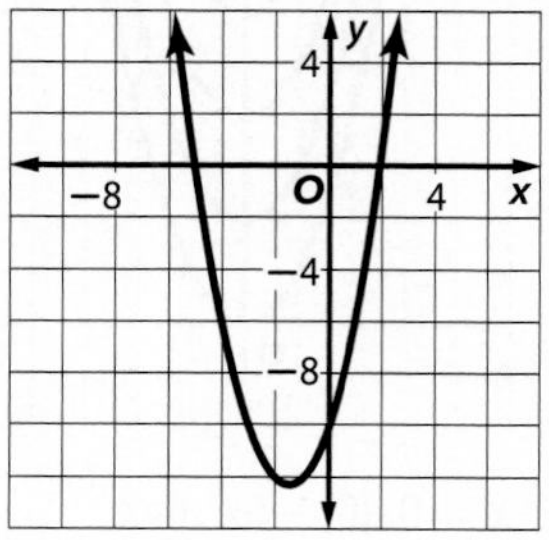

2.
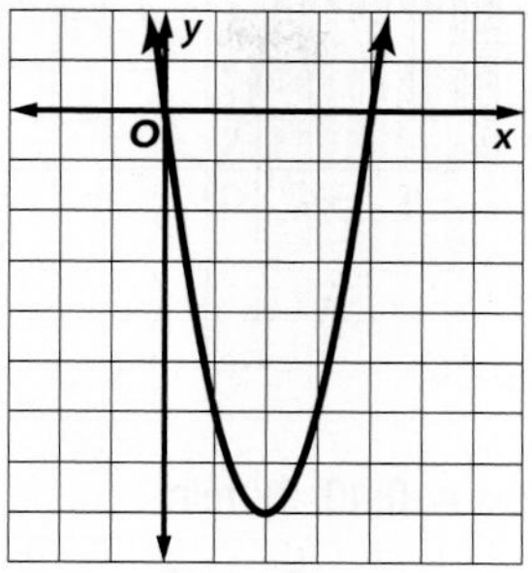

3.
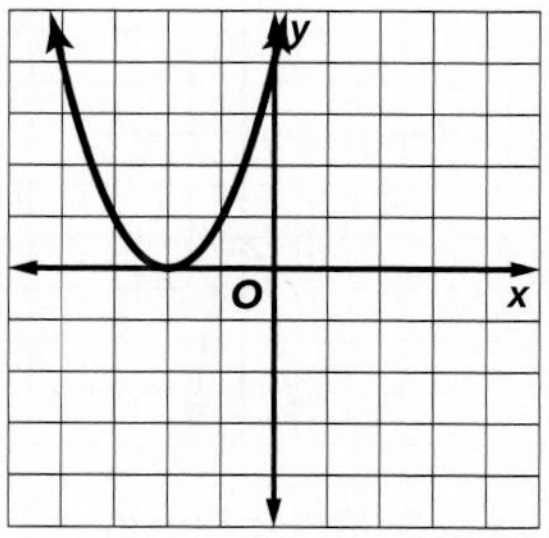

4.
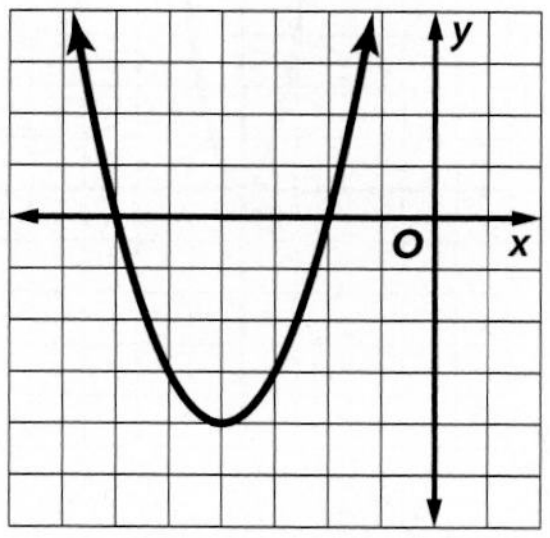

5.
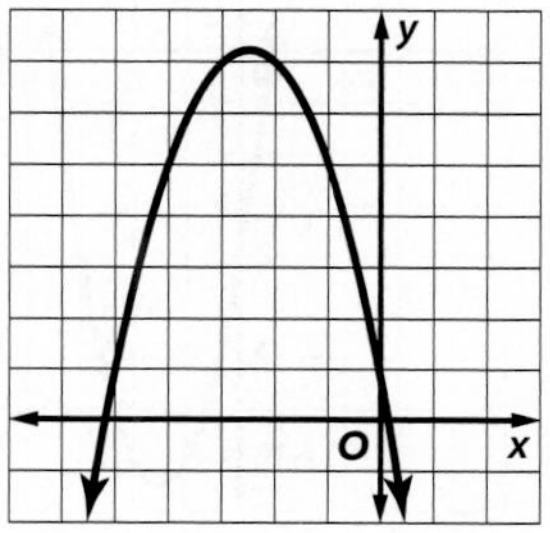

6.
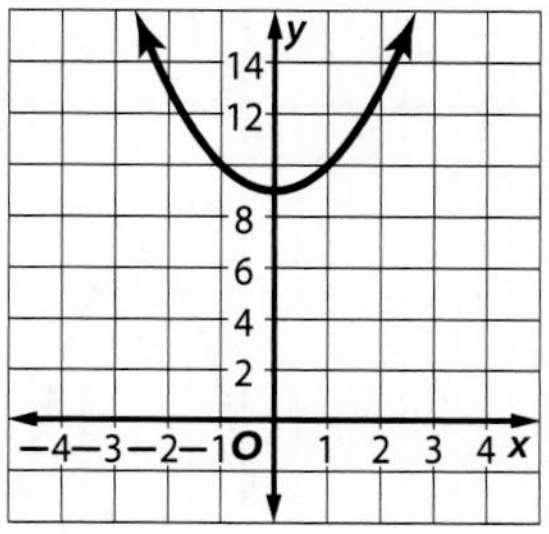

7.
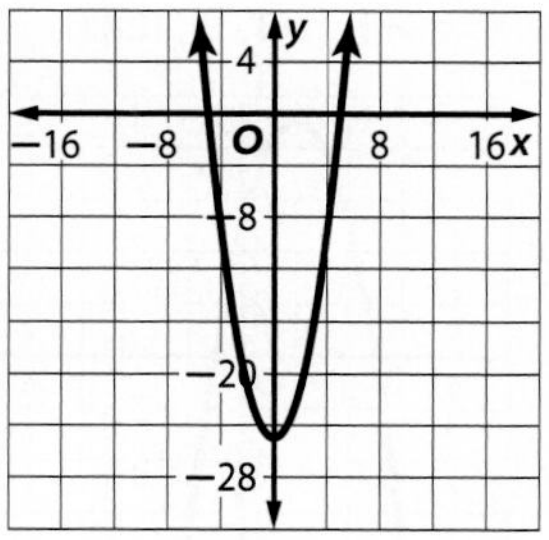

8.
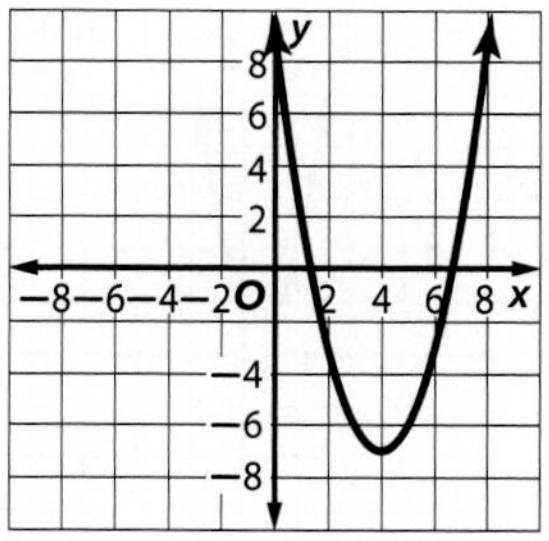

10.
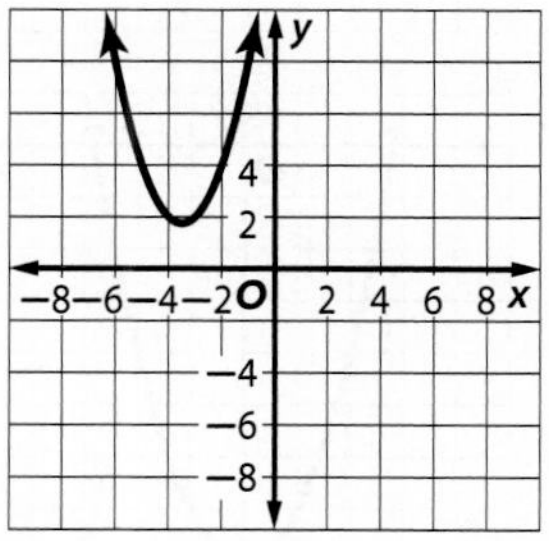

11.
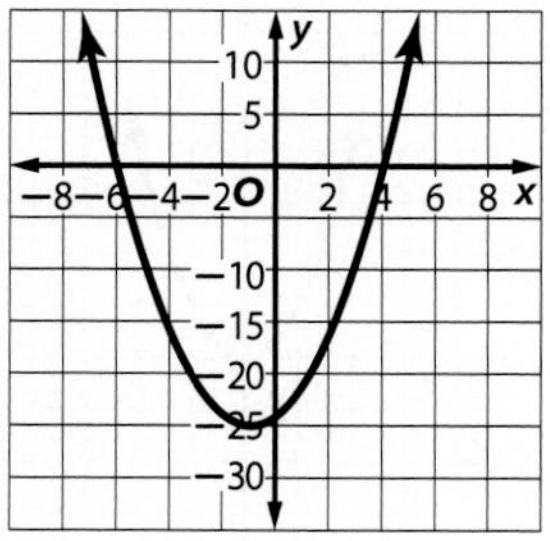

12.
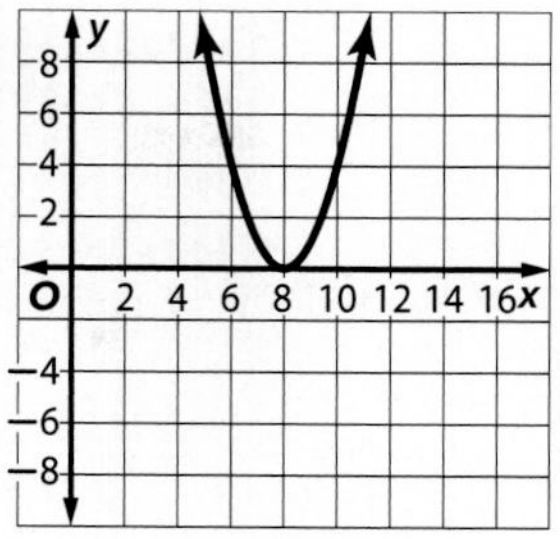

13.
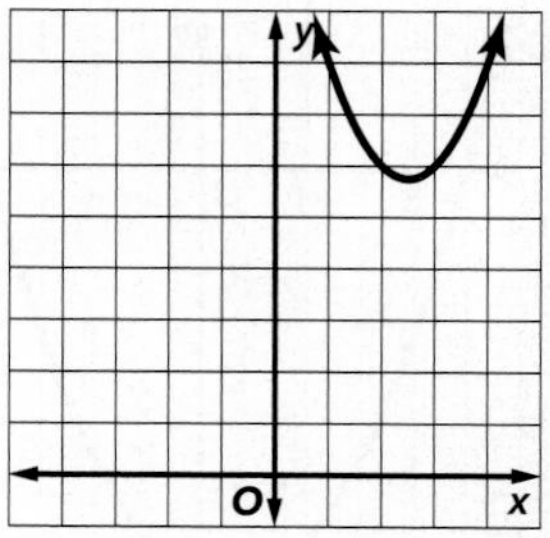

14.
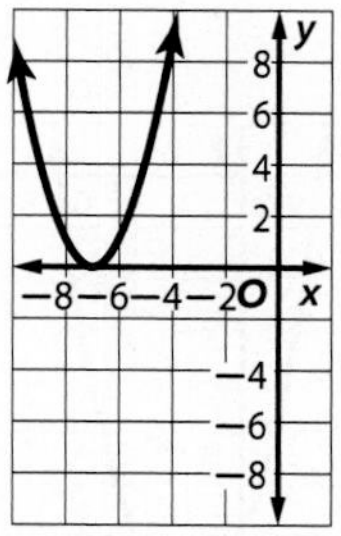

15.
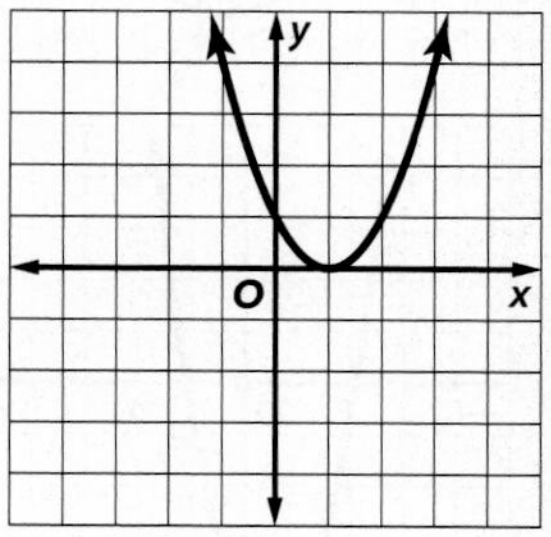

16.
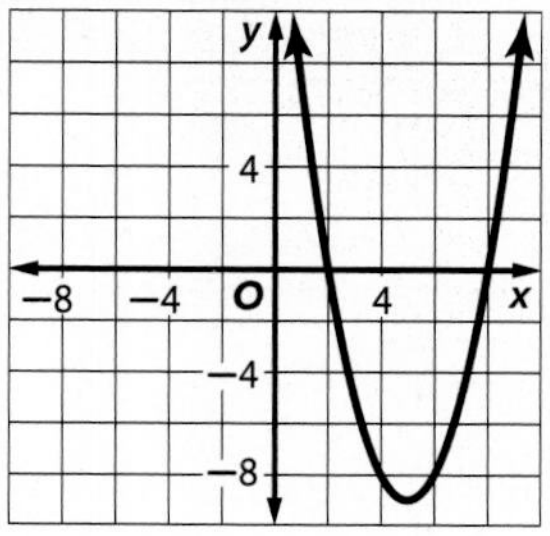

17.
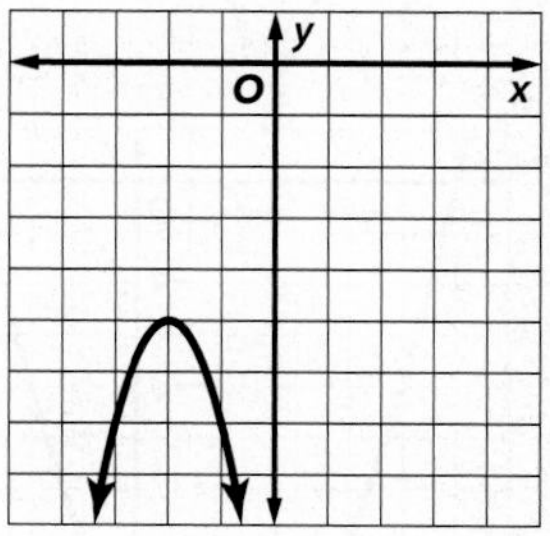

18.
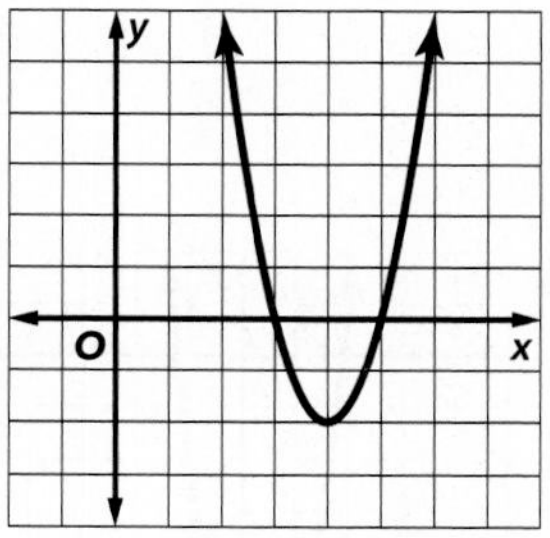

19.
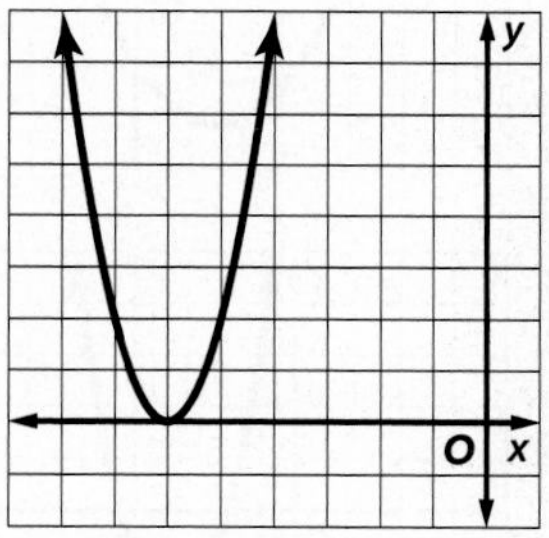

20.
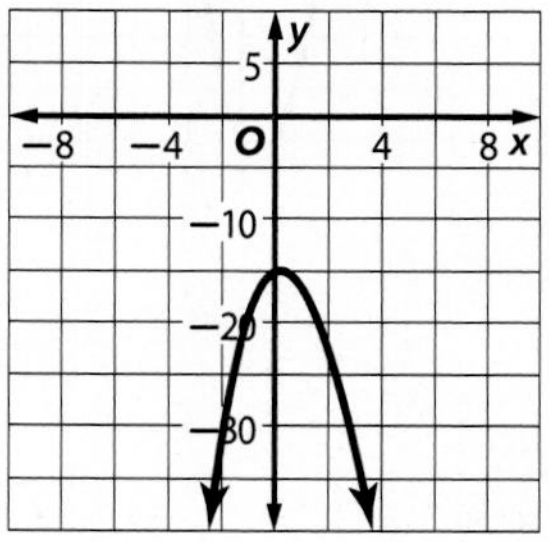

Chapter 9 Answer Appendix

21.
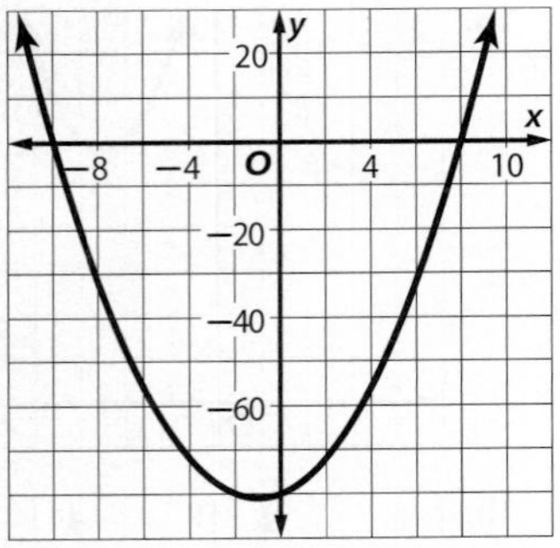

22.
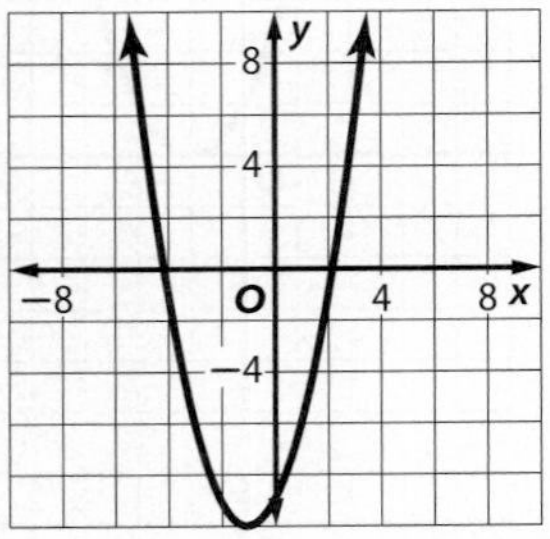

23.
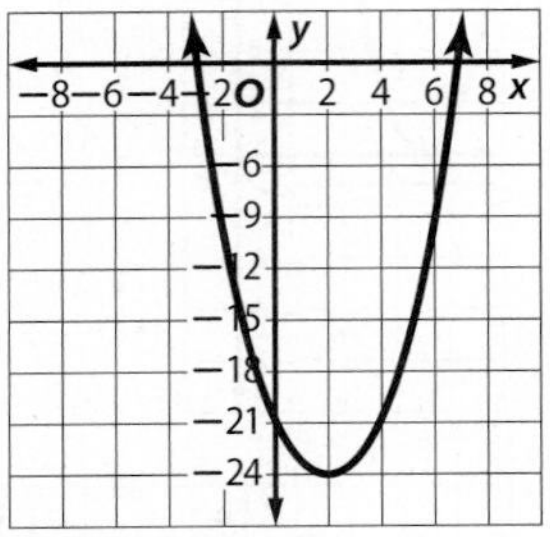

24.
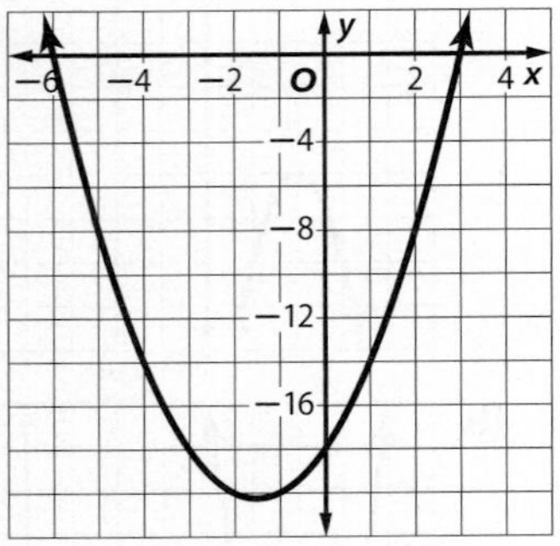

25.
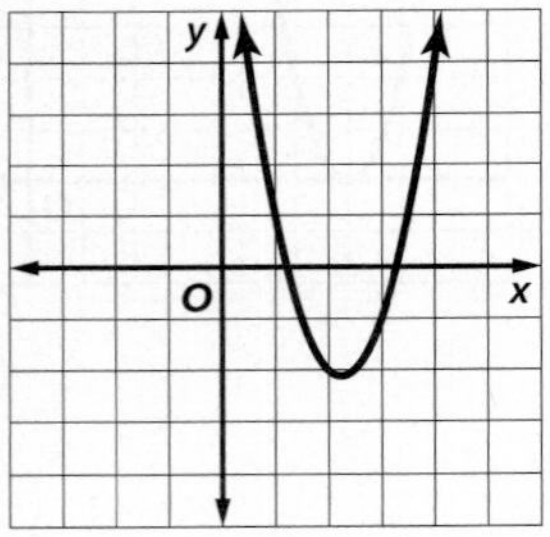

26.
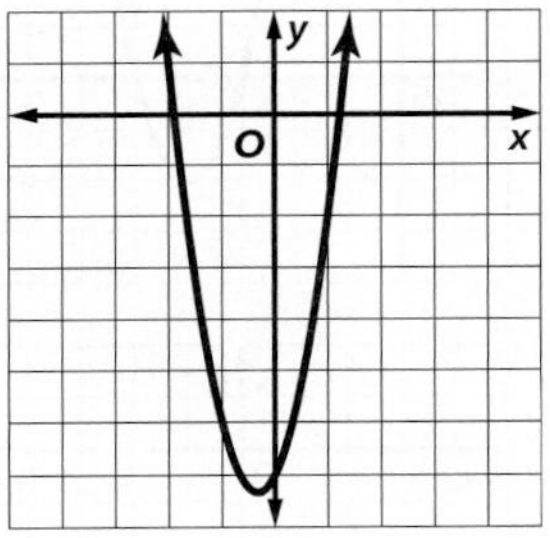

27.
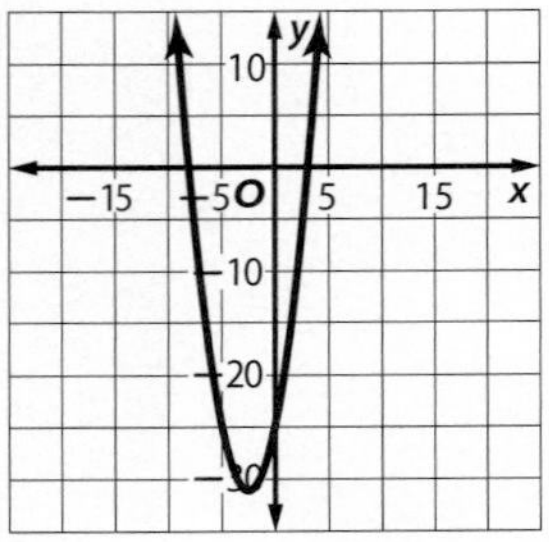

38a.
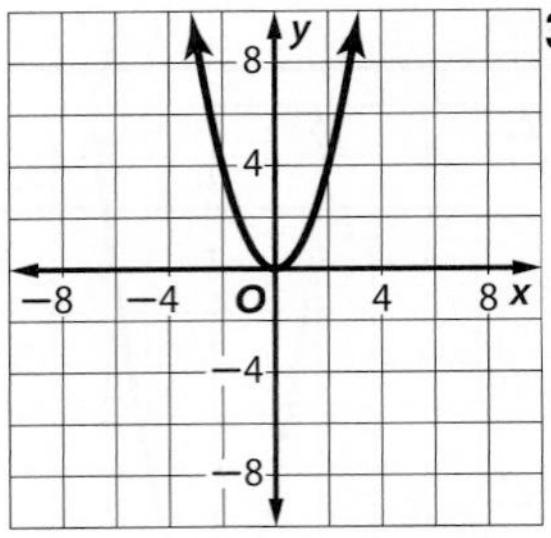

38c.
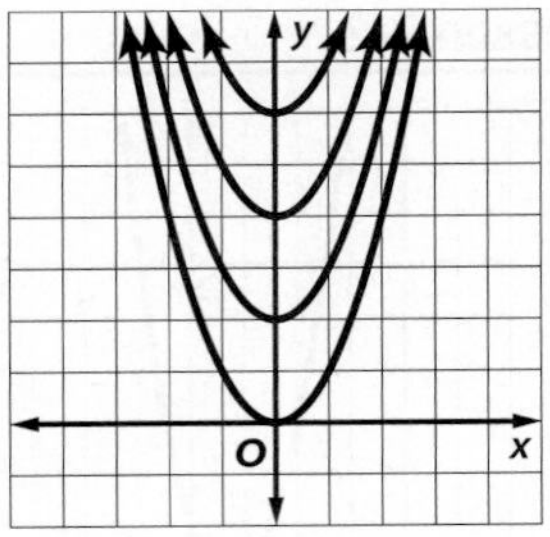

51. $x = 0$; $(0, 0)$; min
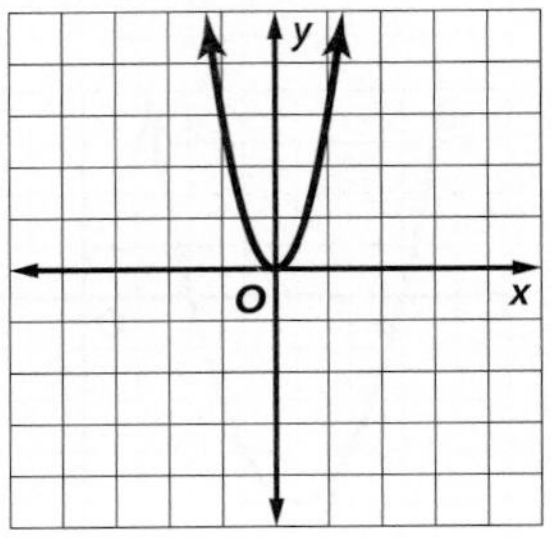

52. $x = 0$; $(0, -5)$; max
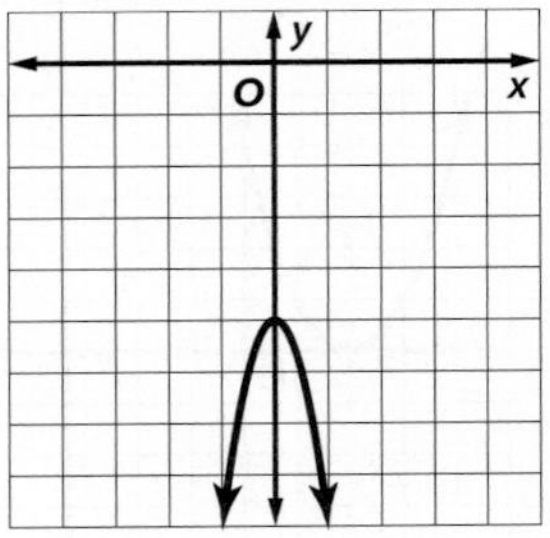

53. $x = 2$; $(2, -3)$; max
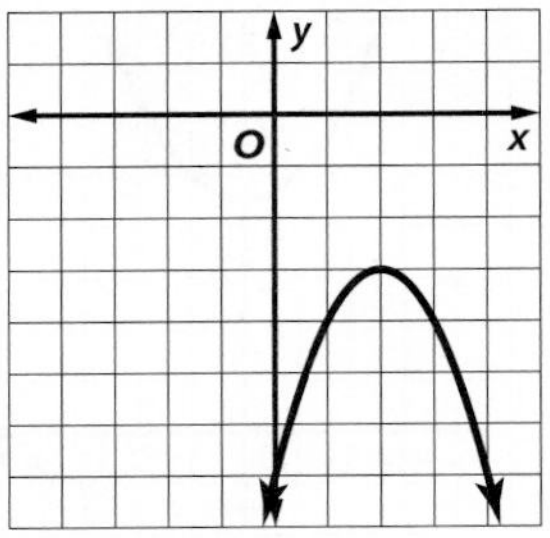

54. $x = 3$; $(3, -17)$; min
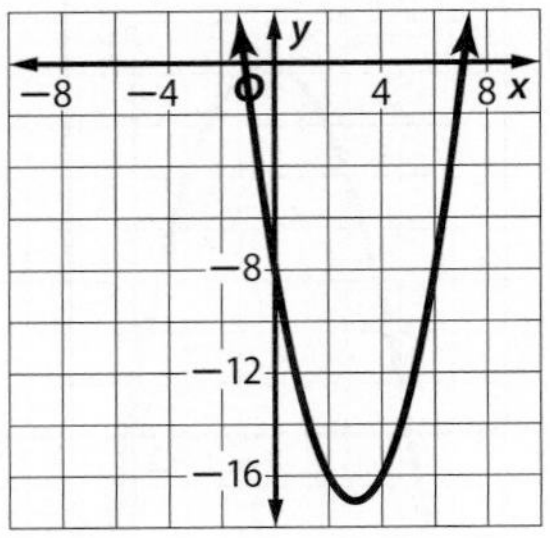

55. $x = -\frac{1}{3}$; $\left(-\frac{1}{3}, \frac{2}{3}\right)$; min
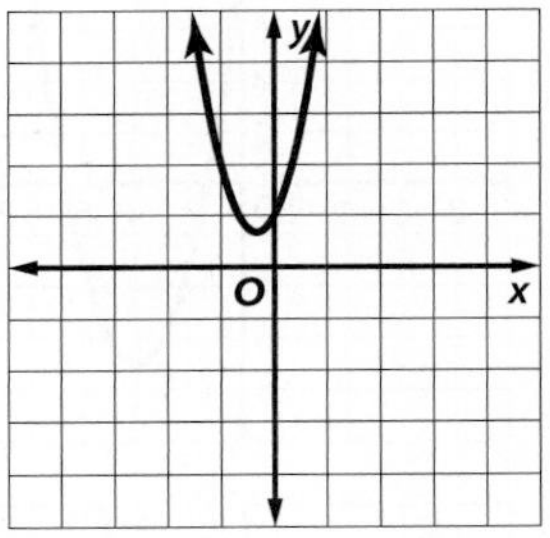

56. $x = -1$, $(-1, 9)$; max
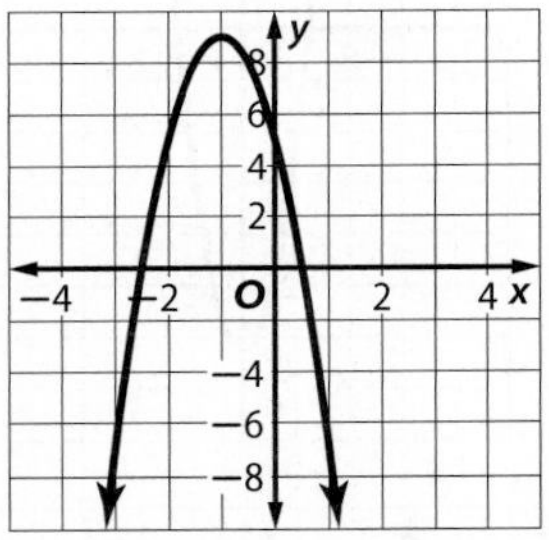

71.
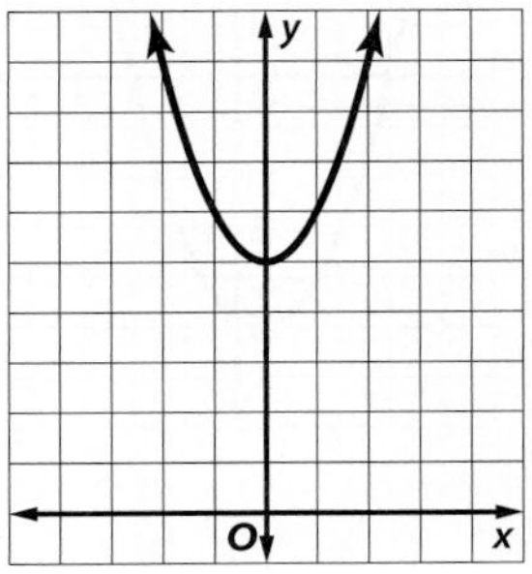

72.
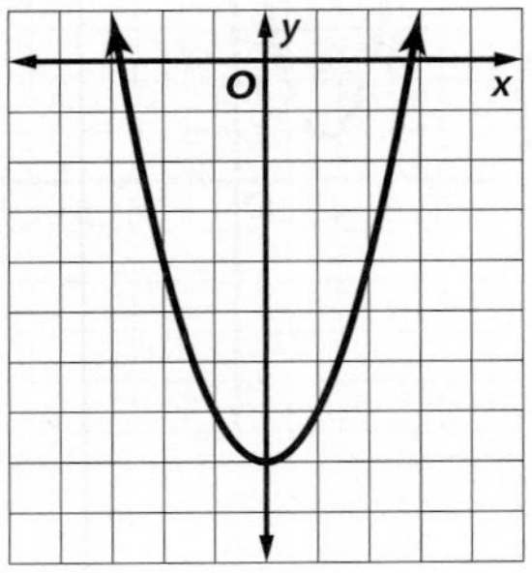

73.
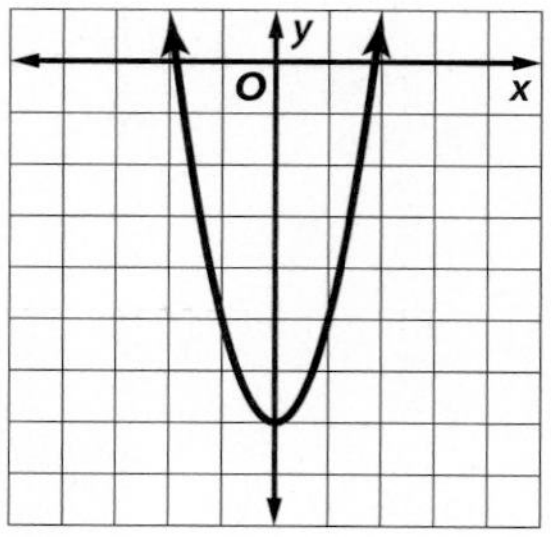

74.
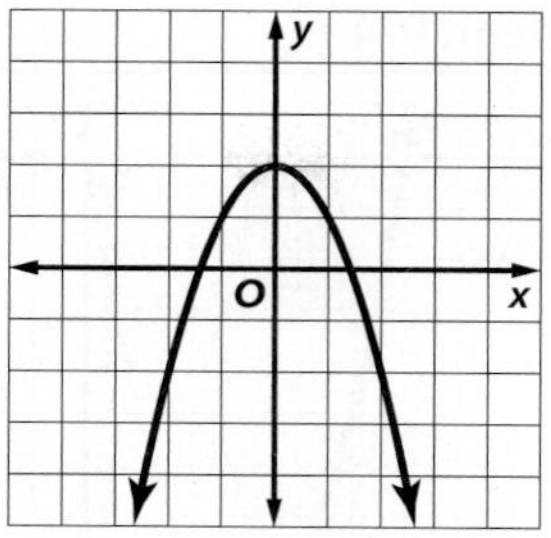

75.
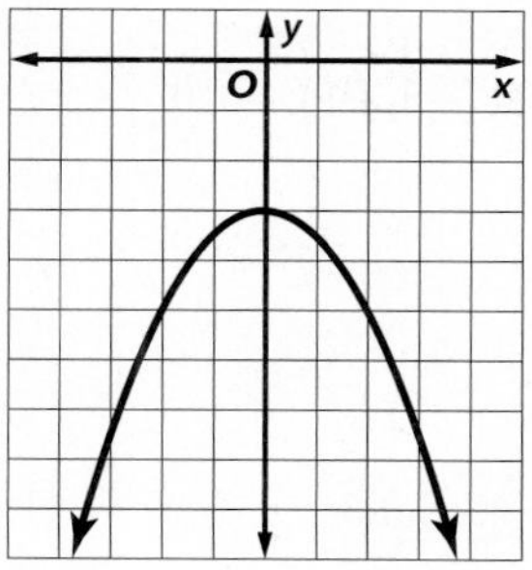

76.
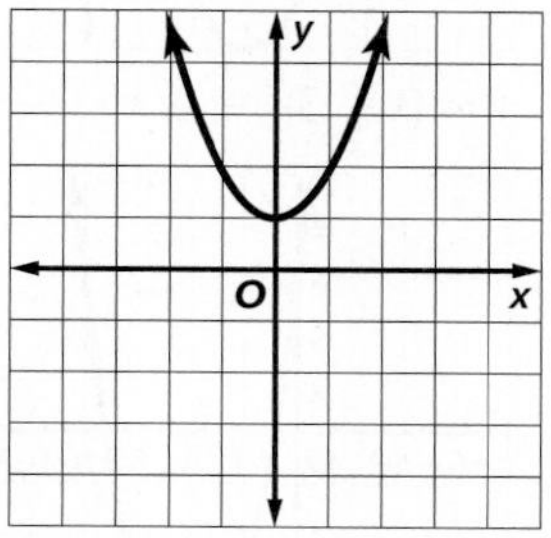

Explore 9-3

4.
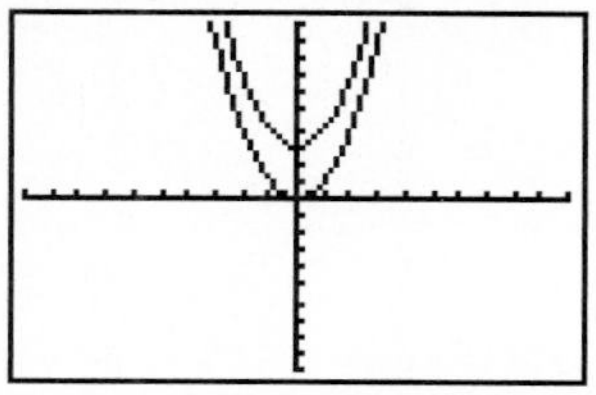

[−10, 10] scl: 1 by [−10, 10] scl: 1

Both graphs have the same shape, but the graph of $y = x^2 + 3$ is 3 units above the graph of $y = x^2$.

5.
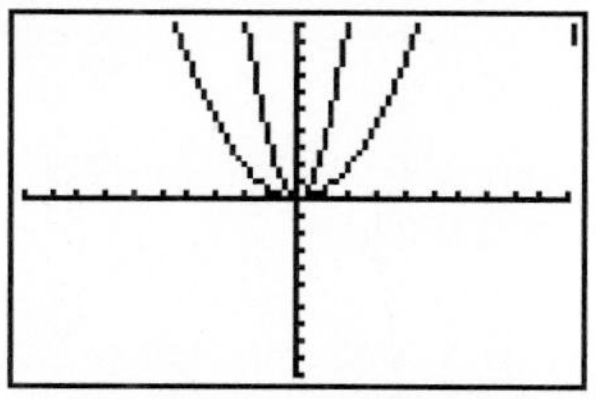

[−10, 10] scl: 1 by [−10, 10] scl: 1

The graph of $y = 3x^2$ is narrower than the graph of $y = \frac{1}{2}x^2$.

6.
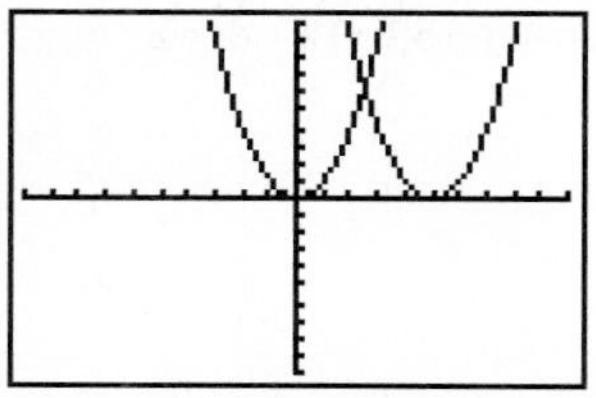

[−10, 10] scl: 1 by [−10, 10] scl: 1

Both graphs have the same shape, but the graph of $y = (x - 5)^2$ is shifted to the right 5 units.

7.
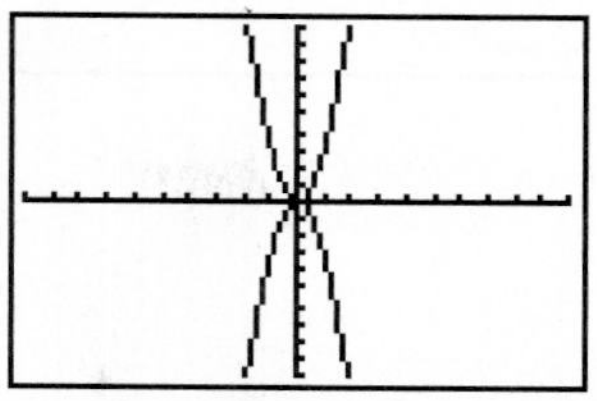

[−10, 10] scl: 1 by [−10, 10] scl: 1

Both graphs have the same shape, but the graph of $y = -3x^2$ opens down while the graph of $y = 3x^2$ opens up.

8.
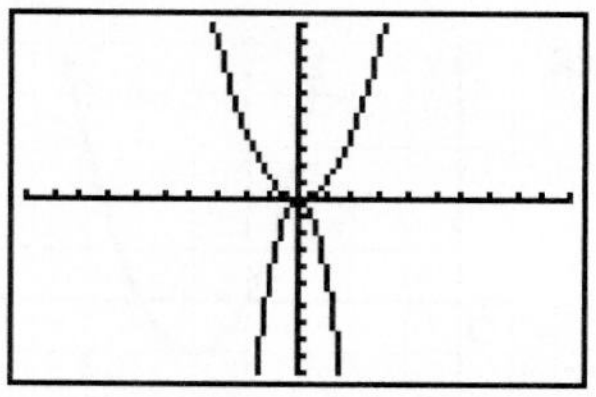

[−10, 10] scl: 1 by [−10, 10] scl: 1

The graph of $y = -4x^2$ opens down and is narrower than the graph of $y = x^2$.

9.
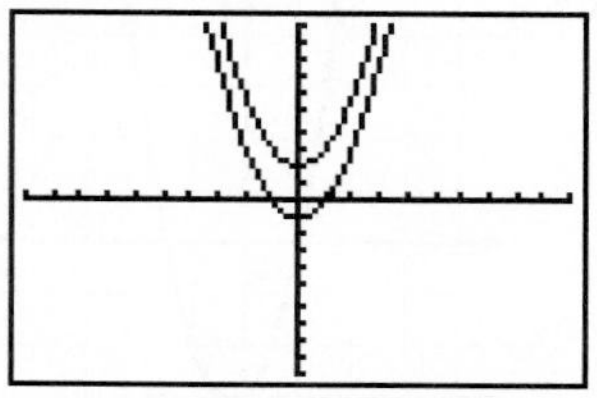

[−10, 10] scl: 1 by [−10, 10] scl: 1

Both graphs have the same shape, but the graph of $y = x^2 + 2$ is 2 units above the x-axis and the graph of $y = x^2 - 1$ is 1 unit below the x-axis.

10.
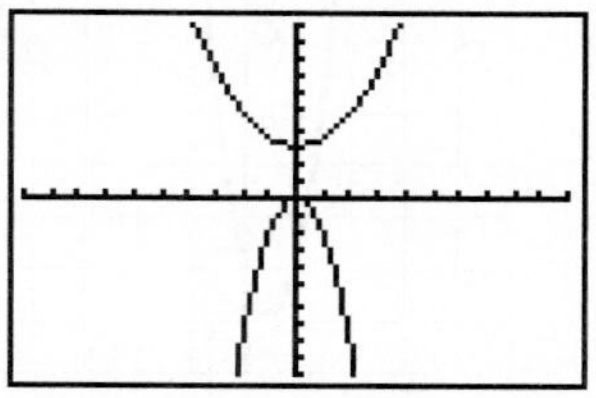

[−10, 10] scl: 1 by [−10, 10] scl: 1

The graph of $y = -2x^2$ opens down and is narrower than the graph of $y = \frac{1}{2}x^2 + 3$; also the graph of $y = \frac{1}{2}x^2 + 3$ is 3 units above the x-axis.

11.
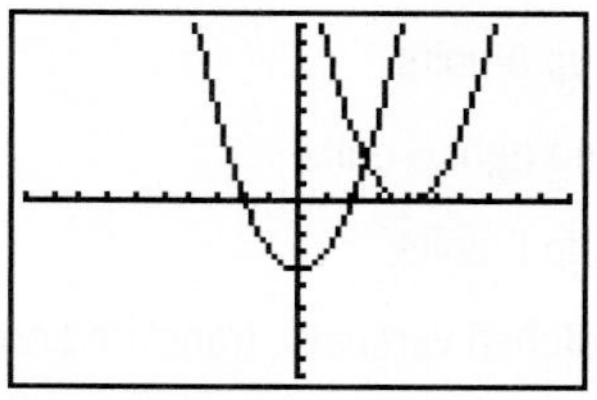

[−10, 10] scl: 1 by [−10, 10] scl: 1

Both graphs have the same shape, but the graph of $y = x^2 - 4$ is 4 units below the x-axis and the graph of $y = (x - 4)^2$ is 4 units to the right of the y-axis.

Lesson 9-3

24. 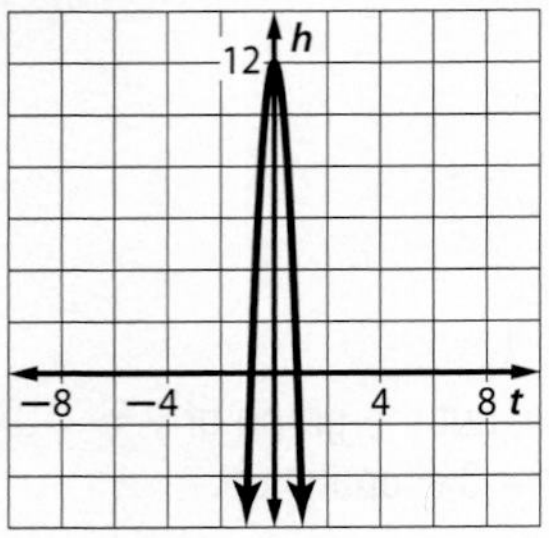

45. 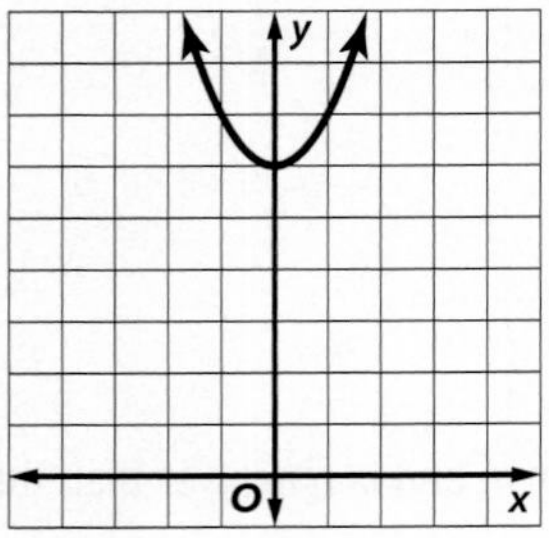

46. 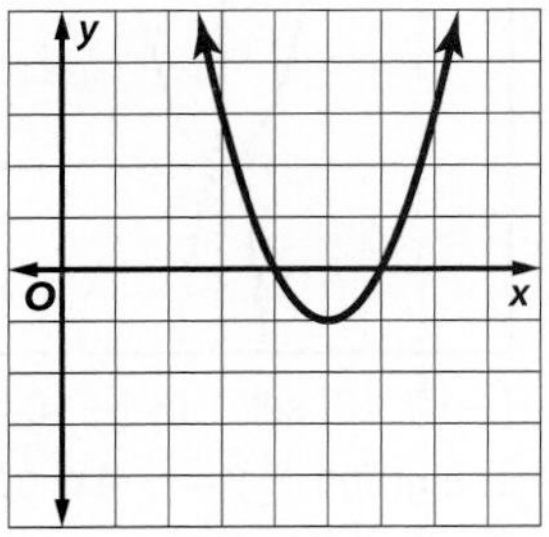

47. 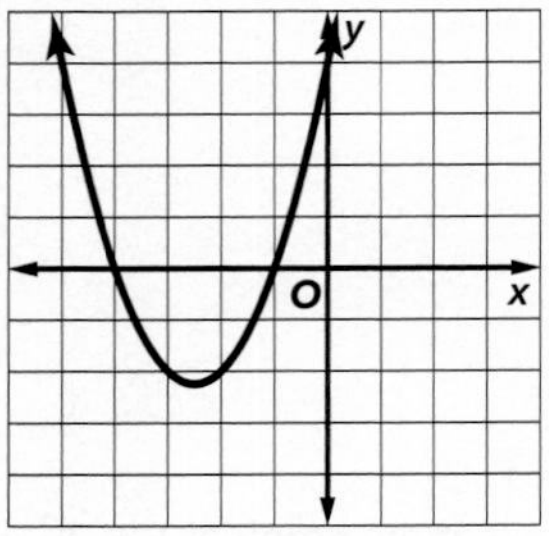

48. 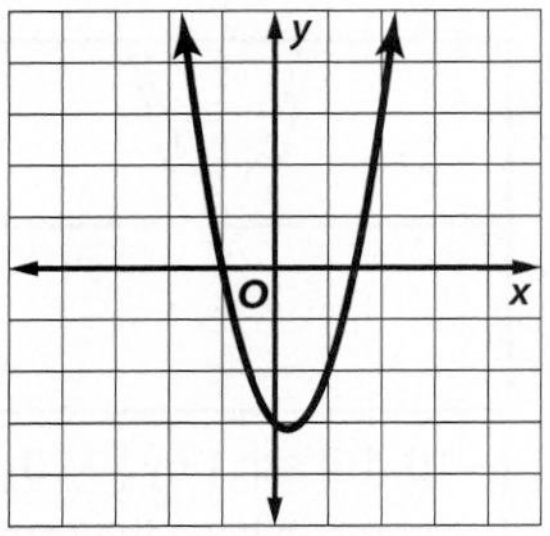

49. 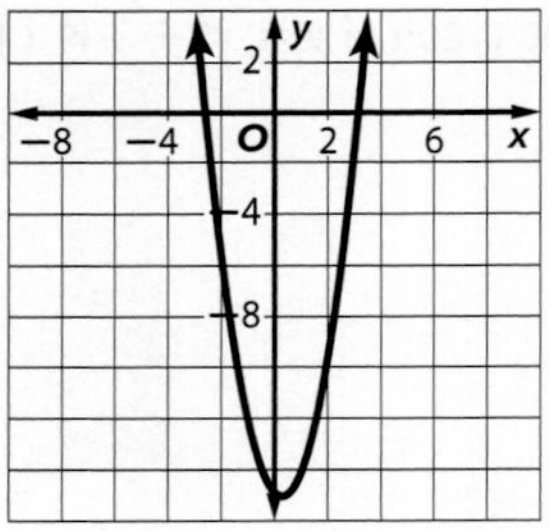

50. 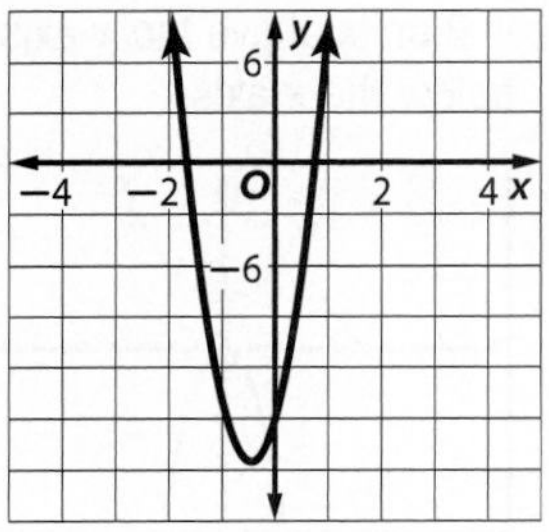

Lesson 9-4

57. translated down 12 units

58. translated left 2 units

59. stretched vertically, translated up 5 units

60. compressed vertically, translated right 6 units

61. stretched vertically, translated up 6 units

62. reflected across the x-axis, stretched vertically, translated down 1 unit

Extend 9-4

2. 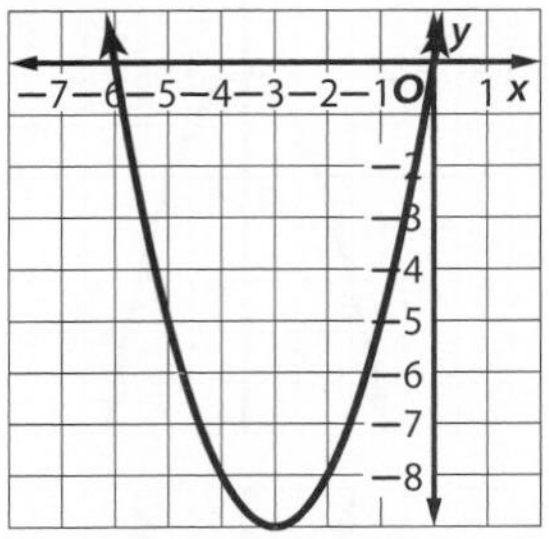

$y = (x + 3)^2 - 9$; $x = -3$; min. at $(-3, -9)$; $-6, 0$

3. 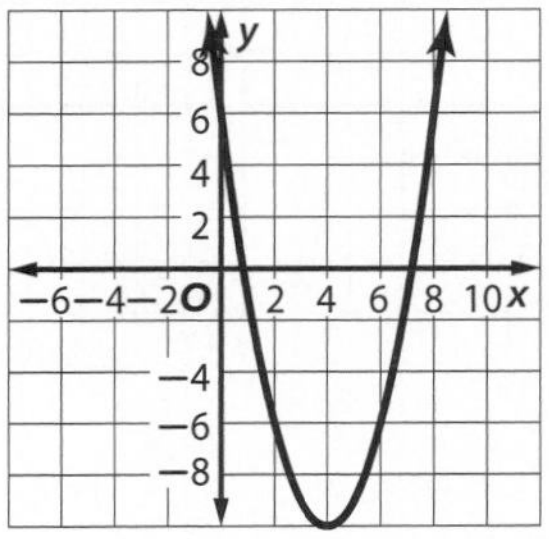

$y = (x - 4)^2 - 10$; $x = 4$; min. at $(4, -10)$; 0.84, 7.16

4. 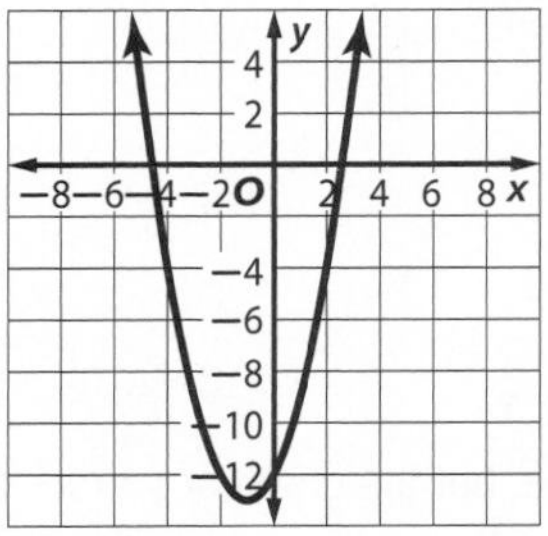

$y = (x + 1)^2 - 13$; $x = -1$; min. at $(-1, -13)$; –4.61, 2.61

5. 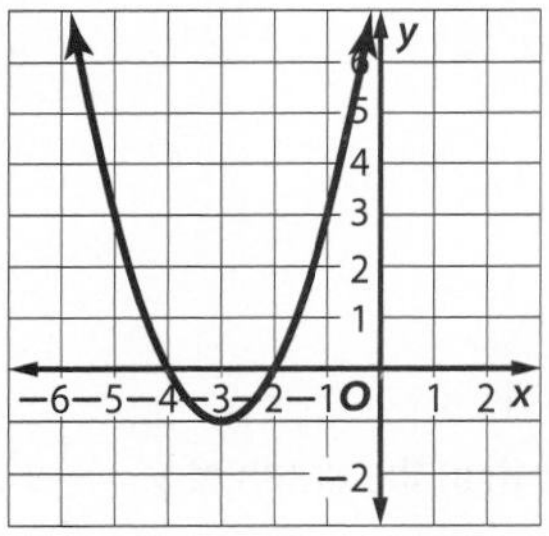

$y = (x + 3)^2 - 1$; $x = -3$; min. at $(-3, -1)$; –4, –2

6.

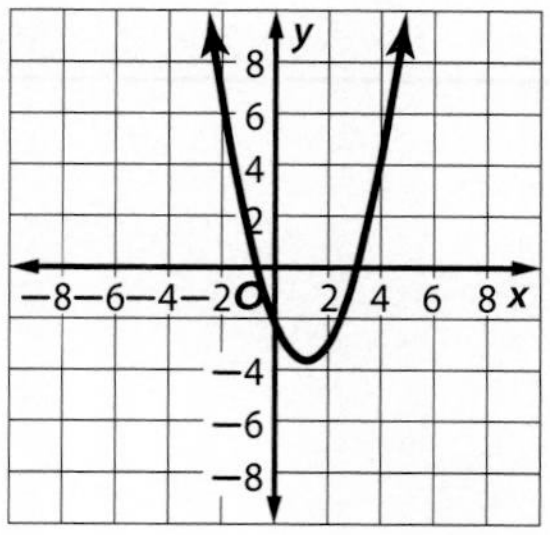

$y = (x - 2)^2 - 1$; $x = 2$; min. at (2, −1); 1, 3

7.

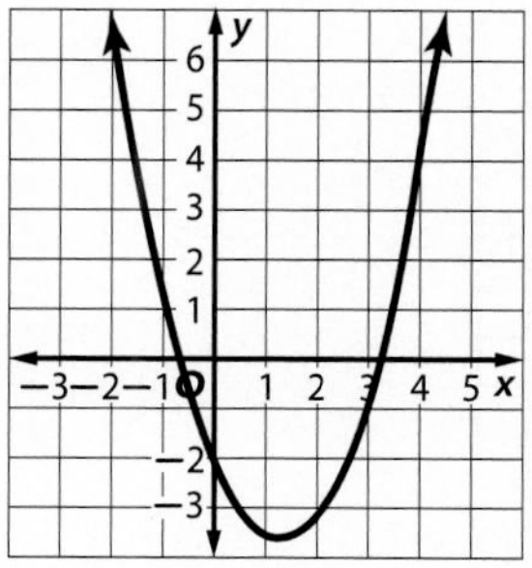

$y = (x - 1.2)^2 - 3.64$; $x = 1.2$; min. at (1.2, −3.64); −0.71, 3.11

8.

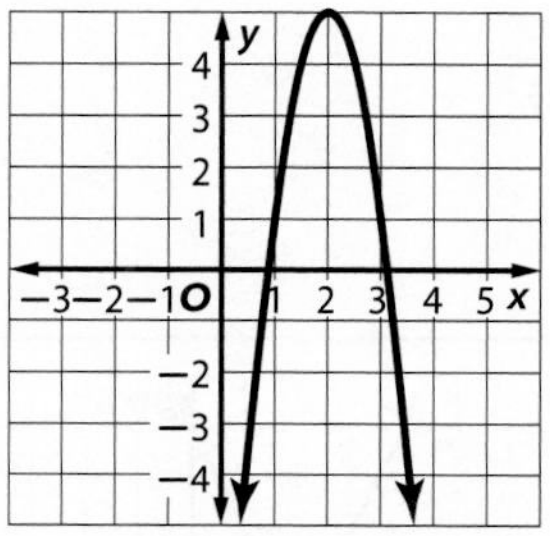

$y = -4(x - 2)^2 + 5$; $x = 2$; max. at (2, 5); 0.88, 3.11

9.

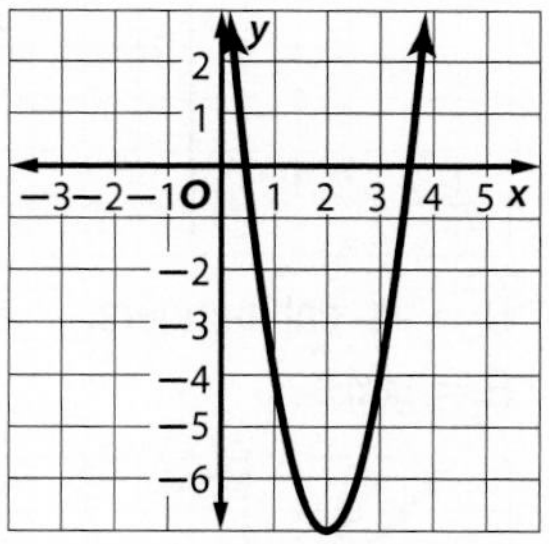

$y = 3(x - 2)^2 - 7$; $x = 2$; min. at (2, −7); 0.5, 3.5

10.

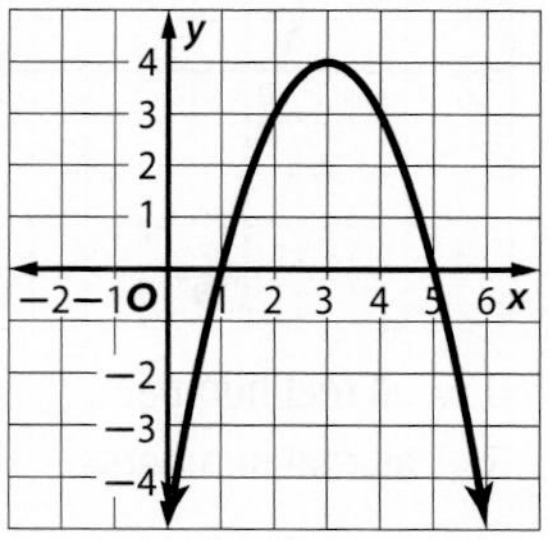

$y = -(x - 3)^2 + 4$; $x = 3$; max. at (3, 4); 1, 5

Mid-Chapter Quiz

1.

x	y
−3	1
−2	−1
−1	−1
0	1
1	5
2	11

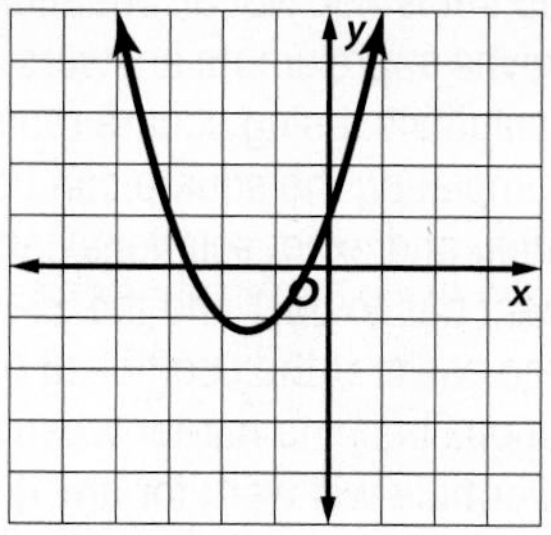

D = {all real numbers}
R = $\{y \mid y \geq -1.25\}$

2.

x	y
−3	33
−2	19
−1	9
0	3
1	1
2	3
3	9

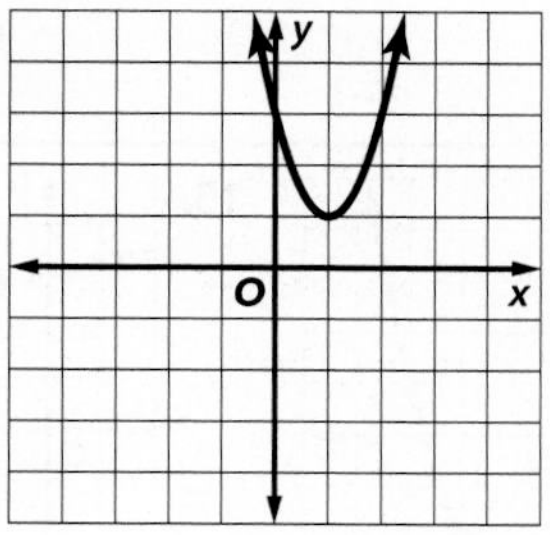

D = {all real numbers}
R = $\{y \mid y \geq 1\}$

3.

x	y
−3	−3
−2	−1
−1	−1
0	−3
1	−7
2	−13

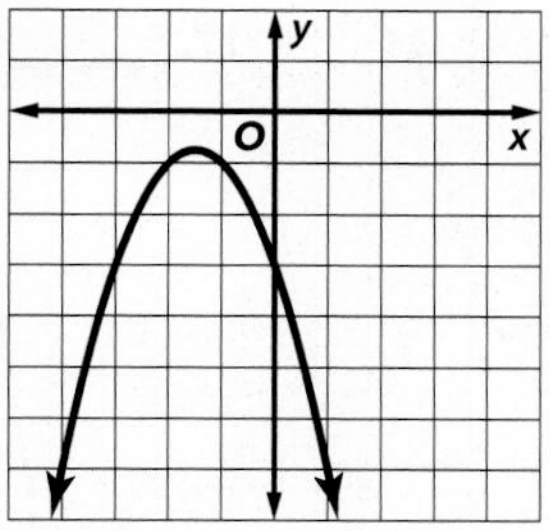

D = {all real numbers}
R = $\{y \mid y \leq -0.75\}$

4.

x	y
−3	−23
−2	−9
−1	−1
0	1
1	−3
2	−13

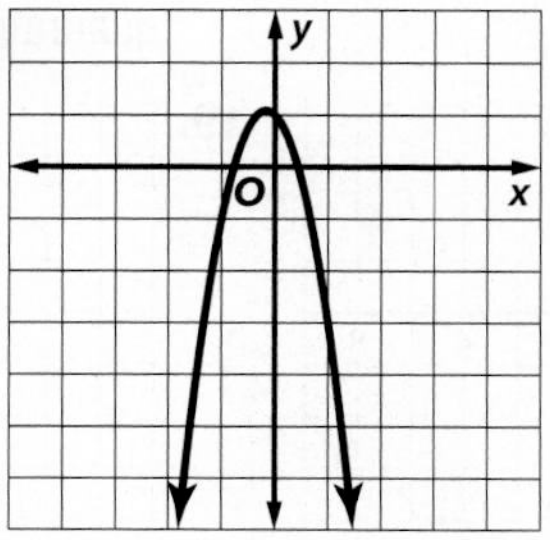

D = {all real numbers}
R = $\left\{y \mid y \leq 1\frac{1}{12}\right\}$

Lesson 9-5

52. Sample answer: The polynomial can be factored to get $f(x) = (x - 4)^2$, so the only real zero is 4. The discriminant is 0, so there is 1 real zero. The discriminant tells us how many real zeros there are. Factoring tells us what they are.

58. Sample answer: Factoring is easy if the polynomial is factorable and complicated if it is not. Not all equations are factorable. Graphing only gives approximate answers, but it is easy to see the number of solutions. Using square roots is easy when there is no x-term. Completing the square can be used for any quadratic equation and exact solutions can be found, but the leading coefficient has to be 1 and the x^2- and x-term must be isolated. It is also easier if the coefficient of the x-term is even; if not, the calculations become harder when dealing with fractions. The Quadratic Formula will work for any quadratic equation and exact solutions can be found. This method can be time consuming, especially if an equation is easily factored. See students' preferences.

Lesson 9-6

14.

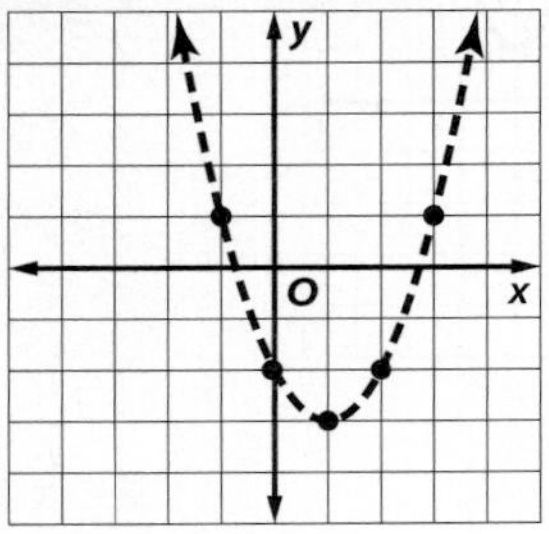

quadratic

15.

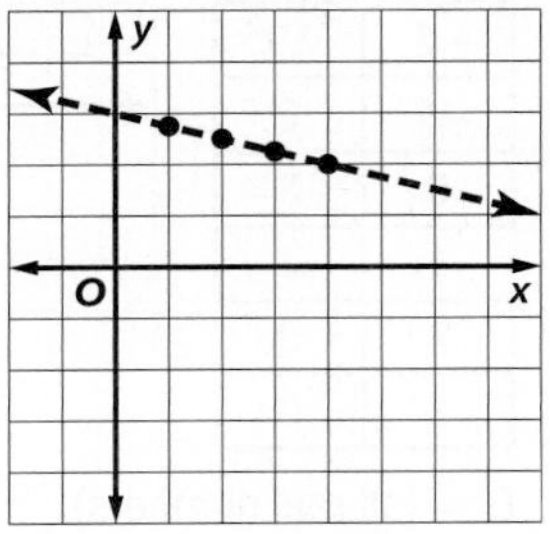

linear

16.

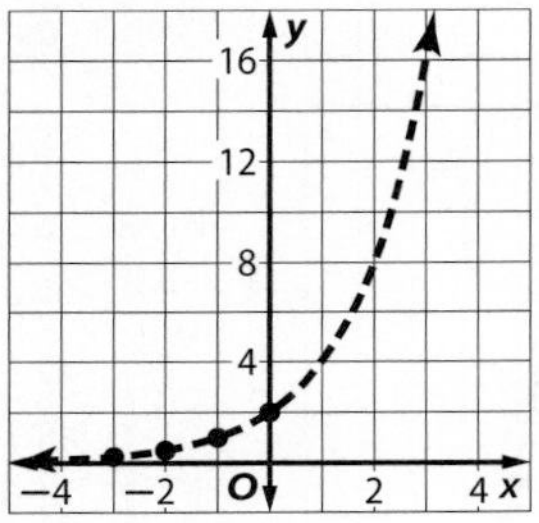

exponential

17.

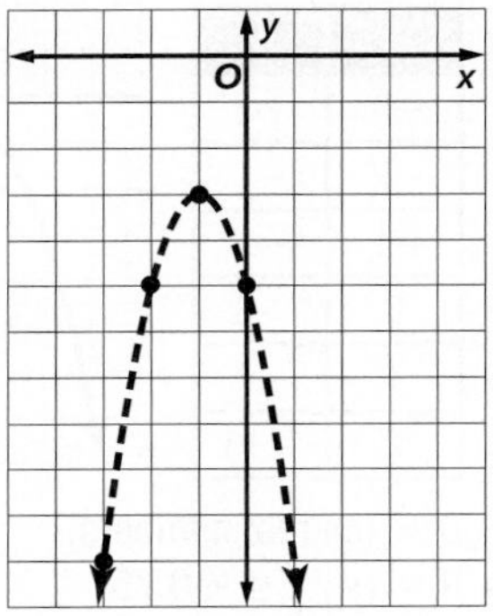

quadratic

18.

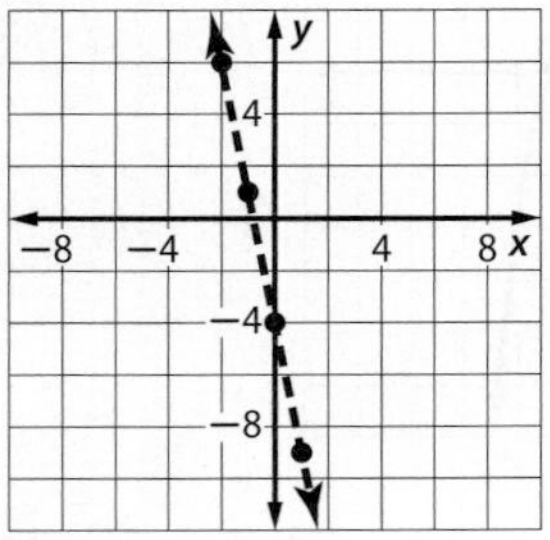

linear

19.

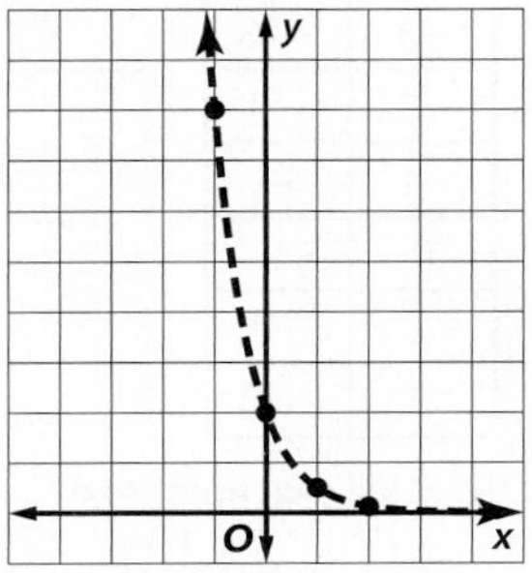

exponential

29a.

Time (hour)	0	1	2	3	4
Amount of Bacteria	12	36	108	324	972

Lesson 9-7 (Guided Practice)

1. D = all real numbers;
R = all even integers

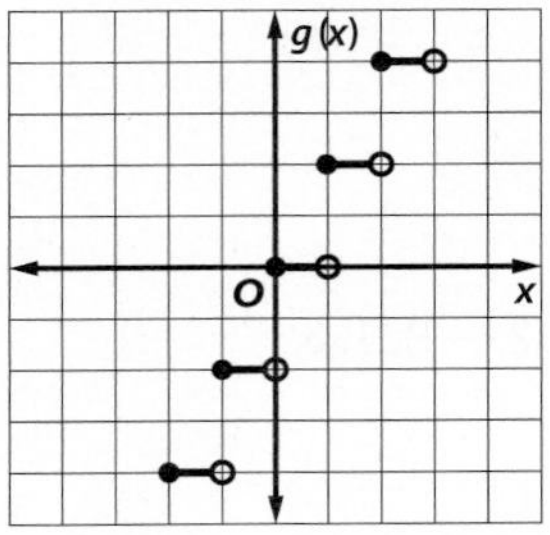

2. **Parking**

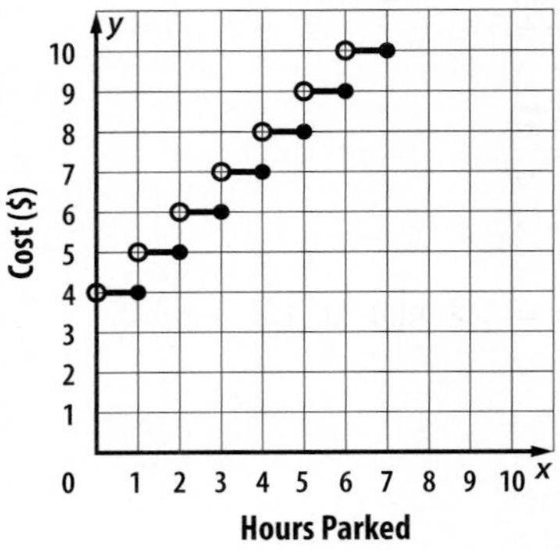

Lesson 9-7

5.

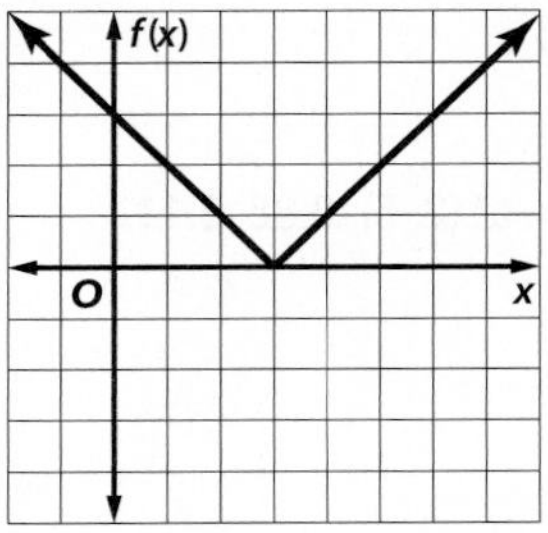

D = all real numbers,
R = $f(x) \geq 0$

6.

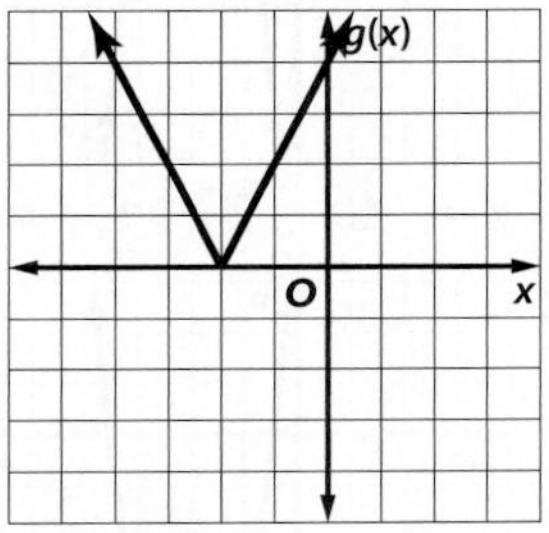

D = all real numbers,
R = $g(x) \geq 0$

7.

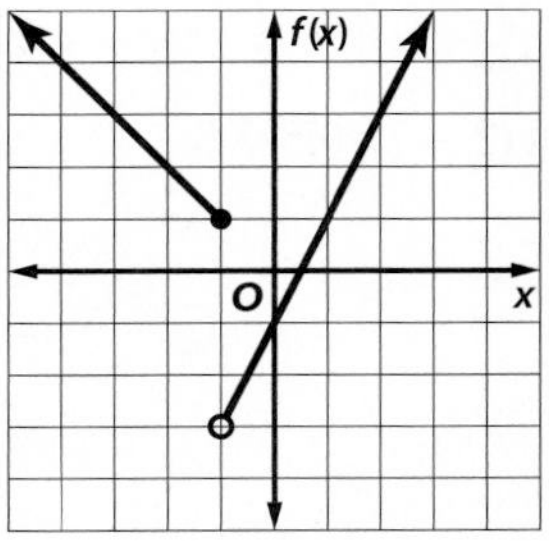

D = all real numbers,
R = $f(x) > -3$

8.

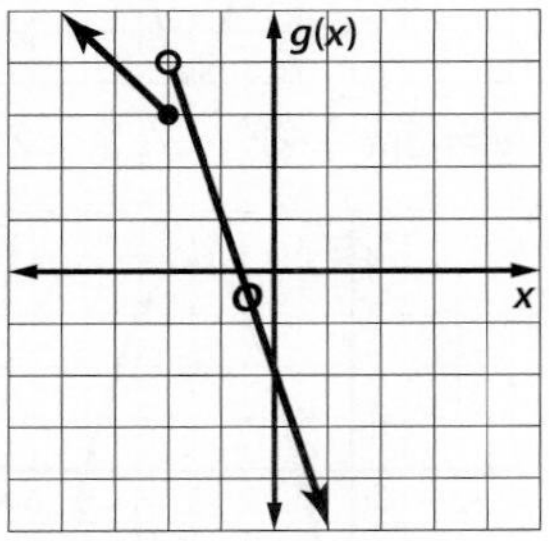

D = all real numbers,
R = all real numbers

9.

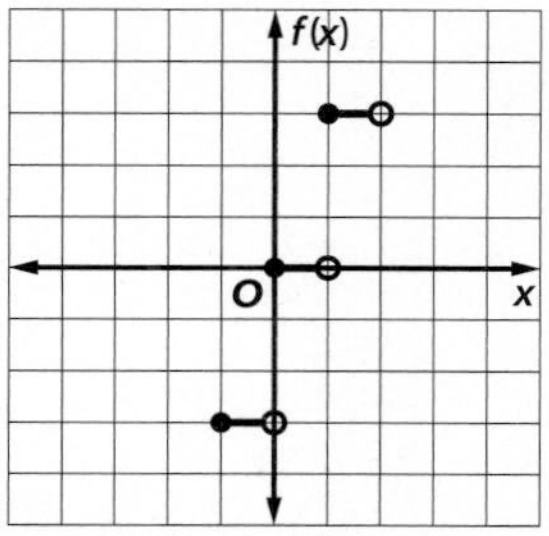

D = all real numbers,
R = all integer multiples of 3

10.

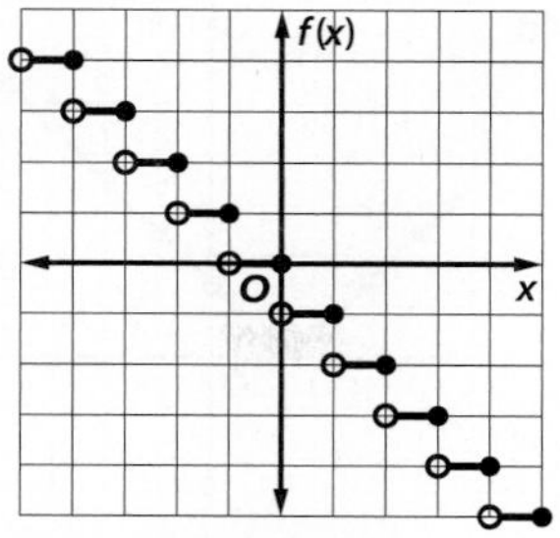

D = all real numbers,
R = all integers

11.

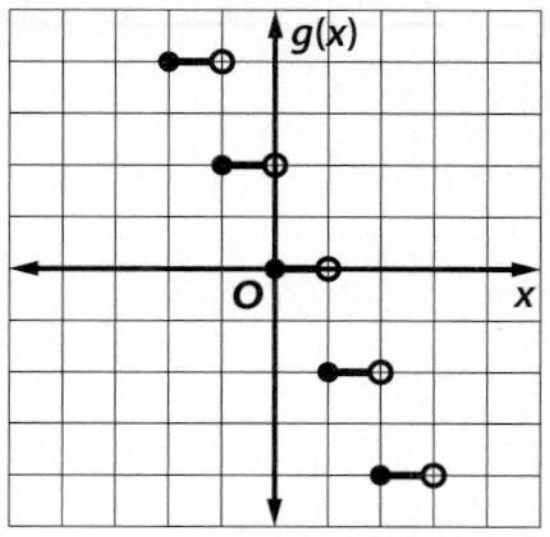

D = all real numbers,
R = all even integers

12.

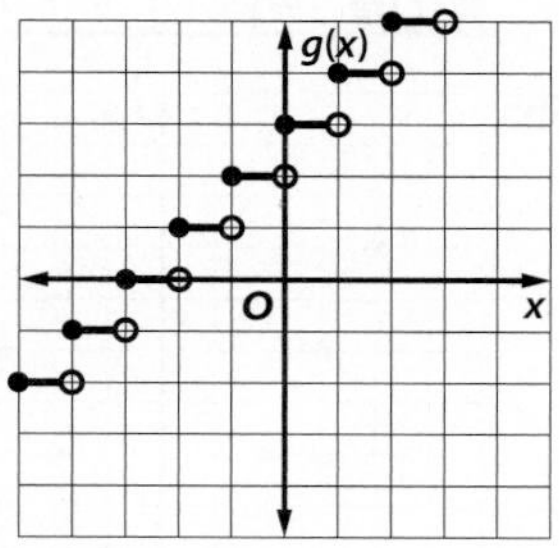

D = all real numbers,
R = all integers

13.

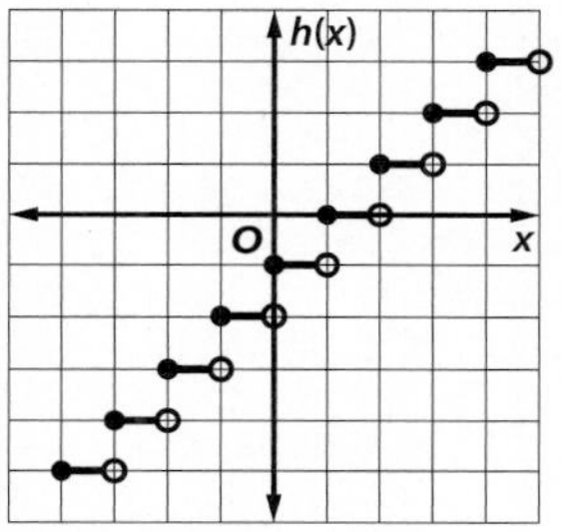

D = all real numbers,
R = all integers

14.

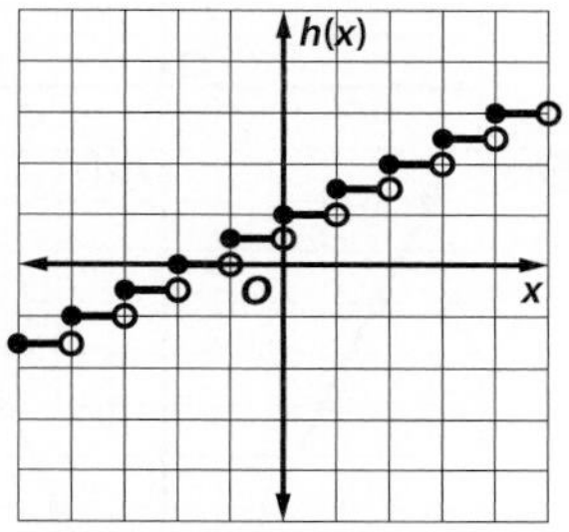

D = all real numbers, R = all integer multiples of 0.5

15a.

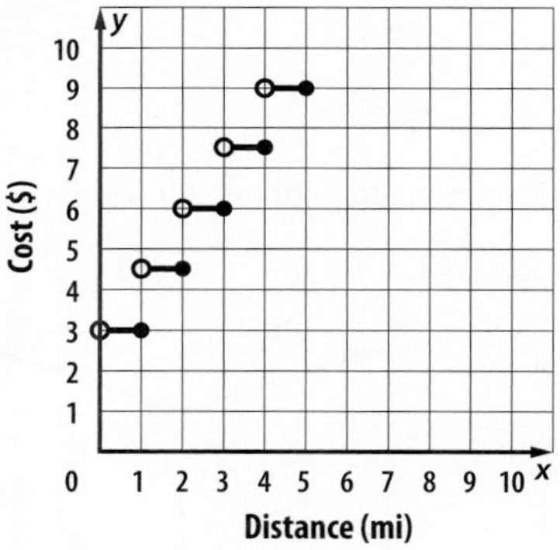

16.

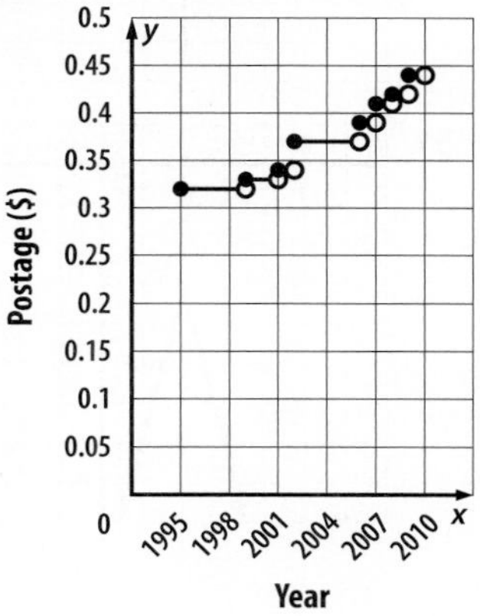

17.

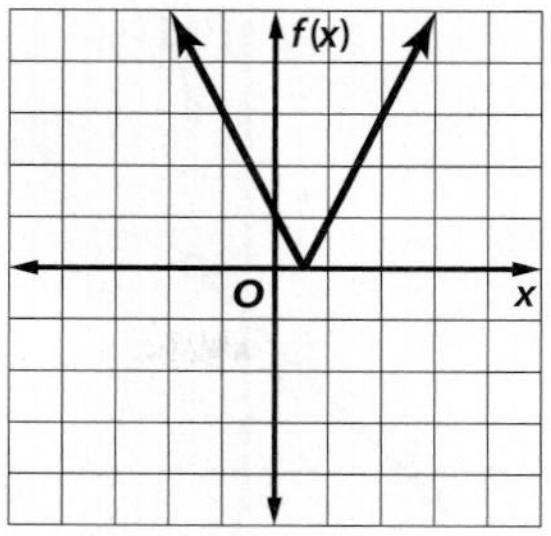

D = all real numbers,
R = $f(x) \geq 0$

18.

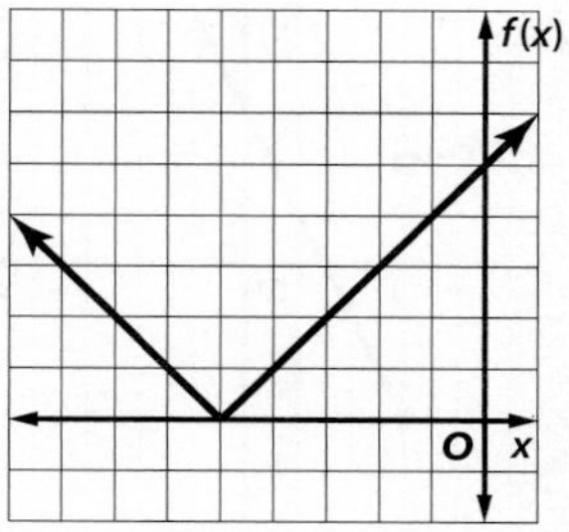

D = all real numbers,
R = $f(x) \geq 0$

19.

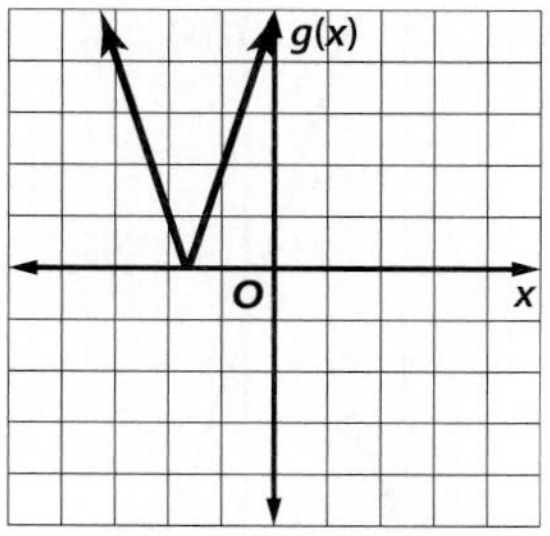

D = all real numbers,
R = $g(x) \geq 0$

20.

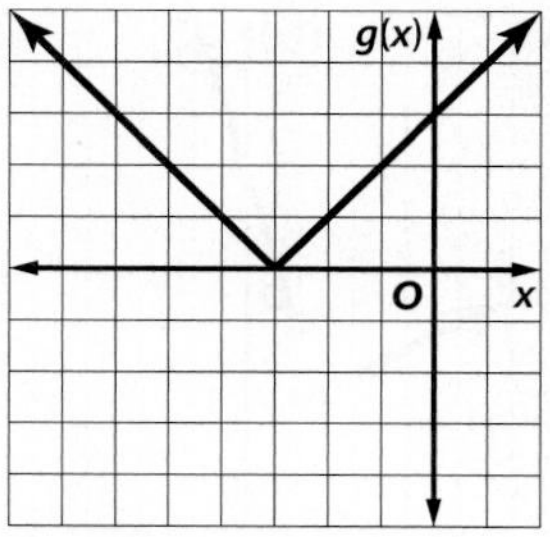

D = all real numbers,
R = $g(x) \geq 0$

21.

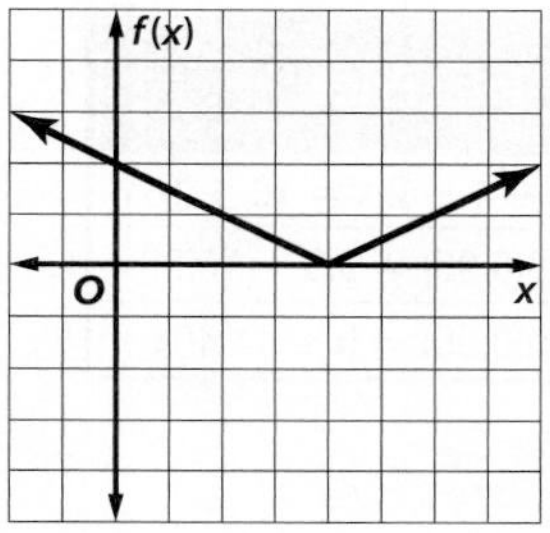

D = all real numbers,
R = $f(x) \geq 0$

22.

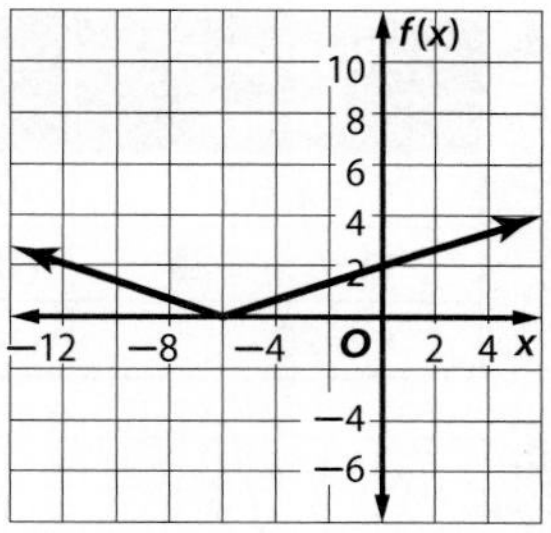

D = all real numbers,
R = $f(x) \geq 0$

23.

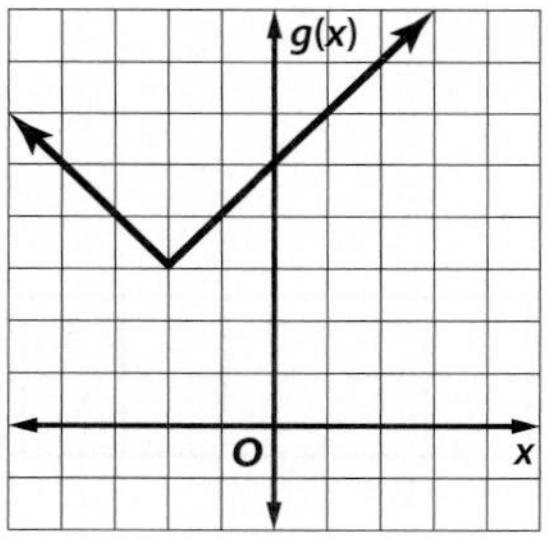

D = all real numbers,
R = $g(x) \geq 3$

24.

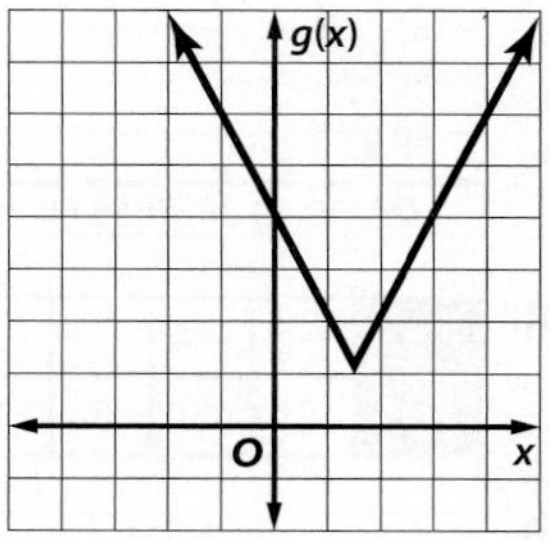

D = all real numbers,
R = $g(x) \geq 1$

25.

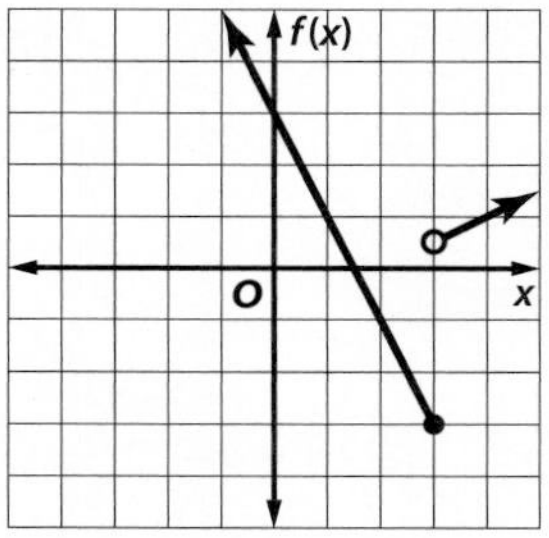

D = all real numbers,
R = $f(x) \geq -3$

26.

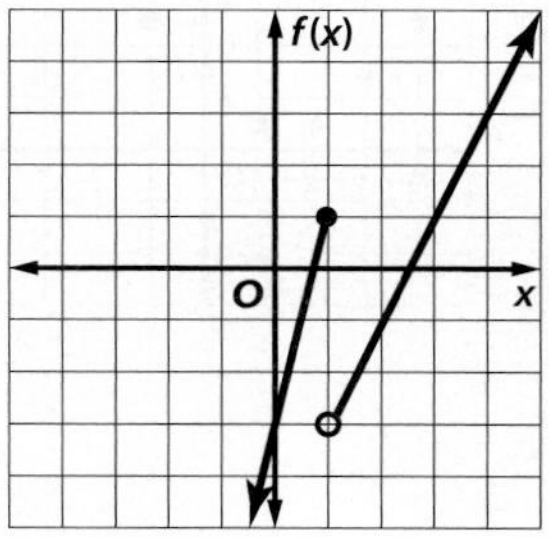

D = all real numbers,
R = all real numbers

27.

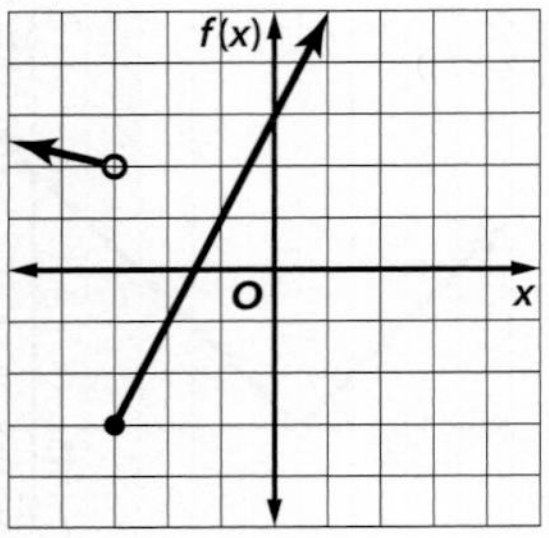

D = all real numbers,
R = all real numbers

28.

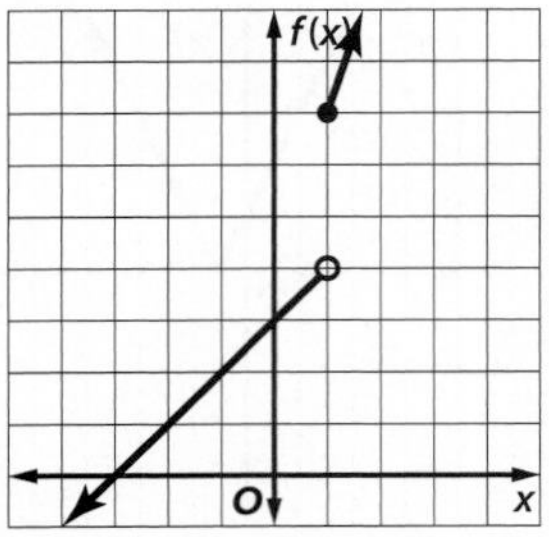

D = all real numbers,
R = $f(x) < 4$ or $f(x) \geq 7$

29.

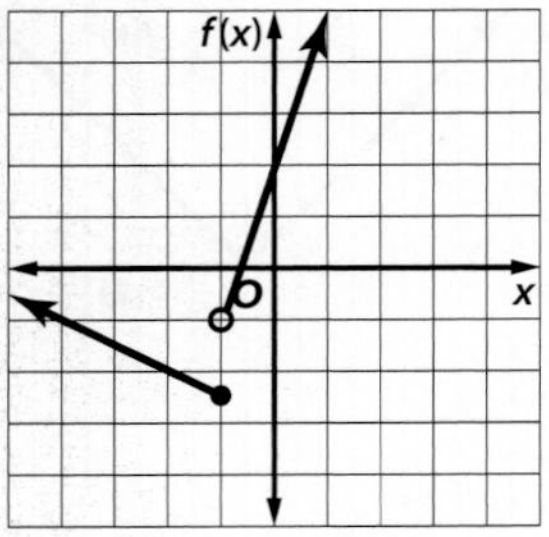

D = all real numbers,
R = $f(x) \geq -2.5$

30.

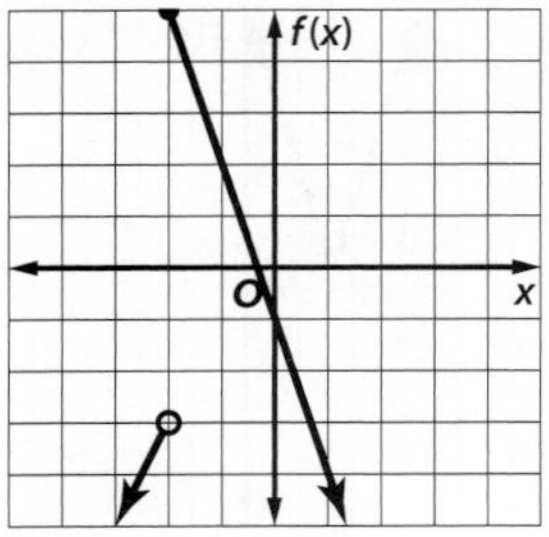

D = all real numbers,
R = $f(x) \leq 5$

43a.

Number of Orders	Total Price
$1 \leq x \leq 10$	$10 + (10 + 4 + 2)x = 10 + 16x$
$11 \leq x < 20$	$(10 + 16x)(0.95) = 9.5 + 15.20x$
$x \geq 20$	$(10 + 16x)(0.90) = 9 + 14.40x$

43c.

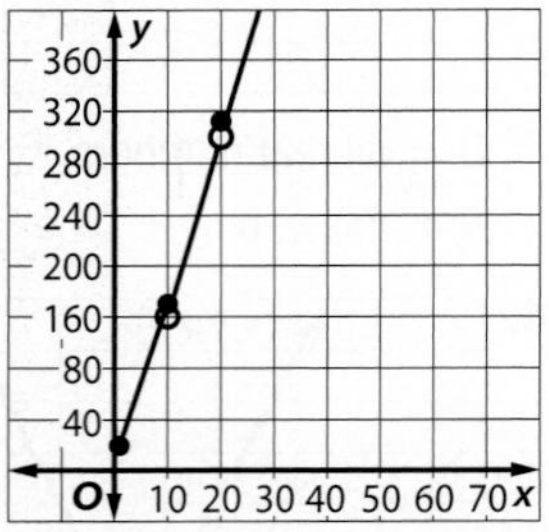

44a.

x	−5	−4	−3	−2	−1	0	1	2	3	4	5
$f(x)$	7	5	3	1	1	3	5	7	9	11	13

44b.

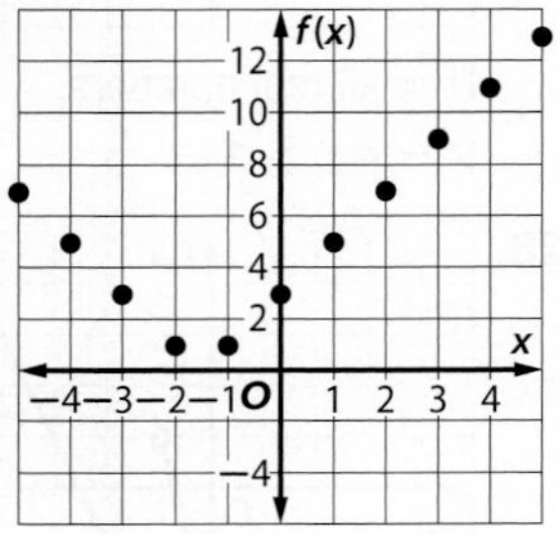

44c.

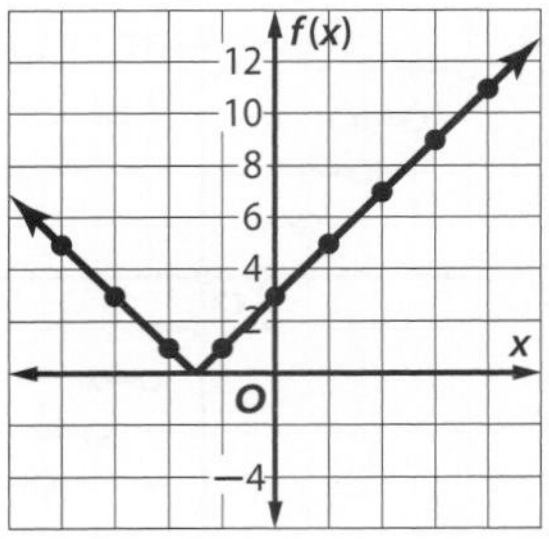

45a.

x	−5	−4	−3	−2	−1	0	1	2	3	4	5
$f(x)$	13	11	9	7	5	3	5	7	9	11	13

45b.

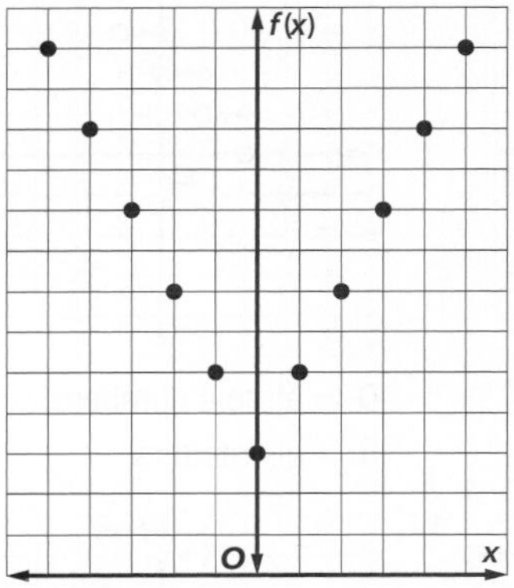

45c.

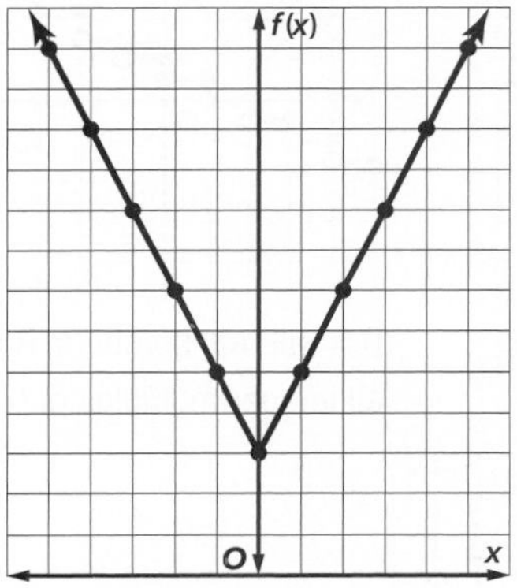

45d. The graph is shifted 1.5 units to the right and 3 units up.

48.

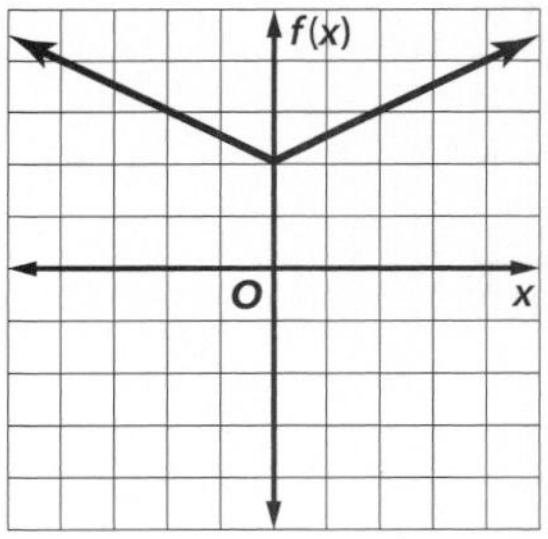

49.

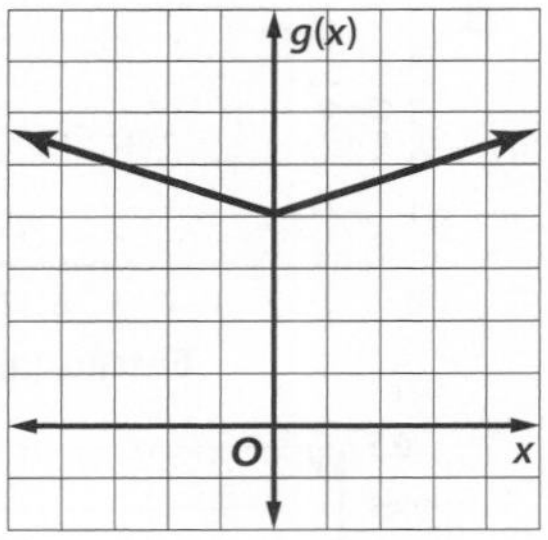

50.

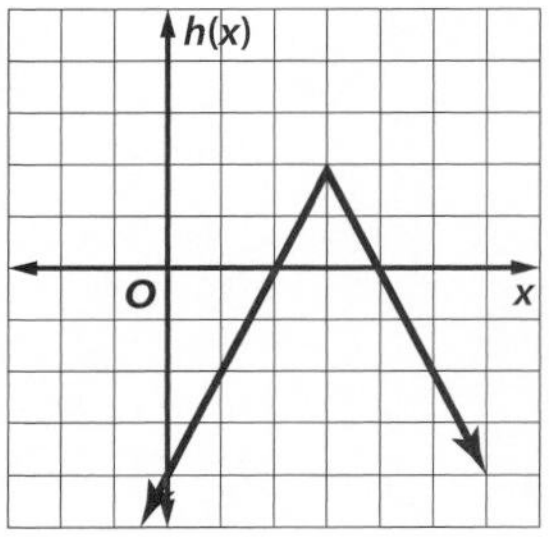

51.

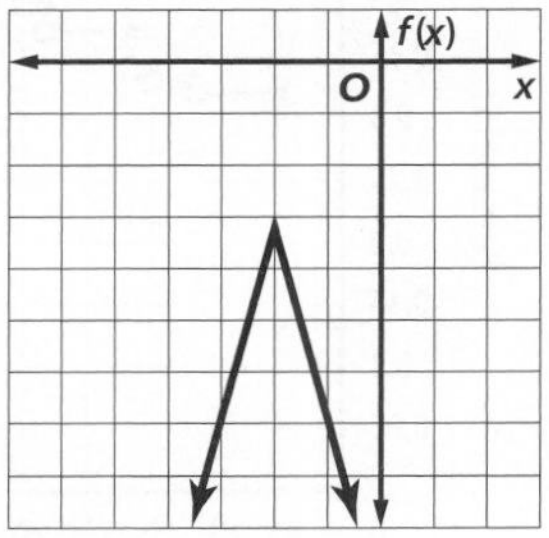

52.

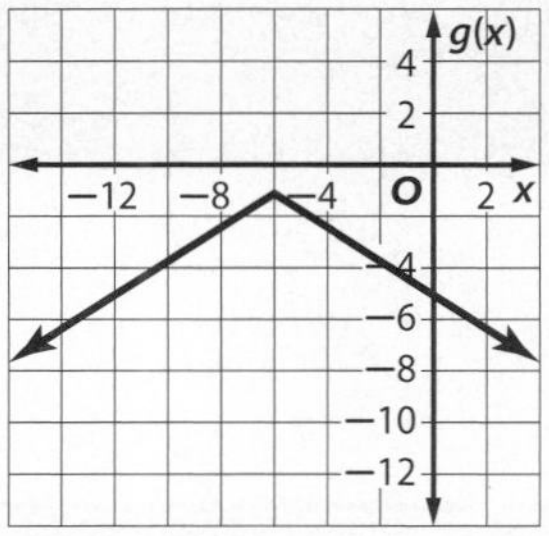

53.

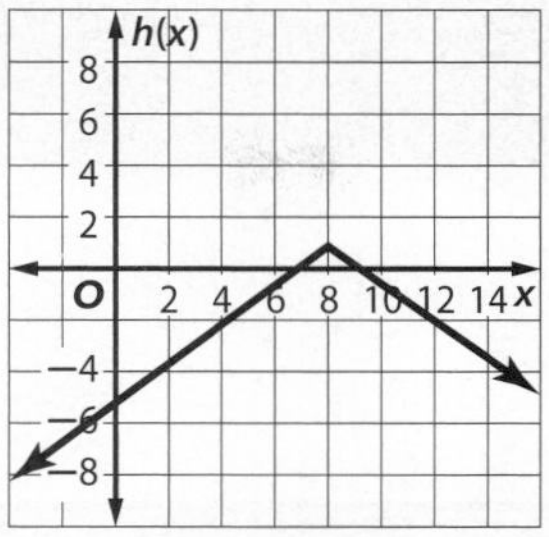

54b.

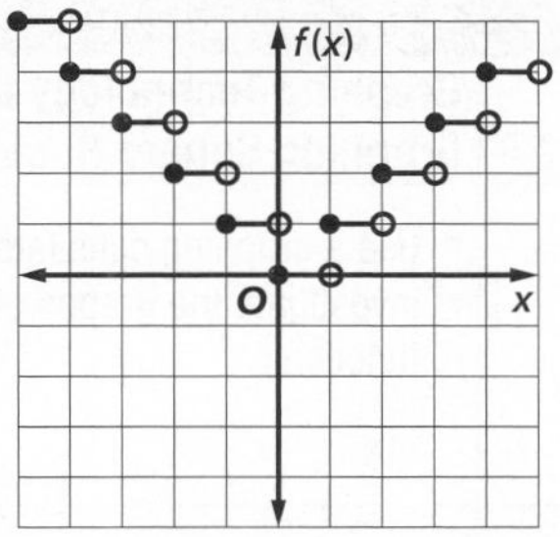

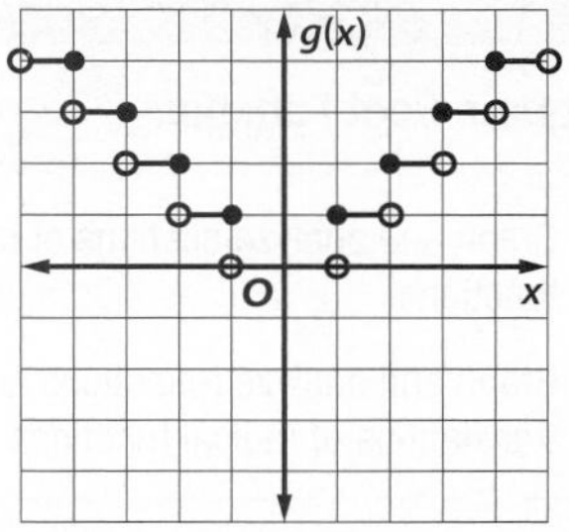

60b.

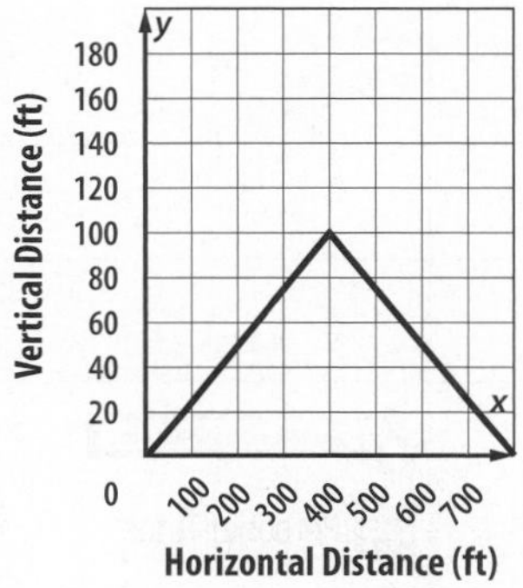

Practice Test

1.

x	y
−3	8
−2	5
−1	4
0	5
1	8
2	13

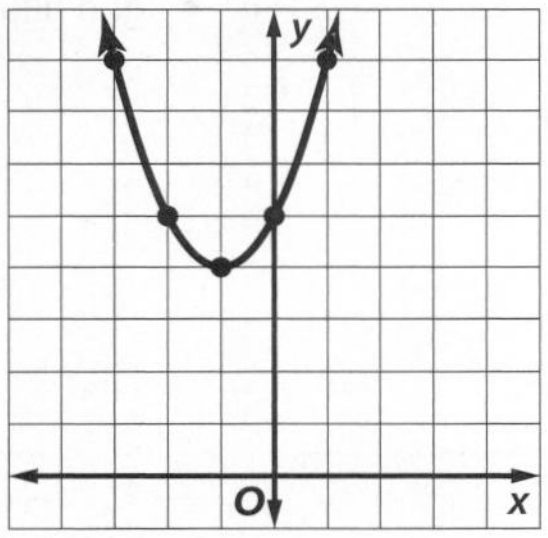

D = {all real numbers}; R = $\{y \mid y \geq 4\}$

2.

x	y
−2	15
−1	6
0	1
1	0
2	3
3	10

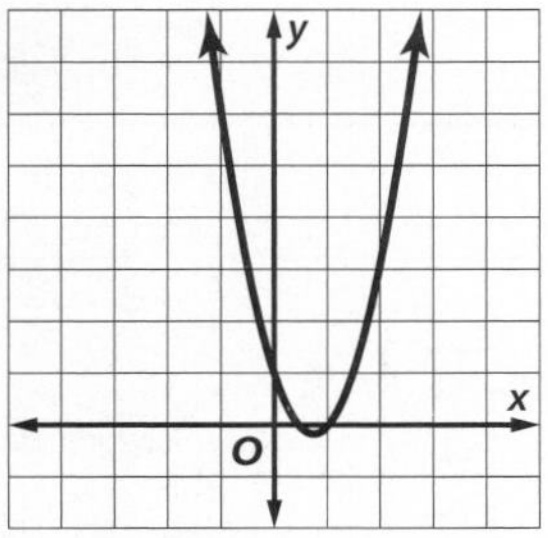

D = {all real numbers}; R = $\{y \mid y \geq -0.125\}$

22.

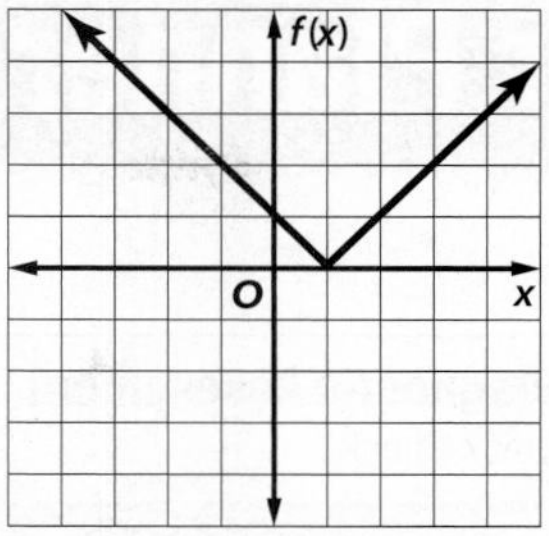

23.

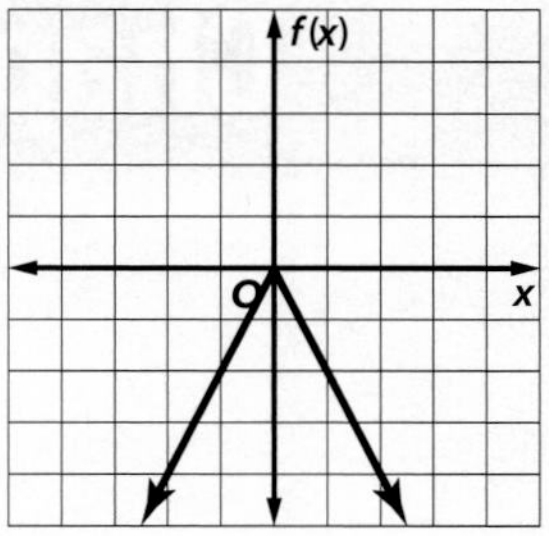

24.

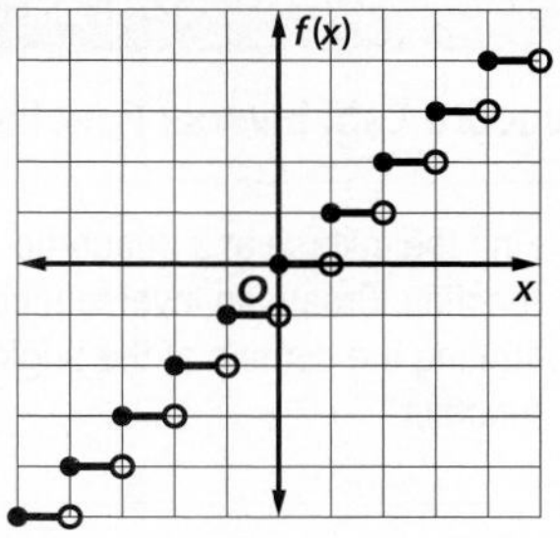

25.

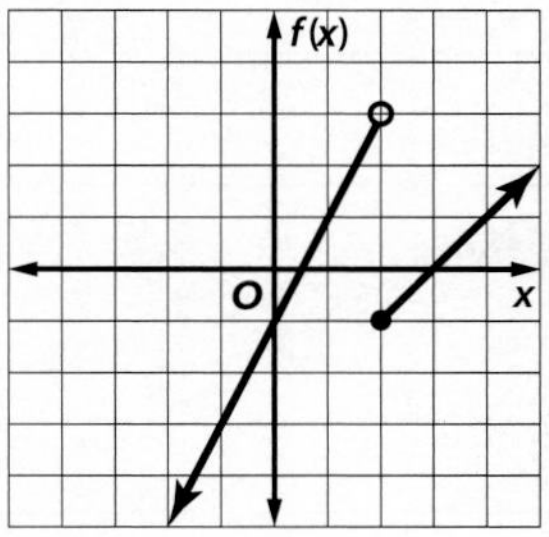

Chapter Planner

Diagnostic Assessment
Quick Check

	EXPLORE 10-1 (45 min: 0.5 day; 90 min: 0.5 day)	LESSON 10-1 (45 min: 1 day; 90 min: 0.5 day)	EXTEND 10-1 (45 min: 0.5 day; 90 min: 0.5 day)
Title	**Algebra Lab: Inverse Functions**	**Square Root Functions**	**Graphing Technology Lab: Graphing Square Root Functions**
Objectives	▪ Find the inverse of a quadratic function. Create an inverse function by limiting the domain of the original function.	▪ Graph and analyze dilations of radical functions. ▪ Graph and analyze reflections and translations of radical functions.	▪ Use a graphing calculator to investigate the graphs of square root functions.
Key Vocabulary		square root function radical function radicand	
Content Standards		PS.6	
Multiple Representations			
Lesson Resources	connectED.mcgraw-hill.com ▪ *Teaching Algebra with Manipulatives* **Materials:** ▪ grid paper	connectED.mcgraw-hill.com Leveled Worksheets Vocabulary Animations Personal Tutor Virtual Manipulatives Self-Check Quiz ▪ *5-Minute Check* ▪ *Study Notebook*	connectED.mcgraw-hill.com Personal Tutor **Materials:** ▪ TI-83/84 Plus or other graphing calculator ▪ grid paper
Resources for Every Lesson	IWB eStudent Edition IWB Interactive Classroom	▪ eTeacher Edition ▪ eSolutions Manual ▪ McGraw-Hill Assessment	
Differentiated Instruction		pp. 623, 626	

IWB All digital assets are Interactive Whiteboard ready.

Suggested Pacing			
Time Periods	Instruction	Review & Assess	Total
45-minute	10 days	2 days	12 days
90-minute	7 days	1 day	8 days

LESSON 10-2 (45 min: 1 day; 90 min: 0.5 day)	EXTEND 10-2 (45 min: 0.5 day; 90 min: 0.5 day)	LESSON 10-3 (45 min: 1 day; 90 min: 0.5 day)	EXTEND 10-3 (45 min: 0.5 day; 90 min: 0.5 day)
Simplifying Radical Expressions	**Algebra Lab: Rational and Irrational Numbers**	**Operations with Radical Expressions**	**Algebra Lab: Simplifying *n*th Root Expressions**
▪ Simplify radical expressions by using the Product Property of Square Roots. ▪ Simplify radical expressions by using the Quotient Property of Square Roots.	▪ Investigate the products and sums of two rational numbers, two irrational numbers, and a rational and irrational number.	▪ Add and subtract radical expressions. ▪ Multiply radical expressions.	▪ Simplify radical expressions with indices greater than 2 and with variables and/or rational numbers in the radicand.
radical expression rationalizing the denominator conjugate	closed		*n*th root index
PS.7, PS.8, AI.RNE.4	AI.RNE.2	PS.2, AI.RNE.4	
connectED.mcgraw-hill.com Leveled Worksheets Quiz 1 Vocabulary Personal Tutor Self-Check Quiz ▪ *5-Minute Check* ▪ *Study Notebook*	connectED.mcgraw-hill.com Vocabulary Personal Tutor	connectED.mcgraw-hill.com Leveled Worksheets Animations Personal Tutor Self-Check Quiz ▪ *5-Minute Check* ▪ *Study Notebook* ▪ *Teaching Algebra with Manipulatives*	connectED.mcgraw-hill.com Vocabulary ▪ *Teaching Algebra with Manipulatives*
IWB eStudent Edition IWB Interactive Classroom	▪ eTeacher Edition ▪ eSolutions Manual ▪ McGraw-Hill eAssessment		
pp. 630, 633		pp. 608, 611	

Chapter Planner

	LESSON 10-4 (45 min: 1 day; 90 min: 0.5 day)	LESSON 10-5 (45 min: 1 day; 90 min: 1 day)	EXTEND 10-5 (45 min: 1 day; 90 min: 0.5 day)
Title	**Radical Equations**	**The Pythagorean Theorem**	**Algebra Lab: Distance on the Coordinate Plane**
Objectives	▪ Solve radical equations. ▪ Solve radical equations with extraneous solutions.	▪ Solve problems by using the Pythagorean Theorem. ▪ Determine whether a triangle is a right triangle.	▪ Investigate distances on the coordinate plane.
Key Vocabulary	radical equations extraneous solutions	hypotenuse legs converse Pythagorean triple	Distance Formula midpoint
Content Standards	PS.3, PS.4	PS.1	
Multiple Representations	✓	✓	
Lesson Resources	connectED.mcgraw-hill.com Leveled Worksheets Quiz 2 Vocabulary Animations Personal Tutor Self-Check Quiz ▪ *5-Minute Check* ▪ *Study Notebook*	connectED.mcgraw-hill.com Leveled Worksheets Quiz 3 Vocabulary Animations Personal Tutor Self-Check Quiz ▪ *5-Minute Check* ▪ *Study Notebook* ▪ *Teaching Algebra with Manipulatives*	connectED.mcgraw-hill.com Vocabulary Virtual Manipulatives ▪ *Teaching Algebra with Manipulatives* **Materials:** ▪ grid paper ▪ ruler
Resources for Every Lesson	IWB eStudent Edition IWB Interactive Classroom	▪ eTeacher Edition ▪ eSolutions Manual ▪ McGraw-Hill eAssessment	
Differentiated Instruction	pp. 613, 616	pp. 619, 623	
	Formative Assessment Mid-Chapter Quiz		

IWB All digital assets are Interactive Whiteboard ready.

EXPLORE 10-6 (45 min: 0.5 day; 90 min: 0.5 day)	LESSON 10-6 (45 min: 1.5 days; 90 min: 1 day)
Algebra Lab: Investigating Trigonometric Ratios	**Trigonometric Ratios**
▪ Investigate trigonometric ratios.	▪ Find trigonometric ratios of angles. ▪ Use trigonometry to solve triangles.
	trigonometry, trigonometric ratio, sine, cosine, tangent, solving the triangle, inverse sine, inverse cosine, inverse tangent
	PS.5
connectED.mcgraw-hill.com Animations Virtual Manipulatives ▪ *Teaching Algebra with Manipulatives* **Materials:** ▪ ruler ▪ protractor ▪ grid paper	connectED.mcgraw-hill.com Leveled Worksheets Quiz 4 Vocabulary Animations Personal Tutor Self-Check Quiz ▪ *5-Minute Check* ▪ *Study Notebook*
IWB eStudent Edition IWB Interactive Classroom	▪ eTeacher Edition ▪ eSolutions Manual ▪ McGraw-Hill eAssessment
	pp. 657, 662
	Summative Assessment Study Guide and Review Practice Test

Assessment and Intervention

SE = Student Edition, **TE** = Teacher Edition, **CRM** = Chapter Resource Masters

	Diagnosis	Prescription
DIAGNOSTIC ASSESSMENT	**Beginning Chapter 10**	
	Get Ready for Chapter 10 **SE**	Response to Intervention **TE**
	Beginning Every Lesson	
	Then, Now, Why? **SE** 5-Minute Check	Chapter 0 **SE** *Quick Review Math Handbook*
FORMATIVE ASSESSMENT	**During/After Every Lesson**	
	Guided Practice **SE**, every example Check Your Understanding **SE** H.O.T. Problems **SE** Spiral Review **SE** Additional Examples **TE** Watch Out! **TE** Step 4, Assess **TE** Chapter 10 Quizzes **CRM**, pp. 45–46 Self-Check Quizzes connectED.mcgraw-hill.com	TIER 1 Intervention Skills Practice **CRM**, Ch. 1–10 connectED.mcgraw-hill.com TIER 2 Intervention Differentiated Instruction **TE** Differentiated Homework Options **TE** Study Guide and Intervention **CRM**, Ch. 1–10 *Quick Review Math Handbook* TIER 3 Intervention *Math Triumphs, Alg. 1*
	Mid-Chapter	
	Mid-Chapter Quiz **SE** Mid-Chapter Test **CRM**, p. 59 McGraw-Hill eAssessment	TIER 1 Intervention Skills Practice **CRM**, Ch. 1–10 connectED.mcgraw-hill.com TIER 2 Intervention Study Guide and Intervention **CRM**, Ch. 1–10; *Quick Review Math Handbook* TIER 3 Intervention *Math Triumphs, Alg. 1*
	Before Chapter Test	
	Chapter Study Guide and Review **SE** Practice Test **SE** Standardized Test Practice **SE** Chapter Test connectED.mcgraw-hill.com Standardized Test Practice connectED.mcgraw-hill.com Vocabulary Review connectED.mcgraw-hill.com McGraw-Hill eAssessment	TIER 1 Intervention Skills Practice **CRM**, Ch. 1–10 connectED.mcgraw-hill.com TIER 2 Intervention Study Guide and Intervention **CRM**, Ch. 1–10; *Quick Review Math Handbook* TIER 3 Intervention *Math Triumphs, Alg. 1*
SUMMATIVE ASSESSMENT	**After Chapter 10**	
	Multiple-Choice Tests, Forms 1, 2A, 2B **CRM**, pp. 49–54 Free-Response Tests, Forms 2C, 2D, 3 **CRM**, pp. 55–60 Vocabulary Test **CRM**, p. 48 Extended Response Test **CRM**, p. 61 Standardized Test Practice **CRM**, pp. 62–64 McGraw-Hill eAssessment	Study Guide and Intervention **CRM**, Ch. 1–10 *Quick Review Math Handbook* connectED.mcgraw-hill.com

Differentiated Instruction

Option 1 Reaching All Learners AL OL BL ELL

Auditory Discuss with your class the parts of a right triangle that are used to define the sine, cosine, and tangent ratios. As a class, determine which side is opposite and which is adjacent to each of the acute angles of a right triangle. Ask students to refer to the Study Tip on p. 657. Explain how SOH-CAH-TOA (pronounced soa • kuh • TOE • uh) can be used to help them remember the definitions for sine, cosine, and tangent.

Visual/Spatial Perfect squares can be removed from under a radical sign and written as a square root. For example, because $\sqrt{25} = 5$, $\sqrt{50} = \sqrt{25 \cdot 2} = 5\sqrt{2}$. Suggest that groups make a colorful poster of all the perfect squares from 0 to 400.

Logical One of the conceptually challenging ideas in working with translations of parent graphs is understanding why $y = \sqrt{x - 4}$ moves a graph right (in the positive direction) and $y = \sqrt{x + 4}$ moves a graph left (in the negative direction). Ask students to develop an explanation using examples to show why this happens.

Option 2 Approaching Level AL

On the board, draw several right triangles oriented in different ways. Then have volunteers label the hypotenuse of each triangle. Ask how they know they chose the correct side. The longest side of a right triangle is always the hypotenuse and is always directly opposite the right angle.

Option 3 English Learners ELL

Have students engage in conversations about the Pythagorean Theorem and how it can be used to find a missing side of a right triangle. Provide groups of students with problems similar to Exercises 29 and 31 on p. 651. Have each group provide a solution to their problem that includes diagrams and equations. Then have them present their solution to the entire class.

Option 4 Beyond Level BL

Ask students to choose several square root functions from Lesson 10-1 and graph them on a coordinate grid. Then have students change the equals sign to an inequality. Ask students to modify their graphs so that they now represent the solutions to their square root inequality. For example, the graph of $y = \sqrt{x + 1}$ and $y \geq \sqrt{x + 1}$ is shown below.

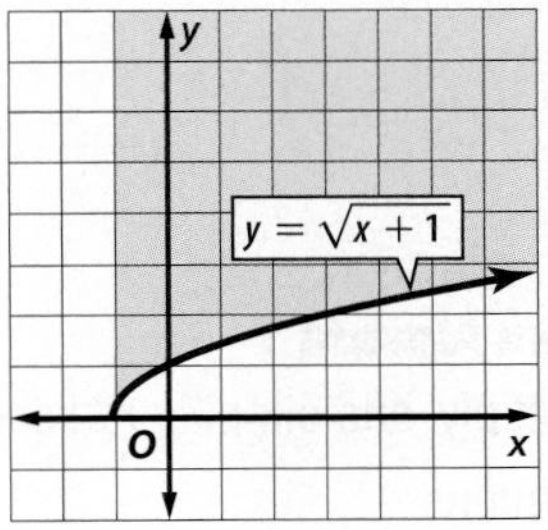

Focus on Mathematical Content

VerticalAlignment

Before Chapter 10

Related Topics before Grade 8

- represent squares and square roots using geometric models
- approximate the values of irrational numbers as they arise from problem situations

Previous Topics from Algebra 1

- use the Distributive Property to simplify algebraic expressions
- solve quadratic equations using algebraic methods
- solve problems involving proportional change
- graph and analyze linear, exponential, and quadratic functions
- rewrite expressions involving radicals and rational exponents using the properties of exponents

Chapter 10

Related Topics from Algebra 1

- add, subtract, multiply, and simplify radical expressions
- solve radical equations
- use the Pythagorean Theorem and trigonometric ratios to solve problems

After Chapter 10

Preparation for Geometry

- use the Pythagorean Theorem
- identify and apply patterns from right triangles to solve meaningful problems
- use formulas for length, slope, and midpoint
- use ratios to solve problems involving similar figures

Preparation for Algebra 2

- formulate equations and inequalities based on square root functions, use a variety of methods to solve them, and analyze the solutions in terms of the situation

Lesson-by-LessonPreview

10-1 Square Root Functions

A square root function is so named because the function contains a variable inside a square root symbol. The parent function of a square root function is $f(x) = \sqrt{x}$. In order for a square root to be a real number, the radicand cannot be negative. When graphing a square root function, numbers that make the radicand negative must be excluded from the domain of the function. The graph of $y = a\sqrt{x}$ starts at the origin and passes through the point $(1, a)$. If a is positive, the graph is in the first quadrant. If a is negative, the graph is a reflection of the graph of $y = |a|\sqrt{x}$ and lies in the fourth quadrant.

10-2 Simplifying Radical Expressions

When an expression contains a square root, it is called a radical expression. When the radicand, the expression under the square root sign, contains no perfect square factors other than 1, it is said to be in simplest form. Properties of square roots can be used to simplify radical expressions.

- Product Property of Square Roots: For any numbers greater than or equal to 0, the square root of their product is equal to the product of each number's square root. For example, $\sqrt{18} = \sqrt{2 \cdot 3 \cdot 3} = \sqrt{2} \cdot \sqrt{3^2} = 3\sqrt{2}$. Principle square roots are never negative, so absolute value symbols must be used to signify that some results are not negative, for example $\sqrt{x^2} = |x|$.
- Quotient Property of Square Roots: For any number greater than or equal to 0 divided by a number greater than 0, the square root of their quotient is equal to the quotient of each number's square root, for example, $\sqrt{\frac{25}{4}} = \frac{\sqrt{25}}{\sqrt{4}} = \frac{5}{2}$.
- When there is a radical expression in the denominator, the expression is not in simplest form. A process called *rationalizing the denominator* eliminates radicals from a denominator. Since squaring and taking a square root are inverse functions, multiply the numerator and the denominator by the same radical expression so that the radical in the denominator contains a perfect square. For example, $\frac{\sqrt{3}}{\sqrt{5}} = \frac{\sqrt{3}}{\sqrt{5}} \cdot \frac{\sqrt{5}}{\sqrt{5}} = \frac{\sqrt{15}}{5}$.
- If the denominator is an expression containing a radical, multiply by its *conjugate* to rationalize the denominator. For example, if the denominator is in the form $a + \sqrt{b}$, multiply both the numerator and the denominator by $a - \sqrt{b}$.

10-3 Operations with Radical Expressions

- Adding or subtracting expressions with radicals uses the process of combining like terms. For terms to be combined, their radicands must be the same.
- Multiplying two radical expressions with two terms is similar to multiplying binomials. The radicands do not have to be like radicands when multiplying.

10-4 Radical Equations

Equations that contain radicals with variables in the radicands are called *radical equations*. To solve radical equations, the radical must first be isolated on one side of the equation. Then both sides are squared. This will eliminate the radical. Squaring each side sometimes produces *extraneous solutions*, results that are not solutions of the original equation. Be sure to substitute all solutions back into the original equation to check their validity.

10-5 The Pythagorean Theorem

The Pythagorean Theorem states that in a right triangle, the square of the length of the hypotenuse equals the sum of the squares of the lengths of the legs, that is, $c^2 = a^2 + b^2$, where c is the length of the hypotenuse and a and b are the lengths of the legs.

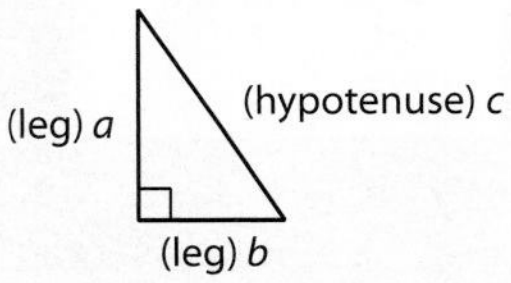

This formula can be used to find the length of any missing side of a right triangle if two sides are known.

Any three nonzero whole numbers that satisfy this equation are known as a *Pythagorean triple*. The triples represent side lengths that always form right triangles. It follows that if three nonzero numbers do not satisfy the Pythagorean Theorem, then a triangle with those lengths will not form a right triangle.

10-6 Trigonometric Ratios

Trigonometry is the study of relationships among the angles and sides of a right triangle. Ratios comparing the measures of two sides of a right triangle are called *trigonometric ratios*. The three most common trigonometric ratios are sine, cosine, and tangent. These ratios can be used to find the missing side lengths or angle measures. If the lengths of two sides of a right triangle or the length of one side and one acute angle measure are known, then the missing lengths and angle measures can be found. This is referred to as *solving the triangle*.

Professional Development

Targeted professional development has been articulated throughout Algebra 1. More quality, customized professional development is available from McGraw-Hill Professional Development. Visit connectED.mcgraw-hill.com for details on each product.

- Online Lessons emphasize the strategies and techniques used to teach Algebra 1. Includes streaming video, interactive pages, and online tools.
- Video Workshops allow mentors, coaches, or leadership personnel to facilitate on-site workshops on educational strategies in mathematics and mathematical concepts.
- MHPD Online (www.mhpdonline.com) offers online professional development with video clips of instructional strategies, links, student activities, and news and issues in education.
- Teaching Today (teachingtoday.glencoe.com) gives secondary teachers practical strategies and materials that inspire excellence and innovation in teaching.

Chapter Project

Ramp It Up

Students use what they have learned about trigonometric ratios to complete a project.

This chapter project addresses global civic literacy, as well as several specific skills identified as being essential to student success by the Framework for 21st Century Learning.

Visit connectED.mcgraw-hill.com for student and teacher handouts.

KeyVocabulary Introduce the key vocabulary in the chapter using the routine below.

Define: A radicand is the expression that is under the radical sign.

Example: $\frac{2ab}{c}$ is the radicand in the expression $\sqrt{\frac{2ab}{c}}$.

Ask: What does the radical sign indicate in regards to the radicand? the square root of the radicand

CHAPTER 10 Radical Functions and Geometry

Then

You solved quadratic and exponential equations.

Now

In this chapter, you will:

- Graph and transform radical functions.
- Simplify, add, subtract, and multiply radical expressions.
- Solve radical equations.
- Use the Pythagorean Theorem.
- Find trigonometric ratios.

Why?

OCEANS Tsunamis, or large waves, are generated by undersea earthquakes. A radical equation can be used to find the speed of a tsunami in meters per second or the depth of the ocean in meters.

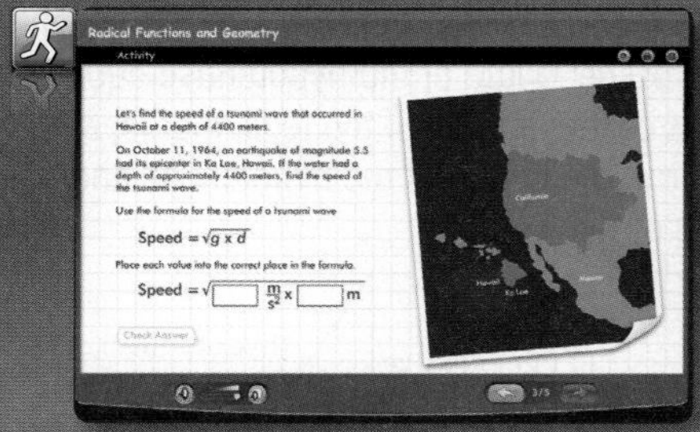

connectED.mcgraw-hill.com Your Digital Math Portal

Animation | Vocabulary | eGlossary | Personal Tutor | Virtual Manipulatives | Graphing Calculator | Audio | Foldables | Self-Check Practice | Worksheets

Content Standards
AI.RNE.2, AI.RNE.4

Process Standards
PS.1, PS.2, PS.3, PS.4, PS.5, PS.6, PS.7, PS.8

Get Ready for the Chapter

Diagnose Readiness | You have two options for checking prerequisite skills.

1 Textbook Option

Take the Quick Check below. Refer to the Quick Review for help.

QuickCheck

Find each square root. If necessary, round to the nearest hundredth.

1. $\sqrt{82}$ **9.06**
2. $\sqrt{26}$ **5.10**
3. $\sqrt{15}$ **3.87**
4. $\sqrt{99}$ **9.95**
5. SANDBOX Isaac is making a square sandbox with an area of 100 square feet. How long is a side of the sandbox? **10 ft**

QuickReview

Example 1 (Used in Lesson 10-2)

Find the square root of $\sqrt{50}$. If necessary, round to the nearest hundredth.

$\sqrt{50} = 7.071067812\ldots$ Use a calculator.

To the nearest hundredth, $\sqrt{50} = 7.07$.

QuickCheck

Simplify each expression.

6. $(21x + 15y) - (9x - 4y)$ **$12x + 19y$**
7. $13x - 5y + 2y$ **$13x - 3y$**
8. $(10a - 5b) + (6a + 5b)$ **$16a$**
9. $6m + 5n + 4 - 3m - 2n + 6$ **$3m + 3n + 10$**
10. $x + y - 3x - 4y + 2x - 8y$ **$-11y$**

QuickReview

Example 2 (Used in Lesson 10-3)

Simplify $3x + 7y - 4x - 8y$.

$3x + 7y - 4x - 8y$

$= (3x - 4x) + (7y - 8y)$ Combine like terms.

$= -x - y$ Simplify.

QuickCheck

Solve each equation. **11–14. See margin.**

11. $2x^2 - 4x = 0$
12. $6x^2 - 5x - 4 = 0$
13. $x^2 - 7x + 10 = 0$
14. $2x^2 + 7x - 5 = -1$
15. GEOMETRY The area of the rectangle is 90 square feet. Find x. **10**

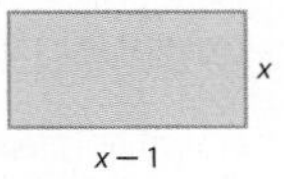

QuickReview

Example 3 (Used in Lesson 10-4)

Solve $x^2 - 5x + 6 = 0$.

$x^2 - 5x + 6 = 0$ Original equation

$(x - 3)(x - 2) = 0$ Factor.

$x - 3 = 0$ or $x - 2 = 0$ Zero Product Property

$x = 3$ $\quad x = 2$ Solve each equation.

2 Online Option

Take an online self-check Chapter Readiness Quiz at connectED.mcgraw-hill.com.

Additional Answers

11. 0, 2
12. $-\frac{1}{2}, \frac{4}{3}$
13. 2, 5
14. $-4, \frac{1}{2}$

Essential Question

- How can you choose a model to represent a real-world situation? Sample answer: To model a set of data, you could create a scatter plot and choose a function with a graph that fits the data. To model a physical situation, you could create a diagram to represent a situation using a figure that has known properties.

Get Ready for the Chapter

Response to Intervention (RtI)

Use the *Quick Check* results and the Intervention Planner chart to help you determine your Response to Intervention. The If-Then statements in the chart below help you decide the appropriate tier of RtI and suggest intervention resources for each tier.

InterventionPlanner

TIER 1 On Level OL

If students miss about 25% of the exercises or less,

Then choose a resource:

SE Lessons 0-2, 1-4, 8-6 and 8-7

Skills Practice, Chapter 1, p. 26, Chapter 8, pp. 39, 45

connectED.mcgraw-hill.com Self-Check Quiz

TIER 2 Strategic Intervention AL

approaching grade level

If students miss about 50% of the exercises,

Then choose a resource:

Study Guide and Intervention, Chapter 1, p. 24, Chapter 8, pp. 37, 43

Quick Review Math Handbook

connectED.mcgraw-hill.com Extra Examples, Personal Tutor, Homework Help

TIER 3 Intensive Intervention

2 or more grades below level

If students miss about 75% of the exercises,

Then use *Math Triumphs, Alg. 1*

connectED.mcgraw-hill.com Extra Examples, Personal Tutor, Homework Help, Review Vocabulary

FOLDABLES StudyOrganizer

Dinah Zike's Foldables®

Focus As students read and study this chapter, they show examples and write notes about radical functions and geometry in their booklet.

Teach Have students make and label their Foldables as illustrated. Before beginning, have them skim the chapter and write down any problems from the chapter that they think are challenging on the right-hand page of the problems' corresponding lessons. As students work through the chapter, ascertain that students are able to find the answers to their problems.

When to Use It Encourage students to add to their Foldables as they work through the chapter and to use them to review for the chapter test.

Differentiated Instruction

Student-Built Glossary, pp. 1–2

Students should complete the chart by providing a definition of each term and an example as they progress through Chapter 10. This study tool can also be used to review for the chapter test.

Get Started on the Chapter

You will learn several new concepts, skills, and vocabulary terms as you study Chapter 10. To get ready, identify important terms and organize your resources. You may wish to refer to Chapter 0 to review prerequisite skills.

FOLDABLES StudyOrganizer

Radical Functions and Geometry Make this Foldable to help you organize your Chapter 10 notes about radical functions and geometry. Begin with four sheets of grid paper.

1 **Fold** in half along the width.

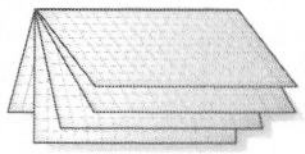

2 **Staple** along the fold.

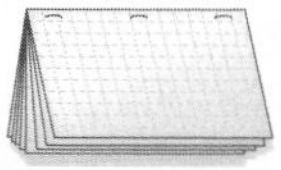

3 **Turn** the fold to the left and write the title of the chapter on the front. On each left-hand page of the booklet, write the title of a lesson from the chapter.

NewVocabulary

English		Español
radicand	p. 621	radicando
radical function	p. 621	función radicales
conjugate	p. 630	conjugado
radical equations	p. 642	ecuaciones radicales
hypotenuse	p. 648	hipotenusa
legs	p. 648	catetos
converse	p. 649	recíproco
midpoint	p. 654	punto medio
sine	p. 656	seno
cosine	p. 656	coseno
tangent	p. 656	tangente
trigonometry	p. 656	trigonometría
inverse cosine	p. 658	coseno inverso
inverse sine	p. 658	seno inverso
inverse tangent	p. 658	tangente inverse

ReviewVocabulary

FOIL method metodo FOIL to multiply two binomials, find the sum of the products of the First terms, Outer terms, Inner terms, and Last terms

perfect square cuadrado perfecto a number with a square root that is a rational number

proportion proporcion an equation of the form $\frac{a}{b} = \frac{c}{d}$, $b \neq 0$, $d \neq 0$ stating that two ratios are equivalent

$$\frac{a}{b} \times \frac{c}{d}$$
$$ad = bc$$

618 | Chapter 10 | Radical Functions and Geometry

EXPLORE 10-1

Algebra Lab
Inverse Functions

You have discovered that every nonhorizontal linear function has an inverse function. You have learned how to find the inverse of any function by exchanging the coordinates for a set of ordered pairs. In the following activity, we will exchange coordinates to find the inverse of a quadratic function and determine whether the inverse is a function.

Activity 1 Exchange Coordinates

Find the inverse of $y = x^2$ by exchanging the coordinates. Is the inverse a function?

Step 1 Make a table of values for $y = x^2$ using x from -3 to 3.

x	-3	-2	-1	0	1	2	3
y	9	4	1	0	1	4	9

Step 2 Write the coordinates as a set of ordered pairs.

$\{(-3, 9), (-2, 4), (-1, 1), (0, 0), (1, 1), (2, 4), (3, 9)\}$

Step 3 Exchange the x- and y-coordinates in each ordered pair to form the inverse.

$\{(9, -3), (4, -2), \mathbf{(1, -1)}, (0, 0), \mathbf{(1, 1)}, (4, 2), (9, 3)\}$

Step 4 Examine the set of ordered pairs and determine if it would be a function. This set of ordered pairs would not be a function because each x-value is not paired with a unique y-value. For example, there are two y-values when $x = 1$.

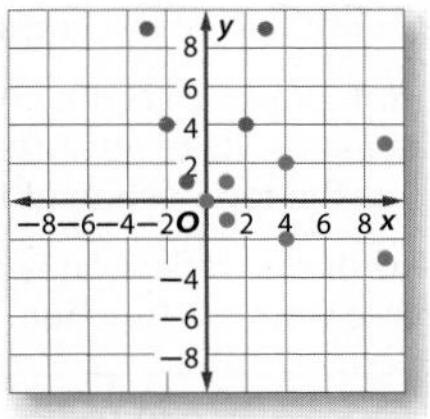

You have also learned how to find the inverse of a linear function algebraically. In the next activity, you will find the inverse of the quadratic function from Activity 1.

Activity 2 Use Algebra

Find the inverse of $y = x^2$ algebraically. Check by graphing the function, its inverse, and the line $y = x$.

Step 1 Find the inverse algebraically.

$y = x^2$	Original function
$x = y^2$	Interchange x and y.
$\sqrt{x} = \sqrt{y^2}$	Take the square root of each side.
$\sqrt{x} = \lvert y \rvert$	Simplify.
$\pm\sqrt{x} = y$	Simplify.

The inverse of $y = x^2$ is $y = \pm\sqrt{x}$.

(continued on the next page)

1 Focus

Objective Find the inverse of a quadratic function. Create an inverse function by limiting the domain of the original function.

Materials for Each Group

- grid paper

Easy to Make Manipulatives

Teaching Algebra with Manipulatives
Template for grid paper, p. 1

Teaching Tip

Before students do the activities, review finding the inverse of a linear function. Recall that each inverse is linear. Remind students that the graph of each quadratic function is a parabola. Ask if they think each inverse of a quadratic function will also be a quadratic function.

2 Teach

Working in Cooperative Groups

Put students in groups of two or three, mixing abilities, to complete Activities 1–3 and Exercises 1, 4, and 8.

Ask:

- Will the reflection of the graph of every quadratic function in the line $y = x$ represent a relation that is not a function? yes
- What feature on the graph of a function determines that its inverse will not be a function? If two or more points lie on the same horizontal line.
- Is the graph of every quadratic function symmetric about the y-axis? If not, where is the axis of symmetry found? No; the axis of symmetry is a vertical line through the vertex of the graph.

Practice Have students complete Exercises 2, 5, and 10.

3 Assess

Formative Assessment

Use Exercises 1 and 4 to assess if students can find the inverse of a quadratic function. Use Exercise 10 to assess if students understand how to restrict the domain to create an inverse function.

From Concrete to Abstract

Have students discuss why it might be necessary to have the inverse be a function. Where is this often observed? It might be necessary for each input to have a unique output. This can be observed on graphing calculators.

In later courses, students will study trigonometric functions. Similar to quadratic functions, the domain of a function will often need to be restricted for its inverse to be a function.

Additional Answers

1. {(6, −3), (1, −2), (−2, −1), (−3, 0), (−2, 1), (1, 2), (6, 3)}; not a function
2. {(16, −3), (9, −2), (4, −1), (1, 0), (0, 1), (1, 2), (4, 3)}; not a function
3. {(18, −3), (8, −2), (2, −1), (0, 0), (2, 1), (8, 2), (18, 3)}; not a function
4. {(25, −3), (10, −2), (1, −1), (−2, 0), (1, 1), (10, 2), (25, 3)}; not a function

Algebra Lab
Inverse Functions *Continued*

Step 2 On a coordinate plane, plot and connect the sets of points from Steps 2 and 3 of Activity 1 with a smooth curve to graph $y = x^2$ and its inverse. Graph the line $y = x$.

Step 3 The graph of $y = \pm\sqrt{x}$ does not pass the vertical line test for a function. The inverse is not a function.

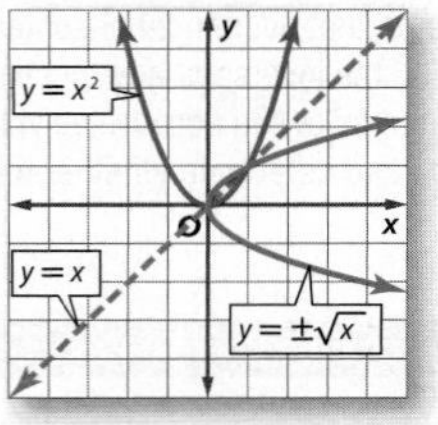

Many functions like $y = x^2$ have inverse relations that are not functions. It is often possible to limit the domains of these functions so that their inverses will be functions.

Activity 3 Restricted Domains

Restrict the domain of $y = x^2$ so that its inverse is a function.

Notice from Activity 2 that the graph of $y = x^2$ is symmetric about the y-axis. If we restrict the domain of $y = x^2$ to either $x \geq 0$ or $x \leq 0$, we are left with half of the graph.

For $x \geq 0$, the graph of $y = x^2$ is now the portion of the parabola to the right of the y-axis. Its inverse is its reflection across the line $y = x$, which is the top portion of the graph of $y = \pm\sqrt{x}$.

Since each x-value of this reflection is paired with a unique y-value, the inverse is now a function.

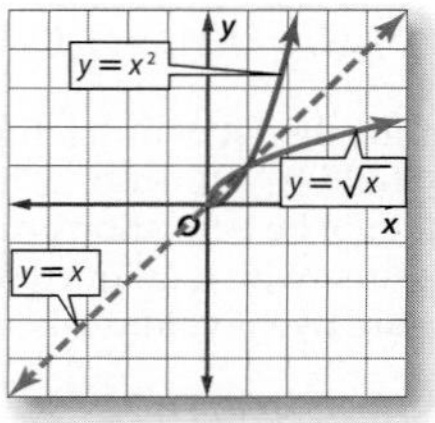

Exercises

Write a set of ordered pairs for the inverse of each function by making a table of values for x from 3 to 3 and exchanging the coordinates. Is the inverse a function? 1–4. See margin.

1. $y = x^2 - 3$
2. $y = (x - 1)^2$
3. $y = 2x^2$
4. $y = 3x^2 - 2$

Find the inverse of each function algebraically. Is the inverse a function?

5. $y = x^2 + 2$ $y = \pm\sqrt{x - 2}$; not a function
6. $y = (x - 1)^2$ $y = 1 \pm \sqrt{x}$; not a function
7. $y = (x + 3)^2 - 4$ $y = \pm\sqrt{x + 4} - 3$; not a function
8. $y = 4x^2 + 2$ $y = \pm\frac{\sqrt{x - 2}}{4}$; not a function

Name a restricted domain for each function for which its inverse would be a function.

9. $y = x^2 - 1$ Sample answer: $x \geq 0$
10. $y = (x + 2)^2$ Sample answer: $x \geq -2$
11. $y = (x - 2)^2 + 1$ Sample answer: $x \geq 2$
12. $y = 3x^2 - 1$ Sample answer: $x \geq 0$

Additional Answers (Lesson 10-1, Guided Practice)

1A. D = $\{x \mid x \geq 0\}$, R = $\{y \mid y \geq 0\}$

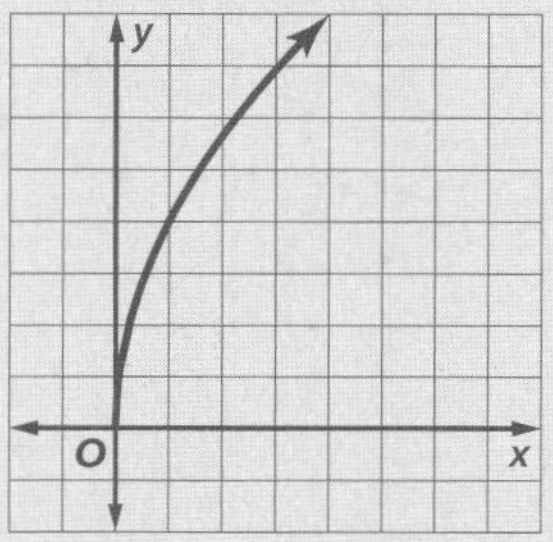

1B. D = $\{x \mid x \geq 0\}$, R = $\{y \mid y \geq 0\}$

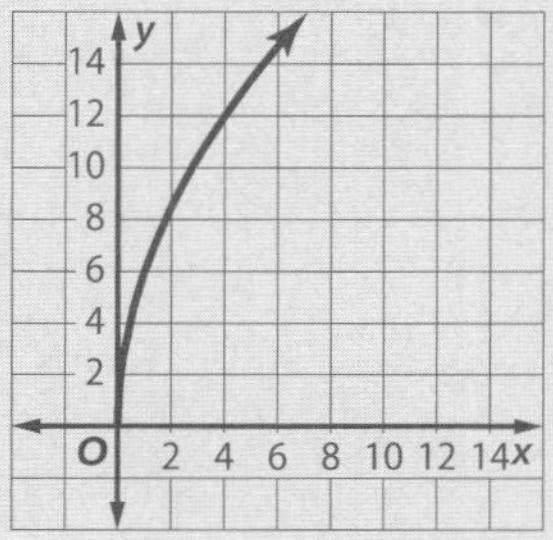

620 | Explore 10-1 | Algebra Lab: Inverse Functions

LESSON 10-1 Square Root Functions

Then

- You graphed and analyzed linear, exponential, and quadratic functions.

Now

1. Graph and analyze dilations of radical functions.
2. Graph and analyze reflections and translations of radical functions.

Why?

- Scientists use sounds of whales to track their movements. The distance to a whale can be found by relating time to the speed of sound in water.

The speed of sound in water can be described by the *square root function* $c = \sqrt{\frac{E}{d}}$, where E represents the bulk modulus elasticity of the water and d represents the density of the water.

NewVocabulary
square root function
radical function
radicand

Process Standards
PS.6

1 Dilations of Radical Functions

A **square root function** contains the square root of a variable. Square root functions are a type of **radical function**. The expression under the radical sign is called the **radicand**. For a square root to be a real number, the radicand cannot be negative. Values that make the radicand negative are not included in the domain.

KeyConcept Square Root Function

Parent Function:	$f(x) = \sqrt{x}$
Type of Graph:	curve
Domain:	$\{x \mid x \geq 0\}$
Range:	$\{y \mid y \geq 0\}$

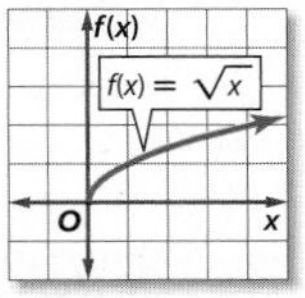

Example 1 Dilation of the Square Root Function

Graph $f(x) = 2\sqrt{x}$. State the domain and range.

Step 1 Make a table.

x	0	0.5	1	2	3	4
$f(x)$	0	≈1.4	2	≈2.8	≈3.5	4

Step 2 Plot points. Draw a smooth curve.

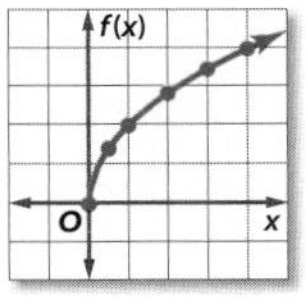

The domain is $\{x \mid x \geq 0\}$, and the range is $\{y \mid y \geq 0\}$. Notice that the graph is increasing on the entire domain, the minimum value is 0, and there is no symmetry.

GuidedPractice 1A–1B. See margin.

1A. $g(x) = 4\sqrt{x}$

1B. $h(x) = 6\sqrt{x}$

1 Focus

VerticalAlignment

Before Lesson 10-1 Graph and analyze linear, exponential, and quadratic functions.

Lesson 10-1 Graph and analyze dilations of radical functions.Graph and analyze reflections and translations of radical functions.

After Lesson 10-1 Solve radical equations.

2 Teach

Scaffolding Questions

Have students read the **Why?** section of the lesson.

Ask:

- What part of the equation indicates that it is a square root function? the radical symbol, which represents a square root
- If the number under the square root symbol cannot be negative, what must be true about $\frac{E}{d}$? The quotient must be greater than or equal to zero.
- If d is constant and E increases, what happens to c? It increases.

Lesson 10-1 Resources

Resource	Approaching Level AL	On Level OL	Beyond Level BL	English Learners ELL
Teacher Edition		▪ Differentiated Instruction, pp. 623, 626	▪ Differentiated Instruction, pp. 623, 626	
Chapter Resource Masters	▪ Study Guide and Intervention, pp. 5–6 ▪ Skills Practice, p. 7 ▪ Practice, p. 8 ▪ Word Problem Practice, p. 9	▪ Study Guide and Intervention, pp. 5–6 ▪ Skills Practice, p. 7 ▪ Practice, p. 8 ▪ Word Problem Practice, p. 9 ▪ Enrichment, p. 10	▪ Practice, p. 8 ▪ Word Problem Practice, p. 9 ▪ Enrichment, p. 10	▪ Study Guide and Intervention, pp. 5–6 ▪ Skills Practice, p. 7 ▪ Practice, p. 8 ▪ Word Problem Practice, p. 9
Other	▪ 5-Minute Check 10-1 ▪ Study Notebook	▪ 5-Minute Check 10-1 ▪ Study Notebook	▪ 5-Minute Check 10-1 ▪ Study Notebook	▪ 5-Minute Check 10-1 ▪ Study Notebook

2 Reflections and Translations of Radical Functions

Recall that when the value of a is negative in the quadratic function $f(x) = ax^2$, the graph of the parent function is reflected across the x-axis.

StudyTip

Graphing Radical Functions Choose perfect squares for x-values that will result in coordinates that are easy to plot.

KeyConcept Graphing $y = a\sqrt{x + h} + k$

Step 1 Draw the graph of $y = a\sqrt{x}$. The graph starts at the origin and passes through $(1, a)$. If $a > 0$, the graph is in quadrant I. If $a < 0$, the graph is reflected across the x-axis and is in quadrant IV.

Step 2 Translate the graph k units up if $k > 0$ and $|k|$ units down if $k < 0$.

Step 3 Translate the graph h units left if $h > 0$ and $|h|$ units right if $h < 0$.

Example 2 Reflection of the Square Root Function

Graph $y = -3\sqrt{x}$. Compare to the parent graph. State the domain and range.

Make a table of values. Then plot the points on a coordinate system and draw a smooth curve that connects them.

x	0	0.5	1	4
y	0	≈−2.1	−3	−6

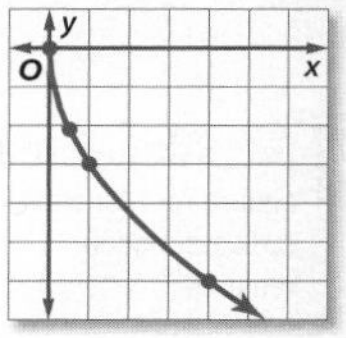

Notice that the graph is in the 4th quadrant. It is obtained by stretching the graph of $y = \sqrt{x}$ vertically and then reflecting across the x-axis. The domain is $\{x \mid x \geq 0\}$, and the range is $\{y \mid y \leq 0\}$.

GuidedPractice **2A–2B. See Ch. 10 Answer Appendix.**

2A. $y = -2\sqrt{x}$ **2B.** $y = -4\sqrt{x}$

StudyTip

Translating Radical Functions If $h > 0$, a radical function $f(x) = \sqrt{x - h}$ is a horizontal translation h units to the right. $f(x) = \sqrt{x + h}$ is a horizontal translation h units to the left.

Example 3 Translation of the Square Root Function

Graph each function. Compare to the parent graph. State the domain and range.

a. $g(x) = \sqrt{x} + 1$

x	0	0.5	1	4	9
y	0	≈1.7	2	3	4

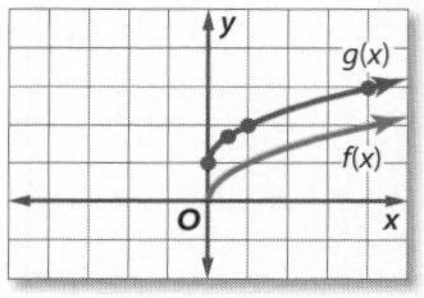

Notice that the values of $g(x)$ are 1 greater than those of $f(x) = \sqrt{x}$. This is a vertical translation 1 unit up from the parent function. The domain is $\{x \mid x \geq 0\}$, and the range is $\{y \mid y \geq 1\}$.

b. $h(x) = \sqrt{x - 2}$

x	2	3	4	6
y	0	1	≈1.4	2

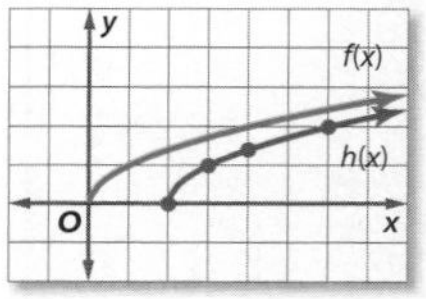

This is a horizontal translation 2 units to the right of the parent function. The domain is $\{x \mid x \geq 2\}$, and the range is $\{y \mid y \geq 0\}$.

1 Dilations of Radical Functions

Example 1 shows how to graph a dilation of a radical function.

Formative Assessment

Use the Guided Practice exercises after each Example to determine students' understanding of concepts.

Additional Example

1 Graph $y = \frac{1}{2}\sqrt{x}$. State the domain and range.
$D = \{x \mid x \geq 0\}$; $R = \{y \mid y \geq 0\}$

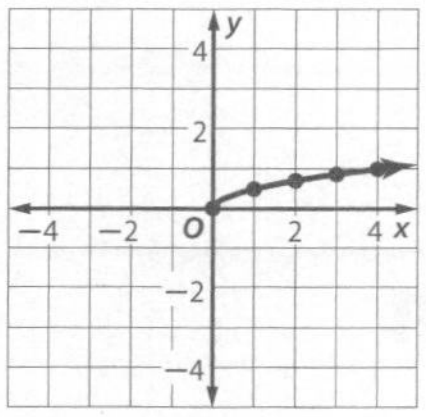

Additional Examples also in Interactive Classroom PowerPoint® Presentations

IWB Interactive White Board READY

2 Reflections and Translations of Radical Functions

Examples 2 and 3 show how to graph reflections and translations of radical functions. **Example 4** shows how to solve a real-world problem involving a radical function. **Example 5** shows how to graph a radical function that has more than one transformation.

Additional Example

2 Graph $y = -\frac{1}{2}\sqrt{x}$. Compare to the parent graph. State the domain and range. vertical compression of $y = \sqrt{x}$ and reflection over the x-axis; $D = \{x \mid x \geq 0\}$; $R = \{y \mid y \leq 0\}$

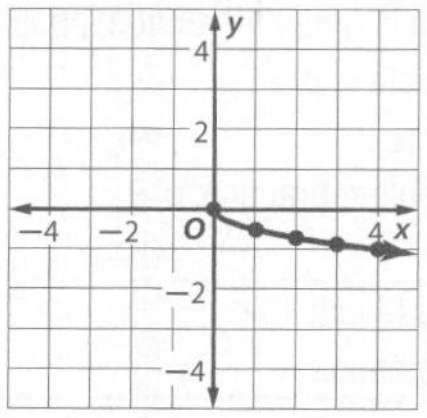

Focus on Mathematical Content

Square Root Functions Square root functions are a type of radical function. The square root function $y = \sqrt{x}$ is the inverse function of $y = x^2$ for $x \geq 0$. It can also be represented as $y = x^{\frac{1}{2}}$. To graph a square root function, exclude any values from the domain that result in a negative radicand.

Tips for New Teachers

Sense-Making Show students that the limits on the domain and range of a square root function are also representative of the inital point of the graph of the function, where x is the minimum value in the domain and y is the minimum value in the range.

GuidedPractice **3A–3B. See Ch. 10 Answer Appendix.**

3A. $g(x) = \sqrt{x} - 4$ **3B.** $h(x) = \sqrt{x + 3}$

Physical phenomena such as motion can be modeled by radical functions. Often these functions are transformations of the parent square root function.

Real-WorldLink

Approximately 39 million cars cross the Golden Gate Bridge in San Francisco each year.

Source: San Francisco Convention and Visitors Bureau

Real-World Example 4 Analyze a Radical Function

BRIDGES The Golden Gate Bridge is about 67 meters above the water. The velocity v of a freely falling object that has fallen h meters is given by $v = \sqrt{2gh}$, where g is the constant 9.8 meters per second squared. Graph the function. If an object is dropped from the bridge, what is its velocity when it hits the water?

Use a graphing calculator to graph the function. To find the velocity of the object, substitute 67 meters for h.

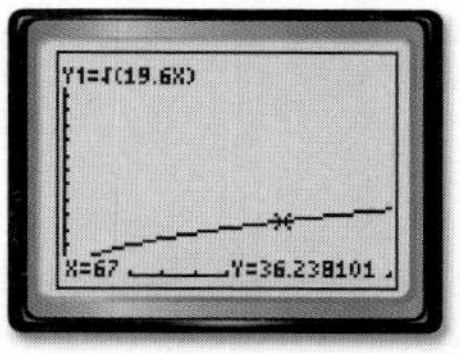

$v = \sqrt{2gh}$	Original function
$= \sqrt{2(9.8)(67)}$	$g = 9.8$ and $h = 67$
$= \sqrt{1313.2}$	Simplify.
≈ 36.2 m/s	Use a calculator.

The velocity of the object is about 36.2 meters per second after dropping 67 meters.

GuidedPractice

4. Use the graph above to estimate the initial height of an object if it is moving at 20 meters per second when it hits the water. **≈20 m**

5A. compressed vertically and translated down 1; D = {x | x ≥ 0}, R = {y | y ≥ −1}

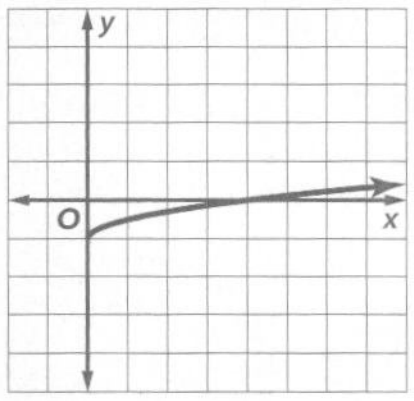

5B. stretched vertically and reflected across the x-axis, and translated right 1; D = {x | x ≥ 1}, R = {y | y ≤ 0}

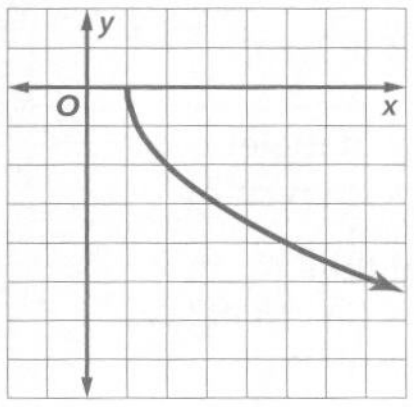

Transformations such as reflections, translations, and dilations can be combined in one equation.

Example 5 Transformations of the Square Root Function

Graph $y = -2\sqrt{x} + 1$, and compare to the parent graph. State the domain and range.

x	0	1	4	9
y	1	−1	−3	−5

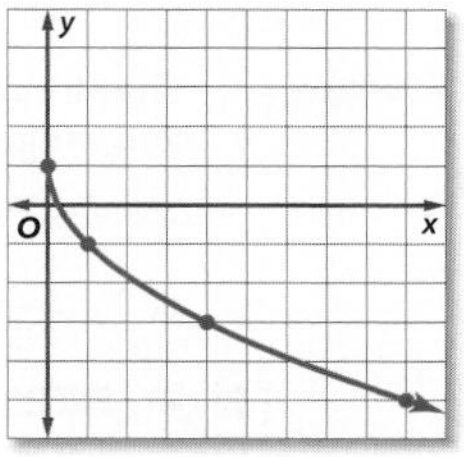

This graph is the result of a vertical stretch of the graph of $y = \sqrt{x}$ followed by a reflection across the x-axis, and then a translation 1 unit up. The domain is $\{x \mid x \geq 0\}$, and the range is $\{y \mid y \leq 1\}$.

GuidedPractice

5A. $y = \frac{1}{2}\sqrt{x} - 1$ **5B.** $y = -2\sqrt{x - 1}$

DifferentiatedInstruction OL BL

If students demonstrate an understanding of the translations of the graphs of square root functions,

Then have students work in pairs or groups to graph square root functions such as $y = \sqrt{x^2 + 2}$, $y = \sqrt{9 - x^2}$, and $y = \sqrt{x^2 - 2x}$. Have them state the domain and range of the functions and describe the graphs. Ask how they might use a graph of the quadratic in the radicand to find the domain and range of the function.

Additional Examples

3 Graph each function. Compare to the parent graph. State the domain and range.

a. $g(x) = \sqrt{x} - 1$ translated 1 unit down; $D = \{x \mid x \geq 0\}$; $R = \{g(x) \mid g(x) \geq -1\}$

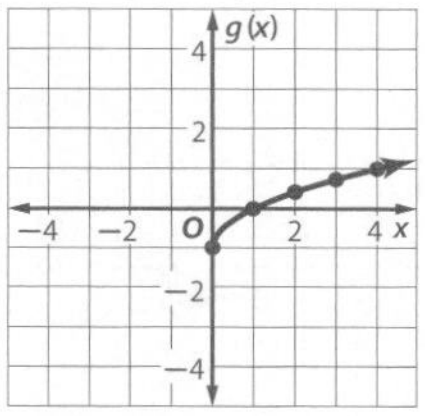

b. $h(x) = \sqrt{x + 1}$ translated 1 unit left; $D = \{x \mid x \geq -1\}$; $R = \{h(x) \mid h(x) \geq 0\}$

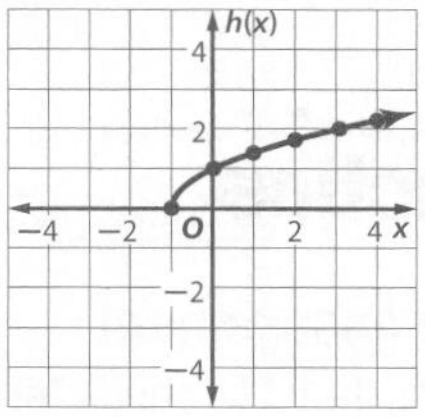

4 **TSUNAMIS** The speed s of a tsunami, in meters per second, is given by $s = 3.1\sqrt{d}$, where d is the depth of the ocean water in meters. Graph the function. If a tsunami is traveling in water 26 meters deep, what is its speed? about 15.8 m/s

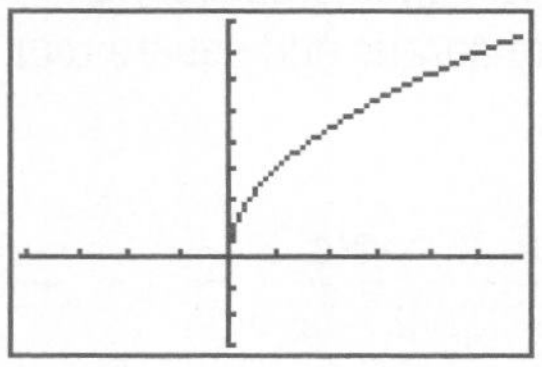

[−5, 5] scl: 1 by [−4, 7] scl: 1

Follow-up

Students have explored square root functions.

Ask:

- Why would you choose a square root function to model a set of data instead of a polynomial function? Sample answer: The end behavior of a square root function might fit the data better. Also, the domain of the square root function is $x \geq 0$, which may be applicable to many real-world situations that involve quantities such as time and distance.

Additional Example

5 Graph $y = 3\sqrt{x-2}$ and compare to the parent graph. State the domain and range. vertical stretch of $y = \sqrt{x}$ translation 2 units right; $D = \{x \mid x \geq 2\}$; $R = \{y \mid y \geq 0\}$

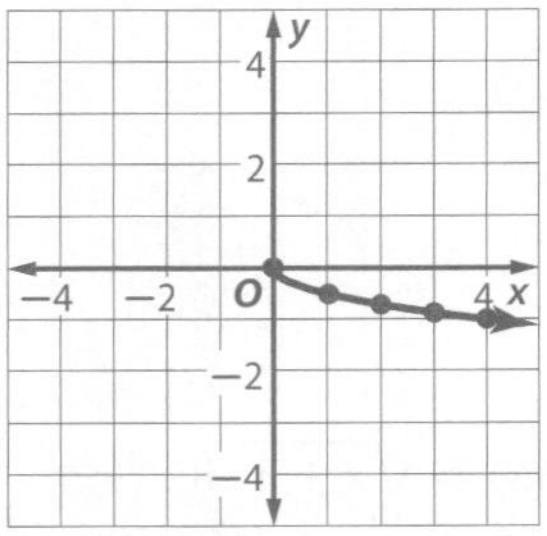

3 Practice

Formative Assessment

Use Exercises 1–13 to check for understanding.

Use the chart at the bottom of this page to customize assignments for your students.

Multiple Representations

In Exercise 44, students use graphs and a piecewise-defined function to compare quadratic and square root functions.

Additional Answers

9.

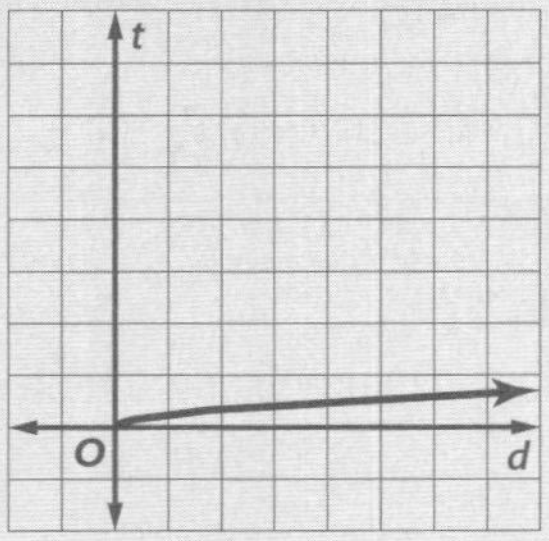

34a.

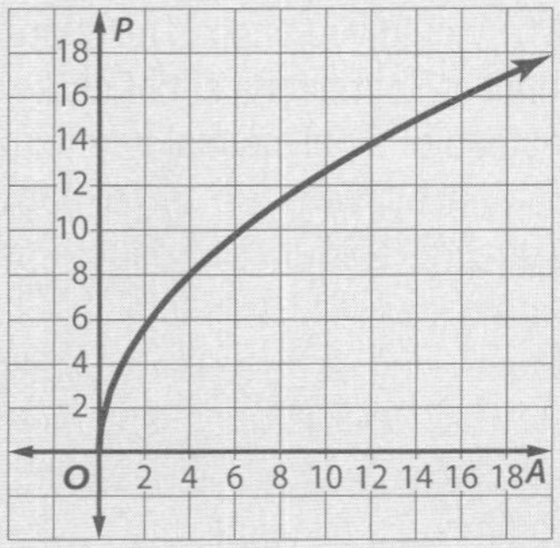

Check Your Understanding

= Step-by-Step Solutions begin on page R13.

Examples 1–3 Graph each function. Compare to the parent graph. State the domain and range. **1–8. See Ch. 10 Answer Appendix.**

1. $y = 3\sqrt{x}$ **2.** $y = -5\sqrt{x}$

3. $y = \frac{1}{3}\sqrt{x}$ **4.** $y = -\frac{1}{2}\sqrt{x}$

5. $y = \sqrt{x} + 3$ **6.** $y = \sqrt{x} - 2$

7. $y = \sqrt{x+2}$ **8.** $y = \sqrt{x-3}$

Example 4 **9. FREE FALL** The time t, in seconds, that it takes an object to fall a distance d, in feet, is given by the function $t = \frac{1}{4}\sqrt{d}$ (assuming zero air resistance). Graph the function, and state the domain and range. **See margin for graph; $D = \{d \mid d \geq 0\}$, $R = \{t \mid t \geq$**

Example 5 Graph each function, and compare to the parent graph. State the domain and range. **10–13. See Ch. 10 Answer Appendix.**

10. $y = \frac{1}{2}\sqrt{x} + 2$ **11.** $y = -\frac{1}{4}\sqrt{x} - 1$

12. $y = -2\sqrt{x+1}$ **13.** $y = 3\sqrt{x-2}$

Practice and Problem Solving

Extra Practice is on page R10.

Examples 1–3 Graph each function. Compare to the parent graph. State the domain and range. **14–33. See Ch. 10 Answer Appendix.**

14. $y = 5\sqrt{x}$ **15.** $y = \frac{1}{2}\sqrt{x}$ **16.** $y = -\frac{1}{3}\sqrt{x}$ **17.** $y = 7\sqrt{x}$

18. $y = -\frac{1}{4}\sqrt{x}$ **19.** $y = -\sqrt{x}$ **20.** $y = -\frac{1}{5}\sqrt{x}$ **21.** $y = -7\sqrt{x}$

22. $y = \sqrt{x} + 2$ **23.** $y = \sqrt{x} + 4$ **24.** $y = \sqrt{x} - 1$

25. $y = \sqrt{x} - 3$ **26.** $y = \sqrt{x} + 1.5$ **27.** $y = \sqrt{x} - 2.5$

28. $y = \sqrt{x+4}$ **29.** $y = \sqrt{x-4}$ **30.** $y = \sqrt{x+1}$

31. $y = \sqrt{x-0.5}$ **32.** $y = \sqrt{x+5}$ **33.** $y = \sqrt{x-1.5}$

Example 4 **34. GEOMETRY** The perimeter of a square is given by the function $P = 4\sqrt{A}$, where A is the area of the square.

a. Graph the function. **See margin.**

b. Determine the perimeter of a square with an area of 225 m^2. **60 m**

c. When will the perimeter and the area be the same value? **When the sides of the square have length 4 m, the perimeter and area are both 16 m.**

Example 5 Graph each function, and compare to the parent graph. State the domain and range. **35–40. See Ch. 10 Answer Appendix.**

35. $y = -2\sqrt{x} + 2$ **36.** $y = -3\sqrt{x} - 3$ **37.** $y = \frac{1}{2}\sqrt{x+2}$

38. $y = -\sqrt{x-1}$ **39.** $y = \frac{1}{4}\sqrt{x-1} + 2$ **40.** $y = \frac{1}{2}\sqrt{x-2} + 1$

B **41. ENERGY** An object has kinetic energy when it is in motion. The velocity in meters per second of an object of mass m kilograms with an energy of E joules is given by the function $v = \sqrt{\frac{2E}{m}}$. Use a graphing calculator to graph the function that represents the velocity of a basketball with a mass of 0.6 kilogram. **See Ch. 10 Answer Appendix.**

Differentiated Homework Options

Level	Assignment	Two-Day Option	
AL Basic	14–40, 47, 49–72	15–39 odd, 53–56	14–40 even, 47, 49–52, 57–72
OL Core	15–39 odd, 41–44, 47, 49–72	14–40, 53–56	41–44, 47, 49–52, 57–72
BL Advanced	41–66, (optional: 67–72)		

624 | Lesson 10-1 | Square Root Functions

42. **GEOMETRY** The radius of a circle is given by $r = \sqrt{\frac{A}{\pi}}$, where A is the area of the circle.

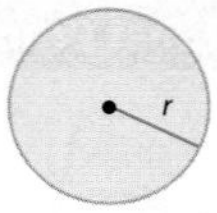

a. Graph the function. **See Ch. 10 Answer Appendix.**

b. Use a graphing calculator to determine the radius of a circle that has an area of 27 in^2. **about 2.9 in.**

43. **SPEED OF SOUND** The speed of sound in air is determined by the temperature of the air. The speed c in meters per second is given by $c = 331.5\sqrt{1 + \frac{t}{273.15}}$, where t is the temperature of the air in degrees Celsius.

a. Use a graphing calculator to graph the function. **See Ch. 10 Answer Appendix.**

b. How fast does sound travel when the temperature is 55°C? **about 363.3 m/s**

c. How is the speed of sound affected when the temperature increases to 65°C?

C 44. **MULTIPLE REPRESENTATIONS** In this problem, you will explore the relationship between the graphs of square root functions and parabolas. **a–e. See Ch. 10 Answer Appendix.**

a. **Graphical** Graph $y = x^2$ on a coordinate system.

b. **Algebraic** Write a piecewise-defined function to describe the graph of $y^2 = x$ in each quadrant.

c. **Graphical** On the same coordinate system, graph $y = \sqrt{x}$ and $y = -\sqrt{x}$.

d. **Graphical** On the same coordinate system, graph $y = x$. Plot the points (2, 4), (4, 2), and (1, 1).

e. **Analytical** Compare the graph of the parabola to the graphs of the square root functions.

43c. When t is 65°C, c is about 368.8 m/s, so this 10-degree increase results in an increase in speed of about 5.5 m/s.

H.O.T. Problems Use Higher-Order Thinking Skills

CHALLENGE Determine whether each statement is *true* or *false*. Provide an example or counterexample to support your answer. **45–46. See Ch. 10 Answer Appendix.**

45. Numbers in the domain of a radical function will always be nonnegative.

46. Numbers in the range of a radical function will always be nonnegative.

47. **WRITING IN MATH** Why are there limitations on the domain and range of square root functions? **See Ch. 10 Answer Appendix.**

48. **TOOLS** Write a radical function with a domain of all real numbers greater than or equal to 2 and a range of all real numbers less than or equal to 5. **Sample answer: $y = -\sqrt{x - 2} + 5$**

49. **WHICH DOES NOT BELONG?** Identify the equation that does not belong. Explain.

$y = 3\sqrt{x}$	$y = 0.7\sqrt{x}$	$y = \sqrt{x} + 3$	$y = \frac{\sqrt{x}}{6}$

See Ch. 10 Answer Appendix.

50. **OPEN ENDED** Write a function that is a reflection, translation, and a dilation of the parent graph $y = \sqrt{x}$. **Sample answer: $y = -3\sqrt{x - 1}$**

51. **REASONING** If the range of the function $y = a\sqrt{x}$ is $\{y \mid y \leq 0\}$, what can you conclude about the value of a? Explain your reasoning. **See Ch. 10 Answer Appendix.**

52. **WRITING IN MATH** Compare and contrast the graphs of $f(x) = \sqrt{x} + 2$ and $g(x) = \sqrt{x + 2}$. **See Ch. 10 Answer Appendix.**

Study Guide and Intervention

AL OL ELL

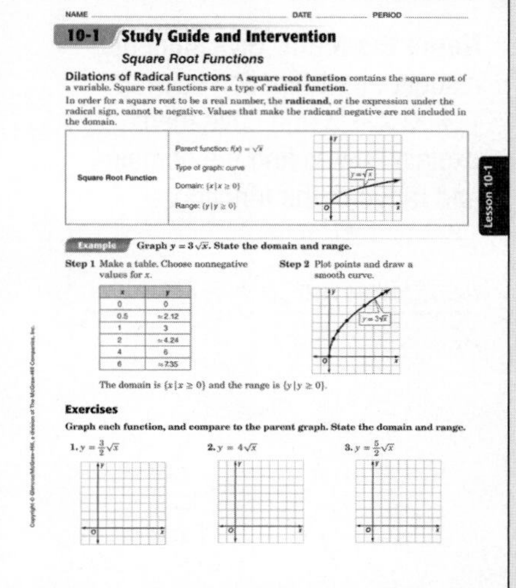
NAME DATE PERIOD

10-1 Study Guide and Intervention

Square Root Functions

Dilations of Radical Functions A square root function contains the square root of a variable. Square root functions are a type of radical function.

In order for a square root to be a real number, the radicand, or the expression under the radical sign, cannot be negative. Values that make the radicand negative are not included in the domain.

Example Graph $y = 3\sqrt{x}$. State the domain and range.

Step 1 Make a table. Choose nonnegative values for x.

Step 2 Plot points and draw a smooth curve.

x	y
0	0
0.5	≈2.12
1	3
2	≈4.24
4	6
6	≈7.35

The domain is $\{x \mid x \geq 0\}$ and the range is $\{y \mid y \geq 0\}$.

Exercises

Graph each function, and compare to the parent graph. State the domain and range.

Practice

AL OL BL ELL

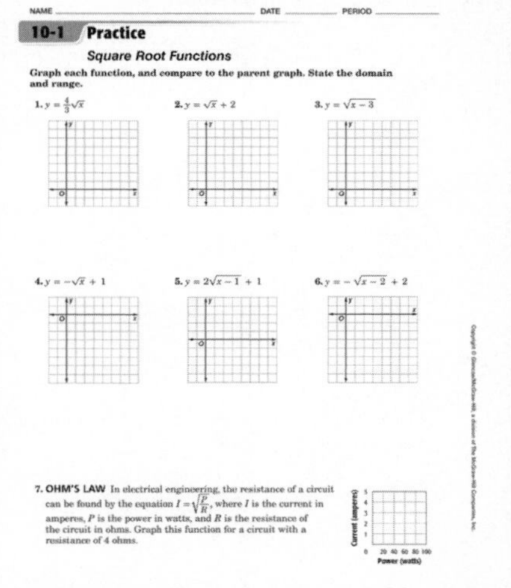
NAME DATE PERIOD

10-1 Practice

Square Root Functions

Graph each function, and compare to the parent graph. State the domain and range.

7. OHM'S LAW

Word Problem Practice

AL OL BL ELL

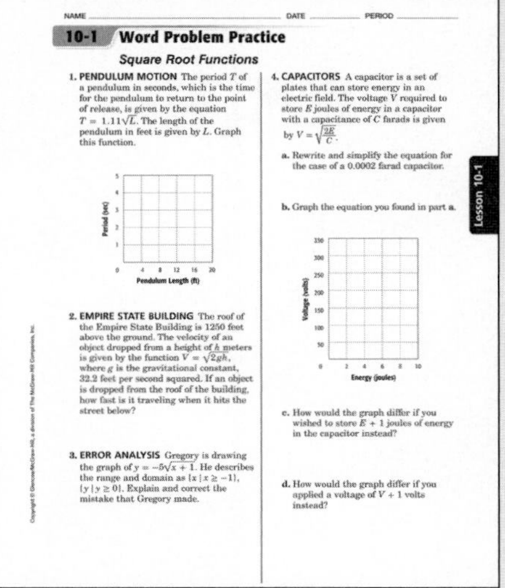
NAME DATE PERIOD

10-1 Word Problem Practice

Square Root Functions

1. PENDULUM MOTION

2. EMPIRE STATE BUILDING

3. ERROR ANALYSIS

4. CAPACITORS

Teaching the Process Standards

Tools Mathematically proficient students consider the available tools when solving a mathematical problem. In Exercise 48, encourage students to consider using graph paper or technology to help as they write their function.

Enrichment

OL BL

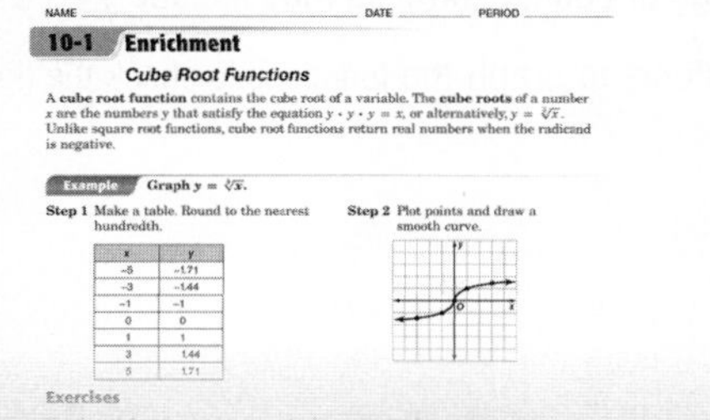
NAME DATE PERIOD

10-1 Enrichment

Cube Root Functions

Example Graph $y = \sqrt[3]{x}$.

Step 1 Make a table. Round to the nearest hundredth.

Step 2 Plot points and draw a smooth curve.

x	y
−5	−1.71
−3	−1.44
−1	−1
0	0
1	1
3	1.44
5	1.71

Exercises

4 Assess

Name the Math Give students a square root function such as $y = \sqrt{x - 5}$ and have them explain how to find the domain and range of the function.

Additional Answers

61.

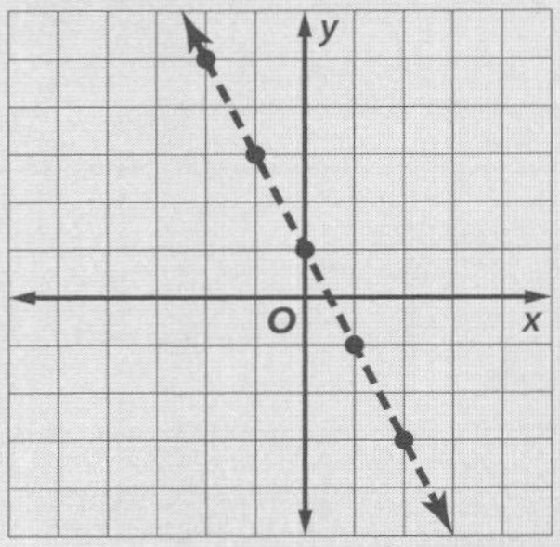

linear

62.

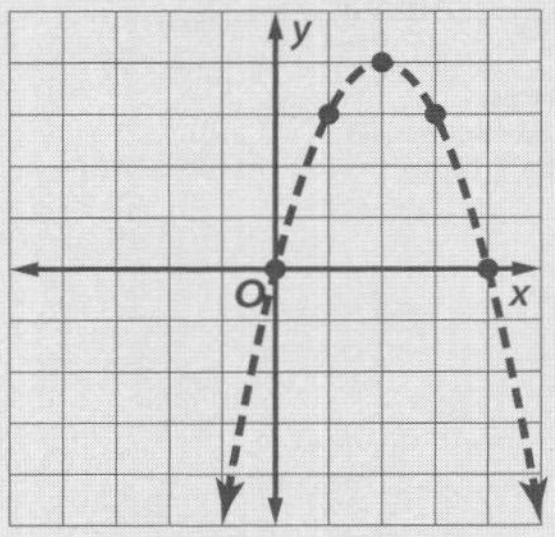

quadratic

63.

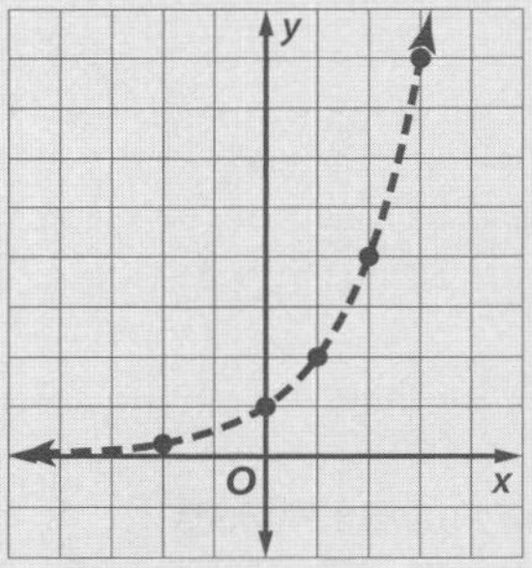

exponential

64.

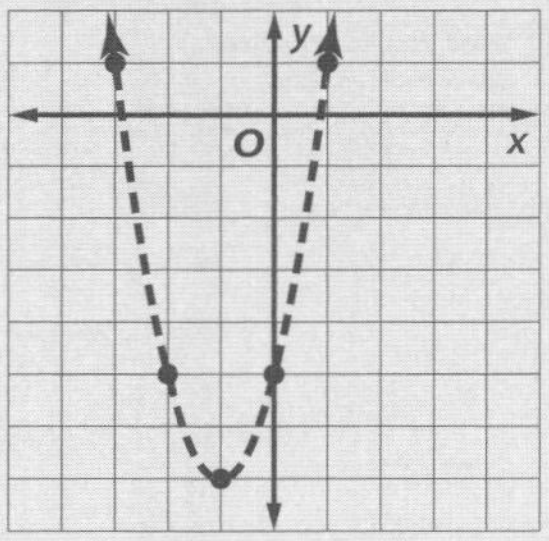

quadratic

Standardized Test Practice

53.

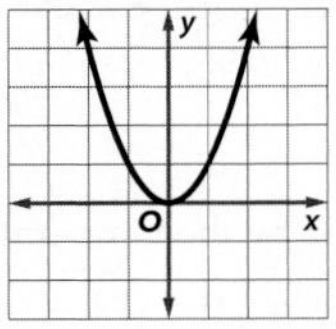

Which function *best* represents the graph? **A**

A $y = x^2$ **C** $y = \sqrt{x}$
B $y = 2^x$ **D** $y = x$

54. The statement "$x < 10$ and $3x - 2 \geq 7$" is true when x is equal to what? **H**

F 0 **H** 8
G 2 **J** 12

55. Which of the following is the equation of a line parallel to $y = -\frac{1}{2}x + 3$ and passing through $(-2, -1)$? **D**

A $y = \frac{1}{2}x$ **C** $y = -\frac{1}{2}x + 2$

B $y = 2x + 3$ **D** $y = -\frac{1}{2}x - 2$

56. SHORT RESPONSE A landscaper needs to mulch 6 rectangular flower beds that are 8 feet by 4 feet and 4 circular flower beds each with a radius of 3 feet. One bag of mulch covers 25 square feet. How many bags of mulch are needed to cover the flower beds? **13 bags of mulch**

Spiral Review

Graph each function. (Lesson 9-7) **57–60. See Ch. 10 Answer Appendix.**

57. $f(x) = |3x + 2|$

58. $f(x) = \begin{cases} x - 2 \text{ if } x > -1 \\ x + 3 \text{ if } x \leq -1 \end{cases}$

59. $f(x) = [\![x + 1]\!]$

60. $f(x) = \left|\frac{1}{4}x - 1\right|$

Graph each set of ordered pairs. Determine whether the ordered pairs represent a *linear* function, a *quadratic* function, or an *exponential* function. (Lesson 9-6) **61–64. See margin.**

61. $\{(-2, 5), (-1, 3), (0, 1), (1, -1), (2, -3)\}$

62. $\{(0, 0), (1, 3), (2, 4), (3, 3), (4, 0)\}$

63. $\left\{\left(-2, \frac{1}{4}\right), (0, 1), (1, 2), (2, 4), (3, 8)\right\}$

64. $\{(-3, 1), (-2, -5), (-1, -7), (0, -5), (1, 1)\}$

65. HEALTH Aida exercises every day by walking and jogging at least 3 miles. Aida walks at a rate of 4 miles per hour and jogs at a rate of 8 miles per hour. Suppose she has at most one half-hour to exercise today. (Lesson 6-6) **a–b. See Ch. 10 Answer Appendix.**

a. Draw a graph showing the possible amounts of time she can spend walking and jogging today.

b. List three possible solutions.

66. NUTRITION Determine whether the graph shows a *positive*, *negative*, or *no* correlation. If there is a positive or negative correlation, describe its meaning in the situation. (Lesson 4-5) **Positive; as the number of grams of fat increases, the amount of Calories increases.**

Fast-Food Choices

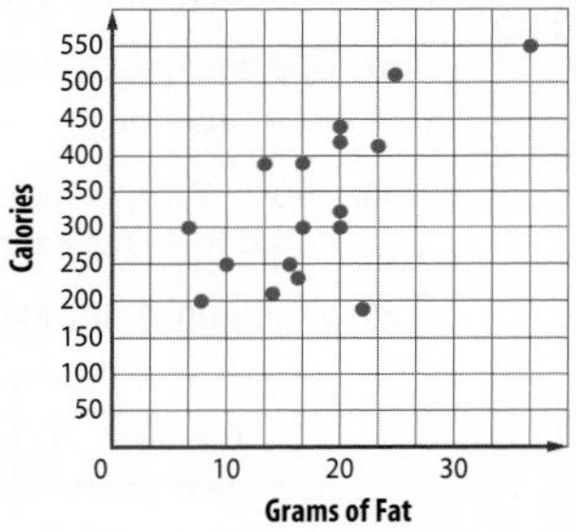

Skills Review

Factor each monomial completely.

67. $28n^3$ $2 \cdot 2 \cdot 7 \cdot n \cdot n \cdot n$

68. $-33a^2b$ $-1 \cdot 3 \cdot 11 \cdot a \cdot a \cdot b$

69. $150rt$ $2 \cdot 3 \cdot 5 \cdot 5 \cdot r \cdot t$

70. $-378nq^2r^2$ $-1 \cdot 2 \cdot 3 \cdot 3 \cdot 3 \cdot 7 \cdot n \cdot q \cdot q \cdot r \cdot r$

71. $225a^3b^2c$ $3 \cdot 3 \cdot 5 \cdot 5 \cdot a \cdot a \cdot a \cdot b \cdot b \cdot c$

72. $-160x^2y^4$ $-1 \cdot 2 \cdot 2 \cdot 2 \cdot 2 \cdot 2 \cdot 5 \cdot x \cdot x \cdot y \cdot y \cdot y \cdot y$

Differentiated Instruction OL BL

Extension Write several square root functions on the board and have students state the domain and range of each. Examples may include $y = \sqrt{3x + 2}$, $y = -5\sqrt{\frac{x + 2}{8}}$, or $y = \sqrt{\frac{1}{x + 2}}$. Encourage students to graph the functions to check the domain and range. $D = \left\{x \mid x \geq -\frac{2}{3}\right\}$; $R = \{y \mid y \geq 0\}$; $D = \{x \mid x \geq -2\}$; $R = \{y \mid y \leq 0\}$; $D = \{x \mid x > -2\}$; $R = \{y \mid y > 0\}$

EXTEND 10-1 Graphing Technology Lab: Graphing Square Root Functions

For a square root to be a real number, the radicand cannot be negative. When graphing a radical function, determine when the radicand would be negative and exclude those values from the domain.

Activity 1 Parent Function

Graph $y = \sqrt{x}$.

Enter the equation in the **Y=** list, and graph in the standard viewing window.

KEYSTROKES: [Y=] [2nd] [$\sqrt{\ }$] [X,T,θ,n] [)] [ZOOM] 6

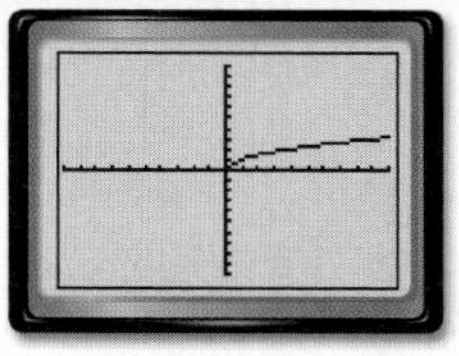

[−10, 10] scl: 1 by [−10, 10] scl: 1

1A. Examine the graph. What is the domain of the function? $\{x \mid x \geq 0\}$

1B. What is the range of the function? $\{y \mid y \geq 0\}$

Activity 2 Translation of Parent Function

Graph $y = \sqrt{x - 2}$.

Enter the equation in the **Y=** list, and graph in the standard viewing window.

KEYSTROKES: [Y=] [2nd] [$\sqrt{\ }$] [X,T,θ,n] [−] 2 [)] [ZOOM] 6

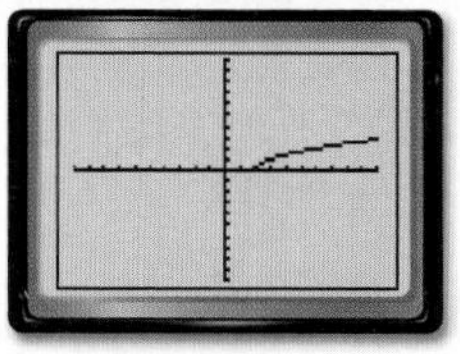

[−10, 10] scl: 1 by [−10, 10] scl: 1

2A. What are the domain and range of the function? $\{x \mid x \geq 2\}$; $\{y \mid y \geq 0\}$

2B. How does the graph of $y = \sqrt{x - 2}$ compare to the graph of the parent function $y = \sqrt{x}$? It is translated 2 units to the right.

Exercises

Graph each equation, and sketch the graph on your paper. State the domain and range. Describe how the graph differs from that of the parent function $y = \sqrt{x}$. 1–8. See Ch. 10 Answer Appendix.

1. $y = \sqrt{x - 1}$
2. $y = \sqrt{x + 3}$
3. $y = \sqrt{x} - 2$
4. $y = \sqrt{-x}$
5. $y = -\sqrt{x}$
6. $y = \sqrt{2x}$
7. $y = \sqrt{2 - x}$
8. $y = \sqrt{x - 3} + 2$

Solve each equation for y. Does the equation represent a function? Explain your reasoning.

9. $x = y^2$
10. $x^2 + y^2 = 4$
11. $x^2 + y^2 = 2$

Write a function with a graph that translates $y = \sqrt{x}$ in each way.

12. shifted 4 units to the left $y = \sqrt{x + 4}$
13. shifted up 7 units $y = \sqrt{x} + 7$
14. shifted down 6 units $y = \sqrt{x} - 6$
15. shifted 5 units to the right and up 3 units $y = \sqrt{x - 5} + 3$

9. $y = \pm\sqrt{x}$; No; you must consider the graph of $y = \sqrt{x}$ and the graph of $y = -\sqrt{x}$. This graph fails the vertical line test.

10. $y = \pm\sqrt{4 - x^2}$; No; there are both positive and negative values of y for most values of x.

11. $y = \pm\sqrt{2 - x^2}$; No; there are both positive and negative values of y for most values of x.

1 Focus

Objective Use a graphing calculator to investigate the graphs of square root functions.

Materials for Each Student

- TI-83/84 Plus or other graphing calculator
- grid paper

Teaching Tip

Before starting this lab, familiarize students with the **ZoomFit** option in the [ZOOM] menu. This option lets the calculator automatically zoom the viewing window to fit the graph. Suggest that students use this option to get a better view of the shape of the graph of a square root function.

2 Teach

Working in Cooperative Groups

Have students work in groups of two or three, mixing abilities, to complete Activities 1 and 2.

- Have students use the value operation from the CALC menu to find the value of the function at different x-values. Press [2nd] [CALC] 1 and then enter an x-value. Students should see that the value of the function is the square root of the radicand of the function.

Practice Have students complete Exercises 1–5.

3 Assess

Formative Assessment

Use Exercise 8 to assess whether students understand how to graph square root functions and can describe how the graph differs from the parent function.

From Concrete to Abstract

Use Exercise 15 to assess whether students can write a function given a description of the graph of the function.

1 Focus

VerticalAlignment

Before Lesson 10-2 Simplify radicals.

Lesson 10-2 Simplify radical expressions by using the Product Property of Square Roots. Simplify radical expressions by using the Quotient Property of Square Roots.

After Lesson 10-2 Add, subtract, and multiply radical expressions.

2 Teach

Scaffolding Questions

Have students read the **Why?** section of the lesson.

Ask:

- Which is the radical expression in the equation for the diameter of a steel cable? $\sqrt{\frac{w}{8}}$
- What does the radical sign in the equation mean? You must find the square root of the value under the radical sign.
- Based on what you know about the order of operations, when do you think you should simplify the radical expression? Simplify the expression under the radical sign before finding the square root.

LESSON 10-2 Simplifying Radical Expressions

Then

- You simplified radicals.

Now

1. Simplify radical expressions by using the Product Property of Square Roots.
2. Simplify radical expressions by using the Quotient Property of Square Roots.

Why?

- The Sunshine Skyway Bridge across Florida's Tampa Bay is supported by 21 steel cables, each 9 inches in diameter.

To find the diameter a steel cable should have to support a given weight, you can use the equation $d = \sqrt{\frac{w}{8}}$, where d is the diameter of the cable in inches and w is the weight in tons.

NewVocabulary
radical expression
rationalizing the denominator
conjugate

Content Standards
AI.RNE.4

Process Standards
PS.7, PS.8

1 Product Property of Square Roots

A **radical expression** contains a radical, such as a square root. Recall the expression under the radical sign is called the radicand. A radicand is in simplest form if the following three conditions are true.

- No radicands have perfect square factors other than 1.
- No radicands contain fractions.
- No radicals appear in the denominator of a fraction.

The following property can be used to simplify square roots.

KeyConcept Product Property of Square Roots

Words	For any nonnegative real numbers a and b, the square root of ab is equal to the square root of a times the square root of b.
Symbols	$\sqrt{ab} = \sqrt{a} \cdot \sqrt{b}$, if $a \geq 0$ and $b \geq 0$
Examples	$\sqrt{4 \cdot 9} = \sqrt{36}$ or 6 $\sqrt{4 \cdot 9} = \sqrt{4} \cdot \sqrt{9} = 2 \cdot 3$ or 6

Example 1 Simplify Square Roots

Simplify $\sqrt{80}$.

$\sqrt{80} = \sqrt{2 \cdot 2 \cdot 2 \cdot 2 \cdot 5}$ Prime factorization of 80

$= \sqrt{2^2} \cdot \sqrt{2^2} \cdot \sqrt{5}$ Product Property of Square Roots

$= 2 \cdot 2 \cdot \sqrt{5}$ or $4\sqrt{5}$ Simplify.

GuidedPractice

1A. $\sqrt{54}$ $3\sqrt{6}$

1B. $\sqrt{180}$ $6\sqrt{5}$

628 | Lesson 10-2

Lesson 10-2 Resources

Resource	Approaching Level AL	On Level OL	Beyond Level BL	English Learners ELL
Teacher Edition	▪ Differentiated Instruction, p. 630	▪ Differentiated Instruction, p. 630	▪ Differentiated Instruction, p. 633	
Chapter Resource Masters	▪ Study Guide and Intervention, pp. 11–12 ▪ Skills Practice, p. 13 ▪ Practice, p. 14 ▪ Word Problem Practice, p. 15	▪ Study Guide and Intervention, pp. 11–12 ▪ Skills Practice, p. 13 ▪ Practice, p. 14 ▪ Word Problem Practice, p. 15 ▪ Enrichment, p. 16	▪ Practice, p. 14 ▪ Word Problem Practice, p. 15 ▪ Enrichment, p. 16	▪ Study Guide and Intervention, pp. 11–12 ▪ Skills Practice, p. 13 ▪ Practice, p. 14 ▪ Word Problem Practice, p. 15
Other	▪ 5-Minute Check 10-2 ▪ Study Notebook	▪ 5-Minute Check 10-2 ▪ Study Notebook	▪ 5-Minute Check 10-2 ▪ Study Notebook	▪ 5-Minute Check 10-2 ▪ Study Notebook

PT

Example 2 Multiply Square Roots

Simplify $\sqrt{2} \cdot \sqrt{14}$.

$$\sqrt{2} \cdot \sqrt{14} = \sqrt{2} \cdot \sqrt{2} \cdot \sqrt{7}$$ Product Property of Square Roots

$$= \sqrt{2^2} \cdot \sqrt{7} \text{ or } 2\sqrt{7}$$ Product Property of Square Roots

GuidedPractice

2A. $\sqrt{5} \cdot \sqrt{10}$ $5\sqrt{2}$ **2B.** $\sqrt{6} \cdot \sqrt{8}$ $4\sqrt{3}$

Consider the expression $\sqrt{x^2}$. It may seem that $x = \sqrt{x^2}$, but when finding the principal square root of an expression containing variables, you have to be sure that the result is not negative. Consider $x = -3$.

$$\sqrt{x^2} \stackrel{?}{=} x$$

$$\sqrt{(-3)^2} \stackrel{?}{=} -3$$ Replace x with -3.

$$\sqrt{9} \stackrel{?}{=} -3$$ $(-3)^2 = 9$

$$3 \neq -3$$ $\sqrt{9} = 3$

Notice in this case, if the right hand side of the equation were $|x|$, the equation would be true. For expressions where the exponent of the variable inside a radical is even and the simplified exponent is odd, you must use absolute value.

$$\sqrt{x^2} = |x| \qquad \sqrt{x^3} = x\sqrt{x} \qquad \sqrt{x^4} = x^2 \qquad \sqrt{x^6} = |x^3|$$

PT

Example 3 Simplify a Square Root with Variables

Simplify $\sqrt{90x^3y^4z^5}$.

$$\sqrt{90x^3y^4z^5} = \sqrt{2 \cdot 3^2 \cdot 5 \cdot x^3 \cdot y^4 \cdot z^5}$$ Prime factorization

$$= \sqrt{2} \cdot \sqrt{3^2} \cdot \sqrt{5} \cdot \sqrt{x^2} \cdot \sqrt{x} \cdot \sqrt{y^4} \cdot \sqrt{z^4} \cdot \sqrt{z}$$ Product Property

$$= \sqrt{2} \cdot 3 \cdot \sqrt{5} \cdot x \cdot \sqrt{x} \cdot y^2 \cdot z^2 \cdot \sqrt{z}$$ Simplify.

$$= 3y^2z^2x\sqrt{10xz}$$ Simplify.

GuidedPractice

3A. $\sqrt{32r^2k^4t^5}$ $4|r|k^2t^2\sqrt{2t}$ **3B.** $\sqrt{56xy^{10}z^5}$ $2|y^5|z^2\sqrt{14xz}$

2 Quotient Property of Square Roots

To divide square roots and simplify radical expressions, you can use the Quotient Property of Square Roots.

ReadingMath

Fractions in the Radicand The expression $\sqrt{\frac{a}{b}}$ is read *the square root of a over b*, or *the square root of the quantity of a over b.*

KeyConcept Quotient Property of Square Roots

Words	For any real numbers a and b, where $a \geq 0$ and $b > 0$, the square root of $\frac{a}{b}$ is equal to the square root of a divided by the square root of b.
Symbols	$\sqrt{\frac{a}{b}} = \frac{\sqrt{a}}{\sqrt{b}}$

Tips for New Teachers

Intervention In order to simplify square roots with the Product Property of Square Roots, students need to be able to find the prime factorization of the radicand. Take a few minutes to review finding prime factorizations so that students can focus on learning the new concept rather than trying to recall earlier material.

1 Product Property of Square Roots

Example 1 shows how to simplify a radical expression in which the radicand is not a perfect square. **Example 2** shows how to multiply square roots. **Example 3** shows how to simplify a square root that contains variables.

Formative Assessment

Use the Guided Practice exercises after each example to determine students' understanding of concepts.

Additional Examples

1. Simplify $\sqrt{52}$. $2\sqrt{13}$
2. Simplify $\sqrt{2} \cdot \sqrt{24}$. $4\sqrt{3}$
3. Simplify $\sqrt{45a^4b^5c^6}$. $3a^2b^2|c^3|\sqrt{5b}$

Additional Examples also in Interactive Classroom PowerPoint® Presentations

IWB **Interactive White Board READY**

Focus on Mathematical Content

Product Property of Square Roots The Product Property can be used to simplify radical expressions. For all nonnegative numbers, the product of each square root equals the square root of the products.

Teach with Tech

Wiki On your secure classroom wiki have half of the students show and explain how they simplified a radical expression. Have different students show how to simplify products and quotients of radicals. When all agree, post on the secure classroom website for additional reference.

2 Quotient Property of Square Roots

Example 4 is a test item that shows how to rationalize the denominator of a radical expression to eliminate radicals from the denominator. **Example 5** shows how to use conjugates to rationalize the denominator of a radical expression.

Focus on Mathematical Content

Quotient Property of Square Roots The Quotient Property can be used to simplify radical expressions. For nonnegative dividends and positive divisors, the square root of a quotient is equal to the quotient of the principal square roots of the numbers.

Additional Examples

4 STANDARDIZED TEST PRACTICE Which expression is equivalent to $\frac{\sqrt{3n}}{\sqrt{8}}$? D

A $\frac{\sqrt{3n}}{8}$ **C** $\frac{\sqrt{6n}}{2}$

B $\frac{\sqrt{3n}}{4}$ **D** $\frac{\sqrt{6n}}{4}$

5 Simplify $\frac{2}{4-\sqrt{5}}$. $\frac{8+2\sqrt{5}}{11}$

Teaching the Process Standards

Structure Mathematically proficient students can see complicated things as single objects or as being composed of several objects. Point out that simplifying the radicand first doesn't change the final answer, but it does simplify the calculations.

You can use the properties of square roots to **rationalize the denominator** of a fraction with a radical. This involves multiplying the numerator and denominator by a factor that eliminates radicals in the denominator.

Test-TakingTip

Structure Look at the radicand to see if it can be simplified first. This may make your computations simpler.

PT

Standardized Test Example 4 Rationalize a Denominator

Which expression is equivalent to $\sqrt{\frac{35}{15}}$?

A $\frac{5\sqrt{21}}{15}$ **B** $\frac{\sqrt{21}}{3}$ **C** $\frac{\sqrt{525}}{15}$ **D** $\frac{\sqrt{35}}{15}$

Read the Test Item The radical expression needs to be simplified.

Solve the Test Item

$\sqrt{\frac{35}{15}} = \sqrt{\frac{7}{3}}$ Reduce $\frac{35}{15}$ to $\frac{7}{3}$.

$= \frac{\sqrt{7}}{\sqrt{3}}$ Quotient Property of Square Roots

$= \frac{\sqrt{7}}{\sqrt{3}} \cdot \frac{\sqrt{3}}{\sqrt{3}}$ Multiply by $\frac{\sqrt{3}}{\sqrt{3}}$.

$= \frac{\sqrt{21}}{3}$ Product Property of Square Roots

The correct choice is B.

GuidedPractice

4. Simplify $\frac{\sqrt{6y}}{\sqrt{12}}$. H

F $\frac{\sqrt{y}}{2}$ **G** $\frac{\sqrt{y}}{4}$ **H** $\frac{\sqrt{2y}}{2}$ **J** $\frac{\sqrt{2y}}{4}$

Binomials of the form $a\sqrt{b} + c\sqrt{d}$ and $a\sqrt{b} - c\sqrt{d}$, where a, b, c, and d are rational numbers, are called **conjugates**. For example, $2 + \sqrt{7}$ and $2 - \sqrt{7}$ are conjugates. The product of two conjugates is a rational number and can be found using the pattern for the difference of squares.

PT

Example 5 Use Conjugates to Rationalize a Denominator

Simplify $\frac{3}{5+\sqrt{2}}$.

$\frac{3}{5+\sqrt{2}} = \frac{3}{5+\sqrt{2}} \cdot \frac{5-\sqrt{2}}{5-\sqrt{2}}$ The conjugate of $5+\sqrt{2}$ is $5-\sqrt{2}$.

$= \frac{3(5-\sqrt{2})}{5^2-(\sqrt{2})^2}$ $(a-b)(a+b) = a^2 - b^2$

$= \frac{15-3\sqrt{2}}{25-2}$ or $\frac{15-3\sqrt{2}}{23}$ $(\sqrt{2})^2 = 2$

GuidedPractice **Simplify each expression.**

5A. $\frac{3}{2+\sqrt{2}}$ $\frac{6-3\sqrt{2}}{2}$ **5B.** $\frac{7}{3-\sqrt{7}}$ $\frac{21+7\sqrt{7}}{2}$

DifferentiatedInstruction AL OL

If students need further practice with conjugates,

Then have students use their calculators to show that using conjugates produces equivalent expressions in Example 5. Have students show that $\frac{3}{5+\sqrt{2}}$, $\frac{3(5-\sqrt{2})}{(5+\sqrt{2})(5-\sqrt{2})}$, and $\frac{15-3\sqrt{2}}{23}$ are equivalent. They should find that each expression is about 0.4677.

Check Your Understanding

= Step-by-Step Solutions begin on page R13.

Examples 1–3 Simplify each expression.

1. $\sqrt{24}$ $2\sqrt{6}$
2. $3\sqrt{16}$ 12
3. $2\sqrt{25}$ 10
4. $\sqrt{10} \cdot \sqrt{14}$ $2\sqrt{35}$
5. $\sqrt{3} \cdot \sqrt{18}$ $3\sqrt{6}$
6. $3\sqrt{10} \cdot 4\sqrt{10}$ 120
7. $\sqrt{60x^4y^7}$ $2x^2y^3\sqrt{15y}$
8. $\sqrt{88m^3p^2r^5}$ $2m|p|r^2\sqrt{22mr}$
9. $\sqrt{99ab^5c^2}$ $3b^2|c|\sqrt{11ab}$

Example 4

10. **MULTIPLE CHOICE** Which expression is equivalent to $\sqrt{\frac{45}{10}}$? D

A $\frac{5\sqrt{2}}{10}$ B $\frac{\sqrt{45}}{10}$ C $\frac{\sqrt{50}}{10}$ D $\frac{3\sqrt{2}}{2}$

Example 5 Simplify each expression.

11. $\frac{3}{3+\sqrt{5}}$ $\frac{9-3\sqrt{5}}{4}$
12. $\frac{5}{2-\sqrt{6}}$ $\frac{10+5\sqrt{6}}{-2}$
13. $\frac{2}{1-\sqrt{10}}$ $\frac{2+2\sqrt{10}}{-9}$
14. $\frac{1}{4+\sqrt{12}}$ $\frac{2-\sqrt{3}}{2}$
15. $\frac{4}{6-\sqrt{7}}$ $\frac{24+4\sqrt{7}}{29}$
16. $\frac{6}{5+\sqrt{11}}$ $\frac{15-3\sqrt{11}}{7}$

Practice and Problem Solving

Extra Practice is on page R10.

Examples 1–3 Simplify each expression.

17. $\sqrt{52}$ $2\sqrt{13}$
18. $\sqrt{56}$ $2\sqrt{14}$
19. $\sqrt{72}$ $6\sqrt{2}$
20. $3\sqrt{18}$ $9\sqrt{2}$
21. $\sqrt{243}$ $9\sqrt{3}$
22. $\sqrt{245}$ $7\sqrt{5}$
23. $\sqrt{5} \cdot \sqrt{10}$ $5\sqrt{2}$
24. $\sqrt{10} \cdot \sqrt{20}$ $10\sqrt{2}$
25. $3\sqrt{8} \cdot 2\sqrt{7}$ $12\sqrt{14}$
26. $4\sqrt{2} \cdot 5\sqrt{8}$ 80
27. $3\sqrt{25t^2}$ $15|t|$
28. $5\sqrt{81q^5}$ $45q^2\sqrt{q}$
29. $\sqrt{28a^2b^3}$ $2|a|b\sqrt{7b}$
30. $\sqrt{75qr^3}$ $5r\sqrt{3qr}$
31. $7\sqrt{63m^3p}$ $21m\sqrt{7mp}$
32. $4\sqrt{66g^2h^4}$ $4|g|h^2\sqrt{66}$
33. $\sqrt{2ab^2} \cdot \sqrt{10a^5b}$ $2a^3b\sqrt{5b}$
34. $\sqrt{4c^3d^3} \cdot \sqrt{8c^3d}$ $4c^3d^2\sqrt{2}$

35. **ROLLER COASTER** Starting from a stationary position, the velocity v of a roller coaster in feet per second at the bottom of a hill can be approximated by $v = \sqrt{64h}$, where h is the height of the hill in feet.
   a. Simplify the equation. $v = 8\sqrt{h}$
   b. Determine the velocity of a roller coaster at the bottom of a 134-foot hill. about 92.6 ft/s

36. **PRECISION** When fighting a fire, the velocity v of water being pumped into the air is modeled by the function $v = \sqrt{2hg}$, where h represents the maximum height of the water and g represents the acceleration due to gravity (32 ft/s^2).
   a. Solve the function for h. $h = \frac{v^2}{2g}$
   b. The Hollowville Fire Department needs a pump that will propel water 80 feet into the air. Will a pump advertised to project water with a velocity of 70 feet per second meet their needs? Explain. See margin.
   c. The Jackson Fire Department must purchase a pump that will propel water 90 feet into the air. Will a pump that is advertised to project water with a velocity of 77 feet per second meet the fire department's need? Explain. See margin.

WatchOut!

Preventing Errors Students may not think the simplified form of a fraction containing radicals looks any simpler than the original fraction. Explain that meeting the three conditions for simplifying a radical expression, not the look of the fraction, dictates whether a fraction containing radicals is simplified.

3 Practice

Formative Assessment

Use Exercises 1–16 to check for understanding.

Use the chart at the bottom of this page to customize assignments for your students.

Teaching the Process Standards

Precision Mathematically proficient students express numerical answers with a degree of precision appropriate for the problem context. In Exercise 36, point out that the calculated values only have to be accurate enough to determine if the needs are met.

Additional Answers

36b. No; sample answer: The advertised pump will pump water only to a maximum height of about 76.6 feet.

36c. Yes; sample answer: The advertised pump will pump water to a maximum height of about 92.6 feet.

Differentiated Homework Options

Level	Assignment	Two-Day Option	
AL Basic	17–48, 52, 54, 55, 57–90	17–47 odd, 58–61	18–48 even, 52, 54, 55, 57, 62–90
OL Core	17–47 odd, 49–52, 54, 55, 57–90	17–48, 58–61	49–52, 54, 55, 57, 62–90
BL Advanced	49–84, (optional: 85–90)		

Study Guide and Intervention

AL OL ELL

NAME ____ DATE ____ PERIOD ____

10-2 Study Guide and Intervention

Simplifying Radical Expressions

Product Property of Square Roots The Product Property of Square Roots and prime factorization can be used to simplify expressions involving irrational square roots. When you simplify radical expressions with variables, use absolute value to ensure nonnegative results.

Product Property of Square Roots	For any numbers a and b, where $a \geq 0$ and $b \geq 0$, $\sqrt{ab} = \sqrt{a} \cdot \sqrt{b}$.

Example 1 Simplify $\sqrt{180}$.

$\sqrt{180} = \sqrt{2 \cdot 2 \cdot 3 \cdot 3 \cdot 5}$ Prime factorization of 180
$= \sqrt{2^2} \cdot \sqrt{3^2} \cdot \sqrt{5}$ Product Property of Square Roots
$= 2 \cdot 3 \cdot \sqrt{5}$ Simplify.
$= 6\sqrt{5}$ Simplify.

Example 2 Simplify $\sqrt{120a^2 \cdot b^5 \cdot c^4}$.

$\sqrt{120a^2 \cdot b^5 \cdot c^4}$
$= \sqrt{2^2 \cdot 2 \cdot 3 \cdot 5 \cdot a^2 \cdot b^5 \cdot c^4}$
$= \sqrt{2^2} \cdot \sqrt{2} \cdot \sqrt{3} \cdot \sqrt{5} \cdot \sqrt{a^2} \cdot \sqrt{b^4} \cdot \sqrt{b} \cdot \sqrt{c^4}$
$= 2 \cdot \sqrt{2} \cdot \sqrt{3} \cdot \sqrt{5} \cdot |a| \cdot b^2 \cdot \sqrt{b} \cdot c^2$
$= 2|a|b^2c^2\sqrt{30b}$

Exercises

Simplify each expression.

1. $\sqrt{28}$ 2. $\sqrt{68}$ 3. $\sqrt{60}$ 4. $\sqrt{75}$
5. $\sqrt{162}$ 6. $\sqrt{3} \cdot \sqrt{6}$ 7. $\sqrt{2} \cdot \sqrt{5}$ 8. $\sqrt{5} \cdot \sqrt{10}$
9. $\sqrt{4a^2}$ 10. $\sqrt{9x^4}$ 11. $\sqrt{300a^4}$ 12. $\sqrt{128c^6}$
13. $4\sqrt{10} \cdot 3\sqrt{6}$ 14. $\sqrt{3x^2} \cdot 3\sqrt{3x^4}$ 15. $\sqrt{20a^2b^4}$ 16. $\sqrt{100x^3y}$
17. $\sqrt{24a^4b^2}$ 18. $\sqrt{81x^4y^2}$ 19. $\sqrt{150a^2b^2c}$
20. $\sqrt{72a^6b^3c^2}$ 21. $\sqrt{45x^2y^5z^8}$ 22. $\sqrt{98x^4y^6z^2}$

Practice

AL OL BL ELL

NAME ____ DATE ____ PERIOD ____

10-2 Practice

Simplifying Radical Expressions

Simplify.

1. $\sqrt{24}$ 2. $\sqrt{60}$
3. $\sqrt{108}$ 4. $\sqrt{8} \cdot \sqrt{6}$
5. $\sqrt{7} \cdot \sqrt{14}$ 6. $3\sqrt{12} \cdot 5\sqrt{6}$
7. $4\sqrt{3} \cdot 3\sqrt{18}$ 8. $\sqrt{27tu^3}$
9. $\sqrt{50p^5}$ 10. $\sqrt{108x^6y^4z^5}$
11. $\sqrt{56m^2n^4p^5}$ 12. $\frac{\sqrt{8}}{\sqrt{6}}$
13. $\sqrt{\frac{2}{10}}$ 14. $\sqrt{\frac{5}{32}}$
15. $\sqrt{\frac{3}{4}} \cdot \sqrt{\frac{4}{5}}$ 16. $\sqrt{\frac{1}{7}} \cdot \sqrt{\frac{7}{11}}$
17. $\frac{\sqrt{3k}}{\sqrt{8}}$ 18. $\sqrt{\frac{18}{x^3}}$
19. $\sqrt{\frac{4y}{3y^2}}$ 20. $\sqrt{\frac{9ab}{4ab^4}}$
21. $\frac{3}{5-\sqrt{2}}$ 22. $\frac{8}{3+\sqrt{3}}$
23. $\frac{5}{\sqrt{7}+\sqrt{3}}$ 24. $\frac{3\sqrt{7}}{-1-\sqrt{27}}$

25. **SKY DIVING** When a skydiver jumps from an airplane, the time t it takes to free fall a given distance can be estimated by the formula $t = \sqrt{\frac{2s}{9.8}}$, where t is in seconds and s is in meters. If Julie jumps from an airplane, how long will it take her to free fall 750 meters?

26. **METEOROLOGY** To estimate how long a thunderstorm will last, meteorologists can use the formula $t = \sqrt{\frac{d^3}{216}}$, where t is the time in hours and d is the diameter of the storm in miles.

a. A thunderstorm is 8 miles in diameter. Estimate how long the storm will last. Give your answer in simplified form and as a decimal.

b. Will a thunderstorm twice this diameter last twice as long? Explain.

Word Problem Practice

AL OL BL ELL

NAME ____ DATE ____ PERIOD ____

10-2 Word Problem Practice

Simplifying Radical Expressions

1. **SPORTS** Jasmine calculated the height of her team's soccer goal to be $\frac{15}{\sqrt{3}}$ feet. Simplify the expression.

2. **NATURE** In 2010, an earthquake below the ocean floor initiated a devastating tsunami in Sumatra. Scientists can approximate the velocity V in feet per second of a tsunami in water of depth d feet with the formula $V = \sqrt{16d}$. Determine the velocity of a tsunami in 300 feet of water. Write your answer in simplified radical form.

3. **AUTOMOBILES** The following formula can be used to find the "zero to sixty" time for a car, or the time it takes for a car to accelerate from a stop to sixty miles per hour.

$V = \sqrt{\frac{2PT}{M}}$

V is the velocity in meters per second, P is the car's average power in watts, M is the mass of the car in kilograms, and T is the time in seconds.

Find the time it takes for a 900-kilogram car with an average 60,000 watts of power to accelerate from stop to 60 miles per hour, which is 26.82 meters per second. Round your answer to the nearest tenth.

4. **PHYSICAL SCIENCE** When a substance such as water vapor is in its gaseous state, the volume and the velocity of its molecules increase as temperature increases. The average velocity V of a molecule with mass m at temperature T is given by the formula $V = \sqrt{\frac{3kT}{m}}$. Solve the equation for k.

5. **GEOMETRY** Suppose Emeryville Hospital wants to build a new helipad on which medic rescue helicopters can land. The helipad will be circular and made of fire resistant rubber.

a. If the area of the helipad is A, write an equation for the radius r.

b. Write an expression in simplified radical form for the radius of a helipad with an area of 288 square meters.

c. Using a calculator, find a decimal approximation for the radius. Round your answer to the nearest hundredth.

Examples 4–5 Simplify each expression.

37. $\sqrt{\frac{32}{t^4}}$ $\frac{4\sqrt{2}}{t^2}$
38. $\sqrt{\frac{27}{m^5}}$ $\frac{3\sqrt{3m}}{m^3}$
39. $\frac{\sqrt{68ac^3}}{\sqrt{27a^2}}$ $\frac{2c\sqrt{51ac}}{9|a|}$
40. $\frac{\sqrt{h^3}}{\sqrt{8}}$ $\frac{h\sqrt{2h}}{4}$
41. $\sqrt{\frac{3}{16}} \cdot \sqrt{\frac{9}{5}}$ $\frac{3\sqrt{15}}{20}$
42. $\sqrt{\frac{7}{2}} \cdot \sqrt{\frac{5}{3}}$ $\frac{\sqrt{210}}{6}$
43. $\frac{7}{5+\sqrt{3}}$ $\frac{35-7\sqrt{3}}{22}$
44. $\frac{9}{6-\sqrt{8}}$ $\frac{27+9\sqrt{2}}{14}$
45. $\frac{3\sqrt{3}}{-2+\sqrt{6}}$ $\frac{6\sqrt{3}+9\sqrt{2}}{2}$
46. $\frac{3}{\sqrt{7}-\sqrt{2}}$ $\frac{3\sqrt{7}+3\sqrt{2}}{5}$
47. $\frac{5}{\sqrt{6}+\sqrt{3}}$ $\frac{5\sqrt{6}-5\sqrt{3}}{3}$
48. $\frac{2\sqrt{5}}{2\sqrt{7}+3\sqrt{3}}$ $4\sqrt{35}-6\sqrt{15}$

B

49. **ELECTRICITY** The amount of current in amperes I that an appliance uses can be calculated using the formula $I = \sqrt{\frac{P}{R}}$, where P is the power in watts and R is the resistance in ohms.

a. Simplify the formula. $I = \frac{\sqrt{PR}}{R}$

b. How much current does an appliance use if the power used is 75 watts and the resistance is 5 ohms? **about 3.9 amps**

50. **KINETIC ENERGY** The speed v of a ball can be determined by the equation $v = \sqrt{\frac{2k}{m}}$, where k is the kinetic energy and m is the mass of the ball.

a. Simplify the formula if the mass of the ball is 3 kilograms. $v = \frac{\sqrt{6k}}{3}$

b. If the ball is traveling 7 meters per second, what is the kinetic energy of the ball in Joules? **73.5 Joules**

51. **SUBMARINES** The greatest distance d in miles that a lookout can see on a clear day is modeled by the formula shown. Determine how high the submarine would have to raise its periscope to see a ship, if the submarine is the given distances away from the ship.

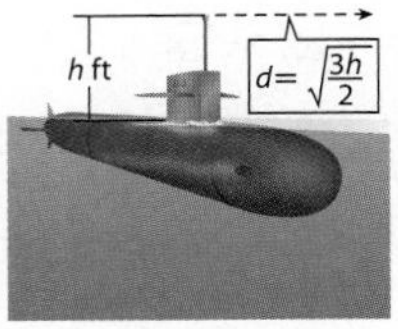

Distance	3	6	9	12	15
Height	6	24	54	96	150

H.O.T. Problems Use Higher-Order Thinking Skills

C

52. **STRUCTURE** Explain how to solve $\frac{\sqrt{3}+2}{x} = \frac{\sqrt{3}-1}{\sqrt{3}}$. **See margin.**

53. **CHALLENGE** Simplify each expression.

a. $\sqrt[3]{27}$ **3** b. $\sqrt[3]{40}$ $2\sqrt[3]{5}$ c. $\sqrt[3]{750}$ $5\sqrt[3]{6}$

54. **REASONING** Marge takes a number, subtracts 4, multiplies by 4, takes the square root, and takes the reciprocal to get $\frac{1}{2}$. What number did she start with? Write a formula to describe the process.

54. 5; $\frac{1}{\sqrt{4(x-4)}} = \frac{1}{2}$

55. **OPEN ENDED** Write two binomials of the form $a\sqrt{b} + c\sqrt{f}$ and $a\sqrt{b} - c\sqrt{f}$. Then find their product.
Sample answer: $1 + \sqrt{2}$ and $1 - \sqrt{2}$; $(1+\sqrt{2}) \cdot (1-\sqrt{2}) = 1 - 2 = -1$

56. **CHALLENGE** Use the Quotient Property of Square Roots to derive the Quadratic Formula by solving the quadratic equation $ax^2 + bx + c = 0$. (*Hint*: Begin by completing the square.) **See Ch. 10 Answer Appendix.**

57. **WRITING IN MATH** Summarize how to write a radical expression in simplest form. **See margin.**

Enrichment

OL BL

NAME ____ DATE ____ PERIOD ____

10-2 Enrichment

Squares and Square Roots From a Graph

The graph of $y = x^2$ can be used to find the squares and square roots of numbers.

To find the square of 3, locate 3 on the x-axis. Then find its corresponding value on the y-axis.

The arrows show that $3^2 = 9$.

To find the square root of 4, first locate 4 on the y-axis. Then find its corresponding value on the x-axis. Following the arrows on the graph, you can see that $\sqrt{4} = 2$.

A small part of the graph at $y = x^2$ is shown below. A 10:1 ratio for unit length on the y-axis to unit length on the x-axis is used.

Example Find $\sqrt{11}$.

The arrows show that $\sqrt{11} = 3.3$ to the nearest tenth.

Teaching the Process Standards

Structure Mathematically proficient students can step back for an overview and shift perspective. In Exercise 52, tell students one way to start is by thinking about when two squared numbers are equal.

Standardized Test Practice

58. Jerry's electric bill is \$23 less than his natural gas bill. The two bills are a total of \$109. Which of the following equations can be used to find the amount of his natural gas bill? **D**

A $g + g = 109$
B $23 + 2g = 109$
C $g - 23 = 109$
D $2g - 23 = 109$

59. Solve $a^2 - 2a + 1 = 25$. **H**

F $-4, -6$
G $4, -6$
H $-4, 6$
J $4, 6$

60. The expression $\sqrt{160x^2y^5}$ is equivalent to which of the following? **C**

A $16|x|y^2\sqrt{10y}$
B $|x|y^2\sqrt{160y}$
C $4|x|y^2\sqrt{10y}$
D $10|x|y^2\sqrt{4y}$

61. GRIDDED RESPONSE Miki earns \$10 an hour and 10% commission on sales. If Miki worked 38 hours and had a total sales of \$1275 last week, how much did she make? **507.50**

Spiral Review

Graph each function. Compare to the parent graph. State the domain and range. (Lesson 10-1) **62–67. See Ch. 10 Answer Appendix.**

62. $y = 2\sqrt{x} - 1$
63. $y = \frac{1}{2}\sqrt{x}$
64. $y = 2\sqrt{x+2}$
65. $y = -\sqrt{x+1}$
66. $y = -3\sqrt{x-3}$
67. $y = -2\sqrt{x} + 1$

Determine the domain and range for each function. (Lesson 9-7) **68–70. See margin.**

68. $f(x) = |2x - 5|$
69. $h(x) = [\![x - 1]\!]$
70. $g(x) = \begin{cases} -3x + 4 \text{ if } x > 2 \\ x - 1 \text{ if } x \le 2 \end{cases}$

Solve each equation by using the Quadratic Formula. Round to the nearest tenth if necessary. (Lesson 9-5)

71. $x^2 - 25 = 0$ **−5, 5**
72. $r^2 + 25 = 0$ **∅**
73. $4w^2 + 100 = 40w$ **5**
74. $2r^2 + r - 14 = 0$ **−2.9, 2.4**
75. $5v^2 - 7v = 1$ **−0.1, 1.5**
76. $11z^2 - z = 3$ **−0.5, 0.6**

Factor each polynomial, if possible. If the polynomial cannot be factored, write *prime*. (Lesson 8-8) **80. $2(4x^2 + y^2)(2x - y)(2x + y)$**

77. $n^2 - 81$ **$(n - 9)(n + 9)$**
78. $4 - 9a^2$ **$(2 - 3a)(2 + 3a)$**
79. $2x^5 - 98x^3$ **$2x^3(x + 7)(x - 7)$**
80. $32x^4 - 2y^4$
81. $4t^2 - 27$ **prime**
82. $x^3 - 3x^2 - 9x + 27$ **$(x + 3)(x - 3)(x - 3)$**

83. POPULATION The country of Latvia has been experiencing a 1.1% annual decrease in population. In 2009, its population was 2,261,294. If the trend continues, predict Latvia's population in 2019. (Lesson 7-6) **about 2,024,510**

84. TOMATOES There are more than 10,000 varieties of tomatoes. One seed company produces seed packages for 200 varieties of tomatoes. For how many varieties do they not provide seeds? (Lesson 5-1) **Sample answer: Let t = the number of tomato varieties for which they do not produce seeds, $t + 200 > 10{,}000$; $\{t \mid t > 9800\}$.**

Skills Review

Write the prime factorization of each number.

85. 24 **$2^3 \cdot 3$**
86. 88 **$2^3 \cdot 11$**
87. 180 **$2^2 \cdot 3^2 \cdot 5$**
88. 31 **31**
89. 60 **$2^2 \cdot 3 \cdot 5$**
90. 90 **$2 \cdot 3^2 \cdot 5$**

DifferentiatedInstruction BL

Extension Find a number other than 1 that has a whole number square root, cube root, and fourth root. Sample answer: 4096

4 Assess

Ticket Out the Door Ask students to write radical expressions in which they need to use a conjugate to rationalize the denominators. Have students simplify the expressions.

Formative Assessment

Check for student understanding of concepts in Lessons 10-1 and 10-2.

Quiz 1, p. 57

Additional Answers

52. Sample answer: Cross multiply then divide. Rationalize the denominator to find that $x = \frac{5\sqrt{3} + 9}{2}$

57. No radicals can appear in the denominator of a fraction. So, rationalize the denominator to get rid of the radicand in the denominator. Then check if any of the radicands have perfect square factors other than 1. If so, simplify.

68. D = {all real numbers}; R = $\{y \mid y \ge 0\}$

69. D = {all real numbers}; R = $\{y \mid y$ is an integer.$\}$

70. D = {all real numbers}; R = $\{y \mid y \le 1\}$

1 Focus

Objective Investigate the products and sums of two rational numbers, two irrational numbers, and a rational and irrational number.

Teaching Tip

Emphasize that using examples with actual numbers cannot actually prove the conclusions made in the activities. This would need to be done algebraically. To increase the reliability of each conclusion, examples should be done using all types of numbers in the set(s).

2 Teach

Working in Cooperative Groups

Have students work in pairs, mixing abilities. Have them first make a list of subsets for rational and irrational numbers. After reading Activities 1 and 2, have them test more pairs of numbers from the subsets they listed.

Ask:

- Did you find any examples that did not agree with the conclusion in each activity? no
- What would finding one example that did not support the conclusion indicate? One example would be a counter example that would prove that the statement is false.

Practice Have students complete Exercises 1–3.

3 Assess

Formative Assessment

Use Exercises 1 and 2 to assess if students can investigate operations completed with specific types of numbers.

EXTEND 10-2 Algebra Lab
Rational and Irrational Numbers

A set is **closed** under an operation if for any numbers in the set, the result of the operation is also in the set. A set may be closed under one operation and not closed under another.

Content Standards
AI.RNE.2

Activity 1 Closure of Rational Numbers and Irrational Numbers

Are the sets of rational and irrational numbers closed under multiplication? under addition?

Step 1 To determine if each set is closed under multiplication, examine several products of two rational factors and then two irrational factors.

Rational: $5 \times 2 = 10$; $-3 \times 4 = -12$; $3.7 \times 0.5 = 1.85$; $\frac{3}{4} \times \frac{2}{3} = \frac{1}{2}$

Irrational: $\pi \times \sqrt{2} = \sqrt{2}\pi$; $\sqrt{3} \times \sqrt{7} = \sqrt{21}$; $\sqrt{5} \times \sqrt{5} = 5$

The product of each pair of rational numbers is rational. However, the products of pairs of irrational numbers are both irrational and rational. Thus, it appears that the set of rational numbers is closed under multiplication, but the set of irrational numbers is not.

Step 2 Repeat this process for addition.

Rational: $3 + 8 = 11$; $-4 + 7 = 3$; $3.7 + 5.82 = 9.52$; $\frac{2}{5} + \frac{1}{4} = \frac{13}{20}$

Irrational: $\sqrt{3} + \pi = \sqrt{3} + \pi$; $3\sqrt{5} + 6\sqrt{5} = 9\sqrt{5}$; $\sqrt{12} + \sqrt{50} = 2\sqrt{3} + 5\sqrt{2}$

The sum of each pair of rational numbers is rational, and the sum of each pair of irrational numbers is irrational. Both sets are closed under addition.

Activity 2 Rational and Irrational Numbers

What kind of numbers are the product and sum of a rational and irrational number?

Step 1 Examine the products of several pairs of rational and irrational numbers.

$3 \times \sqrt{8} = 6\sqrt{2}$; $\frac{3}{4} \times \sqrt{2} = \frac{3\sqrt{2}}{4}$; $1 \times \sqrt{7} = \sqrt{7}$; $0 \times \sqrt{5} = 0$

The product is rational only when the rational factor is 0. The product of each nonzero rational number and irrational number is irrational.

Step 2 Find the sums of several pairs of a rational and irrational number.

$5 + \sqrt{3} = 5 + \sqrt{3}$; $\frac{2}{3} + \sqrt{5} = \frac{2 + 3\sqrt{5}}{3}$; $-4 + \sqrt{6} = -1(4 - \sqrt{6})$

The sum of each rational and irrational number is irrational.

Analyze the Results

1. What kinds of numbers are the difference of two unique rational numbers, two unique irrational numbers, and a rational and an irrational number? **1. The difference of any two unique rational numbers is always a rational number. The difference of any two unique irrational numbers is always irrational. The difference of any rational and irrational numbers is always irrational.**
2. Is the quotient of every rational and irrational number always another rational or irrational number? If not, provide a counterexample. **No; sample answer: $\frac{\sqrt{5}}{0}$ does not equal a real number.**
3. **CHALLENGE** Recall that rational numbers are numbers that can be written in the form $\frac{a}{b}$, where a and b are integers and $b \neq 0$. Using $\frac{a}{b}$ and $\frac{c}{d}$ show that the sum and product of two rational numbers must always be a rational number. **See margin.**

From Concrete to Abstract

After students complete Exercise 3, ask the class for possible ways that irrational numbers could be represented and used to test the product prediction from Activity 1.

Additional Answer

3. $\frac{a}{b} + \frac{c}{d} = \frac{ad + bc}{bd}$ and $\frac{a}{b} \cdot \frac{c}{d} = \frac{ac}{bd}$ The sum and product of two integers is always an integer, so $(ad + bc)$, ac, and bd are all integers. By definition of a rational number, the sum and product of the two rational numbers are rational.

LESSON 10-3 Operations with Radical Expressions

Then

- You simplified radical expressions.

Now

1. Add and subtract radical expressions.
2. Multiply radical expressions.

Why?

- Conchita is going to run in her neighborhood to get ready for the soccer season. She plans to run the course that she has laid out three times each day.

  How far does Conchita have to run to complete the course that she laid out?

  How far does she run every day?

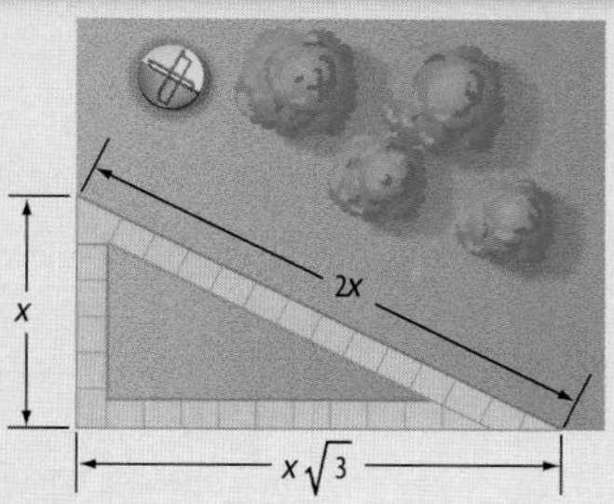

Content Standards
AI.RNE.4

Process Standards
PS.2

1 Add or Subtract Radical Expressions

To add or subtract radical expressions, the radicands must be alike in the same way that monomial terms must be alike to add or subtract.

Monomials	Radical Expressions
$4a + 2a = (4 + 2)a$ $= 6a$	$4\sqrt{5} + 2\sqrt{5} = (4 + 2)\sqrt{5}$ $= 6\sqrt{5}$
$9b - 2b = (9 - 2)b$ $= 7b$	$9\sqrt{3} - 2\sqrt{3} = (9 - 2)\sqrt{3}$ $= 7\sqrt{3}$

Notice that when adding and subtracting radical expressions, the radicand does not change. This is the same as when adding or subtracting monomials.

Example 1 Add and Subtract Expressions with Like Radicands

PT

Simplify each expression.

a. $5\sqrt{2} + 7\sqrt{2} - 6\sqrt{2}$

$5\sqrt{2} + 7\sqrt{2} - 6\sqrt{2} = (5 + 7 - 6)\sqrt{2}$ Distributive Property

$= 6\sqrt{2}$ Simplify.

b. $10\sqrt{7} + 5\sqrt{11} + 4\sqrt{7} - 6\sqrt{11}$

$10\sqrt{7} + 5\sqrt{11} + 4\sqrt{7} - 6\sqrt{11} = (10 + 4)\sqrt{7} + (5 - 6)\sqrt{11}$ Distributive Property

$= 14\sqrt{7} - \sqrt{11}$ Simplify.

Guided Practice

1C. $4\sqrt{3} - 8\sqrt{5}$ 1D. $-2\sqrt{3} + 6\sqrt{7}$

1A. $3\sqrt{2} - 5\sqrt{2} + 4\sqrt{2}$ $2\sqrt{2}$

1B. $6\sqrt{11} + 2\sqrt{11} - 9\sqrt{11}$ $-\sqrt{11}$

1C. $15\sqrt{3} - 14\sqrt{5} + 6\sqrt{5} - 11\sqrt{3}$

1D. $4\sqrt{3} + 3\sqrt{7} - 6\sqrt{3} + 3\sqrt{7}$

Not all radical expressions have like radicands. Simplifying the expressions may make it possible to have like radicands so that they can be added or subtracted.

1 Focus

Vertical Alignment

Before Lesson 10-3 Simplify radical expressions.

Lesson 10-3 Add and subtract radical expressions. Multiply radical expressions.

After Lesson 10-3 Solve radical equations.

2 Teach

Scaffolding Questions

Have students read the **Why?** section of the lesson.

Ask:

- What expression shows the length of the course? $x + 2x + x\sqrt{3}$
- Which terms in the expression can be combined? Explain. x and $2x$ because they are like terms
- Which term cannot be combined? Explain. $x\sqrt{3}$ because it contains a radical
- What expression shows how far Conchita will run each day? $x(3 + \sqrt{3})$

Lesson 10-3 Resources

Resource	Approaching Level AL	On Level OL	Beyond Level BL	English Learners ELL
Teacher Edition	▪ Differentiated Instruction, p. 636	▪ Differentiated Instruction, pp. 636, 639	▪ Differentiated Instruction, p. 639	▪ Differentiated Instruction, p. 636
Chapter Resource Masters	▪ Study Guide and Intervention, pp. 17–18 ▪ Skills Practice, p. 19 ▪ Practice, p. 20 ▪ Word Problem Practice, p. 21	▪ Study Guide and Intervention, pp. 17–18 ▪ Skills Practice, p. 19 ▪ Practice, p. 20 ▪ Word Problem Practice, p. 21 ▪ Enrichment, p. 22	▪ Practice, p. 20 ▪ Word Problem Practice, p. 21 ▪ Enrichment, p. 22	▪ Study Guide and Intervention, pp. 17–18 ▪ Skills Practice, p. 19 ▪ Practice, p. 20 ▪ Word Problem Practice, p. 21
Other	▪ 5-Minute Check 10-3 ▪ Study Notebook ▪ Teaching Algebra with Manipulatives	▪ 5-Minute Check 10-3 ▪ Study Notebook ▪ Teaching Algebra with Manipulatives	▪ 5-Minute Check 10-3 ▪ Study Notebook	▪ 5-Minute Check 10-3 ▪ Study Notebook ▪ Teaching Algebra with Manipulatives

1 Add or Subtract Radical Expressions

Example 1 shows how to use the Distributive Property to add or subtract like radicands in a radical expression. **Example 2** shows how to simplify the radicals in a radical expression with unlike radicands.

Formative Assessment

Use the Guided Practice exercises after each example to determine students' understanding of concepts.

Additional Examples

1 Simplify each expression.

a. $6\sqrt{5} + 2\sqrt{5} - 5\sqrt{5}$ $3\sqrt{5}$

b. $7\sqrt{2} + 8\sqrt{11} - 4\sqrt{11} - 6\sqrt{2}$ $\sqrt{2} + 4\sqrt{11}$

2 Simplify $6\sqrt{27} + 8\sqrt{12} + 2\sqrt{75}$. $44\sqrt{3}$

Additional Examples also in Interactive Classroom PowerPoint® Presentations

IWB **Interactive White Board READY**

2 Multiply Radical Expressions

Example 3 shows how to multiply radical expressions with different radicands. **Example 4** shows how to multiply radical expressions to find the area of a rectangle.

Additional Example

3 Simplify each expression.

a. $2\sqrt{3} \cdot 4\sqrt{6}$ $24\sqrt{2}$

b. $4\sqrt{2}(3\sqrt{2} + 2\sqrt{6})$ $24 + 16\sqrt{3}$

StudyTip

Simplify First Simplify each radical term first. Then perform the operations needed.

Example 2 Add and Subtract Expressions with Unlike Radicands

Simplify $2\sqrt{18} + 2\sqrt{32} + \sqrt{72}$.

$2\sqrt{18} + 2\sqrt{32} + \sqrt{72} = 2(\sqrt{3^2} \cdot \sqrt{2}) + 2(\sqrt{4^2} \cdot \sqrt{2}) + (\sqrt{6^2} \cdot \sqrt{2})$ Product Property

$= 2(3\sqrt{2}) + 2(4\sqrt{2}) + (6\sqrt{2})$ Simplify.

$= 6\sqrt{2} + 8\sqrt{2} + 6\sqrt{2}$ Multiply.

$= 20\sqrt{2}$ Simplify.

GuidedPractice

2A. $4\sqrt{54} + 2\sqrt{24}$ $16\sqrt{6}$

2B. $4\sqrt{12} - 6\sqrt{48}$ $-16\sqrt{3}$

2C. $3\sqrt{45} + \sqrt{20} - \sqrt{245}$ $4\sqrt{5}$

2D. $\sqrt{24} - \sqrt{54} + \sqrt{96}$ $3\sqrt{6}$

2 Multiply Radical Expressions Multiplying radical expressions is similar to multiplying monomial algebraic expressions. Let $x \geq 0$.

Monomials	Radical Expressions
$(2x)(3x) = 2 \cdot 3 \cdot x \cdot x$	$(2\sqrt{x})(3\sqrt{x}) = 2 \cdot 3 \cdot \sqrt{x} \cdot \sqrt{x}$
$= 6x^2$	$= 6x$

You can also apply the Distributive Property to radical expressions.

WatchOut!

Multiplying Radicands Make sure that you multiply the radicands when multiplying radical expressions. A common mistake is to add the radicands rather than multiply.

Example 3 Multiply Radical Expressions

Simplify each expression.

a. $3\sqrt{2} \cdot 2\sqrt{6}$

$3\sqrt{2} \cdot 2\sqrt{6} = (3 \cdot 2)(\sqrt{2} \cdot \sqrt{6})$ Associative Property

$= 6(\sqrt{12})$ Multiply.

$= 6(2\sqrt{3})$ Simplify.

$= 12\sqrt{3}$ Multiply.

b. $3\sqrt{5}(2\sqrt{5} + 5\sqrt{3})$

$3\sqrt{5}(2\sqrt{5} + 5\sqrt{3}) = (3\sqrt{5} \cdot 2\sqrt{5}) + (3\sqrt{5} \cdot 5\sqrt{3})$ Distributive Property

$= [(3 \cdot 2)(\sqrt{5} \cdot \sqrt{5})] + [(3 \cdot 5)(\sqrt{5} \cdot \sqrt{3})]$ Associative Property

$= [6(\sqrt{25})] + [15(\sqrt{15})]$ Multiply.

$= [6(5)] + [15(\sqrt{15})]$ Simplify.

$= 30 + 15\sqrt{15}$ Multiply.

GuidedPractice

3A. $2\sqrt{6} \cdot 7\sqrt{3}$ $42\sqrt{2}$

3B. $9\sqrt{5} \cdot 11\sqrt{15}$ $495\sqrt{3}$

3C. $3\sqrt{2}(4\sqrt{3} + 6\sqrt{2})$ $12\sqrt{6} + 36$

3D. $5\sqrt{3}(3\sqrt{2} - \sqrt{3})$ $15\sqrt{6} - 15$

You can also multiply radical expressions with more than one term in each factor. This is similar to multiplying two algebraic binomials with variables.

DifferentiatedInstruction AL OL ELL

If students struggle with the FOIL method in Example 4,

Then have students rewrite the example in five steps to facilitate an understanding of First terms, Outer terms, Inner terms, and Last terms. For example, in Step 1, have students write the original expression, underline the first terms, and then multiply to find the product of the first terms. Students continue this process until they have found the products of all of the terms. Then for the fifth step, have them combine and simplify the results of the previous four steps.

636 | Lesson 10-3 | Operations with Radical Expressions

Real-World Example 4 Multiply Radical Expressions

GEOMETRY Find the area of the rectangle in simplest form.

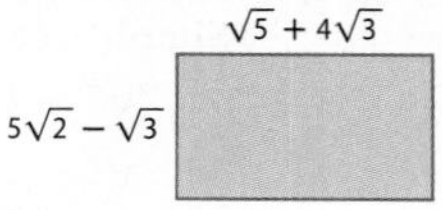

$A = (5\sqrt{2} - \sqrt{3})(\sqrt{5} + 4\sqrt{3})$ $\quad A = \ell \cdot w$

First Terms, Outer Terms, Inner Terms, Last Terms

$= (5\sqrt{2})(\sqrt{5}) + (5\sqrt{2})(4\sqrt{3}) + (-\sqrt{3})(\sqrt{5}) + (\sqrt{3})(4\sqrt{3})$

$= 5\sqrt{10} + 20\sqrt{6} - \sqrt{15} - 4\sqrt{9}$ Multiply.

$= 5\sqrt{10} + 20\sqrt{6} - \sqrt{15} - 12$ Simplify.

Review Vocabulary

FOIL Method Multiply two binomials by finding the sum of the products of the First terms, the Outer terms, the Inner terms, and the Last terms.

Guided Practice

4. GEOMETRY The area A of a rhombus can be found using the equation $A = \frac{1}{2}d_1d_2$, where d_1 and d_2 are the lengths of the diagonals. What is the area of the rhombus at the right? $A = 120 - 8\sqrt{15} - 9\sqrt{30} + 9\sqrt{2}$

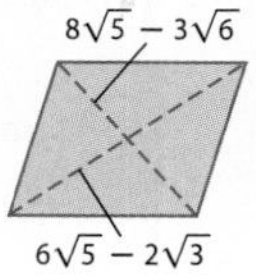

Concept Summary Operations with Radical Expressions

Operation	Symbols	Example
addition, $b \geq 0$	$a\sqrt{b} + c\sqrt{b} = (a + c)\sqrt{b}$ like radicands	$4\sqrt{3} + 6\sqrt{3} = (4 + 6)\sqrt{3} = 10\sqrt{3}$
subtraction, $b \geq 0$	$a\sqrt{b} - c\sqrt{b} = (a - c)\sqrt{b}$ like radicands	$12\sqrt{5} - 8\sqrt{5} = (12 - 8)\sqrt{5} = 4\sqrt{5}$
multiplication, $b \geq 0, g \geq 0$	$a\sqrt{b}(f\sqrt{g}) = af\sqrt{bg}$ Radicands do not have to be like radicands.	$3\sqrt{2}(5\sqrt{7}) = (3 \cdot 5)(\sqrt{2 \cdot 7}) = 15\sqrt{14}$

Check Your Understanding

= Step-by-Step Solutions begin on page R13.

Examples 1–3 Simplify each expression.

1. $3\sqrt{5} + 6\sqrt{5}$ $9\sqrt{5}$
2. $8\sqrt{3} + 5\sqrt{3}$ $13\sqrt{3}$
3. $\sqrt{7} - 6\sqrt{7}$ $-5\sqrt{7}$
4. $10\sqrt{2} - 6\sqrt{2}$ $4\sqrt{2}$
5. $4\sqrt{5} + 2\sqrt{20}$ $8\sqrt{5}$
6. $\sqrt{12} - \sqrt{3}$ $\sqrt{3}$
7. $\sqrt{8} + \sqrt{12} + \sqrt{18}$ $5\sqrt{2} + 2\sqrt{3}$
8. $\sqrt{27} + 2\sqrt{3} - \sqrt{12}$ $3\sqrt{3}$
9. $9\sqrt{2}(4\sqrt{6})$ $72\sqrt{3}$
10. $4\sqrt{3}(8\sqrt{3})$ 96
11. $\sqrt{3}(\sqrt{7} + 3\sqrt{2})$ $\sqrt{21} + 3\sqrt{6}$
12. $\sqrt{5}(\sqrt{2} + 4\sqrt{2})$ $5\sqrt{10}$

Example 4

13. **GEOMETRY** The area A of a triangle can be found by using the formula $A = \frac{1}{2}bh$, where b represents the base and h is the height. What is the area of the triangle at the right? $14.5 + 3\sqrt{15}$

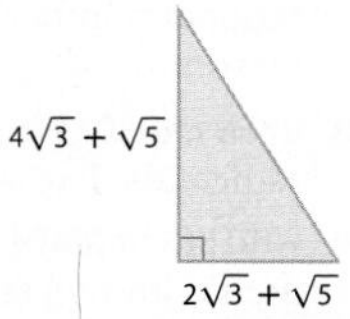

Focus on Mathematical Content

Operations with Radical Expressions Radical expressions can be added or subtracted only if the radicands are the same. Radical expressions can be multiplied whether the radicands are the same or different.

Additional Example

4 **GEOMETRY** Find the area of a rectangle in simplest form with a width of $4\sqrt{6} - 2\sqrt{10}$ and a length of $5\sqrt{3} + 7\sqrt{5}$. $18\sqrt{30} - 10\sqrt{2}$

3 Practice

Formative Assessment

Use Exercises 1–13 to check for understanding.

Use the chart at the bottom of this page to customize assignments for your students.

Teach with Tech

Interactive Whiteboard Write an expression on the board to add or subtract radical expressions. As you simplify the expression, drag the like terms to group them together. Then combine like terms and simplify the expression.

Differentiated Homework Options

Level	Assignment	Two-Day Option	
AL Basic	14–26, 37–68	15–25 odd, 40–43	14–26 even, 37–39, 44–68
OL Core	15–33 odd, 34, 35, 37–68	14–26, 40–43	27–35, 37–39, 44–68
BL Advanced	27–62, (optional: 63–68)		

Study Guide and Intervention

AL OL ELL

NAME ______________ DATE ________ PERIOD ________

10-3 Study Guide and Intervention

Operations with Radical Expressions

Add or Subtract Radical Expressions When adding or subtracting radical expressions, use the Associative and Distributive Properties to simplify the expressions. If radical expressions are not in simplest form, simplify them.

Example 1 Simplify $10\sqrt{6} - 5\sqrt{3} + 6\sqrt{3} - 4\sqrt{6}$.

$10\sqrt{6} - 5\sqrt{3} + 6\sqrt{3} - 4\sqrt{6} = (10 - 4)\sqrt{6} + (-5 + 6)\sqrt{3}$ Associative and Distributive Properties

$= 6\sqrt{6} + \sqrt{3}$ Simplify.

Example 2 Simplify $3\sqrt{12} + 5\sqrt{75}$.

$3\sqrt{12} + 5\sqrt{75} = 3\sqrt{2^2 \cdot 3} + 5\sqrt{5^2 \cdot 3}$ Factor 12 and 75.

$= 3 \cdot 2\sqrt{3} + 5 \cdot 5\sqrt{3}$ Simplify.

$= 6\sqrt{3} + 25\sqrt{3}$ Multiply.

$= 31\sqrt{3}$ Distributive Property

Exercises

Simplify each expression.

1. $2\sqrt{5} + 4\sqrt{5}$
2. $\sqrt{6} - 4\sqrt{6}$
3. $\sqrt{8} - \sqrt{2}$
4. $3\sqrt{75} + 2\sqrt{5}$
5. $\sqrt{20} + 2\sqrt{5} - 3\sqrt{5}$
6. $2\sqrt{3} + \sqrt{6} - 5\sqrt{3}$
7. $\sqrt{12} + 2\sqrt{3} - 5\sqrt{3}$
8. $3\sqrt{6} + 3\sqrt{2} - \sqrt{50} + \sqrt{24}$
9. $\sqrt{8a} - \sqrt{2a} + 5\sqrt{2a}$
10. $\sqrt{54} + \sqrt{24}$
11. $\sqrt{3} + \sqrt{\frac{1}{3}}$
12. $\sqrt{12} + \sqrt{\frac{1}{3}}$
13. $\sqrt{54} - \sqrt{\frac{1}{6}}$
14. $\sqrt{80} - \sqrt{20} + \sqrt{180}$
15. $\sqrt{50} + \sqrt{18} - \sqrt{75} + \sqrt{27}$
16. $2\sqrt{3} - 4\sqrt{45} + 2\sqrt{\frac{1}{3}}$
17. $\sqrt{125} - 2\sqrt{\frac{1}{5}} + \sqrt{\frac{1}{3}}$
18. $\sqrt{\frac{2}{3}} + 3\sqrt{3} - 4\sqrt{\frac{1}{12}}$

Lesson 10-3

Practice

AL OL BL ELL

NAME ______________ DATE ________ PERIOD ________

10-3 Practice

Operations with Radical Expressions

Simplify each expression.

1. $8\sqrt{30} - 4\sqrt{30}$
2. $2\sqrt{5} - 7\sqrt{5} - 5\sqrt{5}$
3. $7\sqrt{13x} - 14\sqrt{13x} + 2\sqrt{13x}$
4. $2\sqrt{45} + 4\sqrt{20}$
5. $\sqrt{40} - \sqrt{10} + \sqrt{90}$
6. $2\sqrt{32} + 3\sqrt{50} - 3\sqrt{18}$
7. $\sqrt{27} + \sqrt{18} + \sqrt{300}$
8. $5\sqrt{8} + 3\sqrt{20} - \sqrt{32}$
9. $\sqrt{14} - \sqrt{\frac{2}{7}}$
10. $\sqrt{50} + \sqrt{32} - \sqrt{\frac{1}{2}}$
11. $5\sqrt{19} + 4\sqrt{28} - 8\sqrt{19} + \sqrt{63}$
12. $3\sqrt{10} + \sqrt{75} - 2\sqrt{40} - 4\sqrt{12}$
13. $\sqrt{6}(\sqrt{10} + \sqrt{15})$
14. $\sqrt{5}(5\sqrt{2} - 4\sqrt{8})$
15. $2\sqrt{7}(3\sqrt{12} + 5\sqrt{8})$
16. $(5 - \sqrt{15})^2$
17. $(\sqrt{10} + \sqrt{6})(\sqrt{30} - \sqrt{18})$
18. $(\sqrt{8} + \sqrt{12})(\sqrt{48} + \sqrt{18})$
19. $(\sqrt{2} + 2\sqrt{8})(3\sqrt{6} - \sqrt{5})$
20. $(4\sqrt{3} - 2\sqrt{5})(3\sqrt{10} + 5\sqrt{6})$

21. **SOUND** The speed of sound V in meters per second near Earth's surface is given by $V = 20\sqrt{t + 273}$, where t is the surface temperature in degrees Celsius.
   a. What is the speed of sound near Earth's surface at 15°C and at 2°C in simplest form?
   b. How much faster is the speed of sound at 15°C than at 2°C?

22. **GEOMETRY** A rectangle is $5\sqrt{7} + 2\sqrt{3}$ meters long and $6\sqrt{7} - 3\sqrt{3}$ meters wide.
   a. Find the perimeter of the rectangle in simplest form.
   b. Find the area of the rectangle in simplest form.

Word Problem Practice

AL OL BL ELL

NAME ______________ DATE ________ PERIOD ________

10-3 Word Problem Practice

Operations with Radical Expressions

1. **ARCHITECTURE** The Pentagon is the building that houses the U.S. Department of Defense. Find the approximate perimeter of the building, which is a regular pentagon. Leave your answer as a radical expression.

2. **EARTH** The surface area S of a sphere with radius r is given by the formula $S = 4\pi r^2$. Assuming that Earth is close to spherical in shape and has a surface area of about 5.1×10^8 square kilometers, what is the radius of Earth to the nearest ten kilometers?

3. **GEOMETRY** The area of a trapezoid is found by multiplying its height by the average length of its bases. Find the area of deck attached to Mr. Wilson's house. Give your answer as a simplified radical expression.

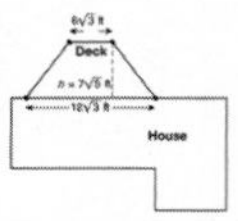

4. **RECREATION** Carmen surveyed a ski slope using a digital device connected to a computer. The computer model assigned coordinates to the top and bottom points of the hill as shown in the diagram. Write a simplified radical expression that represents the slope of the hill.

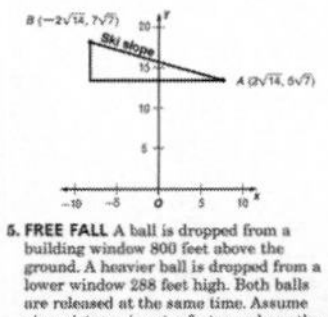

5. **FREE FALL** A ball is dropped from a building window 800 feet above the ground. A heavier ball is dropped from a lower window 288 feet high. Both balls are released at the same time. Assume air resistance is not a factor and use the following formula to find how many seconds t it will take a ball to fall h feet.
$$t = \frac{1}{4}\sqrt{h}$$
   a. How much time will pass between when the first ball hits the ground and when the second ball hits the ground? Give your answer as a simplified radical expression.
   b. Which ball lands first?
   c. Find a decimal approximation of the answer for part **a**. Round your answer to the nearest tenth.

Lesson 10-3

Practice and Problem Solving

Extra Practice is on page R10.

Examples 1–3 **Simplify each expression.** **18. $12\sqrt{3} + \sqrt{2}$**

14. $7\sqrt{5} + 4\sqrt{5}$ **$11\sqrt{5}$**
15. $2\sqrt{6} + 9\sqrt{6}$ **$11\sqrt{6}$**
16. $3\sqrt{5} - 2\sqrt{20}$ **$-\sqrt{5}$**
17. $3\sqrt{50} - 3\sqrt{32}$ **$3\sqrt{2}$**
18. $7\sqrt{3} - 2\sqrt{2} + 3\sqrt{2} + 5\sqrt{3}$
19. $\sqrt{5}(\sqrt{2} + 4\sqrt{2})$ **$5\sqrt{10}$**
20. $\sqrt{6}(2\sqrt{10} + 3\sqrt{2})$ **$4\sqrt{15} + 6\sqrt{3}$**
21. $4\sqrt{5}(3\sqrt{5} + 8\sqrt{2})$ **$60 + 32\sqrt{10}$**
22. $5\sqrt{3}(6\sqrt{10} - 6\sqrt{3})$ **$30\sqrt{30} - 90$**
23. $(\sqrt{3} - \sqrt{2})(\sqrt{15} + \sqrt{12})$
24. $(3\sqrt{11} + 3\sqrt{15})(3\sqrt{3} - 2\sqrt{2})$
25. $(5\sqrt{2} + 3\sqrt{5})(2\sqrt{10} - 5)$ **$5\sqrt{5} + 5\sqrt{2}$**

23. $3\sqrt{5} + 6 - \sqrt{30} - 2\sqrt{6}$

24. $9\sqrt{33} - 6\sqrt{22} + 27\sqrt{5} - 6\sqrt{30}$

Example 4

26. **GEOMETRY** Find the perimeter and area of a rectangle with a width of $2\sqrt{7} - 2\sqrt{5}$ and a length of $3\sqrt{7} + 3\sqrt{5}$. **$10\sqrt{7} + 2\sqrt{5}$ units; 12 units^2**

Simplify each expression. **30. $8\sqrt{5}$**

B

27. $\sqrt{\frac{1}{5}} - \sqrt{5}$ **$\frac{-4\sqrt{5}}{5}$**
28. $\sqrt{\frac{2}{3}} + \sqrt{6}$ **$\frac{4\sqrt{6}}{3}$**
29. $2\sqrt{\frac{1}{2}} + 2\sqrt{2} - \sqrt{8}$ **$\sqrt{2}$**
30. $8\sqrt{\frac{5}{4}} + 3\sqrt{20} - 10\sqrt{\frac{1}{5}}$
31. $(3 - \sqrt{5})^2$ **$14 - 6\sqrt{5}$**
32. $(\sqrt{2} + \sqrt{3})^2$ **$5 + 2\sqrt{6}$**

33. **ROLLER COASTERS** The velocity v in feet per second of a roller coaster at the bottom of a hill is related to the vertical drop h in feet and the velocity v_0 of the coaster at the top of the hill by the formula $v_0 = \sqrt{v^2 - 64h}$.
   a. What velocity must a coaster have at the top of a 225-foot hill to achieve a velocity of 120 feet per second at the bottom? **0 ft/s**
   b. Explain why $v_0 = v - 8\sqrt{h}$ is not equivalent to the formula given.

34. **FINANCIAL LITERACY** Tadi invests $225 in a savings account. In two years, Tadi has $232 in his account. You can use the formula $r = \sqrt{\frac{v_2}{v_0}} - 1$ to find the average annual interest rate r that the account has earned. The initial investment is v_0, and v_2 is the amount in two years. What was the average annual interest rate that Tadi's account earned? **about 1.5%**

33b. Sample answer: In the formula, we are taking the square root of the difference, not the square root of each term.

35. **ELECTRICITY** Electricians can calculate the electrical current in amps A by using the formula $A = \frac{\sqrt{w}}{\sqrt{r}}$, where w is the power in watts and r the resistance in ohms. How much electrical current is running through a microwave oven that has 850 watts of power and 5 ohms of resistance? Write the number of amps in simplest radical form, and then estimate the amount of current to the nearest tenth. **$\sqrt{170}$; about 13 amps**

H.O.T. Problems Use Higher-Order Thinking Skills

C

36. **CHALLENGE** Determine whether the following statement is *true* or *false*. Provide a proof or counterexample to support your answer. **See margin.**
$$x + y > \sqrt{x^2 + y^2} \text{ when } x > 0 \text{ and } y > 0$$

37. **ARGUMENTS** Make a conjecture about the sum of a rational number and an irrational number. Is the sum *rational* or *irrational*? Is the product of a nonzero rational number and an irrational number *rational* or *irrational*? Explain your reasoning. **See margin.**

38. **OPEN ENDED** Write an equation that shows a sum of two radicals with different radicands. Explain how you could combine these terms. **See margin.**

39. **WRITING IN MATH** Describe step by step how to multiply two radical expressions, each with two terms. Write an example to demonstrate your description. **See margin.**

Enrichment

OL BL

NAME ______________ DATE ________ PERIOD ________

10-3 Enrichment

The Wheel of Theodorus

The Greek mathematicians were intrigued by problems of representing different numbers and expressions using geometric constructions.

Theodorus, a Greek philosopher who lived about 425 B.C., is said to have discovered a way to construct the sequence $\sqrt{1}, \sqrt{2}, \sqrt{3}, \sqrt{4}, \ldots$.

The beginning of his construction is shown. You start with an isosceles right triangle with sides 1 unit long.

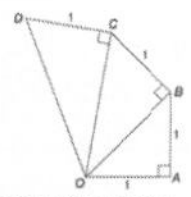

Use the figure above. Write each length as a radical expression in simplest form.

1. line segment AO
2. line segment BO
3. line segment CO
4. line segment DO
5. Describe how each new triangle is added to the figure.
6. The length of the hypotenuse of the first triangle is $\sqrt{2}$. For the second triangle, the length is $\sqrt{3}$. Write an expression for the length of the hypotenuse of the nth triangle.

Teaching the Process Standards

Arguments Mathematically proficient students make conjectures and build a logical progression of statements to explore the truth of their conjectures. In Exercise 37, suggest that students use a calculator to find several sums and products.

Standardized Test Practice

40. SHORT RESPONSE The population of a town is 13,000 and is increasing by about 250 people per year. This can be represented by the equation $p = 13{,}000 + 250y$, where y is the number of years from now and p represents the population. In how many years will the population of the town be 14,500? **6 years**

41. GEOMETRY Which expression represents the sum of the lengths of the 12 edges on this rectangular solid? **C**

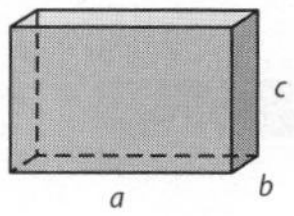

A $2(a + b + c)$
B $3(a + b + c)$
C $4(a + b + c)$
D $12(a + b + c)$

42. Evaluate $\sqrt{n - 9}$ and $\sqrt{n} - \sqrt{9}$ for $n = 25$. **G**

F 4; 4 G 4; 2
H 2; 4 J 2; 2

43. The current I in a simple electrical circuit is given by the formula $I = \frac{V}{R}$, where V is the voltage and R is the resistance of the circuit. If the voltage remains unchanged, what effect will doubling the resistance of the circuit have on the current? **C**

A The current will remain the same.
B The current will double its previous value.
C The current will be half its previous value.
D The current will be two units more than its previous value.

Spiral Review

Simplify. (Lesson 10-2)

44. $\sqrt{18}$ $\mathbf{3\sqrt{2}}$
45. $\sqrt{24}$ $\mathbf{2\sqrt{6}}$
46. $\sqrt{60}$ $\mathbf{2\sqrt{15}}$
47. $\sqrt{50a^3b^5}$ $\mathbf{5ab^2\sqrt{2ab}}$
48. $\sqrt{169x^4y^7}$ $\mathbf{13x^2y^3\sqrt{y}}$
49. $\sqrt{63c^3d^4f^5}$ $\mathbf{3cd^2f^2\sqrt{7cf}}$

Graph each function. Compare to the parent graph. State the domain and range. (Lesson 10-1) **50–55. See Ch. 10 Answer Appendix.**

50. $y = 2\sqrt{x}$
51. $y = -3\sqrt{x}$
52. $y = \sqrt{x + 1}$
53. $y = \sqrt{x - 4}$
54. $y = \sqrt{x} + 3$
55. $y = \sqrt{x} - 2$

Factor each trinomial. (Lesson 8-5)

56. $x^2 + 12x + 27$ $\mathbf{(x + 3)(x + 9)}$
57. $y^2 + 13y + 30$ $\mathbf{(y + 10)(y + 3)}$
58. $p^2 - 17p + 72$ $\mathbf{(p - 8)(p - 9)}$
59. $x^2 + 6x - 7$ $\mathbf{(x - 1)(x + 7)}$
60. $y^2 - y - 42$ $\mathbf{(y - 7)(y + 6)}$
61. $-72 + 6w + w^2$ $\mathbf{(w + 12)(w - 6)}$

62. FINANCIAL LITERACY Determine the value of an investment if $400 is invested at an interest rate of 7.25% compounded quarterly for 7 years. (Lesson 7-6) **$661.44**

Skills Review

Solve each equation. Round each solution to the nearest tenth, if necessary.

63. $-4c - 1.2 = 0.8$ $\mathbf{-0.5}$
64. $-2.6q - 33.7 = 84.1$ $\mathbf{-45.3}$
65. $0.3m + 4 = 9.6$ $\mathbf{18.7}$
66. $-10 - \frac{n}{5} = 6$ $\mathbf{-80}$
67. $\frac{-4h - (-5)}{-7} = 13$ $\mathbf{24}$
68. $3.6t + 6 - 2.5t = 8$ $\mathbf{1.8}$

DifferentiatedInstruction OL BL

Extension Write $\sqrt{6} + \sqrt{3} = \sqrt{9} = 3$ and $\sqrt{40} = \sqrt{36} + \sqrt{4} = 8$ on the board. Ask students to explain the errors. You cannot add radical expressions unless they can be written with the same radicand, and you cannot write the square root of a sum as the sum of the square roots.

4 Assess

Crystal Ball Ask students to write how they think what they learned today about adding, subtracting, and multiplying radical expressions will connect with the next lesson on radical equations.

Additional Answers

36. True; $(x + y)^2 > \left(\sqrt{x^2 + y^2}\right)^2$
$x^2 + 2xy + y^2 > x^2 + y^2$
$2xy > 0$
Because $x > 0$ and $y > 0$, $2xy > 0$ is always true.
So, $x + y > \sqrt{x^2 + y^2}$ is true for all $x > 0$ and $y > 0$.

37. Irrational; irrational; no rational number could be added to or multiplied by an irrational number so that the result is rational.

38. Sample answer: $\sqrt{12} + \sqrt{27} = 5\sqrt{3}$; When you simplify $\sqrt{12}$, you get $2\sqrt{3}$. When you simplify $\sqrt{27}$, you get $3\sqrt{3}$. Because $2\sqrt{3}$ and $3\sqrt{3}$ have the same radicand, you can add them.

39. Sample answer: You can use the FOIL method. You multiply the first terms within the parentheses. Then you multiply the outer terms within the parentheses. Then you would multiply the inner terms within the parentheses. And, then you would multiply the last terms within each parentheses. Combine any like terms and simplify any radicals. For example, $(\sqrt{2} + \sqrt{3})(\sqrt{5} + \sqrt{7}) = \sqrt{10} + \sqrt{14} + \sqrt{15} + \sqrt{21}$.

1 Focus

Objective Simplify radical expressions with indices greater than 2 and with variables and/or rational numbers in the radicand.

Teaching Tip

For Example 3, discuss the similarity between rules for adding radical expressions with the rules of adding and subtracting like terms in polynomials.

2 Teach

Working in Cooperative Groups

Put students in groups of two or three, mixing abilities.

- Have them write all of the new rules discussed in this lab.
- Have them include one example for when each rule is used and one example for when each rule is violated.

EXTEND 10-3

Algebra Lab: Simplifying *n*th Root Expressions

The inverse of raising a number to the *n*th power is finding the **nth root** of a number. The **index** of a radical expression indicates to what root the value under the radicand is being taken. The fourth root of a number is indicated with an index of 4. When simplifying a radical expression in which there is a variable with an exponent in the radicand, divide the exponent by the index.

$13 \div 5 = 2 \text{ R } 3 \longrightarrow$ index $\rightarrow \sqrt[5]{x^{13}} = x^2 \cdot \sqrt[5]{x^3}$ (quotient: x^2; remainder: x^3)

Example 1 Simplify Expressions

Simplify each expression.

a. $\sqrt[3]{x^7}$

$\sqrt[3]{x^7} = x^2\sqrt[3]{x}$ $7 \div 3 = 2 \text{ R } 1$

b. $\sqrt[5]{32x^9}$

$\sqrt[5]{32x^9} = \sqrt[5]{32} \cdot \sqrt[5]{x^9}$ Multiplication Property

$= 2x\sqrt[5]{x^4}$ $9 \div 5 = 1 \text{ R } 4$

The properties of square roots (and *n*th roots) also apply when the radicand contains fractions. Separate the numerator and denominator and then simplify them individually.

Example 2 Simplify Expressions with Fractions

Simplify $\sqrt[3]{\frac{27x^5}{8y^3}}$.

$\sqrt[3]{\frac{27x^5}{8y^3}} = \frac{\sqrt[3]{27}}{\sqrt[3]{8}} \cdot \frac{\sqrt[3]{x^5}}{\sqrt[3]{y^3}}$ Multiplication Property of Radicals

$= \frac{3}{2} \cdot \frac{x\sqrt[3]{x^2}}{y}$ Simplify.

$= \frac{3x\sqrt[3]{x^2}}{2y}$ Multiplication Property of Radicals

The indices *and* the radicands must be alike in order to add or subtract radical expressions.

Example 3 Combine Like Terms

Simplify $8\sqrt[4]{\frac{4}{3}} + \sqrt[4]{\frac{5}{4}} - 3\sqrt[4]{\frac{4}{3}} + \sqrt[3]{\frac{4}{3}}$.

Combine the expressions with identical indices and radicands. Then simplify.

$8\sqrt[4]{\frac{4}{3}} + \sqrt[4]{\frac{5}{4}} - 3\sqrt[4]{\frac{4}{3}} + \sqrt[3]{\frac{4}{3}} = (8-3)\sqrt[4]{\frac{4}{3}} + \sqrt[4]{\frac{5}{4}} + \sqrt[3]{\frac{4}{3}}$ Associative Property

$= 5\sqrt[4]{\frac{4}{3}} + \sqrt[4]{\frac{5}{4}} + \sqrt[3]{\frac{4}{3}}$ Simplify.

When multiplying radical expressions, ensure that the indices are the same. Then multiply the radicands and simplify if possible. Once none of the remaining terms can be combined or simplified, the expression is considered simplified.

Example 4 Simplify Expressions with Products

Simplify $5\sqrt[4]{6} \cdot 2\sqrt[4]{12} \cdot \sqrt[3]{10}$.

Multiply the radicands with identical indexes.

$5\sqrt[4]{6} \cdot 2\sqrt[4]{12} \cdot \sqrt[3]{10} = (5 \cdot 2)(\sqrt[4]{6} \cdot \sqrt[4]{12}) \cdot \sqrt[3]{10}$ Associative Property

$= 10 \cdot (\sqrt[4]{6} \cdot \sqrt[4]{12}) \cdot \sqrt[3]{10}$ Multiply.

$= 10\sqrt[4]{72}\sqrt[3]{10}$ Multiply.

The properties of radical expressions still hold when variables are in the radicand.

Example 5 Simplify Expressions with Several Operations

Simplify $6\sqrt[4]{x} \cdot \sqrt[4]{x^3} + 3(\sqrt[3]{x} + 2\sqrt[3]{x})$.

Follow the order of operations and the properties of radical expressions.

$6\sqrt[4]{x} \cdot \sqrt[4]{x^3} + 3(\sqrt[3]{x} + 2\sqrt[3]{x}) = 6\sqrt[4]{x} \cdot \sqrt[4]{x^3} + 3(3\sqrt[3]{x})$ Add like terms.

$= 6\sqrt[4]{x \cdot x^3} + 3(3\sqrt[3]{x})$ Associative Property

$= 6\sqrt[4]{x^4} + 9\sqrt[3]{x}$ Multiply.

$= 6x + 9\sqrt[3]{x}$ Simplify.

Exercises

Simplify each expression. 9. $2\sqrt[5]{a^4} - 10\sqrt[5]{a}$

1. $\sqrt[3]{c^6}$ c^2
2. $\sqrt[4]{16d^9}$ $2d^2\sqrt[4]{d}$
3. $\sqrt[3]{9} \cdot \sqrt[3]{6} \cdot \sqrt[3]{3}$ $3\sqrt[3]{6}$
4. $\sqrt[3]{\frac{8a^4}{125b^7}}$ $\frac{2a\sqrt[3]{a}}{5b^2\sqrt[3]{b}}$
5. $\sqrt[5]{\frac{32x^4}{5y^6z^5}}$ $\frac{2\sqrt[5]{x^4}}{yz\sqrt[5]{5y}}$
6. $\sqrt[4]{\frac{3}{2}} + 5\sqrt[4]{\frac{3}{2}} - 2\sqrt[4]{\frac{2}{3}}$ $6\sqrt[4]{\frac{3}{2}} - 2\sqrt[4]{\frac{2}{3}}$
7. $3\sqrt[3]{6} \cdot 4\sqrt[3]{6} \cdot 5\sqrt[4]{8}$ $4\sqrt[3]{6} \cdot 30\sqrt[3]{3}$
8. $3\sqrt[4]{x^2} + 2\sqrt[4]{x} \cdot 4\sqrt[4]{x}$ $11\sqrt[4]{x^2}$
9. $\sqrt[5]{a} \cdot 2\sqrt[5]{a^3} - 2(\sqrt[5]{a} + 4\sqrt[5]{a})$
10. $\sqrt[4]{\frac{x}{4}} + 5\sqrt[4]{\frac{x}{4}} - 2\sqrt[4]{\frac{2x}{3}}$ $6\sqrt[4]{\frac{x}{4}} - 2\sqrt[4]{\frac{2x}{3}}$
11. $\sqrt[4]{\frac{8a^2}{15b^3}} \cdot 3\sqrt[4]{\frac{2a^3}{27b}}$ $\frac{2a}{b}\sqrt[4]{\frac{a}{5}}$
12. $\sqrt[4]{\frac{16x^3}{81y^5}} + 3\sqrt[4]{\frac{x^3}{y}} + \sqrt[3]{\frac{16x}{y^8}}$ $\frac{2+9y}{3y}\sqrt[4]{\frac{x^3}{y}} + \frac{2}{y^2}\sqrt[3]{\frac{2x}{y^2}}$

Think About It

13. Provide an example in which two radical expressions with *unlike* radicands can be combined by addition. **Sample answer: $\sqrt[3]{81} + \sqrt[3]{24} = 3\sqrt[3]{3} + 2\sqrt[3]{3} = 5\sqrt[3]{3}$**
14. Provide an example in which two radical expressions with identical indices and with like variables in the radicand *cannot* be combined by addition. **Sample answer: $\sqrt[3]{x} + \sqrt[3]{x^2}$**

Practice Have students complete Exercises 1–14.

Teaching Tip

Remind students that the product of two or more radical expressions may be able to be simplified, as is done in Exercise 3.

3 Assess

Formative Assessment

Use Exercises 13 and 14 to assess whether students understand the rules of simplifying radical expressions.

Ticket Out the Door

Make several copies each of five different operations involving two radical expressions. As students leave the room, ask them to determine whether the expressions can be combined.

1 Focus

VerticalAlignment

Before Lesson 10-4 Add, subtract, and multiply radical expressions.

Lesson 10-4 Solve radical equations. Solve radical equations with extraneous solutions.

After Lesson 10-4 Apply radical equations to trigonometry.

2 Teach

Scaffolding Questions

Have students read the **Why?** section of the lesson.

Ask:

- If you know the value for h, what do you need to isolate to solve the equation? $\sqrt{\ell}$
- How can you isolate it? Divide each side by 1.34.
- How can you remove the radical sign? Square each side of the equation.

LESSON 10-4 Radical Equations

Then

- You added, subtracted, and multiplied radical expressions.

Now

1. Solve radical equations.
2. Solve radical equations with extraneous solutions.

Why?

- The waterline length of a sailboat is the length of the line made by the water's edge when the boat is full. A sailboat's hull speed is the fastest speed that it can travel.

You can estimate hull speed h by using the formula $h = 1.34\sqrt{\ell}$, where ℓ is the length of the sailboat's waterline.

NewVocabulary
radical equations
extraneous solutions

Process Standards
PS.3, PS.4

1 Radical Equations

Equations that contain variables in the radicand, like $h = 1.34\sqrt{\ell}$, are called **radical equations**. To solve, isolate the desired variable on one side of the equation first. Then square each side of the equation to eliminate the radical.

KeyConcept Power Property of Equality

Words	If you square both sides of a true equation, the resulting equation is still true.
Symbols	If $a = b$, then $a^2 = b^2$.
Examples	If $\sqrt{x} = 4$, then $(\sqrt{x})^2 = 4^2$.

Real-World Example 1 Variable as a Radicand

SAILING **Idris and Sebastian are sailing in a friend's sailboat. They measure the hull speed at 9 nautical miles per hour. Find the length of the sailboat's waterline. Round to the nearest foot.**

Understand You know how fast the boat will travel and that it relates to the length.

Plan The boat travels at 9 nautical miles per hour. The formula for hull speed is $h = 1.34\sqrt{\ell}$.

Solve

$h = 1.34\sqrt{\ell}$ Formula for hull speed

$9 = 1.34\sqrt{\ell}$ Substitute 9 for h.

$\frac{9}{1.34} = \frac{1.34\sqrt{\ell}}{1.34}$ Divide each side by 1.34.

$6.72 \approx \sqrt{\ell}$ Simplify.

$(6.72)^2 \approx (\sqrt{\ell})^2$ Square each side of the equation.

$45.16 \approx \ell$ Simplify.

The sailboat's waterline length is about 45 feet.

Check Check by substituting the estimate into the original formula.

$h = 1.34\sqrt{\ell}$ Formula for hull speed

$9 \stackrel{?}{=} 1.34\sqrt{45}$ $h = 9$ and $\ell = 45$

$9 \approx 8.98899327$ ✓ Multiply.

Lesson 10-4 Resources

Resource	Approaching Level AL	On Level OL	Beyond Level BL	English Learners ELL
Teacher Edition		▪ Differentiated Instruction, p. 643	▪ Differentiated Instruction, pp. 643, 646	
Chapter Resource Masters	▪ Study Guide and Intervention, pp. 23–24 ▪ Skills Practice, p. 25 ▪ Practice, p. 26 ▪ Word Problem Practice, p. 27 ▪ Graphing Calculator, p. 29	▪ Study Guide and Intervention, pp. 23–24 ▪ Skills Practice, p. 25 ▪ Practice, p. 26 ▪ Word Problem Practice, p. 27 ▪ Enrichment, p. 28 ▪ Graphing Calculator, p. 29	▪ Practice, p. 26 ▪ Word Problem Practice, p. 27 ▪ Enrichment, p. 28 ▪ Graphing Calculator, p. 29	▪ Study Guide and Intervention, pp. 23–24 ▪ Skills Practice, p. 25 ▪ Practice, p. 26 ▪ Word Problem Practice, p. 27 ▪ Graphing Calculator, p. 29
Other	▪ 5-Minute Check 10-4 ▪ Study Notebook	▪ 5-Minute Check 10-4 ▪ Study Notebook	▪ 5-Minute Check 10-4 ▪ Study Notebook	▪ 5-Minute Check 10-4 ▪ Study Notebook

Guided Practice

1. **DRIVING** The equation $v = \sqrt{2.5r}$ represents the maximum velocity that a car can travel safely on an unbanked curve when v is the maximum velocity in miles per hour and r is the radius of the turn in feet. If a road is designed for a maximum speed of 65 miles per hour, what is the radius of the turn? **1690 ft**

To solve a radical equation, isolate the radical first. Then square both sides of the equation.

Example 2 Expression as a Radicand

Solve $\sqrt{a+5} + 7 = 12$.

$\sqrt{a+5} + 7 = 12$	Original equation
$\sqrt{a+5} = 5$	Subtract 7 from each side.
$(\sqrt{a+5})^2 = 5^2$	Square each side.
$a + 5 = 25$	Simplify.
$a = 20$	Subtract 5 from each side.

WatchOut!
Squaring Each Side Remember that when you square each side of the equation, you must square the entire side of the equation, even if there is more than one term on the side.

Guided Practice

Solve each equation.

2A. $\sqrt{c-3} - 2 = 4$ **39**

2B. $4 + \sqrt{h+1} = 14$ **99**

2 Extraneous Solutions

Squaring each side of an equation sometimes produces a solution that is not a solution of the original equation. These are called **extraneous solutions**. Therefore, you must check all solutions in the original equation.

Example 3 Variable on Each Side

Solve $\sqrt{k+1} = k - 1$. Check your solution.

$\sqrt{k+1} = k - 1$	Original equation
$(\sqrt{k+1})^2 = (k-1)^2$	Square each side.
$k + 1 = k^2 - 2k + 1$	Simplify.
$0 = k^2 - 3k$	Subtract k and 1 from each side.
$0 = k(k-3)$	Factor.
$k = 0$ or $k - 3 = 0$	Zero Product Property
$k = 3$	Solve.

CHECK

$\sqrt{k+1} = k - 1$	Original equation	$\sqrt{k+1} = k - 1$	Original equation
$\sqrt{0+1} \stackrel{?}{=} 0 - 1$	$k = 0$	$\sqrt{3+1} \stackrel{?}{=} 3 - 1$	$k = 3$
$\sqrt{1} \stackrel{?}{=} -1$	Simplify.	$\sqrt{4} \stackrel{?}{=} 2$	Simplify.
$1 \neq -1$ ✗	False	$2 = 2$ ✓	True

Since 0 does not satisfy the original equation, 3 is the only solution.

StudyTip
Extraneous Solutions When checking solutions for extraneous solutions, we are only interested in principal roots.

Guided Practice

Solve each equation. Check your solution.

3A. $\sqrt{t+5} = t + 3$ **−1**

3B. $x - 3 = \sqrt{x-1}$ **5**

1 Radical Equations

Example 1 shows how to solve a real-world problem with a variable in the radicand. **Example 2** shows how to solve a radical equation with a radical expression as the radicand.

Formative Assessment

Use the Guided Practice exercises after each example to determine students' understanding of concepts.

Additional Examples

1 **FREE-FALL HEIGHT** An object is dropped from an unknown height and reaches the ground in 5 seconds. Use the equation $t = \frac{\sqrt{h}}{4}$, where t is time in seconds and h is height in feet, to find the height from which the object was dropped. 400 ft

2 Solve $\sqrt{x-3} + 8 = 15$. 52

Additional Examples also in Interactive Classroom PowerPoint® Presentations

IWB Interactive White Board READY

2 Extraneous Solutions

Example 3 shows how to determine extraneous solutions when solving a radical equation with a variable on each side of the equal sign.

Additional Example

3 Solve $\sqrt{2-y} = y$. Check your solution. 1

Focus on Mathematical Content

Solutions to Radical Equations When solving radical equations, it is always important to check all solutions in the *original* equation, since one or more of the solutions could be extraneous.

Differentiated Instruction OL BL

If students are familiar with graphing calculators,

Then have students graph the equation in Example 3 to check the solution. Have them subtract $k - 1$ from both sides of the equation and then enter the equation as $Y_1 = \sqrt{x+1} - x + 1$ [GRAPH]. Press [2nd] [CALC] 2 to calculate the zero point or x-intercept of the graph. Move the cursor to the left of the x-intercept for left bound, press [ENTER], and to the right of the x-intercept for right bound and press [ENTER]. Press [ENTER] to give the coordinates of the x-intercept.

3 Practice

Formative Assessment

Use Exercises 1–7 to check for understanding.

Use the chart at the bottom of this page to customize assignments for your students.

Multiple Representations

In Exercise 29, students solve a radical equation algebraically and by use of a graphing calculator and compare the solutions.

Exercise Alert

Graphing For Exercise 29, students will need a graphing calculator.

Teaching the Process Standards

Critique Mathematically proficient students distinguish correct logic or reasoning from that which is flawed. In Exercise 31, have students carefully check each step in the two solutions. Have them identify the step in which the error was made and the likely cause. Have students discuss ways they can avoid similar errors.

Additional Answers

8c. Increases; sample answer: As the leg length increases, the value of the radicand also increases.

21b. Increases; sample answer: If the length is longer, the quotient and square root will be a greater number than before.

29a.

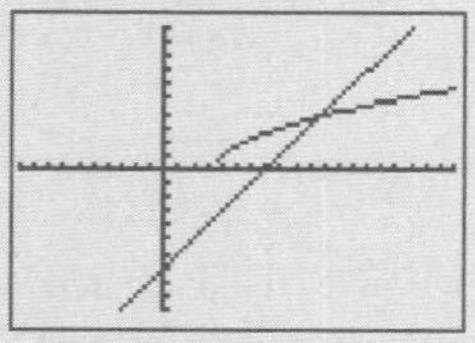

[−10, 20] scl: 1 by [−10, 10] scl: 1

29c.

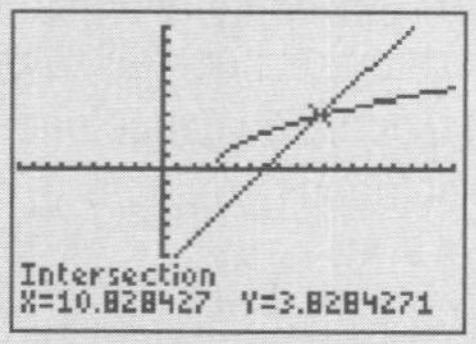

[−10, 20] scl: 1 by [−10, 10] scl: 1

Check Your Understanding

= Step-by-Step Solutions begin on page R13.

Example 1

1. GEOMETRY The surface area of a basketball is x square inches. What is the radius of the basketball if the formula for the surface area of a sphere is $SA = 4\pi r^2$? $r = \frac{\sqrt{\pi x}}{2\pi}$

Examples 2–3 **Solve each equation. Check your solution.**

2. $\sqrt{10h} + 1 = 21$ **40**

3. $\sqrt{7r + 2} + 3 = 7$ **2**

4. $5 + \sqrt{g - 3} = 6$ **4**

5. $\sqrt{3x - 5} = x - 5$ **10**

6. $\sqrt{2n + 3} = n$ **3**

7. $\sqrt{a - 2} + 4 = a$ **6**

Practice and Problem Solving

Extra Practice is on page R10.

Example 1

8. EXERCISE Suppose the function $S = \pi\sqrt{\frac{9.8\ell}{1.6}}$, where S represents speed in meters per second and ℓ is the leg length of a person in meters, can approximate the maximum speed that a person can run.

a. What is the maximum running speed of a person with a leg length of 1.1 meters to the nearest tenth of a meter? **8.2 m/s**

b. What is the leg length of a person with a running speed of 6.7 meters per second to the nearest tenth of a meter? **0.7 m**

c. As leg length increases, does maximum speed increase or decrease? Explain. **See margin.**

Examples 2–3 **Solve each equation. Check your solution.**

9. $\sqrt{a} + 11 = 21$ **100**

10. $\sqrt{t} - 4 = 7$ **121**

11. $\sqrt{n - 3} = 6$ **39**

12. $\sqrt{c + 10} = 4$ **6**

13. $\sqrt{h - 5} = 2\sqrt{3}$ **17**

14. $\sqrt{k + 7} = 3\sqrt{2}$ **11**

15. $y = \sqrt{12 - y}$ **3**

16. $\sqrt{u + 6} = u$ **3**

17. $\sqrt{r + 3} = r - 3$ **6**

18. $\sqrt{1 - 2t} = 1 + t$ **0**

19. $5\sqrt{a - 3} + 4 = 14$ **7**

20. $2\sqrt{x - 11} - 8 = 4$ **47**

B

21. RIDES The amount of time t, in seconds, that it takes a simple pendulum to complete a full swing is called the *period*. It is given by $t = 2\pi\sqrt{\frac{\ell}{32}}$, where ℓ is the length of the pendulum, in feet.

a. The Giant Swing completes a period in about 8 seconds. About how long is the pendulum's arm? Round to the nearest foot. **52 ft**

b. Does increasing the length of the pendulum increase or decrease the period? Explain. **See margin.**

Solve each equation. Check your solution.

22. $\sqrt{6a - 6} = a + 1$ **no solution**

23. $\sqrt{x^2 + 9x + 15} = x + 5$ **no solution**

24. $6\sqrt{\frac{5k}{4}} - 3 = 0$ $\frac{1}{5}$

25. $\sqrt{\frac{5y}{6}} - 10 = 4$ **235.2**

26. $\sqrt{2a^2 - 121} = a$ **11**

27. $\sqrt{5x^2 - 9} = 2x$ **3**

28. REASONING The formula for the slant height c of a cone is $c = \sqrt{h^2 + r^2}$, where h is the height of the cone and r is the radius of its base. Find the height of the cone if the slant height is 4 units and the radius is 2 units. Round to the nearest tenth. $2\sqrt{3}$ **or ≈ 3.5 units**

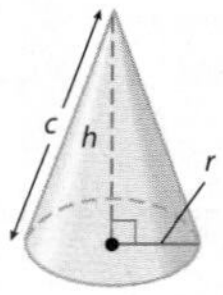

Differentiated Homework Options

Level	Assignment	Two-Day Option	
AL Basic	8–20, 31–35, 37–67	9–19 odd, 38–41	8–20 even, 31–35, 37, 42–67
OL Core	9–27 odd, 28–35, 37–67	8–20, 38–41	21–35, 37, 42–67
BL Advanced	21–61, (optional: 62–67)		

29. **MULTIPLE REPRESENTATIONS** Consider $\sqrt{2x-7} = x - 7$.

a. **Graphical** Clear the **Y=** list. Enter the left side of the equation as **Y1** $= \sqrt{2x-7}$. Enter the right side of the equation as **Y2** $= x - 7$. Press GRAPH. **See margin.**

b. **Graphical** Sketch what is shown on the screen. **See students' work.**

c. **Analytical** Use the **intersect** feature on the **CALC** menu to find the point of intersection. **See margin.**

d. **Analytical** Solve the radical equation algebraically. How does your solution compare to the solution from the graph? **About 10.83; they are the same.**

30. PACKAGING A cylindrical container of chocolate drink mix has a volume of 162 cubic inches. The radius r of the container can be found by using the formula $r = \sqrt{\frac{V}{\pi h}}$, where V is the volume of the container and h is the height.

a. If the radius is 2.5 inches, find the height of the container. Round to the nearest hundredth. **8.25 in.**

b. If the height of the container is 10 inches, find the radius. Round to the nearest hundredth. **2.27 in.**

32. B; The solution of the given equation is 2. Choice B is the only equation that is true when $x = 2$.

H.O.T. Problems Use Higher-Order Thinking Skills

31. CRITIQUE Jada and Fina solved $\sqrt{6-b} = \sqrt{b+10}$. Is either of them correct? Explain. **Jada; Fina had the wrong sign for $2b$ in the fourth step.**

Jada

$\sqrt{6-b} = \sqrt{b+10}$
$(\sqrt{6-b})^2 = (\sqrt{b+10})^2$
$6 - b = b + 10$
$-2b = 4$
$b = -2$
Check $\sqrt{6-(-2)} \stackrel{?}{=} \sqrt{(-2)+10}$
$\sqrt{8} = \sqrt{8}$ ✓

Fina

$\sqrt{6-b} = \sqrt{b+10}$
$(\sqrt{6-b})^2 = (\sqrt{b+10})^2$
$6 - b = b + 10$
$2b = 4$
$b = 2$
Check $\sqrt{6-(2)} \stackrel{?}{=} \sqrt{(2)+10}$
$\sqrt{4} \neq \sqrt{12}$ ✗
no solution

33. Sample answer: In the first equation, you have to isolate the radical first by subtracting 1 from each side. Then square each side to find the value of x. In the second equation, the radical is already isolated, so square each side to start. Then subtract 1 from each side to solve for x.

32. REASONING Which equation has the same solution set as $\sqrt{4} = \sqrt{x+2}$? Explain.

A. $\sqrt{4} = \sqrt{x} + \sqrt{2}$ **B.** $4 = x + 2$ **C.** $2 - \sqrt{2} = \sqrt{x}$

33. REASONING Explain how solving $5 = \sqrt{x} + 1$ is different from solving $5 = \sqrt{x+1}$.

34. OPEN ENDED Write a radical equation with a variable on each side. Then solve the equation. **Sample answer: $\sqrt{2x-1} = x$; 1**

35. REASONING Is the following equation *sometimes*, *always* or *never* true? Explain.

$$\sqrt{(x-2)^2} = x - 2$$

Sometimes; the equation is true for $x \geq 2$, but false for $x < 2$.

36. CHALLENGE Solve $\sqrt{x+9} = \sqrt{3} + \sqrt{x}$. **3**

37. WRITING IN MATH Write some general rules about how to solve radical equations. Demonstrate your rules by solving a radical equation. **See margin.**

Additional Answer

37. Sample answer: Use addition/subtraction to isolate the term containing the radical on one side. Multiply/divide to change the coefficient of the radical to ±1. Square each side of the equation to eliminate the radical. Solve the resulting equation using the most appropriate method. Check the answers for any extraneous solutions. See students' examples.

Study Guide and Intervention

AL OL ELL

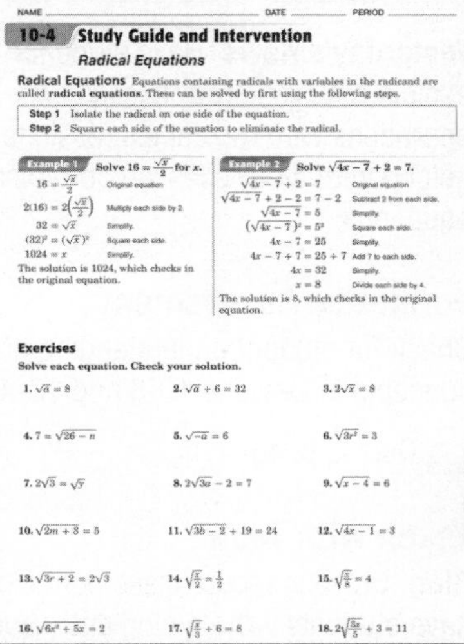
10-4 Study Guide and Intervention
Radical Equations

Practice

AL OL BL ELL

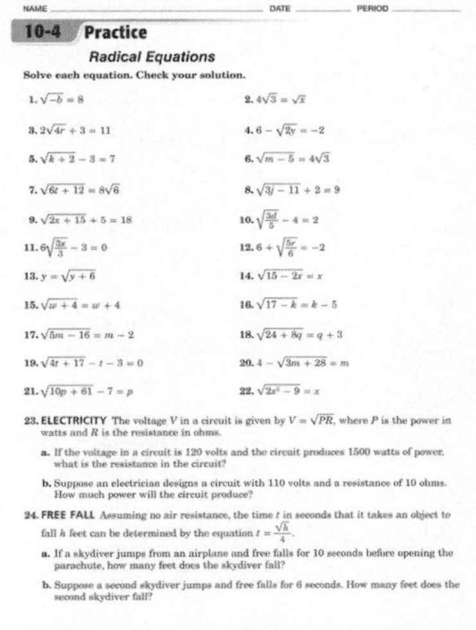
10-4 Practice
Radical Equations

Word Problem Practice

AL OL BL ELL

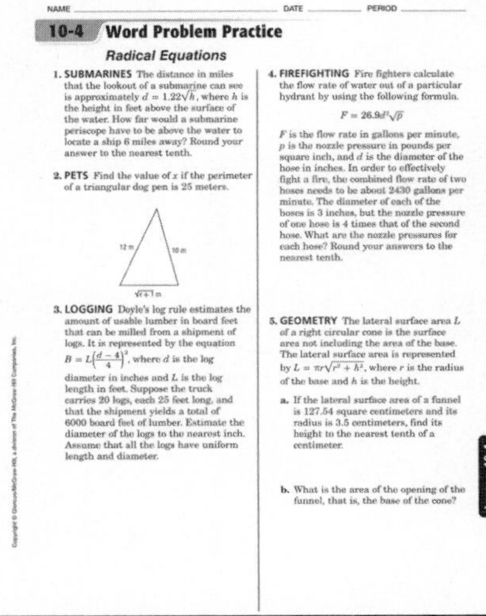
10-4 Word Problem Practice
Radical Equations

Enrichment

OL BL

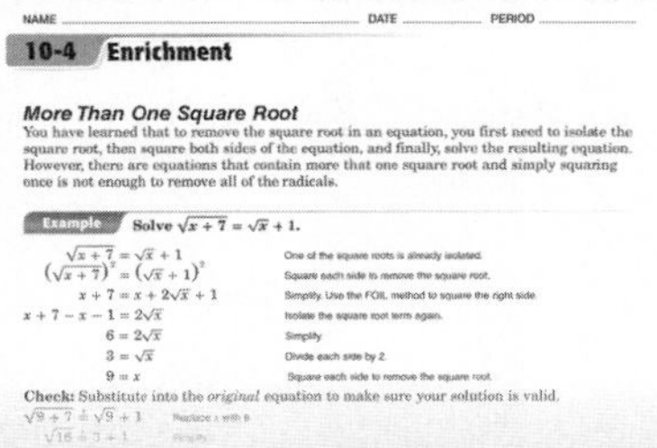
10-4 Enrichment
More Than One Square Root

4 Assess

Yesterday's News Have students explain how yesterday's lesson on operations with radical expressions helped with today's lesson on radical equations.

Formative Assessment

Check for student understanding of concepts in Lessons 10-3 and 10-4.

Quiz 2, p. 45

Teach with Tech

Blog On your secure classroom blog have students write a blog entry about extraneous solutions. Have them explain what extraneous solutions are and how they can check their solutions both graphically and algebraically.

Additional Answers

56. Yes; 12 is a real number and therefore a monomial.

57. Yes; $4x^3$ is the product of a number and three variables.

58. No; $a - 2b$ shows subtraction, not multiplication alone of numbers and variables.

59. No; $4n + 5p$ shows addition, not multiplication alone of numbers and variables.

60. No; $\frac{x}{y^2}$ has a variable in the denominator.

61. Yes; $\frac{1}{5}abc^{14}$ is the product of a number, $\frac{1}{5}$, and several variables.

Standardized Test Practice

38. SHORT RESPONSE Zack needs to drill a hole at A, B, C, D, and E on circle P.

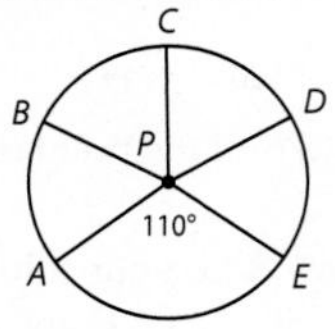

If Zack drills holes so that $m\angle APE = 110°$ and the other four angles are congruent, what is $m\angle CPD$? **62.5°**

39. Which expression is undefined when $w = 3$? **C**

A $\frac{w-3}{w+1}$ **C** $\frac{w+1}{w^2-3w}$

B $\frac{w^2-3w}{3w}$ **D** $\frac{3w}{3w^2}$

40. What is the slope of a line that is parallel to the line? **H**

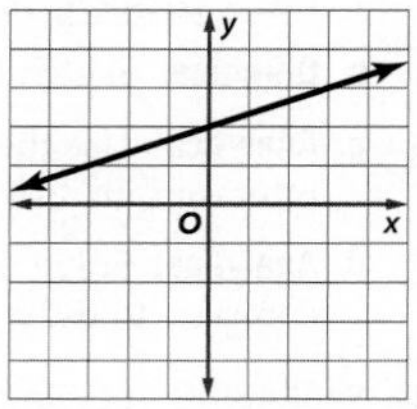

F -3 **H** $\frac{1}{3}$

G $-\frac{1}{3}$ **J** 3

41. What are the solutions of $\sqrt{x+3} - 1 = x - 4$? **D**

A 1, 6 **C** 1

B −1, −6 **D** 6

Spiral Review

42. ELECTRICITY The voltage V required for a circuit is given by $V = \sqrt{PR}$, where P is the power in watts and R is the resistance in ohms. How many more volts are needed to light a 100-watt light bulb than a 75-watt light bulb if the resistance of both is 110 ohms? (Lesson 10-3) **about 14**

Simplify each expression. (Lesson 10-2)

43. $\sqrt{6} \cdot \sqrt{8}$ **$4\sqrt{3}$** **44.** $\sqrt{3} \cdot \sqrt{6}$ **$3\sqrt{2}$** **45.** $7\sqrt{3} \cdot 2\sqrt{6}$ **$42\sqrt{2}$**

46. $\sqrt{\frac{27}{a^2}}$ **$\frac{3\sqrt{3}}{|a|}$** **47.** $\sqrt{\frac{5c^5}{4d^5}}$ **$\frac{c^2\sqrt{5cd}}{2d^3}$** **48.** $\frac{\sqrt{9x^3y}}{\sqrt{16x^2y^2}}$ **$\frac{3\sqrt{xy}}{4|y|}$**

49. PHYSICAL SCIENCE A projectile is shot straight up from ground level. Its height h, in feet, after t seconds is given by $h = 96t - 16t^2$. Find the value(s) of t when h is 96 feet. (Lesson 9-5) **about 1.3 s and 4.7 s**

Factor each trinomial, if possible. If the trinomial cannot be factored using integers, write *prime*. (Lesson 8-7)

50. $2x^2 + 7x + 5$ **$(2x+5)(x+1)$** **51.** $6p^2 + 5p - 6$ **$(2p+3)(3p-2)$** **52.** $5d^2 + 6d - 8$ **$(5d-4)(d+2)$**

53. $8k^2 - 19k + 9$ **prime** **54.** $9g^2 - 12g + 4$ **$(3g-2)(3g-2)$** **55.** $2a^2 - 9a - 18$ **$(2a+3)(a-6)$**

Determine whether each expression is a monomial. Write *yes* or *no*. Explain. (Lesson 7-1) **56–61. See margin.**

56. 12 **57.** $4x^3$ **58.** $a - 2b$ **59.** $4n + 5p$ **60.** $\frac{x}{y^2}$ **61.** $\frac{1}{5}abc^{14}$

Skills Review

Simplify.

62. 9^2 **81** **63.** 10^6 **1,000,000** **64.** 4^5 **1024**

65. $(8v)^2$ **$64v^2$** **66.** $\left(\frac{w^3}{9}\right)^2$ **$\frac{w^6}{81}$** **67.** $(10y^2)^3$ **$1000y^6$**

Differentiated Instruction BL

Extension Explain that the *geometric mean* of two positive numbers is the positive square root of their product. Ask students to find a pair of consecutive positive even integers whose geometric mean is $4\sqrt{5}$. Since $4\sqrt{5} = \sqrt{x(x+2)}$, $x = 8$ or -10. Since the two numbers are positive, x must equal to 8 and, therefore, $x + 2 = 10$. The two numbers are 8 and 10.

CHAPTER 10

Mid-Chapter Quiz

Lessons 10-1 through 10-4

Graph each function. Compare to the parent graph. State the domain and range. (Lesson 10-1)

1. $y = 2\sqrt{x}$ **1–6. See Ch. 10 Answer Appendix.**
2. $y = -4\sqrt{x}$
3. $y = \frac{1}{2}\sqrt{x}$
4. $y = \sqrt{x} - 3$
5. $y = \sqrt{x - 1}$
6. $y = 2\sqrt{x - 2}$

7. **MULTIPLE CHOICE** The length of the side of a square is given by the function $s = \sqrt{A}$, where A is the area of the square. What is the length of the side of a square that has an area of 121 square inches? (Lesson 10-1) **C**

   A 121 inches **C** 11 inches
   B 44 inches **D** 10 inches

Simplify each expression. (Lesson 10-2)

8. $2\sqrt{25}$ **10**
9. $\sqrt{12} \cdot \sqrt{8}$ $4\sqrt{6}$
10. $\sqrt{72xy^5z^6}$ $6y^2|z^3|\sqrt{2xy}$
11. $\frac{3}{1 + \sqrt{5}}$ $\frac{-3 + 3\sqrt{5}}{4}$
12. $\frac{1}{5\sqrt{7}}$ $\frac{5 + \sqrt{7}}{18}$

13. **SATELLITES** A satellite is launched into orbit 200 kilometers above Earth. The orbital velocity of a satellite is given by the formula $v = \sqrt{\frac{Gm_E}{r}}$. v is velocity in meters per second, G is a given constant, m_E is the mass of Earth, and r is the radius of the satellite's orbit in meters. (Lesson 10-2)

   a. The radius of Earth is 6,380,000 meters. What is the radius of the satellite's orbit in meters? **6,580,000 m**

   b. The mass of Earth is 5.97×10^{24} kilograms, and the constant G is $6.67 \times 10^{-11}\ \text{N} \cdot \frac{\text{m}^2}{\text{kg}^2}$ where N is in Newtons. Use the formula to find the orbital velocity of the satellite in meters per second. **about 7779 m/s**

14. **MULTIPLE CHOICE** Which expression is equivalent to $\sqrt{\frac{16}{32}}$? (Lesson 10-2) **G**

   F $\frac{1}{2}$
   G $\frac{\sqrt{2}}{2}$
   H 2
   J 4

Simplify each expression. (Lesson 10-3)

15. $3\sqrt{2} + 5\sqrt{2}$ $8\sqrt{2}$
16. $\sqrt{11} - 3\sqrt{11}$ $-2\sqrt{11}$
17. $6\sqrt{2} + 4\sqrt{50}$ $26\sqrt{2}$
18. $\sqrt{27} - \sqrt{48}$ $-\sqrt{3}$
19. $4\sqrt{3}(2\sqrt{6})$ $24\sqrt{2}$
20. $3\sqrt{20}(2\sqrt{5})$ **60**
21. $(\sqrt{5} + \sqrt{7})(\sqrt{20} + \sqrt{3})$ $10 + \sqrt{15} + 2\sqrt{35} + \sqrt{21}$

22. **GEOMETRY** Find the area of the rectangle. (Lesson 10-3) $36\sqrt{5}$

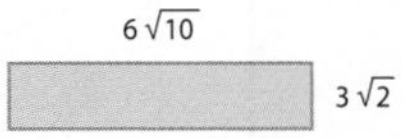

Solve each equation. Check your solution. (Lesson 10-4)

23. $\sqrt{5x} - 1 = 4$ **5**
24. $\sqrt{a - 2} = 6$ **38**
25. $\sqrt{15 - x} = 4$ **−1**
26. $\sqrt{3x^2 - 32} = x$ **4**
27. $\sqrt{2x - 1} = 2x - 7$ **5**
28. $\sqrt{x + 1} + 2 = 4$ **3**

29. **GEOMETRY** The lateral surface area S of a cone can be found by using the formula $S = \pi r\sqrt{r^2 + h^2}$, where r is the radius of the base and h is the height of the cone. Find the height of the cone. (Lesson 10-4) **about 12.5 in.**

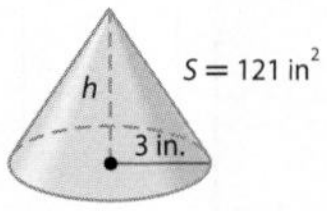

Formative Assessment

Use the Mid-Chapter Quiz to assess students' progress in the first half of the chapter.

For problems answered incorrectly, have students review the lessons indicated in parentheses.

Summative Assessment

Mid-Chapter Test, p. 47

McGraw-Hill eAssessment Customize and create multiple versions of your Mid-Chapter Quiz and their answer keys.

FOLDABLES StudyOrganizer

Dinah Zike's Foldables®

Before students complete the Mid-Chapter Quiz, encourage them to review the information for Lessons 10-1 through 10-4 in their Foldables.

InterventionPlanner

TIER 1 On Level OL	TIER 2 Strategic Intervention AL approaching grade level	TIER 3 Intensive Intervention 2 or more grades below level
If students miss about 25% of the exercises or less,	**If** students miss about 50% of the exercises,	**If** students miss about 75% of the exercises,
Then choose a resource: SE Lessons 10-1, 10-2, 10-3, and 10-4 Skills Practice, pp. 7, 13, 19, and 25 TE Chapter Project connectED.mcgraw-hill.com Self-Check Quiz	**Then** choose a resource: Study Guide and Intervention, Chapter 10, pp. 5, 11, 17, and 23 *Quick Review Math Handbook* connectED.mcgraw-hill.com Extra Examples, Personal Tutor, Homework Help	**Then** use *Math Triumphs, Alg. 1* connectED.mcgraw-hill.com Extra Examples, Personal Tutor, Homework Help, Review Vocabulary

1 Focus

VerticalAlignment

Before Lesson 10-5 Solve quadratic equations by using the Square Root Property.

Lesson 10-5 Solve problems by using the Pythagorean Theorem. Determine whether a triangle is a right triangle.

After Lesson 10-5 Use trigonometry to solve triangles.

2 Teach

Scaffolding Questions

Have students read the **Why?** section of the lesson.

Ask:

- What is the shape of most television screens? rectangles
- Which measurement on a television is longest: the height, the width, or the diagonal? diagonal
- If you draw a triangle to represent the height, width, and diagonal of the television, which side is opposite the right angle? diagonal

LESSON 10-5 The Pythagorean Theorem

Then

- You solved quadratic equations by using the Square Root Property.

Now

1. Solve problems by using the Pythagorean Theorem.
2. Determine whether a triangle is a right triangle.

Why?

- Televisions are measured along the diagonal of the screen. If the height and width of the screen is known, the Pythagorean Theorem can be used to find the measure of the diagonal.

NewVocabulary
hypotenuse
legs
converse
Pythagorean triple

Process Standards
PS.1

1 The Pythagorean Theorem

In a right triangle, the side opposite the right angle, called the **hypotenuse**, is always the longest. The other two sides are the **legs**.

KeyConcept The Pythagorean Theorem

Words If a triangle is a right triangle, then the square of the length of the hypotenuse is equal to the sum of the squares of the lengths of the legs.

Symbols $c^2 = a^2 + b^2$

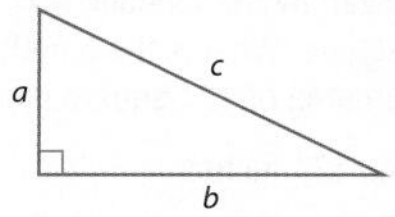

PT

Example 1 Find the Length of a Side

Find each missing length. If necessary, round to the nearest hundredth.

a.

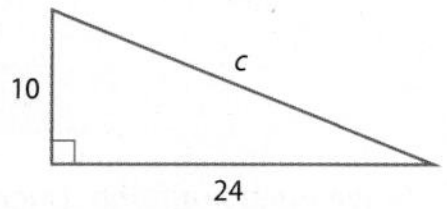

$c^2 = a^2 + b^2$	Pythagorean Theorem
$c^2 = 10^2 + 24^2$	$a = 10$ and $b = 24$
$c^2 = 100 + 576$	Evaluate squares.
$c^2 = 676$	Simplify.
$c = \pm\sqrt{676}$	Take the square root of each side.
$c = \pm 26$	$(\pm 26)^2 = 676$

Length cannot be negative, so the missing length is 26 units.

b.

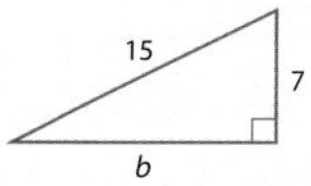

$c^2 = a^2 + b^2$	Pythagorean Theorem
$15^2 = 7^2 + b^2$	$a = 7$ and $c = 15$
$225 = 49 + b^2$	Evaluate squares.
$176 = b^2$	Subtract 49 from each side.
$\pm\sqrt{176} = b$	Take the square root of each side.
$\pm 13.27 \approx b$	Use a calculator to evaluate $\sqrt{176}$.

The missing length is 13.27 units.

GuidedPractice

1A.

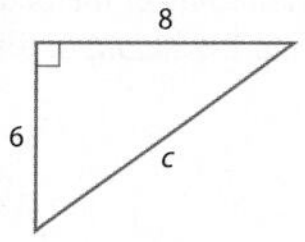

10

1B.

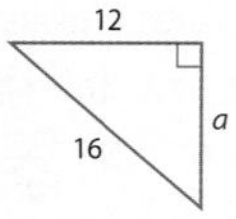

10.58

648 | Lesson 10-5

Lesson 10-5 Resources

Resource	Approaching Level AL	On Level OL	Beyond Level BL	English Learners ELL
Teacher Edition	▪ Differentiated Instruction, p. 649	▪ Differentiated Instruction, p. 649	▪ Differentiated Instruction, p. 653	
Chapter Resource Masters	▪ Study Guide and Intervention, pp. 30–31 ▪ Skills Practice, p. 32 ▪ Practice, p. 33 ▪ Word Problem Practice, p. 34 ▪ Spreadsheet Activity, p. 36	▪ Study Guide and Intervention, pp. 30–31 ▪ Skills Practice, p. 32 ▪ Practice, p. 33 ▪ Word Problem Practice, p. 34 ▪ Enrichment, p. 35 ▪ Spreadsheet Activity, p. 36	▪ Practice, p. 33 ▪ Word Problem Practice, p. 34 ▪ Enrichment, p. 35 ▪ Spreadsheet Activity, p. 36	▪ Study Guide and Intervention, pp. 30–31 ▪ Skills Practice, p. 32 ▪ Practice, p. 33 ▪ Word Problem Practice, p. 34 ▪ Spreadsheet Activity, p. 36
Other	▪ 5-Minute Check 10-5 ▪ Study Notebook ▪ Teaching Algebra with Manipulatives	▪ 5-Minute Check 10-5 ▪ Study Notebook ▪ Teaching Algebra with Manipulatives	▪ 5-Minute Check 10-5 ▪ Study Notebook	▪ 5-Minute Check 10-5 ▪ Study Notebook ▪ Teaching Algebra with Manipulatives

Real-World Example 2 Find the Length of a Side

SAILING The sail of a keelboat forms a right triangle as shown. Find the height of the sail.

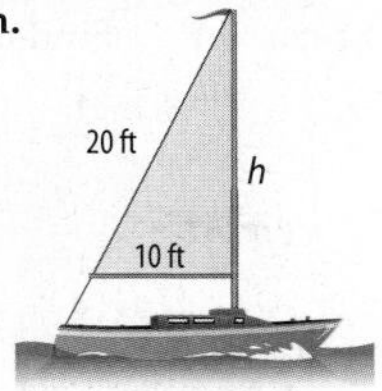

$20^2 = h^2 + 10^2$	Pythagorean Theorem
$400 = h^2 + 100$	Evaluate squares.
$300 = h^2$	Subtract 100 from each side.
$\pm 17.32 \approx h$	Take the square root of each side.
$17.32 \approx h$	Use the positive value.

The sail is approximately 17.32 feet high.

Guided Practice

2. Suppose the longest side of the sail is 30 feet long and the shortest side is 14 feet long. Find the height of the sail. **about 26.53 ft**

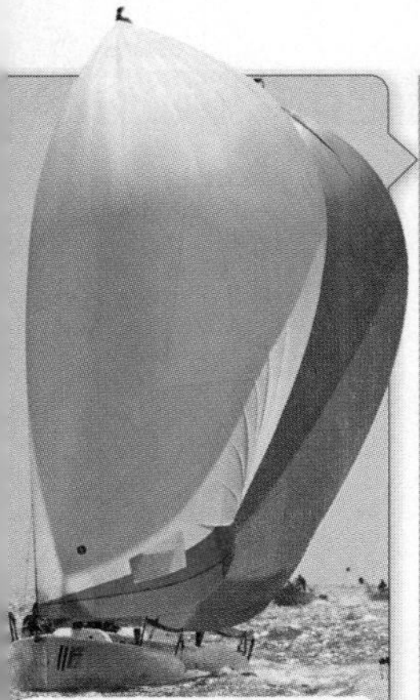

Real-World Link

A keelboat is a sailboat with a weighted keel, a vertical fin at the bottom of the boat. Keels are 20 to 30 inches in length.

Source: United States Sailing Association

2 Right Triangles

If you exchange the phrases after *if* and *then* of an if-then statement, the result is the **converse** of the statement. The converse of the Pythagorean Theorem can be used to determine whether a triangle is a right triangle.

Key Concept Converse of the Pythagorean Theorem

If a triangle has side lengths *a*, *b*, and *c* such that $c^2 = a^2 + b^2$, then the triangle is a right triangle. If $c^2 \neq a^2 + b^2$, then the triangle is not a right triangle.

A **Pythagorean triple** is a group of three counting numbers that satisfy the equation $c^2 = a^2 + b^2$, where *c* is the greatest number. Examples include (3, 4, 5) and (5, 12, 13). Multiples of Pythagorean triples also satisfy the converse of the Pythagorean Theorem, so (6, 8, 10) is also a Pythagorean triple.

Example 3 Check for Right Triangles

Determine whether 9, 12, and 16 can be the lengths of the sides of a right triangle.

Since the measure of the longest side is 16, let $c = 16$, $a = 9$, and $b = 12$.

$c^2 = a^2 + b^2$	Pythagorean Theorem
$16^2 \stackrel{?}{=} 9^2 + 12^2$	$a = 9$, $b = 12$, and $c = 16$
$256 \stackrel{?}{=} 81 + 144$	Evaluate squares.
$256 \neq 225$	Add.

Since $c^2 \neq a^2 + b^2$, segments with these measures cannot form a right triangle.

Guided Practice

Determine whether each set of measures can be the lengths of the sides of a right triangle.

3A. 30, 40, 50 **yes; $30^2 + 40^2 = 50^2$**

3B. 6, 12, 18 **no; $6^2 + 12^2 \neq 18^2$**

Differentiated Instruction AL OL

If students would benefit from further exploration of Pythagorean triples,

Then have them use manipulatives with equivalent lengths to build triangles with side lengths that form Pythagorean triples. Manipulatives could include algebra tiles, blocks, integer rods, or cubes.

1 The Pythagorean Theorem

Example 1 shows how to use the Pythagorean Theorem to find the missing length of a side of a right triangle. **Example 2** shows how to use the Pythagorean Theorem to solve a real-world problem.

Formative Assessment

Use the Guided Practice exercises after each Example to determine students' understanding of concepts.

Additional Examples

1 Find each missing length. If necessary, round to the nearest hundredth.

a. 30 units

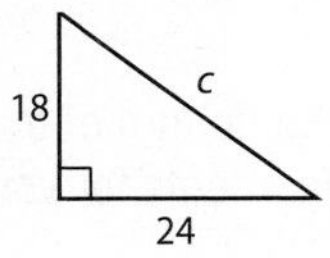

b. 13.23 units

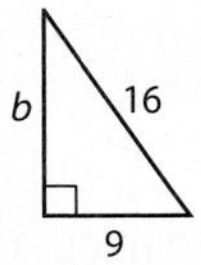

2 TELEVISION The diagonal of a television screen is 32 inches. The width of the screen is 21 inches. Find the height of the screen. $\approx$24.15 in.

Additional Examples also in Interactive Classroom PowerPoint® Presentations

IWB Interactive White Board READY

2 Right Triangles

Example 3 shows how to use the converse of the Pythagorean Theorem to determine whether a triangle is a right triangle.

Additional Example

3 Determine whether 7, 12, and 15 can be the lengths of the sides of a right triangle.
no; $7^2 + 12^2 \neq 15^2$

Focus on Mathematical Content

Pythagorean Theorem The Pythagorean Theorem can be used to find the length of a side of a right triangle when the lengths of the other two sides are known. To find the length of a side, rewrite the formula for the Pythagorean Theorem in terms of that side; for example, to find the length of the hypotenuse, solve for c: $c = \sqrt{a^2 + b^2}$.

3 Practice

Formative Assessment

Use Exercises 1–9 to check for understanding.

Use the chart at the bottom of this page to customize assignments for your students.

WatchOut!

Preventing Errors Point out to students that with Pythagorean triples, the greatest value is always the measure of the hypotenuse, and the two lesser values are the measures of the two legs.

Converses Tell students that the converses of theorems are not necessarily true. But the converse of the Pythagorean Theorem is true.

Teach with Tech

Document Camera Have students bring in objects, or photos of objects that have right triangles to be displayed (such as a toy boat with a triangular sail). Measure two of the sides and have student use the Pythagorean Theorem to find the length of the third side.

Check Your Understanding

= Step-by-Step Solutions begin on page R13.

Example 1 **Find each missing length. If necessary, round to the nearest hundredth.**

1. 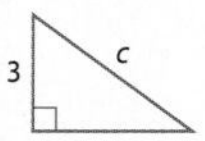

5

2. 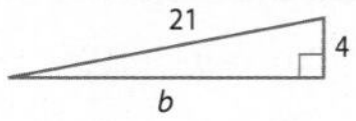

20.62

3. 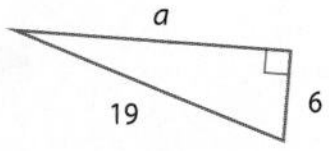

18.03

4. 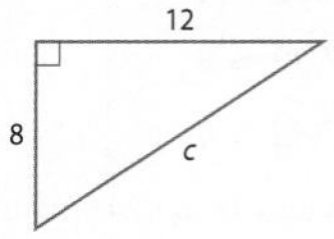

14.42

Example 2

5. **BASEBALL** A baseball diamond is a square. The distance between consecutive bases is 90 feet.

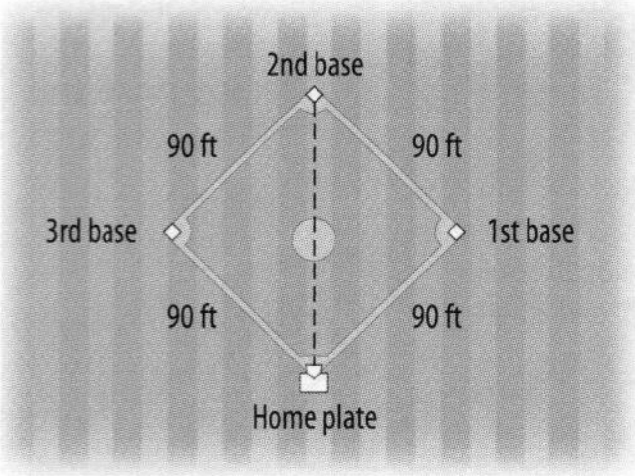

a. How far does a catcher have to throw the ball from home plate to second base? **about 127 ft**

b. How far does a third baseman throw the ball to the first baseman from a point in the baseline 15 feet from third to second base? **about 117 ft**

c. A base runner going from first to second base is 100 feet from home plate. How far is the runner from second base? **about 46 ft**

Example 3 **Determine whether each set of measures can be the lengths of the sides of a right triangle.**

6. 8, 12, 16 **no**

7. 28, 45, 53 **yes**

8. 7, 24, 25 **yes**

9. 15, 25, 45 **no**

Practice and Problem Solving

Extra Practice is on page R10.

Example 1 **Find each missing length. If necessary, round to the nearest hundredth.**

10. 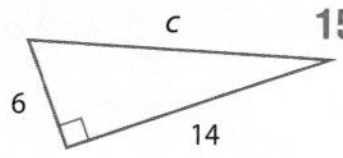

15.23

11. 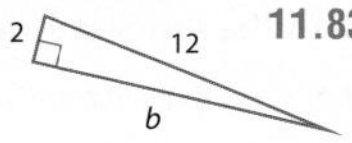

11.83

12. 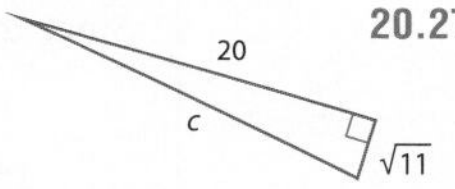

20.27

13. 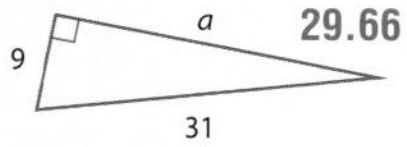

29.66

14. 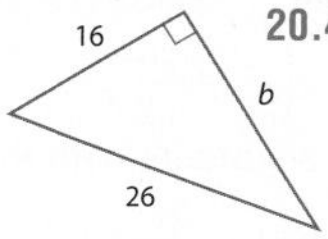

20.49

15. 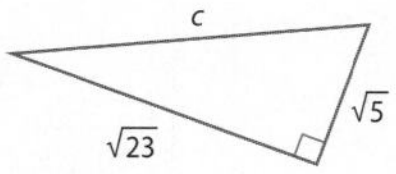

5.29

16. 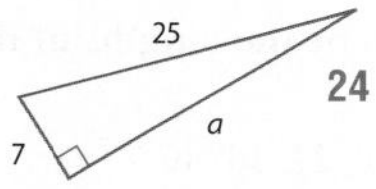

24

17. 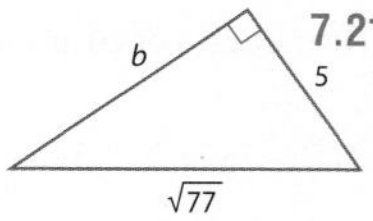

7.21

18. 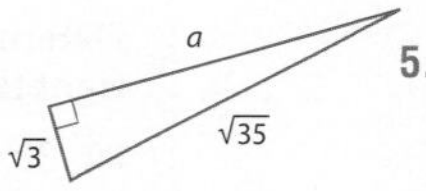

5.66

Differentiated Homework Options

Level	Assignment	Two-Day Option	
AL Basic	10–18, 46, 48–84	11–17 odd, 51–54	10–18 even, 46, 48–50, 55–84
OL Core	11–27 odd, 29–37, 39–43 odd, 44–46, 48–84	10–18, 51–54	19–46, 48–50, 55–84
BL Advanced	29–80, (optional: 81–84)		

Example 2 **19.** **TELEVISION** Larry is buying an entertainment stand for his television. The diagonal of his television is 42 inches. The space for the television measures 30 inches by 36 inches. Will Larry's television fit? Explain. **Yes; sample answer: The diagonal of the space in the TV stand is 46.9 inches, so Larry's TV will fit.**

Example 3 **Determine whether each set of measures can be the lengths of the sides of a right triangle. Then determine whether they form a Pythagorean triple.**

20. 9, 40, 41 **yes; yes**

21. $3, 2\sqrt{10}, \sqrt{41}$ **no; no**

22. $4, \sqrt{26}, 12$ **no; no**

23. $\sqrt{5}, 7, 14$ **no; no**

24. 8, 31.5, 32.5 **yes; no**

25. $\sqrt{65}, 6\sqrt{2}, \sqrt{97}$ **no; no**

26. 18, 24, 30 **yes; yes**

27. 36, 77, 85 **yes; yes**

28. 17, 33, 98 **no; no**

B **29.** **GEOMETRY** Refer to the triangle at the right.

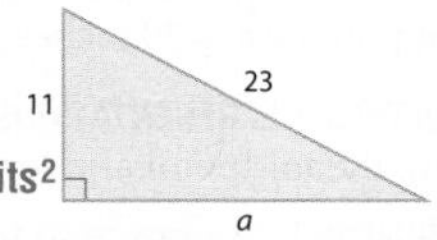

a. What is a? **about 20.20 units**

b. Find the area of the triangle. **about 111.1 units^2**

30. **GARDENING** Khaliah wants to plant flowers in a triangular plot. She has three lengths of plastic garden edging that measure 8 feet, 15 feet, and 17 feet. Determine whether these pieces form a right triangle. Explain.

31. **LADDER** Mr. Takeo is locked out of his house. The only open window is on the second floor. There is a bush along the edge of the house, so he places the neighbor's ladder 10 feet from the house. To the nearest foot, what length of ladder does he need to reach the window? **a 30-ft ladder**

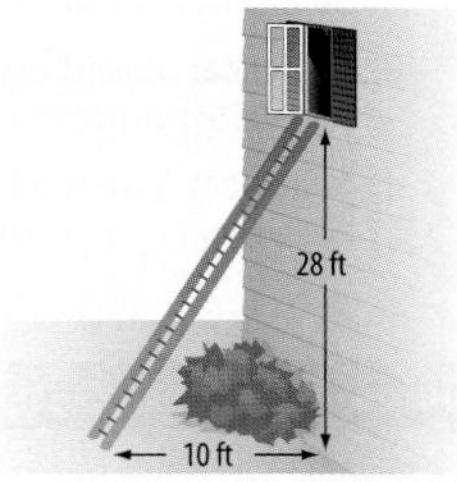

30. Yes; sample answer: $8^2 + 15^2 = 17^2$, so the pieces form a right triangle by the converse of the Pythagorean Theorem.

TOOLS **Find the length of the hypotenuse. Round to the nearest hundredth.**

32. **12.21**

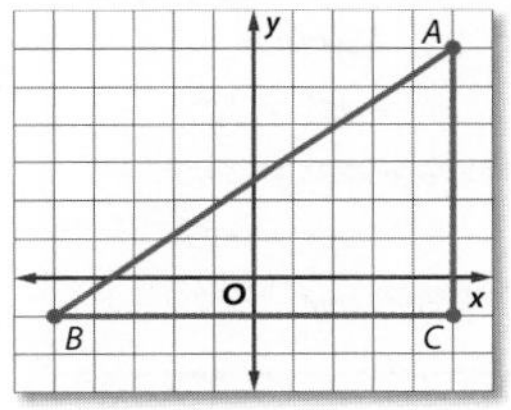

33. **8.06**

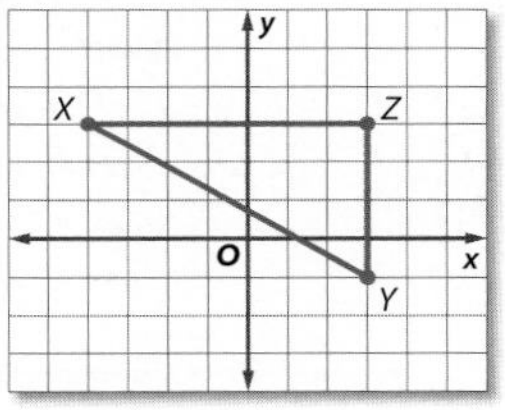

34. **DOLLHOUSE** Alonso is building a dollhouse for his sister's birthday. The roof is 24 inches across and the slanted side is 16 inches long as shown. Find the height of the roof to the nearest tenth of an inch. **10.6 in.**

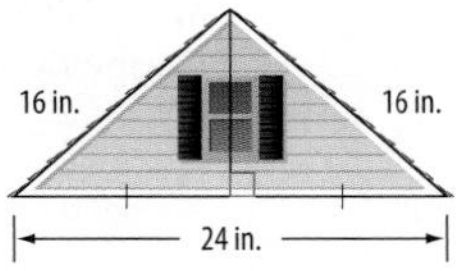

35. **GEOMETRY** Each side of a cube is 5 inches long. Find the length of a diagonal of the cube. **$5\sqrt{3}$ in. or about 8.66 in.**

36. **TOWN SQUARES** The largest town square in the world is Tiananmen Square in Beijing, China, covering 98 acres.

a. One square mile is 640 acres. Assuming that Tiananmen Square is a square, how many feet long is a side to the nearest foot? **2066 ft**

b. To the nearest foot, what is the diagonal distance across Tiananmen Square? **2922 ft**

Teaching the Process Standards

Tools Mathematically proficient students detect possible errors by strategically using estimation. In Exercises 32 and 33, point out to students that determining the length from the graph doesn't provide a precise answer, but it would allow for an estimate that would serve as a check.

The Math Forum

Have your students refer to the Math Forum's Ask Dr. Math to learn more about Pythagorean triples. They can start their search at connectED.mcgraw-hill.com.

connectED.mcgraw-hill.com 651

Study Guide and Intervention

AL OL ELL

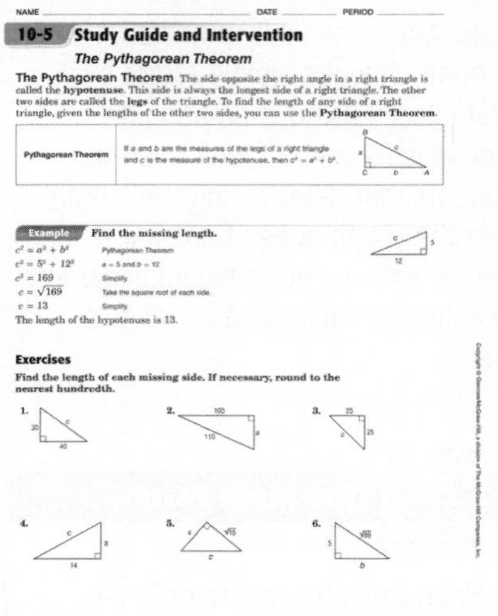
NAME ______ DATE ______ PERIOD ______

10-5 Study Guide and Intervention

The Pythagorean Theorem

The Pythagorean Theorem The side opposite the right angle in a right triangle is called the **hypotenuse**. This side is always the longest side of a right triangle. The other two sides are called the **legs** of the triangle. To find the length of any side of a right triangle, given the lengths of the other two sides, you can use the **Pythagorean Theorem**.

Pythagorean Theorem: If a and b are the measures of the legs of a right triangle and c is the measure of the hypotenuse, then $c^2 = a^2 + b^2$.

Example Find the missing length.

$c^2 = a^2 + b^2$ Pythagorean Theorem
$c^2 = 5^2 + 12^2$ a = 5 and b = 12
$c^2 = 169$ Simplify.
$c = \sqrt{169}$ Take the square root of each side.
$c = 13$ Simplify.

The length of the hypotenuse is 13.

Exercises

Find the length of each missing side. If necessary, round to the nearest hundredth.

Practice

AL OL BL ELL

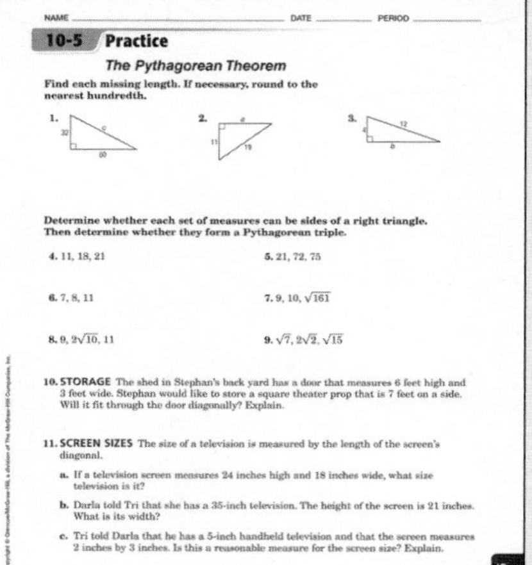
NAME ______ DATE ______ PERIOD ______

10-5 Practice

The Pythagorean Theorem

Find each missing length. If necessary, round to the nearest hundredth.

Determine whether each set of measures can be sides of a right triangle. Then determine whether they form a Pythagorean triple.

4. 11, 18, 21
5. 21, 72, 75
6. 7, 8, 11
7. 9, 10, $\sqrt{161}$
8. 9, $2\sqrt{10}$, 11
9. $\sqrt{7}$, $2\sqrt{2}$, $\sqrt{15}$

10. **STORAGE** The shed in Stephan's back yard has a door that measures 6 feet high and 3 feet wide. Stephan would like to store a square theater prop that is 7 feet on a side. Will it fit through the door diagonally? Explain.

11. **SCREEN SIZES** The size of a television is measured by the length of the screen's diagonal.
a. If a television screen measures 24 inches high and 18 inches wide, what size television is it?
b. Darla told Tri that she has a 35-inch television. The height of the screen is 21 inches. What is its width?
c. Tri told Darla that he has a 5-inch handheld television and that the screen measures 2 inches by 3 inches. Is this a reasonable measure for the screen size? Explain.

Word Problem Practice

AL OL BL ELL

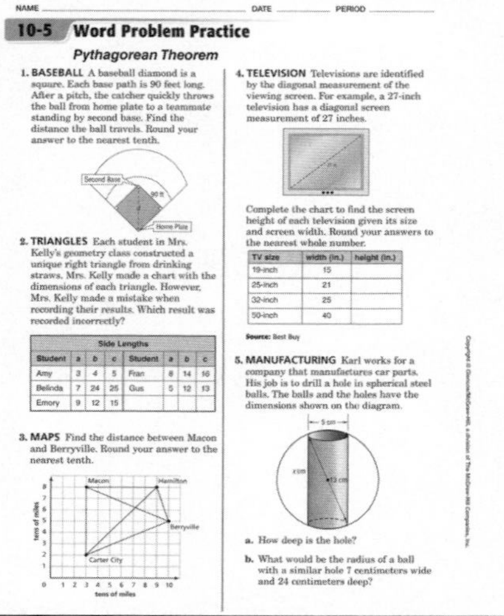
NAME ______ DATE ______ PERIOD ______

10-5 Word Problem Practice

Pythagorean Theorem

1. **BASEBALL** A baseball diamond is a square. Each base path is 90 feet long. After a pitch, the catcher quickly throws the ball from home plate to a teammate standing by second base. Find the distance the ball travels. Round your answer to the nearest tenth.

2. **TRIANGLES** Each student in Mrs. Kelly's geometry class constructed a unique right triangle from drinking straws. Mrs. Kelly made a chart with the dimensions of each triangle. However, Mrs. Kelly made a mistake when recording their results. Which result was recorded incorrectly?

Student	a	b	c	Student	a	b	c
Amy	3	4	5	Fran	8	14	16
Belinda	7	24	25	Gus	5	12	13
Emory	9	12	15				

3. **MAPS** Find the distance between Macon and Berryville. Round your answer to the nearest tenth.

4. **TELEVISION** Televisions are identified by the diagonal measurement of the viewing screen. For example, a 27-inch television has a diagonal screen measurement of 27 inches.

Complete the chart to find the screen height of each television given its size and screen width. Round your answers to the nearest whole number.

TV size	width (in.)	height (in.)
19-inch	15	
25-inch	21	
32-inch	25	
50-inch	40	

Source: Best Buy

5. **MANUFACTURING** Karl works for a company that manufactures car parts. His job is to drill a hole in spherical steel balls. The balls and the holes have the dimensions shown on the diagram.
a. How deep is the hole?
b. What would be the radius of a ball with a similar hole 7 centimeters wide and 24 centimeters deep?

37. **TRUCKS** Violeta needs to construct a ramp to roll a cart of moving boxes from her garage into the back of her truck. How long does the ramp to have to be? **about 6.7 ft**

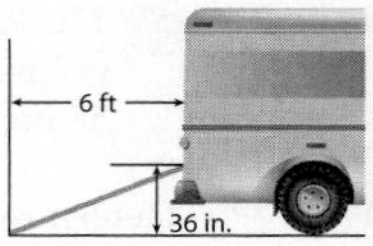

If c is the measure of the hypotenuse of a right triangle, find each missing measure. If necessary, round to the nearest hundredth.

38. $a = x, b = x + 41, c = 85$ **$a = 36$; $b = 77$**
39. $a = 8, b = x, c = x + 2$ **$b = 15$; $c = 17$**
40. $a = 12, b = x - 2, c = x$ **$b = 35$; $c = 37$**
41. $a = x, b = x + 7, c = 97$ **$a = 65$; $b = 72$**
42. $a = x - 47, b = x, c = x + 2$ **$a = 16$; $b = 63$; $c = 65$**
43. $a = x - 32, b = x - 1, c = x$ **$a = 9$; $b = 40$; $c = 41$**

44. **GEOMETRY** A right triangle has one leg that is 8 inches shorter than the other leg. The hypotenuse is 30 inches long. Find the length of each leg. **about 24.83 in. and about 16.83 in.**

45. **MULTIPLE REPRESENTATIONS** In this problem, you will derive a method for finding the midpoint and length of a segment on the coordinate plane.

a. **Graphical** Use a graph to find the lengths of the segments between (3, 2) and (8, 2) and between (4, 1) and (4, 9). Then find the midpoint of each segment. **5 units, 8 units; (5.5, 2), (4, 5)**

b. **Logical** Use what you learned in part **a** to write expressions for the lengths of the segments between (x_1, y) and (x_2, y) and between (x, y_1) and (x, y_2). What would be the midpoint of each segment?

c. **Analytical** Based on your results from part **b**, find the midpoint of the segment with endpoints at (x_1, y_1), and (x_2, y_2).

d. **Analytical** Use the Pythagorean Theorem to write an expression for the distance between (x_1, y_1), and (x_2, y_2).

45b. $|x_2 - x_1|$ **units,** $|y_2 - y_1|$ **units;** $\left(\frac{x_1 + x_2}{2}, y\right), \left(x, \frac{y_1 + y_2}{2}\right)$

45c. $\left(\frac{x_1 + x_2}{2}, \frac{y_1 + y_2}{2}\right)$

45d. $\sqrt{(x_2 - x_1)^2 + (y_2 - y_1)^2}$ **units**

H.O.T. Problems Use Higher-Order Thinking Skills

46. **ERROR ANALYSIS** Wyatt and Dario are determining whether 36, 77, and 85 form a Pythagorean triple. Is either of them correct? Explain your reasoning.

Wyatt	Dario
$36^2 + 77^2 \stackrel{?}{=} 85^2$	$36^2 + 85^2 \stackrel{?}{=} 77^2$
$1296 + 5929 \stackrel{?}{=} 7225$	$1296 + 7725 \stackrel{?}{=} 5929$
$7225 = 7225$	$9021 \neq 5929$
yes	no

46. Wyatt; the square of the greatest value should be equal to the sum of the squares of the two smaller values. Since this is the case, the numbers form a Pythagorean triple.

47. **PERSEVERANCE** Find the value of x in the figure. **$8\sqrt{2}$**

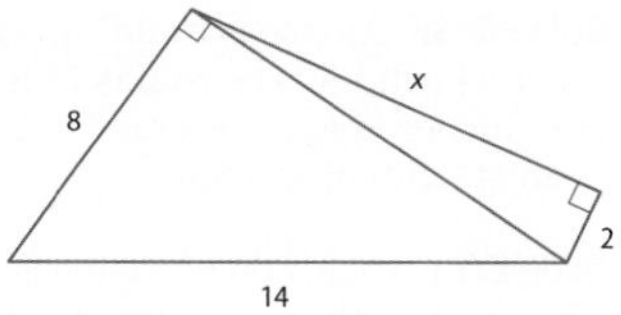

48. **REASONING** Provide a counterexample that is a specific case to show that the statement is false. *Any two right triangles with the same hypotenuse have the same area.* **See margin.**

49. **OPEN ENDED** Draw a right triangle that has a hypotenuse of $\sqrt{72}$ units. **See margin.**

50. **WRITING IN MATH** Explain how to determine whether segments in three lengths could form a right triangle. **See margin.**

652 | Lesson 10-5 | The Pythagorean Theorem

Enrichment

OL BL

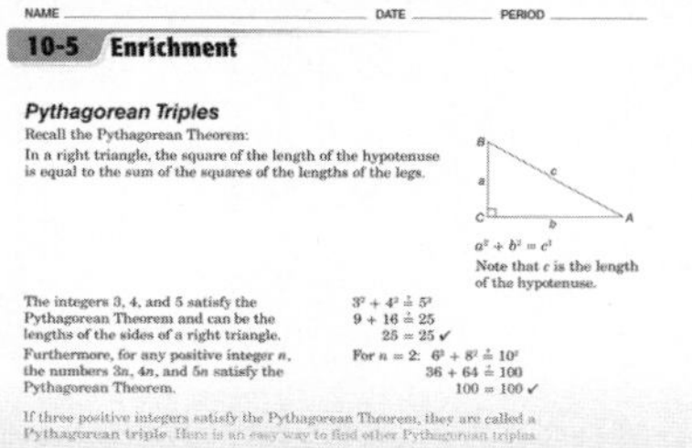
NAME ______ DATE ______ PERIOD ______

10-5 Enrichment

Pythagorean Triples

Recall the Pythagorean Theorem:
In a right triangle, the square of the length of the hypotenuse is equal to the sum of the squares of the lengths of the legs.

$a^2 + b^2 = c^2$
Note that c is the length of the hypotenuse.

The integers 3, 4, and 5 satisfy the Pythagorean Theorem and can be the lengths of the sides of a right triangle.

$3^2 + 4^2 \stackrel{?}{=} 5^2$
$9 + 16 \stackrel{?}{=} 25$
$25 = 25$ ✓

Furthermore, for any positive integer n, the numbers 3n, 4n, and 5n satisfy the Pythagorean Theorem.

For n = 2: $6^2 + 8^2 \stackrel{?}{=} 10^2$
$36 + 64 \stackrel{?}{=} 100$
$100 = 100$ ✓

If three positive integers satisfy the Pythagorean Theorem, they are called a Pythagorean triple. Here is an easy way to find other Pythagorean triples.

Multiple Representations

In Exercise 45, students use a graph and the Pythagorean Theorem to derive the Midpoint Formula.

Standardized Test Practice

51. GEOMETRY Find the missing length. **C**

A -17
B $-\sqrt{161}$
C $\sqrt{161}$
D 17

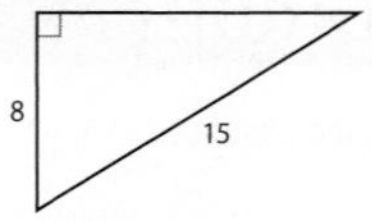

52. What is a solution of this equation? **H**

$$x + 1 = \sqrt{x + 1}$$

F 0, 3
G 3
H 0
J no solutions

53. SHORT RESPONSE A plumber charges \$40 for the first hour of each house call plus \$8 for each additional half hour. If the plumber works for 4 hours, how much does he charge? **\$88**

54. Find the next term in the geometric sequence $4, 3, \frac{9}{4}, \frac{27}{16}, \ldots$. **B**

A $\frac{64}{81}$ B $\frac{81}{64}$ C $\frac{4}{3}$ D $\frac{243}{64}$

Spiral Review

Solve each equation. Check your solution. (Lesson 10-4)

55. $\sqrt{x} = 16$ **256**
56. $\sqrt{4x} = 64$ **1024**
57. $\sqrt{10x} = 10$ **10**
58. $\sqrt{8x} + 1 = 65$ **512**
59. $\sqrt{x + 1} + 2 = 4$ **3**
60. $\sqrt{x - 15} = 3 - \sqrt{x}$ **no real solution**

Simplify each expression. (Lesson 10-3)

61. $2\sqrt{3} + 5\sqrt{3}$ $7\sqrt{3}$
62. $4\sqrt{5} - 2\sqrt{5}$ $2\sqrt{5}$
63. $6\sqrt{7} + 2\sqrt{28}$ $10\sqrt{7}$
64. $\sqrt{18} - 4\sqrt{2}$ $-\sqrt{2}$
65. $3\sqrt{5} - 5\sqrt{3} + 9\sqrt{5}$ $12\sqrt{5} - 5\sqrt{3}$
66. $4\sqrt{3} + 6\sqrt{12}$ $16\sqrt{3}$

Describe how the graph of each function is related to the graph of $f(x) = x^2$. (Lesson 9-3)

67. $g(x) = x^2 - 8$ **translated down 8**
68. $h(x) = \frac{1}{4}x^2$ **compressed vertically**
69. $h(x) = -x^2 + 5$ **reflected across the x-axis, translated up 5**
70. $g(x) = (x + 10)^2$ **translated left 10**
71. $g(x) = -2x^2$ **See margin.**
72. $h(x) = -x^2 - \frac{4}{3}$ **reflected across the x-axis, translated down $\frac{4}{3}$**

73. ROCK CLIMBING While rock climbing, Damaris launches a grappling hook from a height of 6 feet with an initial upward velocity of 56 feet per second. The hook just misses the stone ledge that she wants to scale. As it falls, the hook anchors on a ledge 30 feet above the ground. How long was the hook in the air? (Lesson 8-7) **3 seconds**

Find each product. (Lesson 8-3)

74. $(b + 8)(b + 2)$ $b^2 + 10b + 16$
75. $(x - 4)(x - 9)$ $x^2 - 13x + 36$
76. $(y + 4)(y - 8)$ $y^2 - 4y - 32$
77. $(p + 2)(p - 10)$ $p^2 - 8p - 20$
78. $(2w - 5)(w + 7)$ $2w^2 + 9w - 35$
79. $(8d + 3)(5d + 2)$ $40d^2 + 31d + 6$

80. BUSINESS The amount of money spent at West Outlet Mall continues to increase. The total $T(x)$ in millions of dollars can be estimated by the function $T(x) = 12(1.12)^x$, where x is the number of years after it opened in 2005. Find the amount of sales in 2015, 2016, and 2017. (Lesson 7-5) **about \$37.27 million; about \$41.74 million; about \$46.75 million**

Skills Review

Solve each proportion.

81. $\frac{x}{5} = \frac{12}{3}$ **20**
82. $\frac{12}{x} = \frac{3}{4}$ **16**
83. $\frac{5}{4} = \frac{10}{x}$ **8**
84. $\frac{3}{5} = \frac{12}{x + 8}$ **12**

DifferentiatedInstruction BL

Extension Tell students that when x equals any odd number, x, $\frac{1}{2}(x^2 - 1)$, and $\frac{1}{2}(x^2 + 1)$ will give them numbers that are Pythagorean triples. Ask students to use the expressions to find a set of Pythagorean triples not given in this lesson. Have students verify that their results are actually Pythagorean triples. Sample answer: $x = 11, 60, 61$; $61^2 = 60^2 + 11^2$, $3721 = 3600 + 121$, $3721 = 3721$

WatchOut!

Error Analysis For Exercise 46, ask students whether Wyatt or Dario represented the Pythagorean Theorem correctly. Why?

Teaching the Process Standards

Perseverance Mathematically proficient students analyze givens, constraints, relationships, and goals. In Exercise 47, point out to students that there are two right triangles in the figure.

4 Assess

Crystal Ball Have students write how they think today's lesson will connect to tomorrow's lesson on trigonometric ratios.

Formative Assessment

Check for student understanding of concepts in Lesson 10-5.

Quiz 3, p. 46

Additional Answers

48. Sample answer: A right triangle with legs measuring 3 cm and 4 cm has a hypotenuse of 5 cm and an area of 6 cm^2. A right triangle with legs measuring 2 cm and $\sqrt{21}$ cm also has a hypotenuse of 5 cm, but its area is $\sqrt{21}$ cm^2, which is not equivalent to 6 cm^2.

49.

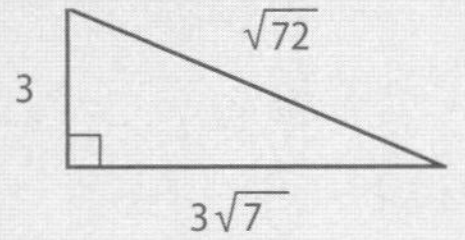

50. Sample answer: From the converse of the Pythagorean Theorem, if $a^2 + b^2 = c^2$, then a, b, and c are the lengths of the side of a right triangle. So, check to see whether the square of the greatest number is equal to the sum of the squares of the other two numbers.

71. reflected across the x-axis, stretched vertically

1 Focus

Objective Investigate distances on the coordinate plane.

Materials for Each Student

- grid paper
- ruler

Easy to Make Manipulatives

Teaching Algebra with Manipulatives

- grid paper, p. 1

Teaching Tip

- Discuss with students why the expressions $(x_2 - x_1)$ and $(y_2 - y_1)$ in the Distance Formula represent the lengths of the sides of the right triangle.

2 Teach

Working in Cooperative Groups

Divide the class into pairs. Ask students to work with their partners to complete the Activity.

Practice Have students complete Exercises 1–13.

3 Assess

Formative Assessment

Use Exercises 1–6 to assess each student's knowledge of the Distance Formula.

From Concrete to Abstract

Ask students to summarize how the Distance Formula is an extension of the Pythagorean Theorem.

EXTEND 10-5

Algebra Lab: Distance on the Coordinate Plane

The Pythagorean Theorem can be extended to develop a formula for finding the distance between two points on a coordinate plane.

Activity Find Distance

Find the distance between the points at $P(4, 3)$ and $Q(1, -2)$.

Step 1 Graph the points and $\overline{PQ}$.

Step 2 Draw a vertical segment down from P and a horizontal segment to the right from Q. Label the the point of intersection R. Notice that $\triangle PQR$ is a right triangle.

Step 3 Use the Pythagorean Theorem.

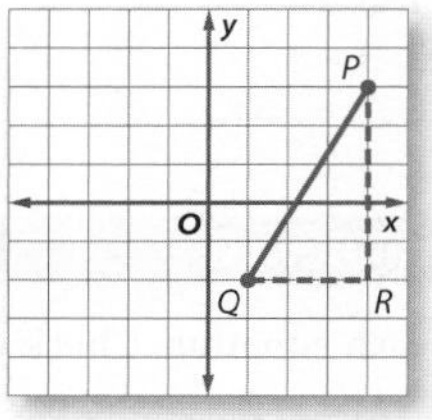

$c^2 = a^2 + b^2$	Pythagorean Theorem
$PQ^2 = 3^2 + 5^2$	$a = 3$ and $c = 5$
$PQ^2 = 9 + 25$	Evaluate squares.
$PQ^2 = 34$	Subtract 49 from each side.
$PQ = \pm\sqrt{34}$	Take the square root of each side.
$PQ \approx 5.83$	Use a calculator to evaluate $\sqrt{34}$. Use the positive value.

The distance between two points can be generalized as follows.

KeyConcept The Distance Formula

Words The distance d between any two points with coordinates (x_1, y_1) and (x_2, y_2) is given by the following formula.

$$d = \sqrt{(x_2 - x_1)^2 + (y_2 - y_1)^2}$$

Model

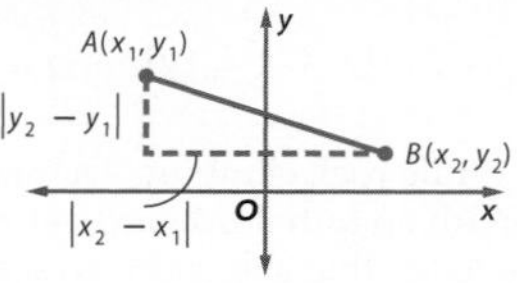

Model and Analyze

Find the distance between the points with the given coordinates.

1. $(6, -2), (12, 8)$ **$2\sqrt{34}$**
2. $(4, 8), (-3, -6)$ **$7\sqrt{5}$**
3. $(3, 0), (6, -2)$ **$\sqrt{13}$**
4. $(-2, -4), (-5, -3)$ **$\sqrt{10}$**
5. $(5, 1), (0, 4)$ **$\sqrt{34}$**
6. $(-5, 2), (4, -2)$ **$\sqrt{97}$**

The Midpoint Formula states that the midpoint M of a line segment with endpoints at (x_1, y_1) and (x_2, y_2) is given by $M = \left(\frac{x_1 + x_2}{2}, \frac{y_1 + y_2}{2}\right)$. Find the coordinates of the midpoint of the segment with the given endpoints.

7. $(5, -10), (5, 8)$ **$(5, -1)$**
8. $(2, -2), (6, 2)$ **$(4, 0)$**
9. $(5, 0), (0, 3)$ **$\left(\frac{5}{2}, \frac{3}{2}\right)$**
10. $(-4, 1), (3, -1)$ **$\left(-\frac{1}{2}, 0\right)$**
11. $(3, -17), (2, -8)$ **$\left(\frac{5}{2}, \frac{-25}{2}\right)$**
12. $(-2, 2), (4, 10)$ **$(1, 6)$**

13. The point that is equidistant from both endpoints is the **midpoint** of a segment. Use the Midpoint Formula to find the midpoint of the segment with endpoints at $(-16, -7)$ and $(-4, -3)$. Then use the Distance Formula to verify that the midpoint you found is correct. (*Hint:* The midpoint must be on the segment.) **See Ch. 10 Answer Appendix.**

EXPLORE 10-6 Algebra Lab: Investigating Trigonometric Ratios

Recall that *similar triangles* have the same shape, but not necessarily the same size. You can use similar triangles to investigate the ratios of the lengths of sides of right triangles.

Activity Collect the Data

Step 1 Use a ruler and grid paper to draw several right triangles with legs in a ratio of 5:8. Include right triangles with the side lengths listed in the table below and several more right triangles similar to these three. Label the vertices of each triangle as A, B, and C, where C is at the right angle, B is opposite the longest leg, and A is opposite the shortest leg.

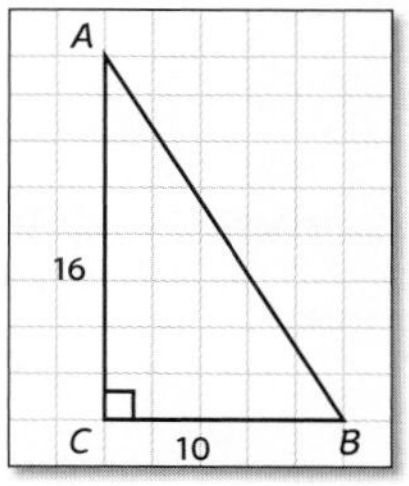

Step 2 Copy the table below. Complete the first three columns by measuring the hypotenuse (side $\overline{AB}$) in each right triangle you created and recording its length to the nearest tenth.

Step 3 Calculate and record the ratios in the middle two columns. Round to the nearest hundredth.

Step 4 Use a protractor to carefully measure angles A and B to the nearest degree in each right triangle. Record the angle measures in the table.

Side Lengths			Ratios		Angle Measures		
side BC	side AC	side AB	$\frac{BC}{AC}$	$\frac{BC}{AB}$	angle A	angle B	angle C
2.5	4	4.7	0.63	0.53	32°	58°	90°
5	8	9.4	0.63	0.53	32°	58°	90°
10	16	18.9	0.63	0.53	32°	58°	90°
15	24	28.3	0.63	0.53	32°	58°	90°
20	32	37.7	0.63	0.53	32°	58°	90°
25	40	47.2	0.63	0.53	32°	58°	90°

Analyze the Results

1. Examine the measures and ratios in the table. What do you notice? Write a sentence or two to describe any patterns you see.
   All ratios and angle measures are the same for any 5:8 right triangle.

Make a Conjecture

2. For any right triangle similar to the ones you have drawn here, what will be the value of the ratio of the length of the shortest leg to the length of the longest leg? 5:8

3. If you draw a right triangle and calculate the ratio of the length of the shortest leg to the length of the hypotenuse to be approximately 0.53, what will be the measure of the larger acute angle in the right triangle? 58°

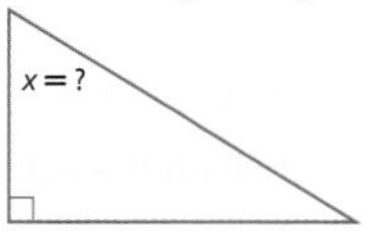

1 Focus

Objective Investigate trigonometric ratios.

Materials for Each Student

- ruler
- protractor
- grid paper

Easy to Make Manipulatives

Teaching Algebra with Manipulatives
Template for:

- grid paper, p. 1

Teaching Tips

- Remind students of the definition of similar triangles. *If two triangles are similar, then the measures of their corresponding angles are equal, and the measures of their corresponding sides are proportional.*
- Explain to students that even though measurements of side lengths and angles may not be exact, the ratios and angle measures should be close. If not, students should recheck the measurements.

2 Teach

Working in Cooperative Groups

Have students work in pairs or groups of three to complete the activity. Suggest that they divide the tasks into drawing the triangles, measuring the hypotenuse and angles, and calculating and recording the data. Students should rotate tasks.

Ask:

- Why are the triangles in the activity similar triangles? the ratios of the corresponding sides are the same for all of the triangles
- If you know the ratio of the shortest leg to the longest leg, what angle measures can you find? all angle measures

Practice Have students complete Exercises 1–3.

3 Assess

Formative Assessment

Use Exercise 1 to assess whether students understand that similar triangles will have the same ratios for the lengths of the corresponding sides and have the same angle measures.

From Concrete to Abstract

Use Exercise 3 to assess whether students understand that they can use the ratios of the sides of a triangle to find unknown measures, including angle measures.

1 Focus

Vertical Alignment

Before Lesson 10-6 Use the Pythagorean Theorem.

Lesson 10-6 Find trigonometric ratios of angles. Use trigonometry to solve triangles.

After Lesson 10-6 Use trigonometric ratios to find angles of elevation or depression.

2 Teach

Scaffolding Questions

Have students read the **Why?** section of the lesson.

Ask:

- Suppose you draw a right triangle to model the 8% grade of the road. Which side represents the horizontal distance of 100 feet? longer leg Which side represents the rise of 8 feet? shorter leg
- Which leg is adjacent to the angle at which the road rises or falls? longer leg Which leg is opposite the angle? shorter leg
- Which ratio would you use to find the measure of the angle? the ratio of the leg opposite the angle to the leg adjacent to the angle

LESSON 10-6 Trigonometric Ratios

Then

- You used the Pythagorean Theorem

Now

1. Find trigonometric ratios of angles.
2. Use trigonometry to solve triangles.

Why?

- If a road has a percent grade of 8%, this means the road rises or falls 8 feet over a horizontal distance of 100 feet. Trigonometric ratios can be used to determine the angle that the road rises or falls.

New Vocabulary

trigonometry
trigonometric ratio
sine
cosine
tangent
solving the triangle
inverse sine
inverse cosine
inverse tangent

Process Standards
PS.5

1 Trigonometric Ratios **Trigonometry** is the study of relationships among the angles and sides of triangles. A **trigonometric ratio** is a ratio that compares the side lengths of two sides of a right triangle. The three most common trigonometric ratios, **sine**, **cosine**, and **tangent**, are described below.

KeyConcept Trigonometric Ratios

Words	Symbols	Model
sine of $\angle A = \frac{\text{leg opposite } \angle A}{\text{hypotenuse}}$	$\sin A = \frac{a}{c}$	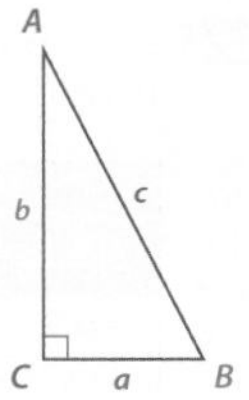
cosine of $\angle A = \frac{\text{leg adjacent to } \angle A}{\text{hypotenuse}}$	$\cos A = \frac{b}{c}$	
tangent of $\angle A = \frac{\text{leg opposite } \angle A}{\text{Leg adjacent to } \angle A}$	$\tan A = \frac{a}{b}$	

Opposite, adjacent, and hypotenuse are abbreviated *opp*, *adj*, and *hyp*, respectively.

Example 1 Find Sine, Cosine, and Tangent Ratios

Find the values of the three trigonometric ratios for angle *A*.

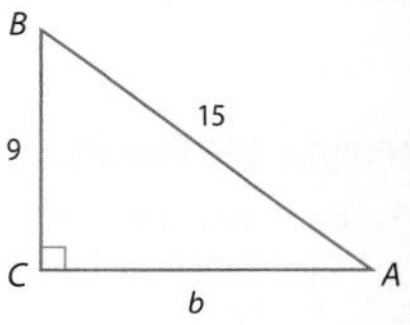

Step 1 Use the Pythagorean Theorem to find b.

$a^2 + b^2 = c^2$ Pythagorean Theorem

$9^2 + b^2 = 15^2$ $a = 9$ and $c = 15$

$81 + b^2 = 225$ Simplify.

$b^2 = 144$ Subtract 81 from each side.

$b = 12$ Take the square root of each side.

Step 2 Use the side lengths to write the trigonometric ratios.

$\sin A = \frac{\text{opp}}{\text{hyp}} = \frac{9}{15} = \frac{3}{5}$ $\cos A = \frac{\text{adj}}{\text{hyp}} = \frac{12}{15} = \frac{4}{5}$ $\tan A = \frac{\text{opp}}{\text{adj}} = \frac{9}{12} = \frac{3}{4}$

Guided Practice

1. Find the values of the three trigonometric ratios for angle *B*. $\sin B = \frac{4}{5}$; $\cos B = \frac{3}{5}$; $\tan B = \frac{4}{3}$

656 | Lesson 10-6

Lesson 10-6 Resources

Resource	Approaching Level AL	On Level OL	Beyond Level BL	English Learners ELL
Teacher Edition	▪ Differentiated Instruction, p. 657	▪ Differentiated Instruction, pp. 657, 662	▪ Differentiated Instruction, p. 662	▪ Differentiated Instruction, p. 657
Chapter Resource Masters	▪ Study Guide and Intervention, pp. 37–38 ▪ Skills Practice, p. 39 ▪ Practice, p. 40 ▪ Word Problem Practice, p. 41	▪ Study Guide and Intervention, pp. 37–38 ▪ Skills Practice, p. 39 ▪ Practice, p. 40 ▪ Word Problem Practice, p. 41 ▪ Enrichment, p. 42	▪ Practice, p. 40 ▪ Word Problem Practice, p. 41 ▪ Enrichment, p. 42	▪ Study Guide and Intervention, pp. 37–38 ▪ Skills Practice, p. 39 ▪ Practice, p. 41 ▪ Word Problem Practice, p. 42
Other	▪ 5-Minute Check 10-6 ▪ Study Notebook	▪ 5-Minute Check 10-6 ▪ Study Notebook	▪ 5-Minute Check 10-6 ▪ Study Notebook	▪ 5-Minute Check 10-6 ▪ Study Notebook

WatchOut!

Tools Make sure your graphing calculator is in degree mode.

Example 2 Use a Calculator to Evaluate Expressions

Use a calculator to find cos 42° to the nearest ten-thousandth.

KEYSTROKES: [COS] 42 [ )] [ENTER]

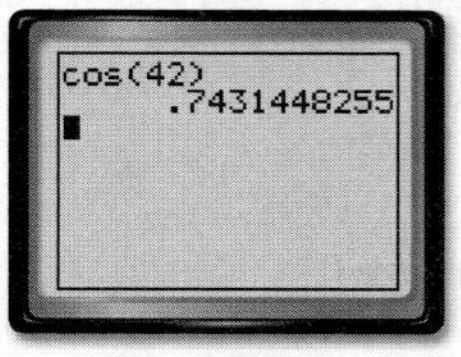

Rounded to the nearest ten-thousandth, cos 42° ≈ 0.7431.

Guided Practice

2A. sin 31° **0.5150** **2B.** tan 76° **4.0108** **2C.** cos 55° **0.5736**

2 Use Trigonometric Ratios

When you find all unknown measures of the sides and angles of a right triangle, you are **solving the triangle**. You can find the missing measures if you know the measure of two sides of the triangle or the measure of one side and the measure of one acute angle.

Example 3 Solve a Triangle

Solve the right triangle. Round each side length to the nearest tenth.

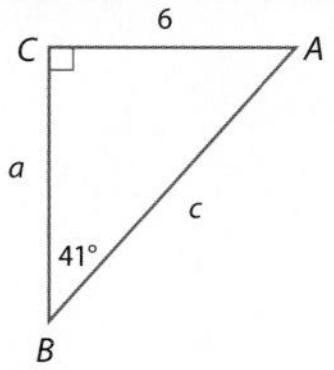

Step 1 Find the measure of $\angle A$. $180° - (90° + 41°) = 49°$
The measure of $\angle A = 49°$.

Step 2 Find a. Since you are given the measure of the side opposite $\angle B$ and are finding the measure of the side adjacent to $\angle B$, use the tangent ratio.

$\tan 41° = \frac{6}{a}$ — Definition of tangent

$a \tan 41° = 6$ — Multiply each side by a.

$a = \frac{6}{\tan 41°}$ or about 6.9 — Divide each side by tan 41°. Use a calculator.

So the measure of a or $\overline{BC}$ is about 6.9.

Step 3 Find c. Since you are given the measure of the side opposite $\angle B$ and are finding the measure of the hypotenuse, use the sine ratio.

$\sin 41° = \frac{6}{c}$ — Definition of sine

$c \sin 41° = 6$ — Multiply each side by c.

$c = \frac{6}{\sin 41°}$ or about 9.1 — Divide each side by sin 41°. Use a calculator.

So the measure of c or $\overline{AB}$ is about 9.1.

StudyTip

Remembering Trigonometric Ratios SOH–CAH–TOA can be used to help you remember the ratios for sine, cosine, and tangent. Each letter represents a word.

$\sin A = \frac{\text{opp}}{\text{hyp}}$

$\cos A = \frac{\text{adj}}{\text{hyp}}$

$\tan A = \frac{\text{opp}}{\text{adj}}$

Guided Practice

3A.

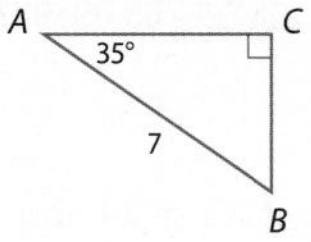

$\angle B = 55°$, $AC \approx 5.7$; $BC \approx 4.0$

3B.

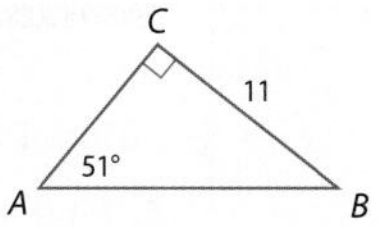

$\angle B = 39°$, $AC \approx 8.9$; $AB \approx 14.2$

Differentiated Instruction AL OL ELL

If students have difficulty remembering the trigonometric ratios,

Then have students work in groups to brainstorm and implement ideas on how to remember them. Prompt students with suggestions such as flash cards, rap verse, or poems. Have groups share their ideas with the class.

1 Trigonometric Ratios

Example 1 shows how to find the trigonometric ratios for an angle of a right triangle. **Example 2** shows how to use a calculator to evaluate a trigonometric expression.

Formative Assessment

Use the Guided Practice exercises after each Example to determine students' understanding of concepts.

Additional Examples

1 Find the values of the three trigonometric ratios for angle B.

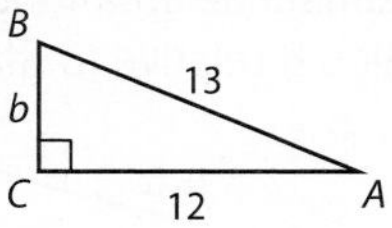

$\sin B = \frac{12}{13}$, $\cos B = \frac{5}{13}$, $\tan B = \frac{12}{5}$

2 Use a calculator to find tan 52° to the nearest ten-thousandth. 1.2799

Additional Examples also in Interactive Classroom PowerPoint® Presentations

IWB Interactive White Board READY

Teaching the Process Standards

Tools Mathematically proficient students are sufficiently familiar with tools appropriate for their course. Point out that calculators can automatically round or truncate answers. Discuss the advantages and disadvantages of rounding or truncating.

2 Use Trigonometric Ratios

Example 3 shows how to solve a right triangle. **Example 4** shows how to use trigonometric ratios to solve a real-world problem. **Example 5** shows how to use the inverse of a trigonometric function to find a missing angle measure.

Additional Examples

3 Solve the right triangle. Round each side to the nearest tenth.

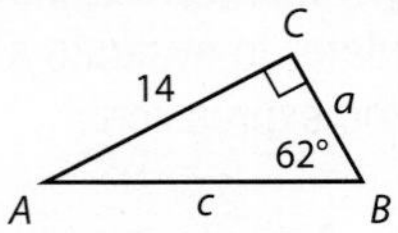

$m\angle A = 28°$; $a \approx 7.4$, $c \approx 15.9$

4 **CONVEYOR BELTS** A conveyor belt moves recycled materials from Station A to Station B. The angle the conveyor belt makes with the floor of the first station is 15°. The conveyor belt is 18 feet long. What is the approximate height of the floor of Station B relative to Station A?

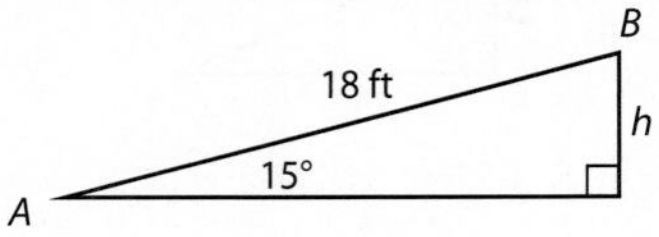

about 4.7 ft

5 Find $m\angle P$ to the nearest degree. 24°

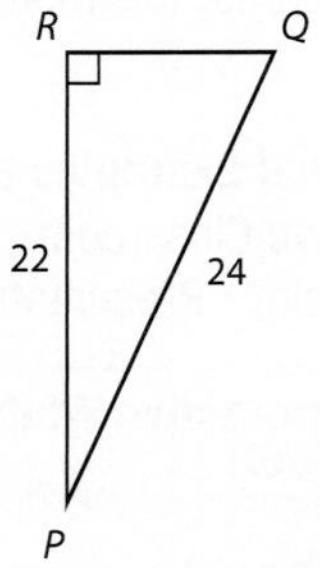

Teach with Tech

Interactive Whiteboard Draw a right triangle on the board and label each of the side lengths. To write the trigonometric ratios, drag the measurement from the side of the triangle to the ratio.

Follow-up

Students have explored trigonometry.

Ask:

- How can trigonometry be useful when modeling? Sample answer: It allows us to solve problems modeled by triangles that cannot be solved using the Pythagorean Theorem.

Real-WorldLink

For optimum health, all adults ages 18–65 should get at least 30 minutes of moderately intense activity five days per week.

Source: American Heart Association

Real-World Example 4 Find a Missing Side Length

EXERCISE A trainer sets the incline on a treadmill to 10°. The walking surface of the treadmill is 5 feet long. About how many inches is the end of the treadmill from the floor?

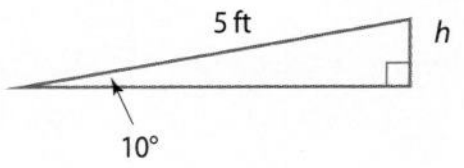

$\sin 10° = \frac{h}{5}$ Definition of sine

$5 \cdot \sin 10° = h$ Multiply each side by 5.

$0.87 \approx h$ Use a calculator.

The value of h is in feet. Multiply 0.87 by 12 to convert feet to inches. The trainer raised the treadmill about 10.4 inches.

GuidedPractice

4. **SKATEBOARDING** The angle that a skateboarding ramp forms with the ground is 25° and the height of the ramp is 6 feet. Determine the length of the ramp. about 14.2 ft

A trigonometric function has a rule given by a trigonometric ratio. If you know the sine, cosine, or tangent of an acute angle, you can use the *inverse* of the trigonometric function to find the measure of the angle.

KeyConcept Inverse Trigonometric Functions

Words	If $\angle A$ is an acute angle and the sine of A is x, then the **inverse sine** of x is the measure of $\angle A$.
Symbols	If $\sin A = x$, then $\sin^{-1} x = m\angle A$.
Words	If $\angle A$ is an acute angle and the cosine of A is x, then the **inverse cosine** of x is the measure of $\angle A$.
Symbols	If $\cos A = x$, then $\cos^{-1} x = m\angle A$.
Words	If $\angle A$ is an acute angle and the tangent of A is x, then the **inverse tangent** of x is the measure of $\angle A$.
Symbols	If $\tan A = x$, then $\tan^{-1} x = m\angle A$.

Example 5 Find a Missing Angle Measure

Find $m\angle Y$ to the nearest degree.

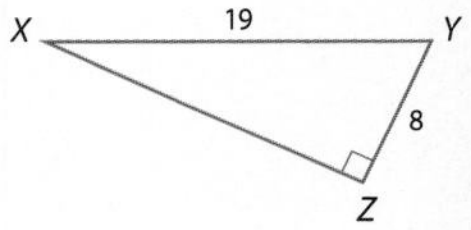

You know the measure of the side adjacent to $\angle Y$ and the measure of the hypotenuse. Use the cosine ratio.

$\cos Y = \frac{8}{19}$ Definition of cosine

Use a calculator and the [COS^{-1}] function to find the measure of the angle.

KEYSTROKES: [2nd] [COS^{-1}] 8 [÷] 19 [)] [ENTER] **65.098937** So, $m\angle Y = 65°$.

GuidedPractice

5. Find $m\angle X$ to the nearest degree if $XY = 14$ and $YZ = 5$. 21°

Focus on Mathematical Content

Trigonometric Ratios The trigonometric ratios include the sine, cosine, and tangent ratios and also the secant, cosecant, and cotangent ratios, which students will use in Algebra 2 and Geometry. The trigonometric ratios give the ratios of the sides of the right triangle in relation to the angles of the triangle. The ratios are used to find missing side lengths. The inverse trigonometric ratios are used to find missing angle measures.

Check Your Understanding

= Step-by-Step Solutions begin on page R13.

Example 1 **Find the values of the three trigonometric ratios for angle A.**

1.

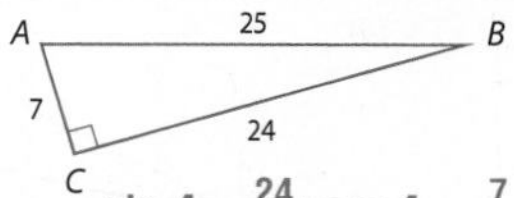

$\sin A = \frac{24}{25}$; $\cos A = \frac{7}{25}$; $\tan A = \frac{24}{7}$

2.

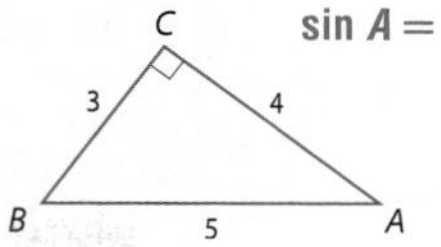

$\sin A = \frac{3}{5}$; $\cos A = \frac{4}{5}$; $\tan A = \frac{3}{4}$

3.

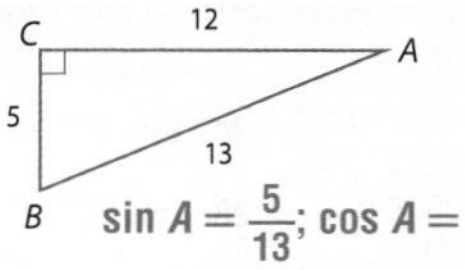

$\sin A = \frac{5}{13}$; $\cos A = \frac{12}{13}$; $\tan A = \frac{5}{12}$

4.

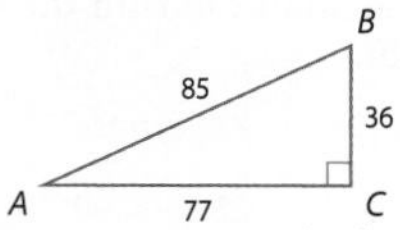

$\sin A = \frac{36}{85}$; $\cos A = \frac{77}{85}$; $\tan A = \frac{36}{77}$

Example 2 **TOOLS Use a calculator to find the value of each trigonometric ratio to the nearest ten-thousandth.**

5. sin 37° **0.6018** **6.** cos 23° **0.9205** **7.** tan 14° **0.2493** **8.** cos 82° **0.1392**

Example 3 **Solve each right triangle. Round each side length to the nearest tenth.**

9.

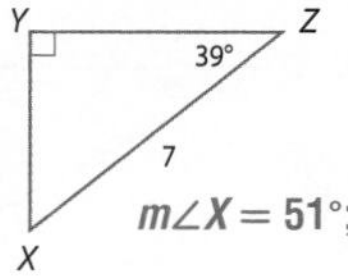

$m\angle X = 51°$; $XY \approx 4.4$; $YZ \approx 5.4$

10.

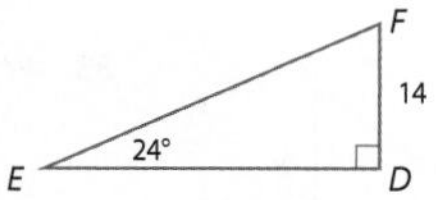

$m\angle F = 66°$; $DE \approx 31.4$; $EF \approx 34.4$

11.

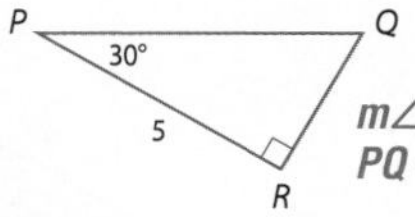

$m\angle Q = 60°$; $RQ \approx 2.9$; $PQ \approx 5.8$

12.

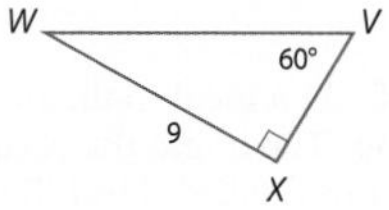

$m\angle W = 30°$; $XV \approx 5.2$; $WV \approx 10.4$

Example 4 **13. SNOWBOARDING** A hill used for snowboarding has a vertical drop of 3500 feet. The angle the run makes with the ground is 18°. Estimate the length of r. **about 11,326.2 ft**

Example 5 **Find $m\angle X$ for each right triangle to the nearest degree.**

14. **34°**

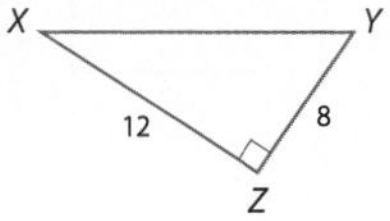

15. **66°**

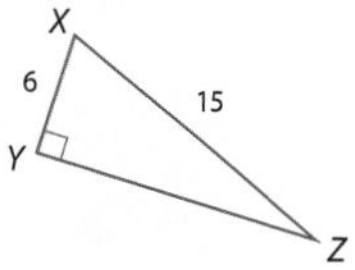

16. **67°**

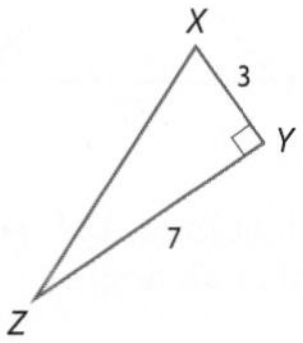

17. **33°**

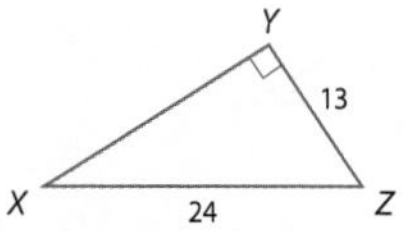

3 Practice

Formative Assessment

Use Exercises 1–17 to check for understanding.

Use the chart at the bottom of the next page to customize assignments for your students

Tips for New Teachers

Reasoning Advise students to be careful not to confuse the notation for inverse trigonometric functions with the notation that is used for negative exponents. For example, $\cos^{-1} x \neq \frac{1}{\cos x}$.

Teaching the Process Standards

Tools Mathematically proficient students are able to identify relevant external mathematical resources. In Exercises 5–8, point out that online and downloadable calculators are available.

WatchOut!

Preventing Errors For Exercises 42–44, suggest that students draw and label right triangles that fit the descriptions in the exercises. Diagrams help students visualize the situation so that they find the correct measures.

connectED.mcgraw-hill.com 659

Multiple Representations

In Exercise 50, students use diagrams, information organized in a table, and verbal analysis to investigate a relationship between the sine and cosine functions.

Teaching the Process Standards

Arguments Mathematically proficient students make conjectures and build a logical progression of statements to explore the truth of their conjectures. In Exercise 54, suggest that students draw a diagram and apply the definitions of sine and cosine.

Additional Answers

18. $\sin B = \frac{15}{17}$; $\cos B = \frac{8}{17}$; $\tan B = \frac{15}{8}$

19. $\sin B = \frac{5}{13}$; $\cos B = \frac{12}{13}$; $\tan B = \frac{5}{12}$

20. $\sin B = \frac{\sqrt{15}}{4}$; $\cos B = \frac{1}{4}$; $\tan B = \sqrt{15}$

29. $m\angle Y = 43°$; $XY \approx 21.9$; $XZ \approx 14.9$

30. $m\angle J = 22°$; $JK \approx 8.3$; $KL \approx 3.4$

31. $m\angle R = 76°$; $QR \approx 7.2$; $PR \approx 1.7$

32. $m\angle B = 56°$; $AB \approx 32.2$; $AC \approx 26.7$

33. $m\angle Y = 39°$; $WU \approx 11.3$; $UY \approx 18.0$

34. $m\angle F = 61°$; $DE \approx 9.0$; $DF \approx 10.3$

45. $\sin A = \frac{\sqrt{7}}{4}$; $\tan A = \frac{\sqrt{7}}{3}$

46. $\tan A = \frac{2\sqrt{5}}{15}$; $\cos A = \frac{3\sqrt{5}}{7}$

47. $\cos A = \frac{\sqrt{15}}{4}$; $\tan A = \frac{\sqrt{15}}{15}$

48. $\sin A = \frac{5\sqrt{34}}{34}$; $\cos A = \frac{3\sqrt{34}}{34}$

52. $$\frac{\sin A}{\cos A} = \frac{\frac{\text{opp}}{\text{hyp}}}{\frac{\text{adj}}{\text{hyp}}} = \frac{\text{opp}}{\text{hyp}} \cdot \frac{\text{hyp}}{\text{adj}} = \frac{\text{opp}}{\text{adj}} = \tan A$$

Practice and Problem Solving

Extra Practice is on page R10.

Example 1 Find the values of the three trigonometric ratios for angle B. **18–20. See margin.**

18. 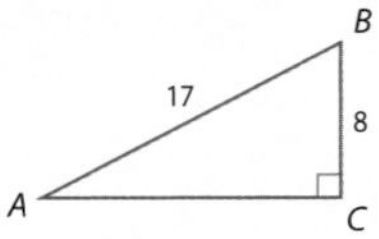

19. 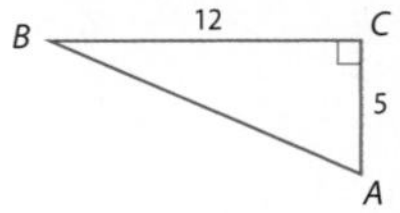

20. 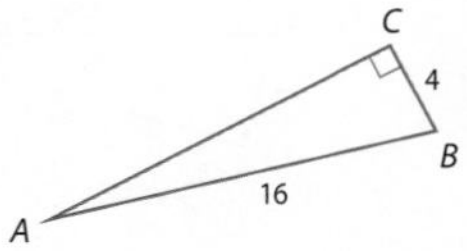

Example 2 **TOOLS** Use a calculator to find the value of each trigonometric ratio to the nearest ten-thousandth.

21. tan 2° **0.0349**
22. sin 89° **0.9998**
23. cos 44° **0.7193**
24. tan 45° **1**
25. sin 73° **0.9563**
26. cos 90° **0**
27. sin 30° **0.5**
28. tan 60° **1.7321**

Example 3 Solve each right triangle. Round each side length to the nearest tenth.

29–34. See margin.

29. 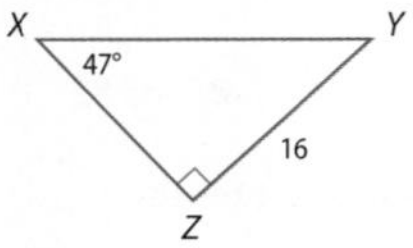

30. 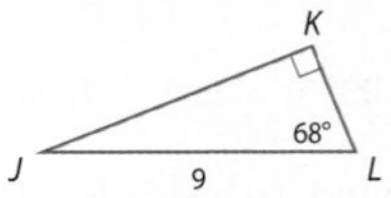

31. 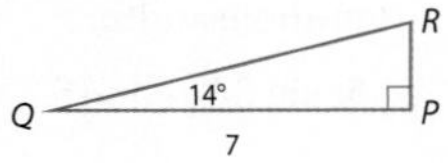

32. 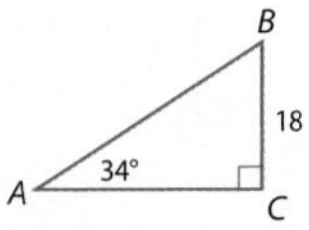

33. 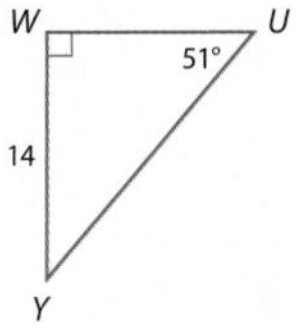

34. 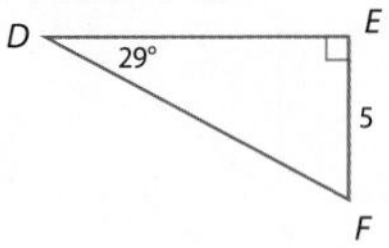

Example 4 35. **ESCALATORS** At a local mall, an escalator is 110 feet long. The angle the escalator makes with the ground is 29°. Find the height reached by the escalator. **about 53 ft**

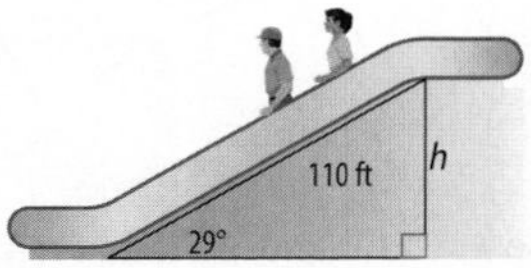

Example 5 Find $m\angle J$ for each right triangle to the nearest degree.

36. **25°** 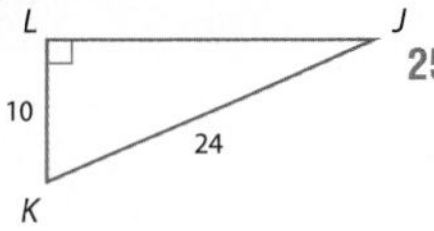

37. **62°** 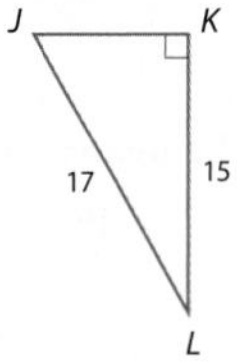

38. **59°** 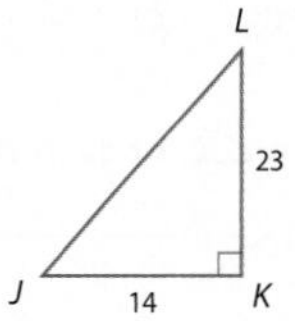

39. **31°** 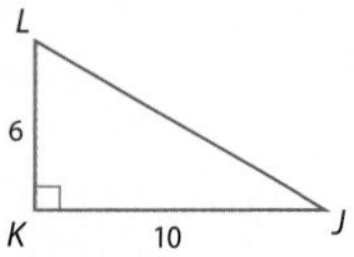

40. **72°** 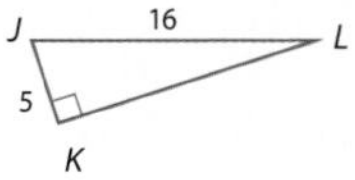

41. **50°** 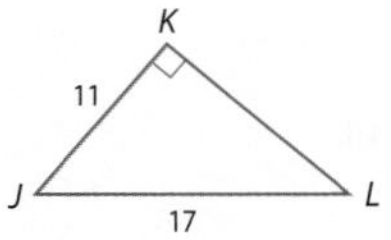

B 42. **MONUMENTS** The Lincoln Memorial building measures 204 feet long, 134 feet wide, and 99 feet tall. Chloe is looking at the top of the monument at an angle of 55°. How far away is she standing from the monument? **about 69 ft**

Differentiated Homework Options

Level	Assignment	Two-Day Option	
AL Basic	18–41, 52–71	19–41 odd, 56–59	18–40 even, 52–55, 60–71
OL Core	19–41 odd, 42–50, 52–71	18–41, 56–59	42–50, 52–55, 60–71
BL Advanced	42–67, (optional: 68–71)		

43. **AIRPLANES** Ella looks down at a city from an airplane window. The airplane is 5000 feet in the air, and she looks down at an angle of 8°. Determine the horizontal distance to the city. **about 35,577 ft**

44. **FORESTS** A forest ranger estimates the height of a tree is about 175 feet. If the forest ranger is standing 100 feet from the base of the tree, what is the measure of the angle formed by the ranger and the top of the tree? **about 60°**

Suppose $\angle A$ is an acute angle of right triangle *ABC*. **45–48. See margin.**

45. Find sin A and tan A if $\cos A = \frac{3}{4}$.

46. Find tan A and cos A if $\sin A = \frac{2}{7}$.

47. Find cos A and tan A if $\sin A = \frac{1}{4}$.

48. Find sin A and cos A if $\tan A = \frac{5}{3}$.

49. **SUBMARINES** A submarine descends into the ocean at an angle of 10° below the water line and travels 3 miles diagonally. How far beneath the surface of the water has the submarine reached? **about 0.5 mi**

C **50.** **MULTIPLE REPRESENTATIONS** In this problem, you will explore a relationship between the sine and cosine functions.

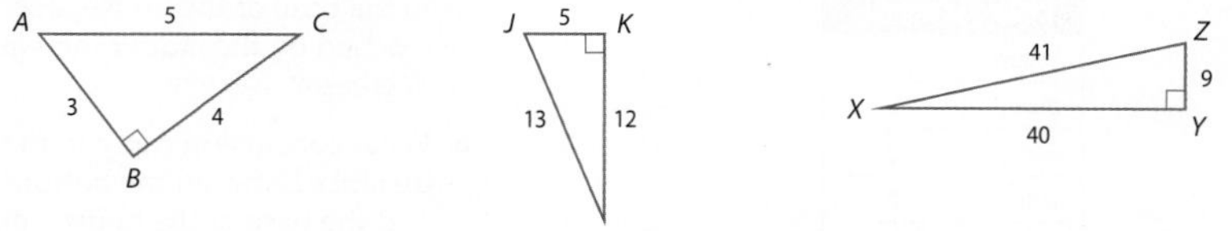

See Ch. 10 Answer Appendix.

a. **Tabular** Copy and complete the table using the triangles shown above.

Triangle	Trigonometric Ratios		$\sin^2$	$\cos^2$	$\sin^2 + \cos^2 =$
ABC	sin $A =$	cos $A =$	$\sin^2 A =$	$\cos^2 A =$	
	sin $C =$	cos $C =$	$\sin^2 C =$	$\cos^2 C =$	
JKL	sin $J =$	cos $J =$	$\sin^2 J =$	$\cos^2 J =$	
	sin $L =$	cos $L =$	$\sin^2 L =$	$\cos^2 L =$	
XYZ	sin $X =$	cos $X =$	$\sin^2 X =$	$\cos^2 X =$	
	sin $Z =$	cos $Z =$	$\sin^2 Z =$	$\cos^2 Z =$	

b. **Verbal** Make a conjecture about the sum of the squares of the sine and cosine functions of an acute angle in a right triangle. **The sum of the squares of the sine and cosine of an acute angle in a right triangle is equal to 1.**

53. Sample answer: Triangles can be used to represent objects or situations with a triangular shape, and trigonometry or the Pythagorean Theorem can be used to find unknown values.

H.O.T. Problems Use Higher-Order Thinking Skills

51. **CHALLENGE** Find a and c in the triangle shown. $a = 5$; $c \approx 7.3$

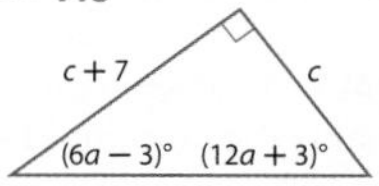

52. **REASONING** Use the definitions of the sine and cosine ratios to define the tangent ratio. **See margin.**

53. **WRITING IN MATH** How can triangles be used to solve problems?

54. **ARGUMENTS** The sine and cosine of an acute angle in a right triangle are equal. What can you conclude about the triangle? **The triangle is an isosceles right triangle. The legs are equal to each other.**

55. **WRITING IN MATH** Explain how to use trigonometric ratios to find the missing length of a side of a right triangle given the measure of one acute angle and the length of one side. **See margin.**

Additional Answer

55. Use the angle given and the measure of the known side to set up one of the trigonometric ratios. The sine ratio uses the opposite side and hypotenuse of the triangle. The cosine ratio uses the adjacent side and hypotenuse of the triangle. The tangent ratio uses the opposite and adjacent sides of the triangle. Set up the ratio and solve for the unknown measure.

Enrichment
OL BL

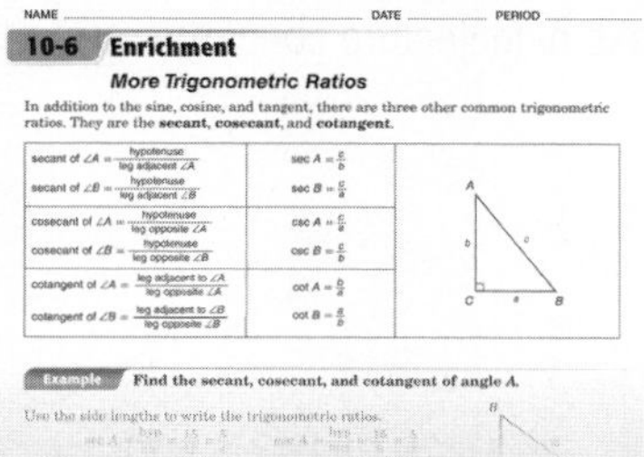
10-6 Enrichment

More Trigonometric Ratios

In addition to the sine, cosine, and tangent, there are three other common trigonometric ratios. They are the **secant, cosecant,** and **cotangent**.

Example Find the secant, cosecant, and cotangent of angle A.

Study Guide and Intervention
AL OL ELL

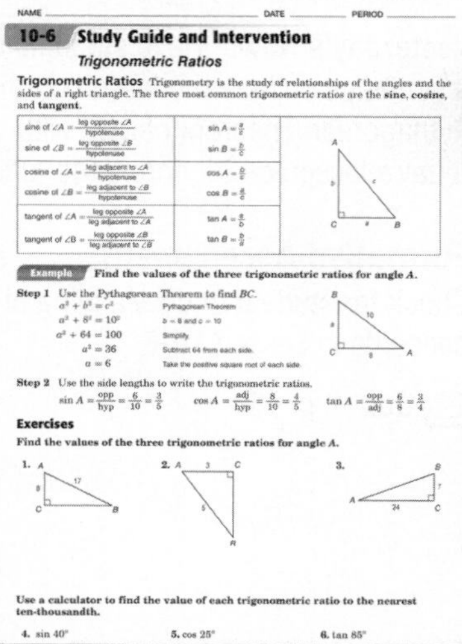
10-6 Study Guide and Intervention

Trigonometric Ratios

Trigonometric Ratios Trigonometry is the study of relationships of the angles and the sides of a right triangle. The three most common trigonometric ratios are the **sine, cosine,** and **tangent**.

Example Find the values of the three trigonometric ratios for angle A.

Step 1 Use the Pythagorean Theorem to find BC.

Step 2 Use the side lengths to write the trigonometric ratios.

Exercises

Find the values of the three trigonometric ratios for angle A.

Use a calculator to find the value of each trigonometric ratio to the nearest ten-thousandth.

4. sin 40° 5. cos 25° 6. tan 85°

Practice
AL OL BL ELL

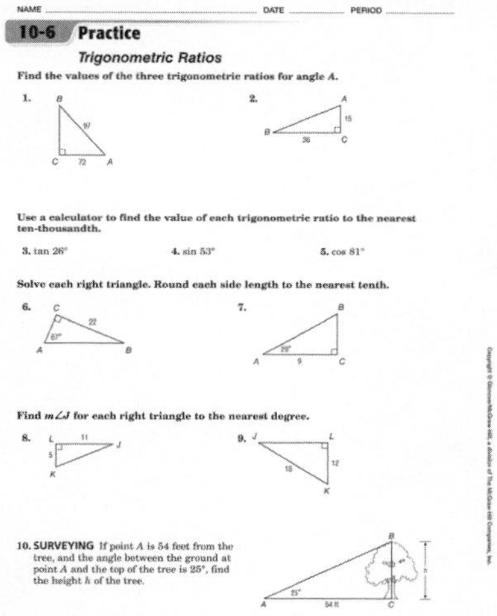
10-6 Practice

Trigonometric Ratios

Find the values of the three trigonometric ratios for angle A.

Use a calculator to find the value of each trigonometric ratio to the nearest ten-thousandth.

3. tan 26° 4. sin 53° 5. cos 81°

Solve each right triangle. Round each side length to the nearest tenth.

Find m∠J for each right triangle to the nearest degree.

10. SURVEYING If point A is 54 feet from the tree, and the angle between the ground at point A and the top of the tree is 25°, find the height h of the tree.

Word Problem Practice
AL OL BL ELL

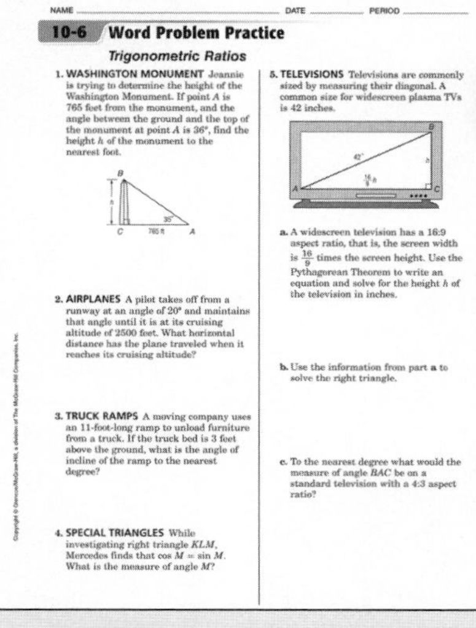
10-6 Word Problem Practice

Trigonometric Ratios

1. WASHINGTON MONUMENT Jeannie is trying to determine the height of the Washington Monument. If point A is 765 feet from the monument, and the angle between the ground and the top of the monument at point A is 36°, find the height h of the monument to the nearest foot.

2. AIRPLANES A pilot takes off from a runway at an angle of 20° and maintains that angle until it is at its cruising altitude of 2500 feet. What horizontal distance has the plane traveled when it reaches its cruising altitude?

3. TRUCK RAMPS A moving company uses an 11-foot-long ramp to unload furniture from a truck. If the truck bed is 3 feet above the ground, what is the angle of incline of the ramp to the nearest degree?

4. SPECIAL TRIANGLES While investigating right triangle KLM, Mercedes finds that cos M = sin M. What is the measure of angle M?

5. TELEVISIONS Televisions are commonly sized by measuring their diagonal. A common size for widescreen plasma TVs is 42 inches.

a. A widescreen television has a 16:9 aspect ratio, that is, the screen width is $\frac{16}{9}$ times the screen height. Use the Pythagorean Theorem to write an equation and solve for the height h of the television in inches.

b. Use the information from part a to solve the right triangle.

c. To the nearest degree what would the measure of angle BAC be on a standard television with a 4:3 aspect ratio?

4 Assess

Yesterday's News Have students write a sentence on how the lesson on the Pythagorean Theorem helped with today's lesson on trigonometric ratios.

Formative Assessment

Check for student understanding of concepts in Lesson 10-6.

Quiz 4, p. 46

Standardized Test Practice

56. Which graph below represents the solution set for $-2 \le x \le 4$? **A**

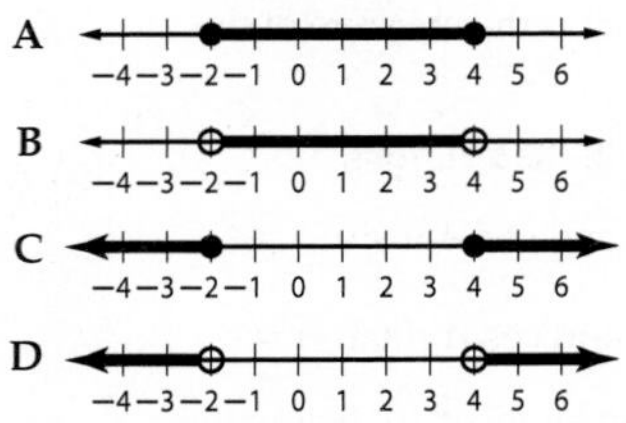

57. PROBABILITY Suppose one chip is chosen from a bin with the chips shown. To the nearest tenth, what is the probability that a green chip is chosen? **F**

Color	Number
yellow	7
blue	9
orange	3
green	5
red	6

F 0.2
G 0.5
H 0.6
J 0.8

58. In the graph, for what value(s) of x is $y = 0$? **D**

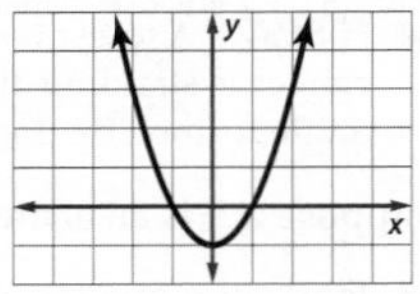

A 0
B −1
C 1
D 1 and −1

59. EXTENDED RESPONSE A 16-foot ladder is placed against the side of a house so that the bottom of the ladder is 8 feet from the base of the house.

a. If the bottom of the ladder is moved closer to the base of the house, does the height reached by the ladder increase or decrease? **increase**

b. What conclusion can you make about the distance between the bottom of the ladder and the base of the house and the height reached by the ladder?

c. How high does the ladder reach if the ladder is 3 feet from the base of the house? **about 15.7 ft**

59b. Sample answer: The sum of their squares is 16^2 or 256.

Spiral Review

If c is the measure of the hypotenuse of a right triangle, find each missing measure. If necessary, round to the nearest hundredth. (Lesson 10-5)

60. $a = 16, b = 63, c = ?$ **65**

61. $b = 3, a = \sqrt{112}, c = ?$ **11**

62. $c = 14, a = 9, b = ?$ **10.72**

63. $a = 6, b = 3, c = ?$ **6.71**

64. $b = \sqrt{77}, c = 12, a = ?$ **8.19**

65. $a = 4, b = \sqrt{11}, c = ?$ **5.20**

66. AVIATION The relationship between a plane's length L in feet and the pounds P its wings can lift is described by $L = \sqrt{kP}$, where k is the constant of proportionality. Find k for this plane to the nearest hundredth. (Lesson 10-4) **0.06**

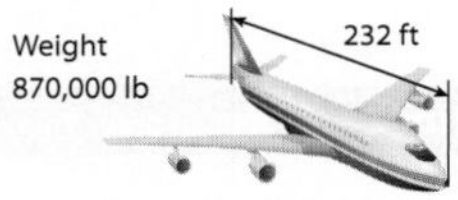

67. FINANCIAL LITERACY A salesperson is paid \$32,000 a year plus 5% of the amount in sales made. What is the amount of sales needed to have an annual income greater than \$45,000? (Lesson 5-3) **The amount of sales must be more than \$260,000.**

Skills Review

Solve each proportion.

68. $\frac{8}{9} = \frac{6}{z}$ **6.75**

69. $\frac{p}{6} = \frac{4}{3}$ **8**

70. $\frac{0.3}{r} = \frac{0.9}{1.7}$ $\mathbf{\frac{17}{30}}$

71. $\frac{0.6}{1.1} = \frac{y}{8.47}$ **4.62**

662 | Lesson 10-6 | Trigonometric Ratios

Differentiated Instruction OL BL

Extension Have students compute the values of sin A, cos A, and tan A for several values of A. Have them make a conjecture about the quotient $\frac{\sin A}{\cos A}$. The value is always tan A.

CHAPTER 10 Study Guide and Review

Study Guide

KeyConcepts

Square Root Functions (Lesson 10-1)

- A square root function contains the square root of a variable.
- The parent function of the family of square root functions is $f(x) = \sqrt{x}$.

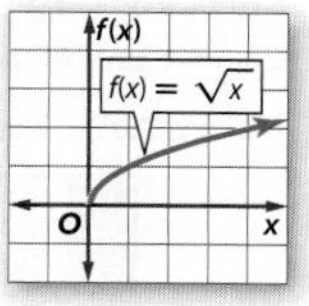

Simplifying Radical Expressions (Lesson 10-2)

- A radical expression is in simplest form when
  - no radicands have perfect square factors other than 1,
  - no radicals contain fractions,
  - and no radicals appear in the denominator of a fraction.

Operations with Radical Expressions and Equations
(Lessons 10-3 and 10-4)

- Radical expressions with like radicals can be added or subtracted.
- Use the FOIL method to multiply radical expressions.

Pythagorean Theorem and Trigonometric Ratios
(Lessons 10-5 and 10-6)

Pythagorean Theorem $c^2 = a^2 + b^2$

$\sin A = \frac{a}{c}$

$\cos A = \frac{b}{c}$

$\tan A = \frac{a}{b}$

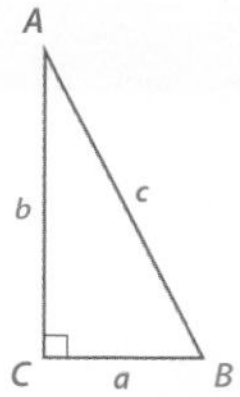

FOLDABLES StudyOrganizer

Be sure the Key Concepts are noted in your Foldable.

KeyVocabulary

conjugate (p. 630)
converse (p. 649)
cosine (p. 656)
Distance Formula (p. 654)
extraneous solution (p. 653)
hypotenuse (p. 648)
inverse cosine (p. 658)
inverse sine (p. 658)
inverse tangent (p. 658)
legs (p. 648)
midpoint (p. 654)
Pythagorean triple (p. 649)
radical equation (p. 642)
radical expression (p. 628)
radical function (p. 621)
radicand (p. 621)
rationalizing the denominator (p. 630)
sine (p. 656)
solving the triangle (p. 657)
square root function (p. 621)
tangent (p. 656)
trigonometric ratio (p. 656)
trigonometry (p. 656)

VocabularyCheck

State whether each sentence is *true* or *false*. If *false*, replace the underlined word, phrase, expression, or number to make a true sentence.

1. A triangle with sides having measures of 3, 4, and 6 is a right triangle. **false; sample answer: 3, 4, and 5**
2. The expressions $12\sqrt{4}$ and $\sqrt{288}$ are equivalent. **false; $12\sqrt{2}$**
3. The expressions $2 + \sqrt{5}$ and $2 - \sqrt{5}$ are conjugates. **true**
4. In the expression $-5\sqrt{2}$, the radicand is 2. **true**
5. The shortest side of a right triangle is the hypotenuse. **false; longest**
6. The cosine of an angle is found by dividing the measure of the side opposite the angle by the hypotenuse. **false; adjacent**
7. The domain of the function $y = \sqrt{x}$ is $\{x \mid x \leq 0\}$. **false; $\{x \mid x \geq 0\}$**
8. After the first step in solving $\sqrt{2x + 4} = x + 5$, you would have $2x + 4 = x^2 + 10x + 25$ **true**
9. The converse of the Pythagorean Theorem is true. **true**
10. The range of the function $y = \sqrt{x}$ is $\{y \mid > 0\}$. **false; $\{y \mid y \geq 0\}$**

Formative Assessment

KeyVocabulary The page reference after each word denotes where that term was first introduced. If students have difficulty answering questions 1–10, remind them that they can use these page references to refresh their memories about the vocabulary terms.

Summative Assessment

Vocabulary Test, p. 48

Vocabulary Review

Vocabulary Review provides students the opportunity to check their understanding of important concepts and terminology in an online game format.

FOLDABLES StudyOrganizer

Dinah Zike's Foldables®

Have students look through the chapter to make sure they have included examples in their Foldables for each lesson of the chapter. Suggest that students keep their Foldables handy while completing the Study Guide and Review pages. Point out that their Foldables can serve as a quick review when studying for the chapter test.

connectED.mcgraw-hill.com 663

Lesson-by-Lesson Review

Intervention If the given examples are not sufficient to review the topics covered by the questions, remind students that the lesson references tell them where to review that topic in their textbooks.

Two-Day Option Have students complete the Lesson-by-Lesson Review. Then you can use McGraw-Hill eAssessment to customize another review worksheet that practices all the objectives of this chapter or only the objectives on which your students need more help.

Additional Answers

11. translated down 3 units; D = $\{x \mid x \geq 0\}$ R = $\{y \mid y \geq 3\}$

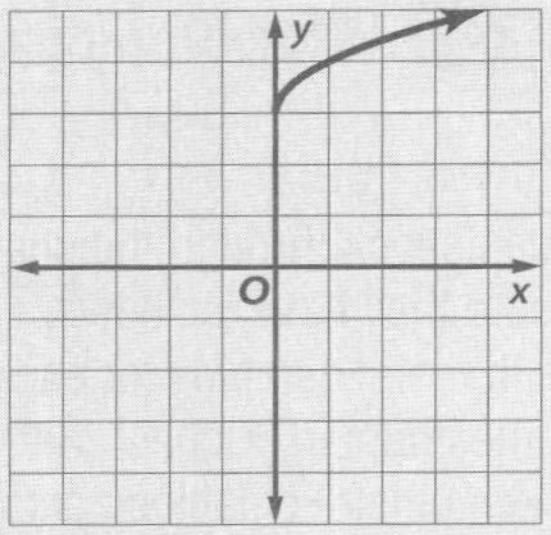

12. translated up 2 units; D = $\{x \mid x \geq 0\}$ R = $\{y \mid y \geq -2\}$

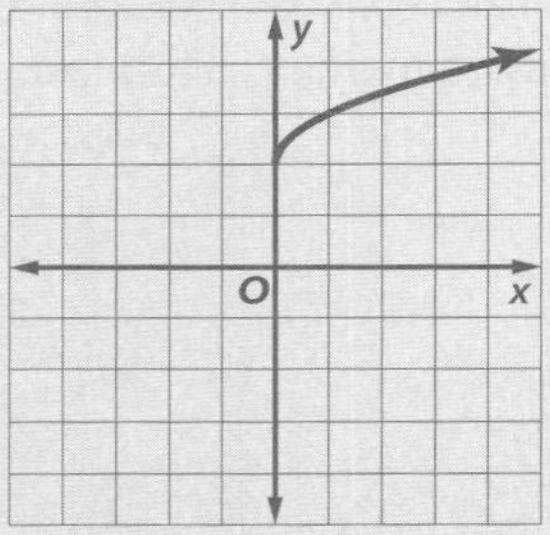

CHAPTER 10

Study Guide and Review *Continued*

Lesson-by-Lesson Review

10-1 Square Root Functions

Graph each function. Compare to the parent graph. State the domain and range. **11–16. See margin.**

11. $y = \sqrt{x} - 3$

12. $y = \sqrt{x} + 2$

13. $y = -5\sqrt{x}$

14. $y = \sqrt{x} - 6$

15. $y = \sqrt{x - 1}$

16. $y = \sqrt{x} + 5$

17. **GEOMETRY** The function $s = \sqrt{A}$ can be used to find the length of a side of a square given its area. Use this function to determine the length of a side of a square with an area of 90 square inches. Round to the nearest tenth if necessary. **9.5 in.**

Example 1

Graph $y = -3\sqrt{x}$. Compare to the parent graph. State the domain and range.

Make a table. Choose nonnegative values for x.

x	0	1	2	3	4
y	0	−3	≈−4.2	≈−5.2	−6

Plot points and draw a smooth curve.

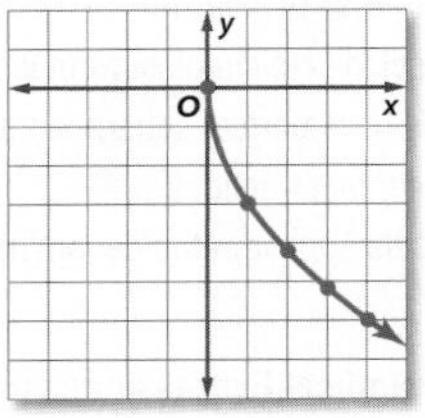

The graph of $y = \sqrt{x}$ is stretched vertically and is reflected across the x-axis.

The domain is $\{x|x \geq 0\}$.

The range is $\{y|y \leq 0\}$.

10-2 Simplifying Radical Expressions

Simplify.

18. $\sqrt{36x^2y^7}$ $6|x|y^3\sqrt{y}$

19. $\sqrt{20ab^3}$ $2b\sqrt{5ab}$

20. $\sqrt{3} \cdot \sqrt{6}$ $3\sqrt{2}$

21. $2\sqrt{3} \cdot 3\sqrt{12}$ 36

22. $(4 - \sqrt{5})^2$ $21 - 8\sqrt{5}$

23. $(1 + \sqrt{2})^2$ $2\sqrt{2} + 3$

24. $\sqrt{\frac{50}{a^2}}$ $\frac{5\sqrt{2}}{|a|}$

25. $\sqrt{\frac{2}{5}} \cdot \sqrt{\frac{3}{4}}$ $\frac{\sqrt{30}}{10}$

26. $\frac{3}{2 - \sqrt{5}}$ $-6 - 3\sqrt{5}$

27. $\frac{5}{\sqrt{7} + 6}$ $\frac{5\sqrt{7} - 30}{-29}$

28. **WEATHER** To estimate how long a thunderstorm will last, use $t = \sqrt{\frac{d^3}{216}}$, where t is the time in hours and d is the diameter of the storm in miles. A storm is 10 miles in diameter. How long will it last? **about 2.15 hours or 2 hours and 9 minutes**

Example 2

Simplify $\frac{2}{4 + \sqrt{3}}$.

$\frac{2}{4 + \sqrt{3}}$ — Original expression

$= \frac{2}{4 + \sqrt{3}} \cdot \frac{4 - \sqrt{3}}{4 - \sqrt{3}}$ — Rationalize the denominator.

$= \frac{2(4) - 2\sqrt{3}}{4^2 - (\sqrt{3})^2}$ — $(a - b)(a + b) = a^2 - b^2$

$= \frac{8 - 2\sqrt{3}}{16 - 3}$ — $(\sqrt{3})^2 = 3$

$= \frac{8 - 2\sqrt{3}}{13}$ — Simplify.

13. stretched vertically and reflected across the x-axis; D = $\{x \mid x \geq 0\}$, R = $\{y \mid y \leq 0\}$

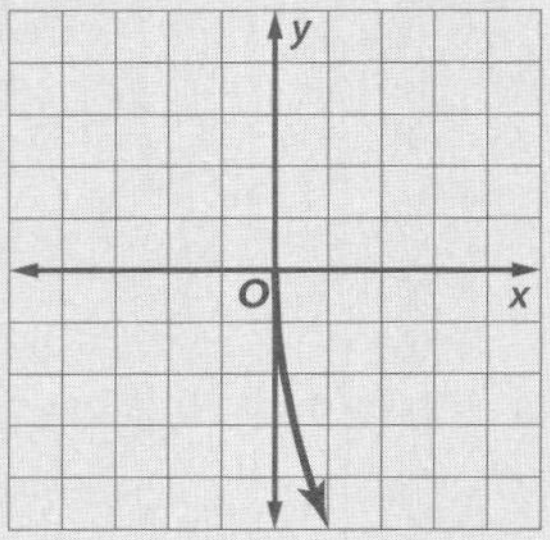

14. translated down 6 units; D = $\{x \mid x \geq 0\}$, R = $\{y \mid y \geq -6\}$

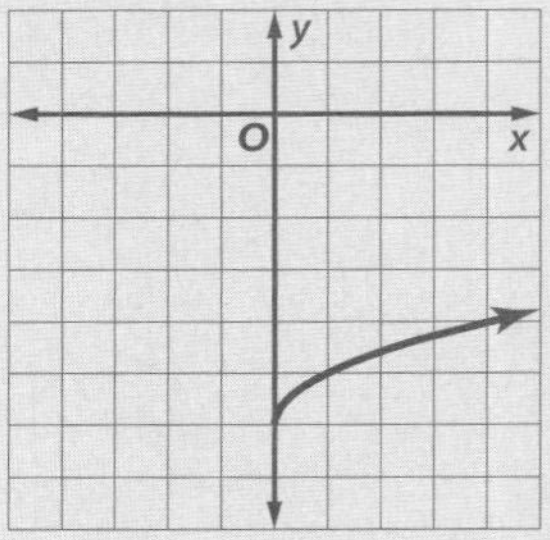

10-3 Operations with Radical Expressions

Simplify each expression.

29. $\sqrt{6} - \sqrt{54} + 3\sqrt{12} + 5\sqrt{3}$ $-2\sqrt{6} + 11\sqrt{3}$

30. $2\sqrt{6} - \sqrt{48}$ $2\sqrt{6} - 4\sqrt{3}$

31. $4\sqrt{3x} - 3\sqrt{3x} + 3\sqrt{3x}$ $4\sqrt{3x}$

32. $\sqrt{50} + \sqrt{75}$ $5\sqrt{2} + 5\sqrt{3}$

33. $\sqrt{2}(5 + 3\sqrt{3})$ $5\sqrt{2} + 3\sqrt{6}$

34. $(2\sqrt{3} - \sqrt{5})(\sqrt{10} + 4\sqrt{6})$ $-2\sqrt{30} + 19\sqrt{2}$

35. $(6\sqrt{5} + 2)(4\sqrt{2} + \sqrt{3})$ $24\sqrt{10} + 8\sqrt{2} + 6\sqrt{15} + 2\sqrt{3}$

36. **MOTION** The velocity of a dropped object when it hits the ground can be found using $v = \sqrt{2gd}$, where v is the velocity in feet per second, g is the acceleration due to gravity, and d is the distance in feet the object drops. Find the speed of a penny when it hits the ground, after being dropped from 984 feet. Use 32 feet per second squared for g. **about 250.95 ft/s**

Example 3

Simplify $2\sqrt{6} - \sqrt{24}$.

$2\sqrt{6} - \sqrt{24} = 2\sqrt{6} - \sqrt{4 \cdot 6}$	Product Property
$= 2\sqrt{6} - 2\sqrt{6}$	Simplify.
$= 0$	Simplify.

Example 4

Simplify $(\sqrt{3} - \sqrt{2})(\sqrt{3} + 2\sqrt{2})$.

$(\sqrt{3} - \sqrt{2})(\sqrt{3} + 2\sqrt{2})$

$= (\sqrt{3})(\sqrt{3}) + (\sqrt{3})(2\sqrt{2}) + (-\sqrt{2})(\sqrt{3}) + (\sqrt{2})(2\sqrt{2})$

$= 3 + 2\sqrt{6} - \sqrt{6} + 4$

$= 7 + \sqrt{6}$

10-4 Radical Equations

Solve each equation. Check your solution.

37. $10 + 2\sqrt{x} = 0$ **no solution**

38. $\sqrt{5 - 4x} - 6 = 7$ -41

39. $\sqrt{a + 4} = 6$ 32

40. $\sqrt{3x} = 2$ $\frac{4}{3}$

41. $\sqrt{x + 4} = x - 8$ 12

42. $\sqrt{3x - 14} + x = 6$ 5

43. **FREE FALL** Assuming no air resistance, the time t in seconds that it takes an object to fall h feet can be determined by $t = \frac{\sqrt{h}}{4}$. If a skydiver jumps from an airplane and free falls for 10 seconds before opening the parachute, how many feet does she free fall? **1600 ft**

Example 5

Solve $\sqrt{7x + 4} - 18 = 5$.

$\sqrt{7x + 4} - 18 = 5$	Original equation
$\sqrt{7x + 4} = 23$	Add 18 to each side.
$(\sqrt{7x + 4})^2 = 23^2$	Square each side.
$7x + 4 = 529$	Simplify.
$7x = 525$	Subtract 4 from each side.
$x = 75$	Divide each side by 7.

CHECK	$\sqrt{7x + 4} - 18 = 5$	Original equation
	$\sqrt{7(75) + 4} - 18 \stackrel{?}{=} 5$	$x = 75$
	$\sqrt{525 + 4} - 18 \stackrel{?}{=} 5$	Multiply.
	$\sqrt{529} - 18 \stackrel{?}{=} 5$	Add.
	$23 - 18 \stackrel{?}{=} 5$	Simplify.
	$5 = 5$ ✓	True.

Additional Answers

15. translated right 1 unit; $D = \{x \mid x \geq 1\}$, $R = \{y \mid y \geq 0\}$

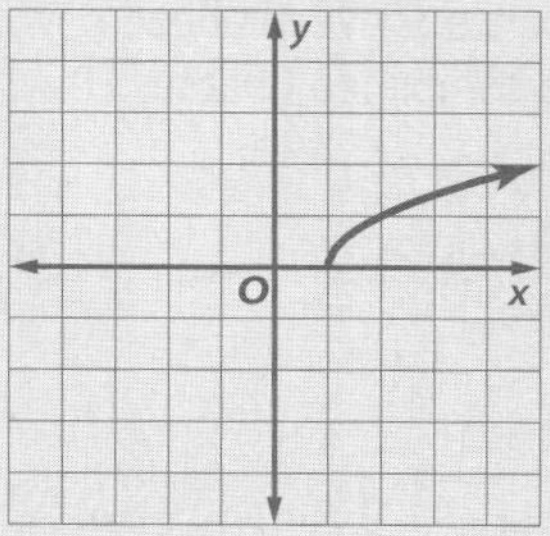

16. translated up 5 units; $D = \{x \mid x \geq 0\}$, $R = \{y \mid y \geq 5\}$

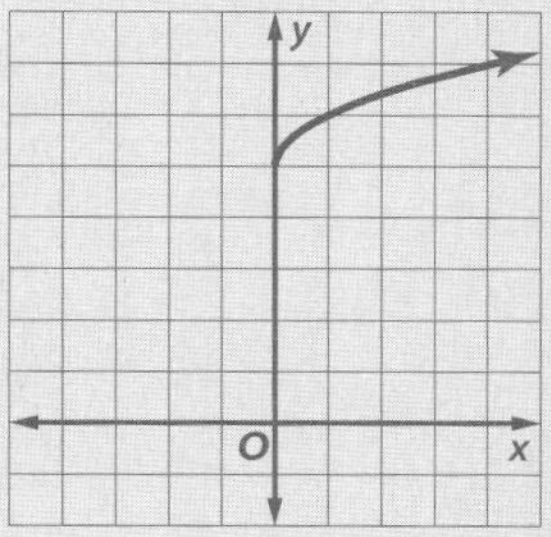

connectED.mcgraw-hill.com 665

Anticipation Guide

Have students complete the Chapter 10 Anticipation Guide and discuss how their responses have changed now that they have completed Chapter 10.

Additional Answers

53. $\cos A = \frac{5}{13}$, $\sin A = \frac{12}{13}$, $\tan A = \frac{12}{5}$

54. $\cos A = \frac{3}{5}$, $\sin A = \frac{4}{5}$, $\tan A = \frac{4}{3}$

CHAPTER 10 Study Guide and Review *Continued*

10-5 The Pythagorean Theorem

Determine whether each set of measures can be the lengths of the sides of a right triangle.

44. 6, 8, 10 **yes**

45. 3, 4, 5 **yes**

46. 12, 16, 21 **no**

47. 10, 12, 15 **no**

48. 2, 3, 4 **no**

49. 7, 24, 25 **yes**

50. 5, 12, 13 **yes**

51. 15, 19, 23 **no**

52. LADDER A ladder is leaning on a building. The base of the ladder is 10 feet from the building, and the ladder reaches up 15 feet on the building. How long is the ladder? **18.0 ft**

Example 6

Determine whether the set of measures 12, 16, and 20 can be the lengths of the sides of a right triangle.

$a^2 + b^2 = c^2$	Pythagorean Theorem
$12^2 + 16^2 \stackrel{?}{=} 20^2$	$a = 12$, $b = 16$, and $c = 20$
$144 + 256 \stackrel{?}{=} 400$	Multiply.
$400 = 400$ ✓	Add.

The measures can be the lengths of the sides of a right triangle.

10-6 Trigonometric Ratios

Find the values of the three trigonometric ratios for angle *A*. **53, 54. See margin.**

53.

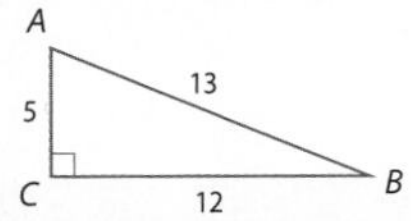

54.

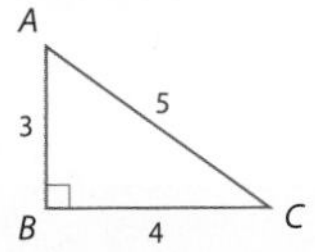

55. RAMPS How long is the ramp? **6 ft**

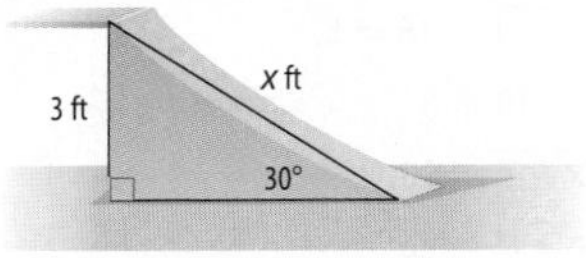

Example 7

Find the values of the three trigonometric ratios for angle *A*.

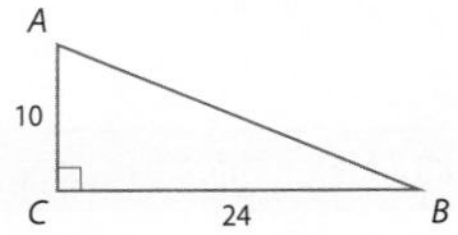

Find the hypotenuse: $c^2 = 10^2 + 24^2$, so $c = 26$.

$$\sin A = \frac{\text{leg opposite } \angle A}{\text{hypotenuse}} = \frac{24}{26} = \frac{12}{13}$$

$$\cos A = \frac{\text{leg adjacent } \angle A}{\text{hypotenuse}} = \frac{10}{26} = \frac{5}{13}$$

$$\tan A = \frac{\text{leg opposite } \angle A}{\text{leg adjacent } \angle A} = \frac{24}{10} = \frac{12}{5}$$

Additional Answers (Practice Test)

1. reflected across the *x*-axis; $D = \{x \mid x \geq 0\}$, $R = \{y \mid y \leq 0\}$

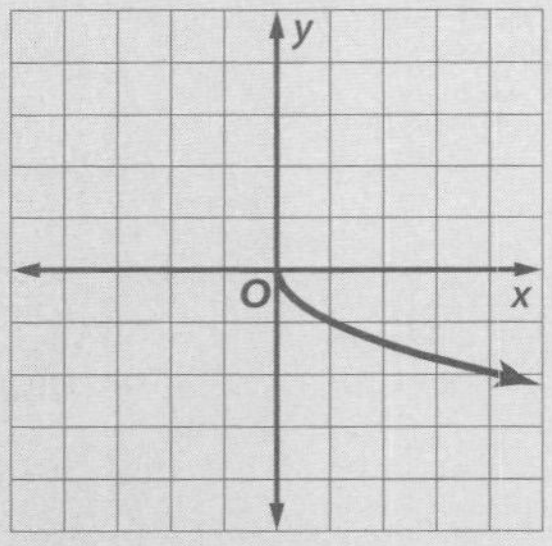

2. compressed vertically; $D = \{x \mid x \geq 0\}$, $R = \{y \mid y \geq 0\}$

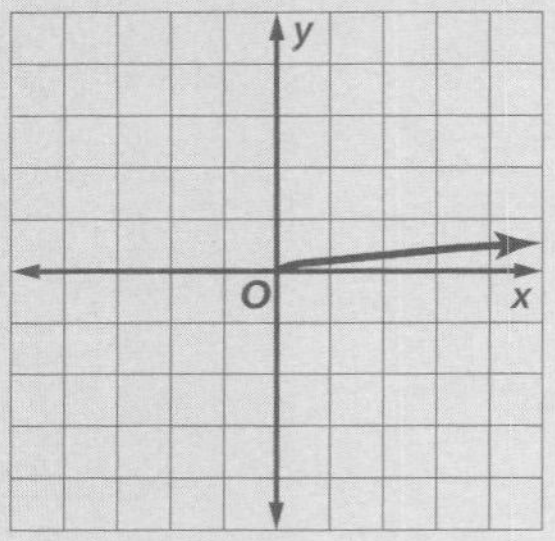

3. translated up 5 units; $D = \{x \mid x \geq 0\}$, $R = \{y \mid y \geq 5\}$

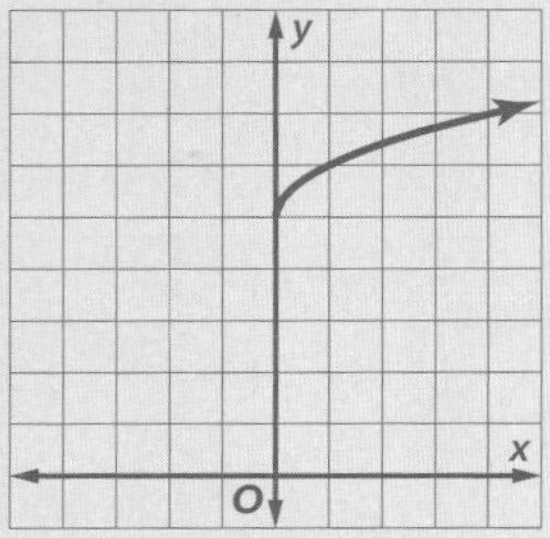

4. translated left 4 units; $D = \{x \mid x \geq -4\}$, $R = \{y \mid y \geq 0\}$

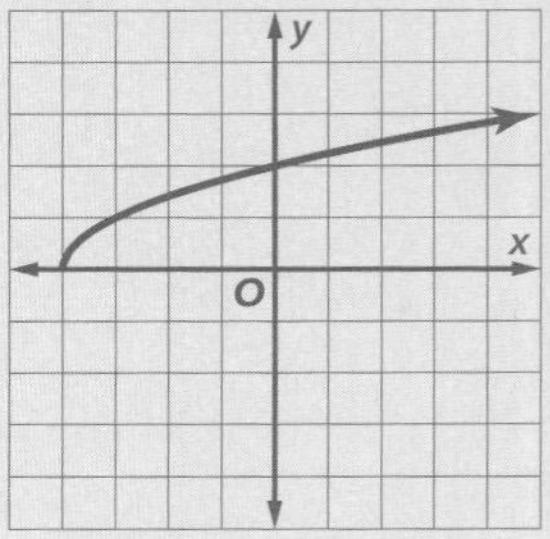

CHAPTER 10 Practice Test

Graph each function, and compare to the parent graph. State the domain and range. 1–4. See margin.

1. $y = -\sqrt{x}$
2. $y = \frac{1}{4}\sqrt{x}$
3. $y = \sqrt{x} + 5$
4. $y = \sqrt{x + 4}$

5. **MULTIPLE CHOICE** The length of the side of a square is given by the function $s = \sqrt{A}$, where A is the area of the square. What is the perimeter of a square that has an area of 64 square inches? C

 A 64 inches

 B 8 inches

 C 32 inches

 D 16 inches

Simplify each expression.

6. $5\sqrt{36}$ 30
7. $\frac{3}{1 - \sqrt{2}}$ $-3 - 3\sqrt{2}$
8. $2\sqrt{3} + 7\sqrt{3}$ $9\sqrt{3}$
9. $3\sqrt{6}(5\sqrt{2})$ $30\sqrt{3}$

10. **MULTIPLE CHOICE** Find the area of the rectangle. H

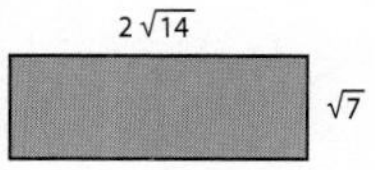

 F $7\sqrt{2}$

 G 14

 H $14\sqrt{2}$

 J $98\sqrt{2}$

Solve each equation. Check your solution.

11. $\sqrt{10x} = 20$ 40
12. $\sqrt{4x - 3} = 6 - x$ 3

13. **PACKAGING** A cylindrical container of chocolate drink mix has a volume of about 162 in^3. The radius of the container can be found by using the formula $r = \sqrt{\frac{V}{\pi h}}$, where r is the radius and h is the height. If the height is 8.25 inches, find the radius of the container. about 2.5 in.

Find each missing length. If necessary, round to the nearest tenth.

14. 10

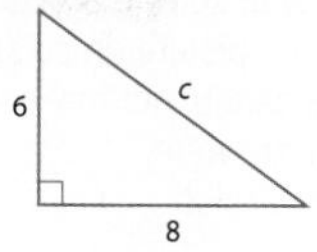

15. 9.2

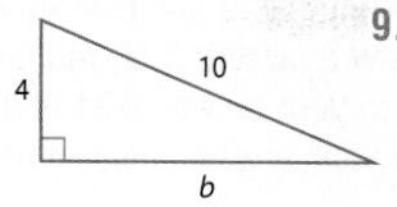

16. **DELIVERY** Ben and Amado are delivering a freezer. The bank in front of the house is the same height as the back of the truck. They set up their ramp as shown. What is the length of the slanted part of the ramp to the nearest foot? 7 ft

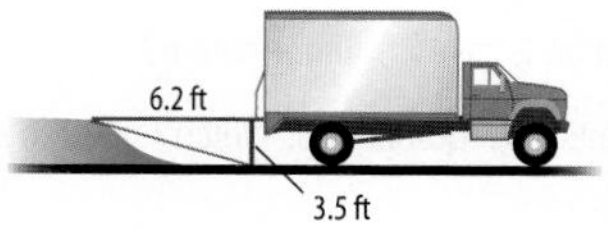

17. Find the values of the three trigonometric ratios for angle A. $\sin A = \frac{4}{5}$, $\cos A = \frac{3}{5}$, $\tan A = \frac{4}{3}$

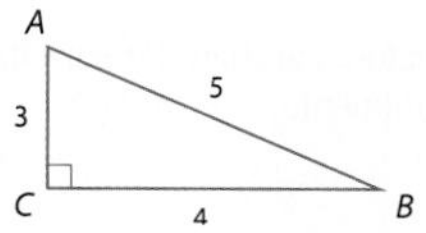

18. Find $m\angle X$ to the nearest degree. 37°

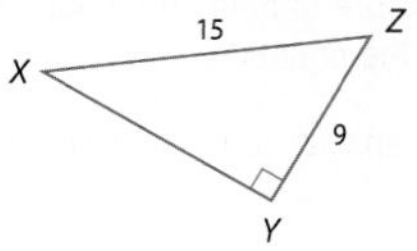

19. **LIGHTHOUSE** How tall is the lighthouse? 128.6 ft

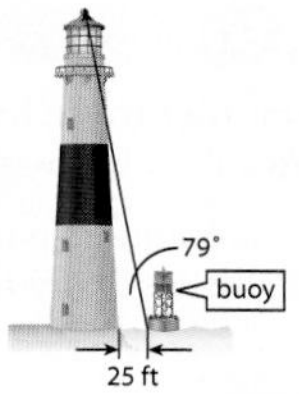

Summative Assessment

Use these alternate leveled chapter tests to differentiate assessment for your students.

Leveled Chapter 10 Tests

Form	Type	Level	Page(s)
1	MC	AL	49–50
2A	MC	OL	51–52
2B	MC	OL	53–54
2C	FR	OL	55–56
2D	FR	OL	57–58
3	FR	BL	59–60
Vocabulary Test			48
Extended-Response Test			61

MC = multiple-choice questions
FR = free-response questions

McGraw-Hill eAssessment Customize and create multiple versions of your chapter tests and their answer keys. All of the questions from the leveled chapter tests in the *Chapter 10 Resource Masters* are also available on McGraw-Hill eAssessment.

InterventionPlanner

Tier 1 On Level OL

If students miss about 25% of the exercises or less,

Then choose a resource:

SE Lessons 10-1, 10-2, 10-3, 10-4, 10-5, and 10-6

Skills Practice, pp. 7, 13, 19, 25, 32, and 39

TE Chapter Project

connectED.mcgraw-hill.com Self-Check Quiz

Tier 2 Strategic Intervention AL
approaching grade level

If students miss about 50% of the exercises,

Then choose a resource:

Study Guide and Intervention, Chapter 10, pp. 5, 11, 17, 23, 30, and 37

Quick Review Math Handbook

connectED.mcgraw-hill.com Extra Examples, Personal Tutor, Homework Help

Tier 3 Intensive Intervention
2 or more grades below level

If students miss about 75% of the exercises,

Then use *Math Triumphs, Alg. 1*

connectED.mcgraw-hill.com Extra Examples, Personal Tutor, Homework Help, Review Vocabulary

1 Focus

Objective Use the strategy of drawing a picture to solve standardized test problems.

2 Teach

Scaffolding Questions

Ask:

- Have you ever drawn a picture to help solve a problem? Answers will vary.
- What kind of information did you include in the picture? Answers will vary.
- Why do you think it is helpful to draw pictures when solving problems? Sample answer: It allows you to see relationships in a different way, which makes it easier to solve the problem.

CHAPTER 10

Preparing for Standardized Tests

Draw a Picture

Sometimes it is easier to visualize how to solve a problem if you draw a picture first. You can sketch your picture on scrap paper or in your test booklet (if allowed). Be careful not make any marks on your answer sheet other than your answers.

Strategies for Drawing a Picture

Step 1

Read the problem statement carefully.

Ask yourself:

- What am I being asked to solve?
- What information is given in the problem?
- What is the unknown quantity for which I need to solve?

Step 2

Sketch and label your picture.

- Draw your picture as clearly and accurately as possible.
- Label the picture carefully. Be sure to include all of the information given in the problem statement.

Step 3

Solve the problem.

- Use your picture to help you model the problem situation with an equation. Then solve the equation.
- Check your answer to make sure it is reasonable.

Standardized Test Example

Read the problem. Identify what you need to know. Then use the information in the problem to solve. Show your work.

An 18-foot ladder is leaning against a building. For stability, the base of the ladder must be 36 inches away from the wall. How far up the wall does the ladder reach?

668 | Chapter 10 | Preparing for Standardized Tests

Read the problem statement carefully. You know the height of the ladder leaning against the building and you know that the base of the ladder must be 36 inches away from the wall. You need to find how far up the wall the ladder reaches.

Scoring Rubric	
Criteria	**Score**
Full Credit: The answer is correct and a full explanation is provided that shows each step.	2
Partial Credit: • The answer is correct, but the explanation is incomplete. • The answer is incorrect, but the explanation is correct.	1
No Credit: Either an answer is not provided or the answer does not make sense.	0

Example of a 2-point response:

First convert all measurements to feet.

36 inches = 3 feet

Use a right triangle to find how high the ladder reaches. Draw and label a triangle to represent the situation.

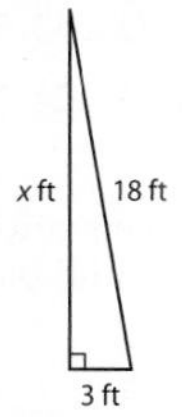

You know the measures of a leg and the hypotenuse, and need to know the length of the other leg. So you can use the Pythagorean Theorem.

$$c^2 = a^2 + b^2$$
$$18^2 = 3^2 + b^2$$
$$324 = 9 + b^2$$
$$315 = b^2$$
$$\pm 315 = b$$
$$17.7 \approx b$$

The ladder reaches about 17.7 feet or about 17 feet 9 inches.

Exercises

Read each problem. Identify what you need to know. Then use the information in the problem to solve. Show your work.

about 86.7 feet

1. A building casts a 15-foot shadow, while a billboard casts a 4.5-foot shadow. If the billboard is 26 feet high, what is the height of the building? Round to the nearest tenth if necessary.

2. A space shuttle is directed toward the Moon, but drifts 1.2° from its intended course. The distance from Earth to the Moon is about 240,000 miles. If the pilot doesn't get the shuttle back on course, how far will the shuttle have drifted from its intended landing position? **about 5027.3 miles**

Additional Example

SHORT RESPONSE Bradley is standing next to a purple martin birdhouse that is on the ground. The bird house casts a shadow that is 2.25 feet long. The Sun is at an elevation of 73°. What is the height of the purple martin bird house? Round to the nearest tenth of a foot.

Sample 2-point response:

Draw and label a right triangle to represent the situation.

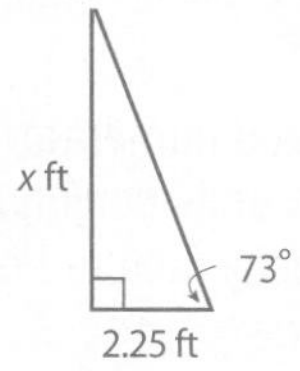

Set up and solve an equation.

$$\tan 73° = \frac{x}{2.25}$$
$$2.25 \tan 73° = x$$
$$7.36 \approx x$$

The purple martin bird house is about 7.4 feet high.

3 Assess

Use Exercises 1 and 2 to assess students' understanding.

connectED.mcgraw-hill.com 669

Diagnose Student Errors

Survey student responses for each item. Class trends may indicate common errors and misconceptions.

1. A error in units translated up from parent graph
B correct
C incorrectly chose positive instead of negative sign to show graph is reflected over *x*-axis
D incorrectly chose positive instead of negative sign to show graph is reflected over *x*-axis and error in units translated up from parent graph

2. F multiplied numerator by $4 + \sqrt{2}$ instead of its conjugate
G incorrectly factored out 2
H correct
J multiplied numerator by $4 + \sqrt{2}$ instead of its conjugate and incorrectly factored out 2

3. A calculation error and added instead of multiplied radicand
B forgot to multiply by $\frac{1}{2}$
C calculation error and added instead of multiplied radicand
D correct

4. F mistakenly divided correct result by 2
G guess
H correct
J guess

5. A correct
B chose measures that are the sides of a right triangle
C chose measures that are the sides of a right triangle
D chose measures that are the sides of a right triangle

6. F error in slope and passes through (4, 0) instead of (4, −4)
G error in slope but passes through (4, −4)
H slope is correct but passes through (0, −4) instead of (4, −4)
J correct

7. A guess or calculation error
B correct
C guess or calculation error
D guess

CHAPTER 10 Standardized Test Practice

Cumulative, Chapters 1 through 10

Multiple Choice

Read each question. Then fill in the correct answer on the answer document provided by your teacher or a sheet of paper.

1. What is the equation of the square root function graphed below? B

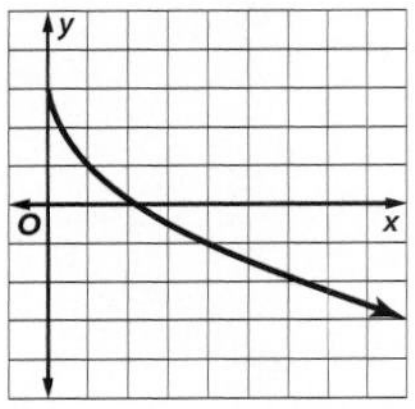

A $y = -2\sqrt{x} + 1$
B $y = -2\sqrt{x} + 3$
C $y = 2\sqrt{x} + 3$
D $y = 2\sqrt{x} + 1$

2. Simplify $\frac{1}{4 + \sqrt{2}}$. H

F $\frac{4 + \sqrt{2}}{14}$
G $\frac{2 - \sqrt{2}}{7}$
H $\frac{4 - \sqrt{2}}{14}$
J $\frac{2 + \sqrt{2}}{7}$

3. What is the area of the triangle below? D

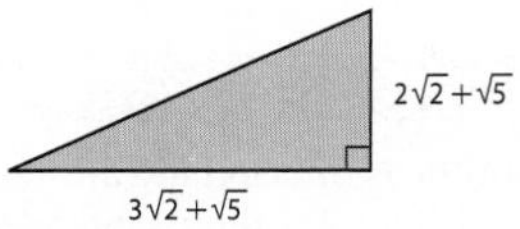

A $3\sqrt{2} + 10\sqrt{5}$
B $17 + 5\sqrt{10}$
C $12\sqrt{2} + 8\sqrt{5}$
D $8.5 + 2.5\sqrt{10}$

4. The formula for the slant height *c* of a cone is $c = \sqrt{h^2 + r^2}$, where *h* is the height of the cone and *r* is the radius of its base. What is the radius of the cone below? Round to the nearest tenth. H

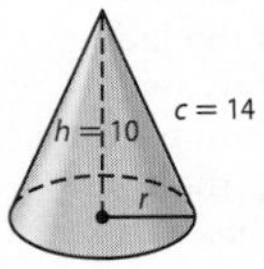

F 4.9
G 6.3
H 9.8
J 10.2

5. Which of the following sets of measures could not be the sides of a right triangle? A

A (12, 16, 24)
B (10, 24, 26)
C (24, 45, 51)
D (18, 24, 30)

6. Which of the following is an equation of the line perpendicular to $4x - 2y = 6$ and passing through (4, −4)? J

F $y = -\frac{3}{4}x + 3$
G $y = -\frac{3}{4}x - 1$
H $y = -\frac{1}{2}x - 4$
J $y = -\frac{1}{2}x - 2$

7. The scale on a map shows that 1.5 centimeters is equivalent to 40 miles. If the distance on the map between two cities is 8 centimeters, about how many miles apart are the cities? B

A 178 miles
B 213 miles
C 224 miles
D 275 miles

Test-Taking Tip
Question 4 Substitute for *c* and *h* in the formula. Then solve for *r*.

Short Response/Gridded Response

Record your answers on the answer sheet provided by your teacher or on a sheet of paper.

8. **GRIDDED RESPONSE** How many times does the graph of $y = x^2 - 4x + 10$ cross the x-axis? **0**

9. Factor $2x^4 - 32$ completely. **$2(x - 2)(x + 2)(x^2 + 4)$**

10. **GRIDDED RESPONSE** In football, a field goal is worth 3 points, and the extra point after a touchdown is worth 1 point. During the 2006 season, John Kasay of the Carolina Panthers scored a total of 100 points for his team by making a total of 52 field goals and extra points. How many field goals did he make? **24**

11. Shannon bought a satellite radio and a subscription to satellite radio. What is the total cost for his first year of service? **$183.87**

Item	Cost
radio	$39.99
subscription	$11.99 per month

12. **GRIDDED RESPONSE** The distance required for a car to stop is directly proportional to the square of its velocity. If a car can stop in 242 meters at 22 kilometers per hour, how many meters are needed to stop at 30 kilometers per hour? **450**

13. The highest point in Kentucky is at an elevation of 4145 feet above sea level. The lowest point in the state is at an elevation of 257 feet above sea level. Write an inequality to describe the possible elevations in Kentucky. **$257 \leq x \leq 4,145$**

14. Simplify the expression below. Show your work.

$$\left(\frac{-2r^{-2}q^5t^2}{5r^4q^2t^{-3}}\right)^{-2}$$

$\frac{25r^{12}}{4q^6t^{10}}$

15. **GRIDDED RESPONSE** For the first home basketball game, 652 tickets were sold for a total revenue of $5216. If each ticket costs the same, how much is the cost per ticket? State your answer in dollars. **$8.00**

Extended Response

Record your answers on a sheet of paper. Show your work.

16. Karen is making a map of her hometown using a coordinate grid. The scale of her map is 1 unit = 2.5 miles.

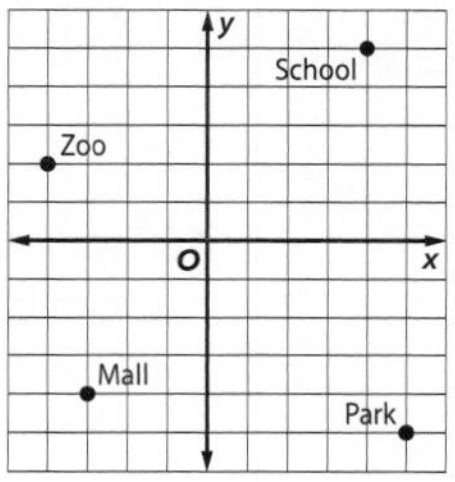

a. Use the Pythagorean Theorem to find the actual distance between Karen's school and the park. Round to the nearest tenth of a mile if necessary. **25.1 mi**

b. Suppose Karen's house is located at (0.5, 0.5). What is farthest from her house, the zoo, the park, the school, or the mall? **the park**

Need ExtraHelp?

If you missed Question...	1	2	3	4	5	6	7	8	9	10	11	12	13	14	15	16
Go to Lesson...	10-1	10-2	10-3	10-4	10-5	4-4	2-6	9-5	8-8	6-4	1-4	3-6	5-4	7-2	2-2	10-5

Formative Assessment

You can use these pages to benchmark student progress.

Standardized Test Practice, pp. 62–64

Answer Sheet Practice

Have students simulate taking a standardized test by recording their answers on a practice recording sheet.

Student Recording Sheet

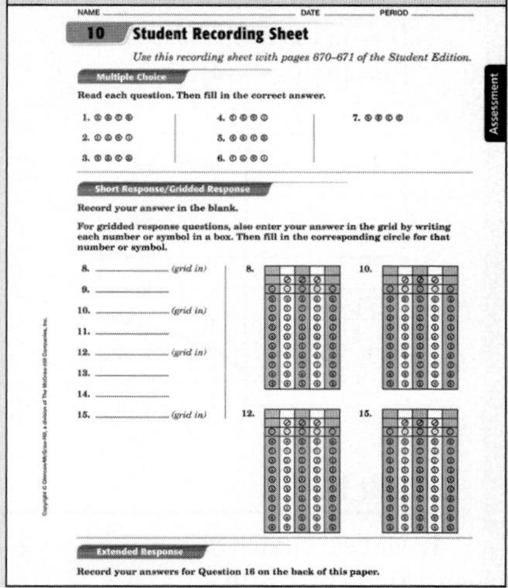
10 Student Recording Sheet

Use this recording sheet with pages 670–671 of the Student Edition.

Multiple Choice

Read each question. Then fill in the correct answer.

Short Response/Gridded Response

Record your answer in the blank.

For gridded response questions, also enter your answer in the grid by writing each number or symbol in a box. Then fill in the corresponding circle for that number or symbol.

Extended Response

Record your answers for Question 16 on the back of this paper.

McGraw-Hill eAssessment Create practice tests that align to your state standards, the Common Core State Standards, and other national standards such as TIMSS and NAEP.

Homework Option

Get Ready for Chapter 11 Assign students the exercises on p. 673 as homework to assess whether they possess the prerequisite skills needed for the next chapter.

Lesson 10-1 (Guided Practice)

2A. stretched vertically and reflected across the x-axis; $D = \{x \mid x \geq 0\}$, $R = \{y \mid y \leq 0\}$

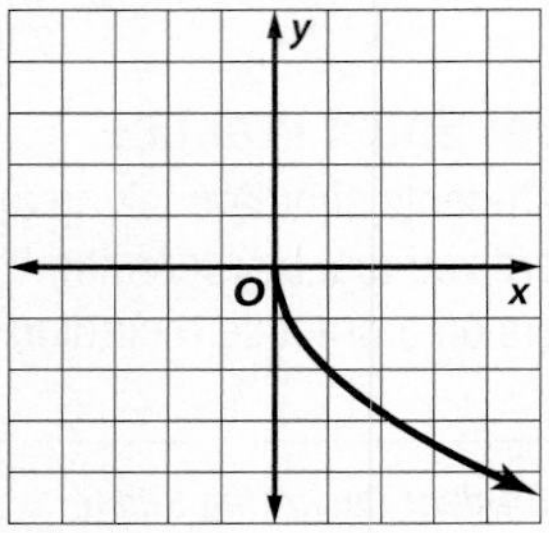

2B. stretched vertically and reflected across the x-axis; $D = \{x \mid x \geq 0\}$, $R = \{y \mid y \leq 0\}$

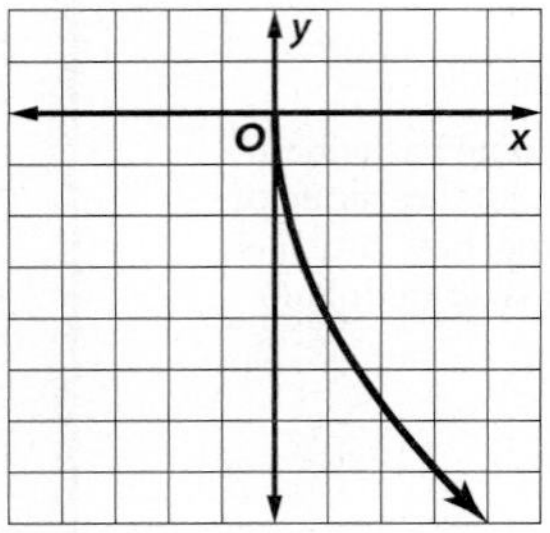

3A. translated down 4 units; $D = \{x \mid x \geq 0\}$, $R = \{y \mid y \geq -4\}$

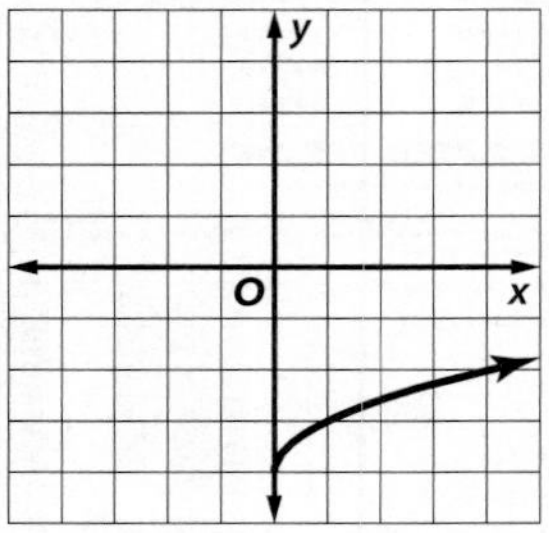

3B. translated left 3 units; $D = \{x \mid x \geq -3\}$, $R = \{y \mid y \geq 0\}$

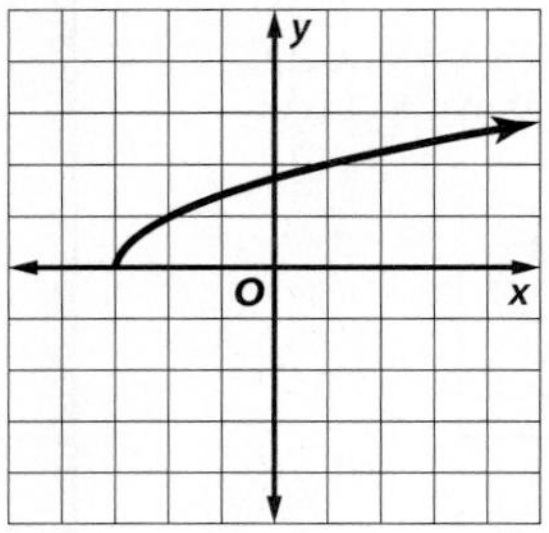

Lesson 10-1

1. vertical stretch of $y = \sqrt{x}$; $D = \{x \mid x \geq 0\}$, $R = \{y \mid y \geq 0\}$

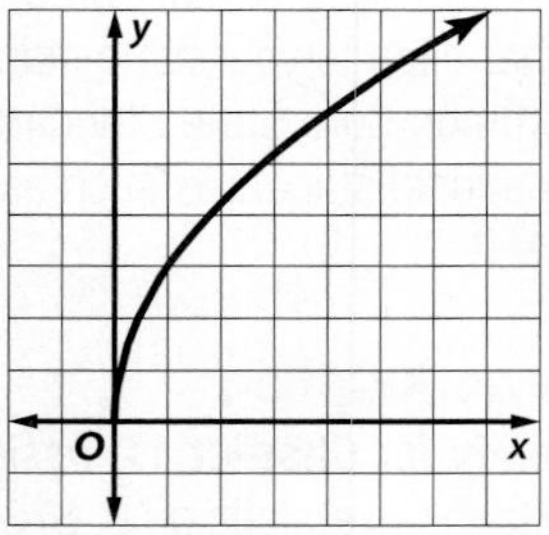

2. vertical stretch of $y = \sqrt{x}$ and a reflection across the x-axis; $D = \{x \mid x \leq 0\}$, $R = \{y \mid y \leq 0\}$

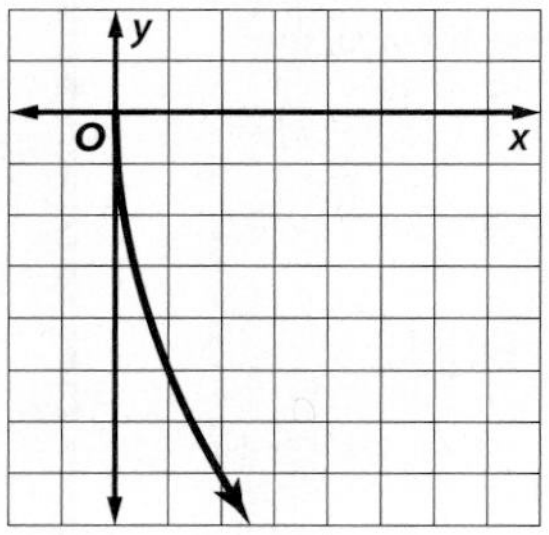

3. vertical compression of $y = \sqrt{x}$; $D = \{x \mid x \geq 0\}$, $R = \{y \mid y \geq 0\}$

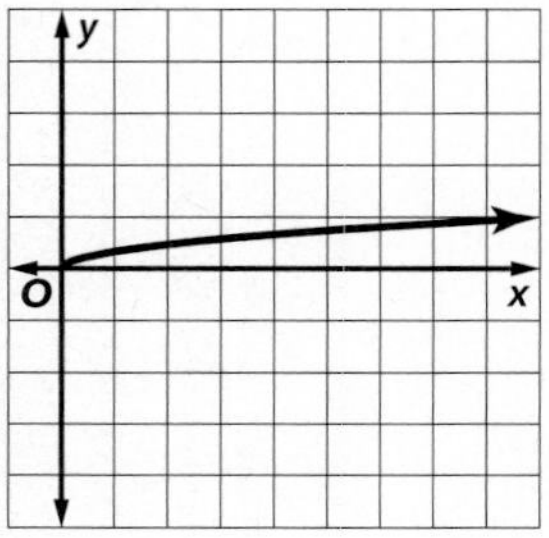

4. vertical compression of $y = \sqrt{x}$ and a reflection across the x-axis; $D = \{x \mid x \geq 0\}$; $R = \{y \mid y \leq 0\}$

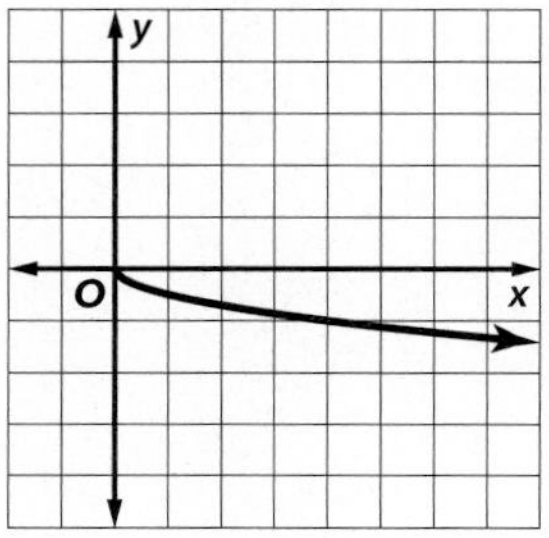

5. translated up 3 units; $D = \{x \mid x \geq 0\}$, $R = \{y \mid y \geq 3\}$

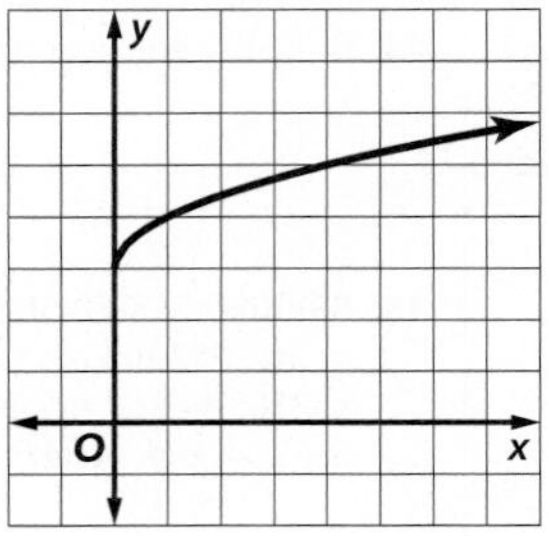

6. translated down 2 units; $D = \{x \mid x \geq 0\}$, $R = \{y \mid y \geq -2\}$

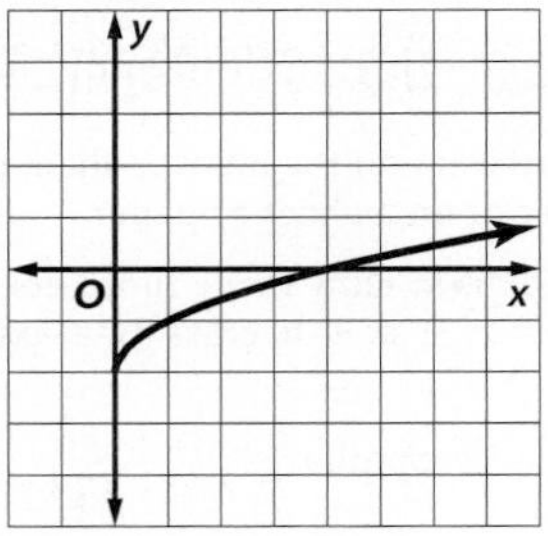

7. translated left 2 units; $D = \{x \mid x \geq -2\}$, $R = \{y \mid y \geq 0\}$

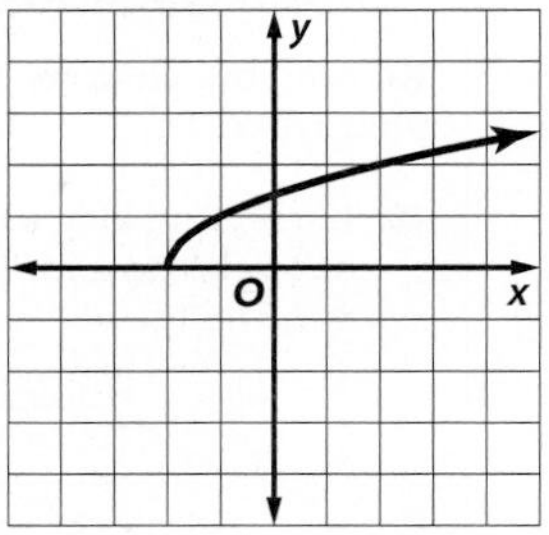

8. translated right 3 units; $D = \{x \mid x \geq 3\}$, $R = \{y \mid y \geq 0\}$

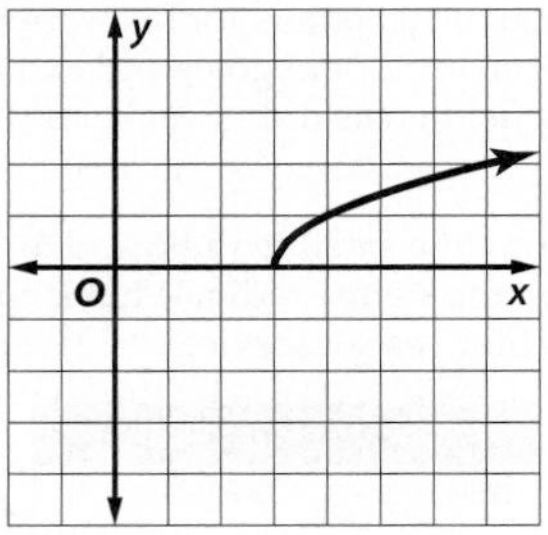

10. vertical compression of $\sqrt{x}$ and translated up 2 units; $D = \{x \mid x \geq 0\}$, $R = \{y \mid y \geq 2\}$

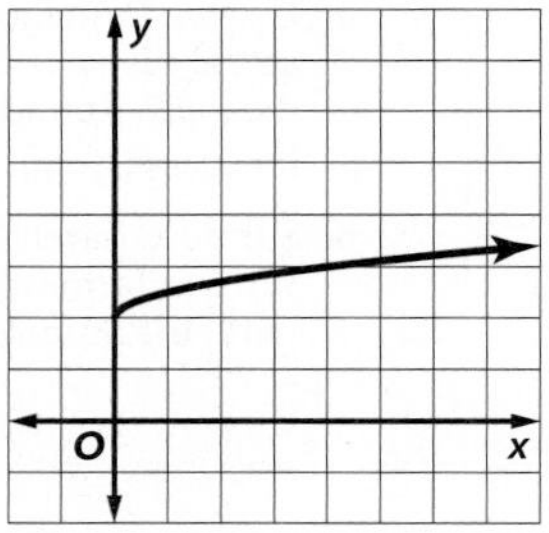

11. vertical compression of $\sqrt{x}$, and reflected across the x-axis and translated down 1 unit; $D = \{x \mid x \geq 0\}$, $R = \{y \mid y \leq -1\}$

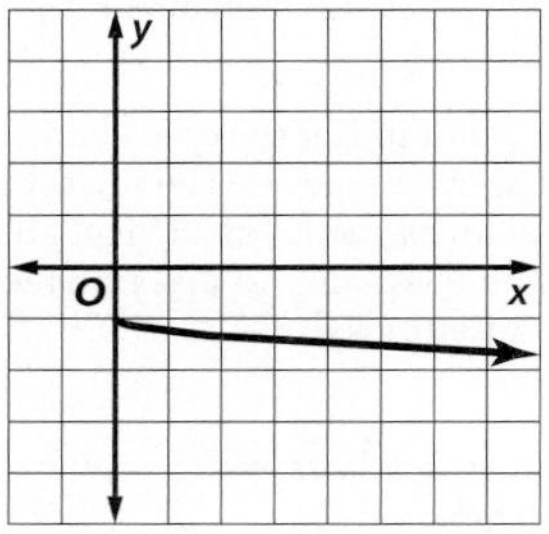

12. translated left 1 unit, vertical stretch and reflected across x-axis; $D = \{x \mid x \geq -1\}$, $R = \{y \mid y \leq 0\}$

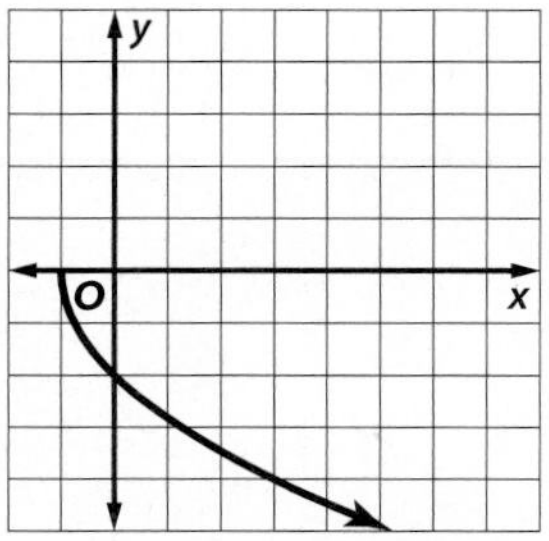

13. translated right 2 units and vertical stretch of $\sqrt{x}$; $D = \{x \mid x \geq 2\}$, $R = \{y \mid y \geq 0\}$

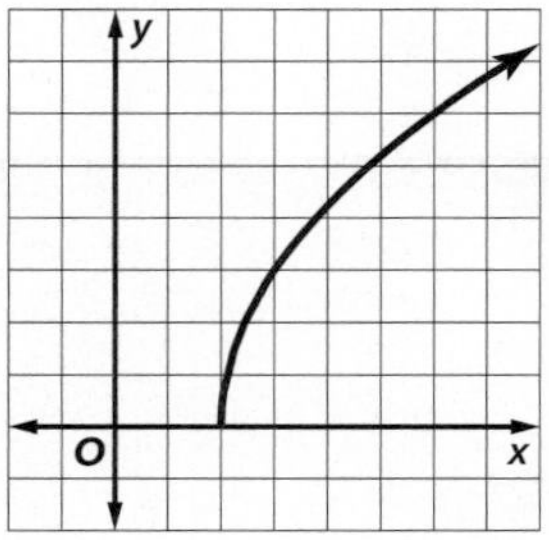

14. vertical stretch of $\sqrt{x}$;
$D = \{x \mid x \geq 0\}$,
$R = \{y \mid y \geq 0\}$

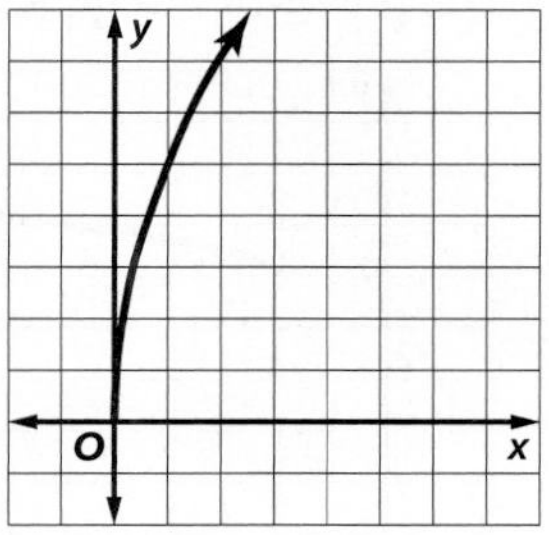

15. vertical compression of $\sqrt{x}$;
$D = \{x \mid x \geq 0\}$,
$R = \{y \mid y \geq 0\}$

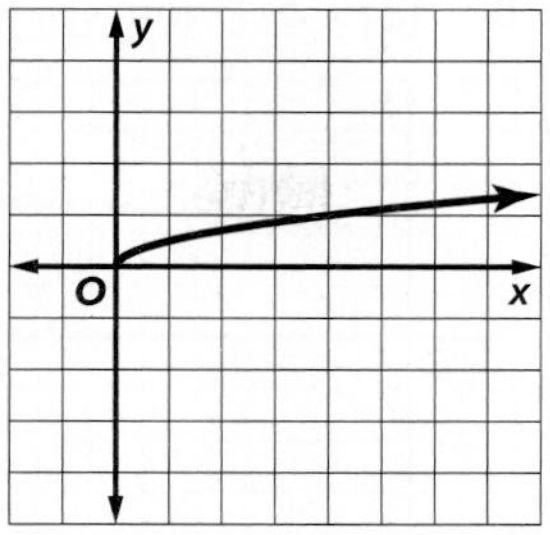

16. vertical compression of $\sqrt{x}$ and reflected across the x-axis; $D = \{x \mid x \geq 0\}$,
$R = \{y \mid y \leq 0\}$

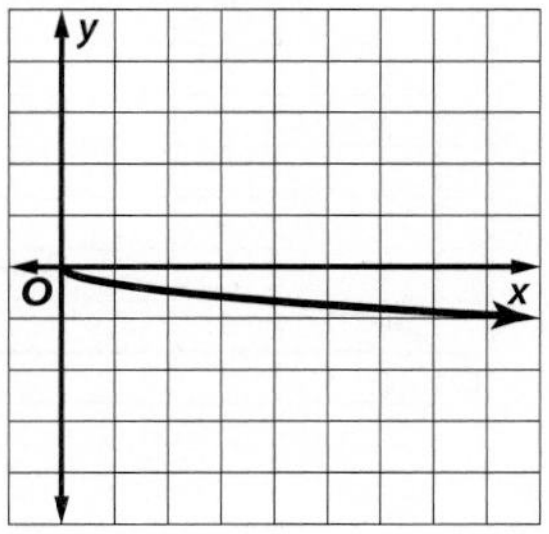

17. vertical stretch of $\sqrt{x}$;
$D = \{x \mid x \geq 0\}$,
$R = \{y \mid y \geq 0\}$

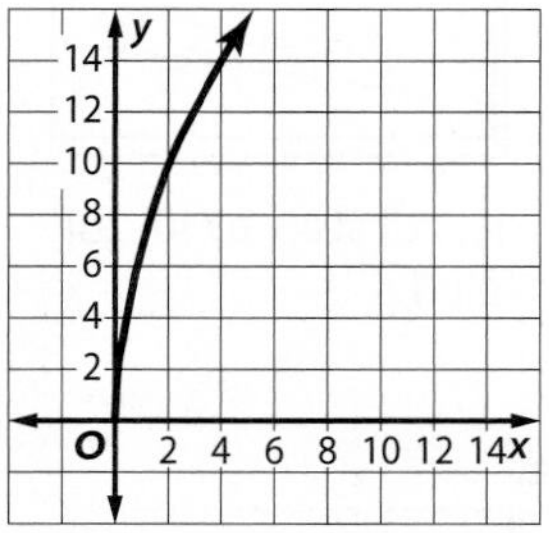

18. vertical compression of $\sqrt{x}$ and reflected across the x-axis; $D = \{x \mid x \geq 0\}$,
$R = \{y \mid y \leq 0\}$

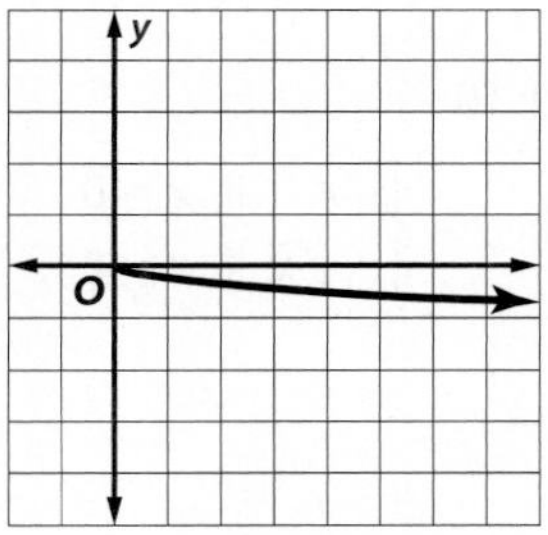

19. reflected across the x-axis;
$D = \{x \mid x \geq 0\}$,
$R = \{y \mid y \leq 0\}$

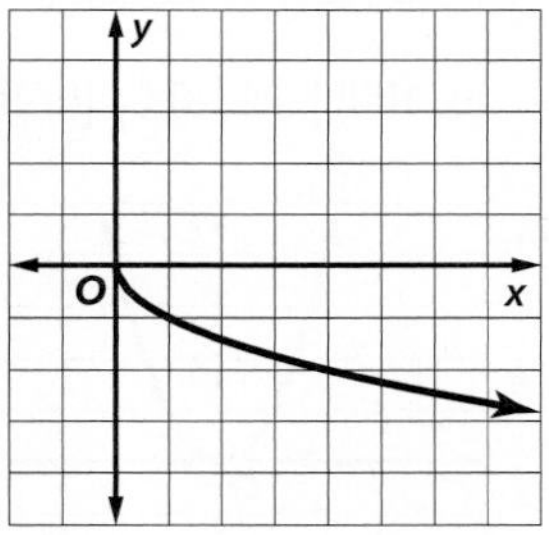

20. vertical compression of $\sqrt{x}$ and reflected across x-axis;
$D = \{x \mid x \geq 0\}$,
$R = \{y \mid y \leq 0\}$

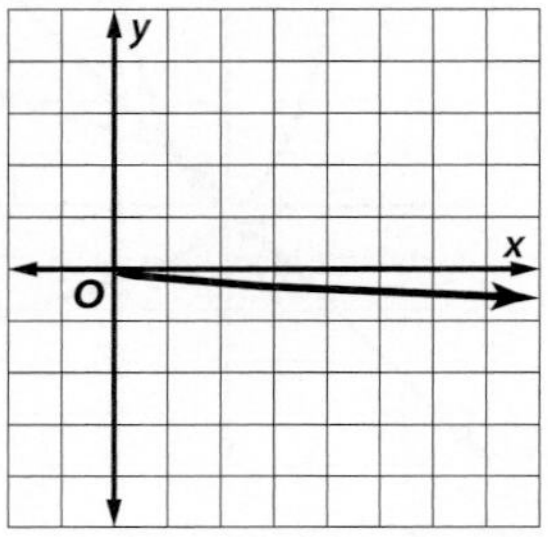

21. vertical stretch of $\sqrt{x}$ and reflected across the x-axis;
$D = \{x \mid x \geq 0\}$,
$R = \{y \mid y \leq 0\}$

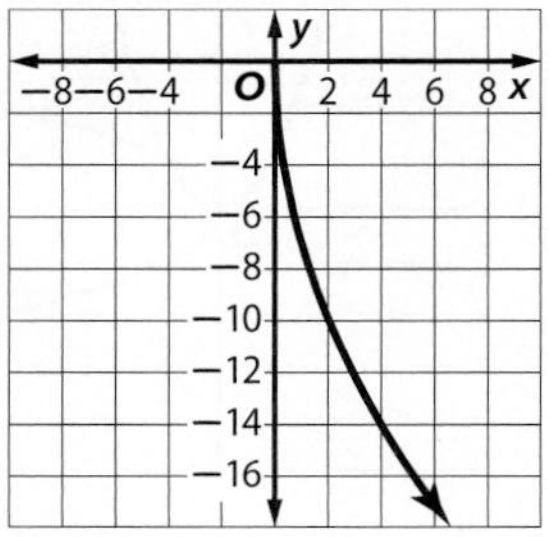

22. translated up 2 units;
$D = \{x \mid x \geq 0\}$,
$R = \{y \mid y \geq 2\}$

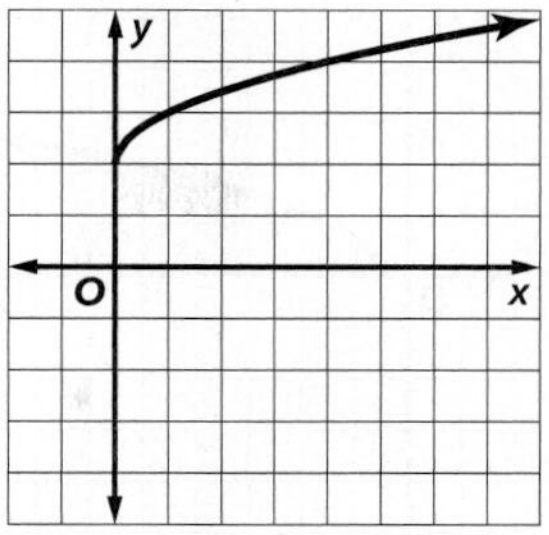

23. translated up 4 units;
$D = \{x \mid x \geq 0\}$,
$R = \{y \mid y \geq 4\}$

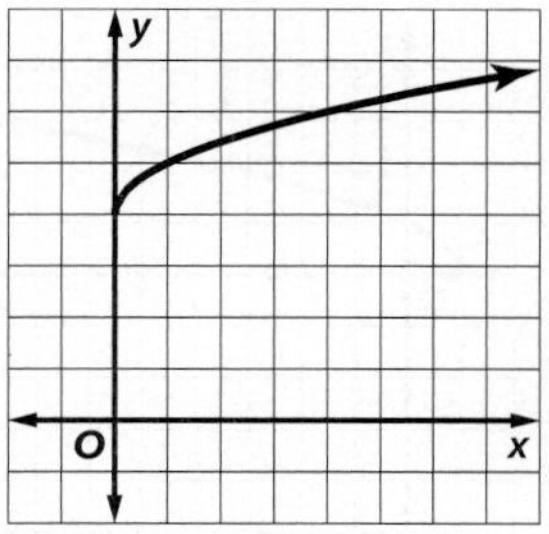

24. translated down 1 unit;
$D = \{x \mid x \geq 0\}$,
$R = \{y \mid y \geq -1\}$

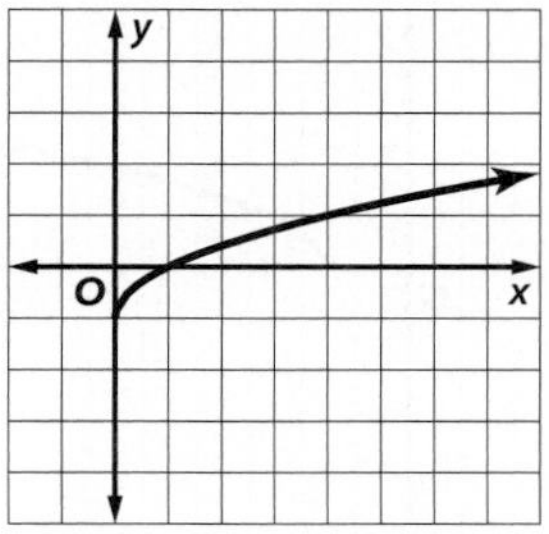

25. translated down 3 units;
$D = \{x \mid x \geq 0\}$,
$R = \{y \mid y \geq -3\}$

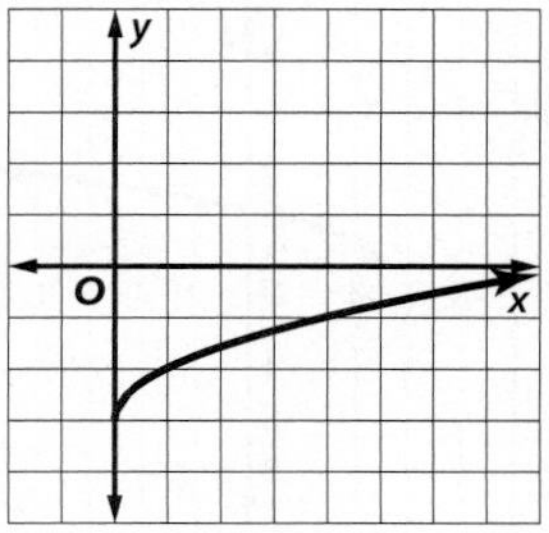

26. translated up 1.5 units;
$D = \{x \mid x \geq 0\}$,
$R = \{y \mid y \geq 1.5\}$

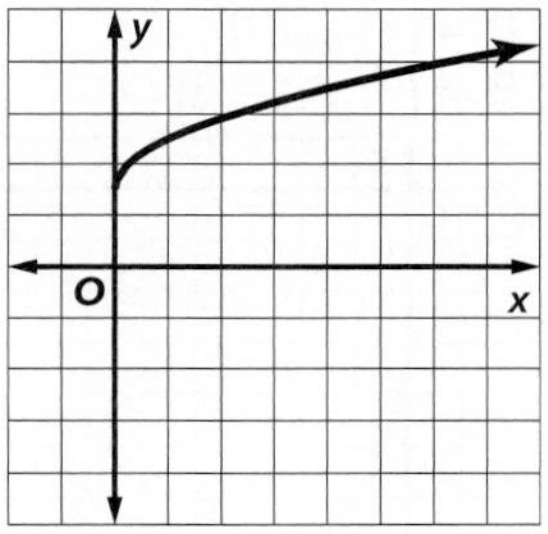

27. translated down 2.5 units;
$D = \{x \mid x \geq 0\}$,
$R = \{y \mid y \geq -2.5\}$

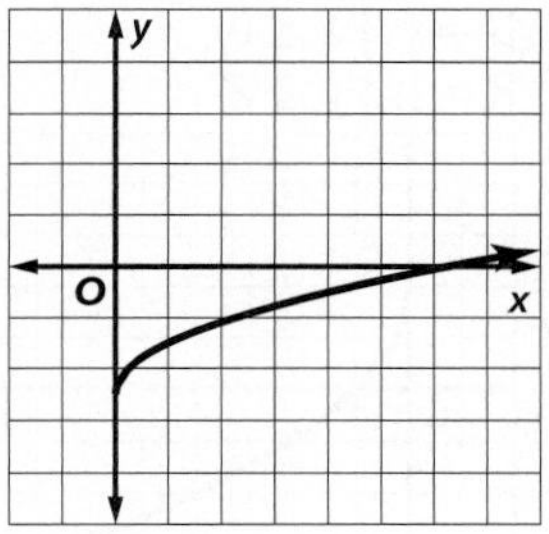

28. translated left 4 units;
$D = \{x \mid x \geq -4\}$,
$R = \{y \mid y \geq 0\}$

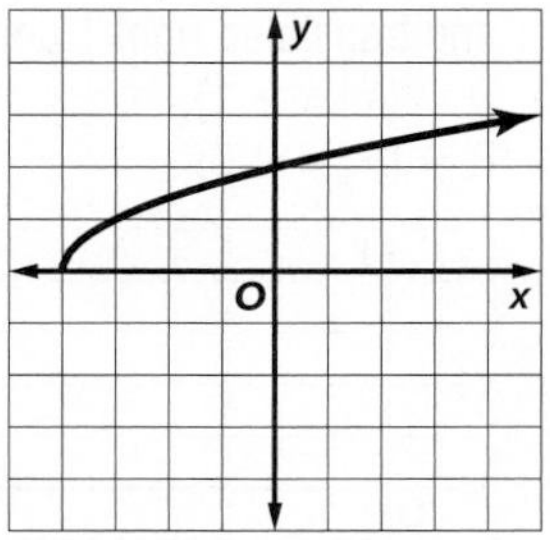

29. translated right 4 units;
$D = \{x \mid x \geq 4\}$,
$R = \{y \mid y \geq 0\}$

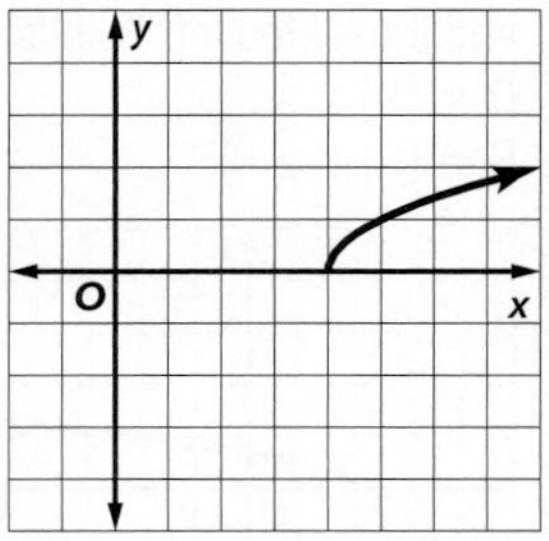

30. translated left 1 unit; D = {x | $x \geq -1$}, R = {y | $y \geq 0$}

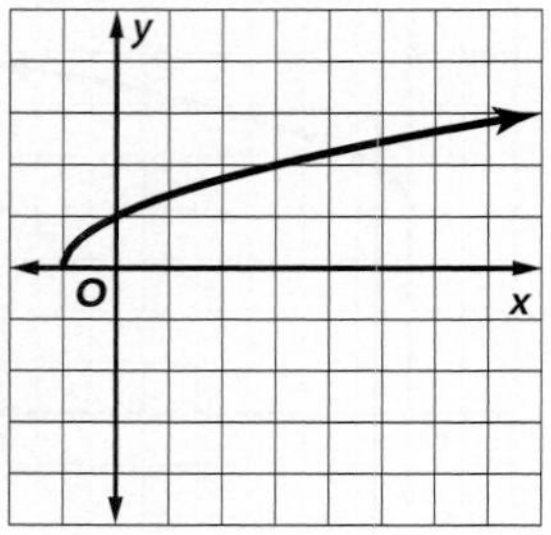

31. translated right 0.5 unit; D = {x | $x \geq 0.5$}, R = {y | $y \geq 0$}

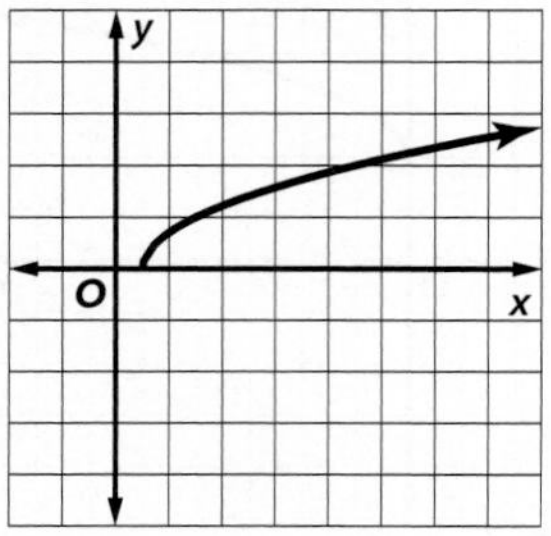

32. translated left 5 units; D = {x | $x \geq -5$}, R = {y | $y \geq 0$}

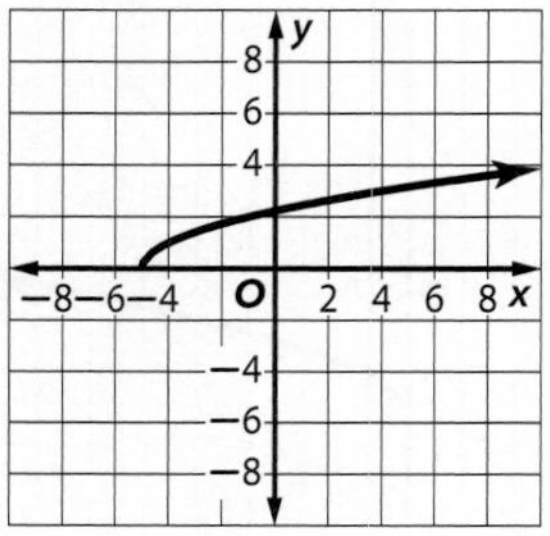

33. translated right 1.5 units; D = {x | $x \geq 1.5$}, R = {y | $y \geq 0$}

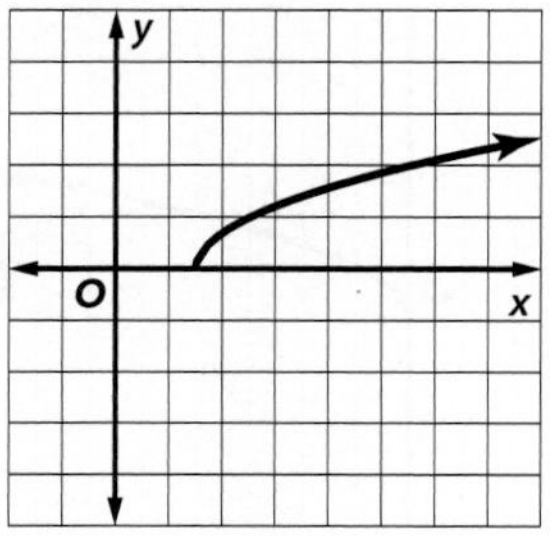

35. vertical stretch of $y = \sqrt{x}$, reflected across the x-axis, and translated up 2 units; D = {x | $x \geq 0$}, R = {y | $y \leq 2$}

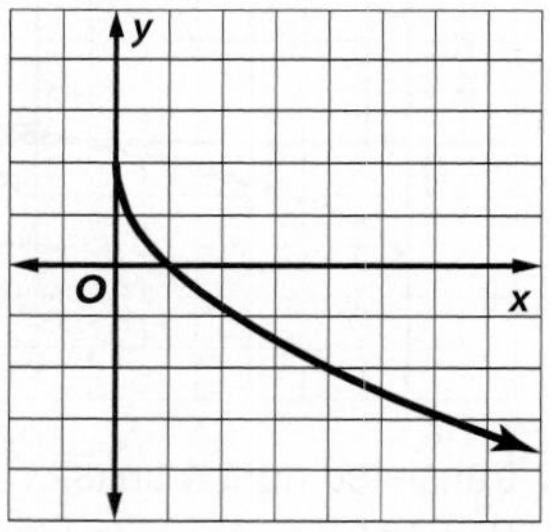

36. vertical stretch of $y = \sqrt{x}$, reflected across the x-axis, and translated down 2 units; D = {x | $x \geq 0$}, R = {y | $y \leq -3$}

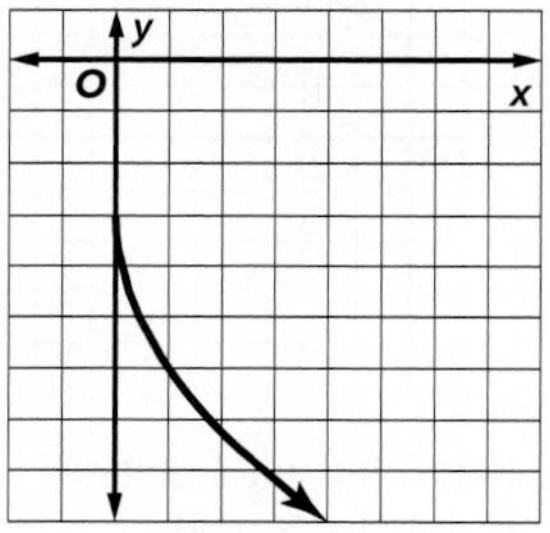

37. vertical compression of $y = \sqrt{x}$ and translated left 2 units; D = {x | $x \geq -2$}, R = {y | $y \geq 0$}

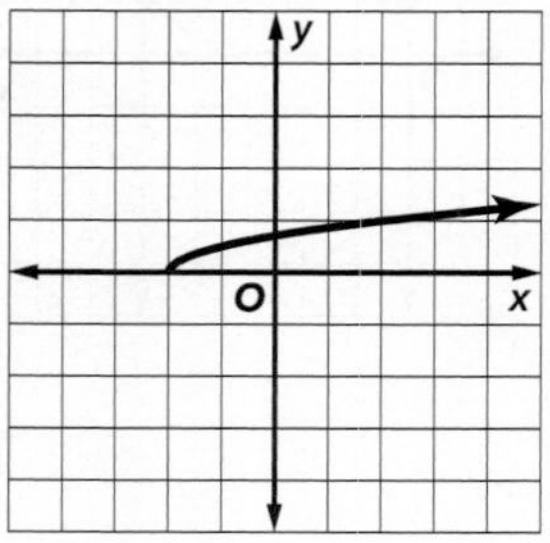

38. reflected across the x-axis and translated right 1 unit; D = {x | $x \geq 1$}, R = {y | $y \leq 0$}

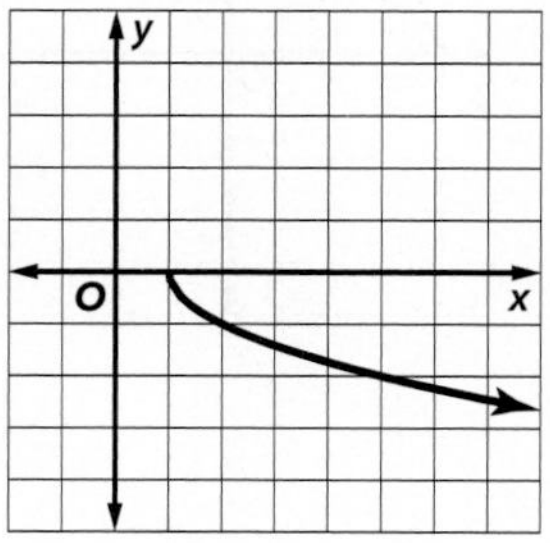

39. vertical compression of $y = \sqrt{x}$ and translated up 2 units and right 1 unit; D = {x | $x \geq 1$}, R = {y | $y \geq 2$}

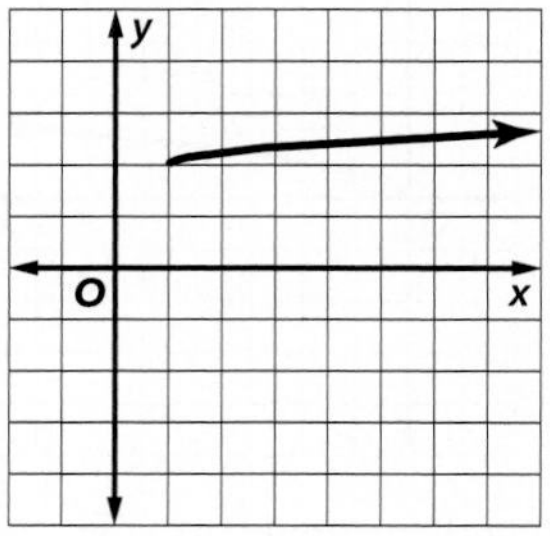

40. vertical compression of $y = \sqrt{x}$ and translated up 1 unit and right 2 units; D = {x | $x \geq 2$}, R = {y | $y \geq 1$}

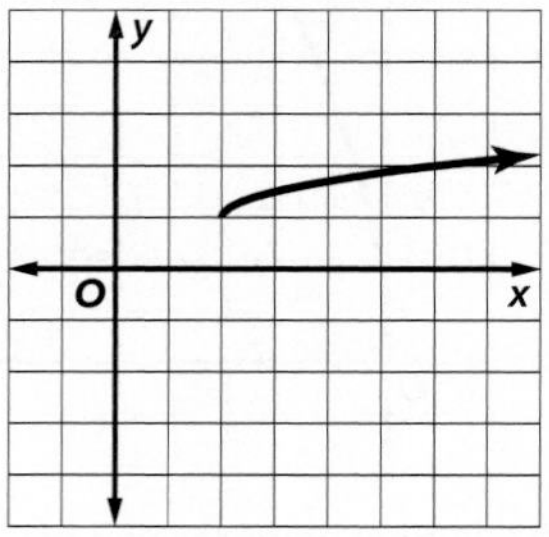

41.

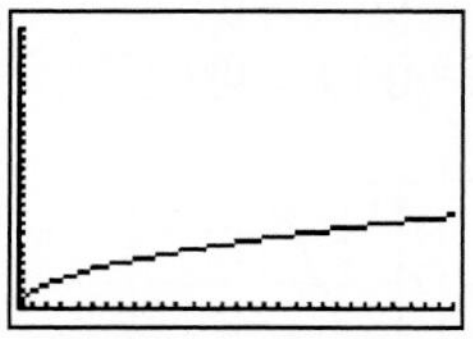

[0, 28] scl: 1 by [0, 28] scl: 1

42a.

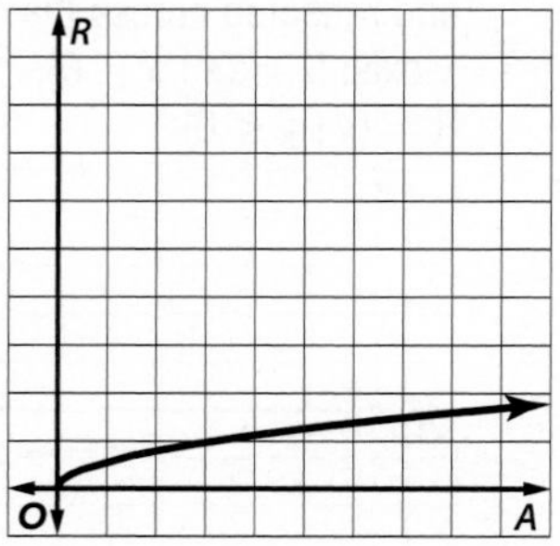

43a.

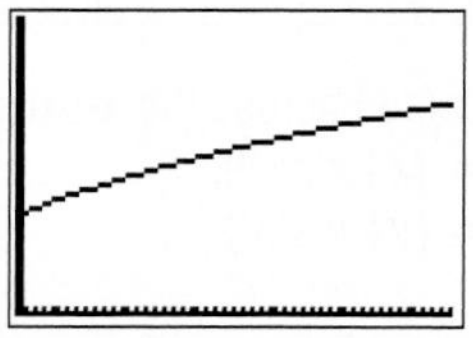

[0, 1000] scl: 20 by [0, 1000] scl: 10

44a.

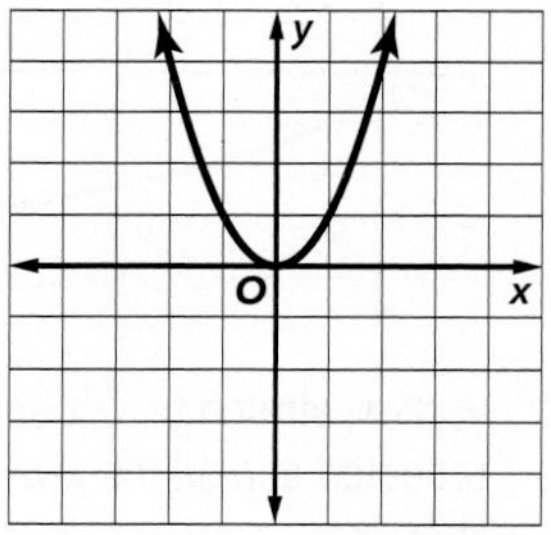

44b. $y = \begin{cases} \sqrt{x} & \text{if } x \geq 0 \\ -\sqrt{x} & \text{if } x \geq 0 \end{cases}$

44c.

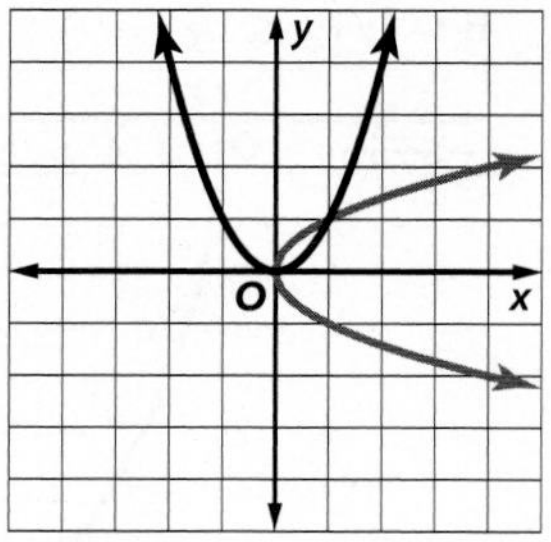

44d.

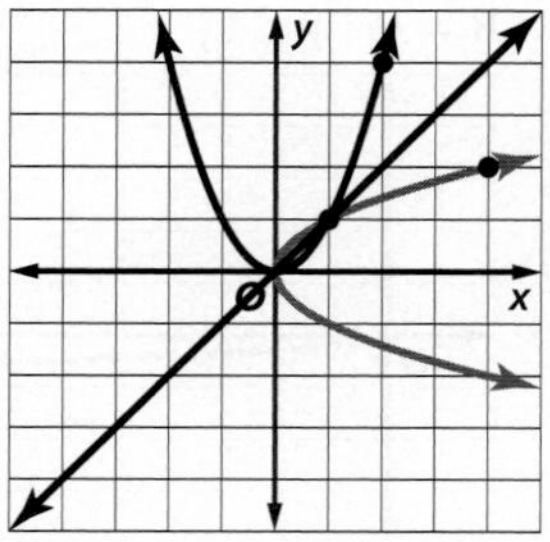

44e. The combined graphs of the square root functions are the same size and shape as the parabola. It is a reflection in the line $y = x$.

45. False; sample answer: The domain of $y = \sqrt{x + 3}$ includes -1, -2, and -3.

46. False; sample answer: -6 and -5 are in the range of $y = \sqrt{x} - 6$.

47. Sample answer: The domain is limited because square roots of negative numbers are imaginary; therefore the radicand must be nonnegative. Since the principal square root of a nonnegative number is a nonnegative number, the range will be nonnegative.

49. $y = \sqrt{x} + 3$; it is a translation of $y = \sqrt{x}$; the other equations represent vertical streches or compressions.

51. The value of a is negative. For the function to have negative y-values, the value of a must be negative.

52. Both functions are translations of the square root function, but $f(x) = \sqrt{x} + 2$ is a translation 2 units up and $g(x) = \sqrt{x + 2}$ is a translation 2 units to the left.

57.

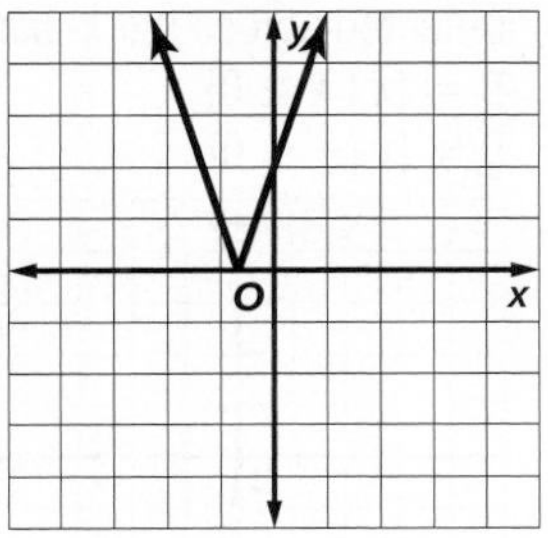

58.

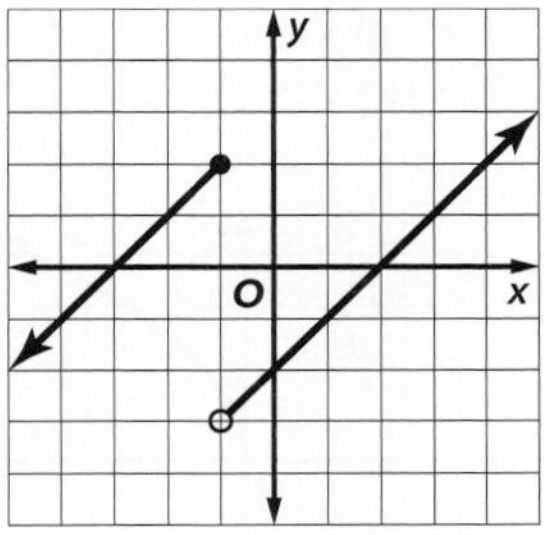

59.

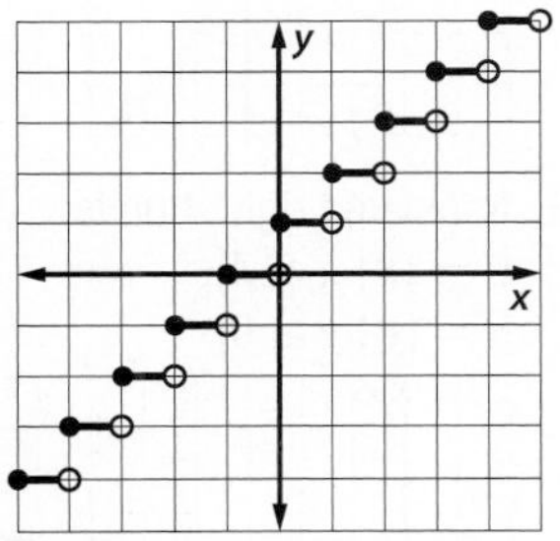

60.

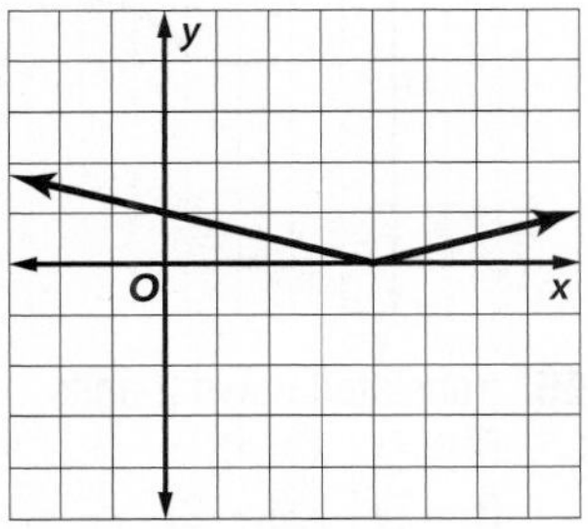

65a.

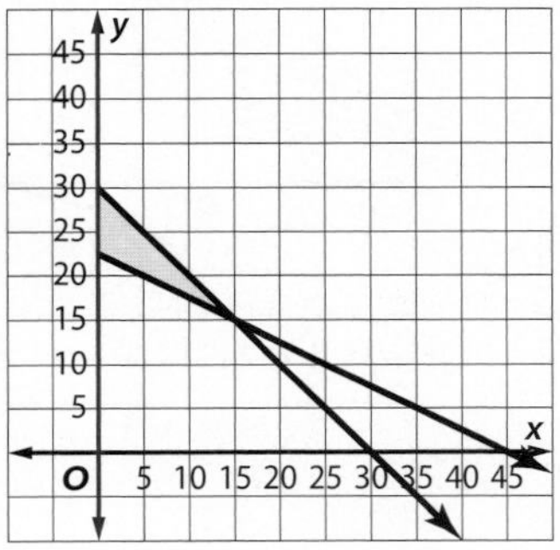

65b. Sample answer: walk: 15 min, jog: 15 min; walk: 10 min, jog: 18 min; walk: 5 min, jog: 23 min

Extend 10-1

1. $\{x \mid x \geq 1\}$, $\{y \mid y \geq 0\}$; moved right 1 unit

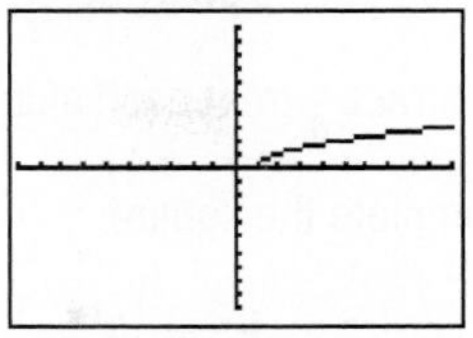

[−10, 10] scl: 1 by [−10, 10] scl: 1

2. $\{x \mid x \geq -3\}$, $\{y \mid y \geq 0\}$; moved left 3 units

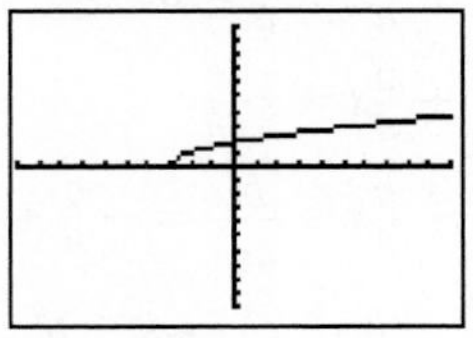

[−10, 10] scl: 1 by [−10, 10] scl: 1

3. $\{x \mid x \geq 0\}$, $\{y \mid y \geq -2\}$; moved down 2 units

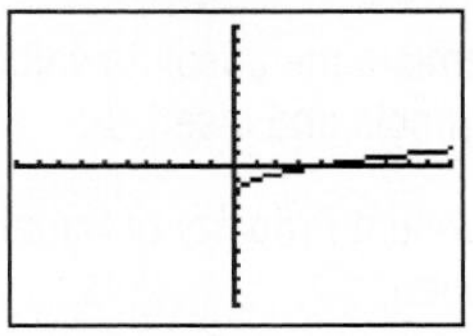

[−10, 10] scl: 1 by [−10, 10] scl: 1

4. $\{x \mid x \leq 0\}$, $\{y \mid y \geq 0\}$; reflected over y-axis

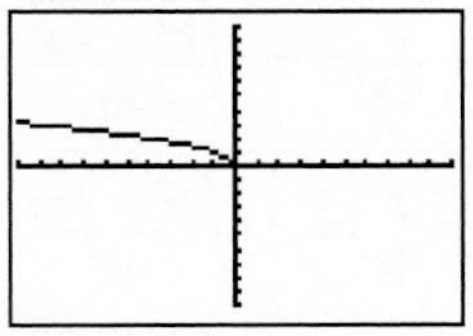

[−10, 10] scl: 1 by [−10, 10] scl: 1

5. $\{x \mid x \geq 0\}$, $\{y \mid y \leq 0\}$; reflected across x-axis

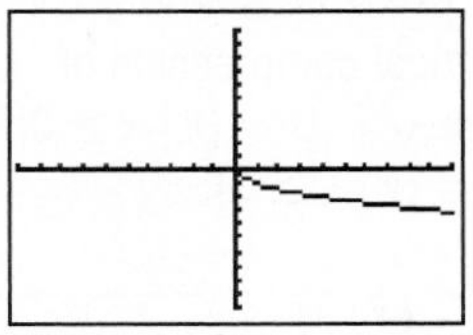

[−10, 10] scl: 1 by [−10, 10] scl: 1

6. $\{x \mid x \geq 0\}$, $\{y \mid y \geq 0\}$; vertical stretch of $y = \sqrt{x}$

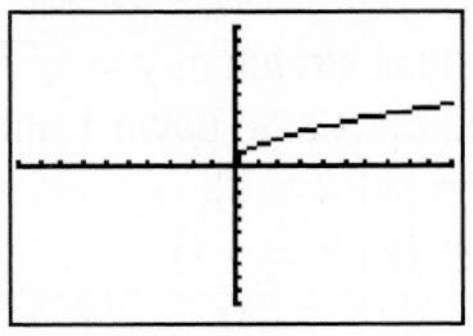

[−10, 10] scl: 1 by [−10, 10] scl: 1

7. $\{x \mid x \leq 2\}$, $\{y \mid y \geq 0\}$; moved right 2 units and reflected across the y-axis

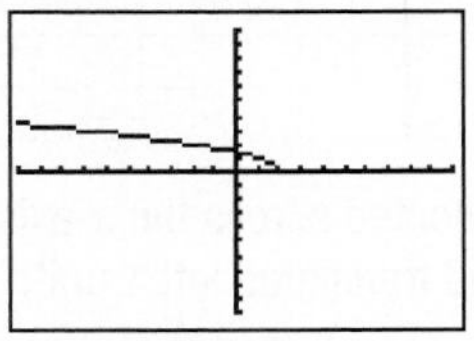

[−10, 10] scl: 1 by [−10, 10] scl: 1

8. $\{x \mid x \geq 3\}$, $\{y \mid y \geq 2\}$; moved right 3 units and up 2 units

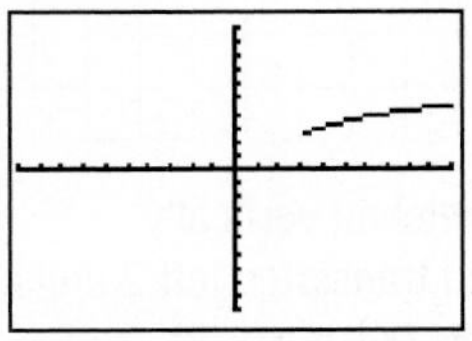

[−10, 10] scl: 1 by [−10, 10] scl: 1

Lesson 10-2

56.

$ax^2 + bx + c = 0$	Original equation
$x^2 + \frac{b}{a}x + \frac{c}{a} = 0$	Divide each side by *a*.
$x^2 + \frac{b}{a}x = -\frac{c}{a}$	Subtract $\frac{c}{a}$ from each side.
$x^2 + \frac{b}{a}x + \frac{b^2}{4a^2} = -\frac{c}{a} + \frac{b^2}{4a^2}$	Complete the square.
$\left(x + \frac{b}{2a}\right)^2 = \frac{-4ac + b^2}{4a^2}$	Factor $x^2 + \frac{b}{a}x + \frac{b^2}{4a^2}$.
$\left\lvert x + \frac{b}{2a}\right\rvert = \sqrt{\frac{b^2 - 4ac}{4a^2}}$	Take the square root of each side.
$x + \frac{b}{2a} = \pm\sqrt{\frac{b^2 - 4ac}{4a^2}}$	Remove the absolute value symbols and insert $\pm$.
$x + \frac{b}{2a} = \pm\sqrt{\frac{b^2 - 4ac}{4a^2}}$	Quotient Property of Square Roots
$x + \frac{b}{2a} = \pm\sqrt{\frac{b^2 - 4ac}{4a^2}}$	$\sqrt{4a^2} = 2a$
$x = \frac{-b \pm \sqrt{b^2 - 4ac}}{2a}$	Subtract $\frac{b}{2a}$ from each side.

62. vertical stretch of $y = \sqrt{x}$ and translated down 1 unit; D = $\{x \mid x \geq 0\}$, R = $\{y \mid y \geq -1\}$

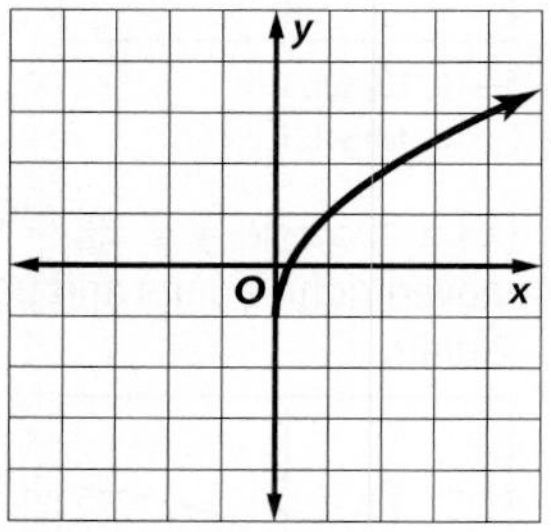

63. vertical compression of $y = \sqrt{x}$, D = $\{x \mid x \geq 0\}$, R = $\{y \mid y \geq 0\}$

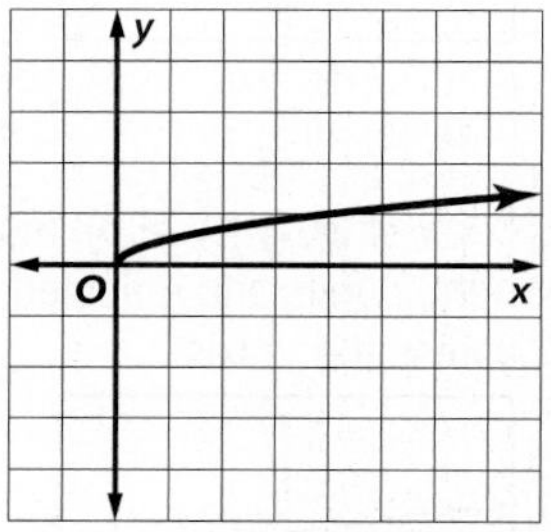

64. stretched vertically and translated left 2 units; D = $\{x \mid x \geq -2\}$, R = $\{y \mid y \geq 0\}$

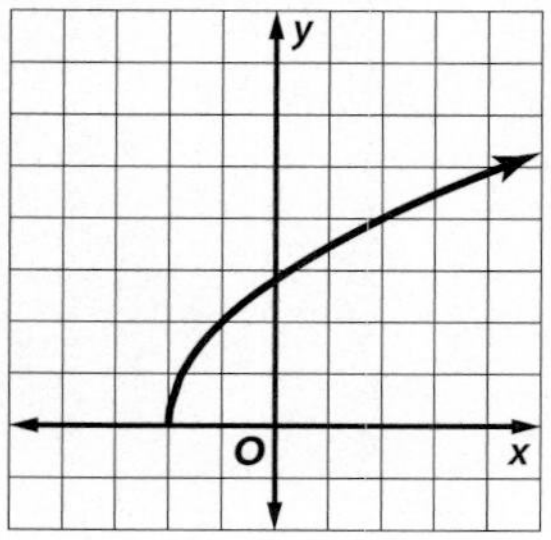

65. reflected across the *x*-axis and translated left 1 unit; D = $\{x \mid x \geq -1\}$, R = $\{y \mid y \leq 0\}$

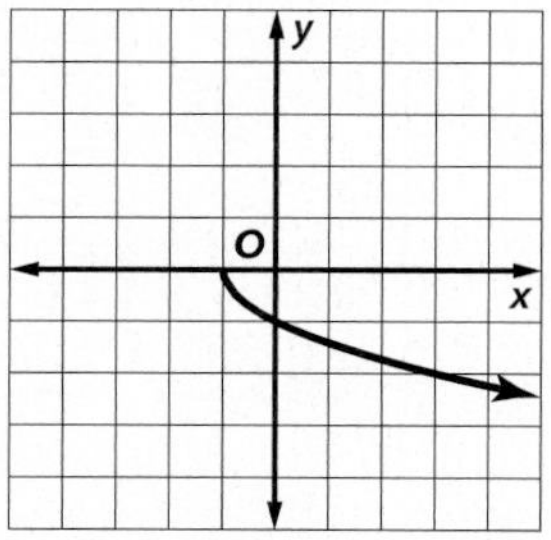

66. stretched vertically, reflected across the *x*-axis, and translated right 3 units; D = $\{x \mid x \geq 3\}$, R = $\{y \mid y \leq 0\}$

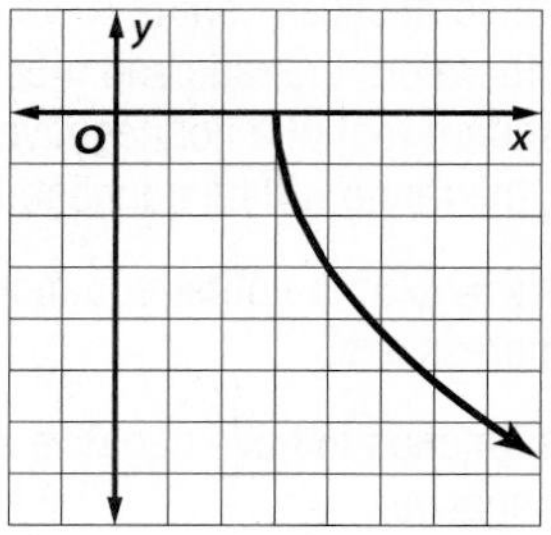

67. stretched vertically, reflected across the *x*-axis, and translated up 1 unit; D = $\{x \mid x \geq 0\}$, R = $\{y \mid y \leq 1\}$

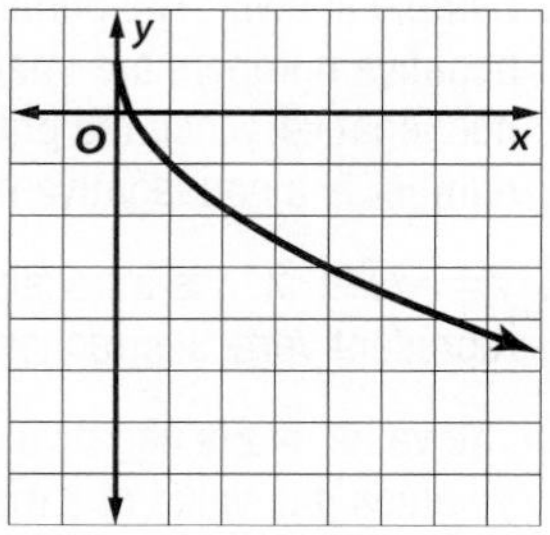

Lesson 10-3

50. stretched vertically; D = $\{x \mid x \geq 0\}$, R = $\{y \mid y \geq 0\}$

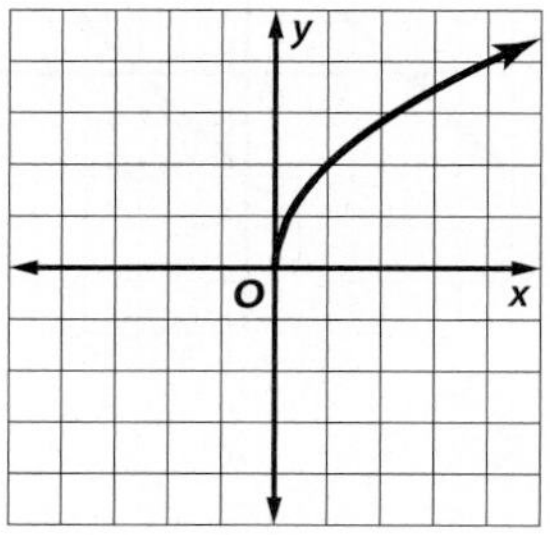

51. stretched vertically, reflected across the *x*-axis, D = $\{x \mid x \geq 0\}$, R = $\{y \mid y \leq 0\}$

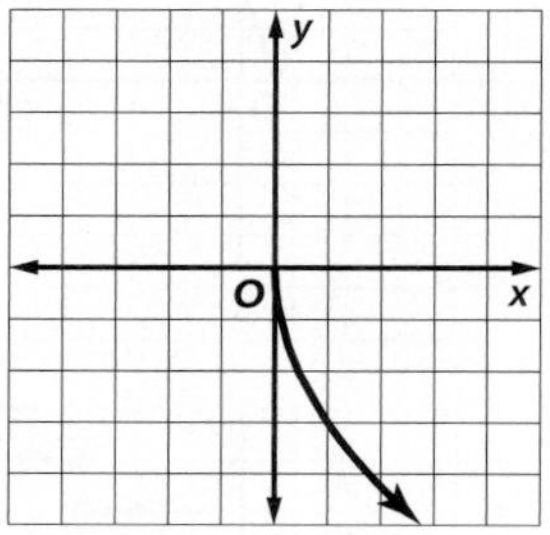

52. translated left 1 unit; D = $\{x \mid x \geq -1\}$, R = $\{y \mid y \geq 0\}$

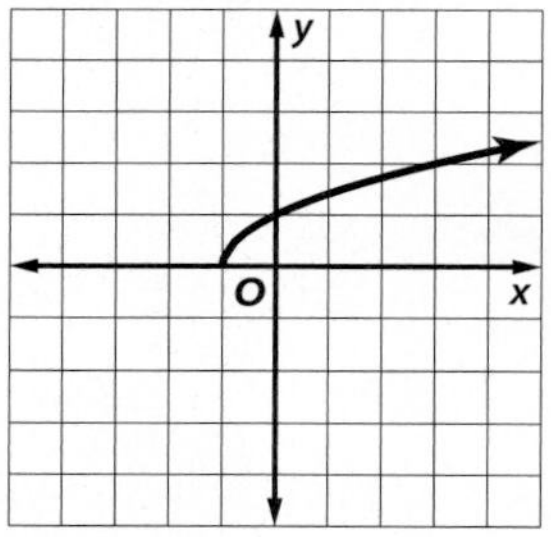

53. translated right 4 units; D = $\{x \mid x \geq 4\}$, R = $\{y \mid y \geq 0\}$

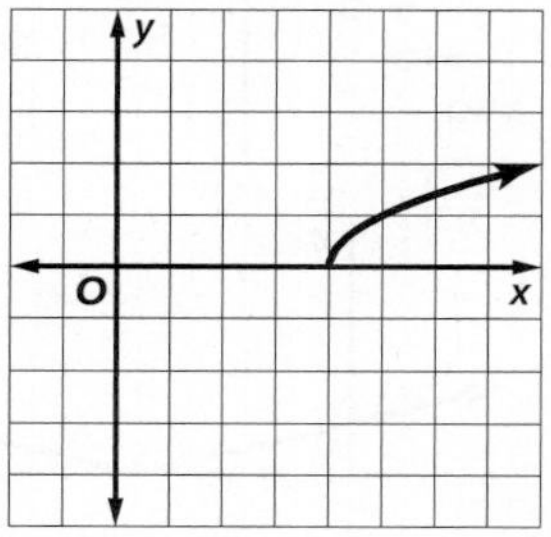

54. translated up 3 units; D = $\{x \mid x \geq 0\}$, R = $\{y \mid y \geq 3\}$

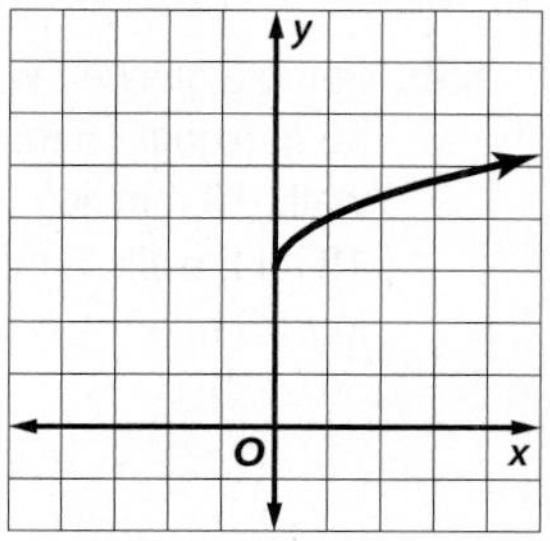

55. translated down 2 units; D = $\{x \mid x \geq 0\}$, R = $\{y \mid y \geq -2\}$

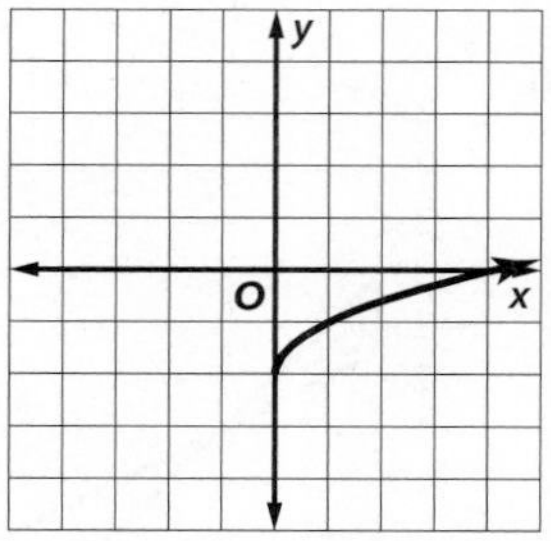

Mid-Chapter Quiz

1. stretched vertically; $D = \{x \mid x \geq 0\}$, $R = \{y \mid y \geq 0\}$

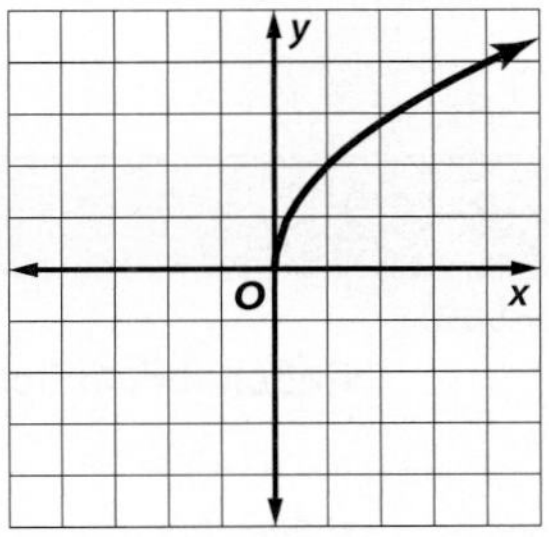

2. vertical stretch of $y = \sqrt{x}$ and reflection across the x-axis $D = \{x \mid x \geq 0\}$, $R = \{y \mid y \leq 0\}$

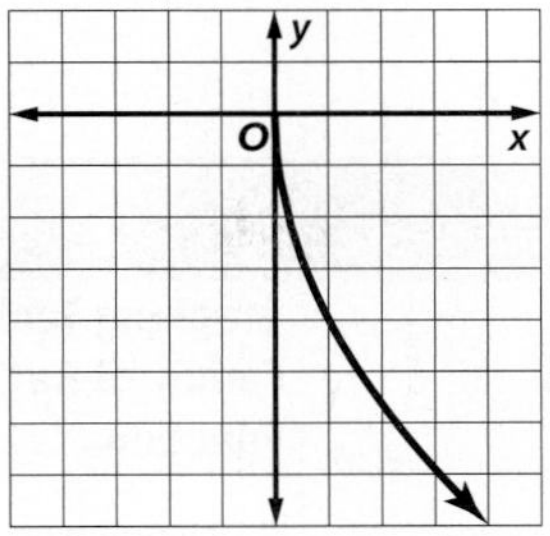

3. compressed vertically; $D = \{x \mid x \geq 0\}$, $R = \{y \mid y \geq 0\}$

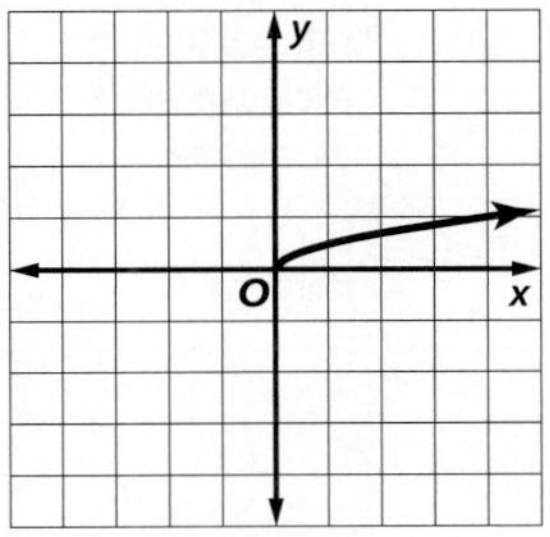

4. translation down 3 units; $D = \{x \mid x \geq 0\}$, $R = \{y \mid y \geq -3\}$

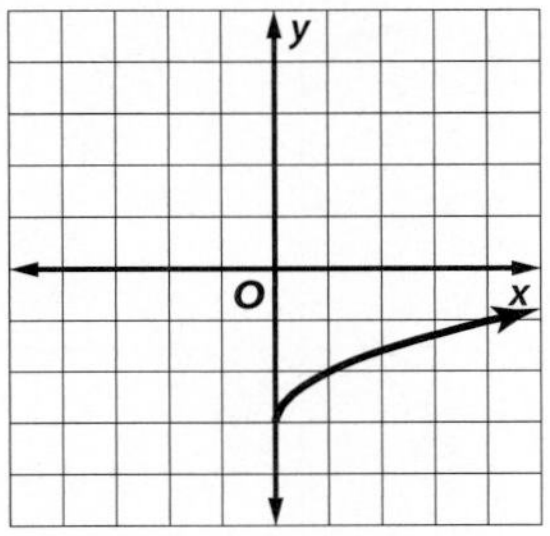

5. translation right 1 unit; $D = \{x \mid x \geq 1\}$, $R = \{y \mid y \geq 0\}$

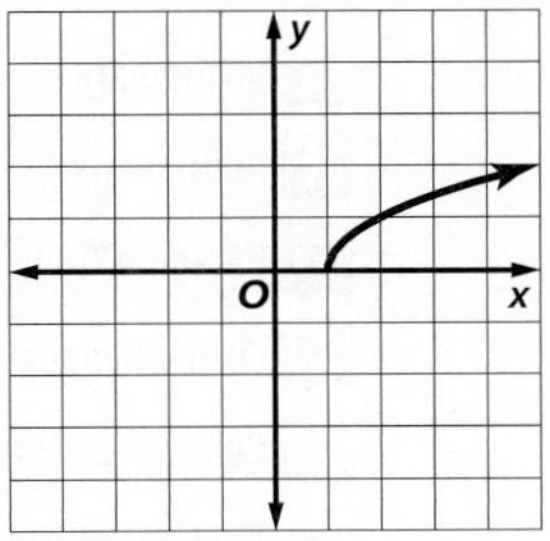

6. stretched vertically and translated right 2 units; $D = \{x \mid x \geq 2\}$, $R = \{y \mid y \geq 0\}$

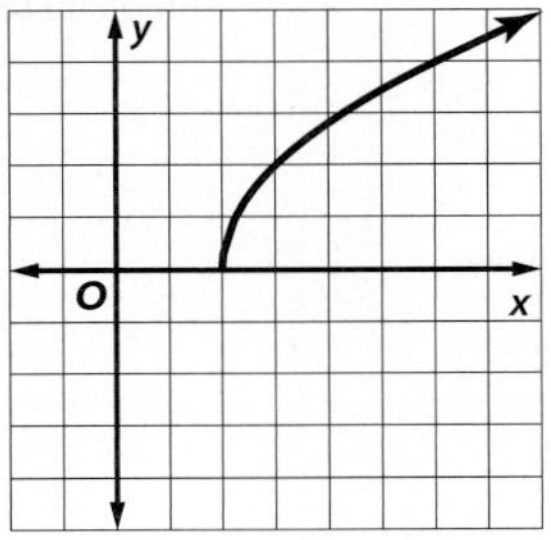

Extend 10-5

13. $(-10, -5)$; Find the distance between each endpoint and $(-10, -5)$.

$(-16, -7)$ and $(-10, -5)$

$$d = \sqrt{(x_2 - x_1)^2 + (y_2 - y_1)^2}$$
$$= \sqrt{(-16 - (-10))^2 + (-7 - (-5))^2}$$
$$= \sqrt{(-6)^2 + (-2)^2}$$
$$= \sqrt{40} \text{ or } 2\sqrt{10}$$

$(-4, -3)$ and $(-10, -5)$

$$d = \sqrt{(x_2 - x_1)^2 + (y_2 - y_1)^2}$$
$$= \sqrt{(-4 - (-10))^2 + (-3 - (-5))^2}$$
$$= \sqrt{(6)^2 + (2)^2}$$
$$= \sqrt{40} \text{ or } 2\sqrt{10}$$

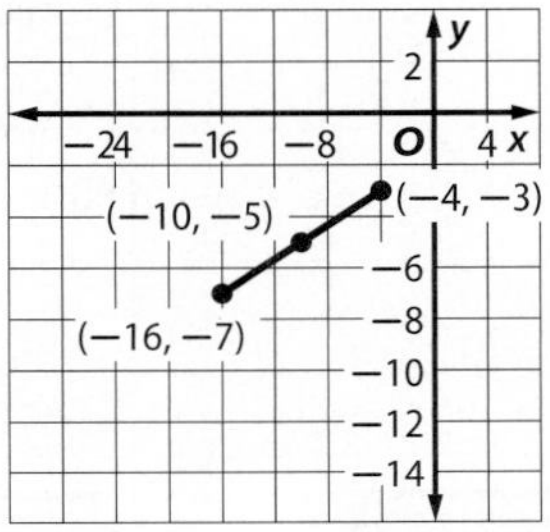

The graph shows that $(-10, -5)$ is on the segment. Since the distances from it to each endpoint are equal, the point is the midpoint of the segment between $(-16, -7)$ and $(-4, -3)$.

Lesson 10-6

50a.

Triangle	Trigonometric Ratios		$\sin^2$	$\cos^2$	$\sin^2 + \cos^2 =$
ABC	$\sin A = \frac{4}{5}$	$\cos A = \frac{3}{5}$	$\sin^2 A = \frac{16}{25}$	$\cos^2 A = \frac{9}{25}$	1
	$\sin C = \frac{3}{5}$	$\cos C = \frac{4}{5}$	$\sin^2 C = \frac{9}{25}$	$\cos^2 C = \frac{16}{25}$	1
JKL	$\sin J = \frac{12}{13}$	$\cos J = \frac{5}{13}$	$\sin^2 J = \frac{144}{169}$	$\cos^2 J = \frac{25}{169}$	1
	$\sin L = \frac{5}{13}$	$\cos L = \frac{12}{13}$	$\sin^2 L = \frac{25}{169}$	$\cos^2 L = \frac{144}{169}$	1
XYZ	$\sin X = \frac{9}{41}$	$\cos X = \frac{40}{41}$	$\sin^2 X = \frac{81}{1681}$	$\cos^2 X = \frac{1600}{1681}$	1
	$\sin Z = \frac{40}{41}$	$\cos Z = \frac{9}{41}$	$\sin^2 Z = \frac{1600}{1681}$	$\cos^2 Z = \frac{81}{1681}$	1

Chapter Planner

Diagnostic Assessment
Quick Check

	EXPLORE 11-1 (45 min: 0.5 day; 90 min: 0.5 day)	LESSON 11-1 (45 min: 1 day; 90 min: 0.5 day)	EXPLORE 11-2 (45 min: 0.5 day; 90 min: 0.5 day)	LESSON 11-2 (45 min: 1 day; 90 min: 0.5 day)
Title	**Graphing Technology Lab: Inverse Variation**	**Inverse Variation**	**Graphing Technology Lab: Family of Rational Functions**	**Rational Functions**
Objectives	■ Collect data to investigate the relationship between volume and pressure.	■ Identify and use inverse variations. ■ Graph inverse variations.	■ Use graphing technology to investigate families of rational functions.	■ Identify excluded values. ■ Identify and use asymptotes to graph rational functions.
Key Vocabulary		inverse variation product rule		rational function excluded value asymptote
Content Standards		PS.1		PS.3, PS.7
Multiple Representations				
Lesson Resources	connectED.mcgraw-hill.com **Materials:** ■ TI-83/84 Plus or other graphing calculator ■ CBL or other data collection device ■ syringe ■ gas pressure sensor	connectED.mcgraw-hill.com Leveled Worksheets Vocabulary Animations Personal Tutor Virtual Manipulatives Self-Check Quiz ■ *5-Minute Check* ■ *Study Notebook*	connectED.mcgraw-hill.com **Materials:** ■ TI-83/84 Plus or other graphing calculator	connectED.mcgraw-hill.com Leveled Worksheets Quiz 1 Vocabulary Animations Personal Tutor Virtual Manipulatives Self-Check Quiz ■ *5-Minute Check* ■ *Study Notebook*
Resources for Every Lesson	IWB eStudent Edition IWB Interactive Classroom	■ eTeacher Edition ■ eSolutions Manual ■ McGraw-Hill eAssessment		
Differentiated Instruction		pp. 679, 682		pp. 685, 689

IWB All digital assets are Interactive Whiteboard ready.

Suggested Pacing			
Time Periods	Instruction	Review & Assess	Total
45-minute	11 days	2 days	13 days
90-minute	6 days	1 day	7 days

LESSON 11-3 (45 min: 1 day; 90 min: 0.75 day)	EXTEND 11-3 (45 min: 0.5 day; 90 min: 0.25 day)	LESSON 11-4 (45 min: 1 day; 90 min: 0.5 day)	LESSON 11-5 (45 min: 1 day; 90 min: 0.5 day)
Simplifying Rational Expressions	**Graphing Technology Lab: Simplifying Rational Expressions**	**Multiplying and Dividing Rational Expressions**	**Dividing Polynomials**
▪ Identify values excluded from the domain of a rational expression. ▪ Simplify rational expressions.	▪ Use a graphing calculator to simplify rational expressions, and verify solutions and excluded values.	▪ Multiply rational expressions. ▪ Divide rational expressions.	▪ Divide a polynomial by a monomial. ▪ Divide a polynomial by a binomial.
rational expression			
AI.RNE.5	AI.RNE.5	AI.RNE.5	PS.8, AI.RNE.5
connectED.mcgraw-hill.com Leveled Worksheets Vocabulary Animations Personal Tutor Self-Check Quiz ▪ *5-Minute Check* ▪ *Study Notebook*	connectED.mcgraw-hill.com Personal Tutor **Materials:** ▪ TI-83/84 Plus or other graphing calculator	connectED.mcgraw-hill.com Leveled Worksheets Quiz 2 Animations Personal Tutor Self-Check Quiz ▪ *5-Minute Check* ▪ *Study Notebook*	connectED.mcgraw-hill.com Leveled Worksheets Animations Personal Tutor Self-Check Quiz ▪ *5-Minute Check* ▪ *Study Notebook* ▪ *Teaching Algebra with Manipulatives*
IWB eStudent Edition IWB Interactive Classroom	▪ eTeacher Edition ▪ eSolutions Manual ▪ McGraw-Hill eAssessment		
pp. 692, 696		pp. 700, 704	pp. 707, 711
		Formative Assessment Mid-Chapter Quiz	

Chapter Planner

	LESSON 11-6 (45 min: 1.5 days; 90 min: 0.5 day)	LESSON 11-7 (45 min: 1 day; 90 min: 0.5 day)	LESSON 11-8 (45 min: 0.5 day; 90 min: 0.5 day)	EXTEND 11-8 (45 min: 0.5 day; 90 min: 0.25 day)
Title	**Adding and Subtracting Rational Expressions**	**Mixed Expressions and Complex Fractions**	**Rational Equations**	**Graphing Technology Lab: Solving Rational Equations**
Objectives	▪ Add and subtract rational expressions with like denominators. ▪ Add and subtract rational expressions with unlike denominators.	▪ Simplify mixed expressions. ▪ Simplify complex fractions.	▪ Solve rational equations. ▪ Use rational equations to solve problems.	▪ Use graphing technology to solve rational equations.
Key Vocabulary	least common multiple (LCM) least common denominator (LCD)	mixed expression complex fraction	rational equation extraneous solution work and rate problems	
Content Standards	PS.6, AI.RNE.5	PS.4, AI.RNE.5	PS.2	PS.5
Multiple Representations				
Lesson Resources	connectED.mcgraw-hill.com Leveled Worksheets Quiz 3 Vocabulary Animations Personal Tutor Self-Check Quiz ▪ *5-Minute Check* ▪ *Study Notebook*	connectED.mcgraw-hill.com Leveled Worksheets Vocabulary Personal Tutor Self-Check Quiz ▪ *5-Minute Check* ▪ *Study Notebook*	connectED.mcgraw-hill.com Leveled Worksheets Quiz 4 Vocabulary Animations Personal Tutor Self-Check Quiz ▪ *5-Minute Check* ▪ *Study Notebook* ▪ *Teaching Algebra with Manipulatives*	connectED.mcgraw-hill.com Personal Tutor **Materials:** ▪ TI-Nspire Technology
Resources for Every Lesson	IWB eStudent Edition IWB Interactive Classroom	▪ eTeacher Edition ▪ eSolutions Manual ▪ McGraw-Hill eAssessment		
Differentiated Instruction	pp. 715, 719	pp. 722, 725	pp. 729, 732	

Summative Assessment
Study Guide and Review
Practice Test

IWB All digital assets are Interactive Whiteboard ready.

Professional Development

Targeted professional development has been articulated throughout Algebra 1. More quality, customized professional development is available from McGraw-Hill Professional Development. Visit connectED.mcgraw-hill.com for details on each product.

- Online Lessons emphasize the strategies and techniques used to teach Algebra 1. Includes streaming video, interactive pages, and online tools.
- Video Workshops allow mentors, coaches, or leadership personnel to facilitate on-site workshops on educational strategies in mathematics and mathematical concepts.
- MHPD Online (www.mhpdonline.com) offers online professional development with video clips of instructional strategies, links, student activities, and news and issues in education.
- Teaching Today (teachingtoday.glencoe.com) gives secondary teachers practical strategies and materials that inspire excellence and innovation in teaching.

What the Research Says...

Collis describes the use of the reciprocal strategy as involving a relatively complex system. Students often mistakenly apply the simpler inverse strategy when the reciprocal strategy is essential.

- Multiplying by the LCD (Lesson 11-8) is an example of using the reciprocal strategy to solve a rational equation.
- Students frequently make the error of multiplying only one term in a rational equation by the LCD (the inverse strategy). They may need to be reminded that every term must be multiplied by the LCD in order to solve it.

Source: Collis, K.F. "Mathematical Thinking in Children," in Ved P. Varma and Phillip Williams (Eds.) *Piaget, Psychology and Education,* Itasca, IL, F.E. Peacock, pp. 144–154.

Project CRISS STUDY SKILL

A sequence map can be used to compare and contrast similar processes. Students often benefit from making sequence maps as a cooperative group activity.

The sample sequence map at the right relates finding percents of increase and decrease. Have students develop their own diagrams to compare the processes of adding, subtracting, and multiplying rational expressions.

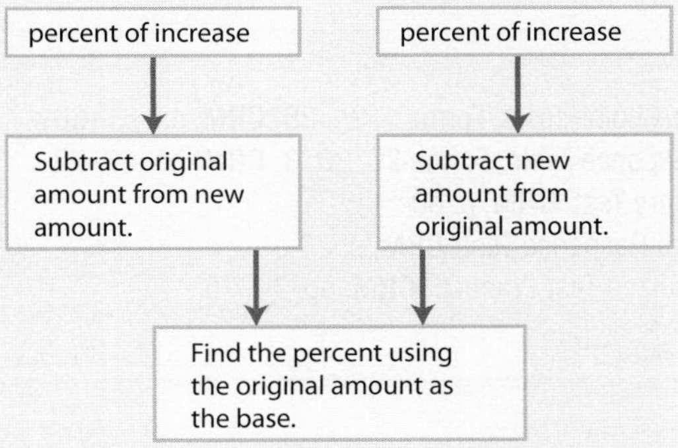

Creating Independence through Student-owned Strategies

Assessment and Intervention

SE = Student Edition, **TE** = Teacher Edition, **CRM** = Chapter Resource Masters

	Diagnosis	Prescription
DIAGNOSTIC ASSESSMENT	**Beginning Chapter 11**	
	Get Ready for Chapter 11 **SE**	Response to Intervention **TE**
	Beginning Every Lesson	
	Then, Now, Why? **SE** 5-Minute Check	Chapter 0 **SE** *Quick Review Math Handbook*
FORMATIVE ASSESSMENT	**During/After Every Lesson**	
	Guided Practice **SE**, every example Check Your Understanding **SE** H.O.T. Problems **SE** Spiral Review **SE** Additional Examples **TE** Watch Out! **TE** Step 4, Assess **TE** Chapter 11 Quizzes **CRM**, pp. 57–58 Self-Check Quizzes connectED.mcgraw-hill.com	TIER 1 Intervention Skills Practice **CRM**, Ch. 1–11 connectED.mcgraw-hill.com TIER 2 Intervention Differentiated Instruction **TE** Study Guide and Intervention **CRM**, Ch. 1–11 *Quick Review Math Handbook* TIER 3 Intervention *Math Triumphs, Alg. 1*
	Mid-Chapter	
	Mid-Chapter Quiz **SE** Mid-Chapter Test **CRM**, p. 59 McGraw-Hill eAssessment	TIER 1 Intervention Skills Practice **CRM**, Ch. 1–11 connectED.mcgraw-hill.com TIER 2 Intervention Study Guide and Intervention **CRM**, Ch. 1–11; *Quick Review Math Handbook* TIER 3 Intervention *Math Triumphs, Alg. 1*
	Before Chapter Test	
	Chapter Study Guide and Review **SE** Practice Test **SE** Standardized Test Practice **SE** Chapter Test connectED.mcgraw-hill.com Standardized Test Practice connectED.mcgraw-hill.com Vocabulary Review connectED.mcgraw-hill.com McGraw-Hill eAssessment	TIER 1 Intervention Skills Practice **CRM**, Ch. 1–11 connectED.mcgraw-hill.com TIER 2 Intervention Study Guide and Intervention **CRM**, Ch. 1–11; *Quick Review Math Handbook* TIER 3 Intervention *Math Triumphs, Alg. 1*
SUMMATIVE ASSESSMENT	**After Chapter 11**	
	Multiple-Choice Tests, Forms 1, 2A, 2B **CRM**, pp. 61–66 Free-Response Tests, Forms 2C, 2D, 3 **CRM**, pp. 67–72 Vocabulary Test **CRM**, p. 60 Extended Response Test **CRM**, p. 73 Standardized Test Practice **CRM**, pp. 74–76 McGraw-Hill eAssessment	Study Guide and Intervention **CRM**, Ch. 1–11 *Quick Review Math Handbook* connectED.mcgraw-hill.com

Differentiated Instruction

Option 1 Reaching All Learners AL OL BL ELL

Social Have students work in groups. Assign each student a polynomial division problem. Tell the students to study their problems for a few minutes to decide on a method for finding the quotient. Then, ask each student to "teach" the group how to find the quotient. Have groups discuss whether the method "taught" is correct.

Auditory In pairs or small groups, students work on Exercise 18 on p. 730 and talk about each step of the solution as they show their work. Have them check their solutions and discuss why one of the solutions is extraneous.

Kinesthetic Average speed *r* is given by the equation $r = \frac{d}{t}$, where *d* is the distance traveled and *t* is the time it takes to travel the distance. Ask students to choose a distance like 50 yards that people are willing to run. Once they have chosen the distance, ask them to create a graph, perform an experiment with the given distance, and then determine whether the graph accurately depicts the performance of their participants. Analyses should be performed to show how the data points relate to the graph.

Option 2 Approaching Level AL

Have students write division problems involving rational expressions on note cards, pieces of scrap paper, or any other item that they can manipulate. Then have students physically "flip" the fractions to multiply by the reciprocal. The act of "flipping" the fractions will help cement the concept in students' minds.

Option 3 English Learners ELL

Place students in small groups. Have students take turns reading example problems to the group. As one student reads, have the other group members record the problem. Then have all members of the group discuss the procedures for solving the problem.

Option 4 Beyond Level BL

Ask students to research a method of dividing polynomials known as synthetic division. Then ask students to compare this method to using the long division method. An example below is shown for $(3x^3 - 5x^2 - 6x - 2) \div (x - 3)$.

Long Division:

$3x^2 + 4x + 6$
$x - 3\overline{)3x^3 - 5x^2 - 6x - 2}$
$\underline{3x^3 - 9x^2}$
$4x^2 - 6x$
$\underline{4x^2 - 12x}$
$6x - 2$
$\underline{6x - 18}$
16

Synthetic Division

$3\,|\;3 \;\; -5 \;\; -6 \;\; -2$
$\underline{\quad\quad\; 9 \;\; 12 \;\; 18}$
$\quad\; 3 \;\; 4 \;\; 6 \;\; 16$

Focus on Mathematical Content

VerticalAlignment

Before Chapter 11

Related Topics before Grade 8

- identify the greatest common factor of a set of positive integers
- convert measures within the same measurement system

Related Topics from Pre-Algebra

- use appropriate operations to solve problems involving rational numbers

Previous Topics from Algebra 1

- solve problems involving proportional change
- simplify and factor polynomial expressions
- transform and solve equations

Chapter 11

Related Topics from Algebra 11

- analyze data and represent situations involving inverse variation using tables, graphs, or algebraic methods
- Graph and analyze rational functions.
- identify excluded values from rational expressions and simplify rational expressions
- multiply and divide rational expressions and use dimensional analysis
- divide a polynomial by a monomial or binomial
- add and subtract rational expressions with like and unlike denominators
- solve rational equations and eliminate extraneous roots

After Chapter 11

Preparation for Algebra 2

- use quotients of polynomials to describe the graphs of rational functions
- analyze various representations of rational functions with respect to problem situations
- determine the solutions of rational equations using graphs, tables, and algebraic methods

Lesson-by-Lesson Preview

11-1 Inverse Variation

Some situations in which y increases as x increases are known as *direct variations* (Lesson 3-4). Some situations in which y decreases as x increases, or vice versa, are known as *inverse variations.* Inverse variations can be represented by equations of the form $y = \frac{k}{x}$ or $xy = k$, where $x \neq 0$ and $y \neq 0$. The value of an inverse variation is undefined when $x = 0$.

The *product* rule of inverse variation states that if (x_1, y_1) and (x_2, y_2) are solutions of an inverse variation, then $x_1y_1 = x_2y_2$ because both $x_1y_1 = k$ and $x_2y_2 = k$. The equation $x_1y_1 = x_2y_2$ can be used to solve for missing values of x and y.

11-2 Rational Functions

A rational function is a function of the form $y = \frac{p}{q}$, where the numerator, p, and denominator, q, are both polynomials. Any value that makes the value of q equal to 0 is called an *excluded value* of the rational function and must be excluded from the domain of the function. Depending on the situation represented by a rational function, there may be additional values excluded as well. The graph of a rational function of the form $y = \frac{a}{x - b}$ (where $a \neq 0$), has two asympotes, the line $x = b$ and the line $y = 0$. The graph of the function *appears* to approach these two lines.

11-3 Simplifying Rational Expressions

Algebraic fractions that have polynomials for numerators and denominators are called rational expressions. All properties that apply to rational numbers also apply to rational expressions. Because division by 0 is undefined, the polynomial in the denominator cannot be 0.

The numerator and denominator of a simplified rational expression will have no common factors other than 1.

- To simplify rational expressions in which both the numerator and denominator are monomials, divide each by the GCF.
- To simplify rational expressions in which both the numerator and denominator are polynomials, first factor each polynomial and then divide each by the common factors.

mathforum.org
The Math Forum @ Drexel University

Get educator support from the Math Forum's T2T. You may want to search for or ask about assessment strategies. Start your search at connectED.mcgraw-hill.com.

11-4 Multiplying and Dividing Rational Expressions

The process of multiplying rational expressions is similar to that of multiplying rational numbers. First, multiply the numerators. Then, multiply the denominators. If either of the rational expressions can be simplified, do so before multiplying.

To divide rational expressions, multiply by the reciprocal of the divisor, just as you would do when dividing rational numbers. Then follow the rules for multiplying rational expressions.

When you multiply or divide fractions or rational expressions that involve units of measure, you can divide by the common units in the same way that you divide by common variables. This process of *dimensional analysis* allows you to convert between units of measure.

11-5 Dividing Polynomials

To divide a polynomial by a monomial, simply divide each term of the polynomial by the monomial.

To divide a polynomial by a binomial, first try to factor the polynomial to see if there is perhaps a common binomial factor. If factoring is not possible, use a division process similar to the one used for dividing whole numbers. Then divide.

Using $(a^3 - 4a) \div (a - 2)$ as an example,

$$\frac{a^3 - 4a}{a - 2} = \frac{a\cancel{(a-2)}(a+2)}{\cancel{a-2}} = a^2 + 2a \text{ or}$$

$$\begin{array}{r} a^2 + 2a \\ a - 2\overline{)\,a^3 + 0a^2 - 4a} \\ \underline{(-)a^3 - 2a^2 } \\ 2a^2 - 4a \\ \underline{(-)2a^2 - 4a} \\ 0 \end{array}$$

11-6 Adding and Subtracting Rational Expressions

When adding/subtracting rational expressions with like denominators, add/subtract the numerators and write the sum/difference over the common denominator.

When adding/subtracting rational expressions with unlike denominators, a common denominator must first be found. Use the following steps to add/subtract rational expressions with unlike denominators.

Step 1 *Identify the LCD by finding the prime factorization of the denominators. Use each factor the greatest number of times it appears in either of the factorizations.*

Step 2 *Rewrite each rational expression as an equivalent expression with the LCD as the denominator.*

Step 3 *Add/subtract.*

Step 4 *Simplify whenever possible.*

11-7 Mixed Expressions and Complex Fractions

A mixed number contains the sum of a whole number and a fraction. Similarly, a *mixed expression* contains the sum of a monomial and a rational expression. To simplify mixed expressions, change them into a single rational expression with the same denominator as the given expression.

A *complex fraction* is a fraction with additional fractions in the numerator, denominator, or both. You can rewrite a complex fraction as a division expression. Divide the numerator of the fraction by the denominator and then write the quotient as a simple fraction.

11-8 Rational Equations

Rational equations are equations that contain rational expressions. If both sides of a rational equation are single fractions, cross products can be used to solve the equation. Or, you can multiply each side of the equation by the LCD of the fractions to eliminate the fractions, and then solve the resulting equation.

When solving a rational equation, more than one solution may result. Always check all solutions in the original equation, as some solutions may be *extraneous solutions.*

Chapter Project

The More You Know

Students use what they have learned about rational functions to complete a project.

This chapter project addresses civic literacy, as well as several specific skills identified as being essential to student success by the Framework for 21st Century Learning.

Visit connectED.mcgraw-hill.com for student and teacher handouts.

Key Vocabulary Introduce the key vocabulary in the chapter using the routine below.

Define: A complex fraction is a fraction that has one or more fractions in the numerator or denominator.

Example: $\frac{\frac{8}{3}}{\frac{7}{5}}$

Ask: What are the two fractions in this complex fraction? $\frac{8}{3}$ and $\frac{7}{5}$

CHAPTER 11 Rational Functions and Equations

Then

You simplified expressions involving monomials and polynomials.

Now

In this chapter, you will:

- Identify and graph inverse variations.
- Identify excluded values of rational functions.
- Multiply, divide, and add rational expressions.
- Divide polynomials.
- Solve rational equations.

Why?

HOCKEY The time it will take for a puck hit from the blue line to reach the goal line is given by the rational expression $\frac{64}{x}$, where x is the speed of the puck in feet per seconds. If a player hits the puck at 100 miles per hour, the puck will reach the goal line in 0.34 second.

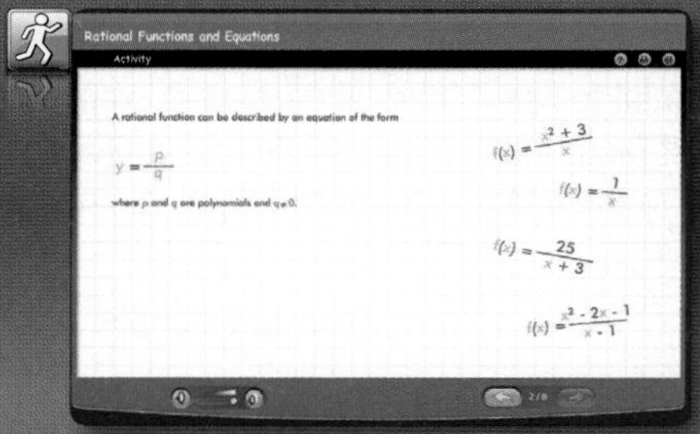

connectED.mcgraw-hill.com Your Digital Math Portal

Animation | Vocabulary | eGlossary | Personal Tutor | Virtual Manipulatives | Graphing Calculator | Audio | Foldables | Self-Check Practice | Worksheets

Content Standards
AI.RNE.5

Process Standards
PS.2, PS.3, PS.5, PS.7

Get Ready for the Chapter

Diagnose Readiness | You have two options for checking prerequisite skills.

1 Textbook Option Take the Quick Check below. Refer to the Quick Review for help.

QuickCheck

Solve each proportion.

1. $\frac{y}{3} = \frac{8}{9}$ $\frac{8}{3}$
2. $\frac{5}{12} = \frac{x}{36}$ 15
3. $\frac{7}{2} = \frac{y}{3}$ $\frac{21}{2}$
4. $\frac{5}{x} = \frac{10}{4}$ 2
5. **DRAWING** Rosie is making a scale drawing. She is using the scale 1 inch = 3 feet. How many inches will represent 10 feet? $\frac{10}{3}$ or $3\frac{1}{3}$ inches

Factor each polynomial, if possible. If the polynomial cannot be factored using integers, write *prime*.

6. $4a - 12$ $4(a - 3)$
7. $2x^2 - 4x$ $2x(x - 2)$
8. $6xy + 15x$ $3x(2y + 5)$
9. $2c^2d - 4c^2d^2$ $2c^2d(1 - 2d)$
10. $d^2 - 12d + 27$ $(d - 3)(d - 9)$
11. $m^2 - m - 132$ $(m - 12)(m + 11)$
12. $3x^2 + 2x - 1$ $(3x - 1)(x + 1)$
13. $6x^2 - 5x - 4$ $(3x - 4)(2x + 1)$
14. **AREA** The area of a rectangle is $x^2 + 5x + 6$. What binomial expressions could represent the side lengths of the rectangle? $(x + 3)$, $(x + 2)$

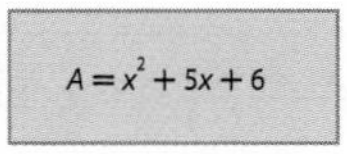

QuickReview

Example 1 (Used in Lesson 11-1)

Solve $\frac{3}{5} = \frac{x}{12}$.

$\frac{3}{5} = \frac{x}{12}$ Original equation

$3 \cdot 12 = 5 \cdot x$ Cross products

$36 = 5x$ Simplify.

$\frac{36}{5} = \frac{5x}{5}$ Divide each side by 5.

$\frac{36}{5} = x$ Simplify.

Example 2 (Used in Lessons 11-4 through 11-8)

Factor $45x^2 + 27x$.

Find the GCF of the terms.

$45x^2 = 3 \cdot 3 \cdot 5 \cdot x \cdot x$

$27x = 3 \cdot 3 \cdot 3 \cdot x$

GCF $= 3 \cdot 3 \cdot x$ or $9x$

$45x^2 + 27x = 9x(5x) + 9x(3)$

$= 9x(5x + 3)$

2 Online Option Take an online self-check Chapter Readiness Quiz at connectED.mcgraw-hill.com.

Essential Question

- How can simplifying mathematical expressions be useful? Sample answer: There are several ways to write an expression, but expressions are often easier to work with when simplified. For example, multiplying by 3 is easier than multiplying by (5 – 2) or $\frac{21}{7}$.

Get Ready for the Chapter

Response to Intervention (RtI)

Use the *Quick Check* results and the Intervention Planner chart to help you determine your Response to Intervention. The If-Then statements in the chart below help you decide the appropriate tier of RtI and suggest intervention resources for each tier.

InterventionPlanner

TIER 1 On Level OL

If students miss about 25% of the exercises or less,

Then choose a resource:

SE Lessons 2-6, 8-5, 8-6, and 8-7

Skills Practice, Chapter 2, p. 38, Chapter 8, pp. 33, 39, 45

connectED.mcgraw-hill.com Self-Check Quiz

TIER 2 Strategic Intervention AL
approaching grade level

If students miss about 50% of the exercises,

Then choose a resource:

Study Guide and Intervention, Chapter 2, p. 36, Chapter 8, pp. 31, 37, 43

Quick Review Math Handbook

connectED.mcgraw-hill.com Extra Examples, Personal Tutor, Homework Help

TIER 3 Intensive Intervention
2 or more grades below level

If students miss about 75% of the exercises,

Then use *Math Triumphs, Alg. 1*

connectED.mcgraw-hill.com Extra Examples, Personal Tutor, Homework Help, Review Vocabulary

FOLDABLES® StudyOrganizer

Dinah Zike's Foldables®

Focus Students write notes about rational expressions and equations as they work through each lesson in this chapter.

Teach Have students make and label their Foldables as illustrated. Ask students to write down the Key Concepts and Concept Summaries in this chapter. Encourage students to reword the information in such a way that someone who did not understand rational functions and equations would understand them after reading what was written.

When to Use It Encourage students to add to their Foldables as they work through the chapter and to use them to review for the chapter test.

Differentiated Instruction

Student-Built Glossary, pp. 1–2

Students should complete the chart by providing a definition of each term and an example as they progress through Chapter 11. This study tool can also be used to review for the chapter test.

Get Started on the Chapter

You will learn several new concepts, skills, and vocabulary terms as you study Chapter 11. To get ready, identify important terms and organize your resources. You may wish to refer to Chapter 0 to review prerequisite skills.

FOLDABLES StudyOrganizer

Rational Functions and Equations Make this Foldable to help you organize your Chapter 11 notes about rational functions and equations. Begin with 3 sheets of notebook paper.

1 **Take** one sheet of paper and fold in half along the width. Cut 1 inch slits on each side of the paper.

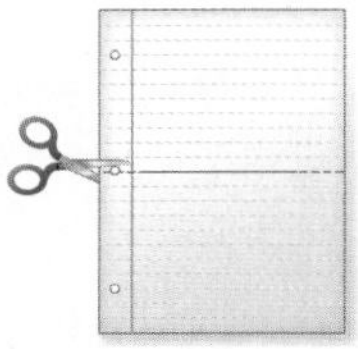

2 **Stack** the two sheets of paper and fold in half along the width. Cut a slit through the center stopping 1 inch from each side.

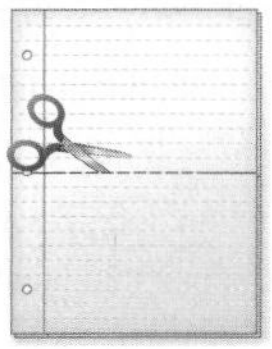

3 **Insert** the first sheet through the second sheets and align the folds to form a booklet. Label the cover with the chapter title.

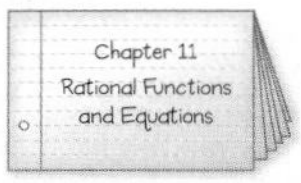

NewVocabulary

English		Español
inverse variation	p. 676	variación inversa
product rule	p. 677	regla del producto
excluded value	p. 684	valores excluidos
rational function	p. 684	función racional
asymptote	p. 685	asíntota
rational expression	p. 690	expresión racional
least common multiple (LCM)	p. 713	mínimo común múltiplo (mcm)
least common denominator (LCD)	p. 714	mínimo común denominador (mcd)
complex fraction	p. 720	fracción compleja
mixed expression	p. 720	expresión mixta
rational equation	p. 726	ecuacion racional
extraneous solutions	p. 727	soluciones extrañas
work problems	p. 728	problemas de trabajo
rate problems	p. 729	problemas de tasas

ReviewVocabulary

direct variation variación directa an equation of the form $y = kx$, where $k \neq 0$

Quotient of Powers cociente de potencia $\frac{a^m}{a^n} = a^{m-n}$

$$\frac{x^5}{x^3} = \frac{x \cdot x \cdot x \cdot x \cdot x}{x \cdot x \cdot x} = x \cdot x \text{ or } x^2$$

$$\frac{x^5}{x^3} = x^{5-3} \text{ or } x^2$$

Zero Product Property propiedad del producto de cero
if the product of two factors is 0, then at least one of the factors must be 0

674 | Chapter 11 | Rational Functions and Equations

EXPLORE 11-1

Graphing Technology Lab Inverse Variation

You can use a data collection device to investigate the relationship between volume and pressure.

Set Up The Lab

- Connect a syringe to the gas pressure sensor. Then connect the data collection device to both the sensor and the calculator as shown.
- Start the collection program and select the sensor.

Activity Collect Data

Step 1 Open the valve between the atmosphere and the syringe. Set the inside ring of the syringe to 20 mL and close the valve. This ensures that the amount of air inside the syringe will be constant throughout the experiment.

Step 2 Press the plunger of the syringe to the 5 mL mark. Wait for the pressure gauge to stop changing, then take the data reading. Enter 5 as the volume in the calculator. The pressure is measured in atmospheres (atm).

Step 3 Repeat step 2, pressing the plunger to 7.5 mL, 10.0 mL, 12.5 mL, 15.0 mL, 17.5 mL, and 20.0 mL. Record the volume from each data reading.

Step 4 After taking the last data reading, use **STAT PLOT** to create a line graph.

Exercises

1. Does the pressure vary directly as the volume? Explain.
2. As the volume changes from 10 to 20 mL, what happens to the pressure?
3. Predict what the pressure of the gas in the syringe would be if the volume increased to 40 mL. **Sample answer: 0.48**
4. Add a column to the data table to find the product of the volume and the pressure for each data reading. What pattern do you observe?
5. **MAKE A CONJECTURE** The relationship between the pressure and volume of a gas is called Boyle's Law. Write an equation relating the volume v in milliliters and pressure p in atmospheres in your experiment. Compare your conjecture to those of two classmates. Formulate mathematical questions about their conjectures. **Sample answer: $pv = 18$; see students' work.**

1. No; the pressure increases as the volume decreases.
2. Sample answer: The pressure decreases by about half.
4. Sample answer: The product is close to constant.

1 Focus

Objective Collect data to investigate the relationship between volume and pressure.

Materials for Each Group

- syringe
- gas pressure sensor
- CBL or other data collection device
- TI–83/84 plus or other graphing calculator

Teaching Tip

Before performing the experiment, ask students to think about what they expect to happen. As they push the plunger in the syringe, do they expect it to get harder or easier to push?

2 Teach

Working in Cooperative Groups

Put students in groups of four or five, mixing abilities, to complete the Activity.

Ask:

- Does the volume of air in the syringe change as you press the plunger? Explain Yes; the volume decreases.
- Does the air pressure in the syringe change as you press the plunger? Explain. Yes; the pressure increases.
- Does the volume of air in the syringe change as you pull the plunger? Explain. Yes; the volume increases.
- Does the air pressure in the syringe change as you pull the plunger? Explain. Yes; the pressure decreases.

Practice Have students complete Exercises 1–5.

3 Assess

Formative Assessment

Use Exercise 5 to assess whether students can determine if there is a relationship between the pressure and volume of gas.

From Concrete to Abstract

Explain that Boyle's Law states that, at constant temperature, the volume of a given mass of gas is inversely proportional to the pressure upon the gas, or $v = \frac{k}{p}$, where v = volume, p = pressure, and k = a constant. Ask students to explain whether the results of the experiment follow the pattern of Boyle's Law.

1 Focus

VerticalAlignment

Before Lesson 11-1 Solve problems involving direct variation.

Lesson 11-1 Identify and use inverse variations. Graph inverse variations.

After Lesson 11-1 Identify and use rational functions.

2 Teach

Scaffolding Questions

Have students read the **Why?** section of the lesson.

Ask:

- If a runner has an average pace of 5 miles an hour, how long will it take the runner to run 10 miles? 2 hours
- If a runner has an average pace of 6 miles an hour, how long will it take the runner to run 10 miles? 1 hour 40 min
- In both cases, what number does not change? the distance, 10 miles

LESSON 11-1 Inverse Variation

Then

- You solved problems involving direct variation.

Now

1. Identify and use inverse variations.
2. Graph inverse variations.

Why?

- The time it takes a runner to finish a race is inversely proportional to the average pace of the runner. The runner's time decreases as the pace of the runner increases. So, these quantities are *inversely proportional.*

NewVocabulary
inverse variation
product rule

Process Standards
PS.1

1 Identify and Use Inverse Variations

An **inverse variation** can be represented by the equation $y = \frac{k}{x}$ or $xy = k$.

KeyConcept Inverse Variation

y varies inversely as x if there is some nonzero constant k such that $y = \frac{k}{x}$ or $xy = k$, where $x, y \neq 0$.

In an inverse variation, the product of two values remains constant. Recall that a relationship of the form $y = kx$ is a *direct variation*. The constant k is called the *constant of variation* or the *constant of proportionality*.

Example 1 Identify Inverse and Direct Variations

Determine whether each table or equation represents an *inverse* or a *direct* variation. Explain.

a.

x	y
1	16
2	8
4	4

In an inverse variation, xy equals a constant k. Find xy for each ordered pair in the table.

$1 \cdot 16 = 16$ $2 \cdot 8 = 16$ $4 \cdot 4 = 16$

The product is constant, so the table represents an inverse variation.

b.

x	y
1	3
2	6
3	9

Notice that xy is not constant. So, the table does not represent an indirect variation.

$3 = k(1)$ $6 = k(2)$ $9 = k(3)$
$3 = k$ $3 = k$ $3 = k$

The table of values represents the direct variation $y = 3x$.

c. $x = 2y$

The equation can be written as $y = \frac{1}{2}x$. Therefore, it represents a direct variation.

d. $2xy = 10$

$2xy = 10$ Write the equation.
$xy = 5$ Divide each side by 2.

The equation represents an inverse variation.

GuidedPractice

1A.

x	1	2	5
y	10	5	2

Inverse; xy equals a constant.

1B. $-2x = y$ Direct; $-2x = y$ is equivalent to $y = -2x$.

Lesson 11-1 Resources

Resource	Approaching Level AL	On Level OL	Beyond Level BL	English Learners ELL
Teacher Edition		▪ Differentiated Instruction, p. 682	▪ Differentiated Instruction, pp. 679, 682	
Chapter Resource Masters	▪ Study Guide and Intervention, pp. 5–6 ▪ Skills Practice, p. 7 ▪ Practice, p. 8 ▪ Word Problem Practice, p. 9	▪ Study Guide and Intervention, pp. 5–6 ▪ Skills Practice, p. 7 ▪ Practice, p. 8 ▪ Word Problem Practice, p. 9 ▪ Enrichment, p. 10	▪ Practice, p. 8 ▪ Word Problem Practice, p. 9 ▪ Enrichment, p. 10	▪ Study Guide and Intervention, pp. 5–6 ▪ Skills Practice, p. 7 ▪ Practice, p. 8 ▪ Word Problem Practice, p. 9
Other	▪ 5-Minute Check 11-1 ▪ Study Notebook	▪ 5-Minute Check 11-1 ▪ Study Notebook	▪ 5-Minute Check 11-1 ▪ Study Notebook	▪ 5-Minute Check 11-1 ▪ Study Notebook

You can use $xy = k$ to write an inverse variation equation that relates x and y.

ReadingMath

Variation Equations For direct variation equations, you say that y *varies directly* as x. For inverse variation equations, you say that y *varies inversely* as x.

Example 2 Write an Inverse Variation

Assume that y varies inversely as x. If $y = 18$ when $x = 2$, write an inverse variation equation that relates x and y.

$xy = k$ — Inverse variation equation

$2(18) = k$ — $x = 2$ and $y = 18$

$36 = k$ — Simplify.

The constant of variation is 36. So, an equation that relates x and y is $xy = 36$ or $y = \frac{36}{x}$.

GuidedPractice

2. Assume that y varies inversely as x. If $y = 5$ when $x = -4$, write an inverse variation equation that relates x and y. $xy = -20$ or $y = \frac{-20}{x}$

If (x_1, y_1) and (x_2, y_2) are solutions of an inverse variation, then $x_1y_1 = k$ and $x_2y_2 = k$.

$x_1y_1 = k$ and $x_2y_2 = k$

$x_1y_1 = x_2y_2$ — Substitute x_2y_2 for k.

The equation $x_1y_1 = x_2y_2$ is called the **product rule** for inverse variations.

KeyConcept Product Rule for Inverse Variations

Words If (x_1, y_1) and (x_2, y_2) are solutions of an inverse variation, then the products x_1y_1 and x_2y_2 are equal.

Symbols $x_1y_1 = x_2y_2$ or $\frac{x_1}{x_2} = \frac{y_2}{y_1}$

Example 3 Solve for x or y

Assume that y varies inversely as x. If $y = 3$ when $x = 12$, find x when $y = 4$.

$x_1y_1 = x_2y_2$ — Product rule for inverse variations

$12 \cdot 3 = x_2 \cdot 4$ — $x_1 = 12$, $y_1 = 3$, and $y_2 = 4$

$36 = x_2 \cdot 4$ — Simplify.

$\frac{36}{4} = x_2$ — Divide each side by 4.

$9 = x_2$ — Simplify.

So, when $y = 4$, $x = 9$.

GuidedPractice

3. If y varies inversely as x and $y = 4$ when $x = -8$, find y when $x = -4$. 8

The product rule for inverse variations can be used to write an equation to solve real-world problems.

Teach with Tech

Interactive Whiteboard Choose a student to work through an example in front of the class. Give the student an x-value and a y-value. Have the student find the constant of variation given that y varies inversely with x.

1 Identify and Use Inverse Variations

Example 1 shows how to identify inverse and direct variations. **Example 2** shows how to write an inverse variation equation to relate x and y. **Example 3** shows how to use the product rule for inverse variations to find a value for x or y. **Example 4** shows how to use the product rule for inverse variations to model a real-world situation.

Formative Assessment

Use the Guided Practice exercises after each Example to determine students' understanding of concepts.

Additional Examples

1 Determine whether each table or equation represents an *inverse* or a *direct* variation. Explain.

a.

x	6	8	10
y	3	4	5

Direct variation; $y = \frac{1}{2}x$.

b.

x	1	2	3
y	12	6	4

Inverse variation; xy is a constant.

c. $-2xy = 20$ Inverse variation; xy is a constant.

d. $x = 0.5y$ Direct variation; the equation can be written in the form $y = kx$.

2 Assume that y varies inversely as x. If $y = 5$ when $x = 3$, write an inverse variation equation that relates x and y. $xy = 15$ or $y = \frac{15}{x}$

3 Assume that y varies inversely as x. If $y = 5$ when $x = 12$, find x when $y = 15$. 4

Additional Examples also in Interactive Classroom PowerPoint® Presentations

IWB Interactive White Board READY

Additional Example

4 **PHYSICAL SCIENCE** When two people are balanced on a seesaw, their distances from the center of the seesaw are inversely proportional to their weights. How far should a 105-pound person sit from the center of the seesaw to balance a 63-pound person sitting 3.5 feet from the center? 2.1 ft

2 Graph Inverse Variations

Example 5 shows how to graph an inverse variation in which there are negative values of *x*.

Additional Example

5 Graph an inverse variation in which $y = 1$ when $x = 4$.

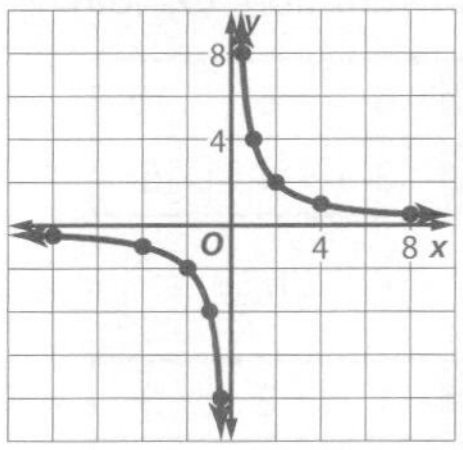

Focus on Mathematical Content

Inverse Variation When the product of two quantities remains constant, the quantities form an inverse variation. As one quantity increases, the other decreases, as long as $k > 0$. The nonzero product of the two quantities xy is called the constant of variation k.

Teaching the Process Standards

Sense-Making Mathematically proficient students consider analogous problems, and try simpler forms of the original problem in order to gain insight into its solution. Point out that the procedure for making a table of values and graphing points is the same for various types of functions.

Real-WorldLink

A standard hockey puck is 1 inch thick and 3 inches in diameter. Its mass is between approximately 156 and 170 grams.

Source: *NHL Rulebook*

Real-World Example 4 Use Inverse Variations

PHYSICS The acceleration a of a hockey puck is inversely proportional to its mass m. Suppose a hockey puck with a mass of 164 grams is hit so that it accelerates 122 m/s². Find the acceleration of a 158-gram hockey puck if the same amount of force is applied.

Make a table to organize the information.

Puck	Mass	Acceleration
1	164 g	122 m/s²
2	158 g	a_2

Let $m_1 = 164$, $a_1 = 122$, and $m_2 = 164$. Solve for a_2.

$m_1a_1 = m_2a_2$ — Use the product rule to write an equation.

$164 \cdot 122 = 158a_2$ — $m_1 = 164$, $a_1 = 122$, and $m_2 = 158$

$20{,}008 = 158a_2$ — Simplify.

$126.6 \approx a_2$ — Divide each side by 158 and simplify.

The 158-gram puck has an acceleration of approximately 126.6 m/s².

GuidedPractice

4. **RACING** Manuel runs an average of 8 miles per hour and finishes a race in 0.39 hour. Dyani finished the race in 0.35 hour. What was her average pace? **about 8.9 mph**

2 Graph Inverse Variations

The graph of an inverse variation is not a straight line like the graph of a direct variation.

Problem-SolvingTip

Sense-Making

Sometimes it is necessary to break a problem into parts, solve each part, and then combine them to find the solution to the problem.

Example 5 Graph an Inverse Variation

Graph an inverse variation equation in which $y = 8$ when $x = 3$.

Step 1 Write an inverse variation equation.

$xy = k$ — Inverse variation equation

$3(8) = k$ — $x = 3, y = 8$

$24 = k$ — Simplify.

The inverse variation equation is $xy = 24$ or $y = \frac{24}{x}$.

Step 2 Choose values for x and y that have a product of 24.

Step 3 Plot each point and draw a smooth curve that connects the points.

x	y
−12	−2
−8	−3
−4	−6
−2	−12
0	undefined
2	12
3	8
6	4
12	2

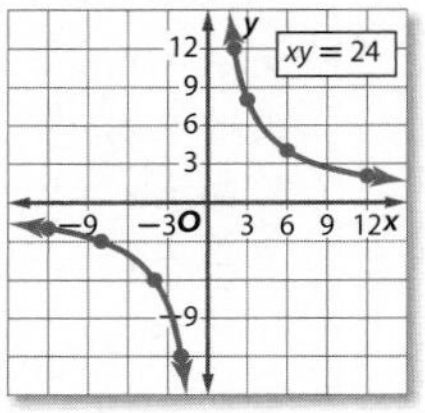

Notice that since y is undefined when $x = 0$, there is no point on the graph when $x = 0$. This graph is called a hyperbola.

GuidedPractice

5. Graph an inverse variation equation in which $y = 16$ when $x = 4$.

5.

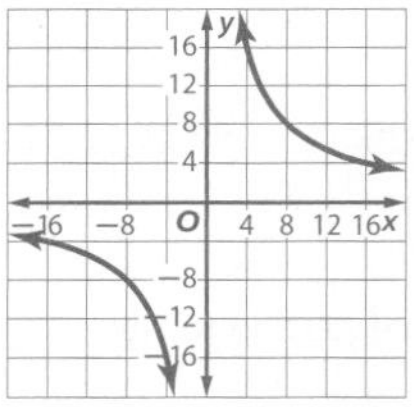

Additional Answers

5.

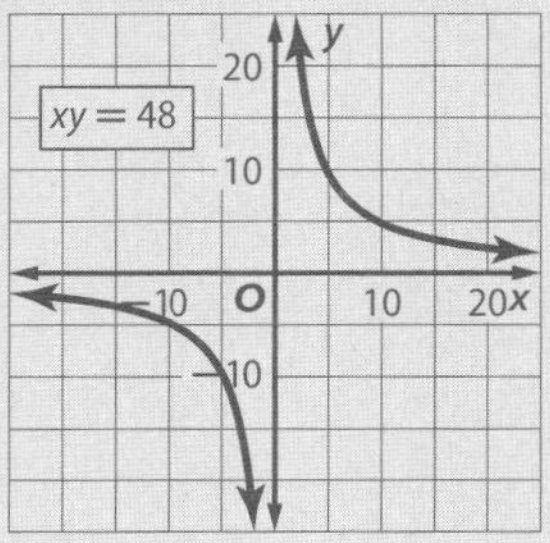

6.

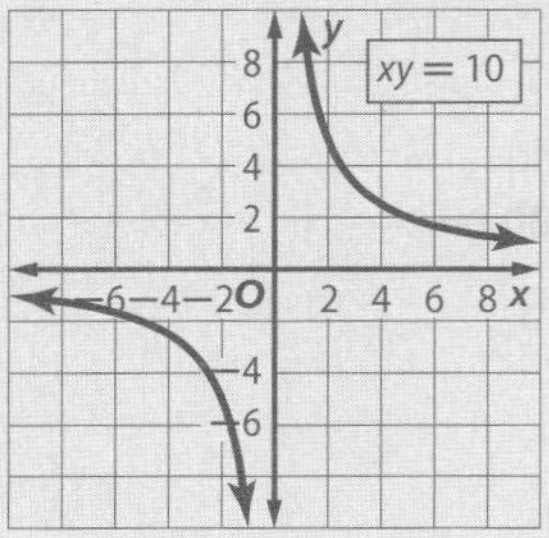

7.

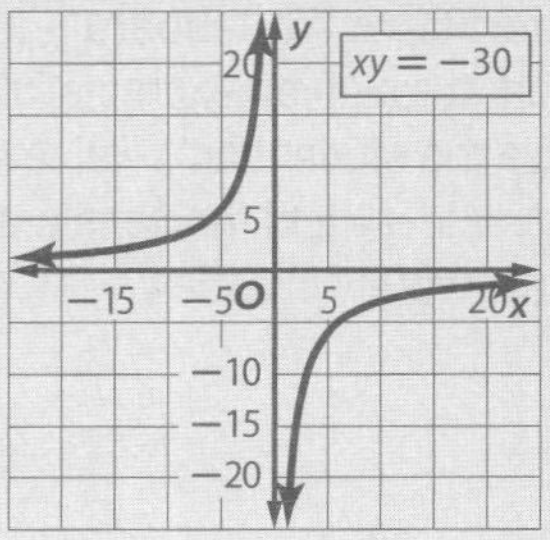

ConceptSummary Direct and Inverse Variations

Direct Variation	Inverse Variation
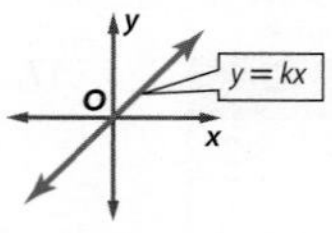 $k > 0$ 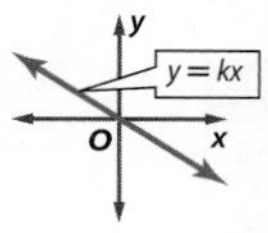 $k < 0$	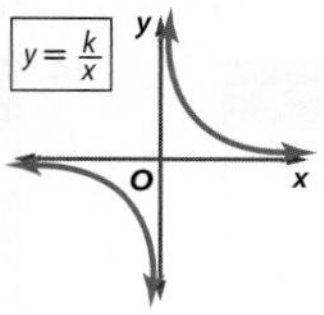 $k > 0$ 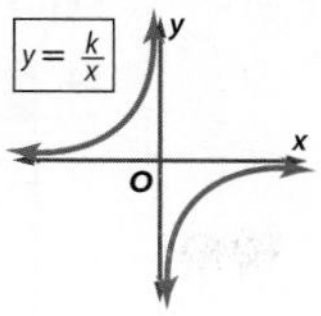 $k < 0$
• $y = kx$ • y varies directly as x. • The ratio $\frac{y}{x}$ is a constant.	• $y = \frac{k}{x}$ • y varies inversely as x. • The product xy is a constant.

Check Your Understanding

= Step-by-Step Solutions begin on page R13.

Example 1 **Determine whether each table or equation represents an *inverse* or a *direct* variation. Explain.**

1.

x	1	4	8	12
y	2	8	16	24

1. Direct; the data in the table can be represented by the equation $y = 2x$.

2. Inverse; $xy = 24$.

x	1	2	3	4
y	24	12	8	6

3. $xy = 4$ Inverse; $xy = 4$.

4. $y = \frac{x}{10}$ Direct; $y = \frac{1}{10}x$.

Examples 2, 5 **Assume that y varies inversely as x. Write an inverse variation equation that relates x and y. Then graph the equation.** 5–8. See margin.

5. $y = 8$ when $x = 6$
6. $y = 2$ when $x = 5$
7. $y = 3$ when $x = -10$
8. $y = -1$ when $x = -12$

Example 3 **Solve. Assume that y varies inversely as x.**

9. If $y = 8$ when $x = 4$, find x when $y = 2$. 16
10. If $y = 7$ when $x = 6$, find y when $x = -21$. −2
11. If $y = -5$ when $x = 9$, find y when $x = 6$. −7.5

Example 4

12. **RACING** The time it takes to complete a go-cart race course is inversely proportional to the average speed of the go-cart. One rider has an average speed of 73.3 feet per second and completes the course in 30 seconds. Another rider completes the course in 25 seconds. What was the average speed of the second rider? 87.96 ft/s

13. **OPTOMETRY** When a person does not have clear vision, an optometrist can prescribe lenses to correct the condition. The power P of a lens, in a unit called diopters, is equal to 1 divided by the focal length f, in meters, of the lens.
    a. Graph the inverse variation $P = \frac{1}{f}$. See margin.
    b. Find the powers of lenses with focal lengths +0.2 to −0.4 meters. 5 to −2.5 diopters

DifferentiatedInstruction BL

If students need a challenge in this lesson,

Then borrow a fulcrum, lever, and weights from a science teacher to recreate Additional Example 4 or Exercise 44. After some experimentation, ask students to calculate where to place the weights for the lever to balance.

3 Practice

Formative Assessment

Use Exercises 1–13 to check for understanding.

Use the chart at the bottom of the next page to customize assignments for your students.

Exercise Alert

Grid Paper For Exercises 5–8, 13, 22–27, and 51 students will need grid paper.

Additional Answers

8.

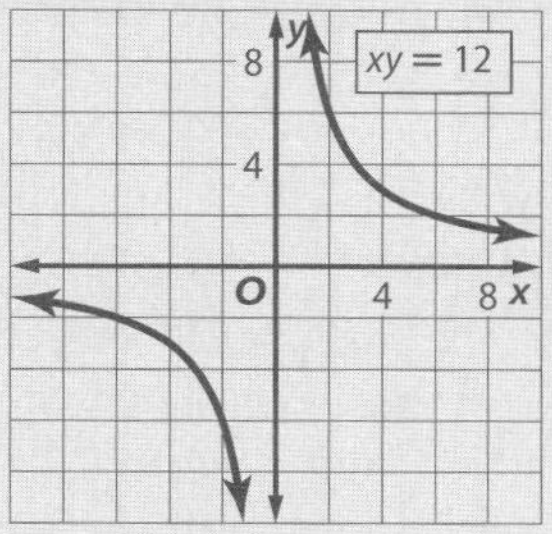

13a.

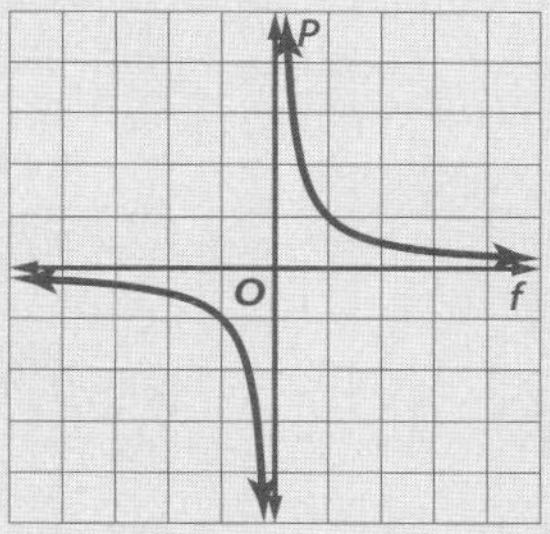

connectED.mcgraw-hill.com 679

Practice and Problem Solving

Extra Practice is on page R11.

Example 1 **Determine whether each table or equation represents an *inverse* or a *direct* variation. Explain.** 14–21. See margin.

14.

x	y
1	30
2	15
5	6
6	5

15.

x	y
2	−6
3	−9
4	−12
5	−15

16.

x	y
−4	−2
−2	−1
2	1
4	2

17.

x	y
−5	8
−2	20
4	−10
8	−5

18. $5x - y = 0$ **19.** $xy = \frac{1}{4}$ **20.** $x = 14y$ **21.** $\frac{y}{x} = 9$

Examples 2, 5 **Assume that y varies inversely as x. Write an inverse variation equation that relates x and y. Then graph the equation.** 22–27. See Ch. 11 Answer Appendix.

22. $y = 2$ when $x = 20$ **23.** $y = 18$ when $x = 4$ **24.** $y = -6$ when $x = -3$

25. $y = -4$ when $x = -3$ **26.** $y = -4$ when $x = 16$ **27.** $y = 12$ when $x = -9$

Example 3 **Solve. Assume that y varies inversely as x.**

28. If $y = 12$ when $x = 3$, find x when $y = 6$. 6

29. If $y = 5$ when $x = 6$, find x when $y = 2$. 15

30. If $y = 4$ when $x = 14$, find x when $y = -5$. −11.2

31. If $y = 9$ when $x = 9$, find y when $x = -27$. −3

32. If $y = 15$ when $x = -2$, find y when $x = 3$. −10

33. If $y = -8$ when $x = -12$, find y when $x = 10$. 9.6

Example 4 **34.** **EARTH SCIENCE** The water level in a river varies inversely with air temperature. When the air temperature was 90° Fahrenheit, the water level was 11 feet. If the air temperature was 110° Fahrenheit, what was the level of water in the river? 9 ft

35. **MUSIC** When under equal tension, the frequency of a vibrating string in a piano varies inversely with the string length. If a string that is 420 millimeters in length vibrates at a frequency of 523 cycles a second, at what frequency will a 707-millimeter string vibrate? approximately 311 cycles per second

Determine whether each situation is an example of an *inverse* or a *direct* variation. Justify your reasoning. 36–39. See margin.

36. The drama club can afford to purchase 10 wigs at $2 each or 5 wigs at $4 each.

37. The Spring family buys several lemonades for $1.50 each.

38. Nicole earns $14 for babysitting 2 hours, and $21 for babysitting 3 hours.

B **39.** Thirty video game tokens are divided evenly among a group of friends.

Determine whether each table or graph represents an *inverse* or a *direct* variation. Explain. 40–43. See margin.

40.

x	y
5	1
8	1.6
11	2.2

41.

x	y
−3	−7
−2	−10.5
4	5.25

42.

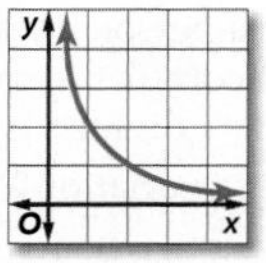

43.

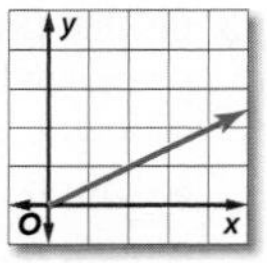

Differentiated Homework Options

Level	Assignment	Two-Day Option	
AL Basic	14–35, 52, 54–78	15–35 odd, 57–60	14–34 even, 52, 54–56, 61–78
OL Core	15–43 odd, 44, 45–49 odd, 50–52, 54–78	14–35, 57–60	36–52, 54–56, 61–78
BL Advanced	36–70, (optional: 71–78)		

Teaching the Process Standards

Critique Mathematically proficient students read the arguments of others and decide whether they make sense. In Exercise 52, point out that a single pair of x- and y-values could represent either a direct or indirect variation. In this problem, x and y vary inversely.

Additional Answers

14. Inverse; $xy = 30$

15. Direct; $y = -3x$

16. Direct; $y = -\frac{1}{2}x$

17. Inverse; $xy = -40$

18. Direct; $y = 5x$

19. Inverse; $xy = \frac{1}{4}$

20. Direct; $y = kx$

21. Direct; $y = 9x$

36. Inverse; the cost per wig times the number of wigs equals the total amount they can spend, $20.

37. Direct; the number of lemonades times the cost per lemonade equals the total cost. So the ratio $\frac{\text{total cost}}{\text{number of lemonades}}$ is a constant $1.50.

38. Direct; the number of hours times the rate per hour equals the total pay. The ratio $\frac{\text{total pay}}{\text{number of hours}}$ is a constant $7.

39. Inverse; the number of friends times the number of tokens per person equals the constant 30.

40. Direct; $y = 0.2x$

41. Inverse; $xy = 21$

42. Inverse; $xy = 2$

43. Direct; $y = \frac{1}{2}x$

55. Sample answer: Newton's Law of Gravitational Force is an example of an inverse variation that models real-world situations. The gravitational force exerted on two objects is inversely proportional to the square of the distances between the two objects. The force exerted on the two objects, times the square of the distance between the two objects, is equal to the gravitational constant times the masses of the two objects.

44. **PHYSICAL SCIENCE** When two people are balanced on a seesaw, their distances from the center of the seesaw are inversely proportional to their weights. If a 118-pound person sits 1.8 meters from the center of the seesaw, how far should a 125-pound person sit from the center to balance the seesaw? **about 1.7 m**

C **Solve. Assume that y varies inversely as x.**

45. If $y = 9.2$ when $x = 6$, find x when $y = 3$. **18.4**

46. If $y = 3.8$ when $x = 1.5$, find x when $y = 0.3$. **19**

47. If $y = \frac{1}{5}$ when $x = -20$, find y when $x = -\frac{8}{5}$. **2.5**

48. If $y = -6.3$ when $x = \frac{2}{3}$, find y when $x = 8$. **−0.525**

49. **SWIMMING** Logan and Brianna each bought a pool membership. Their average cost per day is inversely proportional to the number of days that they go to the pool. Logan went to the pool 25 days for an average cost per day of $5.60. Brianna went to the pool 35 days. What was her average cost per day? **$4**

50. **PHYSICAL SCIENCE** The amount of force required to do a certain amount of work in moving an object is inversely proportional to the distance that the object is moved. Suppose 90 N of force is required to move an object 10 feet. Find the force needed to move another object 15 feet if the same amount of work is done. **60 N**

51. **DRIVING** Lina must practice driving 40 hours with a parent or guardian before she is allowed to take the test to get her driver's license. She plans to practice the same number of hours each week. **a, c. See Ch. 11 Answer Appendix.**
    a. Let h represent the number of hours per week that she practices driving. Make a table showing the number of weeks w that she will need to practice for the following values of h: 1, 2, 4, 5, 8, and 10.
    b. Describe how the number of weeks changes as the number of hours per week increases. **The number of weeks decreases.**
    c. Write and graph an equation that shows the relationship between h and w.

H.O.T. Problems Use Higher-Order Thinking Skills

52. **CRITIQUE** Christian and Trevor found an equation such that x and y vary inversely, and $y = 10$ when $x = 5$. Is either of them correct? Explain.

Trevor; the constant of variation is 5(10) or 50, so the correct equation is $xy = 50$ or $y = \frac{50}{x}$. Christian found an equation for a direct variation.

Christian

$k = \frac{y}{x}$

$= \frac{10}{2}$ or 5

$y = 5x$

Trevor

$k = xy$

$= (5)(10)$ or 50

$y = \frac{50}{x}$

53. **CHALLENGE** Suppose f varies inversely with g, and g varies inversely with h. What is the relationship between f and h? **direct variation**

54. **REASONING** Does $xy = -k$ represent an inverse variation when $k \neq 0$? Explain. **Yes; the product of x and y is a nonzero constant.**

55. **OPEN ENDED** Give a real-world situation or phenomena that can be modeled by an inverse variation equation. Use the correct terminology to describe your example and explain why this situation is an inverse variation. **See margin.**

56. **WRITING IN MATH** Compare and contrast direct and inverse variation. Include a description of the relationship between slope and the graphs of a direct and inverse variation. **See margin.**

Additional Answer

56. Direct variation can be written as $y = kx$ where k is the constant of proportionality. The graph of a direct variation is a line through the origin with a slope of k. An inverse variation is written in the form $y = \frac{k}{x}$. The graph is a two-part curve (a hyperbola).

Enrichment
OL BL

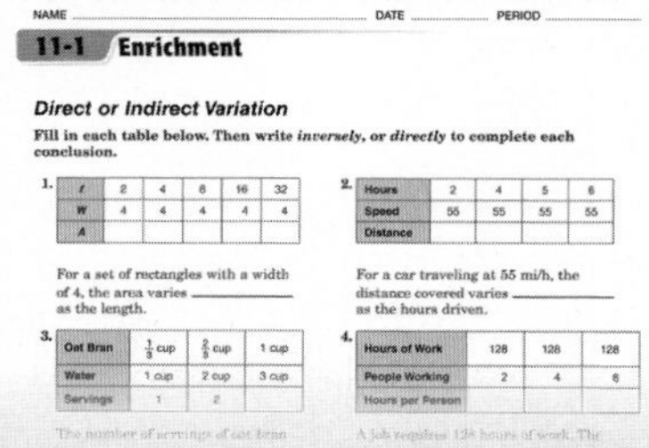

Study Guide and Intervention
AL OL ELL

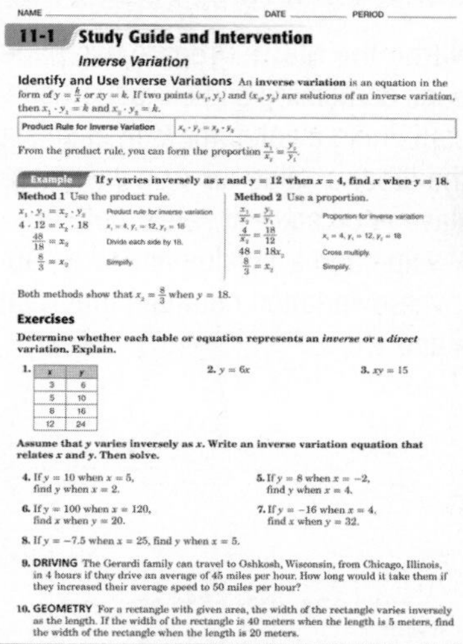

Practice
AL OL BL ELL

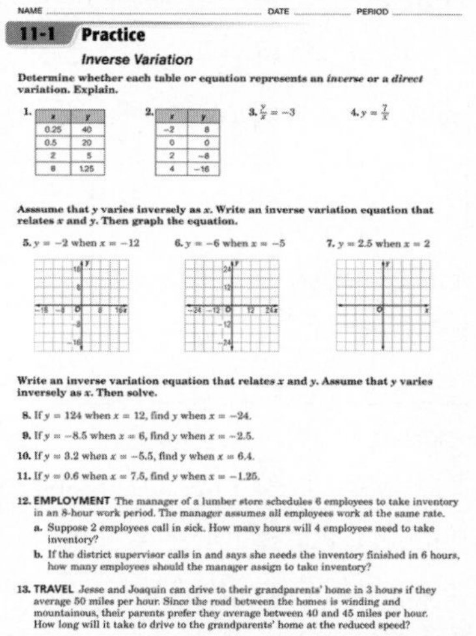

Word Problem Practice
AL OL BL ELL

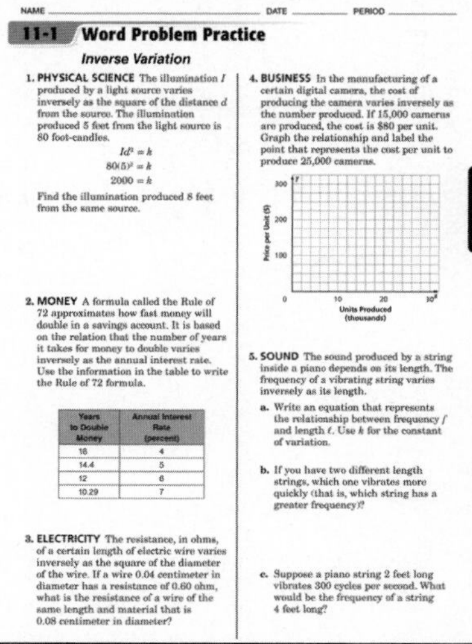

4 Assess

Name the Math Prepare two paper bags containing slips of paper: one containing a value for x on each slip, the other a value for y on each slip. Have each student select both an x-value and a y-value and write an inverse variation equation that relates x and y.

Additional Answers (Explore 11-2)

2. 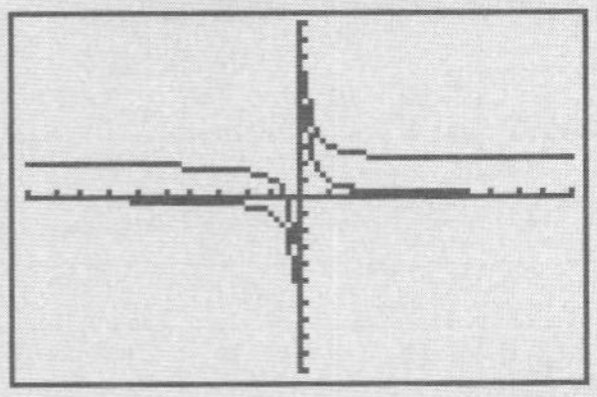

[−10, 10] scl: 1 by [−10, 10] scl: 1

Both graphs have the same shape, but the graph of $y = \frac{1}{x} + 2$ is 2 units above the graph of $y = \frac{1}{x}$.

3. 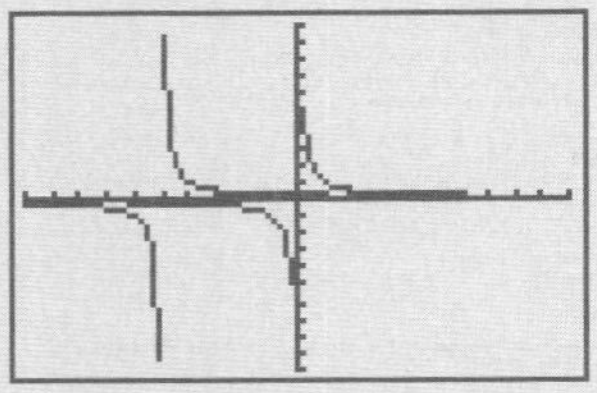

[−10, 10] scl: 1 by [−10, 10] scl: 1

Both graphs have the same shape, but the graph of $y = \frac{1}{x+5}$ is 5 units to the left of the graph of $y = \frac{1}{x}$.

4. 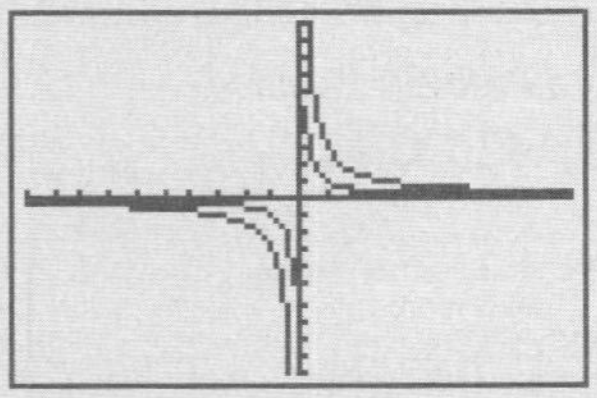

[−10, 10] scl: 1 by [−10, 10] scl: 1

The graph of $y = \frac{3}{x}$ is farther from the axes than the graph of $y = \frac{1}{x}$.

Standardized Test Practice

57. Given a constant force, the acceleration of an object varies inversely with its mass. Assume that a constant force is acting on an object with a mass of 6 pounds resulting in an acceleration of 10 ft/s^2. The same force acts on another object with a mass of 12 pounds. What would be the resulting acceleration? **B**

A 4 ft/s^2
B 5 ft/s^2
C 6 ft/s^2
D 7 ft/s^2

58. Fiona had an average of 56% on her first seven tests. What would she have to make on her eighth test to average 60% on 8 tests? **G**

F 82%
G 88%
H 98%
J 100%

59. Anthony takes a picture of a 1-meter snake beside a brick wall. When he develops the pictures, the 1-meter snake is 2 centimeters long and the wall is 4.5 centimeters high. What was the actual height of the brick wall? **C**

A 2.25 cm
B 22.5 cm
C 225 cm
D 2250 cm

60. SHORT RESPONSE Find the area of the rectangle. **$x^2 + 15x + 36$ cm^2**

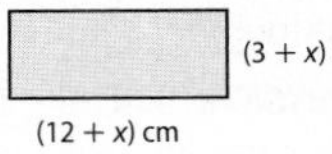

Spiral Review

For each triangle, find sin A, cos A, and tan A to the nearest ten-thousandth. (Lesson 10-6)

61. 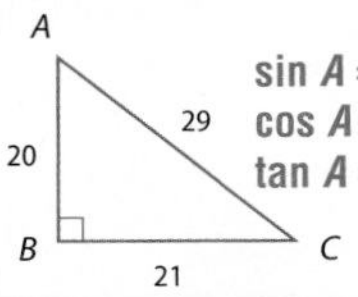

sin A = 0.7241, cos A = 0.6897, tan A = 1.05

62. 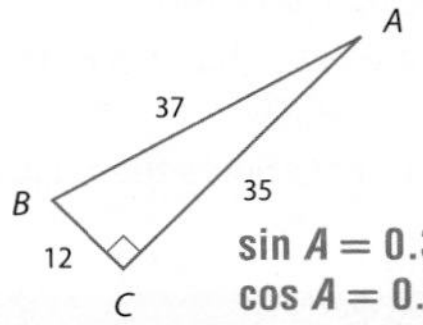

sin A = 0.3243, cos A = 0.9459, tan A = 0.3429

63. 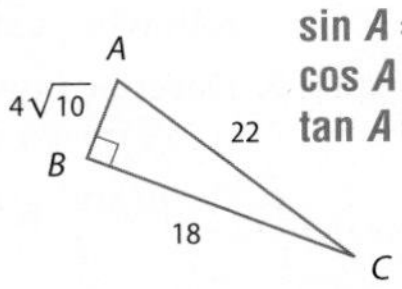

sin A = 0.8182, cos A = 0.5750, tan A = 1.4230

64. CRAFTS Jane is making a stained glass window using several triangular pieces of glass like the one shown. What is the length of the third side? (Lesson 10-5) **$2\sqrt{2}$ in.**

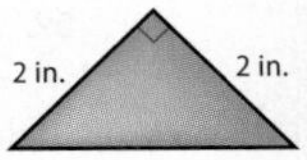

Solve each equation. (Lesson 10-4)

65. $\sqrt{10c} + 2 = 5$ **$\frac{9}{10}$**

66. $\sqrt{9h + 19} = 9$ **$6\frac{8}{9}$**

67. $\sqrt{7k + 2} + 2 = 5$ **1**

68. $\sqrt{5r - 1} = r - 5$ **13**

69. $6 + \sqrt{2x + 11} = -x$ **no solution**

70. $4 + \sqrt{4t - 4} = t$ **10**

Skills Review

Simplify. Assume that no denominator is equal to zero.

71. $\frac{7^8}{7^6}$ **7^2 or 49**

72. $\frac{x^8y^{12}}{x^2y^7}$ **x^6y^5**

73. $\frac{5pq^7}{10p^6q^3}$ **$\frac{q^4}{2p^5}$**

74. $\left(\frac{2c^3d}{7z^2}\right)^3$ **$\frac{8c^9d^3}{343z^6}$**

75. $\left(\frac{4a^2b}{2c^3}\right)^2$ **$\frac{4a^4b^2}{c^6}$**

76. $y^0(y^5)(y^{-9})$ **$\frac{1}{y^4}$**

77. $\frac{(4m^{-3}n^5)^0}{mn}$ **$\frac{1}{mn}$**

78. $\frac{(3x^2y^5)^0}{(21x^5y^2)^0}$ **1**

Differentiated Instruction OL BL

Extension Write $k = 4$ on the board. Ask students to write and graph an inverse variation equation that uses 4 as the constant of variation. $xy = 4$

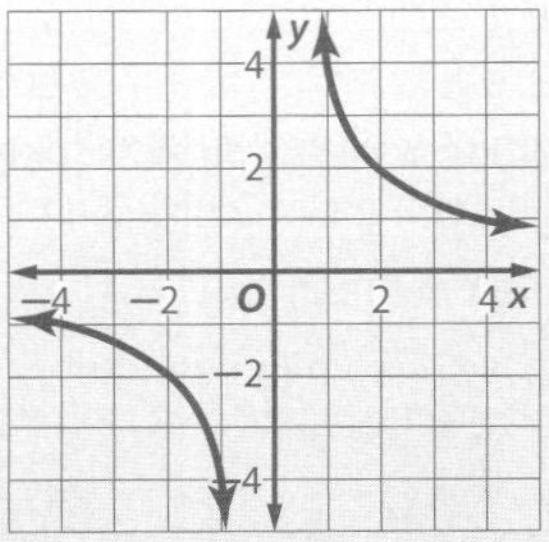

682 | Lesson 11-1 | Inverse Variation

Graphing Technology Lab
Family of Rational Functions

You can use a graphing calculator to analyze how changing the parameters a and b in $y = \frac{a}{x - b} + c$ affects the graphs in the family of rational functions.

Activity Change Parameters

Graph each set of equations on the same screen in the standard viewing window. Describe any similarities and differences among the graphs.

a. $y = \frac{1}{x}$, $y = \frac{1}{x} + 2$, $y = \frac{1}{x} - 4$

Enter the equations in the Y= list and graph in the standard viewing window.

The graphs have the same shape. Each graph approaches the y-axis on both sides. However, the graphs have different vertical positions.

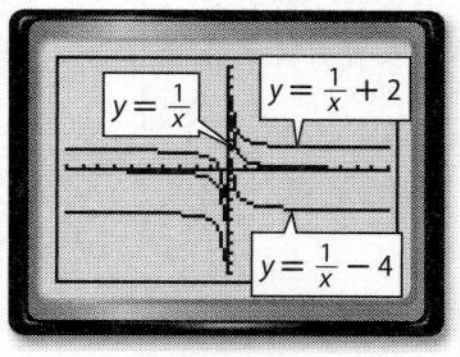

[−10, 10] scl: 1 by [−10, 10] scl: 1

b. $y = \frac{1}{x}$, $y = \frac{1}{x + 2}$, $y = \frac{1}{x - 4}$

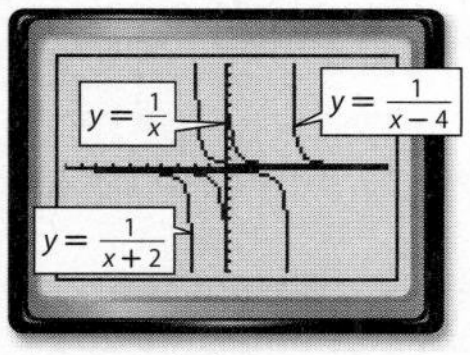

[−10, 10] scl: 1 by [−10, 10] scl: 1

The graphs have the same shape, and all approach the x-axis from both sides. However, the graphs have different horizontal positions.

c. $y = \frac{1}{x}$, $y = \frac{2}{x}$, $y = \frac{4}{x}$

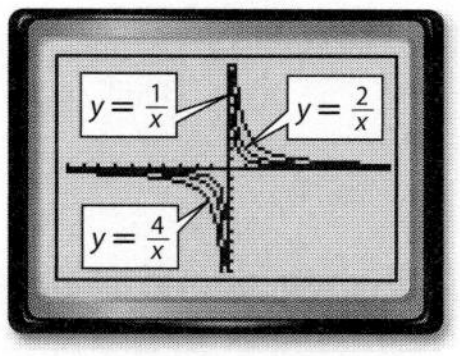

[−10, 10] scl: 1 by [−10, 10] scl: 1

The graphs all approach the x-axis and the y-axis from both sides. However, the graphs have different shapes.

Model and Analyze

1. How do a, b, and c affect the graph of $y = \frac{a}{x - b} + c$? Give examples. **See margin.**

Examine each pair of equations and predict the similarities and differences in their graphs. Use a graphing calculator to confirm your predictions. Write a sentence or two comparing the two graphs. **2–4. See margin.**

2. $y = \frac{1}{x}$, $y = \frac{1}{x} + 2$
3. $y = \frac{1}{x}$, $y = \frac{1}{x + 5}$
4. $y = \frac{1}{x}$, $y = \frac{3}{x}$

Additional Answer

1. The value of c affects the vertical position of the graph. The value of b affects the horizontal position of the graph. The value of a affects the shape of the graph. Sample answer: The graph of $y = \frac{1}{x} + 5$ is 5 units above the x-axis. The graph of $y = \frac{1}{x + 5}$ is 5 units to the left of the y-axis. The graph of $y = \frac{5}{x}$ is farther from the axes than the graph of $y = \frac{1}{x}$.

1 Focus

Objective Use graphing technology to investigate families of rational functions.

Materials

- TI-83/84 Plus or other graphing calculator

Teaching Tips

- Remind students to use ZOOM 6 to show graphs in the standard viewing window.
- In parts b and c, students will need to clear the Y= lists. To do this, they can use CLEAR.
- Use TRACE and ▼ or ▲ to display the equation for a graph.

2 Teach

Working in Cooperative Groups

Divide the class into pairs. Work through the Activity. Then ask students to work with their partners to complete Exercise 1.

Practice Have students complete Exercises 2–4.

3 Assess

Formative Assessment

Use Exercises 2–4 to assess each student's ability to predict similarities and differences in rational functions.

From Concrete to Abstract

Ask students to summarize using technology to investigate families of rational functions.

1 Focus

VerticalAlignment

Before Lesson 11-2 Write inverse variation equations.

Lesson 11-2 Identify excluded values. Identify and use asymptotes to graph rational functions.

After Lesson 11-2 Use rational equations to solve problems.

2 Teach

Scaffolding Questions

Have students read the **Why?** section of the lesson.

Ask:

- What does the average number of pages Trina reads each day depend on? the number of days she reads
- What happens to the value of y as x increases? It decreases.
- What values of x are excluded from consideration? x cannot equal 0 or any negative number.

LESSON 11-2 Rational Functions

Then

- You wrote inverse variation equations.

Now

1. Identify excluded values.
2. Identify and use asymptotes to graph rational functions.

Why?

- Trina is reading a 300-page book. The average number of pages she reads each day y is given by $y = \frac{300}{x}$, where x is the number of days that she reads.

NewVocabulary
rational function
excluded value
asymptote

Process Standards
PS.3, PS.7

1 Identify Excluded Values

The function $y = \frac{300}{x}$ is an example of a **rational function**. This function is nonlinear.

KeyConcept Rational Functions

Words A rational function can be described by an equation of the form $y = \frac{p}{q}$, where p and q are polynomials and $q \neq 0$.

Parent function:	$f(x) = \frac{1}{x}$
Type of graph:	hyperbola
Domain:	$\{x \mid x \neq 0\}$
Range:	$\{y \mid y \neq 0\}$

Graph

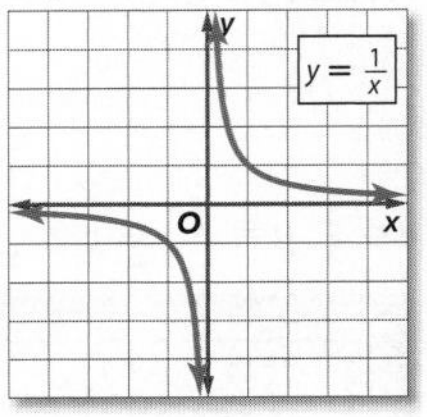

Since division by zero is undefined, any value of a variable that results in a denominator of zero in a rational function is excluded from the domain of the function. These are called **excluded values** for the rational function.

PT

Example 1 Find Excluded Values

State the excluded value for each function.

a. $y = -\frac{2}{x}$

The denominator cannot equal 0. So, the excluded value is $x = 0$.

b. $y = \frac{2}{x+1}$

$x + 1 = 0$ Set the denominator equal to 0.

$x = -1$

The excluded value is $x = -1$.

c. $y = \frac{5}{4x - 8}$

$4x - 8 = 0$

$4x = 8$

$x = 2$

The excluded value is $x = 2$.

GuidedPractice

1A. $y = \frac{5}{2x}$ $x = 0$ **1B.** $y = \frac{x}{x-7}$ $x = 7$ **1C.** $y = \frac{4}{3x+9}$ $x = -3$

684 | Lesson 11-2

Lesson 11-2 Resources

Resource	Approaching Level AL	On Level OL	Beyond Level BL	English Learners ELL
Teacher Edition	▪ Differentiated Instruction, p. 685	▪ Differentiated Instruction, pp. 685, 689	▪ Differentiated Instruction, p. 689	▪ Differentiated Instruction, p. 685
Chapter Resource Masters	▪ Study Guide and Intervention, pp. 11–12 ▪ Skills Practice, p. 13 ▪ Practice, p. 14 ▪ Word Problem Practice, p. 15	▪ Study Guide and Intervention, pp. 11–12 ▪ Skills Practice, p. 13 ▪ Practice, p. 14 ▪ Word Problem Practice, p. 15 ▪ Enrichment, p. 16	▪ Practice, p. 14 ▪ Word Problem Practice, p. 15 ▪ Enrichment, p. 16	▪ Study Guide and Intervention, pp. 11–12 ▪ Skills Practice, p. 13 ▪ Practice, p. 14 ▪ Word Problem Practice, p. 15
Other	▪ 5-Minute Check 11-2 ▪ Study Notebook	▪ 5-Minute Check 11-2 ▪ Study Notebook	▪ 5-Minute Check 11-2 ▪ Study Notebook	▪ 5-Minute Check 11-2 ▪ Study Notebook

Depending on the real-world situation, in addition to excluding x-values that make a denominator zero from the domain of a rational function, additional values might have to be excluded from the domain as well.

Real-WorldLink

As the temperature of the gas inside a hot air balloon increases, the density of the gas decreases. A hot air balloon rises because the density of the air inside it is less than the density of the air outside.

Source: Goddard Space Flight Center

Real-World Example 2 Graph Real-Life Rational Functions

BALLOONS If there are x people in the basket of a hot air balloon, the function $y = \frac{20}{x}$ represents the number of square feet y per person. Graph this function.

Since the number of people cannot be zero or less, it is reasonable to exclude negative values and only use positive values for x.

Number of People x	2	4	5	10
Square Feet per Person y	10	5	4	2

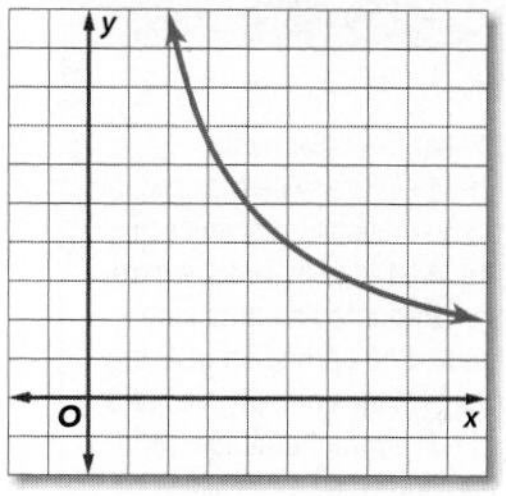

Notice that as x increases y approaches 0. This is reasonable since as the number of people increases, the space per person gets closer to 0.

GuidedPractice

2. GEOMETRY A rectangle has an area of 18 square inches. The function $\ell = \frac{18}{w}$ shows the relationship between the length and width. Graph the function. See Ch. 11 Answer Appendix.

2 Identify and Use Asymptotes

In Example 2, an excluded value is $x = 0$. Notice that the graph approaches the vertical line $x = 0$, but never touches it.

The graph also approaches but never touches the horizontal line $y = 0$. The lines $x = 0$ and $y = 0$ are called *asymptotes*. An **asymptote** is a line that the graph of a function approaches.

StudyTip

Use Asymptotes Asymptotes are helpful for graphing rational functions. However, they are not part of the graph.

KeyConcept Asymptotes

Words A rational function in the form $y = \frac{a}{x-b} + c$, $a \neq 0$, has a vertical asymptote at the x-value that makes the denominator equal zero, $x = b$. It has a horizontal asymptote at $y = c$.

Model

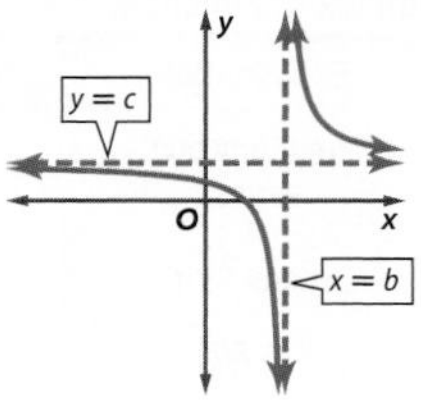

Example

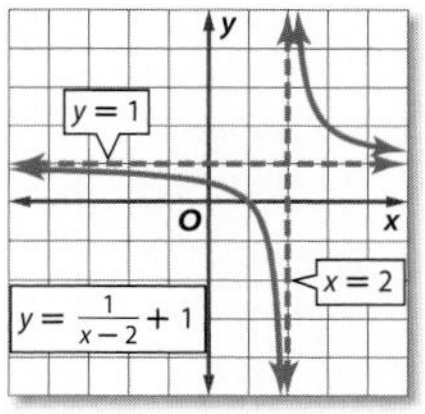

The domain of $y = \frac{a}{x-b} + c$ is all real numbers except $x = b$. The range is all real numbers except $y = c$. Rational functions cannot be traced with a pencil that never leaves the paper, so choose x-values on both sides of the vertical asymptote to graph both portions of the function.

DifferentiatedInstruction AL OL ELL

Logical Learners Most students understand that a fraction with a denominator equal to 0 is undefined, thus the vertical asymptote. To help students understand that a horizontal asymptote occurs at $y = c$ in a function in the form $y = \frac{a}{x-b} + c$ (where $a \neq 0$), have students make a table of values for x and y and a graph using the example shown in the Key Concept, $y = \frac{1}{x-2} + 1$. Have students extend the table of values and the graph until they all agree that, as x gets greater and greater, $y = \frac{1}{x-2}$ approaches 0, and y gets closer and closer to 1, the value for c.

1 Identify Excluded Values

Example 1 shows how to find excluded values for rational functions. **Example 2** shows how to graph real-life rational functions and determine which values should be excluded.

Formative Assessment

Use the Guided Practice exercises after each example to determine students' understanding of concepts.

Additional Examples

1 State the excluded value for each function.

a. $y = \frac{3}{x}$ $x = 0$

b. $y = \frac{3}{x+2}$ $x = -2$

c. $y = \frac{8}{2x+1}$ $x = -\frac{1}{2}$

2 TALENT SHOW If x students will compete in a talent show lasting 100 minutes, the function $y = \frac{100}{x}$ represents the number of minutes available for each act. Graph this function. graph of positive values for $y = \frac{100}{x}$ as shown below, through (10, 10) (5, 20), (20, 5), (25, 4)

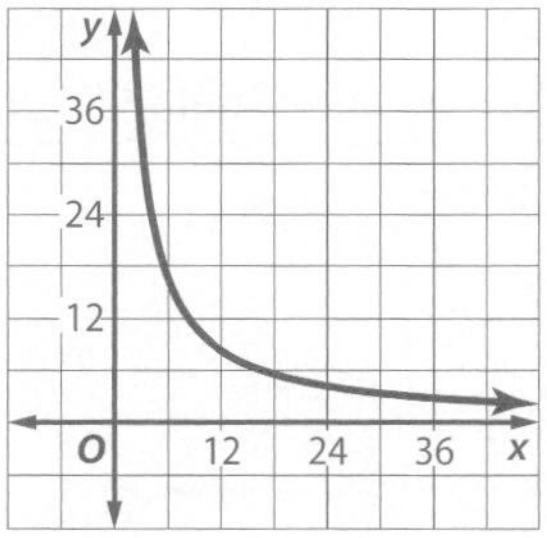

Additional Examples also in Interactive Classroom PowerPoint® Presentations

IWB Interactive White Board READY

Tips for New Teachers

Discrete vs. Continuous The functions used in Real World Example 2 and Additional Example 2 are discrete, not continuous.

2 Identify and Use Asymptotes

Example 3 shows how to identify the asymptotes of a function and use them to graph the function.

Additional Example

3 Identify the asymptotes for each function. Then graph the function.

a. $y = \frac{3}{x} - 4$ $x = 0; y = -4$

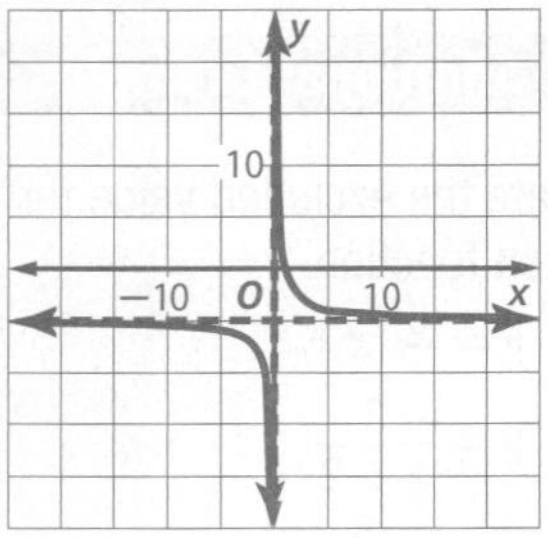

b. $y = \frac{2}{x+2}$ $x = -2; y = 0$

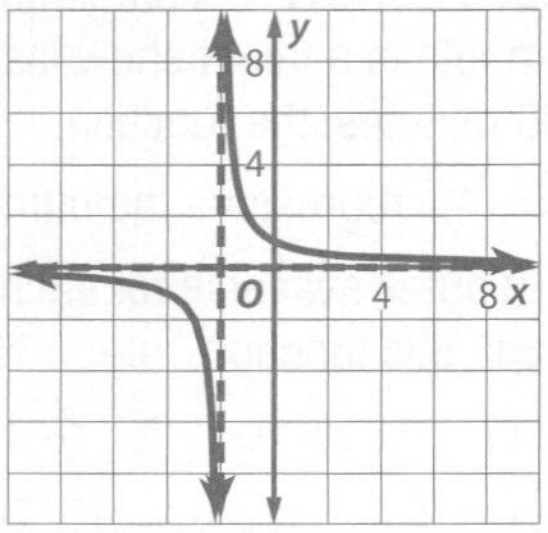

Additional Answers (Guided Practice)

3A. $x = 0; y = 0$

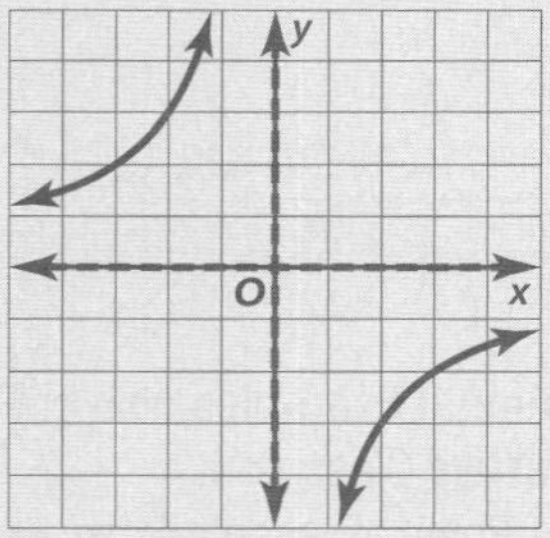

3B. $x = 3; y = 0$

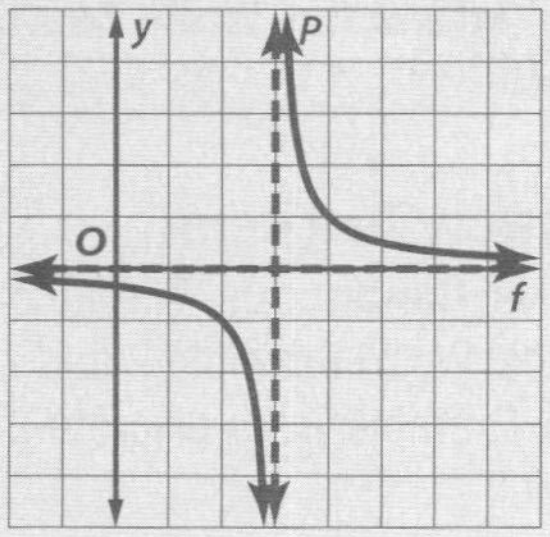

3C. $x = -2; y = 1$

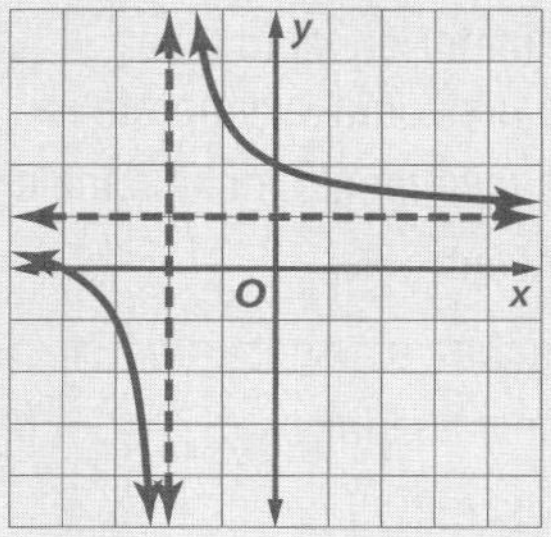

Math HistoryLink

Evelyn Boyd Granville (1924–) Granville majored in mathematics and physics at Smith College in 1945, where she graduated summa cum laude. She earned an M.A. in mathematics and physics and a Ph.D. in mathematics from Yale University. Granville's doctoral work focused on functional analysis.

Example 3 Identify and Use Asymptotes to Graph Functions

Identify the asymptotes of each function. Then graph the function.

a. $y = \frac{2}{x} - 4$

Step 1 Identify and graph the asymptotes using dashed lines.

vertical asymptote: $x = 0$

horizontal asymptote: $y = -4$

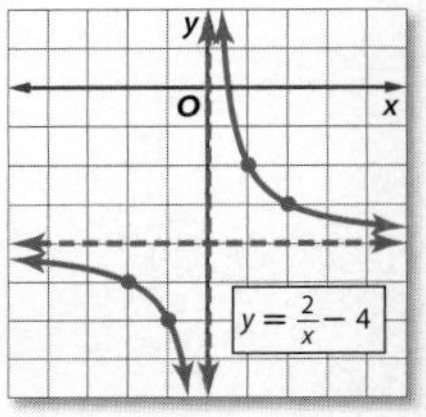

Step 2 Make a table of values and plot the points. Then connect them.

x	−2	−1	1	2
y	−5	−6	−2	−3

b. $y = \frac{1}{x+1}$

Step 1 To find the vertical asymptote, find the excluded value.

$x + 1 = 0$ Set the denominator equal to 0.

$x = -1$ Subtract 1 from each side.

vertical asymptote: $x = -1$

horizontal asymptote: $y = 0$

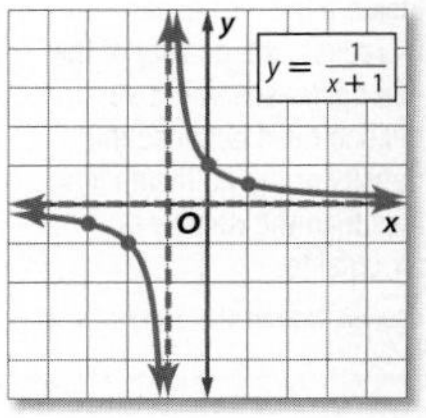

Step 2

x	−3	−2	0	1
y	−0.5	−1	1	0.5

GuidedPractice **3A–3C. See margin.**

3A. $y = -\frac{6}{x}$ **3B.** $y = \frac{1}{x-3}$ **3C.** $y = \frac{2}{x+2} + 1$

Four types of nonlinear functions are shown below.

ConceptSummary Families of Functions

Quadratic	Exponential	Radical	Rational
Parent function: $y = x^2$	Parent function: varies	Parent function: $y = \sqrt{x}$	Parent function: $y = \frac{1}{x}$
General form: $y = ax^2 + bx + c$	General form: $y = ab^x$	General form: $y = \sqrt{x - b} + c$	General form: $y = \frac{a}{x - b} + c$
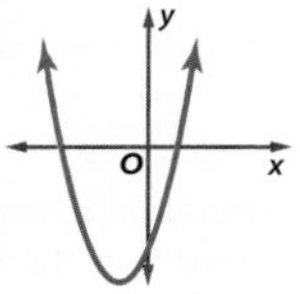	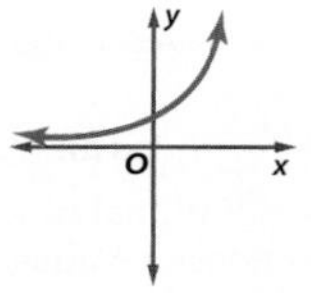	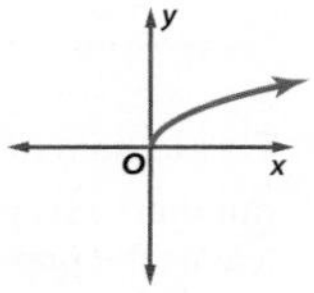	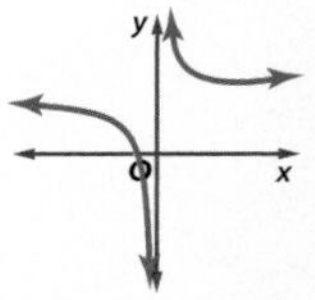

Teach with Tech

Video Recording Have students create video recordings showing how to graph a rational function. Have students first describe how to find the horizontal and vertical asymptotes, and then use a table of values to draw the graph.

Check Your Understanding

= Step-by-Step Solutions begin on page R13.

Example 1 **State the excluded value for each function.**

1. $y = \frac{5}{x}$ $x = 0$ **2.** $y = \frac{1}{x+3}$ $x = -3$ **3.** $y = \frac{x+2}{x-1}$ $x = 1$ **4.** $y = \frac{x}{2x-8}$ $x = 4$

Example 2 **5.** **PARTY PLANNING** The cost of decorations for a party is \$32. This is split among a group of friends. The amount each person pays y is given by $y = \frac{32}{x}$, where x is the number of people. Graph the function. See margin.

6–11. See Ch. 11 Answer Appendix.

Example 3 **Identify the asymptotes of each function. Then graph the function.**

6. $y = \frac{2}{x}$ **7.** $y = \frac{3}{x} - 1$ **8.** $y = \frac{1}{x-2}$

9. $y = \frac{-4}{x+2}$ **10.** $y = \frac{3}{x-1} + 2$ **11.** $y = \frac{2}{x+1} - 5$

Practice and Problem Solving

Extra Practice is on page R11.

Example 1 **State the excluded value for each function.** 14. $x = -2$ 15. $x = -6$

17. $x = -5$
18. $x = 2$
19. $x = -7$

12. $y = \frac{-1}{x}$ $x = 0$ **13.** $y = \frac{8}{x-8}$ $x = 8$ **14.** $y = \frac{x}{x+2}$ **15.** $y = \frac{4}{x+6}$

16. $y = \frac{x+1}{x-3}$ $x = 3$ **17.** $y = \frac{2x+5}{x+5}$ **18.** $y = \frac{7}{5x-10}$ **19.** $y = \frac{x}{2x+14}$

Example 2 **20.** **ANTELOPES** A pronghorn antelope can run 40 miles without stopping. The average speed is given by $y = \frac{40}{x}$, where x is the time it takes to run the distance.

a. Graph $y = \frac{40}{x}$. See Ch. 11 Answer Appendix.

b. Describe the asymptotes. $x = 0$ and $y = 0$

21. **CYCLING** A cyclist rides 10 miles each morning. Her average speed y is given by $y = \frac{10}{x}$, where x is the time it takes her to ride 10 miles. Graph the function. See margin.

22–33. See Ch. 11 Answer Appendix.

Example 3 **Identify the asymptotes of each function. Then graph the function.**

22. $y = \frac{5}{x}$ **23.** $y = \frac{-3}{x}$ **24.** $y = \frac{2}{x} + 3$

25. $y = \frac{1}{x} - 2$ **26.** $y = \frac{1}{x+3}$ **27.** $y = \frac{1}{x-2}$

28. $y = \frac{-2}{x+1}$ **29.** $y = \frac{4}{x-1}$ **30.** $y = \frac{1}{x-2} + 1$

31. $y = \frac{3}{x-1} - 2$ **32.** $y = \frac{2}{x+1} - 4$ **33.** $y = \frac{-1}{x+4} + 3$

B **34.** **READING** Refer to the application at the beginning of the lesson.

a. Graph the function. Interpret key features of the graph in terms of the situation. See Ch. 11 Answer Appendix.

b. Choose a point on the graph, and describe what it means in the context of the situation. Sample answer: (6, 50); if she reads for 6 days, she will read 50 pages per day.

35. **STRUCTURE** The graph shows a translation of the graph of $y = \frac{1}{x}$.

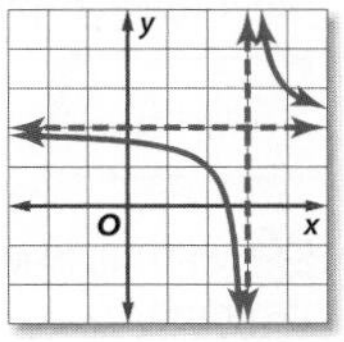

a. Describe the asymptotes. $x = 3$ and $y = 2$

b. Write a possible function for the graph. $y = \frac{1}{x-3} + 2$

3 Practice

Formative Assessment

Use Exercises 1–11 to check for understanding.

Use the chart at the bottom of this page to customize assignments for your students.

4 Assess

Ticket Out the Door On small pieces of paper, write one of five different rational functions similar to those in this lesson. Give one to each student. Ask them to tell you the horizontal and vertical asymptotes.

Formative Assessment

Check for student understanding of concepts in Lessons 11-1 and 11-2.

Quiz 1, p. 57

Teaching the Process Standards

Structure Mathematically proficient students look closely to discern a pattern or structure. In Exercise 35, remind students that they have experience with transformations of the graphs of many types of functions.

Additional Answers

5.

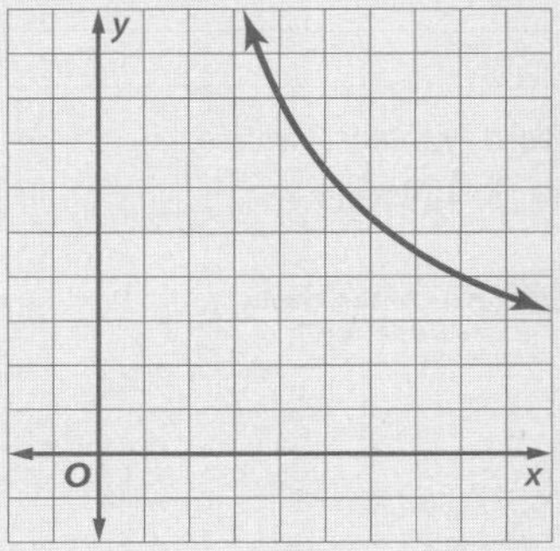

21.

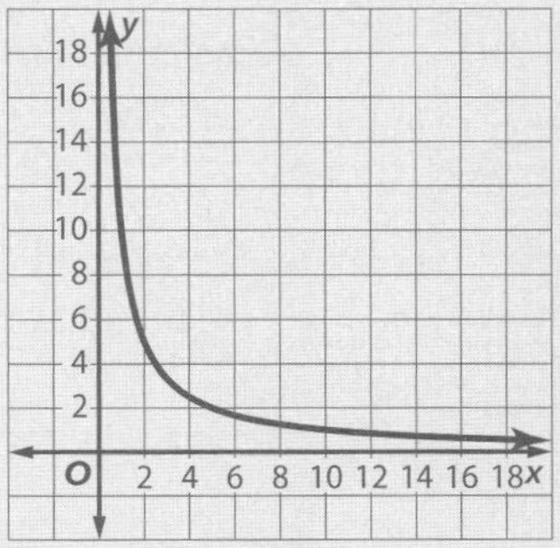

Differentiated Homework Options

Level	Assignment	Two-Day Option	
AL Basic	12–33, 43–77	13–33 odd, 48–51	12–32 even, 43–47, 52–77
OL Core	13–33 odd, 34–37, 39, 41, 43–77	12–33, 48–51	34–41, 43–47, 52–77
BL Advanced	34–65, (optional: 66–77)		

Study Guide and Intervention

AL OL ELL

NAME ______ DATE ______ PERIOD ______

11-2 Study Guide and Intervention

Rational Functions

Identify Excluded Values The function $y = \frac{10}{x}$ is an example of a **rational function**. Because division by zero is undefined, any value of a variable that results in a denominator of zero must be excluded from the domain of that variable. These are called **excluded values** of the rational function.

Example State the excluded value for each function.

a. $y = \frac{3}{x}$
The denominator cannot equal zero.
The excluded value is $x = 0$.

b. $y = \frac{4}{x-5}$
$x - 5 = 0$ Set the denominator equal to 0.
$x = 5$ Add 5 to each side.
The excluded value is $x = 5$.

Exercises

State the excluded value for each function.

1. $y = \frac{2}{x}$ 2. $y = \frac{1}{x-4}$ 3. $y = \frac{x-3}{x+1}$
4. $y = \frac{4}{x-2}$ 5. $y = \frac{x}{2x-4}$ 6. $y = -\frac{5}{3x}$
7. $y = \frac{3x-2}{x+3}$ 8. $y = \frac{x-1}{5x+10}$ 9. $y = \frac{x+1}{x}$
10. $y = \frac{x-7}{2x+8}$ 11. $y = \frac{x-5}{6x}$ 12. $y = \frac{x-2}{x+11}$
13. $y = \frac{7}{3x+21}$ 14. $y = \frac{3x-4}{x+4}$ 15. $y = \frac{x}{7x-35}$

16. **DINING** Mya and her friends are eating at a restaurant. The total bill of $36 is split among x friends. The amount each person pays y is given by $y = \frac{36}{x}$, where x is the number of people. Graph the function.

Bill per Person ($) — Number of People

Lesson 11-2

Practice

AL OL BL ELL

NAME ______ DATE ______ PERIOD ______

11-2 Practice

Rational Functions

State the excluded value for each function.

1. $y = \frac{-1}{x}$ 2. $y = \frac{3}{x+5}$ 3. $y = \frac{2x}{x-5}$
4. $y = \frac{x-1}{12x+36}$ 5. $y = \frac{x+1}{2x+3}$ 6. $y = \frac{1}{5x-2}$

Identify the asymptotes of each function. Then graph the function.

7. $y = \frac{1}{x}$ 8. $y = \frac{3}{x}$ 9. $y = \frac{2}{x-1}$
10. $y = \frac{2}{x+2}$ 11. $y = \frac{1}{x-3} + 2$ 12. $y = \frac{2}{x+1} - 1$

13. **AIR TRAVEL** Denver, Colorado, is located approximately 1000 miles from Indianapolis, Indiana. The average speed of a plane traveling between the two cities is given by $y = \frac{1000}{x}$, where x is the total flight time. Graph the function.

Average Speed (mph) — Total Flight Time

Word Problem Practice

AL OL BL ELL

NAME ______ DATE ______ PERIOD ______

11-2 Word Problem Practice

Rational Functions

1. **BULLET TRAINS** The Shinkansen, or Japanese bullet train network, provides high-speed transportation throughout Japan. Trains regularly operate at speeds in excess of 200 kilometers per hour. The average speed of a bullet train traveling between Tokyo and Kyoto is given by $y = \frac{515}{x}$, where x is the total travel time in hours. Graph the function.

Average Speed (km/h) — Time (hours)

2. **DRIVING** Peter is driving to his grandparents' house 40 miles away. During the trip, Peter makes a 30-minute stop for lunch. The average speed of Peter's trip is given by $y = \frac{40}{x+0.5}$, where x is the total time spent in the car. What are the asymptotes of the function?

3. **ERROR ANALYSIS** Nicolas is graphing the equation $y = \frac{20}{x+3} - 6$ and draws a graph with asymptotes at $y = 3$ and $x = -6$. Explain the error that Nicolas made in his graph.

4. **USED CARS** While researching cars to purchase online, Ms. Jacobs found that the value of a used car is inversely proportional to the age of the car. The average price of a used car is given by $y = \frac{17{,}900}{x+1.2} + 100$, where x is the age of the car. What are the asymptotes of the function? Explain why $x = 0$ cannot be an asymptote.

5. **FAMILY REUNION** The Gaudet family is holding their annual reunion at Watkins Park. It costs $50 to get a permit to hold the reunion at the park, and the family is spending $8 per person on food. The Gaudets have agreed to split the cost of the event evenly among all those attending.

a. Write an equation showing the cost per person y if x people attend the reunion.

b. What are the asymptotes of the equation?

c. Now assume that the family wants to let a long-lost cousin attend for free. Rewrite the equation to find the new cost per paying person y.

d. What are the asymptotes for the new equation?

Lesson 11-2

36. **BIRDS** A long-tailed jaeger is a sea bird that can migrate 5000 miles or more each year. The average rate in miles per hour r can be given by the function $r = \frac{5000}{t}$, where t is the time in hours. Use the function to determine the average rate of the bird if it spends 250 hours flying. **20 mi per hour**

37. **CLASS TRIP** The freshmen class is going to a science museum. As part of the trip, each person is also contributing an equal amount of money to name a star.

a. Write a verbal description for the cost per person.

b. Write an equation to represent the total cost y per person if p people go to the museum. $y = \frac{95}{p} + 8.50$

c. Use a graphing calculator to graph the equation. Interpret key features of the graph in terms of the situation. **See margin.**

d. Estimate the number of people needed for the total cost of the trip to be about $15. **Sample answer: 15 people**

37a. Sample answer: The total cost of the trip equals the cost of a ticket plus the cost of the star-naming package divided by the number of people.

Welcome to The Museum

Admission $8.50
As a special memory of your visit,
name a star for $95

Graph each function. Identify the asymptotes. 38–40. See Ch. 11 Answer Appendix.

38. $y = \frac{4x+3}{2x-4}$ 39. $y = \frac{x^2}{x^2-1}$ 40. $y = \frac{x}{x^2-9}$

C 41. **GEOMETRY** The equation $h = \frac{2(64)}{b_1 + 8}$ represents the height h of a trapezoid with an area of 64 square units. The trapezoid has two opposite sides that are parallel and h units apart; one is b_1 units long and another is 8 units long.

a. Describe a reasonable domain and range for the function.

b. Graph the function in the first quadrant. **See margin.**

c. Use the graph to estimate the value of h when $b_1 = 10$. **about 7 units**

41a. D = {all positive real numbers}; R = {all positive real numbers}

43. The graph of $y = \frac{1}{x+5} - 2$ is the graph of $y = \frac{1}{x}$ translated 5 units to the left and 2 units down.

H.O.T. Problems Use Higher-Order Thinking Skills

42. **CHALLENGE** Graph $y = \frac{1}{x^2 - 4}$. State the domain and the range of the function. **See margin.**

43. **REASONING** Without graphing, describe the transformation that takes place between the graph of $y = \frac{1}{x}$ and the graph of $y = \frac{1}{x+5} - 2$.

44. **OPEN ENDED** Write a rational function if the asymptotes of the graph are at $x = 3$ and $y = 1$. Explain how you found the function. **See margin.**

45. **ARGUMENTS** Is the following statement *true* or *false*? If false, give a counterexample. **False; sample answer: The graph of $y = \frac{1}{x}$ has no x- or y-intercepts.**

The graph of a rational function will have at least one intercept.

46. **WHICH ONE DOESN'T BELONG** Identify the function that does not belong with the other three. Explain your reasoning.

$y = \frac{4}{x}$	$y = \frac{6}{x+1}$	$y = \frac{8}{x} + 1$	$y = \frac{10}{2x}$

46. Sample answer: The graph of $y = \frac{8}{x} + 1$ is the only one that does not have $y = 0$ as an asymptote.

47. **WRITING IN MATH** How are the properties of a rational function reflected in its graph? **See margin.**

Enrichment

OL BL

NAME ______ DATE ______ PERIOD ______

11-2 Enrichment

Inequalities involving Rational Functions

Inequalities involving rational functions can be graphed much like those involving linear functions.

Example Graph $y \geq \frac{1}{x}$.

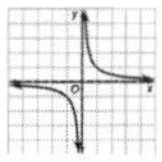

Step 1 Plot points and draw a smooth solid curve. Because the inequality involves a greater than or equal to sign, solutions that satisfy $y = \frac{1}{x}$ will be a part of the graph.

Step 2 Plot the asymptotes, $x = 0$ and $y = 0$, as dashed lines.

Step 3 Begin testing values. A value must be tested between each set of lines, including asymptotes.

Region 1 Test (–1, 1). This returns a true value for the inequality.

Region 2 Test (–1, –0.5). This returns a true value for the inequality.

Region 3 Test (–1, –2). This returns a false value for the inequality.

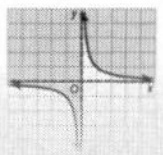

Teaching the Process Standards

Arguments Mathematically proficient students are able to analyze situations by breaking them into cases, and can recognize and use counterexamples. In Exercise 45, suggest that students graph a rational function and visualize moving the graph to test the conjecture.

Standardized Test Practice

48. Simplify $\frac{2a^2d}{3bc} \cdot \frac{9b^2c}{16ad^2}$. **D**

A $\frac{abd}{c}$ **C** $\frac{6a}{4bd}$

B $\frac{ab}{d}$ **D** $\frac{3ab}{8d}$

49. SHORT RESPONSE One day Lola ran 100 meters in 15 seconds, 200 meters in 45 seconds, and 300 meters over low hurdles in one and a half minutes. How many more seconds did it take her to run 300 meters over low hurdles than the 200-meter dash? **45 seconds**

50. Scott and Ian started a T-shirt printing business. The total start-up costs were $450. It costs $5.50 to print one T-shirt. Write a rational function $A(x)$ for the average cost of producing x T-shirts. **F**

F $A(x) = \frac{450 + 5.5x}{x}$ **H** $A(x) = 450x + 5.5$

G $A(x) = \frac{450}{x} + 5.5$ **J** $A(x) = 450 + 5.5x$

51. GEOMETRY Which of the following is a quadrilateral with exactly one pair of parallel sides? **D**

A parallelogram **C** square

B rectangle **D** trapezoid

Spiral Review

52. TRAVEL The Brooks family can drive to the beach, which is 220 miles away, in 4 hours if they drive 55 miles per hour. Kendra says that they would save at least a half an hour if they were to drive 65 miles per hour. Is Kendra correct? Explain. (Lesson 11-1) **Yes; sample answer: At 65 mph, the family can travel 220 miles in about 3 hours and 23 minutes, saving them about 37 minutes.**

Use a calculator to find the measure of each angle to the nearest degree. (Lesson 10-6)

53. $\sin C = 0.9781$ **78°** **54.** $\tan H = 0.6473$ **33°** **55.** $\cos K = 0.7658$ **40°**

56. $\tan Y = 3.6541$ **75°** **57.** $\cos U = 0.5000$ **60°** **58.** $\sin N = 0.3832$ **23°**

If c is the measure of the hypotenuse of a right triangle, find each missing measure. If necessary round to the nearest hundredth. (Lesson 10-5)

59. $a = 15, b = 60, c = ?$ **61.85** **60.** $a = 17, c = 35, b = ?$ **30.59** **61.** $a = \sqrt{110}, b = 1, c = ?$ **10.54**

62. $a = \sqrt{17}, b = \sqrt{12}, c = ?$ **5.39** **63.** $a = 6, c = 11, b = ?$ **9.22** **64.** $a = 9, b = 6, c = ?$ **10.82**

65. SIGHT The formula $d = \sqrt{\frac{3h}{2}}$ represents the distance d in miles that a person h feet high can see. Irene is standing on a cliff that is 310 feet above sea level. How far can Irene see from the cliff? Write a simplified radical expression and a decimal approximation. (Lesson 10-2) **$\sqrt{465}$ or about 21.56 mi**

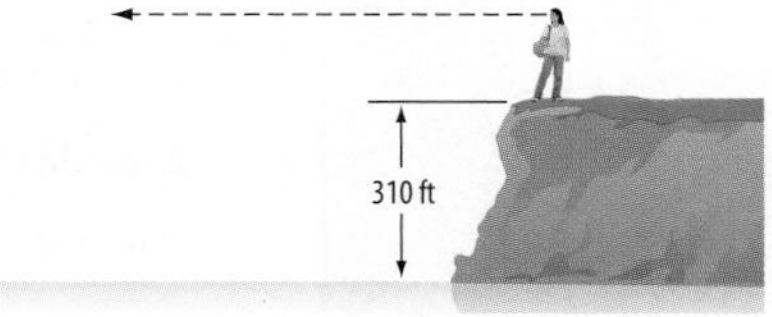

66. $(x + 3)(x + 8)$ **67.** $(w + 16)(w - 3)$ **68.** $(p - 7)(p + 5)$
69. $(3 + a)(24 + a)$ **70.** $(c + 7)(c + 5)$ **71.** $(d - 2)(d - 5)$

Skills Review

72. $(g - 15)(g - 4)$ **73.** $(n + 9)(n - 6)$ **74.** $(5x + 2)(x + 5)$
75. $(4b - 3)(6b + 1)$ **76.** $(4a + 5)(3a - 7)$ **77.** $2(x - 3)(3x + 2)$

Factor each trinomial.

66. $x^2 + 11x + 24$ **67.** $w^2 + 13w - 48$ **68.** $p^2 - 2p - 35$ **69.** $72 + 27a + a^2$

70. $c^2 + 12c + 35$ **71.** $d^2 - 7d + 10$ **72.** $g^2 - 19g + 60$ **73.** $n^2 + 3n - 54$

74. $5x^2 + 27x + 10$ **75.** $24b^2 - 14b - 3$ **76.** $12a^2 - 13a - 35$ **77.** $6x^2 - 14x - 12$

Differentiated Instruction OL BL

Extension Ask students to graph the function $y = \frac{x - 1}{x - 1}$. Then ask students to describe the graph. The graph is a horizontal line, $y = 1$, with a hole at (1, 1).

Additional Answers

37c.

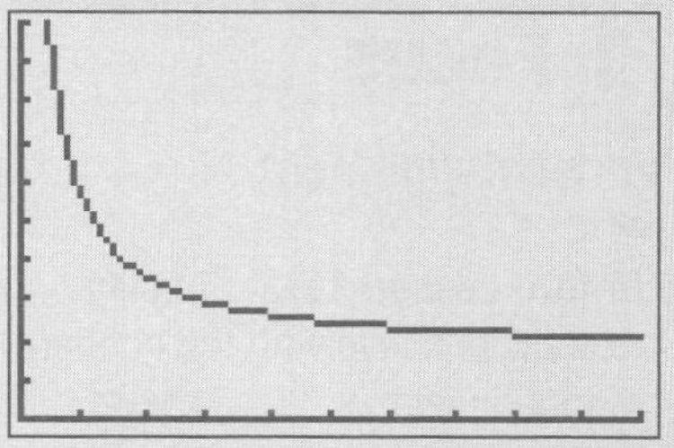

[0, 50] scl: 5 by [0,50] scl: 5

Sample answer: The end behavior indicates that as the number of people increases, the cost per person approaches 0. Since there is no x-intercept, the cost per person will never be 0.

41b.

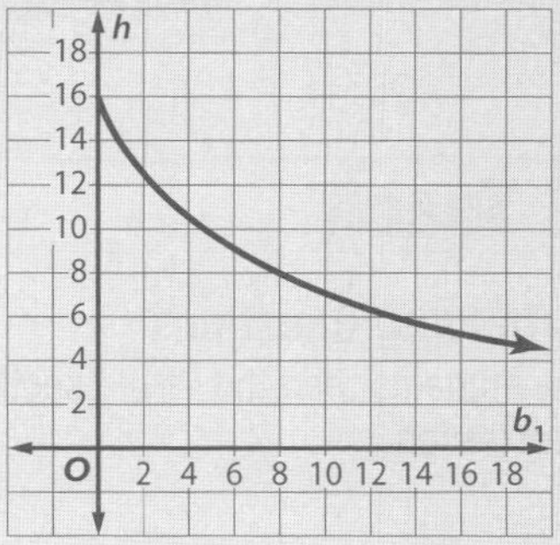

42.

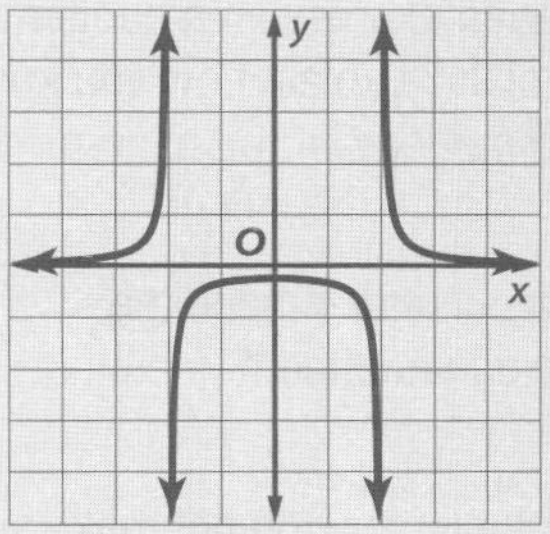

D = all real numbers except $x = -2$ and $x = 2$;
$R = \left\{y \mid y > 0 \text{ or } y \leq -\frac{1}{4}\right\}$

44. Sample answer: $y = \frac{1}{x - 3} + 1$; use the equation $y = \frac{a}{x - b} + c$. The vertical asymptote is $x = b$. So, $b = 3$. The horizontal asymptote is $y = c$. So, $c = 1$. Substituting the values for b and c and letting $a = 1$, the equation becomes $y = \frac{1}{x - 3} + 1$.

47. Sample answer: Vertical asymptotes occur at values that make the denominator 0; horizontal asymptotes occur at $y = c$ for any rational function of the form $y = \frac{a}{x - b} + c$.

1 Focus

Vertical Alignment

Before Lesson 11-3 Simplify expressions involving the quotient of monomials.

Lesson 11-3 Identify values excluded from the domain of a rational expression. Simplify rational expressions.

After Lesson 11-3 Simplify mixed expressions and complex fractions.

2 Teach

Scaffolding Questions

Have students read the **Why?** section of the lesson.

Ask:

- Is the given expression a quotient of polynomials? Explain how you know. Yes; the numerator and denominator are one-term polynomials.
- What value(s) for r make the expression undefined? r cannot equal 0.
- What value(s) for r do not make sense for this situation? r cannot be a negative value.

LESSON 11-3 Simplifying Rational Expressions

Then

- You simplified expressions involving the quotient of monomials.

Now

1. Identify values excluded from the domain of a rational expression.
2. Simplify rational expressions.

Why?

- Big-O is a "hubless" Ferris wheel in Tokyo, Japan. The *centripetal force*, or the force acting toward the center, is given by $\frac{mv^2}{r}$, where m is the mass of the Ferris wheel, v is the velocity, and r is the radius.

New Vocabulary
rational expression

Content Standards
AI.RNE.5

1 Identify Excluded Values The expression $\frac{mv^2}{r}$ is an example of a rational expression. A **rational expression** is an algebraic fraction whose numerator and denominator are polynomials. Since division by zero is undefined, the polynomial in the denominator cannot be 0.

PT

Example 1 Find Excluded Values

State the excluded values for each rational expression.

a. $\frac{-8}{r^2 - 36}$

Exclude the values for which $r^2 - 36 = 0$.

$r^2 - 36 = 0$		The denominator cannot be zero.
$(r - 6)(r + 6) = 0$		Factor.
$r - 6 = 0$ or	$r + 6 = 0$	Zero Product Property
$r = 6$	$r = -6$	Therefore, r cannot equal 6 or −6.

b. $\frac{n^2}{n^2 + 4n - 5}$

Exclude the values for which $n^2 + 4n - 5 = 0$.

$n^2 + 4n - 5 = 0$		The denominator cannot be zero.
$(n - 1)(n + 5) = 0$		Factor.
$n - 1 = 0$ or	$n + 5 = 0$	Zero Product Property
$n = 1$	$n = -5$	Therefore, n cannot equal 1 or −5.

Guided Practice

1A. $\frac{5x}{x^2 - 81}$ 9, −9

1B. $\frac{3a - 2}{a^2 + 6a + 8}$ −2, −4

Lesson 11-3 Resources

Resource	Approaching Level AL	On Level OL	Beyond Level BL	English Learners ELL
Teacher Edition	▪ Differentiated Instruction, p. 692	▪ Differentiated Instruction, p. 692	▪ Differentiated Instruction, p. 696	▪ Differentiated Instruction, p. 692
Chapter Resource Masters	▪ Study Guide and Intervention, pp. 17–18 ▪ Skills Practice, p. 19 ▪ Practice, p. 20 ▪ Word Problem Practice, p. 21	▪ Study Guide and Intervention, pp. 17–18 ▪ Skills Practice, p. 19 ▪ Practice, p. 20 ▪ Word Problem Practice, p. 21 ▪ Enrichment, p. 22	▪ Practice, p. 20 ▪ Word Problem Practice, p. 21 ▪ Enrichment, p. 22	▪ Study Guide and Intervention, pp. 17–18 ▪ Skills Practice, p. 19 ▪ Practice, p. 20 ▪ Word Problem Practice, p. 21
Other	▪ 5-Minute Check 11-3 ▪ Study Notebook	▪ 5-Minute Check 11-3 ▪ Study Notebook	▪ 5-Minute Check 11-3 ▪ Study Notebook	▪ 5-Minute Check 11-3 ▪ Study Notebook

StudyTip

Cylinder The volume of a cylinder is $V = \pi r^2 h$. The height of a cylinder with volume V and radius r is given by $\frac{V}{\pi r^2}$.

Real-World Example 2 Use Rational Expressions

GEOMETRY Find the height of a cylinder that has a volume of 821 cubic inches and a radius of 7 inches. Round to the nearest tenth.

Understand You have a rational expression with two variables, V and r.

Plan Substitute 821 for V and 7 for r and simplify.

Solve $\frac{V}{\pi r^2} = \frac{821}{\pi(7)^2}$ Replace V with 821 and r with 7.

≈ 5.3 The height of the cylinder is about 5.3 inches.

Check Use estimation to determine whether the answer is reasonable.

$\frac{800}{3(50)} \approx 5$ ✓ The solution is reasonable.

GuidedPractice

2. Find the height of the cylinder that has a volume of 710 cubic inches and a diameter of 18 inches. **2.8 in.**

2 Simplify Expressions

A rational expression is in simplest form when the numerator and denominator have no common factors except 1. To simplify a rational expression, divide out any common factors of the numerator and denominator.

KeyConcept Simplifying Rational Expressions

Words	Let a, b, and c, be polynomials with $a \neq 0$ and $c \neq 0$.
Symbols	$\frac{ba}{ca} = \frac{b \cdot a}{c \cdot a} = \frac{b}{c}$ **Example** $\frac{3x - 9}{4x - 12} = \frac{3(x-3)}{4(x-3)} = \frac{3}{4}$

Test-TakingTip

Eliminate Possibilities Since there is only one negative factor in the expression in Example 3, the simplified expression should have a negative sign. So, you can eliminate choices A and B.

Standardized Test Example 3 Use GCF to Simplify an Expression

Which expression is equivalent to $\frac{(-3x^2)(4x^5)}{9x^6}$?

A $\frac{4}{3}x$ B $\frac{4}{3x}$ C $-\frac{4}{3x}$ D $-\frac{4}{3}x$

Read the Test Item The expression represents the product of two monomials and the division of that product by another monomial.

Solve the Test Item

Step 1 Factor the numerator and denominator, using their GCF. $\frac{(3x^6)(-4x)}{(3x^6)(3)}$

Step 2 Simplify. The correct answer is D. $\frac{\overset{1}{\cancel{(3x^6)}}(-4x)}{\underset{1}{\cancel{(3x^6)}}(3)}$ or $-\frac{4}{3}x$

GuidedPractice

3. Which expression is equivalent to $\frac{16c^2b^4}{8c^3b}$? F

F $\frac{2b^3}{c}$ G $\frac{b^3}{2c}$ H $\frac{1}{2b^3c}$ J $2b^3c$

WatchOut!

Excluded Values Students may assume that excluded values are determined from the simplified expression. This may or may not be true. Stress that excluded values must *always* be determined from the original denominator.

Teach with Tech

Blog On your secure classroom blog, have students write entries explaining why they need to find the excluded values when simplifying a rational expression. Make sure students explain that they need to check the denominator of the *original* expression for values where the denominator is zero.

1 Identify Excluded Values

Example 1 shows how to determine the excluded values for rational expressions. **Example 2** shows how to use rational expressions to solve real-world problems.

Formative Assessment

Use the Guided Practice exercises after each example to determine students' understanding of concepts.

Additional Examples

1 State the excluded value(s) for each expression.

a. $\frac{3b - 2}{b + 7}$ b cannot equal -7.

b. $\frac{5a^2 + 2}{a^2 - a - 12}$ a cannot equal -3 or 4.

c. $y = \frac{8}{2x + 1}$ x cannot equal $-\frac{1}{2}$.

2 **GEOMETRY** Suppose the cylinder in Example 2 has a volume of 770 cubic inches and a diameter of 12 inches. Find the height of the cylinder. Round to the nearest tenth. 6.8 in.

Additional Examples also in Interactive Classroom PowerPoint® Presentations

IWB Interactive White Board READY

2 Simplify Expressions

Example 3 shows how to simplify a rational expression using the greatest common factor of the numerator and the denominator. **Example 4** shows the importance of finding the excluded values of a rational expression by using the denominator of the original expression rather than that of the simplified expression. **Example 5** shows how to simplify rational expressions containing binomials that are opposites. **Example 6** shows how to find the zeros of a rational function.

Additional Examples

3 STANDARDIZED TEST PRACTICE Which expression is equivalent to $\frac{32x^5y^2}{4xy^7}$? B

A $\frac{8x^5}{y^5}$ **C** $\frac{8x^6}{y^9}$

B $\frac{8x^4}{y^5}$ **D** $\frac{24x^4}{y^5}$

4 Simplify $\frac{4x + 16}{x^2 - 5x - 36}$. State the excluded values of x. $\frac{4}{x - 9}$; $x \neq -4$ and $x \neq 9$

5 Simplify $\frac{25 - x^2}{8x - 40}$. State the excluded values of x. $\frac{-5 + x}{8}$; $x \neq 5$

Focus on Mathematical Content

Simplifying Rational Expressions

A rational expression is simplified when the numerator and denominator of the expression have no factors in common other than ± 1. Identifying excluded values should be the first step in the simplification process since all restrictions found in a problem should be included in the answer.

WatchOut!

Preventing Errors Refer students to Chapter 8 if they need to review how to factor polynomials.

Teaching the Process Standards

Structure Mathematically proficient students can see complicated things, such as rational expressions, as single objects or as being composed of several objects. To convince students of the importance of using the original expression to determine excluded values point out that in Example 4, -9 is excluded in the original expression and is not excluded from the simplified expression.

You can use the same procedure to simplify a rational expression in which the numerator and denominator are polynomials.

Example 4 Simplify Rational Expressions

Simplify $\frac{2r + 18}{r^2 + 8r - 9}$. State the excluded values of r.

$\frac{2r + 18}{r^2 + 8r - 9} = \frac{2(r + 9)}{(r + 9)(r - 1)}$ Factor.

$= \frac{2\cancel{(r + 9)}^{1}}{\cancel{(r + 9)}_{1}(r - 1)}$ or $\frac{2}{r - 1}$ Divide the numerator and denominator by the GCF, $r + 9$.

Exclude the values for which $r^2 + 8r - 9$ equals 0.

$r^2 + 8r - 9 = 0$ The denominator cannot equal zero.

$(r + 9)(r - 1) = 0$ Factor.

$r = -9$ or $r = 1$ Zero Product Property

So, $r \neq -9$ and $r \neq 1$.

StudyTip

Structure Determine the excluded values using the original expression rather than the simplified expression.

GuidedPractice

Simplify each rational expression. State the excluded values of the variables.

4A. $\frac{n + 3}{n^2 + 10n + 21}$ $\frac{1}{n + 7}$; $-3, -7$ **4B.** $\frac{y^2 + 9y - 10}{2y + 20}$ $\frac{y - 1}{2}$; -10

When simplifying rational expressions, look for binomials that are opposites. For example, $5 - x$ and $x - 5$ are opposites because $5 - x = -1(x - 5)$. So, you can write $\frac{x - 5}{5 - x}$ as $\frac{x - 5}{-1(x - 5)}$.

Example 5 Recognize Opposites

Simplify $\frac{36 - t^2}{5t - 30}$. State the excluded values of t.

$\frac{36 - t^2}{5t - 30} = \frac{(6 - t)(6 + t)}{5(t - 6)}$ Factor.

$= \frac{-1(t - 6)(6 + t)}{5(t - 6)}$ Rewrite $6 - t$ as $-1(t - 6)$.

$= \frac{-1\cancel{(t - 6)}^{1}(6 + t)}{5\cancel{(t - 6)}_{1}}$ or $-\frac{6 + t}{5}$ Divide out the common factor, $t - 6$.

Exclude the values for which $5t - 30$ equals 0.

$5t - 30 = 0$ The denominator cannot equal zero.

$5t = 30$ Add 30 to each side.

$t = 6$ Divide each side by 5.

So, $t \neq 6$.

GuidedPractice

Simplify each expression. State the excluded values of x.

5A. $\frac{12x + 36}{x^2 - x - 12}$ $\frac{12}{x - 4}$; 4 and -3 **5B.** $\frac{x^2 - 2x - 35}{x^2 - 9x + 14}$ $\frac{x + 5}{x - 2}$; 2 and 7

DifferentiatedInstruction AL OL ELL

If you think students may benefit from working with a partner,

Then place students in pairs to work through Examples 1, 3, 4, 5, and 6. Have one student factor the numerator, and the other the denominator. Then ask students to jointly find the excluded values and the simplified expression.

StudyTip

Zeros Once simplified, a rational function has zeros at the values that make the numerator 0.

Recall that to find the zeros of a quadratic function, you need to find the values of x when $f(x) = 0$. The zeros of a rational function are found in the same way.

Example 6 Rational Functions

Find the zeros of $f(x) = \frac{x^2 + 3x - 18}{x - 3}$.

$f(x) = \frac{x^2 + 3x - 18}{x - 3}$ Original function

$0 = \frac{x^2 + 3x - 18}{x - 3}$ $f(x) = 0$

$0 = \frac{(x + 6)(x - 3)}{x - 3}$ Factor.

$0 = \frac{(x + 6)\cancel{(x - 3)}^{1}}{\cancel{x - 3}_{1}}$ Divide out common factors.

$0 = x + 6$ Simplify.

When $x = -6$, the numerator becomes 0, so $f(x) = 0$. Therefore, the zero of the function is -6.

GuidedPractice

Find the zeros of each function.

6A. $f(x) = \frac{x^2 + 2x - 15}{x + 1}$ **−5, 3**

6B. $f(x) = \frac{x^2 + 6x + 8}{x^2 + x - 2}$ **−4**

Check Your Understanding

= Step-by-Step Solutions begin on page R13.

Example 1 **State the excluded values for each rational expression.**

1. $\frac{8}{x^2 - 16}$ **4, −4**

2. $\frac{3m}{m^2 - 6m + 5}$ **1, 5**

Example 2

3. PHYSICAL SCIENCE A 0.16-kilogram ball attached to a string is being spun in a circle 7.26 meters per second. The expression $\frac{mv^2}{r}$, where m is the mass of the ball, v is the velocity, and r is the radius, can be used to find the force that keeps the ball spinning in a circle. If the circle has a radius of 0.5 meter, find the force that must be exerted to keep the ball spinning. Round to the nearest tenth. **16.9 units of force**

Examples 3–5 **Simplify each expression. State the excluded values of the variables.**

4. $\frac{28ab^3}{16a^2b}$ $\frac{7b^2}{4a}$; $a \neq 0, b \neq 0$

5. $\frac{(-3r)(10r^4)}{6r^5}$ **−5; 0**

6. $\frac{5d + 15}{d^2 - d - 12}$ $\frac{5}{d - 4}$; **4, −3**

7. $\frac{x^2 + 11x + 28}{x + 4}$ $x + 7$; **−4**

8. $\frac{2r - 12}{r^2 - 36}$ $\frac{2}{r + 6}$; **6, −6**

9. $\frac{3y - 27}{81 - y^2}$ $-\frac{3}{9 + y}$; **−9, 9**

Example 6 **Find the zeros of each function.**

10. $f(x) = \frac{x^2 - x - 12}{x - 2}$ **4, −3**

11. $f(x) = \frac{x^2 - x - 6}{x^2 + 8x + 12}$ **3**

Additional Example

6 Find the zeros of $f(x) = \frac{x^2 + 8x + 7}{x + 1}$. -7

3 Practice

Formative Assessment

Use Exercises 1–11 to check for understanding.

Use the chart at the bottom of the next page to customize assignments for your students.

Follow-up

Students have explored rational expressions.

Ask:

- How are simplifying rational expressions similar to reducing a fraction? Sample answer: To reduce a fraction, the numerator and denominator are each divided by a common factor. This applies to simplifying a rational expression. Once the expressions in the numerator and denominator have been simplified, look for a factor common to the numerator and denominator.

Exercise Alert

Formulas For Exercises 17 and 41, students will need to know the formulas for the circumference and area of a circle, the surface area and volume of a rectangular solid, and the surface area and volume of a cylinder.

Teaching the Process Standards

Reasoning Mathematically proficient students make sense of quantities and their relationships in problem situations. In Exercise 37, encourage students to start by defining variable(s).

WatchOut!

Error Analysis For Exercise 43, ask students to identify the person who listed the excluded values correctly and also the person who simplified the expression correctly.

Additional Answers

38. $b^3 + 3a - 2a^3$; $a, b \neq 0$

39. $\frac{4x^4 - 5y^2}{y^3}$; $x, y \neq 0$

40. $\frac{1}{3x-1}$; $\frac{1}{3}$, -5

44. Sample answer: The intercepts and end behavior of the graphs are the same. The graphs appear to be identical, but the second graph has an excluded value at $x = -7$, so there is a hole in the graph at $(-7, -9)$.

45. Every polynomial P can be written as $\frac{P}{1}$, where the numerator and denominator are polynomials; hence every polynomial is also a rational expression.

46. Sample answer: $\frac{1}{x^2-4}$; since the excluded values are 2 and -2, the denominator of the rational expression must contain the factors $x - 2$ and $x + 2$.

Practice and Problem Solving

Extra Practice is on page R11.

Example 1 State the excluded values for each rational expression.

12. $\frac{-n}{n^2 - 49}$ **7, −7**

13. $\frac{5x + 1}{x^2 - 1}$ **1, −1**

14. $\frac{12a}{a^2 - 3a - 10}$ **5, −2**

15. $\frac{k^2 - 4}{k^2 + 5k - 24}$ **3, −8**

Example 2

16. **GEOMETRY** The volume of a rectangular prism is $3x^3 + 34x^2 + 72x - 64$. If the height is $x + 4$, what is the area of the base of the prism? **$3x^2 + 22x - 16$**

17. **GEOMETRY** Use the circle at the right to write the ratio $\frac{\text{circumference}}{\text{area}}$. Then simplify. State the excluded value of the variable. **$\frac{2\pi(5t)}{\pi(5t)^2} = \frac{2}{5t}$; 0**

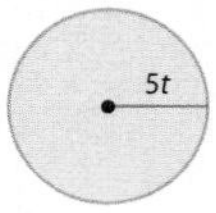

Examples 3–5 Simplify each expression. State the excluded values of the variables.

18. $\frac{15x^4y^2}{40x^3y^3}$ **$\frac{3x}{8y}$; $x \neq 0$, $y \neq 0$**

19. $\frac{32n^2p}{2n^4p}$ **$\frac{16}{n^2}$; $n \neq 0$, $p \neq 0$**

20. $\frac{(4t^3)(2t)}{20t^2}$ **$\frac{2t^2}{5}$; 0**

21. $\frac{(7c^2)(-6c^3)}{21c^4}$ **$-2c$; 0**

22. $\frac{4x - 24}{x^2 - 12x + 36}$ **$\frac{4}{x-6}$; 6**

23. $\frac{a^2 + 3a}{a^2 - 3a - 18}$ **$\frac{a}{a-6}$; 6, −3**

24. $\frac{n^2 + 7n - 18}{n - 2}$ **$n + 9$; 2**

25. $\frac{x^2 + 4x - 32}{x + 8}$ **$x - 4$; −8**

26. $\frac{x^2 - 25}{x^2 + 5x}$ **$\frac{x-5}{x}$; 0, −5**

27. $\frac{2p^2 - 14p}{p^2 - 49}$ **$\frac{2p}{p+7}$; 7, −7**

28. $\frac{2x - 10}{25 - x^2}$ **$\frac{2}{-(x+5)}$; 5, −5**

29. $\frac{64 - c^2}{c^2 - 7c - 8}$ **$\frac{-(8+c)}{c+1}$; 8, −1**

Example 6 Find the zeros of each function.

30. $f(x) = \frac{x^2 - x - 12}{x^2 + 2x - 35}$ **−3, 4**

31. $f(x) = \frac{x^2 + 3x - 4}{x^2 + 9x + 20}$ **1**

32. $f(x) = \frac{2x^2 + 11x - 40}{2x + 5}$ **$-8, \frac{5}{2}$**

33. $f(x) = \frac{3x^2 - 18x + 24}{x - 6}$ **2, 4**

34. $f(x) = \frac{x^3 + x^2 - 6x}{x - 1}$ **0, −3, 2**

35. $f(x) = \frac{x^3 - 4x^2 - 12x}{x + 2}$ **0, 6**

B

36. **PYRAMIDS** The perimeter of the base of the Pyramid of the Sun is 4π times the height. The perimeter of the base of the Great Pyramid of Giza is 2π times the height. Write and simplify each ratio comparing the base perimeters. **a. about 0.97**

Pyramid	Height (ft)
Pyramid of the Sun (Mexico)	233.5
Great Pyramid (Egypt)	481.4

a. Pyramid of the Sun to the Great Pyramid

b. Great Pyramid to the Pyramid of the Sun **about 1.03**

37. **REASONING** George Ferris built the first Ferris wheel for the World's Columbian Exposition in 1893. It had a diameter of 250 feet.

a. To find the speed traveled by a car located on the wheel, you can find the circumference of a circle and divide by the time it takes for one rotation. Write a rational expression for the speed of a car rotating in time t. **$\frac{250\pi}{t}$**

b. Suppose the first Ferris wheel rotated once every 5 minutes. What was the speed of a car on the circumference in feet per minute? **about 157 ft/min**

Simplify each expression. State the excluded values of the variables. **38–40. See margin.**

38. $\frac{3a^2b^4 + 9a^3b - 6a^5b}{3a^2b}$

39. $\frac{8x^5 - 10xy^2}{2xy^3}$

40. $\frac{x + 5}{3x^2 + 14x - 5}$

Differentiated Homework Options

Level	Assignment	Two-Day Option	
AL Basic	12–35, 43, 45–76	13–35 odd, 49–52	12–34 even, 43, 45–48, 53–76
OL Core	13–35 odd, 36, 37, 39, 41–43, 45–76	12–35, 49–52	36–43, 45–48, 53–76
BL Advanced	36–70, (optional: 71–76)		

41. PACKAGING To minimize packaging expenses, a company uses packages that have the least surface area to volume ratio. For each figure, write a ratio comparing the surface area to the volume. Then simplify. State the excluded values of the variables.

a. $\frac{10x^2}{2x^3} = \frac{5}{x}$; 0

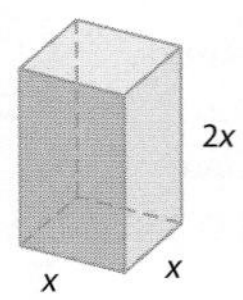

b. $\frac{2\pi a^2 + 2\pi ab}{\pi a^2 b} = \frac{2a + 2b}{ab}$; 0, 0

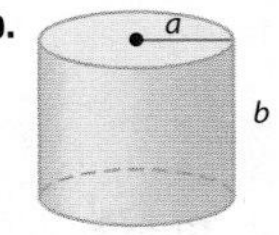

C **42. HISTORY** The diagram shows how a lever may have been used to move blocks.

a. The mechanical advantage of a lever is $\frac{L_A}{L_R}$, where L_A is the length of the effort arm and L_R is the length of the resistance arm. Find the mechanical advantage of the lever shown. **4**

b. The force placed on the rock is the product of the mechanical advantage and the force applied to the end of the lever. If the Egyptian worker can apply a force of 180 pounds, what is the greatest weight he can lift with the lever? **720 lb**

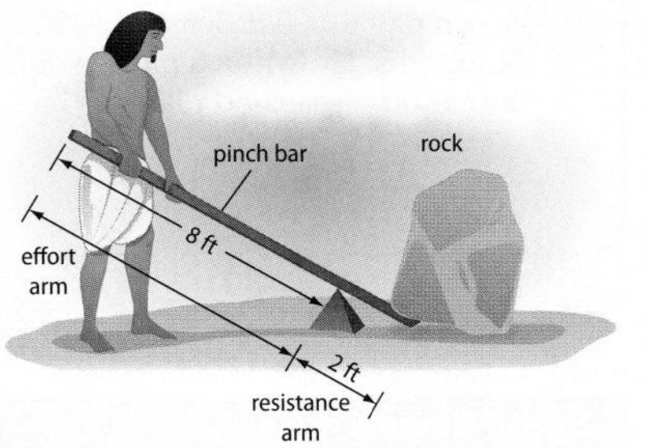

c. To lift a 535-pound rock using a 7-foot lever with the fulcrum 2 feet from the rock, how much force will have to be used? **214 lb**

H.O.T. Problems Use Higher-Order Thinking Skills

43. ERROR ANALYSIS Colleen and Sanson examined $\frac{12x + 36}{x^2 - x - 12}$ and found the excluded value(s). Is either of them correct? Explain.

No; Colleen did not show the simplified expression and Sanson used the simplified expression to find the excluded values.

Colleen	Sanson
$\frac{12x+36}{x^2-x-12} = \frac{12(x+3)}{(x-4)(x+3)}$ The excluded values are 4 and -3.	$\frac{12x+36}{x^2-x-12} = \frac{12(x+3)}{(x-4)(x+3)} = \frac{12\cancel{(x+3)}}{(x-4)\cancel{(x+3)}} = \frac{12}{x-4}$ The excluded value is 4.

44. PRECISION Compare and contrast the key features of the graphs of $y = x - 2$ and $y = \frac{x^2 + 5x - 14}{x + 7}$. **See margin.**

45. REASONING Explain why every polynomial is also a rational expression. **See margin.**

46. OPEN ENDED Write a rational expression with excluded values −2 and 2. Explain how you found the expression. **See margin.**

47. REASONING Is $\frac{2x^2 - 4x}{x - 2}$ in simplest form? Justify your answer. **See margin.**

48. WRITING IN MATH List the steps you would use to simplify $\frac{x^2 + x - 20}{x + 5}$. State the excluded value. **See margin.**

Additional Answers

47. No; the numerator and denominator have $x - 2$ as a common factor.

48. Sample Answer: To simplify any rational expression, look for a factor common to the numerator and denominator. After factoring the numerator as $(x + 5)(x - 4)$ divide the numerator and the denominator by the GCF, $x + 5$. The simplified expression is $x - 4$. The excluded value is $x = -5$.

Study Guide and Intervention
AL OL ELL

11-3 Study Guide and Intervention — Simplifying Rational Expressions

Practice
AL OL BL ELL

11-3 Practice — Simplifying Rational Expressions

Word Problem Practice
AL OL BL ELL

11-3 Word Problem Practice — Simplifying Rational Expressions

Enrichment
OL BL

11-3 Enrichment — Shannon's Juggling Theorem

4 Assess

Crystal Ball Ask them to write how they think what they have learned today will connect with the next lesson on multiplying and dividing rational expressions.

Additional Answers (Extend 11-3)

1.

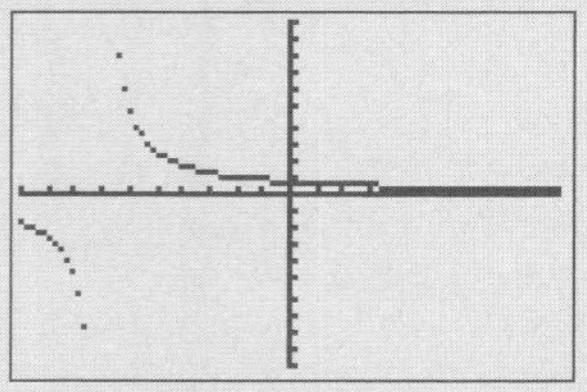

[−10, 10] scl: 1 by [−10,10] scl: 1

2.

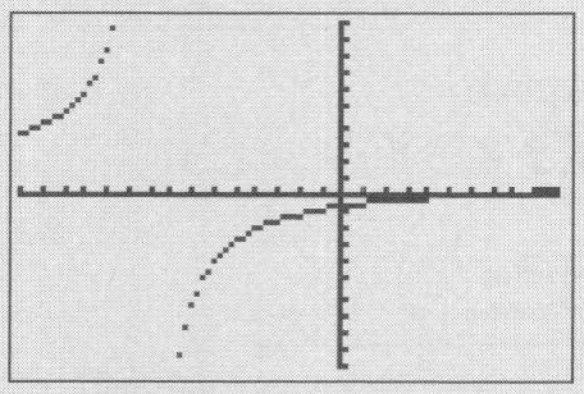

[−15, 10] scl: 1 by [−10,10] scl: 1

3.

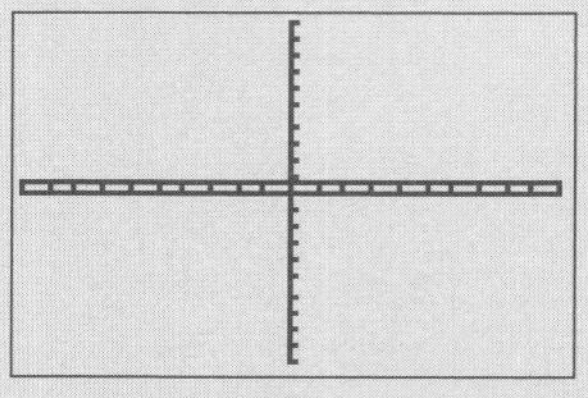

[−10, 10] scl: 1 by [−10,10] scl: 1

Standardized Test Practice

49. Simplify $\frac{2x+4}{2}$. **C**

A $x + 1$
B x
C $x + 2$
D $\frac{x}{2}$

50. SHORT RESPONSE Shiro is buying a car for $5800. He can pay the full amount in cash, or he can pay $1000 down and $230 a month for 24 months. How much more would he pay for the car on the second plan? **$720**

51. GEOMETRY What is the name of the figure? **G**

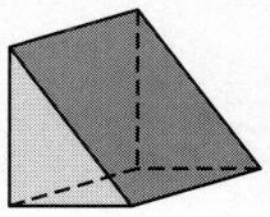

F triangular pyramid
G triangular prism
H rectangular prism
J rectangular pyramid

52. A rectangle has a length of 10 inches and a width of 5 inches. Another rectangle has the same area as the first rectangle but its width is 2 inches. Find the length of the second rectangle. **D**

A 60 in. **C** 30 in.
B 45 in. **D** 25 in.

Spiral Review

State the excluded value for each function. (Lesson 11-2)

53. $y = \frac{6}{x}$ **0**
54. $y = \frac{2}{x-5}$ **5**
55. $y = \frac{x-4}{x-3}$ **3**
56. $y = \frac{3x}{2x+6}$ **−3**

Solve. Assume that y varies inversely as x. (Lesson 11-1)

57. If $y = 10$ when $x = 4$, find x when $y = 2$. **20**

58. If $y = 12$ when $x = 3$, find x when $y = 6$. **6**

59. If $y = -5$ when $x = 3$, find x when $y = -3$. **5**

60. If $y = 21$ when $x = -6$, find x when $y = 7$. **−18**

61. CRAFTS Melinda is working on a quilt using the pattern shown. She has several right triangular pieces of material with two sides that measure 6 inches. What is the length of the third side? (Lesson 10-5) **8.4 in.**

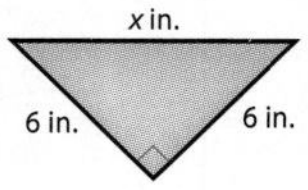

Simplify. (Lesson 10-2)

62. $\sqrt{20}$ **$2\sqrt{5}$**
63. $\sqrt{18}$ **$3\sqrt{2}$**
64. $\sqrt{2} \cdot \sqrt{8}$ **4**
65. $2\sqrt{32}$ **$8\sqrt{2}$**
66. $\sqrt{5} \cdot \sqrt{6}$ **$\sqrt{30}$**
67. $\sqrt{40a^2}$ **$2|a|\sqrt{10}$**
68. $\sqrt{\frac{t}{8}}$ **$\frac{\sqrt{2t}}{4}$**
69. $\sqrt{\frac{2}{7}} \cdot \sqrt{\frac{7}{3}}$ **$\frac{\sqrt{6}}{3}$**

70. FINANCIAL LITERACY Determine the amount of an investment if $250 is invested at an interest rate of 7.3% compounded quarterly for 40 years. (Lesson 9-3) **about $4514.89**

Skills Review

Find the greatest common factor for each set of monomials.

71. $2x, 8x^2$ **$2x$**
72. $3y^2, 7y^3$ **y^2**
73. $7g, 10h$ **1**
74. $21c^2d^3, 14cd^2$ **$7cd^2$**
75. $9qt^2, 18q^2t^2, 27qt$ **$9qt$**
76. $10ab, 25a^2b^2, 30a^2b$ **$5ab$**

Differentiated Instruction BL

Extension Write the expression $\frac{7}{x-9} + 5$ on the board. Ask students to explain how adding 5 to the rational expression $\frac{7}{x-9}$ affects the excluded values in the expression. The excluded value is 9 whether or not 5 is added to $\frac{7}{x-9}$.

EXTEND 11-3 Graphing Technology Lab
Simplifying Rational Expressions

When simplifying rational expressions, you can use a graphing calculator to support your answer. If the graphs of the original expression and the simplified expression overlap, they are equivalent. You can also use the graphs to see excluded values.

Content Standards
AI.RNE.5

Activity Simplify a Rational Expression

Simplify $\frac{x^2-16}{x^2+8x+16}$.

Step 1 Factor the numerator and denominator.

$$\frac{x^2-16}{x^2+8x+16} = \frac{(x-4)(x+4)}{(x+4)(x+4)}$$
$$= \frac{(x-4)}{(x+4)}$$

When $x = -4$, $x + 4 = 0$. Therefore, x cannot equal -4 because you cannot divide by zero.

Step 2 Graph the original expression.

- Set the calculator to Dot mode.
- Enter $\frac{x^2-16}{x^2+8x+16}$ as Y1 and graph in the standard viewing window.

KEYSTROKES: [MODE] [▼] [▼] [▼] [▼] [▶] [ENTER] [Y=] [(] [X,T,θ,n] [x²] [−] 16 [)] [÷] [(] [X,T,θ,n] [x²] [+] 8 [X,T,θ,n] [+] 16 [)] [ZOOM] 6

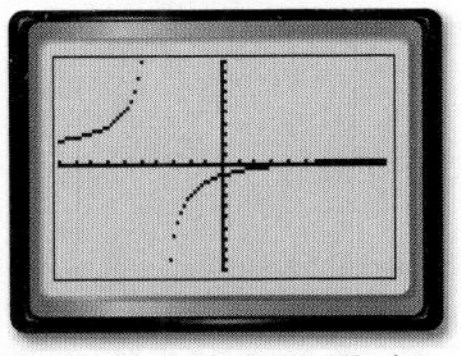

[−10, 10] scl: 1 by [−10, 10] scl: 1

Step 3 Graph the simplified expression.

Enter $\frac{(x-4)}{(x+4)}$ as Y2 and graph.

KEYSTROKES: [Y=] [▼] [(] [X,T,θ,n] [−] 4 [)] [÷] [(] [X,T,θ,n] [+] 4 [)] [GRAPH]

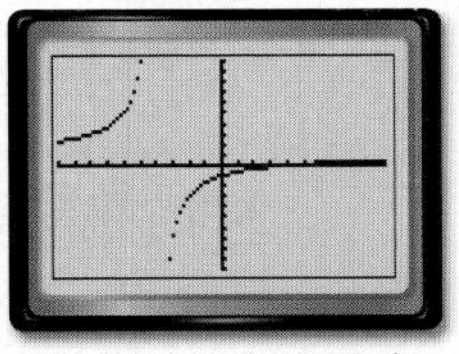

[−10, 10] scl: 1 by [−10, 10] scl: 1

Since the graphs overlap, the two expressions are equivalent.

Exercises

Simplify each expression. Then verify your answer graphically. Name the excluded values. 1–3. See margin for graphs.

1. $\frac{5x+15}{x^2+10x+21}$ $\frac{5}{x+7}$; −3, −7
2. $\frac{x^2-8x+12}{x^2+7x-18}$ $\frac{x-6}{x+9}$; −9, 2
3. $\frac{2x^2+6x+4}{3x^2+9x+6}$ $\frac{2}{3}$; −1, −2
4. a. Simplify $\frac{3x-8}{6x^2-16x}$. $\frac{1}{2x}$
   b. How can you use the **TABLE** function to verify that the original expression and the simplified expression are equivalent? Sample answer: Examine the values and verify that they are identical.
   c. How does the **TABLE** function show you that an x-value is an excluded value? It displays ERROR.

1 Focus

Objective Use a graphing calculator to simplify rational expressions, and verify solutions and excluded values with technology.

Materials for Each Student

- TI-83/84 Plus or other graphing calculator

Teaching Tip

Be sure students understand that when they enter two functions that should produce identical graphs, it is impossible to tell from the screen whether there are two graphs or one. To make sure there are two graphs and that they overlap, have students press [TRACE]. Tell students to use the up and down arrow keys to switch between the two graphs. Each time they press the keys, the equation in the upper left-hand corner of the screen should change but the values for x and y at the bottom of the screen should stay the same.

2 Teach

Working in Cooperative Groups

Put students in groups of two or three, mixing abilities. Have groups complete the Activity and Exercises 1–3.

- Make sure students enter the equations exactly as shown in the keystrokes. If students fail to put the numerator and denominator in parentheses, the resulting graph may be incorrect.

Practice Have students complete Exercise 4.

3 Assess

Formative Assessment

Ask students when they would use a graphing calculator to confirm the simplification of a rational expression. Sample answer: when the simplification is very complicated

From Concrete to Abstract

Ask: Will the graphs of the original expression and the simplified expression always be the same? Graph $\frac{x^2-64}{x-8}$ and its simplified version, $x + 8$. Explain how the graphs are different. When there are excluded values for the original rational expression and not for the simplified expression, the graphs might be slightly different; the first graph has a hole at $x = 8$ because it is an excluded value of the equation.

1 Focus

VerticalAlignment

Before Lesson 11-4 Multiplied polynomials and divided monomials.

Lesson 11-4 Multiply rational expressions. Divide rational expressions.

After Lesson 11-4 Divide a polynomial by a monomial or a binomial.

2 Teach

Scaffolding Questions

Have students read the **Why?** section of the lesson.

Ask:

- What is the simplification of the expression shown? 20,250 minutes
- In what way are the units in these expressions similar to variables? The common units in the numerator and denominator can be factored out.
- How do you know that you ended up with the correct units at the end of the simplification? The problem states that you want to know the number of minutes. The final unit left is minutes, which is the correct unit.

LESSON 11-4 Multiplying and Dividing Rational Expressions

Then

- You multiplied polynomials and divided monomials.

Now

- 1 Multiply rational expressions.
- 2 Divide rational expressions.

Why?

- A recent survey showed 10- to 17-year olds talk or text on their cell phones an average of 3.75 hours per day during the summer. The expression below can be used to find the average number of minutes youth talk or text on their phones during summer, approximately 90 days.

$$90 \text{ days} \cdot \frac{3.75 \text{ hours}}{\text{day}} \cdot \frac{60 \text{ minutes}}{1 \text{ hour}} = 20{,}250 \text{ minutes}$$

Content Standards
AI.RNE.5

1 Multiply Rational Expressions

To multiply fractions, you multiply numerators and multiply denominators. Use this same method to multiply rational expressions.

KeyConcept Multiplying Rational Expressions

Words Let a, b, c, and d be polynomials with $b \neq 0$ and $d \neq 0$. Then, $\frac{a}{b} \cdot \frac{c}{d} = \frac{ac}{bd}$.

Example $\frac{x}{2x-3} \cdot \frac{4x^2}{5} = \frac{4x^3}{5(2x-3)}$

Example 1 Multiply Expressions Involving Monomials

Find each product.

a. $\frac{r^2x}{9t^3} \cdot \frac{3t^4}{r}$

Divide by the common factors before multiplying.

$$\frac{r^2x}{9t^3} \cdot \frac{3t^4}{r} = \frac{\overset{r}{\cancel{r^2}}x}{\underset{3\ 1}{\cancel{9}\cancel{t^3}}} \cdot \frac{\overset{1\ t}{\cancel{3}\cancel{t^4}}}{\underset{1}{\cancel{r}}}$$ Divide by the common factors 3, r, and t^3.

$$= \frac{rxt}{3}$$ Simplify.

b. $\frac{a+4}{a^2} \cdot \frac{a}{a^2+2a-8}$

$$\frac{a+4}{a^2} \cdot \frac{a}{a^2+2a-8} = \frac{a+4}{a^2} \cdot \frac{a}{(a+4)(a-2)}$$ Factor the denominator.

$$= \frac{\overset{1}{\cancel{a+4}}}{\underset{a}{\cancel{a^2}}} \cdot \frac{\overset{1}{\cancel{a}}}{\underset{1}{\cancel{(a+4)}}(a-2)}$$ The GCF is $a(a+4)$.

$$= \frac{1}{a(a-2)} \text{ or } \frac{1}{a^2-2a}$$ Simplify.

GuidedPractice

1A. $\frac{3x}{16x^2} \cdot \frac{8x^2}{3}$ $\frac{x}{2}$

1B. $\frac{x+3}{x} \cdot \frac{5}{x^2+7x+12}$ **1B.** $\frac{5}{x^2+4x}$

1C. $\frac{y^2-3y-4}{y+5} \cdot \frac{y+5}{y^2-4y}$ **1C.** $\frac{y+1}{y}$

Lesson 11-4 Resources

Resource	Approaching Level AL	On Level OL	Beyond Level BL	English Learners ELL
Teacher Edition		▪ Differentiated Instruction, p. 704	▪ Differentiated Instruction, pp. 700, 704	
Chapter Resource Masters	▪ Study Guide and Intervention, pp. 23–24 ▪ Skills Practice, p. 25 ▪ Practice, p. 26 ▪ Word Problem Practice, p. 27	▪ Study Guide and Intervention, pp. 23–24 ▪ Skills Practice, p. 25 ▪ Practice, p. 26 ▪ Word Problem Practice, p. 27 ▪ Enrichment, p. 28 ▪ Spreadsheet Activity, p. 29	▪ Practice, p. 26 ▪ Word Problem Practice, p. 27 ▪ Enrichment, p. 28	▪ Study Guide and Intervention, pp. 23–24 ▪ Skills Practice, p. 25 ▪ Practice, p. 26 ▪ Word Problem Practice, p. 27
Other	▪ 5-Minute Check 11-4 ▪ Study Notebook	▪ 5-Minute Check 11-4 ▪ Study Notebook	▪ 5-Minute Check 11-4 ▪ Study Notebook	▪ 5-Minute Check 11-4 ▪ Study Notebook

StudyTip

Rational Expressions From this point on, assume that no denominator of a rational expression has a value of zero.

When you multiply fractions that involve units of measure, you can divide by the units in the same way that you divide by variables. Recall that this process is called *dimensional analysis*. You can use dimensional analysis to convert units of measure within a system and between systems.

PT

Real-World Example 2 Dimensional Analysis

SKI RACING Ann Proctor won the 2007 World Waterski Racing Championship race in her category when she finished the 88-kilometer course in 51.23 minutes. What was her average speed in miles per hour? (*Hint*: 1 km ≈ 0.62 mi)

$$\frac{88\text{ km}}{51.23\text{ min}} \cdot \frac{0.62\text{ mi}}{1\text{ km}} \cdot \frac{60\text{ min}}{1\text{ h}} = \frac{88\,\cancel{\text{km}}}{51.23\,\cancel{\text{min}}} \cdot \frac{0.62\text{ mi}}{1\,\cancel{\text{km}}} \cdot \frac{60\,\cancel{\text{min}}}{1\text{ h}}$$

$$= \frac{88 \cdot 0.62\text{ mi} \cdot 60}{51.23 \cdot 1 \cdot 1\text{ h}} \quad \text{Simplify.}$$

$$= \frac{3273.6\text{ mi}}{51.23\text{ h}} \quad \text{Multiply.}$$

$$\approx \frac{63.9\text{ mi}}{\text{h}} \quad \text{Divide the numerator and the denominator by 51.23.}$$

Her average speed was 63.9 miles per hour.

GuidedPractice

2. SKI RACING What was Ann Proctor's speed in feet per second? **about 93.72 ft/s**

2 Divide Rational Expressions

To divide by a fraction, you multiply by the reciprocal. You can use this same method to divide by a rational expression.

KeyConcept Dividing Rational Expressions

Symbols Let a, b, c, and d be polynomials with $b \neq 0$, $c \neq 0$, and $d \neq 0$. Then, $\frac{a}{b} \div \frac{c}{d} = \frac{a}{b} \cdot \frac{d}{c} = \frac{ad}{bc}$.

Example $\frac{x-3}{x} \div \frac{2x^2}{5} = \frac{x-3}{x} \cdot \frac{5}{2x^2} = \frac{5(x-3)}{2x^3}$

PT

Example 3 Divide by a Rational Expression

Find $\frac{4}{15n^3} \div \frac{12}{25n}$.

$$\frac{4}{15n^3} \div \frac{12}{25n} = \frac{4}{15n^3} \cdot \frac{25n}{12} \quad \text{Multiply by } \frac{25n}{12}\text{, the reciprocal of } \frac{12}{25n}.$$

$$= \frac{\overset{1}{\cancel{4}}}{\underset{3n^2}{\cancel{15n^3}}} \cdot \frac{\overset{5}{\cancel{25n}}}{\underset{3}{\cancel{12}}} \quad \text{Divide by common factors 4, 5, and } n.$$

$$= \frac{5}{9n^2} \quad \text{Simplify.}$$

GuidedPractice

Find each quotient.

3A. $\frac{15y^2}{4x} \div \frac{5y}{8x^3}$ $\mathbf{6x^2y}$

3B. $\frac{12a^2}{5b} \div \frac{25a}{6b^2}$ $\mathbf{\frac{72ab}{125}}$

1 Multiply Rational Expressions

Example 1a shows how to multiply rational expressions involving monomials. **Example 1b** shows how to factor a quadratic expression before simplifying a product of rational expressions involving polynomials that are not monomials. **Example 2** shows how to use a process called *dimensional analysis* to multiply fractions in a real-world problem that involves units of measure.

Formative Assessment

Use the Guided Practice exercises after each example to determine students' understanding of concepts.

Additional Examples

1 Find each product.

a. $\frac{7x^2y}{12z^3} \cdot \frac{14z}{49xy^4}$ $\frac{x}{6y^3z^2}$

b. $\frac{b+3}{4b-12} \cdot \frac{b^2-4b+3}{b^2-7b-30}$ $\frac{b-1}{4b-40}$

2 **SPACE** The velocity that a spacecraft must have in order to escape Earth's gravitational pull is called the *escape velocity*. The escape velocity for a spacecraft leaving Earth is about 40,320 kilometers per hour. What is this speed in meters per second? 11,200 m/s

Additional Examples also in Interactive Classroom PowerPoint® Presentations

IWB Interactive White Board READY

Focus on Mathematical Content

Dimensional Analysis Dimensional analysis is the process of analyzing units to decide which conversion factors to use when converting between different units.

WatchOut!

Student Misconceptions The **Study Tip** states that, from this point forward, students can assume that no denominator of a rational expression has a value of zero. Ask students to discuss why this is an important assumption.

2 Divide Rational Expressions

Example 3 shows how to multiply by the reciprocal when dividing rational expressions. **Example 4** shows how to divide by rational expressions and polynomials. **Example 5** shows how to factor a quadratic expression before dividing a rational expression.

Additional Examples

3 Find $\frac{8}{20x^3} \div \frac{44}{25x^2}$. $\frac{5}{22x}$

4 Find each quotient.

a. $\frac{3x+9}{x^2} \div (x+3)$ $\frac{3}{x^2}$

b. $\frac{y-6}{2y+6} \div \frac{y+2}{y+3}$ $\frac{y-6}{2y+4}$

5 Find $\frac{x-5}{x^2-9x+18} \div \frac{x^2-25}{x-6}$. $\frac{1}{(x-3)(x+5)}$

Teach with Tech

Interactive Whiteboard Use the board to help demonstrate canceling out common factors. Cross out the common factors as you simplify the expression, and drag the remaining factors to create the simplified expression.

ReadingMath

Rational Expressions In a rational expression, the fraction bar acts as a grouping symbol. In Example 4a, $\frac{2x+6}{x^2}$ is read *the quantity two x plus six divided by x squared.*

PT

Example 4 Divide by Rational Expressions and Polynomials

Find each quotient.

a. $\frac{2x+6}{x^2} \div (x+3)$

$\frac{2x+6}{x^2} \div (x+3) = \frac{2x+6}{x^2} \div \frac{x+3}{1}$ Write the binomial as a fraction.

$= \frac{2x+6}{x^2} \cdot \frac{1}{x+3}$ Multiply by the reciprocal of $x + 3$.

$= \frac{2(x+3)}{x^2} \cdot \frac{1}{x+3}$ Factor $4x + 6$.

$= \frac{2\cancel{(x+3)}^{1}}{x^2} \cdot \frac{1}{\cancel{x+3}_{1}}$ or $\frac{2}{x^2}$ Divide out the common factor and simplify.

b. $\frac{a-2}{4a+4} \div \frac{a+5}{a+1}$

$\frac{a-2}{4a+4} \div \frac{a+5}{a+1} = \frac{a-2}{4a+4} \cdot \frac{a+1}{a+5}$ Multiply by the reciprocal.

$= \frac{a-2}{4\cancel{(a+1)}_{1}} \cdot \frac{\cancel{a+1}^{1}}{a+5}$ Factor $4a + 4$.

$= \frac{a-2}{4(a+5)}$ The GCF is $a + 1$ and simplify.

GuidedPractice

4A. $\frac{4d-8}{2d-6} \div \frac{2d-4}{d-4}$ $\frac{d-4}{d-3}$

4B. $\frac{b+4}{3b+2} \div \frac{3b+12}{b+1}$ $\frac{b+1}{3(3b+2)}$

Sometimes you must factor a quadratic expression before you can simplify the quotient of rational expressions.

PT

Example 5 Expression Involving Polynomials

Find $\frac{y-3}{y^2-10y+16} \div \frac{y^2-9}{y-8}$.

$\frac{y-3}{y^2-10y+16} \div \frac{y^2-9}{y-8}$

$= \frac{y-3}{y^2-10y+16} \cdot \frac{y-8}{y^2-9}$ Multiply by the reciprocal, $\frac{y-8}{y^2-9}$.

$= \frac{y-3}{(y-2)(y-8)} \cdot \frac{y-8}{(y-3)(y+3)}$ Factor $y^2 - 10y + 16$ and $y^2 - 9$.

$= \frac{\cancel{y-3}^{1}}{(y-2)\cancel{(y-8)}_{1}} \cdot \frac{\cancel{y-8}^{1}}{\cancel{(y-3)}_{1}(y+3)}$ The GCF is $(y - 3)(y - 8)$.

$= \frac{1}{(y-2)(y+3)}$ Simplify.

StudyTip

Canceling Remember that only factors can be canceled, not individual terms.

GuidedPractice

Find each quotient.

5A. $\frac{p^2-4}{5p} \div \frac{p-2}{p+q}$ $\frac{(p+2)(p+q)}{5p}$

5B. $\frac{q^2+3q+2}{12} \div \frac{q+1}{q^2+4}$ $\frac{(q+2)(q^2+4)}{12}$

DifferentiatedInstruction BL

Logical Learners Challenge students to write one division and one multiplication problem consisting of two rational expressions that simplify to $\frac{x-1}{x-2}$.

Check Your Understanding

◯ = Step-by-Step Solutions begin on page R13.

Example 1 Find each product.

1. $\frac{2x^3}{7x}\cdot\frac{14}{x}$ $4x$
2. $\frac{3ab}{4c^4}\cdot\frac{16c^2}{9b}$ $\frac{4a}{3c^2}$
3. $\frac{t^2}{(t-5)(t+5)}\cdot\frac{t+5}{6t}$ $\frac{t}{6(t-5)}$
4. $\frac{8}{r+1}\cdot\frac{r^2-1}{2}$ $4(r-1)$

Example 2

5. **PRECISION** The slowest land mammal is the three-toed sloth. It travels 0.07 mile per hour on the ground. What is this speed in feet per minute? **6.16 ft/min**

6. **EXERCISE** One hour of moderate inline skating burns approximately 330 Calories. If Nelia plans to do inline skating for 3 hours a week, how many Calories will she burn in a year from the skating? **51,480 Calories**

Examples 3–5 Find each quotient.

7. $\frac{8}{3x^2}\div\frac{4}{x}$ $\frac{2}{3x}$
8. $\frac{c^5}{2}\div\frac{c^3}{6d^2}$ $3c^2d^2$
9. $\frac{b^2+6b+5}{6b+6}\div(b+5)$ $\frac{1}{6}$
10. $\frac{2x+8}{x+3}\div\frac{x+4}{x^2+6x+9}$ $2(x+3)$

Practice and Problem Solving

Extra Practice is on page R11.

Example 1 Find each product.

11. $\frac{10n^2}{4}\cdot\frac{2}{n}$ $5n$
12. $\frac{12c^3}{21b}\cdot\frac{14b^2}{6c}$ $\frac{4bc^2}{3}$
13. $\frac{x^5y}{2z^3}\cdot\frac{18z^4}{xy}$ $9x^4z$
14. $\frac{5c^3d}{c^4d}\cdot\frac{f^2d^3c}{10cf^4}$ $\frac{d^3}{2cf^2}$
15. $\frac{9}{t-2}\cdot\frac{(t+2)(t-2)}{3}$ $3(t+2)$
16. $\frac{(a+4)(a-5)}{a^2}\cdot\frac{6a}{a+4}$ $\frac{6(a-5)}{a}$
17. $\frac{(k+6)(k-1)}{k+2}\cdot\frac{(k+1)(k+2)}{(k+1)(k-1)}$ $k+6$
18. $\frac{(r-8)(r+3)}{r}\cdot\frac{2r}{(r+8)(r+3)}$ $\frac{2(r-8)}{r+8}$
19. $\frac{n^2+n-2}{n+2}\cdot\frac{4n}{n-1}$ $4n$
20. $\frac{y^2-1}{y^2-49}\cdot\frac{y-7}{y+1}$ $\frac{y-1}{y+7}$

Example 2

21. **FINANCIAL LITERACY** A scarf bought in Italy cost 18 Euros. The exchange rate at the time was 1 U.S. dollar = 0.73 Euro.
    a. How much did the scarf cost in U.S. dollars? **about \$24.66**
    b. If the exchange rate at the time was 1 Canadian dollar = 0.69 Euro, how much did the scarf cost in Canadian dollars? **about \$26.09**

22. **ROLLER COASTERS** A roller coaster has 6 trains. Each train has 3 cars, and each car seats 4 people. Write and simplify an expression including units to find the total number of people that can ride the roller coaster at one time.
    $6 \text{ trains}\cdot\frac{3 \text{ cars}}{1 \text{ train}}\cdot\frac{4 \text{ people}}{1 \text{ car}}$; 72 people

27. $\frac{b-2}{(b+5)(2b+3)}$
28. $\frac{5(k+3)}{k}$
29. $\frac{x}{2(x-4)}$
31. $\frac{(r+2)^2}{4}$

Examples 3–5 Find each quotient.

23. $\frac{x^5}{y}\div\frac{x}{y^2}$ x^4y
24. $\frac{3r^4}{k^2}\div\frac{18r^3}{k}$ $\frac{r}{6k}$
25. $\frac{21b^3}{4c^2}\div\frac{7}{6c^2}$ $\frac{9b^3}{2}$
26. $\frac{f^4g^2h}{x^2y}\div f^3g$ $\frac{fgh}{x^2y}$
27. $\frac{6b-12}{b+5}\div(12b+18)$
28. $\frac{k+3}{k+2}\div\frac{k}{5k+10}$
29. $\frac{5x^2}{x^2-5x+4}\div\frac{10x}{x-1}$
30. $\frac{n^2+7n+12}{16n^2}\div\frac{n+3}{2n}$ $\frac{n+4}{8n}$
31. $\frac{r+2}{r+1}\div\frac{4}{r^2+3r+2}$
32. $\frac{3a}{a^2+2a+1}\div\frac{a-1}{a+1}$ $\frac{3a}{(a+1)(a-1)}$

3 Practice

Formative Assessment

Use Exercises 1–10 to check for understanding.

Use the chart at the bottom of this page to customize assignments for your students.

Teaching the Process Standards

Precision Mathematically proficient students are careful about specifying units of measure. In real-world problems involving dimensional analysis, suggest that students highlight like units to avoid confusion.

Differentiated Homework Options

Level	Assignment	Two-Day Option	
AL Basic	11–34, 53, 54, 56–89	11–33 odd, 60–63	12–34 even, 53, 54, 56–59, 64–89
OL Core	11–33 odd, 35–44, 45–49 odd, 50–54, 56–89	11–34, 60–63	35–54, 56–59, 64–89
BL Advanced	35–83, (optional: 84–89)		

Exercise Alert

Formulas For Exercises 44 and 52, students will need to know the formula for the volume of a rectangular prism.

WatchOut!

Error Analysis For Exercise 53, students encounter two of the most common errors made when dividing and multiplying rational expressions. Suggest students write out each step to find the correct solution to the problem.

Tips for New Teachers

Sense-Making Discuss with students how they can verify that a dimensional analysis problem has been set up correctly. Also, encourage students to check the reasonableness of their answers when they solve a problem.

Additional Answers

43. $\frac{1 \text{ cup}}{1 \text{ beat}} \cdot \frac{70 \text{ beats}}{1 \text{ minute}} \cdot \frac{1 \text{ gallon}}{16 \text{ cups}} \cdot \frac{60 \text{ minutes}}{1 \text{ hour}} = 262.5 \text{ gal/h}$

52a.

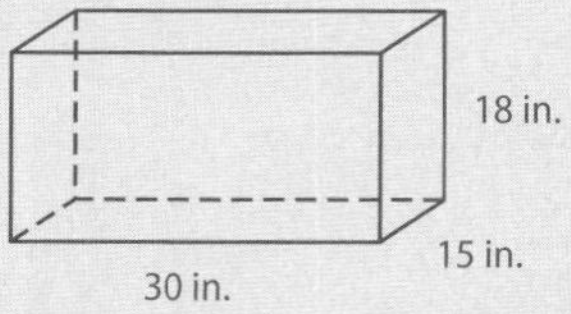

8100 in^3

56. Sample answer: You can use dimensional analysis in situations that involve units of measure when dividing rational expressions. For example, to change 30 miles/hour to feet/second, multiply $\frac{30 \text{ miles}}{1 \text{ hour}} \cdot \frac{5280 \text{ feet}}{1 \text{ mile}} \cdot \frac{1 \text{ hour}}{60 \text{ min}} \cdot \frac{1 \text{ min}}{60 \text{ s}}$

33. BEARS A grizzly bear runs 110 feet in 5 seconds. What is the average speed of the bear in miles per hour? **15 mi/h**

34. SEWING The fabric that Megan wants to buy for a costume she is making costs \$7.50 per yard. To the nearest tenth, how many meters can she buy with \$24? (*Hint*: 1 inch = 2.54 centimeters) **2.9 m**

B **35. TRAVEL** A plane flies 1250 kilometers at an average speed of 540 miles per hour.

a. Write a product to find the number of hours it took for the plane to make the trip. Include the units. (*Hint*: 1 mile = 1.609 kilometers). $\frac{1250 \text{ km}}{1} \cdot \frac{1 \text{ mi}}{1.609 \text{ km}} \cdot \frac{1 \text{ h}}{540 \text{ mi}}$

b. Find the number of hours it took for the plane to make the trip. Round to the nearest tenth. **1.4 h**

36. VOLUNTEERING Tyree is passing out cups of orange drink from a 3.5-gallon cooler. If each cup of orange drink is 4.25 ounces, about how many cups can he hand out? (*Hint*: There are 128 ounces in a gallon.) **about 105.4 cups**

37. LAND Louisiana loses about 30 square miles of land each year to coastal erosion, hurricanes, and other natural and human causes. Approximately how many square yards of land are lost per month? (*Hint*: Use 1 square mile = 3,097,600 square yards.) **7,744,000 yd²/mo**

38. GEOMETRY Write an expression to represent the length of the rectangle. $(x + 6)(x - 3)$

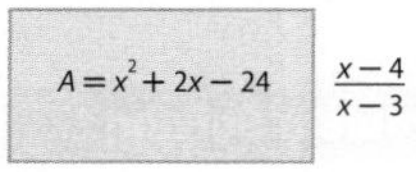

Convert each rate. Round to the nearest tenth.

39. 46 feet per second to miles per hour **about 31.4 mi/h**

40. 29.5 meters per second to kilometers per hour **106.2 km/h**

41. 28 milliliters per second to cups per minute. (*Hint*: 1 liter ≈ 0.908 quart) **6.1 c/min**

42. 32.4 meters per second to miles per hour. (*Hint*: 1 mile ≈ 1.609 kilometers) **72.5 mi/h**

43. LIFE SCIENCE A human heart pumps about a cup of blood each time it beats. On average, a person's heart beats about 70 times a minute. Write and simplify an expression to find how many gallons of blood are pumped per hour. **See margin.**

44. GEOMETRY Refer to the prism at the right.

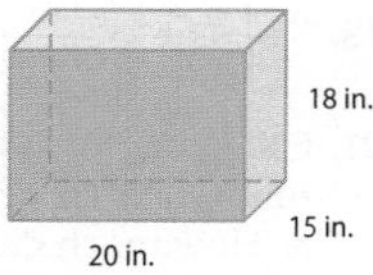

a. Find the volume in cubic inches. **5400 in³**

b. Use the ratio $\frac{1 \text{ foot}^3}{1728 \text{ inches}^3}$ to write a multiplication expression to convert the volume to cubic feet. Then convert the volume. $5400 \text{ in}^3 \cdot \frac{1 \text{ ft}^3}{1728 \text{ in}^3}$; **3.125 ft³**

PRECISION Find each product. Describe what the final answer represents.

45. $\frac{\$9.80}{1 \text{ hour}} \cdot \frac{15 \text{ hours}}{1 \text{ week}} \cdot \frac{52 \text{ weeks}}{1 \text{ year}}$ **\$7644/yr; Sample answer: earnings per year**

46. $\frac{\$2.85}{1 \text{ gallon of gasoline}} \cdot \frac{15 \text{ gallons of gasoline}}{1 \text{ fill-up}} \cdot \frac{3 \text{ fill-ups}}{1 \text{ month}} \cdot \frac{1 \text{ month}}{30 \text{ days}}$ **about \$4.28/day; the average cost of gasoline per day**

47. $\frac{32 \text{ meters}}{1 \text{ second}} \cdot \frac{60 \text{ seconds}}{1 \text{ minute}} \cdot \frac{60 \text{ minutes}}{1 \text{ hour}} \cdot \frac{1 \text{ kilometer}}{1000 \text{ meters}} \cdot \frac{1 \text{ mile}}{1.609 \text{ kilometers}}$ **about 71.6 mi/h; converting 32 meters per second to miles per hour**

48. $\frac{\$32{,}000}{1 \text{ year}} \cdot \frac{1 \text{ year}}{52 \text{ weeks}} \cdot \frac{1 \text{ week}}{40 \text{ hours}}$ **about \$15.38; converting yearly salary to hourly wage**

49. SPACE The highest speed at which any spacecraft has ever escaped from Earth is 35,800 miles per hour by the *New Horizons* probe, which was launched in 2006. Convert this speed to feet per second. Round to the nearest tenth. **about 52,506.7 ft/s**

57. Sample answer: The height of a cylinder when you know an expression for the volume and radius;
$\frac{V}{\pi r^2} = h$;
$V = \pi(x^3 - 6x^2 + 9x)$,
$r = (x - 3)$.

59. Sample answer: Write ratios comparing the number of days in one year and the number of hours in one day. Then multiply the ratios: $\frac{365 \text{ days}}{1 \text{ year}} \cdot \frac{24 \text{ hours}}{1 \text{ day}} = 8760$ hours.

50. **ELECTRICITY** Simplify the expression below to find the cost of running a 3500-watt air conditioner for one week. **$58.80**

$$3500 \text{ watts} \cdot \frac{1 \text{ kilowatt}}{1000 \text{ watts}} \cdot \frac{168 \text{ hours}}{1 \text{ week}} \cdot \frac{10 \text{ cents}}{1 \text{ kilowatt} \cdot \text{hours}} \cdot \frac{1 \text{ dollar}}{100 \text{ cents}}$$

51. **AMUSEMENT PARKS** In a ride, riders stand along the wall of a circular room with a radius of 3.1 meters. The room completes 27 rotations per minute.

51a. $\frac{27 \text{ rotations}}{1 \text{ min}} \cdot \frac{1 \text{ min}}{60 \text{ s}} \cdot \frac{2\pi(3.1) \text{ m}}{1 \text{ rotation}}$

a. Write an expression for the number of meters the room moves per second.

b. Simplify the expression you wrote in Part **a** and describe what it means. **About 8.8 m/s; the room spins at a rate of 8.8 m/s.**

C 52. **AQUARIUMS** An aquarium is a rectangular prism 30 inches long, 15 inches wide, and 18 inches high. **52b. Sample answer: Multiply the volume in cubic inches by the ratio; 4.7 ft³.**

a. Sketch and label a diagram of the aquarium. Then find its volume in cubic inches. **See margin.**

b. Describe how to use the ratio $\frac{1 \text{ ft}^3}{1728 \text{ in}^3}$ to find the volume of the tank in cubic feet. Then find the volume. Round to the nearest tenth.

c. Pure water weighs 62 pounds per cubic foot. How much would the water in the tank weigh if the tank were filled? **about 291.4 lb**

d. A saltwater aquarium requires 2 pounds of minerals for each cubic foot of water. Find the percent concentration by weight of the saltwater by dividing the weight of the minerals by the sum of the weights of the minerals and the water. **3.125%**

e. Kim accidentally added twice the required minerals. Find the percent concentration by weight. Is it twice the recommended concentration? Explain. **6.06%; No, the numerator is doubled and the denominator is changed.**

H.O.T. Problems Use Higher-Order Thinking Skills

53. **ERROR ANALYSIS** Mei and Tamika are finding $\frac{2x+6}{x+5} \div \frac{2}{x+5}$. Is either of them correct? Explain.

Neither; Tamika did not multiply by the reciprocal, and Mei incorrectly factored out the 2 in $2x + 6$.

Mei

$\frac{2x+6}{x+5} \div \frac{2}{x+5}$

$= \frac{\not{2}x+6}{\not{x+5}} \cdot \frac{\not{x+5}}{\not{2}}$

$= x + 6$

Tamika

$\frac{2x+6}{x+5} \div \frac{2}{x+5}$

$= \frac{\not{2}(x+3)}{\not{x+5}} \cdot \frac{\not{2}}{\not{x+5}}$

$= \frac{4(x+3)}{(x+5)^2}$

54. **REASONING** Find the missing term in $\frac{?}{7} \div \frac{10x^3}{21} = \frac{3}{2x}$. Justify your answer. $\frac{5x^2}{7}$; $\frac{3}{2x} \cdot \frac{10x^3}{21} = \frac{5x^2}{7}$

55. **PERSEVERANCE** Find $\frac{x^2 - 3x - 10}{x^2 + 2x - 35} \cdot \frac{x^2 + 4x - 21}{x^2 + 9x + 14}$. Write in simplest form. $\frac{x-3}{x+7}$

56. **WRITING IN MATH** Give an example and describe how you could use dimensional analysis to solve a real-world problem involving rational expressions. **See margin.**

57. **OPEN ENDED** Give an example of a real-world situation that could be modeled by the quotient of two rational expressions. Provide an example of this quotient. **See margin.**

58. **WRITE A QUESTION** A classmate found that the product of two rational expressions is $\frac{9x-3}{(x+3)(3x+1)}$. Write a question to help her find the excluded values. **Sample answer: What values of x make the denominators that were multiplied equal to 0?**

59. **WRITING IN MATH** Describe how to use dimensional analysis to find the number of hours in one year. **See margin.**

Study Guide and Intervention

AL OL ELL

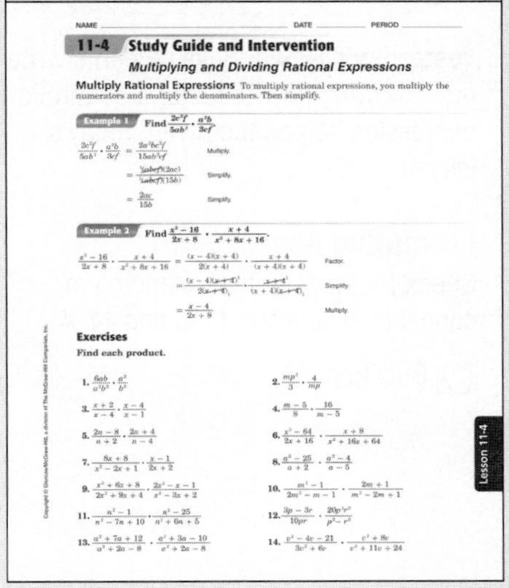

Practice

AL OL BL ELL

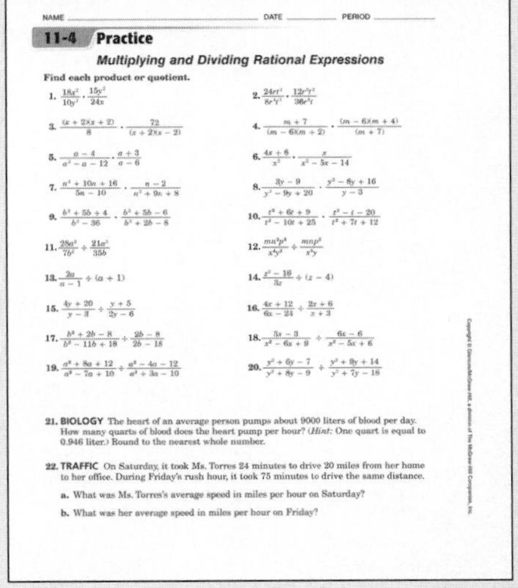

Word Problem Practice

AL OL BL ELL

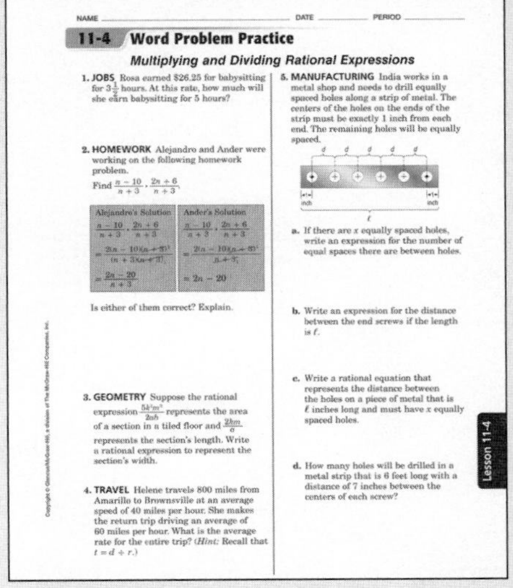

Teaching the Process Standards

Perseverance Mathematically proficient students consider analogous problems, and try simpler forms of the original problem. In Exercise 55, remind students that rational expressions can be treated like rational numbers. Simplifying before multiplying can make the computations easier.

Enrichment

OL BL

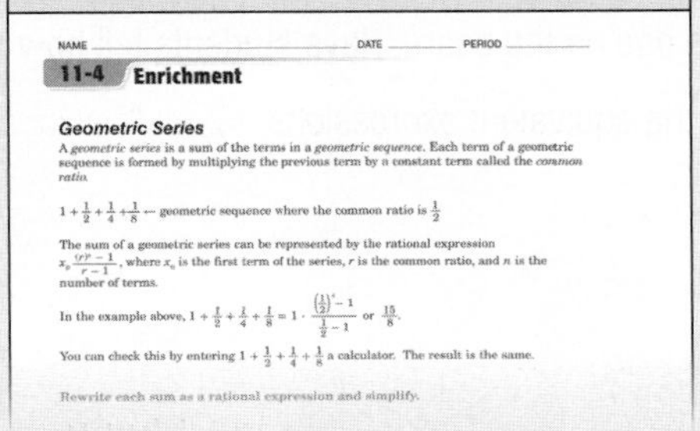

4 Assess

Yesterday's News Have students write how knowing how to factor a quadratic expression helped them with today's lesson.

Formative Assessment

Check for student understanding of concepts in Lessons 11-3 and 11-4.

Quiz 2, p. 57

Standardized Test Practice

60. GEOMETRY The perimeter of a rectangle is 30 inches. Its area is 54 square inches. Find the length of the longest side. **B**

A 6 inches
B 9 inches
C 12 inches
D 30 inches

61. Find $\frac{c^2 - c - 6}{2c - 10} \div \frac{2c + 4}{3c - 15}$. **F**

F $\frac{3(c-3)}{4}$ H $\frac{4(c-3)}{3}$
G $\frac{c+5}{c-3}$ J $\frac{c-3}{c-5}$

62. EXTENDED RESPONSE The weekly salaries of six employees at a fast food restaurant are \$140, \$220, \$90, \$180, \$140, \$200.

a. What is the mean of the six salaries? **\$161.67**

b. What is the median of the six salaries? **\$160**

c. What is the mode of the six salaries? **\$140**

63. Tito has three times as many CDs as Dasan. Dasan has two thirds as many CDs as Brant. Brant has 27 CDs. How many CDs does Tito have? **A**

A 54 C 27
B 32 D 18

Spiral Review

Simplify each expression. State the excluded values of the variables. (Lesson 11-3)

64. $\frac{20x^2y}{25xy}$ $\frac{4}{5}x$; $x \neq 0, y \neq 0$

65. $\frac{14g^3h^2}{42gh^3}$ $\frac{g^2}{3h}$; $g \neq 0, h \neq 0$

66. $\frac{64qt}{16q^2t^3}$ $\frac{4}{qt^2}$; $q \neq 0, t \neq 0$

67. $\frac{y^2 + 10y + 16}{y + 2}$ $y + 8$; -2

68. $\frac{p^2 - 9}{p^2 - 5p + 6}$ $\frac{p+3}{p-2}$; 3, 2

69. $\frac{z^2 + z - 2}{z^2 - 3z + 2}$ $\frac{z+2}{z-2}$; 2, 1

Identify the asymptotes of each function. (Lesson 11-2)

70. $y = \frac{2}{x}$ $x = 0, y = 0$

71. $y = \frac{3}{x} + 5$ $x = 0, y = 5$

72. $y = \frac{1}{x-5} - 4$ $x = 5, y = -4$

73. $y = \frac{1}{x+3}$ $x = -3, y = 0$

74. $y = \frac{-1}{x+6} + 7$ $x = -6, y = 7$

75. $y = \frac{2}{x-8} - 3$ $x = 8, y = -3$

76. FORESTRY The number of board feet B that a log will yield can be estimated by using the formula $B = \frac{L}{16}(D^2 - 8D + 16)$, where D is the diameter in inches and L is the log length in feet. For logs that are 16 feet long, what diameter will yield approximately 256 board feet? (Lesson 8-9) **20 in.**

Find the degree of each polynomial. (Lesson 8-1)

77. 2 **0**

78. $-3a$ **1**

79. $5x^2 + 3x$ **2**

80. $d^4 - 6c^2$ **4**

81. $2x^3 - 4z + 8xz$ **3**

82. $3d^4 + 5d^3 - 4c^2 + 1$ **4**

83. DRIVING Tires should be kept within 2 pounds per square inch (psi) of the manufacturer's recommended tire pressure. If the recommendation for a tire is 30 psi, what is the range of acceptable pressures? (Lesson 5-5) $\{p \mid 28 \leq p \leq 32\}$

Skills Review

Factor each polynomial.

84. $x^2 - 18x - 40$ $(x + 2)(x - 20)$

85. $x^2 - 5x + 6$ $(x - 2)(x - 3)$

86. $x^2 - 2x - 24$ $(x + 4)(x - 6)$

87. $3x^2 + 7x - 20$ $(x + 4)(3x - 5)$

88. $2x^2 + x - 15$ $(x + 3)(2x - 5)$

89. $8x^2 - 4x - 40$ $4(x + 2)(2x - 5)$

Differentiated Instruction OL BL

Extension Write $\frac{3}{x+4}$ on the board. Ask students to write rational expressions that are equivalent to the one on the board. Have students tell how the excluded values change from the original expression to the equivalent expressions. Sample answer: $\frac{3x - 12}{x^2 - 16}$; the excluded value in $\frac{3}{x+4}$ is $x = -4$; the excluded values in $\frac{3x-12}{x^2-16}$ are $x = -4$ and $x = 4$.

CHAPTER 11

Mid-Chapter Quiz

Lessons 11-1 through 11-4

1. Determine whether the table represents an inverse variation. Explain. (Lesson 11-1)

x	y
2	8
4	4
8	2
16	1

Yes, each product is 16.

Assume that y varies inversely as x. Write an inverse variation equation that relates x and y. (Lesson 11-1)

2. $y = 5$ when $x = 10$ **$y = \frac{50}{x}$**
3. $y = -2$ when $x = 12$ **$y = \frac{-24}{x}$**

Solve. Assume that y varies inversely as x. (Lesson 11-1)

4. If $y = 6$ when $x = 3$, find x when $y = 5$. **3.6**
5. If $y = 3$ when $x = 2$, find y when $x = 4$. **1.5**

State the excluded value for each function. (Lesson 11-2)

6. $y = \frac{2}{x}$ **0**
7. $y = \frac{1}{x-6}$ **6**

Identify the asymptotes of each function. (Lesson 11-2)

8. $y = \frac{3}{2x+4}$ **$x = -2, y = 0$**
9. $y = \frac{2}{x-4}$ **$x = 4, y = 0$**

10. **MULTIPLE CHOICE** Jorge has $x^2 + 8x + 15$ square yards of carpet. He wants to carpet rooms that have areas of $x^2 + 5x + 6$ square yards. Write and simplify an expression to show how many rooms he can carpet. (Lesson 11-3) **B**

A $\frac{x+5}{x+3}$

B $\frac{x+5}{x+2}$

C $\frac{x+3}{x+2}$

D $\frac{x+5}{x+6}$

Simplify each expression. State the excluded values of the variables. (Lesson 11-3)

11. $\frac{16x^2y^3}{8xy}$ **$2xy^2$; $x \neq 0$, $y \neq 0$**
12. $\frac{z-5}{z^2-7z+10}$ **$\frac{1}{z-2}$; 2, 5**
13. $\frac{3x-15}{x^2-25}$ **$\frac{3}{x+5}$; −5, 5**

Find each product. (Lesson 11-4)

14. $\frac{(x+5)(x-3)}{x^3} \cdot \frac{5x}{x-3}$ **$\frac{5x+25}{x^2}$**
15. $\frac{a^2+2a+1}{a+1} \cdot \frac{a-1}{a^2-1}$ **1**
16. $\frac{m}{m^2+3m+2} \cdot \frac{m+2}{m^2}$ **$\frac{1}{m^2+m}$**

17. **MULTIPLE CHOICE** Find the area of the rectangle. (Lesson 11-4) **J**

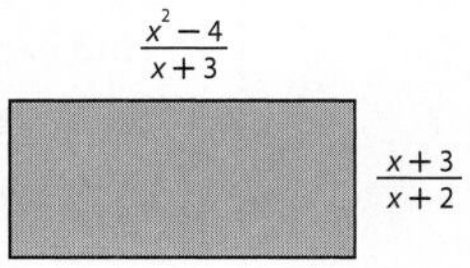

F $\frac{x+2}{x-2}$

G $\frac{x+3}{x-2}$

H 1

J $x - 2$

Find each quotient. (Lesson 11-4)

18. $\frac{x^4}{y^2} \div \frac{x}{y}$ **$\frac{x^3}{y}$**
19. $\frac{x+3}{2x+6} \div \frac{3x-6}{4x-8}$ **$\frac{2}{3}$**
20. $\frac{x^2+7x+12}{x^2-25} \div \frac{x^2-9}{2x+10}$ **$\frac{2(x+4)}{(x-5)(x-3)}$**

21. **ANIMALS** American quarter horses excel at sprinting short distances. A quarter horse named Evening Snow holds the world record for the quarter mile with a time of 20.94 seconds. What is this speed in miles per hour and in meters per second? (Lesson 11-4) **42.98 mi/h, 19.26 m/s**

Formative Assessment

Use the Mid-Chapter Quiz to assess students' progress in the first half of the chapter.

For problems answered incorrectly, have students review the lessons indicated in parentheses.

Summative Assessment

Mid-Chapter Test, p. 59

McGraw-Hill eAssessment Customize and create multiple versions of your Mid-Chapter Quiz and their answer keys.

FOLDABLES StudyOrganizer

Dinah Zike's Foldables®

Before students complete the Mid-Chapter Quiz, encourage them to review the information for Lessons 11-1 through 11-4 in their Foldables.

InterventionPlanner

TIER 1 On Level OL	TIER 2 Strategic Intervention AL approaching grade level	TIER 3 Intensive Intervention 2 or more grades below level
If students miss about 25% of the exercises or less,	**If** students miss about 50% of the exercises,	**If** students miss about 75% of the exercises,
Then choose a resource: SE Lessons 11-1, 11-2, 11-3 and 11-4 Skills Practice, pp. 7, 13, 19 and 25 TE Chapter Project connectED.mcgraw-hill.com Self-Check Quiz	**Then** choose a resource: Study Guide and Intervention, Chapter 11, pp. 5, 11, 17 and 23 *Quick Review Math Handbook* connectED.mcgraw-hill.com Extra Examples, Personal Tutor, Homework Help	**Then** use *Math Triumphs, Alg. 1* connectED.mcgraw-hill.com Extra Examples, Personal Tutor, Homework Help, Review Vocabulary

1 Focus

Vertical Alignment

Before Lesson 11-5 Divide rational expressions.

Lesson 11-5 Divide a polynomial by a monomial. Divide a polynomial by a binomial.

After Lesson 11-5 Simplify complex fractions involving polynomials.

2 Teach

Scaffolding Questions

Have students read the **Why?** section of the lesson.

Ask:

- How might you read the expression given? the quantity v squared minus four squared, divided by two a
- How can the fraction be written so that the denominator divides each term in the numerator? $\frac{v^2}{2a} - \frac{4^2}{2a}$
- Why does $\frac{4^2}{2a}$ not equal $\frac{2^2}{a}$? You have to follow the order of operations: $4^2 = 16$, then divide by $2a$ to get $\frac{8}{a}$.

LESSON 11-5 Dividing Polynomials

Then

- You divided rational expressions.

Now

1. Divide a polynomial by a monomial.
2. Divide a polynomial by a binomial.

Why?

- The equation below describes the distance d a horse travels when its initial velocity is 4 m/s, its final velocity is v m/s, and its acceleration is a m/s^2.

$$d = \frac{v^2 - 4^2}{2a}$$

There are different ways to simplify the expression.

Keep as one fraction.

$$\frac{v^2 - 4^2}{2a} = \frac{v^2 - 16}{2a}$$

Divide each term by $2a$.

$$\frac{v^2 - 4^2}{2a} = \frac{v^2}{2a} - \frac{4^2}{2a} = \frac{v^2}{2a} - \frac{8}{a}$$

Content Standards
A1.RNE.5

Process Standards
PS.8

1 Divide Polynomials by Monomials

To divide a polynomial by a monomial, divide each term of the polynomial by the monomial.

Example 1 Divide Polynomials by Monomials

Find each quotient.

a. $(2x^2 + 16x) \div 2x$

$$(2x^2 + 16x) \div 2x = \frac{2x^2 + 16x}{2x}$$ Write as a fraction.

$$= \frac{2x^2}{2x} + \frac{16x}{2x}$$ Divide each term by $2x$.

$$= \frac{\overset{x}{\cancel{2x^2}}}{\underset{1}{\cancel{2x}}} + \frac{\overset{8}{\cancel{16x}}}{\underset{1}{\cancel{2x}}}$$ Divide out common factors.

$$= x + 8$$ Simplify.

b. $(b^2 + 12b - 14) \div 3b$

$$(b^2 + 12b - 14) \div 3b = \frac{b^2 + 12b - 14}{3b}$$ Write as a fraction.

$$= \frac{b^2}{3b} + \frac{12b}{3b} - \frac{14}{3b}$$ Divide each term by $3b$.

$$= \frac{\overset{b}{\cancel{b^2}}}{\underset{3}{\cancel{3b}}} + \frac{\overset{4}{\cancel{12b}}}{\underset{1}{\cancel{3b}}} - \frac{14}{3b}$$ Divide out common factors.

$$= \frac{b}{3} + 4 - \frac{14}{3b}$$ Simplify.

Guided Practice

1A. $(3q^3 - 6q) \div 3q$ $q^2 - 2$

1B. $(4t^5 - 5t^2 - 12) \div 2t^2$ $2t^3 - \frac{5}{2} - \frac{6}{t^2}$

1C. $(4r^6 + 3r^4 - 2r^2) \div 2r$ $2r^5 + \frac{3}{2}r^3 - r$

1D. $(6w^3 - 3w) \div 4w^2$ $\frac{3}{2}w - \frac{3}{4w}$

Lesson 11-5 Resources

Resource	Approaching Level AL	On Level OL	Beyond Level BL	English Learners ELL
Teacher Edition	▪ Differentiated Instruction, p. 707	▪ Differentiated Instruction, pp. 707, 711	▪ Differentiated Instruction, pp. 707, 711	▪ Differentiated Instruction, p. 707
Chapter Resource Masters	▪ Study Guide and Intervention, pp. 30–31 ▪ Skills Practice, p. 32 ▪ Practice, p. 33 ▪ Word Problem Practice, p. 34	▪ Study Guide and Intervention, pp. 30–31 ▪ Skills Practice, p. 32 ▪ Practice, p. 33 ▪ Word Problem Practice, p. 34 ▪ Enrichment, p. 35 ▪ TI-Nspire Activity, p. 36	▪ Practice, p. 33 ▪ Word Problem Practice, p. 34 ▪ Enrichment, p. 35	▪ Study Guide and Intervention, pp. 30–31 ▪ Skills Practice, p. 32 ▪ Practice, p. 33 ▪ Word Problem Practice, p. 34
Other	▪ 5-Minute Check 11-5 ▪ Study Notebook ▪ Teaching Algebra with Manipulatives	▪ 5-Minute Check 11-5 ▪ Study Notebook ▪ Teaching Algebra with Manipulatives	▪ 5-Minute Check 11-5 ▪ Study Notebook	▪ 5-Minute Check 11-5 ▪ Study Notebook ▪ Teaching Algebra with Manipulatives

2 Divide Polynomials by Binomials

You can also divide polynomials by binomials. When a polynomial can be factored and common factors can be divided out, write the division as a rational expression and simplify.

PT

Example 2 Divide a Polynomial by a Binomial

Find $(h^2 + 9h + 18) \div (h + 6)$.

$(h^2 + 9h + 18) \div (h + 6) = \frac{h^2 + 9h + 18}{h + 6}$ Write as a rational expression.

$= \frac{(h + 3)(h + 6)}{h + 6}$ Factor the numerator.

$= \frac{(h + 3)\overset{1}{\cancel{(h + 6)}}}{\underset{1}{\cancel{h + 6}}}$ Divide out common factors.

$= h + 3$ Simplify.

GuidedPractice **Find each quotient.**

2A. $(b^2 - 2b - 15) \div (b + 3)$ **$b - 5$**

2B. $(x^2 + 11x + 24) \div (x + 8)$ **$x + 3$**

If the polynomial cannot be factored or if there are no common factors by which to divide, you must use long division.

WatchOut!

Polynomials When using long division, be sure the dividend is written in standard form. That is, the terms are written so that the exponents decrease from left to right.

$y^2 + 4y + 12$ yes

$4y + y^2 + 12$ no

PT

Example 3 Use Long Division

Find $(y^2 + 4y + 12) \div (y + 3)$ by using long division.

Step 1 Divide the first term of the dividend, y^2, by the first term of the divisor, y.

$$\begin{array}{r} y \\ y+3 \overline{) y^2 + 4y + 12} \\ (-)\ y^2 + 3y \\ \hline 1y + 12 \end{array}$$

$y^2 \div y = y$

Multiply y and $y + 3$

Subtract. Bring down the 12.

Step 2 Divide the first term of the partial dividend, $1y$, by the first term of the divisor, y.

$$\begin{array}{r} y + 1 \\ y+3 \overline{) y^2 + 4y + 12} \\ (-)\ y^2 + 3y \\ \hline 1y + 12 \\ (-)\ y + 3 \\ \hline 9 \end{array}$$

Subtract. Bring down the 12.

Multiply 1 and $y + 3$.

Subtract.

So, $(y^2 + 4y + 12) \div (y + 3)$ is $y + 1$ with a remainder of 9. This answer can be written as $y + 1 + \frac{9}{y + 3}$.

GuidedPractice **Find each quotient.** **3A.** $3x - 6 + \frac{15}{x + 5}$ **3B.** $n + 8 + \frac{18}{n - 2}$

3A. $(3x^2 + 9x - 15) \div (x + 5)$

3B. $(n^2 + 6n + 2) \div (n - 2)$

DifferentiatedInstruction AL OL BL ELL

If some students are able to read, comprehend, and explain the steps in the examples in this lesson easily,

Then pair those students with others who are having difficulty. Have the pairs work several example problems.

1 Divide Polynomials by Monomials

Example 1 shows how to divide a polynomial by a monomial by dividing each term of the polynomial by the monomial.

Formative Assessment

Use the Guided Practice exercises after each example to determine students' understanding of concepts.

Additional Example

1 Find each quotient.

a. $(4x^2 - 18x) \div 2x$ $2x - 9$

b. $(2y^2 - 3y - 9) \div 3y$

$\frac{2y}{3} - 1 - \frac{3}{y}$

Additional Examples also in Interactive Classroom PowerPoint® Presentations

IWB **Interactive White Board READY**

WatchOut!

Preventing Errors As an alternative to dividing each term of the polynomial by the monomial, students can factor and then eliminate the GCF.

Remind students that only factors can be divided, not the terms.

2 Divide Polynomials by Binomials

Example 2 shows how to divide a polynomial by a binomial by factoring the dividend. **Example 3** shows how to use long division to divide a polynomial by a binomial when the polynomial cannot be factored. **Example 4** shows how to divide polynomials to solve a real-world problem. **Example 5** shows how to rename a polynomial with a missing term in order to divide the polynomial by a binomial.

Additional Examples

2 Find $(2r^2 + 5r - 3) \div (r + 3)$. $2r - 1$

3 Find $(x^2 + 7x - 15) \div (x - 2)$ by using long division. $x + 9 + \frac{3}{x-2}$

4 **GEOMETRY** The area of a rectangle is represented by $3x + 90$. Its length is $(x - 3)$. Find $(3x + 90) \div (x - 3)$ to find the width of the rectangle. $3 + \frac{99}{x-3}$

5 Find $(x^3 - 34x + 45) \div (x - 5)$. The quotient is $x^2 + 5x - 9$.

WatchOut!

Preventing Errors Remind students to pay close attention to the signs in the binomials as they perform long division. For the binomial being subtracted, the sign of each term changes.

Real-World Example 4 Divide Polynomials to Solve a Problem

PARTIES The expression $5x + 250$ represents the cost of renting a picnic shelter and food for x people. The total cost is divided evenly among all the people except for the two who bought decorations. Find $(5x + 250) \div (x - 2)$ to determine how much each person pays.

$$\begin{array}{r} 5 \\ x-2\overline{)5x+250} \\ (-)\,5x-\ \ 10 \\ \hline 260 \end{array}$$

So, $5 + \frac{260}{x-2}$ represents the amount each person pays.

Guided Practice

4. GEOMETRY The area of a rectangle is $(2x^2 + 10x - 1)$ square units, and the width is $(x + 1)$ units. What is the length? $2x + 8 + \frac{-9}{x+1}$ units

When a dividend is written in standard form and a power is missing, add a term of that power with a coefficient of zero.

Example 5 Insert Missing Terms

Find $(c^3 + 5c - 6) \div (c - 1)$.

$$\begin{array}{rl} c^2 + c + 6 & \\ c-1\overline{)c^3 + 0c^2 + 5c - 6} & \text{Insert a } c^2\text{-term that has a coefficient of 0.} \\ (-)\,c^3 - c^2 \qquad\qquad & \text{Multiply } c^2 \text{ and } c - 1. \\ c^2 + 5c \qquad & \text{Subtract. Bring down the } 5c. \\ (-)\,c^2 - \ \ c \qquad & \text{Multiply } c \text{ and } c - 1. \\ 6c - 6 & \text{Subtract. Bring down the } -6. \\ (-)\,6c - 6 & \text{Multiply 6 and } c - 1. \\ 0 & \text{Subtract.} \end{array}$$

So, $(c^3 + 5c - 6) \div (c - 1) = c^2 + c + 6$.

Guided Practice Find each quotient. **5A.** $2r^2 + 4r + 4$ **5B.** $x^3 + 6 - \frac{22}{x+2}$

5A. $(2r^3 + 2r^2 - 4) \div (r - 1)$ **5B.** $(x^4 + 2x^3 + 6x - 10) \div (x + 2)$

Check Your Understanding

◯ = Step-by-Step Solutions begin on page R13.

Examples 1–2 Find each quotient.

1. $(8a^2 + 20a) \div 4a$ $2a + 5$
2. $(4z^3 + 1) \div 2z$ $2z^2 + \frac{1}{2z}$
3. $(12n^3 - 6n^2 + 15) \div 6n$ $2n^2 - n + \frac{5}{2n}$
4. $(t^2 + 5t + 4) \div (t + 4)$ $t + 1$
5. $(x^2 + 3x - 28) \div (x + 7)$ $x - 4$
6. $(x^2 + x - 20) \div (x - 4)$ $x + 5$

Example 4

7. **CHEMISTRY** The number of beakers that can be filled with $50 + x$ milliliters of a solution is given by $(400 + 3x) \div (50 + x)$. How many beakers can be filled. $3 + \frac{250}{x+50}$

Examples 3–5 Find each quotient. Use long division. **10.** $2h^2 - \frac{3}{2h+3}$ **11.** $3n^2 + n - 4 + \frac{4}{3n-1}$

8. $(n^2 + 3n + 10) \div (n - 1)$ $n + 4 + \frac{14}{n-1}$
9. $(4y^2 + 8y + 3) \div (y + 2)$ $4y + \frac{3}{y+2}$
10. $(4h^3 + 6h^2 - 3) \div (2h + 3)$
11. $(9n^3 - 13n + 8) \div (3n - 1)$

3 Practice

Formative Assessment

Use Exercises 1–11 to check for understanding.

Use the chart at the bottom of the next page to customize assignments for your students.

Teach with Tech

Video Recording Record yourself as you work through examples showing how to divide polynomials. After class, post the videos to a video sharing Web site so students may use them for reference outside of class.

Focus on Mathematical Content

Long Division Long division can be used to divide a polynomial by a binomial whether or not the polynomial can be factored. If the polynomial is missing a term, use 0 for the coefficient of the missing term, then divide by the binomial. This is possible because a term with a zero coefficient has a value of zero, so it does not affect the quotient. It is simply a placeholder.

Practice and Problem Solving

Extra Practice is on page R11.

Examples 1–2 Find each quotient. 26. $2x + 5 - \frac{20}{x} + \frac{13}{x^2}$

12. $(14x^2 + 7x) \div 7x$ $2x + 1$
13. $(a^3 + 4a^2 - 18a) \div a$ $a^2 + 4a - 18$
14. $(5q^3 + q) \div q$ $5q^2 + 1$
15. $(6n^2 - 12n + 3) \div 3n$ $2n - 4 + \frac{1}{n}$
16. $(8k^2 - 6) \div 2k$ $4k - \frac{3}{k}$
17. $(9m^2 + 5m) \div 6m$ $\frac{3}{2}m + \frac{5}{6}$
18. $(a^2 + a - 12) \div (a - 3)$ $a + 4$
19. $(x^2 - 6x - 16) \div (x + 2)$ $x - 8$
20. $(r^2 - 12r + 11) \div (r - 1)$ $r - 11$
21. $(k^2 - 5k - 24) \div (k - 8)$ $k + 3$
22. $(y^2 - 36) \div (y^2 + 6y)$ $\frac{y - 6}{y}$
23. $(a^3 - 4a^2) \div (a - 4)$ a^2
24. $(c^3 - 9c) \div (c - 3)$ $c^2 + 3c$
25. $(4t^2 - 1) \div (2t + 1)$ $2t - 1$
26. $(6x^3 + 15x^2 - 60x + 39) \div (3x^2)$
27. $(2h^3 + 8h^2 - 3h - 12) \div (h + 4)$ $2h^2 - 3$

Example 4

28. **GEOMETRY** The area of a rectangle is $(x^3 - 4x^2)$ square units, and the width is $(x - 4)$ units. What is the length? x^2 units

29. $-n + 18 + \frac{850}{n}$

29. **MANUFACTURING** The expression $-n^2 + 18n + 850$ represents the number of baseball caps produced by n workers. Find $(-n^2 + 18n + 850) \div n$ to write an expression for average number of caps produced per person.

32. $2y + 1 + \frac{3}{y - 2}$ 34. $p^2 - 3p - 3 + \frac{6}{p - 1}$ 36. $3x^2 - 2x + 3$

Examples 3, 5 Find each quotient. Use long division.

30. $(b^2 + 3b - 9) \div (b + 5)$ $b - 2 + \frac{1}{b + 5}$
31. $(a^2 + 4a + 3) \div (a - 1)$ $a + 5 + \frac{8}{a - 1}$
32. $(2y^2 - 3y + 1) \div (y - 2)$
33. $(4n^2 - 3n + 6) \div (n - 2)$ $4n + 5 + \frac{16}{n - 2}$
34. $(p^3 - 4p^2 + 9) \div (p - 1)$
35. $(t^3 - 2t - 4) \div (t + 4)$ $t^2 - 4t + 14 - \frac{60}{t + 4}$
36. $(6x^3 + 5x^2 + 9) \div (2x + 3)$
37. $(8c^3 + 6c - 5) \div (4c - 2)$ $2c^2 + c + 2 - \frac{1}{4c - 2}$

B 38. **GEOMETRY** The volume of a prism with a triangular base is $10w^3 + 23w^2 + 5w - 2$. The height of the prism is $2w + 1$, and the height of the triangle is $5w - 1$. What is the measure of the base of the triangle? (*Hint*: $V = Bh$) $2w + 4$

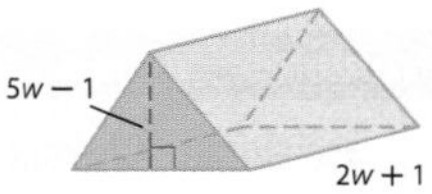

Use long division to find the expression that represents the missing length.

39. $x + 3$

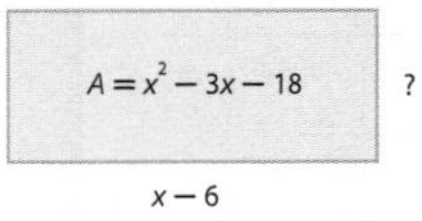

40. $2x + 4$

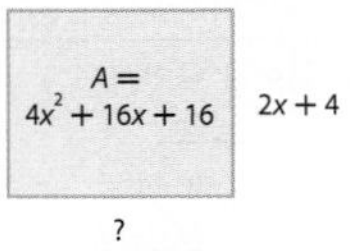

41. Determine the quotient when $x^3 + 11x + 14$ is divided by $x + 2$. $x^2 - 2x + 15 - \frac{16}{x + 2}$

42. What is $14y^5 + 21y^4 - 6y^3 - 9y^2 + 32y + 48$ divided by $2y + 3$? $7y^4 - 3y^2 + 16$

43. **STRUCTURE** Consider $f(x) = \frac{3x + 4}{x - 1}$. 43c. The graph of the quotient ignoring the remainder is an asymptote of the graph of the function.

a. Rewrite the function as a quotient plus a remainder. Then graph the quotient, ignoring the remainder. See margin.

b. Graph the original function using a graphing calculator. See margin.

c. How are the graphs of the function and quotient related?

d. What happens to the graph near the excluded value of x? As x approaches 1 from the left, y approaches negative infinity. As x approaches 1 from the right, y approaches positive infinity.

Differentiated Homework Options

Level	Assignment	Two-Day Option	
AL Basic	12–37, 47, 49–75	13–37 odd, 51–54	12–36 even, 47, 49, 50, 55–75
OL Core	13–37 odd, 38, 39, 41–47, 49–75	12–37, 51–54	38–47, 49, 50, 55–75
BL Advanced	38–73, (optional: 74, 75)		

Exercise Alert

Grid Paper For Exercise 43, students will need grid paper.

Tips for New Teachers

Reasoning Remind students that they can use multiplication to check their answers. For example, in Exercise 30 students could check their answer by multiplying $(b + 5)(b - 2) + 1$.

Teaching the Process Standards

Structure Mathematically proficient students can step back for an overview and shift perspective. In Exercise 43, suggest that students graph both functions together to compare.

Additional Answers

43a. $f(x) = 3 + \frac{7}{x - 1}$

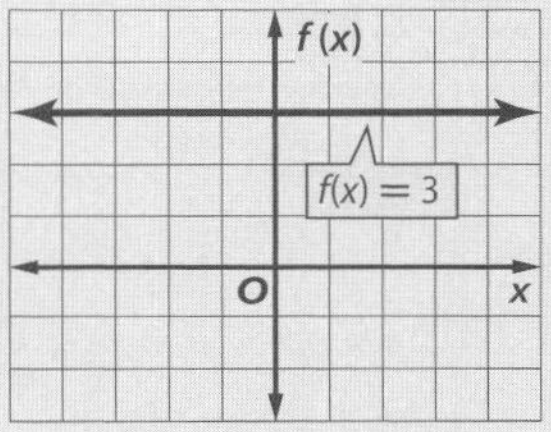

43b.

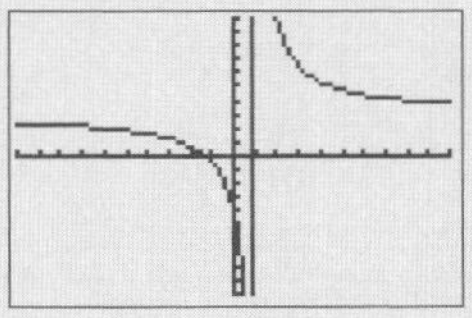

[−10, 10] scl:1 by [−10, 10] scl:1

Study Guide and Intervention

AL OL ELL

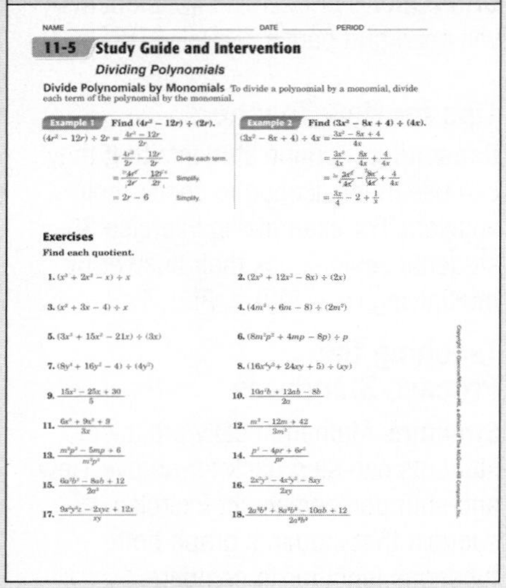
11-5 Study Guide and Intervention
Dividing Polynomials
Divide Polynomials by Monomials To divide a polynomial by a monomial, divide each term of the polynomial by the monomial.
Exercises
Find each quotient.

Practice

AL OL BL ELL

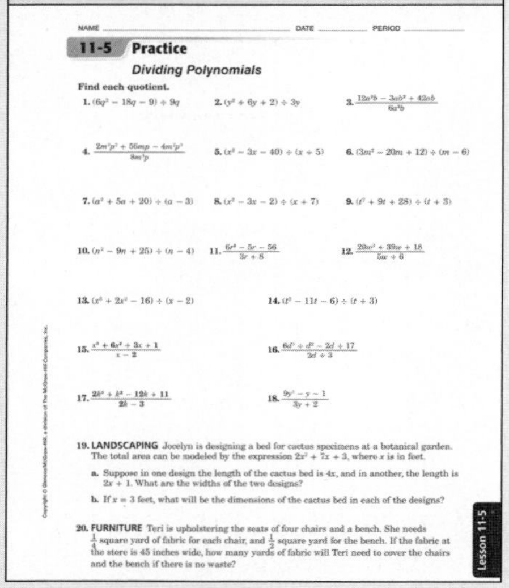
11-5 Practice
Dividing Polynomials
Find each quotient.

Word Problem Practice

AL OL BL ELL

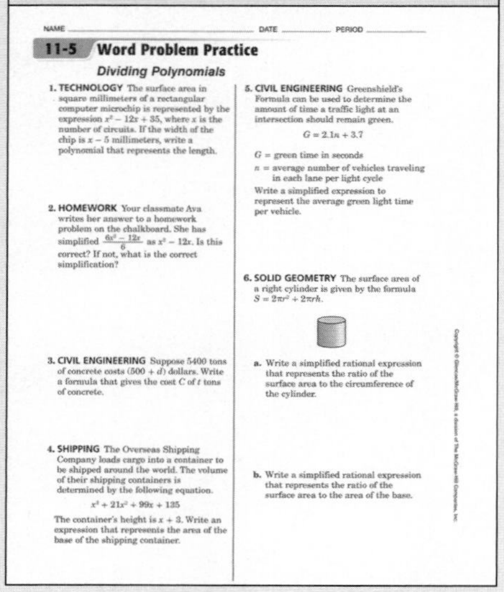
11-5 Word Problem Practice
Dividing Polynomials

44. **ROAD TRIP** The first Ski Club van has been on the road for 20 minutes, and the second van has been on the road for 35 minutes.

   a. Write an expression for the amount of time that each van has spent on the road after an additional t minutes. **$t + 20$; $t + 35$**

   b. Write a ratio for the first van's time on the road to the second van's time on the road and use long division to rewrite this ratio as an expression. Then find the ratio of the first van's time on the road to the second van's time on the road after 60 minutes, 200 minutes. **$\frac{t+20}{t+35}$; $1 - \frac{15}{t+35}$; about 0.84; about 0.94**

45. **BOILING POINT** The temperature at which water boils decreases by about 0.9°F for every 500 feet above sea level. The boiling point at sea level is 212°F.

   a. Write an equation for the temperature T at which water boils x feet above sea level. **$T = 212 - 0.9\left(\frac{x}{500}\right)$**

   b. Mount Whitney, the tallest point in California, is 14,494 feet above sea level. At approximately what temperature does water boil on Mount Whitney? **185.9°F**

C 46. **MULTIPLE REPRESENTATIONS** In this problem, you will use picture models to help divide expressions.

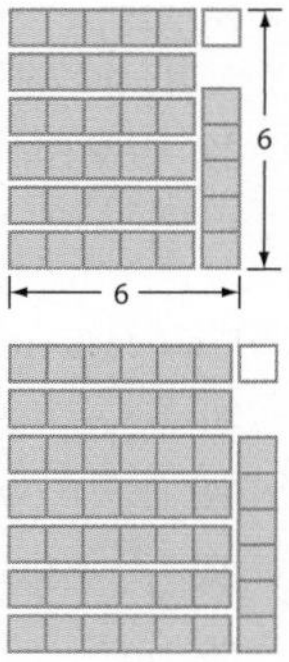

   a. **Analytical** The first figure models $6^2 \div 7$. Notice that the square is divided into seven equal parts. What are the quotient and the remainder? What division problem does the second figure model? **$5\frac{1}{7}$; $7^2 \div 8$**

   b. **Concrete** Draw figures for $3^2 \div 4$ and $2^2 \div 3$.

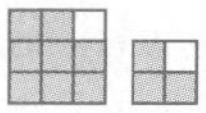

   c. **Verbal** Do you observe a pattern in the previous exercises? Express this pattern algebraically.

   d. **Analytical** Use long division to find $x^2 \div (x + 1)$. Does this result match your expression from part **c**?
   $x - 1 + \frac{1}{x+1}$; yes **46c. $x^2 \div (x + 1) = x - 1 + \frac{1}{x+1}$**

H.O.T. Problems Use Higher-Order Thinking Skills

47. **ERROR ANALYSIS** Alvin and Andrea are dividing $c^3 + 6c - 4$ by $c + 2$. Is either of them correct? Explain your reasoning. **Andrea; Alvin did not take into account the missing term.**

Alvin	Andrea
$c^2 + 4c - 12$	$c^2 - 2c + 10$
$c + 2 \overline{)c^3 + 6c - 4}$	$c + 2 \overline{)c^3 + 0c^2 + 6c - 4}$
$c^3 + 2c^2$	$c^3 + 2c^2$
$4c^2 - 4$	$-2c^2 + 6c$
$4c^2 + 8c$	$-2c^2 - 4c$
$-12c$	$10c - 4$
$-12c - 24$	$10c + 20$
24	-24

48. **REGULARITY** The quotient of two polynomials is $4x^2 - x - 7 + \frac{11x + 15}{x^2 + x + 2}$. What are the polynomials? **Sample answer: $4x^4 + 3x^3 + 2x + 1$ and $x^2 + x + 2$**

49. **OPEN ENDED** Write a division problem involving polynomials that you would solve by using long division. Explain your answer.

49. Sample answer: $(a^2 + 4a - 22) \div (a - 3)$; The polynomial $a^2 + 4a - 22$ is prime, so the problem can be solved by using long division.

50. **WRITING IN MATH** Describe the steps to find $(w^2 - 2w - 30) \div (w + 7)$. **See margin.**

710 | Lesson 11-5 | Dividing Polynomials

Enrichment

OL BL

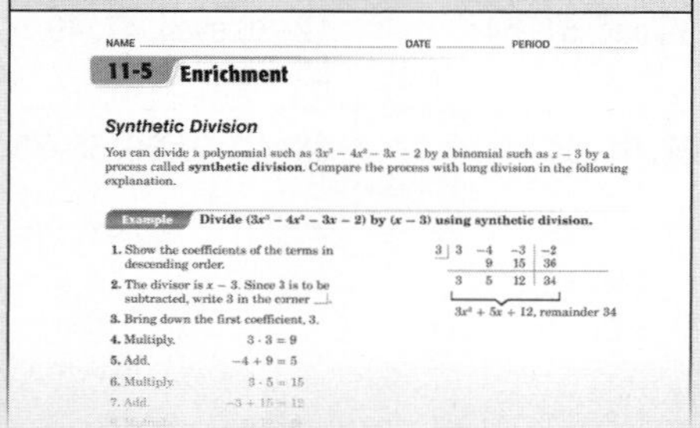
11-5 Enrichment
Synthetic Division
You can divide a polynomial such as $3x^3 - 4x^2 - 3x - 2$ by a binomial such as $x - 3$ by a process called synthetic division. Compare the process with long division in the following explanation.

Multiple Representations

In Exercise 46, students use verbal analysis and pictorial models to illustrate division of algebraic expressions.

Standardized Test Practice

51. Simplify $\frac{21x^3 - 35x^2}{7x}$. **A**

A $3x^2 - 5x$ C $3x - 5$

B $4x^2 - 6x$ D $5x - 3$

52. EXTENDED RESPONSE The box shown is designed to hold rice.

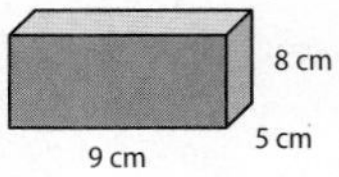

a. What is the volume of the box? **360 cm³**

b. What is the area of the label on the box, if the label covers all surfaces? **314 cm²**

53. Simplify $\frac{x^2 + 7x + 12}{x^2 + 5x + 6}$. **G**

F $x + 4$ H $x + 2$

G $\frac{x + 4}{x + 2}$ J $\frac{x + 2}{x + 4}$

54. Susana bought cards at 6 for $10. She decorated them and sold them at 4 for $10. She made $60 in profit. How many cards did she buy and sell if she had none left? **D**

A 25   C 60

B 53   D 72

Spiral Review

Find each product. (Lesson 11-4) **57.** $\frac{t}{6(t + 4)}$

55. $\frac{3x^3}{8x} \cdot \frac{16}{x}$ **6x**

56. $\frac{3ad}{4c^4} \cdot \frac{8c^2}{6d}$ $\frac{a}{c^2}$

57. $\frac{t^2}{(t - 4)(t + 4)} \cdot \frac{t - 4}{6t}$

58. $\frac{10}{r - 2} \cdot \frac{r^2 - 4}{2}$ **5(r + 2)**

Find the zeros of each function. (Lesson 11-3)

59. $f(x) = \frac{x + 2}{x^2 - 6x + 8}$ **−2**

60. $f(x) = \frac{x^2 - 3x - 4}{x^2 - x - 12}$ **−1**

61. $f(x) = \frac{x^2 + 6x + 9}{x^2 - 9}$ **no zero**

62. SHADOWS A flagpole casts a shadow that is 10 feet long when the Sun is at an elevation of 68°. How tall is the flagpole? (Lesson 10-6) **about 24.75 ft**

Solve each equation. Check your solution. (Lesson 10-4) **64. no solution**

63. $\sqrt{h} = 9$ **81**

64. $\sqrt{x + 3} = -5$

65. $3 + 5\sqrt{n} = 18$ **9**

66. $\sqrt{x - 5} = 2\sqrt{6}$ **29**

Solve each equation by using the Quadratic Formula. Round to the nearest tenth if necessary. (Lesson 9-5)

67. $v^2 + 12v + 20 = 0$ **−10, −2**

68. $3t^2 - 7t - 20 = 0$ $-\frac{5}{3}$**, 4**

69. $5y^2 - y - 4 = 0$ **−0.8, 1**

70. $2x^2 + 98 = 28x$ **7**

71. $2n^2 - 7n - 3 = 0$ **−0.4, 3.9**

72. $2w^2 = -(7w + 3)$ **−3, −0.5**

73. THEATER A backdrop for a play uses a series of thin metal arches attached to the stage floor. For each arch the height y, in feet, is modeled by the equation $y = -x^2 + 6x$, where x is the distance, in feet, across the bottom of the arch. (Lesson 9-2)

a. Graph the related function and determine the width of the arch at the floor. **See margin.**

b. What is the height at the top of the arch? **9 ft**

Skills Review

Find each sum.

74. $(3a^2 + 2a - 12) + (8a + 7 - 2a^2)$ $a^2 + 10a - 5$

75. $(2c^3 + 3cd - d^2) + (-5cd - 2c^3 + 2d^2)$ $-2cd + d^2$

Differentiated Instruction OL BL

Extension Ask half the class to find the value of $(2x^2 - 13x + 15) \div (2x - 3)$ for $x = 12$ by first substituting, then simplifying. Ask the other half of the class to divide first, then substitute. Have students discuss which of the two methods made it easier to evaluate the expression. For both methods, the resulting value is 7.

WatchOut!

Error Analysis For Exercise 47, remind students that, just as in division with whole numbers, an answer can be checked by multiplying the divisor by the quotient and then adding the remainder.

Teaching the Process Standards

Regularity Mathematically proficient students look both for general methods and for shortcuts. In Exercise 48, remind students that they have found quotients given dividends and divisors. Since they are given the quotient, they will be working backward in this problem.

4 Assess

Name the Math On an index card, have students divide $x^2 + 9x - 2$ by $x + 1$. Beside each step, have students write one or two sentences explaining and justifying their methods.

Additional Answers

50. Sample answer: Divide the first term of the dividend, w^2, by the first term of the divisor, w. Write the answer, w, above the division bar and multiply w and $w + 7$. Subtract and bring down the −30 to get $-9w - 30$. Divide the first term of the partial dividend, $-9w$, by the first term of the divisor, w. Write the answer, −9, above the division bar and multiply −9 and $w + 7$. Subtract. The answer is $w - 9 + \frac{33}{w + 7}$.

73a.

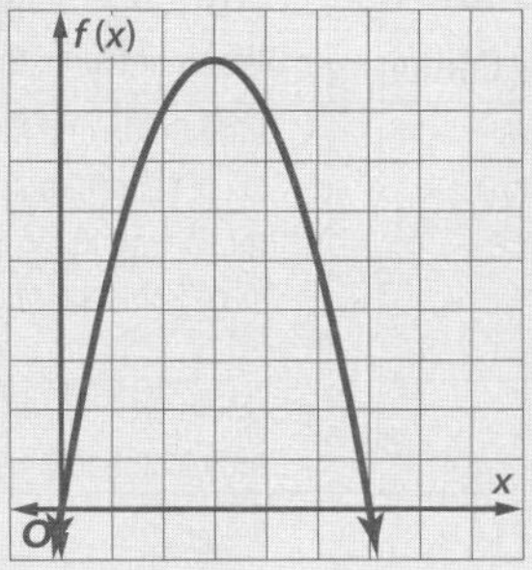

6 ft

1 Focus

VerticalAlignment

Before Lesson 11-6 Add and subtract polynomials.

Lesson 11-6 Add and subtract rational expressions with like denominators. Add and subtract rational expressions with unlike denominators.

After Lesson 11-6 Solve rational equations.

2 Teach

Scaffolding Questions

Have students read the **Why?** section of the lesson.

Ask:

- What conditions must be met to add fractions? They must have like denominators.
- Do you really need to change percents into fractions before adding them? Explain. No; percents are fractions of 100, so they can be added without converting them to fraction form.
- How do you simplify $\frac{38}{100}$? Divide the numerator and denominator by the common factor 2 to get $\frac{19}{50}$.

LESSON 11-6 Adding and Subtracting Rational Expressions

Then

- You added and subtracted polynomials.

Now

1. Add and subtract rational expressions with like denominators.
2. Add and subtract rational expressions with unlike denominators.

Why?

- A survey asked families how often they eat takeout. To determine the fraction of those surveyed who eat takeout more than once a week, you can add. Remember that percents can be written as fractions with denominators of 100.

2–3 times a week	plus	daily	equals	more than once a week.
$\frac{30}{100}$	$+$	$\frac{8}{100}$	$=$	$\frac{38}{100}$

Thus, $\frac{38}{100}$ or 38% eat takeout more than once a week.

How Many Times a Week Families Eat Takeout

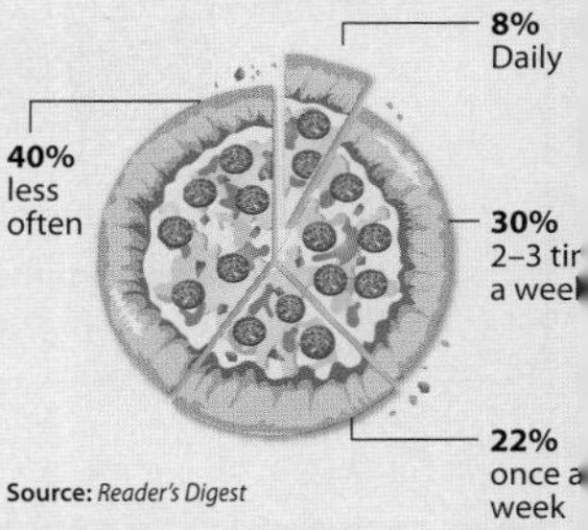

Source: *Reader's Digest*

NewVocabulary
least common multiple (LCM)
least common denominator (LCD)

Content Standards
AI.RNE.5

Process Standards
PS.6

1 Add and Subtract Rational Expressions with Like Denominators

To add or subtract rational expressions that have the same denominator, add or subtract the numerators and write the sum or difference over the common denominator.

KeyConcept Add or Subtract Rational Expressions with Like Denominators

Let *a*, *b*, and *c* be polynomials with $c \neq 0$.

$$\frac{a}{c} + \frac{b}{c} = \frac{a+b}{c} \qquad \frac{a}{c} - \frac{b}{c} = \frac{a-b}{c}$$

Example 1 Add Rational Expressions with Like Denominators

Find $\frac{5n}{n+3} + \frac{15}{n+3}$.

$\frac{5n}{n+3} + \frac{15}{n+3} = \frac{5n+15}{n+3}$ — The common denominator is $n + 3$.

$= \frac{5(n+3)}{n+3}$ — Factor the numerator.

$= \frac{5(n+3)^{1}}{(n+3)_{1}}$ — Divide by the common factor, $n + 3$.

$= \frac{5}{1}$ or 5 — Simplify.

GuidedPractice

Find each sum.

1A. $\frac{8c}{6} + \frac{5c}{6}$ $\frac{13c}{6}$

1B. $\frac{4t}{5xy} + \frac{7}{5xy}$ $\frac{4t+7}{5xy}$

1C. $\frac{3y}{3+y} + \frac{y^2}{3+y}$ y

712 | Lesson 11-6

Lesson 11-6 Resources

Resource	Approaching Level AL	On Level OL	Beyond Level BL	English Learners ELL
Teacher Edition	▪ Differentiated Instruction, p. 715	▪ Differentiated Instruction, pp. 715, 719	▪ Differentiated Instruction, p. 719	
Chapter Resource Masters	▪ Study Guide and Intervention, pp. 37–38 ▪ Skills Practice, p. 39 ▪ Practice, p. 40 ▪ Word Problem Practice, p. 41	▪ Study Guide and Intervention, pp. 37–38 ▪ Skills Practice, p. 39 ▪ Practice, p. 40 ▪ Word Problem Practice, p. 41 ▪ Enrichment, p. 42	▪ Practice, p. 40 ▪ Word Problem Practice, p. 41 ▪ Enrichment, p. 42	▪ Study Guide and Intervention, pp. 37–38 ▪ Skills Practice, p. 39 ▪ Practice, p. 40 ▪ Word Problem Practice, p. 41
Other	▪ 5-Minute Check 11-6 ▪ Study Notebook	▪ 5-Minute Check 11-6 ▪ Study Notebook	▪ 5-Minute Check 11-6 ▪ Study Notebook	▪ 5-Minute Check 11-6 ▪ Study Notebook

Example 2 Subtract Rational Expressions with Like Denominators

Find $\frac{3m-5}{m+4} - \frac{4m+2}{m+4}$.

$$\frac{3m-5}{m+4} - \frac{4m+2}{m+4} = \frac{(3m-5)-(4m+2)}{m+4}$$ The common denominator is $m + 4$.

$$= \frac{(3m-5)+[-(4m+2)]}{m+4}$$ The additive inverse of $(4m + 2)$ is $-(4m + 2)$.

$$= \frac{3m-5-4m-2}{m+4}$$ Distributive Property

$$= \frac{-m-7}{m+4}$$ Simplify.

StudyTip

Checking Answers You can check whether you have simplified a rational expression correctly by substituting values, but this does not guarantee that the expressions are always equal. If the results are different, check for an error.

GuidedPractice

Find each difference.

2A. $\frac{2h+4}{h+1} - \frac{5+h}{h+1}$ $\frac{h-1}{h+1}$

2B. $\frac{17h+4}{15h-5} - \frac{2h-6}{15h-5}$ $\frac{3h+2}{3h-1}$

You can sometimes use additive inverses to form like denominators.

Example 3 Inverse Denominators

Find $\frac{3n}{n-4} + \frac{6n}{4-n}$.

$$\frac{3n}{n-4} + \frac{6n}{4-n} = \frac{3n}{n-4} + \frac{6n}{-(n-4)}$$ Rewrite $4 - n$ as $-(n - 4)$.

$$= \frac{3n}{n-4} - \frac{6n}{n-4}$$ Rewrite so the denominators are the same.

$$= \frac{3n-6n}{n-4} \text{ or } -\frac{3n}{n-4}$$ Subtract the numerators and simplify.

GuidedPractice

Find each sum or difference.

3A. $\frac{t^2}{t-3} + \frac{3}{3-t}$ $\frac{t^2-3}{t-3}$

3B. $\frac{2p}{p-1} - \frac{2p}{1-p}$ $\frac{4p}{p-1}$

2 Add and Subtract with Unlike Denominators

The **least common multiple (LCM)** is the least number that is a multiple of two or more numbers or polynomials.

Example 4 LCMs of Polynomials

Find the LCM of each pair of polynomials.

a. $6x$ and $4x^3$

Step 1 Find the prime factors of each expression.

$6x = 2 \cdot 3 \cdot x$ $\quad$ $4x^3 = 2 \cdot 2 \cdot x \cdot x \cdot x$

Step 2 Use each prime factor, 2, 3, and x, the greatest number of times it appears in either of the factorizations.

$6x = 2 \cdot 3 \cdot x$ $\quad$ $4x^3 = 2 \cdot 2 \cdot x \cdot x \cdot x$

LCM $= 2 \cdot 2 \cdot 3 \cdot x \cdot x \cdot x$ or $12x^3$

Focus on Mathematical Content

Adding Rational Expressions Whether the denominators of rational expressions are numbers, monomials, or binomials, the denominators must be the same in order to add two or more rational expressions. If the denominators are the same, the numerator of the sum is found by adding the numerators of the addends. The denominator of the sum is the same as for the addends. Sums should be simplified.

1 Add and Subtract Rational Expressions with Like Denominators

Example 1 shows how to add rational expressions with the same denominator. **Example 2** shows how to subtract rational expressions with like denominators by adding the additive inverse of the numerator of the expression being subtracted. **Example 3** shows how to add rational expressions with denominators that are additive inverses.

Formative Assessment

Use the Guided Practice exercises after each example to determine students' understanding of concepts.

Additional Examples

1 Find $\frac{4b}{15} + \frac{16b}{15}$. $\frac{4b}{3}$

2 Find $\frac{7x+9}{x-3} - \frac{x-5}{x-3}$. $\frac{2(3x+7)}{x-3}$

3 Find $\frac{3x}{11-x} + \frac{-5x}{x-11}$. $\frac{8x}{11-x}$

Additional Examples also in Interactive Classroom PowerPoint® Presentations

IWB **Interactive White Board READY**

2 Add and Subtract Rational Expressions with Unlike Denominators

Example 4 shows how to find the least common multiple of two or more polynomials. **Example 5** shows how to add rational expressions with unlike denominators by using the least common multiple of the denominators to get equivalent expressions with a common denominator. **Example 6** shows how to add rational expressions to solve a real-world problem. **Example 7** shows how to subtract rational expressions with unlike denominators.

Additional Examples

4 Find the LCM of each pair of polynomials.

a. $12b^4c^5$ and $32bc^2$ $96b^4c^5$

b. $x^2 - 3x - 28$ and $x^2 - 8x + 7$ $(x + 4)(x - 7)(x - 1)$

5 Find $\frac{x+7}{x^2 - 6x + 9} + \frac{x+3}{x-3}$. $\frac{(x+2)(x-1)}{(x-3)^2}$

Focus on Mathematical Content

Subtracting Rational Expressions Whether the denominators of rational expressions are numbers, monomials, or binomials, the denominators must be the same in order to subtract the rational expressions. If the denominators are the same, add the inverse of the numerator of the rational expression to the numerator from which it is being subtracted, use the common denominator, and simplify.

Teach with Tech

Wiki Have students demonstrate how to distinguish between equivalent expressions with a LCD from ones without a common denominator. Be sure they clearly explain how to find the LCD. Once all agree, post the results to your classroom Web site.

Follow-up

Students have explored rational expressions.

Ask:

- What should you consider when simplifying a rational expression? Sample answer: You should completely factor the numerator and denominator before dividing by the GCF. You should also consider excluded values, which need to be determined by analyzing the original expression rather than the simplified expression.

Review Vocabulary

Factored Form A monomial is in factored form when it is expressed as the product of prime numbers and variables, and no variable has an exponent greater than 1.

b. $n^2 + 5n + 4$ and $(n + 1)^2$

$n^2 + 5n + 4 = (n + 1)(n + 4)$ Factor each expression.

$(n + 1)^2 = (n + 1)(n + 1)$

$(n + 1)$ is a factor twice in the second expression. $(n + 4)$ is a factor once.

LCM $= (n + 1)(n + 1)(n + 4)$ or $(n + 1)^2(n + 4)$

Guided Practice

4A. $8m^2t$ and $12m^2t^3$ $24m^2t^3$

4B. $x^2 - 2x - 8$ and $x^2 - 5x - 14$ $(x + 2)(x - 4)(x - 7)$

To add or subtract fractions with unlike denominators, you need to rename the fractions using the least common multiple of the denominators, called the **least common denominator (LCD)**.

Key Concept Add or Subtract Rational Expressions with Unlike Denominators

Step 1 Find the LCD.

Step 2 Write each rational expression as an equivalent expression with the LCD as the denominator.

Step 3 Add or subtract the numerators and write the result over the common denominator.

Step 4 Simplify if possible.

Watch Out!

Precision Remember that every term of the numerator and the denominator must be multiplied or divided by the same number for the fraction to be equivalent to the original.

Example 5 Add Rational Expressions with Unlike Denominators

Find $\frac{3t+2}{t^2 - 2t - 3} + \frac{t+1}{t-3}$.

Find the LCD. Since $t^2 - 2t - 3 = (t - 3)(t + 1)$, the LCD is $(t - 3)(t + 1)$.

$\frac{3t+2}{t^2-2t-3} + \frac{t+1}{t-3} = \frac{3t+2}{(t-3)(t+1)} + \frac{t+1}{t-3}$ Factor $t^2 - 2t - 3$.

$= \frac{3t+2}{(t-3)(t+1)} + \frac{t+1}{t-3}\left(\frac{t+1}{t+1}\right)$ Write $\frac{t+1}{t-3}$ using the LCD.

$= \frac{3t+2}{(t-3)(t+1)} + \frac{t^2+2t+1}{(t-3)(t+1)}$ Simplify.

$= \frac{3t+2+t^2+2t+1}{(t-3)(t+1)}$ Add the numerators.

$= \frac{t^2+5t+3}{(t-3)(t+1)}$ Simplify.

Guided Practice

5A. $\frac{4d^2}{d} + \frac{d+2}{d^2}$ $\frac{4d^3+d+2}{d^2}$

5B. $\frac{b+3}{b} + \frac{b-5}{b+1}$ $\frac{2b^2-b+3}{b^2+b}$

Teaching the Process Standards

Precision Mathematically proficient students calculate accurately and efficiently. Remind students to treat rational expressions as they would rational numbers.

The formula time $= \frac{\text{distance}}{\text{rate}}$ is helpful in solving real-world applications.

Real-WorldLink

The distance a hang glider can travel is determined by its *glide ratio*, or the ratio of the forward distance traveled to the vertical distance dropped.

Source: HowStuffWorks

Real-World Example 6 Add Rational Expressions

HANG GLIDING For the first 5000 meters, a hang glider travels at a rate of x meters per minute. Then, due to a stronger wind, it travels 6000 meters at a speed that is 3 times as fast.

a. Write an expression to represent how much time the hang glider is flying.

Understand For the first 5000 meters, the hang glider's speed is x. For the last 6000 meters, the hang glider's speed is $3x$.

Plan Use the formula $d = r \times t$ or $t = \frac{d}{r}$ to represent the time t of each section of the hang glider's trip, with rate r and distance d.

Solve Time to fly 5000 meters: $\frac{d}{r} = \frac{5000}{x}$ $d = 5000, r = x$

Time to fly 6000 meters: $\frac{d}{r} = \frac{6000}{3x}$ $d = 6000, r = 3x$

Total flying time: $\frac{5000}{x} + \frac{6000}{3x}$

$\frac{5000}{x} + \frac{6000}{3x} = \frac{5000}{x}\left(\frac{3}{3}\right) + \frac{6000}{3x}$ The LCD is $3x$.

$= \frac{15{,}000}{3x} + \frac{6000}{3x}$ Multiply.

$= \frac{\overset{7000}{\cancel{21{,}000}}}{\underset{1}{\cancel{3}}x}$ or $\frac{7000}{x}$ Simplify.

Check $\frac{5000}{x} + \frac{6000}{3x} = \frac{5000}{1} + \frac{6000}{3(1)}$ Let $x = 1$ in the original expression.

$= 5000 + 2000$ or 7000 Simplify.

$\frac{7000}{x} = \frac{7000}{1}$ or 7000 Let $x = 1$ in the answer expression. Simplify.

Since the expressions have the same value for $x = 1$, the answer is reasonable. ✓

b. If the hang glider is flying at a rate of 600 meters per minute for the first 5000 meters, find the total amount of time that the hang glider is flying.

$\frac{7000}{x} = \frac{7000}{600}$ Substitute 600 for x in the expression.

≈ 11.7 Simplify.

So, the hang glider is flying for approximately 11.7 minutes.

c. If the hang glider flew for approximately 15 minutes, find the rate the hang glider flew for the first 5000 meters.

$\frac{7000}{x} = 15$ Set the expression equal to 15.

$7000 = 15x$ Multiply each side by x.

$466.7 \approx x$ Divide each side by 15 and simplify.

The hang glider was flying at a rate of 466.7 meters per minute.

GuidedPractice

6. TRAINS A train travels 5 miles from Lynbrook to Long Beach and then back. The train travels about 1.2 times as fast returning from Long Beach. If r is the train's speed from Lynbrook to Long Beach, write and simplify an expression for the total time of the round trip. $\frac{5}{r} + \frac{5}{1.2r}; \frac{11}{1.2r}$

Additional Example

6 BIKING For the first 15 miles, a biker travels at x miles per hour. Then, due to a downhill slope, the biker travels 2 miles at a speed that is 2 times as fast.

a. Write an expression to represent how much time the biker is bicycling. $\frac{15}{x} + \frac{2}{2x}$ or $\frac{16}{x}$

b. If the biker is bicycling at a rate of 8 miles per hour for the first 15 miles, find the total amount of time the biker is bicycling. 2 hours

Tips for New Teachers

Additive Inverses Tell students to pay close attention to signs any time that they are dealing with additive inverses. It is easy to forget to change a sign when finding the additive inverse of an expression. Encourage students to use the Distributive Property to help them change the signs correctly.

DifferentiatedInstruction AL OL

If you think students should visualize the need to rename rational expressions using the LCD before they can actually add or subtract rational expressions,

Then have students highlight rational expressions, like those in Example 5, using a different color for each different denominator. Once the student rewrites the rational expressions with the same denominator, have him or her highlight them all with the same color.

Additional Example

7 Find $\frac{3}{x} - \frac{5x-2}{8x}$. $\frac{26-5x}{8x}$

3 Practice

Formative Assessment

Use Exercises 1–14 to check for understanding.

Use the chart at the bottom of this page to customize assignments for your students.

To subtract rational expressions with unlike denominators, rename the expressions using the LCD. Then subtract the numerators.

Example 7 Subtract Rational Expressions with Unlike Denominators

Find $\frac{5}{x} - \frac{2x+1}{4x}$.

$\frac{5}{x} - \frac{2x+1}{4x} = \frac{5}{x}\left(\frac{4}{4}\right) - \frac{2x+1}{4x}$ — Write $\frac{5}{x}$ using the LCD, $4x$.

$= \frac{20}{4x} - \frac{2x+1}{4x}$ — Simplify.

$= \frac{20-(2x+1)}{4x}$ — Subtract the numerators.

$= \frac{20-2x-1}{4x}$ or $\frac{19-2x}{4x}$ — Simplify.

StudyTip
Simplifying Answers
When simplifying a rational expression, you can leave the denominator in factored form, or multiply the terms.

GuidedPractice

Find each difference.

7A. $\frac{6}{t+3} - \frac{7}{t}$ $\frac{-t-21}{t(t+3)}$

7B. $\frac{y}{y-3} - \frac{2}{y^2+y-12}$ $\frac{y^2+4y-2}{(y-3)(y+4)}$

Check Your Understanding

(circled) = Step-by-Step Solutions begin on page R13.

Examples 1–3 Find each sum or difference. **3.** $\frac{16r}{9-r}$

1. $\frac{3}{7n} + \frac{2}{7n}$ $\frac{5}{7n}$ **2.** $\frac{x+8}{2} + \frac{x}{2}$ $x+4$ **3.** $\frac{14r}{9-r} - \frac{2r}{r-9}$ **4.** $\frac{7}{5t} - \frac{3+t}{5t}$ $\frac{4-t}{5t}$

Example 4 Find the LCM of each pair of polynomials.

5. $3t, 8t^2$ $24t^2$ **6.** $5m+15, 2m+6$ $10(m+3)$

7. $(x^2-8x+7), (x^2+x-2)$ $(x-7)(x-1)(x+2)$

Examples 5–7 Find each sum or difference.

8. $\frac{6}{n^4} + \frac{2}{n^2}$ $\frac{6+2n^2}{n^4}$ **9.** $\frac{3}{4x} + \frac{2}{5y}$ $\frac{15y+8x}{20xy}$ **10.** $\frac{4}{5n} - \frac{1}{10n^3}$ $\frac{8n^2-1}{10n^3}$

11. $\frac{8}{3c} - \frac{-5}{6d}$ $\frac{16d+5c}{6cd}$ **12.** $\frac{a}{a+4} + \frac{6}{a+2}$ **13.** $\frac{x}{x-3} - \frac{3}{x+2}$

Example 6 **14. EXERCISE** Joseph walks 10 times around the track at a rate of x laps per hour. He runs 8 times around the track at a rate of $3x$ laps per hour. Write and simplify an expression for the total time it takes him to go around the track 18 times.

12. $\frac{a^2+8a+24}{(a+4)(a+2)}$ **13.** $\frac{x^2-x+9}{x^2-x-6}$ **14.** $\frac{10}{x} + \frac{8}{3x}$; $\frac{38}{3x}$

Practice and Problem Solving

Extra Practice is on page R11.

Examples 1–3 Find each sum or difference.

(15) $\frac{a}{4} + \frac{3a}{4}$ a **16.** $\frac{1}{6m} + \frac{5m}{6m}$ $\frac{1+5m}{6m}$ **17.** $\frac{5y}{6} - \frac{y}{6}$ $\frac{2y}{3}$

18. $\frac{11}{4r} - \frac{-1}{4r}$ $\frac{3}{r}$ **19.** $\frac{8b}{ab} + \frac{3a}{ab}$ $\frac{8b+3a}{ab}$ **20.** $\frac{t+2}{3} + \frac{t+5}{3}$ $\frac{2t+7}{3}$

21. $\frac{3c-7}{2c-1} + \frac{2c+1}{1-2c}$ $\frac{c-8}{2c-1}$ **22.** $\frac{15x}{33x-9} + \frac{3}{9-33x}$ **23.** $\frac{n+6}{10} - \frac{n+1}{10}$ $\frac{1}{2}$

24. $\frac{5x+2}{2x+5} - \frac{x-8}{2x+5}$ 2 **25.** $\frac{w+2}{8w} - \frac{2w-3}{8w}$ **26.** $\frac{3a+1}{a-1} - \frac{a+4}{a-1}$ $\frac{2a-3}{a-1}$

22. $\frac{5x-1}{11x-3}$ **25.** $\frac{-w+5}{8w}$

Differentiated Homework Options

Level	Assignment	Two-Day Option	
AL Basic	15–50, 72, 74–95	15–49 odd, 76–79	16–50 even, 72, 74, 75, 80–95
OL Core	15–51 odd, 52, 53–69, odd, 70, 72, 74–95	15–50, 76–79	51–70, 72, 74, 75, 80–95
BL Advanced	51–92, (optional: 93–95)		

Example 4 **Find the LCM of each pair of polynomials.**

27. x^3y, x^2y^2 x^3y^2

28. $5ab, 10b$ $10ab$

29. $(3r-1), (r+2)$ $(3r-1)(r+2)$

30. $2n-10, 4n-20$ $4(n-5)$

31. $(x^2+9x+18), x+3$ $(x+6)(x+3)$

32. $(k^2-2k-8), (k+2)^2$ $(k-4)(k+2)^2$

Examples 5, 7 **Find each sum or difference.**

33. $\frac{5}{4x}+\frac{1}{10x}$ $\frac{27}{20x}$

34. $\frac{6}{r}+\frac{2}{r^2}$ $\frac{6r+2}{r^2}$

35. $\frac{3}{2a}+\frac{1}{5b}$ $\frac{15b+2a}{10ab}$

36. $\frac{6g}{g+5}-\frac{g-2}{2g}$

37. $\frac{7}{4k+8}-\frac{k}{k+2}$ $\frac{7-4k}{4(k+2)}$

38. $\frac{5}{2d+2}-\frac{d}{d+5}$

39. $\frac{-2}{7r}+\frac{4}{t}$ $\frac{-2t+28r}{7rt}$

40. $\frac{n}{n-2}+\frac{n}{n+1}$

41. $\frac{d}{d+5}+\frac{7}{d-1}$

42. $\frac{4}{a}-\frac{1}{3a}$ $\frac{11}{3a}$

43. $\frac{6}{5t^2}-\frac{2}{3t}$ $\frac{18-10t}{15t^2}$

44. $\frac{7}{4r}-\frac{3}{t}$ $\frac{7t-12r}{4rt}$

36. $\frac{11g^2-3g+10}{2g(g+5)}$

38. $\frac{-2d^2+3d+25}{(2d+2)(d+5)}$

40. $\frac{2n^2-n}{(n-2)(n+1)}$

41. $\frac{d^2+6d+35}{(d+5)(d-1)}$

45. $\frac{w-3}{w^2-w-20}+\frac{w}{w+4}$ $\frac{w^2-4w-3}{(w+4)(w-5)}$

46. $\frac{n}{2n+10}+\frac{1}{n^2-25}$ $\frac{n^2-5n+2}{2(n+5)(n-5)}$

47. $\frac{2x}{x^2+8x+15}-\frac{x+3}{x+5}$ $\frac{-x^2-4x-9}{(x+3)(x+5)}$

48. $\frac{r-3}{r^2+6r+9}-\frac{r-9}{r^2-9}$ $\frac{36}{(r-3)(r+3)^2}$

Example 6

49. **TRAVEL** Grace walks to her friend's house 2 miles away and then jogs back home. Her jogging speed is 2.5 times her walking speed w.

a. Write and simplify an expression to represent the amount of time Grace spends going to and coming from her friend's house. $\frac{2}{w}+\frac{2}{2.5w}$; $\frac{7}{2.5w}$

b. If Grace walks about 3.5 miles per hour, how many minutes did she spend going to and from her friend's house? **48 min**

50. **BOATS** A boat travels 3 miles downstream and then goes 6 miles upstream. The speed of a boat going downstream is $x+2$ miles per hour and going upstream is $x-2$ miles per hour, where x is the speed of the boat in still water.

a. Write and simplify an expression to represent the total time it takes the boat to travel 3 miles downstream and 6 miles upstream.

b. If the rate of the boat in still water x is 4 miles per hour, how long did it take the boat to travel the 9 miles? **3.5 hours**

50a. $\frac{3}{x+2}+\frac{6}{x-2}$; $\frac{9x+6}{(x+2)(x-2)}$

B 51. **SCHOOL** On Saturday, Mr. Kim graded 2 geometry tests and all his algebra tests a. On Sunday, he graded 7 more geometry tests. Write an expression to represent the fraction of tests he graded if he had 18 more geometry tests than algebra tests. **See margin.**

52. **REASONING** A total of 1248 people attended the school play. The same number x attended each of the two Sunday performances. There were twice as many people at the Saturday performance than at both Sunday performances. Write an expression to represent the fraction of people who attended on Saturday. $\frac{4x}{1248}$ or $\frac{x}{312}$

Find each sum or difference. **53–64. See margin.**

53. $\frac{x+5}{x^2-4}-\frac{3}{x^2-4}$

54. $\frac{18y}{9y+2}-\frac{-4}{-2-9y}$

55. $\frac{k^2-26}{k-5}-\frac{1}{5-k}$

56. $\frac{8}{c-1}+\frac{c}{1-c}$

57. $\frac{2}{x-1}+\frac{3}{x+1}-\frac{4x-2}{x^2-1}$

58. $\frac{x^2-x-12}{x^2-11x+30}-\frac{x-4}{18-x}$

59. $\frac{a^2-5a}{3a-18}-\frac{7a-36}{3a-18}$

60. $\frac{8n-3}{n^2+8n+12}-\frac{5n-9}{n^2+8n+12}$

61. $\frac{x^2-16}{x^3}+\frac{x^3+1}{x^4}$

62. $\frac{x}{7x-3}+\frac{x+2}{15x+30}$

63. $\frac{5x}{3x^2+19x-14}-\frac{1}{9x^2-12x+4}$

64. $\frac{2x+7}{x^2-y^2}+\frac{-5}{x^2-2xy+y^2}$

Tips for New Teachers

LCM or LCD Review with students that the least common multiple, LCM, is used to find a number or polynomial that is the least number that is a common multiple of two or more numbers or polynomials. The least common denominator, LCD, is the LCM of two or more denominators. We say that y^2x^2 is the LCM of y^2x and yx^2, while y^2x^2 is the LCD of $\frac{8}{y^2x}$ and $\frac{6}{yx^2}$.

Teaching the Process Standards

Reasoning Mathematically proficient students abstract a situation, represent it symbolically and manipulate the symbols as if they have a life of their own. In Exercise 52, suggest that students write the ratios using words before writing them with numbers and variables.

Additional Answers

51. $\frac{a+9}{2a+18}$ or $\frac{1}{2}$

53. $\frac{1}{x-2}$

54. $\frac{18y-4}{9y+2}$

55. $k+5$

56. $\frac{8-c}{c-1}$

57. $\frac{1}{x-1}$

58. $\frac{2x^3-34x^2+80x+96}{(x-5)(x-6)(x-18)}$

59. $\frac{a-6}{3}$

60. $\frac{3}{n+6}$

61. $\frac{2x^3-16x+1}{x^4}$

62. $\frac{22x-3}{15(7x-3)}$

63. $\frac{15x^2-11x-7}{(3x-2)^2(x+7)}$

64. $\frac{2x^2+2x-2xy-12y}{(x-y)^2(x+y)}$

connectED.mcgraw-hill.com 717

Study Guide and Intervention

AL OL ELL

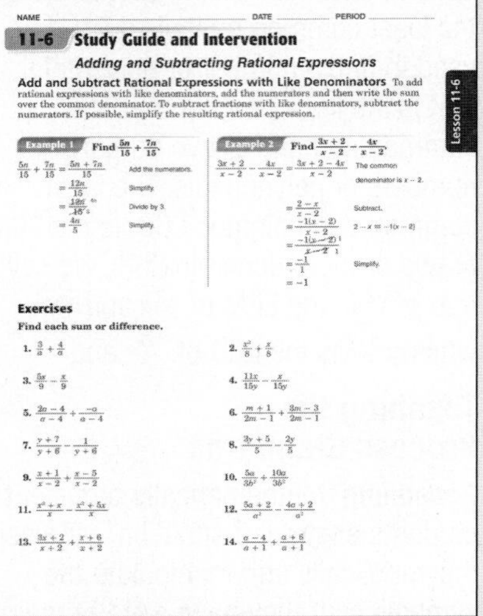

NAME ____ DATE ____ PERIOD ____

11-6 Study Guide and Intervention

Adding and Subtracting Rational Expressions

Add and Subtract Rational Expressions with Like Denominators To add rational expressions with like denominators, add the numerators and then write the sum over the common denominator. To subtract fractions with like denominators, subtract the numerators. If possible, simplify the resulting rational expression.

Exercises

Find each sum or difference.

Practice

AL OL BL ELL

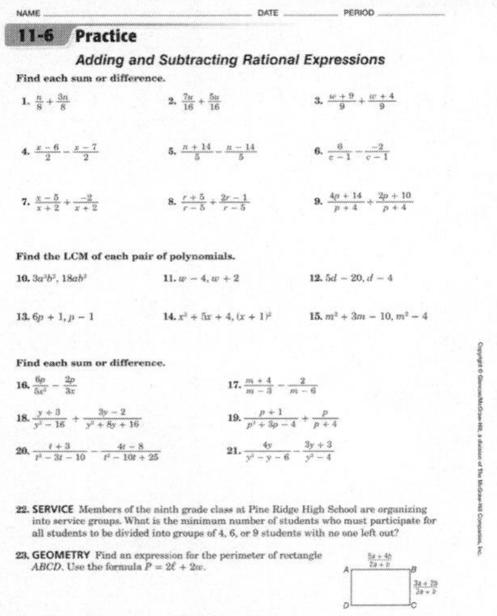

NAME ____ DATE ____ PERIOD ____

11-6 Practice

Adding and Subtracting Rational Expressions

Find each sum or difference.

Find the LCM of each pair of polynomials.

Find each sum or difference.

22. SERVICE Members of the ninth grade class at Pine Ridge High School are organizing into service groups. What is the minimum number of students who must participate for all students to be divided into groups of 4, 6, or 9 students with no one left out?

23. GEOMETRY Find an expression for the perimeter of rectangle ABCD. Use the formula $P = 2\ell + 2w$.

Word Problem Practice

AL OL BL ELL

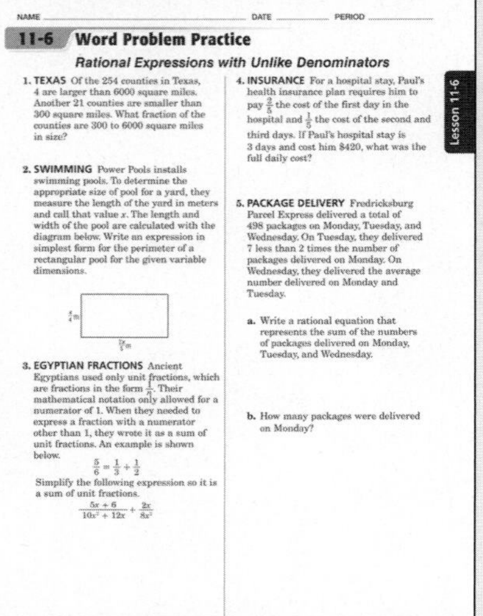

NAME ____ DATE ____ PERIOD ____

11-6 Word Problem Practice

Rational Expressions with Unlike Denominators

Enrichment

OL BL

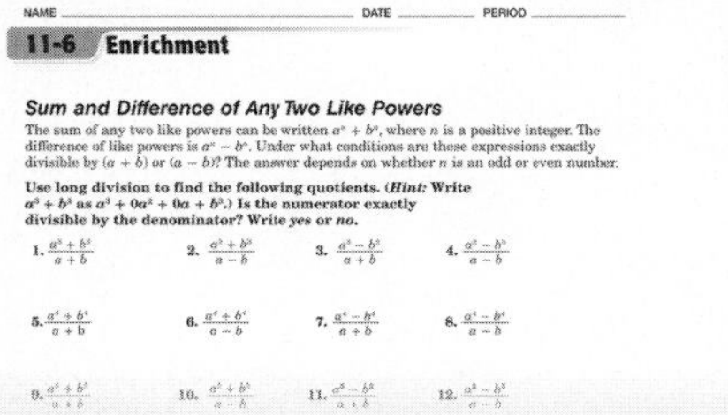

NAME ____ DATE ____ PERIOD ____

11-6 Enrichment

Sum and Difference of Any Two Like Powers

65. TRIATHLONS In a sprint triathlon, athletes swim 400 meters, bike 20 kilometers, and run 5 kilometers. An athlete bikes 12 times as fast as she swims and runs 5 times as fast as she swims.

a. Simplify $\frac{400}{x} + \frac{20{,}000}{12x} + \frac{5000}{5x}$, an expression that represents the time it takes the athlete to complete the sprint triathlon. **$\frac{9200}{3x}$**

b. If the athlete swims 40 meters per minute, find the total time it takes her to complete the triathlon. **about 76 min 40 seconds**

GEOMETRY Write an expression for the perimeter of each figure.

C **66.** 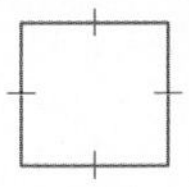 $\frac{t+1}{2t}$ **$\frac{2t+2}{t}$**

67. 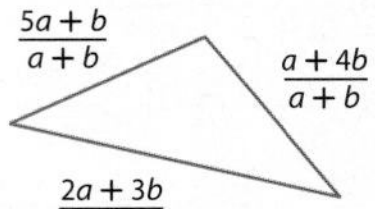 $\frac{5a+b}{a+b}$, $\frac{a+4b}{a+b}$, $\frac{2a+3b}{a+b}$ **8**

68. 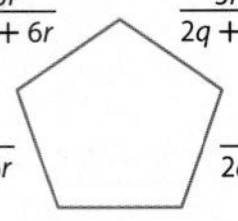 $\frac{5r}{2q+6r}$, $\frac{5r}{2q+6r}$, $\frac{9r}{2q+6r}$, $\frac{9r}{2q+6r}$, $\frac{4r}{2q+6r}$ **$\frac{16r}{q+3r}$**

69. BIKES Marina rides her bike at an average rate of 10 miles per hour. On one day, she rides 9 miles and then rides around a large loop x miles long. On the second day, she rides 5 miles and then rides around the loop three times.

a. Write an expression to represent the total time she spent riding her bike on those two days. Then simplify the expression. **$\frac{9+x}{10} + \frac{5+3x}{10}$; $\frac{7+2x}{5}$**

b. If the loop is 2 miles long, how long did Marina ride on those two days? **2.2 hours**

70. TRAVEL The Showalter family drives 80 miles to a college football game. On the trip home, their average speed is about 3 miles per hour slower.

a. Let x represent the average speed of the car on the way to the game. Write and simplify an expression to represent the total time it took driving to the game and then back home. **$\frac{80}{x} + \frac{80}{x-3}$; $\frac{160x-240}{x(x-3)}$**

b. If their average speed on the way to the game was 68 miles per hour, how long did it take the Showalter family to drive to the game and back? Round to the nearest tenth. **2.4 hours**

H.O.T. Problems Use Higher-Order Thinking Skills

71. PERSEVERANCE Find $\left(\frac{4}{7y-2} + \frac{7y}{2-7y}\right)\left(\frac{y+5}{6} - \frac{y+3}{6}\right)$. **$\frac{4-7y}{21y-6}$**

72. WRITING IN MATH Describe in words the steps you use to find the LCD in an addition or subtraction of rational expressions with unlike denominators. **See margin.**

73. CHALLENGE Is the following statement *sometimes*, *always*, or *never* true? Explain. **See margin.**

$$\frac{a}{x} + \frac{b}{y} = \frac{ay+bx}{xy};\ x \neq 0,\ y \neq 0$$

74. OPEN ENDED Describe a real-life situation that could be expressed by adding two rational expressions that are fractions. Explain what the denominator and numerator represent in both expressions. **See margin.**

75. WRITING IN MATH Describe how to add rational expressions with denominators that are additive inverses. **See margin.**

Additional Answer

72. Sample answer: If possible, factor the polynomial in the denominator of each rational expression. The LCM of the denominators is the product of these factors each used the greatest number of times it appears in any of the factorizations. Write all the rational expressions using this product as the LCD.

718 | Lesson 11-6 | Adding and Subtracting Rational Expressions

Standardized Test Practice

76. SHORT RESPONSE An object is launched upwards with an initial velocity of 19.6 meters per second from a 58.8-meter-tall platform. The equation for the object's height h, in meters, at time t seconds after launch is $h(t) = -4.9t^2 + 19.6t + 58.8$. How long after the launch does the object strike the ground? **6 seconds**

77. Simplify $\frac{2}{5} + \frac{3}{25} + \frac{1}{10}$. **C**

A $\frac{2}{5}$ C $\frac{31}{50}$

B $\frac{3}{5}$ D $\frac{5}{3}$

78. STATISTICS Courtney has grades of 84, 65, and 76 on three math tests. What grade must she earn on the next test to have an average of exactly 80 for the four tests? **J**

F 80 H 92

G 84 J 95

79. Simplify $\frac{2}{x} + \frac{3}{x^2} + \frac{1}{2x}$. **C**

A $\frac{3x+2}{x^2}$ C $\frac{5x+6}{2x^2}$

B $\frac{6}{2x^2}$ D $\frac{6+x}{x^2}$

Spiral Review

Find each quotient. (Lesson 11-5) **81.** $5y^2 + \frac{14}{3}$ **82.** $2a^2 - 4a + 1$

80. $(6x^2 + 10x) \div 2x$ **$3x + 5$**

81. $(15y^3 + 14y) \div 3y$

82. $(10a^3 - 20a^2 + 5a) \div 5a$

Convert each rate. Round to the nearest tenth if necessary. (Lesson 11-4)

83. 23 feet per second to miles per hour **about 15.7 mi/h**

84. 118 milliliters per second to quarts per hour (*Hint*: 1 liter ≈ 1.06 quarts) **450.3 qt/h**

Find the length of the missing side. If necessary, round to the nearest hundredth. (Lesson 10-5)

85. 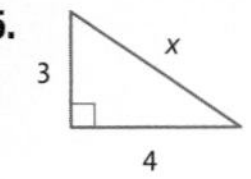

5

86. 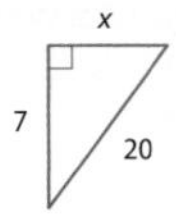

18.73

87. 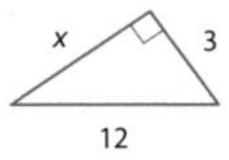

11.62

88. AMUSEMENT RIDE The height h in feet of a car above the exit ramp of a free-fall ride can be modeled by $h(t) = -16t^2 + s$, where t is the time in seconds after the car drops, and s is the starting height of the car in feet. If the designer wants the free fall to last 3 seconds, what should be the starting height in feet? (Lesson 8-9) **144 ft**

Express each number in scientific notation. (Lesson 7-4)

89. 12,300 **1.23×10^4**

90. 0.0000375 **3.75×10^{-5}**

91. 1,255,000 **1.255×10^6**

92. FINANCIAL LITERACY Ruben has \$13 to order pizza. The pizza costs \$7.50 plus \$1.25 per topping. He plans to tip 15% of the total cost. Write and solve an inequality to find out how many toppings he can order. (Lesson 5-3)
$7.50 + 1.25t + 0.15(7.50 + 1.25t) \leq 13$; 3 or fewer toppings

Skills Review

Find each quotient.

93. $\frac{12}{3x^2} \div \frac{6}{x}$ **$\frac{2}{3x}$**

94. $\frac{g^4}{2} \div \frac{g^3}{8d^2}$ **$4gd^2$**

95. $\frac{4y-8}{y+1} \div (y-2)$ **$\frac{4}{y+1}$**

Differentiated Instruction OL BL

Extension Ask students to find $\frac{3x-4}{x^2-5x+4} + \frac{x+4}{x^2+3x-4}$. $\frac{4x-8}{(x-1)(x-4)}$

Teaching the Process Standards

Perseverance Mathematically proficient students can understand the approaches of others to solving complex problems and identify correspondences between different approaches. In Exercise 71, allow students to discuss and compare their methods.

4 Assess

Ticket Out the Door Ask students to choose two letters from A through F. On the board write the letters A through F. Under each letter write a different rational expression, three with the same denominator and three with denominators that are the additive inverse denominator of the first three. Ask students to first add the rational expressions that are under their two letters. Then have students subtract the rational expressions.

Formative Assessment

Check for student understanding of Lessons 11-5 and 11-6.

Quiz 3, p. 58

Additional Answers

73. always; $\frac{a}{x} + \frac{b}{y} = \frac{a}{x} \cdot \frac{y}{y} + \frac{b}{y} \cdot \frac{x}{x} = \frac{ay}{xy} + \frac{bx}{yx} = \frac{ay + bx}{xy}$

74. Sample answer: Survey data can be represented with rational expressions that are fractions; $\frac{a}{d} + \frac{3a-12}{d}$; the numerator is the number of people who gave a certain response to a survey and the denominator is the number of people who took the survey.

75. First, factor −1 out of one of the denominators so that it is like the other. Then rewrite the denominator without parentheses. Finally, add or subtract the numerators and write the result over the like denominator.

1 Focus

VerticalAlignment

Before Lesson 11-7 Simplify rational expressions.

Lesson 11-7 Simplify mixed expressions. Simplify complex fractions.

After Lesson 11-7 Solve rational equations.

2 Teach

Scaffolding Questions

Have students read the **Why?** section of the lesson.

Ask:

- What is the denominator of the complex fraction shown? $4\frac{2}{5}$
- What operation does the fraction bar represent? division
- How do you divide by a mixed number? Sample answer: Convert it to an improper fraction and multiply by the reciprocal.

LESSON 11-7 Mixed Expressions and Complex Fractions

Then

- You simplified rational expressions.

Now

1. Simplify mixed expressions.
2. Simplify complex fractions.

Why?

- A Top Fuel dragster can cover $\frac{1}{4}$ mile in $4\frac{2}{5}$ seconds. The average speed in miles per second can be described by the expression below. It is called a complex fraction.

$$\frac{\frac{1}{4}\text{ mile}}{4\frac{2}{5}\text{ seconds}}$$

New Vocabulary
mixed expression
complex fraction

Content Standards
AI.RNE.5

1 Simplify Mixed Expressions

An expression like $2 + \frac{4}{x+1}$ is called a **mixed expression** because it contains the sum of a monomial, 2, and a rational expression, $\frac{4}{x+1}$. You can use the LCD to change a mixed expression to a rational expression.

PT

Example 1 Change Mixed Expressions to Rational Expressions

Write $2 + \frac{4}{x-1}$ as a rational expression.

$2 + \frac{4}{x-1} = \frac{2(x-1)}{x-1} + \frac{4}{x-1}$ — The LCD is $x - 1$.

$= \frac{2(x-1)+4}{x-1}$ — Add the numerators.

$= \frac{2x-2+4}{x-1}$ — Distributive Property

$= \frac{2x+2}{x-1}$ — Simplify.

GuidedPractice

Write each mixed expression as a rational expression.

1A. $2 + \frac{5}{x}$ $\frac{2x+5}{x}$

1B. $\frac{6y}{4y+8} + 5y$ $\frac{10y^2+23y}{2y+4}$

2 Simplify Complex Fractions

A **complex fraction** has one or more fractions in the numerator or denominator. You can simplify by using division.

numerical complex fraction

$$\frac{\frac{2}{3}}{\frac{5}{8}} = \frac{2}{3} \div \frac{5}{8} = \frac{2}{3} \times \frac{8}{5} = \frac{16}{15}$$

algebraic complex fraction

$$\frac{\frac{a}{b}}{\frac{c}{d}} = \frac{a}{b} \div \frac{c}{d} = \frac{a}{b} \times \frac{d}{c} = \frac{ad}{bc}$$

To simplify a complex fraction, write it as a division expression. Then find the reciprocal of the second expression and multiply.

Lesson 11-7 Resources

Resource	Approaching Level AL	On Level OL	Beyond Level BL	English Learners ELL
Teacher Edition		▪ Differentiated Instruction, pp. 722, 725	▪ Differentiated Instruction, pp. 722, 725	▪ Differentiated Instruction, p. 722
Chapter Resource Masters	▪ Study Guide and Intervention, pp. 43–44 ▪ Skills Practice, p. 45 ▪ Practice, p. 46 ▪ Word Problem Practice, p. 47	▪ Study Guide and Intervention, pp. 43–44 ▪ Skills Practice, p. 45 ▪ Practice, p. 46 ▪ Word Problem Practice, p. 47 ▪ Enrichment, p. 48	▪ Practice, p. 46 ▪ Word Problem Practice, p. 47 ▪ Enrichment, p. 48	▪ Study Guide and Intervention, pp. 43–44 ▪ Skills Practice, p. 45 ▪ Practice, p. 46 ▪ Word Problem Practice, p. 47
Other	▪ 5-Minute Check 11-7 ▪ Study Notebook	▪ 5-Minute Check 11-7 ▪ Study Notebook	▪ 5-Minute Check 11-7 ▪ Study Notebook	▪ 5-Minute Check 11-7 ▪ Study Notebook

Real-WorldLink

A Jr. Dragster is a half-scale verson of a Top Fuel dragster. This car, which can go $\frac{1}{8}$ mile in $7\frac{9}{10}$ seconds, is designed to be driven by kids ages 8–17 in the NHRA Jr. Drag Racing League.

Source: NHRA

PT

Real-World Example 2 Use Complex Fractions to Solve Problems

RACING Refer to the application at the beginning of the lesson. Find the average speed of the Top Fuel dragster in miles per minute.

$$\frac{\frac{1}{4}\text{ mile}}{4\frac{2}{5}\text{ seconds}} = \frac{\frac{1}{4}\text{ mile}}{4\frac{2}{5}\text{ seconds}} \times \frac{60\text{ seconds}}{1\text{ minute}}$$ Convert seconds to minutes. Divide by common units.

$$= \frac{\frac{1}{4} \times 60}{4\frac{2}{5}}$$ Simplify.

$$= \frac{\frac{60}{4}}{\frac{22}{5}}$$ Express each term as an improper fraction.

$$= \frac{\overset{15}{\cancel{60}} \times 5}{\underset{1}{\cancel{4}} \times 22}$$ Use the rule $\frac{\frac{a}{b}}{\frac{c}{d}} = \frac{ad}{bc}$.

$$= \frac{75}{22} \text{ or } 3\frac{9}{22}$$ Simplify.

So, the average speed of the Top Fuel dragster is $3\frac{9}{22}$ miles per minute.

GuidedPractice

2. **RACING** Refer to the information about the Jr. Dragster at the left. What is the average speed of the car in feet per second? $83\frac{43}{79}$ ft/s

To simplify complex fractions, you can either use the rule as in Example 2, or you can rewrite the fraction as a division expression, as shown below.

PT

Example 3 Complex Fractions Involving Monomials

Simplify $\frac{\frac{8t^2}{v}}{\frac{4t}{v^3}}$.

$$\frac{\frac{8t^2}{v}}{\frac{4t}{v^3}} = \frac{8t^2}{v} \div \frac{4t}{v^3}$$ Write as a division expression.

$$= \frac{8t^2}{v} \times \frac{v^3}{4t}$$ To divide, multiply by the reciprocal.

$$= \frac{\overset{2t}{\cancel{8t^2}}}{\underset{1}{\cancel{v}}} \times \frac{\overset{v^2}{\cancel{v^3}}}{\underset{1}{\cancel{4t}}} \text{ or } 2tv^2$$ Divide by the common factors $4t$ and v and simplify.

GuidedPractice

Simplify each expression.

3A. $\frac{\frac{g^3h}{b}}{\frac{gh^3}{b^2}}$ $\frac{g^2b}{h^2}$

3B. $\frac{\frac{-24m^3t^5}{p^2h}}{\frac{16pm^2}{t^4h}}$ $\frac{-3mt^9}{2p^3}$

1 Simplify Mixed Expressions

Example 1 shows how to change a mixed expression to a rational expression.

Formative Assessment

Use the Guided Practice exercises after each example to determine students' understanding of concepts.

Additional Example

1 Write $3 + \frac{7}{x-2}$ as a rational expression. $\frac{3x+1}{x-2}$

Additional Examples also in Interactive Classroom PowerPoint® Presentations

IWB Interactive White Board READY

2 Simplify Complex Fractions

Example 2 shows how to use complex fractions to solve problems.
Example 3 shows how to simplify a complex fraction involving monomials.
Example 4 shows how to simplify a complex fraction involving polynomials.

Additional Examples

2 **RACING** Refer to the application at the beginning of the lesson. If the dragster can cover $\frac{1}{4}$ mile in $3\frac{1}{8}$ seconds, what is its average speed in miles per minute? $4\frac{4}{5}$ miles per minute

3 Simplify $\frac{\frac{a^5b}{c^2}}{\frac{ab^4}{c^4}}$. $\frac{a^4c^2}{b^3}$

WatchOut!

Preventing Errors Point out that since one of the terms of a mixed expression is a monomial, the LCD will be the same as the denominator of the rational expression. Suggest that students still having difficulty write 3 as $\frac{3}{1}$ and then find the LCD.

Teach with Tech

Interactive Whiteboard Display a complex fraction on the board. Rewrite this as a product of two fractions by dragging the fraction from the denominator and writing its reciprocal.

Focus on Mathematical Content

Complex Fractions You can simplify an algebraic complex fraction in the same way that you simplify a numerical complex fraction. Multiply the numerator by the reciprocal of the denominator.

Additional Example

4 Simplify each expression.

a. $\dfrac{b + \frac{2}{b+3}}{b-4}$ $\dfrac{(b+2)(b+1)}{(b+3)(b-4)}$

b. $\dfrac{\frac{c^2-4c+3}{c^2+9c+14}}{\frac{c^2-9}{c+2}}$ $\dfrac{c-1}{(c+7)(c+3)}$

WatchOut!

Preventing Errors When simplifying complex fractions, there are many steps in which errors can occur, even for those students who clearly understand the concept. Encourage students to write out each step of the simplifying process.

Complex fractions may also involve polynomials.

Real-WorldCareer

Lab Technician Lab technicians work with scientists, running experiments, conducting research projects, and running routine diagnostic samples. Lab technicians in any field need at least a two-year associate degree.

Example 4 Complex Fractions Involving Polynomials

Simplify each expression.

a. $\dfrac{\frac{2}{y+3}}{\frac{5}{y^2-9}}$

$\dfrac{\frac{2}{y+3}}{\frac{5}{y^2-9}} = \dfrac{2}{y+3} \div \dfrac{5}{y^2-9}$ Write as a division expression.

$= \dfrac{2}{y+3} \times \dfrac{y^2-9}{5}$ To divide, multiply by the reciprocal.

$= \dfrac{2}{y+3} \times \dfrac{(y-3)(y+3)}{5}$ Factor $y^2 - 9$.

$= \dfrac{2}{\cancel{y+3}_{1}} \times \dfrac{(y-3)\cancel{(y+3)}^{1}}{5}$ Divide by the GCF, $y + 3$.

$= \dfrac{2(y-3)}{5}$ Simplify.

b. $\dfrac{\frac{n^2+7n-18}{n^2-2n+1}}{\frac{n^2-81}{n-1}}$

$\dfrac{\frac{n^2+7n-18}{n^2-2n+1}}{\frac{n^2-81}{n-1}} = \dfrac{n^2+7n-18}{n^2-2n+1} \div \dfrac{n^2-81}{n-1}$ Write as a division expression.

$= \dfrac{n^2+7n-18}{n^2-2n+1} \times \dfrac{n-1}{n^2-81}$ Multiply by the reciprocal.

$= \dfrac{(n-2)(n+9)}{(n-1)(n-1)} \times \dfrac{n-1}{(n-9)(n+9)}$ Factor the polynomials.

$= \dfrac{(n-2)\cancel{(n+9)}^{1}}{(n-1)\cancel{(n-1)}_{1}} \times \dfrac{\cancel{n-1}^{1}}{(n-9)\cancel{(n+9)}_{1}}$ Divide out the common factors.

$= \dfrac{n-2}{(n-1)(n-9)}$ Simplify.

StudyTip

Factoring When simplifying fractions involving polynomials, factor the numerator and the denominator of each expression if possible.

GuidedPractice

4A. $\dfrac{\frac{a+7}{4}}{\frac{a^2-49}{10}}$ $\dfrac{5}{2(a-7)}$

4B. $\dfrac{\frac{x+4}{x-1}}{\frac{x^2+6x+8}{2x-2}}$ $\dfrac{2}{x+2}$

4C. $\dfrac{\frac{c-d}{j+p}}{\frac{c^2-d^2}{j^2-p^2}}$ $\dfrac{j-p}{c+d}$

4D. $\dfrac{\frac{n^2+4n-21}{n^2-9n+18}}{\frac{n^2+3n-28}{n^2-10n+24}}$ 1

DifferentiatedInstruction OL BL ELL

Intrapersonal Learners Ask students to write their own Key Concepts for this lesson. Tell them to include simplifying mixed expressions as well as simplifying complex fractions. Have students share their Key Concepts with the class.

722 | Lesson 11-7 | Mixed Expressions and Complex Fractions

Check Your Understanding

= Step-by-Step Solutions begin on page R13.

Example 1 **Write each mixed expression as a rational expression.**

1. $\frac{2}{n} + 4$ $\frac{2+4n}{n}$

2. $r + \frac{1}{3r}$ $\frac{3r^2+1}{3r}$

3. $6 + \frac{5}{t+1}$ $\frac{6t+11}{t+1}$

4. $\frac{x+7}{2x} - 5x$ $\frac{-10x^2+x+7}{2x}$

Example 2

5. **ROWING** Rico rowed a canoe $2\frac{1}{2}$ miles in $\frac{1}{3}$ hour.
   a. Write an expression to represent his speed in miles per hour. $\frac{2\frac{1}{2}\text{ mi}}{\frac{1}{3}\text{ h}}$
   b. Simplify the expression to find his average speed. $\frac{15}{2}$ or $7\frac{1}{2}$ mi/h

Examples 3–4 **Simplify each expression.**

6. $\frac{2\frac{1}{3}}{1\frac{2}{5}}$ $\frac{5}{3}$ or $1\frac{2}{3}$

7. $\frac{\frac{4}{5}}{6\frac{2}{3}}$ $\frac{3}{25}$

8. $\frac{\frac{a^2}{b^3}}{\frac{b^5}{a}}$ $\frac{a^3}{b^8}$

9. $\frac{\frac{y^4}{x^2}}{\frac{xy^2}{2x^2}}$ $\frac{2y^2}{x}$

10. $\frac{\frac{6}{x-2}}{\frac{3}{x^2-x-2}}$ $2(x+1)$

11. $\frac{\frac{r+s}{x^2-y^2}}{\frac{(r+s)^2}{x-y}}$ $\frac{1}{(x+y)(r+s)}$

12. $\frac{\frac{2+q}{q^2-4}}{\frac{q+4}{q^2-6q+8}}$ $\frac{q-4}{q+4}$

13. $\frac{\frac{p+3}{p^2+p-6}}{\frac{p^2+4p+3}{p^2+6p+9}}$ $\frac{p+3}{p^2-p-2}$

Practice and Problem Solving

Extra Practice is on page R11.

Example 1 **Write each mixed expression as a rational expression.** 18–22. See margin.

14. $10 + \frac{6}{f}$ $\frac{10f+6}{f}$

15. $p - \frac{7}{2p}$ $\frac{2p^2-7}{2p}$

16. $5a - \frac{2a}{b}$ $\frac{5ab-2a}{b}$

17. $3h + \frac{1+h}{h}$ $\frac{3h^2+h+1}{h}$

18. $t + \frac{v+w}{v-w}$

19. $n^2 + \frac{n-1}{n+4}$

20. $(k+2) + \frac{k-1}{k-2}$

21. $(d-6) + \frac{d+1}{d-7}$

22. $\frac{h-3}{h+5} - (h+2)$

Example 2

23. **READING** Ebony reads $6\frac{3}{4}$ pages of a book in 9 minutes. What is her average reading rate in pages per minute? $\frac{3}{4}$ page/min

24. **HORSES** A thoroughbred can run $\frac{1}{2}$ mile in about $\frac{3}{4}$ minute. What is the horse's speed in miles per hour? 40 mi/h

Examples 3–4 **Simplify each expression.**

25. $\frac{2\frac{2}{9}}{3\frac{1}{3}}$ $\frac{2}{3}$

26. $\frac{5\frac{3}{5}}{2\frac{1}{7}}$ $2\frac{46}{75}$

27. $\frac{\frac{g^2}{h}}{\frac{g^5}{h^2}}$ $\frac{h}{g^3}$

28. $\frac{\frac{5n^4}{p^3}}{\frac{6n}{5p}}$ $\frac{25n^3}{6p^2}$

29. $\frac{\frac{2}{a}}{\frac{1}{a+6}}$ $\frac{2a+12}{a}$

30. $\frac{\frac{t+5}{9}}{\frac{t^2-t-30}{12}}$ $\frac{4}{3(t-6)}$

31. $\frac{\frac{j^2-16}{j^2+10j+16}}{\frac{15}{j+8}}$ $\frac{(j-4)(j+4)}{15(j+2)}$

32. $\frac{\frac{x-3}{x^2+3x+2}}{\frac{x^2-9}{x+1}}$ $\frac{1}{(x+2)(x+3)}$

B 33. **MODELING** The Centralville High School Cooking Club has $12\frac{1}{2}$ pounds of flour with which to make tortillas. There are $3\frac{3}{4}$ cups of flour in a pound, and it takes about $\frac{1}{3}$ cup of flour per tortilla. How many tortillas can they make? about 140

3 Practice

Formative Assessment

Use Exercises 1–13 to check for understanding.

Use the chart at the bottom of this page to customize assignments for your students.

Teaching the Process Standards

Modeling Mathematically proficient students can apply the mathematics they know to solve problems arising in everyday life. In Exercise 33, remind students to use dimensional analysis.

Additional Answers

18. $\frac{tv - tw + v + w}{v - w}$

19. $\frac{n^3 + 4n^2 + n - 1}{n + 4}$

20. $\frac{k^2 + k - 5}{k - 2}$

21. $\frac{d^2 - 12d + 43}{d - 7}$

22. $\frac{-h^2 - 6h - 13}{h + 5}$

Differentiated Homework Options

Level	Assignment	Two-Day Option	
AL Basic	14–32, 43, 44, 46–80	15–31 odd, 48–51	14–32 even, 43, 44, 46, 47, 52–80
OL Core	15–31 odd, 33–36, 37–43 odd, 44, 46–80	14–32, 48–51	33–44, 46, 47, 52–80
BL Advanced	33–74, (optional: 75–80)		

Study Guide and Intervention

AL OL ELL

NAME _______ DATE _______ PERIOD _______

11-7 Study Guide and Intervention

Mixed Expressions and Complex Fractions

Simplify Mixed Expressions Algebraic expressions such as $a + \frac{b}{c}$ and $5 + \frac{x+y}{x+3}$ are called **mixed expressions**. Changing mixed expressions to rational expressions is similar to changing mixed numbers to improper fractions.

Example 1 Simplify $5 + \frac{2}{n}$.

$5 + \frac{2}{n} = \frac{5 \cdot n}{n} + \frac{2}{n}$ LCD is n.

$= \frac{5n + 2}{n}$ Add the numerators.

Therefore, $5 + \frac{2}{n} = \frac{5n+2}{n}$.

Example 2 Simplify $2 + \frac{3}{n+3}$.

$2 + \frac{3}{n+3} = \frac{2(n+3)}{n+3} + \frac{3}{n+3}$

$= \frac{2n+6}{n+3} + \frac{3}{n+3}$

$= \frac{2n+6+3}{n+3}$

$= \frac{2n+9}{n+3}$

Therefore, $2 + \frac{3}{n+3} = \frac{2n+9}{n+3}$.

Lesson 11-7

Exercises

Write each mixed expression as a rational expression.

1. $4 + \frac{6}{a}$
2. $\frac{1}{2x} - 3$
3. $3x - \frac{1}{x^2}$
4. $\frac{4}{x^2} - 2$
5. $10 + \frac{60}{x+5}$
6. $\frac{h}{h+4} + 2$
7. $\frac{y}{y-2} + y^2$
8. $4 - \frac{4}{2x+1}$
9. $1 + \frac{1}{x}$
10. $\frac{4}{m-2} - 2m$
11. $x^2 + \frac{x+2}{x-3}$
12. $a - 3 + \frac{a-2}{a+3}$
13. $4m + \frac{3p}{2t}$
14. $2q^2 + \frac{q}{p+q}$
15. $\frac{2}{y^2-1} - 4y^2$
16. $t^2 + \frac{p+t}{p-t}$

Practice

AL OL BL ELL

NAME _______ DATE _______ PERIOD _______

11-7 Practice

Mixed Expressions and Complex Fractions

Write each mixed expression as a rational expression.

1. $14 - \frac{9}{a}$
2. $7d + \frac{4d}{c}$
3. $3n + \frac{6-n}{n}$
4. $5b - \frac{b+3}{2b}$
5. $3 + \frac{t+5}{t^2-1}$
6. $2a + \frac{a-1}{a+1}$
7. $2p + \frac{p+1}{p-3}$
8. $4n^2 + \frac{n-1}{n^2-1}$
9. $(t+1) + \frac{4}{t+5}$

Simplify each expression.

10.–18. [complex fractions]

19. **TRAVEL** Ray and Jan are on a $12\frac{1}{2}$-hour drive from Springfield, Missouri, to Chicago, Illinois. They stop for a break every $3\frac{1}{4}$ hours.
 a. Write an expression to model this situation.
 b. How many stops will Ray and Jan make before arriving in Chicago?

20. **CARPENTRY** Tai needs several $2\frac{1}{4}$-inch wooden rods to reinforce the frame on a futon. She can cut the rods from a $24\frac{1}{2}$-inch dowel purchased from a hardware store. How many wooden rods can she cut from the dowel?

Word Problem Practice

AL OL BL ELL

NAME _______ DATE _______ PERIOD _______

11-7 Word Problem Practice

Mixed Expressions and Complex Fractions

1. **CYCLING** Natalie rode in a bicycle event for charity on Saturday. It took her $\frac{2}{3}$ of an hour to complete the 18-mile race. What was her average speed in miles per hour?

2. **QUILTING** Mrs. Tantora sews and sells Amish baby quilts. She bought $42\frac{3}{4}$ yards of backing fabric, and $2\frac{1}{4}$ yards are needed for each quilt she sews. How many quilts can she make with the backing fabric she bought?

3. **TRAVEL** The Franz family traveled from Galveston to Waco for a family reunion. Driving their minivan, they averaged 30 miles per hour on the way to Waco and 45 miles per hour on the return trip home to Galveston. What is their average rate for the entire trip? (*Hint:* Remember that average rate equals total distance divided by total time and that time can be represented as a ratio of distance to rate.)

4. **PHYSICAL SCIENCE** The volume of a gas varies directly as the Kelvin temperature T and inversely as the pressure P, where k is the constant of variation.

$V = k\left(\frac{T}{P}\right)$

If $k = \frac{13}{157}$, find the volume in liters of helium gas at 273 degrees Kelvin and $\frac{13}{3}$ atmospheres of pressure. Round your answer to the nearest hundredth.

5. **SAFETY** The Occupational Safety and Health Administration provides safety standards in the workplace to keep workers free from dangerous working conditions. OSHA recommends that for general construction there be 5 foot-candles of illumination in which to work. A foreman using a light meter finds that the illumination of a construction light on a surface 8 feet from the source is 11 foot-candles. The illumination produced by a light source varies inversely as the square of the distance from the source.

$I = \frac{k}{d^2}$ I is illumination (in foot-candles), d is the distance from the source (in feet), k is a constant.

 a. Find the illumination of the same light at a distance of $15\frac{1}{2}$ feet. Round your answer to the nearest hundredth.
 b. Is there enough illumination at this distance to meet OSHA requirements for lighting?
 c. In order to comply with OSHA, what is the maximum allowable working distance from this light source? Round your decimal answer to nearest tenth.

Lesson 11-7

34. **SCOOTER** The speed v of an object spinning in a circle equals the circumference of the circle divided by the time T it takes the object to complete one revolution.
 a. Use the variables v, r (the radius of the circle), and T to write a formula describing the speed of a spinning object. $v = \frac{2\pi r}{T}$
 b. A scooter has tires with a radius of $3\frac{1}{2}$ inches. The tires make one revolution every $\frac{1}{10}$ second. Find the speed in miles per hour. Round to the nearest tenth. **12.5 mi/h**

35. **SCIENCE** The *density* of an object equals $\frac{m}{V}$, where m is the mass of the object and V is the volume. The densities of four metals are shown in the table. Identify the metal of each ball described below. (*Hint*: The volume of a sphere is $V = \frac{4}{3}\pi r^3$.)

Metal	Density (kg/m³)
copper	8900
gold	19,300
iron	7800
lead	11,300

 a. A metal ball has a mass of 15.6 kilograms and a radius of 0.0748 meter. **copper**
 b. A metal ball has a mass of 285.3 kilograms and a radius of 0.1819 meter. **lead**

36. **SIRENS** As an ambulance approaches, the siren sounds different than if it were sitting still. If the ambulance is moving toward you at v miles per hour and blowing the siren at a frequency of f, then you hear the siren as if it were blowing at a frequency h. This can be described by the equation $h = \frac{f}{1 - \frac{v}{s}}$, where s is the speed of sound, approximately 760 miles per hour.
 a. Simplify the complex fraction in the formula. $\frac{fs}{s - v}$
 b. Suppose a siren blows at 45 cycles per minute and is moving toward you at 65 miles per hour. Find the frequency of the siren as you hear it. **49.21 cycles/min**

C Simplify each expression.

37. $15 - \frac{17x+5}{5x+10}$ $\frac{58x+145}{5x+10}$

38. $\frac{\frac{b}{b+3} + 2}{b^2 - 2b - 8}$ $\frac{3}{(b+3)(b-4)}$

39. $\frac{1 + \frac{2c^2 - 6c - 10}{c+7}}{2c+1}$ $\frac{c-3}{c+7}$

40. $\frac{y - \frac{12}{y-4}}{y - \frac{18}{y-3}}$ $\frac{(y+2)(y-3)}{(y-4)(y+3)}$

41. $\frac{\frac{x^2-4x-32}{x+1}}{\frac{x^2+6x+8}{x^2-1}}$ $\frac{(x-8)(x-1)}{x+2}$

42. $\frac{\frac{r^2-9r}{r^2+7r+10}}{\frac{r^2+5r}{r^2+r-2}}$ $\frac{(r-9)(r-1)}{(r+5)^2}$

H.O.T. Problems Use Higher-Order Thinking Skills

43. **REASONING** Describe the first step to simplify the expression below.

$$\frac{\left(\frac{y}{x} - \frac{x}{y}\right)}{\frac{x+y}{xy}}$$

43. **Find the lowest common denominator for the fractions in the numerator and simplify to $\frac{y^2 - x^2}{xy}$.**

44. **REASONING** Is $\frac{n}{1 - \frac{5}{p}} + \frac{n}{\frac{5}{p} - 1}$ *sometimes*, *always*, or *never* equal to 0? Explain.

44. **Always; the expression can be simplified to $\frac{n}{1-\frac{5}{p}} - \frac{n}{1-\frac{5}{p}}$, $p \neq 0$.**

45. **PERSEVERANCE** Simplify the rational expression below.

$$\frac{\frac{1}{t-1} + \frac{1}{t+1}}{\frac{1}{t} - \frac{1}{t^2}}$$ $\frac{2t^3}{(t-1)(t^2-1)}$

46. **OPEN ENDED** Write a complex fraction that, when simplified, results in $\frac{1}{x}$. **Sample answer: $\frac{\frac{x}{a}}{\frac{x^2}{a}}$**

47. **WRITING IN MATH** Explain how complex fractions can be used to solve a problem involving distance, rate, and time. Give an example. **See Ch. 11 Answer Appendix.**

Enrichment

OL BL

NAME _______ DATE _______ PERIOD _______

11-7 Enrichment

Continued Fractions

Continued fractions are a special type of complex fraction. Each fraction in a continued fraction has a numerator of 1.

$1 + \frac{1}{2 + \frac{1}{3 + \frac{1}{4}}}$

Example 1 Evaluate the continued fraction above. Start at the bottom and work your way up.

Step 1 $3 + \frac{1}{4} = \frac{12}{4} + \frac{1}{4} = \frac{13}{4}$

Step 2 $\frac{1}{3 + \frac{1}{4}} = \frac{4}{13}$

Step 3 $2 + \frac{4}{13} = \frac{26}{13} + \frac{4}{13} = \frac{30}{13}$

Example 2 Change $\frac{13}{7}$ into a continued fraction.

Step 1 $\frac{13}{7} = \frac{7}{7} + \frac{6}{7} = 1 + \frac{6}{7}$

Step 2 $\frac{6}{7} = \frac{1}{\frac{7}{6}}$

Step 3 $\frac{7}{6} = 1 + \frac{1}{6}$

Exercise Alert

Formula For Exercise 34, students will need to know the formula for the circumference of a circle, $C = \pi d$ or $C = 2\pi r$.

Standardized Test Practice

48. A number is between 44 squared and 45 squared. 5 squared is one of its factors, and it is a multiple of 13. Find the number. **A**

A 1950

B 2000

C 2025

D 2050

49. SHORT RESPONSE Bernard is reading a 445-page book. He has already read 157 pages. If he reads 24 pages a day, how long will it take him to finish the book? **12 days**

50. GEOMETRY Angela wanted a round rug to fit her room that is 16 feet wide. The rug should just meet the edges. What is the area of the rug rounded to the nearest tenth? **J**

F 50.3 ft^2 H 152.2 ft^2

G 100.5 ft^2 J 201.1 ft^2

51. Simplify $7x + \frac{10}{2xy}$. **B**

A $\frac{7x + 10}{2xy}$ C $\frac{17x}{2xy}$

B $\frac{7x^2y + 5}{xy}$ D $\frac{7xy + 5}{x^2y}$

Spiral Review

Find each sum or difference. (Lesson 11-6)

52. $\frac{6}{7x} - \frac{5 + x}{7x}$ $\mathbf{\frac{1 - x}{7x}}$

53. $\frac{4}{d - 1} + \frac{d}{1 - d}$ $\mathbf{\frac{-d + 4}{d - 1}}$

54. $\frac{3q + 2}{2q + 1} + \frac{q - 5}{2q + 1}$ $\mathbf{\frac{4q - 3}{2q + 1}}$

55. $\frac{2}{5m} - \frac{1}{15m^3}$ $\mathbf{\frac{6m^2 - 1}{15m^3}}$

56. $\frac{10}{3g} - \frac{-3}{4h}$ $\mathbf{\frac{9g + 40h}{12gh}}$

57. $\frac{b}{b + 3} + \frac{6}{b - 2}$ $\mathbf{\frac{b^2 + 4b + 18}{(b + 3)(b - 2)}}$

Find each quotient. Use long division. (Lesson 11-5) **58–63. See margin.**

58. $(x^2 - 2x - 30) \div (x + 7)$

59. $(a^2 + 4a - 22) \div (a - 3)$

60. $(3q^2 + 20q + 11) \div (q + 6)$

61. $(3y^3 + 8y^2 + y - 7) \div (y + 2)$

62. $(6t^3 - 9t^2 + 6) \div (2t - 3)$

63. $(9h^3 + 5h - 8) \div (3h - 2)$

64. GEOMETRY A rectangle has a base of 8 meters and a height of 14 meters. What is the length of the diagonal? (Lesson 10-5) $\mathbf{2\sqrt{65}}$ **or about 16.1 m**

Graph each function. Determine the domain and range. (Lesson 10-1) **65–67. See margin.**

65. $y = 2\sqrt{x}$

66. $y = -3\sqrt{x}$

67. $y = \frac{1}{4}\sqrt{x}$

Factor each polynomial. If the polynomial cannot be factored, write *prime*. (Lesson 8-8)

68. $x^2 - 81$ $\mathbf{(x - 9)(x + 9)}$

69. $a^2 - 121$ $\mathbf{(a - 11)(a + 11)}$

70. $n^2 + 100$ **prime**

71. $-25 + 4y^2$ $\mathbf{(2y - 5)(2y + 5)}$

72. $p^4 - 16$ $\mathbf{(p - 2)(p + 2)(p^2 + 4)}$

73. $4t^4 - 4$ $\mathbf{4(t - 1)(t + 1)(t^2 + 1)}$

74. PARKS A youth group traveling in two vans visited Mammoth Cave in Kentucky. The number of people in each van and the total cost of the cave are shown. Find the adult price and the student price of the tour. (Lesson 6-3) **adult: $16; student: $9**

Van	Number of Adults	Number of Students	Total Cost
A	2	5	$77
B	2	7	$95

Skills Review

Solve each equation.

75. $6x = 24$ **4**

76. $5y - 1 = 19$ **4**

77. $2t + 7 = 21$ **7**

78. $\frac{p}{3} = -4.2$ **−12.6**

79. $\frac{2m + 1}{4} = -5.5$ **−11.5**

80. $\frac{3}{4}g = \frac{1}{2}$ $\mathbf{\frac{2}{3}}$

Differentiated Instruction OL BL

Extension Write $1 + \cfrac{1}{1 + \cfrac{1}{1 + \cfrac{1}{x}}}$ on the board. Ask students to write this mixed expression as a rational expression. $\frac{3x + 2}{2x + 1}$

4 Assess

Name the Math Have students tell what mathematical procedures they used to simplify the expression in Exercise 31. Then have students substitute 2 for j in the original expression and in their simplified expressions. Students should see that when $j = 2$, the value of both expressions is $-\frac{1}{5}$.

Additional Answers

58. $x - 9 + \frac{33}{x + 7}$

59. $a + 7 - \frac{1}{a - 3}$

60. $3q + 2 - \frac{1}{q + 6}$

61. $3y^2 + 2y - 3 - \frac{1}{y + 2}$

62. $3t^2 + \frac{6}{2t - 3}$

63. $3h^2 + 2h + 3 - \frac{2}{3h - 2}$

65.

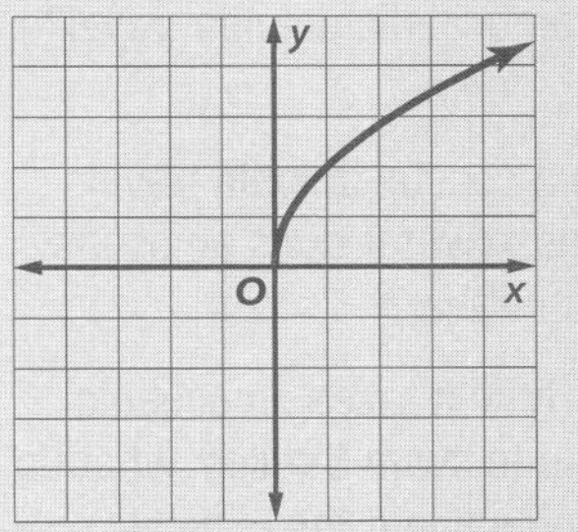

$D = \{x \mid x \geq 0\}$; $R = \{y \mid y \geq 0\}$

66.

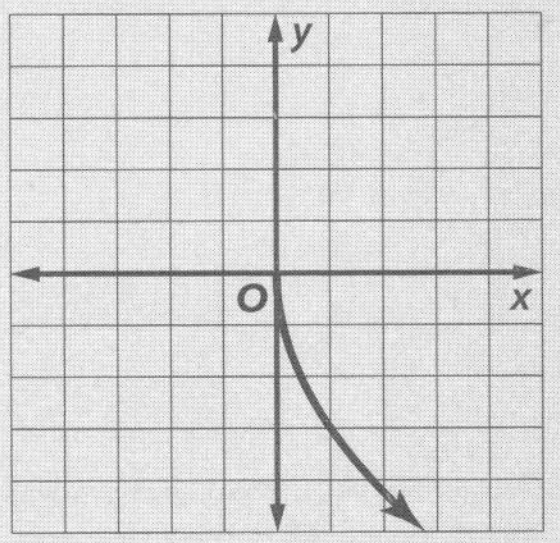

$D = \{x \mid x \geq 0\}$; $R = \{y \mid y \leq 0\}$

67.

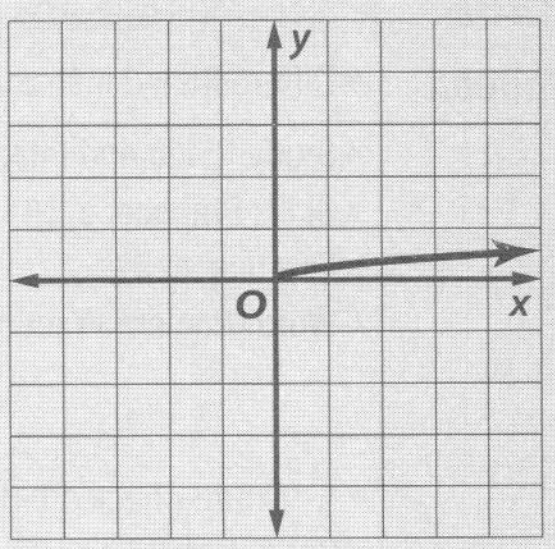

$D = \{x \mid x \geq 0\}$; $R = \{y \mid y \geq 0\}$

1 Focus

VerticalAlignment

Before Lesson 11-8 Solve proportions.

Lesson 11-8 Solve rational equations. Use rational equations to solve problems.

After Lesson 11-8 Solve rational inequalities.

2 Teach

Scaffolding Questions

Have students read the **Why?** section of the lesson.

Ask:

- When a coastal dolphin travels at x miles per hour, at what rate does an oceanic dolphin travel? $(x + 5)$ mi/h
- When a coastal dolphin travels 2 miles, how far does an oceanic dolphin travel? 3 miles
- In the time it takes an oceanic dolphin to swim 6 miles, what do you know about the coastal dolphin? It can swim 4 miles.

LESSON 11-8 Rational Equations

Then

- You solved proportions.

Now

1. Solve rational equations.
2. Use rational equations to solve problems.

Why?

- Oceanic species of dolphins can swim 5 miles per hour faster than coastal species of dolphins. An oceanic dolphin can swim 3 miles in the same time that it takes a coastal dolphin to swim 2 miles.

Dolphins			
Species	**Distance**	**Rate**	**Time**
coastal	2 miles	x mph	t hours
oceanic	3 miles	x + 5 mph	t hours

Since time = $\frac{\text{distance}}{\text{rate}}$, the equation below represents this situation.

Time an oceanic dolphin swims 3 miles equals time a coastal dolphin swims 2 miles.

$$\frac{3}{x+5} = \frac{2}{x}$$

(distance → numerator, rate → denominator)

NewVocabulary

rational equation
extraneous solution
work problem
rate problem

Process Standards
PS.2

1 Solve Rational Equations

A **rational equation** contains one or more rational expressions. When a rational equation is a proportion, you can use cross products to solve it.

Real-World Example 1 Use Cross Products to Solve Equations

DOLPHINS **Refer to the information above. Solve $\frac{3}{x+5} = \frac{2}{x}$ to find the speed of a coastal dolphin. Check the solution.**

$\frac{3}{x+5} = \frac{2}{x}$ — Original equation

$3x = 2(x + 5)$ — Find the cross products.

$3x = 2x + 10$ — Distributive Property

$x = 10$ — Subtract $2x$ from each side.

So, a coastal dolphin can swim 10 miles per hour.

CHECK $\frac{3}{x+5} = \frac{2}{x}$ — Original equation

$\frac{3}{10+5} \stackrel{?}{=} \frac{2}{10}$ — Replace x with 10.

$\frac{3}{15} \stackrel{?}{=} \frac{1}{5}$ — Simplify.

$\frac{1}{5} = \frac{1}{5}$ ✓ — Simplify.

GuidedPractice

Solve each equation. Check the solution.

1A. $\frac{7}{y-3} = \frac{3}{y+1}$ −4

1B. $\frac{13}{10} = \frac{2f + 0.2}{7}$ 4.45

Lesson 11-8 Resources

Resource	Approaching Level AL	On Level OL	Beyond Level BL	English Learners ELL
Teacher Edition	▪ Differentiated Instruction, p. 729	▪ Differentiated Instruction, pp. 729, 732	▪ Differentiated Instruction, p. 732	▪ Differentiated Instruction, p. 729
Chapter Resource Masters	▪ Study Guide and Intervention, pp. 49–50 ▪ Skills Practice, p. 51 ▪ Practice, p. 52 ▪ Word Problem Practice, p. 53	▪ Study Guide and Intervention, pp. 49–50 ▪ Skills Practice, p. 51 ▪ Practice, p. 52 ▪ Word Problem Practice, p. 53 ▪ Enrichment, p. 54 ▪ Graphing Calculator, p. 55	▪ Practice, p. 52 ▪ Word Problem Practice, p. 53 ▪ Enrichment, p. 54	▪ Study Guide and Intervention, pp. 49–50 ▪ Skills Practice, p. 51 ▪ Practice, p. 52 ▪ Word Problem Practice, p. 53
Other	▪ 5-Minute Check 11-8 ▪ Study Notebook ▪ Teaching Algebra with Manipulatives	▪ 5-Minute Check 11-8 ▪ Study Notebook ▪ Teaching Algebra with Manipulatives	▪ 5-Minute Check 11-8 ▪ Study Notebook	▪ 5-Minute Check 11-8 ▪ Study Notebook ▪ Teaching Algebra with Manipulatives

Another method that can be used to solve any rational equation is to find the LCD of all the fractions in the equation. Then multiply each side of the equation by the LCD to eliminate the fractions.

PT

Example 2 Use the LCD to Solve Rational Equations

Solve $\frac{4}{y} + \frac{5y}{y+1} = 5$. Check the solution.

Step 1 Find the LCD.

The LCD of $\frac{4}{y}$ and $\frac{5y}{y+1}$ is $y(y + 1)$.

Step 2 Multiply each side of the equation by the LCD.

$$\frac{4}{y} + \frac{5y}{y+1} = 5 \quad \text{Original equation}$$

$$y(y+1)\left(\frac{4}{y} + \frac{5y}{y+1}\right) = y(y+1)(5) \quad \text{Multiply each side by the LCD, } y(y+1).$$

$$\left(\frac{\cancel{y}^{1}(y+1)}{1} \cdot \frac{4}{\cancel{y}_{1}}\right) + \left(\frac{y\cancel{(y+1)}^{1}}{1} \cdot \frac{5y}{\cancel{y+1}_{1}}\right) = y(y+1)(5) \quad \text{Distributive Property}$$

$$(y+1)4 + y(5y) = y(y+1)(5) \quad \text{Simplify.}$$

$$4y + 4 + 5y^2 = 5y^2 + 5y \quad \text{Multiply.}$$

$$4y + 4 + 5y^2 - 5y^2 = 5y^2 - 5y^2 + 5y \quad \text{Subtract } 5y^2 \text{ from each side.}$$

$$4y + 4 = 5y \quad \text{Simplify.}$$

$$4y - 4y + 4 = 5y - 4y \quad \text{Subtract } 4y \text{ from each side.}$$

$$4 = y \quad \text{Simplify.}$$

CHECK

$$\frac{4}{y} + \frac{5y}{y+1} = 5 \quad \text{Original equation}$$

$$\frac{4}{4} + \frac{5(4)}{4+1} \stackrel{?}{=} 5 \quad \text{Replace } y \text{ with 4.}$$

$$1 + 4 \stackrel{?}{=} 5 \quad \text{Simplify.}$$

$$5 = 5 \checkmark \quad \text{Simplify.}$$

StudyTip

Solutions It is important to check the solutions of rational equations to be sure that they satisfy the original equation.

GuidedPractice

Solve each equation. Check your solutions.

2A. $\frac{2b-5}{b-2} - 2 = \frac{3}{b+2}$ 1

2B. $1 + \frac{1}{c+2} = \frac{28}{c^2+2c}$ 4, −7

2C. $\frac{y+2}{y-2} - \frac{2}{y+2} = -\frac{7}{3}$ $-1, \frac{2}{5}$

2D. $\frac{n}{3n+6} - \frac{n}{5n+10} = \frac{2}{5}$ −3

VocabularyLink

extraneous
Everyday Use irrelevant or unimportant

extraneous solution
Math Use a result that is not a solution of the original equation

Recall that any value of a variable that makes the denominator of a rational expression zero must be excluded from the domain.

In the same way, when a solution of a rational equation results in a zero in the denominator, that solution must be excluded. Such solutions are called **extraneous solutions**.

$$\frac{4+x}{x-5} + \frac{1}{x} = \frac{2}{x+1} \quad \text{5, 0, and } -1 \text{ cannot be solutions.}$$

1 Solve Rational Equations

Example 1 shows how to use cross products to solve rational expressions when both sides of the equation are single fractions. **Example 2** shows how to solve rational equations by multiplying each side of the equation by the LCD to eliminate fractions. **Example 3** shows how to determine which solutions are extraneous solutions when both sides of a rational equation are multiplied by the LCD of the rational expressions that make up the equation.

Formative Assessment

Use the Guided Practice exercises after each example to determine students' understanding of concepts.

Additional Examples

1 **FRIENDS** Cabrini can run 3 miles an hour faster than Michael. Cabrini can run 5 miles in the same time it takes Michael to run 3 miles. Solve $\frac{5}{x+3} = \frac{3}{x}$ to find how fast Michael can run. Check the solution. $4\frac{1}{2}$ miles per hour

2 Solve $\frac{5}{x+1} - \frac{1}{x} = \frac{2}{x^2+x}$. Check the solution. $\frac{3}{4}$

Additional Examples also in Interactive Classroom PowerPoint® Presentations

IWB Interactive White Board READY

Teach with Tech

Interactive Whiteboard Display the graph of the radical function on the board. Solve the equation algebraically, and show students how this solution relates to the graph. Save your notes as a PDF and post on your class Web site.

WatchOut!

Preventing Errors Suggest students make a mental note of the values for the variable that make the denominator equal to zero.

Suggest that students check their solutions by substituting them back into the original equation.

Additional Example

3 Solve $\frac{3x}{x-1} + \frac{6x-9}{x-1} = 6$. State any extraneous solutions. no solution; 1

WatchOut!

Student Misconceptions Emphasize that the equation must be solved in order to find the solution(s) and to determine whether the solutions are extraneous. The value of the variable that would make the denominator zero is not necessarily an extaneous solution of the rational equation.

Focus on Mathematical Content

Extraneous Roots It is always important to check a solution to an equation in the original equation, but it is especially important when each side of an equation has been multiplied by a variable. If your solution is an approximation, it is sometimes difficult to determine whether a discrepancy is due to rounding or if it is an incorrect solution.

2 Use Rational Equations to Solve Problems

Example 4 shows how to use rational equations to solve real-world work problems. **Example 5** shows how to use rational equations to solve real-world rate problems.

Additional Example

4 **TV INSTALLATION** On Saturdays, Lee helps her father install satellite TV systems. The jobs normally take Lee's father about $2\frac{1}{2}$ hours. But when Lee helps, the jobs only take them $1\frac{1}{2}$ hours. If Lee were installing a satellite system herself, how long would the job take? $3\frac{3}{4}$ hours

PT

Example 3 Extraneous Solutions

Solve $\frac{2n}{n-5} + \frac{4n-30}{n-5} = 5$. State any extraneous solutions.

$\frac{2n}{n-5} + \frac{4n-30}{n-5} = 5$	Original equation
$(n-5)\left(\frac{2n}{n-5} + \frac{4n-30}{n-5}\right) = (n-5)5$	Multiply each side by the LCD, $n-5$.
$\left(\frac{\cancel{n-5}^{1}}{1} \cdot \frac{2n}{\cancel{n-5}_{1}}\right) + \left(\frac{\cancel{n-5}^{1}}{1} \cdot \frac{4n-30}{\cancel{n-5}_{1}}\right) = (n-5)5$	Distributive Property
$2n + 4n - 30 = 5n - 25$	Simplify.
$6n - 30 = 5n - 25$	Add like terms.
$6n - 5n - 30 = 5n - 5n - 25$	Subtract $5n$ from each side.
$n - 30 = -25$	Simplify.
$n - 30 + 30 = -25 + 30$	Add 30 to each side.
$n = 5$	Simplify.

Since $n = 5$ results in a zero in the denominator of the original equation, it is an extraneous solution. So, the equation has no solution.

StudyTip

Solutions It is possible to get both a valid solution and an extraneous solution when solving a rational equation.

GuidedPractice

3. Solve $\frac{n^2-3n}{n^2-4} - \frac{10}{n^2-4} = 2$. State any extraneous solutions. **−1; extraneous solution: −2**

2 Use Rational Equations to Solve Problems

You can use rational equations to solve **work problems**, or problems involving work rates.

PT

Real-World Example 4 Work Problem

JOBS At his part-time job at the zoo, Ping can clean the bird area in 2 hours. Natalie can clean the same area in 1 hour and 15 minutes. How long would it take them if they worked together?

Understand It takes Ping 2 hours to complete the job and Natalie $1\frac{1}{4}$ hours.

You need to find the rate that each person works and the total time t that it will take them if they work together.

Plan Find the fraction of the job that each person can do in an hour.

Ping's rate ⟶ $\frac{1 \text{ job}}{2 \text{ hours}} = \frac{1}{2}$ job per hour

Natalie's rate ⟶ $\frac{1 \text{ job}}{1\frac{1}{4} \text{ hours}}$ or $\frac{1 \text{ job}}{\frac{5}{4} \text{ hours}} = \frac{4}{5}$ job per hour

Since rate • time = fraction of job done, multiply each rate by the time t to represent the amount of the job done by each person.

728 | Lesson 11-8 | Rational Equations

StudyTip

Reasoning When solving work problems, remember that each term should represent the portion of a job completed in one unit of time.

Solve Fraction of job Ping completes plus fraction of job Natalie completes equals 1 job.

$$\frac{1}{2}t + \frac{4}{5}t = 1$$

$$10\left(\frac{1}{2}t + \frac{4}{5}t\right) = 10(1) \quad \text{Multiply each side by the LCD, 10.}$$

$$10\left(\frac{1}{2}t\right) + 10\left(\frac{4}{5}t\right) = 10 \quad \text{Distributive Property}$$

$$5t + 8t = 10 \quad \text{Simplify.}$$

$$t = \frac{10}{13} \quad \text{Add like terms and divide each side by 13.}$$

So, it would take them $\frac{10}{13}$ hour or about 46 minutes to complete the job if they work together.

Check In $\frac{10}{13}$ hour, Ping would complete $\frac{1}{2} \cdot \frac{10}{13}$ or $\frac{5}{13}$ of the job and Natalie would complete $\frac{4}{5} \cdot \frac{10}{13}$ or $\frac{8}{13}$ of the job. Together, they complete $\frac{5}{13} + \frac{8}{13}$ or 1 whole job. So, the answer is reasonable.✓

GuidedPractice

4. RAKING Jenna can rake the leaves in 2 hours. It takes her brother Benjamin 3 hours. How long would it take them if they worked together? **$1\frac{1}{5}$ hour**

Rational equations can also be used to solve **rate problems**.

Real-World Example 5 Rate Problem

AIRPLANES An airplane takes off and flies an average of 480 miles per hour. Another plane leaves 15 minutes later and flies to the same city traveling 560 miles per hour. How long will it take the second plane to pass the first plane?

Record the information that you know in a table.

Plane	Distance	Rate	Time
1	d miles	480 mi/h	t hours
2	d miles	560 mi/h	$t - \frac{1}{4}$ hours

← Plane 2 took off 15 minutes, or $\frac{1}{4}$ hour, after Plane 1

Since both planes will have traveled the same distance when Plane 2 passes Plane 1, you can write the following equation.

Distance for Plane 1 = Distance for Plane 2

$$480 \cdot t = 560 \cdot \left(t - \frac{1}{4}\right) \quad \text{distance = rate • time}$$

$$480t = (560 \cdot t) - \left(560 \cdot \frac{1}{4}\right) \quad \text{Distributive Property}$$

$$480t = 560t - 140 \quad \text{Simplify.}$$

$$-80t = -140 \quad \text{Subtract } 560t \text{ from each side.}$$

$$t = 1.75 \quad \text{Divide each side by } -80.$$

So, the second plane passes the first plane after 1.75 hours.

Real-WorldLink

The longest nonstop commercial flight was 13,422 miles from Hong Kong Airport in China to London Heathrow in the United Kingdom. It took 22 hours and 42 minutes.

Source: *Guinness Book of World Records*

GuidedPractice

5. Lenora leaves the house walking at 3 miles per hour. After 10 minutes, her mother leaves the house riding a bicycle at 10 miles per hour. In how many minutes will Lenora's mother catch her? **$14\frac{2}{7}$ min**

Additional Example

5 BUS A bus leaves a station and travels an average of 50 miles per hour towards a city. Another bus leaves the same station 20 minutes later and travels to the same city traveling 60 miles per hour. How long will it take the second bus to pass the first bus? 1 hour 40 minutes, or $1\frac{2}{3}$ hours

Teaching the Process Standards

Reasoning Mathematically proficient students make sense of quantities and their relationships in problem situations. Encourage students to start problems they work on their own by planning and writing an equation as shown in Example 4.

DifferentiatedInstruction AL OL ELL

If you think students would benefit by acting out a concept in this lesson,

Then have students refer to Example 5. Ask students to design a rate problem that two students can act out, such as walking a certain distance. Have the two students start at different times. The student who starts later should take more steps per second than the other. Have another student record the time the one student passes the other. Then work out the problem to see if the calculations reflect the actual time.

3 Practice

Formative Assessment

Use Exercises 1–8 to check for understanding.

Use the chart at the bottom of this page to customize assignments for your students.

Teaching the Process Standards

Reasoning Mathematically proficient students create a coherent representation of the problem at hand. In Exercise 28, remind students to examine their solution in terms of the situation.

Arguments Mathematically proficient students can recognize and use counterexamples. In Exercise 39, remind students that a counterexample is a specific case in which the statement is false. So they need to write a rational equation that has a solution of 0.

Additional Answers

25a. line

25b. $f(x) = \frac{x(x+5)(x-6)}{x-6}$
$= x + 5$

25c. -5

26a. parabola

26b. $f(x) = \frac{x(x+2)(x-1)}{x+2}$
$= x(x-1)$

26c. 0, 1

27a. parabola

27b. $f(x) = x^2 + 6x + 12$

27c. no real zeros

Check Your Understanding

● = Step-by-Step Solutions begin on page R13.

Examples 1–3 **Solve each equation. State any extraneous solutions.** **6.** $-\frac{4}{3}$; **extraneous: 1**

1. $\frac{2}{x+1} = \frac{4}{x}$ **−2**

2. $\frac{t+3}{5} = \frac{2t+3}{9}$ **12**

3. $\frac{a+3}{a} - \frac{6}{5a} = \frac{1}{a}$ $-\frac{4}{5}$

4. $4 - \frac{p}{p-1} = \frac{2}{p-1}$ **2**

5. $\frac{2t}{t+1} + \frac{4}{t-1} = 2$ **−3**

6. $\frac{x+3}{x^2-1} - \frac{2x}{x-1} = 1$

Example 4

7. WEEDING Maurice can weed the garden in 45 minutes. Olinda can weed the garden in 50 minutes. How long would it take them to weed the garden if they work together? $\frac{15}{38}$ **hour or about 0.4 hour**

Example 5

8. LANDSCAPING Hunter is filling a 3.5-gallon bucket to water plants at a faucet that flows at a rate of 1.75 gallons a minute. If he were to add a hose that flows at a rate of 1.45 gallons per minute, how many minutes would it take him to fill the bucket? Round to the nearest tenth. **1.1 min**

Practice and Problem Solving

Extra Practice is on page R11.

Examples 1–3 **Solve each equation. State any extraneous solutions.**

9. $\frac{8}{n} = \frac{3}{n-5}$ **8**

10. $\frac{6}{t+2} = \frac{4}{t}$ **4**

11. $\frac{3g+2}{12} = \frac{g}{2}$ $\frac{2}{3}$

12. $\frac{5h}{4} + \frac{1}{2} = \frac{3h}{8}$ $-\frac{4}{7}$

13. $\frac{2}{3w} = \frac{2}{15} + \frac{12}{5w}$ **−13**

14. $\frac{c-4}{c+1} = \frac{c}{c-1}$ $\frac{2}{3}$

15. $\frac{x-1}{x+1} - \frac{2x}{x-1} = -1$ **0**

16. $\frac{y+4}{y-2} + \frac{6}{y-2} = \frac{1}{y+3}$ **−4, −8**

17. $\frac{a}{a+3} + \frac{a^2}{a+3} = 2$ **−2, 3**

18. $\frac{12}{a+3} + \frac{6}{a^2-9} = \frac{8}{a+3}$ $\frac{3}{2}$

19. $\frac{3n}{n-1} + \frac{6n-9}{n-1} = 6$ **no solution; extraneous: 1**

20. $\frac{n^2-n-6}{n^2-n} - \frac{n-5}{n-1} = \frac{n-3}{n^2-n}$ **no solution; extraneous: 1**

Example 4

21. PAINTING It takes Noah 3 hours to paint one side of a fence. It takes Gilberto 5 hours. How long would it take them if they worked together? $\frac{15}{8}$ **hours or** $1\frac{7}{8}$ **hours**

22. DISHWASHING Ron works as a dishwasher and can wash 500 plates in two hours and 15 minutes. Chris can finish the 500 plates in 3 hours. About how long would it take them to finish all of the plates if they work together? $\frac{9}{7}$ **hours or** $1\frac{2}{7}$ **hours**

Example 5

23. ICE A hotel has two ice machines in its kitchen. How many hours would it take both machines to make 60 pounds of ice? Round to the nearest tenth. **26.2 hours**

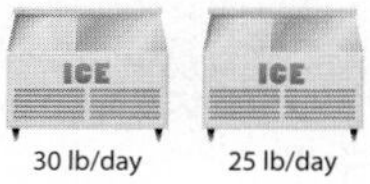

24. CYCLING Two cyclists travel in opposite directions around a 5.6-mile circular trail. They start at the same time. The first cyclist completes the trail in 22 minutes and the second in 28 minutes. At what time do they pass each other? **12.32 min**

25–27. See margin.

B **GRAPHING CALCULATOR** **For each function, a) describe the shape of the graph, b) use factoring to simplify the function, and c) find the zeros of the function.**

25. $f(x) = \frac{x^2 - x - 30}{x - 6}$

26. $f(x) = \frac{x^3 + x^2 - 2x}{x + 2}$

27. $f(x) = \frac{x^3 + 6x^2 + 12x}{x}$

28. REASONING Morgan can paint a standard-sized house in about 5 days. For his latest job, Morgan hires two assistants. At what rate must these assistants work for Morgan to meet a deadline of two days? **They must paint** $\frac{3}{10}$ **of the house each day for 2 days.**

Differentiated Homework Options

Level	Assignment	Two-Day Option	
AL Basic	9–24, 37–63	9–23 odd, 41–44	10–24 even, 37–40, 45–63
OL Core	9–27 odd, 28–31, 33, 35, 37–63	9–24, 41–44	25–35, 37–40, 45–63
BL Advanced	25–60, (optional: 61–63)		

730 | Lesson 11-8 | Rational Equations

29. AIRPLANES Headwinds push against a plane and reduce its total speed, while tailwinds push on a plane and increase its total speed. Let w equal the speed of the wind, r equal the speed set by the pilot, and s equal the total speed.

a. Write an equation for the total speed with a headwind and an equation for the total speed with a tailwind. **$s = r - w$; $s = r + w$**

b. Use the rate formula to write an equation for the distance traveled by a plane with a headwind and another equation for the distance traveled by a plane with a tailwind. Then solve each equation for time instead of distance. **$d = t(r - w)$, $d = t(r + w)$; $t = \frac{d}{r - w}$, $t = \frac{d}{r + w}$**

C **30. MIXTURES** A pitcher of fruit juice has 3 pints of pineapple juice and 2 pints of orange juice. Erin wants to add more orange juice so that the fruit juice mixture is 60% orange juice. Let x equal the pints of orange juice that she needs to add.

a. Copy and complete the table below.

Juice	Pints of Orange Juice	Total Pints of Juice	Percent of Orange Juice
original mixture	**2**	5	**0.4**
final mixture	2 + x	**5 + x**	0.6

b. Write and solve an equation to find the pints of orange juice to add. **$\frac{2 + x}{5 + x} = 0.6$; 2.5 pt**

31. DORMITORIES The number of hours h it takes to clean a dormitory varies inversely with the number of people cleaning it c and directly with the number of people living there p.

a. Write an equation showing how h, c, and p are related. (*Hint*: Include the constant k.) **$h = \frac{kp}{c}$**

b. It takes 8 hours for 5 people to clean the dormitory when there are 100 people there. How long will it take to clean the dormitory if there are 10 people cleaning and the number of people living in the dorm stays the same? **4 hours**

Solve each equation. State any extraneous solutions.

32. $\frac{4b + 2}{b^2 - 3b} + \frac{b + 2}{b} = \frac{b - 1}{b}$ **1**

33. $\frac{x^2 - x - 3}{x - 1} + \frac{x^3 + 2x^2}{x - 1} = 3$ **0, −4; extraneous: 1**

34. $\frac{y^2 + 5y - 6}{y^3 - 2y^2} = \frac{5}{y} - \frac{6}{y^3 - 2y^2}$ **$\frac{15}{4}$; extraneous: 0**

35. $\frac{x - \frac{6}{5}}{x} - \frac{x - 10\frac{1}{2}}{x - 5} = \frac{x + 21}{x^2 - 5x}$ **$\frac{50}{11}$**

H.O.T. Problems Use Higher-Order Thinking Skills

36. CHALLENGE Solve $\frac{2x}{x - 2} + \frac{x^2 + 3x}{(x + 1)(x - 2)} = \frac{2}{(x + 1)(x - 2)}$. **$-2, \frac{1}{3}$**

37. REASONING How is an excluded value of a rational expression related to an extraneous solution of a corresponding rational equation? Explain. **37. The extraneous solution of a rational equation is an excluded value of one of the expressions in the equation.**

38. WRITING IN MATH Why should you check solutions of rational equations? **See margin.**

39. ARGUMENTS Find a counterexample for the following statement.

The solution of a rational equation can never be zero. **Sample answer: $\frac{x}{x - 8} = 0$**

40. WRITING IN MATH Describe the steps for solving a rational equation that is not a proportion. **Sample answer: First, find the LCD of the fractions in the equation. Then multiply each side of the equation by the LCD. Simplify and use the order of operations to solve for the variable.**

Additional Answer

38. Sample answer: Multiplying each side of a rational equation by the LCD can result in extraneous solutions. Therefore, all solutions should be checked to make sure that they satisfy the original equation.

Study Guide and Intervention

AL OL ELL

NAME ______ DATE ______ PERIOD ______

11-8 Study Guide and Intervention

Rational Equations

Solve Rational Equations **Rational equations** are equations that contain rational expressions. To solve equations containing rational expressions, multiply each side of the equation by the least common denominator.

Rational equations can be used to solve **work problems** and **rate problems**.

Example 1 Solve $\frac{x - 3}{3} + \frac{x}{2} = 4$.

$\frac{x - 3}{3} + \frac{x}{2} = 4$

$6\left(\frac{x - 3}{3} + \frac{x}{2}\right) = 6(4)$ The LCD is 6.

$2(x - 3) + 3x = 24$ Distributive Property

$2x - 6 + 3x = 24$ Distributive Property

$5x = 30$ Simplify.

$x = 6$ Divide each side by 5.

The solution is 6.

Example 2 Solve $\frac{15}{x^2 - 1} = \frac{5}{2(x - 1)}$. State any extraneous solutions.

$\frac{15}{x^2 - 1} = \frac{5}{2(x - 1)}$ Original equation

$30(x - 1) = 5(x^2 - 1)$ Cross multiply.

$30x - 30 = 5x^2 - 5$ Distributive Property

$0 = 5x^2 - 30x + 30 - 5$ Add −30x + 30 to each side.

$0 = 5x^2 - 30x + 25$ Simplify.

$0 = 5(x^2 - 6x + 5)$ Factor.

$0 = 5(x - 1)(x - 5)$ Factor.

$x = 1$ or $x = 5$ Zero Product Property

The number 1 is an extraneous solution, since 1 is an excluded value for x. So, 5 is the solution of the equation.

Lesson 11-8

Exercises

Solve each equation. State any extraneous solutions.

1. $\frac{x - 5}{5} + \frac{x}{4} = 8$
2. $\frac{3}{x} = \frac{6}{x + 1}$
3. $\frac{x - 1}{5} = \frac{2x - 2}{15}$
4. $\frac{8}{n - 1} = \frac{10}{n + 1}$
5. $t - \frac{4}{t + 3} = t + 3$
6. $\frac{m + 4}{m} + \frac{m}{3} = \frac{m}{3}$
7. $\frac{q + 4}{q - 1} + \frac{q}{q + 1} = 2$
8. $\frac{5 - 2x}{2} - \frac{4x + 3}{6} = \frac{7x + 2}{6}$
9. $\frac{m + 1}{m - 1} - \frac{m}{1 - m} = 1$
10. $\frac{x^2 - 9}{x - 3} + x^2 = 9$
11. $\frac{2}{x^2 - 36} - \frac{1}{x - 6} = 0$
12. $\frac{4z}{z^2 + 4z + 3} = \frac{6}{z + 3} + \frac{4}{z + 1}$
13. $\frac{4}{4 - p} - \frac{p^2}{p - 4} = 4$
14. $\frac{x^2 - 16}{x - 4} + x^2 = 16$

Practice

AL OL BL ELL

NAME ______ DATE ______ PERIOD ______

11-8 Practice

Rational Equations

Solve each equation. State any extraneous solutions.

1. $\frac{5}{n + 2} = \frac{7}{n + 6}$
2. $\frac{x}{x - 5} = \frac{x + 4}{x - 6}$
3. $\frac{k + 5}{k} = \frac{k - 1}{k + 9}$
4. $\frac{2h}{h - 1} = \frac{2h + 1}{h + 2}$
5. $\frac{4y}{3} + \frac{1}{2} = \frac{5y}{6}$
6. $\frac{y - 2}{4} - \frac{y + 2}{5} = -1$
7. $\frac{2q - 1}{6} - \frac{q}{3} = \frac{q + 4}{18}$
8. $\frac{5}{p - 1} - \frac{3}{p + 2} = 0$
9. $\frac{3t}{3t - 3} - \frac{1}{9t + 3} = 1$
10. $\frac{4x}{2x + 1} - \frac{2x}{2x + 3} = 1$
11. $\frac{d - 3}{d} - \frac{d - 4}{d - 2} = \frac{1}{d}$
12. $\frac{3y - 2}{y - 2} + \frac{y^2}{2 - y} = -3$
13. $\frac{2}{m + 2} - \frac{m + 2}{m - 2} = \frac{7}{3}$
14. $\frac{n + 2}{n} + \frac{n + 5}{n + 3} = -\frac{1}{n}$
15. $\frac{1}{z + 1} - \frac{6 - z}{6z} = 0$
16. $\frac{2p}{p - 2} + \frac{p + 2}{p^2 - 4} = 1$
17. $\frac{x + 7}{x^2 - 9} - \frac{x}{x + 3} = 1$
18. $\frac{2n}{n - 4} - \frac{n + 6}{n^2 - 16} = 1$

19. **PUBLISHING** Tracey and Alan publish a 10-page independent newspaper once a month. At production, Alan usually spends 6 hours on the layout of the paper. When Tracey helps, layout takes 3 hours and 20 minutes.

a. Write an equation that could be used to determine how long it would take Tracey to do the layout by herself.

b. How long would it take Tracey to do the job alone?

20. **TRAVEL** Emilio made arrangements to have Lynda pick him up from an auto repair shop after he dropped his car off. He called Lynda to tell her he would start walking and to look for him on the way. Emilio and Lynda live 10 miles from the auto shop. It takes Emilio $2\frac{1}{4}$ hours to walk the distance and Lynda 15 minutes to drive the distance.

a. If Emilio and Lynda leave at the same time, when should Lynda expect to spot Emilio on the road?

b. How far will Emilio have walked when Lynda picks him up?

Word Problem Practice

AL OL BL ELL

NAME ______ DATE ______ PERIOD ______

11-8 Word Problem Practice

Rational Equations

1. **ELECTRICITY** The current in a simple electric circuit varies inversely as the resistance. If the current is 20 amps when the resistance is 5 ohms, find the current when the resistance is 8 ohms.

2. **MASONRY** Sam and Belai are masons who are working to build a stone wall that will be 120 feet long. Sam works from one end and is able to build one ten-foot section in 5 hours. Belai works from the other end and is able to finish a ten-foot section in 4 hours. How long will it take Sam and Belai to finish building the wall?

3. **NUMBERS** The formula to find the sum of the first n whole numbers is sum $= \frac{n^2 + n}{2}$. In order to encourage students to show up early to a school dance, the dance committee decides to charge less for those who come to the dance early. Their plan is to charge the first student to arrive 1 penny. The second student through the door is charged 2 pennies; the third student through the door is charged 3 pennies, and so on. How much money, in total, would paid by the first 150 students?

4. **NAUTICAL** A ferry captain keeps track of the progress of his ship in the ship's log. One day, he records the following entry.

With the recent spring snow melt, the current is running strong today. The six-mile trip downstream to Whyte's landing was very quick. However, we only covered two miles in the same amount of time when we headed back upstream.

Write a rational equation using b for the speed of the boat and c for the speed of the stream and solve for b in terms of c.

5. **HEALTH CARE** The total number of Americans waiting for kidney and heart transplants is approximately 66,500. The ratio of those awaiting a kidney transplant to those awaiting a heart transplant is about 20 to 1.

a. How many people are on each of the waiting lists? Round your answers to the nearest hundred.

b. These two groups make up about $\frac{3}{4}$ of the transplant candidates for all organs. About how many organ transplant candidates are there altogether? Round your answer to the nearest thousand.

Lesson 11-8

Enrichment

OL BL

NAME ______ DATE ______ PERIOD ______

11-8 Enrichment

Winning Distances

In 1999, Hicham El Guerrouj set a world record for the mile run with a time of 3:43.13 (3 min 43.13 s). In 1954, Roger Bannister ran the first mile under 4 minutes at 3:59.4. Had they run those times in the same race, how far in front of Bannister would El Guerrouj have been at the finish?

Use $\frac{d}{t} = r$. Since 3 min 43.13 s = 223.13 s, and 3 min 59.4 s = 239.4 s, El Guerrouj's rate was $\frac{5280 \text{ ft}}{223.13 \text{ s}}$ and Bannister's rate was $\frac{5280 \text{ ft}}{239.4 \text{ s}}$.

	r	t	d
El Guerrouj	$\frac{5280}{223.13}$	223.13	5280 feet
Bannister	$\frac{5280}{239.4}$	223.13	$\frac{5280}{239.4} \cdot 223.13$ or 4921.2 feet

Therefore, when El Guerrouj hit the tape, he would be 5280 − 4921.2, or 358.8 feet, ahead of Bannister. Let's see whether we can develop a formula for this type of problem.

Let D = the distance raced,

4 Assess

Yesterday's News Have students write how knowing how to simplify mixed expressions helped them with today's lesson.

Formative Assessment

Check for student understanding of Lessons 11-7 and 11-8.

Quiz 4, p. 58

Standardized Test Practice

41. It takes Cheng 4 hours to build a fence. If he hires Odell to help him, they can do the job in 3 hours. If Odell built the same fence alone, how long would it take him? **D**

A $1\frac{5}{7}$ hours C 8 hours

B $3\frac{2}{3}$ hours D 12 hours

42. In the 1000-meter race, Zoe finished 35 meters ahead of Taryn and 53 meters ahead of Evan. How far was Taryn ahead of Evan? **F**

F 18 m G 35 m H 53 m J 88 m

43. Twenty gallons of lemonade were poured into two containers of different sizes. Express the amount of lemonade poured into the smaller container in terms of g, the amount poured into the larger container. **D**

A $g + 20$ C $g - 20$

B $20 + g$ D $20 - g$

44. GRIDDED RESPONSE The gym has 2-kilogram and 5-kilogram disks for weight lifting. They have fourteen disks in all. The total weight of the 2-kilogram disks is the same as the total weight of the 5-kilogram disks. How many 2-kilogram disks are there? **10**

Spiral Review

Simplify each expression. (Lesson 11-7)

45. $\dfrac{\frac{c^2}{d}}{\frac{c^3}{d^2}}$ $\mathbf{\frac{d}{c}}$

46. $\dfrac{\frac{5g^3}{h^2}}{\frac{6g}{5h}}$ $\mathbf{\frac{25g^2}{6h}}$

47. $\dfrac{\frac{2}{b}}{\frac{4}{b-3}}$ $\mathbf{\frac{b-3}{2b}}$

48. $\dfrac{\frac{q-2}{9}}{\frac{q^2-6q+8}{12}}$ $\mathbf{\frac{4}{3(q-4)}}$

Find the LCM of each pair of polynomials. (Lesson 11-6)

49. $2h, 4h^2$ $\mathbf{4h^2}$

50. $5c^2, 12c^3$ $\mathbf{60c^3}$

51. $x - 4, x + 2$ $\mathbf{(x-4)(x+2)}$

52. $p - 7, 2(p - 14)$ $\mathbf{2(p-7)(p-14)}$

Look for a pattern in each table of values to determine which kind of model best describes the data. (Lesson 9-6)

53.

x	0	1	2	3	4
y	4	5	6	7	8

linear

54.

x	1	2	3	4	5
y	2	4	8	16	32

exponential

55.

x	−3	−2	−1	0	1
y	14	9	6	5	6

quadratic

56.

x	3	4	5	6	7
y	3	5	7	9	11

linear

57. GENETICS Brown genes B are dominant over blue genes b. A person with genes BB or Bb has brown eyes. Someone with genes bb has blue eyes. Mrs. Dunn has brown eyes with genes Bb, and Mr. Dunn has blue eyes. Write an expression for the possible eye coloring of their children. Then find the probability that a child would have blue eyes. (Lesson 8-4) $\mathbf{0.5Bb + 0.5b^2; \frac{1}{2}}$

Solve each inequality. Check your solution. (Lesson 5-2)

58. $\frac{b}{10} \leq 5$ $\mathbf{\{b \mid b \leq 50\}}$

59. $-7 > -\frac{r}{7}$ $\mathbf{\{r \mid r > 49\}}$

60. $\frac{5}{8}y \geq -15$ $\mathbf{\{y \mid y \geq -24\}}$

Skills Review

Determine the probability of each event if you randomly select a marble from a bag containing 9 red marbles, 6 blue marbles, and 5 yellow marbles.

61. P(blue) **0.3**

62. P(red) **0.45**

63. P(not yellow) **0.75**

Differentiated Instruction OL BL

Extension Solve $\frac{a}{x} = \frac{2}{3}$ for x in terms of a. $x = \frac{3a}{2}$

EXTEND 11-8 Graphing Technology Lab
Solving Rational Equations

You can use TI-Nspire Technology to solve rational equations by graphing, by using tables, and by using a computer algebra system (CAS).

Process Standards
PS.5

To solve by graphing, graph both sides of the equation and locate the point(s) of intersection.

Activity 1 Solve a Rational Equation by Graphing

Solve $\frac{5}{x+2} = \frac{3}{x}$ by graphing.

Step 1 Add a new **Graphs** page.

Step 2 Use the **Window Settings** option from the **Window/Zoom** menu to adjust the window to −20 to 20 for both x and y. Set both scales to 2.

Step 3 Enter $\frac{5}{x+2}$ into **f1(*x*)** and $\frac{3}{x}$ into **f2(*x*)**.

Step 4 Change the thickness of the graph of **f1(*x*)** by selecting the graph of **f1(*x*)** and the **ctrl menu Attributes** option.

Step 5 Use the **Intersection Point(s)** tool from the **Points & Lines** menu to find the intersection of the two graphs. Select the graph of **f1(*x*) enter** and then the graph of **f2(*x*) enter**.

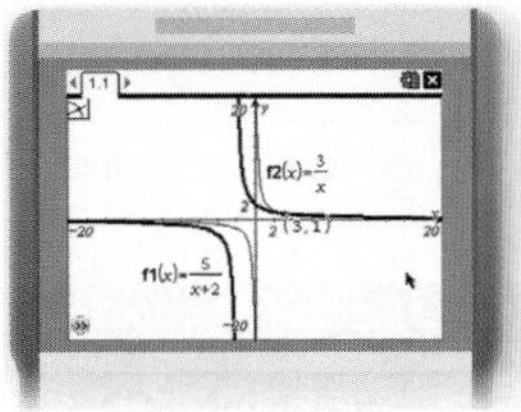

[−20, 20] scl: 2 by [−20, 20] scl: 2

The graphs intersect at (3, 1). This means that $\frac{5}{x+2}$ and $\frac{3}{x}$ both equal 1 when $x = 3$. Thus, the solution of $\frac{5}{x+2} = \frac{3}{x}$ is $x = 3$.

Exercises

Use a graphing calculator to solve each equation.

1. $\frac{5}{x} + \frac{4}{x} = 10$ **$\frac{9}{10}$**
2. $\frac{12}{x} + \frac{3}{4} = \frac{3}{2}$ **16**
3. $\frac{6}{x} + \frac{3}{2x} = 12$ **$\frac{5}{8}$**
4. $\frac{4}{x} + \frac{3}{4x} = \frac{1}{8}$ **38**
5. $\frac{4}{x} + \frac{x-2}{2x} = x$ **$-\frac{3}{2}$ or 2**
6. $\frac{3}{3x-2} + \frac{5}{x} = 0$ **$\frac{5}{9}$**
7. $\frac{2x+1}{2} + \frac{3}{2x} = \frac{2}{x}$ **−1 or $\frac{1}{2}$**
8. $\frac{x}{x+2} + x = \frac{5x+8}{x+2}$ **4**
9. $\frac{1}{2x} + \frac{5}{x} = \frac{3}{x-1}$ **$\frac{11}{5}$**
10. $\frac{4x-3}{x-2} + \frac{2x+5}{x-2} = 6$ **no solution**

1 Focus

Objective Use graphing technology to solve rational equations.

Materials

- TI-Nspire Technology

Teaching Tips

- For Activity 1 step 3, remind students that to enter $\frac{5}{x+2}$, they will need to put parentheses around the denominator. Then they will need to use the **tab** key to move the curser to the entry line to type $\frac{3}{x}$ into ***f2(x)***.
- When changing the windows settings, use the **tab** key to move from one field to another.
- A spreadsheet program can also be used to complete Activity 2.
- For Activity 3, remind students that they cannot edit a line once they press **enter**. However, they can use **ctrl c** and **ctrl x** to copy and paste a line, and then make edits.

2 Teach

Working in Cooperative Groups

Divide the class into pairs. Work through Activity 1 as a class. Then ask students to work with their partners to complete Exercises 1 to 10 and Activities 2 and 3.

Practice Have students complete Exercises 11 to 15.

3 Assess

Tips for New Teachers

Using Tables Point out to students that the table method only works when their table includes the x-value(s) of the solution(s). If a solution is not found with a table with integer values of x, students should adjust their x-values or use another method to find any solutions.

Formative Assessment

Use Exercises 16–19 to assess each student's knowledge of solving rational equations.

From Concrete to Abstract

Ask students to summarize the use of technology to find the solutions to rational equations.

Graphing Technology Lab
Solving Rational Equations *Continued*

Activity 2 Solve a Rational Equation by Using a Table

Solve $\frac{2x+1}{3} = \frac{x+2}{2}$ using a table.

Step 1 Add a new **Lists & Spreadsheet** page.

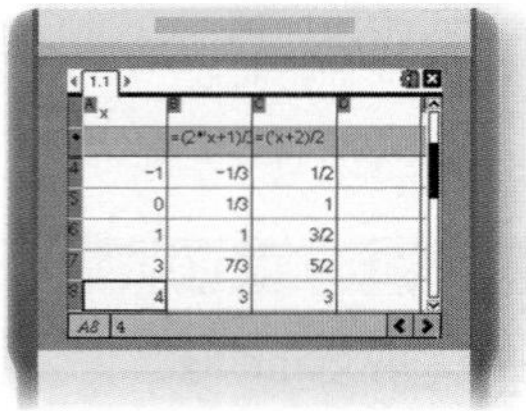

Step 2 Label column A as x. Enter values from −4 to 4 in cells A1 to A9.

Step 3 In column B in the formula row, enter the left side of the rational equation, with parenthesis around the binomials. In column C in the formula row, enter the right side of the rational equation, with parenthesis around the binomials. Specify **Variable Reference** when prompted.

Scroll until you see where the values in Columns B and C are equal. This occurs at $x = 4$. Therefore the solution of $\frac{2x+1}{3} = \frac{x+2}{2}$ is 4.

You can also use a computer algebra system (CAS) to solve rational equations.

Activity 3 Solve a Rational Equation by Using a CAS

Solve $\frac{x-3}{x} - \frac{x-4}{x-2} = \frac{1}{x}$ using a CAS.

Step1 Add a new **Calculator** page.

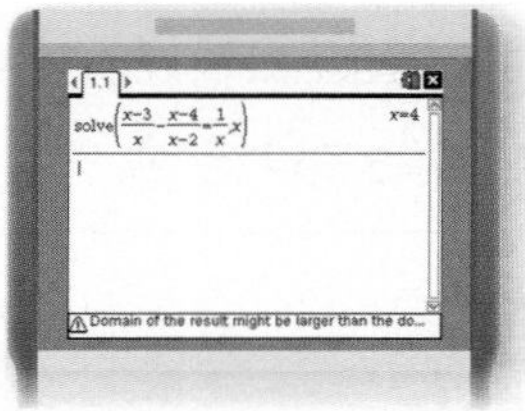

Step 2 To solve, select the **Solve** tool from the **Algebra** menu. Enter the left side of the equation with parenthesis around the binomials. Enter = and the right side of the equation. Then type a comma, followed by x, and then **enter**.

The solution of 4 is displayed.

Exercises

Use a table or CAS to solve each equation.

11. $\frac{2}{x} + \frac{2+x}{2} = \frac{x+3}{2}$ **4**
12. $\frac{4}{x-2} = -\frac{1}{x+3}$ **−2**
13. $\frac{3}{x+2} + \frac{4}{x-1} = 0$ **$-\frac{5}{7}$**
14. $\frac{1}{x+1} + \frac{2}{x-1} = 0$ **$-\frac{1}{3}$**
15. $\frac{2}{x+4} + \frac{4}{x-1} = 0$ **$-\frac{7}{3}$**
16. $\frac{1}{x-2} + \frac{x+2}{4} = 2x$ **0 or $\frac{16}{7}$**
17. $\frac{2x}{x+3} + \frac{x+1}{2} = x$ **−1 or 3**
18. $\frac{2}{x-3} + \frac{3}{x-2} = \frac{4}{x}$ **$\frac{-7 \pm \sqrt{145}}{2}$**
19. $\frac{x^2}{x+1} + \frac{x}{x-1} = x$ **0**

CHAPTER 11 Study Guide and Review

Study Guide

KeyConcepts

Inverse Variation (Lesson 11-1)

- You can use $\frac{x_1}{x_2} = \frac{y_2}{y_1}$ to solve problems involving inverse variation.

Rational Functions (Lesson 11-2)

- Excluded values are values of a variable that result in a denominator of zero.
- If vertical asymptotes occur, it will be at excluded values.

Rational Expressions (Lessons 11-3 and 11-4)

- Multiplying rational expressions is similar to multiplying rational numbers.
- Divide rational expressions by multiplying by the reciprocal of the divisor.

Dividing Polynomials (Lesson 11-5)

- To divide a polynomial by a monomial, divide each term of the polynomial by the monomial.

Adding and Subtracting Rational Expressions (Lesson 11-6)

- Rewrite rational expressions with unlike denominators using the least common denominator (LCD). Then add or subtract.

Complex Fractions (Lesson 11-7)

- Simplify complex fractions by writing them as division problems.

Solving Rational Equations (Lesson 11-8)

- Use cross products to solve rational equations with a single fraction on each side of the equals sign.

FOLDABLES StudyOrganizer

Be sure the Key Concepts are noted in your Foldable.

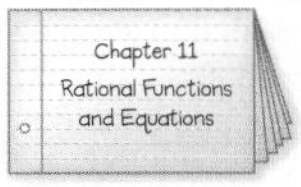

KeyVocabulary

asymptote (p. 685)
complex fraction (p. 720)
excluded value (p. 684)
extraneous solution (p. 727)
inverse variation (p. 676)
least common denominator (LCD) (p. 714)
least common multiple (LCM) (p. 713)
mixed expression (p. 720)
product rule (p. 677)
rate problems (p. 729)
rational equation (p. 726)
rational expression (p. 690)
rational function (p. 684)
work problems (p. 728)

VocabularyCheck

State whether each sentence is *true* or *false*. If *false*, replace the underlined word, phrase, expression, or number to make a true sentence.

1. The least common multiple for $x^2 - 25$ and $x - 5$ is <u>$x - 5$</u>. **false; $x^2 - 25$**
2. If the product of two variables is a nonzero constant, the relationship is an <u>inverse variation</u>. **true**
3. If the line $x = a$ is a vertical <u>asymptote</u> of a rational function, then a is an excluded value. **true**
4. A rational expression is a fraction in which the numerator and denominator are <u>fractions</u>. **false; polynomials**
5. The excluded values for $\frac{x}{x^2 + 5x + 6}$ are <u>-2 and -3</u>. **true**
6. The equation $\frac{3x}{x-2} = \frac{6}{x-2}$ has an extraneous solution, <u>2</u>. **true**
7. A <u>rational expression</u> has one or more fractions in the numerator and denominator. **false; complex fraction**
8. The expression $\frac{\frac{1}{2}}{\frac{3}{4}}$ can be simplified to <u>$\frac{2}{3}$</u>. **true**
9. A <u>direct variation</u> can be represented by an equation of the form $k = xy$, where k is a nonzero constant. **false; inverse variation**
10. The rational function $y = \frac{2}{x-1} + 3$ has a horizontal asymptote at <u>$y = 3$</u>. **true**

Formative Assessment

KeyVocabulary The page references after each word denote where that term was first introduced. If students have difficulty answering questions 1–10, remind them that they can use these page references to refresh their memories about the vocabulary.

Summative Assessment

Vocabulary Test, p. 60

Vocabulary Review

Vocabulary Review provides students the opportunity to check their understanding of important concepts and terminology in an online game format.

FOLDABLES StudyOrganizer

Dinah Zike's Foldables®

Have students look through the chapter to make sure they have included examples in their Foldables for each lesson of the chapter. Suggest that students keep their Foldables handy while completing the Study Guide and Review pages. Point out that their Foldables can serve as a quick review when studying for the chapter test.

Lesson-by-Lesson Review

Intervention If the given examples are not sufficient to review the topics covered by the questions, remind students that the lesson references tell them where to review that topic in their textbook.

Two-Day Option Have students complete the Lesson-by-Lesson Review. Then you can use McGraw-Hill eAssessment to customize another review worksheet that practices all the objectives of this chapter or only the objectives on which your students need more help.

Additional Answer

19.

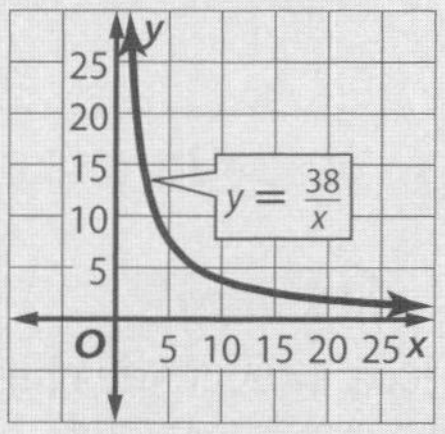

The vertical asymptote is at $x = 0$ and the horizontal asymptote is at $y = 0$.

CHAPTER 11 Study Guide and Review *Continued*

Lesson-by-Lesson Review

11-1 Inverse Variation

Solve. Assume that y varies inversely as x.

11. If $y = 4$ when $x = 1$, find x when $y = 12$ $\frac{1}{3}$

12. If $y = -1$ when $x = -3$, find y when $x = -9$ $-\frac{1}{3}$

13. If $y = 1.5$ when $x = 6$, find y when $x = -16$ $-\frac{9}{16}$

14. **PHYSICS** A 135-pound person sits 5 feet from the center of a seesaw. How far from the center should a 108-pound person sit to balance the seesaw? **6.25 ft or 6 ft 3 in.**

Example 1

If y varies inversely as x and $y = 28$ when $x = 42$, find y when $x = 56$.

Let $x_1 = 42$, $x_2 = 56$, and $y_1 = 28$. Solve for y_2.

$\frac{x_1}{x_2} = \frac{y_2}{y_1}$ Proportion for inverse variation

$\frac{42}{56} = \frac{y_2}{28}$ Substitution

$1176 = 56y_2$ Cross multiply.

$21 = y_2$

Thus, $y = 21$ when $x = 56$.

11-2 Rational Functions

State the excluded value for each function.

15. $y = \frac{1}{x-3}$ 3

16. $y = \frac{2}{2x-5}$ $\frac{5}{2}$

17. $y = \frac{3}{3x-6}$ 2

18. $y = \frac{-1}{2x+8}$ -4

19. **PIZZA PARTY** Katelyn ordered pizza and soda for her study group for \$38. The cost per person y is given by $y = \frac{38}{x}$, where x is the number of people in the study group. Graph the function and describe the asymptotes. **See margin.**

Example 2

State the excluded value for the function $y = \frac{1}{4x+16}$.

Set the denominator equal to zero.

$4x + 16 = 0$

$4x + 16 - 16 = 0 - 16$ Subtract 16 from each side.

$4x = -16$ Simplify.

$x = -4$ Divide each side by 4.

11-3 Simplifying Rational Expressions

Simplify each expression.

20. $\frac{2xy^2}{16xyz}$ $\frac{y}{8z}$

21. $\frac{x+4}{x^2+12x+32}$ $\frac{1}{x+8}$

22. $\frac{x^2+10x+21}{x^3+x^2-42x}$ $\frac{x+3}{x(x-6)}$

23. $\frac{y^2-25}{y^2+3y-10}$ $\frac{y-5}{y-2}$

24. $\frac{3x^3}{3x^3+6x^2}$ $\frac{x}{x+2}$

25. $\frac{4y^2}{8y^4+16y^3}$ $\frac{1}{2y(y+2)}$

State the excluded values for each function.

26. $y = \frac{x}{x^2+9x+18}$ $-6, -3$

27. $y = \frac{10}{6x^2+7x-3}$ $-\frac{3}{2}, \frac{1}{3}$

Example 3

Simplify $\frac{a^2-7a+12}{a^2-13a+36}$.

Factor and simplify.

$\frac{a^2-7a+12}{a^2-13a+36} = \frac{(a-3)(a-4)}{(a-9)(a-4)}$ Factor.

$= \frac{a-3}{a-9}$ Simplify.

736 | Chapter 11 | Study Guide and Review

11-4 Multiplying and Dividing Rational Expressions

Find each product or quotient.

28. $\frac{6x^2y^4}{12} \cdot \frac{3x^3y^2}{xy}$ $\frac{3x^4y^5}{2}$

29. $\frac{3x-6}{x^2-9} \cdot \frac{x+3}{x^2-2x}$ $\frac{3}{x^2-3x}$

30. $\frac{x^2}{x+4} \div \frac{3x}{x^2-16}$ $\frac{x(x-4)}{3}$

31. $\frac{3b-12}{b+4} \div (b^2-6b+8)$ $\frac{3}{(b+4)(b-2)}$

32. $\frac{2a^2+7a-15}{a+5} \div \frac{9a^2-4}{3a+2}$ $\frac{2a-3}{3a-2}$

33. **GEOMETRY** Find the area of the rectangle shown. Write the answer in simplest form. xy

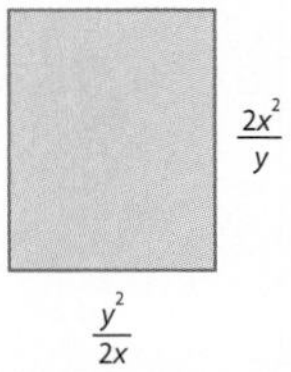

Example 4

Find $\frac{7b^2}{9} \cdot \frac{6a^2}{b}$.

$\frac{7b^2}{9} \cdot \frac{6a^2}{b} = \frac{42a^2b^2}{9b}$ Multiply.

$= \frac{14a^2b}{3}$ Simplify.

Example 5

Find $\frac{x^2-25}{x^2-9} \div \frac{x+5}{x-3}$.

$\frac{x^2-25}{x^2-9} \div \frac{x+5}{x-3} = \frac{(x+5)(x-5)}{(x+3)(x-3)} \div \frac{x+5}{x-3}$ Factor.

$= \frac{\overset{1}{\cancel{(x+5)}}(x-5)}{(x+3)\underset{1}{\cancel{(x-3)}}} \cdot \frac{\overset{1}{\cancel{x-3}}}{\underset{1}{\cancel{x+5}}}$ Multiply by the reciprocal.

$= \frac{x-5}{x+3}$ Simplify.

11-5 Dividing Polynomials

Find each quotient.

34. $(x^3-2x^2-22x+21) \div (x-3)$ $x^2+x-19-\frac{36}{x-3}$

35. $(x^3+7x^2+10x-6) \div (x+3)$ x^2+4x-2

36. $(5x^2y^2-10x^2y+5xy) \div 5xy$ $xy-2x+1$

37. $(48y^2+8y+7) \div (12y-1)$ $4y+1+\frac{8}{12y-1}$

38. **GEOMETRY** The area of a rectangle is $x^2+7x+13$. If the length is $(x+4)$, what is the width of the rectangle? $x+3+\frac{1}{x+4}$

Example 6

Find $(4x^2+17x-1) \div (4x+1)$.

$$\begin{array}{r} x+4 \\ 4x+1\overline{)4x^2+17x-1} \\ \underline{4x^2+x} \\ 16x-1 \\ \underline{16x+4} \\ -5 \end{array}$$

Multiply x and $4x+1$.
Subtract, bring down -1.
Multiply 4 and $4x+1$.
Subtract.

The quotient is $x+4-\frac{5}{4x+1}$.

11-6 Adding and Subtracting Rational Expressions

Find each sum or difference.

39. $\frac{5a}{b} - \frac{2a}{b}$ $\frac{3a}{b}$

40. $\frac{-3}{2n-3} + \frac{2n}{2n-3}$ 1

41. $\frac{3}{y+1} - \frac{y}{y-3}$

42. $\frac{1}{x+1} + \frac{3}{x-2}$

43. **DESIGN** Miguel is decorating a model of a room that is $\frac{2x}{x+4}$ feet long and $\frac{8}{x+4}$ feet wide. What is the perimeter of the room? 4 ft

41. $\frac{-y^2+2y-9}{(y+1)(y-3)}$

42. $\frac{4x+1}{(x+1)(x-2)}$

Example 7

Find $\frac{x^2}{x+1} + \frac{2x+1}{x+1}$.

$\frac{x^2}{x+1} + \frac{2x+1}{x+1} = \frac{x^2+2x+1}{x+1}$ Add the numerators.

$= \frac{(x+1)(x+1)}{x+1}$ Factor.

$= x+1$ Simplify.

connectED.mcgraw-hill.com 737

Anticipation Guide

Have students complete the Chapter 11 Anticipation Guide and discuss how their responses have changed now that they have completed Chapter 11.

CHAPTER 11 Study Guide and Review *Continued*

11-7 Mixed Expressions and Complex Fractions

Simplify each expression.

44. $\dfrac{\frac{a^2b^4}{c}}{\frac{a^3b}{c^2}}$ $\frac{b^3c}{a}$

45. $\dfrac{x-\frac{35}{x+2}}{x+\frac{42}{x+13}}$ $\frac{x^2+8x-65}{x^2+8x+12}$

46. $\dfrac{\frac{x^2-25}{x+2}}{\frac{x-5}{x^2-4}}$ $(x+5)(x-2)$

47. $\dfrac{y+9-\frac{6}{y+4}}{y+4+\frac{2}{y+1}}$ $\frac{y^2+11y+10}{y^2+6y+8}$

48. **FABRICS** Donna makes sets of three different sized tablecloths to sell. A small one takes one-half yard of fabric, a medium one takes five-eighths yard, and a large one takes one and one-quarter yards.

 a. How many yards of fabric does she need to make a tablecloth of each size? $2\frac{3}{8}$ yd

 b. If Donna can make a tablecloth of each size in 38 minutes, what is the average rate of fabric she uses in yards per hour?

Example 8

Simplify $\dfrac{\frac{x+3}{6}}{\frac{x^2-2x-15}{x}}$.

Write as a division expression.

$$\dfrac{\frac{x+3}{6}}{\frac{x^2-2x-15}{x}} = \frac{x+3}{6} \div \frac{x^2-2x-15}{x}$$
$$= \frac{x+3}{6} \cdot \frac{x}{x^2-2x-15}$$
$$= \frac{x+3}{6} \cdot \frac{x}{(x+3)(x-5)}$$
$$= \frac{x}{6(x-5)}$$

48b. 3.75 yds/hr

11-8 Rational Equations

Solve each equation. State any extraneous solutions.

49. $\frac{5n}{6}+\frac{1}{n-2}=\frac{n+1}{3(n-2)}$ $\frac{2}{5}$, extraneous: 2

50. $\frac{4x}{3}+\frac{7}{2}=\frac{7x}{12}-14$ $-\frac{70}{3}$

51. $\frac{11}{2x}+\frac{2}{4x}=\frac{1}{4}$ 24

52. $\frac{1}{x+4}-\frac{1}{x-1}=\frac{2}{x^2+3x-4}$ no solution

53. $\frac{1}{n-2}=\frac{n}{8}$ −2, 4

54. **PAINTING** Anne can paint a room in 6 hours. Oljay can paint a room in 4 hours. How long will it take them to paint the room working together? $\frac{12}{5}$ or $2\frac{2}{5}$ hours

Example 9

Solve $\frac{3}{x^2+3x}+\frac{x+2}{x+3}=\frac{1}{x}$.

$$\frac{3}{x^2+3x}+\frac{x+2}{x+3}=\frac{1}{x}$$
$$x(x+3)\left(\frac{3}{x(x+3)}\right)+x(x+3)\left(\frac{x+2}{x+3}\right)=x(x+3)\left(\frac{1}{x}\right)$$
$$3+x(x+2)=1(x+3)$$
$$3+x^2+2x=x+3$$
$$x^2+x=0$$
$$x(x+1)=0$$
$$x=0 \text{ or } x=-1$$

The solution is −1, and there is an extraneous solution of 0.

738 | Chapter 11 | Study Guide and Review

CHAPTER 11 Practice Test

Determine whether each table represents an inverse variation. Explain.

1.

x	y
2	10
4	12
8	14

No; the products are not the same.

2.

x	y
2	2
4	1
8	$\frac{1}{2}$

yes; $y = \frac{4}{x}$

Find each product or quotient.

3. $\frac{(x+6)(x-2)}{x^3} \cdot \frac{7x^2}{x-3}$ $\frac{7(x+6)(x-2)}{x(x-3)}$

4. $\frac{(x+3)}{y^2} \div \frac{x^2-9}{y}$ $\frac{1}{y(x-3)}$

Solve. Assume that y varies inversely as x.

5. If $y = 3$ when $x = 9$, find x when $y = 1$. 27

6. If $y = 2$ when $x = 0.5$, find y when $x = 3$. $\frac{1}{3}$

Simplify each expression. State the excluded values of the variables.

7. $\frac{z-6}{z^2-3z-18}$ $\frac{1}{z+3}$; $-3, 6$

8. $\frac{4x-28}{x^2-49}$ $\frac{4}{x+7}$; $-7, 7$

9. **MULTIPLE CHOICE** The area of a rectangle is $x^2 + 5x + 6$ square feet. If the width is $x + 2$, what is the length of the rectangle? B

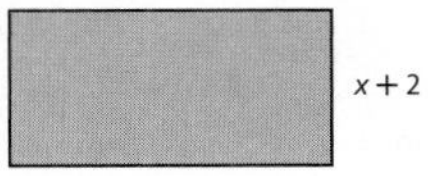

A $x + 2$

B $x + 3$

C 1

D 3

12. $\frac{a-3}{(a+1)(a+4)}$

13. $\frac{(y+4)(2y-5)}{(y+3)(3y-1)}$

Simplify each expression.

10. $\frac{2\frac{1}{3}}{3\frac{1}{2}}$ $\frac{2}{3}$

11. $\frac{\frac{x^2-25}{x-2}}{\frac{x-5}{x-2}}$ $x + 5$

12. $\frac{\frac{a-4}{a^2+6a+8}}{\frac{a^2-3a-4}{a^2-a-6}}$

13. $\frac{\frac{y^2+10y+24}{y^2-9}}{\frac{3y^2+17y-6}{2y^2-11y+15}}$

Find each quotient.

14. $(2x^2 + 10x) \div 2x$ $x + 5$

15. $(4x^2 - 8x + 5) \div (2x + 1)$ $2x - 5 + \frac{10}{2x+1}$

16. $(3x^2 - 14x - 3) \div (x - 5)$ $3x + 1 + \frac{2}{x-5}$

Assume that y varies inversely as x. Write an inverse variation equation that relates x and y.

17. $y = 2$ when $x = 8$ $y = \frac{16}{x}$

18. $y = -3$ when $x = 1$ $y = -\frac{3}{x}$

Find each sum or difference.

19. $\frac{15}{x} - \frac{6}{x}$ $\frac{9}{x}$

20. $\frac{t-5}{t-6} + \frac{t+8}{t-6}$ $\frac{2t+3}{t-6}$

21. $\frac{1}{x-6} + \frac{3}{x-2}$ $\frac{4x-20}{(x-6)(x-2)}$

22. $\frac{2x^2+8x+5}{x^2-2x-24} - \frac{x}{x-6}$ $\frac{x^2+4x+5}{x^2-2x-24}$

State the excluded value or values for each function.

23. $y = \frac{6}{x-1}$ 1

24. $y = \frac{5}{x^2-5x-24}$ $-3, 8$

Identify the asymptotes of each function.

25. $y = \frac{2}{(x-4)(x+2)}$ $x = 4$, $x = -2$, $y = 0$

26. $y = \frac{4}{x^2+3x-28} + 2$ $x = 4$, $x = -7$, $y = 2$

27. **MULTIPLE CHOICE** Lee can shovel the driveway in 3 hours, and Susan can shovel the driveway in 2 hours. How long will it take them working together? J

F 6 hours

G 5 hours

H $\frac{3}{2}$ hours

J $\frac{6}{5}$ hours

28. **PAINTING** Sydney can paint a 60-square foot wall in 40 minutes. Working with her friend Cleveland, the two of them can paint the wall in 25 minutes. How long would it take Cleveland to do the job himself? $\frac{10}{9}$ or $1\frac{1}{9}$ hours

Summative Assessment

Use these alternate leveled chapter tests to differentiate assessment for your students.

Leveled Chapter 11 Tests

Form	Type	Level	Page(s)
1	MC	AL	61–62
2A	MC	OL	63–64
2B	MC	OL	65–66
2C	FR	OL	67–68
2D	FR	OL	69–70
3	FR	BL	71–72
Vocabulary Test			60
Extended-Response Test			73

MC = multiple-choice questions
FR = free-response questions

McGraw-Hill eAssessment Customize and create multiple versions of your chapter test and their answer keys. All of the questions from the leveled chapter tests in the *Chapter 11 Resource Masters* are also available on McGraw-Hill eAssessment.

InterventionPlanner

Tier 1 On Level OL

If students miss about 25% of the exercises or less,

Then choose a resource:

SE Lessons 11-1, 11-2, 11-3, 11-4, 11-5, 11-6, 11-7, 11-8

Skills Practice, pp. 7, 13, 19, 25, 32, 38, 44 and 50

TE Chapter Project

connectED.mcgraw-hill.com Self-Check Quiz

Tier 2 Strategic Intervention AL
approaching grade level

If students miss about 50% of the exercises,

Then choose a resource:

Study Guide and Intervention, Chapter 11, pp. 5, 11, 17, 23, 30, 36, 42 and 48

Quick Review Math Handbook

connectED.mcgraw-hill.com Extra Examples, Personal Tutor, Homework Help

Tier 3 Intensive Intervention
2 or more grades below level

If students miss about 75% of the exercises,

Then use *Math Triumphs, Alg. 1*

connectED.mcgraw-hill.com Extra Examples, Personal Tutor, Homework Help, Review Vocabulary

1 Focus

Objective Use the strategy of modeling with an equation to solve standardized test problems.

2 Teach

Scaffolding Questions

Ask:

- What are the benefits of using an equation to model a situation? Sample answer: The equation can help you see the relationship between the parts of a complex problem.
- What do you look for when you are solving a problem that can be modeled by an equation? Sample answer: Unknown and known quantities and words to show how they are related

CHAPTER 11

Preparing for Standardized Tests

Model with an Equation

In order to successfully solve some standardized test questions, you will need to be able to write equations to model different situations. Use this lesson to practice solving these types of problems.

Strategies for Modeling with Equations

Step 1

Read the problem statement carefully.

Ask yourself:

- What am I being asked to solve?
- What information is given in the problem?
- What is the unknown quantity that I need to find?

Step 2

Translate the problem statement into an equation.

- Assign a variable to the unknown quantity.
- Write the word sentence as a mathematical number sentence.
- Look for keywords such as *is, is the same as, is equal to,* or *is identical to* that indicate where to place the equals sign.

Step 3

Solve the equation.

- Solve for the unknown in the equation.
- Check your answer to be sure it is reasonable and that it answers the question in the problem statement.

Standardized Test Example

Read the problem. Identify what you need to know. Then use the information in the problem to solve.

It takes Craig 75 minutes to paint a small room. If Delsin can paint the same room in 60 minutes, how long would it take them to paint the room if they work together? Round to the nearest tenth.

A about 33.3 minutes **C** about 45.1 minutes

B about 38.4 minutes **D** about 50.3 minutes

740 | Chapter 11 | Preparing for Standardized Tests

Read the problem carefully. You know how long it takes Craig and Delsin to paint a room individually. Model the situation with an equation to find how long it would take them to paint the room if they work together.

Find the rate that each person works when painting individually.

Craig's rate: $\frac{1 \text{ job}}{75 \text{ minutes}} = \frac{1}{75}$ job per minute

Delsin's rate: $\frac{1 \text{ job}}{60 \text{ minutes}} = \frac{1}{60}$ job per minute

Let t represent the number of minutes it would take them to complete the job working together. Multiply each rate by the time t to represent the portion of the job done by each painter. Add these expressions and set them equal to 1 job. Then solve for t.

Portion that Craig completes	plus	portion that Delsin completes	equals	1 job.
$\frac{1}{75}t$	$+$	$\frac{1}{60}t$	$=$	1

Solve for t:

$\frac{1}{75}t + \frac{1}{60}t = 1$ Original equation

$300\left(\frac{1}{75}t + \frac{1}{60}t\right) = 300(1)$ Multiply each side by the LCD, 300.

$4t + 5t = 300$ Simplify.

$9t = 300$ Combine like terms.

$t \approx 33.3$ Divide each side by 9.

So, it would take Craig and Delsin about 33.3 minutes to paint the room working together. The correct answer is A.

Exercises

Read each problem. Identify what you need to know. Then use the information in the problem to solve.

1. Hana can finish a puzzle in 6 hours, while Eric can finish one in 5 hours. How long would it take them to finish a puzzle together? Round to the nearest tenth. D

   A about 1.8 hours
   B about 2.4 hours
   C about 2.5 hours
   D about 2.7 hours

2. Roberto wants to print 500 flyers for his landscaping business. His printer can complete the job in 35 minutes, and his brother's printer can print them in 45 minutes. How long would it take to print the flyers using both printers? Round to the nearest whole minute. H

   F about 15 minutes
   G about 18 minutes
   H about 20 minutes
   J about 23 minutes

Additional Example

STANDARDIZED TEST PRACTICE
Cody and Alyssa work as lab assistants for a chemistry teacher. If Cody can prepare a lab for a class in 95 minutes and Alyssa can prepare a lab in 80 minutes, how long would it take them to prepare a lab together? Round to the nearest whole minute. A

A about 43 minutes
B about 46 minutes
C about 50 minutes
D about 61 minutes

3 Assess

Use Exercises 1 and 2 to assess students' understanding.

Diagnose Student Errors

Survey student responses for each item. Class trends may indicate common errors and misconceptions.

1. A chose direct variation equation
B chose direct variation equation
C guess
D correct

2. F error in calculating denominator
G error in addition or multiplication and/or dividing by common factor
H error dividing by common factor in denominator
J correct

3. A guess or calculation error
B guess or calculation error
C guess or calculation error
D correct

4. F guess
G correct
H guess
J calculation error

5. A guess
B correct
C guess
D chose the number of bicycles instead of scooters

6. F switched x- and y-variables and made calculation error
G used (240, 14) and (300, 13) to write linear regression equation
H correct
J switched x- and y-variables

CHAPTER 11 Standardized Test Practice

Cumulative, Chapters 1 through 11

Multiple Choice

Read each problem. Then fill in the correct answer on the answer document provided by your teacher or on a sheet of paper.

1. What is the inverse variation equation for the numbers shown in the table? D

x	y
−8	16
−4	32
2	−64
8	−16
16	−8

A $y = -2x$

B $y = 8x$

C $xy = 24$

D $xy = -128$

2. Suppose a square has a side length given by the expression $\frac{x+5}{8x}$. What is the perimeter of the square? J

F $\frac{4x+20}{5x}$

G $\frac{2x+10}{x}$

H $\frac{x+5}{4x}$

J $\frac{x+5}{2x}$

3. Find the length of the hypotenuse if the legs of a right triangle are 2 centimeters and 10 centimeters. D

A 8.1 cm

B 8.5 cm

C 9.6 cm

D 10.2 cm

Test-TakingTip

Question 1 Sometimes you can eliminate answer choices as unreasonable because they do not fit the requirements of the problem. Choices A and B show direct variation equations, so they can be eliminated.

4. In 1990, the population of a country was about 3.66 million people. By 2010, this number had grown to about 4.04 million people. What was the annual rate of change in population from 1990 to 2010? G

F about 15,000 people per year

G about 19,000 people per year

H about 24,000 people per year

J about 38,000 people per year

5. Ricky's Rentals rented 12 more bicycles than scooters last weekend for a total revenue of \$2,125. How many scooters were rented? B

Item	Rental Fee
Bicycle	\$20
Scooter	\$45

A 26

B 29

C 37

D 41

6. The table shows the relationship between calories and fat grams contained in orders of french fries from various restaurants.

Calories	Fat Grams
240	14
280	15
310	16
260	12
340	16
350	18
300	13

Assuming the data can best be described by a linear model, how many fat grams would be expected to be contained in a 315-calorie order of french fries? H

F 12 fat grams

G 13 fat grams

H 16 fat grams

J 8051 fat grams

Short Response/Gridded Response

Record your answers on the answer sheet provided by your teacher or on a sheet of paper.

7. Suppose the first term of a geometric sequence is 3 and the fourth term is 192.

a. What is the common ratio of the sequence? **4**

b. Write an equation that can be used to find the nth term of the sequence. $a_n = 3 \times 4^{n-1}$

c. What is the sixth term of the sequence? **3072**

8. GRIDDED RESPONSE Peggy is having a cement walkway installed around the perimeter of her swimming pool with the dimensions shown below. If $x = 3$ find the area, in square feet, of the pool and walkway. **390**

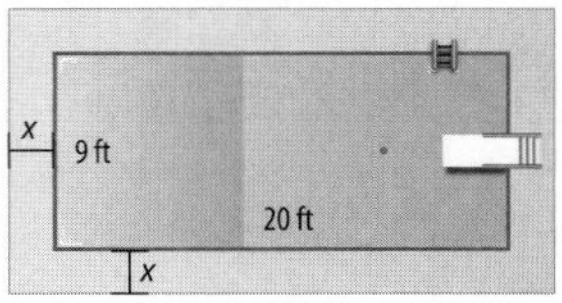

9. Use the equation $y = 2(4 + x)$ to answer each question.

x	y
1	10
2	12
3	14
4	16
5	18
6	20

a. Complete the following table for the different values of x.

b. Plot the points from the table on a coordinate grid. What do you notice about the points?
Check students' graphs. Sample answer: The points lie in a straight line.

10. Jason received a $50 gift certificate for his birthday. He wants to buy a DVD and a poster from a media store. (Assume that sales tax is included in the prices.) Write and solve a linear inequality to show how much he would have left to spend after making these purchases.
$x + 14.95 + 10.99 \leq 50$; $x \leq 24.06$

11. Simplify the complex fraction. Show your work. $\frac{5x+10}{x-6}$

$$\frac{\frac{5}{x-3}}{\frac{x-6}{x^2-x-6}}$$

Extended Response

Record your answers on a sheet of paper. Show your work.

12. Carl's father is building a tool chest that is shaped like a rectangular prism. He wants the tool chest to have a surface area of 62 square feet. The height of the chest will be 1 foot shorter than the width. The length will be 3 feet longer than the height.

a. Sketch a model to represent the problem. **See margin.**

b. Write a polynomial that represents the surface area of the tool chest. $6w^2 + 4w - 4$

c. What are the dimensions of the tool chest?
2 feet high by 3 feet wide by 5 feet long

Need ExtraHelp?

If you missed Question...	1	2	3	4	5	6	7	8	9	10	11	12
Go to Lesson...	11-1	11-6	10-5	3-3	6-2	4-5	7-7	8-3	1-4	5-1	11-7	8-9

Formative Assessment

You can use these pages to benchmark student progress.

Standardized Test Practice, pp. 74–76

Answer Sheet Practice

Have students simulate taking a standardized test by recording their answers on a practice recording sheet.

Student Recording Sheet

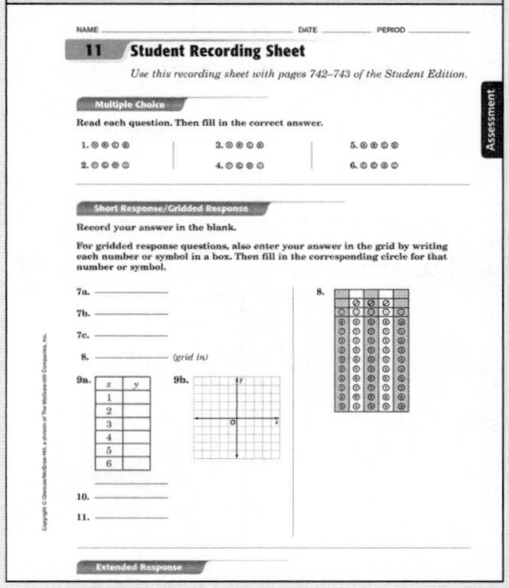

McGraw-Hill eAssessment Create practice tests that align to your state standards, the Common Core State Standards, and other national standards such as TIMSS and NAEP.

Homework Option

Get Ready for Chapter 12 Assign students the exercises on p. 745 as homework to assess whether they possess the prerequisite skills needed for the next chapter.

Additional Answer

12a. Sample answer:

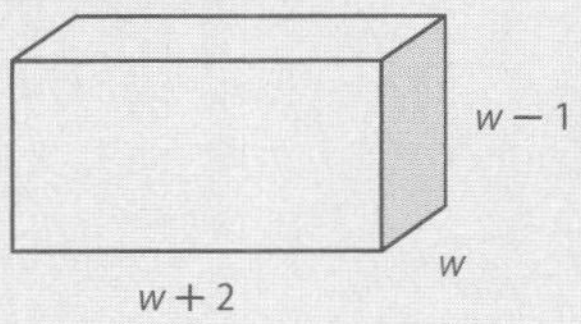

Lesson 11-1

22. $xy = 40$

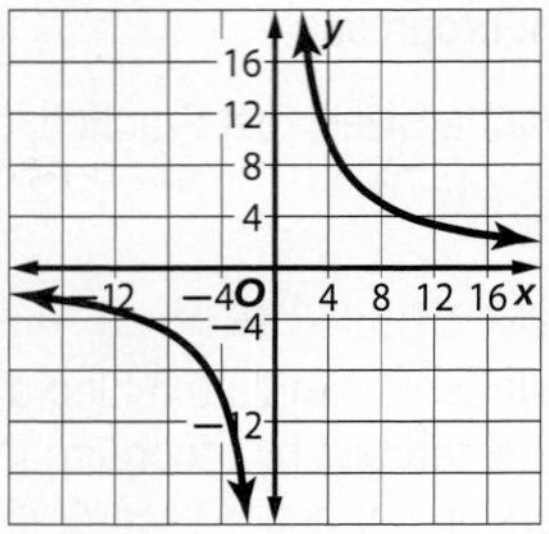

23. $xy = 72$

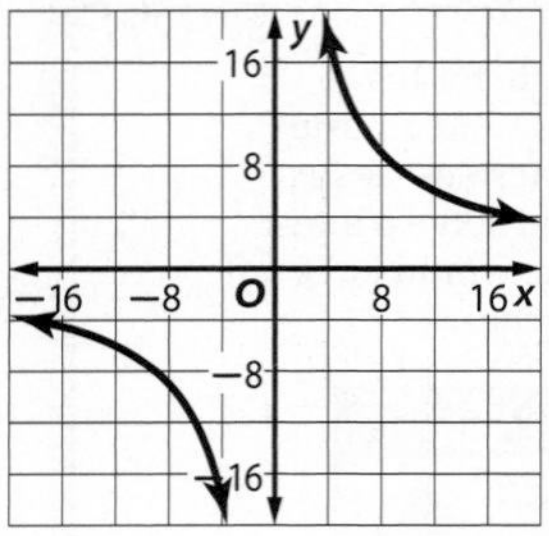

24. $xy = 18$

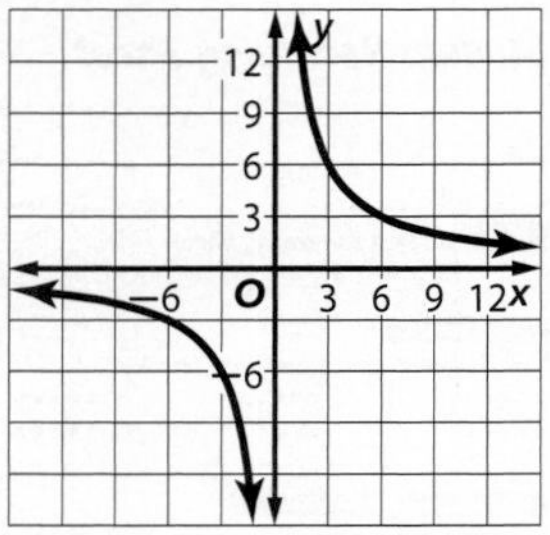

25. $xy = 12$

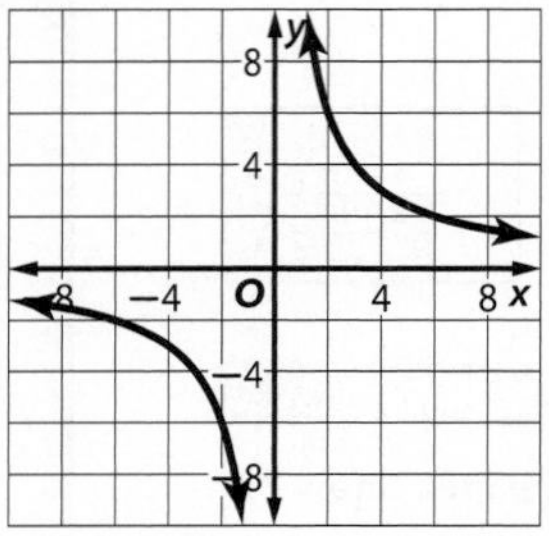

26. $xy = -64$

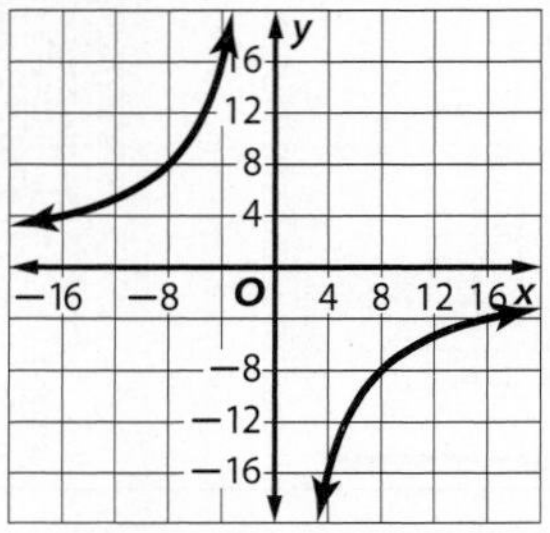

27. $xy = -108$

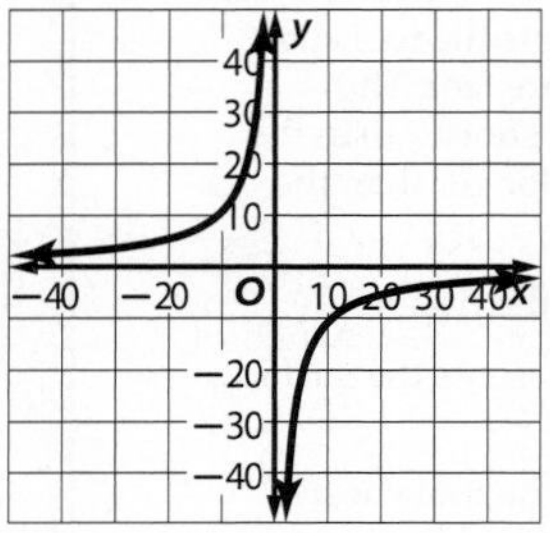

51a.

Hours per Week *h*	Number of Weeks *w*
1	40
2	20
4	10
5	8
8	5
10	4

51c. $hw = 40$ or $w = \frac{40}{h}$

Driving

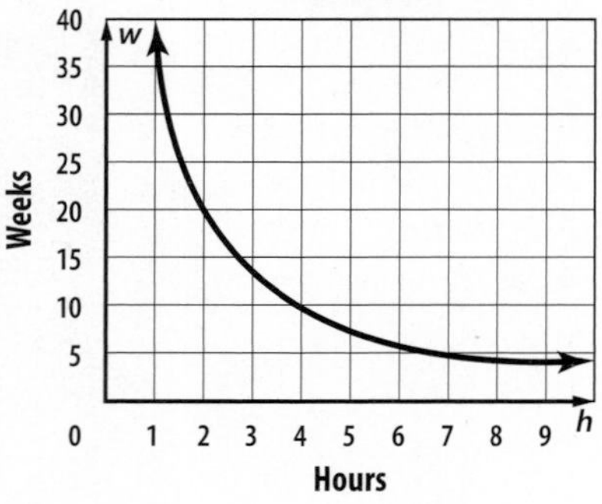

Lesson 11-2 (Guided Practice)

2.

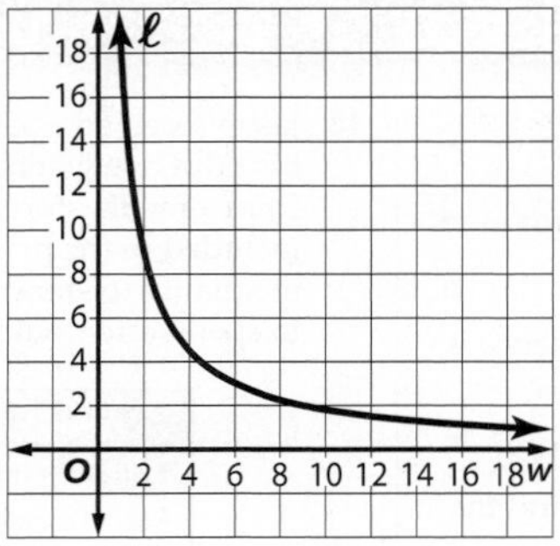

Lesson 11-2

6. $x = 0$; $y = 0$

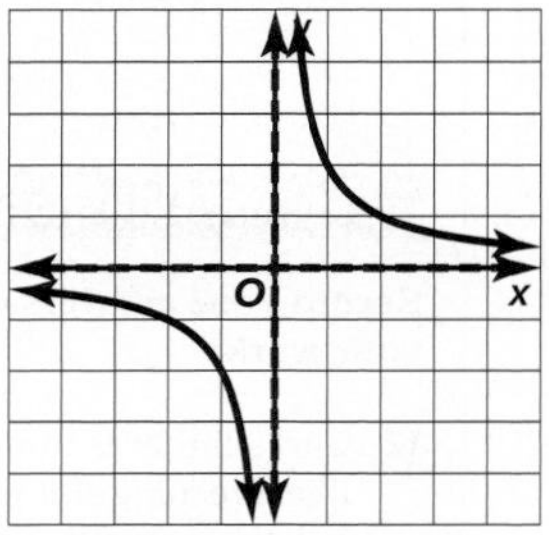

7. $x = 0$; $y = -1$

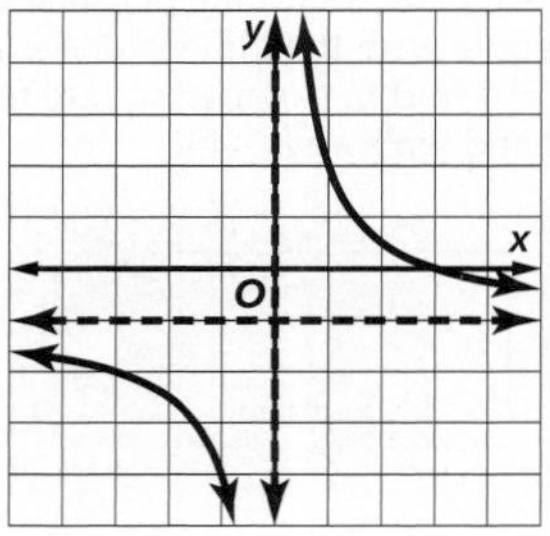

8. $x = 2$; $y = 0$

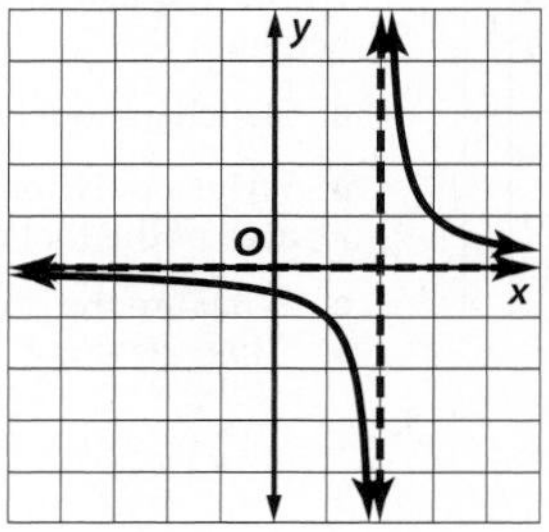

9. $x = -2$; $y = 0$

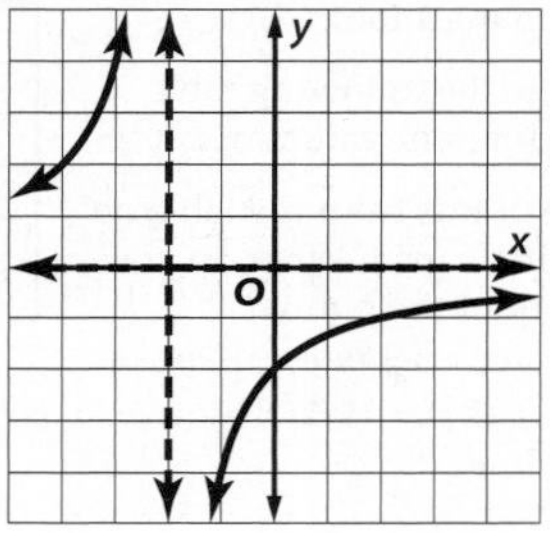

10. $x = 1$; $y = 2$

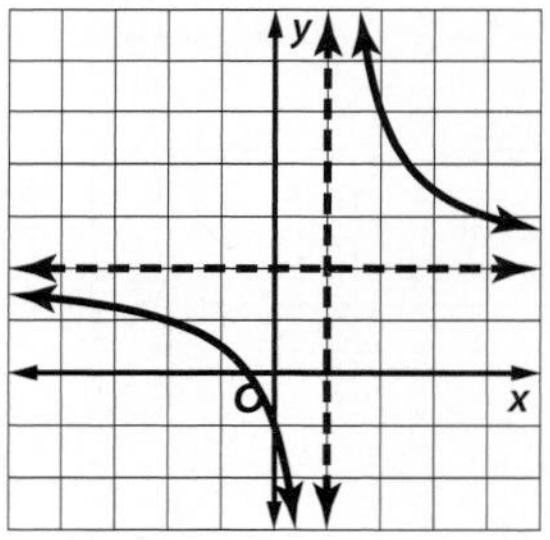

11. $x = -1$; $y = -5$

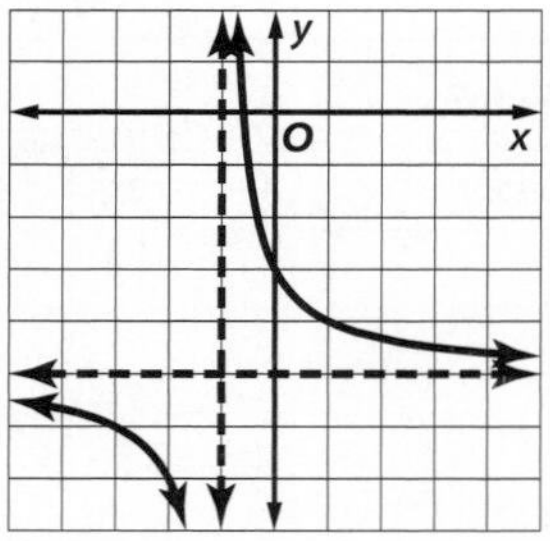

20a.

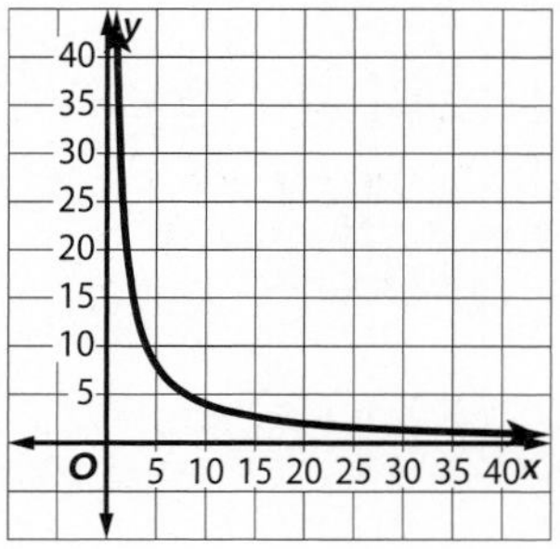

22. $x = 0$; $y = 0$

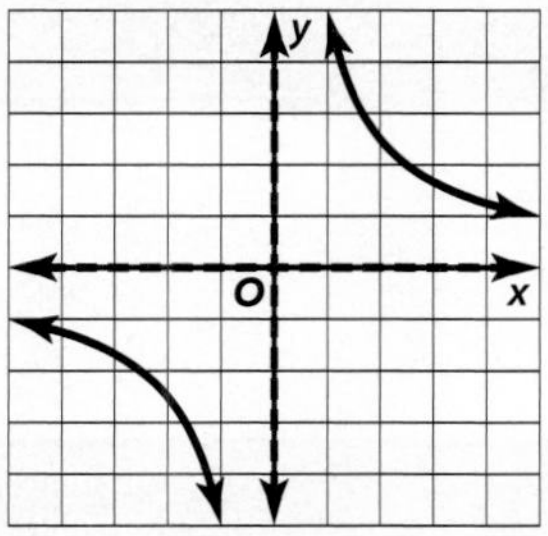

23. $x = 0$; $y = 0$

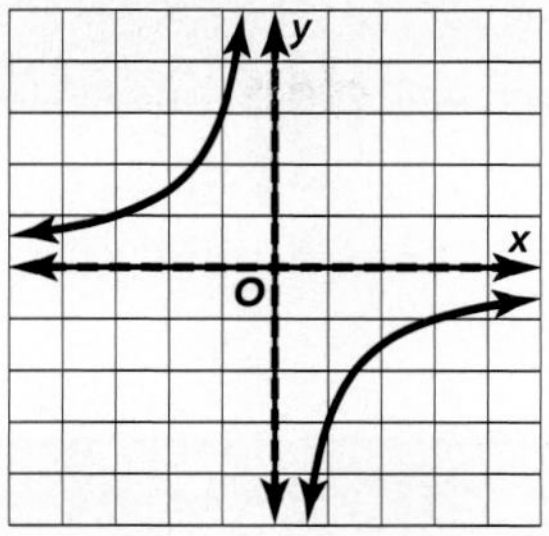

24. $x = 0$; $y = 3$

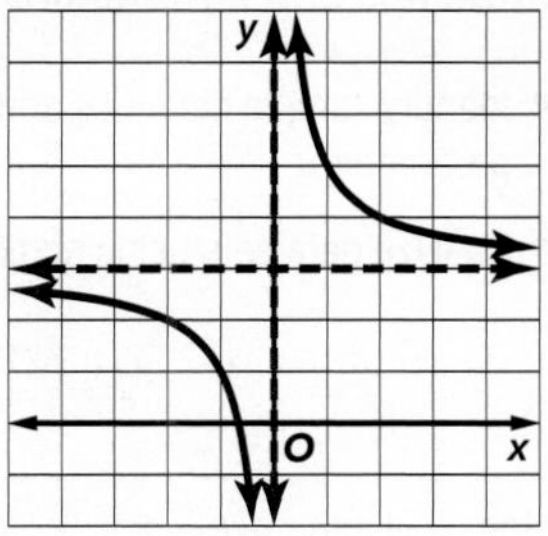

25. $x = 0$; $y = -2$

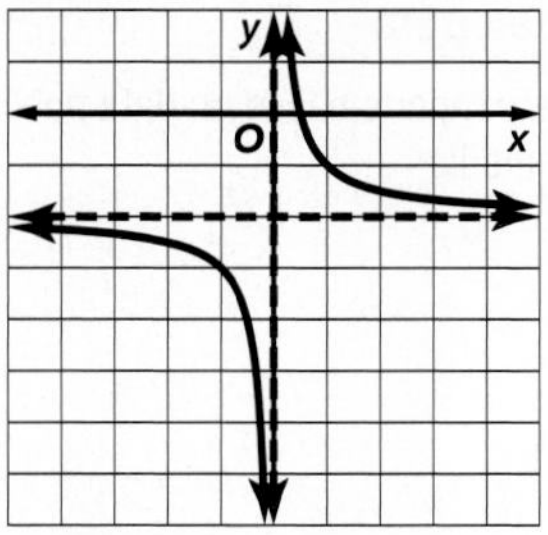

26. $x = -3$; $y = 0$

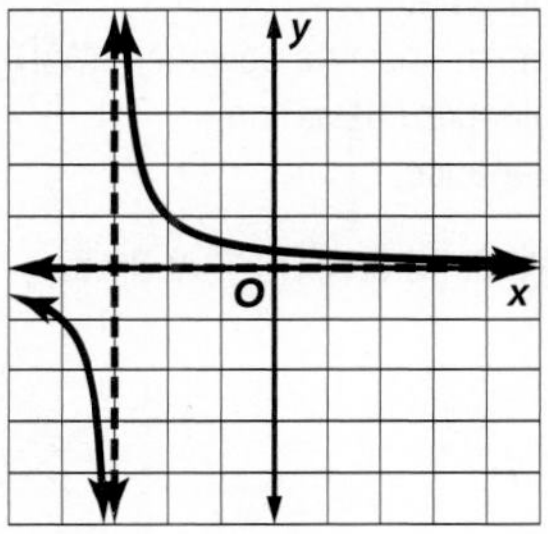

27. $x = 2$; $y = 0$

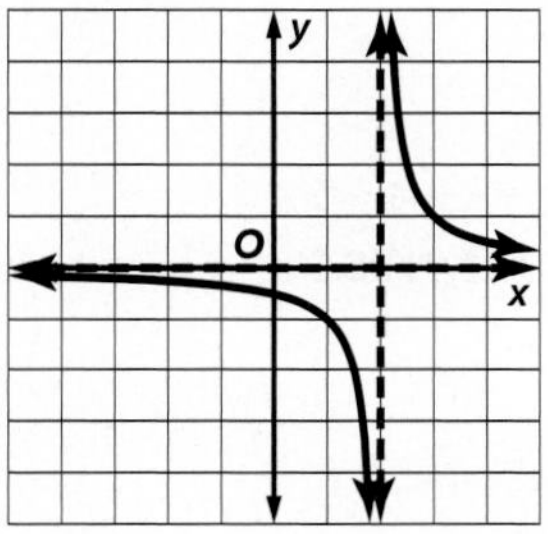

28. $x = -1$; $y = 0$

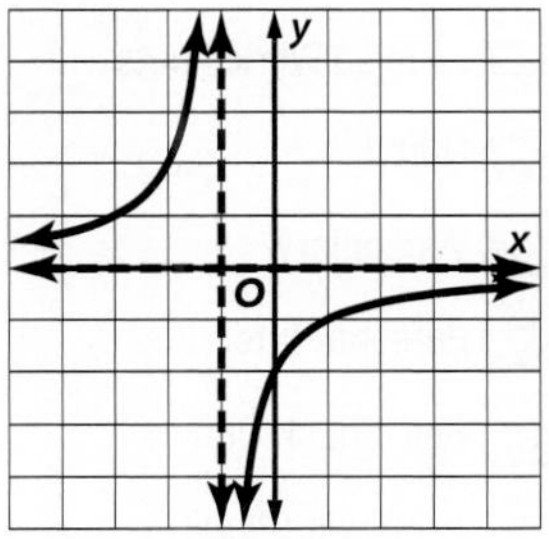

29. $x = 1$; $y = 0$

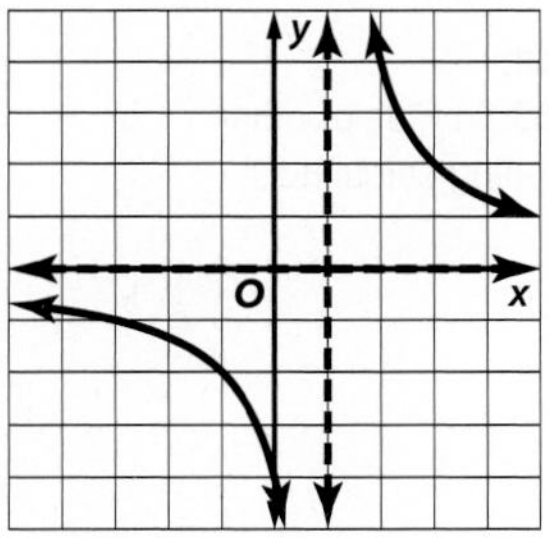

30. $x = 2$; $y = 1$

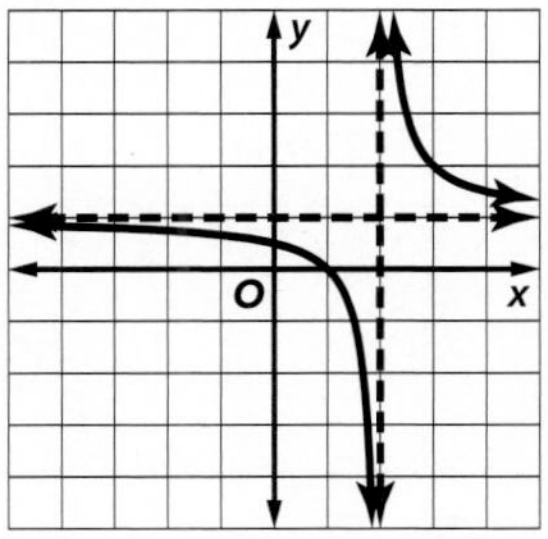

31. $x = 1$; $y = -2$

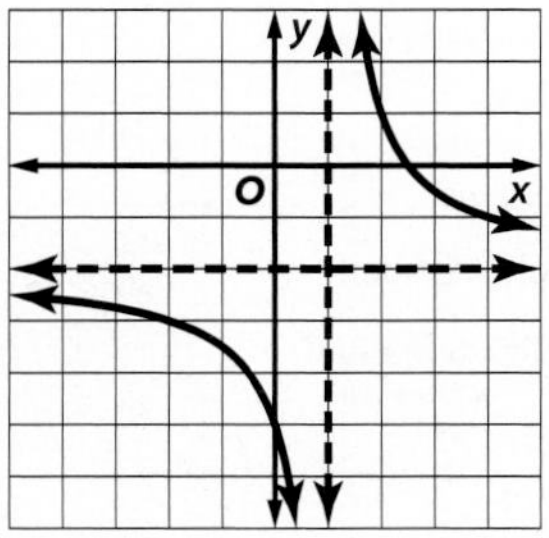

32. $x = -1$; $y = -4$

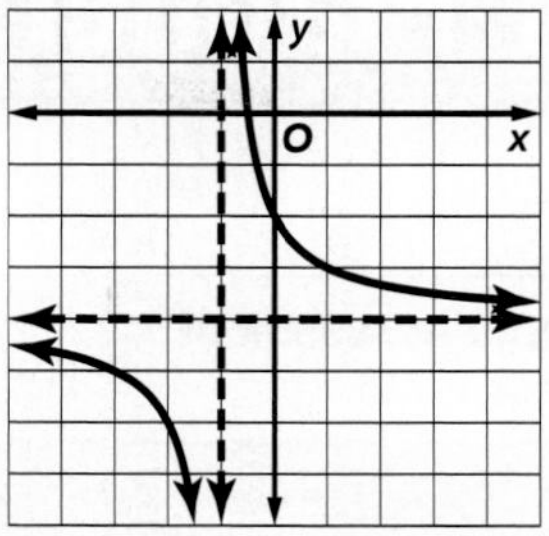

33. $x = -4$; $y = 3$

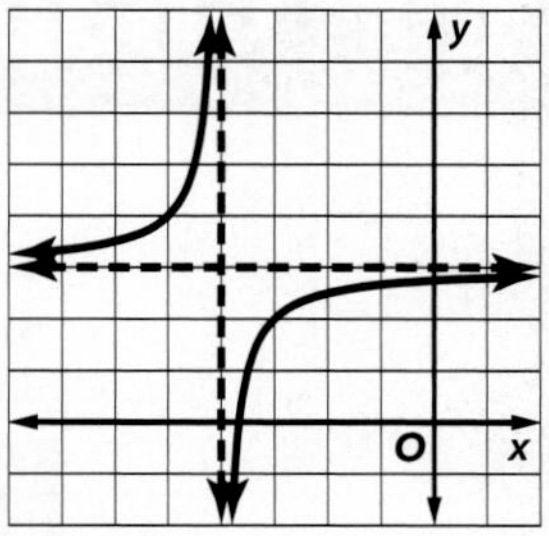

34a.

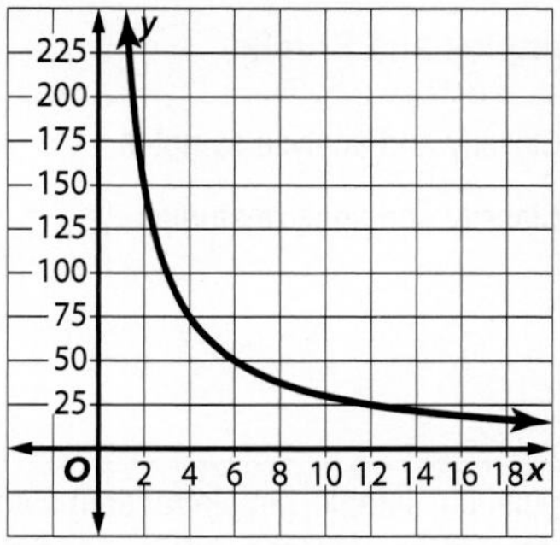

Sample answer: The end behavior indicates that as the number of days increases, the number of pages per day approaches 0. Since there is no *x*-intercept the number of pages per day will never be 0.

38.

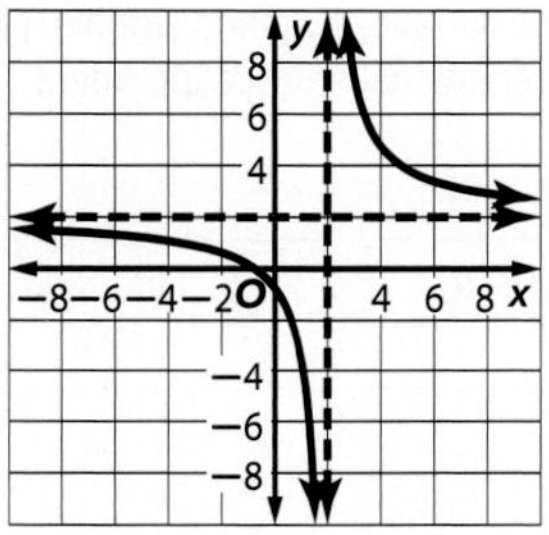

$x = 2$; $y = 2$

39.

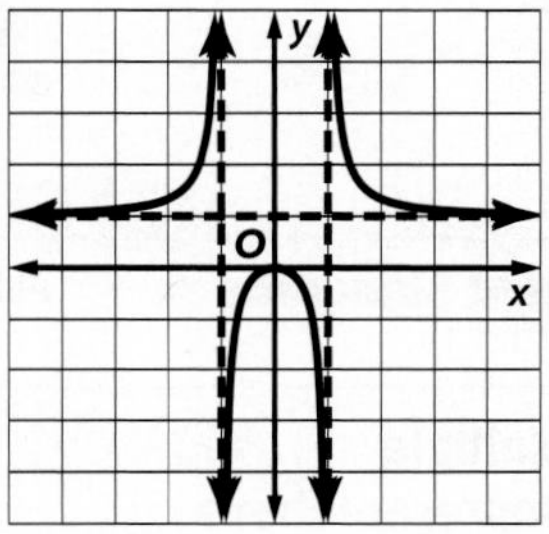

$x = -1, x = 1$; $y = 1$

40.

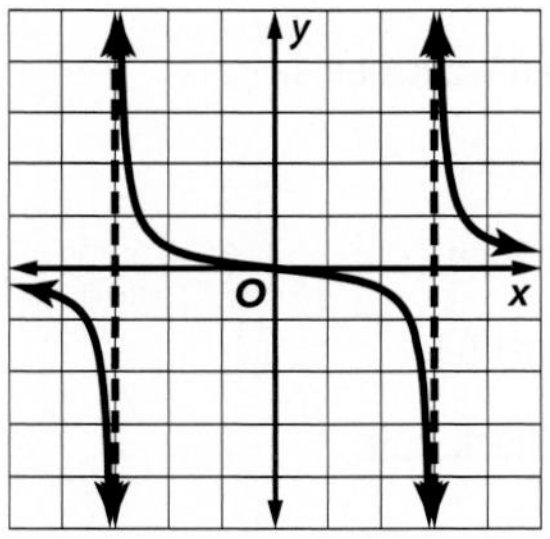

$x = 3, x = -3$; $y = 0$

Lesson 11-7

47. Sample answer: Time equals distance divided by rate or $\frac{d}{r}$. When the distance or the rate is given as a fraction or mixed number, the expression $\frac{d}{r}$ becomes a complex fraction.
Example: Someone walks $\frac{3}{4}$ mile in $10\frac{1}{2}$ minutes; the time in miles per minute is $\frac{\frac{3}{4}}{10\frac{1}{2}}$, which simplifies to $\frac{1}{14}$ mi/min.

Chapter Planner

Diagnostic Assessment
Quick Check, p. 745

	LESSON 12-1 (45 min: 0.75 day; 90 min: 0.75 day)	EXTEND 12-1 (45 min: 0.25 day; 90 min: 0.25 day)	LESSON 12-2 (45 min: 1 day; 90 min: 0.5 day)
Title	**Samples and Studies**	**Algebra Lab: Evaluating Published Data**	**Statistics and Parameters**
Objectives	■ Classify and analyze samples. ■ Classify and analyze studies.	■ Evaluate reports based on data published in the media.	■ Identify sample statistics and population parameters. ■ Analyze data sets using statistics.
Key Vocabulary	population, sample, simple random sample, systematic sample, self-selected sample, convenience sample, stratified sample, bias, survey, observational study, experiment		statistical inference statistic parameter mean absolute deviation (MAD) standard deviation variance
Content Standards	AI.DS.1, AI.DS.6	PS.3: AI.DS.1, AI.DS.6	PS.2, PS.6, AI.DS.1, AI.DS.6
Multiple Representations			
Lesson Resources	connectED.mcgraw-hill.com Leveled Worksheets Vocabulary Animations Personal Tutor Self-Check Quiz ■ *5-Minute Check* ■ *Study Notebook*	connectED.mcgraw-hill.com **Materials:** ■ TI-83/84 Plus or other graphing calculator	connectED.mcgraw-hill.com Leveled Worksheets Quiz 1 Vocabulary Personal Tutor Self-Check Quiz ■ *5-Minute Check* ■ *Study Notebook*
Resources for Every Lesson	IWB eStudent Edition IWB Interactive Classroom	■ eTeacher Edition ■ eSolutions Manual ■ McGraw-Hill eAssessment	
Differentiated Instruction	pp. 749, 754		pp. 758, 763

IWB All digital assets are Interactive Whiteboard ready.

Suggested Pacing			
Time Periods	Instruction	Review & Assess	Total
45-minute	9 days	2 days	11 days
90-minute	6 days	1 day	7 days

LESSON 12-3 **45 min:** 1 day **90 min:** 0.5 day	LESSON 12-4 **45 min:** 1 day **90 min:** 0.5 day	LESSON 12-5 **45 min:** 1 day **90 min:** 0.5 day	LESSON 12-6 **45 min:** 1 day **90 min:** 0.5 day
Distributions of Data	**Comparing Sets of Data**	**Simulations**	**Permutations and Combinations**
▪ Describe the shape of a distribution. ▪ Use the shapes of distributions to select appropriate statistics.	▪ Determine the effect that transformations of data have on measures of central tendency and variation. ▪ Compare data using measures of central tendency and variation.	▪ Calculate experimental probabilities. ▪ Design simulations and summarize data from simulations.	▪ Use permutations. ▪ Use combinations.
distribution negatively skewed distribution symmetric distribution positively skewed distribution	linear transformation	theoretical probability experimental probability relative frequency simulation probability model	permutation factorial combination
PS.5	PS.1	PS.4	PS.8
connectED.mcgraw-hill.com Leveled Worksheets Vocabulary Personal Tutor Virtual Manipulatives Self-Check Quiz ▪ *5-Minute Check* ▪ *Study Notebook*	connectED.mcgraw-hill.com Leveled Worksheets Quiz 2 Vocabulary Animations Personal Tutor Virtual Manipulatives Self-Check Quiz ▪ *5-Minute Check* ▪ *Study Notebook*	connectED.mcgraw-hill.com Leveled Worksheets Vocabulary Personal Tutor Virtual Manipulatives Self-Check Quiz ▪ *5-Minute Check* ▪ *Study Notebook* ▪ *Teaching Algebra with Manipulatives*	connectED.mcgraw-hill.com Leveled Worksheets Quiz 3 Vocabulary Animations Personal Tutor Self-Check Quiz ▪ *5-Minute Check* ▪ *Study Notebook*
IWB eStudent Edition IWB Interactive Classroom	▪ eTeacher Edition ▪ eSolutions Manual ▪ McGraw-Hill eAssessment		
pp. 765, 766, 770	pp. 772, 778	pp. 782, 785	pp. 788, 792

Formative Assessment
Mid-Chapter Quiz

Chapter Planner

	LESSON 12-7 (45 min: 1 day; 90 min: 0.5 day)	EXTEND 12-7 (45 min: 0.5 day; 90 min: 0.5 day)	LESSON 12-8 (45 min: 1 day; 90 min: 1 day)	EXTEND 12-8 (45 min: 0.5 day; 90 min: 0.5 day)
Title	**Probability of Compound Events**	**Algebra Lab: Two-Way Frequency Tables**	**Probability Distributions**	**Graphing Technology Lab: The Normal Curve**
Objectives	▪ Find probabilities of independent and dependent events. ▪ Find probabilities of mutually exclusive events.	▪ Use two-way frequency tables to find marginal, joint, and conditional relative frequencies.	▪ Find probabilities by using random variables. ▪ Find the expected value of a probability distribution.	▪ Use a graphing calculator to explore normal distribution curves.
Key Vocabulary	compound event joint probability independent events dependent events mutually exclusive events	two-way frequency table joint frequencies marginal frequencies relative frequency conditional relative frequency	random variable discrete random variable probability distribution probability graph expected value	normal distribution normal curve *z*-score
Content Standards		AI.DS.5	PS.7	
Multiple Representations	✓		✓	
Lesson Resources	connectED.mcgraw-hill.com Leveled Worksheets Vocabulary Animations Personal Tutor Virtual Manipulatives Self-Check Quiz ▪ *5-Minute Check* ▪ *Study Notebook* ▪ *Teaching Algebra with Manipulatives*	connectED.mcgraw-hill.com Personal Tutor Vocabulary	connectED.mcgraw-hill.com Leveled Worksheets Quiz 4 Vocabulary Personal Tutor Virtual Manipulatives Self-Check Quiz ▪ *5-Minute Check* ▪ *Study Notebook* ▪ *Teaching Algebra with Manipulatives*	connectED.mcgraw-hill.com Personal Tutor Vocabulary **Materials:** ▪ TI-83/84 Plus or other graphing calculator
Resources for Every Lesson	IWB eStudent Edition IWB Interactive Classroom	▪ eTeacher Edition ▪ eSolutions Manual ▪ McGraw-Hill eAssessment		
Differentiated Instruction	pp. 795, 800		pp. 805, 809	

Summative Assessment
Study Guide and Review
Practice Test

IWB All digital assets are Interactive Whiteboard ready.

What the Research Says . . .

According to Wilkins (1999), there is an increased emphasis to have students create experimental and theoretical models to analyze real-world situations. Students should perform experiments using basic probability models, such as flipping coins and rolling dice.

- In Lesson 12-5, students use random number generators to simulate inspections, contests, and games.
- In Exercise 10 of Lesson 12-5, students use the results of a simulation to draw conclusions about an expected outcome.

Source: Wilkins, Jesse L.M. (1999). "The Cereal Box Problem Revisited." *School Science and Mathematics*, 99, Issue 3, pp.117–123.

Project CRISS SM

STUDY SKILL

Most students begin Chapter 12 having some background in the topics presented there. Using a **K**now-**W**ant to Learn-**L**earned(KWL) chart will help them build on their prior knowledge.

Before beginning this chapter, draw a KWL chart like the one at the right on an overhead transparency. Name some topics covered in the chapter, such as the probability of compound events. Have students tell what they already know about the topics as you record their ideas. Next, have them list what they would like to know about the topics. Then, after the chapter has been completed, have students complete the last column, describing what they learned.

Compound Events		
Know	**What to Learn**	**Learned**
The probability of two independent events *A* and *B* occurring is the product of the probability of *A* and the probability of *B*.	What is the probability of two events that cannot occur at the same time?	

C Reating **I**ndependence through **S**tudent-owned **S**trategies

Assessment and Intervention

SE = Student Edition, **TE** = Teacher Edition, **CRM** = Chapter Resource Masters

	Diagnosis	Prescription
DIAGNOSTIC ASSESSMENT	**Beginning Chapter 12**	
	Get Ready for Chapter 12 **SE**	Response to Intervention **TE**
	Beginning Every Lesson	
	Then, Now, Why? **SE** 5-Minute Check	Chapter 0 **SE** *Quick Review Math Handbook*
FORMATIVE ASSESSMENT	**During/After Every Lesson**	
	Guided Practice **SE**, every example Check Your Understanding **SE** H.O.T. Problems **SE** Spiral Review **SE** Additional Examples **TE** Watch Out! **TE** Step 0, Assess **TE** Chapter 12 Quizzes **CRM**, pp. 57–58 Self-Check Quizzes connectED.mcgraw-hill.com	TIER 1 Intervention Skills Practice **CRM**, Ch. 1–12 connectED.mcgraw-hill.com TIER 2 Intervention Differentiated Instruction **TE** Study Guide and Intervention **CRM**, Ch. 1–12 *Quick Review Math Handbook* TIER 3 Intervention *Math Triumphs, Alg. 1,* Ch. 6
	Mid-Chapter	
	Mid-Chapter Quiz **SE** Mid-Chapter Test **CRM**, p. 59 McGraw-Hill eAssessment	TIER 1 Intervention Skills Practice **CRM**, Ch. 1–12 connectED.mcgraw-hill.com TIER 2 Intervention Study Guide and Intervention **CRM**, Ch. 1–12; *Quick Review Math Handbook* TIER 3 Intervention *Math Triumphs, Alg. 1,* Ch. 6
	Before Chapter Test	
	Chapter Study Guide and Review **SE** Practice Test **SE** Standardized Test Practice **SE** Chapter Test connectED.mcgraw-hill.com Standardized Test Practice connectED.mcgraw-hill.com Vocabulary Review connectED.mcgraw-hill.com McGraw-Hill eAssessment	TIER 1 Intervention Skills Practice **CRM**, Ch. 1–12 connectED.mcgraw-hill.com TIER 2 Intervention Study Guide and Intervention **CRM**, Ch. 1–12; *Quick Review Math Handbook* TIER 3 Intervention *Math Triumphs, Alg. 1,* Ch. 6
SUMMATIVE ASSESSMENT	**After Chapter 12**	
	Multiple-Choice Tests, Forms 1, 2A, 2B **CRM**, pp. 61–66 Free-Response Tests, Forms 2C, 2D, 3 **CRM**, pp. 67–72 Vocabulary Test **CRM**, p. 60 Extended Response Test **CRM**, p. 73 Standardized Test Practice **CRM**, pp. 74–76 McGraw-Hill eAssessment	Study Guide and Intervention **CRM**, Ch. 1–12 *Quick Review Math Handbook* connectED.mcgraw-hill.com

Differentiated Instruction

Option 1 Reaching All Learners AL OL BL ELL

Logical Have students write the digits 0–7 on index cards. Have them rearrange the cards in different ways to help them visualize how the combination formula relates to the cards. Compare their results with the calculations in Example 3 on p. 788 (Lesson 12-6).

Interpersonal Have students work in small groups. Tell them they will design a survey for the following situation: *You own a company that designs rides for amusement parks. You want to know which rides are liked best by the children who attend these types of parks.*

The survey should produce valid results and include the following:

- how they will conduct the survey,
- who will complete the survey,
- the size of the sample and why it is representative of the larger population,
- the type of sample(s) used for the survey, and
- the question(s) asked in the survey.

Have groups discuss how they might display the results and how they might use them as a business owner.

Option 2 Approaching Level AL

Review with students how to display a sample space with a tree diagram. Explain that the results show the possible outcomes and can help you find the probability of an event, but it is not a very useful method to use when the sample space is very large.

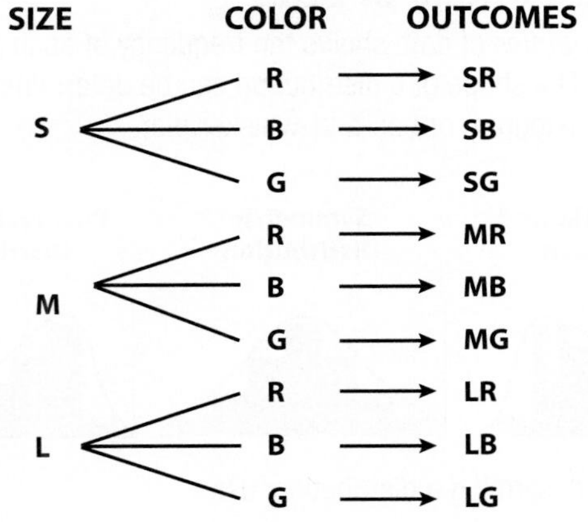

Option 3 English Learners ELL

Have students work in pairs or small groups to create a probability word scramble using the vocabulary words from this chapter. On one side of their paper, they should list the scrambled vocabulary words. On the other side they should list, in a different order, the definition of the words. Then have groups trade papers, unscramble the words, and connect each word with its definition.

Option 4 Beyond Level BL

Allow students to design their own experiments to find experimental probability, such as finding the probability of tossing a paper cup into a wastebasket, the probability of a student being able to read more than 10 words in 10 seconds, and so on.

Statistics and Probability

Focus on Mathematical Content

VerticalAlignment

Before Chapter 12

Related Topics before Pre-Algebra

- find the probabilities of dependent and independent events
- use theoretical probabilities and experimental results to make predictions and decisions
- select and use different models to simulate an event
- evaluate methods of sampling to determine validity of an inference made from a set of data
- recognize misuses of graphical or numerical information and evaluate predictions and conclusions based on data analysis

Chapter 12

Related Topics from Algebra 1

- identify various sampling techniques and recognize a biased sample
- count outcomes using the Fundamental Counting Principle
- use combinations and permutations to determine probabilities
- find the probability of two independent events or dependent events, and find the probability of two mutually exclusive or inclusive events
- use random variables to compute probability, and use probability distributions to solve real-world problems
- use probability simulations to model real-world situations

After Chapter 12

Preparation for Algebra 2

This chapter reinforces skills needed in Algebra 2.

Lesson-by-Lesson Preview

12-1 Samples and Studies

A *sample* is a portion of a larger group called a *population.* Five types of samples are:

- *simple random*—each member has an equal chance of being selected
- *systematic*—members are selected according to a specified interval
- *self-selected*—members volunteer
- *convenience*—members that are readily available are chosen
- *stratified sample*—members are divided into subgroups and are then selected

After a sample is selected, information can be collected from the sample by conducting a survey, an observational study, or an experiment.

12-2 Statistics and Parameters

A *statistic* is a measure that describes a characteristic of a sample, while a *parameter* is a measure that describes a characteristic of the population.

Univariate data can be represented by the mean, median, and mode, as well as by measures of variation, including

- *mean absolute deviation*—the average of the absolute values of the differences between the mean and each value in the data set,
- *standard deviation*—a value that shows how the data deviates from the mean of the set of data found by taking the square root of the variance, and
- *variance*—the square of the standard deviation.

12-3 Distributions of Data

A *distribution* of data shows the frequency of each possible data value. The shape of a distribution can be determined by looking at its histogram or box-and-whisker plot.

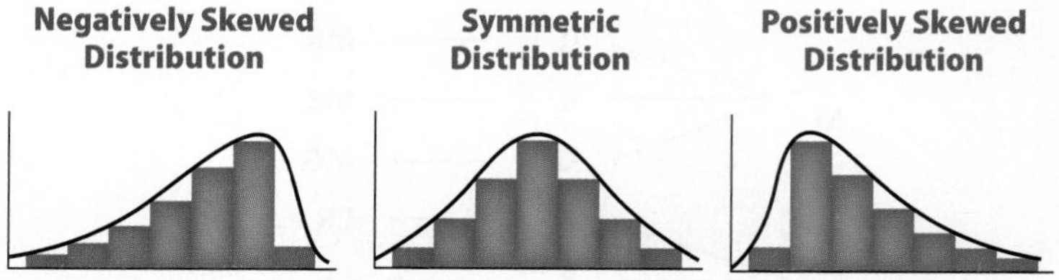

When describing a distribution, use

- the mean and standard deviation if the distribution is symmetric, or
- the five-number summary if the distribution is skewed.

12-4 Comparing Sets of Data

If a real number k is added to every value in a set of data,

- the mean, median, and mode of the new data set can be found by adding k to the mean, median, and mode of the original data set, and
- the range and standard deviation will not change.

If every value in a set of data is multiplied by a constant k, $k > 0$, then the mean, median, mode, range, and standard deviation of the new data set can be found by multiplying each original statistic by k.

When comparing two sets of data, use

- the means and standard deviations if the distributions are both symmetric, or
- the five-number summaries if the distributions are both skewed, or if one distribution is symmetric and the other is skewed.

12-5 Simulations

Theoretical probability describes what is expected to happen. *Experimental probability* describes what happens based on repeated experiments.

A *simulation* provides a way to find experimental probability by "acting out" an event that might be difficult to perform. It uses a *probability model* such as dice, coins, spinners, or random number generators to simulate an event.

12-6 Permutations and Combinations

A *permutation* is an arrangement or listing in which the order or placement of the arrangement is important.

- You can find the number of permutations by using the formula $\frac{n!}{(n-r)!}$, where n is the number of items to choose from, and r is the number of items to be chosen. The symbol for the number of permutations is ${}_nP_r$ or $P(n, r)$.

A *combination* is an arrangement or listing in which the order or placement is not important.

- The formula for finding the number of combinations is $\frac{n!}{(n-r)!r!}$, where n is the number of items to choose from and r is the number of items to be chosen. The symbol for the number of combinations is ${}_nC_r$ or $C(n, r)$.

12-7 Probability of Compound Events

A simple event is one event, while a *compound event* consists of two or more simple events.

- To find the probability of *independent events*, multiply the probability of the first event by the probability of the second event: $P(A) \cdot P(B)$.
- To find the probability of two *dependent events*, multiply the probability of the first event by the probability of the second event after the first event occurs: $P(A) \cdot P(B \text{ following } A)$.
- If event A and event B are mutually exclusive, then the probability that either A or B occurs is $P(A) + P(B)$.
- If event A and event B are not mutually exclusive, then the probability that either A or B occurs is $P(A) + P(B) - P(A \text{ and } B)$.

12-8 Probability Distributions

A *random variable* is a variable with a value that is the outcome of a random event. A *probability distribution* shows all of the possible values of the random variable, X.

- The probabilities for each value of X add up to 1.
- Probability distributions can be shown in tables or graphs.

The *expected value* of a discrete random variable X is the sum of the products of every possible value of X and its associated probability.

Professional Development

Targeted professional development has been articulated throughout Algebra 1. More quality, customized professional development is available from McGraw-Hill Professional Development. Visit connectED.mcgraw-hill.com for details on each product.

- Online Lessons emphasize the strategies and techniques used to teach Algebra 1. Includes streaming video, interactive pages, and online tools.
- Video Workshops allow mentors, coaches, or leadership personnel to facilitate on-site workshops on educational strategies in mathematics and mathematical concepts.
- MHPD Online (www.mhpdonline.com) offers online professional development with video clips of instructional strategies, links, student activities, and news and issues in education.
- Teaching Today (teachingtoday.glencoe.com) gives secondary teachers practical strategies and materials that inspire excellence and innovation in teaching.

Chapter Project

I Have the Best Idea for a Show…

Students use what they have learned about distributions of data to complete a project.

This chapter project addresses business literacy, as well as several specific skills identified as being essential to student success by the Framework for 21st Century Learning.

Visit connectED.mcgraw-hill.com for student and teacher handouts.

Key Vocabulary Introduce the key vocabulary in the chapter using the routine below.

Define: A random sample is a sample that is chosen without any preference, representative of the entire population.

Example: Thirty students are in a class. Three of the thirty students are chosen at random to answer a survey.

Ask: If the three students were chosen for a certain reason, would this be a random sample? Explain why or why not. No; for it to be a random sample, the sample must be picked without preferences.

CHAPTER 12 Statistics and Probability

Then

You calculated simple probability.

Now

In this chapter, you will:

- Design surveys and evaluate results.
- Use permutations and combinations.
- Find probabilities of compound events.
- Design and use simulations.

Why?

RESTAURANTS A restaurant may ask their customers to complete a survey about their visit. The survey data can be analyzed using statistical methods. The restaurant staff can learn more about their customers and how to improve their experiences in the restaurant.

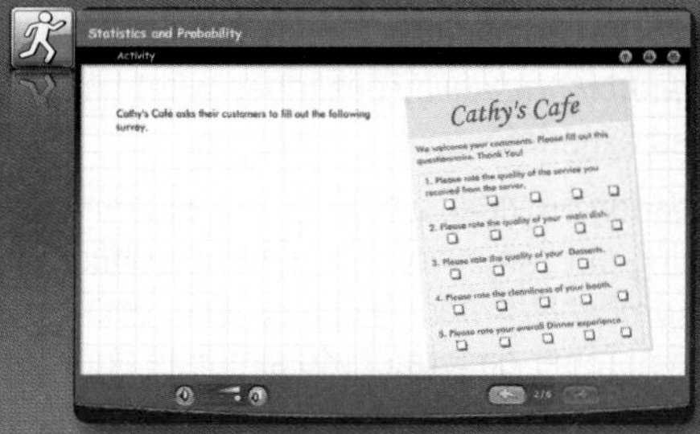

connectED.mcgraw-hill.com Your Digital Math Portal

Animation | Vocabulary | eGlossary | Personal Tutor | Virtual Manipulatives | Graphing Calculator | Audio | Foldables | Self-Check Practice | Worksheets

Content Standards
AI.DS.1, AI.DS.5, AI.DS.6

Process Standards
PS.1, PS.2, PS.3, PS.4, PS.5, PS.6, PS.7, PS.8

Get Ready for the Chapter

Diagnose Readiness | You have two options for checking prerequisite skills.

1 Textbook Option Take the Quick Check below. Refer to the Quick Review for help.

QuickCheck

Determine the probability of each event if you randomly select a cube from a bag containing 6 red cubes, 4 yellow cubes, 3 blue cubes, and 1 green cube.

1. *P*(red) $\frac{3}{7}$
2. *P*(blue) $\frac{3}{14}$
3. *P*(not red) $\frac{4}{7}$
4. *P*(white) 0
5. Jim rolls a die with 6 sides. What is the probability of rolling a 5? $\frac{1}{6}$
6. Malika spins a spinner that is divided into 8 equal sections. Each section is a different color, including blue. What is the probability the spinner lands on the blue section? $\frac{1}{8}$

Find each product.

7. $\frac{5}{4} \cdot \frac{2}{3}$ $\frac{5}{6}$
8. $\frac{4}{19} \cdot \frac{7}{20}$ $\frac{7}{95}$
9. $\frac{4}{32} \cdot \frac{7}{32}$ $\frac{7}{256}$
10. $\frac{5}{12} \cdot \frac{6}{11}$ $\frac{5}{22}$
11. $\frac{56}{100} \cdot \frac{24}{100}$ $\frac{84}{625}$
12. $\frac{9}{34} \cdot \frac{17}{27}$ $\frac{1}{6}$

Write each fraction as a percent. Round to the nearest tenth.

13. $\frac{14}{17}$ 82.4%
14. $\frac{7}{8}$ 87.5%
15. $\frac{107}{125}$ 85.6%
16. $\frac{625}{1024}$ 61.0%
17. **SHOPPERS** At the mall, 700 of the 2000 people shopping were under the age of 21. What percent of the shoppers were under 21? 35%

QuickReview

Example 1 (Used in Lessons 12-4 and 12-5)

Determine the probability of selecting a green cube if you randomly select a cube from a bag containing 6 red cubes, 4 yellow cubes, and 1 green cube.

There is 1 green cube and a total of 11 cubes in the bag.

$\frac{1}{11} = \frac{\text{number of green cubes}}{\text{total number of cubes}}$

The probability of selecting a green cube is $\frac{1}{11}$.

Example 2 (Used in Lesson 12-6)

Find $\frac{4}{5} \cdot \frac{3}{4}$.

$\frac{4}{5} \cdot \frac{3}{4} = \frac{4 \cdot 3}{5 \cdot 4}$ Multiply the numerators and the denominators.

$= \frac{12}{20}$ Simplify.

$= \frac{3}{5}$ Rename in simplest form.

Example 3 (Used in Lesson 12-7)

Write the fraction $\frac{33}{80}$ as a percent. Round to the nearest tenth.

$\frac{33}{80} \approx 0.413$ Simplify and round.

$0.413 \cdot 100 = 41.3$ Multiply the decimal by 100.

$\frac{33}{80}$ written as a percent is about 41.3%.

2 Online Option Take an online self-check Chapter Readiness Quiz at connectED.mcgraw-hill.com.

Get Ready for the Chapter

Response to Intervention (RtI)

Use the *Quick Check* results and the Intervention Planner chart to help you determine your Response to Intervention. The If-Then statements in the chart below help you decide the appropriate tier of RtI and suggest intervention resources for each tier.

InterventionPlanner

TIER 1 On Level OL

If students miss about 25% of the exercises or less,

Then choose a resource:

SE Lessons 0-5, 0-6, and 0-11

connectED.mcgraw-hill.com Self-Check Quiz

TIER 2 Strategic Intervention AL approaching grade level

If students miss about 50% of the exercises,

Then choose a resource:

Quick Review Math Handbook

connectED.mcgraw-hill.com Extra Examples, Personal Tutor, Homework Help

TIER 3 Intensive Intervention 2 or more grades below level

If students miss about 75% of the exercises,

Then use *Math Triumphs, Alg. 1*, Ch. 6

connectED.mcgraw-hill.com Extra Examples, Personal Tutor, Homework Help, Review Vocabulary

Essential Question

- How are statistics and probability used in the real world?

Sample answer: Statistics are used in charts, graphs, and articles or reports in Web sites, newspapers, magazines, and television news. Probability is used in the lottery, games of chance, and in news reports of unlikely events (for example, odds of being struck by lightning).

FOLDABLES® Study Organizer

Dinah Zike's Foldables®

Focus Students write notes about probability and statistics for each lesson in this chapter.

Teach Have students make and label their Foldables as illustrated. For each lesson have students record definitions and examples on the appropriate sheets.

When to Use It Encourage students to add to their Foldables as they work through the chapter and to use them to review for the chapter test.

Differentiated Instruction

Student-Built Glossary, pp. 1–2

Students should complete the chart by providing a definition of each term and an example as they progress through Chapter 12. This study tool can also be used to review for the chapter test.

Get Started on the Chapter

You will learn several new concepts, skills, and vocabulary terms as you study Chapter 12. To get ready, identify important terms and organize your resources. You may wish to refer to Chapter 0 to review prerequisite skills.

FOLDABLES Study Organizer

Statistics and Probability Make this Foldable to help you organize your Chapter 12 notes about Statistics and Probability. Begin with 8 sheets of $8\frac{1}{2}$" by 11" paper.

1 **Fold** each sheet of paper in half. Cut 1 inch from the end to the fold. Then cut 1 inch along the fold.

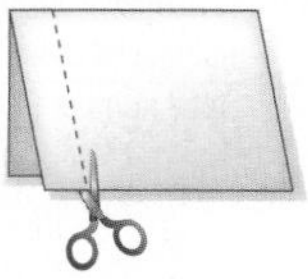

2 **Label** 7 of the 8 sheets with the lesson number and title.

3 **Label** the inside of each sheet with Definitions and Examples.

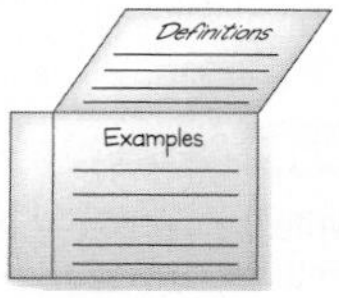

4 **Stack** the sheets. Staple along the left side. Write the title of the chapter on the first page.

New Vocabulary

English		Español
population	p. 747	población
sample	p. 747	muestra
bias	p. 748	tendencia
observational study	p. 749	estudio de observación
experiment	p. 749	experimento
statistic	p. 757	estadística
parameter	p. 757	parámetro
standard deviation	p. 759	desviación estándar
distribution	p. 764	distribución
symmetric distribution	p. 764	distribución simétrica
theoretical probability	p. 780	probabilidad teórica
experimental probability	p. 780	probabilidad experimental
simulation	p. 781	simulación
permutation	p. 786	permutación
combination	p. 787	combinación
compound event	p. 793	evento compuesto
independent events	p. 793	eventos independientes
dependent events	p. 794	eventos dependientes
mutually exclusive	p. 795	mutuamente exclusivos
random variable	p. 803	variable aleatoria
probability distribution	p. 804	distribución de probabilidad
expected value	p. 805	valor esperado

Review Vocabulary

probability probilidad the ratio of favorable outcomes to the total possible outcomes

sample space espacio muestral the list of all possible outcomes

746 | Chapter 12 | Statistics and Probability

LESSON 12-1 Samples and Studies

:: Then	:: Now	:: Why?
• You displayed results from studies.	1 Classify and analyze samples. 2 Classify and analyze studies.	• A high school principal is trying to determine whether the school should change its mascot and decides to survey some of the students.

NewVocabulary
population
sample
simple random sample
systematic sample
self-selected sample
convenience sample
stratified sample
bias
survey
observational study
experiment

Content Standards
AI.DS.1, AI.DS.6

1 Sampling

A **population** consists of all of the members of a group of interest. Since it may be impractical to examine every member of a population, a **sample** or subset is sometimes selected to represent the population. The sample can then be analyzed to draw conclusions about the entire population. For instance, in the example above, the population is the entire student body. The sample is the students who participate in the survey.

In a **simple random sample**, each member of the population has an equal chance of being selected as part of the sample. The principal can generate a simple random sample by randomly drawing student ID numbers from a hat that contains the ID number of every student.

Some other types of samples are described below.

In a **systematic sample**, members are selected according to a specified interval from a random starting point, such as selecting every third student.

In a **self-selected sample**, members volunteer to be included in the sample.

In a **convenience sample**, members that are readily available or easy to reach are selected, such as the students on a particular bus.

In a **stratified sample**, the population is first divided into similar, nonoverlapping groups. Members are then randomly selected from each group.

Factors that can influence the type of sample used include cost, time, and the availability of willing participants.

1 Focus

VerticalAlignment

Before Lesson 12-1 You displayed results from studies.

Lesson 12-1 Classify and analyze samples and studies.

After Lesson 12-1 You will analyze data sets using statistics.

2 Teach

Scaffolding Questions

Have students read the **Why?** section of the lesson.

Ask:

- How should the principal go about choosing which students to ask? The principal should select a random sample of students from the entire population by using a random number generator or some other form of simulation.
- What would be wrong with the principal only asking the football players? This sample is not random and could be biased to favor a specific result. None of the other students in the school are represented.

Lesson 12-1 Resources

Resource	Approaching Level AL	On Level OL	Beyond Level BL	English Learners ELL
Teacher Edition	▪ Differentiated Instruction, p. 749	▪ Differentiated Instruction, pp. 749, 754	▪ Differentiated Instruction, p. 754	
Chapter Resource Masters	▪ Study Guide and Intervention, pp. 5–6 ▪ Skills Practice, p. 7 ▪ Practice, p. 8 ▪ Word Problem Practice, p. 9	▪ Study Guide and Intervention, pp. 5–6 ▪ Skills Practice, p. 7 ▪ Practice, p. 8 ▪ Word Problem Practice, p. 9 ▪ Enrichment, p. 10	▪ Practice, p. 8 ▪ Word Problem Practice, p. 9 ▪ Enrichment, p. 10	▪ Study Guide and Intervention, pp. 5–6 ▪ Skills Practice, p. 7 ▪ Practice, p. 8 ▪ Word Problem Practice, p. 9
Other	▪ 5-Minute Check 12-1 ▪ Study Notebook	▪ 5-Minute Check 12-1 ▪ Study Notebook	▪ 5-Minute Check 12-1 ▪ Study Notebook	▪ 5-Minute Check 12-1 ▪ Study Notebook

1 Sampling

Example 1 shows how to classify a random sample. **Example 2** shows how to identify a sample as biased or unbiased.

Formative Assessment

Use the Guided Practice exercises after each example to determine students' understanding of concepts.

Additional Examples

1 **MOVIES** Every fifth person walking out of a movie theater is asked to name their favorite type of movie.

a. Identify the sample, and suggest a population from which it is selected. Sample: every fifth person leaving the theater. population: all moviegoers

b. Classify the sample as *simple*, *systematic*, *self-selected*, *convenience*, or *stratified*. Explain your reasoning. Systematic; members are selected according to a specified interval.

2 Identify each sample as *biased* or *unbiased*. Explain your reasoning.

a. STUDENT COUNCIL The student council surveys the students in one classroom to decide the theme for the spring dance. Biased; it includes only the students in one classroom.

b. SCHOOL The Parent Association surveys the parents of every fifth student to decide whether to hold a fund-raiser. Unbiased; the parents are picked randomly, and all have an equal chance of being picked.

Additional Examples also in Interactive Classroom PowerPoint® Presentations

IWB Interactive White Board READY

Real-WorldLink

The Jamaican Jerk Festival is held annually in Pembroke Pines, Florida. Cooks may enter a competition where each entrant must prepare any three dishes from the following categories: jerked pork, jerked chicken, jerked seafood, or other.

Source: Jamaican Jerk Festival

Real-World Example 1 Classify a Random Sample

ZOOS Animals in a zoo are divided by species. Then two animals are selected at random from each group to have their blood tested.

a. Identify the sample, and suggest a population from which it was selected.

Sample: the two animals selected from each species
Population: all of the animals in the zoo

b. Classify the sample as *simple, systematic, self-selected, convenience,* or *stratified.* Explain your reasoning.

This is a stratified sample. The animals were divided into categories before there was a random selection.

GuidedPractice

Identify each sample, and suggest a population from which it was selected. Then classify the sample as *simple, systematic, self-selected, convenience,* or *stratified.* Explain your reasoning.

1A. CONTESTS Refer to the information at the left. After the competition, contestants were asked to complete an online survey about possible future categories.

1B. FOOD At a popular diner, the manager checks the quality of the burgers every 20 minutes, starting at a randomly selected time.

1A. Sample: the contestants that completed a survey; population: all of the contestants; self-selected: the contestants voluntarily complete the online survey.

1B. Sample: the burgers selected every 20 minutes; population: the burgers at the restaurant; systematic: the burgers were selected according to a specified time interval.

Sample data are often used to estimate a characteristic of a population. Therefore, a sample should be selected so that it is representative of the entire population. Also, the larger the sample size, or the more samples taken, the more closely it approximates the population.

A **bias** is an error that results in a misrepresentation of a population. If a sample favors one conclusion over another, the sample is biased and the data are invalid.

Example 2 Biased and Unbiased Samples

Identify each sample as *biased* or *unbiased*. Explain your reasoning.

a. MUSIC **Every fifth person coming into a grocery store is asked to name their favorite radio station.**

The sample is unbiased because the participants are randomly selected. The fact that the sample is selected at a grocery store has no bearing on the conclusion because many different kinds of people shop at grocery stores.

b. MUSIC **Every fifth person at the Country Music Showcase is asked to name their favorite radio station.**

The sample is biased because the participants are selected at a country music show, and therefore people may be more likely to select a country music station.

GuidedPractice

2A. Biased; sample answer: The group of Young Republicans probably share common political opinions, and are not a good representation of the entire student body.

2A. POLITICS A journalist surveys 15 student members of the Young Republicans to determine the overall political opinions of the student body.

2B. SHOES A shoe store conducts a study of which shoes are most popular. The store surveys every third girl and boy that enters the store.

2B. Unbiased; sample answer: The sample is random, and does not favor one outcome over another.

Focus on Mathematical Content

Samples and Populations By taking a sample of a population, you can estimate the characteristics of the population and make predictions based on the characteristics. A sample is a portion of a group, and the population is the group from which the sample is taken.

Teach with Tech

Student Response System Give students a list of several data finding situations. Have students enter whether this situation is a *survey*, *observational study*, or *experiment*. The same can be done with different types of sampling. This will help you track student understanding of these new concepts.

2 Studies

Studies After a sample is selected, information can be collected using one of the following study types.

KeyConcept Study Types

Type	Definition	Example
survey	Data are collected from responses given by a sample regarding their characteristics, behaviors, or opinions.	To determine whether the student body is happy with the spring dance theme, the dance committee asks a sample of students for their opinion.
observational study	Members of a sample are measured or observed without being affected by the study.	A gaming company watches a group of teens play a selection of video games and notes the ones they play the most.
experiment	The sample is divided into two groups: • an *experimental group* that undergoes a change, and • a *control group* that does not undergo the change. The effect on the experimental group is then compared to the control group.	A teacher administers a paper-and-pencil test to one of two Algebra classes. He administers a computer-based test that covers the same material to the other class. The teacher compares the scores and the completion times of the two classes.

StudyTip

Census A *census* is a survey in which every member of the population is questioned. So there is no sample when a census is conducted.

Factors that can influence the type of study conducted are cost, time, and the objective of the study.

Example 3 Classify Study Techniques

Determine whether each situation describes a *survey*, an *observational study*, or an *experiment*. Explain your reasoning.

a. CHARITY **A local charity is interested in finding out whether residents would use a curbside pick-up service for donations. They distribute 30 questionnaires to people living in the neighborhood.**

This is a survey. The data are gathered from responses given by members of the sample.

b. ADVERTISING **A company shows five different commercials that advertise the same product to a group of students. The company records the students' reactions to each.**

This is an observational study. The data are gathered from observing the students.

GuidedPractice

Determine whether each situation describes a *survey*, an *observational study*, or an *experiment*. Explain your reasoning.

Group 1 Food with sugar — Group 2 Food with no sugar

3A. RESEARCH Scientists study the behavior of two groups of rats to determine their reaction to sugar.

3B. RECREATION The city council wants to build a community recreational center. They call 1000 random citizens asking if they would consider paying a fee to join if the center is built.

. Experiment; sample answer: The rats are divided into two groups, one of which undergoes a change.

. Survey; sample answer: The data is obtained from opinions given by citizens that are called.

2 Studies

Example 3 shows how to classify data collection techniques. **Example 4** shows how to identify survey questions as biased or unbiased. **Example 5** shows how to identify experimental designs as biased or unbiased.

Additional Example

3 Determine whether each situation describes a *survey*, an *observational study*, or an *experiment*. Explain your reasoning.

a. RETAIL A retailer wants to evaluate their performance in customer service. They contact 1000 random customers asking if they would complete an evaluation form. Survey; the data are gathered from responses given by members of the sample.

b. VITAMINS Researchers analyze the reactions of rats to a vitamin. Experiment; rats that did not get the vitamin are the control group and rats that got the vitamin are the experimental group.

DifferentiatedInstruction AL OL

If students need further practice to understand the different types of random samples,

Then place students in small groups. Give each group a different number of colored beads to serve as a population. Have the groups model the different types of random samples with the beads. For example, for stratified random samples, students would first divide the beads into groups by color and then take random beads from each group. Have students describe how they would take a systematic random sample.

connectED.mcgraw-hill.com 749

Additional Examples

4 **Identify each survey question as *biased* or *unbiased*. If biased, explain your reasoning.**

a. How often do you exercise? unbiased

b. Do you like basketball? If so, do you prefer watching high school, college, or professional? Biased; the question addresses more than one issue.

5 **BASEBALL** A baseball bat manufacturer wants to test a new grip on their bats. They select 75 high school baseball players to try out the bat with the new grips and 75 other players to try out the old grips. Identify the experiment as *biased* or *unbiased*. If biased, explain your reasoning. Biased; members of the control group and the experimental group are not randomly selected.

Tips for New Teachers

Bias in Observational Studies
Students will review an observational study in Exercises 31 and 32.

The design of a survey can introduce bias. Survey questions should not:

- be confusing,
- encourage the members of the sample to answer a certain way,
- cause a strong reaction, or
- address more than one issue at a time.

PT

Example 4 Biased and Unbiased Survey Questions

Identify each survey question as *biased* or *unbiased*. If biased, explain your reasoning.

a. Is your favorite ice cream flavor plain vanilla or delicious chocolate?

This question is biased. It limits the responses to vanilla or chocolate and encourages the participant to answer a certain way by using the adjectives *plain* and *delicious*.

b. What type(s) of reading material(s) do you enjoy?

This question is unbiased. It does not encourage participants to answer a certain way, and it is clearly stated.

GuidedPractice

Identify each survey question as *biased* or *unbiased*. If biased, explain your reasoning.

4A. Do you like animals, and would you ever consider having a dog, a cat, or a hamster as a pet? **Biased; sample answer: The question is asking about two issues.**

4B. How much time do you spend working on school work each night? **unbiased**

Real-WorldCareer

Dog Trainer Dog trainers may seek professional certification by passing an examination after compiling 300 hours experience in dog training, acquiring a high school diploma, and obtaining three letters of reference.

Source: Certification Council for Professional Dog Trainers

Bias can also be introduced in the design of an experiment. To avoid this, members of the control group and the experimental group should be randomly selected. Also, the only difference between the two groups should be the change being observed.

PT

Real-World Example 5 Biased and Unbiased Experimental Designs

TRAINER A dog trainer wants to test training speed with a new method. She selects three terriers as the control group and teaches a trick using her normal method. She selects three greyhounds as the experimental group and teaches the same trick using the new method. She then compares the training times. Identify the experiment as *biased* or *unbiased*. If biased, explain your reasoning.

This experiment is biased. A terrier may be more apt to learn tricks than a greyhound, or vice versa. The bias could be corrected by using a random sample consisting entirely of terriers or greyhounds.

GuidedPractice

5. TRACK A track coach wants to test whether new shoes that claim to increase speed will produce faster times for his runners. He randomly selects five runners as the control group and records their times throughout the season using their normal shoes. He randomly selects five runners as the experimental group and records their times throughout the season using the new shoes. At the end of the season, he compares any improvements made by each group. Identify the experiment as *biased* or *unbiased*. If biased, explain your reasoning. **unbiased**

Check Your Understanding

◯ = Step-by-Step Solutions begin on page R13.

Example 1 **Identify each sample, and suggest a population from which it was selected. Then classify the sample as *simple, systematic, self-selected, convenience,* or *stratified.* Explain your reasoning.** 1–6. See margin.

1. **SHOWER** At a bridal shower, a sticker was placed on the bottom of three random plates. The guests who receive the stickered plates will win a prize.

2. **BOOK CLUB** Mr. Peterson surveys the students in his English classes to gauge the student body's interest in forming a book club.

Example 2 **Identify each sample as *biased* or *unbiased*. Explain your reasoning.**

3. **ELECTION** A group of students stands at the door of the school and asks every tenth student who they would vote for in the upcoming class elections and why.

4. **SHOPPING** Every fifteenth shopper at a clothing store is asked what they would want most for their birthday.

Example 3 **Determine whether each situation describes a *survey*, an *observational study*, or an *experiment*. Explain your reasoning.**

5. **TELEVISION** A television network wants to conduct a cartoon marathon. To choose the episodes, they mail a questionnaire to people selected at random throughout the country.

6. **FOOD** A frozen food company is considering creating frozen meals with tofu instead of meat. At a testing, they randomly give half of a group of 100 people the meals with meat and the other half the same meals with tofu and ask the people how they like the meals.

Example 4 **Identify each survey question as *biased* or *unbiased*. If biased, explain your reasoning.**

7. What are you planning to do over summer vacation? unbiased

8. Do you think we should serve mouth-watering steak or chicken? See margin.

9. Don't you think Suzanne should be the class president? See margin.

10. What type of music do you listen to? unbiased

Example 5 **Identify the experiment as *biased* or *unbiased*. If biased, explain your reasoning.**

11. **POOLS** A national pool manufacturer wants to determine if a new advertising strategy will increase sales. The company continues to use the normal advertising strategy in its stores located in Indiana, Pennsylvania, and Kentucky. The company uses the new advertising strategy in Florida, Louisiana, and Georgia. The company then compares the sales. See margin.

12. **EDUCATION** A school district wants to determine if having school in session year-round will improve the performance of students. They select one of their schools to be in session year-round and compare the test scores of those students with the test scores of the other students in the district. See margin.

Check out our beautiful pools that can be used year-round!

Differentiated Homework Options

Level	Assignment	Two-Day Option	
AL Basic	13–30, 37, 39–57	13–29 odd, 42–45	14–30 even, 37, 39–41, 46–57
OL Core	13–29 odd, 31–37, 39–57	13–30, 42–45	31–37, 39–41, 46–57
BL Advanced	31–56, (optional: 57)		

3 Practice

Formative Assessment

Use Exercises 1–12 to check for understanding.

Use the chart at the bottom of this page to customize assignments for your students.

Additional Answers

1. Sample: the guests who receive the stickered plates; population: all of the guests; simple: all of the guests have an equal chance of receiving a stickered plate.
2. Sample: the students in Mr. Peterson's classes; population: the student body: convenience: Mr. Peterson is only surveying the students that are in his classes.
3. Unbiased; sample answer: The sample is random, and does not favor one outcome over another.
4. Biased; sample answer: Shoppers at a clothing store are more likely to say clothes.
5. Survey; sample answer: The data is obtained from opinions given by people that return the questionnaire.
6. Experiment; sample answer: The people are divided into two groups, one of which undergoes a change.
8. Biased; sample answer: The adjective *mouth-watering* encourages the participants to select steak.
9. Biased; sample answer: The survey question encourages the members of the sample to choose Suzanne as class president.
11. Biased; sample answer: The normal advertising strategy was used in states that have a cooler climate than the states where the new advertising strategy was used.
12. Biased; sample answer: The district selected a specific school to be tested. The school could already be high-performing or low-performing compared to the rest of the district which would influence the test results.

WatchOut!

Error Analysis Have the class discuss the factors that make a survey representative of the population. Then have students analyze the descriptions given by Amy and Esteban in Exercise 37. Encourage them to give specific reasons why they think the descriptions of the two students do or do not increase the accuracy of a survey.

Practice and Problem Solving

Extra Practice is on page R12.

Example 1 **Identify each sample, and suggest a population from which it was selected. Then classify the sample as *simple, systematic, self-selected, convenience,* or *stratified.* Explain your reasoning.** 13–16. See margin.

13. **SPORTS CARDS** Greg divides his baseball cards by teams. Then he randomly selects four cards from each team and records the players' RBIs.

14. **CARS** The service manager at a car dealership inspects every fifth car to make sure that cars are detailed after being serviced.

15. **RAFFLE** The students who attended a prom committee meeting were each given a raffle ticket for a drawing of five prizes.

16. **MUSIC** A music store asks its customers to submit suggestions for local bands that should play on Friday nights.

Example 2 **Identify each sample as *biased* or *unbiased.* Explain your reasoning.** 17–20. See margin.

17. **ACTORS** A random sample of ten people is asked to name their favorite actor.

18. **BASKETBALL** Every fifth athlete at a basketball camp is asked to name their favorite brand of basketball shoe.

19. **TELEVISION** Every tenth person entering a gas station is asked to name their favorite television program.

20. **MUSIC** Every fifth person entering a play is asked to name their favorite style of music.

Example 3 **Determine whether each situation describes a *survey,* an *observational study,* or an *experiment.* Explain your reasoning.** 21–24. See margin.

21. **PARTIES** Federico is throwing a party for one of his friends. He is trying to decide on a theme. He sends a piece of paper in each invitation, asking guests questions to get their opinions.

22. **VOLUNTEER** Jaime finds 50 students, half of whom volunteer at a homeless shelter, and compares their grade point averages, extracurricular activities, and involvement in school clubs.

23. **SOCCER** A researcher organizes a soccer game in hot weather. One team wears short-sleeved shirts, while the other team wears long sleeves.

24. **SALONS** A salon emails customers, asking them to rate their experience during their last appointment.

Example 4 **Identify each survey question as *biased* or *unbiased.* If biased, explain your reasoning.**

25. What outdoor activities do you enjoy? unbiased

26. Do you think the comedian's stupid antics are funny? See margin.

27. Do you like to listen to music, read a book, or watch movies? See margin.

28. What is your favorite Web site? unbiased

Example 5 **Identify the experiment as *biased* or *unbiased.* If biased, explain your reasoning.**

29. **EMPLOYMENT** The management of a company hopes to increase the morale of their employees. They select some employees at random and move them into two identical office buildings. They build a recreation room in one of the buildings for employees to use. They then compare the morale of the employees in each building. unbiased

30. **CONCERTS** The manager of a band wants to see if a light show will improve their concerts. For the final date of the band's tour in their hometown, they perform while doing the light show. The manager then compares the reviews of this concert with the reviews of the rest of the tour. See margin.

Additional Answers

13. Sample: the cards that Greg selects; population: all of Greg's baseball cards; stratified: Greg divides the cards by teams before the sample is selected.

14. Sample: every fifth car serviced; population: all cars serviced; systematic: each selection was made at a regular interval.

15. Sample: the five students who win the raffle; population: all of the students at the meeting; simple: each student has an equal chance of winning.

16. Sample: the customers who submit suggestions; population: all customers; self-selected: the customers voluntarily submit suggestions.

17. Biased; sample answer: The sample is too small and doesn't represent the population.

18. Unbiased; sample answer: The participants are randomly selected. The fact that the sample is selected at a basketball camp does not influence the responses of the selected sample.

19. Unbiased; sample answer: The participants are randomly selected. The fact that the sample is selected at a gas station has no bearing on the conclusion because many different kinds of people enter gasoline stations.

20. Biased; sample answer: The participants are selected at a play and will likely prefer a certain type of music.

21. Survey; sample answer: The data is obtained from opinions given by guests that return the paper.

22. Observational study; sample answer: The students are observed and compared without them being affected by the study.

23. Experiment; sample answer: The control group is the team in short sleeves, while the experimental group is wearing long sleeves. The different affects of the clothes in the heat are analyzed.

24. Survey; sample answer: The data are obtained from opinions given by customers who respond to the email.

26. Biased; sample answer: The question encourages the participant to answer a certain way.

B **Identify the observational study as *biased* or *unbiased*. If biased, explain your reasoning.** 32. See margin.

31. **GOLF** A golf club manufacturer watches a group of randomly selected golfers test a prototype club and notes their performances and reactions. unbiased

32. **MOVIES** A production company sets up a test audience of friends and family of the production crew to view the new movie and notes their reactions.

Determine whether each situation calls for a *survey*, an *experiment*, or an *observational study*. Explain your reasoning. 33–35. See Ch. 12 Answer Appendix.

33. **GYMS** A gym owner wants to test whether changing the color of the walls improves member satisfaction.

34. **GAMING** A manufacturer invites twenty randomly selected teens to try out a new gaming system and notes their reactions as they play.

35. **SCHOOLS** A student asks 100 randomly selected neighbors if they think the school should build a new football field.

36a. customers that use the Web site; all athletic shoe customers

36. **SHOES** A shoe company's Web site allows customers to design their own shoes. This program keeps a count of styles and colors chosen by customers.
   a. Identify the sample. From what population was the sample selected?
   b. State the method of data collection. observational study
   c. Tell whether the sample is *biased* or *unbiased*. Explain.
   d. If unbiased, classify the sample as *simple, stratified, systematic, self-selected,* or *convenience.* self-selected

   36c. Unbiased; each person is equally likely to be chosen.

H.O.T. Problems Use Higher-Order Thinking Skills

C 37. **ERROR ANALYSIS** Amy and Esteban are describing one way to increase the accuracy of a survey. Is either of them correct? Explain your reasoning. Both; both Amy and Esteban's methods can result in an accurate survey.

Amy	Esteban
The survey should include as many people in the population as possible.	The sample for the survey should be chosen randomly. Several random samples should be taken.

38. **CRITIQUE** Consider the following survey proposal. See Ch. 12 Answer Appendix.

   Question: How do students feel about the new dress code?
   Method: Take a simple random sample from each of the four classes. Use this sample to conduct the survey.
   Discuss the strengths and weaknesses of this survey.

39. **REASONING** Charlie wants to determine who the most popular athlete is. He conducts three different surveys. For the first survey, he asks 20 random students at school. For the second survey, he asks 50 random people at the mall. For the third survey, he asks 150 random people at a concert. The most popular athlete was different for each survey. Which survey do you think would most likely represent the population? Explain your reasoning. See Ch. 12 Answer Appendix.

40. **OPEN ENDED** Design and conduct a simple experiment. See students' work.

41. **WRITING IN MATH** Why are accurate studies important to companies? See Ch. 12 Answer Appendix.

Additional Answers

27. Biased; sample answer: The question addresses more than one issue.

30. Biased; sample answer: The band did the light show in their hometown where they should already expect positive reviews.

32. Biased; sample answer: The sample is not randomly selected and is made up of people who would be partial to giving the movie a favorable review.

Study Guide and Intervention
AL OL ELL

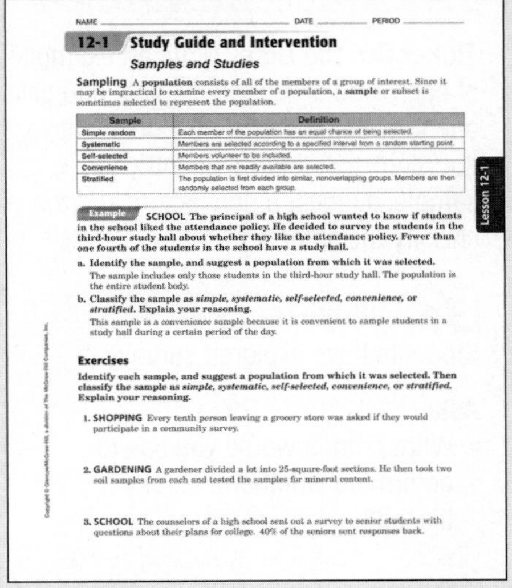
12-1 Study Guide and Intervention
Samples and Studies

Sampling A population consists of all of the members of a group of interest. Since it may be impractical to examine every member of a population, a sample or subset is sometimes selected to represent the population.

Sample	Definition
Simple random	Each member of the population has an equal chance of being selected.
Systematic	Members are selected according to a specified interval from a random starting point.
Self-selected	Members volunteer to be included.
Convenience	Members that are readily available are selected.
Stratified	The population is first divided into similar, nonoverlapping groups. Members are then randomly selected from each group.

Example SCHOOL The principal of a high school wanted to know if students in the school liked the attendance policy. He decided to survey the students in the third-hour study hall about whether they like the attendance policy. Fewer than one fourth of the students in the school have a study hall.

a. Identify the sample, and suggest a population from which it was selected. The sample includes only those students in the third-hour study hall. The population is the entire student body.

b. Classify the sample as simple, systematic, self-selected, convenience, or stratified. Explain your reasoning. This sample is a convenience sample because it is convenient to sample students in a study hall during a certain period of the day.

Exercises
Identify each sample, and suggest a population from which it was selected. Then classify the sample as simple, systematic, self-selected, convenience, or stratified. Explain your reasoning.

1. SHOPPING Every tenth person leaving a grocery store was asked if they would participate in a community survey.
2. GARDENING A gardener divided a lot into 25-square-foot sections. He then took two soil samples from each and tested the samples for mineral content.
3. SCHOOL The counselors of a high school sent out a survey to senior students with questions about their plans for college. 40% of the seniors sent responses back.

Practice
AL OL BL ELL

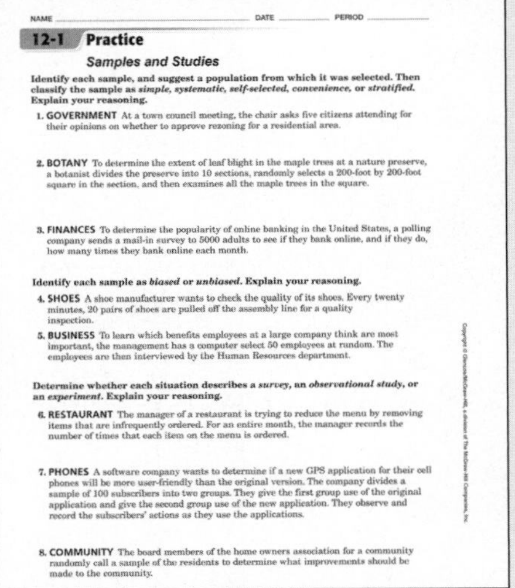
12-1 Practice
Samples and Studies

Identify each sample, and suggest a population from which it was selected. Then classify the sample as simple, systematic, self-selected, convenience, or stratified. Explain your reasoning.

1. GOVERNMENT At a town council meeting, the chair asks five citizens attending for their opinions on whether to approve rezoning for a residential area.
2. BOTANY To determine the extent of leaf blight in the maple trees at a nature preserve, a botanist divides the preserve into 10 sections, randomly selects a 200-foot by 200-foot square in the section, and then examines all the maple trees in the square.
3. FINANCES To determine the popularity of online banking in the United States, a polling company sends a mail-in survey to 5000 adults to see if they bank online, and if they do, how many times they bank online each month.

Identify each sample as biased or unbiased. Explain your reasoning.

4. SHOES A shoe manufacturer wants to check the quality of its shoes. Every twenty minutes, 20 pairs of shoes are pulled off the assembly line for a quality inspection.
5. BUSINESS To learn which benefits employees at a large company think are most important, the management has a computer select 50 employees at random. The employees are then interviewed by the Human Resources department.

Determine whether each situation describes a survey, an observational study, or an experiment. Explain your reasoning.

6. RESTAURANT The manager of a restaurant is trying to reduce the menu by removing items that are infrequently ordered. For an entire month, the manager records the number of times that each item on the menu is ordered.
7. PHONES A software company wants to determine if a new GPS application for their cell phones will be more user-friendly than the original version. The company divides a sample of 100 subscribers into two groups. They give the first group use of the original application and give the second group use of the new application. They observe and record the subscribers' actions as they use the applications.
8. COMMUNITY The board members of the home owners association for a community randomly call a sample of the residents to determine what improvements should be made to the community.

Word Problem Practice
AL OL BL ELL

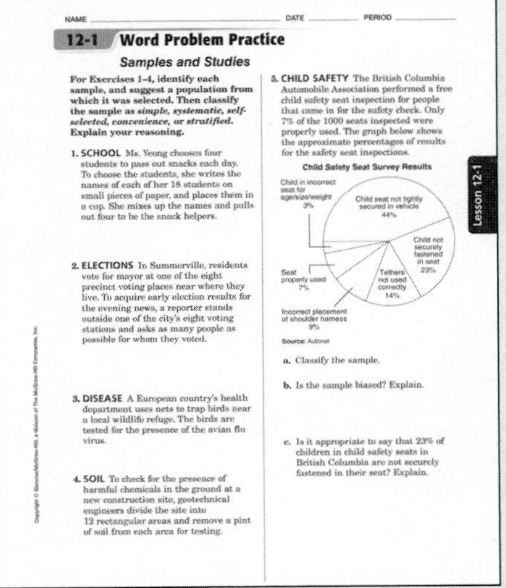
12-1 Word Problem Practice
Samples and Studies

For Exercises 1–4, identify each sample, and suggest a population from which it was selected. Then classify the sample as simple, systematic, self-selected, convenience, or stratified. Explain your reasoning.

1. SCHOOL Ms. Yeong chooses four students to pass out snacks each day. To choose the students, she writes the names of each of her 18 students on small pieces of paper, and places them in a cup. She mixes up the names and pulls out four to be the snack helpers.
2. ELECTIONS In Summerville, residents vote for mayor at one of the eight precinct voting places near where they live. To acquire early election results for the evening news, a reporter stands outside one of the city's eight voting stations and asks as many people as possible for whom they voted.
3. DISEASE A European country's health department uses nets to trap birds near a local wildlife refuge. The birds are tested for the presence of the avian flu virus.
4. SOIL To check for the presence of harmful chemicals in the ground at a new construction site, geotechnical engineers divide the site into 12 rectangular areas and remove a pint of soil from each area for testing.
5. CHILD SAFETY The British Columbia Automobile Association performed a free child safety seat inspection for people that came in for the safety check. Only 7% of the 1000 seats inspected were properly used. The graph below shows the approximate percentages of results for the safety seat inspections.

Child Safety Seat Survey Results
Source: Autonet

a. Classify the sample.
b. Is the sample biased? Explain.
c. Is it appropriate to say that 23% of children in child safety seats in British Columbia are not securely fastened in their seat? Explain.

Enrichment
OL BL

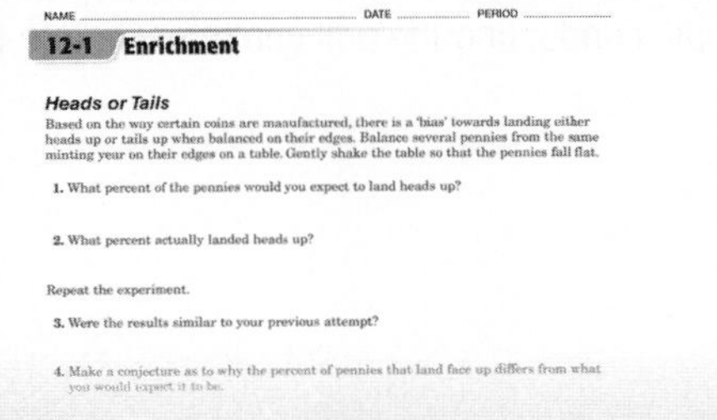
12-1 Enrichment

Heads or Tails
Based on the way certain coins are manufactured, there is a 'bias' towards landing either heads up or tails up when balanced on their edges. Balance several pennies from the same minting year on their edges on a table. Gently shake the table so that the pennies fall flat.

1. What percent of the pennies would you expect to land heads up?
2. What percent actually landed heads up?

Repeat the experiment.

3. Were the results similar to your previous attempt?
4. Make a conjecture as to why the percent of pennies that land face up differs from what you would expect it to be.

4 Assess

Ticket Out the Door Write an example of each type of random sample and give one to each student. As students leave the room, ask them to identify the sample, suggest a population, and then classify the sample.

Follow-up

Students have explored surveys.

Ask:

- What criteria would you use to determine whether a survey is biased? Sample answer: how the survey participants were chosen, the questions that were asked, the number of participants

Additional Answer

57.

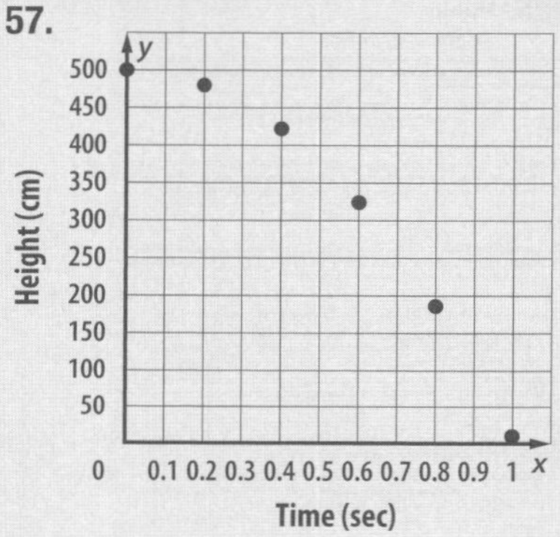

Standardized Test Practice

42. GRIDDED RESPONSE The first stage of a rocket burns 28 seconds longer than the second stage. If the total burning time for both stages is 152 seconds, how many seconds does the first stage burn? **90**

43. Ms. Brinkman invested \$30,000; part at 5%, and part at 8%. The total interest on the investment was \$2100 after one year. How much did she invest at 8%? **C**

A \$10,000	**C** \$20,000
B \$15,000	**D** \$25,000

44. A pair of \$25 jeans is on sale for 15% off. What is the sale price? **F**

F \$21.25	**H** \$23.25
G \$22.25	**J** \$24.25

45. GEOMETRY A piece of wire 42 centimeters long is bent into the shape of a rectangle with a width that is twice its length. Find the dimensions of the rectangle. **B**

A 5 cm, 12 cm	**C** 9 cm, 16 cm
B 7 cm, 14 cm	**D** 11 cm, 18 cm

Spiral Review

Solve each equation. State any extraneous solutions. (Lesson 11-8)

46. $\frac{3}{c} = \frac{2}{c+2}$ **−6**

47. $\frac{4}{f} = \frac{2}{f-3}$ **6**

48. $\frac{j}{j+2} = \frac{j-6}{j-2}$ **−6**

49. $\frac{h-2}{h} = \frac{h-2}{h-5}$ **2**

50. $\frac{3m}{4} + \frac{1}{3} = \frac{3m+4}{6}$ $\mathbf{\frac{4}{3}}$

51. $\frac{6}{5} + \frac{4p}{3} = \frac{8p}{5}$ $\mathbf{\frac{9}{2}}$

52. $\frac{r-2}{r+2} - \frac{3r}{r-2} = -2$ $\mathbf{-\frac{2}{5}}$

53. $\frac{t-3}{t+3} - \frac{2t}{t-3} = -1$ **0**

54. $\frac{4v}{2v+3} - \frac{2v}{2v-3} = 1$ $\mathbf{\frac{1}{2}}$

55. SPORTS When air is pumped into a ball, the pressure required can be computed by using the formula $P = \frac{3412.94}{\frac{4\pi r^3}{3}}$, where P represents the pressure in pounds per square inch (psi), and r is the radius of the ball in inches. (Lesson 11-7)

a. Simplify the complex fraction. $P = \frac{2559.705}{\pi r^3}$

b. Suppose the air pressure inside the ball is 8 psi. Approximate the radius of the ball to the nearest hundredth. **4.67 in.**

56. ROLLER COASTERS Suppose a roller coaster climbs 208 feet higher than its starting point, while making a horizontal advance of 360 feet. When it comes down, it makes a horizontal advance of 44 feet. (Lesson 10-5)

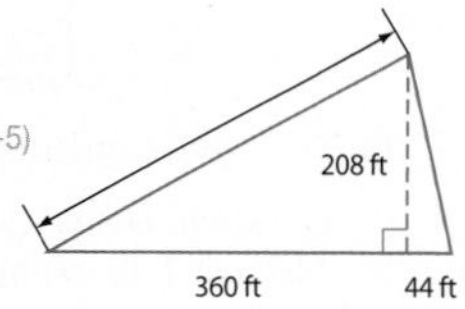

a. How far will it travel to get to the top of the ride? **about 415.8 ft**

b. How far will it travel on the downhill track? **about 212.6 ft**

Skills Check

57. PHYSICAL SCIENCE Mr. Blackwell's students recorded the height of an object above the ground at several intervals after it was dropped from a height of 5 meters. **See margin.**

Time (s)	0	0.2	0.4	0.6	0.8	1
Height (cm)	500	480	422	324	186	10

Draw a graph showing the relationship between the height of the falling object and time.

Differentiated Instruction OL BL

Extension Pass out examples of opinion polls taken from news magazines and newspapers. Have students identify the sample and the population for the poll. Then have students describe how the people conducting the poll could make sure the sample was not biased.

754 | Lesson 12-1 | Samples and Studies

EXTEND 12-1

Algebra Lab
Evaluating Published Data

An article in the *International Business Times* asserts that "the rate of decline in teen smoking in the United States has slowed down." This claim is supported by survey results from a study by the Centers for Disease Control and Prevention (CDC). This survey was conducted over an 18-year period from 1991 to 2009 and included a minimum of 10,904 to a maximum of 16,410 students in 110 to 159 high schools. The study reported cigarette use among high school students as shown in the following table. Current use was defined as smoking a cigarette at least one day in the last 30, while frequent use was defined as smoking at least 20 days in the last 30.

Content Standards
AI.DS.1, AI.DS.6

Process Standards
PS.3

Year	1991	1993	1995	1997	1999	2001	2003	2005	2007	2009
Current Use (%)	27.5	30.5	34.8	36.4	34.8	28.5	21.9	23.0	20.0	19.5
Frequent Use (%)	12.7	13.8	16.1	16.7	16.8	13.8	9.7	9.4	8.1	7.3

The report contained the following graph comparing the numbers of current high school smokers and adults who consider themselves smokers.

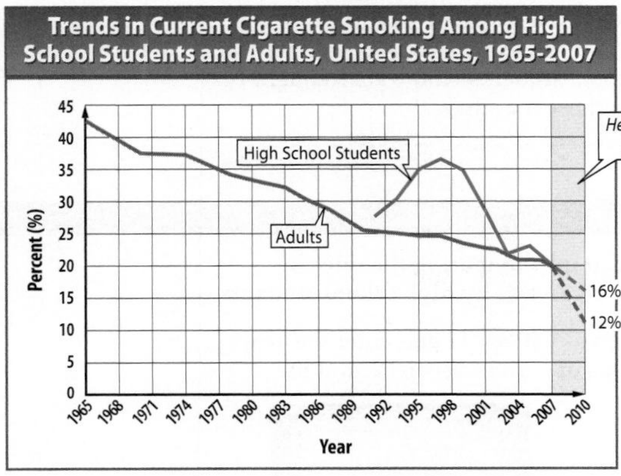

Activity 1 Evaluate the Design of a Study

Evaluate the design of this study and the source of the data.

a. What might be a problem that could occur when conducting this survey?

b. What biases could occur from their choice of a sample group?

a. A survey about activities that are deemed unacceptable might not get truthful responses from all students who complete the survey. Many students may refuse to complete the survey if they think the data might be used to punish them.

b. The study does not identify what types of schools were used in the survey. The sample may not represent all ethnic and economic groups that are found throughout the United States.

(continued on the next page)

1 Focus

Objective Evaluate reports based on data published in the media.

Materials for Each Student
- TI-83/84 Plus or other graphing calculator

Teaching Tip
Prior to beginning the activity, ask students to recall any examples of data used in the media to support a conclusion they believed to be invalid. Have the students discuss what errors may have been made in the study.

2 Teach

Working in Cooperative Groups
Have students work in groups of two or three to complete Activities 1, 2, and 3 and Exercises 3 and 4.

- Before starting Activity 1, have each group examine the report and discuss any problems that might affect the conclusions. Remind students to refer to Lesson 12-1 to review the biases that can occur in a study.
- Each student should make the double line graph on a graphing calculator. Have students help each other with keystrokes and commands.
- Students may use the Internet, magazines, or newspapers to find a report to evaluate for Exercise 4.

connectED.mcgraw-hill.com 755

3 Assess

Formative Assessment
Use Exercise 3 to assess whether students can evaluate a report based on data.

From Concrete to Abstract
After students complete Exercise 4, have each group present their evaluations to the entire class. Ask the class for possible reasons that the report was presented in a misleading way.

Algebra Lab
Evaluating Published Data *Continued*

Bias may be introduced when data are collected or by how the results are analyzed or reported.

Activity 2 Evaluate an Analysis and Display

For this study, evaluate how the data are analyzed and displayed.

a. **Is there a problem with the conclusion made in the article that the rate of decline in teen smoking is slowing? If so, what is it?**

b. **The graph appears to show that percentage of high school smokers is greater than the percentage of adult smokers. Is this accurate? Explain.**

a. The assertion generalizes all teens, while the survey was taken from high school students. Teens who have graduated or dropped out of school were not included and may have vastly different smoking habits than the sample group.

b. The line labeled *Adults* represents the percent of adults who classify themselves as current cigarette smokers. These adults would most likely be those who smoke on a daily basis. The line labeled *High School Students* is for those students who have smoked at least once in the last 30 days. A better comparison with adult smokers would be those high school students who were frequent smokers. These percents would be less than those for adults.

Activity 3 Compare Data

On a graphing calculator, make a double line graph comparing the rates of change of the current use and frequent use of cigarettes by high school students.

Step 1 First enter the data into **L1**, **L2**, and **L3**. Press STAT 1 and enter the years from 1991 to 2009 in **L1**, then the percents of current use in **L2**, and the percents for frequent use in **L3**.

Step 2 Use the **Stat Plot** function to produce a double line graph. Use **Plot1** to graph the line for the current use and **Plot2** to graph the line for the frequent use.

Step 3 Next, adjust the window settings and graph the double line graph.

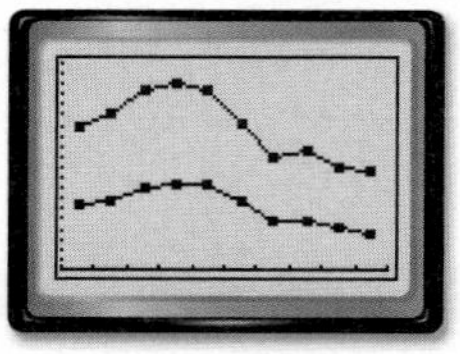

[1990, 2010] scl: 2 by [0, 40] scl: 2

Analyze the Results

1. Would a graph of frequent smokers imply a conclusion similar to the one implied by the graph of current smokers for all high school students? Explain. **Yes; sample answer: The graphs display similar patterns in their slopes.**
2. What might be a reason that the CDC would use the percents of current use rather than frequent use? **Sample answer: The greater percent would illustrate a greater need for continued antismoking programs for high school students.**
3. List five things to consider whenever you are evaluating published data in the media. **See margin.**
4. Find a report in the media and evaluate the published data using your list from Exercise 3. **See students' work.**

Additional Answer

3. Sample answer: What is the population for the data? Does the sample accurately represent the population? Were the data collected using the most appropriate type of study? If a survey was used, did the question(s) have any bias? Are any conclusions supported by the data? Do any graphs provided have consistent intervals on their axes? Are any comparisons being done on an equal basis?

LESSON 12-2 Statistics and Parameters

Then

- You analyzed data collection techniques.

Now

1. Identify sample statistics and population parameters.
2. Analyze data sets using statistics.

Why?

- At the start of every class period for one week, each of Mr. Day's algebra students randomly draws 9 pennies from a jar of 1000 pennies. Each student calculates the mean age of the random sample of pennies drawn and then returns the pennies to the jar.

How does the mean age for 9 pennies compare to the mean age of all 1000 pennies?

NewVocabulary
statistical inference
statistic
parameter
mean absolute deviation (MAD)
standard deviation
variance

Content Standards
AI.DS.1, AI.DS.6

Process Standards
PS.2, PS.6

1 Statistics and Parameters

The statistics of a sample are used to draw conclusions about the entire population. This is called **statistical inference**. In the scenario above, each student takes a random sample of pennies from the jar. The jar of 1000 pennies represents the population.

A **statistic** is a measure that describes a characteristic of a sample. A **parameter** is a measure that describes a characteristic of a population. Parameters are fixed values that can be determined by the entire population, but are typically estimated based on the statistics of a carefully chosen random sample. A statistic can and usually will vary from sample to sample. A parameter will not change, for it represents the entire population.

Example 1 Statistics and Parameters

Identify the sample and the population for each situation. Then describe the sample statistic and the population parameter.

a. At a local university, a random sample of 40 scholarship applicants is selected. The mean grade-point average of the 40 applicants is calculated.

Sample: the group of 40 scholarship applicants
Population: all applicants
Sample statistic: mean grade-point average of the sample
Population parameter: mean grade-point average of all applicants

b. A stratified random sample of registered nurses is selected from all hospitals in a three-county area, and the median salary is calculated.

Sample: randomly selected registered nurses from hospitals in the three-county area
Population: all nurses at the hospitals in the same region
Sample statistic: median salary of nurses in the sample
Population parameter: median salary of all nurses in all hospitals in a three-county area.

GuidedPractice

1. sample: boxes that are removed and weighed; population: all boxes made in the factory; sample statistic: mode weight of the weighed boxes; population parameter: mode weight of all boxes

1. **CEREAL** Starting with a randomly selected box of cereal from the manufacturing line, every 50th box of cereal is removed and weighed. The mode weight of a day's sample is calculated.

1 Focus

VerticalAlignment

Before Lesson 12-2 Analyze data collection techniques.

Lesson 12-2 Use statistics to analyze data.

After Lesson 12-2 Analyze distributions of data.

2 Teach

Scaffolding Questions

Have students read the **Why?** section of the lesson.

Ask:

- Will the mean ages of the students' samples of pennies vary? Explain. Sample answer: Yes; the samples are random, so each sample will have a different mix of ages of pennies.
- How is the mean of a sample of pennies different from the mean of all of the pennies? The mean of the samples will vary, but the mean of all of the pennies will not vary.

Lesson 12-2 Resources

Resource	Approaching Level AL	On Level OL	Beyond Level BL	English Learners ELL
Teacher Edition		▪ Differentiated Instruction, pp. 758, 763	▪ Differentiated Instruction, pp. 758, 763	
Chapter Resource Masters	▪ Study Guide and Intervention, pp. 11–12 ▪ Skills Practice, p. 13 ▪ Practice, p. 14 ▪ Word Problem Practice, p. 15	▪ Study Guide and Intervention, pp. 11–12 ▪ Skills Practice, p. 13 ▪ Practice, p. 14 ▪ Word Problem Practice, p. 15 ▪ Enrichment, p. 16	▪ Practice, p. 14 ▪ Word Problem Practice, p. 15 ▪ Enrichment, p. 16	▪ Study Guide and Intervention, pp. 11–12 ▪ Skills Practice, p. 13 ▪ Practice, p. 14 ▪ Word Problem Practice, p. 15
Other	▪ 5-Minute Check 12-2 ▪ Study Notebook	▪ 5-Minute Check 12-2 ▪ Study Notebook	▪ 5-Minute Check 12-2 ▪ Study Notebook	▪ 5-Minute Check 12-2 ▪ Study Notebook

1 Statistics and Parameters

Example 1 shows how to identify statistics in a sample and the parameters in a population.

Formative Assessment

Use the Guided Practice exercises after each example to determine students' understanding of concepts.

Additional Example

1 Identify the sample and the population for each situation. Then describe the sample statistic and the population parameter.

a. A movie rental business selects a random sample of 50 orders in one day. The median number of rentals per order is calculated. sample: 50 movie orders; population: all movie orders for the day of the sample; sample statistic: median number of rentals per order in the sample; population parameter: median number of rentals per order for all rentals the day of the sample

b. A stratified random sample of 2 trees of each species is selected from all trees at a nursery. The mean height of trees in the sample is calculated. sample: 2 trees of each species found at the nursery; population: all trees at the nursery; sample statistic: mean height of trees in the sample; population parameter: mean height of all trees at the nursery

Additional Examples also in Interactive Classroom PowerPoint® Presentations

IWB Interactive White Board READY

2 Statistical Analysis

As shown in Lesson 0-12, univariate data can be represented by measures of central tendency, such as the mean, median, and mode. Univariate data can also be represented by measures of variation that assess the variability of the data. Some examples are the range, quartiles, interquartile range, mean absolute deviation, and standard deviation.

The **mean absolute deviation (MAD)** is the average of the absolute values of the differences between the mean and each value in the data set. The mean absolute deviation is used to predict errors and judge how well the mean represents the data.

StudyTip

Ellipsis The ellipsis in the formula for MAD denotes "and so on". All of the terms between the second term and the last term are implied to save space.

KeyConcept Mean Absolute Deviation

Step 1 Find the mean, $\bar{x}$.

Step 2 Find the absolute value of the difference between each data value x_n and the mean, $|\bar{x} - x_n|$.

Step 3 Find the sum of all of the values in Step 2.

Step 4 Divide the sum by the number of values in the set of data n.

Formula $\text{MAD} = \frac{|\bar{x} - x_1| + |\bar{x} - x_2| + \ldots + |\bar{x} - x_n|}{n}$

Example 2 Mean Absolute Deviation

MARKETING **Each person who visited the Comic Book Shoppe's Web site was asked to enter the number of comic books they buy each month. They received the following responses in one day: {2, 2, 3, 4, 14}. Find and interpret the mean absolute deviation.**

Step 1 Find the mean.

$\bar{x} = \frac{2 + 2 + 3 + 4 + 14}{5}$ or 5

Step 2 Find the absolute values of the differences.

$x_1 = 2: |\bar{x} - x_1| = |5 - 2|$ or 3 $x_2 = 2: |\bar{x} - x_2| = |5 - 2|$ or 3

$x_3 = 3: |\bar{x} - x_3| = |5 - 3|$ or 2 $x_4 = 4: |\bar{x} - x_4| = |5 - 4|$ or 1

$x_5 = 14: |\bar{x} - x_5| = |5 - 14|$ or 9

Step 3 Find the sum.

$3 + 3 + 2 + 1 + 9 = 18$

Step 4 Find the mean absolute deviation.

$\text{MAD} = \frac{|\bar{x} - x_1| + |\bar{x} - x_2| + \ldots + |\bar{x} - x_n|}{n}$ Formula for Mean Absolute Deviation

$= \frac{18}{5}$ or 3.6 The sum is 18 and $n = 5$.

A mean absolute deviation of 3.6 indicates that the data, on average, are 3.6 units away from the mean. This value is significantly influenced by the outlier 14. Without the outlier, the data set would have a mean of 2.75 and a mean absolute deviation of 0.75.

GuidedPractice

2. 9; Sample answer: On average, daily ticket sales are 9 tickets away from the mean of 36 tickets.

2. DANCES The prom committee kept a count of how many tickets it sold each day during lunch: {12, 32, 36, 41, 22, 47, 51, 33, 37, 49}. Find and interpret the mean absolute deviation of these data.

DifferentiatedInstruction OL BL

If students demonstrate understanding of how to use mean absolute deviation,

Then have students describe how they can use the mean absolute deviation to predict errors and to judge equality. For example, what does a greater or lesser value for the mean absolute deviation indicate when predicting the number of comics a certain group of people will purchase each month? Encourage students to use examples to explain their reasoning.

In a set of data, the **standard deviation** shows how the data deviate from the mean. A low standard deviation indicates that the data tend to be very close to the mean, while a high standard deviation indicates that the data are spread out over a larger range of values.

The standard deviation is represented by the lowercase Greek letter sigma, σ. The **variance** σ^2 of the data is the square of the standard deviation.

StudyTip

Symbols The mean of a sample and the mean of a population are calculated the same way. $\bar{x}$ refers to the mean of a sample and μ refers to the mean of a population. In this text, $\bar{x}$ will refer to both.

KeyConcept Standard Deviation

Step 1 Find the mean, $\bar{x}$.

Step 2 Find the square of the difference between each data value x_n and the mean, $(\bar{x} - x_n)^2$.

Step 3 Find the sum of all of the values in Step 2.

Step 4 Divide the sum by the number of values in the set of data n. This value is the variance.

Step 5 Take the square root of the variance.

Formula $\sigma = \sqrt{\dfrac{(\bar{x} - x_1)^2 + (\bar{x} - x_2)^2 + \ldots + (\bar{x} - x_n)^2}{n}}$

PT

Example 3 Variance and Standard Deviation

ELECTRONICS Ed surveys his classmates to find out how many electronic gadgets each person has in their home. Find and interpret the standard deviation of the data set.

{9, 10, 11, 6, 9, 11, 9, 8, 11, 8, 7, 9, 11, 11, 5}

Step 1 Find the mean.

$$\bar{x} = \frac{9 + 10 + 11 + 6 + 9 + 11 + 9 + 8 + 11 + 8 + 7 + 9 + 11 + 11 + 5}{15} \text{ or } 9$$

Step 2 Find the square of the differences, $(\bar{x} - x_n)^2$.

$(9-9)^2 = 0$	$(9-10)^2 = 1$	$(9-11)^2 = 4$	$(9-6)^2 = 9$	$(9-9)^2 = 0$
$(9-11)^2 = 4$	$(9-9)^2 = 0$	$(9-8)^2 = 1$	$(9-11)^2 = 4$	$(9-8)^2 = 1$
$(9-7)^2 = 4$	$(9-9)^2 = 0$	$(9-11)^2 = 4$	$(9-11)^2 = 4$	$(9-5)^2 = 16$

Step 3 Find the sum.

$$0 + 1 + 4 + 9 + 0 + 4 + 0 + 1 + 4 + 1 + 4 + 0 + 4 + 4 + 16 = 52$$

Step 4 Find the variance.

$$\sigma^2 = \frac{(\bar{x} - x_1)^2 + (\bar{x} - x_2)^2 + \ldots + (\bar{x} - x_n)^2}{n} \qquad \text{Formula for Variance}$$

$$= \frac{52}{15} \text{ or about } 3.47 \qquad \text{The sum is 52 and } n = 15.$$

Step 5 Find the standard deviation.

$$\sigma = \sqrt{\sigma^2} \qquad \text{Square Root of the Variance}$$

$$\approx \sqrt{3.47} \text{ or about } 1.86$$

A standard deviation of 1.86 is small compared to the mean of 9. This suggests that most of the data values are relatively close to the mean.

GuidedPractice

3. 67.8; Sample answer: the standard deviation is very small compared to the mean, so most of the data values are very close to the mean of 2007 Calories.

3. DIET Caleb tracked his Calorie intake for a week. Find and interpret the standard deviation of his Calorie intake.

1950, 2000, 2100, 2000, 1900, 2100, 2000

Statistical Analysis

Example 2 shows how to find and interpret the mean absolute deviation of a data set. **Example 3** shows how to find and interpret the standard deviation of a data set. **Example 4** shows how to compare two sets of data using the mean and standard deviation.

Additional Examples

2 PETS A rescue agency records the number of pets adopted each month: {14, 18, 12, 17, 15, 20}. Find and interpret the mean absolute deviation. ≈ 2.3; On average, the monthly number of pets adopted each month is about 2.3 pets from the mean of 16 pets.

3 SCORES Leo tracked his homework scores for the past week: {100, 0, 100, 50, 0}. Find and interpret the standard deviation of the data set. ≈ 44.7; A standard deviation very close to the mean suggests that the data deviate quite a bit. Most of Leo's scores are far away from the mean of 50.

Teach with Tech

Interactive Whiteboard Use a spreadsheet or other software program to calculate various statistics from data collected from a survey. Keep this information displayed on the board as you teach students what it means and how to interpret it.

Focus on Mathematical Content

Measures of Variation Measures of variation show the spread of the data. Range describes the spread of all values in the data. Quartiles and interquartile range describe the spread in the middle half of the data. Mean absolute deviation, variance, and standard deviation describe the spread around the mean. Two data sets can have the same range and mean, but the spread around the mean can be quite different.

The Math Forum

mathforum.org The Math Forum @ Drexel University

Have your students refer to the Math Forum's Ask Dr. Math to learn more about the measures of dispersion. They can start their search at connectED.mcgraw-hill.com.

Additional Example

4 **BASEBALL** Kyle can throw a baseball left-handed or right-handed. Below are the speeds in miles per hour of 16 throws from each hand. Compare the means and standard deviations.

Left-Handed			
68	71	70	69
67	67	73	71
74	68	68	71
72	70	66	70

Right-Handed			
71	78	77	70
81	72	74	80
70	69	79	83
81	68	83	82

Sample answer: The left-handed throws had a mean of about 69.7 miles per hour with a standard deviation of about 2.2. The right-handed throws had a mean of about 76.1 miles per hour with a standard deviation of about 5.3. While the right-handed throws had a higher average speed, there was also greater variability in the speeds of the throws.

3 Practice

Formative Assessment

Use Exercises 1–4 to check for understanding.

Use the chart at the bottom of this page to customize assignments for your students.

Additional Answer

1. sample: 1000 college students; population: all college students in the United States; sample statistic: mean of the money spent on books in a year by the sample; population parameter: mean of money spent on books by all college students in the United States

The mean and standard deviation can be used to compare two different sets of data.

StudyTip

Symbols The standard deviation of a sample s and the standard deviation of a population σ are calculated in different ways. In this text, you will calculate the standard deviation of a population.

Example 4 Compare Two Sets of Data

Miguel plays golf at Table Rock and Blackhawk golf courses. Compare the means and standard deviations of each set of Miguel's scores.

Table Rock				
81	78	79	82	80
80	79	83	81	80

Blackhawk				
84	79	86	78	77
88	85	79	87	86

Use a graphing calculator to find the mean and standard deviation. Clear all lists. Then press STAT ENTER, and enter each data value into L1. To view the statistics, press STAT ▶ 1 ENTER.

Table Rock

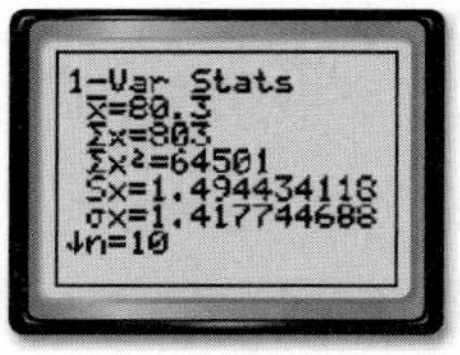

Blackhawk

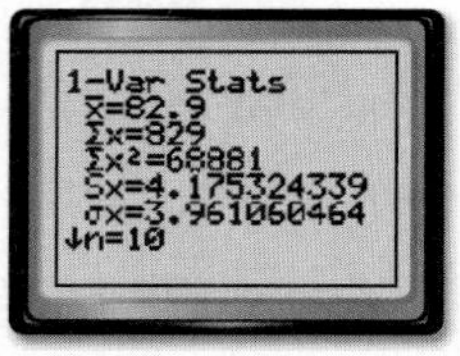

Miguel's mean score at Table Rock is 80.3 with a standard deviation of about 1.4. His mean score at Blackhawk is 82.9 with a standard deviation of about 4.0. Therefore, he tends to score lower at Table Rock. The greater standard deviation at Blackhawk indicates that there is greater variability to his scores at that course, but he is more consistent at Table Rock.

GuidedPractice

4. **SWIMMING** Anna is considering two different lineups for her 4 × 100 relay team. Below are the times in minutes recorded for each lineup. Compare the means and standard deviations of each set of data.

Lineup A				
4.25	4.31	4.19	4.40	4.23
4.18	4.71	4.56	4.32	4.39

Lineup B				
4.47	4.68	4.25	4.41	4.49
4.18	4.27	4.69	4.32	4.44

4. Sample answer: Lineup A had a mean time of 4.354 with a standard deviation of 0.16 while Lineup B had a mean time of 4.42 with a standard deviation of 0.16. Therefore, since the times for both lineups have the same variability and Lineup A has a lower mean time, Anna should use Lineup A.

Check Your Understanding

○ = Step-by-Step Solutions begin on page R13.

1–4. See margin.

Example 1 — 1. **BOOKS** A stratified random sample of 1000 college students in the United States is surveyed about how much money they spend on books per year. Identify the sample and the population. Then describe the sample statistic and the population parameter.

Example 2 — 2. **AMUSEMENT PARKS** An amusement park manager kept track of how many bags of cotton candy they sold each hour on a Saturday: {16, 24, 15, 17, 22, 16, 18, 24, 17, 13, 25, 21}. Find and interpret the mean absolute deviation.

Example 3 — 3. **PART-TIME JOBS** Ms. Johnson asks all of the members of the girls' tennis team to find the number of hours each week they work at part-time jobs: {10, 12, 0, 6, 9, 15, 12, 10, 11, 20}. Find and interpret the standard deviation of the data set.

Example 4 — 4. **MODELING** Mr. Jones recorded the number of pull-ups done by his students. Compare the means and standard deviations of each group.
Boys: {5, 16, 3, 8, 4, 12, 2, 15, 0, 1, 9, 3} Girls: {2, 4, 0, 3, 5, 4, 6, 1, 3, 8, 3, 4}

Differentiated Homework Options

Level	Assignment	Two-Day Option	
AL Basic	5–13, 16–18, 20–38	5–13 (odd), 22–25	6–12 (even), 16–18, 20, 21, 26–38
OL Core	5–13 (odd), 14–18, 20–38	5–13, 22–25	14–18, 20, 21, 26–38
BL Advanced	14–32, (optional: 33–38)		

Practice and Problem Solving

Extra Practice is on page R12.

Example 1 **Identify the sample and the population for each situation. Then describe the sample statistic and the population parameter.** 5–7. See margin.

5. **POLITICS** A random sample of 1003 Mercy County voters is asked if they would vote for the incumbent for governor. The percent responding *yes* is calculated.

6. **ACTIVITIES** A stratified random sample of high school students from each school in the county was polled about the time spent each week on extracurricular activities.

7. **MONEY** A stratified random sample of 2500 high school students across the country was asked how much money they spent each month.

Example 2

8. **DVDS** A math teacher asked all of his students to count the number of DVDs they owned. Find and interpret the mean absolute deviation. See margin.

Number of DVDs					
26	39	5	82	12	14
0	3	15	19	41	6
2	0	11	1	19	29

9. **SWIMMING** The owner of a public swimming pool tracked the daily attendance. Find and interpret the mean absolute deviation. See margin.

Daily Attendance					
86	45	91	104	95	88
111	85	79	102	166	103
89	94	79	103	88	84

Example 3

10. **REASONING** Samantha wants to see if she is getting a fair wage for babysitting at $8.50 per hour. She takes a survey of her friends to see what they charge per hour. The results are {$8.00, $8.50, $9.00, $7.50, $15.00, $8.25, $8.75}. Find and interpret the standard deviation of the data. See margin.

11. **ARCHERY** Carla participates in competitive archery. Each competition allows a maximum of 90 points. Carla's results for the last 8 competitions are {76, 78, 81, 75, 80, 80, 76, 77}. Find and interpret the standard deviation of the data. See margin.

Example 4

12. **BASKETBALL** The coach of the Wildcats basketball team is comparing the number of fouls called against his team with the number called against their rivals, the Trojans. He records the number of fouls called against each team for each game of the season. Compare the means and standard deviations of each set of data. See Chapter 12 Answer Appendix.

Wildcats			
15	12	13	9
11	12	14	12
8	16	9	9
11	13	12	14

Trojans			
9	10	14	13
7	8	10	10
9	7	11	9
12	11	13	8

13. **MOVIE RATINGS** Two movies were rated by the same group of students. Ratings were from 1 to 10, with 10 being the best. See Chapter 12 Answer Appendix.

a. Compare the means and standard deviations of each set of data.

b. Provide an argument for why Movie A would be preferred. Movie B?

Movie A			
7	8	7	6
8	6	7	8
6	8	8	6
7	7	8	8

Movie B			
9	5	10	6
3	10	9	4
8	3	9	9
2	8	10	3

Additional Answers

2. 3.5; Sample answer: On average, hourly cotton candy sales are 3.5 bags away from the mean of 19 bags.
3. 4.98; Sample answer: The standard deviation is relatively high due to outliers 0 and 20.
4. Sample answer: The boys had a mean of 6.5 pull-ups with a standard deviation of about 5.2 pull-ups. The girls had a mean of about 3.6 pull-ups with a standard deviation of about 2.1 pull-ups. The boys had a higher average, but there was much more variability in the data set. The girls had a lower average number of pull-ups, but their data values were more consistent.
5. sample: 1003 voters in Mercy County; population: all voters in Mercy County; sample statistic: the number of people in the sample who would vote for the incumbent candidate; population parameter: the number of people in the county who would vote for the incumbent candidate
6. sample: stratified random sample from schools in the county; population: all high school students in the county; sample statistic: time spent each week on extracurricular activities by the sample; population parameter: time spent each week on extracurricular activities by all students in the county
7. sample: stratified random sample of 2500; population: high school students in the country; sample statistic: how much money the 2500 students spent each month; population parameter: how much money all the students in the country spent each month
8. 14.3; Sample answer: On average, each data value is about 14 DVDs away from the mean of 18 DVDs. The mean absolute deviation is so close to the mean of the data because the data are very spread out with many of the values either very high (82, 41, 39) or very low (0, 0, 1).

9. 14; Sample answer: On average, each day's attendance is 14 people from the mean of 94 people. The mean absolute deviation is affected by outliers 45 and 166.
10. 2.4; Sample answer: With a mean of about $9.29, the standard deviation of about $2.38 suggests that there is a good amount of deviation to the data. This deviation is mostly caused by the outlier of $15.00. If this outlier were removed, the new mean of the data would be about $8.33 with a standard deviation of about $0.49.
11. 2.1; Sample answer: With a mean of 77.875, the standard deviation of about 2.1 suggests that there is a very little deviation to the data. Therefore, you can conclude that Carla's archery scores are pretty consistent.

B **14. PENNIES** Mr. Day has another jar of pennies on his desk. There are 30 pennies in this jar. Theo chooses 5 pennies from the jar. Lola chooses 10 pennies, and Peter chooses 20 pennies. Pennies are chosen and replaced.

a. Theo's pennies are {1974, 1975, 1981, 1999, 1992}. Find the mean absolute deviation. **≈9.0**

b. Lola's pennies are {2004, 1999, 2004, 2005, 1991, 2003, 2005, 2000, 2001, 1998}. Find the mean absolute deviation. **≈3.2**

c. Peter's pennies are {2007, 2005, 1975, 2003, 2005, 1997, 1992, 1994, 1991, 1992, 2000, 1999, 2005, 1982, 2005, 2004, 1998, 2001, 2002, 2006}. Find the mean absolute deviation. **≈6.5**

Years of Pennies in Jar					
2001	1990	2000	1982	1991	1975
2007	1981	2005	2007	2003	2005
1997	1974	1992	1994	1991	1992
2000	1995	1999	2005	2006	2005
2004	2004	1998	2001	2002	2006

d. Find the mean absolute deviation for all of the pennies in the jar. Which sample most accurately reflected the population mean? Explain. **See margin.**

15. RUNNING The results of a 5K race are published in a local paper. Over a thousand people participated, but only the times of the top 15 finishers are listed.

15th Annual 5K Road Race					
Place	Time (min:s)	Place	Time (min:s)	Place	Time (min:s)
1	15:56	6	16:34	11	17:14
2	16:06	7	16:41	12	17:46
3	16:11	8	16:54	13	17:56
4	16:21	9	17:00	14	17:57
5	16:26	10	17:03	15	18:03

a. Find the mean and standard deviation of the top 15 running times. (*Hint*: Convert each time to seconds.) **≈16.9 min, ≈41.4 seconds**

b. Identify the sample and population. **See margin.**

c. Analyze the sample. Classify the data as *quantitative* or *qualitative*. Can a statistical analysis of the sample be applied to the population? Explain your reasoning. **See margin.**

H.O.T. Problems Use Higher-Order Thinking Skills

C **16. CRITIQUE** Jennifer and Megan are determining one way to decrease the size of the standard deviation of a set of data. Is either of them correct? Explain. **See margin.**

Jennifer	Megan
Remove the outliers from the data set.	Add data values to the data set that are equal to the mean.

17. REASONING Determine whether the statement *Two random samples taken from the same population will have the same mean and standard deviation* is *sometimes*, *always*, or *never* true. Explain. **See margin.**

18. OPEN ENDED Describe a situation in which it would be useful to use a sample mean to help estimate a population mean. How could you collect a random sample? **See Ch. 12 Answer Appendix.**

19. CHALLENGE Write a set of data with a standard deviation that is equal to the mean absolute deviation. **See Ch. 12 Answer Appendix.**

WRITING IN MATH Compare and contrast each of the following. **20, 21. See Ch. 12 Answer Appendix.**

20. statistics and parameters

21. standard deviation and mean absolute deviation

Additional Answer

14d. ≈7.1; Peter's sample was the most accurate. The mean year of his sample was 1 year off from the actual mean year. The samples that had more pennies were more accurate.

Study Guide and Intervention
AL OL ELL

NAME ______ DATE ______ PERIOD ______

12-2 Study Guide and Intervention

Statistics and Parameters

Statistics and Parameters A **statistic** is a measure that describes a characteristic of a sample. A **parameter** is a measure that describes a characteristic of a population. Statistics can change from sample to sample while parameters do not.

Example **Identify the sample and the population for each situation. Then describe the sample statistic and the population parameter.**

a. At a local supermarket, a random sample of 50 shoppers is selected. The median amount spent at the supermarket is calculated for the sample.

Sample: the group of 50 shoppers
Population: all shoppers at the supermarket
Sample statistic: median amount of time spent by shoppers in the sample
Population parameter: median amount by all shoppers spent at the supermarket

b. Every 20 minutes at a furniture factory, a finished sofa is pulled from the assembly line and checked for defects. The percentage of sofas in the sample which are defective is then calculated.

Sample: the sofas checked for defects
Population: all sofas manufactured
Sample statistic: percentage of defective sofas in the sample
Population parameter: percentage of all sofas which are defective

Exercises

Identify the sample and the population for each situation. Then describe the sample statistic and the population parameter.

1. **WEATHER** A meteorologist places ten weather stations in a county to measure rainfall. The mean annual rainfall is calculated for the sample.

2. **BOTANY** A scientist randomly selects 20 trees in a forest. The mean height of the 20 trees is then calculated.

3. **POLITICS** A political reporter randomly selects 25 congressional districts across the country. The mean number of votes cast in the 25 congressional districts is calculated.

Lesson 12-2

Practice
AL OL BL ELL

NAME ______ DATE ______ PERIOD ______

12-2 Practice

Statistics and Parameters

Identify the sample and the population for each situation. Then describe the sample statistic and the population parameter.

1. **MARINE BIOLOGY** A marine biologist randomly selects 30 oysters from a research tank. The mean weight of the 30 oysters is calculated.

2. **CIVIL ENGINEERING** A civic engineer randomly selects 10 city intersections with traffic lights. The mean length of a red light is calculated for the sample.

3. **BASEBALL** A baseball commissioner randomly selects 10 home games played by a major league team. The mean attendance is calculated for the games in the sample.

Find and interpret the mean absolute deviation.

4. **INVESTING** A stock broker keeps a record of the daily closing price of a share of stock in Bicsomm Corporation: {45.20, 46.10, 46.85, 42.55, 40.80}.

5. **GOLF** A golfer keeps track of his scores for each round: {78, 81, 86, 77, 75}.

Find and interpret the standard deviation of each set of data.

6. {6, 11, 19, 9}

7. {2, 5, 8, 11, 4}

8. {145, 166, 171, 150, 188}

9. {13, 24, 22, 17, 14, 19, 15, 22}

10. **QUALITY CONTROL** An inspector checks each automobile that comes off of the assembly line. He keeps a record of the number of defective cars each day: {3, 1, 2, 0, 0, 4, 3, 6, 1, 2}. Find and interpret the standard deviation.

Word Problem Practice
AL OL BL ELL

NAME ______ DATE ______ PERIOD ______

12-2 Word Problem Practice

Statistics and Parameters

1. **GAS PRICES** Renee is planning a road trip to her aunt's house. To estimate how much the trip will cost, she goes online and finds the price of a gallon of gasoline for 5 randomly selected gas stations along the route. She then calculates the mean price per gallon for the 5 selected gas stations.
   a. Identify the sample and the population.
   b. Describe the sample statistic and the population parameter.

2. **FOOTBALL** The following table shows information about the number of carries a running back had over a number of years. Find and interpret the standard deviation of the number of carries.

Year	Number of Carries	Yards per Carry	Yards	Touchdowns
2006	31	4.8	148	0
2007	90	4.2	378	2
2008	105	4.0	420	3
2009	115	3.3	379	7
2010	162	3.7	602	9

3. **HOCKEY** A hockey team keeps track of how many goals it scores each game: {2, 4, 0, 3, 7, 2}. Find and interpret the standard deviation of the data.

4. **ERROR ANALYSIS** Myau hypothesizes that the variance of a set of data will always be greater than the standard deviation. Alice believes that the standard variation can be a greater number than the variance. Who is correct? Explain.

5. **HEALTH CLUBS** To plan their future equipment purchases, the Northville Health Club randomly chooses 8 patrons and tracks how many minutes they spend on the treadmill: {30, 30, 45, 20, 60, 30, 30, 45}. The mean treadmill time is then calculated.
   a. Identify the sample and the population. Then describe the sample statistic and the population parameter.
   b. Find the sample statistic specified in part **a**.
   c. Find and interpret the mean absolute deviation and standard deviation for the sample.

Lesson 12-2

Enrichment
OL BL

NAME ______ DATE ______ PERIOD ______

12-2 Enrichment

Standard Error and Confidence Limits

You just learned about standard deviation, which measures how widely spread data points in a sample are—essentially, how far data points are from the mean.

Another key statistical measure is the **standard error of the mean**, or $S_{\bar{x}}$. The standard error of the mean describes the uncertainty of how the sample mean represents the population mean, and is given by the equation $S_{\bar{x}} = \frac{\sigma}{\sqrt{n}}$, where σ is the standard deviation and n is the sample size.

The equation for the standard error indicates that the larger the sample size is, the smaller the standard error will be. The standard error is often described in terms of percentages called **confidence limits**.

$$95\% \text{ confidence limit interval} = \bar{x} \pm 1.96S_{\bar{x}}$$
$$99\% \text{ confidence limit interval} = \bar{x} \pm 2.58S_{\bar{x}}$$

Example **The standard deviation of the weight of individual apples at Mr. Maguire's stand is 0.8 ounces. The mean weight of a sample of 25 apples is 5.2 ounces. Find the 99% confidence interval for the mean.**

Standardized Test Practice

22. Melina bought a shirt that was marked 20% off. She paid \$15.75. What was the original price? **D**

A \$16.69 C \$18.69
B \$17.69 D \$19.69

23. SHORT RESPONSE A group of student ambassadors visited the Capitol building. Twenty students met with the local representative. This was 16% of the students. How many student ambassadors were there altogether? **125**

24. The tallest 7 trees in a park have heights in meters of 19, 24, 17, 26, 24, 20, and 18. Find the mean absolute deviation of their heights. **F**

F 3.0 H 3.4
G 3.2 J 21

25. It takes 3 hours for a boat to travel 27 miles upstream. The same boat can travel 30 miles downstream in 2 hours. Find the speed of the boat. **C**

A 3 mph C 12 mph
B 5 mph D 14 mph

Spiral Review

Identify each sample as *biased* or *unbiased*. Explain your reasoning. (Lesson 12-1)

26. SHOPPING Every tenth person walking into the mall is asked to name their favorite store. **Unbiased; the sample is a random selection of people with no evidence of influence.**

27. MUSIC Every fifth person at a rock concert is asked to name their favorite radio station. **Biased; because they are at a rock concert, they are more likely to select a rock music station.**

Simplify each expression. (Lesson 11-3)

28. $\frac{x^2-8x+15}{x^2+3x-18} \quad \frac{x-5}{x+6}$

29. $\frac{x^2-x-12}{x^2-6x+8} \quad \frac{x+3}{x-2}$

30. $\frac{x^2-x-30}{x^2-4x-12} \quad \frac{x+5}{x+2}$

31. SOCCER The number of members of the local soccer association has increased by 6% every year. As of the beginning of 2010, there were 880 members. (Lesson 7-6)

a. Write an equation for the number of members of the association t years after 2010. $y = 880(1.06)^t$

b. If this trend continues, predict how many members the association will have in 2020. **about 1576 members**

32. GEOMETRY If the side length of a cube is s, the volume is represented by s^3, and the surface area is represented by $6s^2$. (Lessons 7-1 and 7-2)

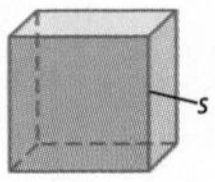

a. Are the expressions for volume and surface area monomials? Explain. **Yes; each is the product of variables and/or a real number.**

b. If the side of a cube measures 3 feet, find the volume and surface area. **27 ft³; 54 ft²**

c. Find a side length s such that the volume and surface area have the same measure. **6 units**

d. The volume of a cylinder can be found by multiplying the radius squared times the height times π, or $V = \pi r^2 h$. Suppose you have two cylinders. Each measure of the second is twice the measure of the first, so $V = \pi(2r)^2(2h)$. What is the ratio of the volume of the first cylinder to the second cylinder? **1:8**

Skills Review

Find the range, median, lower quartile, and upper quartile for each set of data.

33. {15, 23, 46, 36, 15, 19} **31; 21; 15; 36**

34. {55, 57, 39, 72, 46, 53, 81} **42; 55; 46; 72**

35. {21, 25, 19, 18, 22, 16, 27} **11; 21; 18; 25**

36. {52, 29, 72, 64, 33, 49, 51, 68} **43; 51.5; 41; 66**

37. {8, 12, 9, 11, 11, 10, 14, 18} **10; 11; 9.5; 13**

38. {133, 119, 147, 94, 141, 106, 118, 149} **55; 126; 112; 144**

Differentiated Instruction OL BL

Extension Have students compute the range and the standard deviation for a few different data sets. Ask them to compare the values and see if they can make any generalizations about the relationship between range and standard deviation. For large data sets, the range is usually from 4 to 6 times as large as the standard deviation. This provides a rule of thumb that is sometimes used to find a quick estimate of standard deviation without going through the complete calculation.

Teaching the Process Standards

Critique Mathematically proficient students are able to compare the effectiveness of two plausible arguments. In Exercise 16, have students make up a data set and test Jennifer's and Megan's statements.

4 Assess

Yesterday's News Have students write a sentence on how yesterday's lesson on summarizing and analyzing survey results helped with today's lesson on sample statistics and population parameters.

Formative Assessment

Check for student understanding of concepts in Lessons 12-1 and 12-2.

Quiz 1, p. 57

Additional Answers

15b. The sample is the first 15 finishers of the race. The population is all of the people who ran the race.

15c. The data is quantitative. No, since the sample is the top 15 runners in the race, it is not random. So, it would not be accurate to apply the mean and standard deviation of the running times to the population.

16. Both; sample answer: When an outlier is removed from a set of data, the spread and standard deviation of the data will decrease. When more values that are equal to the mean of a data set are added to the data set, the mean will be stronger and outliers will have less influence.

17. Sometimes; if the samples are truly random, they would rarely contain identical elements and the mean and standard deviation would differ. If the sample produces identical elements, the mean and standard deviation would be the same.

1 Focus

VerticalAlignment

Before Lesson 12-3 You calculated measures of central tendency and variation.

Lesson 12-3 Describe the shape of a distribution. Use the shapes of distributions to select appropriate statistics.

After Lesson 12-3 Compare sets of data using appropriate statistics.

2 Teach

Scaffolding Questions

Have students read the **Why?** section of the lesson.

Ask:

- Why is Sarah's average time so much different than her median time? Sample answer: The times that Sarah recorded after pulling a muscle in her back probably raised her average time. Her median time was less affected by the higher times.
- Which time is a better representation of Sarah's 100-meter dash time? Explain. Sample answer: Her median time is probably a better representation since it is less affected by any outliers or times that are not a true reflection of Sarah's normal times.

LESSON 12-3 Distributions of Data

Then

- You calculated measures of central tendency and variation.

Now

1. Describe the shape of a distribution.
2. Use the shapes of distributions to select appropriate statistics.

Why?

- While training for the 100-meter dash, Sarah pulled a muscle in her lower back. After being cleared for practice, she continued to train. Sarah's median time was about 12.34 seconds, but her average time dropped to about 12.53 seconds.

NewVocabulary
distribution
negatively skewed distribution
symmetric distribution
positively skewed distribution

Process Standards
PS.5

1 Describing Distributions

A **distribution** of data shows the observed or theoretical frequency of each possible data value. Recall that a histogram is a type of bar graph used to display data that have been organized into equal intervals. A histogram is useful when viewing the overall distribution of the data within a set over its range. You can see the shape of the distribution by drawing a curve over the histogram.

KeyConcept Symmetric and Skewed Distributions

Negatively Skewed Distribution

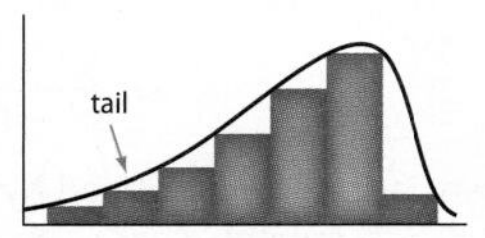

The majority of the data are on the right.

Symmetric Distribution

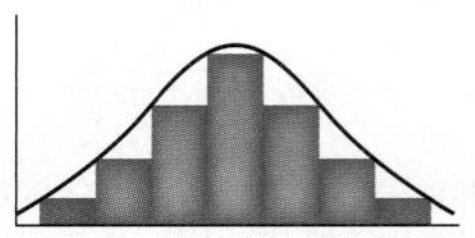

The data are evenly distributed.

Positively Skewed Distribution

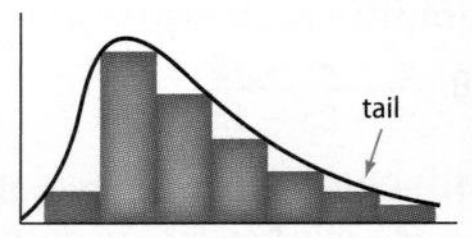

The majority of the data are on the left.

Example 1 Distribution Using a Histogram

Use a graphing calculator to construct a histogram for the data, and use it to describe the shape of the distribution.

25, 22, 31, 25, 26, 35, 18, 39, 22, 32, 34, 26, 42, 23, 40, 36, 18, 30
26, 30, 37, 23, 19, 33, 24, 29, 39, 21, 43, 25, 34, 24, 26, 30, 21, 22

First, press STAT ENTER and enter each data value. Then, press 2nd [STAT PLOT] ENTER ENTER and choose [histogram icon]. Press ZOOM [ZoomStat] to adjust the window.

The graph is high on the left and has a tail on the right. Therefore, the distribution is positively skewed.

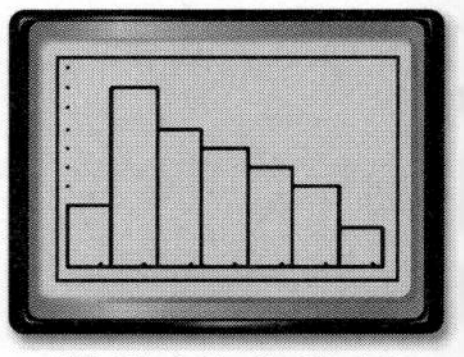

[17, 45] scl: 4 by [0, 10] scl: 1

GuidedPractice

1. Use a graphing calculator to construct a histogram for the data, and use it to describe the shape of the distribution. **See Ch. 12 Answer Appendix.**

8, 11, 15, 25, 21, 26, 20, 12, 32, 20, 31, 14, 19, 27, 22, 21, 14, 8
6, 23, 18, 16, 28, 25, 16, 20, 29, 24, 17, 35, 20, 27, 10, 16, 22, 12

764 | Lesson 12-3

Lesson 12-3 Resources

Resource	Approaching Level AL	On Level OL	Beyond Level BL	English Learners ELL
Teacher Edition	▪ Differentiated Instruction, p. 765	▪ Differentiated Instruction, pp. 765, 766, 770	▪ Differentiated Instruction, pp. 765, 766, 770	
Chapter Resource Masters	▪ Study Guide and Intervention, pp. 17–18 ▪ Skills Practice, p. 19 ▪ Practice, p. 20 ▪ Word Problem Practice, p. 21	▪ Study Guide and Intervention, pp. 17–18 ▪ Skills Practice, p. 19 ▪ Practice, p. 20 ▪ Word Problem Practice, p. 21 ▪ Enrichment, p. 22	▪ Practice, p. 20 ▪ Word Problem Practice, p. 21 ▪ Enrichment, p. 22	▪ Study Guide and Intervention, pp. 17–18 ▪ Skills Practice, p. 19 ▪ Practice, p. 20 ▪ Word Problem Practice, p. 21
Other	▪ 5-Minute Check 12-3 ▪ Study Notebook	▪ 5-Minute Check 12-3 ▪ Study Notebook	▪ 5-Minute Check 12-3 ▪ Study Notebook	▪ 5-Minute Check 12-3 ▪ Study Notebook

A box-and-whisker plot can also be used to identify the shape of a distribution. Recall from Lesson 0-13 that a box-and-whisker plot displays the spread of a data set by dividing it into four quartiles. The data from Example 1 are displayed below.

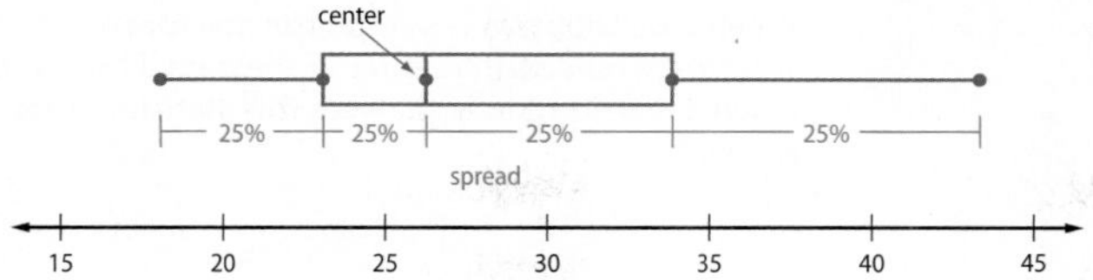

Notice that the left whisker is shorter than the right whisker, and that the line representing the median is closer to the left whisker. This represents a peak on the left and a tail to the right.

KeyConcept Symmetric and Skewed Box-and-Whisker Plots

Negatively Skewed	Symmetric	Positively Skewed
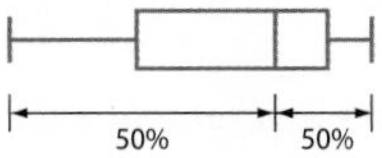 50% 50%	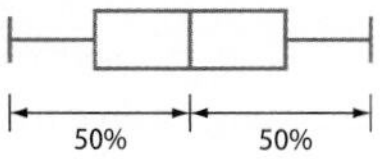 50% 50%	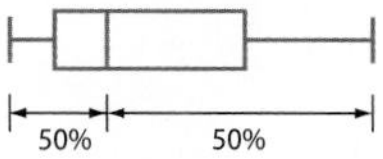 50% 50%
The left whisker is longer than the right. The median is closer to the shorter whisker.	The whiskers are the same length. The median is in the center of the data.	The right whisker is longer than the left. The median is closer to the shorter whisker.

Example 2 Distribution Using a Box-and-Whisker Plot

Use a graphing calculator to construct a box-and-whisker plot for the data, and use it to determine the shape of the distribution.

9, 17, 15, 10, 16, 2, 17, 19, 10, 18, 14, 8, 20, 20, 3, 21, 12, 11
5, 26, 15, 28, 12, 5, 27, 26, 15, 53, 12, 7, 22, 11, 8, 16, 22, 15

Enter the data as **L1**. Press 2nd [STAT PLOT] ENTER ENTER and choose the box plot icon. Adjust the window to the dimensions shown.

The lengths of the whiskers are approximately equal, and the median is in the middle of the data. This indicates that the data are equally distributed to the left and right of the median. Thus, the distribution is symmetric.

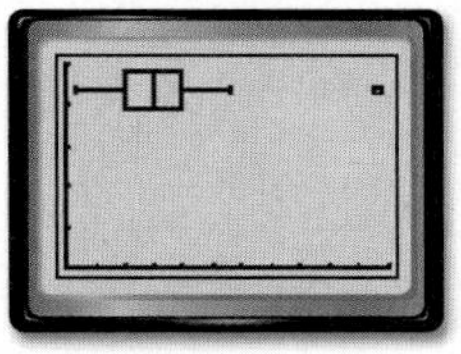

[0, 55] scl: 5 by [0, 5] scl: 1

StudyTip
Outliers In Example 2, notice that the outlier does not affect the shape of the distribution.

GuidedPractice

2. Use a graphing calculator to construct a box-and-whisker plot for the data, and use it to describe the shape of the distribution.

40, 50, 35, 48, 43, 31, 52, 42, 54, 38, 50, 46, 49, 43, 40, 50, 32, 53
51, 43, 47, 41, 49, 50, 34, 54, 51, 44, 54, 39, 47, 35, 51, 44, 48, 37

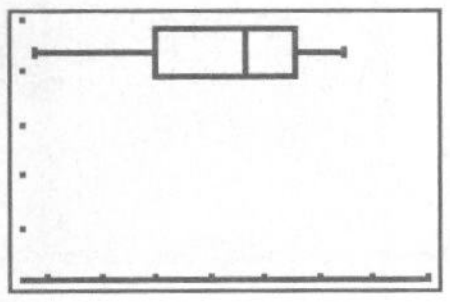

[30, 60] scl: 4 by [0, 5] scl: 1

negatively skewed

DifferentiatedInstruction AL OL BL

Interpersonal Learners Have students work in pairs to think of ways to help them remember how to recognize the different shapes of the distributions from histograms and box-and-whisker plots.

1 Describing Distributions

Example 1 shows how to describe the shape of a distribution using a histogram. **Example 2** shows how to describe the shape of a distribution using a box-and-whisker plot.

Formative Assessment

Use the Guided Practice exercises after each example to determine students' understanding of concepts.

Additional Examples

1 Use a graphing calculator to construct a histogram for the data, and use it to describe the shape of the distribution.

9, 18, 22, 12, 24, 25, 19, 25, 2
5, 28, 12, 22, 19, 28, 15, 23, 6
8, 27, 17, 14, 22, 21, 13, 24, 21
9, 25, 16, 24, 16, 25, 27, 21, 10

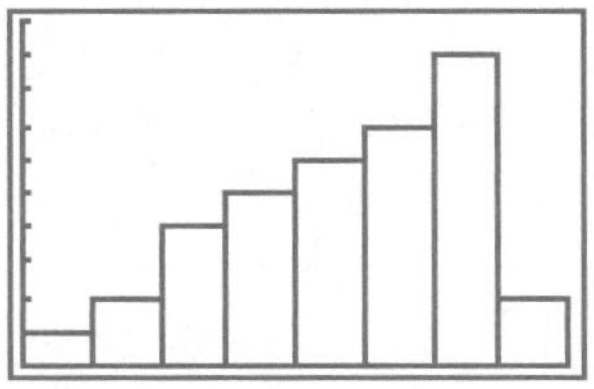

[0, 32] scl: 4 by [0, 10] scl: 1

negatively skewed

2 Use a graphing calculator to construct a box-and-whisker plot for the data, and use it to determine the shape of the distribution.

9, 18, 22, 12, 24, 25, 19, 25, 2
5, 28, 12, 22, 19, 28, 15, 23, 6
8, 27, 17, 14, 22, 21, 13, 24, 21
9, 25, 16, 24, 16, 25, 27, 21, 10

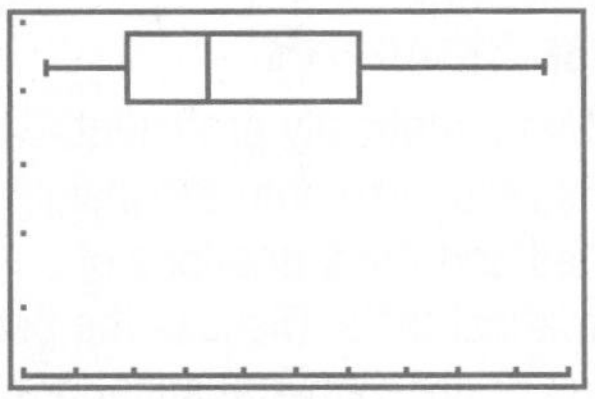

[50, 100] scl: 5 by [0, 5] scl: 1

positively skewed

2 Analyzing Distributions

Example 3 shows how to choose appropriate statistics to describe a set of data using a histogram. **Example 4** shows how to choose appropriate statistics to describe a set of data using a box-and-whisker plot.

Additional Example

3 Describe the center and spread of the data using either the mean and standard deviation or the five-number summary. Justify your choice by constructing a histogram for the data.

78, 68, 72, 71, 79, 67, 71, 78, 70
80, 76, 82, 82, 70, 84, 72, 71, 85
67, 86, 74, 86, 73, 72, 77, 87, 70
66, 88, 75, 72, 76, 71, 90, 69, 94

Sample answer: The distribution is skewed, so use the five-number summary. The range is 94 − 66 or 28. The median is 74.5, and half of the data are between 71 and 82.

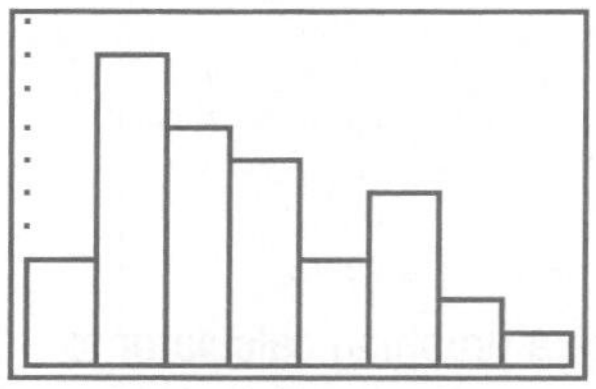

[64, 96] scl: 4 by [0, 10] scl: 1

Additional Examples also in Interactive Classroom PowerPoint® Presentations

IWB Interactive White Board READY

Teaching the Process Standards

Tools Mathematically proficient students recognize both the insight to be gained and the limitations of mathematical tools. Discuss the pros and cons of creating statistical graphs with graphing calculators. Allow students to work together with these tools.

2 Analyzing Distributions

You have learned that data can be described using statistics. The mean and median describe the center. The standard deviation and quartiles describe the spread. You can use the shape of the distribution to choose the most appropriate statistics that describe the center and spread of a set of data.

When a distribution is symmetric, the mean accurately reflects the center of the data. However, when a distribution is skewed, this statistic is not as reliable.

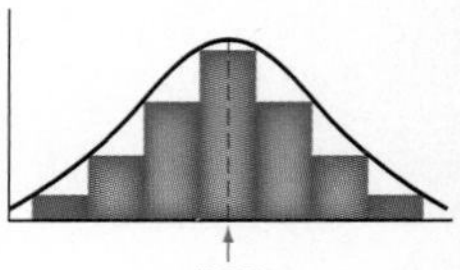

In Lesson 0-12, you discovered that outliers can have a strong effect on the mean of a data set, while the median is less affected. So, when a distribution is skewed, the mean lies away from the majority of the data toward the tail. The median is less affected and stays near the majority of the data.

Negatively Skewed Distribution

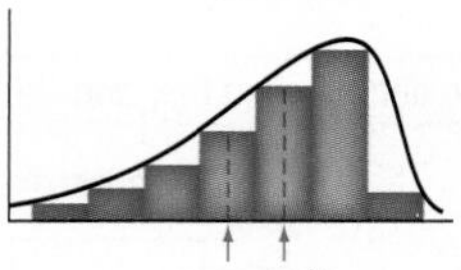

Positively Skewed Distribution

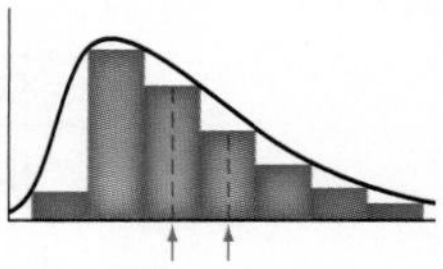

When choosing appropriate statistics to represent a set of data, first determine the shape of the distribution.

- If the distribution is relatively symmetric, the mean and standard deviation can be used.
- If the distribution is skewed or has outliers, use the five-number summary.

Example 3 Choose Appropriate Statistics

Describe the center and spread of the data using either the mean and standard deviation or the five-number summary. Justify your choice by constructing a histogram for the data.

21, 28, 16, 30, 25, 34, 21, 47, 18, 36, 24, 28, 30, 15, 33, 24, 32, 22
27, 38, 23, 29, 15, 27, 33, 19, 34, 29, 23, 26, 19, 30, 25, 13, 20, 25

Use a graphing calculator to create a histogram. The graph is high in the middle and low on the left and right. Therefore, the distribution is symmetric.

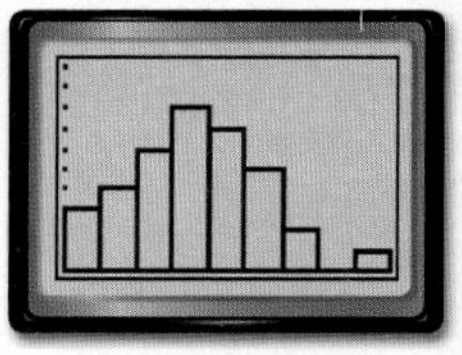

[12, 48] scl: 4 by [0, 10] scl: 1

The distribution is symmetric, so use the mean and standard deviation to describe the center and spread. Press STAT ▶ ENTER ENTER.

The mean $\overline{x}$ is about 26.1 with standard deviation σ of about 7.1.

TechnologyTip

Tools On a graphing calculator, each bar is called a *bin*. The width of each bin can be adjusted by pressing WINDOW and changing Xscl. View the histogram using different bin widths and compare the results to determine the appropriate bin width.

DifferentiatedInstruction OL BL

Interpersonal Learners Have students work in pairs to generate a set of data, create a histogram using the data, and describe the shape of the distribution. Then have the students describe the center and spread of the data using either the mean and standard deviation or the five-number summary.

3. Sample answer: The distribution is skewed, so use the five-number summary. The range is 32 − 2 or 30. The median is 24, and half of the data are between 18 and 26.

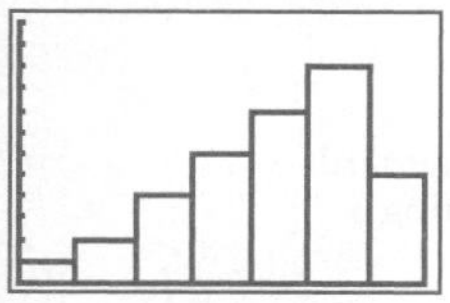

[0, 35] scl: 5 by [0, 12] scl: 1

Real-WorldLink

Volunteers in the Peace Corps must be at least 18 years old, and more than 90% of volunteers have college degrees. Volunteers work in another country for 27 months and are placed in host countries that have the greatest needs for skilled volunteers.

Source: Peace Corps

4. Sample answer: The distribution is symmetric, so use the mean and standard deviation to describe the center and spread. The mean amount raised was $36.70 with a standard deviation of about $18.58.

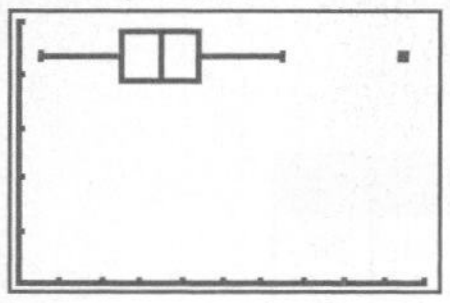

[0, 100] scl: 10 by [0, 5] scl: 1

GuidedPractice

3. Describe the center and spread of the data using either the mean and standard deviation or the five-number summary. Justify your choice by creating a histogram for the data.

19, 2, 25, 14, 24, 20, 27, 30, 14, 25, 19, 32, 21, 31, 25, 16, 24, 22
29, 6, 26, 32, 17, 26, 24, 26, 32, 10, 28, 19, 26, 24, 11, 23, 19, 8

A box-and-whisker plot is helpful when viewing a skewed distribution since it is constructed using the five-number summary.

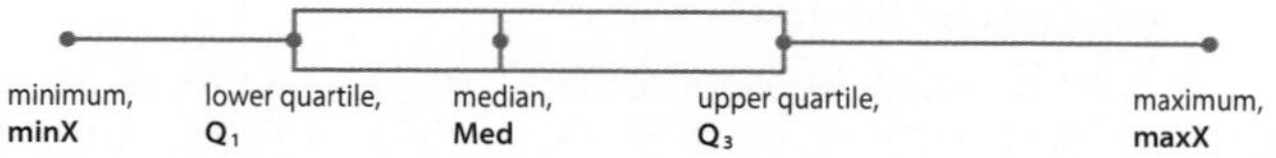

Real-World Example 4 Choose Appropriate Statistics

COMMUNITY SERVICE The number of community service hours each of Ms. Tucci's students completed is shown. Describe the center and spread of the data using either the mean and standard deviation or the five-number summary. Justify your choice by constructing a box-and-whisker plot for the data.

Community Service Hours												
6	13	8	7	19	12	2	19	11	22	7	33	13
3	8	10	5	25	16	6	14	7	20	10	30	

Use a graphing calculator to create a box-and-whisker plot. The right whisker is longer than the left and the median is closer to the left whisker. Therefore, the distribution is positively skewed.

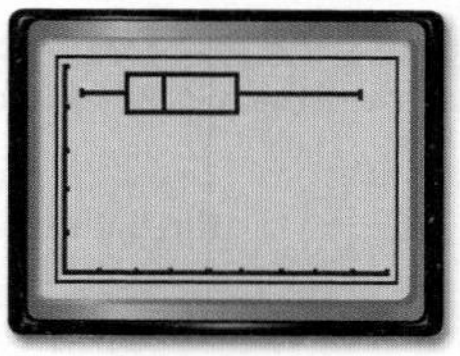

[0, 36] scl: 4 by [0, 5] scl: 1

The distribution is positively skewed, so use the five-number summary. The range is 33 – 2 or 31. The median number of hours completed is 11, and half of the students completed between 7 and 19 hours.

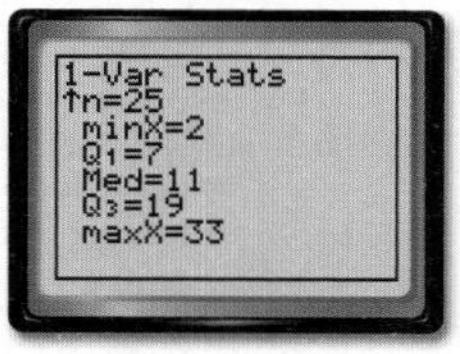

GuidedPractice

4. FUNDRAISER The money raised per student in Mr. Bulanda's 5th period class is shown. Describe the center and spread of the data using either the mean and standard deviation or the five-number summary. Justify your choice by creating a box-and-whisker plot for the data.

Money Raised per Student (dollars)									
41	27	52	18	42	32	16	95	27	65
36	45	5	34	50	15	62	38	57	20
38	21	33	58	25	42	31	8	40	28

Additional Example

4 BOWLING The averages for the bowlers on five teams are shown below. Describe the center and spread of the data using either the mean and standard deviation or the five-number summary. Justify your choice by constructing a box-and-whisker plot for the data.

Bowling Average				
142	180	161	131	201
179	152	177	196	148
198	123	203	170	187
159	193	176	137	183

Sample answer: The distribution is skewed, so use the five-number summary. The range is 203 − 123 or 80. The median bowling average is 176.5, and half of the bowlers have an average between 150 and 190.

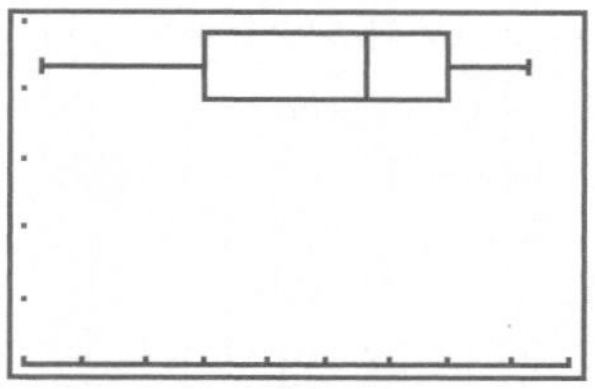

[120, 210] scl: 10 by [0, 5] scl: 1

3 Practice

Formative Assessment

Use Exercises 1–4 to check for understanding.

Use the chart at the bottom of this page to customize assignments for your students.

Additional Answers

1.

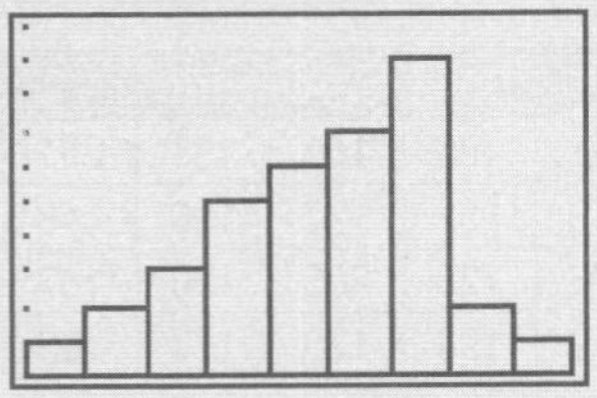

[56, 92] scl: 4 by [0, 10] scl: 1

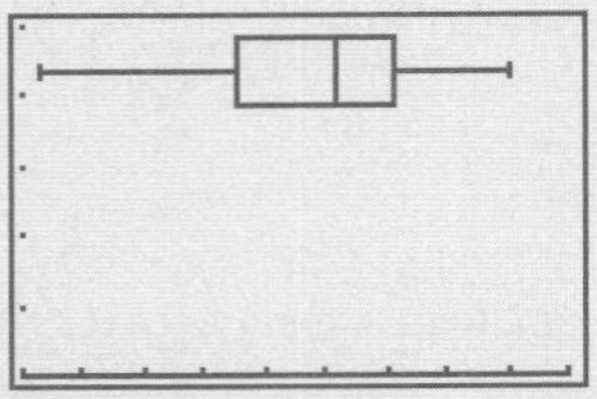

[56, 92] scl: 4 by [0, 5] scl: 1

negatively skewed

2.

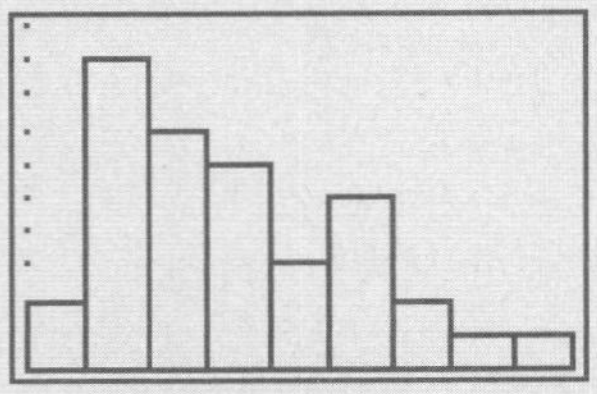

[10, 100] scl: 10 by [0, 10] scl: 1

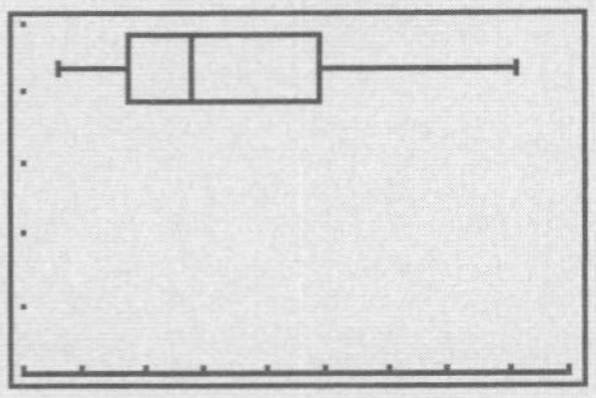

[10, 100] scl: 10 by [0, 5] scl: 1

positively skewed

3. Sample answer: The distribution is skewed, so use the five-number summary. The range is 92 − 52 or 40. The median is 65, and half of the data are between 59.5 and 74.

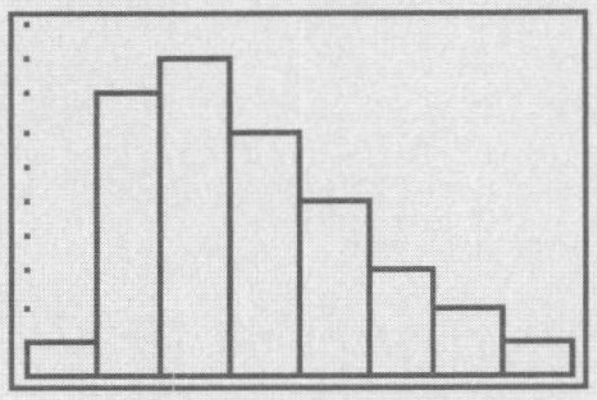

[48, 96] scl: 6 by [0, 10] scl: 1

Check Your Understanding

◯ = Step-by-Step Solutions begin on page R13.

Examples 1–2 **Use a graphing calculator to construct a histogram and a box-and-whisker plot for the data. Then describe the shape of the distribution.** 1–2. See margin.

1. 80, 84, 68, 64, 57, 88, 61, 72, 76, 80, 83, 77, 78, 82, 65, 70, 83, 78
73, 79, 70, 62, 69, 66, 79, 80, 86, 82, 73, 75, 71, 81, 74, 83, 77, 73

2. 30, 24, 35, 84, 60, 42, 29, 16, 68, 47, 22, 74, 34, 21, 48, 91, 66, 51
33, 29, 18, 31, 54, 75, 23, 45, 25, 32, 57, 40, 23, 32, 47, 67, 62, 23

Example 3 **Describe the center and spread of the data using either the mean and standard deviation or the five-number summary. Justify your choice by constructing a histogram for the data.** See margin.

3. 58, 66, 52, 75, 60, 56, 78, 63, 59, 54, 60, 67, 72, 80, 68, 88, 55, 60
59, 61, 82, 70, 67, 60, 58, 86, 74, 61, 92, 76, 58, 62, 66, 74, 69, 64

Example 4

4. **PRESENTATIONS** The length of the students' presentations in Ms. Monroe's 2nd period class are shown. Describe the center and spread of the data using either the mean and standard deviation or the five-number summary. Justify your choice by constructing a box-and-whisker plot for the data. See Chapter 12 Answer Appendix.

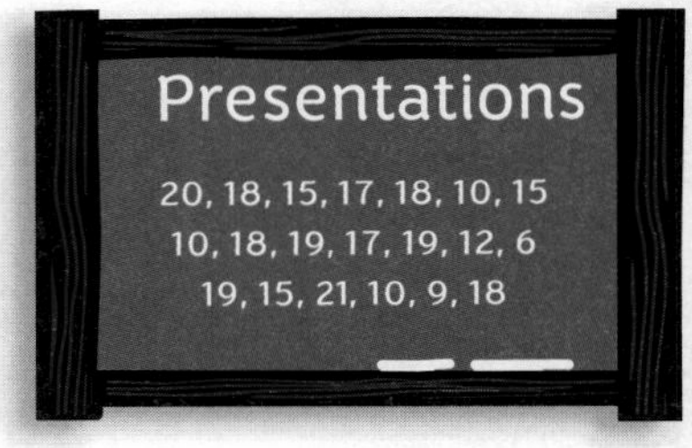

Practice and Problem Solving

Extra Practice is on page R12.

Examples 1–2 **Use a graphing calculator to construct a histogram and a box-and-whisker plot for the data. Then describe the shape of the distribution.** 5–6. See Chapter 12 Answer Appendix.

5. 55, 65, 70, 73, 25, 36, 33, 47, 52, 54, 55, 60, 45, 39, 48, 55, 46, 38
50, 54, 63, 31, 49, 54, 68, 35, 27, 45, 53, 62, 47, 41, 50, 76, 67, 49

6. 42, 48, 51, 39, 47, 50, 48, 51, 54, 46, 49, 36, 50, 55, 51, 43, 46, 37
50, 52, 43, 40, 33, 51, 45, 53, 44, 40, 52, 54, 48, 51, 47, 43, 50, 46

Example 3 **Describe the center and spread of the data using either the mean and standard deviation or the five-number summary. Justify your choice by constructing a histogram for the data.** 7–8. See Chapter 12 Answer Appendix.

7. 32, 44, 50, 49, 21, 12, 27, 41, 48, 30, 50, 23, 37, 16, 49, 53, 33, 25
35, 40, 48, 39, 50, 24, 15, 29, 37, 50, 36, 43, 49, 44, 46, 27, 42, 47

8. 82, 86, 74, 90, 70, 81, 89, 88, 75, 72, 69, 91, 96, 82, 80, 78, 74, 94
85, 77, 80, 67, 76, 84, 80, 83, 88, 92, 87, 79, 84, 96, 85, 73, 82, 83

Example 4

9. **WEATHER** The daily low temperatures for New Carlisle over a 30-day period are shown. Describe the center and spread of the data using either the mean and standard deviation or the five-number summary. Justify your choice by constructing a box-and-whisker plot for the data. See Chapter 12 Answer Appendix.

Temperature (°F)														
48	50	55	53	57	53	44	61	57	49	51	58	46	54	57
50	55	47	57	48	58	53	49	56	59	52	48	55	53	51

Differentiated Homework Options

Level	Assignment	Two-Day Option	
AL Basic	5–9, 15–39	5–9 odd, 18–21	6, 8, 15–17, 22–39
OL Core	5–11, 15–39	5–9, 18–21	10, 11, 15–17, 22–39
BL Advanced	10–33 (optional: 34–39)		

10. TRACK Refer to the beginning of the lesson. Sarah's 100-meter dash times are shown. **a–c. See Ch. 12 Answer Appendix.**

100-meter dash (seconds)				
12.20	12.35	13.60	12.24	12.72
12.18	12.06	12.41	12.28	13.06
12.87	12.04	12.38	12.20	13.12
12.30	13.27	12.93	12.16	12.02
12.50	12.14	11.97	12.24	13.09
12.46	12.33	13.57	11.96	13.34

a. Use a graphing calculator to create a box-and-whisker plot. Describe the center and spread of the data.

b. Sarah's slowest time prior to pulling a muscle was 12.50 seconds. Use a graphing calculator to create a box-and-whisker plot that *does not* include the times that she ran after pulling the muscle. Then describe the center and spread of the new data set.

c. What effect does removing the times recorded after Sarah pulled a muscle have on the shape of the distribution and on how you should describe the center and spread?

11. MENU The prices for entrees at a restaurant are shown.

Entree Prices ($)				
9.00	11.25	16.50	9.50	13.00
18.50	7.75	11.50	13.75	9.75
8.00	16.50	12.50	10.25	17.75
13.00	10.75	16.75	8.50	11.50

a. Use a graphing calculator to create a box-and-whisker plot. Describe the center and spread of the data. **a, b. See Ch. 12 Answer Appendix.**

b. The owner of the restaurant decides to eliminate all entrees that cost more than $15. Use a graphing calculator to create a box-and-whisker plot that reflects this change. Then describe the center and spread of the new data set.

H.O.T. Problems Use Higher-Order Thinking Skills

CHALLENGE **Identify the box-and-whisker plot that corresponds to each of the following histograms.**

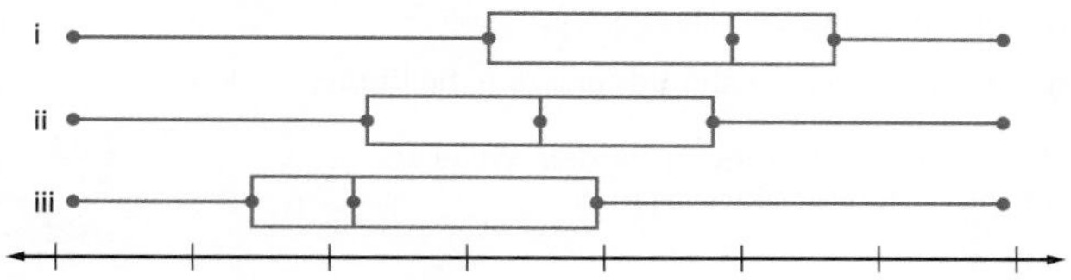

12. 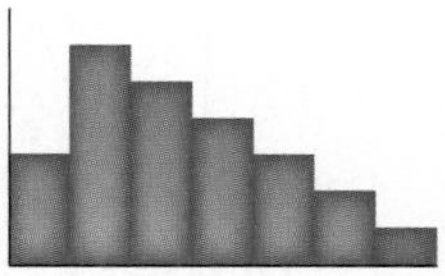 iii

13. 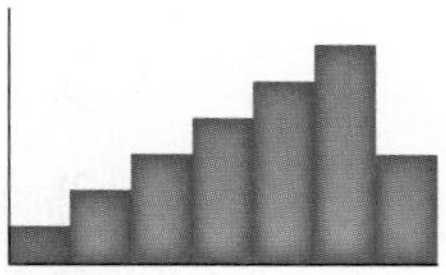 i

14. 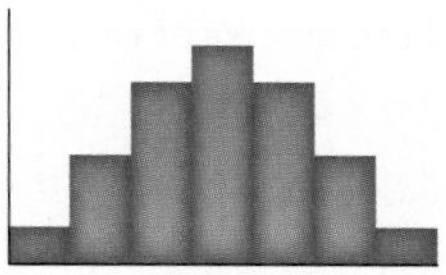 ii

15. ARGUMENTS Research and write a definition for a *bimodal distribution*. How can the measures of center and spread of a bimodal distribution be described? **15–17. See Ch. 12 Answer Appendix.**

16. OPEN ENDED Give an example of a set of real-world data with a distribution that is symmetric and one with a distribution that is not symmetric.

17. WRITING IN MATH Explain why the mean and standard deviation are used to describe the center and spread of a symmetrical distribution and the five-number summary is used to describe the center and spread of a skewed distribution.

Teaching the Process Standards

Arguments Mathematically proficient students use previously established results in constructing arguments. In Exercise 15, have students use what they have learned about distributions to discuss how to analyze a bimodal distribution.

Study Guide and Intervention
AL OL ELL

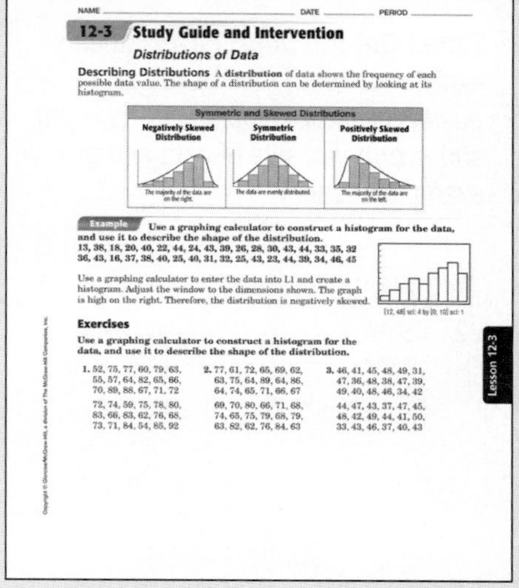
12-3 Study Guide and Intervention
Distributions of Data

Practice
AL OL BL ELL

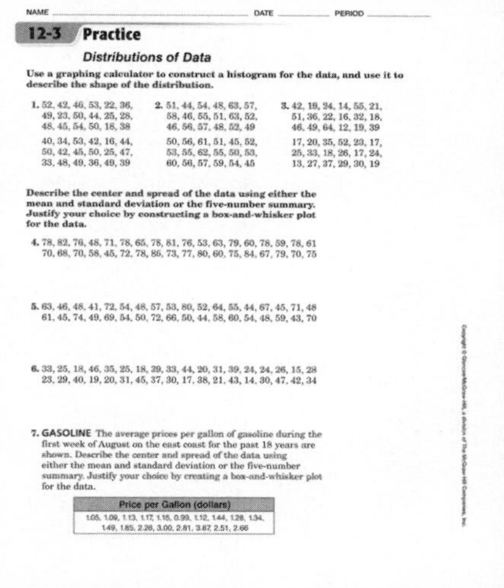
12-3 Practice
Distributions of Data

Word Problem Practice
AL OL BL ELL

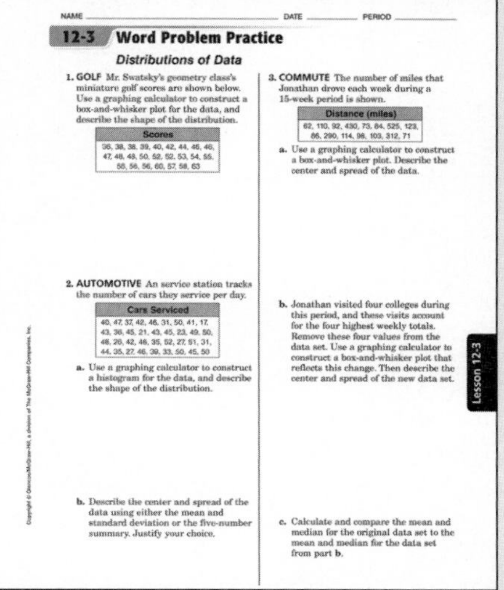
12-3 Word Problem Practice
Distributions of Data

Enrichment
OL BL

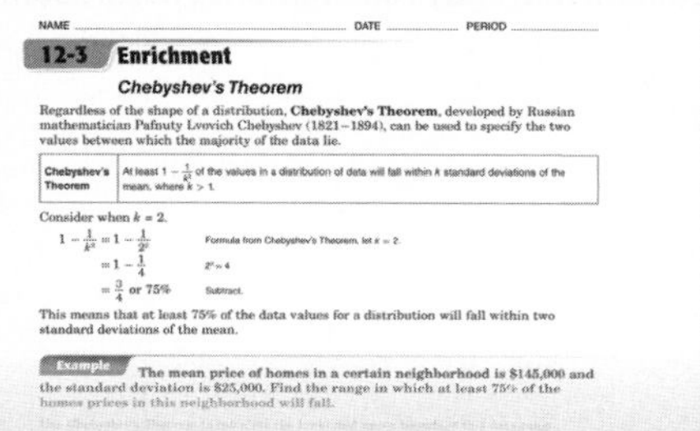
12-3 Enrichment
Chebyshev's Theorem

4 Assess

Ticket Out the Door Have students explain the difference between *positively skewed, negatively skewed,* and *symmetric* sets of data and give an example of each.

Additional Answers

22. sample: systematic sample of 250 guests; population: all of the guests; sample statistic: the median amount of money spent on concessions by the sample; population parameter: the median amount of money spent on concession by all guests

23. sample: random sample of 100 seniors; population: all seniors at North Boyton High School; sample statistic: the mean amount of money the sample spent on prom; population parameter: the mean amount of money seniors at North Boyton High School spent on prom

24. Biased; sample answer: The question addresses more than one issue, and assumes that the participant likes reality television shows.

26. Biased; sample answer: The question encourages a certain response. The phrase "don't you agree" encourages the participant to agree.

Standardized Test Practice

18. At the county fair, 1000 tickets were sold. Adult tickets cost \$8.50, children's tickets cost \$4.50, and a total of \$7300 was collected. How many children's tickets were sold? **D**

A 700 C 400
B 600 D 300

19. Edward has 20 dimes and nickels, which together total \$1.40. How many nickels does he have? **F**

F 12 H 8
G 10 J 6

20. If 4.5 kilometers is about 2.8 miles, about how many miles is 6.1 kilometers? **C**

A 3.2 miles C 3.8 miles
B 3.6 miles D 4.0 miles

21. EXTENDED RESPONSE Three times the width of a certain rectangle exceeds twice its length by three inches, and four times its length is twelve more than its perimeter.

a. Translate the sentences into equations.
b. Find the dimensions of the rectangle.
c. What is the area of the rectangle? **315 in^2**

21a. $3w = 2\ell + 3$; $4\ell = 12 + P$ **21b.** 21 in., 15 in.

Spiral Review

Identify the sample and the population for each situation. Then describe the sample statistic and the population parameter. (Lesson 12-2)

22. AMUSEMENT PARK A systematic sample of 250 guests is asked how much money they spent on concessions inside the park. The median amount of money is calculated. **See margin.**

23. PROM A random sample of 100 high school seniors at North Boyton High School is surveyed, and the mean amount of money spent on prom by a senior is calculated. **See margin.**

Identify each survey question as *biased* or *unbiased*. If biased, explain your reasoning. (Lesson 12-1)

24. What do you like the most about reality television shows, and which one is your favorite? **See margin.**

25. Are you planning on seeing the school play? **unbiased**

26. Don't you agree that the school should renovate the library? **See margin.**

27. GARDENING Trey planted a triangular garden. Write an expression for the perimeter of the triangle. (Lesson 11-6) $\frac{11a+7}{a+1}$

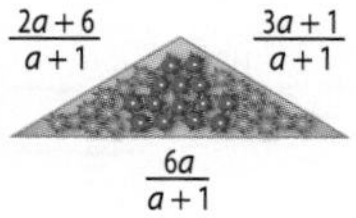

Find the inverse of each function. (Lesson 4-7)

28. $f(x) = 2x - 14$ $f^{-1}(x) = \frac{1}{2}x + 7$

29. $f(x) = 17 - 5x$ $f^{-1}(x) = -\frac{1}{5}x + \frac{17}{5}$

30. $f(x) = \frac{1}{4}x + 3$ $f^{-1}(x) = 4x - 12$

31. $f(x) = -\frac{1}{7}x - 1$ $f^{-1}(x) = -7x - 7$

32. $f(x) = \frac{2}{3}x + 6$ $f^{-1}(x) = \frac{3}{2}x - 9$

33. $f(x) = 12 - \frac{3}{5}x$ $f^{-1}(x) = -\frac{5}{3}x + 20$

Skills Review

A bowl contains 3 red chips, 6 green chips, 5 yellow chips, and 8 orange chips. A chip is drawn randomly. Find each probability.

34. red $\frac{3}{22}$

35. orange $\frac{4}{11}$

36. yellow or green $\frac{1}{2}$

37. not orange $\frac{7}{11}$

38. not green $\frac{8}{11}$

39. red or orange $\frac{1}{2}$

Differentiated Instruction OL BL

Extension Have students generate a set of data that is neither skewed nor symmetrical. Discuss situations that may result in data that resembles such distributions.

LESSON 12-4 Comparing Sets of Data

:: Then

- You calculated measures of central tendency and variation.

:: Now

1. Determine the effect that transformations of data have on measures of central tendency and variation.
2. Compare data using measures of central tendency and variation.

:: Why?

- Tom gets paid hourly to do landscaping work. Because he is such a good employee, Tom is planning to ask his boss for a bonus. Tom's initial pay for a month is shown. He is trying to decide whether he should ask for an extra $5 per day or a 10% increase in his daily wages.

Tom's Pay ($)		
44	52	50
40	48	46
44	52	54
58	42	52
54	50	52
42	52	46
56	48	44
50	42	

NewVocabulary
linear transformation

Process Standards
PS.1

1 Transformations of Data

To see the effect that an extra $5 per day would have on Tom's daily pay, we can find the new daily pay values and compare the measures of center and variation for the two sets of data. The new data can be found by performing a *linear transformation*. A **linear transformation** is an operation performed on a data set that can be written as a linear function. Tom's daily pay after the $5 bonus can be found using $y = 5 + x$, where x represents his original daily pay and y represents his daily pay after the bonus.

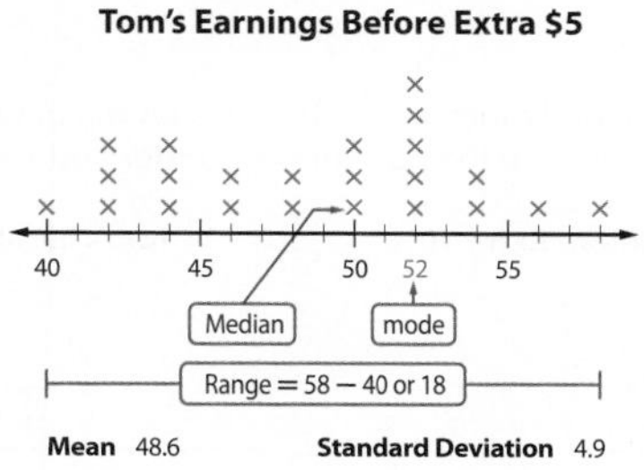

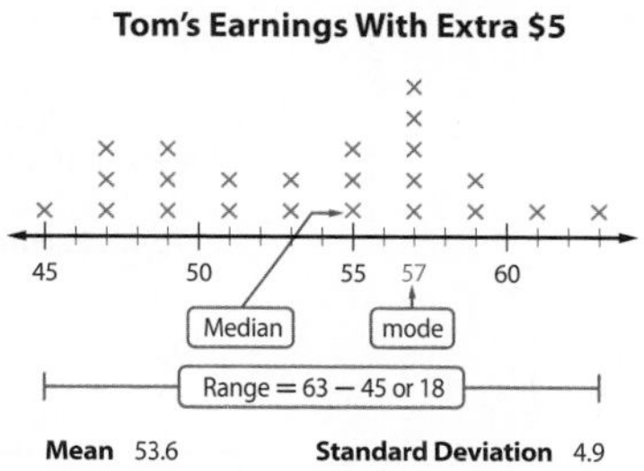

Notice that each value was translated 5 units to the right. Thus, the mean, median, and mode increased by 5. Since the new minimum and maximum values also increased by 5, the range remained the same. The standard deviation is unchanged because the amount by which each value deviates from the mean stayed the same.

These results occur when any positive or negative number is added to every value in a set of data.

KeyConcept Transformations Using Addition

If a real number k is added to every value in a set of data, then:

- the mean, median, and mode of the new data set can be found by adding k to the mean, median, and mode of the original data set, and
- the range and standard deviation will not change.

1 Focus

VerticalAlignment

Before Lesson 12-4 You calculated measures of central tendency and variation.

Lesson 12-4 Determine the effect that transformations of data have on measures of central tendency and variation.

After Lesson 12-4 Summarize data from simulations.

2 Teach

Scaffolding Questions

Have students read the **Why?** section of the lesson.

Ask:

- How can Tom calculate the effect of each bonus? Sample answer: For the extra $5 per day, Tom can add $5 to each daily total. For the 10% increase, Tom can multiply each daily total by 1.10.
- When is it to Tom's benefit that he accepts the extra $5 over the 10% increase and vice versa? Explain. Sample answer: On days when Tom makes less than $50, he should take the extra $5 because 10% of any value less than $50 will be less than $5. On days when Tom makes more than $50, he should take the 10% increase because 10% of any value greater than $50 will be greater than $5. When Tom makes $50, the bonuses are equal.

Lesson 12-4 Resources

Resource	Approaching Level AL	On Level OL	Beyond Level BL	English Learners ELL
Teacher Edition	▪ Differentiated Instruction, p. 772	▪ Differentiated Instruction, pp. 772, 778	▪ Differentiated Instruction, pp. 772, 778	▪ Differentiated Instruction, p. 772
Chapter Resource Masters	▪ Study Guide and Intervention, pp. 23–24 ▪ Skills Practice, p. 25 ▪ Practice, p. 26 ▪ Word Problem Practice, p. 27	▪ Study Guide and Intervention, pp. 23–24 ▪ Skills Practice, p. 25 ▪ Practice, p. 26 ▪ Word Problem Practice, p. 27 ▪ Enrichment, p. 28	▪ Practice, p. 26 ▪ Word Problem Practice, p. 27 ▪ Enrichment, p. 28	▪ Study Guide and Intervention, pp. 23–24 ▪ Skills Practice, p. 25 ▪ Practice, p. 26 ▪ Word Problem Practice, p. 27
Other	▪ 5-Minute Check 12-4 ▪ Study Notebook	▪ 5-Minute Check 12-4 ▪ Study Notebook	▪ 5-Minute Check 12-4 ▪ Study Notebook	▪ 5-Minute Check 12-4 ▪ Study Notebook

1 Transformations of Data

Example 1 shows how to calculate descriptive statistics for a set of data that has been transformed using addition. **Example 2** shows how to calculate descriptive statistics for a set of data that has been transformed using multiplication.

Formative Assessment

Use the Guided Practice exercises after each example to determine students' understanding of concepts.

Additional Examples

1 Find the mean, median, mode, range, and standard deviation of the data set obtained after adding 12 to each value.

73, 78, 61, 54, 88, 90, 63, 78, 80, 61, 86, 78 86.2, 90, 90, 36, 11.3

2 Find the mean, median, mode, range, and standard deviation of the data set obtained after multiplying each value by 2.5.

4, 2, 3, 1, 4, 6, 2, 3, 7, 5, 1, 4 mean: 8.75; median: 8.75; mode: 10; range: 15; standard deviation: 4.5

Additional Examples also in Interactive Classroom PowerPoint® Presentations

IWB Interactive White Board READY

Tips for New Teachers

Transformations Using Multiplication If every value in a set of data is multiplied by a negative constant *k*, then the mean, median, and mode of the new data set can be found by multiplying the mean, median, and mode of the original data set by *k*. The range and standard deviation of the new data set can be found by multiplying the range and standard deviation of the original data set by |*k*|. Students will explore this in Exercise 22.

TechnologyTip

1-Var Stats To quickly calculate the mean $\bar{x}$, median **Med**, standard deviation σ, and range of a data set, enter the data as **L1** in a graphing calculator, and then press STAT ▶ ENTER ENTER. Subtract **minX** from **maxX** to find the range.

PT

Example 1 Transformation Using Addition

Find the mean, median, mode, range, and standard deviation of the data set obtained after adding 7 to each value.

13, 5, 8, 12, 7, 4, 5, 8, 14, 11, 13, 8

Method 1 Find the mean, median, mode, range, and standard deviation of the original data set.

Mean	9	Mode	8	Standard Deviation	3.3
Median	8	Range	10		

Add 7 to the mean, median, and mode. The range and standard deviation are unchanged.

Mean	16	Mode	15	Standard Deviation	3.3
Median	15	Range	10		

Method 2 Add 7 to each data value.

20, 12, 15, 19, 14, 11, 12, 15, 21, 18, 20, 15

Find the mean, median, mode, range, and standard deviation of the new data set.

Mean	16	Mode	15	Standard Deviation	3.3
Median	15	Range	10		

GuidedPractice

1. Find the mean, median, mode, range, and standard deviation of the data set obtained after adding −4 to each value. **30, 32.5, 22, 38, 10.1**

27, 41, 15, 36, 26, 40, 53, 38, 37, 24, 45, 26

To see the effect that a daily increase of 10% has on the data set, we can multiply each value by 1.10 and recalculate the measures of center and variation.

Tom's Earnings Before Extra 10%

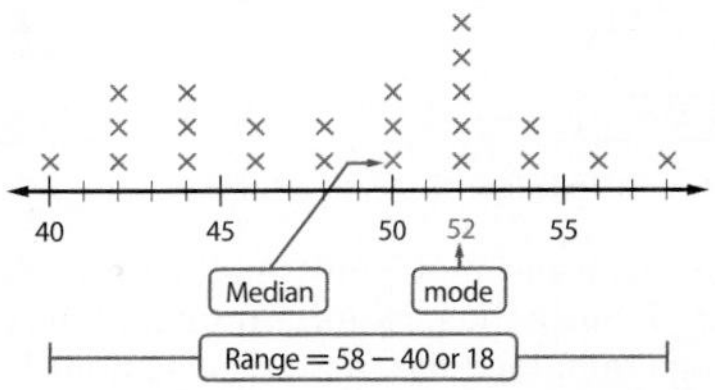

Mean 48.6 **Standard Deviation** 4.9

Tom's Earnings With Extra 10%

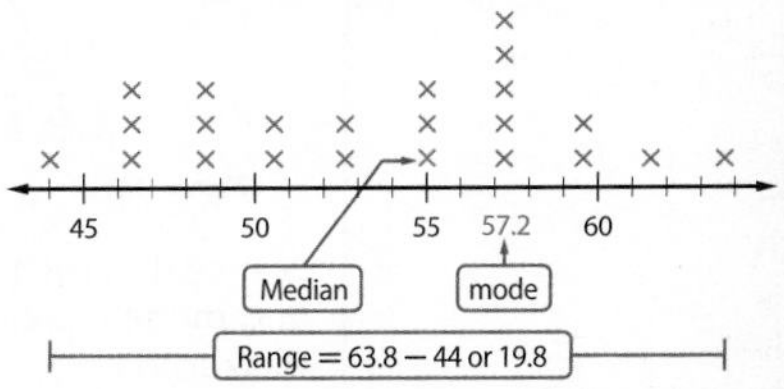

Mean 53.5 **Standard Deviation** 5.4

Notice that each value did not increase by the same amount, but did increase by a factor of 1.10. Thus, the mean, median, and mode increased by a factor of 1.10. Since each value was increased by a constant percent and not by a constant amount, the range and standard deviation both changed, also increasing by a factor of 1.10.

KeyConcept Transformations Using Multiplication

If every value in a set of data is multiplied by a constant *k*, $k > 0$, then the mean, median, mode, range, and standard deviation of the new data set can be found by multiplying each original statistic by *k*.

DifferentiatedInstruction AL OL BL ELL

Interpersonal Learners Have students work in pairs to perform transformations on data sets. Have each student create a data set and then determine an operation that should be done to each value. The students should exchange data sets, and then find the mean, median, mode, range, and standard deviation of the original data set and of the new data set after the operation is performed.

Since the medians for both bonuses are equal and the means are approximately equal, Tom should ask for the bonus that he thinks he has the best chance of receiving.

Example 2 Transformation Using Multiplication

Find the mean, median, mode, range, and standard deviation of the data set obtained after multiplying each value by 3.

21, 12, 15, 18, 16, 10, 12, 19, 17, 18, 12, 22

Find the mean, median, mode, range, and standard deviation of the original data set.

Mean	16	Mode	12	Standard Deviation	3.7
Median	16.5	Range	12		

Multiply the mean, median, mode, range, and standard deviation by 3.

Mean	48	Mode	36	Standard Deviation	11.1
Median	49.5	Range	36		

GuidedPractice

2. Find the mean, median, mode, range, and standard deviation of the data set obtained after multiplying each value by 0.8. **44, 44.4, 48, 13.6, 4.2**

63, 47, 54, 60, 55, 46, 51, 60, 58, 50, 56, 60

2 Comparing Distributions

Recall that when choosing appropriate statistics to represent data, you should first analyze the shape of the distribution. The same is true when comparing distributions.

- Use the mean and standard deviation to compare two symmetric distributions.
- Use the five-number summaries to compare two skewed distributions or a symmetric distribution and a skewed distribution.

Example 3 Compare Data Using Histograms

QUIZ SCORES **Robert and Elaine's quiz scores for the first semester of Algebra 1 are shown below.**

Robert's Quiz Scores
85, 95, 70, 87, 78, 82, 84, 84, 85, 99, 88, 74, 75, 89, 79, 80, 92, 91, 96, 81

Elaine's Quiz Scores
89, 76, 87, 86, 92, 77, 78, 83, 83, 82, 81, 82, 84, 85, 85, 86, 89, 93, 77, 85

a. Use a graphing calculator to construct a histogram for each set of data. Then describe the shape of each distribution.

Enter Robert's quiz scores as L1 and Elaine's quiz scores as L2.

Robert's Quiz Scores

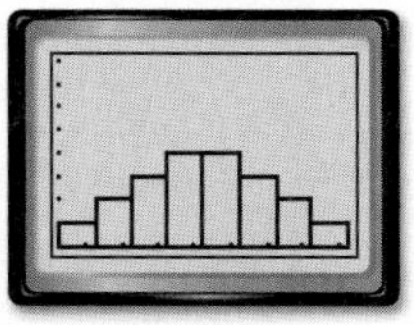

[69, 101] scl: 4 by [0, 8] scl: 1

Elaine's Quiz Scores

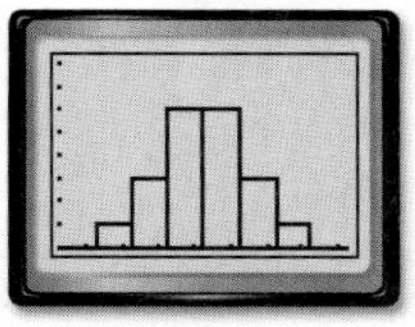

[69, 101] scl: 4 by [0, 8] scl: 1

Both distributions are high in the middle and low on the left and right. Therefore, both distributions are symmetric.

TechnologyTip

Histograms To create a histogram for a set of data in L2, press 2nd [STAT PLOT] ENTER ENTER, choose the histogram icon, and enter L2 for Xlist.

2 Comparing Distributions

Example 3 shows how to use histograms to compare the distributions of two data sets. **Example 4** shows how to use box-and-whisker plots to compare the distributions of two data sets.

Additional Example

3 GAMES Brittany and Justin are playing a computer game. Their high scores for each game are shown below.

Brittany's Scores
29, 43, 54, 58, 39, 44, 39, 53, 32, 48, 39, 49, 38, 31, 41, 44, 44, 45, 48, 31

Justin's Scores
48, 26, 28, 53, 39, 28, 30, 58, 45, 37, 30, 31, 40, 32, 30, 44, 33, 35, 43, 35

a. Use a graphing calculator to create a histogram for each set of data. Then describe the shape of each distribution. See bottom margin for graphs; Brittany, symmetric; Justin, positively skewed

b. Compare the distributions using either the means and standard deviations or the five-number summaries. Justify your choice. Sample answer: One distribution is symmetric and the other is skewed, so use the five-number summaries. Both distributions have a maximum of 58, but Brittany's minimum score is 29 compared to Justin's minimum scores of 26. The median for Brittany's scores is 43.5 and the upper quartile for Justin's scores is 43.5. This means that 50% of Brittany's scores are between 43.5 and 58, while only 25% of Justin's scores fall within this range. Therefore, we can conclude that overall, Brittany's scores are higher than Justin's scores.

Additional Answer (Additional Example)

3a.

Brittany's Scores

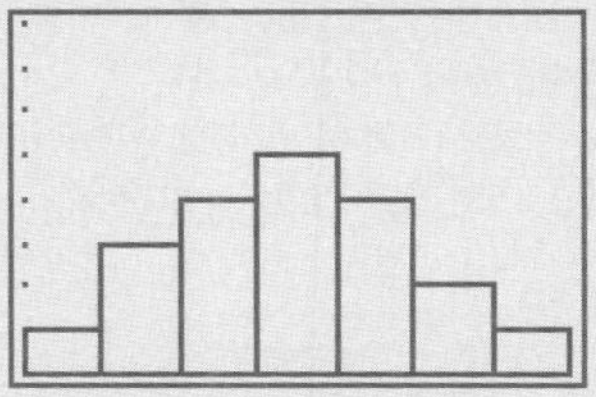

[25, 60] scl: 5 by [0, 8] scl: 1

Justin's Scores

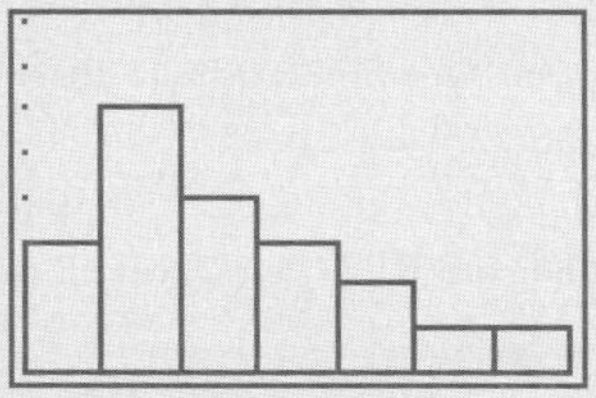

[25, 60] scl: 5 by [0, 8] scl: 1

Additional Example

4 FISHING Steve and Kurt went fishing for the weekend. The weights of the fish they each caught are shown below.

Steve's Fish (pounds)
1.6, 2.1, 2.6, 1.3, 2.7, 3.2, 1.4, 2.3, 3.5, 1.9, 2.2, 2.7, 3.5, 1.4, 3.7, 3.4, 1.8, 2.5, 3.0

Kurt's Fish (pounds)
1.1, 3.2, 2.3, 3.7, 1.7, 2.7, 2.1, 4.0, 1.0, 2.9, 2.9, 1.2, 3.3, 2.3, 4.5, 2.4, 3.9

a. Use a graphing calculator to create a box-and-whisker plot for each data set. Then describe the shape of the distribution for each data set.

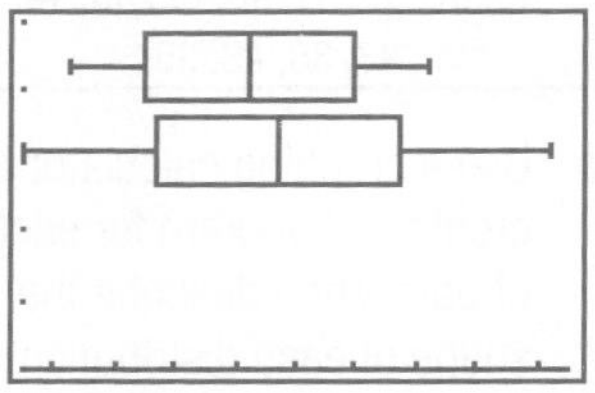

[1, 4.6] scl: 0.4 by [0, 5] scl: 1

both symmetric

b. Compare the distributions using either the means and standard deviations or the five-number summaries. Justify your choice. The distributions are symmetric, so use the means and standard deviations. The mean weight for Steve's fish is about 2.5 pounds with standard deviation of about 0.8 pound. The mean weight for Kurt's fish is about 2.7 pounds with standard deviation of about 1 pound. While the mean weight for Kurt's fish is greater, the weights of Kurt's fish also have more variability. This means the weights for Steve's fish are generally closer to his mean than the weights for Kurt's fish.

TechnologyTip

Multiple Data Sets In order to calculate statistics for a set of data in **L2**, press STAT ▶ ENTER 2nd [L2] ENTER.

3A.

2nd Period

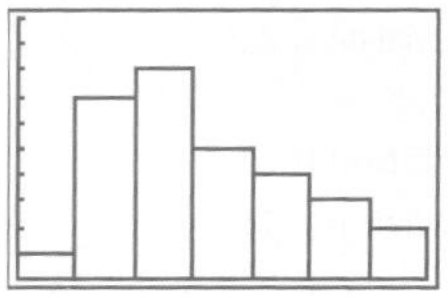

[0, 35] scl: 5 by [0, 10] scl: 1

7th Period

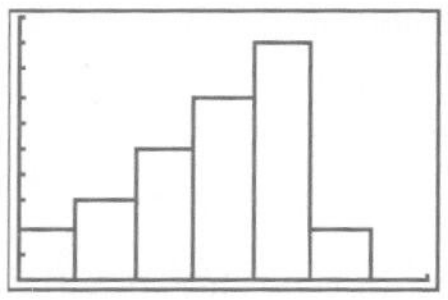

[0, 35] scl: 5 by [0, 10] scl: 1

2nd period, positively skewed; 7th period, negatively skewed

b. Compare the data sets using either the means and standard deviations or the five-number summaries. Justify your choice.

Both distributions are symmetric, so use the means and standard deviations to describe the centers and spreads.

Robert's Quiz Scores

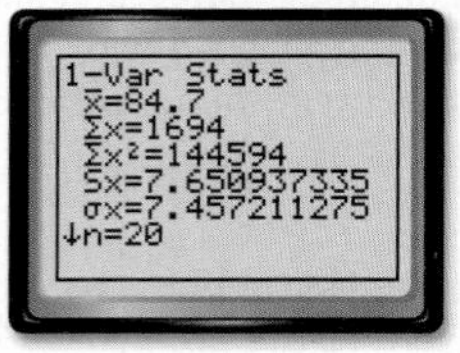

Elaine's Quiz Scores

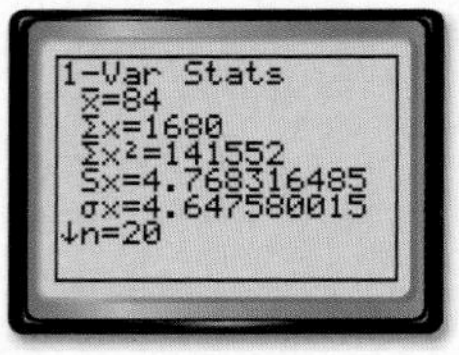

The means for the students' quiz scores are approximately equal, but Robert's quiz scores have a much higher standard deviation than Elaine's quiz scores. This means that Elaine's quiz scores are generally closer to her mean than Robert's quiz scores are to his mean.

GuidedPractice

COMMUTE The students in two of Mr. Martin's classes found the average number of minutes that they each spent traveling to school each day.

3A. Use a graphing calculator to construct a histogram for each set of data. Then describe the shape of each distribution.

3B. Compare the data sets using either the means and standard deviations or the five-number summaries. Justify your choice. **See margin.**

2nd Period (minutes)
8, 4, 18, 7, 13, 26, 12, 6, 20, 5, 9, 24, 8, 16, 31, 13, 17, 10, 8, 22, 12, 25, 13, 11, 18, 12, 16, 22, 25, 33

7th Period (minutes)
21, 4, 20, 13, 22, 6, 10, 23, 13, 25, 14, 16, 19, 21, 19, 8, 20, 18, 9, 14, 21, 17, 19, 22, 4, 19, 21, 26

Box-and-whisker plots are useful for comparisons of data because they can be displayed on the same screen.

Real-WorldLink

Only about 2% of all high school student athletes attend a college with the aid of athletic scholarships.

Source: NCAA

Real-World Example 4 Compare Data Using Box-and-Whisker Plots

FOOTBALL Kurt's total rushing yards per game for his junior and senior seasons are shown.

Junior Season (yards)					
16	20	72	4	25	18
34	10	42	17	56	12

Senior Season (yards)					
77	54	109	60	156	72
39	83	73	101	46	80

a. Use a graphing calculator to construct a box-and-whisker plot for each set of data. Then describe the shape of each distribution.

Enter Kurt's rushing yards from his junior season as **L1** and his rushing yards from his senior season as **L2**. Graph both box-and-whisker plots on the same screen by graphing **L1** as **Plot1** and **L2** as **Plot2**.

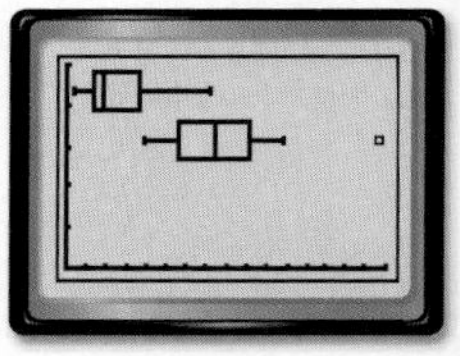

[0, 160] scl: 10 by [0, 5] scl: 1

For Kurt's junior season, the right whisker is longer than the left, and the median is closer to the left whisker. The distribution is positively skewed.

For Kurt's senior season, the lengths of the whiskers are approximately equal, and the median is in the middle of the data. The distribution is symmetric.

Additional Answer

3B. Sample answer: The distributions are skewed, so use the five-number summaries. Both classes have a minimum of 4, but 2nd period has a median of 13 and 7th period has a lower quartile of 13. This means that the lower 50% of the data from 2nd period spans the same range as the lower 25% of the data from 7th period. The upper 50% of the data from 2nd period spans from 13 to 33, while the upper 75% of data from 7th period spans from 13 to 26. Therefore, we can conclude that while the median for 7th period is significantly higher than the median for 2nd period, the data from 2nd period is dispersed over a wider range than the data from 7th period.

b. Compare the data sets using either the means and standard deviations or the five-number summaries. Justify your choice.

One distribution is symmetric and the other is skewed, so use the five-number summaries to compare the data.

The upper quartile for Kurt's junior season was 38, while the minimum for his senior season was 39. This means that Kurt rushed for more yards in every game during his senior season than 75% of the games during his junior season.

The maximum for Kurt's junior season was 72, while his median for his senior season was 75. This means that in half of his games during his senior year, he rushed for more yards than in any game during his junior season. Overall, we can conclude that Kurt rushed for many more yards during his senior season than during his junior season.

StudyTip

Box-and-Whisker Plots Recall that a box-and-whisker plot displays the spread of a data set by dividing it into four quartiles. Each quartile accounts for 25% of the data.

4A.

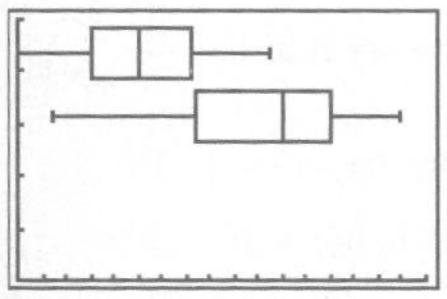

[0, 34] scl: 2 by [0, 5] scl: 1

junior season, symmetric; senior season, negatively skewed

GuidedPractice

BASKETBALL The points Vanessa scored per game during her junior and senior seasons are shown.

4A. Use a graphing calculator to construct a histogram for each set of data. Then describe the shape of each distribution.

4B. Compare the data sets using either the means and standard deviations or the five-number summaries. Justify your choice. **See margin.**

Junior Season (points)
10, 12, 6, 10, 13, 8, 12, 3, 21, 14, 7, 0, 15, 6, 16, 8, 17, 3, 17, 2

Senior Season (points)
10, 32, 3, 22, 20, 30, 26, 24, 5, 22, 28, 32, 26, 21, 6, 20, 24, 18, 12, 25

Check Your Understanding

◯ = Step-by-Step Solutions begin on page R13.

Example 1 **Find the mean, median, mode, range, and standard deviation of each data set that is obtained after adding the given constant to each value.**

1. 10, 13, 9, 8, 15, 8, 13, 12, 7, 8, 11, 12; + (−7) **3.5, 3.5, 1, 8, 2.4**

2. 38, 36, 37, 42, 31, 44, 37, 45, 29, 42, 30, 42; + 23 **60.8, 60.5, 65, 16, 5.5**

Example 2 **Find the mean, median, mode, range, and standard deviation of each data set that is obtained after multiplying each value by the given constant.**

3. 6, 10, 3, 7, 4, 9, 3, 8, 5, 11, 2, 1; × 3 **17.3, 16.5, 9, 30, 9.4**

4. 42, 39, 45, 44, 37, 42, 38, 37, 41, 49, 42, 36; × 0.5 **20.5, 20.8, 21, 6.5, 1.8**

Example 3 **5. TRACK** Mark and Kyle's long jump distances are shown.

Kyle's Distances (ft)
17.2, 18.28, 18.56, 17.28, 17.36, 18.08, 17.43, 17.71, 17.46, 18.26, 17.51, 17.58, 17.41, 18.21, 17.34, 17.63, 17.55, 17.26, 17.18, 17.78, 17.51, 17.83, 17.92, 18.04, 17.91

Mark's Distances (ft)
18.88, 19.24, 17.63, 18.69, 17.74, 19.18, 17.92, 18.96, 18.19, 18.21, 18.46, 17.47, 18.49, 17.86, 18.93, 18.73, 18.34, 18.67, 18.56, 18.79, 18.47, 18.84, 18.87, 17.94, 18.7

a. Use a graphing calculator to construct a histogram for each set of data. Then describe the shape of each distribution. **a–b. See margin.**

b. Compare the data sets using either the means and standard deviations or the five-number summaries. Justify your choice.

Differentiated Homework Options

Level	Assignment	Two-Day Option	
AL Basic	7–18, 22–47	7–17 odd, 26–29	8–18 even, 22–25, 30–47
OL Core	7–19 odd, 23–47	7–18, 26–29	19–20, 22–25, 30–47
BL Advanced	19–41, (optional: 42–47)		

3 Practice

Formative Assessment

Use Exercises 1–6 to check for understanding.

Use the chart at the bottom of this page to customize assignments for your students.

Additional Answer (Guided Practice)

4B. Sample answer: One distribution is symmetric and the other is skewed, so use the five-number summaries. The maximum for Vanessa's junior season is 21, while the median for her senior season is 22. This means that in half of her games during her senior season, Vanessa scored more points than in any of the games during her junior season. Therefore, we can conclude that overall, Vanessa scored more points during her senior season.

Additional Answers

5a. Kyle's Distances

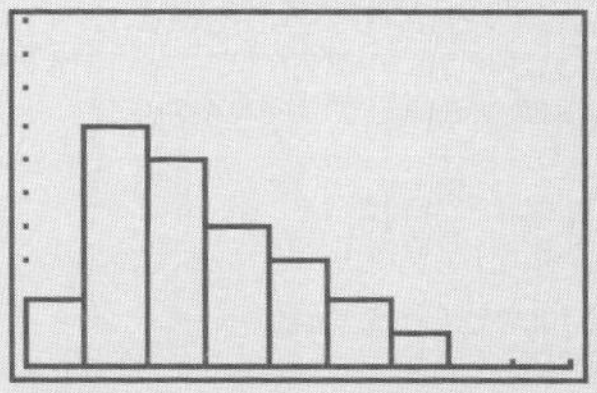

[17, 19.25] scl: 0.25 by [0, 10] scl: 1

Mark's Distances

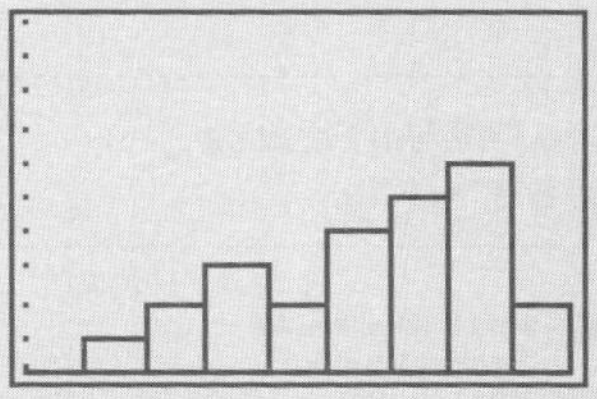

[17, 19.25] scl: 0.25 by [0, 10] scl: 1

Kyle, positively skewed; Mark, negatively skewed

5b. Sample answer: The distributions are skewed, so use the five-number summaries. Kyle's upper quartile is 17.98, while Mark's lower quartile is 18.065. This means that 75% of Mark's distances are greater than 75% of Kyle's distances. Therefore, we can conclude that overall, Mark's distances are higher than Kyle's.

Study Guide and Intervention

AL OL ELL

NAME ______ DATE ______ PERIOD ______

12-4 Study Guide and Intervention

Comparing Sets of Data

Transformation of Data When an operation is performed on every value of a data set, the statistics for the new set of data can be found using the statistics from the original set of data.

Transformations Using Addition
If a real number k is added to every value in a set of data, then:
- the mean, median, and mode of the new data set can be found by adding k to the mean, median, and mode of the original data set, and
- the range and standard deviation will not change.

Transformations Using Multiplication
If every value in a set of data is multiplied by a constant k, k > 0, then the mean, median, mode, range, and standard deviation of the new data set can be found by multiplying each original statistic by k.

Example 1 Find the mean, median, mode, range, and standard deviation of the data set obtained after adding 9 to each value.
12, 10, 15, 17, 15, 9, 10, 15, 12, 14
The mean, median, mode, range, and standard deviation of the original data set are 12.9, 13, 15, 8, and about 2.5, respectively. Add 9 to the mean, median, and mode. The range and standard deviation are unchanged.
Mean 21.9 Median 24 Mode 22
Range 8 Standard Deviation 2.5

Example 2 Find the mean, median, mode, range, and standard deviation of the data set obtained after multiplying each value by 1.5.
4, 3, 7, 6, 2, 6, 8, 5, 4, 6, 7, 2
The mean, median, mode, range, and standard deviation of the original data set are 5, 5.5, 6, 6, and about 1.9, respectively. Multiply the mean, median, mode, range, and standard deviation by 1.5.
Mean 7.5 Median 8.3 Mode 9
Range 9 Standard Deviation 2.9

Exercises

Find the mean, median, mode, range, and standard deviation of each data set that is obtained after adding the given constant to each value.

1. 33, 38, 29, 35, 27, 34, 36, 28, 41, 26; + 11
2. 8, 9, 3, 6, 12, 9, 3, 16, 9, 11; + (−3)

Find the mean, median, mode, range, and standard deviation of each data set that is obtained after multiplying each value by the given constant.

3. 2, 1, 8, 6, 3, 1, 7, 5, 7, 2, 4, 2; × 4
4. 22, 26, 30, 27, 25, 23, 31, 20; × 0.5

Practice

AL OL BL ELL

NAME ______ DATE ______ PERIOD ______

12-4 Practice

Comparing Sets of Data

Find the mean, median, mode, range, and standard deviation of each data set that is obtained after adding the given constant to each value.

1. 62, 58, 57, 65, 68, 71, 49, 48, 52, 47; + 5.8
2. 2, 8, 1, 5, 1, 3, 1, 7, 5, 4, 3, 1; + (−0.3)
3. 4.3, 3.8, 3.1, 4.5, 3.7, 4.4, 4.9, 3.9; + (−2.4)
4. 17, 21, 18, 32, 29, 24, 19, 32; + 7.6

Find the mean, median, mode, range, and standard deviation of each data set that is obtained after multiplying each value by the given constant.

5. 94, 90, 88, 92, 85, 92, 86, 98, 92, 90; × 0.8
6. 41, 44, 47, 40, 43, 41, 42, 48; × 2.3
7. 63, 62, 59, 68, 67, 72, 70, 75, 64, 61; × $\frac{1}{3}$
8. 9, 7, 5, 2, 8, 4, 5, 6, 9, 5, 2, 1; × $\frac{4}{9}$

9. RECYCLING The weekly totals of recycled paper in pounds for two neighboring high schools are shown below.

a. Use a graphing calculator to construct a box-and-whisker plot for each set of data. Then describe the shape of each distribution.

b. Compare the data sets using either the means and standard deviations or the five-number summaries. Justify your choice.

Word Problem Practice

AL OL BL ELL

NAME ______ DATE ______ PERIOD ______

12-4 Word Problem Practice

Comparing Sets of Data

1. DIVING The weights of 15 swimmers going scuba diving are shown below.

a. Find the mean, median, mode, range, and standard deviation of the swimmers' weights.

b. The scuba gear that the swimmers will be wearing weighs 56 pounds. Find the statistics of the swimmers' weights while wearing the scuba gear.

2. COMPETITION The distances that 18 participants threw a football are shown.

a. Find the mean, median, mode, range, and standard deviation of the participants' distances.

b. Find the statistics of the participants' distances in yards.

3. TEMPERATURE The monthly average high temperatures for Lexington, Kentucky are shown.

a. Find the mean, median, mode, range, and standard deviation of the temperatures.

b. Find the statistics of the temperatures in degrees Celsius. Recall that $C = \frac{5}{9}(F - 32)$.

4. FANTASY SPORTS The weekly total points of Scott's and Jen's fantasy baseball teams are shown.

a. Use a graphing calculator to construct a box-and-whisker plot for each set of data. Then describe the shape of each distribution.

b. Compare the data sets using either the means and standard deviations or the five-number summaries. Justify your choice.

c. How does eliminating the outliers of each data set affect the statistics and comparison from part b?

Example 4

6. **TIPS** Miguel and Stephanie are servers at a restaurant. The tips that they earned to the nearest dollar over the past 15 workdays are shown.

Miguel's Tips ($)	Stephanie's Tips ($)
14, 68, 52, 21, 63, 32, 43, 35, 70, 37, 42, 16, 47, 38, 48	34, 52, 43, 39, 41, 50, 46, 36, 37, 47, 39, 49, 44, 36, 50

a. Use a graphing calculator to construct a box-and-whisker plot for each set of data. Then describe the shape of each distribution. **a, b. See margin.**

b. Compare the data sets using either the means and standard deviations or the five-number summaries. Justify your choice.

Practice and Problem Solving

Extra Practice is on page R12.

Example 1

Find the mean, median, mode, range, and standard deviation of each data set that is obtained after adding the given constant to each value.

7. 52, 53, 49, 61, 57, 52, 48, 60, 50, 47; + 8 **60.9, 60, 60, 14, 4.7**
8. 101, 99, 97, 88, 92, 100, 97, 89, 94, 90; + (−13) **81.7, 82.5, 84, 13, 4.5**
9. 27, 21, 34, 42, 20, 19, 18, 26, 25, 33; + (−4) **22.5, 21.5, no mode, 24, 7.4**
10. 72, 56, 71, 63, 68, 59, 77, 74, 76, 66; + 16 **84.2, 85.5, no mode, 21, 6.8**

Example 2

Find the mean, median, mode, range, and standard deviation of each data set that is obtained after multiplying each value by the given constant.

11. 11, 7, 3, 13, 16, 8, 3, 11, 17, 3; × 4 **36.8, 38, 12, 56, 20.0**
12. 64, 42, 58, 40, 61, 67, 58, 52, 51, 49; × 0.2 **10.8, 11, 11.6, 5.4, 1.7**
13. 33, 37, 38, 29, 35, 37, 27, 40, 28, 31; × 0.8 **26.8, 27.2, 29.6, 10.4, 3.5**
14. 1, 5, 4, 2, 1, 3, 6, 2, 5, 1; × 6.5 **19.5, 16.3, 6.5, 32.5, 11.6**

Example 3

15. **BOOKS** The page counts for the books that the students chose are shown.

1st Period	6th Period
388, 439, 206, 438, 413, 253, 311, 427, 258, 511, 283, 578, 291, 358, 297, 303, 325, 506, 331, 482, 343, 372, 456, 267, 484, 227	357, 294, 506, 392, 296, 467, 308, 319, 485, 333, 352, 405, 359, 451, 378, 490, 379, 401, 409, 421, 341, 438, 297, 440, 500, 312, 502

a. Use a graphing calculator to construct a histogram for each set of data. Then describe the shape of each distribution. **a, b. See margin.**

b. Compare the data sets using either the means and standard deviations or the five-number summaries. Justify your choice.

16. **TELEVISIONS** The prices for a sample of televisions are shown.

The Electronics Superstore	Game Central
46, 25, 62, 45, 30, 43, 40, 46, 33, 53, 35, 38, 39, 40, 52, 42, 44, 48, 50, 35, 32, 55, 28, 58	53, 49, 26, 61, 40, 50, 42, 35, 45, 48, 31, 48, 33, 50, 35, 55, 38, 50, 42, 53, 44, 54, 48, 58

a. Use a graphing calculator to construct a histogram for each set of data. Then describe the shape of each distribution. **a, b. See Ch. 12 Answer Appendix.**

b. Compare the data sets using either the means and standard deviations or the five-number summaries. Justify your choice.

Example 4

17. **BRAINTEASERS** The time that it took Leon and Cassie to complete puzzles is shown.

Leon's Times (minutes)	Cassie's Times (minutes)
4.5, 1.8, 3.2, 5.1, 2.0, 2.6, 4.8, 2.4, 2.2, 2.8, 1.8, 2.2, 3.9, 2.3, 3.3, 2.4	2.3, 5.8, 4.8, 3.3, 5.2, 4.6, 3.6, 5.7, 3.8, 4.2, 5.0, 4.3, 5.5, 4.9, 2.4, 5.2

a. Use a graphing calculator to construct a box-and-whisker plot for each set of data. Then describe the shape of each distribution. **a, b. See Ch. 12 Answer Appendix.**

b. Compare the data sets using either the means and standard deviations or the five-number summaries. Justify your choice.

Enrichment

OL BL

NAME ______ DATE ______ PERIOD ______

12-4 Enrichment

Sample Deviation of Sample Data

You have calculated the variance σ^2 and standard deviation σ of a population to describe its measures of variation. When the population is large, the variance and standard deviation of a sample are often used to estimate these parameters for the entire population. Unlike other sample statistics, the variance for the sample is calculated differently than the variance for the population.

The *sample variance* s^2 is the sum of the squares of the deviations from the sample mean divided by one less than the number of values in the data set. The *sample standard deviation* s is the square root of the sample variance.

Follow these steps to calculate the sample variance and standard deviation.

Step 1 Calculate the sample mean. For example, suppose a sample contains the numbers {2, 5, 6, 9, 11}. The sample mean is $\bar{X} = \frac{2+5+6+9+11}{5}$ or 6.6.

Step 2 Find the sum of the squares of the deviations from the mean. $(6.6-2)^2 + (6.6-5)^2 + (6.6-6)^2 + (6.6-9)^2 + (6.6-11)^2 = 49.2$

Step 3 Since there are 5 numbers in the sample, find the variance by dividing the sum by 5 − 1, or 4. $s^2 = \frac{49.2}{4}$ or 12.3

Additional Answer

6a.

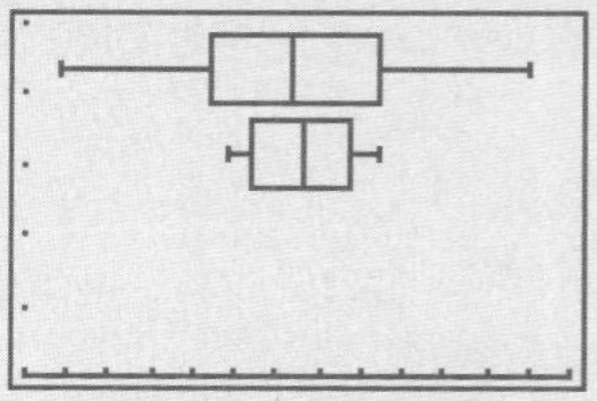

[10, 75] scl: 5 by [0, 5] scl: 1

both symmetric

18. **DANCE** The total amount of money that a sample of students spent to attend the homecoming dance is shown.

Boys (dollars)
114, 98, 131, 83, 91, 64, 94, 77, 96, 105, 72, 108, 87, 112, 58, 126

Girls (dollars)
124, 74, 105, 133, 85, 162, 90, 109, 94, 102, 98, 171, 138, 89, 154, 76

a. Use a graphing calculator to construct a box-and-whisker plot for each set of data. Then describe the shape of each distribution. **a, b. See Ch. 12 Answer Appendix.**

b. Compare the data sets using either the means and standard deviations or the five-number summaries. Justify your choice.

B 19. **LANDSCAPING** Refer to the beginning of the lesson. Rhonda, another employee that works with Tom, earned the following over the past month.

Rhonda's Pay ($)		
45	55	53
47	53	54
44	56	59
63	47	53
60	57	62
44	50	45
60	53	49
62	47	

a. Find the mean, median, mode, range, and standard deviation of Rhonda's earnings. **52.96, 53, 53, 19, 6.08**

b. A $5 bonus had been added to each of Rhonda's daily earnings. Find the mean, median, mode, range, and standard deviation of Rhonda's earnings before the $5 bonus. **47.96, 48, 48, 19, 6.08**

20. **SHOPPING** The items Lorenzo purchased are shown.

Baseball hat	*$14.98*
Jeans	*$24.61*
T-shirt	*$12.84*
T-shirt	*$16.05*
Backpack	*$42.80*
Folders	*$2.14*
Sweatshirt	*$19.26*

a. Find the mean, median, mode, range, and standard deviation of the prices. **18.95, 16.05, no mode, 40.66, 11.62**

b. A 7% sales tax was added to the price of each item. Find the mean, median, mode, range, and standard deviation of the items without the sales tax. **17.71, 15, no mode, 38, 10.86**

H.O.T. Problems Use Higher-Order Thinking Skills

C 21. **CHALLENGE** A salesperson has 15 SUVs priced between $33,000 and $37,000 and 5 luxury cars priced between $44,000 and $48,000. The average price for all of the vehicles is $39,250. The salesperson decides to reduce the prices of the SUVs by $2000 per vehicle. What is the new average price for all of the vehicles? **$37,750**

22. **REASONING** If every value in a set of data is multiplied by a constant k, $k < 0$, then how can the mean, median, mode, range, and standard deviation of the new data set be found? **See Ch. 12 Answer Appendix.**

23. **WRITING IN MATH** Compare and contrast the benefits of displaying data using histograms and box-and-whisker plots. **23–25. See Ch.12 Answer Appendix.**

24. **REGULARITY** If k is added to every value in a set of data, and then each resulting value is multiplied by a constant m, $m > 0$, how can the mean, median, mode, range, and standard deviation of the new data set be found? Explain your reasoning.

25. **WRITING IN MATH** Explain why the mean and standard deviation are used to compare the center and spread of two symmetrical distributions and the five-number summary is used to compare the center and spread of two skewed distributions or a symmetric distribution and a skewed distribution.

WatchOut!

Transformations In Exercises 19 and 20, the data given has already been transformed. Students will need to subtract $5 from each of Rhonda's daily earnings, and will need to subtract 7% sales tax from each item Lorenzo purchased.

Teaching the Process Standards

Regularity Mathematically proficient students notice if calculations are repeated, and look both for general methods and for shortcuts. In Exercise 24, have students look at the transformations they have done to make a conclusion.

Additional Answers

6b. Sample answer: The distributions are symmetric, so use the means and standard deviations. The mean for Miguel's tips is about $41.73 with standard deviation of about $16.64. The mean for Stephanie's tips is about $42.87 with standard deviation of about $5.73. While the means only differ by $1.14, the standard deviations show that Stephanie's tips are generally closer to her mean than Miguel's tips.

15a. 1st Period

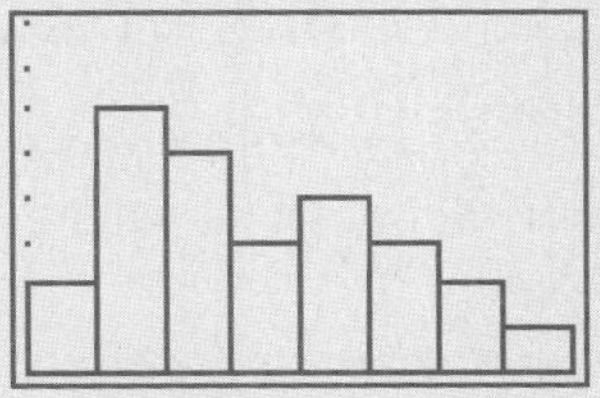

[200, 600] scl: 50 by [0, 8] scl: 1

6th Period

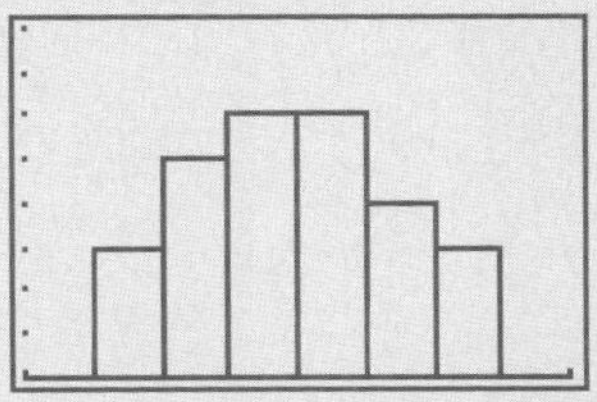

[200, 600] scl: 50 by [0, 8] scl: 1

1st period, positively skewed; 6th period, symmetric

15b. Sample answer: One distribution is symmetric and the other is skewed, so use the five-number summaries. The lower quartile for 1st period is 291 pages, while the minimum for 6th period is 294 pages. This means that the lower 25% of data for 1st period is lower than any data from 6th period. The range for 1st period is 578 − 206 or 372 pages. The range for 6th period is 506 − 294 or 212 pages. The median for 1st period is about 351 pages, while the median for 6th period is 392 pages. This means that, while the median for 6th period is greater, 1st period's pages have a greater range and include greater values than 1st period.

4 Assess

Ticket Out the Door Have students summarize how the mean, median, mode, range, and standard deviation of a new data set can be found after a transformation is performed on the original data set.

Formative Assessment

Check for student understanding of concepts in Lessons 12-3 and 12-4.

Quiz 2, p. 57

Standardized Test Practice

26. A store manager recorded the number of customers each day for a week: {46, 57, 63, 78, 91, 110, 101}. Find the mean absolute deviation. **C**

A 16.8 C 19.4
B 18.1 D 22.7

27. SHORT RESPONSE Solve the right triangle. Round each side length to the nearest tenth. **$m\angle A = 36°$, $c \approx 9.9$, $a \approx 5.8$**

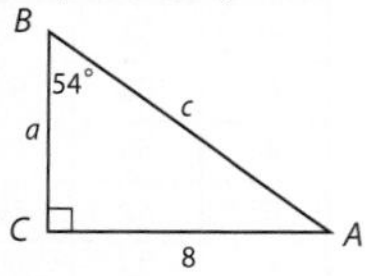

28. A research company divides a group of volunteers by age, and then randomly selects volunteers from each group to complete a survey. What type of sample is this? **J**

F simple H self-selected
G systematic J stratified

29. Which set of measures can be the measures of the sides of a right triangle? **D**

A 6, 7, 9
B 9, 12, 19
C 12, 15, 17
D 14, 48, 50

31. 5.58; Sample answer: The standard deviation is relatively high compared to the mean of 6.4 due to the outlier 23. If this outlier were removed, the new mean of the data would be about 5.2 with a standard deviation of about 3.51.

Spiral Review

30. Use a graphing calculator to construct a histogram for the data, and use it to describe the shape of the distribution. (Lesson 12-3)

23, 45, 50, 22, 37, 24, 36, 46, 24, 52, 25, 42, 25, 26, 54, 47, 27, 55
63, 28, 29, 30, 45, 31, 55, 43, 32, 34, 30, 23, 30, 35, 27, 35, 38, 40

30.

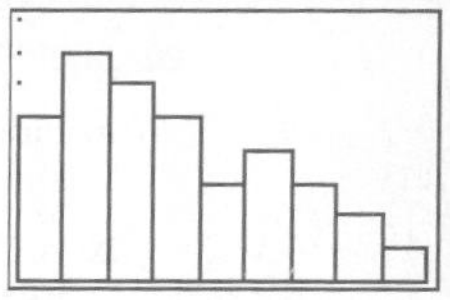

[20, 65] scl: 5 by [0, 10] scl: 1

positively skewed

31. SUBSCRIPTIONS Ms. Wilson's students are selling magazine subscriptions. Her students recorded the total number of subscriptions they each sold: {8, 12, 10, 7, 4, 3, 0, 4, 9, 0, 5, 3, 23, 6, 2}. Find and interpret the standard deviation of the data set. (Lesson 12-2)

Find the value of x for each figure. Round to the nearest tenth if necessary. (Lesson 9-4)

32. $A = 45 \text{ in}^2$ **2**

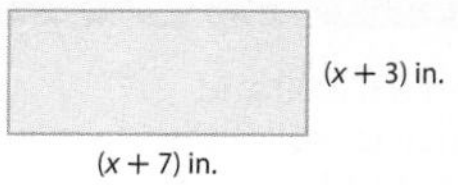

33. $A = 20 \text{ ft}^2$ **4**

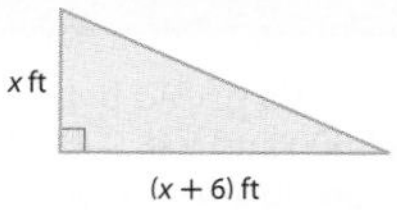

34. $A = 42 \text{ m}^2$ **2.9**

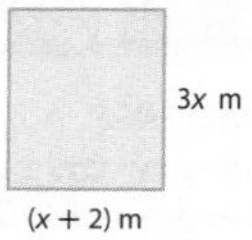

Factor each polynomial. (Lesson 8-6)

35. $x^2 - 4x - 21$ **$(x + 3)(x - 7)$**

36. $11x + x^2 + 30$ **$(x + 6)(x + 5)$**

37. $32 + x^2 - 12x$ **$(x - 8)(x - 4)$**

38. $-36 - 9x + x^2$ **$(x - 12)(x + 3)$**

39. $x^2 + 12x + 20$ **$(x + 10)(x + 2)$**

40. $-x + x^2 - 42$ **$(x - 7)(x + 6)$**

41. MANUFACTURING A company is designing a box for dry pasta in the shape of a rectangular prism. The length is 2 inches more than twice the width, and the height is 3 inches more than the length. Write an expression for the volume of the box. (Lesson 8-3) **$4w^3 + 14w^2 + 10w$**

Skills Review

Find the degree of each polynomial.

42. $2x^2 + 5y - 21$ **2**

43. $16xy^3 - 17x^2y - 16z^3$ **4**

44. $3ac^3d + 14a^2$ **5**

45. 18 **0**

46. $3a^2b^3 + 11ab^2c$ **5**

47. $7x + 11$ **1**

Differentiated Instruction OL BL

Extension Have students research the Internet to find data about two cities in the United States. This could include population, median household incomes, or other data. Ask students to make box-and-whisker plots of each data set and compare them. Their analyses should include a comparison using either the means and standard deviations or the five-number summaries.

778 | Lesson 12-4 | Comparing Sets of Data

CHAPTER 12 Mid-Chapter Quiz
Lessons 12-1 through 12-4

Identify each sample, and suggest a population from which it was selected. Then classify the sample as *simple, systematic, self-selected, convenience,* or *stratified.* Explain your reasoning. (Lesson 12-1)

1. **CEREAL** A cereal company invites 100 random children and parents to test a new cereal and records the reactions. **See margin.**
2. **SCHOOL LUNCH** A school is creating a new lunch menu. They send out a questionnaire to all students with odd homeroom numbers to determine what items should be on the new menu. **See margin.**
3. **MASCOTS** The cheerleaders send out a flyer with pictures of possible options for the new mascot to all the girls in the school. The girls mark their favorite mascot and send it back. The new mascot is chosen from the survey. **Sample: all the girls in the school; population: all the students in the school; convenience: only the girls in the school are being surveyed.**

Identify each sample as *biased* or *unbiased.* Explain your reasoning. (Lesson 12-1)

4. **ART** Every fifth person leaving the art museum is asked to name their favorite piece. **Unbiased; each museum visitor has an equal chance of being the fifth person leaving the museum.**
5. **SHOPPING** Each person leaving the Earring Pagoda is asked to name their favorite store in the mall. **Biased; since the respondents are leaving a particular store in the mall, their responses may be biased.**
6. **FOOTBALL** Every 10th student leaving the student union at Ohio State is asked to name their favorite college football team. **Biased; since the respondents are students at Ohio State, they are more likely to choose their own football team.**

Identify the sample and the population for each situation. Then describe the sample statistic and the population parameter. (Lesson 12-2) **7–9. See Ch.12 Answer Appendix.**

7. **DINING** At a restaurant, a random sample of 15 diners is selected. The amount of money spent on each meal is recorded.
8. **POOLS** A random sample of 25 children at a community pool is asked if they visit the pool at least once each week. The percent responding *yes* is calculated.
9. **PLAY AREA** Ian listed the ages of the children playing at the play area at the mall. Find and interpret the standard deviation of the data set. (Lesson 12-2)

   {2, 3, 2, 2, 4, 2, 3, 2, 8, 3, 4, 2}

10. **MULTIPLE CHOICE** Several friends are chipping in to buy a gift for their teacher. Indigo is keeping track of how much each friend spends. Find the mean absolute deviation. (Lesson 12-2) **A**

    {$10, $5, $3, $6, $7, $8}

    A $1.83 **C** $2.40
    B $2.22 **D** $6.50

11. Use a graphing calculator to construct a histogram for the data, and use it to describe the shape of the distribution. (Lesson 12-3) **See Chapter 12 Answer Appendix.**

    19, 36, 26, 36, 40, 31, 30, 33, 23, 38, 23, 46

12. Describe the center and spread of the data using either the mean and standard deviation or the five-number summary. Justify your choice by constructing a box-and-whisker plot for the data. (Lesson 12-3) **See Chapter 12 Answer Appendix.**

    9, 11, 2, 6, 8, 10, 6, 3, 10, 11, 9, 8, 3, 8, 5, 11, 14, 6, 8, 6, 11, 5, 9, 10, 8

13. **MULTIPLE CHOICE** Which pair of box-and-whisker plots depicts two positively skewed sets of data in which 75% of one set of data is larger than 75% of the other set of data? (Lesson 12-4) **F**

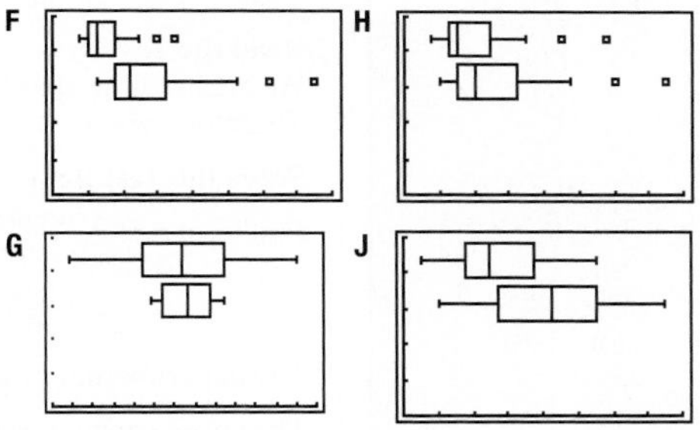

Find the mean, median, mode, range, and standard deviation of each data set that is obtained after adding the given constant to each value. (Lesson 12-4)

14. 6, 9, 0, 15, 9, 14, 11, 13, 9, 5, 8, 6; +(−3) **5.75, 6, 6, 15, 4.04**
15. 19, 22, 10, 17, 26, 24, 12, 22, 18, 17; +8 **26.7, 26.5, 30, 16, 4.80**

connectED.mcgraw-hill.com **779**

Formative Assessment

Use the Mid-Chapter Quiz to assess students' progress in the first half of the chapter.

For problems answered incorrectly, have students review the lessons indicated in parentheses.

Summative Assessment

Mid-Chapter Test, p. 59

McGraw-Hill eAssessment Customize and create multiple versions of your Mid-Chapter Test and their answer keys.

FOLDABLES® StudyOrganizer

Dinah Zike's Foldables®

Before students complete the Mid-Chapter Quiz, encourage them to review the information for Lessons 12-1 through 12-4 in their Foldables.

Additional Answers

1. Sample: the 100 children and parents; population: all parents and children; simple: all children and parents are given the same cereal.
2. Sample: all students with odd homeroom numbers; population: all students in the school; systematic: only the students from the odd homeroom numbers are selected.

InterventionPlanner

TIER 1 On Level (OL)

If students miss about 25% of the exercises or less,

Then choose a resource:

SE Lessons 12-1, 12-2, 12-3, and 12-4

Skills Practice, pp. 7, 13, 19, and 25

TE Chapter Project, p. 714

connectED.mcgraw-hill.com Self-Check Quiz

TIER 2 Strategic Intervention (AL) approaching grade level

If students miss about 50% of the exercises,

Then choose a resource:

Study Guide and Intervention, Chapter 12, pp. 5, 11, 17, and 23

Quick Review Math Handbook

connectED.mcgraw-hill.com Extra Examples, Personal Tutor, Homework Help

TIER 3 Intensive Intervention 2 or more grades below level

If students miss about 75% of the exercises,

Then *use Math Triumphs, Alg. 1,* Ch. 6

connectED.mcgraw-hill.com Extra Examples, Personal Tutor, Homework Help, Review Vocabulary

1 Focus

VerticalAlignment

Before Lesson 12-5 You calculated simple probability.

Lesson 12-5 Calculate experimental probabilities. Design simulations and summarize data from simulations.

After Lesson 12-5 Find probabilities using permutations and combinations.

2 Teach

Scaffolding Questions

Have students read the **Why?** section of the lesson.

Ask:

- If Alex thinks he can make at least 66% of his goal kicks, how many out of 50 kicks should he expect to make? at least 33
- How did Alex's actual performance compare with his prediction? Sample answer: He made 70% of his kicks, which agrees with his prediction.

1 Experimental Probability

Example 1 shows how to calculate experimental probability.

LESSON 12-5 Simulations

:: Then	:: Now	:: Why?
You calculated simple probability.	1 Calculate experimental probabilities. 2 Design simulations and summarize data from simulations.	Alex has been practicing his penalty kicks. He expects to be able to make at least 66% of his penalty kicks. To test this, he takes 50 penalty kicks, of which he makes 35.

NewVocabulary
theoretical probability
experimental probability
relative frequency
simulation
probability model

Process Standards
PS.4

1 Experimental Probability

A **theoretical probability** is the ratio of the number of favorable outcomes to the total number of outcomes. The theoretical probability that a coin lands heads up is $\frac{1}{2}$ or 50%. The theoretical probability suggests that 5 of 10 tosses will most likely result in the coin landing heads up.

We can toss a coin 10 times and record the outcomes. The **experimental probability**, or **relative frequency**, is determined using data from experiments. It is the ratio of the number of times an outcome occurs to the total number of events or trials. In this case, the experimental probability of tossing the coin and having it land heads up is $\frac{3}{10}$ or 30%.

Outcome	Frequency
heads	3
tails	7

Standardized Test Example 1 Find Experimental Probability

A die is rolled 50 times and the results are recorded. Find the experimental probability of rolling at least a 5.

A $\frac{6}{50}$ **B** $\frac{7}{50}$ **C** $\frac{13}{50}$ **D** $\frac{37}{50}$

Outcome	Frequency
1	6
2	10
3	14
4	7
5	6
6	7

Read the Test Item

We are asked to find the probability of rolling at least a 5. Therefore, we need to consider rolling a 5 and rolling a 6.

Solve the Test Item

$$P(\text{at least a 5}) = \frac{\text{number of 5s and 6s rolled}}{\text{total number of rolls}}$$

$$= \frac{6+7}{50} \text{ or } \frac{13}{50}$$

The experimental probability of rolling at least a 5 is $\frac{13}{50}$ or 26%.

The correct answer is C.

GuidedPractice

1. Students were asked how they travel to school each morning. Find the experimental probability of randomly selecting a student who does not ride in a car or bus. F

F $\frac{9}{47}$ **G** $\frac{17}{47}$ **H** $\frac{21}{47}$ **J** $\frac{38}{47}$

Mode	Frequency
bike	3
bus	21
car	17
walk	6

Lesson 12-5 Resources

Resource	Approaching Level AL	On Level OL	Beyond Level BL	English Learners ELL
Teacher Edition	▪ Differentiated Instruction, p. 782	▪ Differentiated Instruction, p. 782	▪ Differentiated Instruction, p. 785	
Chapter Resource Masters	▪ Study Guide and Intervention, pp. 29–30 ▪ Skills Practice, p. 31 ▪ Practice, p. 32 ▪ Word Problem Practice, p. 33	▪ Study Guide and Intervention, pp. 29–30 ▪ Skills Practice, p. 31 ▪ Practice, p. 32 ▪ Word Problem Practice, p. 33 ▪ Enrichment, p. 34	▪ Practice, p. 32 ▪ Word Problem Practice, p. 33 ▪ Enrichment, p. 34	▪ Study Guide and Intervention, pp. 29–30 ▪ Skills Practice, p. 31 ▪ Practice, p. 32 ▪ Word Problem Practice, p. 33
Other	▪ 5-Minute Check 12-5 ▪ Study Notebook	▪ 5-Minute Check 12-5 ▪ Study Notebook	▪ 5-Minute Check 12-5 ▪ Study Notebook	▪ 5-Minute Check 12-5 ▪ Study Notebook

Notice that the experimental probability of rolling a 3 was $\frac{7}{25}$ or 28%, but the theoretical probability is $\frac{1}{6}$ or about 16.7%. This is because theoretical probability is what *is expected to* happen and experimental probability is what *actually* happens.

2 Simulations

An experiment that would be difficult or impractical to perform can be modeled by a **simulation**. In a simulation, a **probability model** is used to recreate a situation so that the experimental probability of an outcome can be found. A probability model is a mathematical model used to represent the theoretical probability of the outcomes in an experiment. Coins, dice, random number generators, or other objects can be used as probability models.

To design a simulation, use the following steps.

KeyConcept Designing a Simulation

Step 1 Determine each possible outcome and its theoretical probability.

Step 2 Describe an appropriate probability model for the situation that accurately represents the theoretical probability of each outcome.

Step 3 Define what a trial is for the situation, and state the number of trials to be conducted.

Real-World Example 2 Design a Simulation

QUALITY CONTROL Eloy inspects bike frames as they come through the assembly line. From previous observations, he expects to find a weld defect in one out of every ten frames and a design defect in one out of every twenty frames that he inspects. Design a simulation using Eloy's expectation of defects. Assume that a frame can only have one of the defects.

Step 1 There are three possible outcomes: weld defect, design defect, and no defects. Use Eloy's expectation of defects to calculate the theoretical probability of each outcome.

Possible Outcomes	Theoretical Probability
Weld defect	10%
Design defect	5%
No defects	85%

Step 2 We can use the random number generator on a graphing calculator. Assign the integers 0–19 to accurately represent the probability data.

Outcome	Represented by
Weld defect	0, 1
Design defect	2
No defects	3–19

Step 3 A trial will represent selecting a frame at random. The simulation can consist of any number of trials. We will use 40.

GuidedPractice

2. FREE AGENT A survey asked team executives for which team they thought free agent Bonny Solomon would choose to play next season. The results are shown. Design a simulation that can be used to estimate the probability that Bonny chooses one of these three teams. **See Chapter 12 Answer Appendix.**

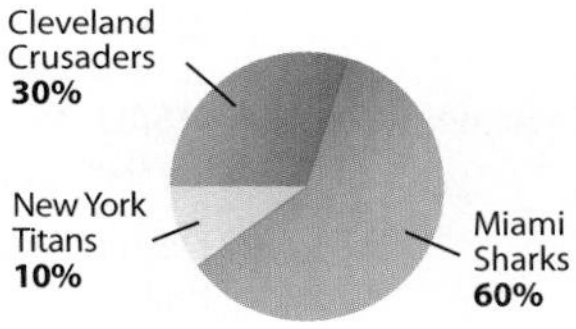

Real-WorldCareer

Assemblers Assemblers may work as part of a team, where all members are capable of performing each task. In the automobile manufacturing industry, the mean wage for a team assembler in 2009 was $49,360.

Source: Bureau of Labor Statistics

StudyTip

Modeling Simulations should involve data that are easier to obtain than the actual data you are modeling. Another probability model for Example 2 would be to place 20 marbles in a bag letting 2 red marbles represent a weld defect, 1 orange marble represent a design defect, and 17 yellow marbles represent no defects.

Formative Assessment

Use the Guided Practice exercises after each example to determine students' understanding of concepts.

Additional Example

1 STANDARDIZED TEST EXAMPLE Using the data in Example 1, find the experimental probability of rolling a prime number. (*Hint:* Recall that 1 is neither prime nor composite.) C

A $\frac{2}{5}$ **C** $\frac{3}{5}$

B $\frac{13}{25}$ **D** $\frac{18}{25}$

Additional Examples also in Interactive Classroom PowerPoint® Presentations

IWB Interactive White Board READY

2 Simulations

Example 2 shows how to design a simulation. **Example 3** shows how to conduct and evaluate a simulation.

Additional Example

2 SOFTBALL Mandy is a pitcher on her high school softball team. Last season, 70% of her pitches were strikes. Design a simulation that can be used to estimate the probability that Mandy's next pitch is a strike. Sample answer: The theoretical probability that Mandy's next pitch is a strike is 70%, and the theoretical probability that it is a ball is 30%. Use a random number generator to generate integers 1 through 10. The integers 1–7 will represent a strike, and the integers 8–10 will represent a ball. The simulation will consist of 50 trials.

Focus on Mathematical Content

Theoretical and Experimental Probability Theoretical probability describes what should occur given the number of events or trials and the sample space. Experimental probability describes the actual results of repeated trials or events. As the number of trials increases, experimental probability more closely approximates theoretical probability.

Teaching the Process Standards

Modeling Mathematically proficient students are comfortable making assumptions and approximations to simplify a complicated situation, realizing that these may need revision later. Discuss various simulation methods and the pros and cons of each.

Additional Example

3 SOFTBALL Conduct the simulation in Additional Example 2. Then report the results.
Sample answer: P(strike) = 72%, P(ball) = 28%

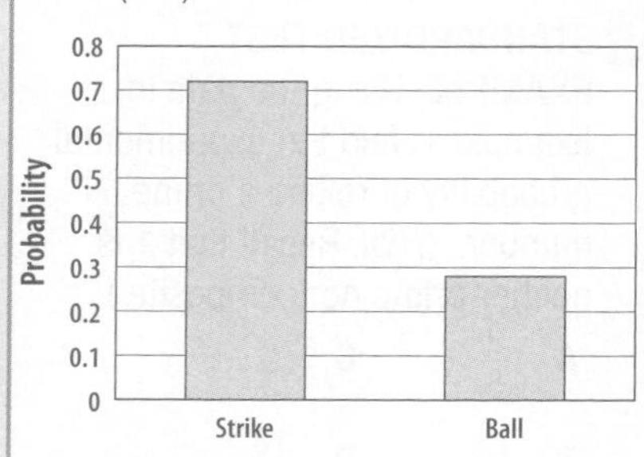

3 Practice

Formative Assessment

Use Exercises 1–2 to check for understanding.

Use the chart at the bottom of the next page to customize assignments for your students.

Additional Answer (Guided Practice)

3. Sample answer:
P(Miami) = 58%,
P(Cleveland) = 34%,
P(New York) = 8%

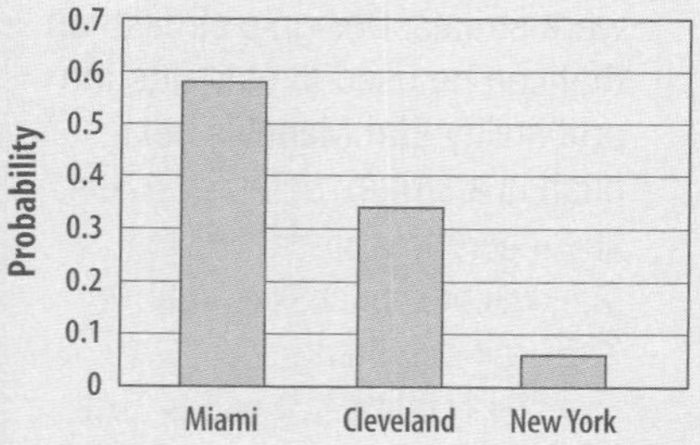

Additional Answer

2a. Sample answer: The theoretical probability that Rico will make an extra point is 94%, and the theoretical probability that he misses is 6%. Use a random number generator to generate integers 1 through 50. The integers 1–47 will represent a made extra point, and the integers 48–50 will represent a missed extra point. The simulation will consist of 40 trials.

After designing a simulation, conduct it and analyze the results.

TechnologyTip
Random Number Generator After running the random number generator, you can store the results as a list by pressing STO▸ and entering L1.

Math HistoryLink
Ada Byron Lovelace (1815–1852) Lovelace is known for generating a sequence of numbers using an early model of a computer. She is credited with being the first computer programmer. In 1980, the U.S. Department of Defense named a programming language after her.

PT

Example 3 Conduct and Evaluate a Simulation

QUALITY CONTROL Refer to the simulation in Example 2. Conduct the simulation and report the results.

Press MATH ◀ and select **[randInt (]**. Then press 0 , 19 , 40) ENTER. Use the left and right arrow buttons to view the results. Make a frequency table and record the results.

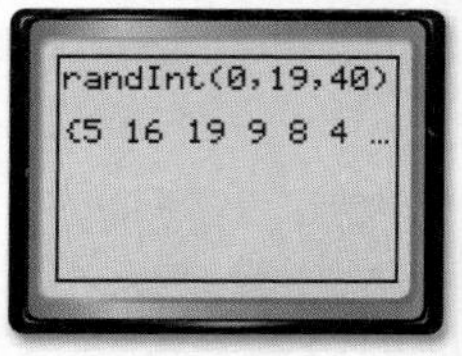

Outcome	Tally	Frequency
Weld defect	|||	3
Design defect	||	2
No defects	𝍸 𝍸 𝍸 𝍸 𝍸 𝍸 𝍸	35
Total		40

Calculate the experimental probability of finding each type of defect.

Weld defect $\frac{3}{40}$ or 0.075 Design defect $\frac{2}{40}$ or 0.05

No defects $\frac{35}{40}$ or 0.875

The experimental probabilities that a frame will have a weld defect, a design defect, or no defects in this case are 7.5%, 5%, and 87.5%, respectively. Notice that the probabilities are close to, and in the case of a design defect, the same as, the theoretical probabilities.

Make a bar graph of these results.

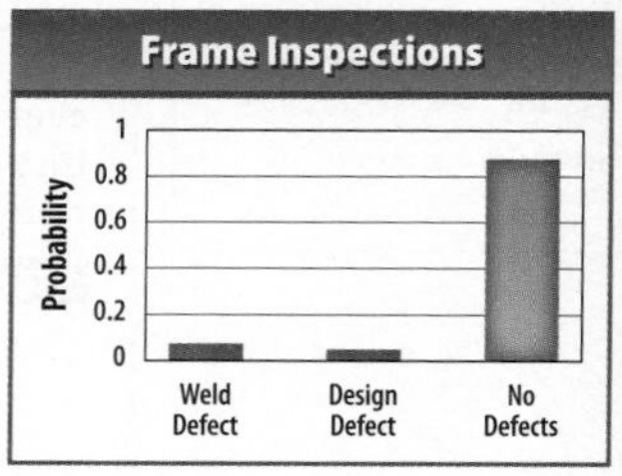

GuidedPractice

3. FREE AGENT Conduct the simulation in Guided Practice 2. Then report the results. **See margin.**

Check Your Understanding

○ = Step-by-Step Solutions begin on page R13.

Example 1

1 MULTIPLE CHOICE A movie theater employee surveyed a sample of customers as they exited the theater. Find the experimental probability of randomly selecting a customer who is older than 12 but younger than 46. **B**

A $\frac{24}{127}$ **C** $\frac{99}{127}$

B $\frac{157}{254}$ **D** $\frac{213}{254}$

Age	Frequency
0–7	13
8–12	28
13–17	48
18–23	42
24–31	27
32–45	40
46–64	33
65+	23

Examples 2–3

2. FOOTBALL Rico is the kicker on the football team. Last season, he made 94% of his extra points.

a. Design a simulation that can be used to estimate the probability that Rico will make his next extra point. **a, b. See margin.**

b. Conduct the simulation, and report the results.

DifferentiatedInstruction AL OL

If students need more practice with probability simulations,

Then give each student or pair of students a single die. Have them toss the die 100 times and then create a probability distribution table to record the number of times each number comes up. Then have them calculate the experimental probability for each number and compare the results to the theoretical probabilities.

Practice and Problem Solving

Extra Practice is on page R12.

Example 1

3. **CARDS** Javier is drawing a card from a standard deck of cards, recording the suit, and then replacing the card in the deck. The table below shows his results. **3a.** $\frac{1}{5}$ **or 20%**

Suit	clubs	diamonds	hearts	spades
Frequency	7	4	5	9

3b. $\frac{16}{25}$ **or 64%**

3c. $\frac{3}{10}$ **or 30%**

a. Find the experimental probability of drawing a heart.

b. Find the experimental probability of drawing a black card.

c. Javier repeated his test. The results of the second test are shown below. Combine the results from the second test with the results from the first test, and then find the experimental probability of drawing a spade.

Suit	clubs	diamonds	hearts	spades
Frequency	5	8	6	6

4. **MUSIC** Shannon's digital media player has a large collection of songs. She randomly toggles through the songs and then records the genre. The graph shows her results.

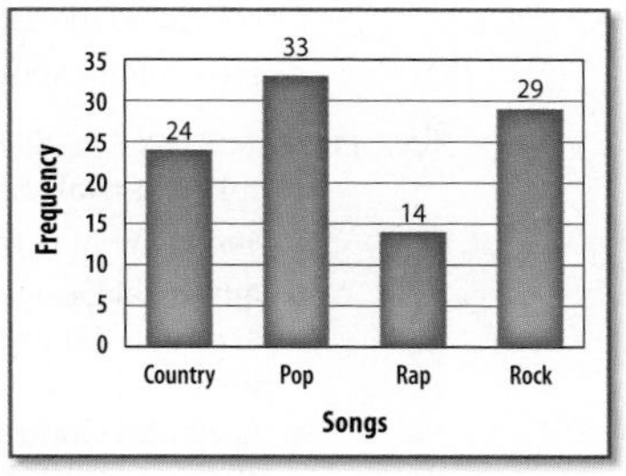

a. Find the experimental probability of selecting a country song. $\frac{6}{25}$ **or 24%**

b. Find the experimental probability of selecting a song that is not rock. $\frac{71}{100}$ **or 71%**

Examples 2–3

5. **BATTING AVERAGE** In a computer baseball game, a player has a batting average of .300. That is, he gets a hit 300 out of 1000, or 30%, of the times he is at bat.

a. Design a simulation that can be used to estimate the probability that the player will get a hit at his next at bat. **a–b. See margin.**

b. Conduct the simulation, and report the results.

6. **JEANS** Julie examines the stitching on pairs of jeans that are produced at a manufacturing plant. She expects to find defects in 1 out of every 20 pairs.

a. Design a simulation that can be used to estimate the probability that the next pair of jeans that Julie examines has a defect. **See margin.**

b. Conduct the simulation, and report the results. **See Chapter 12 Answer Appendix.**

7. **FOOD** For a promotion, the concession stands at a football stadium are giving away free items. For every tenth customer, a wheel is spun to choose the customer's prize. Each prize is equally likely. **a–b. See Chapter 12 Answer Appendix.**

a. Design a simulation that can be used to estimate the probability that the next spin is one of the five prizes.

b. Conduct the simulation, and report the results.

8. **MODELING** For its twentieth anniversary, a store randomly gives each customer a prize from the following choices: a free music download, a free game download, a free bag of popcorn, or a free DVD. The chances of winning each prize are equal. **a–b. See Chapter 12 Answer Appendix.**

a. Design a simulation that can be used to estimate the probability that the next prize given is one of the four prizes.

b. Conduct the simulation, and report the results.

Differentiated Homework Options

Level	Assignment	Two-Day Option	
AL Basic	3–8, 12, 13, 15–35	3–7 odd, 17–20	4–8 even, 12, 13, 15, 16, 21–35
OL Core	3–7 odd, 9–13, 15–35	3–8, 17–20	9–13, 15, 16, 21–35
BL Advanced	9–29 (optional: 30–35)		

Additional Answers

2b. Sample answer:
P(made) = 92.5%,
P(missed) = 7.5%

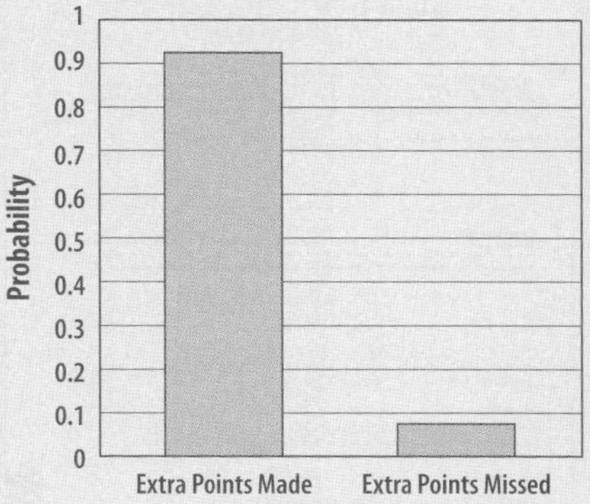

5a. Sample answer: The theoretical probability that the player gets a hit is 30%, and the theoretical probability that he does not get a hit is 70%. Use a random number generator to generate integers 1 through 10. The integers 1–3 will represent a hit, and the integers 4–10 will represent the player not getting a hit. The simulation will consist of 50 trials.

5b. Sample answer:
P(hit) = 28%,
P(not a hit) = 72%

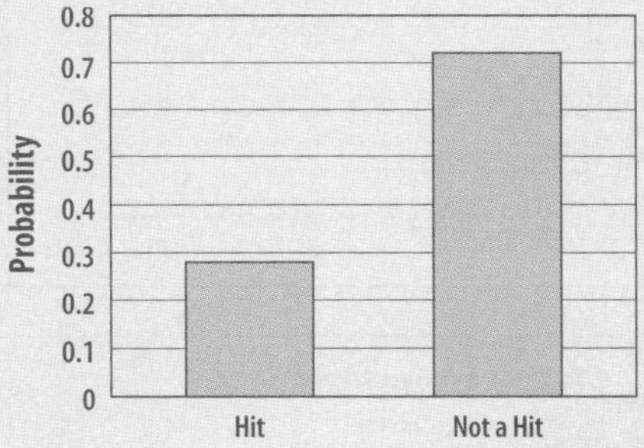

6a. Sample answer: The theoretical probability that the next pair of jeans has a defect is 5%, and the theoretical probability that the jeans do not have a defect is 95%. Use a random number generator to generate integers 1 through 20. The integer 1 will represent a pair of jeans with a defect, and the integers 2–20 will represent a pair of jeans without a defect. The simulation will consist of 40 trials.

Study Guide and Intervention

AL OL ELL

NAME ______________ DATE ________ PERIOD ________

12-5 Study Guide and Intervention

Simulations

Experimental Probability A **theoretical probability** is the ratio of the number of feasible outcomes to the total number of outcomes. For example, the theoretical probability of rolling a 4 with a number cube is $\frac{1}{6}$, or $P(4) = \frac{1}{6}$. **Experimental probability** is the ratio of the number of times an outcome occurs in an experiment to the total number of events or trials, known as the **relative frequency**.

Experimental Probability	$P = \frac{\text{frequency of an outcome}}{\text{total number of trials}}$

Example 1 **Matt recorded that it rained 8 times in November and snowed 3 times. The other days, it was sunny. There are 30 days in November. Find the experimental probability that a day in November is sunny.**

$$\text{Experimental Probability} = \frac{\text{frequency of outcome}}{\text{total number of trials}} = \frac{(30 - 8 - 3)}{30} = \frac{19}{30} = 63.3\%$$

The experimental probability that it was sunny on a day in November is 63.3%.

Example 2 **A football team noticed that 9 of the last 20 coin tosses to choose which team would receive the ball first resulted in tails. What is the experimental probability of the coin landing on tails? What is the theoretical probability?**

$$\text{Experimental Probability} = \frac{\text{frequency of outcome}}{\text{total number of trials}} = \frac{\text{number of tails}}{\text{total number of tosses}} = \frac{9}{20}$$

In this case, the experimental probability that a coin toss will be tails is $\frac{9}{20}$ or 45%. If the coin is fair, the theoretical probability is $\frac{1}{2}$ or 50%.

Exercise

DIE ROLL A math class decided to test whether a die is fair, that is, whether the experimental probability equals the theoretical probability. The results for 100 rolls are shown at the right.

1: 6	2: 15
3: 4	4: 13
5: 15	6: 47

a. What is the theoretical probability of rolling a 6?

b. What is the experimental probability of rolling a 6?

c. Is the die fair? Explain your reasoning.

Lesson 12-5

Practice

AL OL BL ELL

NAME ______________ DATE ________ PERIOD ________

12-5 Practice

Simulations

1. **MARBLES** Place 5 red, 4 yellow, and 7 green marbles in a box. Randomly draw two marbles from the box, record each color, and then return the marbles to the box. Repeat this procedure 50 times.
   a. Based on your results, what is the experimental probability of selecting two yellow marbles?
   b. Based on your results, what is the experimental probability of selecting a green marble and a yellow marble?
2. **OPTOMETRY** Color blindness occurs in 4% of the male population. Design a simulation that can be used to estimate the probability that a randomly chosen male will be color blind.
3. **SCHOOL CURRICULUM** Laurel Woods High randomly selected students for a survey to determine the most important school issues among the student body. The school wants to develop a curriculum that addresses these issues. The survey results are shown in the table.

School Issues	
Issue	Number Ranking Issue Most Important
grades	37
school standards	17
popularity	84
dating	76
violence	68
drugs, including tobacco	29

   a. Find the experimental probability for the importance of each issue.
   b. Based on the survey, what is the experimental probability that a student chosen at random thinks the most important issue is grades or school standards?
   c. The enrollment in the 9th and 10th grades at Laurel Woods High is 168. If their opinions are reflective of those of the school as a whole, how many of them would you expect to have chosen popularity as the most important issue?
   d. Suppose the school develops a curriculum incorporating the top three issues. What is the probability that a student selected at random will think the curriculum addresses the most important issue at school?

Word Problem Practice

AL OL BL ELL

NAME ______________ DATE ________ PERIOD ________

12-5 Word Problem Practice

Simulations

1. **GAMES** Suppose you spin the spinner below 20 times. You get 6 red, 4 blue, 5 yellow, and 5 green. What is the theoretical probability of spinning red? What is the experimental probability of spinning red?

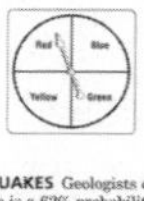

2. **EARTHQUAKES** Geologists conclude that there is a 62% probability of a magnitude 6.7 or greater quake striking the San Francisco Bay region before 2032. Design a simulation that can be used to estimate the probability that such an earthquake occurs.
3. **TOYS** There is a toy that is sold as a mother dog with 2, 3, or 4 puppies. The number of puppies in the package is a surprise. The toy company states that one half of the packages contain 2 puppies, one third contain 3 puppies, and one sixth contain 4 puppies. Describe a simulation for determining the probability of randomly receiving a certain number of puppies.
4. **AUTOMOBILES** A consumer group surveyed its members and found that many of them had flats or blowouts with a certain brand of tire. Out of a total of 20,224 tires purchased, 984 developed problems within the first 1000 miles. Lea has just had one of these tires installed on her car. What is the probability that her tire will have a flat or blowout in the first 1000 miles?
5. **BASKETBALL** Liam plays basketball. Last year, he made 80% of his attempted free throws. Design a simulation that can be used to estimate the probability that Liam makes his next free throw.
6. **POLYGRAPH TESTING** A former FBI detective has developed a voice stress analysis device to determine whether or not a person is telling the truth. He claims that the device is accurate 95% of the time. Design a simulation that can be used to estimate the probability that the test is accurate the next time it is administered.

Lesson 12-5

B 9. **GAMES** Games at the fair require the majority of players to lose in order for game owners to make a profit. New games are tested to make sure they have sufficient difficulty. The results of three test groups are listed in the table. The owners want a maximum of 33% of players to win. There were 50 participants in each test group.

Result	Group 1	Group 2	Group 3
Winners	13	15	19
Losers	37	35	31

a. What is the experimental probability that the participant was a winner in the second group? **$\frac{3}{10}$ or 30%**

b. What is the experimental probability of winning for all three groups?

9b. $\frac{47}{150}$ or about 31.3%

c. **DECISION MAKING** Should this game be used? Explain your reasoning. **See margin.**

10. **TEST** Jack forgot to study for his multiple-choice science quiz and is going to guess for each question. There are 20 questions, each with 4 possible answers.
    a. Design a simulation that can be used to estimate the number of questions that Jack answers correctly.
    b. Conduct the experiment from part **a** five times, and complete the table. **a–c. See margin.**
    c. How many should Jack expect to answer correctly?

Simulation	Number of Correct Answers
1	
2	
3	
4	
5	

C 11. **MULTIPLE REPRESENTATIONS** In this problem, you will explore the effect the number of trials has on the experimental probability of an event. **b–e. See Ch. 12 Answer Appendix.**
   a. **Verbal** What is the probability of rolling a 1 on a die? **$\frac{1}{6}$**
   b. **Analytical** Design a simulation that can be used to estimate the probability that the next number rolled on a die is a 1.
   c. **Analytical** Conduct the simulation from part **b** for 10, 20, 50, and 100 trials, and complete the table.
   d. **Analytical** As the number of trials increases, what is happening to the experimental probability?
   e. **Verbal** The *Law of Large Numbers* states that as the number of trials increases, the experimental probability gets closer to the theoretical probability. If you continued the simulation, each time increasing the number of trials, what would you expect the experimental probability for rolling a 1 to approach?

Rolling a 1		
Trials	Frequency	Experimental Probability
10		
20		
50		
100		

12. Never; sample answer: The theoretical probability of getting heads from a coin toss is one half, or 7.5 times of 15 tosses. However, when you toss a coin 15 times, getting 7.5 heads is not possible.

H.O.T. Problems Use Higher-Order Thinking Skills

12. **ARGUMENTS** The experimental probability of heads when a coin is tossed 15 times is *sometimes*, *never*, or *always* equal to the theoretical probability. Explain your reasoning.
13. **OPEN ENDED** Describe a situation at your school that could be represented by a simulation. Then design the simulation. **See Ch. 12 Answer Appendix.**
14. **CHALLENGE** *True* or *false*: If the theoretical probability of an event is 1, the experimental probability of the event cannot be 0. Explain your reasoning. **See Ch. 12 Answer Appendix.**
15. **REASONING** Jeremy tosses a coin several times and finds that the experimental probability for it landing heads up is 25%. Should Jeremy be concerned about the fairness of the coin? Explain your reasoning. **See Ch. 12 Answer Appendix.**
16. **WRITING IN MATH** What should you consider when using the results of a simulation to make a prediction? **See Ch. 12 Answer Appendix.**

Enrichment

OL BL

NAME ______________ DATE ________ PERIOD ________

12-5 Enrichment

Game Shows

On a popular game show of the 1970s, contestants were presented with three doors. Behind one of the doors was a prize. Behind the other two doors were gag prizes. A contestant was asked to select a door. Instead of showing the contestant what was behind the selected door; the host would reveal a gag prize behind one of the doors that was not chosen. After the gag prize was revealed, the contestant was given the choice to switch doors or stay with the door originally chosen. In this simulation, you will determine whether it is better to stay, switch, or if it does not matter.

1. Make a conjecture as to whether it is better to stay, switch, or does not matter once a gag prize is shown.
2. Find another person to do this simulation with. Use three colored cards to represent the three doors. Two of the cards should be the same color and the third should be a different color. One person should act as the "host" and the other as the "contestant." The "contestant" wins if the

	Won	Lost
Stay		
Switch		

Additional Answer

9c. Yes; sample answer: In total there were 150 participants with a success rate of about 31%. This is lower than the 33% success rate required by the owners.

Standardized Test Practice

17. GEOMETRY Suppose a covered water tank in the shape of a right circular cylinder is thirty feet long and eight feet in diameter. What is the surface area of the cylinder? **A**

A 272π ft^2
B 248π ft^2
C 224π ft^2
D 153π ft^2

18. SHORT RESPONSE Two consecutive numbers have a sum of 91. What are the numbers? **45 and 46**

19. Solve $\frac{2x}{x-2} + \frac{8}{x} = 6$. **G**

F 1
G 1, 4
H 2
J 2, 6

20. Mr. Bahn has $20,000 to invest. He invests part at 6% and the rest at 7%. He earns $1280 in interest within a year. How much did he invest at 7%? **D**

A $12,000
B $11,275
C $9950
D $8000

Spiral Review

Find the mean, median, mode, range, and standard deviation of each data set that is obtained after adding the given constant to each value. (Lesson 12-4)

21. 12, 16, 4, 8, 7, 11, 9, 4; + 5 **13.9, 13.5, 9, 12, 3.8**

22. 1, 4, 3, 9, 12, 6, 7, 3; + 12 **17.6, 17, 15, 11, 3.4**

23. 18, 12, 8, 13, 7, 15, 8, 6; + (−3) **7.9, 7, 5, 12, 4.0**

24. DANCE RECITAL The number of dance students in each act of a dance recital is shown. Describe the center and spread of the data using either the mean and standard deviation or the five-number summary. Justify your choice by constructing a box-and-whisker plot for the data. (Lesson 12-3) **See Chapter 12 Answer Appendix.**

Number of Dance Students														
13	15	1	20	14	4	18	2	17	10	22	1	22	15	17
21	10	18	14	18	2	10	20	15	18	4	19	12	16	5

25. PARTIES Student Council is planning a party for the school volunteers. There are five 66-ounce unopened bottles of soda left from a recent dance. When poured over ice, $5\frac{1}{2}$ ounces of soda fills a cup. How many servings of soda do they have? (Lesson 11-7) **60**

Write an inverse variation equation that relates x and y. Assume that y varies inversely as x. Then solve. (Lesson 11-1)

26. If $y = 8.5$ when $x = -1$, find x when $y = -1$. **$xy = -8.5$; 8.5**

27. If $y = 8$ when $x = 1.55$, find x when $y = -0.62$. **$xy = 12.4$; −20**

28. If $y = 6.4$ when $x = 4.4$, find x when $y = 3.2$. **$xy = 28.16$; 8.8**

29. DELIVERY Ben and Amado are delivering a freezer. The bank in front of the house is the same height as the back of the truck. They set up their ramp as shown. What is the length of the slanted part of the ramp to the nearest tenth of a foot? (Lesson 10-5) **7.1 ft**

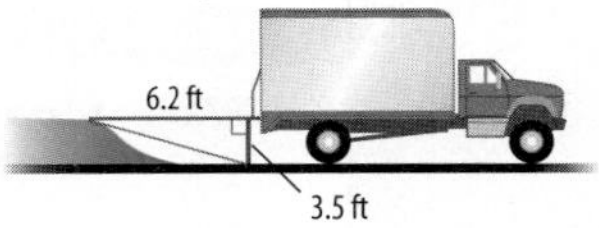

Skills Review

Write each fraction as a percent rounded to the nearest whole number.

30. $\frac{26}{58}$ **45%**

31. $\frac{55}{125}$ **44%**

32. $\frac{14}{128}$ **11%**

33. $\frac{82}{110}$ **75%**

34. $\frac{76}{124}$ **61%**

35. $\frac{23}{86}$ **27%**

Differentiated Instruction BL

Extension Have students work in groups of three or four to design an experiment that has eight possible outcomes. Have them brainstorm ways to simulate the outcome and then select a method and build the simulator. Students should create a frequency table and compare the theoretical and experimental probabilities of the situation. Have students present their results to the class.

4 Assess

Ticket Out the Door Have students explain why simulations are sometimes used instead of collecting actual data. Then have them give an example of an instance when a simulation is more practical than collecting actual data.

Teach with Tech

Interactive Whiteboard Use the student response system as a way to collect random data. For example, you could simulate rolling a number cube by giving students 6 letters to choose from as answer choices. Have each student choose one letter at random. Or, use either the Interactive Classroom software or the whiteboard software to roll simulated dice. Discuss the results of the simulation with the class.

Additional Answers

10a. Sample answer: The theoretical probability of Jack answering a question correctly is 25%, and the theoretical probability of Jack answering a question incorrectly is 75%. Use a random number generator to generate the integers 1 through 4. The integer 1 will represent a correct answer, and the integers 2–4 will represent an incorrect answer. The simulation will consist of 20 trials.

10b. Sample answer:

Simulation	Number of Correct Answers
1	4
2	5
3	8
4	5
5	7

10c. Sample answer: The average number of questions that Jack answered correctly after 5 trials is $\frac{29}{5}$ or 5.8 questions. Since a fraction of a question cannot be correct, Jack should expect to answer 5 questions correctly.

1 Focus

VerticalAlignment

Before Lesson 12-6 Use the Fundamental Counting Principle.

Lesson 12-6 Use permutations and combinations.

After Lesson 12-6 Find probabilities of compound events.

2 Teach

Scaffolding Questions

Have students read the **Why?** section of the lesson.

Ask:

- Can a player be listed more than once in the team's lineup? no
- When the coach chooses a group of players to play in the game, is the order in which she chooses them important? no
- When the coach lists the players in the lineup, is the order in which she lists them important? yes

LESSON 12-6 Permutations and Combinations

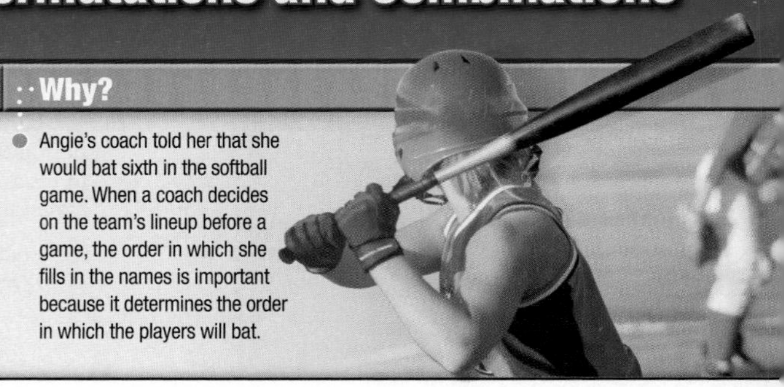

Then

- You used the Fundamental Counting Principle.

Now

1 Use permutations.

2 Use combinations.

Why?

- Angie's coach told her that she would bat sixth in the softball game. When a coach decides on the team's lineup before a game, the order in which she fills in the names is important because it determines the order in which the players will bat.

NewVocabulary
permutation
factorial
combination

Process Standards
PS.8

1 Permutations

When the objects in a sample space are arranged so that order is important, each possible arrangement is called a **permutation**. Three permutations of batting orders for the first four batters are shown below.

Use the Fundamental Counting Principle to find the total number of permutations.

number of permutations		choices for 1st batter		choices for 2nd batter		choices for 3rd batter		choices for 4th batter
Permutations =		4	$\cdot$	3	$\cdot$	2	$\cdot$	1
= 24								

There are 24 ways to arrange the first four batters. The expression used to find the number of arrangements, $4 \cdot 3 \cdot 2 \cdot 1$, can be written as 4!, which is read *4 factorial*.

Key Concept Factorial

Words The **factorial** of a positive integer n is the product of the positive integers less than or equal to n. 0! is defined to be 1.

Symbols $n! = n \cdot (n - 1) \cdot (n - 2) \cdot \ldots \cdot 1$, where $n \geq 1$

PT

Example 1 Permutations Using Factorials

TRAVEL A travel agency is planning a European vacation package. How many ways can the agency arrange the 5 cities along the tour?

There are five choices for the first city, four choices for the second city, and so on.

Number of ways to arrange the cities = 5!

$= 5 \cdot 4 \cdot 3 \cdot 2 \cdot 1$ or 120

There are 120 ways to arrange the cities.

GuidedPractice

1. **MOVIES** Lloyd and five friends go to a movie. In how many different ways can they sit together in a row of 6 empty seats? 720

Lesson 12-6 Resources

Resource	Approaching Level AL	On Level OL	Beyond Level BL	English Learners ELL
Teacher Edition	▪ Differentiated Instruction, p. 788	▪ Differentiated Instruction, pp. 788, 792	▪ Differentiated Instruction, p. 792	
Chapter Resource Masters	▪ Study Guide and Intervention, pp. 35–36 ▪ Skills Practice, p. 37 ▪ Practice, p. 38 ▪ Word Problem Practice, p. 39	▪ Study Guide and Intervention, pp. 35–36 ▪ Skills Practice, p. 37 ▪ Practice, p. 38 ▪ Word Problem Practice, p. 39 ▪ Enrichment, p. 40	▪ Practice, p. 38 ▪ Word Problem Practice, p. 39 ▪ Enrichment, p. 40	▪ Study Guide and Intervention, pp. 35–36 ▪ Skills Practice, p. 37 ▪ Practice, p. 38 ▪ Word Problem Practice, p. 39
Other	▪ 5-Minute Check 12-6 ▪ Study Notebook	▪ 5-Minute Check 12-6 ▪ Study Notebook	▪ 5-Minute Check 12-6 ▪ Study Notebook	▪ 5-Minute Check 12-6 ▪ Study Notebook

Suppose Angie's coach had 5 players in mind for the first 3 spots in the lineup. How many different batting orders could she make?

choices for 1st batter		choices for 2nd batter		choices for 3rd batter	
5	$\cdot$	4	$\cdot$	3	= 60 permutations

Once the 3 spots are filled, there are 5 − 3 or 2 players left over. Notice that $5 \cdot 4 \cdot 3$ can also be written as $= \frac{5 \cdot 4 \cdot 3 \cdot 2 \cdot 1}{2 \cdot 1} = \frac{5!}{2!}$ or $\frac{5!}{(5-3)!}$. This result is generalized below.

ReadingMath

Notation The number of permutations $P(n, r)$ of n objects taken r at a time can also be written as ${}_nP_r$.

KeyConcept Permutation Formula

Words The number of permutations of n objects taken r at a time is the quotient of $n!$ and $(n - r)!$.

Symbols $P(n, r) = \frac{n!}{(n-r)!}$

Example 2 Use the Permutation Formula

LIBRARY The librarian is placing 6 of 10 magazines in a school showcase. How many ways can she arrange the magazines in the case?

$P(n, r) = \frac{n!}{(n-r)!}$ — Permutation Formula

$P(10, 6) = \frac{10!}{(10-6)!}$ — $n = 10$ and $r = 6$

$= \frac{10!}{4!}$ — Simplify.

$= \frac{10 \cdot 9 \cdot 8 \cdot 7 \cdot 6 \cdot 5 \cdot \cancel{4} \cdot \cancel{3} \cdot \cancel{2} \cdot \cancel{1}}{\cancel{4} \cdot \cancel{3} \cdot \cancel{2} \cdot \cancel{1}}$ — Divide by common factors.

$= 151{,}200$ — Simplify.

There are 151,200 ways for the librarian to arrange the magazines.

GuidedPractice

2. **TROPHIES** James wants to place 5 of his 8 trophies on the fireplace. How many ways can he arrange the trophies? **6720**

StudyTip

Permutations and Combinations If order matters in a group, the group is a *permutation*. If order does not matter in a group, the group is a *combination*.

2 Combinations

Recall that the coach had 60 possible lineups when considering 5 players for 3 spots. What if order didn't matter and he only cares *if* players are in the lineup? A selection of objects in which order is *not* important is called a **combination**. From how many combinations of 3 players can the coach choose?

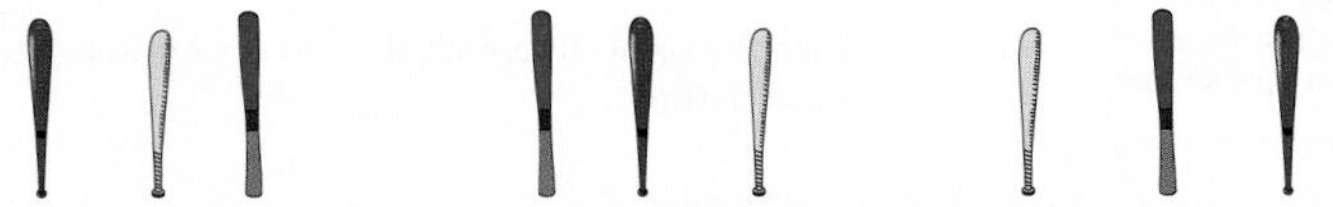

Angie Beth Cora — Cora Angie Beth — Beth Cora Angie

This same combination of players can be arranged 3! or 6 different ways. So 6 out of the 60 possible lineups include Angie, Beth, and Cora. The same will be true of every other combination. Therefore, out of the 60 possible lineups, there are $\frac{60}{6}$ or 10 different combinations of players.

1 Permutations

Example 1 shows how to use the Fundamental Counting Principle to find the number of permutations.
Example 2 shows how to use the Permutation Formula.

Formative Assessment

Use the Guided Practice exercises after each example to determine students' understanding of concepts.

Additional Examples

1. **CODES** Shaquille has a 4-digit pass code to access his e-mail account. The code is made up of the even digits 2, 4, 6, and 8. Each digit can be used only once. How many different pass codes could Shaquille have? 24

2. **CODES** A word processing program requires a user to enter a 5-digit registration code made up of the digits 1, 2, 3, 4, 5, 6, and 7. No digit can be used more than once. How many different registration codes are possible? 2520

Additional Examples also in Interactive Classroom PowerPoint® Presentations

IWB Interactive White Board READY

Teach with Tech

Portable Media Player Have students look at their portable media player and find the number of songs on their favorite album. Then, have students calculate the number of 5-song playlists that could be created for that album, given that the order of the songs *does* matter. Discuss individual results with the class.

Focus on Mathematical Content

Permutations A permutation is an arrangement or listing in which order is important. For example, if the arrangement of DVDs on a shelf is alphabetical, then the order in which they are arranged is important and this situation is a permutation. The number of permutations is expressed as $P(n, r)$ or ${}_nP_r$, where n is the number of items to choose from and r is the number of items to be chosen. To find the number of permutations, use the formula ${}_nP_r = \frac{n!}{(n-r)!}$.

Combinations

Example 3 shows how to use the Combination Formula. **Example 4** shows how to identify permutations and combinations. **Example 5** shows how to find the probability of an event by using permutations and combinations.

Additional Examples

3 **SCHOOL** A group of 4 seniors, 5 juniors, and 7 sophomores have volunteered to be on a fundraising committee. Mr. Davidson needs to choose 12 students out of the group. How many ways can the 12 students be chosen? 1820

4 Identify each situation as a *permutation* or a *combination*.

a. During a fire drill, a teacher checks the students in her row to see if everyone is present. combination

b. In preparing for a competition, a tennis coach lists his players in order of ability. permutation

Tips for New Teachers

Pacing Because permutations and combinations are frequently confused, consider discussing many examples of each. For each example, show how to find the number of permutations or combinations.

Notice that we divided the number of permutations by the number of possible arrangements for every combination of elements $r!$ to obtain the number of combinations.

StudyTip

Combination Formula The number of combinations is the quotient of the number of permutations of n objects taken r at a time and the number of permutations of r objects.

KeyConcept Combination Formula

Words The number of combinations of n objects taken r at a time is the quotient of $n!$ and $(n-r)!r!$.

Symbols $C(n, r) = \frac{n!}{(n-r)!r!}$

PT

Example 3 Use the Combination Formula

RETAIL Marques works part-time at a local department store. His manager asked him to make a display using 5 different styles of shirts from 8 available styles. How many ways can Marques choose the shirts?

$C(n, r) = \frac{n!}{(n-r)!r!}$ Combination Formula

$C(8, 5) = \frac{8!}{(8-5)!5!}$ $n = 8$ and $r = 5$

$= \frac{8!}{3!5!}$ Simplify.

$= \frac{8 \cdot 7 \cdot 6 \cdot \cancel{5} \cdot \cancel{4} \cdot \cancel{3} \cdot \cancel{2} \cdot \cancel{1}}{3 \cdot 2 \cdot 1 \cdot \cancel{5} \cdot \cancel{4} \cdot \cancel{3} \cdot \cancel{2} \cdot \cancel{1}}$ Divide by common factors.

$= \frac{336}{6}$ or 56 Simplify.

GuidedPractice

3. SPRING DANCE A group of four students is selecting corsages and boutonnières to wear to the spring dance. They can choose from 4 roses, 6 carnations, and 8 tulips. If all of the flowers are different, in how many ways can 4 flowers be chosen? **3060**

Part of the difficulty in learning permutations and combinations is distinguishing between them. Remember that order matters with permutations.

PT

Example 4 Identifying Permutations and Combinations

Identify each situation as a *permutation* or a *combination*.

a. A playlist of songs on a digital media player is being played so that songs do not repeat. In how many ways can the songs be played?

Since the question is really about the different orders of songs, this is a permutation.

b. Amy orders an ice cream cone with three different flavors. There are 26 possible flavors. How many different sets of three flavors can she choose?

Since the order in which the flavors are selected is not important, this is a combination.

WatchOut!

Wording Notice that if we were asked for the order that the scoops were placed on the cone, then this would have been a permutation.

GuidedPractice

4A. A teacher uses a random number generator to create a seating chart for 20 students. **permutation**

4B. Ten athletes enter a race. The top three finishers move on to the next round. **combination**

DifferentiatedInstruction AL OL

Logical Learners After students learn how to calculate the number of combinations in Example 3, discuss the difference between combinations and permutations. In Example 3, the order in which the shirts are chosen does not matter because only a group of shirts is being chosen. However, if Marques were deciding where in the display to place each shirt, then the order would matter.

We can use permutations or combinations to find the probability of an event.

PT

Example 5 Probability with Permutations and Combinations

SPANISH CLUB The Spanish club is forming two teams for the International Festival. Rebekah and Lydia are among the nine who volunteered to lead a team. If the advisor assigns positions at random, what is the probability that Rebekah is chosen to lead the food team and Lydia is chosen to lead the tickets team?

Step 1 Find the total number of outcomes.
Since we care about specific positions, this is a permutation. Find the number of permutations of 9 people taken 2 at a time.

$P(n, r) = \frac{n!}{(n-r)!}$ Permutation Formula

$P(9, 2) = \frac{9!}{(9-2)!}$ or 72 $n = 9$ and $r = 2$

There are 72 possible outcomes

Step 2 Find the successes.
Of the 72 permutations, only one has Rebekah leading the food team and Lydia leading the tickets team.

Step 3 Find the probability.

$P = \frac{\text{number of successes}}{\text{number of possible outcomes}} = \frac{1}{72}$ Probability Formula

The probability of Rebekah leading the food team and Lydia leading the tickets team is $\frac{1}{72}$.

StudyTip
Probability Find the probability of an event by dividing the number of favorable outcomes by the number of possible outcomes.

GuidedPractice

5. **STUDENT COUNCIL** Four of the twelve members of the student council are being randomly selected to hand out flyers at the mall. What is the probability that Hasina, Amy, Bonny, and Tim are all selected? $\frac{1}{495}$

Check Your Understanding

= Step-by-Step Solutions begin on page R13.

Example 1

1. **CHARITY** A youth charity group is holding a raffle and wants to display a picture of the 6 prizes on a flyer. How many ways can they arrange the prizes in a row? **720**

Examples 2–4 **Identify each situation as a *permutation* or a *combination*.**

2. choosing 3 different pizza toppings from a list of 12 **combination**
3. choosing team captains for a football team **combination**
4. choosing the first-, second-, and third-place winner of an art competition **permutation**

Evaluate each expression.

5. $P(7, 2)$ **42**
6. $P(9, 3)$ **504**
7. $C(6, 4)$ **15**
8. $C(5, 2)$ **10**
9. **MENUS** There are 14 toppings listed in a pizza menu. How many different six-topping pizzas are possible? **3003**

Example 5

10. **MODELING** Students are given 5-digit passwords for their accounts on the school's computer system. If no numbers can repeat, what is the probability that a student's password is 93152? $\frac{1}{30{,}240}$

Additional Example

5 TABLE TENNIS Sixteen people signed up for a table tennis tournament. If players are put into groups of 4 and the draw is determined randomly, what is the probability that Heather, Erin, Michele, and Patrick are put into the same group? $\frac{1}{1820}$

Focus on Mathematical Content

Combinations A combination is an arrangement or listing in which order is not important. For example, when choosing the decorations for a school party, the order in which the decorations are chosen does not matter, so this situation is a combination. The number of combinations are expressed as $C(n, r)$ or ${}_nC_r$, where n is the number of items to choose from and r is the number of items to be chosen. To find the number of combinations, use the formula $C(n, r) = \frac{n!}{(n-r)!r!}$.

3 Practice

Formative Assessment

Use Exercises 1–10 to check for understanding.

Use the chart on the bottom of the next page to customize assignments for your students.

Teaching the Process Standards

Modeling Mathematically proficient students can apply the mathematics they know to solve problems arising in everyday life. In Exercise 10, point out that it may not seem so, but a random password of 12345 is as likely as 92152.

WatchOut!

Error Analysis For Exercise 39, ask students if order is important in this problem. Then remind them that when the order is not important, the Combination Formula should be used.

Teaching the Process Standards

Tools Mathematically proficient students consider the available tools when solving a problem. These tools might include pencil and paper, and concrete models. In exercises where students are finding numbers of permutations or combinations, pictures or concrete models can help to visualize the situations.

Perseverance Mathematically proficient students draw diagrams of important features and relationships. In Exercise 40, suggest that students draw a picture to start to solve the problem.

Additional Answers

37c. Sample answer: A random number generator can be used with 1-4 representing freshmen, 5-9 representing sophomores, 10-15 representing juniors, and 16-23 representing seniors.

37d. Sample answer: Assume the first number generated is a 3 and the first selection is a freshman. The random number generator can be reconfigured to 1-3 representing freshmen, 4-8 representing sophomores, 9-14 representing juniors, and 15-22 representing seniors. An easier method would be to use the original number generator and ignore any repeats of the number 3. Follow this process for each remaining selection.

Practice and Problem Solving

Extra Practice is on page R12.

Example 1

11. SCIENCE FAIR There are 8 finalists in a science fair competition. How many ways can they stand on the stage? **40,320**

Evaluate each expression.

12. $P(6, 6)$ **720** **13.** $P(5, 1)$ **5** **14.** $P(4, 1)$ **4** **15.** $P(7, 3)$ **210**

16. $C(7, 6)$ **7** **17.** $C(5, 3)$ **10** **18.** $C(5, 5)$ **1** **19.** $C(3, 0)$ **1**

Examples 2–4

Identify each situation as a *permutation* or a *combination*.

20. selecting 5 books to read from a list of 8 **combination**

21. an arrangement of the letters in the word *probability* **permutation**

22. a list of students by class ranking **permutation**

23. a playlist of songs on a digital media player **combination**

24. selecting 4 different ingredients out of 8 for a salad **combination**

25. TOOLS Abigail works at the jewelry store in the mall. Her manger asks her to place 3 of the 12 birthstone necklaces in the front display case. How many ways can she arrange the necklaces in the display case? **1320**

26. RECYCLING Juana is setting two recycling bins at the end of her driveway for pick-up. She has four bins from which to choose. How many ways can she pick the bins to set out? **6**

Example 5

27. MUSIC What is the probability that the first 8 songs that are played on Kenneth's playlist are country songs? $\frac{1}{43{,}758}$

Exercise Playlist

Country	8 songs
Rock	6 songs
Rap	4 songs

28. AMUSEMENT PARKS Tino is entering an amusement park with 5 of his friends. At the gate they must go through a turnstile one at a time. How many ways can Tino and his friends go through the turnstile? **720**

29. PAGEANTS The Teen Miss USA pageant has 51 delegates. If the judges choose Teen Miss USA and four runners-up, how many ways can they be chosen? **281,887,200**

30. BASKETBALL A coach has to select 5 of 12 players on the basketball team to start the game. How many different groups of players could be selected as starters? **792 groups**

31. ICE CREAM How many ways can a customer choose 3 flavors of ice cream at The Dairy Barn? **455**

THE DAIRY BARN
5 varieties of chocolate
4 varieties of candy-flavor
6 varieties of berry-flavor

32. GAMES Tonisha is playing a board game in which you make words to score points. There are 12 letters left in the box, and she must choose 4. She cannot see the letters.

a. Suppose the 12 letters are all different. How many ways can she choose 4 of the 12? **495**

b. She chooses *A*, *T*, *R*, and *E*. How many different arrangements of three letters can she make from these letters? **24 arrangements**

c. How many of the three-letter arrangements are words? List them. **9; ART, ATE, ARE, TAR, TEA, RAT, EAT, EAR, ERA**

33. DANCE At the spring dance, Christy and 7 of her friends sit on one side of a table. How many ways can Christy and her friends fill the 8 empty seats? **40,320**

Differentiated Homework Options

Level	Assignment	Two-Day Option	
AL Basic	11–31, 39, 41–64	11–31 odd, 44–47	10–30 even, 39, 41–43, 48–64
OL Core	11–31 odd, 32–39, 41–64	11–31, 44–47	32–39, 48–64
BL Advanced	32–58, (optional: 59–64)		

790 | Lesson 12-6 | Permutations and Combinations

34. HORSEBACK RIDING Trish and Charliqua entered a horseback riding camp with 22 other people. Six riders are randomly selected to work with the head instructor. How many different groups of people can be placed with the head instructor? **134,596**

35) BOWLING Chris and Kelly entered a bowling tournament.

a. What is the probability that Chris and Kelly are selected to bowl against each other in *any* lane? $\frac{1}{496}$

b. What is the probability that Chris and Kelly are selected to bowl against each other in the *last* lane? $\frac{1}{7936}$

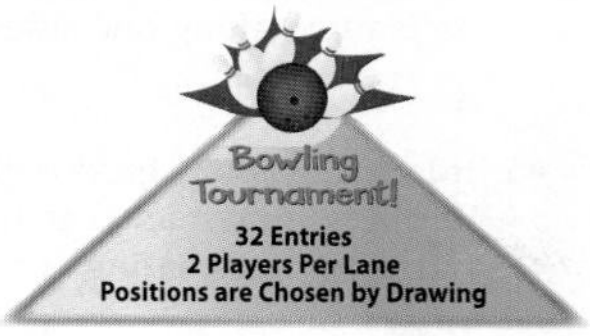

36. SECURITY Banks lock an account after three incorrect PIN entries. Suppose a bank that uses four-digit PINs in which the digits cannot repeat allowed unlimited incorrect entries. What is the maximum time it would take a hacker using a computer program that can enter 100 different codes per second to enter the correct PIN? **50.4 seconds**

C **37. DECISION MAKING** Westerville High School is putting on a play. In all, 4 freshmen, 5 sophomores, 6 juniors, and 8 seniors tried out for the 12 open spots.

a. How many ways can the 12 spots be chosen? **1,352,078**

b. If the students are chosen randomly, what is the probability that at least one senior will be chosen? **about 99.97%**

c. What probability model can we use to randomly select the first spot? **See margin.**

d. How does this model change when selecting the second spot? **See margin.**

38. COMPOUND PROBABILITY There are 7 red marbles, 8 purple marbles, and 6 green marbles in a bag. Fifteen marbles are randomly selected. Use the following steps to determine the probability of selecting 5 of each color.

a. Find the number of possible outcomes. **54,264**

b. Find the number of successes for selecting 5 of 7 red marbles, for selecting 5 of 8 purple marbles, and for selecting 5 of 6 green marbles. **21; 56; 6**

c. Use the Fundamental Counting Principle to find the total number of successes. **7056**

d. Determine the probability of selecting 5 of each color. **about 13%**

H.O.T. Problems Use Higher-Order Thinking Skills

39. ERROR ANALYSIS Sydney and Ming are determining how many 4-person committees are possible if 10 people are available. Is either of them correct? Explain.

Sydney	Ming
${}_{10}P_4 = \frac{10!}{(10-4)!}$	${}_{10}C_4 = \frac{10!}{(10-4)!4!}$
$= 5040$	$= 210$

Ming; since order is not important, combinations should have been used.

41. Determining class rank in a senior class; this is the only situation in which order matters.

40. PERSEVERANCE Seven identical mathematics books and 4 identical science books are to be stored on one shelf. How many different ways can the books be arranged? **330**

41. WHICH ONE DOESN'T BELONG? Determine which situation does not belong. Explain.

choosing 5 players on a quiz team	choosing 10 colored marbles from a bag
choosing 4 horses from 6 to run a race	ranking students in a senior class

42. REASONING Determine whether the statement ${}_nP_r = {}_nC_r$ is *sometimes*, *always*, or *never* true. Explain your reasoning. **Sometimes; the statement is true when $r = 1$ because order is irrelevant when choosing 1 item.**

43. WRITING IN MATH Write a situation in which 3 of 8 objects are selected and order is not important. **Sample answer: choosing 3 clubs out of 8 to join**

Study Guide and Intervention

AL OL ELL

NAME ______ DATE ______ PERIOD ______

12-6 Study Guide and Intervention

Permutations and Combinations

Permutations An arrangement or listing in which order or placement is important is called a **permutation.** For example, the arrangement AB of choices A and B is different from the arrangement BA of these same two choices.

Permutations	The number of permutations of n objects taken r at a time is $P(n, r) = \frac{n!}{(n-r)!}$.

Example 1 Find $P(6, 2)$.

$P(n, r) = \frac{n!}{(n-r)!}$ Permutation Formula

$P(6, 2) = \frac{6!}{(6-2)!}$ $n = 6, r = 2$

$= \frac{6!}{4!}$ Simplify.

$= \frac{6 \cdot 5 \cdot 4 \cdot 3 \cdot 2 \cdot 1}{4 \cdot 3 \cdot 2 \cdot 1}$ Definition of factorial

$= 6 \cdot 5$ or 30 Simplify.

There are 30 permutations of 6 objects taken 2 at a time.

Example 2 **PASSWORDS A specific program requires the user to enter a 5-digit password. The digits cannot repeat and can be any five of the digits 1, 2, 3, 4, 7, 8, and 9.**

a. How many different passwords are possible?

$P(n, r) = \frac{n!}{(n-r)!}$

$P(7, 5) = \frac{7!}{(7-5)!}$

$= \frac{7 \cdot 6 \cdot 5 \cdot 4 \cdot 3 \cdot 2 \cdot 1}{2 \cdot 1}$

$= 7 \cdot 6 \cdot 5 \cdot 4 \cdot 3$ or 2520

There are 2520 ways to create a password.

b. What is the probability that the first two digits are odd numbers with the other digits any of the remaining numbers?

$P(\text{first two digits odd}) = \frac{\text{number of favorable outcomes}}{\text{number of possible outcomes}}$

favorable outcomes: There are 4 choices for the first 2 digits and 5 choices for the remaining 3 digits. $P(4, 2) \cdot P(5, 3)$

possible outcomes: There are 7 choices for the 5 digits. $P(7, 5)$

The probability is $\frac{P(4, 2) \cdot P(5, 3)}{P(7, 5)} = \frac{720}{2520}$ or about 28.6%.

Exercises

Evaluate each expression.

1. $P(7, 4)$ 2. $P(12, 7)$ 3. $[P(9, 9)]$

4. **CLUBS** A club with ten members wants to choose a president, vice-president, secretary, and treasurer. Six of the members are women, and four are men.
a. How many different sets of officers are possible?
b. What is the probability that all officers will be women.

Lesson 12-6

Practice

AL OL BL ELL

NAME ______ DATE ______ PERIOD ______

12-6 Practice

Permutations and Combinations

Identify each situation as a *permutation* or a *combination*.

1. choosing the order of 16 songs to burn to a CD
2. choosing friends to invite to a party
3. choosing 5 players for a basketball team
4. choosing your top 10 favorite actors
5. choosing where to sit at a restaurant

Evaluate each expression.

6. $P(20, 5)$ 7. $P(11, 7)$ 8. $P(13, 1)$

9. $C(19, 16)$ 10. $P(15, 4)$ 11. $C(14, 7)$

12. **SPORTS** In how many orders can the top five finishers in a race finish?

13. **JUDICIAL PROCEDURE** The court system in a community needs to assign 3 out of 8 judges to a docket of criminal cases. Five of the judges are male and three are female.
a. Does the selection of judges involve a permutation or a combination?
b. In how many ways could three judges be chosen?
c. If the judges are chosen randomly, what is the probability that all 3 judges are male?

14. **PRESENTATIONS** Mrs. Harper is randomly selecting 4 students to give their presentations today. If there are 16 boys and 14 girls in the class, what is the probability that the first two students selected are girls and the next two are boys?

15. **DIAMONDS** A bag contains 16 fake diamonds and 8 real diamonds that are identically shaped. If 5 diamonds are randomly selected from the bag, what is the probability that 2 are fake and 3 are real?

Word Problem Practice

AL OL BL ELL

NAME ______ DATE ______ PERIOD ______

12-6 Word Problem Practice

Permutations and Combinations

1. **CHORES** In Ashley's family there are 4 children and their mother and father. If two of the six must help clear the table after dinner, how many ways can two people be paired?

2. **PUBLIC SERVICE** A county computer randomly selects jurors from the lawyer-approved potential juror list. How many ways are there for 12 jurors to be chosen from a pool of 20?

Potential Jurors	
Fred	Jennifer
Sally	Carla
Mike	Sam
Tom	Sylvia
Maria	Jamal
Ted	Greg
Carlos	Todd
Dorothy	Lauren
Irene	Maya
Trish	Luke

3. **SPORTS** Hans' basketball team decides to choose two captains each week so that many players get the chance to be captain. Each week, each of the 11 players writes his name on a slip of paper. The papers are then placed in a container and mixed. The last week's captains draw two slips of paper from the container; these two people are captains for the following week. How many different pairs of captains can be formed?

4. **PUZZLES** A popular newspaper puzzle involves a series of letters that can be rearranged to form a word. Will is writing his own version of the game for a school project. He wants to scramble the following word for his puzzle.

numbers

How many ways are there to arrange the letters with the letter *b* as the first letter?

5. **HORSE RACING** There are 15 contenders in a horse race.
a. How many different ways can the horses finish the race?
b. How many different ways can horses place first, second, and third?
c. If all 15 horses have an equal chance of winning and 6 of the horses are female, what is the probability that a female horse places first, second, and third?

Lesson 12-6

Enrichment

OL BL

NAME ______ DATE ______ PERIOD ______

12-6 Enrichment

A Great Pizza Deal

A television commercial advertised a pizza deal in which customers could choose two pizzas each with up to five toppings chosen from a set of eleven toppings. On the commercial, a boy claims that there are 1,048,576 ways for the customer to choose the two pizzas. Is this a valid claim?

Pizza Deal!!
For a limited time, you can choose 2 pizzas with up to 5 toppings for only
$7.99!!!!!!!

Topping	Yes	No
Pepperoni	☐	☐
Sausage	☐	☐
Tomato	☐	☐
Green olives	☐	☐
Black olives	☐	☐
Mushrooms	☐	☐
Extra Cheese	☐	☐
Peppers	☐	☐
Onions	☐	☐

4 Assess

Crystal Ball Have students explain how today's concepts on permutations and combinations might help them with finding probabilities of compound events in the next lesson.

Formative Assessment

Check for student understanding of concepts in Lessons 12-5 and 12-6.

Quiz 3, p. 58

Follow-up

Students have explored probability.

Ask:

- What is the difference between a combination and a permutation? When are each of these used in the real world? Sample answer: If order is important, then permutations are used. If order is not important, then combinations are used. Finding the first, second, and third places in a competition would involve a permutation. Choosing 3 toppings for a salad from a menu of 8 options would involve a combination.

Standardized Test Practice

44. In how many ways can 3 of 8 different flowers be planted along one side of a road? **C**

A 342 B 338 C 336 D 328

45. If Jack can eat 21 hard-boiled eggs in 15 minutes, how many can he eat in 25 minutes if he continues eating at the same pace? **G**

F 18 G 35 H 36 J 37

46. Shante has 30 coins, quarters and dimes, that total \$5.70. How many quarters does she have? **C**

A 12 C 18
B 15 D 20

47. SHORT RESPONSE There are 3 red candies in a bag of 20 candies. What is the probability of selecting a red candy? $\frac{3}{20}$

Spiral Review

Vacationers were asked how many evenings they spent eating out during their trip. Find each experimental probability. (Lesson 12-5)

Number of Evenings	Frequency
0	14
1	39
2	28
3	21
4	10
5+	13

48. a vacationer ate out at least once **88.8%**

49. a vacationer ate out less than three times **64.8%**

50. Find the mean, median, mode, range, and standard deviation of the data set obtained after multiplying each value by 1.3. (Lesson 12-4)

26, 15, 19, 31, 47, 44, 38, 26, 28, 19 **38.09, 35.1, 24.7, 41.6, 13.3**

51. PET CARE Kendra takes care of pets while their owners are out of town. One week she has three dogs that all eat the same kind of dog food. How many bags of food should Kendra buy for one week? (Lesson 11-6) **2 bags**

Max
12 days/bag

Miles
15 days/bag

Stormy
16 days/bag

Find each product. (Lesson 11-4)

52. $\frac{8}{x^2} \cdot \frac{x^4}{4x}$ $2x$

53. $\frac{10r^3}{6n^3} \cdot \frac{42n^2}{35r^3}$ $\frac{2}{n}$

54. $\frac{10y^3z^2}{6wx^3} \cdot \frac{12w^2x^2}{25y^2z^4}$ $\frac{4wy}{5xz^2}$

55. $\frac{(n-1)(n+1)}{(n+1)} \cdot \frac{(n-4)}{(n-1)(n+4)}$ $\frac{n-4}{n+4}$

56. $\frac{(x-8)}{(x+8)(x-3)} \cdot \frac{(x+4)(x-3)}{(x-8)}$ $\frac{x+4}{x+8}$

57. $\frac{3a^2b}{2gh} \cdot \frac{24g^2h}{15ab^2}$ $\frac{12ag}{5b}$

58. COOKING The formula $t = \frac{40(25 + 1.85a)}{50 - 1.85a}$ relates the time t in minutes that it takes to cook an average-size potato in an oven at an altitude of a thousands of feet. (Lesson 11-3)

a. What is the value of a for an altitude of 4500 feet? **4.5**

b. Calculate the time it takes to cook a potato at an altitude of 3500 feet and at 7000 feet. How do your cooking times compare at these two altitudes? **29; 41; The difference is 12 minutes.**

Skills Review

Ten red tiles, 12 blue tiles, 8 green tiles, 4 yellow tiles, 10 red tiles, and 12 black tiles are placed in a bag and selected at random. Find each probability.

59. P(blue) $\frac{6}{23}$

60. P(red) $\frac{5}{23}$

61. P(black or yellow) $\frac{8}{23}$

62. P(green or red) $\frac{9}{23}$

63. P(not blue) $\frac{17}{23}$

64. P(not green) $\frac{19}{23}$

Differentiated Instruction OL BL

Extension Ask students whether they would expect the number of combinations of n items taken r at a time to be less or more than the number of permutations of n items taken r at a time. Have them explain their reasoning by using real-life examples. The number of combinations would be less than the number of permutations. Sample answer: If you listen to jazz recording A and jazz recording B in no particular order, this is a combination, and AB and BA are the same. If the order in which you listen to the recordings is important, then listening to the recordings in the order AB is different from listening to the recordings in the order BA. The number of combinations is therefore less than the number of permutations.

LESSON 12-7 Probability of Compound Events

:: Then	:: Now	:: Why?
● You calculated simple probability.	● **1** Find probabilities of independent and dependent events. **2** Find probabilities of mutually exclusive events.	● Evita is flying from Cleveland to Honolulu. The airline reports that the flight from Cleveland to Honolulu has a 40% on-time record. The airline also reported that they lose luggage 5% of the time. What is the probability that both the flight will be on time and Evita's luggage will arrive?

NewVocabulary
compound event
joint probability
independent events
dependent events
mutually exclusive events

1 Independent and Dependent Events Recall that one event, like flying from Cleveland to Honolulu, is called a *simple event*. A **compound event** is made up of two or more simple events. So, the probability that the flight will be on time and the luggage arrives is an example of a compound event. The probability of compound events is called **joint probability**.The plane being on time may not affect whether luggage is lost. These two events are called **independent events** because the outcome of one event does not affect the outcome of the other.

KeyConcept Probability of Independent Events

Words If two events, *A* and *B*, are independent, then the probability of both events occurring is the product of the probability of *A* and the probability of *B*.

Symbols $P(A \text{ and } B) = P(A) \cdot P(B)$

Model

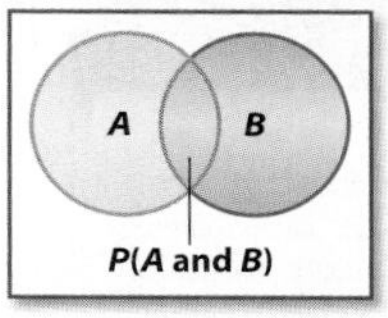

Real-World Example 1 Independent Events

MARBLES **A bag contains 6 black marbles, 9 blue marbles, 4 yellow marbles, and 2 green marbles. A marble is selected, replaced, and a second marble is selected. Find the probability of selecting a black marble, then a yellow marble.**

First marble: $P(\text{black}) = \frac{6}{21}$ ← number of black marbles / ← total number of marbles

Second marble: $P(\text{yellow}) = \frac{4}{21}$ ← number of yellow marbles / ← total number of marbles

$P(\text{black, yellow}) = P(\text{black}) \cdot P(\text{yellow})$ Probability of independent events

$= \frac{6}{21} \cdot \frac{4}{21}$ or $\frac{24}{441}$ Substitution

The probability is $\frac{24}{441}$ or about 5.4%.

GuidedPractice **Find each probability.**

1A. $P(\text{blue, green})$ $\frac{18}{441}$ **or about 4.1%**

1B. $P(\text{not black, blue})$ $\frac{135}{441}$ **or about 30.6%**

1 Focus

VerticalAlignment

Before Lesson 12-7 Calculate simple probability.

Lesson 12-7 Find probabilities of independent and dependent events. Find probabilities of mutually exclusive events.

After Lesson 12-7 Construct probability distributions.

2 Teach

Scaffolding Questions

Have students read the **Why?** section of the lesson.

Ask:

- Suppose the flight is on time. Does this affect whether Evita's luggage is lost? no
- What does the word *independent* mean? free or unrelated
- Could the word *independent* be used to describe the relationship between "flight is on time" and "luggage is lost"? Yes, because a flight being on time does not affect whether luggage is lost; the events are independent of each other.

Lesson 12-7 Resources

Resource	Approaching Level AL	On Level OL	Beyond Level BL	English Learners ELL
Teacher Edition	▪ Differentiated Instruction, p. 795	▪ Differentiated Instruction, pp. 795, 800	▪ Differentiated Instruction, p. 800	
Chapter Resource Masters	▪ Study Guide and Intervention, pp. 41–42 ▪ Skills Practice, p. 43 ▪ Practice, p. 44 ▪ Word Problem Practice, p. 45	▪ Study Guide and Intervention, pp. 41–42 ▪ Skills Practice, p. 43 ▪ Practice, p. 44 ▪ Word Problem Practice, p. 45 ▪ Enrichment, p. 46 ▪ Graphing Calculator Activity, p. 47	▪ Practice, p. 44 ▪ Word Problem Practice, p. 45 ▪ Enrichment, p. 46	▪ Study Guide and Intervention, pp. 41–42 ▪ Skills Practice, p. 43 ▪ Practice, p. 44 ▪ Word Problem Practice, p. 45
Other	▪ 5-Minute Check 12-7 ▪ Study Notebook ▪ Teaching Algebra with Manipulatives	▪ 5-Minute Check 12-7 ▪ Study Notebook ▪ Teaching Algebra with Manipulatives	▪ 5-Minute Check 12-7 ▪ Study Notebook	▪ 5-Minute Check 12-7 ▪ Study Notebook ▪ Teaching Algebra with Manipulatives

1 Independent and Dependent Events

Example 1 shows how to find the probability of two independent events occurring. **Example 2** shows how to find the probability of dependent events occurring.

Formative Assessment

Use the Guided Practice exercises after each example to determine students' understanding of concepts.

Additional Examples

1 FLIGHTS Rae is flying from Birmingham to Chicago on a flight with a 90% on-time record. On the same day, the chances of rain in Denver are predicted to be 50%. What is the probability that Rae's flight will be on time and that it will rain in Denver? 45%

2 GAMES At the school carnival, winners in the ring-toss game are randomly given a prize from a bag that contains 4 sunglasses, 6 hairbrushes, and 5 key chains. Three prizes are randomly chosen from the bag and not replaced. Find each probability.

a. P(sunglasses, hairbrush, keychain) $\frac{4}{91}$

b. P(hairbrush, hairbrush, not a hairbrush) $\frac{9}{91}$

Additional Examples also in Interactive Classroom PowerPoint® Presentations

IWB Interactive White Board READY

When the outcome of one event affects the outcome of another event, they are **dependent events**. In Example 1, if the marble was not placed back in the bag, then drawing the two marbles would have been dependent events. The probability of drawing the second marble depends on what marble was drawn first.

KeyConcept Probability of Dependent Events

Words	If two events, A and B, are dependent, then the probability of both events occurring is the product of the probability of A and the probability of B after A occurs.
Symbols	$P(A \text{ and } B) = P(A) \cdot P(B \text{ following } A)$

Recall that the complement of a set is the set of all objects that do *not* belong to the given set. In a standard deck of cards, the complement of drawing a heart is drawing a diamond, club, or spade. So, the probability of drawing a heart is $\frac{13}{52}$, and the probability of not drawing a heart is $\frac{52-13}{52}$ or $\frac{39}{52}$.

The sum of the probabilities for any two complementary events is 1.

Real-WorldLink

A standard deck of cards consists of 52 cards. There are 4 suits: hearts, diamonds, clubs, and spades. There are 13 cards of each suit. An ace, 2, 3, 4, 5, 6, 7, 8, 9, 10, jack, queen, and king. The hearts and diamonds are red, and the clubs and spades are black.

Real-World Example 2 Dependent Events

CARDS Cynthia randomly draws three cards from a standard deck one at a time without replacement. Find the probability that the cards are drawn in the given order.

a. P(diamond, spade, diamond)

First card: $P(\text{diamond}) = \frac{13}{52}$ or $\frac{1}{4}$ ← $\frac{\text{number of diamonds}}{\text{total number of cards}}$

Second card: $P(\text{spade}) = \frac{13}{51}$ ← $\frac{\text{number of spades}}{\text{number of cards remaining}}$

Third card: $P(\text{diamond}) = \frac{12}{50}$ or $\frac{6}{25}$ ← $\frac{\text{number of diamonds remaining}}{\text{number of cards remaining}}$

$P(\text{diamond, spade, diamond}) = P(\text{diamond}) \cdot P(\text{spade}) \cdot P(\text{diamond})$

$= \frac{1}{4} \cdot \frac{13}{51} \cdot \frac{6}{25}$ or $\frac{13}{850}$ Substitution

The probability is $\frac{13}{850}$ or about 1.5%.

b. P(four, four, not a jack)

After Cynthia draws the first two fours from the deck of 52 cards, there are 50 cards left. Since neither of these cards are jacks, there are still four jacks left in the deck. So, there are $52 - 2 - 4$ or 46 cards that are not jacks.

$P(\text{four, four, not a jack}) = P(\text{four}) \cdot P(\text{four}) \cdot P(\text{not a jack})$

$= \frac{4}{52} \cdot \frac{3}{51} \cdot \frac{46}{50}$

$= \frac{552}{132{,}600}$ or $\frac{23}{5525}$

The probability is $\frac{23}{5525}$ or about 0.4%.

Problem-SolvingTip

Tools Acting out the situation can help you understand what the question is asking. Use a deck of cards to represent the situation described in the problem.

GuidedPractice

Find each probability. **2A.** $\frac{94}{16{,}575}$ or about 0.6% **2B.** $\frac{39}{850}$ or about 5%

2A. P(two, five, not a five) **2B.** P(heart, not a heart, heart)

Teaching the Process Standards

Tools Mathematically proficient students make sound decisions about when tools might be helpful, recognizing both the insight to be gained and their limitations. Discuss how and when using tools such as cards can be helpful.

Teach with Tech

Interactive Whiteboard Use a Venn diagram to help students visualize a simple example using inclusive events. Let one circle represent condition A and let the other circle represent condition B. List each of the possible outcomes, and drag it into the appropriate part of the Venn diagram. Show students that you must subtract $P(A \text{ and } B)$ because it is the intersection of the two sets.

2 Mutually Exclusive Events

Events that cannot occur at the same time are called **mutually exclusive events**. Suppose you wanted to find the probability of drawing a heart or a diamond. Since a card cannot be both a heart and a diamond, the events are mutually exclusive.

> **StudyTip**
> *and* and *or* While probabilities involving *and* deal with independent and dependent events, probabilities involving *or* deal with mutually exclusive and non-mutually exclusive events.

KeyConcept Probability of Mutually Exclusive Events

Words If two events, A and B, are mutually exclusive, then the probability that either A or B occurs is the sum of their probabilities.

Symbols $P(A \text{ or } B) = P(A) + P(B)$

Model

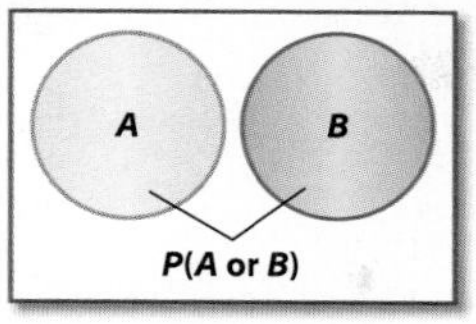

Real-World Example 3 Mutually Exclusive Events

A die is being rolled. Find each probability.

a. $P(3 \text{ or } 5)$

Since a die cannot show both a 3 and a 5 at the same time, these events are mutually exclusive.

$P(\text{rolling a } 3) = \frac{1}{6}$ ← number of sides with a 3 / total number of sides

$P(\text{rolling a } 5) = \frac{1}{6}$ ← number of sides with a 5 / total number of sides

$P(3 \text{ or } 5) = P(\text{rolling a } 3) + P(\text{rolling a } 5)$ — Probability of mutually exclusive events

$= \frac{1}{6} + \frac{1}{6}$ — Substitution

$= \frac{2}{6} \text{ or } \frac{1}{3}$ — Add.

The probability of rolling a 3 or a 5 is $\frac{1}{3}$ or about 33%.

> **StudyTip**
> Alternative Method In Example 3a, you could have placed the number of possible outcomes over the total number of outcomes.
> $\frac{1+1}{6} = \frac{2}{6} \text{ or } \frac{1}{3}$

b. $P(\text{at least } 4)$

Rolling at least a 4 means you can roll either a 4, 5, or a 6. So, you need to find the probability of rolling a 4, 5, or a 6.

$P(\text{rolling a } 4) = \frac{1}{6}$ ← number of sides with a 4 / total number of sides

$P(\text{rolling a } 5) = \frac{1}{6}$ ← number of sides with a 5 / total number of sides

$P(\text{rolling a } 6) = \frac{1}{6}$ ← number of sides with a 6 / total number of sides

$P(\text{at least } 4) = P(\text{rolling a } 4) + P(\text{rolling a } 5) + P(\text{rolling a } 6)$ — Mutually exclusive events

$= \frac{1}{6} + \frac{1}{6} + \frac{1}{6}$ — Substitution

$= \frac{3}{6} \text{ or } \frac{1}{2}$ — Add.

The probability of rolling at least a 4 is $\frac{1}{2}$ or about 50%.

GuidedPractice

3A. $P(\text{less than } 3)$ $\frac{1}{3}$ **or about 33%**　　**3B.** $P(\text{even})$ $\frac{1}{2}$ **or about 50%**

2 Mutually Exclusive Events

Example 3 shows how to find the probability that either one or the other of two mutually exclusive events will occur. **Example 4** shows how to find the probability that either one or the other of two non-mutually exclusive events will occur.

Additional Example

3 A card is being drawn from a standard deck. Find each probability.

a. $P(7 \text{ or } 8)$ $\frac{2}{13}$

b. $P(\text{neither club nor heart})$ $\frac{1}{2}$

Focus on Mathematical Content

Mutually Exclusive Events Events that cannot occur at the same time are mutually exclusive. For example, if you randomly draw either a blue marble or a yellow marble from a bag of marbles, these events are mutually exclusive since you cannot draw a blue marble and a yellow marble at the same time. You find the probability of mutually exclusive events by finding the sum of the probabilities of each event. For example, if the probability of drawing a blue marble from the bag is $\frac{3}{8}$ and the probability of drawing a yellow marble is $\frac{1}{4}$, the probability of drawing either a blue marble or a yellow marble is $\frac{3}{8} + \frac{1}{4} = \frac{5}{8}$.

DifferentiatedInstruction AL OL

Spatial/Visual Learners Bring a packet of raw sunflower seeds or other fast-sprouting seeds to class. Ensure that there are slightly more seeds than students. Explain that each student will take a seed and plant it either on school grounds or in a small plant pot. As students take a seed from the packet, lead them to understand that the number of seeds from which they can choose is a dependent event for all but the first student who chooses.

Additional Example

4 GAMES In the game of bingo, balls or tiles are numbered 1 through 75. These numbers correspond to columns on a bingo card, as shown in the table. A number is selected at random. What is the probability that it is a multiple of 5 or is in the N column? $\frac{9}{25}$

B	I	N	G	O
1–15	16–30	31–45	46–60	61–75

Tips for New Teachers

Sense-Making Point out to students that the Venn diagram of two mutually exclusive events does not have overlapping circles, while the Venn diagrams of two events that are not mutually exclusive will have overlapping circles. Ask students to explain why the diagrams are drawn that way.

ReadingMath
A or *B* Unlike everyday language, the expression *A* or *B* allows the possibility of both *A* and *B* occurring.

Suppose you want to find the probability of randomly drawing a 2 or a diamond from a standard deck of cards. Since it is possible to draw a card that is both a 2 and a diamond, these events are not mutually exclusive.

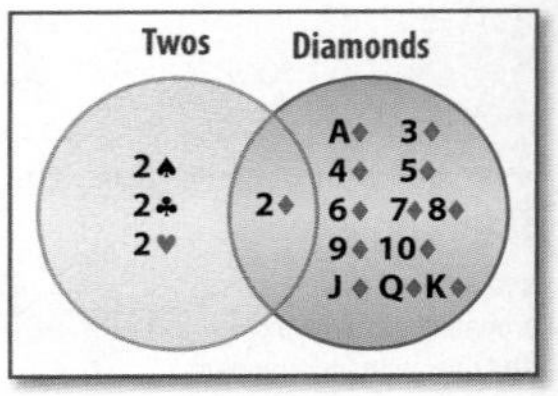

$P(2)$	$P(\text{diamond})$	$P(2, \text{diamond})$
$\frac{4}{52}$	$\frac{13}{52}$	$\frac{1}{52}$

In the first two fractions above, the probability of drawing the two of diamonds is counted twice, once for a two and once for a diamond. To find the correct probability, subtract $P(2 \text{ of diamonds})$ from the sum of the first two probabilities.

$$P(2 \text{ or a diamond}) = P(2) + \text{P}(\text{diamond}) - P(2 \text{ of diamonds})$$
$$= \frac{4}{52} + \frac{13}{52} - \frac{1}{52}$$
$$= \frac{16}{52} \text{ or } \frac{4}{13}$$

The probability is $\frac{4}{13}$ or about 31%.

WatchOut!
Intersection of Events When determining the probability of events that are not mutually exclusive, you may count the intersection of the events twice since it occurs in both events. It only actually occurs once.

KeyConcept Probability of Events that are Not Mutually Exclusive

Words If two events, *A* and *B*, are not mutually exclusive, then the probability that either *A* or *B* occurs is the sum of their probabilities decreased by the probability of both occurring.

Symbols $P(A \text{ or } B) = P(A) + P(B) - P(A \text{ and } B)$

Model

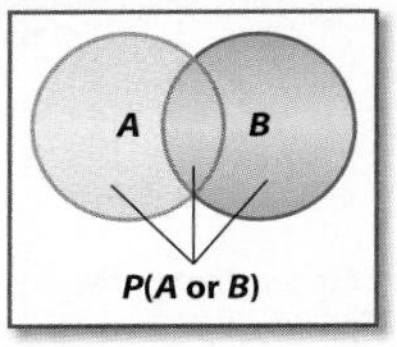

Real-World Example 4 Events that are Not Mutually Exclusive

STUDENT ATHLETES Of 240 girls, 176 are on the Honor Roll, 48 play sports, and 36 are on the Honor Roll and play sports. What is the probability that a randomly selected student plays sports or is on the Honor Roll?

Since some students play sports and are on the Honor Roll, the events are not mutually exclusive.

$P(\text{sports}) = \frac{48}{240}$ $\quad P(\text{Honor Roll}) = \frac{176}{240}$ $\quad P(\text{sports and Honor Roll}) = \frac{36}{240}$

$$P(\text{sports or Honor Roll}) = P(\text{sports}) + P(\text{HR}) - P(\text{sports and HR})$$
$$= \frac{48}{240} + \frac{176}{240} - \frac{36}{240} \quad \text{Substitution}$$
$$= \frac{188}{240} \text{ or } \frac{47}{60} \quad \text{Simplify.}$$

The probability is $\frac{47}{60}$ or about 78%.

GuidedPractice

4. PETS Out of 5200 households surveyed, 2107 had a dog, 807 had a cat, and 303 had both a dog and a cat. What is the probability that a randomly selected household has a dog or a cat? $\frac{2611}{5200}$ **or about 50%**

796 | Lesson 12-7 | Probability of Compound Events

Check Your Understanding

● = Step-by-Step Solutions begin on page R13.

Examples 1–2 Determine whether the events are *independent* or *dependent*. Then find the probability.

1. **BABYSITTING** A toy bin contains 12 toys, 8 stuffed animals, and 3 board games. Marsha randomly chooses 2 items for the child she is babysitting. What is the probability that she chose 2 stuffed animals as the first two choices? **dependent; $\frac{28}{253}$ or about 11%**

2. **FRUIT** A basket contains 6 apples, 5 bananas, 4 oranges, and 5 peaches. Drew randomly chooses one piece of fruit, eats it, and chooses another. What is the probability that he chose a banana and then an apple? **dependent; $\frac{3}{38}$ or about 8%**

3. **MONEY** Nakos has 4 quarters, 3 dimes, and 2 nickels in his pocket. Nakos randomly picks two coins out of his pocket. What is the probability that he did not choose a dime either time, if he replaced the first coin before choosing a second coin? **independent; $\frac{4}{9}$ or about 44%**

4. **BOOKS** Joanna needs a book to prop up a table leg. She randomly selects a book, puts it back on the shelf, and selects another book. What is the probability that Joanna selected two math books? **independent; $\frac{64}{289}$ or about 22%**

Examples 3–4 A card is drawn from a standard deck of playing cards. Determine whether the events are *mutually exclusive* or *not mutually exclusive*. Then find the probability.

5. *P*(two or queen) **mutually exclusive; $\frac{2}{13}$ or about 15%**
6. *P*(diamond or heart) **mutually exclusive; $\frac{1}{2}$ or about 50%**
7. *P*(seven or club) **not mutually exclusive; $\frac{4}{13}$ or about 31%**
8. *P*(spade or ace) **not mutually exclusive; $\frac{4}{13}$ or about 31%**

Practice and Problem Solving

Extra Practice is on page R12.

Examples 1–2 Determine whether the events are *independent* or *dependent*. Then find the probability.

9. independent; $\frac{1}{16}$ or about 6% **10. independent; $\frac{5}{6}$ or about 83%**

9. **COINS** If a coin is tossed 4 times, what is the probability of getting tails all 4 times?

10. **DICE** A die is rolled twice. What is the probability of rolling two different numbers?

11. **CANDY** A box of chocolates contains 10 milk chocolates, 8 dark chocolates, and 6 white chocolates. Sung randomly chooses a chocolate, eats it, and then randomly chooses another. What is the probability that Sung chose a milk chocolate and then a white chocolate? **dependent; $\frac{5}{46}$ or about 11%**

12. **DICE** A die is rolled twice. What is the probability of rolling the same numbers? **independent; $\frac{1}{6}$ or about 17%**

13. **PETS** Chuck and Rashid went to a pet store to buy dog food. They chose from 10 brands of dry food, 6 brands of canned food, and 3 brands of pet snacks. What is the probability that both chose dry food, if Chuck randomly chose first and liked the first brand he picked up? **independent; $\frac{100}{361}$ or about 28%**

14. **MODELING** A rental agency has 12 white sedans, 8 gray sedans, 6 red sedans, and 3 green sedans for rent. Mr. Escobar rents a sedan, returns it because the radio is broken, and gets another sedan. Assuming the returned sedan remains in circulation, what is the probability that Mr. Escobar was given a green sedan and then a gray sedan? **dependent; $\frac{6}{203}$ or about 3%**

3 Practice

Formative Assessment

Use Exercises 1–8 to check for understanding.

Use the chart at the bottom of this page to customize assignments for your students.

WatchOut!

Preventing Errors Students are often confused about whether compound events are dependent, independent, mutually exclusive, or inclusive. You might want to preview Exercises 9–18 with the class before they begin the exercises. Ask students to identify the type of compound event in each exercise. If students consistently fail to identify the type of event, suggest that they review each of the examples in the lesson.

Teaching the Process Standards

Modeling Mathematically proficient students identify important quantities in a practical situation and map their relationships. In Exercise 14, write each quantity in the problem and draw a diagram to show how the quantities are related.

Differentiated Homework Options

Level	Assignment	Two-Day Option	
AL Basic	9–18, 34, 36–56	9–17 odd, 39–42	10–18 even, 34, 36–38, 43–56
OL Core	9–29 odd, 30–34, 36–56	9–18, 39–42	19–34, 36–38, 43–56
BL Advanced	19–50, (optional: 51–56)		

connectED.mcgraw-hill.com 797

Study Guide and Intervention

AL OL ELL

NAME ______________ DATE ________ PERIOD ________

12-7 Study Guide and Intervention

Probability of Compound Events

Independent and Dependent Events Compound events are made up of two or more simple events. The events can be **independent events** or they can be **dependent events**.

Probability of Independent Events	Outcome of first event does not affect outcome of second.	$P(A \text{ and } B) = P(A) \cdot P(B)$	Example: rolling a 6 on a die and then rolling a 5
Probability of Dependent Events	Outcome of first event does affect outcome of second.	$P(A \text{ and } B) = P(A) \cdot P(B \text{ following } A)$	Example: without replacing the first card, choosing an ace and then a king from a deck of cards

Example 1 **Find the probability that you will roll a six and then a five when you roll a die twice.**

By the definition of independent events, $P(A \text{ and } B) = P(A) \cdot P(B)$

First roll: $P(6) = \frac{1}{6}$

Second roll: $P(5) = \frac{1}{6}$

$P(6 \text{ and } 5) = P(6) \cdot P(5) = \frac{1}{6} \cdot \frac{1}{6} = \frac{1}{36}$

The probability that you will roll a six and then roll a five is $\frac{1}{36}$.

Example 2 **A bag contains 3 red marbles, 2 green marbles, and 4 blue marbles. Two marbles are drawn randomly from the bag and not replaced. Find the probability that both marbles are blue.**

By the definition of dependent events, $P(A \text{ and } B) = P(A) \cdot P(B \text{ following } A)$

First marble: $P(\text{blue}) = \frac{4}{9}$

Second marble: $P(\text{blue}) = \frac{3}{8}$

$P(\text{blue, blue}) = \frac{4}{9} \cdot \frac{3}{8} = \frac{12}{72} = \frac{1}{6}$

The probability of drawing two blue marbles is $\frac{1}{6}$.

Lesson 12-7

Exercises

A bag contains 3 red, 4 blue, and 6 yellow marbles. One marble is selected at a time, and once a marble is selected, it is not replaced. Find each probability.

1. P(2 yellow)
2. P(red, yellow)
3. P(blue, red, yellow)
4. George has two red socks and two white socks in a drawer. What is the probability of picking a red sock and a white sock in that order if the first sock is not replaced?
5. Phyllis drops a penny in a pond, and then she drops a nickel in the pond. What is the probability that both coins land with tails showing?
6. A die is rolled and a penny is dropped. Find the probability of rolling a two and showing a tail.

Practice

AL OL BL ELL

NAME ______________ DATE ________ PERIOD ________

12-7 Practice

Probability of Compound Events

A bag contains 5 red, 3 brown, 6 yellow, and 2 blue marbles. Once a marble is selected, it is not replaced. Find each probability.

1. P(brown, then yellow, then red)
2. P(red, then red, then blue)
3. P(yellow, then yellow, then *not* blue)
4. P(brown, then brown, then *not* yellow)

A die is rolled and a card is drawn from a standard deck of 52 cards. Find each probability.

5. P(6 and king)
6. P(odd number and black)
7. P(less than 3 and heart)
8. P(greater than 1 and black ace)

A card is being drawn from a standard deck of playing cards. Determine whether the events are *mutually exclusive* or *not* mutually exclusive. Then find the probability.

9. P(spade or numbered card)
10. P(ace or red queen)
11. P(red or *not* face card)
12. P(heart or *not* queen)

Tiles numbered 1 through 25 are placed in a box. Tiles numbered 11 through 30 are placed in a second box. The first tile is randomly drawn from the first box. The second tile is randomly drawn from the second box. Find each probability.

13. P(both are greater than 15 and less than 20)
14. The first tile is greater than 10 and the second tile is less than 25 or even.
15. The first tile is a multiple of 3 or prime and the second tile is a multiple of 5.
16. The first tile is less than 9 or odd and the second tile is a multiple of 4 or less than 21.
17. **WEATHER** The forecast predicts a 40% chance of rain on Tuesday and a 60% chance on Wednesday. If these probabilities are independent, what is the chance that it will rain on both days?
18. **FOOD** Tomaso places favorite recipes in a bag for 4 pasta dishes, 5 casseroles, 3 types of chili, and 8 desserts.
    a. If Tomaso chooses one recipe at random, what is the probability that he selects a pasta dish or a casserole?
    b. If Tomaso chooses one recipe at random, what is the probability that he does *not* select a dessert?
    c. If Tomaso chooses two recipes at random without replacement, what is the probability that the first recipe he selects is a casserole and the second recipe he selects is a dessert?

Word Problem Practice

AL OL BL ELL

NAME ______________ DATE ________ PERIOD ________

12-7 Word Problem Practice

Probability of Compound Events

1. **BIRTHDAYS** On Juanita's birthday, her grandmother sends her a card. What is the probability that the man who delivered the mail has a birthday either the same day or one day before or after? Disregard February 29 as a possible birthday, and assume that all days are equally likely.
2. **SPORTS** The World Series is a "best of seven" game championship in which up to seven games are played, and one team has to win four games to win the Series. In the 2007 World Series, the Boston Red Sox swept the Colorado Rockies, meaning that they won the series by winning the first four games. If you assume that each team has an equal chance of winning each game, what is the probability of a World Series sweep?
3. **BUSINESS** At Corrugated Packaging, Inc., a team of six employees is in charge of marketing and selling the company's products; three are women and three are men. The president of the company decides to send four team members to a national cardboard box conference. He wants to make sure he chooses names fairly, so he decides to put the names of his six sales employees in a hat and draw four names to see who will go to the conference. What is the probability that the team will consist of three women and one man?
4. **MAGIC** Iris performs a magic trick in which she holds a standard deck of cards and has each of three people randomly choose a card from the deck. Each person keeps his or her card as the next person draws. What is the probability that all three people will draw a heart?

5. **STOCKS** Bruce has just purchased 100 shares of Out Clone, Inc. stock. The company is seeking FDA approval for a treatment that relieves the common cold. According to pharmaceutical experts, there is a 50% chance that FDA approval will be granted, and according to market insiders there is an 85% chance the value of the stock will double if FDA approval is granted.
    a. What is the probability that the FDA will approve the treatment and the value of Bruce's investment will double?
    b. What is the probability that the FDA will approve the treatment and the value of your stock will not double?
    c. Are these events dependent or independent?

Lesson 12-7

Examples 3–4 **Determine whether the events are *mutually exclusive* or *not mutually exclusive*. Then find the probability.**

15. **BOWLING** Cindy's bowling records indicate that for any frame, the probability that she will bowl a strike is 30%, a spare 45%, and neither 25%. What is the probability that she will bowl either a spare or a strike for any given frame? **mutually exclusive; $\frac{3}{4}$ or 75%**
16. **SPORTS CARDS** Dario owns 145 baseball cards, 102 football cards, and 48 basketball cards. What is the probability that he randomly selects a baseball or a football card? **16. mutually exclusive; $\frac{247}{295}$ or about 84%**
17. **SCHOLARSHIPS** 3000 essays were received for a $5000 college scholarship. 2865 essays were the required length, 2577 of the applicants had the minimum required grade-point average, and 2486 had the required length and minimum grade-point average. What is the probability that an essay selected at random will have the required length or the required grade-point average? **not mutually exclusive; $\frac{739}{750}$ or about 98.5%**
18. **KITTENS** Ruby's cat had 8 kittens. The litter included 2 orange females, 3 mixed-color females, 1 orange male, and 2 mixed-color males. Ruby wants to keep one kitten. What is the probability that she randomly chooses a kitten that is female or orange? **not mutually exclusive; $\frac{3}{4}$ or about 75%**

B **CHIPS** **A restaurant serves red, blue, and yellow tortilla chips. The bowl of chips Gabriel receives has 10 red chips, 8 blue chips, and 12 yellow chips. After Gabriel chooses a chip, he eats it. Find each probability.**

19. P(red, blue) **$\frac{8}{87}$ or about 9%**
20. P(blue, yellow) **$\frac{16}{145}$ or about 11%**
21. P(yellow, not blue) **$\frac{42}{145}$ or about 29%**
22. P(red, not yellow) **$\frac{17}{87}$ or about 20%**
23. **SOCKS** Damon has 14 white socks, 6 black socks, and 4 blue socks in his drawer. If he chooses two socks at random, what is the probability that the first two socks are white? **$\frac{91}{276}$ or about 33%**

TOOLS **Cards are being randomly drawn from a standard deck of cards. Find each probability.** **24–29. See margin.**

24. P(heart or spade)
25. P(spade or club)
26. P(queen or heart)
27. P(jack or spade)
28. P(five or prime number)
29. P(ace or black)

C 30. **CANDY** A bag contains 10 red, 6 green, 7 yellow, and 5 orange jelly beans. What is the probability of randomly choosing a red jelly bean, replacing, randomly choosing another red jelly bean, replacing, and then randomly choosing an orange jelly bean? **$\frac{125}{5488}$ or about 2%**

31. **SPORTS** The extracurricular activities in which the senior class at Valley View High School participate are shown in the Venn diagram.

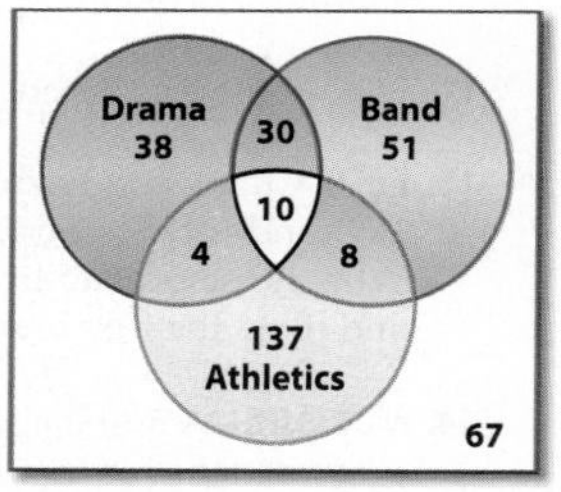

    a. How many students are in the senior class? **345**
    b. How many students participate in athletics? **159**
    c. If a student is randomly chosen, what is the probability that the student participates in athletics or drama? **$\frac{227}{345}$ or about 66%**
    d. If a student is randomly chosen, what is the probability that the student participates in only drama and band? **$\frac{2}{23}$ or about 9%**

Enrichment

OL BL

NAME ______________ DATE ________ PERIOD ________

12-7 Enrichment

Happy Birthday

On a reality show, a contestant must randomly choose enough people to go into a room so that the probability that at least one of those people has the same birthday (month and date) as the contestant is greater than 50%. Time is of the essence, so the contestant doesn't want any more people than necessary. What number of people should the contestant gather?

1. Make a conjecture about the number of people needed.
2. When the probability that every person in the room has a different birthday is less than 50%, the probability that two of them will share a birthday is greater than 50%. Explain why.
3. Observe this pattern:
   If there are two people in the room, the probability that they all have different

Additional Answers

24. $\frac{1}{2}$ or 50%
25. $\frac{1}{2}$ or 50%
26. $\frac{4}{13}$ or about 31%
27. $\frac{4}{13}$ or about 31%
28. $\frac{4}{13}$ or about 31%
29. $\frac{7}{13}$ or about 54%

32. TILES Kirsten and José are playing a game. Kirsten places tiles numbered 1 to 50 in a bag. José selects a tile at random. If he selects a prime number or a number greater than 40, then he wins the game. What is the probability that José will win on his first turn? $\frac{11}{25}$ or 44%

33. MULTIPLE REPRESENTATIONS In this problem, you will explore **conditional probability**, which is the probability that event B occurs given that event A has already occurred. It is calculated by dividing the probability of the occurrence of both events by the probability of the occurrence of the first event. The notation for conditional probability is $P(B \mid A)$, read *the probability of B, given A.*

a. **Graphical** Draw a Venn diagram to illustrate $P(A \text{ and } B)$. See margin.

b. **Verbal** Tell how to find $P(B \mid A)$ given the Venn diagram. **33b.** Divide the overlap of the two circles by the $P(A)$ circle.

c. **Analytical** A jar contains 12 marbles, of which 8 marbles are red and 4 marbles are green. If marbles are chosen without replacement, find P(red) and P(red, green). $P(\text{red}) = \frac{2}{3}$; $P(\text{red, green}) = \frac{8}{33}$

d. **Analytical** Using the probabilities from part **c** and the Venn diagram in part **a**, determine the probability of choosing a green marble on the second selection, given that the first marble selected was red.

33d. $P(\text{green}|\text{red}) = \dfrac{\frac{8}{33}}{\frac{2}{3}} = \frac{4}{11}$

e. **Analytical** Write a formula for finding a conditional probability. $P(B|A) = \dfrac{P(A \text{ and } B)}{P(A)}$

f. **Analytical** Use the definition from part **e** to answer the following: At a basketball game, 80% of the fans cheered for the home team. In the same crowd, 20% of the fans were waving banners and cheering for the home team. What is the probability that a fan waved a banner given that the fan cheered for the home team? 25%

H.O.T. Problems Use Higher-Order Thinking Skills

34. ERROR ANALYSIS George and Aliyah are determining the probability of randomly choosing a blue or red marble from a bag of 8 blue marbles, 6 red marbles, 8 yellow marbles, and 4 white marbles. Is either of them correct? Explain.

George

$P(\text{blue or red}) = P(\text{blue}) \cdot P(\text{red})$
$= \frac{8}{26} \cdot \frac{6}{26}$
$= \frac{48}{676}$
about 7%

Aliyah

$P(\text{blue or red}) = P(\text{blue}) + P(\text{red})$
$= \frac{8}{26} + \frac{6}{26}$
$= \frac{14}{26}$
about 54%

34. Aliyah; the individual probabilities should be added since we want the probability of blue *or* red, two mutually exclusive events.

35. CHALLENGE In some cases, if one bulb in a string of holiday lights fails to work, the whole string will not light. If each bulb in a set has a 99.5% chance of working, what is the maximum number of lights that can be strung together with at least a 90% chance that the whole string will light? 21

36. REGULARITY Suppose there are three events A, B, and C that are not mutually exclusive. List all of the probabilities you would need to consider in order to calculate $P(A \text{ or } B \text{ or } C)$. Then write the formula you would use to calculate it. See margin.

37. OPEN ENDED Describe a situation in your life that involves dependent and independent events. Explain why the events are dependent or independent. See margin.

38. WRITING IN MATH Explain why the subtraction occurs when finding the probability of two events that are not mutually exclusive. See margin.

Multiple Representations

In Exercise 33, students use formulas, Venn diagrams, and analysis to find a conditional probability.

WatchOut!

Error Analysis For Exercise 34, point out to students that when two events are connected by the word *or*, the probability of the compound event is found by adding the individual event probabilities.

Teaching the Process Standards

Regularity Mathematically proficient students pay attention to their calculations. In Exercise 36, instruct students to examine what they know in order to write a formula.

Additional Answers

33a.

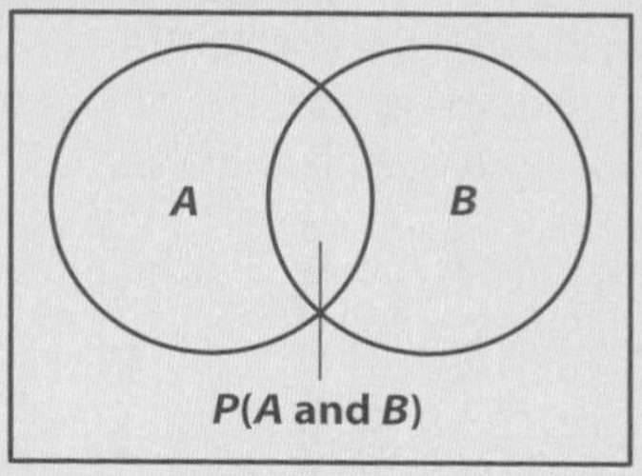

36. $P(A)$, $P(B)$, $P(C)$, $P(A \text{ and } B)$, $P(A \text{ and } C)$, $P(B \text{ and } C)$, $P(A \text{ and } B \text{ and } C)$; $P(A \text{ or } B \text{ or } C) = P(A) + P(B) + P(C) - P(A \text{ and } B) - P(A \text{ and } C) - P(B \text{ and } C) + P(A \text{ and } B \text{ and } C)$.

37. Sample answer: Choosing a CD to listen to, putting it back, and then choosing another CD to listen to would represent independent events since the CD was placed back before the second CD was chosen. Choosing a pair of jeans to wear would represent dependent events if I did not like the first pair chosen and I did not put them back.

38. If two events are not mutually exclusive, they have item(s) in common. So the subtraction is needed to get rid of the items counted twice.

4 Assess

Ticket Out the Door Write probability examples on slips of paper, using each type of compound event. Give each student one of the examples. As students walk out the door, have them tell whether their events are independent, dependent, mutually exclusive, or inclusive, and have them give the probabilities of the events.

Additional Answers

44a. Sample answer: The theoretical probability that the next client that makes an appointment will schedule a basic haircut is 70%, and the theoretical probability that the client will make an appointment for another service is 30%. Use a random number generator to generate integers 1 through 10. The integers 1–7 will represent a basic haircut, and the integers 8–10 will represent another service. The simulation will consist of 40 trials.

44b. Sample answer: $P(\text{haircut}) = 65\%$, $P(\text{other}) = 35\%$

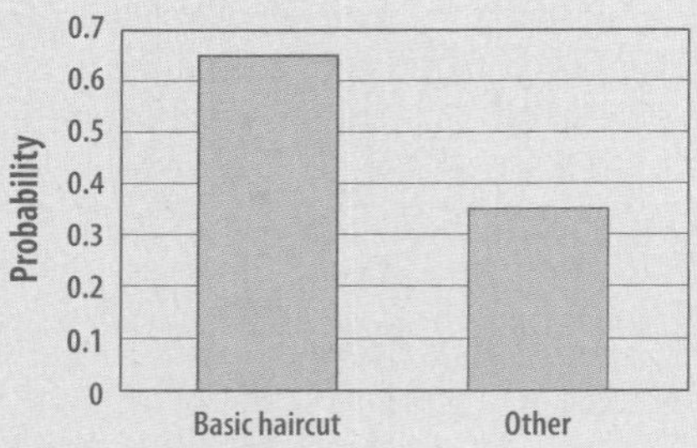

Standardized Test Practice

39. In how many ways can a committee of 4 be selected from a group of 12 people? **C**

A 48
B 483
C 495
D 11,880

40. A total of 925 tickets were sold for \$5925. If adult tickets cost \$7.50 and children's tickets cost \$3.00, how many adult tickets were sold? **F**

F 700 | H 325
G 600 | J 225

41. SHORT RESPONSE A circular swimming pool with a diameter of 28 feet has a deck of uniform width built around it. If the area of the deck is 60π square feet, find its width. **2 ft**

42. The probability of heads landing up when you flip a coin is $\frac{1}{2}$. What is the probability of getting tails if you flip it again? **C**

A $\frac{1}{4}$ | C $\frac{1}{2}$
B $\frac{1}{3}$ | D $\frac{3}{4}$

Spiral Review

43. SHOPPING The Millers have twelve grandchildren, 5 boys and 7 girls. For their anniversary, the grandchildren decided to pool their money and have three of them shop for the entire group. (Lesson 12-6)

a. Does this situation represent a *combination* or *permutation*? **combination**

b. How many ways are there to choose the three? **220**

c. What is the probability that all three will be girls? $\frac{210}{1320}$ **or 16%**

44. HAIR STYLIST Tia is a hair stylist. Last week, 70% of her clients who called to make appointments made an appointment for a basic haircut. (Lesson 12-5) **a–b. See margin.**

a. Design a simulation that can be used to estimate the probability that the next client that makes an appointment will schedule a basic haircut.

b. Conduct the simulation, and report the results.

Solve each equation. State any extraneous solutions. (Lesson 11-8)

45. $\frac{4}{a} = \frac{3}{a-2}$ **8**

46. $\frac{3}{x} = \frac{1}{x-2}$ **3**

47. $\frac{x}{x+1} = \frac{x-6}{x-1}$ $-\frac{3}{2}$

48. $\frac{2n}{3} + \frac{1}{2} = \frac{2n-3}{6}$ **−3**

49. COOKING Hannah was making candy using a two-quart pan. As she stirred the mixture, she noticed that the pan was about $\frac{2}{3}$ full. If each piece of candy has a volume of about $\frac{3}{4}$ ounce, approximately how many pieces of candy will Hannah make? (*Hint:* There are 32 ounces in a quart.) (Lesson 11-3) **about 57 pieces**

50. GEOMETRY A rectangle has a width of $3\sqrt{5}$ centimeters and a length of $4\sqrt{10}$ centimeters. Find the area of the rectangle. Write as a simplified radical expression. (Lesson 10-2) $60\sqrt{2}$ **cm²**

Skills Review

Solve each equation. Check your solution.

51. $\sqrt{-3a} = 6$ **−12**

52. $\sqrt{a} = 100$ **10,000**

53. $\sqrt{-k} = 4$ **−16**

54. $5\sqrt{2} = \sqrt{x}$ **50**

55. $3\sqrt{7} = \sqrt{-y}$ **−63**

56. $3\sqrt{4a} - 2 = 10$ **4**

Differentiated Instruction OL BL

Extension Have students write an example of how they could use probability calculations in their daily lives. The example should include both a description of how the probability calculation could be used and a sample calculation with sample data.

EXTEND 12-7 Algebra Lab: Two-Way Frequency Tables

Joana sent out a survey to the freshmen and sophomores, asking if they were planning on attending the dance. One way of organizing her responses is to use a two-way frequency table. A **two-way frequency table** or *contingency table* is used to show the frequencies of data from a survey or experiment classified according to two categories, with the rows indicating one category and the columns indicating the other.

Content Standards
AI.DS.5

For Joana's survey, the two categories are *class* and *attendance*. These categories can be split into subcategories: *freshman* and *sophomore* for *class*, and *attending* and *not attending* for *attendance*.

Class	Attending	Not Attending	Totals
Freshman			
Sophomore			
Totals			

subcategories

Activity 1 Two-Way Frequency Table

DANCE **Sixty-six freshmen responded to the survey, with 32 saying that they would be attending. Of the 84 sophomores that responded, 46 said they would attend. Organize the data in a two-way table.**

Step 1 Find the values for every combination of subcategories. One combination is freshmen/not attending. Since 32 of 66 freshmen are attending, 66 − 32 or 34 freshmen are *not* attending. These combinations are called **joint frequencies.**

Step 2 Place every combination in the corresponding cell.

Step 3 Find the totals of each subcategory and place them in their corresponding cell. These values are called **marginal frequencies.**

Step 4 Find the sum of each set of marginal frequencies. These two sums should be equal. Place the value in the bottom right corner.

Class	Attending	Not Attending	Totals
Freshman	32	34	66
Sophomore	46	38	84
Totals	78	72	150

joint frequencies
marginal frequencies
marginal frequencies

Analyze the Results 4–7. See margin.

1. How many students responded to the survey? 150
2. How many of the students that were surveyed are attending the dance? 78
3. How many of the surveyed sophomores are not attending the dance? 38
4. What does each of the joint frequencies represent?
5. What does each of the marginal frequencies represent?
6. WORK Heather sent out a survey asking who was working during the holiday. Of the 50 boys who responded, 34 said *yes*. Of the 45 girls who responded, 21 said *no*. Create a two-way frequency table of the results.
7. SOCCER Pamela asked if anyone would be interested in a co-ed soccer team. Of the 28 boys who responded, 18 said that they would play and 4 were undecided. Of the 22 girls who responded, 6 said they did not want to play and 3 were undecided. Create a two-way frequency table of the results.

7.

Gender	Playing	Not Playing	Undecided	Totals
Boys	18	6	4	28
Girls	13	6	3	22
Totals	31	12	7	50

1 Focus

Objective Use two-way frequency tables to find marginal, joint, and conditional relative frequencies.

Teaching Tips

Using Media Two-way frequency tables are often used to present data in newspapers and other media. Have students find and discuss examples.

Marginal Frequencies Point out to students that the marginal frequencies are on the outside of the table, like the margins of a sheet of paper.

2 Teach

Working in Cooperative Groups

Have student work in mixed ability pairs. Have students alternate the steps of the activities.

Additional Answers

4. The joint frequencies represent every viable combination of subcategories. These include the frequency of freshmen attending, freshmen not attending, sophomores attending, and sophomores not attending.
5. The marginal frequencies represent the total frequency of every subcategory. In other words, they indicate how many times that particular subcategory occurred.
6.

Gender	Working	Not Working	Totals
Boys	34	16	50
Girls	24	21	45
Totals	58	37	95

Practice Have students complete Activities 1 and 2 and Exercises 1–13.

3 Assess

Formative Assessment

Use Exercises 8 and 12 to assess each student's ability to use two-way frequency tables to determine probabilities.

From Concrete to Abstract

Ask students to summarize what they learned about two-way frequency tables.

Additional Answers

9. Each conditional relative frequency represents the probability that one subcategory occurred given the knowledge that another subcategory already is known. For example, the probability that a person is not attending if you already know she is a freshman.

10. The sums of the columns (for attending) do not equal 100% because the conditional relative frequency table is organized by class. The probability of freshmen attending and the probability of sophomores attending are not mutually exclusive. The sums of the rows equal 100% because those events *are* mutually exclusive.

Algebra Lab

Two-Way Frequency Tables *Continued*

A **relative frequency** is the ratio of the number of observations in a category to the total number of observations. Relative frequencies are also probabilities. To create a relative frequency two-way table, divide each of the values by the total number of observations and replace them with their corresponding decimals or percents.

Class	Attending	Not Attending	Totals
Freshman	$\frac{32}{150} \approx 21.3\%$	22.7%	44%
Sophomore	30.7%	25.3%	56%
Totals	52%	48%	100%

A **conditional relative frequency** is the ratio of the joint frequency to the marginal frequency. For example, given that a student is a freshman, what is the conditional relative frequency that he or she is going to the dance? In other words, what is the probability that a freshman is going to the dance?

Activity 2 Two-Way Conditional Relative Frequency Table

DANCE **Joana wants to determine the conditional relative frequencies (or probabilities) given the fact that she knows the class of the respondents.**

Step 1 Refer to the table in Activity 1. A total of 66 freshmen responded, and 32 said *yes*. Therefore, the conditional relative frequency that a respondent said *yes* given that the respondent is a freshman is $\frac{32}{66}$.

Step 2 Place every conditional relative frequency in the corresponding cell.

Step 3 The conditional relative frequencies for each row should sum to 100%.

Conditional Relative Frequencies by Class			
Class	Attending	Not Attending	Totals
Freshman	$\frac{32}{66} \approx 48\%$	$\frac{34}{66} \approx 52\%$	100%
Sophomore	$\frac{46}{84} \approx 55\%$	$\frac{38}{84} \approx 45\%$	100%

Analyze the Results 9–11. See margin.

8. Given that a respondent was a sophomore, what is the probability that he or she said *no*? 45%

9. What does each of the conditional relative frequencies represent?

10. Why do you think that the columns do not sum to 100%?

11. Create a two-way conditional relative frequency table for the category *attendance*.

12. Given that a respondent was not attending, what is the probability that he or she is a freshman? 47%

13. ACTIVITIES The managers, staff, and assistants were given three options for the holiday activity: a potluck, a dinner at a restaurant, and a gift exchange. Five of the 11 managers want a dinner, while 3 want a potluck. Eleven of the 45 staff members want a gift exchange, while 18 want a dinner. Ten of the 32 assistants want a dinner, while 8 of them want a gift exchange.
    a. Create a two-way frequency table. **a–b. See margin.**
    b. Convert the two-way frequency table into a relative frequency table.
    c. Create two conditional relative frequency tables: one for the activities and one for the employees. **See Chapter 12 Answer Appendix.**

802 | Extend 12-7 | Algebra Lab: Two-Way Frequency Tables

11.

Conditional Relative Frequencies by Attending		
Class	Attending	Not Attending
Freshman	41%	47%
Sophomore	59%	53%
Totals	100%	100%

13a.

Employees	Potluck	Dinner	Gifts	Totals
Managers	3	5	3	11
Staff	16	18	11	45
Assistants	14	10	8	32
Totals	33	33	22	88

13b.

Employees	Potluck	Dinner	Gifts	Totals
Managers	3.4%	5.7%	3.4%	12.5%
Staff	18.2%	20.4%	12.5%	51.1%
Assistants	15.9%	11.4%	9.1%	36.4%
Totals	37.5%	37.5%	25%	100%

LESSON 12-8 Probability Distributions

Then

- You found probabilities of events.

Now

1. Find probabilities by using random variables.
2. Find the expected value of a probability distribution.

Why?

- A gaming software company with five online games on the market is interested in how many games each of their customers play. They surveyed 1000 randomly chosen customers. The results of the survey are shown.

Number of Computer Games	Number of Customers
1	130
2	110
3	150
4	500
5	110

NewVocabulary
random variable
discrete random variable
probability distribution
probability graph
expected value

Process Standards
PS.7

1 Random Variables and Probability

A variable with a value that is the numerical outcome of a random event is called a **random variable**. A random variable with a countable number of possibilities is a **discrete random variable**. We can let the random variable G represent the number of different games. So, G can equal 1, 2, 3, 4, or 5.

Example 1 Random Variables

A graduation supply company offers five items that can be purchased for graduation: a diploma frame, graduation picture, cap and gown, senior key ring, and class pin. The school takes a poll of the seniors to see how many of these items each senior is buying. The results are shown.

Number of Items Being Purchased	Number of Seniors
0	12
1	122
2	134
3	115
4	145
5	97

a. Find the probability that a randomly chosen senior is buying 3 items.

Let X represent the number of items being purchased. There is only one outcome in which 3 items are being purchased, and there is a total of 625 seniors.

$$P(X = 3) = \frac{\text{3 items being purchased}}{\text{seniors surveyed}}$$

$P(X = n)$ is the probability of X occurring n times.

$$= \frac{115}{625} \text{ or } \frac{23}{125}$$

The probability is $\frac{23}{125}$ or 18.4%.

b. Find the probability that a randomly chosen senior buys at least 4 items.

There are 145 + 97 or 242 seniors who are purchasing at least 4 items.

$P(X \geq 4) = \frac{242}{625}$ The probability is $\frac{242}{625}$ or about 38.7%.

GuidedPractice

GRADES After an algebra test, there are 7 students with As, 9 with Bs, 11 with Cs, 3 with Ds, and 2 with Fs.

1A. Find the probability that a randomly chosen student has a C. $\frac{11}{32}$ or about 34.3%

1B. Find the probability that a randomly chosen student has at least a B. $\frac{1}{2}$ or 50%

1 Focus

VerticalAlignment

Before Lesson 12-8 Conduct simulations.

Lesson 12-8 Find probabilities by using random variables. Solve real-world problems using distributions.

2 Teach

Scaffolding Questions

Have students read the **Why?** section of the lesson.

Ask:

- Could a particular customer appear in more than one row of the table? no
- What percent of the customers played only 1 game? 13%
- What is the total of the percents of customers represented by all the rows of the table? 100%

1 Random Variables and Probability

Example 1 shows how to use random variables to find probabilities.

Lesson 12-8 Resources

Resource	Approaching Level AL	On Level OL	Beyond Level BL	English Learners ELL
Teacher Edition	▪ Differentiated Instruction, p. 805	▪ Differentiated Instruction, p. 805	▪ Differentiated Instruction, p. 809	
Chapter Resource Masters	▪ Study Guide and Intervention, pp. 48–49 ▪ Skills Practice, p. 50 ▪ Practice, p. 51 ▪ Word Problem Practice, p. 52	▪ Study Guide and Intervention, pp. 48–49 ▪ Skills Practice, p. 50 ▪ Practice, p. 51 ▪ Word Problem Practice, p. 52 ▪ Enrichment, p. 53	▪ Practice, p. 51 ▪ Word Problem Practice, p. 52 ▪ Enrichment, p. 53	▪ Study Guide and Intervention, pp. 48–49 ▪ Skills Practice, p. 50 ▪ Practice, p. 51 ▪ Word Problem Practice, p. 52
Other	▪ 5-Minute Check 12-8 ▪ Study Notebook	▪ 5-Minute Check 12-8 ▪ Study Notebook	▪ 5-Minute Check 12-8 ▪ Study Notebook	▪ 5-Minute Check 12-8 ▪ Study Notebook

Formative Assessment

Use the Guided Practice exercises after each example to determine students' understanding of concepts.

Additional Examples

1 **PETS** A pet store owner asked customers how many pets they own. The results are shown.

Number of Pets	0	1	2	3	4
Number of Customers	3	37	33	18	9

a. Find the probability that a randomly chosen customer has 2 pets. $\frac{33}{100}$ or 33%

b. Find the probability that a randomly chosen customer has at least 3 pets. $\frac{27}{100}$ or 27%

2 **POPULATION** The table shows the probability distribution of students in each grade at Sunnybrook High School.

X = Grade	$P(X)$
9	0.29
10	0.26
11	0.25
12	0.2

a. Show that the distribution is valid. For each value of X, the probability is greater than or equal to 0 and less than or equal to 1. Also, $0.29 + 0.26 + 0.25 + 0.2 = 1$.

b. If a student is chosen at random, what is the probability that he or she is in grade 11 or 12? $P(X = 11) + P(X = 12) = 0.45$

c. Make a probability graph of the data.

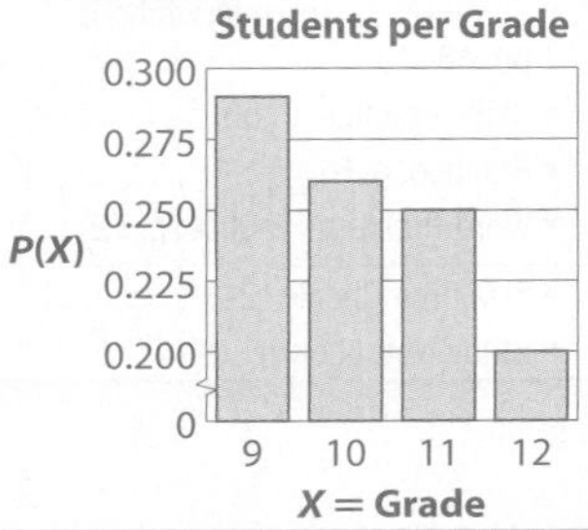

StudyTip

Discrete and Continuous Data Data are *discrete* if the observations can be counted. For example, the number of kittens in a litter is discrete data. Data are *continuous* if the data can take on any value within an interval. For example, the height of each person in a sample is continuous data.

2 Probability Distributions

A **probability distribution** is the probability of every possible value of the random variable. A **probability graph** is a bar graph that displays a probability distribution.

KeyConcept Properties of Probability Distributions

- The probability of each value of X is greater than or equal to 0 and is less than or equal to 1.
- The sum of the probabilities of all values of X is 1.

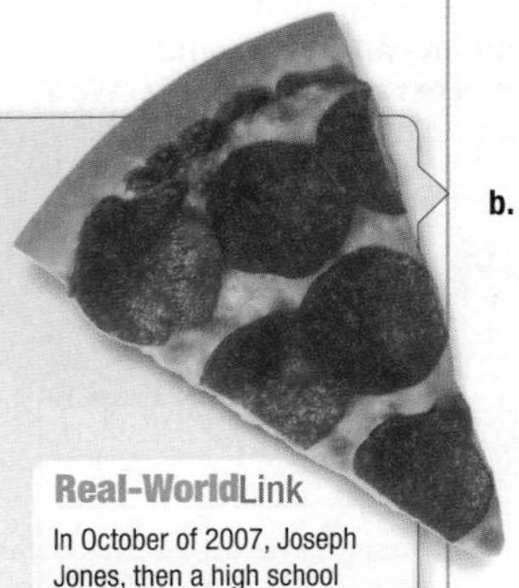

Real-WorldLink

In October of 2007, Joseph Jones, then a high school senior, ate 83 slices of pepperoni pizza within 10 minutes at an eating competition.

Source: About Pizza

Real-World Example 2 Probability Distribution

PIZZA The table shows the probability distribution of the number of times a customer orders pizza each month.

Pizzas Ordered Per Month

X = Number of Pizzas	Probability
0	0.10
1	0.12
2	0.44
3	0.24
4+	0.10

a. Show that the distribution is valid.

- For each value of X, the probability is greater than or equal to 0 and less than or equal to 1.
- The sum of the probabilities, $0.10 + 0.12 + 0.44 + 0.24 + 0.10$, is 1.

b. What is the probability that a customer orders pizza fewer than three times per month?

The probability of a compound event is the sum of the probabilities of each individual event. The probability of a customer ordering fewer than 3 times per month is the sum of the probability of ordering 2 times per month plus the probability of ordering one time per month.

$P(X < 3) = P(X = 2) + P(X = 1) + P(X = 0)$ Sum of individual probabilities

$= 0.44 + 0.12 + 0.10$ $P(X = 2) = 0.44$, $P(X = 1) = 0.12$, and $P(X = 0) = 0.10$

$= 0.66$ Add.

c. Make a probability graph of the data.

Use the data from the probability distribution table to draw a bar graph. Remember to label each axis and give the graph a title.

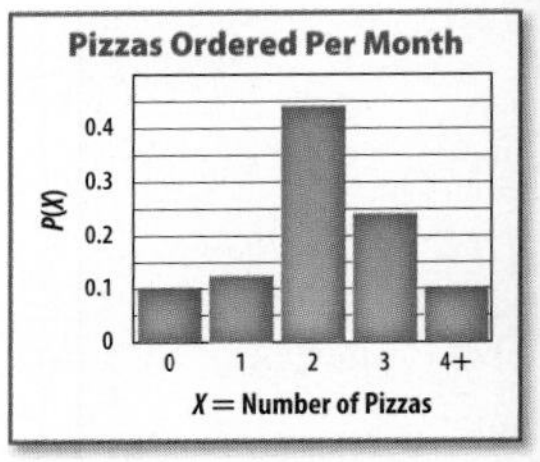

GuidedPractice

The table shows the probability distribution of adults who play golf by age range.

Golfers By Age

A = Ages	Probability
18–24	0.13
25–34	0.18
35–44	0.21
45–54	0.19
55–64	0.12
65+	0.17

2A. Show that the distribution is valid.

2B. What is the probability that an adult golfer is 35 years old or older? **0.69 = 69%**

2C. Make a probability graph of the data. **See Ch. 12 Answer Appendix.**

2A. Each value is greater than 0 and less than 1; $0.13 + 0.18 + 0.21 + 0.19 + 0.12 + 0.17 = 1$.

Teach with Tech

Interactive Whiteboard Choose two students to work through an example in front of the class. Have one student explain how to calculate a frequency distribution, and have the other student explain how to create a graph.

Focus on Mathematical Content

Discrete vs. Continuous All the random variables discussed in this lesson are discrete, which means that only certain values are possible for the variable. For a continuous random variable, all real numbers interval are possible values for the variable.

The **expected value $E(X)$** of a discrete random variable is the weighted average of the variable. The "weight" applied to each value is its theoretical probability. The expected value tells you what average value to expect after many trials.

KeyConcept Expected Value of a Discrete Random Variable

Words	The expected value of a discrete random variable is the weighted average of the values of the variable. It is calculated by finding the sum of the products of every possible value of X and its associated probability $P(X)$.
Symbols	$E(X) = [X_1 \cdot P(X_1)] + [X_2 \cdot P(X_2)] + \ldots + [X_n \cdot P(X_n)]$, where n is the total number of values of X

Real-WorldLink

Sweepstakes The odds of winning the grand prize in some sweepstakes can be 1 in over 500 million.

Real-World Example 3 Expected Value

GAMES **A candy bar manufacturer is holding a contest. The potential prizes and the probability of winning each prize are shown in the table.**

Prize	gift certificate	year supply of candy bars	trip	new car
Prize Value	$50	$250	$4000	$25,000
Probability	1 in 500	1 in 2000	1 in 2,000,000	1 in 20,000,000

a. Create a probability distribution.

Find the probability associated with each prize. Note that the probability of winning $0 is found by subtracting the probability of winning something from 1.

X	P(X)
$50	0.002
$250	0.0005
$4000	0.0000005
$25,000	0.00000005
$0	0.99749945

StudyTip

Probability of Winning $0 The probability of winning $0 is included in order for the sum of the probabilities in the probability distribution to equal 1.

b. Calculate the expected value.

$E(X) = [X_1 \cdot P(X_1)] + [X_2 \cdot P(X_2)] + \ldots + [X_n \cdot P(X_n)]$

$= 50(0.002) + 250(0.0005) + 4000(0.0000005) + 25{,}000(0.00000005) + 0(0.997\ldots)$

$= 0.1 + 0.125 + 0.002 + 0.00125 + 0$ or 0.22825

The expected value is 0.22825 or about $0.23.

c. Interpret your results.

The expected value of 0.22825 means that one candy bar purchase can be expected to win about $0.23.

GuidedPractice

3. **CONTEST** Wendy entered a contest with the following prize values.

Prize Value	$100	$500	$5000	$50,000
Probability	1 in 1000	1 in 5000	1 in 100,000	1 in 1,000,000

A. Create a probability distribution. **See Ch. 12 Answer Appendix.**

B. Calculate the expected value. **$0.30**

C. Interpret your results.

3C. Sample answer: One ticket will be expected to win about $0.30. Therefore, once purchased, one ticket will be worth about $0.30. The maker of the contest can expect to spend about $0.30 per ticket.

DifferentiatedInstruction AL OL

Visual/Spatial Learners Give small groups of students the following probability distribution. The number of hours a student spends on homework in an average week, X is: 0, 1, 2, 3, 4, 5+. The probability $P(x)$ is: 0.05, 0.05, 0.10, 0.15, 0.45, 0.20. Have students prepare a probability graph of the data. Use the graph to determine the probability that a student studies 4 hours or more in an average week. 0.65 or 65%

Probability Distributions

Example 2 shows how to determine whether a probability distribution for a real-world situation is valid, and how to use a probability table and graph to represent the probability distribution. **Example 3** shows how to find the expected value of a discrete random variable.

Additional Example

3 Nikki paid $5 for an entry into a contest with the following prize values.

Prize Value	Probability
$500	1 in 5000
$5000	1 in 50,000
$20,000	1 in 500,000
$50,000	1 in 2,000,000

a. Create a probability distribution.

X	P(X)
$500	0.0002
$5000	0.00002
$20,000	0.000002
$50,000	0.0000005
$0	0.9997775

b. Calculate the expected value. $0.265

c. Interpret your results. Sample answer: One entry can be expected to win about $0.27 once the purchase is made. Assuming that a large number of entries is sold, the maker of the contest can expect to spend about $0.27 per entry. Therefore, with a cost of $5, they can expect to earn about $4.73 per entry.

Additional Examples also in Interactive Classroom PowerPoint® Presentations

IWB **Interactive White Board READY**

3 Practice

Formative Assessment

Use Exercises 1–3 to check for understanding.

Use the chart at the bottom of this page to customize assignments for your students.

Teaching the Process Standards

Arguments Mathematically proficient students reason inductively about data, making plausible arguments that take into account the context from which the data arose. In Exercises 3 and 8, encourage students to discuss their interpretations of the results.

Additional Answers

2c.

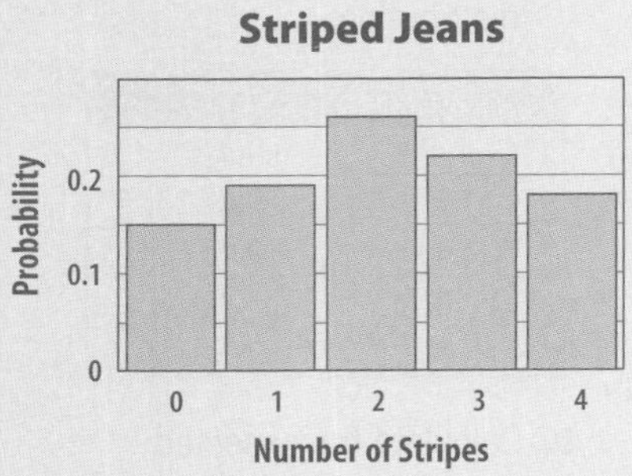

3a.

X	$P(X)$
\$1000	0.0125
\$5000	0.005
\$25,000	0.001
\$100,000	0.0001
\$0	0.9814

6c.

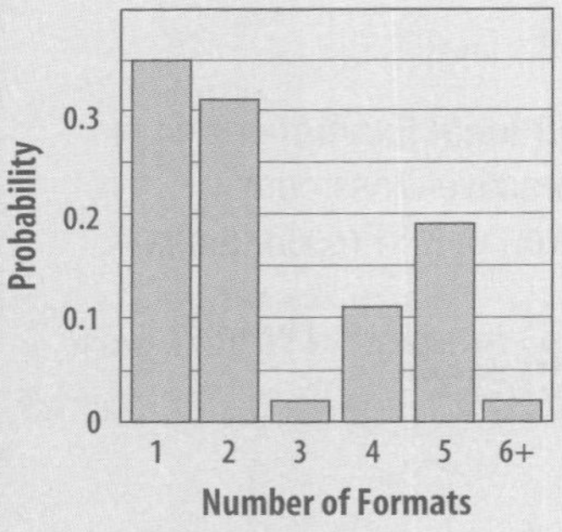

Check Your Understanding

= Step-by-Step Solutions begin on page R13.

Example 1

1. GPS A car dealership surveys 10,000 of its customers with a GPS system in their vehicles to ask how often they have used the system within the past year. The results are shown in the table.

a. Find the probability that a randomly chosen customer will have used the GPS system more than 20 times. **4.7%**

b. Find the probability that a randomly chosen customer will have used the GPS system no more than 10 times. **57.4%**

Customers Using the GPS System

Uses	Customers
0	1382
1–5	2350
6–10	2010
11–15	1863
16–20	1925
21+	470

Example 2

2. JEANS A fashion boutique ordered jeans with different numbers of stripes down the outside seams. The table shows the probability distribution of the number of each type of jean that was sold in a particular week.

a. Show that the distribution is valid.

2a. All of the values are between 0 and 1; 0.15 + 0.19 + 0.26 + 0.22 + 0.18 = 1.

b. What is the probability that a randomly chosen pair of jeans has fewer than 3 stripes? **60%**

c. Make a probability graph of the data. **See margin.**

Types of Jeans Sold

Number of Stripes	Probability
0	0.15
1	0.19
2	0.26
3	0.22
4	0.18

Example 3

3. ARGUMENTS The producers of a game show provided the probability of winning the prizes for one of the games.

a. Create a probability distribution. **See margin.**

b. Calculate the expected value. **\$72.50**

c. Interpret your results.

3c. Sample answer: The game show producers expect to lose about \$72.50 each time a certain game is played.

Prize Value	Probability
\$1000	1 in 80
\$5000	1 in 200
\$25,000	1 in 1000
\$100,000	1 in 10,000

Practice and Problem Solving

Extra Practice is on page R12.

Example 1

4. HOME THEATER An electronics store sells components and speakers for home theaters individually. The store surveyed its home theater customers to see how many of the 10 components they bought. The results are shown in the table.

a. Find the probability that a randomly chosen customer bought 5 or 6 components. **20%**

b. Find the probability that a randomly chosen customer bought fewer than 5 components. **41.2%**

Home Theater Purchases

Components	Customers
0–2	26
3–4	42
5–6	33
7–8	24
9–10	40

5. FOOD DRIVE Ms. Valdez's biology class held a food drive that lasted four days. The class kept track of the number of packages donated each day.

a. Find the probability that a randomly chosen product was donated on the fourth day. **39.1%**

b. Find the probability that a randomly chosen product was donated on the first or second day. **50.4%**

Food Drive Donations Count

Day	Packages
1	36
2	22
3	12
4	45

Differentiated Homework Options

Level	Assignment	Two-Day Option	
AL Basic	4–9, 15–41	5–9 odd, 21–24	4–8 even, 15–20, 25–41
OL Core	5–9 odd, 10–13, 15–41	4–9, 21–24	10–13, 15–20, 25–41
BL Advanced	10–41		

806 | Lesson 12-8 | Probability Distributions

Example 2 **6. MUSIC** A Web site conducted a survey on the number of different formats on which teens have music. The table shows a probability distribution of the results.

Formats	Probability
1	0.35
2	0.31
3	0.19
4	0.11
5	0.02
6+	0.02

a. Show that the distribution is valid.

b. What is the probability that a student randomly chosen will have music on 2 or more formats? **65%**

c. Make a probability graph of the data. **See margin.**

6a. All of the values are between 0 and 1; $0.35 + 0.31 + 0.19 + 0.11 + 0.02 + 0.02 = 1$.

7. GRADES Mr. Rockwell's Algebra class took a chapter test last week. The table shows the probability distribution of the results.

Score	Probability
4	0.29
3	0.43
2	0.17
1	0.11
0	0

a. Show that the distribution is valid.

b. What is the probability that a student chosen at random will have no higher than a 3? **71%**

c. Make a probability graph of the data. **See margin.**

All of the values are between 0 and 1; $0.29 + 0.43 + 0.17 + 0.11 + 0 = 1$.

Example 3 **8. ARGUMENTS** Kylie entered a drawing at the county fair. The table shows the value and probability of winning each prize.

Prize Value	Probability
$20	1 in 50
$50	1 in 100
$100	1 in 250
$250	1 in 1000

a. Create a probability distribution. **See margin.**

b. Calculate the expected value. **$1.55**

c. Interpret your results.

ample answer: ylie's ticket is orth about 1.55. If the rganizers of the air expect to nake any money ff of the rawing, they will eed to charge nore than $1.55 er ticket.

9. CONTESTS Nikia entered a contest where each ticket cost $1. The table shows the value and probability of each prize.

Prize Value	Probability
$200	1 in 500
$1000	1 in 5000
$5000	1 in 25,000
$25,000	1 in 100,000

a. Create a probability distribution. **See margin.**

b. Calculate the expected value. **$1.05**

c. Interpret your results.

ample answer: he makers of ie contest expect ɔ lose $1.05 for ach ticket valued t $1.00 Therefore, ney can expect to ɔse money by oing this contest.

10. MARKETING A retail marketing group conducted a survey on teen shopping habits and asked the teens for the number of stores they visited to complete their holiday shopping. The table shows the probability distribution of the results.

Number of Stores	0–2	3–5	6–8	9–11	12+
Probability	0.35	0.32	0.17	0.11	0.05

a. Show that the distribution is valid. **All of the values are between 0 and 1; $0.35 + 0.32 + 0.17 + 0.11 + 0.05 = 1$.**

b. What is the probability that a shopper chosen at random will shop at more than 5 stores but fewer than 12? **28%**

c. Make a probability graph of the data. **See margin.**

11. DECISION MAKING An auto insurance company uses many variables to calculate each driver's six-month payment. The table at the right shows the probability of a specific driver getting into an accident that will cost the company $10,000.

Variable	Probability
driving record	1 in 50
vehicle type	1 in 500
age	1 in 250
gender	1 in 200
residence	1 in 1000

a. Taking all of the probabilities into account, what is the probability of the driver having an accident? **3.2%**

b. What is the company's expected payout for this driver? **$320**

c. What should the company charge the driver for a six-month policy? Explain your reasoning.

Sample answer: The company should charge at least $320 to cover their expected costs. However, in order to cover other costs such as paying employees and other business expenses and still earn a profit, the company should charge around $600 for the policy.

4 Assess

Yesterday's News Have students describe how the lesson on simulations helped prepare them for today's lesson on probability distributions.

Formative Assessment

Check for student understanding of concepts in Lessons 12-7 and 12-8.

Quiz 4, p. 58

Additional Answers

7c.

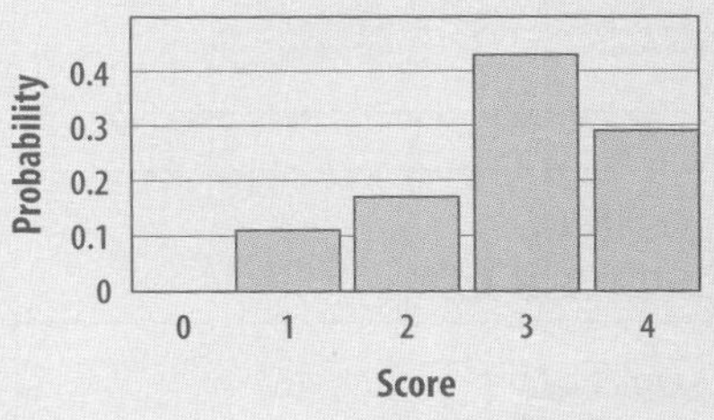

8a.

X	$P(X)$
$20	0.02
$50	0.01
$100	0.004
$250	0.001
$0	0.965

9a.

X	$P(X)$
$200	0.002
$1000	0.0002
$5000	0.00004
$25,000	0.00001
$0	0.99775

10c. **Shopping Places**

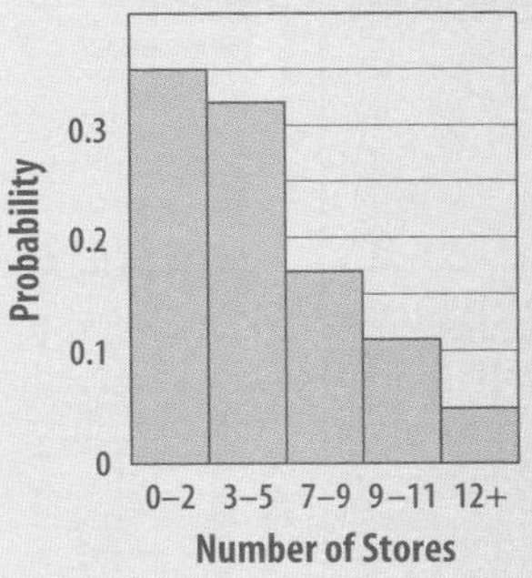

12. **DECISION MAKING** Amber is investing in stocks for her math class. After analyzing five stocks, she has determined the following probabilities.

Stock	Cost Per Share	Probability of \$20 Gain	Probability of No Gain	Probability of \$30 Loss
A	\$100	47%	25%	28%
B	\$200	40%	40%	20%
C	\$200	50%	20%	30%
D	\$200	60%	0%	40%
E	\$300	30%	60%	10%

a. Calculate the expected gain or loss for one share of each stock. **\$1; \$2; \$1; \$0; \$3**

b. If Amber is allowed to spend \$1000, what combination of stocks should she purchase to ensure the greatest expected value? Explain your reasoning. **See Ch. 12 Answer Appendix.**

13. **MULTIPLE REPRESENTATIONS** In this problem, you will investigate probability distributions and simulations. **a, b, d, e. See Ch. 12 Answer Appendix.**

a. **Tabular** Construct a relative-frequency table showing the theoretical probability for the sum obtained from rolling a die and spinning the spinner at the right.

b. **Graphical** Make a probability graph of the data.

c. **Analytical** Calculate the expected value of one spin. **6.75**

d. **Concrete** Design a simulation for 50 trials. Explain your reasoning. Conduct the simulation and tally your results.

e. **Graphical** Make a probability graph of the data in the simulation. Compare and contrast the two graphs.

H.O.T. Problems

14. **CHALLENGE** What is wrong with the probability distribution shown? Explain your reasoning. **See margin.**

15. **REASONING** Suppose two dice are rolled twelve times. Which sum is most likely to occur? Make a table to show the probability distribution. Then make a probability graph to confirm your answer. **See Ch. 12 Answer Appendix.**

16. **STRUCTURE** Explain why the sum of the probabilities in a probability distribution should always be 1. Include an example. **See margin.**

17. **REASONING** Determine whether the following statement is *true* or *false*. Explain your reasoning. **See margin.**

Discrete random variables can take on an infinite number of values.

18. **OPEN ENDED** Write a real-world problem in which you could find a probability distribution. Create a probability graph for your data. **See Ch. 12 Answer Appendix.**

19. **REASONING** Determine whether the following statement is *true* or *false*. Explain your reasoning. **See margin.**

The expected value of a random variable is the value for the random variable most likely to occur.

20. **WRITING IN MATH** Write a real-world story in which you are the owner of a business. Explain how you could use a probability distribution to help you make a business decision. **See margin.**

Study Guide and Intervention
AL OL ELL

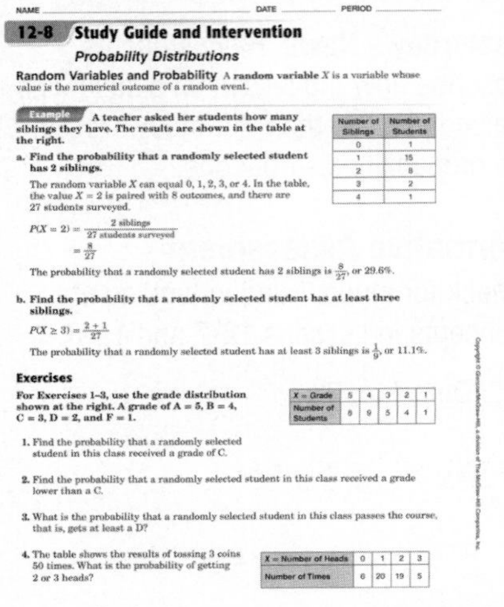
12-8 Study Guide and Intervention
Probability Distributions

Practice
AL OL BL ELL

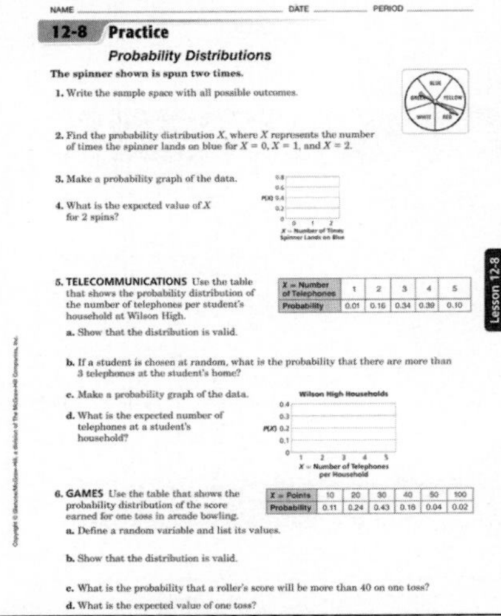
12-8 Practice
Probability Distributions

Word Problem Practice
AL OL BL ELL

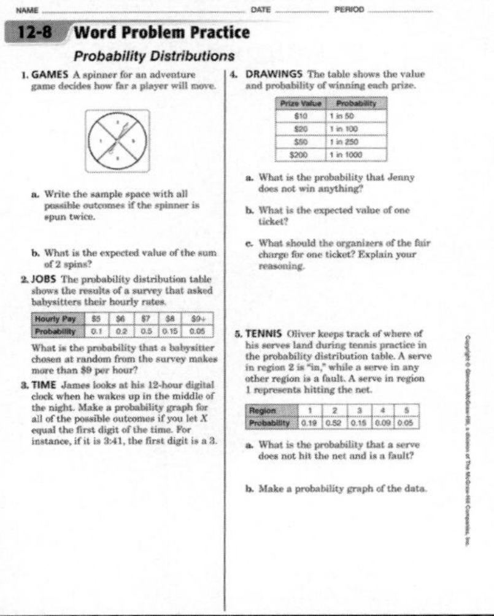
12-8 Word Problem Practice
Probability Distributions

Enrichment
OL BL

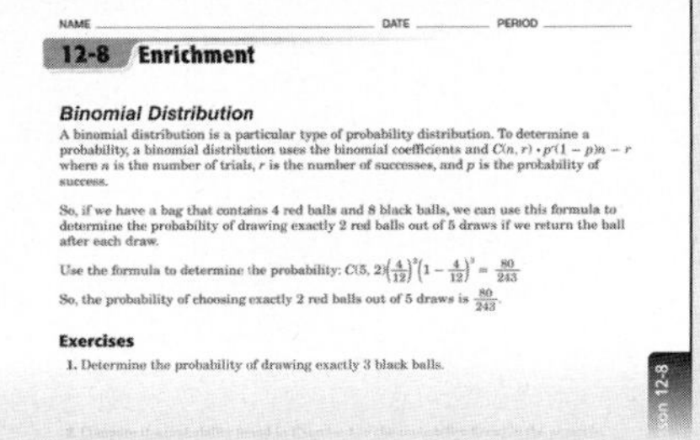
12-8 Enrichment
Binomial Distribution

Multiple Representations
In Exercise 13, students use a die, spinner, and random number generator to show the difference between theoretical probability and experimental probability.

Standardized Test Practice

21. A coin is flipped and a die is rolled. What is the probability of the coin landing heads up and rolling a 3? **A**

A $\frac{1}{12}$ C $\frac{1}{8}$

B $\frac{1}{9}$ D $\frac{2}{3}$

22. **SHORT RESPONSE** How many different ways can the letters P, Q, R, S be arranged? **24**

23. Suppose there are 10 tickets in a box for a drawing numbered as follows: 1, 2, 2, 3, 4, 4, 6, 6, 9, and 9. A single ticket is randomly chosen from the box. What is the probability of drawing a ticket with a number less than 10? **H**

F $\frac{1}{5}$ G $\frac{3}{10}$ H 1 J 0

24. **GEOMETRY** The height of a triangle is five inches less than the length of its base. If the area of the triangle is 52 square inches, find the base and the height. **C**

A 15 in., 9 in. C 13 in., 8 in.

B 11 in., 7 in. D 17 in., 11 in.

Spiral Review

25. **PET TOYS** Johnda is looking for 2 puppy toys at the pet store. They have a box of clearance items that contains 6 balls, 5 tug toys, 8 rawhide chews, and 4 chew toys. If Johnda reaches in the box and pulls out two items, what is the probability that she will pull out two tug toys? (Lesson 12-7) **$\frac{10}{253}$ or about 4%**

26. **GAMES** For a certain game, each player rolls four dice at the same time. (Lesson 12-6)
   a. Do the outcomes of rolling the four dice represent a permutation or combination? Explain. **Combination; order is not important in this case.**
   b. How many outcomes are possible? **1296**
   c. What is the probability that four dice show the same number on a single roll? **$\frac{1}{216}$**

Find each sum. (Lesson 11-6)

27. $\frac{4}{a^2} + \frac{6}{a}$ **$\frac{6a+4}{a^2}$**

28. $\frac{3}{b^3} + \frac{7}{b^2}$ **$\frac{7b+3}{b^3}$**

29. $\frac{4}{d+6} + \frac{5}{d-5}$ **$\frac{9d+10}{(d+6)(d-5)}$**

30. $\frac{f}{f+5} + \frac{4}{f-4}$ **$\frac{f^2+20}{(f+5)(f-4)}$**

31. $\frac{8h}{h+6} + \frac{h}{h-3}$ **$\frac{9h(h-2)}{(h+6)(h-3)}$**

32. $\frac{7k}{k-3} + \frac{k}{k+2}$ **$\frac{k(8k+11)}{(k-3)(k+2)}$**

Find the values of the three trigonometric ratios for angle A. (Lesson 10-6)

33.
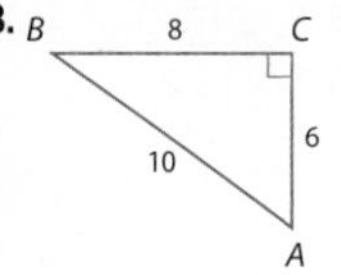

$\sin A = \frac{4}{5}$; $\cos A = \frac{3}{5}$; $\tan A = \frac{4}{3}$

34.
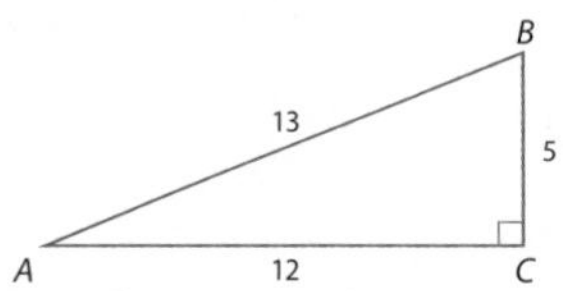

$\sin A = \frac{5}{13}$; $\cos A = \frac{12}{13}$; $\tan A = \frac{5}{12}$

35.
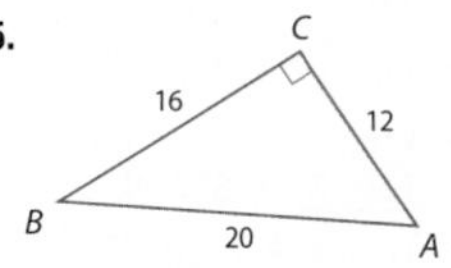

$\sin A = \frac{4}{5}$; $\cos A = \frac{3}{5}$; $\tan A = \frac{4}{3}$

Simplify each expression. (Lesson 10-2)

36. $\sqrt{\frac{50}{x^4}}$ **$\frac{5\sqrt{2}}{x^2}$**

37. $\frac{\sqrt{t^3}}{\sqrt{18}}$ **$\frac{t\sqrt{t}}{3\sqrt{2}}$**

38. $\sqrt{\frac{15}{14}} \cdot \sqrt{\frac{21}{10}}$ **$\frac{3}{2}$**

39. $\frac{6}{3-\sqrt{5}}$ **$\frac{9+3\sqrt{5}}{2}$**

40. $\frac{3}{\sqrt{7}+\sqrt{6}}$ **$3\sqrt{7}-3\sqrt{6}$**

41. $\frac{\sqrt{2}}{\sqrt{8}-\sqrt{6}}$ **$2+\sqrt{3}$**

Differentiated Instruction BL

Extension While two probability distributions may have the same expected value, one of the distributions may show more *risk* than the other. The risk of the probability distribution for a stock can be found by calculating the standard deviation of the distribution. For each value of X, subtract the mean from X and square the difference. Then multiply by the probability of X. The sum of each of these products is the variance. The standard deviation is the square root of the variance. The stock with the larger standard deviation is the stock with the greater risk. Of stocks A and C in Exercise 14, which is the riskiest? Stock C

Additional Answers

14. Sample answer: The problem with this probability distribution is that shooting foul shots is not a random event. Events involving athletic ability should not be considered when making probability distributions.

16. Since the probability is found by dividing the number of desired outcomes by the number of possible outcomes, the sum of the probability of each outcome is 1. For example, if a jar contains 2 red marbles, 1 green marble, and 3 blue marbles the probability of drawing a red marble is $\frac{2}{2+1+3}$ or $\frac{1}{3}$, the probability of drawing a green marble is $\frac{1}{2+1+3}$ or $\frac{1}{6}$, and the probability of drawing a blue marble is $\frac{3}{2+1+3}$ or $\frac{1}{2}$. The sum of the probabilities in the distribution is 1.

17. True; sample answer: While a discrete random variable is a countable variable, it can still take on an infinite number of values. For example, the number of hits a Web site receives is countable, but can be infinite.

19. False; sample answer: False; sample answer: The expected value of a random variable is the weighted average of the variable. The expected value of a random variable does not have to be a possible value. For example the expected value when a die is rolled is 3.5. This value cannot occur.

20. Sample answer: I own a cosmetics store. As part of my inventory, I keep track of each type of cosmetic that I sell. This allows me to decide how much of each type of item to keep in stock.

1 Focus

Objective Use a graphing calculator to explore normal distribution curves.

Materials for Each Student

- TI-83/84 Plus or other graphing calculator

Teaching Tip

Before starting students on the activity, discuss normal distributions using the graphic on the page. Some other examples of normally distributed random variables are lengths of newborn babies, blood pressure, lengths of objects made by machines, and useful lives of some manufactured items.

2 Teach

Working in Cooperative Groups

Have students work in pairs, mixing abilities to work through Activities 1 and 2.

- For a continuous normally distributed variable, the height of the curve represents only a probability density.
- The total area under the curve is equal to 1.
- The probability that a variable takes on a value within a given interval is equal to the area under the curve between the endpoints of the curve interval.
- The probability that the height (to the nearest inch) of a particular 15-year old is 67 inches is equal to the area under the normal curve from 66.5 inches to 67.5 inches.

EXTEND 12-8 Graphing Technology Lab: The Normal Curve

When there are a large number of values in a data set, the frequency distribution tends to cluster around the mean of the set in a distribution (or shape) called a **normal distribution**. The graph of a normal distribution is called a **normal curve**. Since the shape of the graph resembles a bell, the graph is also called a *bell curve*.

Data sets that have a normal distribution include reaction times of drivers that are the same age, achievement test scores, and the heights of people that are the same age.

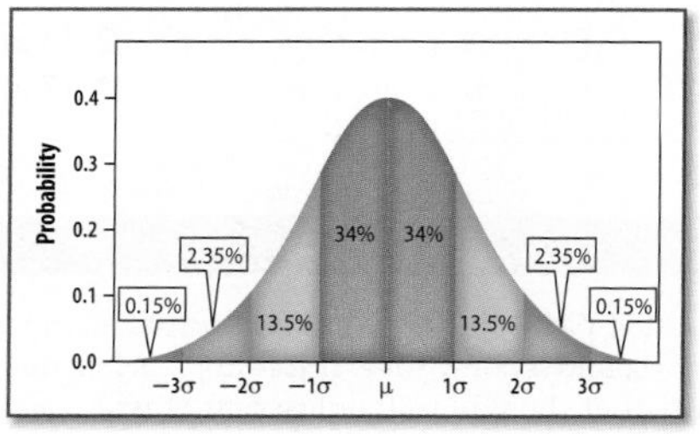

You can use a graphing calculator to graph and analyze a normal distribution if the mean and standard deviation of the data are known.

Activity 1 Graph a Normal Distribution

HEIGHT **The mean height of 15-year-old boys in the city where Isaac lives is 67 inches, with a standard deviation of 2.8 inches. Use a normal distribution to represent these data.**

Step 1 Set the viewing window. [WINDOW]

- Xmin = 67 [−] 3 [×] 2.8 [ENTER] 58.6
- Xmax = 67 [+] 3 [×] 2.8 [ENTER] 75.4
- Xscl = 2.8 [ENTER]
- Ymin = 0 [ENTER]
- Ymax = 1 [÷] [(] 2 [×] 2.8 [)] [ENTER] .17857142...
- Yscale = 1 [ENTER]

Step 2 By entering the mean and standard deviation into the calculator, we can graph the corresponding normal curve. Enter the values using the following keystrokes.

KEYSTROKES: [Y=] [2nd] [DISTR] [ENTER] [X,T,θ,n] [,] 67 [,] 2.8 [)] [GRAPH]

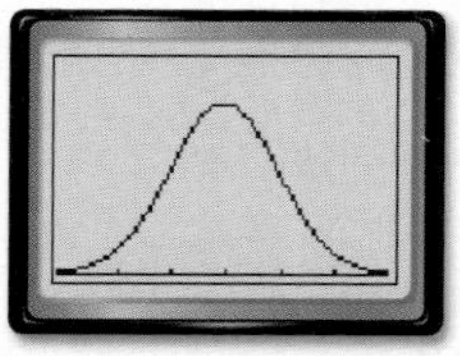

[58.6, 75.4] scl: 2.8 by [0, 0.17857142] scl: 1

810 | Extend 12-8 | Graphing Technology Lab: The Normal Curve

Graphing Technology Lab
The Normal Curve *Continued*

The probability of a range of values is the area under the curve.

Activity 2 Analyze a Normal Distribution

Use the graph to answer questions about the data. What is the probability that Isaac will be at most 67 inches tall when he is 15?

The sum of all the y-values up to $x = 67$ would give us the probability that Isaac's height will be less than or equal to 67 inches. This is also the area under the curve. We will shade the area under the curve from negative infinity to 67 inches and find the area of the shaded portion of the graph.

Step 1 Use the **ShadeNorm** function.

KEYSTROKES: [2nd] [DISTR] [▶] [ENTER]

Step 2 Shade the graph.

Next enter the lowest value, highest value, mean, and standard deviation.

On the TI-84 Plus, -1×10^{99} represents negative infinity.

KEYSTROKES: [(−)] 1 [2nd] [EE] 99 [,] 67 [,] 67 [,] 2.8 [)] [ENTER]

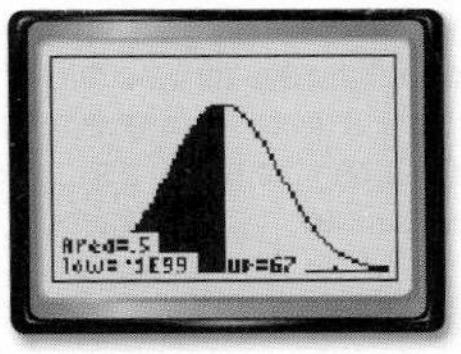

[58.6, 75.4] scl: 2.8 by [0, 0.17857142] scl: 1

The area is given as 0.5. The probability that Isaac will be 67 inches tall is 0.5 or 50%. Since the mean value is 67, we expect the probability to be 50%.

Exercises

1. What is the probability that Isaac will be at least 6 feet tall when he is 15? **about 4%**
2. What is the probability that Isaac will be between 65 and 68 inches? **about 40%**
3. The **z-score** represents the number of standard deviations that a given data value is from the mean. The z-score for a data value X is given by $z = \frac{X - \mu}{\sigma}$, where μ is the mean and σ is the standard deviation. Find and interpret the z-score of a height of 73 inches. **About 2.14; 73 in. is 2.14 standard deviations above the mean.**
4. Find and interpret the z-score of a height of 61 inches. **About −2.14; 61 in. is 2.14 standard deviations below the mean.**

Extension
Refer to the curve at the right.

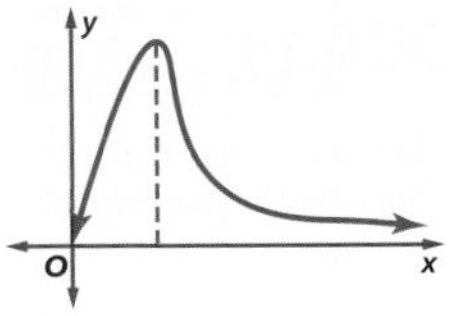

5. Compare this curve to the normal curve in Activity 1. **5. Both curves have a bell shape. This curve has a longer tail at the right.**
6. Describe where an outlier of the data set would be graphed on this curve. **6. On this curve, an outlier is plotted at the right, where the y-values are smaller.**

Practice Have students complete Exercises 1–6.

3 Assess

Formative Assessment

Use Exercise 2 to assess whether students can use the **normalpdf** command to find normal probabilities.

From Concrete to Abstract

Exercise 4 asks students to find an open ended probability using a different normal distribution.

connectED.mcgraw-hill.com 811

Formative Assessment

KeyVocabulary The page reference after each word denotes where that term was first introduced. If students have difficulty answering questions 1–5, remind them that they can use these page references to refresh their memories about the vocabulary terms.

Summative Assessment

Vocabulary Test, p. 60

Vocabulary Review

Vocabulary Review provides students the opportunity to check their understanding of important concepts and terminology in an online game format.

FOLDABLES StudyOrganizer

Dinah Zike's Foldables®

Have students look through the chapter to make sure they have included examples in their Foldables for each lesson of the chapter. Suggest that students keep their Foldables handy while completing the Study Guide and Review pages. Point out that their Foldables can serve as a quick review when studying for the chapter test.

CHAPTER 12 Study Guide and Review

Study Guide

KeyConcepts

Samples and Studies (Lesson 12-1)

- Some types of samples are simple random, systematic, convenience, self-selected, and stratified.
- Three study types are the survey, observational study, and experiment.

Statistics and Parameters (Lesson 12-2)

- The mean absolute deviation is used to predict errors and judge how well the mean represents the data.
- A low standard deviation indicates that the data tend to be very close to the mean, while a high standard deviation indicates that the data are spread out over a larger range.

Distributions of Data and Comparing Sets of Data (Lessons 12-3 and 12-4)

- In a negatively skewed distribution, the majority of the data are on the right. In a positively skewed distribution, the majority of the data are on the left. In a symmetric distribution, the data are evenly distributed.

Simulations (Lesson 12-5)

- Simulations are used to perform experiments that would be difficult or impossible to perform in real life.

Permutations and Combinations and Probability of Compound Events (Lessons 12-6 and 12-7)

- A selection of objects in which order is important is called a permutation. A selection of objects in which order is not important is called a combination.
- For independent events, the outcome of one does not affect the outcome of the other.

Probability Distributions (Lesson 12-8)

- For each value of X, $0 \leq P(X) \leq 1$. The sum of the probabilities of each value of X is 1.
- The expected value $E(X)$ of a discrete random variable of a probability distribution is its weighted average.

FOLDABLES StudyOrganizer

Be sure the Key Concepts are noted in your Foldable.

KeyVocabulary

bias (p. 748)
combination (p. 787)
compound event (p. 793)
convenience sample (p. 747)
dependent events (p. 794)
discrete random variable (p. 803)
distribution (p. 764)
expected value $E(X)$ (p. 805)
experiment (p. 749)
experimental probability (p. 780)
independent events (p. 793)
linear transformation (p. 771)
mean absolute deviation (MAD) (p. 758)
mutually exclusive events (p. 795)
observational study (p. 749)
parameter (p. 757)
permutation (p. 786)
population (p. 747)
probability distribution (p. 804)
probability graph (p. 804)
random variable (p. 803)
sample (p. 747)
self-selected sample (p. 747)
simple random sample (p. 747)
simulation (p. 781)
standard deviation (p. 759)
statistic (p. 757)
statistical inference (p. 757)
stratified sample (p. 747)
survey (p. 749)
systematic sample (p. 747)
theoretical probability (p. 780)
variance (p. 759)

VocabularyCheck

Choose the term that best completes each sentence.

1. An arrangement in which order is important is called a (combination, permutation). **permutation**
2. A (parameter, statistic) is a measure that describes the characteristic of a sample. **statistic**
3. A (sample, population) consists of all of the members of a group. **population**
4. (Experimental probability, Theoretical probability) is the ratio of the number of favorable outcomes to the total number of outcomes. **Theoretical probability**
5. A variable with a value that is the numerical outcome of a random event is called a (discrete random variable, random variable). **random variable**

Lesson-by-Lesson Review

12-1 Samples and Studies

Identify the sample as *biased* or *unbiased*. Explain your reasoning.

6. GOVERNMENT To determine whether voters support a new trade agreement, 5 people from the list of registered voters in each state are selected at random. See margin.

Determine whether each situation describes a *survey*, an *observational study*, or an *experiment*. Explain your reasoning. 7–8. See margin.

7. SCHOOL DANCE The homecoming dance committee sends out a questionnaire to all the girls in the school to decide on a theme for the homecoming dance.

8. MILKSHAKE Mary wants to test her milkshake recipe using honey instead of sugar. She randomly gives half of her 6 friends milkshakes sweetened with honey and the other half the same milkshakes sweetened with sugar. Then she asks them how they like the milkshakes.

Example 1

MUSIC A randomly selected group of people who listen to a country music radio station is asked to name their favorite type of music. Identify the sample as *biased* or *unbiased*. Explain your reasoning.

The sample is biased. People listening to a country music radio station are likely to vote for country music.

Example 2

BOOK COVER An artist is trying to choose a cover for a children's book. She sends out a flyer with the two covers to all of the students at one school. She asks them to check the favorite cover. Determine whether this situation describes a *survey*, an *observational study*, or an *experiment*. Explain your reasoning.

This is a survey. The data are gathered from the responses given by members in the sample.

12-2 Statistics and Parameters

9. SHOVELING Ben shovels driveways to raise money. The number of driveways he shovels each day is {2, 4, 3, 5, 3}. Find and interpret the mean absolute deviation. See margin.

10. CANDY BARS Luci is keeping track of the number of candy bars each member of the drill team sold. The results are {20, 25, 30, 50, 40, 60, 20, 10, 42}. Find and interpret the mean absolute deviation. See margin.

11. FOOD A fast food company polls a random sample of its day and night customers to find how many times a month they eat out. Compare the means and standard deviations of each data set. See margin.

Day Customers	Night Customers
10, 3, 12, 15, 7, 8, 4, 12, 9, 14, 12, 9	15, 12, 13, 9, 11, 12, 14, 12, 8, 16, 9, 9

Example 3

GIFTS Joshua is collecting money from his family for a Mother's Day gift. He keeps track of how much each person has donated: {10, 5, 20, 15, 10}. Find and interpret the mean absolute deviation.

Step 1 Find the mean: $\bar{x} = \frac{10 + 5 + 20 + 15 + 10}{5}$ or 12.

Step 2 Find the absolute values of the differences.

$x_1 = 10: |12 - 10|$ or 2 $\quad x_2 = 5: |12 - 5|$ or 7

$x_3 = 20: |12 - 20|$ or 8 $\quad x_4 = 15: |12 - 15|$ or 3

$x_5 = 10: |12 - 10|$ or 2

Step 3 Find the sum: $2 + 7 + 8 + 3 + 2 = 22$.

Step 4 Find the mean absolute deviation.

$$\text{MAD} = \frac{|\bar{x} - x_1| + |\bar{x} - x_2| + \ldots + |\bar{x} - x_n|}{n}$$

$$= \frac{22}{5} \text{ or } 4.4$$

A mean absolute deviation of 4.4 indicates that the data, on average, are 4.4 units away from the mean.

Lesson-by-Lesson Review

Intervention If the given examples are not sufficient to review the topics covered by the questions, remind students that the lesson references tell them where to review that topic in their textbooks.

Two-Day Option Have students complete the Lesson-by-Lesson Review. Then you can use McGraw-Hill eAssessment to customize another review worksheet that practices all the objectives of this chapter or only the objectives on which your students need more help.

Additional Answers

6. Unbiased; sample answer: The sample represents part of the population.
7. Survey; sample answer: The data are obtained from opinions given by the girls that return the questionnaire.
8. Experiment; sample answer: The people are divided into two groups, one of which undergoes a change.
9. 0.88; Sample answer: On average, the number of driveways that Ben shovels each day is 0.88 away from the mean of 3.4.
10. 13.33; Sample answer: On average, the number of candy bars sold is 13.33 away from the mean of 33. The mean absolute deviation is affected by outliers 10 and 60.
11. The day customers had a mean of about 9.6 times per month with a standard deviation of about 3.5. The night customers had a mean of about 11.7 times per month with a standard deviation of about 2.5. The night customers had a higher average and their data values were more consistent.

Additional Answers

12.

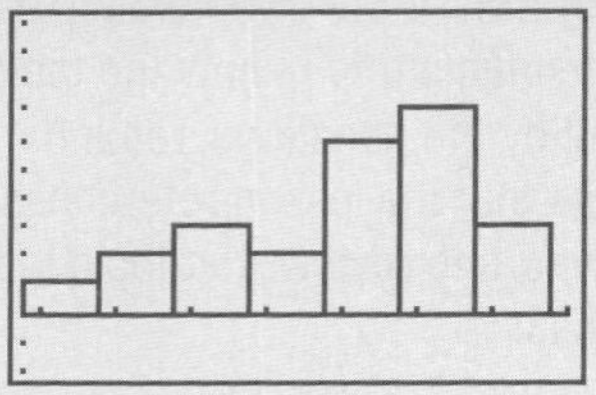

[8, 80] scl: 10 by [−2, 10] scl: 1

negatively skewed

13.

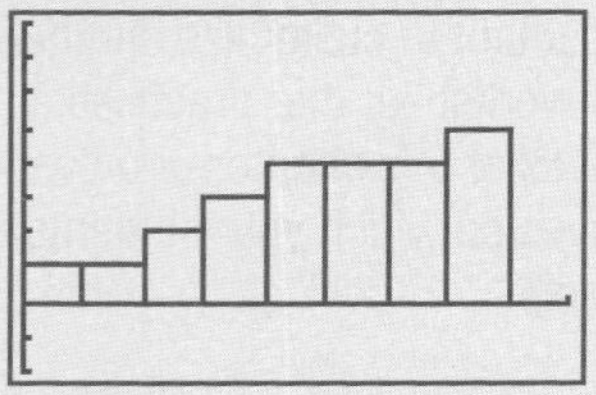

[0, 90] scl: 10 by [−2, 8] scl: 1

negatively skewed

14.

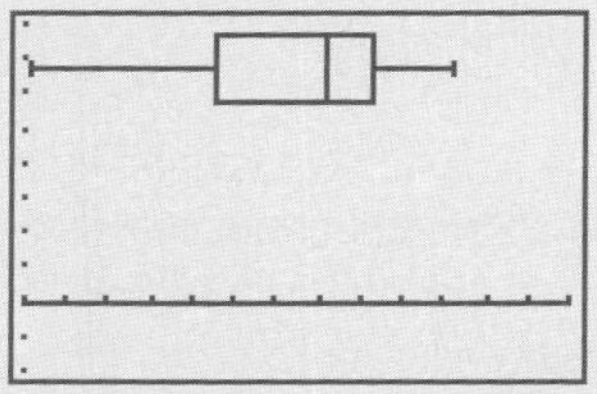

[175, 500] scl: 25 by [−2, 8] scl: 1

Sample answer: The data are negatively skewed, so use the five-number summary. The range is 252 gallons. The median is 354.5 gallons. Half of the data are between 288 and 383 gallons.

17a.

Ms. Miller:

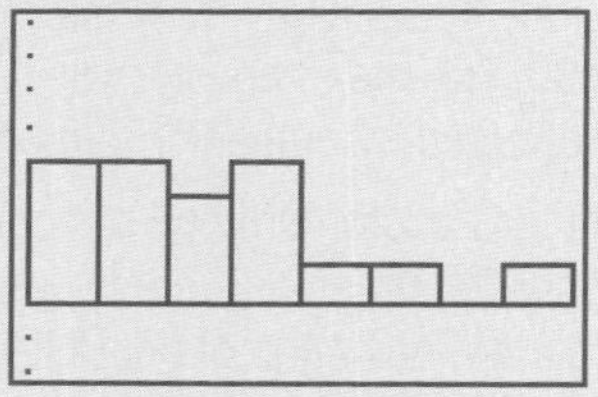

[9, 17] scl: 1 by [−2, 8] scl: 1

Ms. Anderson:

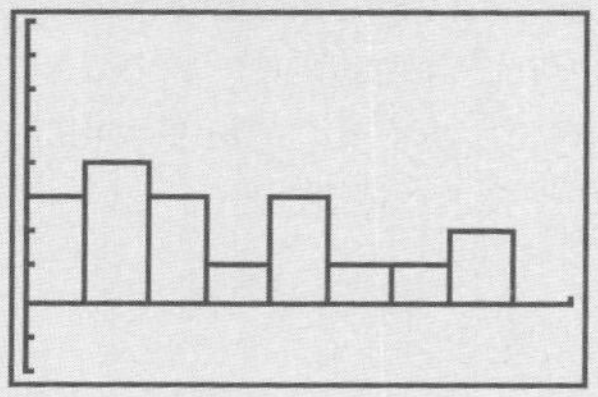

[0, 9] scl: 1 by [−2, 8] scl: 1

CHAPTER 12 Study Guide and Review *Continued*

12-3 Distributions of Data

Use a graphing calculator to construct a histogram for the data. Then describe the shape of the distribution.

12. 55, 62, 32, 56, 31, 59, 19, 61, 8, 48, 41, 69, 32, 63, 48, 60, 43, 66, 71, 70, 49, 56, 21, 67

12–14. See margin.

13. 4, 19, 62, 28, 26, 59, 33, 39, 36, 72, 46, 48, 49, 44, 72, 76, 55, 53, 55, 62, 66, 69, 71, 74

14. MILK A grocery store manager tracked the amount of milk in gallons sold each day. Describe the center and spread of the data using either the mean and standard deviation or the five-number summary. Justify your choice by constructing a box-and-whisker plot for the data.

Gallons of Milk Sold Per Day					
383	296	354	288	195	372
421	367	411	355	296	321
403	357	432	229	180	266

Example 4

DRIVING TESTS Several driving test results are shown. Describe the center and spread of the data using either the mean and standard deviation or the five-number summary. Justify your choice by constructing a box-and-whisker plot for the data.

Driving Test Scores					
80	95	100	95	95	100
100	90	75	60	90	80

Use a graphing calculator to create a box-and-whisker plot.

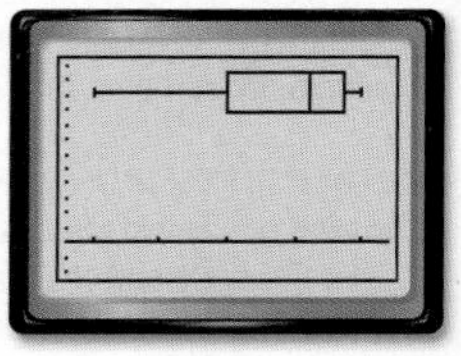

[56, 104] scl: 10 by [−2, 12] scl: 1

The left whisker is longer than the right and the median is closer to the right whisker. Therefore, the distribution is negatively skewed.

Use the five-number summary. The range is 40. The median score is 92.5, and half of the drivers scored between 80 and 97.5.

15. 22.5, 21.5, no mode, 24, 7.4

16. 84.2, 85.5, no mode, 21, 6.8

12-4 Comparing Sets of Data

Find the mean, median, mode, range, and standard deviation of each data set that is obtained after adding the given constant to each value.

15. 27, 21, 34, 42, 20, 19, 18, 26, 25, 33; +(−4)

16. 72, 56, 71, 63, 68, 59, 77, 74, 76, 66; +16

17. SCHOOL Principal Andrews tracked the number of disciplinary actions given by Ms. Miller and Ms. Anderson to their students each week. **See margin.**

Ms. Miller	Ms. Anderson
9, 16, 12, 11, 12, 9, 10, 14, 13, 10, 9, 10, 11, 9, 12, 10, 11, 12	7, 1, 0, 4, 2, 1, 6, 2, 2, 1, 4, 3, 0, 7, 0, 2, 5, 0

a. Use a graphing calculator to construct a histogram for each set of data. Then describe the shape of each distribution.

b. Compare the data sets using either the means and standard deviations or the five-number summaries. Justify your choice.

Example 5

Find the mean, median, mode, range, and standard deviation of the data set obtained after adding 6 to each value.

12, 15, 11, 12, 14, 16, 15, 12, 10, 13

Find the mean, median, mode, range, and standard deviation of the original data set.

Mean 13 Mode 12 Standard Deviation 1.8

Median 12.5 Range 6

Add 6 to the mean, median, and mode. The range and standard deviation are unchanged.

Mean 19 Mode 18 Standard Deviation 1.8

Median 18.5 Range 6

17b. Sample answer: Use the five-number summaries. The range for Ms. Miller is 7. The median is 11. Half of the data are between 10 and 12. The range for Ms. Anderson is 7. The median is 2. Half of the data are between 1 and 4. All of the data in Ms. Anderson's distribution are less than all of the data in Ms. Miller's distribution. Therefore, Ms. Miller will more than likely hand out more disciplinary actions than Ms. Anderson.

12-5 Simulations

18. GAMES While watching a game at a carnival where participants guess which of three shells is covering a ball, Jeremy tallies the following results.

Ball Location	left	middle	right
Frequency	16	18	33

a. Find the experimental probability of the ball being under the right shell. $\frac{33}{67}$ **or about 50%**

b. Find the experimental probability of the ball not being under the middle shell. $\frac{49}{67}$ **or about 73%**

19. SCHOOL BUS Christy has determined that the school bus is late 60% of the time. **a–b. See margin.**

a. Design a simulation that can be used to estimate the probability that the school bus is late today.

b. Conduct the simulation, and report the results.

Example 6

GROUPS Before the random drawing of groups, Dawn has determined that she is 20% likely to get placed in the same group as Sherry. Design a simulation that can be used to estimate the probability of Dawn and Sherry being in the same group.

Step 1 There are two possible outcomes.

Possible Outcomes	Theoretical Probability
Grouped together	20%
Not grouped together	80%

Step 2 We can use the random number generator on a graphing calculator. Assign the integers 1–5 to accurately represent the probability data.

Outcome	Represented by
Grouped together	1
Not grouped together	2–5

Step 3 A trial will represent one drawing of groups. The simulation can consist of any number of trials. We will use 20.

12-6 Permutations and Combinations

Identify each situation as a *permutation* or a *combination*.

20. selecting 3 different toppings for pizza from a list of 15 **combination**

21. an arrangement of textbooks on a bookshelf **permutation**

22. a list of teams participating in a tournament **combination**

23. a ranking of students by scores **permutation**

24. CLASS PHOTO The Spanish teacher at South High School wants to arrange 7 students who traveled to Mexico for a yearbook photo. In how many ways can the students be arranged? **5040**

25. GOLF BALLS A golf bag contains 5 white golf balls, 6 yellow golf balls, and 4 orange golf balls. Two balls are pulled from the bag at random. What is the probability that both balls are orange golf balls? $\frac{2}{35}$

Example 7

BOOK COVERS An artist is trying to choose five covers for children's books. There are 10 different covers to choose from. How many ways can the artist choose the covers?

$C(n, r) = \frac{n!}{(n-r)!r!}$ Combination Formula

$C(10, 5) = \frac{10!}{(10-5)!5!}$ $n = 10$ and $r = 5$

$= \frac{10!}{5!5!}$ Simplify.

$= \frac{10 \cdot 9 \cdot 8 \cdot 7 \cdot 6 \cdot \cancel{5} \cdot \cancel{4} \cdot \cancel{3} \cdot \cancel{2} \cdot \cancel{1}}{5 \cdot 4 \cdot 3 \cdot 2 \cdot 1 \cdot \cancel{5} \cdot \cancel{4} \cdot \cancel{3} \cdot \cancel{2} \cdot \cancel{1}}$

$= \frac{30{,}240}{120}$ or 252 Simplify.

There are 252 ways for the aritist to choose 5 covers.

Additional Answers

19a. Sample answer: The theoretical probability that the bus is late is 60%, and the theoretical probability that the bus is not late is 40%. Use a random number generator to generate integers 1 through 5. The integers 1–3 will represent the bus being late, and the integers 4–5 will represent the bus not being late. The simulation will consist of 50 trials.

19b. Sample answer: P(late) = 58%

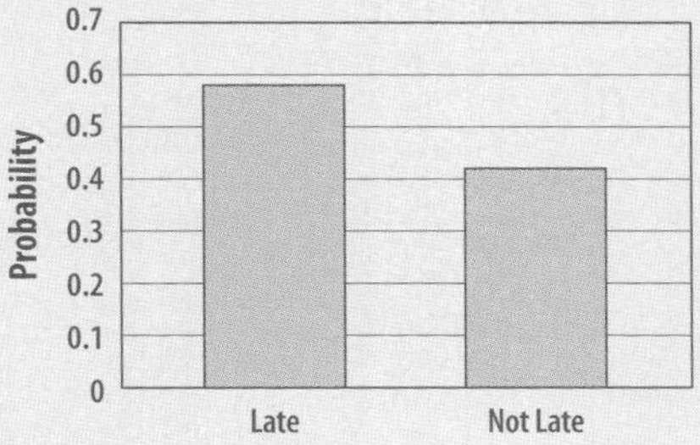

Additional Answers (Practice Test)

6. Biased; since the survey is done from subscribers to a particular newspaper, the respondents are more likely to choose the *Dispatch*.
7. Unbiased; the respondents are not more likely to choose one store over another.
8. 2.57; Sample answer: This value is significantly influenced by the outlier 12. Without the outlier, the data set would have a mean of about 2.67 and a mean absolute deviation of about 13.3.

CHAPTER 12 Study Guide and Review *Continued*

12-7 Probability of Compound Events

26. **MUSIC** Tracie is playing a mix playlist with 6 classic rock, 8 pop, and 4 dance songs. $\frac{2}{81}$
    a. If she selects random play and the songs can repeat, what is the probability that she hears 2 classic rock songs and then a dance song?
    b. If the songs cannot repeat, what is the probability that she hears 3 dance songs in a row? $\frac{1}{204}$

A box contains 8 red chips, 6 blue chips, and 12 white chips. Chips are randomly drawn from the box and are not replaced. Find each probability.

27. *P*(red, white, blue)
28. *P*(red, red, red) $\frac{7}{325}$
29. *P*(red, white, white)
30. *P*(blue, blue) $\frac{3}{65}$

One card is randomly drawn from a standard deck of 52 cards. Find each probability.

31. *P*(heart or red) $\frac{1}{2}$
32. *P*(10 or spade) $\frac{4}{13}$

27. $\frac{12}{325}$

29. $\frac{22}{325}$

Example 8

Determine if rolling a die three times is an *independent* or *dependent* event. Then find the probability of rolling a 5 all three times.

These events are independent because the outcome of one does not affect the outcome of the others.

The probability of rolling a 5 is $\frac{1}{6}$.

$P(5, 5, 5) = P(5) \cdot P(5) \cdot P(5)$

$= \frac{1}{6} \cdot \frac{1}{6} \cdot \frac{1}{6}$ or $\frac{1}{216}$

Example 9

A bag of colored paper clips contains 30 red clips, 22 blue clips, and 22 green clips. Three clips are drawn randomly from the bag and are not replaced. Find *P*(blue, red, green).

First clip: $P(\text{blue}) = \frac{22}{74}$ Second clip: $P(\text{red}) = \frac{30}{73}$

Third clip: $P(\text{green}) = \frac{22}{72}$

$P(\text{blue, red, green}) = \frac{22}{74} \cdot \frac{30}{73} \cdot \frac{22}{72}$ or $\frac{605}{16{,}206}$

12-8 Probability Distributions

A local cable provider asked its subscribers how many television sets they had in their homes. The results of their survey are shown in the probability distribution.

X = Number of Televisions	Probability
1	0.18
2	0.36
3	0.34
4	0.08
5+	0.04

33. Show that the probability distribution is valid.
34. If a household is selected at random, what is the probability that it has fewer than 4 televisions? 0.88

33. For each *X*, the probability is greater than or equal to 0 and less than or equal to 1, 0.18 + 0.36 + 0.34 + 0.08 + 0.04 = 1, so the sum of the probabilities is 1.

Example 10

The table shows the probability distribution for the number of extracurricular activities in which students at Midpark High School participate.

X = Number of Activities	Probability
0	0.04
1	0.12
2	0.37
3	0.30
4+	0.17

a. **Show that the distribution is valid.**

For each *X*, the probability is greater than or equal to 0 and less than or equal to 1.

0.04 + 0.12 + 0.37 + 0.30 + 0.17 = 1

b. **What is the probability that a randomly chosen student participates in 1 to 3 activities?**

$P(1 \leq X \leq 3) = P(X = 1) + P(X = 2) + P(X = 3)$

$= 0.12 + 0.37 + 0.30 = 0.79$ or 79%

CHAPTER 12 Practice Test

1. **CHOCOLATE** Rico is selling candy. If Marisa randomly selects two candy bars to purchase, what is the probability that she buys a milk chocolate bar followed by a caramel bar? **8%**

2. A die is rolled 200 times. What is the experimental probability of rolling less than 3? **28%**

Outcome	Frequency
1	30
2	26
3	44
4	38
5	22
6	40

3. **MULTIPLE CHOICE** Use a graphing calculator to construct a histogram for the data, and use it to describe the shape of the distribution. **A**

16, 18, 14, 31, 19, 18, 10, 29,
12, 12, 28, 19, 17, 26, 15, 20

A positively skewed
B negatively skewed
C symmetric
D none of the above

Find the mean, median, mode, range, and standard deviation of each data set that is obtained after multiplying each value by the given constant.

4. 9, 17, 31, 21, 17, 25, 13, 9, 12, 9; × 3

5. 16, 14, 23, 41, 38, 29, 18, 13, 16; × 0.25

4. 48.9, 45, 51, 66, 21.3 **5. 5.78, 4.5, 4, 7, 2.48**

Identify each sample as *biased* or *unbiased*. Explain your reasoning. **6–7. See margin.**

6. **NEWSPAPERS** A survey is sent to all people who subscribe to the *Dispatch* to determine what newspaper people prefer to read.

7. **SHOPPING** Each person leaving the Maxtowne Mall is asked to name their favorite clothing store in the mall.

8. **SALES** Nate is keeping track of how much people spent at the school bookstore in one day. Find and interpret the mean absolute deviation for the data: 1, 1, 2, 3, 4, 5, 12. **See margin.**

9. **PIZZA** How many ways can 3 different toppings be chosen from a list of 10 toppings? **120**

10. **EDUCATION** Kristin surveys 200 people in her school to determine how many nights per week students do homework. The results are shown in the table.

Number of Nights	Number of Students
0	10
1	30
2	50
3	90
4	10
5 or more	10

a. Find the probability that a randomly chosen student will have studied more than 4 nights. **5%**

b. Find the probability that a randomly chosen student will have studied no more than 3 nights. **90%**

11. **MULTIPLE CHOICE** The second graders are divided into boys and girls. Then 2 girls and 2 boys are chosen at random to represent the class at the Pride Assembly. Which of the following best describes the sample? **G**

F simple
G stratified
H systematic
J self-selected

Identify each situation as a *permutation* or a *combination*.

12. a student's daily class schedule **permutation**

13. a list of teachers' names at school **combination**

14. gold, silver, and bronze medalists **permutation**

15. **RAFFLE** Carmen is considering paying $1 for a raffle ticket. What is the expected value of this ticket? **−$0.70**

Prize Value	$10	$50	$500
Probability	1 in 100	1 in 500	1 in 5000

Summative Assessment

Use these alternate leveled chapter tests to differentiate assessment for your students.

Leveled Chapter 12 Tests

Form	Type	Level	Page(s)
1	MC	AL	61–62
2A	MC	OL	63–64
2B	MC	OL	65–66
2C	FR	OL	67–68
2D	FR	OL	69–70
3	FR	BL	71–72
Vocabulary Test			60
Extended-Response Test			73

MC = multiple-choice questions
FR = free-response questions

McGraw-Hill eAssessment Customize and create multiple versions of your chapter tests and their answer keys. All of the questions from the leveled chapter test in the *Chapter 12 Resource Masters* are also available on McGraw-Hill eAssessment.

InterventionPlanner

Tier 1 On Level OL

If students miss about 25% of the exercises or less,

Then choose a resource:

SE Lessons 12-1, 12-2, 12-3, 12-4, 12-5, 12-6, 12-7, 12-8

Skills Practice, pp. 7, 13, 19, 25, 31, 37, 43, and 50

TE Chapter Project

connectED.mcgraw-hill.com Self-Check Quiz

Tier 2 Strategic Intervention AL approaching grade level

If students miss about 50% of the exercises,

Then choose a resource:

Study Guide and Intervention, Chapter 12, pp. 5, 11, 17, 23, 29, 35, 41, and 48

connectED.mcgraw-hill.com Extra Examples, Personal Tutor, Homework Help

Tier 3 Intensive Intervention 2 or more grades below level

If students miss about 75% of the exercises,

Then use *Math Triumphs, Alg. 1*, ch. 6

connectED.mcgraw-hill.com Extra Examples, Personal Tutor, Homework Help, Review Vocabulary

1 Focus

Objective Use the strategy of organizing data to solve standardized test problems.

2 Teach

Scaffolding Questions

Ask:

- What are some ways in which you can organize data? Sample answers: lists, tables, graphs, Venn diagrams, tree diagrams
- Is it possible to organize data in more than one way? Explain. Answers will vary.
- What factors do you consider when you are thinking of ways in which you can organize data? Sample answers: the type of graph that would best represent the data; the type of method I am most familiar with or most comfortable using; the type of organizing that works best with the data

CHAPTER 12 Preparing for Standardized Tests

Organize Data

Sometimes you may be given a set of data that you need to analyze in order to solve problems on a standardized test. Use this lesson to practice organizing data to help you solve problems.

Strategies for Organizing Data

Step 1

When you are given a problem statement containing data, consider:

- **making a list** of the data.
- **using a table** to organize the data.
- **using a data display** (such as a bar graph, Venn diagram, circle graph, line graph, or box-and-whisker plot) to organize the data.

Step 2

Organize the data.

- Create your table, list, or data display.
- If possible, fill in any missing values that can be found by intermediate computations.

Step 3

Analyze the data to solve the problem.

- Reread the problem statement to determine what you are being asked to solve.
- Use the properties of algebra to work with the organized data and solve the problem.
- If time permits, go back and check your answer.

Standardized Test Example

Read the problem. Identify what you need to know. Then use the information in the problem to solve. Show your work.

Of the 24 students in a music class, 10 play the flute, 14 play the piano, and 13 play the guitar. Two students play the flute only, 5 the piano only, and 7 the guitar only. One student plays the flute and the guitar but not the piano. Two students play the piano and guitar but not the flute. Three students play all the instruments. If a student is selected at random, what is the probability that he or she plays the piano and flute, but not the guitar?

Scoring Rubric	
Criteria	Score
Full Credit: The answer is correct and a full explanation is provided that shows each step.	2
Partial Credit: • The answer is correct, but the explanation is incomplete. • The answer is incorrect, but the explanation is correct.	1
No Credit: Either an answer is not provided or the answer does not make sense.	0

Read the problem carefully. The data is difficult to analyze as it is presented. Use a Venn diagram to organize the data and solve the problem.

Example of a 2-point response:

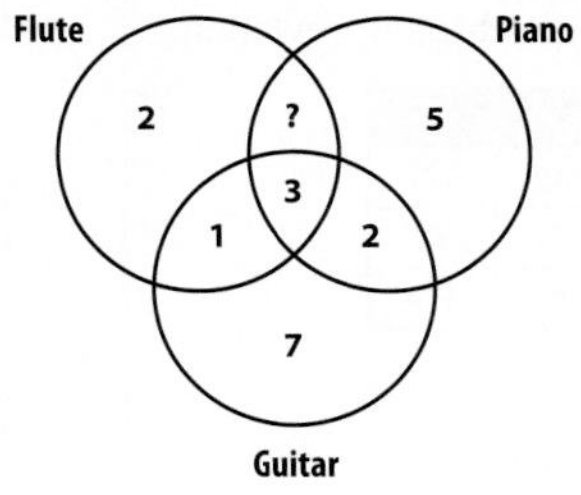

Use a Venn diagram to organize the data. Fill in all of the information given in the problem statement. There are 14 students who play the piano, so $14 - 5 - 2 - 3$ or 4 students play the piano and the flute, but not the guitar. Find the probability.

$P(\text{piano and flute}) = \frac{4}{24}$ or $\frac{1}{6}$

So, the probability that a randomly selected student plays the piano and flute but not the guitar is $\frac{1}{6}$.

Exercises

Read the problem. Identify what you need to know. Then use the information in the problem to solve. Show your work.

1. There are 40 students, 9 camp counselors, and 5 teachers at Camp Kern. Each person is assigned to one activity this afternoon. There are 9 students going hiking and 17 students going horseback riding. Of the camp counselors, 2 will supervise the hike and 3 will help with the canoe trip. There are 2 teachers helping with the canoe trip and 2 going horseback riding. Suppose a person is selected at random during the afternoon activities. What is the probability that the one selected is a student on the canoe trip or a camp counselor on a horse? Express your answer as a fraction. $\frac{1}{3}$

2. The table shows the number of coins in a piggy bank.

Coin	Number
Penny	16
Nickel	18
Dime	20
Quarter	10

a. Find the probability that a randomly selected coin will be a dime. $\frac{5}{16}$

b. Find the probability that a randomly selected coin will be either a nickel or a quarter. $\frac{7}{16}$

3. It takes Craig 40 minutes to mow his family's lawn. His brother Jacob can do the same job in 50 minutes. How long would it take them to mow the lawn together? Round your answer to the nearest tenth of a minute. **22.2**

Additional Example

SHORT RESPONSE Of the 32 students in a class, 22 own dogs, 17 own cats, and 8 own birds. Nine students own dogs only, 7 own cats only, and 2 own birds only. One student owns a dog, a cat, and a bird. Eight students own a cat and a dog, but not a bird. One student owns a cat and a bird, but not a dog. If a student is selected at random, what is the probability that the student owns a dog and a bird, but not a cat?

SAMPLE 2-POINT RESPONSE

Use a Venn diagram to organize the data. Then fill in the information given in the problem.

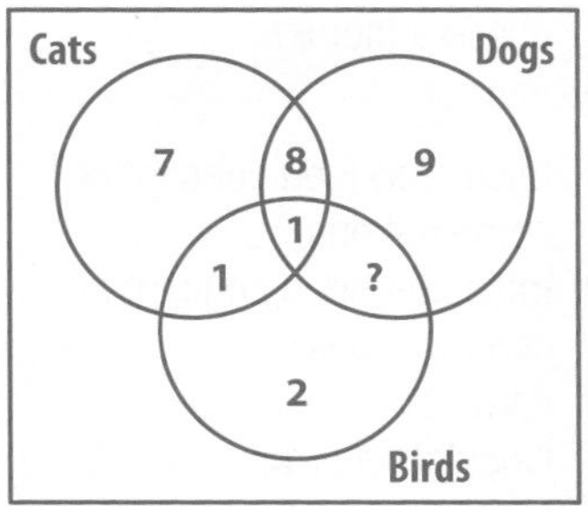

There are 22 students who own dogs, so $22 - 9 - 8 - 1 = 4$ students who own a dog and a bird, but not a cat.

Find the probability: $P(\text{only dog and bird}) = \frac{4}{32}$ or $\frac{1}{8}$.

So, the probability of randomly selecting a student who owns a dog and a bird, but not a cat is 0.125 or 12.5%.

3 Assess

Use Exercises 1–3 to assess students' understanding.

Diagnose Student Errors

Survey student responses for each item. Class trends may indicate common errors and misconceptions.

1. A correct
B guess
C factored incorrectly
D factored numerator instead of denominator

2. F correct
G guess or used wrong numbers to calculate
H guess or used wrong numbers to calculate
J did not find absolute values of the differences

3. A chose a factor
B chose a factor
C chose a factor
D correct

4. F misunderstood concept of combinations
G misunderstood concept of combinations
H correct
J calculation error

5. A chose feature that describes graph
B chose feature that describes graph
C correct
D chose feature that describes graph

6. F interpreted *y*-intercept incorrectly instead of slope
G interpreted *y*-intercept instead of slope
H correct
J interpreted slope incorrectly

7. A guess or used wrong numbers to calculate
B guess or used wrong numbers to calculate
C correct
D guess or used wrong numbers to calculate

CHAPTER 12

Standardized Test Practice

Cumulative, Chapters 1 through 12

Multiple Choice

Read each question. Then fill in the correct answer on the answer document provided by your teacher or on a sheet of paper.

1. What are the excluded values of the variable in the expression $\frac{x^2 - x - 12}{x^2 - x - 2}$? **A**

A $-1, 2$
B $-2, 2$
C $-2, 1$
D $-3, 4$

2. The table shows the number of Calories in twelve different snacks. Find the mean absolute deviation. **F**

Number of Calories in Snacks			
122	91	149	121
64	138	342	72
179	105	99	114

F 46
G 43
H 1.5
J 0.8

3. Which of the following is *not* a factor of $x^4 - 6x^2 - 27$? **D**

A $x^2 + 3$
B $x - 3$
C $x + 3$
D $x^2 - 3$

4. Eduardo has 20 CDs. He wants to choose 3 of them at random to take on a road trip. How many different ways can he do this if the order is *not* important? **H**

F 60
G 84
H 1140
J 6840

5. Which of the following does *not* accurately describe the graph $y = -2x^2 + 4$? **C**

A The parabola is symmetric about the y-axis.
B The parabola opens downward.
C The parabola has the origin as its vertex.
D The parabola crosses the x-axis in two different places.

6. The highest point in North Carolina is Mt. Mitchell at an elevation of 2,037 meters above sea level. Suppose the position of a hiker is given by the function $p(t) = -2.5t + 2{,}037$, where t is the number of minutes. Which of the following is the best interpretation of the slope of the function? **H**

F The hiker's initial position was 2,037 feet below sea level.
G The hiker's initial position was 2,037 feet above sea level.
H The hiker is descending at a rate of 2.5 meters per minute.
J The hiker is ascending at a rate of 2.5 meters per minute

7. Jorge has made 39 out of 52 free throw attempts this season. What is the experimental probability that he makes a free throw? **C**

A 54%
B 68%
C 75%
D 79%

8. The graph of which equation passes through the points $(-1, -3)$ and $(-2, 3)$? **F**

F $y = -6x - 9$
G $y = -\frac{1}{4}x + 3$
H $y = 4x - 5$
J $y = \frac{2}{3}x + 1$

9. At a museum, each child admission costs \$5.75 and each adult costs \$8.25. How much does it cost a family that consists of 2 adults and 4 children? **B**

A \$34.50
B \$39.50
C \$44.50
D \$49.50

Test-Taking Tip

Question 4 Since order is not important, you are looking for the number of combinations of CDs that can be chosen.

8. F correct
G misunderstood how to calculate slope and *y*-intercept
H misunderstood how to calculate slope and *y*-intercept
J misunderstood how to calculate slope and *y*-intercept

9. A guess or calculation error
B correct
C switched costs for children and adults
D guess or calculation error

Short Response/Gridded Response

Record your answers on the answer sheet provided by your teacher or on a sheet of paper.

10. GRIDDED RESPONSE Suppose Colleen spins the spinner below 80 times and records the results in a frequency table. How many times should she expect to spin a vowel? 32

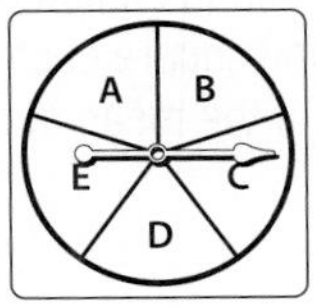

11. What is the value of sin *B*? Express your answer as a fraction. $\frac{5}{13}$

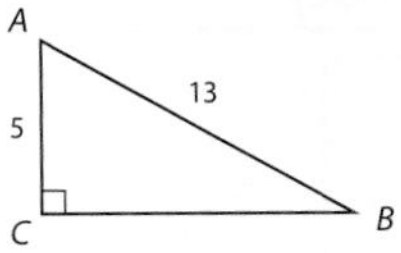

12. Graph $f(x) \geq |x - 2|$ on a coordinate grid. See margin.

13. GRIDDED RESPONSE Find the standard deviation of the set of data below to the nearest tenth. 3.4

14	11	9	6
10	16	15	13
9	12	19	10

14. Larissa has 5 peanut butter cookies, 7 chocolate chip cookies, 4 sugar cookies, and 9 oatmeal raisin cookies in a jar. If she picks two cookies at random without replacing them, what is the probability that she will choose a peanut butter cookie then a sugar cookie? Express your answer as a fraction. $\frac{1}{30}$

15. Write an expression that describes the area in square units of a triangle with a height of $4c^3d^2$ and a base of $3cd^4$. $6c^4d^6$

16. Casey made 84 field goals during the basketball season for a total of 183 points. Each field goal was worth either 2 or 3 points. How many 2-point and 3-point field goals did Casey make during the season? 15 3-point field goals and 69 2-point field goals

17. GRIDDED RESPONSE The booster club pays $180 to rent a concession stand at a football game. They purchase cans of soda for $0.25 and sell them at the game for $1.15. How many cans of soda must they sell to break even? 200

Extended Response

Record your answers on a sheet of paper. Show your work.

18. To predict whether or not an issue on a ballot will pass or fail, a committee randomly calls 250 houses with area codes that are inside the voting district and asks the opinions of registered voters. Based on these efforts, the committee determines that 71% (±2.5%) of the voting population supports the issue. The committee concludes that the issue will pass. a–e. See margin.

a. Identify the sample.

b. Describe the population.

c. What method of data collection did the committee use: survey, experiment, or observational survey? Explain.

d. Is the sample *biased* or *unbiased*. Explain.

e. If unbiased, classify the sample as *simple, systematic, self-selected, convenience,* or *stratified.* Explain.

Need ExtraHelp?

If you missed Question...	1	2	3	4	5	6	7	8	9	10	11	12	13	14	15	16	17	18
Go to Lesson...	11-3	12-2	8-9	12-6	9-3	3-3	12-5	4-2	1-3	12-5	10-6	9-7	12-2	12-7	7-1	6-5	2-4	12-1

Formative Assessment

You can use these pages to benchmark student progress.

Standardized Test Practice, pp. 74–76

Answer Sheet Practice

Have students simulate taking a standardized test by recording their answers on a practice recording sheet.

Student Recording Sheet

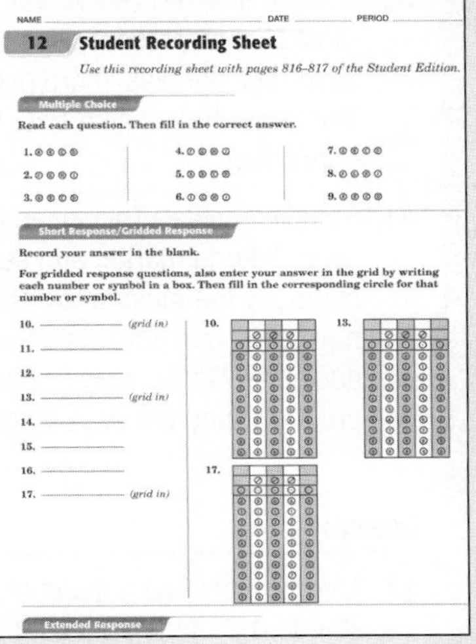
NAME DATE PERIOD

12 Student Recording Sheet

Use this recording sheet with pages 816–817 of the Student Edition.

Multiple Choice

Read each question. Then fill in the correct answer.

1. 2. 3. 4. 5. 6. 7. 8. 9.

Short Response/Gridded Response

Record your answer in the blank.

For gridded response questions, also enter your answer in the grid by writing each number or symbol in a box. Then fill in the corresponding circle for that number or symbol.

10. (grid in)
11.
12.
13. (grid in)
14.
15.
16.
17. (grid in)

Extended Response

McGraw-Hill eAssessment Create practice worksheets or tests that align to your state's standards, as well as TIMSS and NAEP tests.

Additional Answers

12.

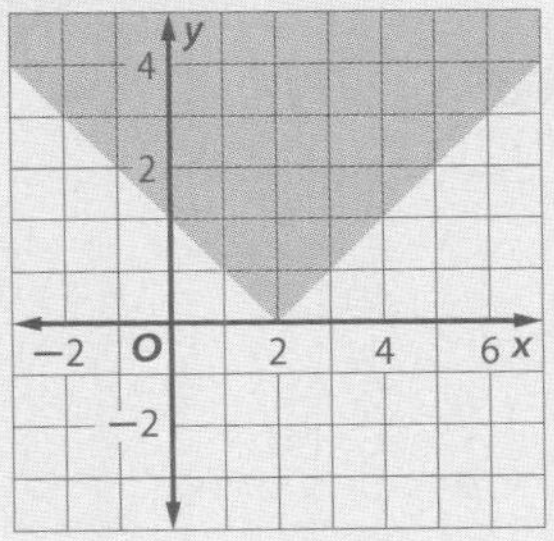

18a. Sample answer: registered voters in the voting district

18b. Sample answer: all registered voters in the voting district

18c. survey; Sample answer: no observations were made and no experiments were ran

18d. Sample answer: unbiased because each voter is equally likely to be called.

18e. simple; Sample answer: each voter in the voting district is equally likely to be called.

Lesson 12-1

33. Experiment; sample answer: The new color will be tested on a sample group. These members will be affected by the study, so it is an experiment.

34. Observational study; sample answer: Members of a sample are observed and are not being affected by the study, so it is an observational study.

35. Survey; sample answer: Data are collected from responses given by members of a population, so it is a survey.

38. Sample answer: This method of selecting a sample is valid. Each student has an equally likely chance of being selected for the sample. A weakness may be that this would not reflect that one grade may feel more strongly about the dress code than another.

39. Sample answer: The survey of 150 people at the concert would most likely represent the population. While each survey may have regional bias, more people were surveyed at the concert. The larger the sample size, the more likely it will reflect the population.

41. Sample answer: They need accurate surveys to make decisions about how to market and sell products that will earn the company the most profit. They also make decisions about marketing and advertising and how to reach their target audience. Finally, they make decisions about the types of products they will develop or continue to sell.

Lesson 12-2

12. The Wildcats had a mean of about 11.9 fouls per game with a standard deviation of about 2.2 fouls. The Trojans had a mean of about 10.1 fouls per game with a standard deviation of about 2.1 fouls. The data sets had nearly the same variability while the Wildcats had a mean of almost 2 fouls more than the Trojans. The Wildcats coach can conclude that his team consistently has about 2 more fouls than the Trojans.

13a. Sample answer: Movie A had a mean of about 7.2 with a standard deviation of about 0.81. Movie B had a mean of about 6.8 with a standard deviation of about 2.86. While both movies had a mean rating of close to 7, the ratings for Movie B had more variability. In other words, some people really liked it while others didn't like it at all. The ratings for Movie A were much more consistent.

13b. Movie A: Sample answer: The reviews are consistent and all are between 6 and 8. You would prefer this movie if you want to see a movie that, while it isn't anyone's favorite, you can assume that it will be decent.

Movie B: Sample answer: While some people didn't like the movie at all, others loved it. You would prefer this movie if you hope to be one of the people that love it.

18. Sample answer: Poll voters to determine if a particular presidential candidate is favored to win the election. Use a stratified random sample to call 100 people throughout the country.

19. Sample answer: Any set of data with identical terms. For example: 5, 5, 5, 5, 5, 5, 5.

20. A statistic is a characteristic that is computed on a sample of the population. A parameter is a characteristic of the entire population. Sample answer: To determine the average height of a student at your high school, you can measure the heights of a random sample of students at your school. The mean height of the sample is a statistic; the actual mean height of the students at your school is a parameter.

21. Both are calculated statistical values that show how each data value deviates from the mean of the data set. The mean absolute deviation is calculated by taking the mean of the absolute values of the differences between each number and the mean of the data set. To find the standard deviation, you square each difference and then take the square root of the mean of the squares.

Lesson 12-3 (Guided Practice)

1.

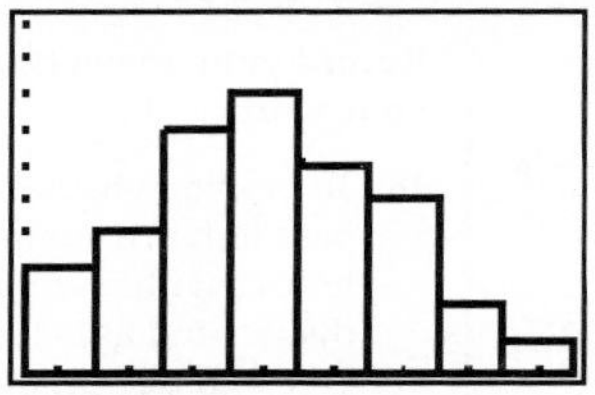

[6, 38] scl: 4 by [0, 10] scl: 1

symmetric

Lesson 12-3

4. Sample answer: The distribution is skewed, so use the five-number summary. The range is 21 − 6 or 15. The median time is 17, and half of the times are between 11 and 18.5 minutes.

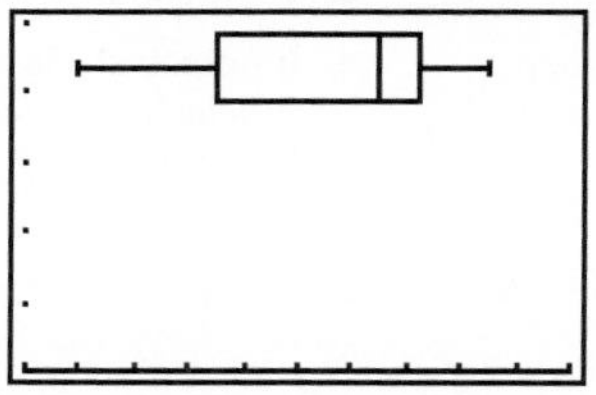

[4, 24] scl: 2 by [0, 5] scl: 1

5.

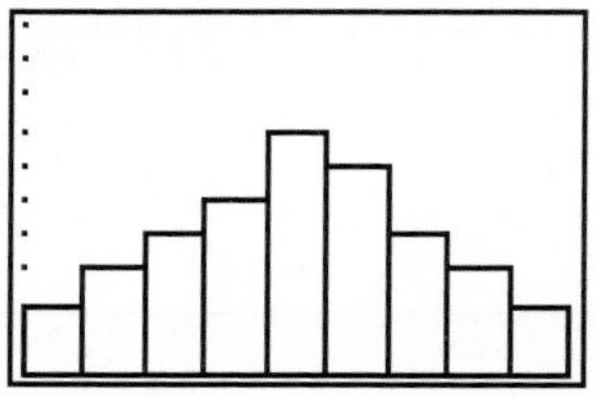

[24, 78] scl: 6 by [0, 10] scl: 1

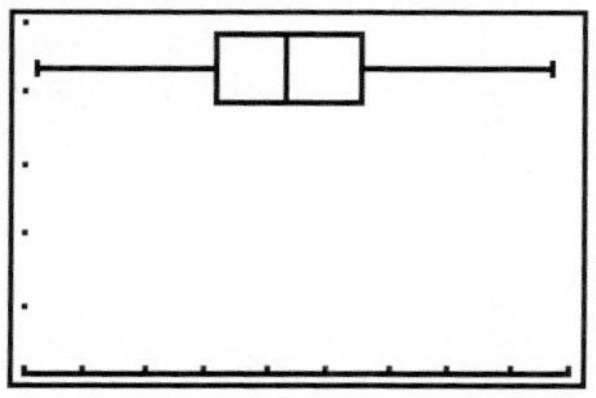

[24, 78] scl: 6 by [0, 5] scl: 1

symmetric

6. 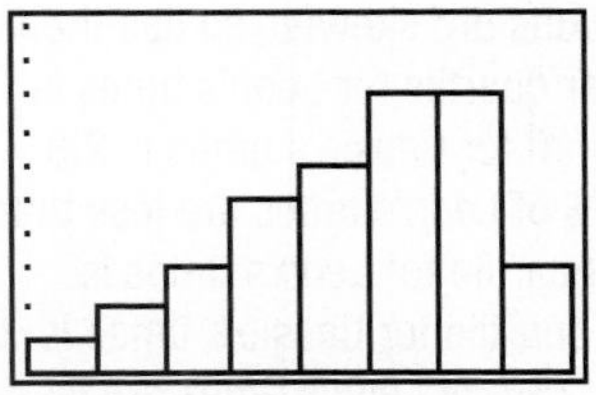

[33, 57] scl: 3 by [0, 10] scl: 1

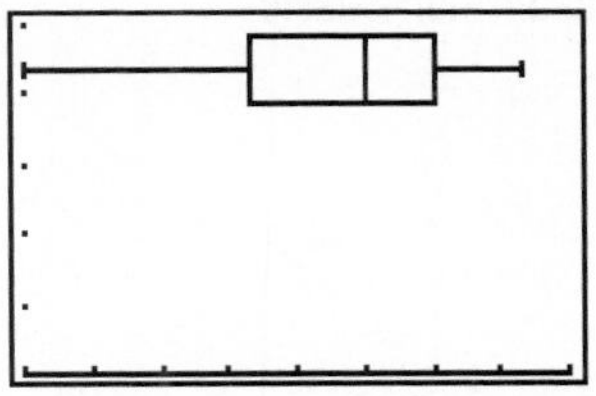

[33, 57] scl: 3 by [0, 5] scl: 1

negatively skewed

7. Sample answer: The distribution is skewed, so use the five-number summary. The range is 53 − 12 or 41. The median is 39.5, and half of the data are between 28 and 48.

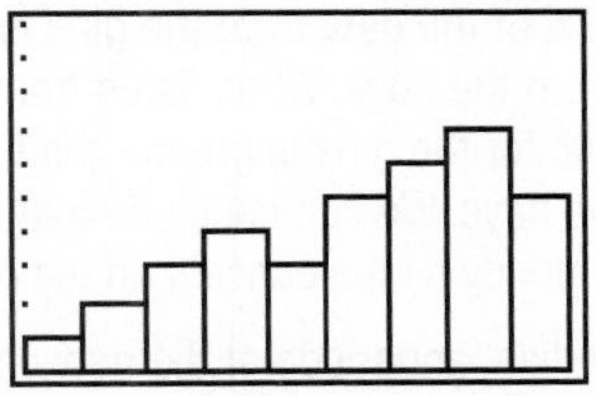

[10, 55] scl: 5 by [0, 10] scl: 1

8. Sample answer: The distribution is symmetric, so use the mean and standard deviation. The mean is 82 with a standard deviation of about 7.4.

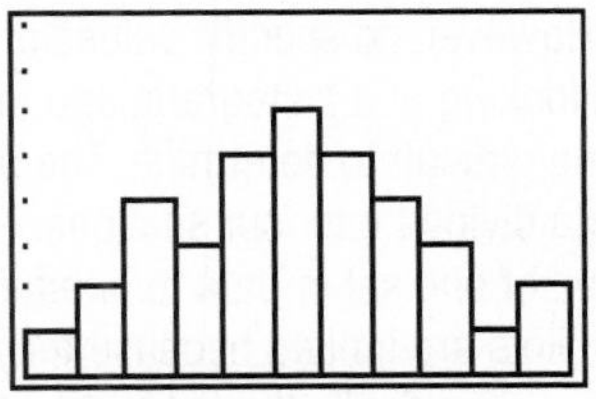

[66, 99] scl: 3 by [0, 8] scl: 1

9. Sample answer: The distribution is symmetric, so use the mean and standard deviation to describe the center and spread. The mean temperature is 52.8° with a standard deviation of about 4.22°.

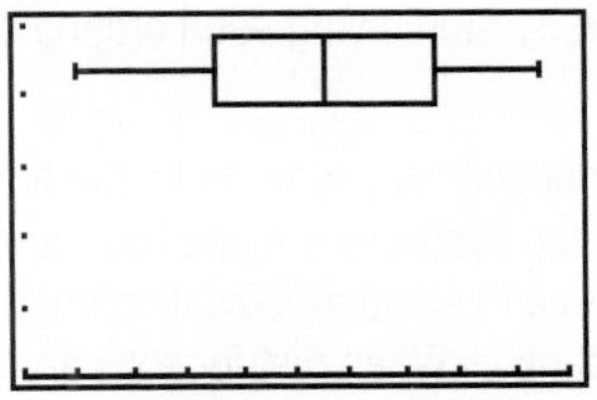

[42, 62] scl: 2 by [0, 5] scl: 1

10a. 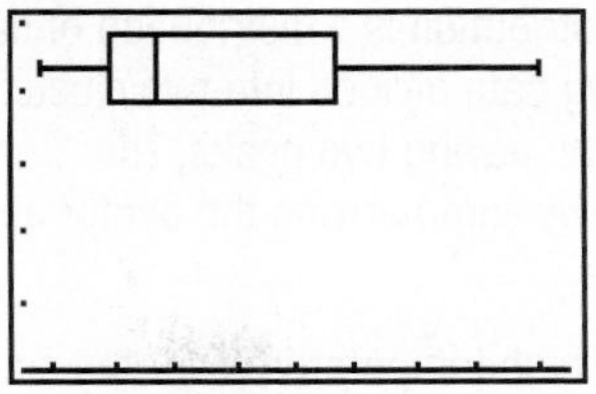

[11.9, 13.7] scl: 0.2 by [0, 5] scl: 1

Sample answer: The distribution is skewed, so use the five-number summary. The range is 13.6 − 11.96 or 1.64. The median time is 12.34, and half of the times are between 12.18 and 12.93 seconds.

10b. 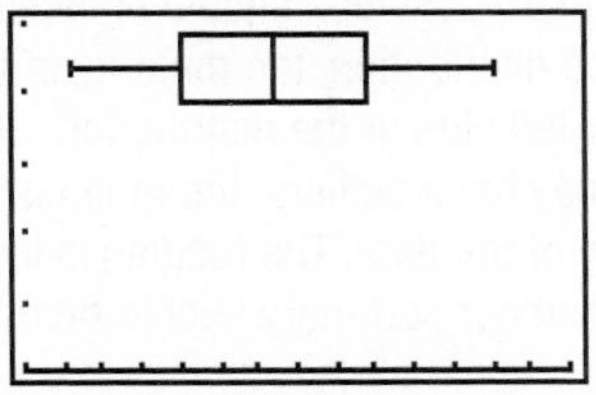

[11.9, 12.6] scl: 0.05 by [0, 5] scl: 1

Sample answer: The distribution is symmetric, so use the mean and standard deviation. The mean is about 12.22 seconds with a standard deviation of about 0.15 second.

10c. Sample answer: Removing the times causes the shape of the distribution to go from being skewed to being symmetric. Therefore, the center and spread should be described using the mean and standard deviation.

11a. 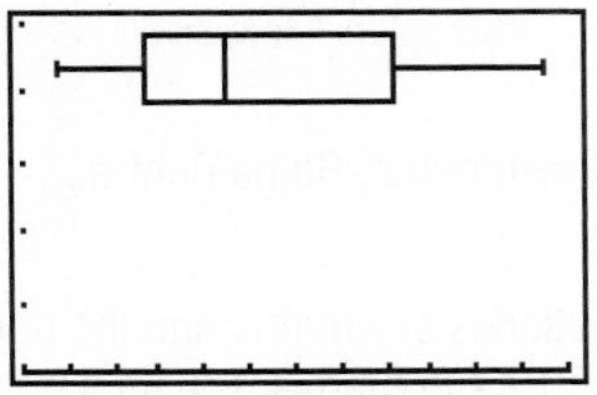

[7, 19] scl: 1 by [0, 5] scl: 1

Sample answer: The distribution is skewed, so use the five-number summary. The range is \$18.50 − \$7.75 or \$10.75. The median price is \$11.50, and half of the prices are between \$9.63 and \$15.13.

11b. 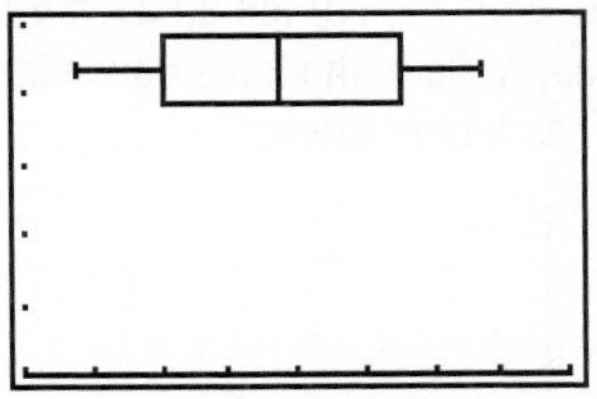

[7, 15] scl: 1 by [0, 5] scl: 1

Sample answer: The distribution is symmetric, so use the mean and standard deviation. The mean is about \$10.67 with a standard deviation of about \$1.84.

15. Sample answer: A bimodal distribution is a distribution of data that is characterized by having data divided into two clusters, thus producing two modes, and having two peaks. The distribution can be described by summarizing the center and spread of each cluster of data.

16. Sample answer: The average high temperature over the course of a year for a city may have a symmetrical distribution. The attendance at a baseball stadium over the course of a season for a team may be skewed.

17. Sample answer: In a symmetrical distribution, the majority of the data are located near the center of the distribution. The mean of the distribution is also located near the center of the distribution. Therefore, the mean and standard deviation should be used to describe the data. In a skewed distribution, the majority of the data lies either on the right or left side of the distribution. Since the distribution has a tail or may have outliers, the mean is pulled away from the majority of the data. The median is less affected. Therefore, the five-number summary should be used to describe the data.

Lesson 12-4

16a.

The Electronics Superstore

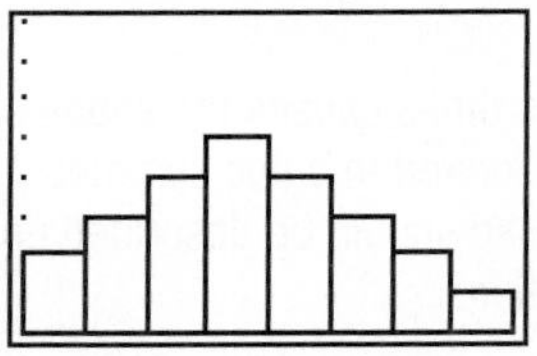

[25, 65] scl: 5 by [0, 8] scl: 1

Game Central

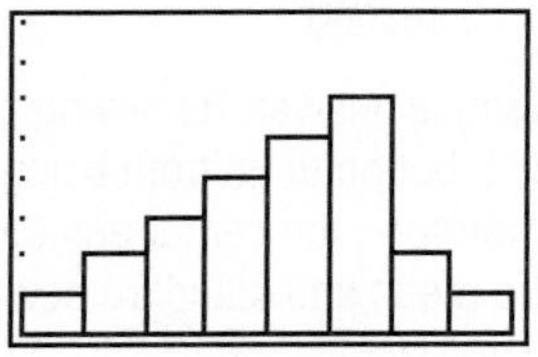

[25, 65] scl: 5 by [0, 8] scl: 1

The Electronics Superstore, symmetric; Game Central, negatively skewed

16b. Sample answer: One distribution is symmetric and the other is skewed, so use the five-number summaries. The minimum and maximum for The Electronic Superstore are \$25 and \$62. The minimum and maximum for Game Stop Central are \$26 and \$61. Therefore, the ranges are approximately equal. The upper quartile for The Electronic Superstore is \$49, while the median for Game Stop Central is \$48. Since these two values are approximately equal, this means that about 50% of the data for Game Stop Central is greater than 75% of the data from The Electronic Superstore. Overall, while both stores have similar ranges, Game Stop Central has higher prices.

17a.

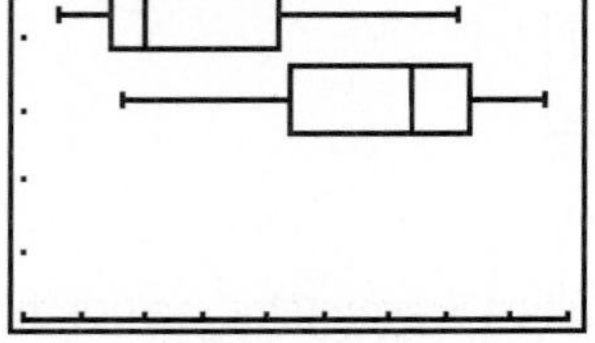

[1.5, 6] scl: 0.5 by [0, 5] scl: 1

Leon, positively skewed; Cassie, negatively skewed

17b. Sample answer: The distributions are skewed, so use the five-number summaries. The lower quartile for Leon's times is 2.2 minutes, while the minimum for Cassie's times is 2.3 minutes. This means that 25% of Leon's times are less than all of Cassie's times. The upper quartile for Leon's times is 3.6 minutes, while the lower quartile for Cassie's times is 3.7 minutes. This means that 75% of Leon's times are less than 75% of Cassie's time. Overall, we can conclude that Leon completed the brainteasers faster than Cassie.

18a.

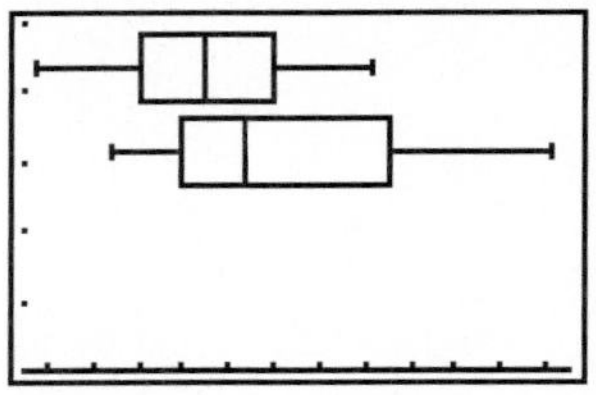

[55, 175] scl: 10 by [0, 5] scl: 1

boys, symmetric; girls, positively skewed

18b. Sample answer: One distribution is symmetric and the other is skewed, so use the five-number summaries. The maximum for the boys is \$131, while the upper quartile for the girls is \$135.50. This means that 25% of the data from the girls is greater than all of the data from the boys. When listed from least to greatest, each statistic for the girls is greater than its corresponding statistic for the boys. We can conclude that in general, the girls spent more money on the dance than the boys.

22. Sample answer: The mean, median, and mode of the new data set can be found by multiplying each original statistic by k. The range and the standard deviation can be found by multiplying each original statistic by $|k|$.

23. Sample answer: Histograms show the frequency of values occurring within set intervals. This makes the shape of the distribution easy to recognize. However, no specific values of the data set can be identified from looking at a histogram, and the overall spread of the data can be difficult to determine. The box-and-whisker plots show the data divided into four sections. This aids when comparing the spread of one set of data to another. However, the box-and-whisker plots are limited because they cannot display the data any more specifically than showing it divided into four sections.

24. Sample answer: The mean, median, and mode of the new data set can be found by adding k to each original statistic, and then multiplying each resulting value by m. Since the range and the standard deviation are not affected when a constant is added to a set of data, they can be found by multiplying each original value by the constant m.

25. Sample answer: When two distributions are symmetric, the first thing to determine is how close the averages are and how spread out each set of data is. The mean and standard deviation are the best values to use for this comparison. When distributions are skewed, we also want to determine the direction and the degree to which it is skewed. The mean and standard deviation cannot provide any information in this regard, but we can get this information by comparing the range, quartiles, and medians found in the five-number summaries. So, if one or both sets of data are skewed, it is best to compare their five-number summaries.

Mid-Chapter Quiz

7. sample: 15 restaurant diners; population: all restaurant diners; sample statistic: amount of money spent each meal by the sample; population parameter: amount of money spent each meal by all restaurant diners

8. sample: 25 children selected; population: all children at the community pool; sample statistic: the percentage of children in the sample visited the pool at least once each week; population parameter: the percentage of children in the community who visits the community pool at least once each week

9. 1.66; Sample answer: With a mean of about 3.08, the standard deviation of about 1.66 suggests that there is some deviation to the data. However, if you remove the outlier, the mean becomes about 2.64 with a standard deviation of about 0.77. Therefore, almost all of the children at the play area are very similar in age.

11. symmetric

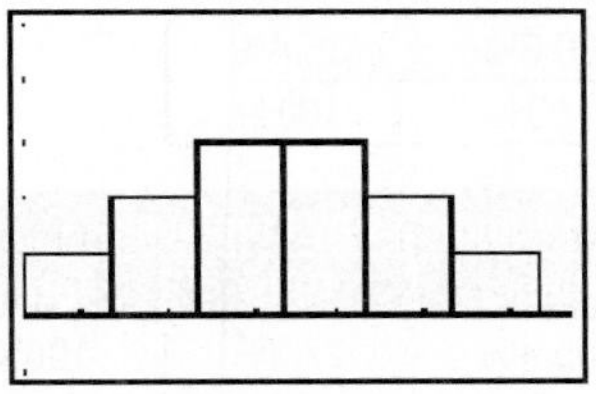

[14, 52] scl: 6 by [−1, 5] scl: 1

12. Sample answer: The distribution is symmetric, so use the mean and standard deviation. The distribution has a mean of 7.88 and a standard deviation of about 2.88.

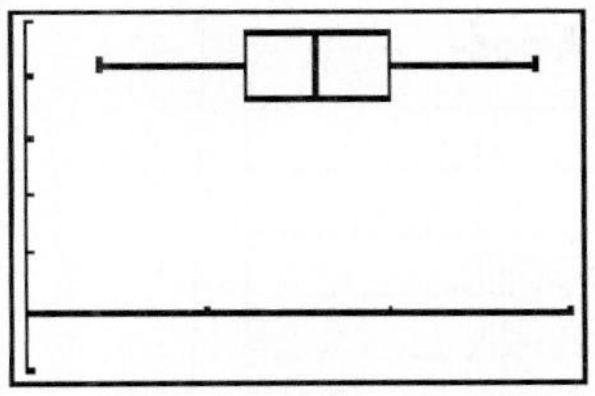

[0, 15] scl: 5 by [−1, 5] scl: 1

Lesson 12-5 (Guided Practice)

2. Sample answer: The theoretical probability that Bonny Solomon chooses Miami is 60%, Cleveland is 30%, and New York is 10%. Use a random number generator to generate integers 1–10. The integers 1–6 will represent Miami, the integers 7–9 will represent Cleveland, and the integer 10 will represent New York. The simulation will consist of 50 trials.

Lesson 12-5

6b. Sample answer: $P(\text{defect}) = 2.5\%$, $P(\text{no defect}) = 97.5\%$

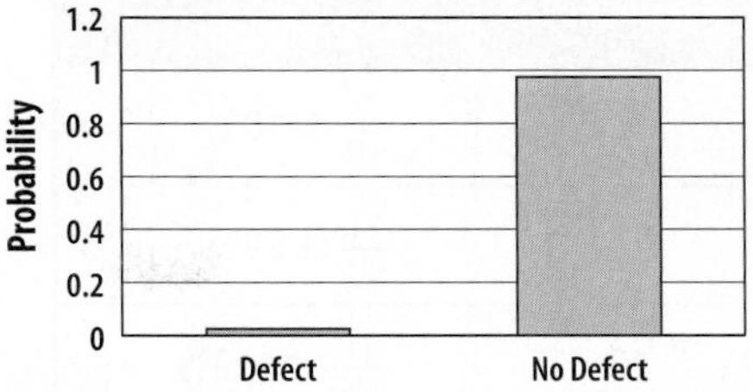

7a. Sample answer: The theoretical probability that a spin results in each prize is 20%. Use a random number generator to generate integers 1 through 5. The integer 1 will represent a hot pretzel, the integer 2 will represent a burger, the integer 3 will represent a large drink, the integer 4 will represent nachos, and the integer 5 will represent a small popcorn. The simulation will consist of 50 trials.

7b. Sample answer: $P(\text{hot pretzel}) = 20\%$, $P(\text{burger}) = 20\%$, $P(\text{large drink}) = 28\%$, $P(\text{nachos}) = 14\%$, $P(\text{small popcorn}) = 18\%$

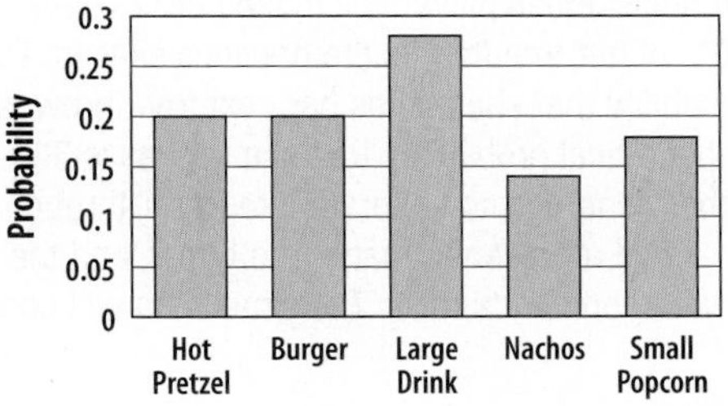

8a. Sample answer: The theoretical probability that a prize results in each outcome is 25%. Use a random number generator to generate integers 1 through 4. The integer 1 will represent a music download, the integer 2 will represent a game download, the integer 3 will represent a bag of popcorn, and the integer 4 will represent a DVD. The simulation will consist of 40 trials.

8b. Sample answer: $P(\text{music download}) = 20\%$, $P(\text{game download}) = 17.5\%$, $P(\text{popcorn}) = 37.5\%$, $P(\text{DVD}) = 25\%$

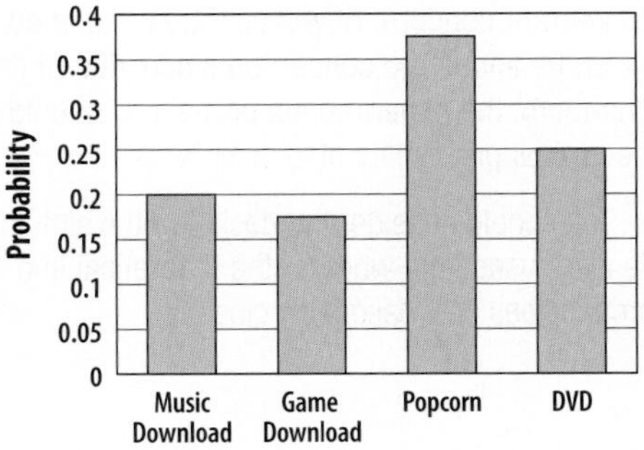

11b. Sample answer: The theoretical probability that a 1 is rolled is $\frac{1}{6}$ or about 17%, and the theoretical probability that a 1 is not rolled is $\frac{5}{6}$ or about 83%. Use a random number generator to generate integers 1 through 6. The integer 1 will represent a 1. The integers 2– 6 will represent the other numbers on the die.

11c. Sample answer:

Rolling a 1		
Trials	**Frequency**	**Experimental Probability**
20	2	$\frac{1}{10}$ or 10%
50	11	$\frac{11}{50}$ or 22%
100	19	$\frac{19}{100}$ or 19%
200	37	$\frac{37}{200}$ or 18.5%

11d. Sample answer: The experimental probability of rolling a 1 is getting closer to the theoretical probability of $\frac{1}{6}$ or 17%.

11e. Sample answer: As the number of trials increases, the experimental probability should approach the theoretical probability of $\frac{1}{6}$ or 17%.

13. Sample answer: A simulation can be designed to estimate the probability that a basketball player will make her next free throw if she made 70% of her free throws the previous season. The theoretical probability that she makes her next free throw is 70%, and the theoretical probability that she misses is 30%. Use a random number generator to generate integers 1 through 10. The integers 1–7 will represent a made free throw, and the integers 8–10 will represent a miss. The simulation will consist of 30 trials.

14. True; Sample answer: The event will always occur when the theoretical probability is 1. Therefore, the experimental probability can never be 0. For example, the theoretical probability of rolling a die and getting a 1, 2, 3, 4, 5, or 6 is 1 since it will always show one of these six numbers. So when a die is rolled, the result will be one of these six numbers, making the experimental probability always greater than 0.

15. Sample answer: Jeremy's concern about the fairness of the coin should be dependent on the number of times he tossed it. If he only completed 4, or even 20 trials, then the sample size is not large enough to warrant concern. However, if he completed 100 or more trials, then he should be concerned since, due to the Law of Large Numbers, the experimental probability should be closer to the theoretical probability of $\frac{1}{2}$ or 50%.

16. Sample answer: You should consider the design of the simulation, how many trials were used, and whether the theoretical and experimental probabilities are reasonably close.

24. Sample answer: The distribution is skewed, so use the five-number summary. The range is 22 − 1 or 21 students. The median is 15 students, and half of the class sizes are between 5 and 18 students.

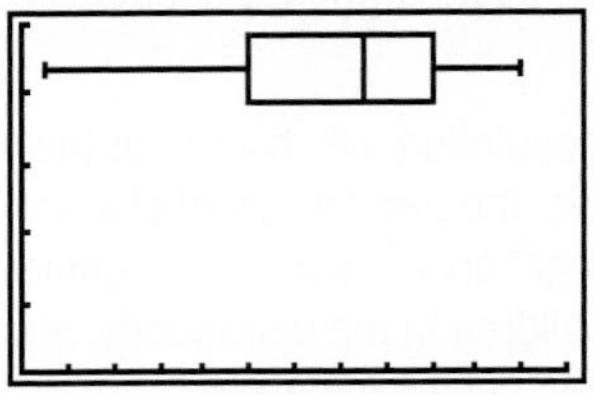

[0, 24] scl: 2 by [0, 5] scl: 1

Extend Lesson 12-7

13c.

Conditional Relative Frequencies by Activities			
Employees	**Potluck**	**Dinner**	**Gifts**
Managers	9.1%	15.2%	13.6%
Staff	48.5%	54.5%	50%
Assistants	42.4%	30.3%	36.4%
Totals	100%	100%	100%

Conditional Relative Frequencies by Employees				
Employees	**Potluck**	**Dinner**	**Gifts**	**Totals**
Managers	27.3%	45.4%	27.3%	100%
Staff	35.6%	40%	24.4%	100%
Assistants	43.8%	31.2%	25%	100%

Lesson 12-8 (Guided Practice)

2C.

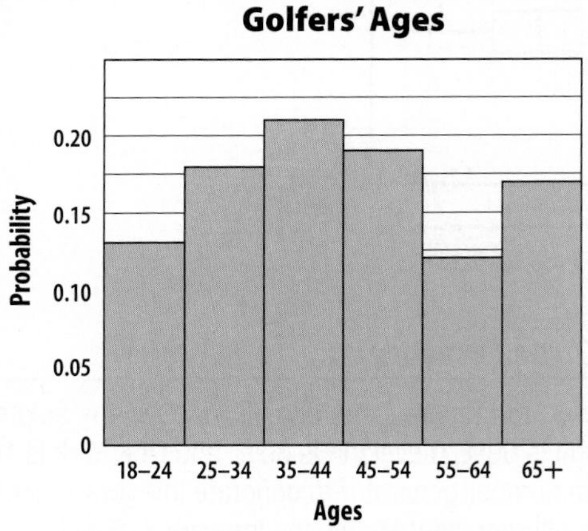

3A.

X	P(X)
$100	0.001
$500	0.0002
$5000	0.00001
$50,000	0.000001
$0	0.998789

12b. Sample answer: Of the stocks that cost $200 per share, Stock B has the greatest expected gain, so it is the best choice. If Amber selects five shares of Stock B, she will spend the entire $1000 and have an expected gain of $10. Amber can also select three shares of Stock E and one share of Stock A and have an expected gain of $10. A third option would be to select 10 shares of Stock A.

13a.

X = Sum	2	3	4	5	6	7	8	9	10	11	12
Frequency	2	3	4	6	7	8	6	5	4	2	1
Probability	$\frac{1}{24}$	$\frac{1}{16}$	$\frac{1}{12}$	$\frac{1}{8}$	$\frac{7}{48}$	$\frac{1}{6}$	$\frac{1}{8}$	$\frac{5}{48}$	$\frac{1}{12}$	$\frac{1}{24}$	$\frac{1}{48}$

13b.

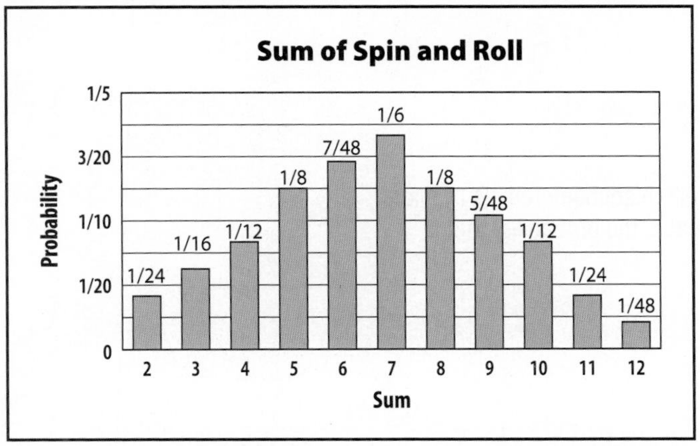

13d. Sample answer: Use values 1–48 in a random number generator. Set up the following representations. This way, the exact probabilities of each sum are accurately represented.

X = Sum	2	3	4	5	6	7	8	9	10	11	12
Range	1–2	3–5	6–9	10–15	16–22	23–30	31–36	37–41	42–45	46–47	48
Tally	2	3	4	2	7	12	8	7	3	2	0

13e.

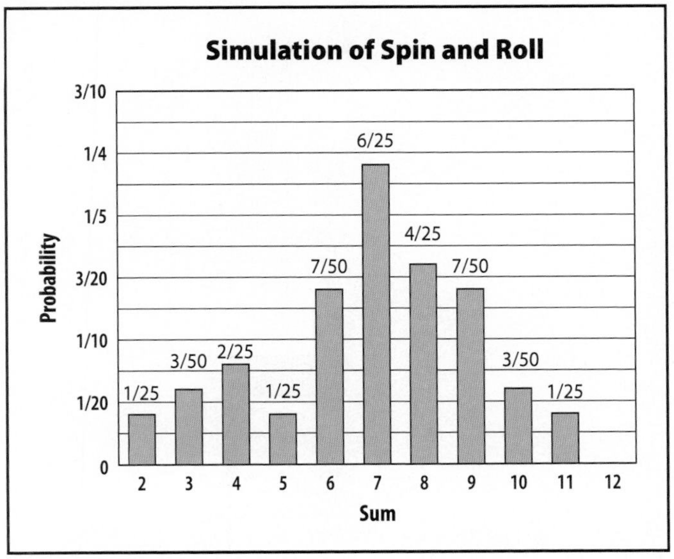

Sample answer: The graph in part b is the theoretical probability, while the graph in part e is the experimental probability. The graphs will be similar in shape, but the experimental probability graph will vary and more than likely will never completely mirror the theoretical probability graph.

15. The sum 7 is most likely to happen.

X = Sum of Dice	2	3	4	5	6	7	8	9	10	11	12
Probability	$\frac{1}{36}$	$\frac{1}{18}$	$\frac{1}{12}$	$\frac{1}{9}$	$\frac{5}{36}$	$\frac{1}{6}$	$\frac{5}{36}$	$\frac{1}{9}$	$\frac{1}{12}$	$\frac{1}{18}$	$\frac{1}{36}$

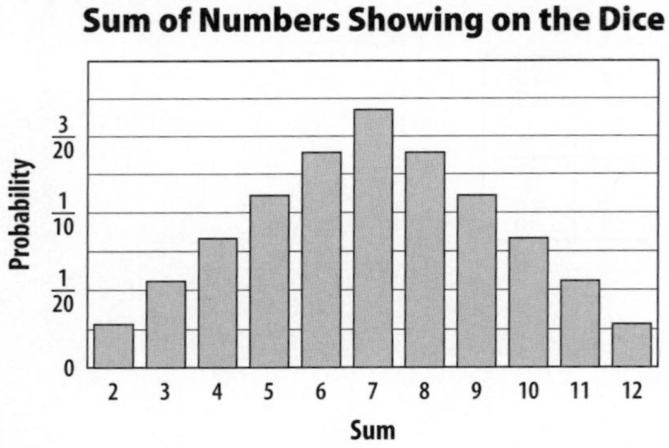

18. Sample answer: There are 870 students in a school: 179 freshmen, 215 sophomores, 211 juniors, and 265 seniors. Find the probability distribution for each class. What is the probability that a randomly chosen student is a sophomore?

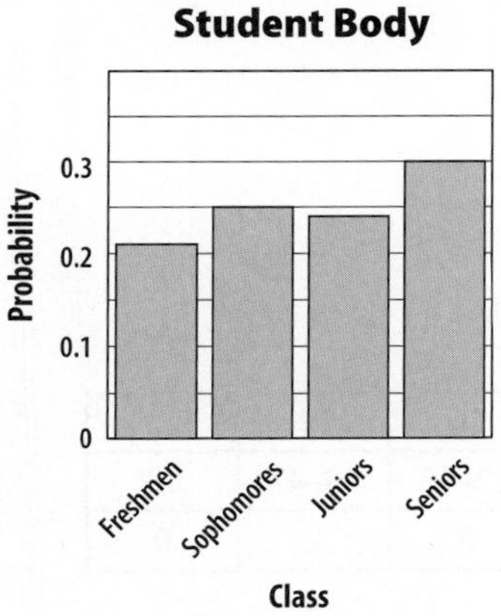

NOTES

Student Handbook

This **Student Handbook** can help you answer these questions.

What if I Need More Practice?

The **Extra Practice** section provides additional problems for each lesson so you have ample opportunity to practice new skills.

What if I Need to Check a Homework Answer?

The answers to odd-numbered problems are included in **Selected Answers and Solutions**.

What if I Forget a Vocabulary Word?

The **English-Spanish Glossary** provides definitions and page numbers of important or difficult words used throughout the textbook.

What if I Need to Find Something Quickly?

The **Index** alphabetically lists the subjects covered throughout the entire textbook and the pages on which each subject can be found.

What if I Forget a Formula?

Formulas and Measures, Symbols and Properties

Following the Index, you will find a list of **Formulas and Symbols** that are used in the book.

Extra Practice

CHAPTER 1 Expressions, Equations, and Functions

Write an algebraic expression for each verbal expression. (Lesson 1-1)

1. 6 times a number m **$6m$**
2. a number t less twelve **$t - 12$**

Evaluate each expression if $m = 2$, $t = 6$, and $z = 5$. (Lesson 1-2)

3. $2(t - z) + \frac{14}{m}$ **9**
4. $(m + 2z)^2 + 12tz$ **504**

5. **SPORTS** Adam mows lawns at an average rate of 40 minutes per lawn. Write and evaluate an expression to find the number of hours Adam spent mowing last weekend. (Lesson 1-2)

Lawns Per Day	
Friday	3
Saturday	11
Sunday	4

$\frac{40(3 + 11 + 4)}{60}$, 12 hours

Evaluate each expression. Name the property used in each step. (Lesson 1-3) **6, 7. See Extra Practice Answer Appendix.**

6. $14\left(5 - \frac{1}{5} \cdot 25\right) + 2 \div (4 \cdot 1)$
7. $3(14 + 8 + 6) - 1 \cdot 18$

8. **PETS** Rosa takes two dogs and one cat to the veterinarian during her vacation. (Lesson 1-3)

Pet	Board	Bath
dog	$25/day	$12
cat	$15/day	$8

   a. Use the table to find the total cost of boarding both dogs and the cat for 5 days. **$325**

   b. If Rosa has the veterinarian give all of the pets a bath while she is on vacation, what is the new total cost? **$357**

Use the Distributive Property to rewrite each expression. Then evaluate. (Lesson 1-4) **9, 10. See Extra Practice Answer Appendix.**

9. $14(102)$
10. $5\frac{1}{6}(30)$

11. **ARTS** Logan sells handmade wooden products. He charges $25 per bowl, $14 per picture frame, and $30 per jewelry box. On Friday, he sells 3 bowls, 6 picture frames, and 2 jewelry boxes. On Saturday, he sells 6 bowls, 14 picture frames, and 3 jewelry boxes. Write and evaluate an expression for his total sales. (Lesson 1-4) **See Extra Practice Answer Appendix.**

Find the solution set for each equation if the replacement sets are $m = \{0, 2, 4, 5, 8\}$ and $n = \{-2, 0, 2, 7, 9\}$. (Lesson 1-5)

12. $4(m - 2) = 8$ **{4}**
13. $6(6 - n) = 24$ **{2}**

Identify the independent and dependent variables for each relation. (Lesson 1-6)

14. Increasing the amount of fertilizer put on a plant increases the rate at which it grows. **14, 15. See Extra Practice Answer Appendix.**
15. Pam babysits to save money. The more kids she babysits, the more money she makes.

16. **INCOME** Jonathan draws the graph at the right to describe his income throughout his career. Describe what is happening in the graph. (Lesson 1-6) **See Extra Practice Answer Appendix.**

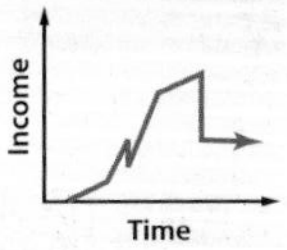

Determine whether the relation is a function. Explain. (Lesson 1-7) **17, 18. See Extra Practice Answer Appendix.**

17. $\{(2, 2), (-5, 2), (6, 6), (9, 4), (4, 9)\}$
18. $\{(0, 2), (1, 7), (0, -6), (4, 8), (-3, -1)\}$

19. Identify the function graphed as *linear* or *nonlinear.* Then estimate and interpret the intercepts of the graph, any symmetry, where the function is positive, negative, increasing, and decreasing, the x-coordinate of any relative extrema, and the end behavior of the graph. (Lesson 1-8) **See Extra Practice Answer Appendix.**

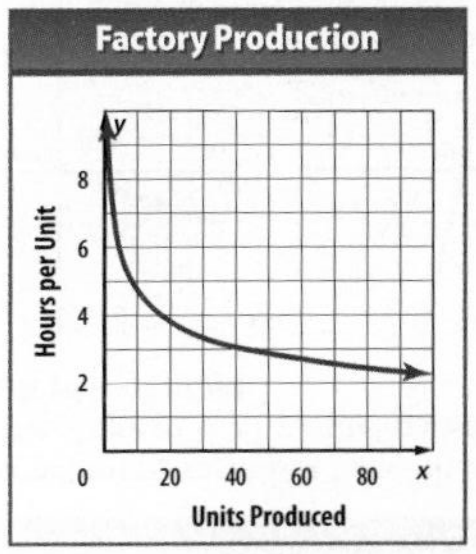

Extra Practice
connectED.mcgraw-hill.com
R1

CHAPTER 2 Linear Equations

Translate each sentence into a formula. (Lesson 2-1)

1. The number of seconds is 60 times the number of minutes. **$s = 60m$**

2. A gallon contains 8 pints. **$g = 8p$**

3. **THEATER** A theater has 1400 seats. Write and use an equation to find the number of rows if each row has 35 seats. (Lesson 2-1) **$35r = 1400$; 40**

Solve each equation. Check your solution. (Lesson 2-2)

4. $-18t + 26 = -19$ **2.5** 5. $\frac{1}{2}b + \frac{3}{4} = \frac{1}{6}$ **$-\frac{7}{6}$**

Write an equation and solve each problem. (Lesson 2-3) **7. $\frac{1}{2}x + 8 = -2$; -20**

6. Find three consecutive even integers with a sum of 78. **$x + (x + 2) + (x + 4) = 78$; 24, 26, 28**

7. Eight more than half a number is negative two.

Solve each equation. Check your solution. (Lesson 2-3)

8. $-3w + 16 = 14.5$ **0.5** 9. $\frac{4}{7} - \frac{k}{3} = \frac{1}{2}$ **$\frac{3}{14}$**

10. **ZOO** The Martin and Smith families went to the zoo. What is the cost of an adult ticket if they spent $75 total? (Lesson 2-3) **$15**

Family	Adults
Martin	2
Smith	3

Solve each equation. Check your solution. (Lesson 2-4)

11. $16x - 8 = 21 - x$ **$\frac{29}{17}$** 12. $\frac{x}{2} + \frac{1}{5} = 3x$ **$\frac{2}{25}$**

13. **GEOMETRY** Find the value of x so that the figures have the same perimeter. (Lesson 2-4) **4**

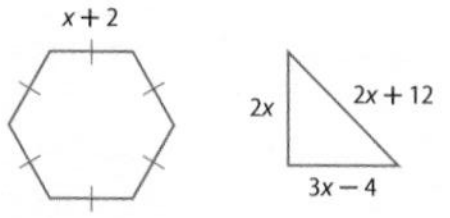

Evaluate each expression if $m = 6$, $n = 15$, and $p = \frac{1}{2}$. (Lesson 2-5)

14. $|m - 12| - 3p$ **4.5** 15. $18p + |n - m|$ **18**

Write an equation involving absolute value for each graph. (Lesson 2-5)

16. 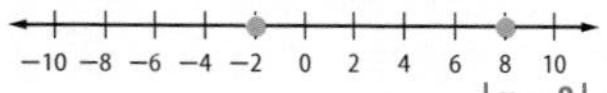

$|x - 3| = 5$

17. 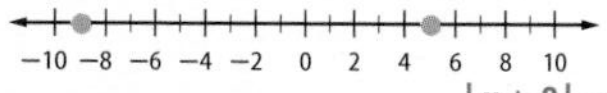

$|x + 2| = 7$

Solve each proportion. If necessary, round to the nearest hundredth. (Lesson 2-6)

18. $\frac{1.7}{n} = \frac{16}{30}$ **3.19** 19. $\frac{418}{83} = \frac{b}{7}$ **35.25** 20. $\frac{30}{y} = \frac{75}{135}$ **54**

21. **ART** Neil is enlarging a photo to hang on the wall. To keep the pictures proportional, what length is the unknown side? (Lesson 2-6) **35 in.**

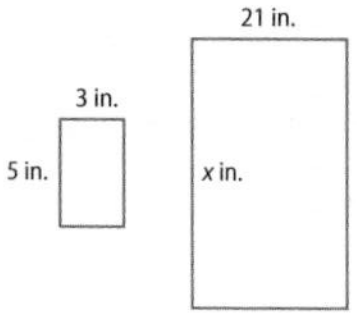

Find the discounted price of each item. (Lesson 2-7)

22. sofa: $575 discount: 20% **$460**
23. cell phone: $80 discount: 12% **$70.40**

24. **CAMPING** Ty's backpack weighs 38.6 pounds. Roger's backpack weighs 15% more. How much does Roger's backpack weigh? (Lesson 2-7) **44.39 lb**

Solve each equation or formula for the variable indicated. (Lesson 2-8)

25. $\frac{2b - a}{c} = -\frac{1}{2}d$, for a **25–27. See Extra Practice Answer Appendix.**

26. $y = w(h - 5)$, for h

27. $3x - 4z = 7 - xy$, for x

28. **WEIGHT** A watermelon weighs 6.3 pounds. One pound is approximately 0.454 kilogram. How many kilograms does the watermelon weigh? (Lesson 2-8) **2.86 kg**

29. **PAINT** Jeff painted 400 square feet in 50 minutes. He then painted 700 square feet in 75 minutes. What is Jeff's average painting speed? (Lesson 2-9) **8.8 ft²/min**

30. **CHEMISTRY** Sarah has 65 milliliters of a 30% solution. How many millimeters of 75% solution should she add to obtain the required 35% solution? (Lesson 2-9) **8.125 mL**

CHAPTER 3 Linear Functions

Determine whether each equation is a linear equation. Write *yes* or *no*. If yes, write the equation in standard form. (Lesson 3-1)

1. $-6xy + 2y = 3x$ **no** 2. $\frac{1}{2}y - 7 = 3x$ **yes; $6x - y = -14$**

Graph each equation by making a table. (Lesson 3-1)

3. $2y - x = 5$ 4. $x + y = 6$
3, 4. See Extra Practice Answer Appendix.

Solve each equation. (Lesson 3-2)

5. $-5x + 14 = 7x - 28$ **3.5**

6. $-\frac{1}{2}x + 8 = 6x - 12 - \frac{13}{2}x$ **no solution**

7. **NURSERY** The function $b = 100 - 2.5f$ represents the remaining balance of store credit Louie has at Blooms Nursery. Find the zero and explain what it means in this situation. (Lesson 3-2)
7–9. See Extra Practice Answer Appendix.

Determine whether each function is linear. Write *yes* or *no*. Explain. (Lesson 3-3)

8.

x	−2	0	2	4	6
y	0	6	12	18	24

9.

x	7	4	1	−2	−5
y	14	2	12	4	10

10. **WEATHER** Refer to the graph. (Lesson 3-3)

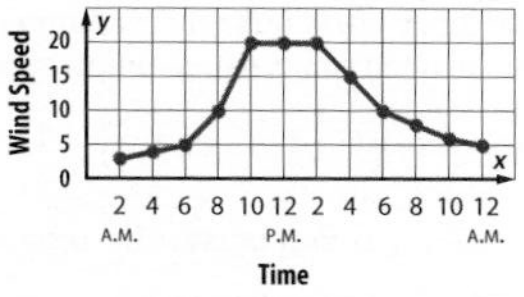

a. Find the rate of change in wind speed between 6 A.M. and 8 A.M. **$\frac{5}{2}$ or 2.5 mph**

b. Is there a greater change in wind speed during the day? If so, when does it occur? **Yes; between 8–10 A.M.**

c. The meteorologist says a storm came through at some point during the day. When do you think this may have happened? Explain your reasoning. **See Extra Practice Answer Appendix.**

Name the constant of variation for each equation. Then find the slope of the line that passes through each pair of points. (Lesson 3-4)

11. 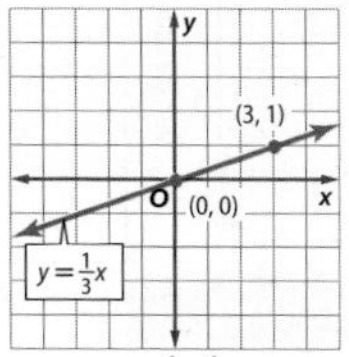

$\frac{1}{3}$; $\frac{1}{3}$

12. 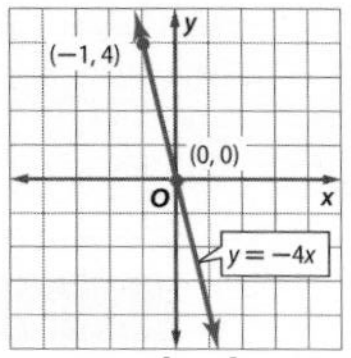

−4; −4

Suppose y varies directly as x. Write a direct variation equation that relates x and y. Then solve. (Lesson 3-4) **13. $y = -\frac{2}{3}x$; 2**

13. If $y = -6$ when $x = 9$, find y when $x = -3$.

14. If $y = -7$ when $x = -1$, find x when $y = 0$. **$y = 7x$; 0**

Determine whether each sequence is an arithmetic sequence. Write *yes* or *no*. Explain. (Lesson 3-5)

15. $-2, 2, -4, 4, -6, 6 \ldots$ **No; there is no common difference.**

16. $-6, -3, 0, 3, 6 \ldots$ **Yes; the common difference is 3.**

17–19a. See Extra Practice Answer Appendix.

Write an equation for the *n*th term of each arithmetic sequence. Then graph the first five terms of the sequence. (Lesson 3-5)

17. 3, 3.5, 4, 4.5… 18. 1, −1.5, −4, −6.5…

19. **NEWSPAPER** The table shows the number of newspapers Daniel delivers. (Lesson 3-6)

Blocks	Papers
5	40
6	48
7	56
8	64

a. Graph the data.

b. Write an equation to describe the relationship. **$y = 8x$**

c. Find the number of papers delivered if he has 11 blocks. **88 papers**

20. $f(x) = \frac{1}{3}x - 1$ 21. $f(x) = -2x + 1$

Write an equation in function notation for each relation. (Lesson 3-6)

20. 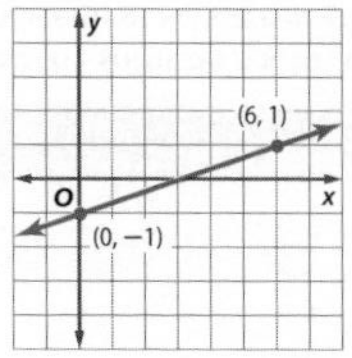

21. 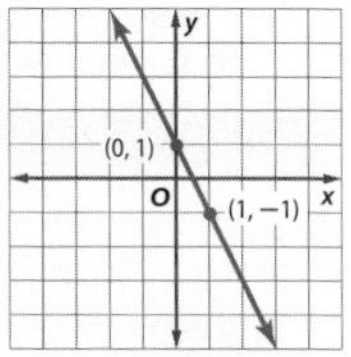

CHAPTER 4 Equations of Linear Functions

Write an equation of a line in slope-intercept form with the given slope and y-intercept. Then graph the equation. (Lesson 4-1)

1. slope: 6, y-intercept: -4 **$y = 6x - 4$**
2. slope: $\frac{1}{3}$, y-intercept: 3 **$y = \frac{1}{3}x + 3$**

Write an equation in slope-intercept form for each graph shown. (Lesson 4-1)

3. 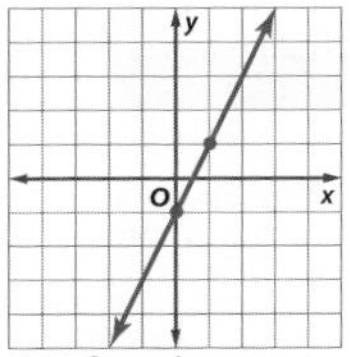
$y = 2x - 1$

4. 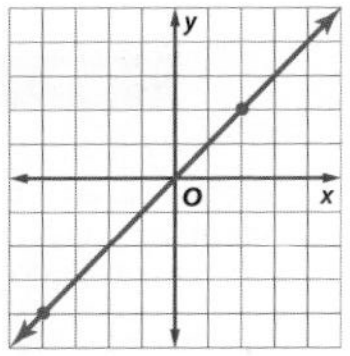
$y = x$

5. **PARTY** Mr. Ramirez paid \$60 for 15 specialty balloons for his son's birthday. (Lesson 4-2)
   a. Write an equation in slope-intercept form to find the cost C of b specialty balloons. **$C = 4b$**
   b. How much would 20 of the balloons cost? **\$80**

Write an equation in slope-intercept form of the line that passes through each pair of points. (Lesson 4-2) **6. $y = \frac{1}{4}x - \frac{1}{2}$**

6. $(2, 0), \left(4, \frac{1}{2}\right)$
7. $(-5, -2), (5, 2)$ **$y = \frac{2}{5}x$**

Write each equation in standard form. (Lesson 4-3)

8. $\frac{1}{2}(y + 2) = 6x$ **$12x - y = 2$**
9. $7y - 13 = 2x + 5$ **$2x - 7y = -18$**

Write each equation in slope-intercept form. (Lesson 4-3) **10. $y = \frac{1}{4}x + \frac{19}{4}$** **11. $y = 3x - \frac{1}{4}$**

10. $2y - 8 = \frac{1}{2}(x + 3)$
11. $y - \frac{1}{2} = 3x - \frac{3}{4}$

Determine whether the graphs of the following equations are *parallel* or *perpendicular*. Explain. (Lesson 4-4) **12. perpendicular**

12. $y = -2x + 6, 2y = x - 3$
13. $y = 3x - 2, -3y = x + 6$ **perpendicular**

14. **MAPS** The director of street repairs wants to first replace curbs on streets that are parallel to each other. Which two streets will get new curbs first? (Lesson 4-4)

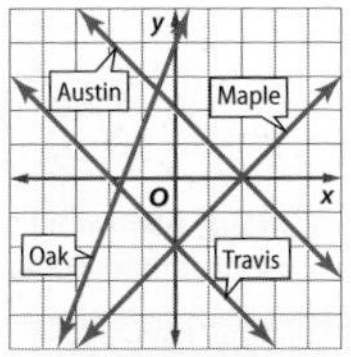

Austin and Travis will receive curbs first because they are parallel.

Write an equation in slope-intercept form for the line that passes through the given point and is parallel to the graph of the equation. (Lesson 4-4)

15. $(-1, 6), y = \frac{1}{4}x - 4$ **$y = \frac{1}{4}x + \frac{25}{4}$**
16. $(5, 7), y = -x + 5$ **$y = -x + 12$**

Determine whether each graph shows a *positive*, *negative*, or *no* correlation. If there is a positive or negative correlation, describe its meaning in the situation. (Lesson 4-5)

17. 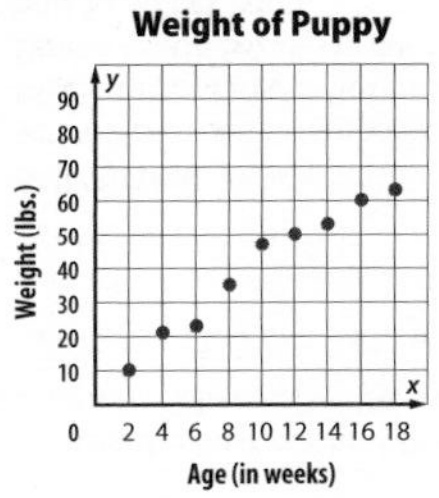

Positive; the older the puppy gets, the more it weighs.

18. 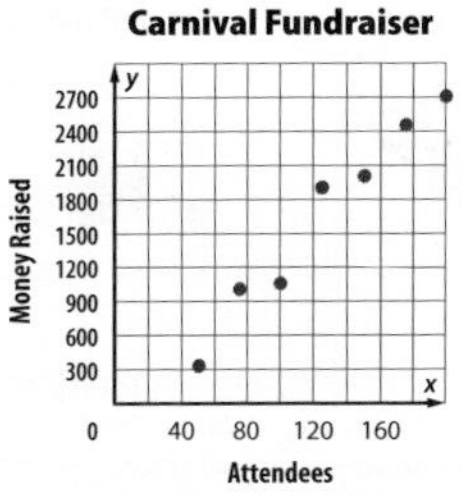

Positive; the more people who attend the carnival, the more money is raised.

Write an equation of the regression line for the data in each table. Then find the correlation coefficient. (Lesson 4-6) **20. $y = -0.02x + 4.34$; -0.97**

19. The table shows the numbers of plants in each garden and turnips produced.

Plants	2	3	4	5	6	7
Turnips	12	19	24	32	34	45

$y = 6.23x - 0.36$; 0.99

20. The table shows the amount of shrimp caught each day and the retail price of the shrimp.

Pounds (1000s)	48	52	60	65	73
Cost/lb (\$)	3.50	3.42	3.35	3.15	3.08

Find the inverse of each function. (Lesson 4-7)

21. $f(x) = -3x + 8$ **$y = -\frac{1}{3}x + \frac{8}{3}$**
22. $f(x) = \frac{1}{2}x + 7$ **$y = 2x - 14$**

CHAPTER 5 Linear Inequalities

Solve each inequality. Then graph the solution set on a number line. (Lesson 5-1)

1. $6t \leq 3$
2. $14 > k + 2$
3. $16 \leq 4n$
4. $6c < 5c + 3$

1–4. See Extra Practice Answer Appendix.

Define a variable, write an inequality, and solve each problem. Check your solution. (Lesson 5-1)

5. The sum of six times a number and three is less than the product of seven and a number.
6. Three times a number is greater than or equal to the sum of twice a number and 12.

5, 6. See Extra Practice Answer Appendix.

Solve each inequality. Graph the solution on a number line. (Lesson 5-2)

7. $\frac{c}{8} > \frac{1}{4}$
8. $-3 \leq 4m$

7–10. See Extra Practice Answer Appendix.

Define a variable, write an inequality, and solve each problem. Then interpret your solution. (Lesson 5-2)

9. **READING** Thomas has a 432-page book to read in 12 days. At least how many pages must he read per day to finish the book on time?
10. **DOGS** Laura has a maximum of 91 minutes to walk 7 dogs. How much time can she spend walking each dog?

Solve each inequality. Graph the solution on a number line. (Lesson 5-3) **11, 12. See Extra Practice Answer Appendix.**

11. $1.2x + 6 < 4.6x - 3$
12. $-4\left(3g + \frac{1}{2}\right) \leq -6(3 + 2g)$
13. **PIZZA** Sam orders 3 large pizzas. Each pizza costs \$12, and each topping costs \$0.50. Sam has \$38 to spend. Write and solve an inequality to find the greatest number of toppings Sam can afford. (Lesson 5-3)

$36 + 0.5x \leq 38$; $x \leq 4$; Sam can buy 4 toppings.

Solve each compound inequality. Then graph the solution set. (Lesson 5-4)

14. $6w + 3 < 9$ or $\frac{1}{2}w \geq 2$
15. $16 \geq 3x - 5$ and $3x - 2 > 2(x - 1)$

14, 15. See Extra Practice Answer Appendix.

16. **COUPON** Victor has a coupon that is valid only for juice sold in containers between 16 and 32 ounces. (Lesson 5-4) **a. $\{x \mid 16 < x < 32\}$**
    a. Write a compound inequality that describes acceptable juice container sizes.
    b. Graph the inequality. **See Extra Practice Answer Appendix.**

Solve each inequality. Then graph the solution set. (Lesson 5-5)

17. $\left|\frac{1}{2}z + 6\right| \leq 4$
18. $|3p + 3| > 1$

17, 18. See Extra Practice Answer Appendix.

19. **SHOP** Kristi is shopping online for gifts for her friends. (Lesson 5-5)

Average Prices	
CD	\$15.50
Book	\$19
Shirt	\$32

   a. If prices ranged from \$1.50 above and below the average CD price, find the range of prices. **$\$14 \leq c \leq \$17$**
   b. Prices for the book varied \$2.25 from the average. Write the range of average book prices. **$\$16.75 \leq b \leq \$21.25$**
   c. Graph the solution set for shirt prices if they varied \$6 below to \$4 above the average. **See Extra Practice Answer Appendix.**

Graph each inequality. (Lesson 5-6)

20. $3(x + y) \geq 6$
21. $\frac{1}{2}y < 2(-1 - x)$

20, 21. See Extra Practice Answer Appendix.

Use a graph to solve each inequality. (Lesson 5-6)

22. $5x + 3 > -2$
23. $y - 8 \leq -3$

22, 23. See Extra Practice Answer Appendix.

24. **DOG WASH** It costs Pups and Suds \$975 a week to operate their business. (Lesson 5-6)

   a. The prices that they charge are shown. Write an inequality to describe how many of each type of dog they need to service to make a profit. **$20x + 30y > 975$**
   b. How many dogs must they wash to make a profit each week? **See Extra Practice Answer Appendix.**

CHAPTER 6 Systems of Linear Equations and Inequalities

Use the graph below to determine whether each system is *consistent* or *inconsistent* and if it is *independent* or *dependent*. (Lesson 6-1)
1. consistent and independent

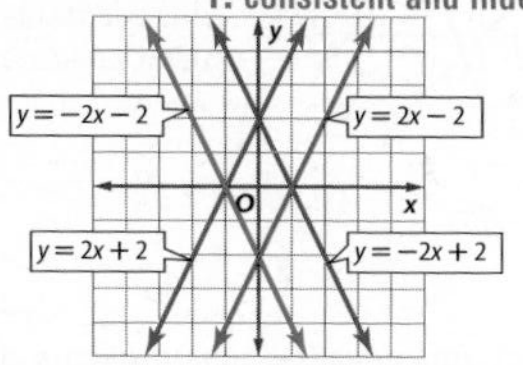

1. $y = 2x + 2$
   $y = -2x - 2$
2. $y = -2x + 2$ **inconsistent**
   $y = -2x - 2$
3. **DANCES** Mario and Tanesha are inflating balloons for the school dance. Mario has 12 balloons inflated and is inflating additional balloons at a rate of 3 balloons per minute. Tanesha has 16 balloons inflated and is inflating additional balloons at a rate of 2 balloons per minute. (Lesson 6-1)
   a. Write a system of equations to represent the situation.
   b. Graph each equation.
   c. How long will it take Mario to have more balloons filled than Tanesha?
   See Extra Practice Answer Appendix.

Use substitution to solve each system of equations. (Lesson 6-2)

4. $x = -y + 3$ **(−1, 4)**
   $3y + 2x = 10$
5. $-x + 2y = 6$ **no solution**
   $4y - 2x = 11$
6. $y - 7x = 2$ $\left(-\frac{7}{33}, \frac{17}{33}\right)$
   $2x + 3 = 5y$
7. $-2y = x + 3$ **infinitely many**
   $\frac{3}{2} = -\frac{1}{2}x - y$
8. **FRUIT** Sarah and Toni each bought fruit for a fundraiser. If Toni spent $4.30 and Sarah spent $2.80, how much does each type of fruit cost? (Lesson 6-3) **apple, $0.30; orange, $0.50**

Girl	Apples	Oranges
Toni	6	5
Sarah	6	2

Use elimination to solve each system of equations. (Lesson 6-3)

9. $2m + 3n = 16$ **9.** $\left(-12, \frac{40}{3}\right)$
   $-3m - 3n = -4$
10. $-5k + 4j = 8$ **(0, 2)**
    $-5k - 6j = -12$
11. The difference of three times a number and a second number is two. The sum of the two numbers is fourteen. What are the two numbers? (Lesson 6-3) **4 and 10**

Use elimination to solve each system of equations. (Lesson 6-4) **13.** $\left(-\frac{2}{3}, -\frac{4}{3}\right)$

12. $1.6x + 2.2y = 5.4$
    $-3.2x + 4y = -2.4$
    (2, 1)
13. $2x + 5y = -8$
    $4x - 2y = 0$
14. **CARNIVALS** Scott and Isaac went to the school carnival. Use the table shown to determine how many tickets a ride and game each cost. (Lesson 6-4)

Rider	Rides	Games	Tickets
Scott	5	4	19
Isaac	7	2	23

ride, 3 tickets; game, 1 ticket

15. **SAVINGS** Caleb made $105 mowing lawns and walking dogs, charging the rates shown. If he mowed half as many lawns as dogs walked, how many lawns did he mow and how many dogs did he walk? (Lesson 6-5) **lawns, 3; dogs, 6**

$7.50 per dog

$20 per lawn

Determine the best method to solve each system of equations. Then solve the system. (Lesson 6-5)

16. $4x + 2y = 12$
    $-y - 4x = 2$
    16. elim (+); (−4, 14)
17. $y + 3x = 11$ **subst; (2, 5)**
    $-2x + 3y = 11$
18. **BABYSITTING** Kelsey and Emma babysit after school to earn extra money. Kelsey made $52 by charging $10 per hour and $4 per child. Emma made $67.50 by charging $15 per hour and $2.50 per child. (Lesson 6-5)
    a. Write a system of equations to represent the situation. $\mathbf{10x + 4y = 52,\ 15x + 2.5y = 67.5}$
    b. How many hours and how many children did each babysit? **4 hours, 3 children**

Solve each system of inequalities by graphing. (Lesson 6-6)

19. $0.5x - y \geq 3$
    $x + y < 3$
20. $y < 2x - 1$
    $y > 4(1 + 0.5x)$

19, 20. See Extra Practice Answer Appendix.

CHAPTER 7 Exponents and Exponential Functions

Simplify each expression. (Lesson 7-1)

1. $(2xy^2)^3(2x^2y^3z)$ $\mathbf{16x^5y^9z}$
2. $(2ab^2c^3)(3ad^2)^2$ $\mathbf{18a^3b^2c^3d^4}$

GEOMETRY Express the area of each triangle as a monomial. (Lesson 7-1)

3. $\mathbf{5a^6b^5c^5}$

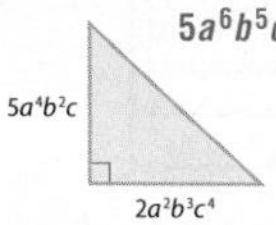

4. $\mathbf{\frac{15}{2}x^3y^4z^5}$

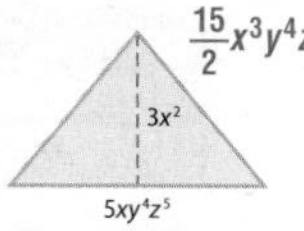

Simplify each expression. Assume that no denominator equals zero. (Lesson 7-2)

5. $\frac{3m^5n^3p^4}{5m^6n^4p^2q^5}$ $\mathbf{\frac{3p^2}{5mnq^5}}$
6. $\left(\frac{x^2yz^3}{2xy^3z^3}\right)^3$ $\mathbf{\frac{x^3}{8y^6}}$
7. $\frac{2a^{-1}b^{-2}c^{-3}}{7a^2b^3c^4d^{-5}}$ $\mathbf{\frac{2d^5}{7a^3b^5c^7}}$
8. $\left(\frac{4x^{-2}y^4z^5}{5x^5y^{-3}z^{-2}}\right)^{-1}$ $\mathbf{\frac{5x^7}{6y^7z^7}}$

Write each expression in radical form, or write each radical in exponential form. (Lesson 7-3)

9. $13^{\frac{1}{3}}$ $\mathbf{\sqrt[3]{13}}$
10. $(7k)^{\frac{1}{2}}$ $\mathbf{\sqrt{7k}}$
11. $\sqrt{17a}$ $\mathbf{(17a)^{\frac{1}{2}}}$
12. $3\sqrt{2xyz^2}$ $\mathbf{3(2xyz^2)^{\frac{1}{2}}}$

Simplify. (Lesson 7-3)

13. $\sqrt[4]{\frac{81}{625}}$ $\mathbf{\frac{3}{5}}$
14. $\sqrt[5]{0.00001}$ **0.1**
15. $4096^{\frac{1}{3}}$ **16**
16. $\left(\frac{125}{343}\right)^{\frac{4}{3}}$ $\mathbf{\frac{625}{2401}}$

Solve each equation. (Lesson 7-3)

17. $81^x = \frac{1}{3}$ $\mathbf{-\frac{1}{4}}$
18. $3^{4x} = 3^{x+1}$ $\mathbf{\frac{1}{3}}$

Express each number in scientific notation. (Lesson 7-4)

19. 22,100,000,000 $\mathbf{2.21 \times 10^{10}}$
20. 0.000000003088 $\mathbf{3.088 \times 10^{-9}}$

Evaluate each product. Express the results in both scientific notation and standard form. (Lesson 7-4) **21, 22. See Extra Practice Answer Appendix.**

21. $(6.2 \times 10^3)(1.77 \times 10^6)$
22. $(4.08 \times 10^{-4})^2$

Graph each equation. Find the *y*-intercept, and state the domain and range. (Lesson 7-5)

23. $f(x) = -3^x - 1$
24. $f(x) = \left(\frac{1}{2}\right)^x + 3$

23–25. See Extra Practice Answer Appendix.

25. Determine whether the set of data shown below displays exponential behavior. Write *yes* or *no*. Explain why or why not. (Lesson 7-5)

x	−1	0	1	2	3	4
y	3	1	$\frac{1}{3}$	$\frac{1}{9}$	$\frac{1}{27}$	$\frac{1}{81}$

26. **POPULATION** A neighborhood had 4518 residents in 2006. The number of residents has been declining by 3.5% each year. How many residents will there be in 2012? (Lesson 7-6) **3648 residents**
27. **MONEY** Sarah put $3000 in an investment that gets 6.2% compounded quarterly for 8 years. What will her investment be worth at the end of the 8 years? (Lesson 7-6) **$4907.71**
28. **SOCCER** The Westside Soccer League has 186 players. They expect a 7.5% increase in players for at least the next 4 years. How many players will they have at that point? (Lesson 7-6) **248 players**

Determine whether each sequence is *arithmetic*, *geometric*, or *neither*. Explain. (Lesson 7-7)

29. $-\frac{1}{2}, -\frac{1}{4}, 0, \frac{1}{4}, \frac{1}{2} \ldots$
30. 100, 90, 85, 75, 60…

29, 30. See Extra Practice Answer Appendix.

Find the next three terms in each geometric sequence. (Lesson 7-7)

31. 48, −96, 192, −384, 768… **−1536, 3072, −6144**
32. 150, 75, 37.5, 18.75, 9.375… **4.6875, 2.3438, 1.1719**

Find the first five terms of each sequence. (Lesson 7-8)

33. $a_1 = 5, a_n = 3.5a_{n-1} + 1, n \geq 2$
34. $a_1 = 12, a_n = -\frac{1}{2}a_{n-1} + \frac{5}{2}, n \geq 2$

33, 34. See Extra Practice Answer Appendix.

Write a recursive formula for each sequence. (Lesson 7-8) **35, 36. See Extra Practice Answer Appendix.**

35. 7, 16, 43, 124, …
36. 729, 243, 81, 27, …

connectED.mcgraw-hill.com

CHAPTER 8 Quadratic Expressions and Equations

Find each sum or difference. (Lesson 8-1)

1. $(7g^3 + 2g^2 - 12) - (-2g^3 - 4g)$ **1.** $9g^3 + 2g^2 + 4g - 12$
2. $(-3h^2 + 3h - 6) + (5h^2 - 3h - 10)$ $2h^2 - 16$

Simplify each expression. (Lesson 8-2)

3. $-\frac{1}{2}n^3p^2(5np^3 - 3n^2p^2 + 8n)$ **3.** $\frac{3}{2}n^5p^4 - \frac{5}{2}n^4p^5 - 4n^4p^2$
4. $6j^2(-3j + 3k^2) - 2k^2(2j + 10j^2)$ **4.** $-18j^3 - 2j^2k^2 - 4jk^2$

Solve each equation. (Lesson 8-2)

5. $-4(b + 3) + b(b - 3) = -b(6 - b) + 2(b - 3)$ -2
6. $3(a - 3) + a(a - 1) + 12 = a(a - 2) + 3(a - 2) + 4$ -5

Find each product. (Lesson 8-3)

7. $(-3t - 16)(5t + 2)$ $-15t^2 - 86t - 32$
8. $\left(4p + \frac{1}{2}\right)\left(\frac{1}{2}p + 4\right)$ **8.** $2p^2 + \frac{65}{4}p + 2$
9. **SIDEWALKS** Reynoldsville is repairing sidewalks. If the sidewalk is the same width around a city block, write an expression for the area of the block and the sidewalk. (Lesson 8-3) $(80 + 2x)(100 + 2x)$; $4x^2 + 360x + 8000$

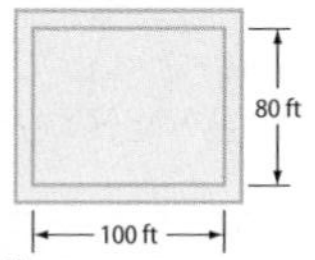

Find each product. (Lesson 8-4)

10. $\left(\frac{1}{2}m + 3\right)^2$
11. $(2n - 6)(2n + 6)$
12. $(5a - 4)^2$
13. $(x - 2y)(x + 2y)$

10–13. See Extra Practice Answer Appendix.

Use the Distributive Property to factor each polynomial. (Lesson 8-5)

14. $4m^3n^2 + 16m^2n^3 - 8m^3n^4$ $4m^2n^2(m + 4n - 2mn^2)$
15. $12j^4k^4 + 36j^3k^2 - 3j^2k^5$ $3j^2k^2(4j^2k^2 + 12j - k^3)$

Factor each polynomial. (Lesson 8-5)

16. $x^2 - 4x + 3xy - 12y$ $(x + 3y)(x - 4)$
17. $4a - 10ab + 6b - 15b^2$ $(2a + 3b)(2 - 5b)$
18. **HEIGHT** The height h of a ball bounced off the ground after t seconds is modeled by the equation $h = -16t^2 + 28.8t$. (Lesson 8-5)
    a. What is the height of the ball at 1.5 seconds? 7.2 ft
    b. How many seconds before the ball hits the ground again? 1.8 s

Factor each polynomial. (Lesson 8-6)

19. $t^2 + 2t - 15$ **19.** $(t - 3)(t + 5)$
20. $d^2 - 3d - 28$ $(d - 7)(d + 4)$
21. $m^2 + 5m - 14$ $(m - 2)(m + 7)$
22. $x^2 - 4x - 45$ $(x - 9)(x + 5)$

Solve each equation. Check your solution. (Lesson 8-6)

23. $h^2 + 3h - 4 = 0$ $-4, 1$
24. $a^2 + 9a + 18 = 0$ $-3, -6$
25. $x^2 - x - 6 = 0$ $-2, 3$
26. $y^2 + 2y - 15 = 0$ $-5, 3$

27–30. See Extra Practice Answer Appendix.

Factor each polynomial, if possible. If the polynomial cannot be factored using integers, write *prime*. (Lesson 8-7)

27. $6x^2 + 21x - 90$
28. $3x^2 - 11x - 42$
29. $6x^2 - 13x - 5$
30. $5y^2 - 3y + 11$
31. **PRIZES** A machine is used to throw T-shirts into the crowd at the Hornets basketball games. (Lesson 8-7)

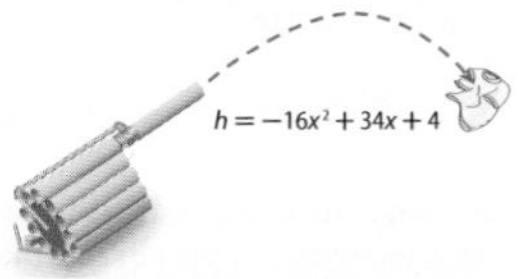

    a. What is the initial height of the T-shirt? 4 ft
    b. If the T-shirt is caught after 2 seconds, what is the height? 8 ft

32–37. See Extra Practice Answer Appendix.

Factor each polynomial. (Lesson 8-8)

32. $\frac{1}{2}t^2 - 162$
33. $25d^3 - 49d$
34. $196t^2u^3 - 144u^3$
35. $169a^4b^6 - 121c^8$
36. $4g^2 - 1296h^2$
37. $18a^3 + 27a^2 - 50a - 75$
38. **FRUIT** An apple fell 25 feet from a tree. The formula $h = -16t^2 + 25$ can be used to approximate the number of seconds it will take the apple to hit the ground. (Lesson 8-8)
    a. How long will it take the apple to hit the ground? 1.25 seconds
    b. If you catch it at 4 feet, how long did the apple drop? about 1.14 seconds

Determine whether each trinomial is a perfect square trinomial. Write *yes* or *no*. If so, factor it. (Lesson 8-9)

39. $64x^2 - 32x + 4$
40. $4a^2 - 12a + 16$
41. $12y^2 - 36y + 27$
42. $75b^3 - 60ab^2 + 12a^2b$

39–42. See Extra Practice Answer Appendix.

CHAPTER 9 Quadratic Functions and Equations

Find the vertex, the equation of the axis of symmetry, and the y-intercept of the graph of each equation. (Lesson 9-1)

1. $y = 4x^2 + 8x - 5$
2. $y = -2x^2 + 8x + 5$
3. $y = x^2 - 8x + 9$
4. $y = 4x^2 + 16x - 6$

1–4. See Extra Practice Answer Appendix.

5. **KICKBALL** A kickball is kicked in the air. The equation $h = -16t^2 + 60t$ gives the height h of the ball in feet after t seconds. (Lesson 9-1)
    a. What is the height of the ball after one second? 44 ft
    b. When will the ball reach its maximum height? 1.875 s
    c. When will the ball hit the ground? 3.75 s

6, 7. See Extra Practice Answer Appendix for graphs.

Solve each equation by graphing. (Lesson 9-2)

6. $-2x^2 - 2x + 4 = 0$ $-2, 1$
7. $x^2 = -2x + 3$ $-3, 1$
8. **MARBLES** Jason shot a marble straight up using a slingshot. The equation $h = -16t^2 + 42t + 5.5$ models the height h, in feet, of the marble after t seconds. After how long will the marble hit the ground? (Lesson 9-2) about 2.7 seconds

Describe how the graph of each function is related to the graph of $f(x) = x^2$. (Lesson 9-3)

9. $g(x) = -x^2 - 4$
10. $h(x) = 7x^2 + 2$

9, 10. See Extra Practice Answer Appendix.

Match each equation to its graph. (Lesson 9-3)

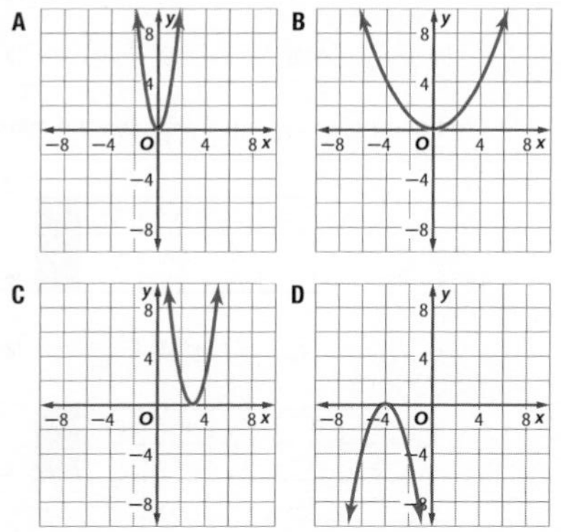

11. $y = 3x^2$ A
12. $y = \frac{1}{4}x^2$ B
13. $y = -(x + 4)^2$ D
14. $y = 2(x - 3)^2$ C
15. **BIOLOGY** The number of cells in a Petri dish can be modeled by the quadratic equation $n = 6t^2 - 4.5t + 74$, where t is the number of hours the cells have been in the dish. When will there be 200 cells in the Petri dish? (Lesson 9-4) after 7 hours.

Solve each equation by completing the square. Round to the nearest tenth if necessary. (Lesson 9-4)

16. $x^2 + 4x - 8 = 5$ $-6.1, 2.1$
17. $3x^2 + 5x = 18$ $-3.4, 1.8$
18. Find the value of x in the figure if the area is 36 square inches. (Lesson 9-4) 4

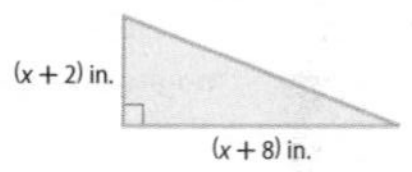

Solve each equation by using the Quadratic Formula. Round to the nearest tenth if necessary. (Lesson 9-5)

19. $3x^2 + 10x = 15$ $-4.5, 1.1$
20. $\frac{1}{2}x^2 - 8x + 6 = 0$ $0.8, 15.2$

State the value of the discriminant. Then determine the number of solutions of the equation. (Lesson 9-5)

21. $4x^2 - 12x = -9$ 0, one real solution
22. $3x^2 + 8 = 9x$ -15, no real solutions

Look for a pattern in each table of values to determine which kind of model best describes the data. (Lesson 9-6)

23. exponential

x	2	3	4	5	6
y	$\frac{9}{4}$	$\frac{27}{8}$	$\frac{81}{16}$	$\frac{243}{32}$	$\frac{729}{64}$

24. quadratic

x	−2	−1	0	1	2
y	−13	−6.25	0	5.75	11

Graph each function. State the domain and range. (Lesson 9-7)

25. $f(x) = |x + 5|$
26. $f(x) = 2[\![x]\!]$

25, 26. See Extra Practice Answer Appendix.

Extra Practice
Extra Practice

CHAPTER 10 Radical Functions and Geometry

Graph each function. Compare to the parent graph. State the domain and range. (Lesson 10-1)

1. $y = 4\sqrt{x+2}$ 2. $y = -3\sqrt{x}$

3. $y = -2\sqrt{x} - 2$ 4. $y = \sqrt{x+2} + 2$

1–4. See Extra Practice Answer Appendix.

5. **PENDULUMS** Find the period T of a pendulum, the time in seconds it takes to swing from one side to the other and back, if the length of the pendulum ℓ is 50 meters and $T = 2\pi\sqrt{\frac{\ell}{g}}$, where g is the gravitational constant, 9.8 meters per second squared. (Lesson 10-1) **about 14.19 seconds**

Simplify each expression. (Lesson 10-2)

6. $\sqrt{24} \cdot 3\sqrt{14}$ **$12\sqrt{21}$** 7. $\sqrt{45x^4y^3z^6}$ **$3x^2y|z^3|\sqrt{5y}$**

8. $\frac{7}{6-\sqrt{10}}$ **$\frac{42+7\sqrt{10}}{26}$** 9. $\frac{3}{8+\sqrt{14}}$ **$\frac{24-3\sqrt{14}}{50}$**

Simplify each expression. (Lesson 10-3) **11. $12 + 9\sqrt{2}$**

10. $6\sqrt{18} + 3\sqrt{2}$ **$21\sqrt{2}$** 11. $\sqrt{6}(\sqrt{24} + 3\sqrt{3})$

12. $4\sqrt{7}(3\sqrt{63})$ **252** 13. $\sqrt{12} + 5\sqrt{48} - 2\sqrt{3}$ **$20\sqrt{3}$**

14. $\sqrt{\frac{1}{3}} - \sqrt{3}$ **$-\frac{2\sqrt{3}}{3}$** 15. $(2\sqrt{3} - 2\sqrt{5})(2\sqrt{15} - 4)$ **$20\sqrt{5} - 28\sqrt{3}$**

16. **PARKS** Crandall Lake has a swimming area shaped like a trapezoid. The area can be found using the formula $A = \frac{1}{2}h(b_1 + b_2)$, where h represents the height and b_1 and b_2 are the lengths of the two bases. What is the area available for swimming? (Lesson 10-3)

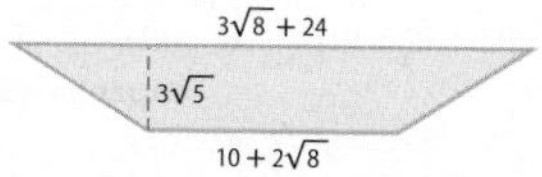

$51\sqrt{5} + 15\sqrt{10}$ units²

Solve each equation. Check your solution. (Lesson 10-4) **19. $6 + 2\sqrt{15}$**

17. $\sqrt{24 - n} = \frac{n}{2}$ **8** 18. $\sqrt{b+6} = 3\sqrt{15}$ **129**

19. $f = 2\sqrt{3f+6}$ 20. $\sqrt{6-m} = m + 6$ **−3**

21. $\sqrt{t} = \sqrt{4t-6}$ **2** 22. $5 + \sqrt{17-m} = m$ **8**

Find each missing length. If necessary, round to the nearest hundredth. (Lesson 10-5)

23. **13.89**

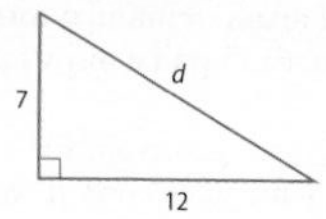

24. **12**

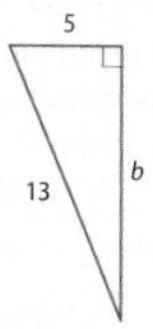

25. **BAKING** Jasmen is cutting triangles from dough to bake for her math class. If she wants the base to be 1.5 inches and the height to be 3 inches, how long is the hypotenuse? (Lesson 10-5) **3.35 in.**

Use a calculator to find the value of each trigonometric ratio to the nearest ten-thousandth. (Lesson 10-6)

26. cos 52° **0.6157** 27. tan 28° **0.5317**

28. sin 17° **0.2924** 29. cos 75° **0.2588**

30. tan 55° **1.4281** 31. sin 65° **0.9063**

Solve each right triangle. Round each side length to the nearest tenth. (Lesson 10-6)

32.

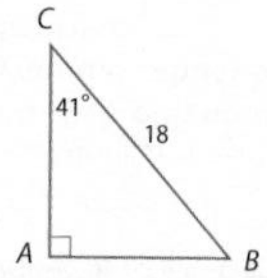

33.

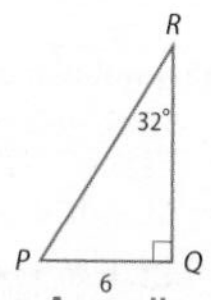

32, 33. See Extra Practice Answer Appendix.

34. **ROLLERBLADING** The path for rollerblading in the park has a vertical rise of 35 feet. The angle the rise makes with the path is 75°. How long is the incline? (Lesson 10-6) **135.2 ft**

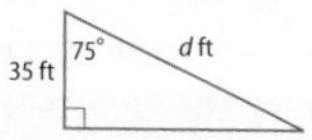

CHAPTER 11 Rational Functions and Equations

Determine whether each table or equation represents an *inverse* or *direct* variation. Explain. (Lesson 11-1) **1. direct; $y = -3x$**

1.

x	1	2	3	4	5
y	−3	−6	−9	−12	−15

2. $y = -\frac{2}{x}$ **inverse; $xy = -2$**

3. **inverse; $xy = 6$**

x	−2	$-\frac{1}{2}$	$\frac{1}{2}$	2
y	−3	−12	12	3

State the excluded value for each function. (Lesson 11-2)

4. $y = \frac{2x-3}{x-5}$ **5** 5. $y = \frac{x+3}{3x-3}$ **1**

Identify the asymptotes of each function. Then graph the function. (Lesson 11-2)

6. $y = \frac{3}{2x-2}$ 7. $y = \frac{2}{3x} - 4$

6, 7. See Extra Practice Answer Appendix.

8. **FUNDRAISER** The Sophomore class has committed to walking 200 miles for a fundraiser. The equation $y = \frac{200}{x}$ models the number of miles each person will walk depending on the number of volunteers. Graph the function. (Lesson 11-2) **See Extra Practice Answer Appendix.**

State the excluded value(s) for each rational expression. (Lesson 11-3)

9. $\frac{6t}{2t^2-18}$ **−3, 3** 10. $\frac{11}{2x^2-x-28}$ **$-\frac{7}{2}$, 4**

11. $\frac{2x+1}{x-4}$ **4** 12. $\frac{7y^2}{2y^2-5y-12}$ **$-\frac{3}{2}$, 4**

Find the zeros of each function. (Lesson 11-3)

13. $f(x) = \frac{x^2-2x-8}{2x^2+8x+6}$ **4, −2** 14. $f(x) = \frac{x^2+7x+10}{x+5}$ **−2**

15. $f(x) = \frac{x^3+x^2-2x}{x^2-2x+1}$ **−2, 0**

Find each quotient. (Lesson 11-4) **17. $\frac{3t-4}{3(t-3)}$**

16. $\frac{3a^3}{6b^2} \div \frac{9a^6}{4b^3}$ **$\frac{2b}{9a^3}$** 17. $\frac{2t-1}{t+2} \div \frac{6t^2-21t+9}{3t^2+2t-8}$

18. $\frac{4x^2yz}{5z^3} \div \frac{2yz^4}{7xy^2z^3}$ **$\frac{14x^3y^2}{5z^3}$** 19. $\frac{4g^2+4g-8}{6h^2+6h-12} \div \frac{5g+10}{5h-5}$ **19. $\frac{2(g-1)}{3(h+2)}$**

20. **BOOKS** John has read 6 books recently. If he reads 40 words per minute, each page has approximately 500 words, and each book has an average of 225 pages, how many hours did John spend reading? (Lesson 11-4) **281.25 hours**

21. **AREA** The area A of a rectangle is given by ℓw. Find the length of the unknown side. (Lesson 11-5) **$x - 1$**

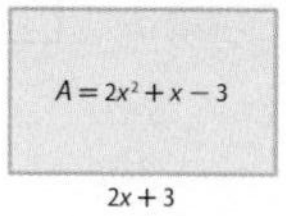

Find each quotient. (Lesson 11-5)

22. $\frac{m^2-m-6}{m} \div (m-3)$ **$\frac{m+2}{m}$**

23. $(2g^2 - 3g - 2) \div (g - 2)$ **$2g + 1$**

Find each sum or difference. (Lesson 11-6)

24. $\frac{7}{g} - \frac{2}{3g}$ **$\frac{19}{3g}$** 25. $\frac{3n}{2n+4} + \frac{n-2}{2n+4}$ **$\frac{2n-1}{n+2}$**

26. $\frac{-6}{k+2} + \frac{k}{k-2}$ **$\frac{k^2-4k+12}{(k+2)(k-2)}$** 27. $\frac{2p-3}{p^2-5p+6} - \frac{5}{p^2-9}$ **$\frac{2p^2-2p+1}{(p-2)(p+3)(p-3)}$**

28. **TRAINING** Miguel is training for a triathlon. He runs 5 miles at x miles per hour and 7 miles at $1.5x$ miles per hour. Write and simplify an expression for the time it takes him to run the 12 miles. (Lesson 11-6) **$\frac{14.5}{1.5x}$**

Simplify each expression. (Lesson 11-7)

29. $\frac{4\frac{2}{5}}{2\frac{5}{9}}$ **$1\frac{83}{115}$** 30. $\frac{\frac{3}{2a+2}}{\frac{1+a}{4a+8}}$ **$\frac{6(a+2)}{(a+1)^2}$**

Solve each equation. State any extraneous solutions. (Lesson 11-8)

31. $\frac{a}{a-1} - 1 = \frac{a}{2}$ **−1 or 2** 32. $\frac{c}{c+2} + c = \frac{5c+8}{c+2}$ **4**

33. $\frac{4}{w-2} = \frac{-1}{w+3}$ **−2** 34. $\frac{1}{y+2} + \frac{1}{y-2} = \frac{3}{y^2-4}$ **$\frac{3}{2}$**

35. **RECYCLING** Jamie and Adam volunteer at a recycle sorting center. Jamie sorts 3 bins in 2 hours. Adam sorts 3 bins in 3 hours. If they work together, how long would it take them to sort the 3 bins? (Lesson 11-8) **1.2 hours**

1, 2. See Extra Practice Answer Appendix.

CHAPTER 12 Statistics and Probability

Determine whether each situation calls for a *survey*, an *experiment*, or an *observational study*. Explain your reasoning. (Lesson 12-1)

1. **AUTO REPAIR** An auto repair company sends each customer a letter asking them to rate their experience during their last service appointment.

2. **ICE CREAM** An ice cream manufacturer is testing a new formula for their chocolate cherry flavor. They randomly give half of a group of 150 people the original formula, and the other half gets the new formula. Both are asked how they like their ice cream.

3. See Extra Practice Answer Appendix.

3. **GAS** A random sample of 1000 car owners in Los Angeles were surveyed about the price they last paid for a gallon of gasoline. Identify the sample and the population for the situation. Then describe the sample statistic and the population parameter. (Lesson 12-2)

4. **BOWLING** Tina's results for 8 bowling games are {110, 123, 147, 119, 153, 142, 113, 143}. Find and interpret the standard deviation of the data. (Lesson 12-2) **16.81**

For Exercises 5 and 6, use these data.
{12, 18, 21, 18, 19, 18, 16, 23, 20, 15, 17, 18}

5. Describe the center and spread of the data using either the mean and standard deviation or the five-number summary. Justify your choice by constructing a histogram. (Lesson 12-3) **See Extra Practice Answer Appendix.**

6. Find the mean, median, mode, range, and standard deviation of the data after multiplying each value by 3. (Lesson 12-4) **53.75; 54; 54; 33; 8.53**

7. **BASKETBALL** Keisha has a 75% free throw average. Describe how to simulate her next 10 free throws. (Lesson 12-5) **See Extra Practice Answer Appendix.**

8. **FLIGHTS** Three airlines have the departure results shown. (Lesson 12-5)

Status	A	B	C
on-time	21	19	24
late	6	3	9

a. What is the experimental probability of each airline having an on-time departure? **A: 78%, B: 86%, C: 73%**

b. What is the experimental probability for an on-time departure for all the airlines? **78%**

Evaluate each expression. (Lesson 12-6)

9. $P(8, 5)$ **6720**

10. $P(7, 3)$ **210**

11. $C(8, 5)$ **56**

12. $C(7, 3)$ **35**

13. **DOG SHOW** There are 12 dogs in the finals for best in show. If 4 dogs will get ribbons, how many ways can the ribbons be awarded? (Lesson 12-6) **11,880**

14. **SOCKS** A drawer contains 4 blue socks, 8 red socks, and 12 white socks. What is the probability of drawing two white socks in successive draws? (Lesson 12-7) $\frac{11}{46}$ **or 24%**

A card is drawn from a standard deck of playing cards. Determine whether the events are *mutually exclusive* or *not mutually exclusive*. Then find the probability. (Lesson 12-7)

15. P(eight or king)

16. P(heart or club)

17. P(two or red card)

18. P(even number or ace)

15–18. See Extra Practice Answer Appendix.

19. **SWEATERS** A local pet store sells five different sizes of dog sweaters. The table shows the probability distribution of each size sold in a month. (Lesson 12-8)

Dog Sweater Sizes	
Size	**Probability**
S	0.38
M	0.29
L	0.13
XL	0.11
XL+	0.09

a. Show that the distribution is valid.

b. What is the probability that a randomly chosen purchase is XL or larger? **0.20**

c. Find the probability that a customer purchased a medium sweater. **0.29**

19a, 20a. See Extra Practice Answer Appendix.

20. **MOVIES** A movie theater surveyed all attendees to a movie on Sunday afternoon to determine the average age. The table shows the results. (Lesson 12-8)

Movie Attendee Age	
Age	**Customers**
0–10	11
11–20	115
21–30	82
31–40	15
41–50	37
51+	28

a. Which category will have the highest probability? Explain.

b. Find the probability of a person being between 21 and 40 years of age. **33.7%**

c. Find the probability of someone being over 40. **23%**

Extra Practice

Extra Practice Chapter 1

6. $14\left(5 - \frac{1}{5} \cdot 25\right) + 2 \div (4 \cdot 1)$
$= 14(5 - 5) + 2 \div (4 \cdot 1)$; Substitution
$= 14(0) + 2 \div (4 \cdot 1)$; Additive Inverse
$= 0 + 2 \div (4 \cdot 1)$; Multiplicative Prop. of Zero
$= 0 + 2 \div 4$; Multiplicative Identity
$= 0 + \frac{1}{2}$; Substitution
$= \frac{1}{2}$; Additive Identity

7. $3(14 + 8 + 6) - 1 \cdot 18$
$= 3(14 + 6 + 8) - 1 \cdot 18$; Commutative (+)
$= 3(20 + 8) - 1 \cdot 18$; Substitution
$= 3(28) - 1 \cdot 18$; Substitution
$= 3(28) - 18$; Multiplicative Identity
$= 84 - 18$; Substitution
$= 66$; Substitution

9. $14(100) + 14(2)$; 1428

10. $\left(5 + \frac{1}{6}\right)(30)$; 155

11. $25(3 + 6) + 14(6 + 14) + 30(2 + 3)$
$= 25(9) + 14(20) + 30(5)$; Substitution
$= 225 + 280 + 150$; Multiply.
$= 655$; Substitution

14. I: fertilizer, D: rate of growth

15. I: kids, D: money made

16. Sample answer: He started out with a low, but increasing salary. Then his salary increased even faster as a young adult. He may have changed jobs where his salary dropped, but then it increased very quickly, and then finally slowed down. He retired and his income dropped to a steady amount.

17. Yes; each element in the domain matches with one element in the range.

18. No; the domain value 0 is paired with both 2 and −6.

19. Nonlinear; the graph intersects the *y*-axis at about (0, 10), so the *y*-intercept is about 10. This means that it took 10 hours to produce the first unit. The graph does not intersect the *x*-axis, so there is no *x*-intercept. This means that it has taken some time to produce each unit. The graph has no symmetry. The function is positive for all values of *x*. The function is decreasing for all values of *x*. The *y*-intercept is a relative maximum, indicating that the first unit took the most time to produce. As *x* increases, *y* appears to approach 2. This indicates that the time to produce each unit decreases until it is about 2 hours. As *x* decreases, *y* increases.

Extra Practice Chapter 2

25. $a = 2b + \frac{1}{2}cd$ or $a = \frac{cd + 4b}{2}$

26. $h = \frac{y + 5w}{w}$ or $h = \frac{y}{w} + 5$

27. $x = \frac{7 + 4z}{3 + y}$

Extra Practice Chapter 3

3.

x	y
3	1
−1	2
1	3
3	4

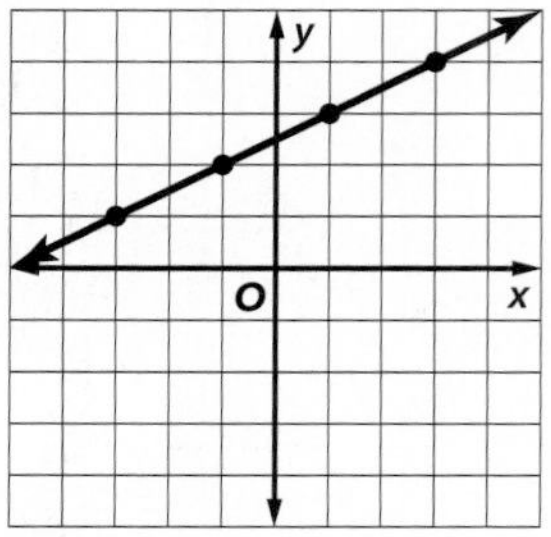

4.

x	y
0	6
6	0
2	4
3	3

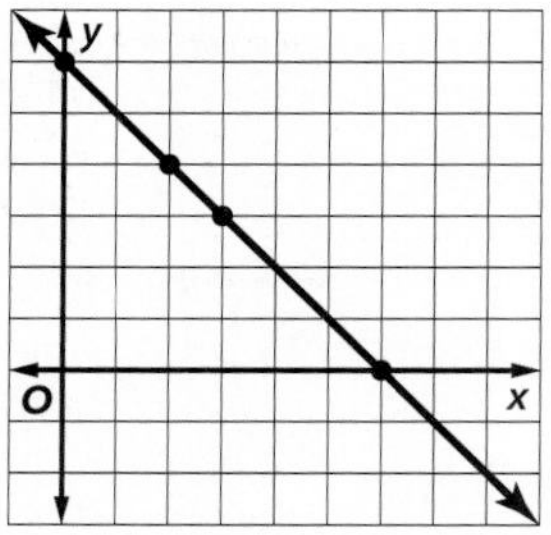

7. $f = 40$; Louie will have spent all of his credit when he purchases 40 flowers.

8. Yes; both the *x*-values and the *y*-values change at a constant rate.

9. No, the *y*-values do not decrease by a constant value.

10c. Sample answer: A storm could have occurred between 8 P.M. and 12 P.M. because the rate of change in wind is greatest during this time.

17. $a_n = 2.5 + .5n$

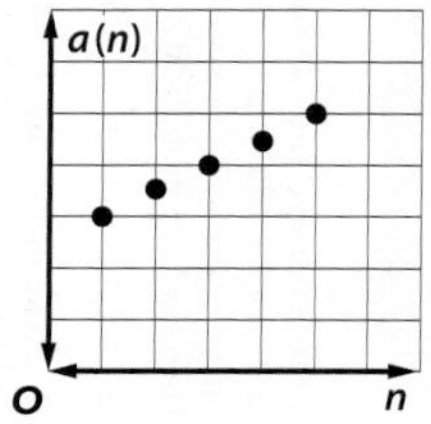

18. $a_n = 3.5 - 2.5n$

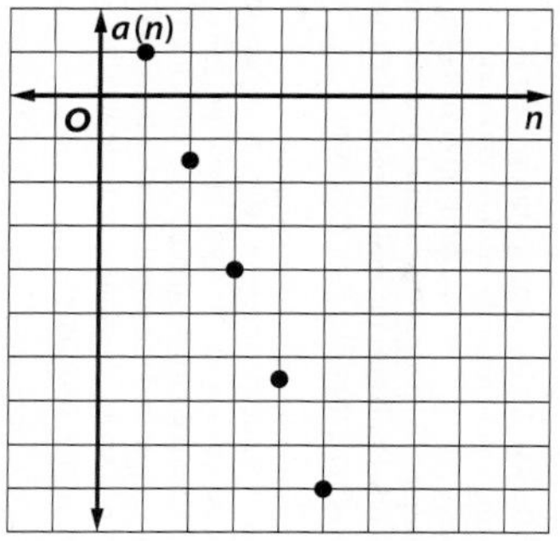

19a.

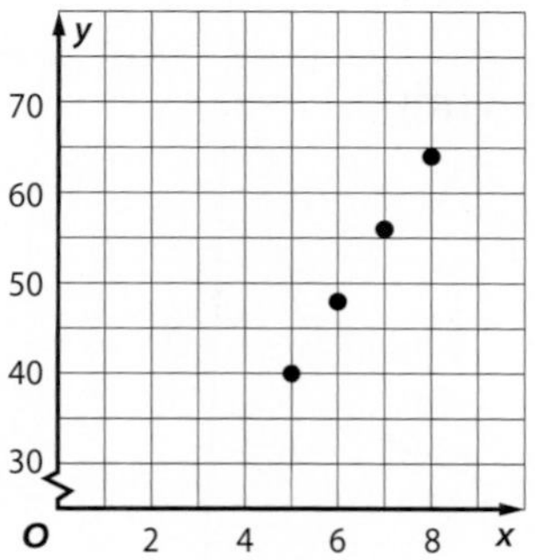

Extra Practice Chapter 5

1. $\left\{t \mid t \leq \frac{1}{2}\right\}$

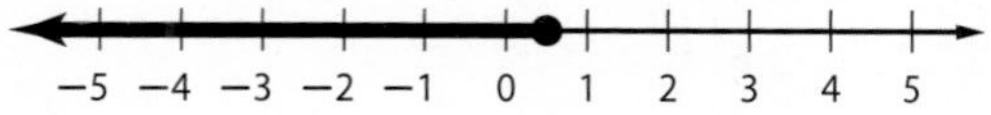

2. $\{k \mid k < 12\}$

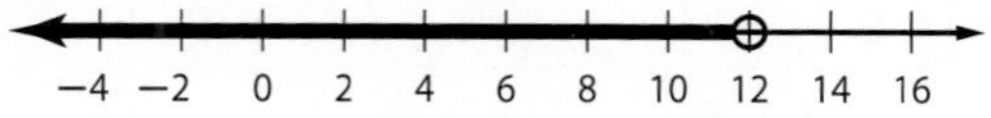

3. $\{n \mid n \geq 4\}$

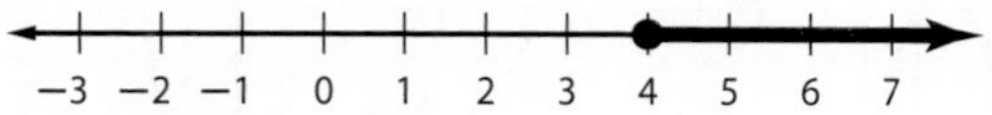

4. $\{c \mid c < 3\}$

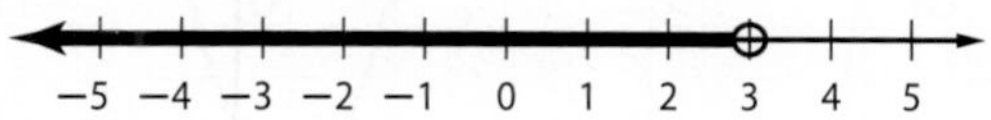

5. $6n + 3 < 7n$; $\{n \mid n > 3\}$

6. $3n \geq 2n + 12$; $\{n \mid n \geq 12\}$

7. $\{c \mid c > 2\}$

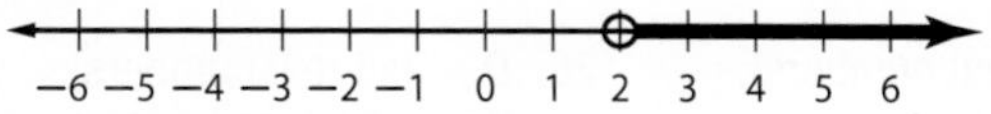

8. $\left\{m \mid m \geq -\frac{3}{4}\right\}$

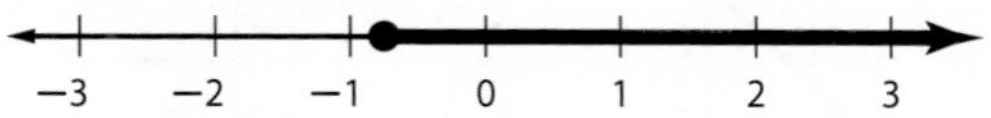

9. Let $x =$ the number of pages that Thomas has to read a day; $\frac{432}{x} < 12$; Thomas needs to read at least 36 pages a day to finish the book in 12 days.

10. Let $m =$ the number of minutes spent walking each dog; $7m \leq 90$; Laura can spend no more than 13 minutes walking each dog.

11. $\{x \mid x > 2.65\}$

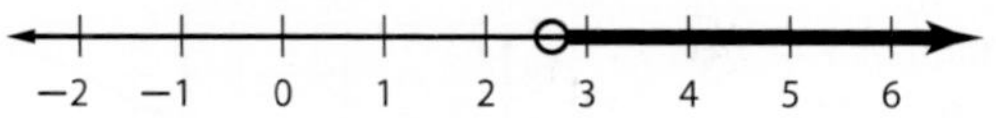

12. no solution

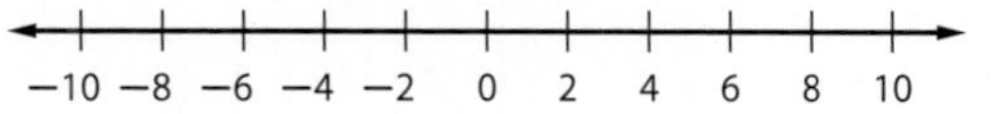

14. $\{w \mid w < 1 \text{ or } w \geq 4\}$

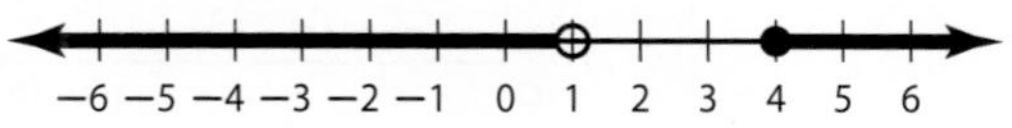

15. $\{x \mid 0 < x \leq 7\}$

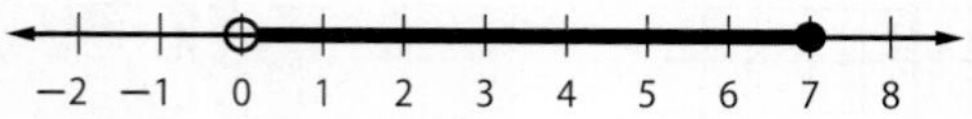

16b.

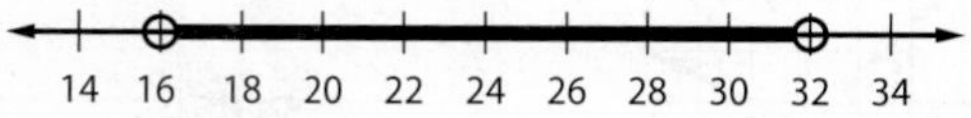

17. $-20 \leq z \leq -4$

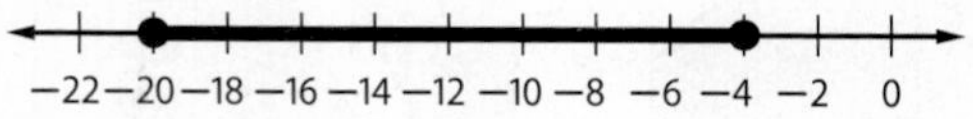

18. $p > -\frac{2}{3}$ and $p < -\frac{4}{3}$

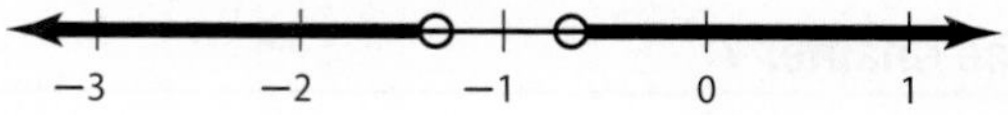

19c. $\$26 \leq s \leq \$36$

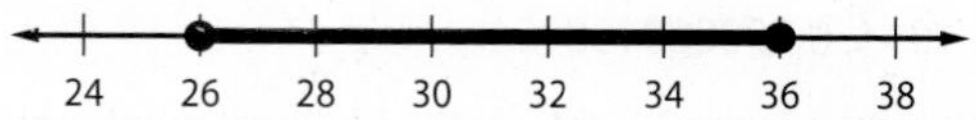

20.

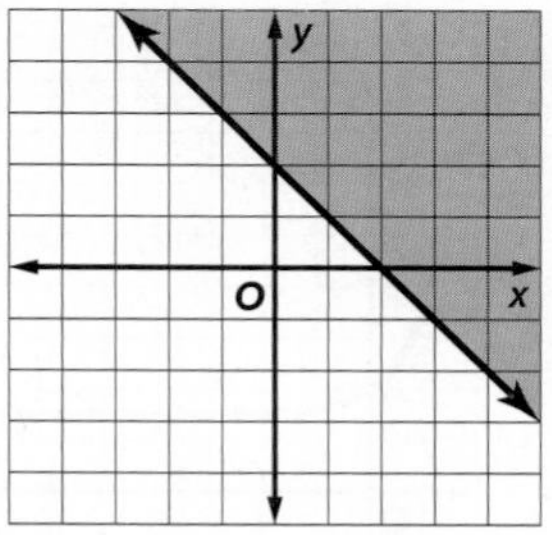

21.

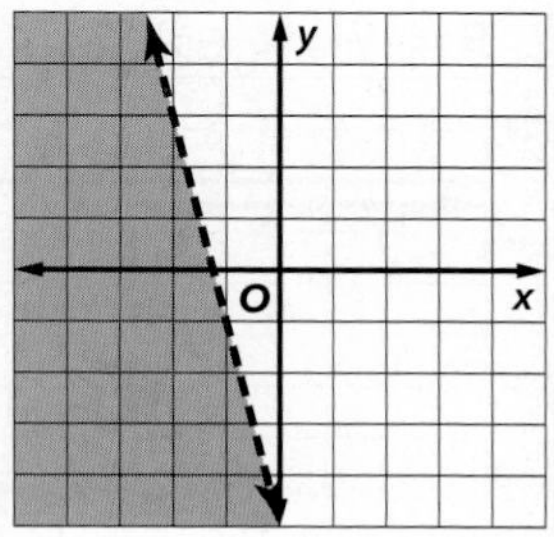

22. $x > -1$

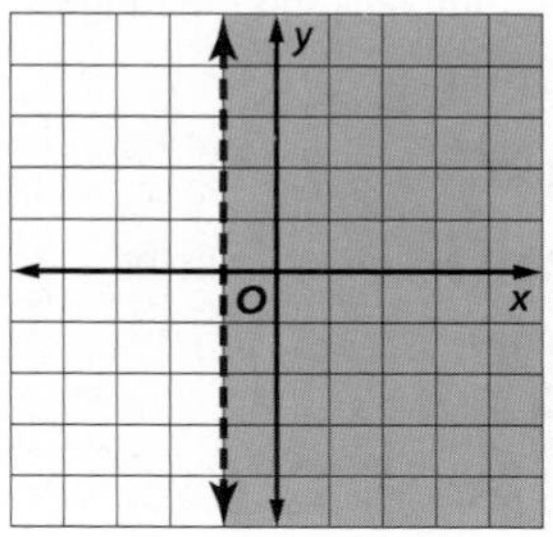

23. $y \leq 5$

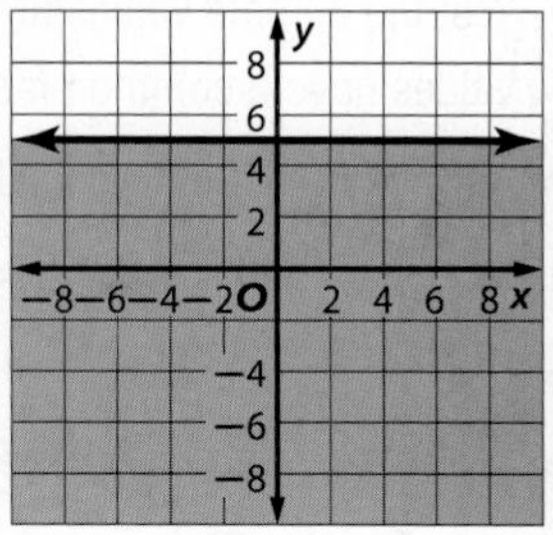

24b. Sample answer: 20 small/medium dogs and 20 large dogs

Extra Practice Chapter 6

3a. Mario: $y = 12 + 3x$, Tanesha: $y = 16 + 2x$

3b.

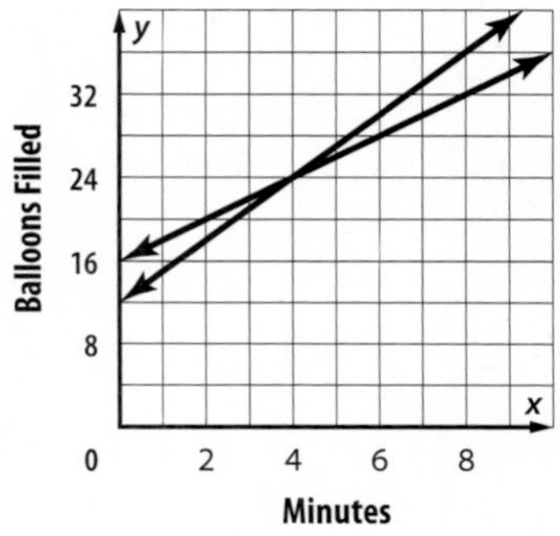

3c. (4, 24); Mario will have more filled balloons after 4 minutes.

Extra Practice Answer Appendix

19.

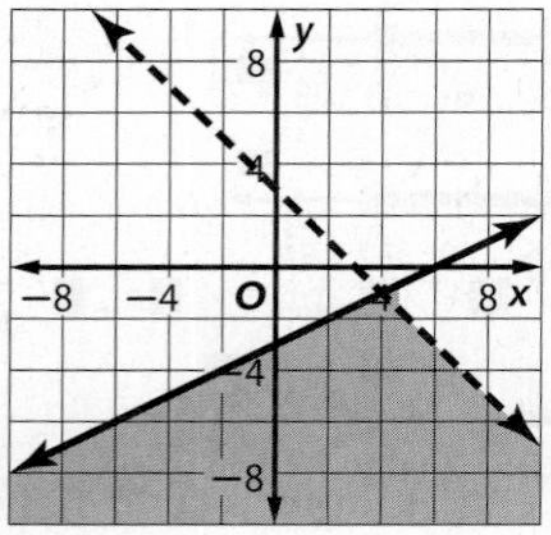

20. no solution

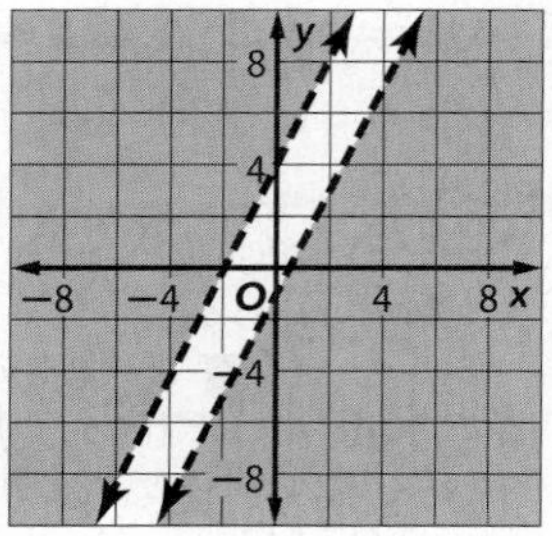

Extra Practice Chapter 7

21. 1.0974×10^{10}, 10,974,000,000

22. 1.66464×10^{-7}, 0.000000166464

23. -2; D = {all real numbers}; R = $\{y \mid y < -1\}$

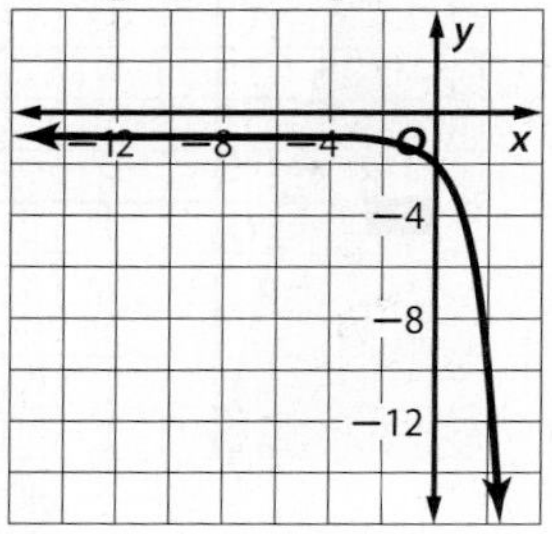

24. 4; D = {all real numbers}; R = $\{y \mid y > 3\}$

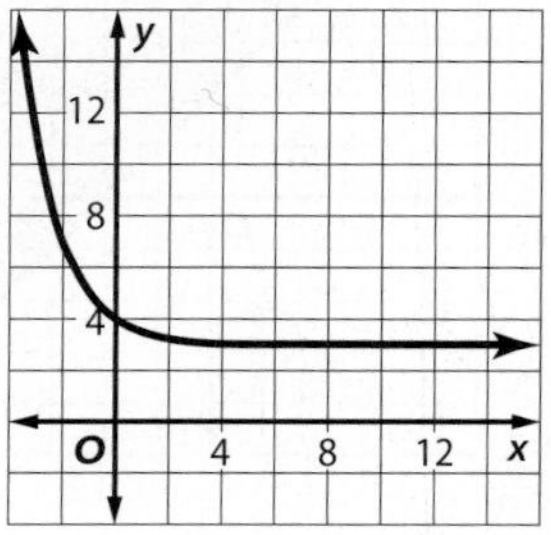

25. Yes; the domain values are at regular intervals and the range values have a common factor of $\frac{1}{3}$.

29. Arithmetic; the difference between terms is $\frac{1}{2}$.

30. Neither; there is no common difference or common factor.

33. 5, 18.5, 65.75, 231.125, 809.9375

34. -3.5, 4.25, 0.375, 2.3125

35. $a_1 = 7$, $a_n = 3a_{n-1} - 5$, $n \geq 2$

36. $a_1 = 729$, $a_n = \frac{1}{3}a_{n-1}$, $n \geq 2$

Extra Practice Chapter 8

10. $\frac{1}{4}m^2 + 3m + 9$

11. $4n^2 - 36$

12. $25a^2 - 40a + 16$

13. $x^2 - 4y^2$

27. $3(2x - 5)(x + 6)$

28. $(3x + 7)(x - 6)$

29. $(2x - 5)(3x + 1)$

30. prime

32. $\frac{1}{2}(t - 18)(t + 18)$

33. $d(5d - 7)(5d + 7)$

34. $4u^3(7t - 6)(7t + 6)$

35. $(13a^2b^3 - 11c^4)(13a^2b^3 + 11c^4)$

36. $4(g + 18h)(g - 18h)$

37. $(3a + 5)(3a - 5)(2a + 3)$

39. yes; $4(4x - 1)(4x - 1)$

40. no

41. yes; $3(2x - 3)(2x - 3)$

42. yes; $3b(5b - 2a)(5b - 2a)$

60a. Sample answer:

Extra Practice Chapter 9

1. $(-1, -9)$; $x = -1$; -5

2. $(2, 13)$; $x = 2$; 5

3. $(4, -7)$; $x = 4$; 9

4. $(-2, -22)$; $x = -2$; -6

6.

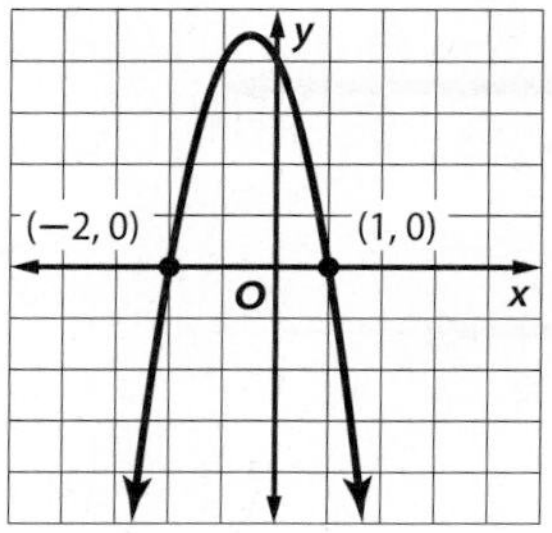

7.

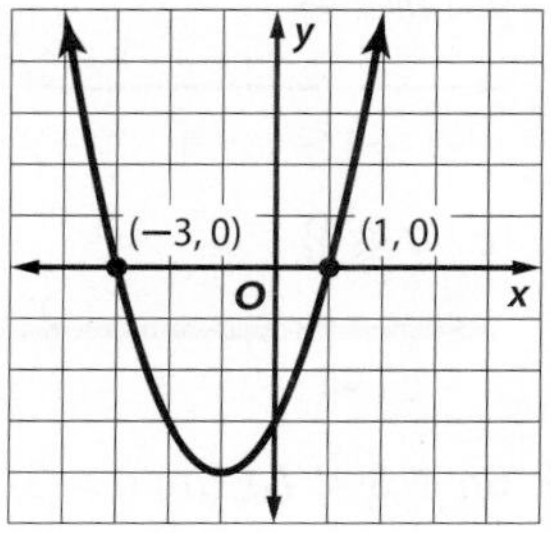

9. reflected across the x-axis, translated down

10. stretched vertically, translated up

25. D = {all real numbers}; R = $\{y \mid y \geq 0\}$

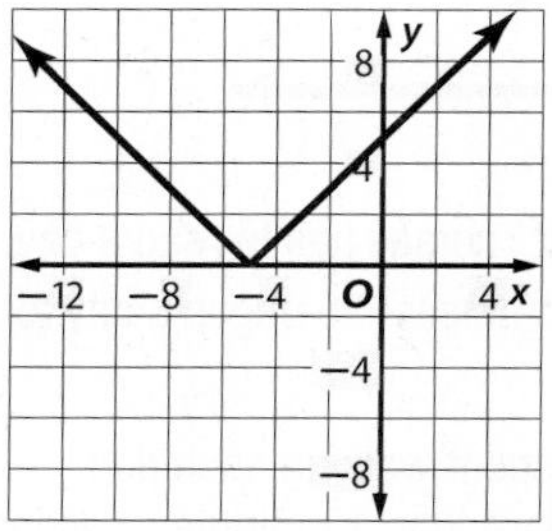

26. D = {all real numbers}; R = {all integer multiples of 2}

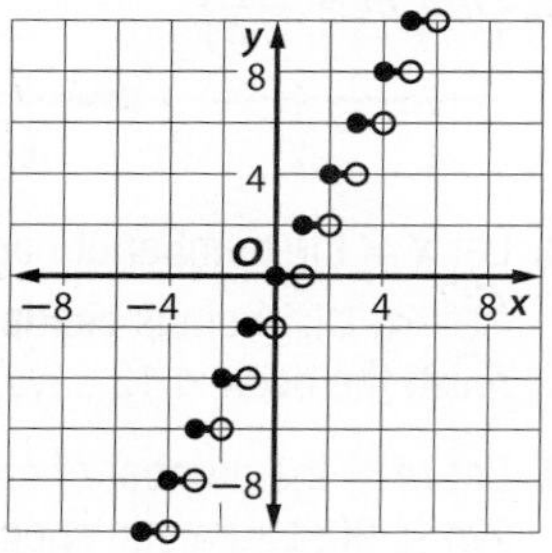

Extra Practice Chapter 10

1. vertical stretch of $y = \sqrt{x}$ translated up 2 units; D = $\{x \mid x \geq 0\}$, R = $\{y \mid y \geq 2\}$

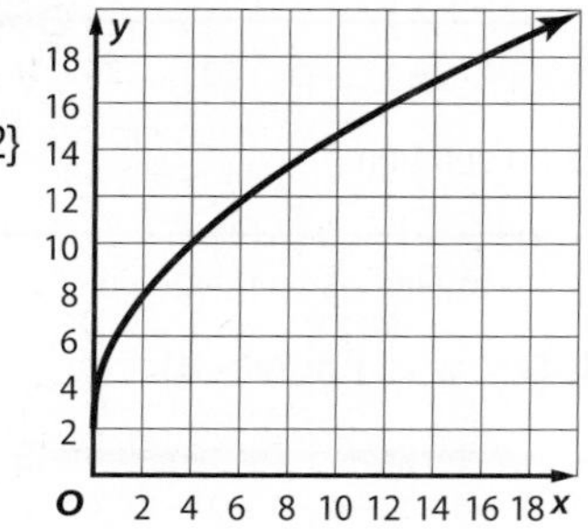

2. vertical stretch of $y = \sqrt{x}$ reflected across the x-axis; $D = \{x \mid x \geq 0\}$, $R = \{y \mid y \leq 0\}$

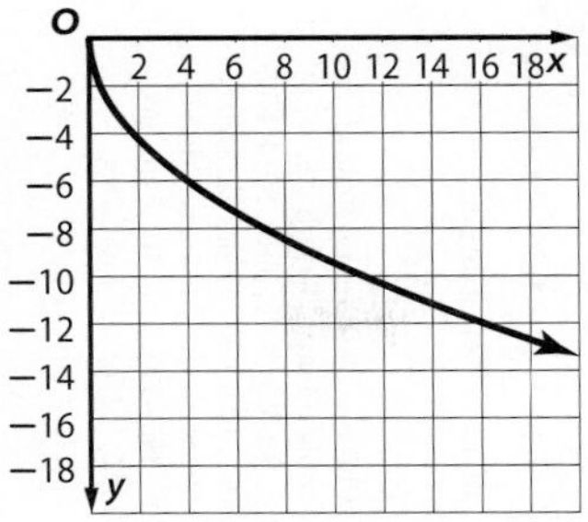

3. vertical stretch of $y = \sqrt{x}$ reflected across the x-axis and translated right 2 units; $D = \{x \mid x \geq 2\}$, $R = \{y \mid y \leq 0\}$

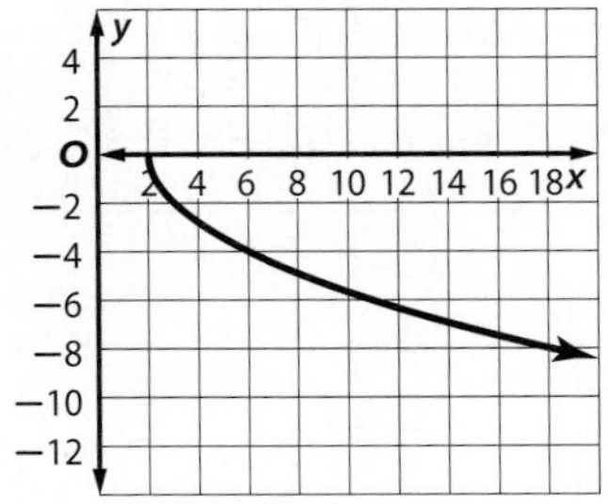

4. translated up 2 units and left 2 units; $D = \{x \mid x \geq -2\}$; $R = \{y \mid y \geq 2\}$

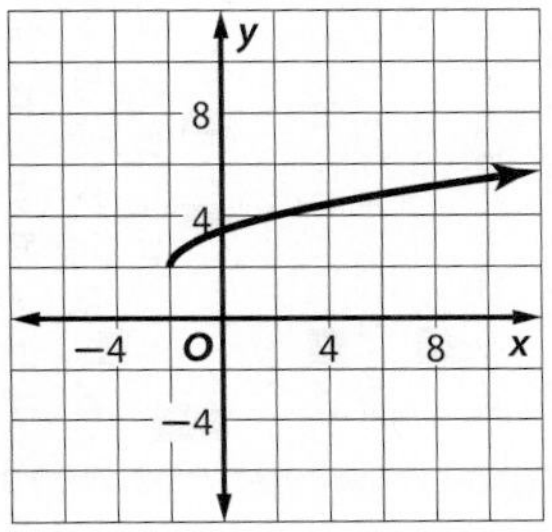

32. $m\angle B = 49$; $AC \approx 13.6$; $AB \approx 11.8$

33. $m\angle P = 58$; $PR \approx 11.3$; $QR \approx 9.6$

Extra Practice Chapter 11

6. $x = 1$; $y = 0$

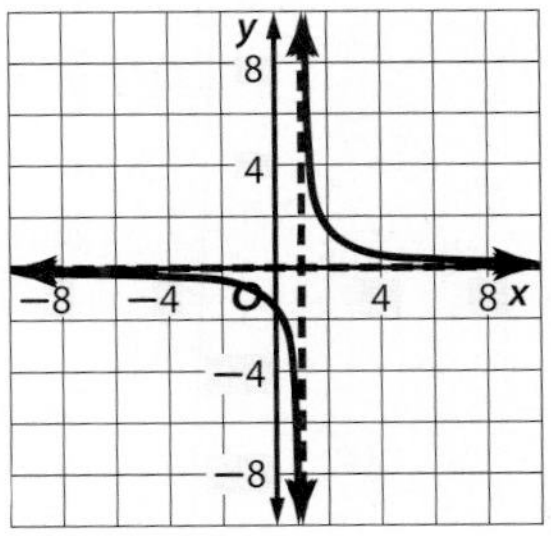

7. $x = 0$; $y = -4$

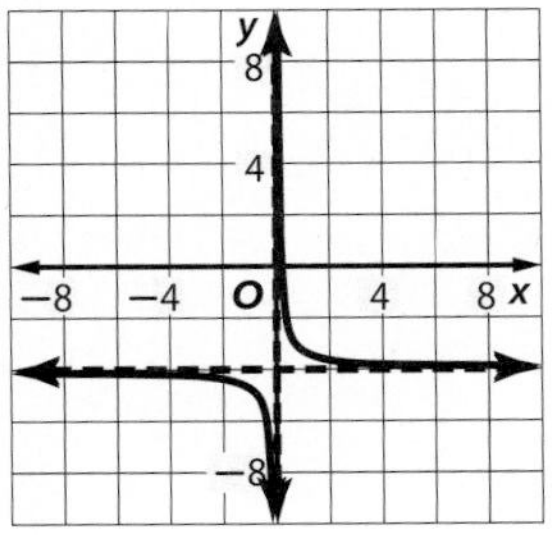

8.

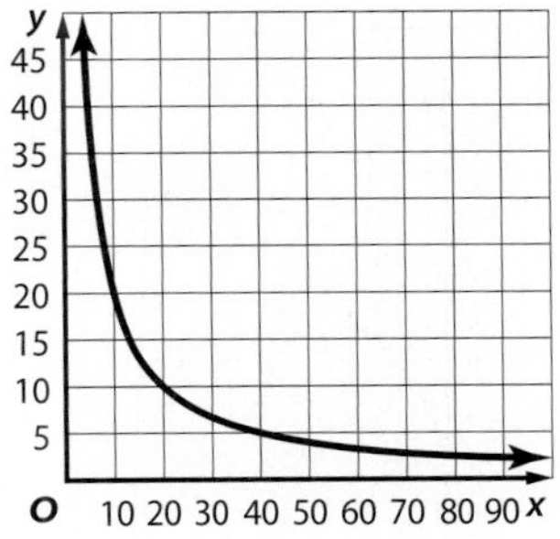

Extra Practice Chapter 12

1. Survey; sample answer: The data are obtained from opinions given by customers who respond to the letter.

2. Experiment; sample answer: The people are divided into two groups, one of which undergoes a change.

3. sample: 1000 car owners in L.A.; population: all car owners in L.A.; sample statistic: mean of the cost of a gallon of gasoline purchased by the sample; population parameter: the mean of the cost of a gallon of gas purchased by the population

5. Sample answer: The distribution is symmetric, so use the mean and standard deviation. The mean is about 17.9 with standard deviation of about 2.8.

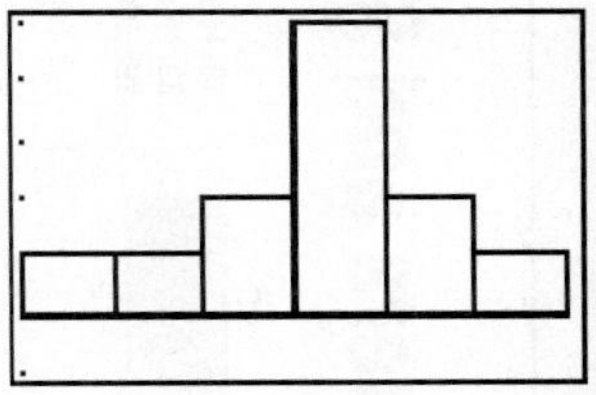

[12, 24] scl: 2 by [−1, 5] scl: 1

7. Spin a 4-part spinner with 3 parts colored the same 10 times and keep track of the color the spinner lands on each time.

15. mutually exclusive, $\frac{2}{13}$

16. mutually exclusive, $\frac{1}{2}$

17. not mutually exclusive, $\frac{7}{13}$

18. mutually exclusive, $\frac{6}{13}$

19a. all probabilities are between 0 and 1, the sum of the probabilities is 1

20a. 11–20 year olds will have the highest probability because it has the greatest number of people of any category.

Selected Answers and Solutions

CHAPTER 0
Preparing for Algebra

Lesson 0-1

1. estimate; about 700 mi **3.** estimate; about 7 times **5.** exact; \$98.75

Lesson 0-2

1. integers, rationals **3.** irrationals **5.** irrationals **7.** rationals **9.** rationals **11.** irrationals
13. $-\frac{6}{5}, -\frac{3}{5}, \frac{3}{4}$, and $\frac{7}{5}$

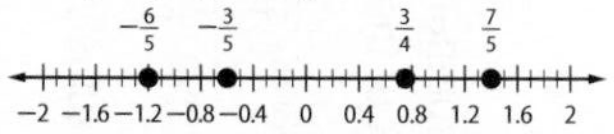

15. $2\frac{1}{4}, 2.\overline{3}, \sqrt{7}$, and $\sqrt{8}$

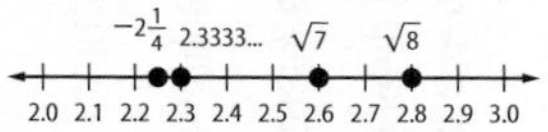

17. $-3\frac{3}{4}, -3.5, -\sqrt{10}$, and $-\frac{15}{5}$

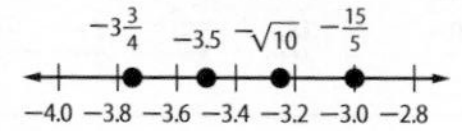

19. $\frac{5}{9}$ **21.** $\frac{13}{99}$ **23.** -5 **25.** ± 6 **27.** ± 1.2 **29.** $\frac{4}{7}$ **31.** $\frac{5}{18}$ **33.** 16 **35.** 26

Lesson 0-3

1. 5 **3.** -27 **5.** -22 **7.** -32 **9.** 22 **11.** 5 **13.** 8 **15.** -9 **17.** -115 **19.** 17° **21.** \$150 **23.** \$125

Lesson 0-4

1. $<$ **3.** $<$ **5.** $=$ **7.** $3.06, 3\frac{1}{6}, 3\frac{3}{4}, 3.8$ **9.** $-0.5, -\frac{1}{9}, \frac{1}{10}, 0.11$ **11.** $\frac{3}{5}$ **13.** $\frac{1}{16}$ **15.** 1 **17.** $2\frac{2}{3}$ **19.** $\frac{1}{9}$ **21.** $\frac{1}{6}$ **23.** $\frac{17}{30}$ **25.** $\frac{1}{4}$ **27.** -36.9 **29.** -19.33 **31.** 153.8 **33.** 93.3 **35.** $-\frac{5}{6}$ **37.** $\frac{9}{20}$ **39.** $\frac{2}{3}$ **41.** $\frac{3}{10}$

Lesson 0-5

1. 0.85 **3.** -7.05 **5.** 60 **7.** -4.8 **9.** -1.52 **11.** $\frac{6}{35}$ **13.** $\frac{2}{33}$ **15.** $\frac{21}{4}$ or $5\frac{1}{4}$ **17.** $-\frac{1}{2}$ **19.** $-\frac{1}{8}$ **21.** $\frac{10}{11}$ **23.** $\frac{5}{2}$ or $2\frac{1}{2}$ **25.** $\frac{7}{6}$ or $1\frac{1}{6}$ **27.** $-\frac{23}{14}$ or $-1\frac{9}{14}$ **29.** $-\frac{3}{16}$ **31.** 2 **33.** 3 **35.** $-\frac{3}{10}$ **37.** $\frac{9}{2}$ or $4\frac{1}{2}$ **39.** $\frac{11}{20}$ **41.** $\frac{5}{18}$ **43.** 3 slices **45.** 34 uniforms **47.** 6 ribbons

Lesson 0-6

1. $\frac{1}{20}$ **3.** $\frac{11}{100}$ **5.** $\frac{39}{50}$ **7.** $\frac{3}{500}$ **9.** 14 **11.** 40% **13.** 160 **15.** 9.5 **17.** 48 **19.** 0.25% **21.** 24.5 **23.** 150% **25.** 90% **27.** 5% **29a.** 20 g **29b.** 2350 mg **29c.** 44% **31.** 6 animals

Lesson 0-7

1. 20 m **3.** 90 in. **5.** 32 in. **7.** 29 ft **9.** 25.0 in. **11.** 31.4 in. **13.** 23.2 m **15.** 848.2 in. **17.** 13.4 cm **19.** 10.3 ft

Lesson 0-8

1. 6 cm^2 **3.** 120 m^2 **5.** 81 ft^2 **7.** 9 ft^2 **9.** 14.1 in^2 **11.** 12.6 ft^2 **13.** 50.3 cm^2 **15.** 201.1 in^2 **17.** 7 ft **19.** 20.5 units^2 **21.** 22.1 cm^2 **23.** 4.0 cm^2

Lesson 0-9

1. 30 cm^3 **3.** 48 yd^3 **5.** 1404 ft^3 **7.** 20 m^3 **9.** 27 m^3 **11.** 2070 in^3 **13.** 1 ft **15.** 4 cm **17.** 2770.9 in^3 **19a.** 128 ft^3 **19b.** 80 ft^3 **19c.** 5 ft 4 in.

Lesson 0-10

1. 68 in^2 **3.** 220 mm^2 **5.** 37 ft^2 **7.** 48 m^2 **9.** 216 in^2 **11.** 480.7 in^2 **13.** 24 m^2 **15.** 77 ft^2 **17.** 40.8 in^2

Lesson 0-11

1. $\frac{4}{15}$ **3.** $\frac{1}{2}$ **5.** $\frac{5}{6}$ **7.** $\frac{1}{2}$ **9.** $\frac{2}{3}$ **11.** 20 **13.** 12 codes **15.** $\frac{11}{24}$ **17.** 1:5 **19.** 13:11 **21.** 16 orders

Lesson 0-12

1. 5 students; 4 students; 3 students; 10 students **3.** 54.75 mph; 54 mph; 53 mph; 8 mph **5.** ≈2.8; 2.75; 2; 4 **7.** 128 **9.** \$309; \$311; \$312; \$314; \$399 **11.** 2 books; 5 books; 10 books; 17 books; 18 books **13.** 16 years old; 19 years old; 21 years old; 24 years old; 45 years old **15.** ≈138.3 mi, 101.5 mi; no outliers **17.** ≈0.286, 0.296; 0.201; ≈0.295, 0.300; mean

Lesson 0-13

1.

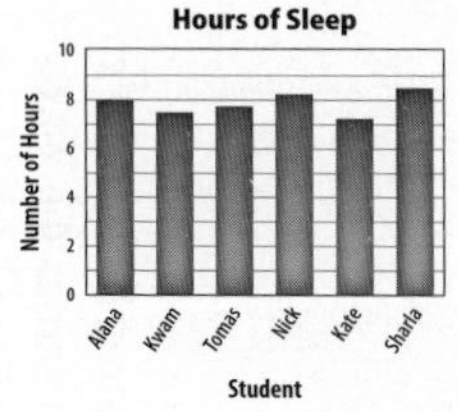

3.

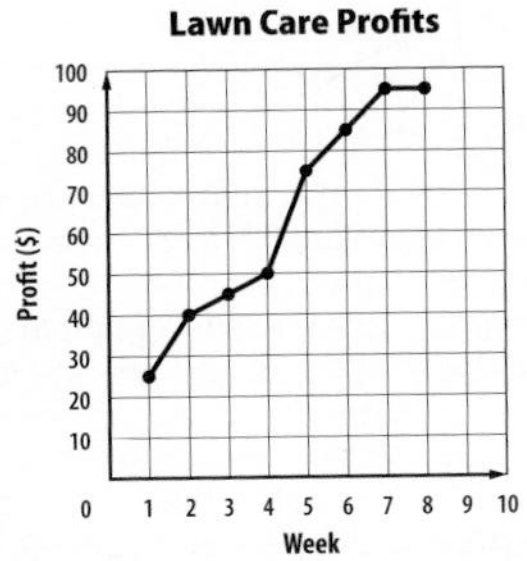

5.

Stem	Leaf
1	8 8
2	1 3 6 6 6 8
3	0 1 1 2 3 4
4	7

Key: 1|8 = 18

Removing 47 leaves Q_1 the same, changes Q_2 to 27 and Q_3 to 31.

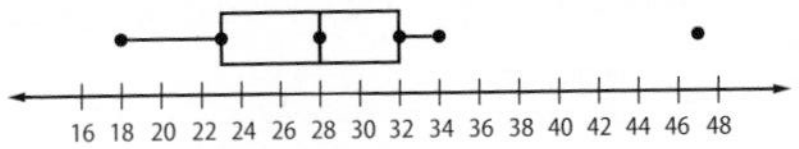

7.

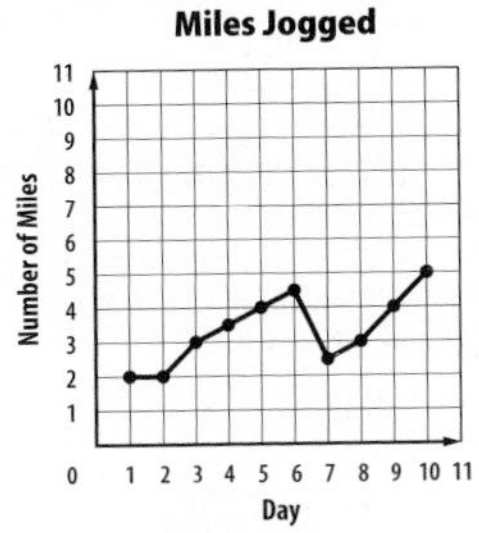

9a.

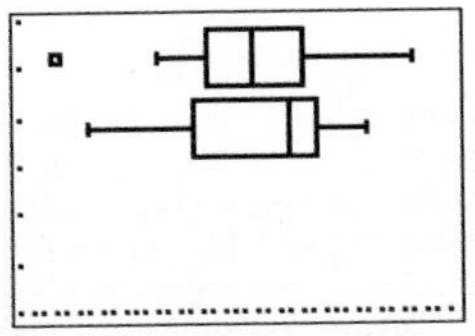

9b. Most of the data for third period are spread fairly evenly from about 80 to 89, with the lowest score being 67 and the highest score being 99. Most of the data for sixth period are between 79 and 91, with the lowest score for the class being 70 and the highest score being 95.
9c. The sixth period class has a smaller range, a higher median, and a larger interquartile range than the third period class.
11. Sample answer: a line graph would show how the cost of a seat changes during those years.

13a.

Stem	Leaf
11	9
12	4 6 9
13	0 0 3 5 6 7 8
14	0

Key: 11|9 = 119

13b.

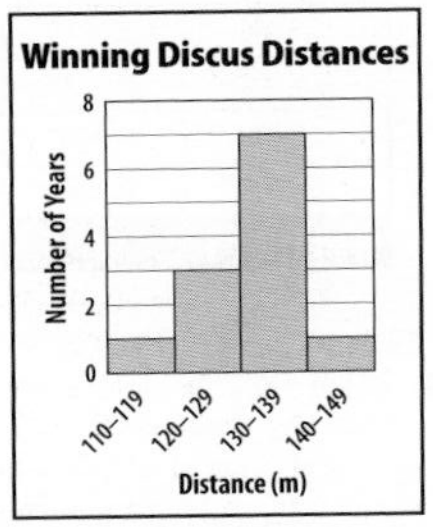

13c. Sample answer: The histogram shows frequencies, while the stem and leaf shows all data points.
13d. Sample answer: The winning distance increased by 16 meters from 2000 to 2010. If this continues, in 2030 the winning distance will be 32 meters more than in 2010, or 172 meters. It is unreasonable to expect that every year girls will be able to throw farther and farther, at some time the distance will level off.

CHAPTER 1 Expressions, Equations, and Functions

Get Ready

1. $\frac{2}{3}$ **3.** 3 **5.** *simplest form* **7.** 19 **9.** $\frac{8}{11}$ **11.** 8.2 cm **13.** 20 m **15.** 34.02 **17.** 1.9 **19.** 0.56

Lesson 1-1

1. Sample answer: the product of 2 and m
3. Sample answer: a squared minus 18 times b
5. $6 - t$ **7.** $1 - \frac{r}{7}$ **9.** $n^3 + 5$ **11.** Sample answer: four times a number q **13.** Sample answer: 15 plus r **15.** Sample answer: 3 times x squared
17 Sample answer: 6 more than the product of 2 and a
19. $7 + x$ **21.** $5n$ **23.** $\frac{f}{10}$ **25.** $3n + 16$ **27.** $k^2 - 11$ **29.** $\pi r^2 h$ **31.** Sample answer: twenty-five plus six times a number squared **33.** Sample answer: three times a number raised to the fifth power divided by two
35 **a.** Words: $\frac{3}{4}$ of the number of dreams
Expression: $\frac{3}{4} \cdot d$
The expression is $\frac{3}{4}d$.
b. $\frac{3}{4}(28) = 21$ dreams

37a.

10^2	·	10^1	=	10 · 10 · 10	=	10^3
10^2	·	10^2	=	10 · 10 · 10 · 10	=	10^4
10^2	·	10^3	=	10 · 10 · 10 · 10 · 10	=	10^5
10^2	·	10^4	=	10 · 10 · 10 · 10 · 10 · 10	=	10^6

37b. $10^2 \cdot 10^x = 10^{(2 + x)}$
37c. The exponent of the product of two powers is the sum of the exponents of the powers with the same base. **39.** Sample answer: x is the number of minutes it takes to walk between my house and school. $2x + 15$ represents the amount of time in minutes I spend walking each day since I walk to and from school and I take my dog on a 15 minute walk. **41.** 6 **43.** D **45.** $\frac{31}{36}$

47.

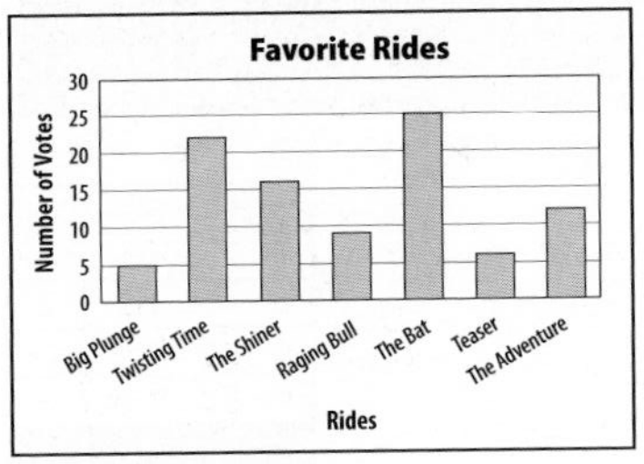

49. mean = 5.6; median = 6.5; mode = 7
51. mean = 15.25; median = 15.5; mode = 24
53. $\frac{21}{55}$ **55.** $\frac{20}{9}$ **57.** 1.46 **59.** 24.61 **61.** 21.16

Lesson 1-2

1. 81 **3.** 243
5 $5 \cdot 5 - 1 \cdot 3 = 25 - 3$
$= 22$
7. 28 **9.** 12 **11.** 20 **13.** $20 + 3 \times 4.95$; \$34.85
15. 49 **17.** 64 **19.** 14 **21.** 36 **23.** 14
25. 142 **27.** 36 **29.** 3 **31.** 1
33 $(2t + 3g) \div 4 = (2(11) + 3(2)) \div 4$
$= (22 + 6) \div 4$
$= (28) \div 4$
$= 7$
35. 149 **37.** $3344 - 148 = 3196$ **39.** 16 **41.** 729
43. 177 **45.** 324 **47.** 29 **49.** 4080 **51.** $\frac{97}{31}$ **53.** 0
55. $28(7) + 12(9.75) + 30(7) + 15(9.75)$; \$669.25
57 **a.**

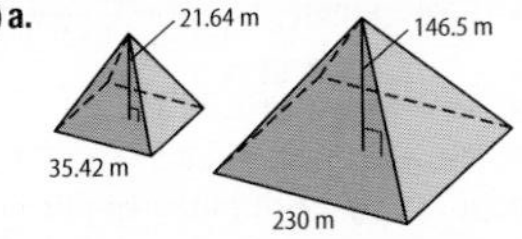

b. Words: one third times 230 squared times 146.5 minus one third times 35.42 squared times 21.64
c. Expression: $\frac{1}{3}(230)^2(146.5) - \frac{1}{3}(35.42)^2(21.64)$
$\approx 2583283.33 - 9049.68$
$\approx 2574233.656 \text{ m}^3$
59. Curtis; Tara subtracted $10 - 9$ before multiplying 4 by 10. **61.** Sample answer: $5 + 4 - 3 - 2 - 1$
63. Sample answer: Area of a trapezoid: $\frac{1}{2}h(b_1 + b_2)$; according to the order of operations, you have to add the lengths of the bases together first and then multiply by the height and by $\frac{1}{2}$. **65.** A **67A.** G
67B. Sample answers given.

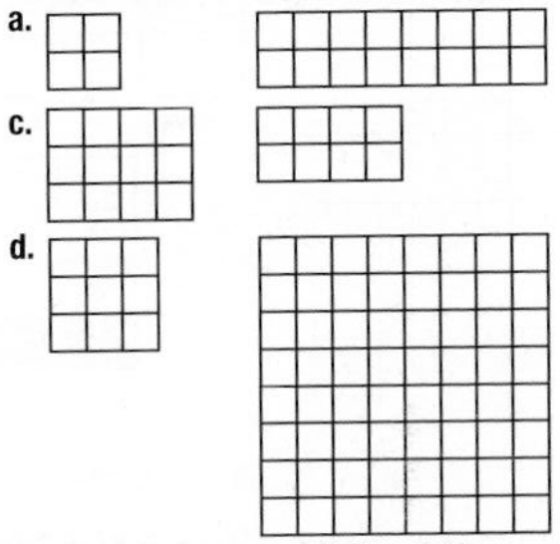

69. 14 minus 9 times c **71.** the difference of 4 and v divided by w **73.** 9π units^2 **75.** $12b$ units^2
77. 2.57 **79.** 13.192 **81.** $\frac{2}{3}$

Lesson 1-3

1. $(1 \div 5)5 \cdot 14$
$= \frac{1}{5} \cdot 5 \cdot 14$ Substitution
$= (1) \cdot 14$ Multiplicative Inverse
$= 14$ Multiplicative Identity
3. $5(14 - 5) + 6(3 + 7) = 5(9) + 6(10)$ Substitution
$= 45 + 60$ Substitution
$= 105$ Substitution
5. $23 + 42 + 37$
$= 23 + 37 + 42$ Commutative (+)
$= (23 + 37) + 42$ Associative (+)
$= 60 + 42$ Substitution
$= 102$ Substitution
7. $3 \cdot 7 \cdot 10 \cdot 2$
$= 3 \cdot 2 \cdot 7 \cdot 10$ Commutative (×)
$= (3 \cdot 2) \cdot (7 \cdot 10)$ Associative (×)
$= 6 \cdot 70$ Substitution
$= 420$ Substitution
9 $3(22 - 3 \cdot 7) = 3(22 - 21)$ Substitution
$= 3(1)$ Substitution
$= 3$ Multiplicative Identity
11. $\frac{3}{4}[4 \div (7 - 4)]$
$= \frac{3}{4}[4 \div 3]$ Substitution
$= \frac{3}{4} \times \frac{4}{3}$ Substitution
$= 1$ Multiplicative Inverse
13. $2(3 \cdot 2 - 5) + 3 \cdot \frac{1}{3}$
$= 2(6 - 5) + 3 \cdot \frac{1}{3}$ Substitution

Selected Answers and Solutions
Selected Answers and Solutions

$= 2(1) + 3 \cdot \frac{1}{3}$ Substitution
$= 2 + 3 \cdot \frac{1}{3}$ Multiplicative Identity
$= 2 + 1$ Multiplicative Inverse
$= 3$ Substitution

15. $2 \cdot \frac{22}{7} \cdot 14^2 + 2 \cdot \frac{22}{7} \cdot 14 \cdot 7$
$= 2 \cdot \frac{22}{7} \cdot 196 + 2 \cdot \frac{22}{7} \cdot 14 \cdot 7$ Substitution
$= \frac{44}{7} \cdot 196 + \frac{44}{7} \cdot 14 \cdot 7$ Substitution
$= 1232 + 616$ Substitution
$= 1848$ Substitution
The surface area is 1848 in^2.

17. $25 + 14 + 15 + 36$
$= 25 + 15 + 14 + 36$ Commutative(+)
$= (25 + 15) + (14 + 36)$ Associative(+)
$= 40 + 50$ Substitution
$= 90$ Substitution

19. $3\frac{2}{3} + 4 + 5\frac{1}{3} = 3\frac{2}{3} + 5\frac{1}{3} + 4$ Commutative (+)
$= \left(3\frac{2}{3} + 5\frac{1}{3}\right) + 4$ Associative (+)
$= 9 + 4$ Substitution
$= 13$ Substitution

21. $4.3 + 2.4 + 3.6 + 9.7$
$= 4.3 + 9.7 + 2.4 + 3.6$ Commutative (+)
$= (4.3 + 9.7) + (2.4 + 3.6)$ Associative (+)
$= 14 + 6$ Substitution
$= 20$ Substitution

23. $12 \cdot 2 \cdot 6 \cdot 5 = 12 \cdot 6 \cdot 2 \cdot 5$ Commutative (×)
$= (12 \cdot 6) \cdot (2 \cdot 5)$ Associative (×)
$= 72 \cdot 10$ Substitution
$= 720$ Substitution

25. $0.2 \cdot 4.6 \cdot 5 = (0.2 \cdot 4.6) \cdot 5$ Associative (×)
$= 0.92 \cdot 5$ Substitution
$= 4.6$ Substitution

27. $1\frac{5}{6} \cdot 24 \cdot 3\frac{1}{11} = 1\frac{5}{6}\left(24 \cdot 3\frac{1}{11}\right)$ Associative (×)
$= 1\frac{5}{6}\left(\frac{24}{1} \cdot \frac{34}{11}\right)$
$= 1\frac{5}{6} \cdot \frac{816}{11}$ Substitution
$= \frac{8976}{66}$ Substitution
$= 136$ Substitution

29a. Sample answer: 2(10.95) + 3(7.5) + 2(5) + 5(18.99); 2(10.95 + 5) + 3(7.5) + 5(18.99) **29b.** \$149.35
(31) $4(-1) + 9(4) - 2(6) = -4 + 36 - 12$
$= 32 - 12$
$= 20$

33. −18 **35.** 192 **37.** Additive Identity; 35 + 0 = 35 **39.** 0; Additive Identity **41.** 7; Reflexive Property **43.** 3; Multiplicative Identity **45.** 2; Commutative Property **47.** 3; Multiplicative Inverse **49.** \$108 **51.** 88 units **(53) a.**

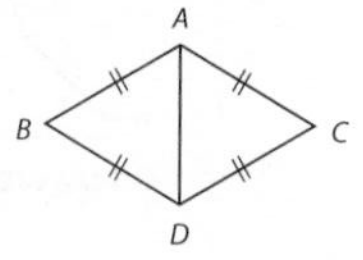

b. $\overline{AD} \cong \overline{AD}$ by the Reflexive Property. The Transitive Property shows that if $\overline{AB} \cong \overline{AC}$ and $\overline{AC} \cong \overline{DC}$, then $\overline{AB} \cong \overline{DC}$ and if $\overline{AB} \cong \overline{BD}$ and $\overline{AB} \cong \overline{AC}$, then $\overline{BD} \cong \overline{AC}$.
c. Since the sides are all congruent, each side has a length x. So, $P = x + x + x + x$.
55. Sample answer: You cannot divide by 0.
57. Sometimes; when a number is subtracted from itself then it holds but otherwise it does not.
59. $(2j)k = 2(jk)$; The other three equations illustrate the Commutative Property of Addition or Multiplication. This equation represents the Associative Property of Multiplication. **61.** D **63.** C **65.** 14 **67.** 6 **69.** 26 ft; 40 ft^2
71. about 64.7 % **73.** $\frac{23}{2}$ **75.** $\frac{6}{35}$ **77.** $\frac{6}{11}$ **79.** 6

Lesson 1-4

1. 25(12 + 15); \$675 **3.** $\left(6 + \frac{1}{9}\right)9$; 55 **5.** $g(5) + (-9)(5)$; $5g - 45$ **7.** simplified
9. $4(2x + 6)$
$= 4(2x) + 4(6)$ Distributive Property
$= 8x + 24$ Multiply.
(11) $4(5 + 3 + 4) = 4(8 + 4)$
$= 4(12)$
$= 48$ activities
13. 6(4) + 6(5); 54 **15.** 6(6) − 6(1); 30 **17.** 14(8) − 14(5); 42 **19.** 4(7) − 4(2); 20 **21.** 7(500 − 3); 3479
23. $36\left(3 + \frac{1}{4}\right)$; 117 **25.** $2(x) + 2(4)$; $2x + 8$
27. $4(8) + (-3m)(8)$; $32 - 24m$ **29.** $18r$ **31.** $2m + 7$
33. $34 - 68n$ **35.** $13m + 5p$ **37.** $4fg + 17g$
39. $7(a^2 + b) - 4(a^2 + b)$
$= 7a^2 + 7b - 4a^2 - 4b$ Substitution
$= 7a^2 - 4a^2 + 7b - 4b$ Commutative (+)
$= (7 - 4)a^2 + (7 - 4)b$ Distributive Prop.
$= 3a^2 + 3b$ Substitution
(41) A hexagon has six sides so an expression for the perimeter is $6(3x + 5)$.
$6(3x + 5) = 6(3x) + 6(5)$
$= 18x + 30$ units
43. $14m + 11g$ **45.** $12k^3 + 12k$ **47.** $19x + 8$
49. $9 - 54b$ **51.** $12c - 6cd^2 + 6d$ **53.** $7y^3 + y^4$
55a. $2(x + 3)$
55b.

Area	Factored form
2x + 6	2(x + 3)
3x + 3	3(x + 1)
3x − 12	3(x − 4)
5x + 10	5(x + 2)

55c. Divide each term of the expression by the same number. Then write the expression as a product.
57. It should be considered a property of both. Both operations are used in $a(b + c) = ab + ac$. **59.** Sample answer: You can use the Distributive Property to calculate quickly by expressing any number as a sum or difference of a more convenient number. Answers should include the following: Both methods result in the correct answer. In one method you multiply then add, and in the other you add then multiply. **61.** G **63.** about $\frac{1}{3}$ or 33%
65. $0.24 \cdot 8 \cdot 7.05 = (0.24 \cdot 8) \cdot 7.05$ Associative (×)
$= 1.92 \cdot 7.05$ Substitution
$= 13.536$ Substitution
67. $\frac{4[6(30) + 3(20)]}{60}$; 16 hours **69.** 21:48
71. 384 in^2 **73.** 15 **75.** 60 **77.** 192

Lesson 1-5

1. {13} **3.** {12} **5.** B **7.** −68 **9.** all real numbers **11.** {12} **13.** {5} **15.** {16} **17.** {3} **19.** 14 **21.** 2 **23.** 2 **25.** 5 **27.** no solution **29.** all real numbers
(31) $(2^4 - 3 \cdot 5)q + 13 = (2 \cdot 9 - 4^2)q + \left(\frac{3 \cdot 4}{12} - 1\right)$
$(16 - 15)q + 13 = (18 - 16)q + (1 - 1)$
$1q + 13 = 2q + 0$
$1q + 13 = 2q$
$13 = 2q - 1q$
$13 = 1q$
$q = 13$
33. 41 students
(35) Words: the number of calories equals 2836 plus 3091
Expression: $C = 2836 + 3091$ Solve: $C = 5927$
37.

x	3x − 2	y
−2	3(−2) − 2	−8
−1	3(−1) − 2	−5
0	3(0) − 2	−2
1	3(1) − 2	1
2	3(2) − 2	4

39. 20 **41.** 66 **43.** 5 **45.** $c = 15$ **47a.** $5 = \frac{1000}{r}$; 20
47b.

Intial Pressure p_1 (mm Hg)	Final Pressure p_2 (mm Hg)	Resistance r (mm Hg/L/min)	Blood Flow Rate F (L/min)
100	0	20	5
100	0	30	≈ 3.33
165	5	40	4
90	30	10	12

49. solution **51.** not a solution **53.** solution
55. solution
57.

x	3x + 5	y
−2	3(−2) + 5	−1
−1	3(−1) + 5	2
0	3(0) + 5	5
1	3(1) + 5	8
2	3(2) + 5	11

59.

x	$\frac{1}{2}x + 2$	y
−2	$\frac{1}{2}(-2) + 2$	1
−1	$\frac{1}{2}(-1) + 2$	1.5
0	$\frac{1}{2}(0) + 2$	2
1	$\frac{1}{2}(1) + 2$	2.5
2	$\frac{1}{2}(2) + 2$	3

61a.

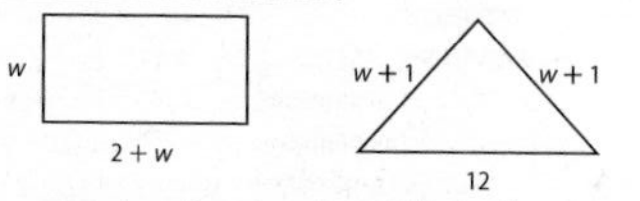

61b. perimeter of rectangle $= 2(2 + w) + 2w$ or $4 + 4w$; perimeter of triangle $= 2(w + 1) + 12 = 2w + 14$.
61c. $4 + 4w = 2w + 14$; $w = 5$ in.
(63) b.

Layers	1	2	3	4	5	6	7
Cubes	4	8	12	16	20	24	28

c. From the table, we can tell that each layer adds 4 more cubes. Notice 8 − 4 = 4; 12 − 8 = 4; 16 − 12 = 4; 20 − 16 = 4; 24 − 20 = 4; 28 − 24 = 4
d. The number of cubes is 4 times the number of layers, or $c = 4L$.
65. Sample answer: $3x + 12 = 3(x + 4)$ **67.** Tom; Li-Cheng added 6 + 4 instead of dividing 6 by 8. She did not follow the order of operations.
69. Sample answer: $3x - 2 = -23$ **71.** C **73.** G
75. 30(500 + 750) **77.** $p = \frac{1}{12}$; Multiplicative Inverse **79.** 1040 in^3 **81.** $\frac{3}{20}$ **83.** estimate; 10 gal
85. 6.74 **87.** 1.65 **89.** $\frac{29}{28}$

Lesson 1-6

1.

x	y
4	3
−2	2
5	−6

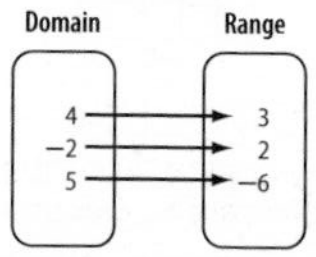

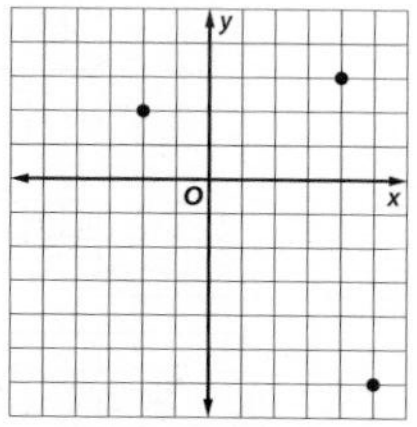

D = {−2, 4, 5}; R = {−6, 2, 3}
3. I: the temperature of the compound; D: the pressure of the compound **5.** I: number of concert tickets, D: cost of tickets **7.** The track team starts by running or walking, and then stops for a short period of time, then continues at the same pace. Finally, they run or walk at a slower pace.

9.

x	y
0	0
−3	2
6	4
−1	1

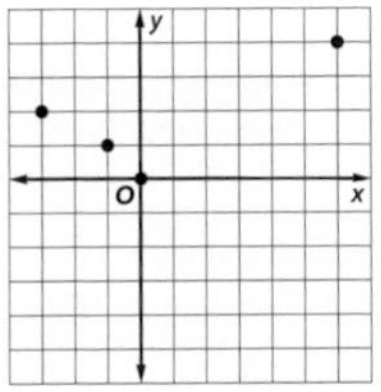

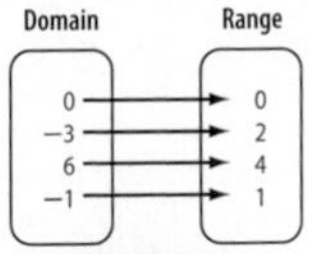

D = {0, −3, 6, −1};
R = {0, 2, 4, 1}

11.

x	y
6	1
4	−3
3	2
−1	−3

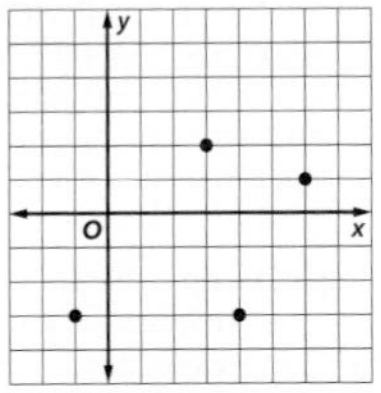

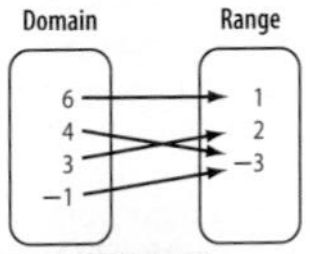

D = {6, 4, 3, −1};
R = {1, −3, 2}

13.

x	y
6	7
3	−2
8	8
−6	2
2	−6

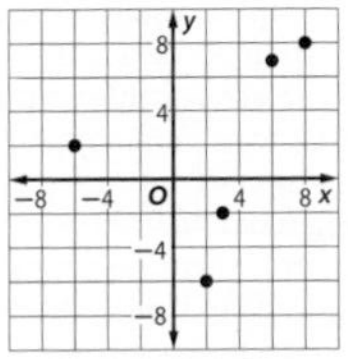

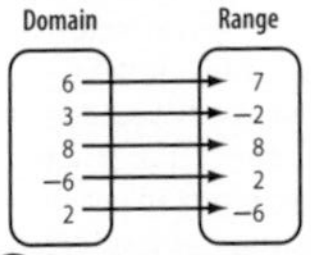

D = {−6, 2, 3, 6, 8};
R = {−6, −2, 2, 7, 8}

15 The number of students who attend is the independent variable because it does not depend on the amount of food there will be. The amount of food is the dependent variable because it depends on the number of students who attend.

17. The bungee jumper starts at the maximum height, and then jumps. After the initial jump, the jumper bounces up and down until coming to a rest.

19 Use the graph to determine what is happening to the value of the baseball card. The values are continually increasing.

21. (1, 5); The dog walker earns $5 for walking 1 dog. **23.** I: number of dogs walked; D: amount earned **25.** (5, 6); In the year 2005, sales were about $6 million. **27.** {(1, 2.50), (2, 4.50), (5, 10.50), (8, 16.50)}; D = {1, 2, 5, 8}; R = {2.50, 4.50, 10.50, 16.50} **29.** {(4, −1), (8, 9), (−2, −6), (7, −3)} **31.** {(4, −2), (−1, 3), (−2,−1), (1, 4)}
33. Sample answer: **35.** Sample answer:

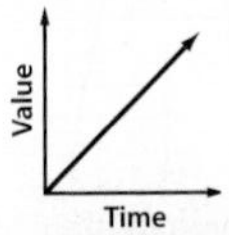

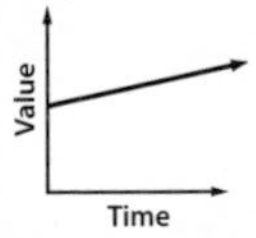

37 a.

b	$w = 2\left(\frac{b}{3}\right)$	w
100	$w = 2\left(\frac{100}{3}\right)$	66.7
105	$w = 2\left(\frac{105}{3}\right)$	70
110	$w = 2\left(\frac{110}{3}\right)$	73.3
115	$w = 2\left(\frac{115}{3}\right)$	76.7
120	$w = 2\left(\frac{120}{3}\right)$	80
125	$w = 2\left(\frac{125}{3}\right)$	83.3
130	$w = 2\left(\frac{130}{3}\right)$	86.7

b. The independent variable is the body weight *b*. The dependent variable is the water weight *w*.

c. The domain is the set of *b* values. D = {100, 105, 110, 115, 120, 125, 130}. The range is the set of all *w* values. R = {66.7, 70, 73.3, 76.7, 80, 83.3, 86.7}

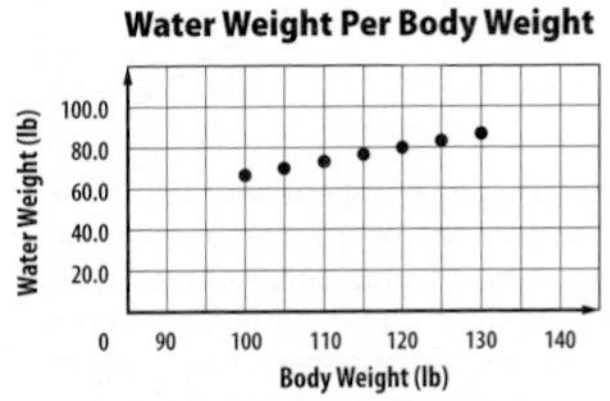

d. Graph the following ordered pairs: (66.7, 100), (70, 105), (73.3, 110), (76.7, 115), (80, 120), (83.3, 125), (86.7, 130).

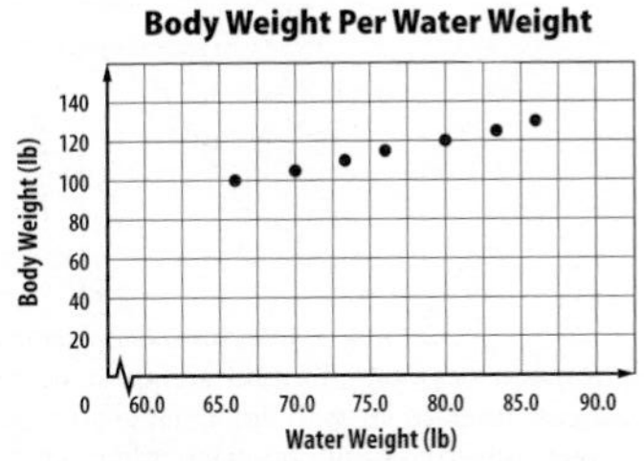

This graph shows what a person's body weight would be based on their water weight.

41. Reversing the coordinates gives (1, 0), (3, 1), (5, 2), and (7, 3).

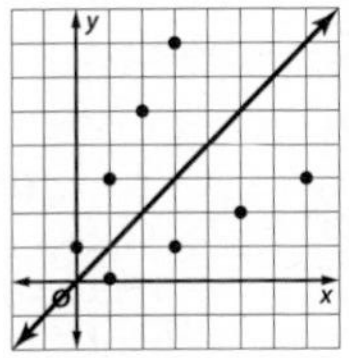

Each point in the original relation is the same distance from the line as the corresponding points of the reverse relation. The graphs are symmetric about the line $y = x$.

43. B **45.** (−1, −3) **47.** 2 **49.** 3 **51.** $\frac{1}{8}$
53. 50.27 cm **55.** 64 **57.** 6.25 **59.** 49

Lesson 1-7

1. Yes; for each input there is exactly one output.
3. No; the domain value 2 is paired with 2 and −4. **5.** No; when $x = 0$, $y = 1$ and $y = 6$.
7. Yes; its graph passes the vertical line test.
9a. {(0, 48,560), (1, 48,710), (2, 48,948), (3, 49,091)}
9b.

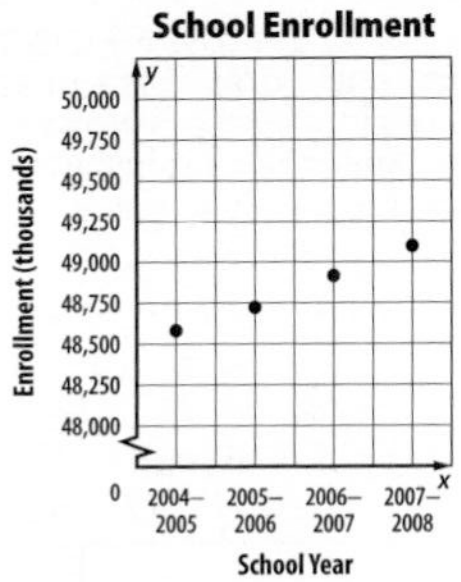

9c. The domain is the school year and the range is the enrollment.

11 $f(-3) = 6(-3) + 7$
$= -18 + 7$
$= -11$

13. $6r - 5$ **15.** $a^2 + 5$ **17.** $6q + 13$ **19.** $b^2 - 4$
21. No; the domain value 4 is paired with both 5 and 6. **23.** Yes; for each input there is exactly one output. **25.** Yes; the graph passes the vertical line test. **27.** yes **29.** yes **31.** yes **33.** −1 **35.** 14
37. −4 **39.** $-8y - 3$ **41.** $-2c + 7$ **43.** $-10d - 15$

45 a. Create a table using the rule given.

t	0.8t + 72	f(t)
0	0.8(0) + 72	72
10	0.8(10) + 72	80
20	0.8(20) + 72	88
30	0.8(30) + 72	96
40	0.8(40) + 72	104
50	0.8(50) + 72	112

Plot the ordered pairs on a coordinate plane.

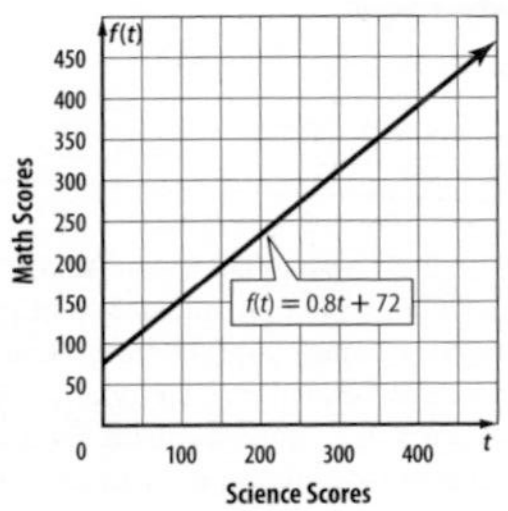

When the science score is 0, the math score is 72. For each point the science score increases, the math score increases by 0.8 points.

b. $308 = 0.8t + 72$
$236 = 0.8t$
$295 = t$

c. The domain is the set of science scores, the range is the set of math scores.

47 The graph represents a function because each *x*-value is paired with only one *y*-value.

49. Sample answer: {(−2, 3), (0, 3), (2, 5)}

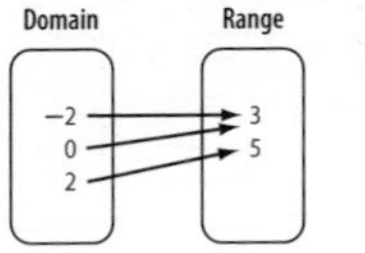

51. $f(g + 3.5) = -4.3g - 17.05$ **53.** Sample answer: $f(x) = 3x + 2$ **55.** Sample answer: You can determine whether each element of the domain is paired with exactly one element of the range. For example, if given a graph, you could use the vertical line test; if a vertical line intersects the graph more than once, then the relation that the graph represents is not a function. **57.** J
59. her first game **61.** $\frac{13}{2}$ **63.** 4(1.99) + 10(0.25) + 4(1.85) = 17.86, so the cost is $17.86. **65.** sample answer: two thirds times *x* **67.** 38.016 cm^3
69. 288,000 mm^3 **71.** −1 **73.** 40 **75.** 65

Lesson 1-8

1. Nonlinear; the *y*-intercept is 0, so there is no change in the stock value at the opening bell. The *x*-intercepts are 0, about 3.2, and about 4.5, so there is no change in the stock value after 0 hours, after about 3.2 hours, and after about 4.5 hours, respectively, after the opening bell. The graph has no line symmetry. The stock went up in value for the first 3.2 hours, then dropped below the starting value from about 3.2 hours until 4.5 hours, and finally went up again after 4.5 hours. The stock value starts the day increasing in value for the first 2 hours, then it goes down in value from 2 hours until 4 hours, and after 4 hours it goes up in value for the remainder of the day. The stock had a relative high value after 2 hours and then a relative low value after 4 hours. As the day goes on, the stock increases in value. **3.** Linear; the y-intercept is about 45, so the temperature was about 45°F when the measurement started. The x-intercept is about 5.5, so after about 5.5 hours, the temperature was 0°F. The graph has no line symmetry. The temperature is above zero for the first 5.5 hours, and then below zero after 5.5 hours. The temperature is going down for the entire time. There are no extrema. As the time increases, the temperature will continue to drop forever, which is not very likely.

5 Since the graph is a curve and not a line, the graph is nonlinear. The graph intersects the y-axis at about (0, 20), so the y-intercept of the graph is about 20. This means that the purchase price of the vehicle was about $20,000. The graph approaches but never intersects the x-axis, so the graph has no x-intercept. This means that the value of the vehicle will never reach 0. There is no line over which the graph can be folded so that both halves match exactly. Therefore the graph has no line symmetry. The graph lies entirely above the x-axis, therefore the function is positive for all values of x. This means that the value of the vehicle is always positive. When viewed from left to right, the graph goes down for all values of x, so the function is decreasing for all values of x, which means that the value of the vehicle is always decreasing. There are no relatively high or low points on the graph, so the function has no extrema. As you move right, the graph goes down, so the end behavior of the graph is that as x increases, y decreases. This means that as the number of years since the car was purchased increases, the value of the vehicle decreases.

7. Nonlinear; the y-intercept is about 100. This means that the Web site had 100 hits before the time began. There is no x-intercept. The function is positive for all values of x. This means that the Web site has never experienced a time of inactivity. The function is increasing for all values of x, with no relative maxima or minima. As x increases, y increases, which means that the upward trend in the number of hits is expected to continue.
9. Nonlinear; the x- and y-intercepts are both 0, which means that a pendulum with no length cannot complete a swing. The function is positive and increasing for all values of x. Also, as x increases, y increases. The function has no relative minima or maxima. This means that as the pendulum gets longer, the time it takes for it to complete one full swing increases. **11.** Sample answer: The function has a y-intercept of 0 and an x-intercept of 0, indicating that the plant started with no height as a seed in the ground. The function is increasing over its domain, so that plant was always getting taller. The function has no relative extrema.

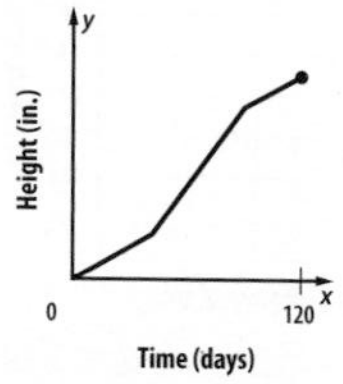

13. Sample answer: The function has a y-intercept of 27, indicating that the initial balance of the loan was $27,000. The x-intercept of 4 indicates that the loan was paid off after 4 years. The function is decreasing over its entire domain, indicating that the amount owed on the loan was always decreasing. The function has no relative extrema.

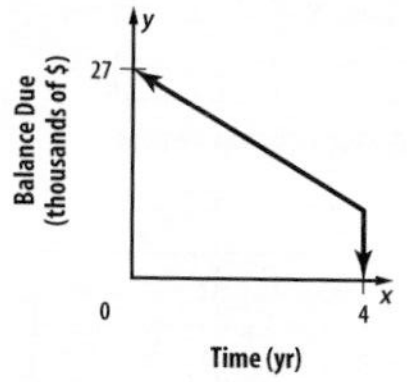

15 Plot the x-intercepts at (−2, 0) and (2, 0) and the y-intercept at (0, −4). Since the graph is nonlinear and decreasing for $x < 0$, draw a smooth curve starting somewhere to the left and above (−2, 0) that moves down through (−2, 0) to (0, −4). Since the graph has a relative minimum at $x = 0$ and is increasing for $x > 0$, turn at the point (0, −4) and draw a smooth curve moving up as you move right, through (2, 0) and continuing to the upper right portion of the graph. Sample graph:

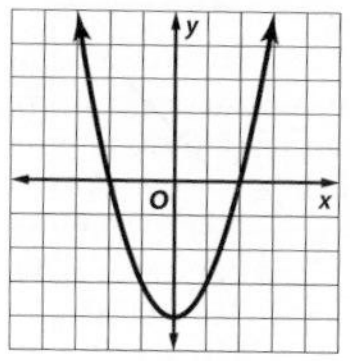

17. Sample graph:

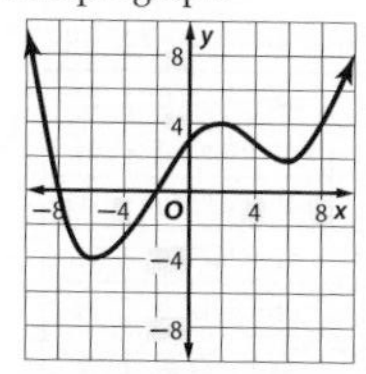

19. As x increases or decreases, y approaches 0.
21. The graph has a relative maximum at about $x = 2$ and a relative minimum at about $x = 4.5$. This means that the weekly gasoline price spiked around week 2 at a high of about \$3.50/gal and dipped around week 5 to a low of about \$1.50/gal.

Average Weekly Gasoline Price

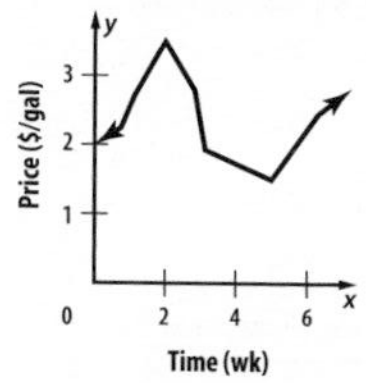

23. C **25.** A **27.** yes **29.** yes **31.** $d^2 + 3d$
33. $3(z - 2x)$ **35.** 49 **37.** 17.64

Chapter 1 Study Guide and Review

1. true **3.** false; not in simplest form **5.** true
7. false; multiplicative identity **9.** the product of 3 and x squared **11.** $x + 9$ **13.** $4x - 5$ **15.** 216
17. $2.50 + 3.25g$ **19.** 18 **21.** 2 **23.** 3 **25.** 5
27. 2.75(3) + 4.25(2); \$16.75

29. $[5 \div (8 - 6)]$
$= [5 \div 2]\frac{2}{5}$ Substitution
$= \frac{5}{2} \cdot \frac{2}{5}$ Substitution
$= 1$ Multiplicative Inverse

31. $2 \cdot \frac{1}{2} + 4(4 \cdot 2 - 7)$
$= 2 \cdot \frac{1}{2} + 4(8 - 7)$ Substitution
$= 2 \cdot \frac{1}{2} + 4(1)$ Substitution
$= 1 + 4(1)$ Multiplicative Inverse
$= 1 + 4$ Multiplicative Identity
$= 5$ Substitution

33. $7\frac{2}{5} + 5 + 2\frac{3}{5}$
$= 7\frac{2}{5} + 2\frac{3}{5} + 5$ Commutative (+)
$= \left(7\frac{2}{5} + 2\frac{3}{5}\right) + 5$ Associative (+)
$= 10 + 5$ Substitution
$= 15$ Substitution

35. $5.3 + 2.8 + 3.7 + 6.2$
$= 5.3 + 3.7 + 2.8 + 6.2$ Commutative (+)
$= (5.3 + 3.7) + (2.8 + 6.2)$ Associative (+)
$= 9 + 9$ Substitution
$= 18$ Substitution

37. (2)6 + (3)6; 30 **39.** 8(6) − 8(2); 32 **41.** −2(5) − (−2)(3); −4 **43.** $3(x) + 3(2); 3x + 6$ **45.** $6(d) - 6(3); 6d - 18$ **47.** $(9y)(-3) - (6)(-3); -27y + 18$
49. 4(3 + 5 + 4); 48 **51.** {7} **53.** {9} **55.** {5} **57.** 9

59.

x	y
1	3
2	4
3	5
4	6

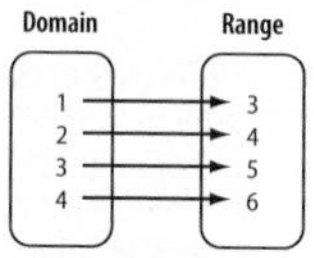

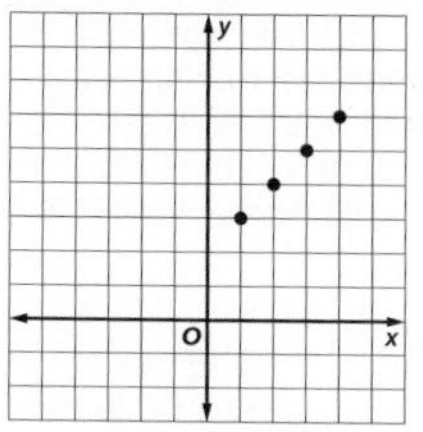

D = {1, 2, 3, 4}; R = {3, 4, 5, 6}

61.

x	y
−2	4
−1	3
0	2
−1	2

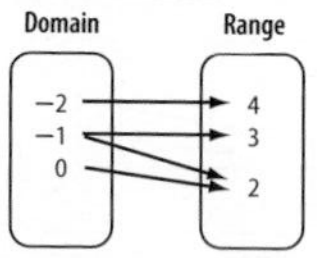

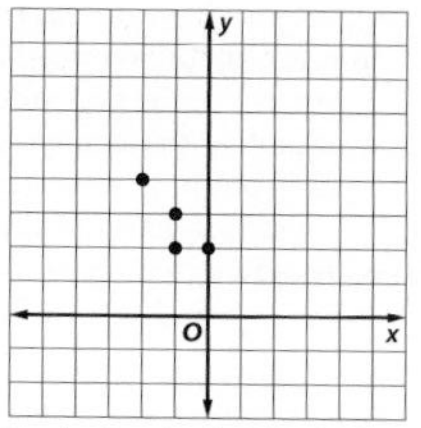

D = {−2, −1, 0}; R = {2, 3, 4}

63. {(−2, −2), (0, −3), (2, −2), (2, 0), (4, −1)}
65. function **67.** not a function **69.** 1 **71.** 13
73. $9p^2 - 3$ **75.** Nonlinear; the graph intersects the y-axis at about (0, 56), so the y-intercept is about 56. This means that about 56,000 U.S. patents were granted in 1980. The graph has no symmetry. The graph does not intersect the x-axis, so there is no x-intercept. This means that in no year were 0 patents granted. The function is positive for all values of x, so the number of patents will always have a positive value. The function is increasing for all values of x. The y-intercept is a relative minimum, so the number of patents granted was at its lowest in 1980. As x increases, y increases. As x decreases, y decreases.

CHAPTER 2
Linear Equations

Get Ready

1. $3n - 4$ **3.** $2b - 11$ **5.** 2 **7.** 11 **9.** 11 **11.** \$28.40 **13.** 20% **15.** 21%

Lesson 2-1

1. $15 - 3r = 6$

(3) Words: A number squared plus 12 is the same as the quotient of p and 4.
Equation: $n^2 + 12 = p \div 4$
The equation is $n^2 + 12 = p \div 4$.

5. $8 + 3k = 5k - 3$ **7.** $\frac{25}{t} + 6 = 2t + 1$ **9.** $1900 + 30w = 2500$; 20 **11.** $P = 5s$ **13.** $4\pi r^2 = S$ **15.** Sample answer: The product of seven and m minus q is equal to 23. **17.** Sample answer: Three times the sum of g and eight is the same as 4 times h minus 10. **19.** Sample answer: A team of gymnasts competed in a regional meet. Each member of the team won 3 medals. There were a total of 45 medals won by the team. How many team members were there? **21.** $f - 5g = 25 - f$ **23.** $4(14 + c) = a^2$ **25.** $3 \cdot 10 = 12f$; $2\frac{1}{2}$ flats

(27) Words: C is five ninths times the difference of F and 32.
Equation: $C = \frac{5}{9} \cdot (F - 32)$
The equation is $C = \frac{5}{9}(F - 32)$.

29. $I = prt$ **31.** Sample answer: Four times m is equal to fifty-two. **33.** Sample answer: Fifteen less than the square of r equals the sum of t and nineteen. **35.** Sample answer: One third minus four fifths of z is four thirds of y cubed. **37.** Sample answer: Ashley has a credit card that charges 12% interest on the principal balance. If Ashley's payment was \$224, what was the principal balance on the credit card? **39.** Sample answer: Fred was teaching his friends a new card game. Each player gets 5 cards, and 7 cards are placed in the center of the table. Since there are 52 cards in a deck, find how many players can play the game. **41.** C **43.** D

(45) Words: the number of tent stakes + packets of drink mix + bottles of water = 17
$d = 3t$
$w = t + 2$
$t + d + w = 17$
$t + 3t + (t + 2) = 17$
$5t + 2 = 17$
$5t + 2 - 2 = 17 - 2$
$5t = 15$
$t = 3$
She brought 3 tent stakes.

47. Sample answer: My favorite television show has 30 new episodes each year. So far eight have aired. How many new episodes are left?

49. $\ell = \frac{P - 2w}{2}$ **51.** C **53.** 180 m **55.** Nonlinear; the graph intersects the y-axis at about (0, 0.8), so the y-intercept is about 0.8. This means that the population of Phoenix was about 800,000 in 1980. The graph has no symmetry. The graph does not intersect the x-axis, so there is no x-intercept. This means that the population will always have a positive value. The function is positive for all values of x. The function is increasing for all values of x. The y-intercept is a relative minimum, so the population was at its lowest in 1980. As x increases, y increases. As x decreases, y decreases.
57a. independent: number of sides; dependent: interior angle sum **57b.** Domain: all integers greater than or equal to 3; Range: all positive integer multiples of 180 **57c.** Discrete; sample answer: There cannot be a polygon with 3.5 sides, so the function cannot be continuous.
59. 1,000,000 **61.** 125

Lesson 2-2

1. 28 **3.** $\frac{5}{6}$ **5.** 9 **7.** -4.1 **9.** $-3\frac{1}{4}$ **11.** 16 **13.** $\frac{10}{9}$ or $1\frac{1}{9}$ **15.** $-\frac{4}{7}$ **17.** \$22.75 **19.** 116 **21.** 22 **23.** -11

(25)
$-16 - (-t) = -45$
$-16 + 16 - (-t) = -45 + 16$
$t = -29$
Check: $-16 + (-29) = -45$
$-45 = -45$ Yes

27. -32 **29.** -7 **31.** $1\frac{1}{8}$ **33.** $1\frac{2}{7}$ **35.** -708 **37.** 33 **39.** -2 **41.** $-1\frac{1}{9}$ **43.** $24.9 = 8.1 + t$; 16.8 hours **45.** -77 **47.** $\frac{16}{3}$ **49.** -10 **51.** $-\frac{10}{7}$ or $-1\frac{3}{7}$ **53.** 18 **55.** 225 **57.** $\frac{2}{3} = -8n$; $n = -\frac{1}{12}$ **59.** $\frac{4}{5} = \frac{10}{16}n$; $n = \frac{32}{25}$

(61) Words: Four and four fifths times a number is one and one fifth.
Equation: $4\frac{4}{5} \cdot n = 1\frac{1}{5}$
The equation is $4\frac{4}{5}n = 1\frac{1}{5}$.
Solve:
$4\frac{4}{5}n = 1\frac{1}{5}$
$\frac{24}{5}n = \frac{6}{5}$
$5\left(\frac{24}{5}n\right) = 5\left(\frac{6}{5}\right)$
$24n = 6$
$n = \frac{6}{24}$
$n = \frac{1}{4}$

63. $555 = 139 + p$; 416 **65.** $180 = t + 154$; 26 s **67.** $1.6 - m = 0.8$; \$0.8 million

(69) Words: 45 million fewer than 57 million is the number who have blogs.
Equation: $57 - 45$
Solve: $57 - 45 = 12$ million

71a. $350 + m = 1000$; \$650 **71b.** $350 + 225 + m = 1000$; \$425 **71c.** $6t = 1000$; 167 **73.** Sample answer: $12 + n = 25$; subtract 12 from each side or add -12 to each side.
75a. Sometimes; $0 + 0 = 0$ but $2 + 2 \neq 2$.
75b. Always; this is the Addition Identity Property. **77a.** $x = \frac{12}{a}$ **77b.** $x = 15 - a$ **77c.** $x = a - 5$ **77d.** $x = 10a$ **79.** C **81.** F **83.** $2r + 3k = 13$ **85.** $m^2 - p^3 = 16$ **87.** $12(5 + 8 + 2)$; 180 hours

Lesson 2-3

(1)
$3m + 4 = -11$
$3m + 4 - 4 = -11 - 4$
$3m = -15$
$m = -5$
Check: $3m + 4 = -11$
$3(-5) + 4 = -11$
$-15 + 4 = -11$
$-11 = -11$ Yes

3. -55 **5.** 61 **7.** $12 - 2n = -34$; 23 **9.** $n + (n + 2) + (n + 4) = 75$; 23, 25, 27 **11.** -5 **13.** -5 **15.** 70 **17.** 27 **19.** 16 **21.** -61

(23) Equation: $49.99 + 0.15m = 100$
$49.99 - 49.99 + 0.15m = 100 - 49.99$
$0.15m = 50.01$
$m \approx 333$
So, he can use the phone for 650 + 333 or 983 minutes.

25. $17 = 6x - 13$; $n = 5$ **27.** $n + (n + 2) + (n + 4) = 141$; 45, 47, 49 **29.** $n + (n + 1) + (n + 2) + (n + 3) = -142$; $-37, -36, -35, -34$ **31.** $-7\frac{3}{5}$ **33.** -72 **35.** 108 **37.** $\frac{4}{5}$ **39.** $\frac{33}{14}$ **41.** $7\frac{1}{4}$ yr or 7 yr 3 mo

(43)
$3.7q + 26.2 = 111.67$
$3.7q + 26.2 - 26.2 = 111.67 - 26.2$
$3.7q = 85.47$
$q = 23.1$

45. 31.6 **47.** -3.5 **49.** 5
51a. $5x + 275 = x(6 + 15 + 9)$; 11 visits

51b.

Visits	Cost for Members	Cost for Nonmembers
3	290	90
6	305	180
9	320	270
12	335	360
15	350	450

51c.

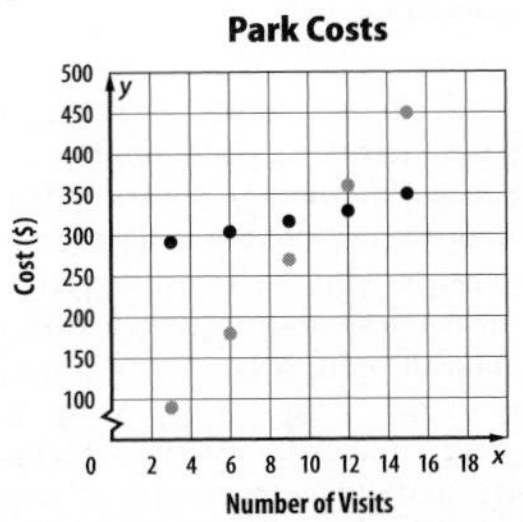

Both functions are linear. If a person is going to visit the park fewer than 11 times, it will be cheaper to be a nonmember. **53.** Sample answer: A pair of designer jeans costs \$60. This is \$40 more than twice the cost of a T-shirt. How much is the T-shirt? The T-shirt costs \$10. **55a.** No; for there to be a solution there must be a number for which $a + 4 = a + 5$. **55b.** Yes; for $b = 0$, $\frac{1 + b}{1 - b} = \frac{1 + 0}{1 - 0}$ or 1.
55c. No; $c - 5 = 5 - c$ when $c = 5$. However, $\frac{c - 5}{5 - c}$ is undefined for $c = 5$ since the fraction represents division by 0. **57.** Sample answer: In order to solve the equation $4k + 20 = 236$, you would first subtract 20 from each side and then divide each side by 4.
59. 84 **61.** B **63.** 1379 **65.** Three times a number h is increased by 7 to equal 20. **67.** Three multiplied by a number p is the same as the difference of 8 times p and r. **69.** The product of $\frac{1}{2}$ and v is equal to the product of $\frac{2}{3}$ and v plus 4.
71. 0; Additive Identity **73.** 4; Additive Inverse **75.** 53 **77.** 1000

Lesson 2-4

1. 4 **3.** -7 **5.** no solution **7.** all numbers **9.** A **11.** 4

(13)
$6 + 3t = 8t - 14$
$6 + 3t - 3t = 8t - 3t - 14$
$6 = 5t - 14$
$6 + 14 = 5t - 14 + 14$
$20 = 5t$
$4 = t$
Check: $6 + 3t = 8t - 14$
$6 + 3(4) = 8(4) - 14$
$6 + 12 = 32 - 14$
$18 = 18$ Yes

15. $2\frac{2}{5}$ **17.** 6 **19.** -5 **21.** 1 **23.** $-4, -2$ **25.** no solution **27.** all numbers **29.** -25 **31.** 15 **33.** 3 **35.** -2 **37.** $-2, 0$

(39) Equation: $1500 + 0.80x = 1.59x$
Solve: $1500 + 0.80x = 1.59x$
$1500 + 0.80x - 0.80x = 1.59x - 0.80x$
$1500 = 0.79x$
$1899 \approx x$

Selected Answers and Solutions

41a. Sample answer: $y = 2x + 4$

x	−2	−1	0	1	2
y	0	2	4	6	8

$y = -x - 2$

x	−2	−1	0	1	2
y	0	−1	−2	−3	−4

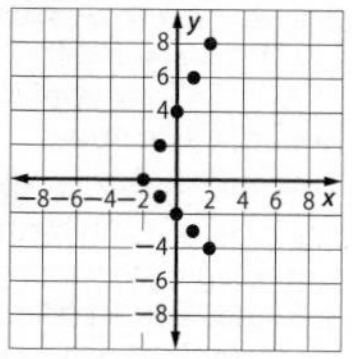

41b. −2 **41c.** Sample answer: The solution in part **b** is the x-coordinate for the point of intersection on the graph.
43. Sample answer: $2x + 1 = \frac{3}{2}x - 2$;
First I chose $\frac{3}{2}$ as the fractional coefficient. Then I chose 2 for the coefficient for the variable on the other side of the equation. After substituting −6 in for x on both sides, 1 must be added to the left and 2 must be subtracted from the right to balance the equation. **45a.** Incorrect; the 2 must be distributed over both g and 5; 6. **45b.** correct **45c.** Incorrect; to eliminate $-6z$ on the right side of the equals sign, $6z$ must be added to each side of the equation; 1.
47. Sample answer: If the equation has variables on both sides of the equation, you must first add or subtract one of the terms from both sides of the equation so that the variable is left on only one side of the equation. Then, solving the equation uses the same steps. **49.** J **51.** A **53.** $-2\frac{2}{3}$
55. −15 **57.** −15 **59.** $34 **61.** 2; Multiplicative Identity **63.** $\frac{2}{3}$; Additive Identity **65.** 7; Substitution **67.** $5(m + k) = 7k$ **69.** 5
71. −24 **73.** 11

Lesson 2-5

1. 15 **3.** −4
5. {4, −2};

7. {−6, −2}

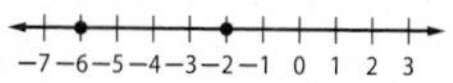

9. ∅

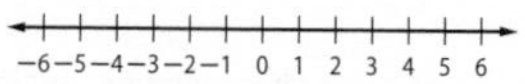

11 Find the point that is the same distance from −2 and 4. This is the midpoint between −2 and 4, which is 1.The distance from −2 to 1 is 3 units. The distance from 4 to 1 is 3 units. So, an equation is $|x - 1| = 3$

13 $|2x + z| + 2y = |2(2.1) + (-4.2)| + 2(3)$
$= |4.2 + (-4.2)| + 6$
$= |0| + 6$
$= 0 + 6$
$= 6$
15. −7.4 **17.** 8.4 **19.** −9.6 **21.** 0.4
23. {−11, −9};

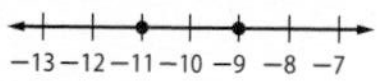

25. {7, −3};

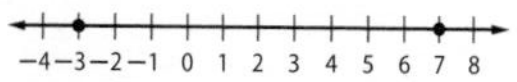

27. ∅

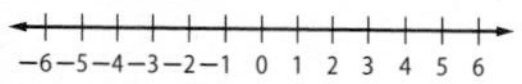

29. {0, 6}

31. 11% to 19% **33.** $|x| = 4$ **35.** $|x - 1| = 4$
37. {−24, 16}

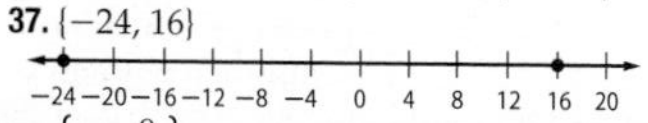

39. $\left\{3, -\frac{9}{5}\right\}$

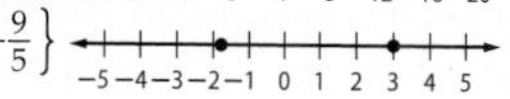

41. no solution

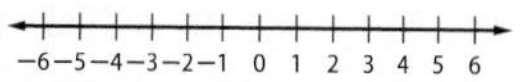

43a. $|x - 52| = 2$; {50, 54} **43b.** $|x - 54| = 1$; {52, 54}
43c. 203 and 214 seconds **45a.** 47 to 53 mph
45b. Sample answer: The speedometer was calibrated more accurately than the speedometer in part **a**.
47. $|x| = 1\frac{1}{2}$ **49.** $\left|x - \frac{1}{4}\right| = \frac{1}{4}$ **51.** $\left|x + \frac{1}{3}\right| = 1$

53 **a.** Let h be the number of people who can clearly hear voices.
Equation: $|h - 20{,}000| = 1000$
b. $|h - 20{,}000| = 1000$
$h - 20{,}000 = 1000$ or $h - 20{,}000 = -1000$
$h - 20{,}000 + 20{,}000 = 1000 + 20{,}000$ or
$h - 20{,}000 + 20{,}000 = -1000 + 20{,}000$
$h = 21{,}000$ or $h = 19{,}000$
c. To find the range, find 21,000 − 19,000 = 2000

55 **a.** Each school could answer every question correctly, earning 50 points. They could also answer every question incorrectly, earning −50 points.
b. Let m = the score on the math section. The maximum distance between m and the initial score of 160 is 50, so $|m - 160| = 50$.
c. Every tenth value between -50 and 50 is possible. Let c = correct, n = incorrect, and u = unanswered. Here are some combinations of answers. $50 = 5c$,
$40 = 4c + 1u$, $30 = 3c + 2u$, $20 = 2c + 3u$,
$10 = 2c + 1n + 2u$, $0 = 2c + 2n + u$,
$-10 = 1n + 4u$, $-20 = 2n + 3u$,
$-30 = 3n + 2u$, $-40 = 4n + u$, $-50 = 5u$.
57. Sometimes; when $x = -1$, the value is 0.
59. Sometimes; when c is a negative value the inequality is true. **61.** An absolute value represents a distance from zero on a number line. A distance can never be a negative number.
63. Wesley; the absolute value of a number cannot be a negative number.
65. D **67.** A **69.** $\frac{1}{2}n + 16 = \frac{2}{3}n - 4$; 120 **71.** 10 in.
73. $\frac{2}{5}n = -24$; −60 **75.** $12 = \frac{1}{5}n$; 60

Lesson 2-6

1. no
3 $\frac{1.4}{2.1}$ is written in simplified form. $\frac{2.8}{4.4} = \frac{1.4}{2.2}$. Since the fractions are not equal, the ratios are not equivalent.
5. 5 **7.** about 253.3 min or 4 hours 13.3 min
9. yes **11.** no **13.** yes **15.** 40 **17.** 29.25 **19.** 9.8
21. 1.32 **23.** 0.84
25 $\frac{t}{0.3} = \frac{1.7}{0.9}$
$0.9t = 1.7(0.3)$
$0.9t = 0.51$
$t \approx 0.57$
27. 6 **29.** 11 **31.** 156 mi **33.** about $262.59 **35.** 18
37. 0.8 **39.** 11 **41.** 130 students
43 **a.** Write each ratio.
for 2003, $\frac{\text{indoor theaters}}{\text{total theaters}} = \frac{35{,}361}{35{,}995}$
for 2004, $\frac{\text{indoor theaters}}{\text{total theaters}} = \frac{36{,}012}{36{,}653}$
for 2005, $\frac{\text{indoor theaters}}{\text{total theaters}} = \frac{37{,}092}{37{,}740}$
for 2006, $\frac{\text{indoor theaters}}{\text{total theaters}} = \frac{37{,}776}{38{,}425}$
for 2007, $\frac{\text{indoor theaters}}{\text{total theaters}} = \frac{38{,}159}{38{,}794}$
for 2008, $\frac{\text{indoor theaters}}{\text{total theaters}} = \frac{38{,}201}{38{,}834}$
for 2009, $\frac{\text{indoor theaters}}{\text{total theaters}} = \frac{38{,}605}{39{,}233}$
b. None of the ratios form a proportion.
45a.

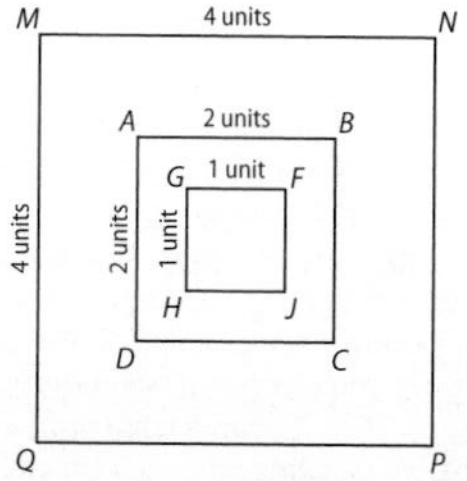

45b.

ABCD		MNPQ		FGHJ	
Side length	2	Side length	4	Side length	1
Perimeter	8	Perimeter	16	Perimeter	4

45c. If the length of a side is increased by a factor, the perimeter is also increased by that factor. If the length of the sides are decreased by a factor, the perimeter is also decreased by the same factor.
47. Ratios and rates each compare two numbers by using division. However, rates compare two measurements that involve different units of measure. **49.** If the tank is about $\frac{9}{16}$ full, he has about $\frac{9}{16} \times 10$ or $5\frac{5}{8}$ gal of gas left. At 32 miles per gallon, he will be able to travel $32 \times 5\frac{5}{8}$ or 180 miles. Since Atlanta is 200 miles away, he will run out of gas about 20 miles before reaching the city if he doesn't stop to get gas. **51.** C **53.** G **55.** ∅
57. {10, −7} **59.** 30 years **61.** −7 **63.** −48 **65.** 13
67. 5.5 **69.** 3.5

Lesson 2-7

1 It is an increase.
$125 - 78 = 47$
$47 \div 78 \approx 0.60$.
The percent of increase is about 60%.
3. inc.; 33% **5.** 146 mi **7.** $38.42 **9.** $53.07
11. $17.21 **13.** $22.10
15 It is a decrease.
$16 - 10 = 6$
$6 \div 16 \approx 0.38$.
The percent of decrease is about 38%.
17. dec.; 77% **19.** inc.; 127% **21.** inc.; 90%
23. $12,400 **25.** $47.48 **27.** $27.31 **29.** $10.66
31. $76.49 **33.** $16.42 **35.** $11.99 **37.** $48.04
39. about 20.7% increase **41a.** First girl's dress - $15; Second girl's dress = $25.50 **41b.** the second girl by $0.50
43 Find the percent of increase or decrease for each grocery item. Milk had the biggest increase with a 38.7% increase.
45. Sample answer: A CD is on sale for $9.99. If tax is 6.5%, what will the CD cost? **47.** Xavier; Maddie divided by the new amount instead of the original amount. **49.** Sample answer: Retail stores use percents of decrease when the prices of items are discounted in a sale; salary increases are usually given as a percent of increase. To find the percent of change, subtract the original from the new amount. Then write a proportion, comparing the change to the original amount. The answer should be written as a percent. **51.** $72 **53.** C
55. 12 **57.** 4 **59.** 5.6 **61.** 3 **63.** −6 **65.** −7
67. $0.99x + 1.29y$ **69.** Sample answer: Six more than twice a number f equals nineteen. **71.** Sample answer: The product of three and a number a when added to 5 is equal to the difference of 27 and two times a. **73.** Sample answer: The fourth power of a number d increased by sixty-four is three times that number d to the third power plus seventy-seven.

Lesson 2-8

1 $5a + c = -8a$
$5a - 5a + c = -8a - 5a$
$c = -13a$
$-\frac{c}{13} = a$

3. $k = -7n - m$ **5a.** $h = \frac{V}{\pi r^2}$ **5b.** 8 in.
7. about 0.43875 ft

9 $x = b - cd$
$x - b = -cd$
$\frac{x-b}{-d} = c$

11. $m = \frac{-n+p}{10}$ **13.** $v = \frac{9}{5}(z - w)$ **15.** $f = \frac{6g - 10}{d}$
17a. $v_f = at + v_i$ **17b.** 10 ft/s^2 **19.** 49.8 L
21. $t = \frac{w - 11v}{31}$ **23.** $c = \frac{-13 + f}{10 - d}$ **25.** 1.0 mm/s
27. 3.9 km/s **29.** $t - 7 = r + 6$; $t = r + 13$
31. $\frac{9}{10}g = 7 + \frac{2}{3}k$; $k = \frac{3}{2}\left[\frac{9}{10}g - 7\right]$

33 $S = 2w(\ell + h) + 2lh$
$214 = 2(6)(7 + h) + 2(7)h$
$214 = 12(7 + h) + 14h$
$214 = 84 + 12h + 14h$
$130 = 26h$
$5 = h$
So, 5 inches.

35. about 364 in^3 **37.** Sandrea; she performed each step correctly; Fernando omitted the negative sign from $-5b$. **39a.** $x = \frac{y-1}{yn-1}$ **39b.** $y = -\frac{1}{3}x$ **41.** D
43. 15 **45.** \$101.76 **47.** \$46.33 **49.** \$56.95
51. 1.67 **53.** 5.14 **55.** 50(7.50) + 90(5.00); \$825
57. −0.5 **59.** −1.5 **61.** 2

Lesson 2-9

1

	Weight	Price	Total Price
Soup	10	0.15	0.15(10)
Salad	x	0.20	0.20x
Total			3.30

$0.15(10) + 0.20x = 3.30$
$1.50 + 0.20x = 3.30$
$0.20x = 1.80$
$x = 9$
She bought 9 oz of salad.

3. 10 mph **5.** 2 hours

7 a.

	Amount	Percent	Total
Metallic Balloons	b	\$2.00	2.00b
Bunches of helium Balloons	b − 36	\$3.50	3.50(b − 36)

b. $2.00b + 3.50(b - 36) = 281$

c. $2.00b + 3.50(b - 36) = 281$
$2b + 3.5b - 126 = 281$
$5.5b = 281 + 126$
$5.5b = 407$
$b = 74$
There were 74 metallic balloons sold.

d. $b - 36 = 74 - 36$
$= 38$
There were 38 bunches of balloons sold.

9. about 16.67 gal 11. about 22.2 mph 13. $1\frac{1}{7}$ hours or 1 h 8 min 34 s **15.** 10 gal **17.** 10.89 mph

19 **a.** $D = rt$
$= 65(6)$
$= 390$ He could drive 390 miles.

b. $D = rt$
$\frac{D}{r} = t$
$\frac{625}{65} = t$
$9.62 \approx t$ It will take about 9.62 hours.

21. 33 mi **23.** Sample answer: For a 50% solution being added to a 100% solution to produce a 75% resulting solution, the quantity of each must be the same. **25.** Sample answer: How many grams of salt must be added to 36 grams of a 15% salt solution to obtain a 50% salt solution? **27.** B
29. C **31.** $\frac{-5+b}{2b}$ **33.** $\frac{A}{2\pi r} - r$ **35.** Sample answer: The quotient of n and −6 is the same as the sum of two times n and one. **37.** Sample answer: The sum of three and twice x squared is equal to twenty-one. **39.** (4, 25); Sample answer: If four cars are washed, \$25 is earned. **41.** \$583.50
43. −2 **45.** −7 **47.** 24

Chapter 2 Study Guide and Review

1. false, variable **3.** true **5.** false, ratio **7.** false, decrease **9.** $5x + 3 = 15$ **11.** $\frac{1}{2}m^3 = 4m - 9$
13. h squared minus five times h plus six is equal to zero. **15.** width: 8 ft, length: 19 ft **17.** −5 **19.** 2.1
21. 6 **23.** 14 **25.** 6 **27.** −11 **29.** 17 **31.** 2
33. 38.1 **35.** 19, 21, 23 **37.** 3 **39.** −2 **41.** 2
43. −8 **45.** 21 **47.** 28 **49.** −144 **51.** {−5, 17}

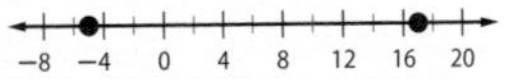

53. {−27, 63}

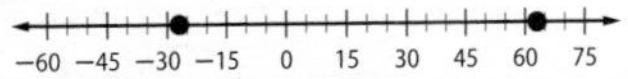

55. yes **57.** 20 **59.** 12 **61.** increase, 25%
63. decrease, 17% **65.** \$52.19 **67.** \$55.20
69. \$33.75 **71.** $y = \frac{9 - 3x}{2}$ **73.** $m = \frac{15 - 9n}{-5}$
75. $y = \frac{5}{2}(m - n)$ **77.** $h = \frac{2A}{a + b}$ **79.** 52 mph

CHAPTER 3
Linear Functions

Get Ready

1.
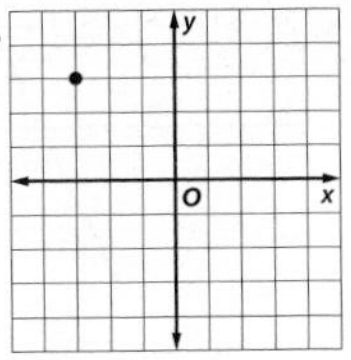

3.
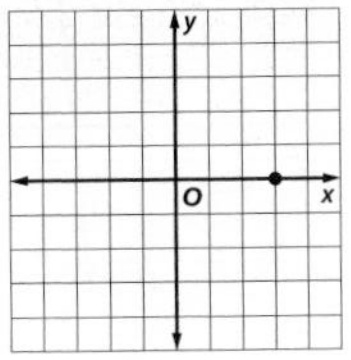

5.
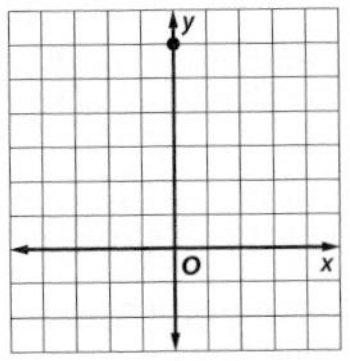

7. (3, −1) **9.** (3, 2)
11. (5, 0) **13.** $y = -3x + 1$
15. $y = \frac{5}{2}x - 6$
17. $y = -10x + 6$
19. $\frac{1}{4}$ **21.** 0 **23.** about \$13.5 million

Lesson 3-1

1. yes; $x - y = -5$ **3.** yes; $y = 1$ **5.** 25, −4; The x-intercept 25 means that after 25 minutes, the temperature is 0°F. The y-intercept −4 means that at time 0, the temperature is −4°F.

7.
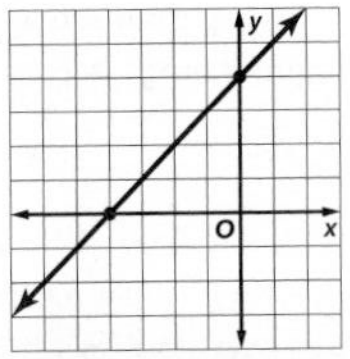

9.

x	$y = 2 - \frac{x}{2}$	y	(x, y)
−4	$y = 2 - \frac{(-4)}{2}$	4	(−4, 4)
−2	$y = 2 - \frac{(-2)}{2}$	3	(−2, 3)
0	$y = 2 - \frac{0}{2}$	2	(0, 2)
2	$y = 2 - \frac{2}{2}$	1	(2, 1)
4	$y = 2 - \frac{4}{2}$	0	(4, 0)

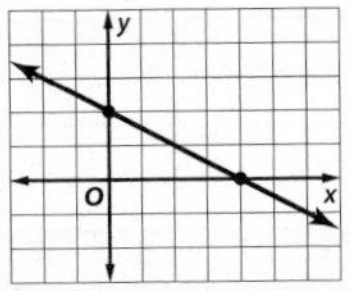

11.

x	y = 3	y	(x, y)
−2	y = 3	3	(−2, 3)
−1	y = 3	3	(−1, 3)
0	y = 3	3	(0, 3)
1	y = 3	3	(1, 3)
2	y = 3	3	(2, 3)

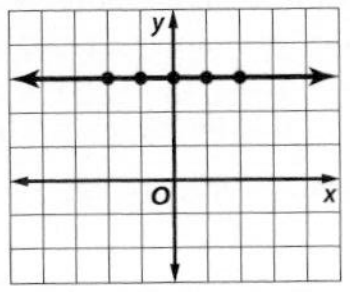

13 $5x + y^2 = 25$
Since the y term is squared, this equation cannot be written in the form $Ax + By = C$, so it is not a linear equation.

15. no **17.** yes; $4x + y = 0$ **19.** 3, 4
21. 6, 20; The x-intercept represents the number of seconds that it takes the eagle to land. The y-intercept represents the initial height of the eagle.

23.
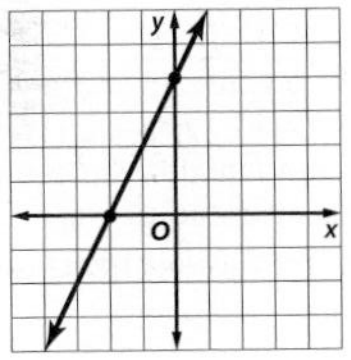

25.
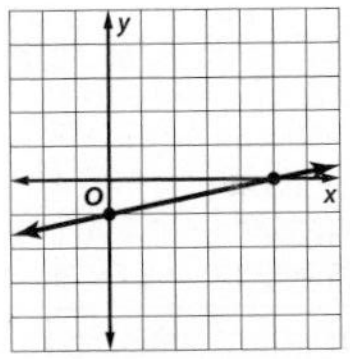

27.
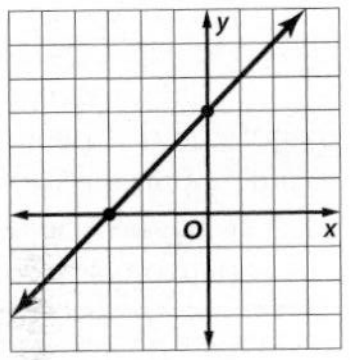

29.

x	y
−2	0
−2	1
−2	2

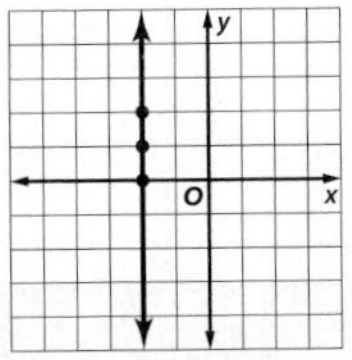

31.

x	y
−1	8
0	0
1	−8

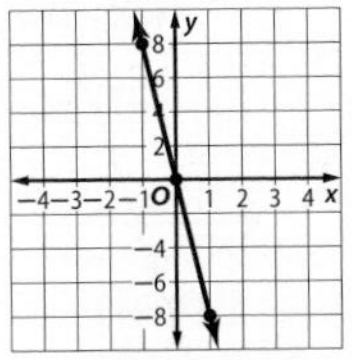

33.

x	y
0	8
1	7
2	6

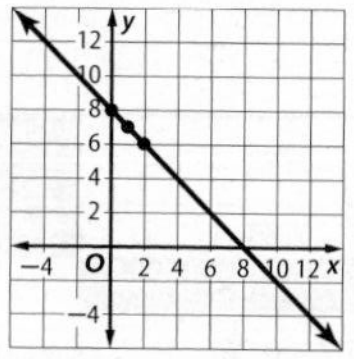

35 **a.** The domain is all real numbers so there are infinitely many solutions. Select values from the domain and make a table.

v	$p = 0.15v$	p	(v, p)
0	$p = 0.15(0)$	0	(0, 0)
2	$p = 0.15(2)$	0.3	(2, 0.3)
4	$p = 0.15(4)$	0.6	(4, 0.6)
6	$p = 0.15(6)$	0.9	(6, 0.9)
8	$p = 0.15(8)$	1.2	(8, 1.2)
10	$p = 0.15(10)$	1.5	(10, 1.5)

b. Create ordered pairs and graph them.

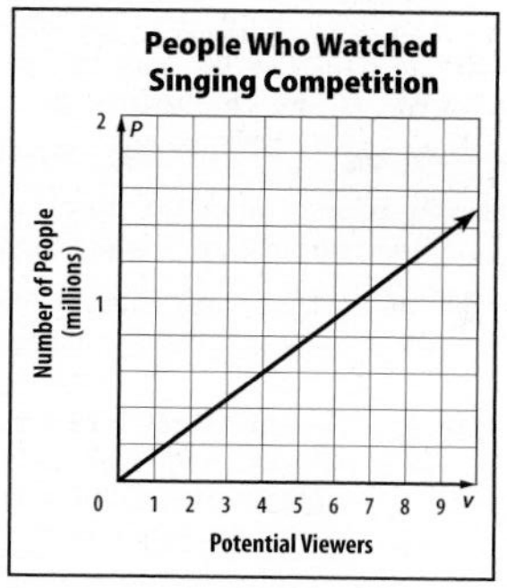

c. Using the graph, when there are 14 million potential viewers, there will about 2.1 million people who watch.

d. A negative does not make sense because you cannot have a negative number of viewers.

37. yes; $3x - 4y = 60$ **39.** yes; $3a = 2$
41. yes; $9m - 8n = -60$

43.

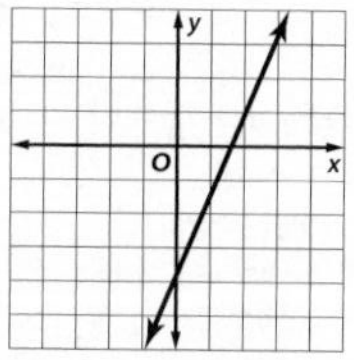

45.

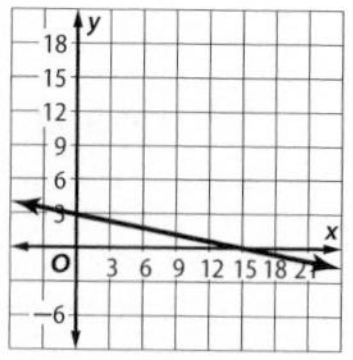

47.

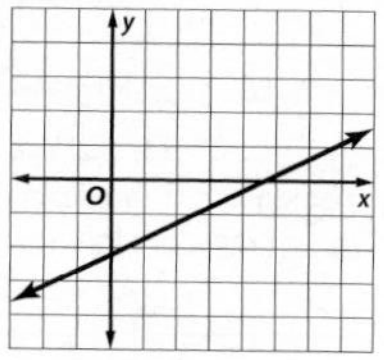

49. No; Sample answer: The rental car would cost \$176. Mrs. Johnson has only \$160 to spend.

51 $5x + 3y = 15$
To find the x-intercept, let $y = 0$.
$5x + 3y = 15$
$5x + 3(0) = 15$
$5x = 15$
$x = 3$
The x-intercept is 3. This means the graph intersects the x-axis at (3, 0).
To find the y-intercept, let $x = 0$.
$5x + 3y = 15$
$5(0) + 3y = 15$
$3y = 15$
$y = 5$
The y-intercept is 5. This means the graph crosses the y-axis at (0, 5).

53. $2\frac{1}{2}; -1\frac{2}{3}$ **55.** 12; −3

57a.

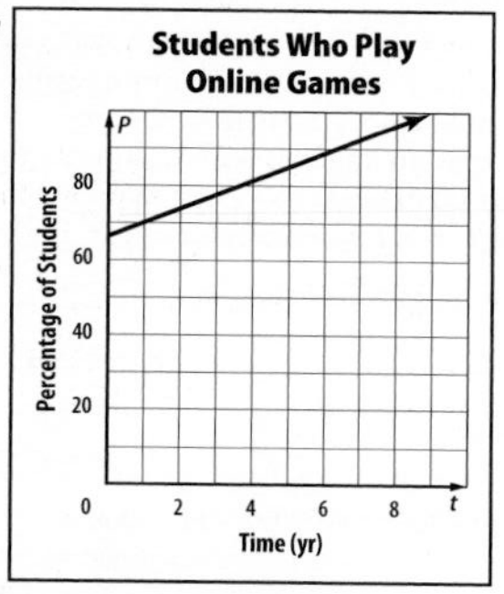

57b. 96%

59.

Perimeter of a Square	
Side Length	Perimeter
1	4
2	8
3	12
4	16

Sample answer: Yes; we used the formula $P = 4s$, which is linear.

Area of a Square	
Side Length	Area
1	1
2	4
3	9
4	16

Sample answer: No; we used the formula $A = s^2$, which is not linear.

Volume of a Cube	
Side Length	Volume
1	1
2	8
3	27
4	64

Sample answer: No; we used the formula $V = s^3$, which is not linear.

61. Sample answer: $y = 8$; horizontal line
63. Sample answer: $x - y = 0$; line through (0, 0)
65. D **67.** \$30 **69.** 270 rolls of solid wrap, 210 rolls of print wrap **71.** $g = \frac{5 + m}{2 + h}$ **73.** $z = \frac{c - b}{2}$
75. $-\frac{23}{14}$ **77.** −56

Lesson 3-2

1. 3 **3.** $\frac{1}{2}$ **5.** no solution **7.** no solution
9. Tyrone must deliver 40 newspapers for the papers in his bag to weigh 0 pounds. **11.** −3
13. no solution **15.** $-\frac{10}{7}$ or $-1\frac{3}{7}$

17
$5x - 5 = 5x + 2$
$5x - 5 + 5 = 5x + 2 + 5$
$5x = 5x + 7$
$5x - 5x = 5x - 5x + 7$
$0 = 7$
There are no solutions.

19. no solution **21.** no solution **23.** 100; She can download a total of 100 songs before the gift card is completely used. **25.** −8 **27.** $\frac{10}{3}$ or $3\frac{1}{3}$
29. $-\frac{34}{13}$ or $-2\frac{8}{13}$ **31.** $\frac{17}{25}$ **33.** $\frac{15}{8}$ or $1\frac{7}{8}$ **35.** 3
37. 4:00 P.M.

39. −3

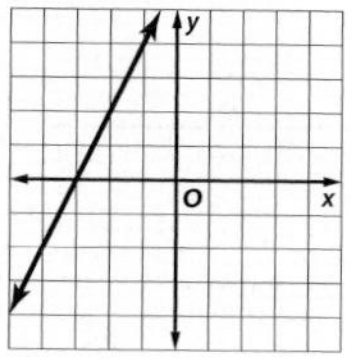

41. −2

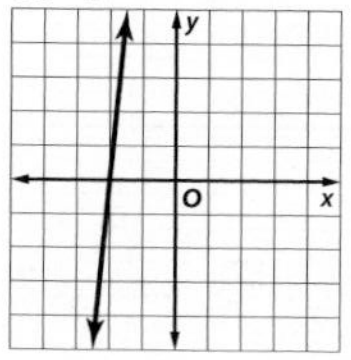

43. $\frac{9}{8}$ or $1\frac{1}{8}$

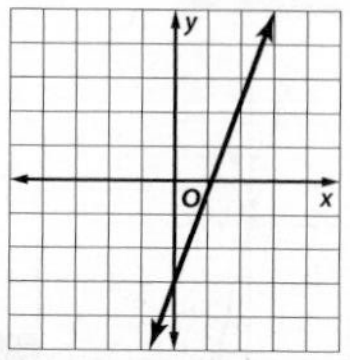

45 **a.** Sample answers given:

Number of Songs Downloaded	Total Cost (\$)	Total Cost / Number Songs Downloaded
2	4	$\frac{4}{2} = 2$
4	8	$\frac{8}{4} = 2$
6	12	$\frac{12}{6} = 2$
8	16	$\frac{16}{8} = 2$
10	20	$\frac{20}{10} = 2$

b. As the number of songs downloaded increases by 2, the cost increases by 4.
c. The value of the total cost divided by the number of songs downloaded represents the cost per song. It costs \$2 per song.

47. 3 **49.** Sample answer: $3 + 4x = 0$; $y = 3 + 4x$ or $f(x) = 3 + 4x$ **51.** A **53.** B **55.** −5, 10 **57.** 7, −2
59. $3m + 2n = \frac{4}{p}$ **61.** $\frac{5}{2}$ **63.** $-\frac{1}{2}$ **65.** $\frac{2}{3}$ **67.** 11

Lesson 3-3

1. $\frac{4}{3}$ **3a.** 1.035; There was an average increase in ticket price of \$1.035 per year. **3b.** Sample answer: 1998–2000; A steeper segment means a greater rate of change. **3c.** Sample answer: 1998–2000; Ticket prices show a sharp increase. **5.** No; the rate of change is not constant. **7.** −1
9. $\frac{7}{9}$ **11.** 0 **13.** −8

15 rate of change $= \frac{\text{change in } y}{\text{change in } x}$
$= \frac{9 - 15}{2 - 1}$
$= \frac{-6}{1}$
$= -6$

17. $\frac{1}{2}$ **19a.** Sample answer: $P = -1221t + 19{,}820$
19b. The car value depreciates by \$1221 each year.
19c. \$11,273 **21.** No; the y-values do not increase at a constant rate. **23.** Yes; both the x-values and the y-values increase at a constant rate.

25 $m = \frac{y_2 - y_1}{x_2 - x_1}$
$= \frac{1 - (-2)}{1 - 8}$
$= \frac{1 + 2}{1 - 8}$
$= -\frac{3}{7}$

27. undefined **29.** $\frac{5}{17}$ **31.** 0 **33.** undefined
35. $\frac{10}{3}$ **37.** $\frac{3}{4}$ **39.** 6 **41.** Sample answer: about -1
43. $\frac{15}{4}$ **45.** $-\frac{2}{3}$

47 a. Plot the ordered pairs on a coordinate plane. Connect the points with a line.

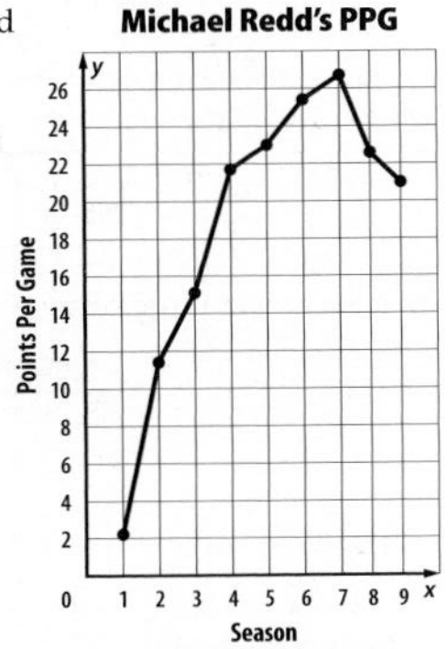

b. The steepest line is between season 1 and season 2, so that is when the PPG increased the most.
c. The rate of change was much more dramatic or steeper in the first four seasons, the rate of change leveled off the next three seasons and is negative and steeper the last two seasons.
49. The rate of change is $2\frac{1}{4}$ inches of growth per week. **51.** Sample answer: Slope can be used to describe a rate of change. Rate of change is a ratio that describes how much one quantity changes with respect to a change in another quantity. The slope of a line is also a ratio and it is the ratio of the change in the y-coordinates to the change in the x-coordinates. **53.** A **55.** $4 **57.** -6 **59.** 4
61. $-1, 2$ **63.** 12 **65.** $\frac{5}{16}$ **67.** 5

Lesson 3-4

1. $-\frac{4}{5}$; $-\frac{4}{5}$

3.

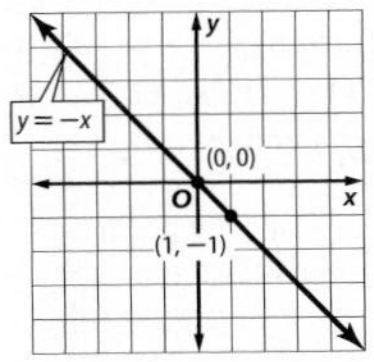

5.

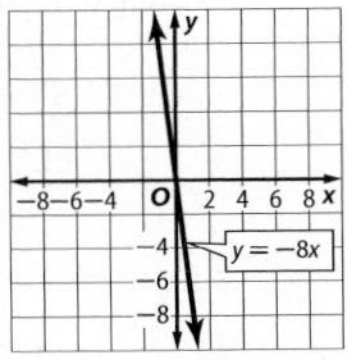

7. $y = \frac{5}{4}x$; 40

9a. $y = \frac{12}{5}x$;

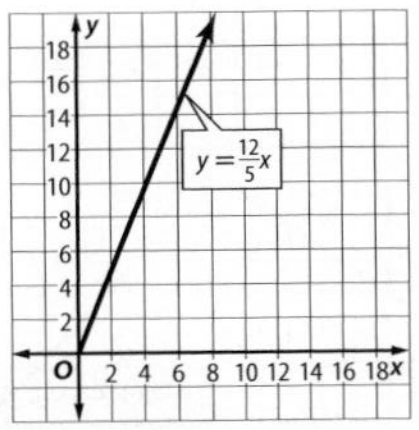

9b. 40

11 The constant of variation is -5.

$m = \frac{5-0}{-1-0}$
$= \frac{5}{-1}$
$= -5$

13. $-\frac{1}{5}$; $-\frac{1}{5}$ **15.** -12; -12

17.

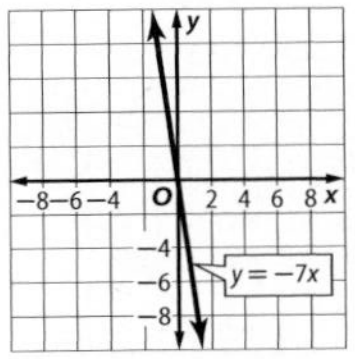

19.

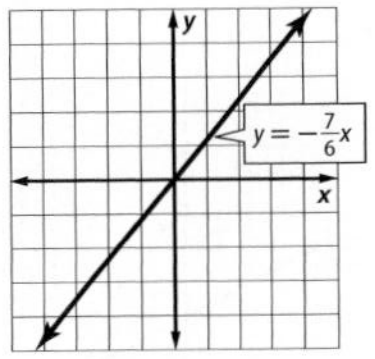

21.

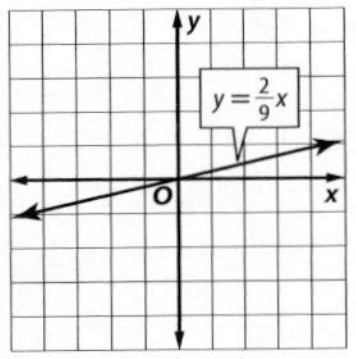

23.

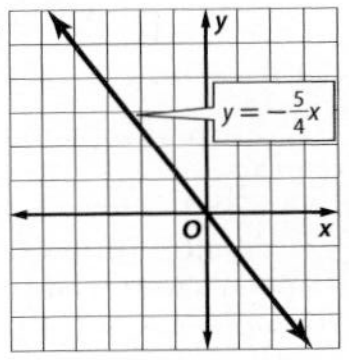

25 $y = kx$
$22 = k(8)$
$\frac{11}{4} = k$
Therefore, the direct variation equation is
$y = \frac{11}{4}x$.
$y = \frac{11}{4}x$
$y = \frac{11}{4}(-16)$ Substitute -16 for x.
$y = 11(-4)$
$y = -44$
Therefore, $y = -44$ when $x = -16$.

27. $y = 14x$; $1\frac{1}{7}$ **29a.** $y = 1800x$ **29b.** 7 yr 6 mo
31. $y = 20x$; $\frac{5}{4}$ **33.** $y = -3.75x$; -30
35. dark green **37.** lime green
39 Since the songs are $0.99 each, the equation is $T = 0.99d$. The graph of the equation runs through the origin with a slope of 0.99.

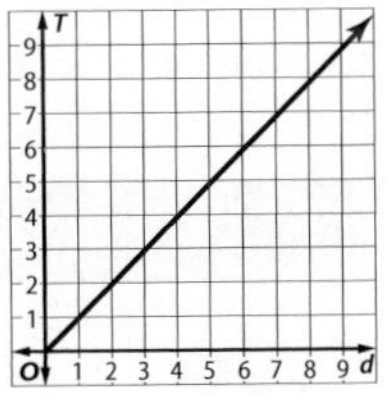

41a.

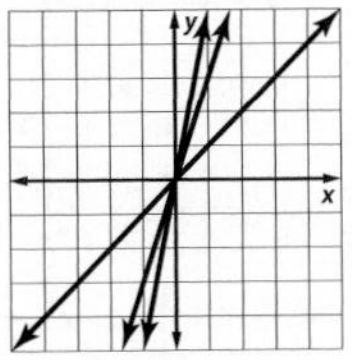

41b. Sample answer: The constant of variation, slope, and rate of change of a graph all have the same value. **41c.** Sample answer: Find the absolute value of k in each equation. The one with the greater value of $|k|$ has the steeper graph.
43. $C = 9.95n$ **45.** $z = \frac{1}{9}x$; It is the only equation that is a direct variation. **47.** Sample answer: $y = 0.50x$ represents the cost of x apples. The rate of change, 0.50, is the cost per apple.

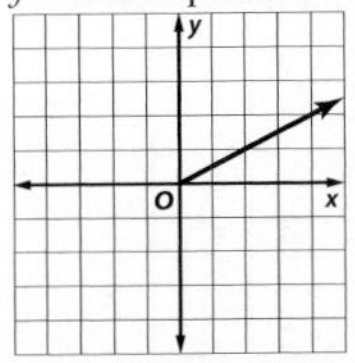

49. Neither; the slope is constant, but it is k.
51. A **53.** D **55.** 6.5; There was an average increase of 6.5 channels per year.

57. -7

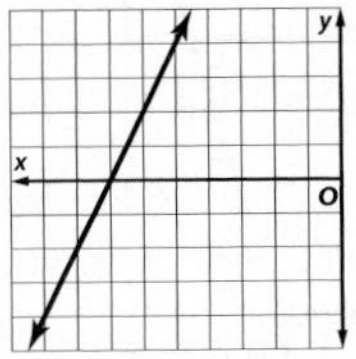

59. -4

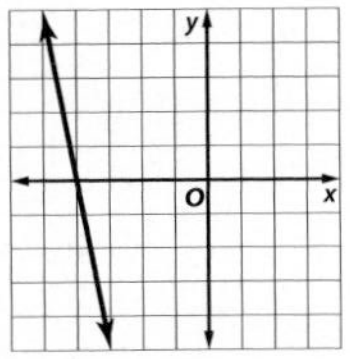

61. 12

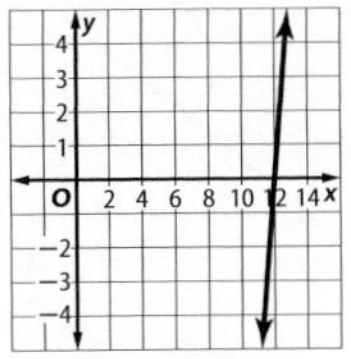

63. 12 **65.** -2
67. -28 **69.** -12
71. -6 **73.** -12

Lesson 3-5

1. No; there is no common difference. **3.** $0, -3, -6$
5. $a_n = 17 - 2n$

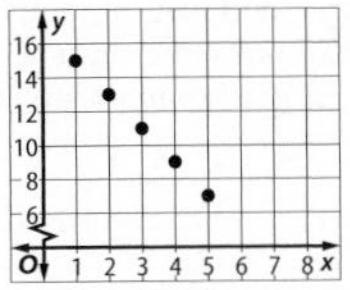

7. $a(n) = 55n + 525$

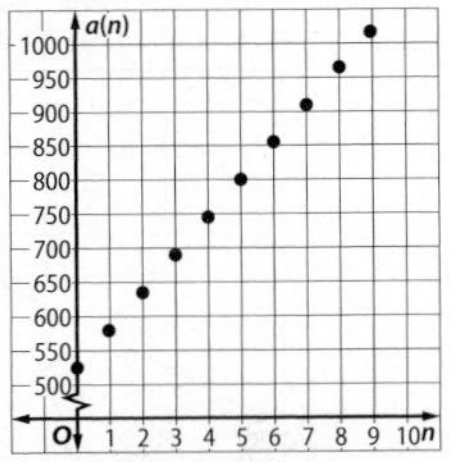

9. No; there is no common difference. **11.** Yes; the common difference is 2.6. **13.** 30, 36, 42

15 Step 1: Find the common difference by subtracting successive terms.

$-\frac{1}{2}$, 0, $\frac{1}{2}$, 1, … (each $+\frac{1}{2}$) The common difference is $\frac{1}{2}$.

Step 2: Add $\frac{1}{2}$ to the last term of the sequence to get the next term.

1, $1\frac{1}{2}$, 2, $2\frac{1}{2}$ (each $+\frac{1}{2}$) The next three terms are $1\frac{1}{2}$, 2, $2\frac{1}{2}$.

17. $3\frac{7}{12}$, $4\frac{1}{3}$, $5\frac{1}{12}$

19. $a_n = 5n - 7$

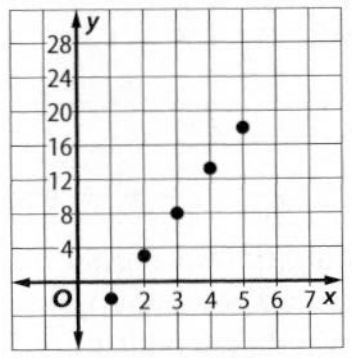

21. $a_n = 0.25n - 1$

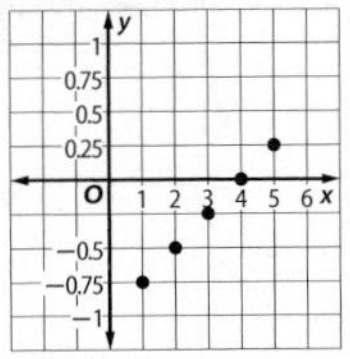

23a. $f(n) = 0.80n$

23b.

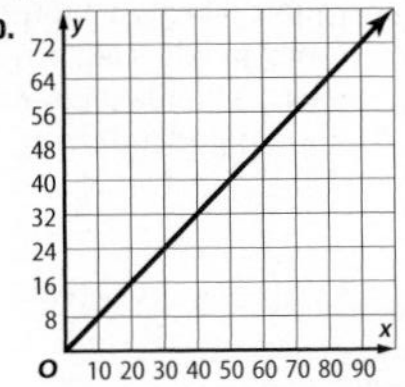

D = {10, 20, 30, 40, …}

(25) The ordered pairs are (10, 7.50), (15, 8.75), (20, 10), (25, 11.25). So, the rate of change is $\frac{8.75 - 7.50}{15 - 10} = \frac{1.25}{5} = 0.25$.
The cost is \$0.25 per word plus a flat fee.
$f(n) = 0.25n + b$
$7.50 = 0.25(10) + b$
$7.50 = 2.50 + b$
$5 = b$
So, the equation is $f(n) = 0.25n + 5$.

27. 77 **29.** 25,646 **31a.** $A_n = 2.5 + 0.5n$ **31b.** week 15 **31c.** Sample answer: No; eventually the number of miles ran per day will become unrealistic. **33.** −1 **35a.** Yes; there is a common difference.; x; $5x + 1, 6x + 1, 7x + 1$. **35b.** No; there is no common difference. **37.** 8 yr **39.** H **41.** 3, 3 **43.** $-\frac{3}{7}$ **45.** 3 **47.** 2 **49.** Sample answer: $453{,}000 - d = 369{,}000$; 84,000
51–55.

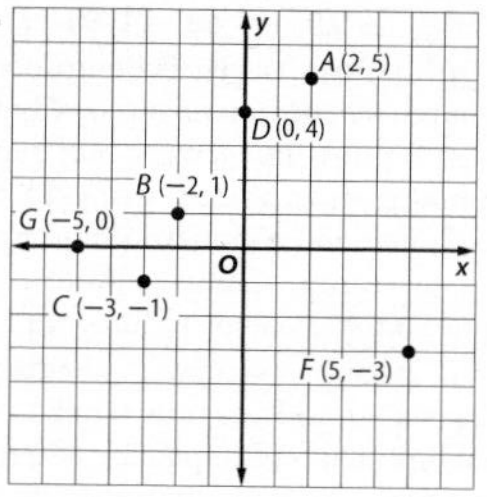

Lesson 3-6

1a.

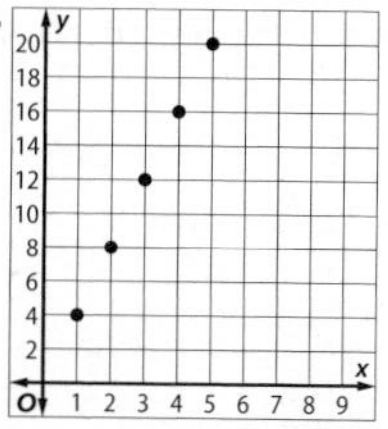

1b. $y = 4x$ **1c.** The perimeter is 4 times the length of the side. **3.** $f(x) = -x + 3$

(5) Select points from the graph and place them in a table.

x	0	1	2	3
y	0	2	4	6

The difference between the x-values is 1, while the difference between the y-values is 2. This suggests that $y = 2x$.
This works for each ordered pair, so the equation is $f(x) = 2x$.

7. $f(x) = 3x - 2$ **9.** $f(n) = 3n - 3$; nonproportional; the function does not describe a direct variation.

11. $y = 2.25x + 2.50$

(13) **a.** Sample answer:

Number of T-shirts ordered	5	10	15	20	25
Cost (\$)	13	23	33	43	53

b. In functional notation, the equation is $C(t) = 2t + 3$.

c. The equation goes through (0, 3) and has a slope of 2.

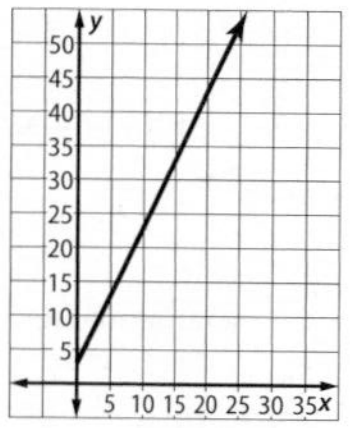

d. The relationship is nonproportional because $\frac{13}{5} \neq \frac{23}{10} \neq \frac{33}{15} \neq \frac{43}{20} \neq \frac{53}{25}$.

15. Sample answer: 4, 7, 10, 13; add a common difference of 3; $a_n = 3n + 1$. **17.** $f(n) = 3n + 2$ is the related function for the arithmetic sequence 5, 8, 11, 14, …, but it is not proportional. The line through (1, 5) and (2, 8) does not pass through (0, 0). **19.** D
21. H **23.** 43, 53, 63 **25.** $\frac{5}{4}, \frac{11}{8}, \frac{3}{2}$ **27.** $y = 7x$; −12 **29a.** $V = \frac{1}{3}\pi r^2 h$ **29b.** about 3142 cm^3
31. $y = 3x - 5$

33.

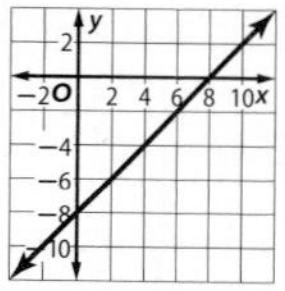

35.

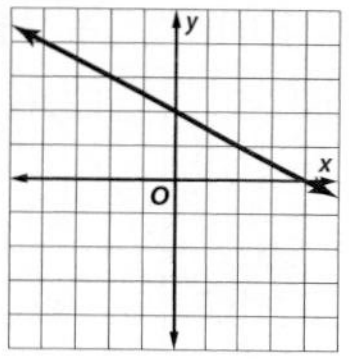

Chapter 3 Study Guide and Review

1. true **3.** false; common difference **5.** true **7.** false; The slope of $y = 5$ is 0. **9.** true **11.** −8, 6

13.

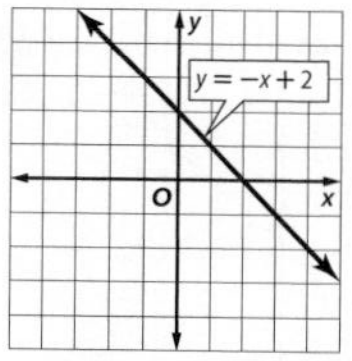

15.

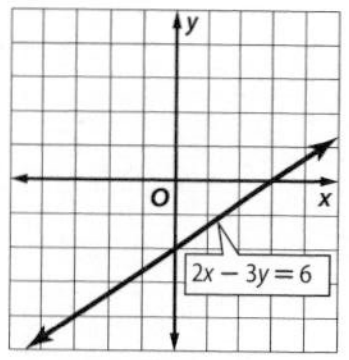

17a.

t	0	1	2	3	4	5
d	0	1.6	3.2	4.8	6.4	8

Speed of Sound

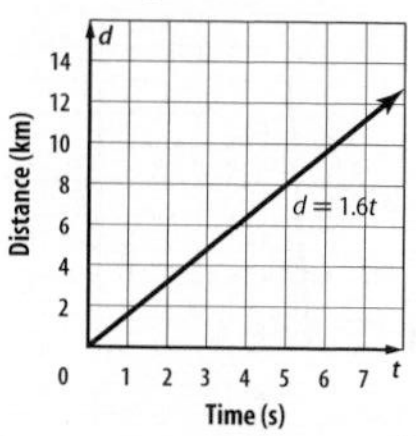

17b. about 11 km **19.** 6 **21.** $-\frac{1}{2}$
23. −7

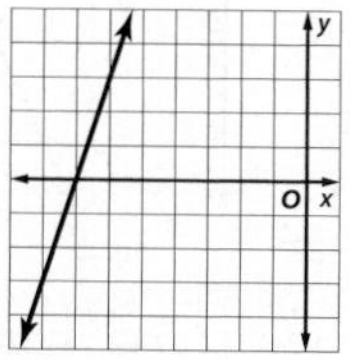

25. 9

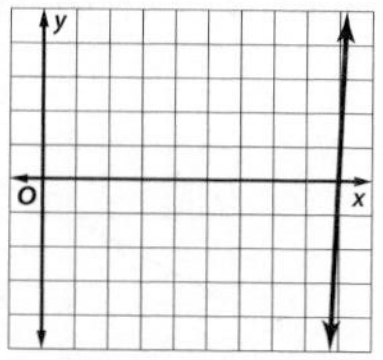

27. 3 **29.** $-\frac{1}{2}$ **31.** −0.05; an average decrease in cost of \$0.05 per year
33.

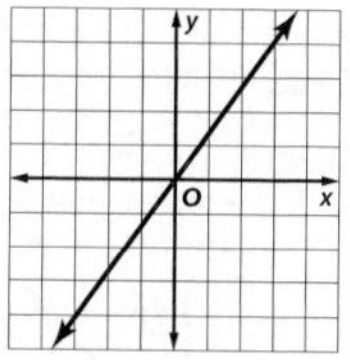

35. $y = 7.5x$; $y = 60$
37. $y = -x$; $y = -7$
39. 26, 31, 36
41. $a_n = 5n + 1$
43. $a_n = 4820n$; 15 s

45a.

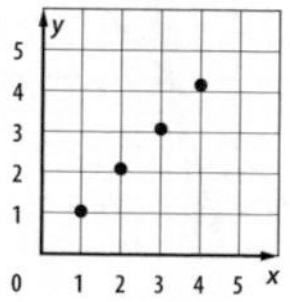

45b. $f(x) = 1.25x$
45c. \$7.50

CHAPTER 4
Equations of Linear Functions

Get Ready

1. 13 **3.** 14 **5.** \$282.50 **7.** $x = 3 + 2y$

9. $x = \frac{3}{4}y + 3$ **11.** (4, 2) **13.** (2, −4) **15.** (−3, −3)

Lesson 4-1

(1) $y = mx + b$
$y = 2x + 4$
To graph, plot the y-intercept (0, 4). Then use the slope of 2 to move up 2 and right 1 from the y-intercept to find the next point. Connect the points with a straight line.

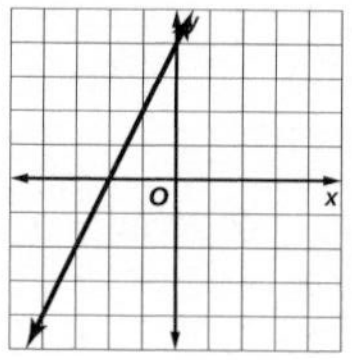

3. $y = \frac{3}{4}x - 1$

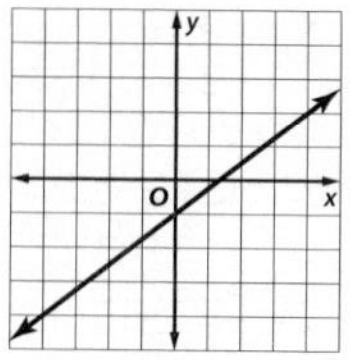

5.

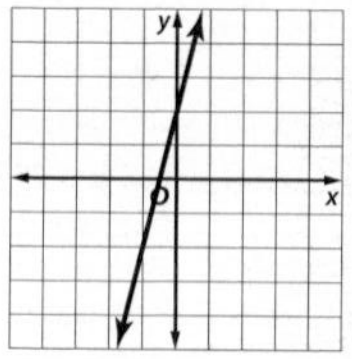

7.

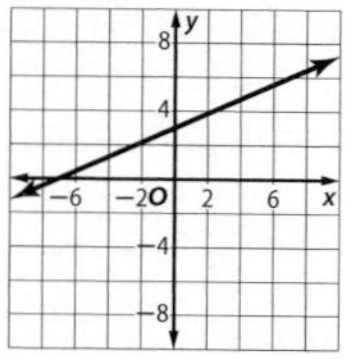

9.

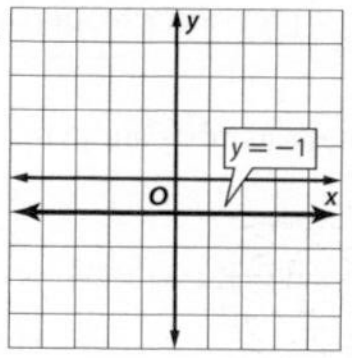

11. $y = \frac{2}{3}x + 2$ **13.** not possible **15a.** $S = 10w + 75$
15b.

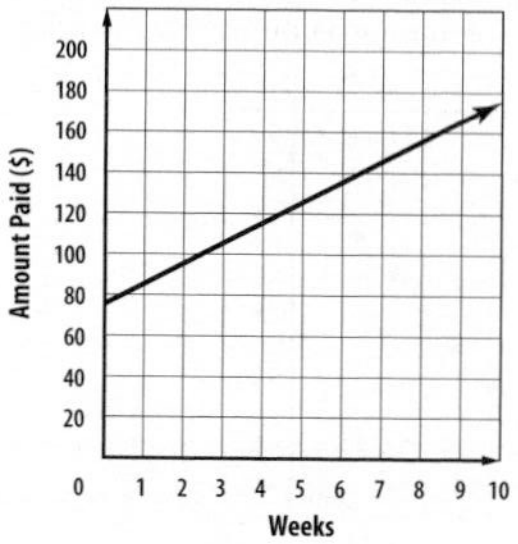

15c. \$155

(17) $y = mx + b$
$y = 5x + 8$
To graph, plot the y-intercept (0, 8). Then use the slope of 5 to move up 5 and right 1 from the y-intercept to find the next point. Connect the points with a straight line.

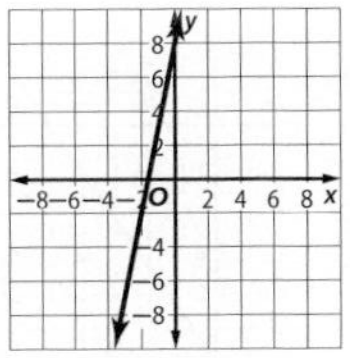

19. $y = -4x + 6$ **21.** $y = 3x - 4$

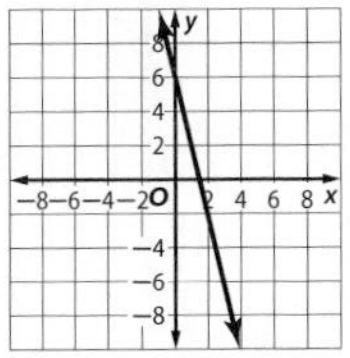

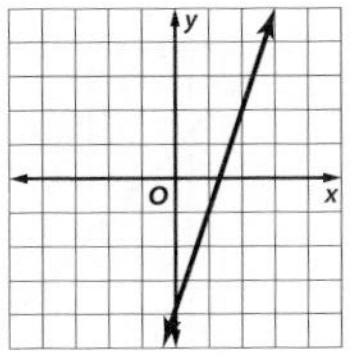

23.

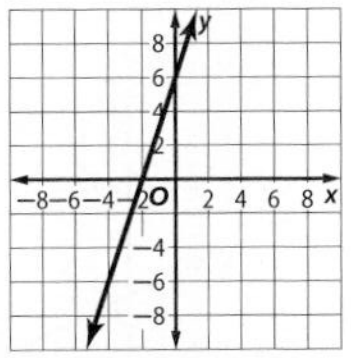

25.

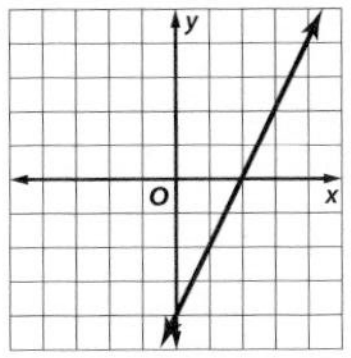

27.

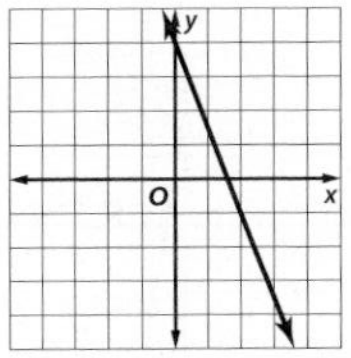

29.

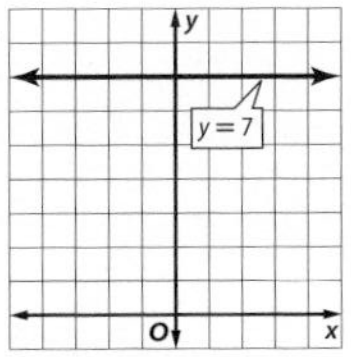

31.

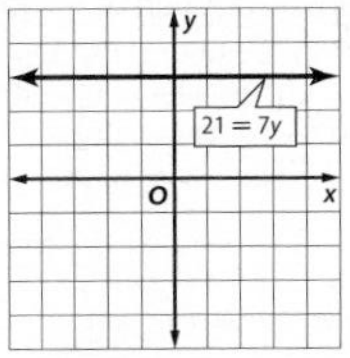

33. $y = -\frac{3}{5}x + 4$
35. $y = \frac{1}{2}x - 3$

(37) a. Words: the population is 1267 plus 123 per year. Equation: $P = 1267 + 123t$

b. Graph the equation by plotting the y-intercept of (0, 1267). Then use the slope of 123 to move 123 up and 1 right.

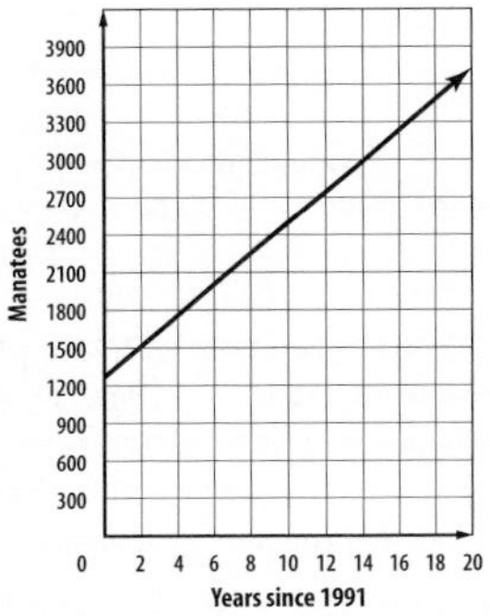

c. $P = 1267 + 123t$
$P = 1267 + 123(15)$
$P = 1267 + 1845$
$P = 3112$ manatees

39. $y = \frac{2}{3}x - 5$ **41.** $y = -\frac{3}{7}x + 2$ **43.** $y = 5$

45.

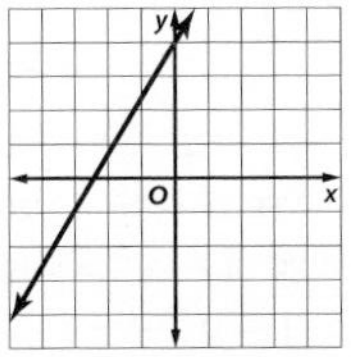

47.

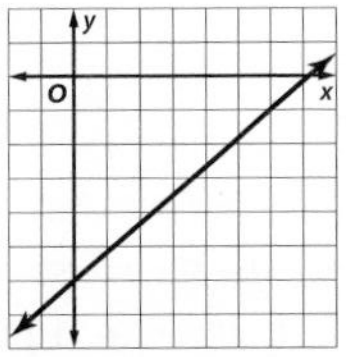

49.

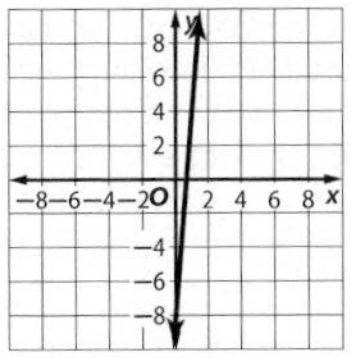

51a. $T = 157c + 218$ **51b.** \$5242 **53.** $y = 0.5x + 7.5$ **55.** $y = -1.5x - 0.25$ **57.** $y = 3x$ **59a.** $C = 45m + 145$ **59b.** the cost per month to maintain the membership **59c.** the start up fee **59d.** \$1225 **61a.** $S = 9125t + 3305$ **61b.** 12 yr **63.** No; because a vertical line has no slope, it cannot be written in slope-intercept form. **65.** Sample answer: Assume that the coefficient of y is not 0. We would first have to rewrite the equation in slope-intercept form. The rate of change is also the slope, so, the coefficient for the x-variable is the rate of change. Assume that the coefficient of y is not 0. **67.** B **69.** C **71.** $a_n = 4n - 1$; nonproportional, does not contain (0, 0) **73.** $a_n = 3n - 3$; nonproportional, does not contain (0, 0) **75a.** \$25,500 **75b.** \$142,500 **77.** $y = -4x; -5$ **79.** $y = 0.8x; -7.5$ **81.** $-\frac{2}{5}$ **83.** 0

Lesson 4-2

1. $y = 3x - 12$ **3.** $y = -x + 6$ **5.** $y = -3x + 9$ **7.** $y = 5x + 8$ **9a.** $C = 35p + 75$ **9b.** \$600

(11) $y = mx + b$
$4 = -1(-1) + b$
$4 = 1 + b$
$3 = b$
So, the equation is $y = -x + 3$.

13. $y = 8x - 55$ **15.** $y = 2x + 2$ **17.** $y = -x + 3$ **19.** $y = 7x - 16$ **21.** $y = 2x$ **23a.** $y = 0.2x + 0.4$ **23b.** 4.4 million **25.** $y = \frac{1}{2}x$ **27.** $y = -\frac{3}{4}x + 8\frac{1}{2}$ **29.** $y = \frac{2}{7}x - 2\frac{4}{7}$ **31a.** $G = 6.4t + 49.7$

31b.

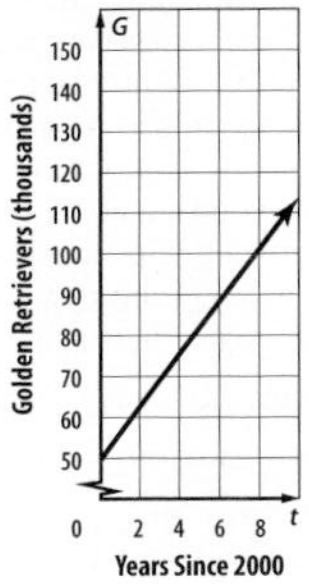

31c. 158,500 **33a.** \$2.75 **33b.** \$35.40

(35) First, find the slope.

$$m = \frac{y_2 - y_1}{x_2 - x_1} = \frac{5 - (-3)}{2 - 5} = \frac{5 + 3}{2 - 5} = \frac{8}{-3} = -\frac{8}{3}$$

Next, use the slope-intercept formula.

$$y = mx + b$$
$$5 = -\frac{8}{3}(2) + b$$
$$5 = -\frac{16}{3} + b$$
$$\frac{31}{3} = b$$
$$10\frac{1}{3} = b$$

So, the equation is $y = -2\frac{2}{3}x + 10\frac{1}{3}$.

37. $y = -x - \frac{7}{12}$ **39.** Yes; substituting 6 and −2 for x and y, respectively, results in an equation that is true. **41.** B; x represents the number of raffle tickets sold, y represents the total amount of money in the treasury. **43a.** 605.2 **43b.** 2032; In that year, the waste would be 0 tons. After that, the waste would be a negative amount, which is impossible.

(45) a. $C = 52t + b$
$275 = 52(5) + b$
$275 = 260 + b$
$15 = b$
So, the equation is $C = 52t + 15$.

b.

Number of tickets	3	4	6	7
Cost (\$)	171	223	327	379

c. Graph the equation by graphing the y-intercept (0, 15) and use the slope of 52 to find the next point.

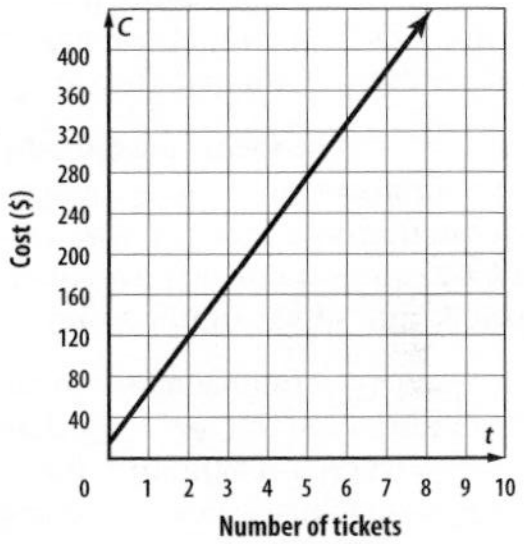

Eight tickets would be \$431.

47. Jacinta; Teresa switched the x- and y-coordinates on the point that she entered in step 3. **49a.** $y = -\frac{A}{B}x + \frac{C}{B}$ **49b.** slope $= -\frac{A}{B}$ **49c.** y-intercept $= \frac{C}{B}$ **49d.** no, $B \neq 0$ **51.** Sample answer: If the problem is about something that could suddenly change, such as weather or prices, the graph could suddenly spike up. You need a constant rate of change to produce a linear graph. **53.** D **55.** B

57.

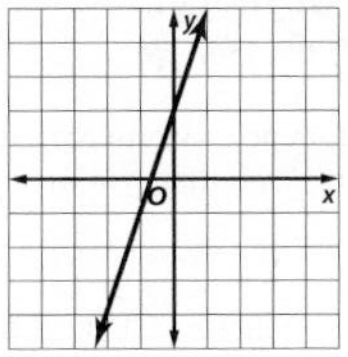

59.

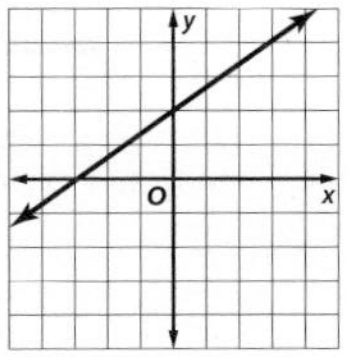

61.

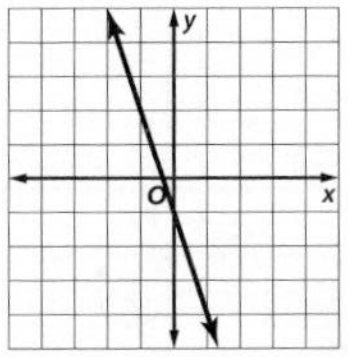

63. $f(x) = -2x$

65a.

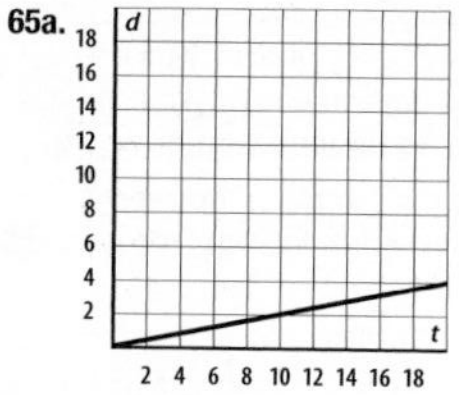

65b. about 14 seconds **67.** −22 **69.** −207 **71.** 1.5 **73.** 7 **75.** −1 **77.** 1

Lesson 4-3

1 $y - y^2 = m(x - x^2)$
$(y - 5) = -6(x - (-2))$
$(y - 5) = -6(x + 2)$
Plot the point (−2, 5) and use the slope of −6 to find the next point.

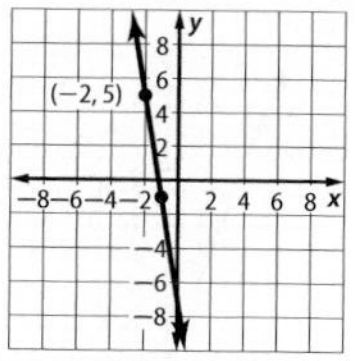

3. $y - 3 = -\frac{1}{2}(x - 4)$

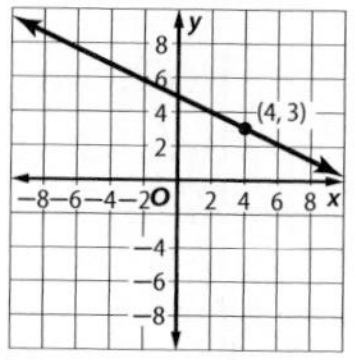

5. $5x + y = -22$ **7.** $y = 4x + 34$ **9.** $y = x + 13$
11. $y - 3 = 7(x - 5)$ **13.** $y + 3 = -1(x + 6)$

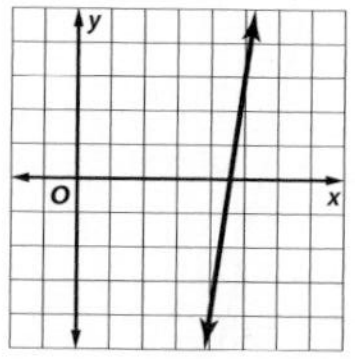

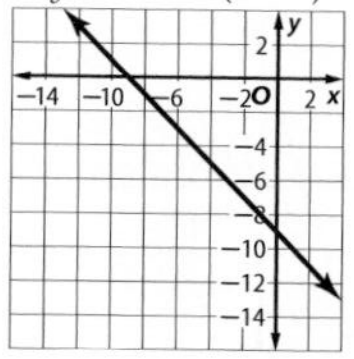

15. $y - 11 = \frac{4}{3}(x + 2)$

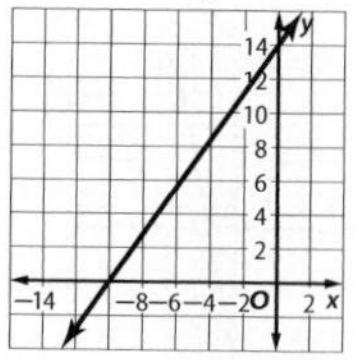

17. $y + 9 = -\frac{7}{5}(x + 2)$ **19.** $2x - y = 6$ **21.** $6x + y = -45$ **23.** $9x - 10y = 43$ **25.** $x + 6y = -7$ **27.** $y = -2x + 20$ **29.** $y = -6x - 47$ **31.** $y = \frac{1}{6}x - \frac{8}{3}$ **33.** $y = -\frac{2}{3}x - 5$

35 The slope is −5 and the point is (6, 4). So, the equation is $y - 4 = -5(x - 6)$. Replace x with 2 to determine how many were rented the second week.
$y - 4 = -5(2 - 6)$
$y - 4 = -5(-4)$
$y - 4 = 20$
$y = 24$
So, 24 copies were rented.

37. $x + y = 6$ **39.** $5x + 4y = 20$
41. $y + 1 = \frac{3}{2}(x + 4)$

43
$$y + \frac{3}{5} = x - \frac{2}{5}$$
$$y + \frac{3}{5} - \frac{3}{5} = x - \frac{2}{5} - \frac{3}{5}$$
$$y = x - \frac{5}{5}$$
$$y = x - 1$$

45. $y = \frac{5}{6}x$ **47.** $y - 4 = \frac{4}{7}(x + 9)$; $y = \frac{4}{7}x + \frac{64}{7}$; $4x - 7y = -64$ **49.** $y + 4 = 3(x + 1)$; The slope-intercept form is not $y = 3x + 2$. **51.** Sample answer: Jocari spent $14 to go to an amusement park and ride ponies. The price she paid included admission. The 5 pony rides cost $2 each; $y - 14 = 2(x - 5)$, $-2x + y = 4$, $y = 2x + 4$. **53.** Sample answer: $y - g = \frac{j - g}{h - f}(x - f)$ **55.** B **57.** J **59.** $y = x - 2$ **61.** $y = -2x + 1$ **63.** $y = -2$ **65.** $y = -2x + 6$ **67.** $y = \frac{1}{2}x + 3$ **69.** $y = 3$ **71.** Yes; there are only 364 seats. **73.** $a = \frac{v - r}{t}$ **75.** $b = \frac{-t + 5}{4}$

Lesson 4-4

1. $y = \frac{1}{2}x + 2\frac{1}{2}$ **3.** Slope of $\overline{AC} = \frac{1 - 7}{-2 - 5}$ or $\frac{6}{7}$; slope of $\overline{BD} = \frac{-3 - 4}{3 - (-3)}$ or $-\frac{7}{6}$; the paths are perpendicular.

5 Graph each line on a coordinate plane.
$y = -2x$ and $4y = 2x + 4$ are perpendicular to $2y = x$; $2y = x$ and $4y = 2x + 4$ are parallel.

7. $y = 2x + 7$ **9.** $y = \frac{3}{2}x$ **11.** $y = x - 5$ **13.** $y = -5x + 2$ **15.** $y = -\frac{3}{4}x + 1\frac{1}{2}$ **17.** Yes; the line containing $\overline{AD}$ and the line containing $\overline{BC}$ have the same slope, $\frac{1}{3}$. Therefore one pair of sides is parallel. The slope of $\overline{AB}$ is undefined and the slope of $\overline{CD}$ is $-\frac{5}{3}$. **19.** Yes; the slopes are −6 and $\frac{1}{6}$. **21.** $2x - 8y = -24$ and $4x + y = -2$ are perpendicular; $2x - 8y = -24$ and $x - 4y = 4$ are parallel.

23 The slope of the given line is −2. So, the slope of a line perpendicular is $\frac{1}{2}$.
$y = mx + b$
$-2 = \frac{1}{2}(-3) + b$
$-2 = -\frac{3}{2} + b$
$-\frac{1}{2} = b$
The equation is $y = \frac{1}{2}x - \frac{1}{2}$.

25. $y = -3x - 7$ **27.** $y = -\frac{1}{5}x + 8\frac{3}{5}$ **29.** $y = 2x + 16$ **31.** $y = -\frac{1}{5}x - \frac{3}{25}$ **33.** neither **35.** perpendicular **37.** neither **39.** $y = 7x$

41 Find the slopes.
$m = \frac{-1 - 6}{4 - 2} = \frac{-7}{2} = -\frac{7}{2}$ $\quad m = \frac{12 - 10}{14 - 7} = \frac{2}{7}$
Since the slopes are opposite reciprocals, the objects are perpendicular.

43a.

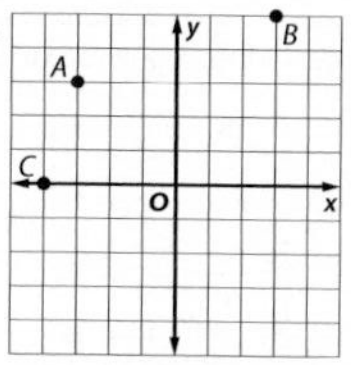

43b. Sample answer: (2, 2); $\overline{AB}$ and $\overline{CD}$ both have slope $\frac{1}{3}$, and $\overline{AC}$ and $\overline{BD}$ both have slope 3.
43c. Two; sample answer: Move C to (−2, 0) and move D to (4, 2). Moving C changes the slope of $\overline{AC}$ to −3. This is the opposite reciprocal of the slope $\overline{AC}$, $\frac{1}{3}$. Moving D also changes the slope of $\overline{BD}$ so $\overline{BD}$ is perpendicular to $\overline{AB}$ and $\overline{CD}$ and it is parallel to $\overline{AC}$. **45.** Sample answer: Parallel lines: similarities: The domain and range are all real numbers, the functions are both either increasing or decreasing on the entire domain, the end behavior is the same; differences: x- and y-intercepts are different. Perpendicular lines: similarities: The domain and range are all real numbers; differences: One function is increasing and the other is decreasing on the entire domain, as x decreases, y increases for one function and decreases for the other and as x increases, y increases for one function and decreases for the other. **47.** Carmen is correct; she correctly determined the slope of the perpendicular line. **49.** A **51.** B **53.** $-4x + y = 5$ **55.** $5x + y = -8$ **57.** $5x - 6y = 14$ **59a.** $C = 10h + 15$ **59b.** $95 **61.** $y = -5x - 21$ **63.** $y = 2x - 1$ **65.** $y = -5x - 6$ **67.** simplified **69a.** 25(5) + 10(8.5) + 35(5) + 12(8.5) **69b.** $487

71.

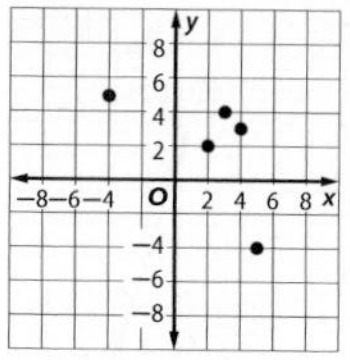

D = {−7, 4, −2, −3}; R = {4, 3, 2, −4, 5}

73.

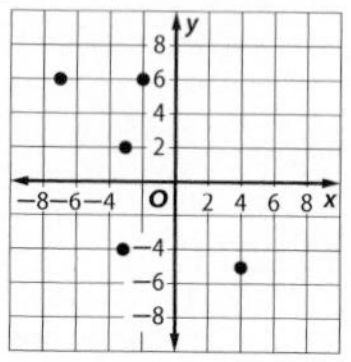

D = {−7, 4, −2, −3}; R = {6, −4, −5, 2}

Lesson 4-5

1. Positive; the longer you practice free throws, the more free throws you will make.

3a.

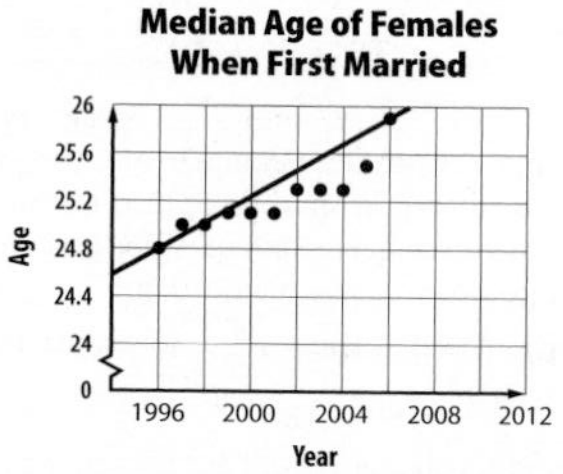

Positive; independent variable is year and dependent variable is median age of females when they were first married. **3b.** See above graph. **3c.** Sample answer: Using (1996, 24.8) and (2006, 25.9) and rounding, $y = 0.11x - 194.8$ **3d.** Sample answer: 27.0 **3e.** Yes, according to the equation, the median age would be 31.4, which is likely.

5 As the height increases, the percentage decreases. The graph shows a slight negative correlation. This correlation means that the taller a player is, the lower their percentage of 3-point shots made is.

7 There is no pattern to the graph, so there is no correlation between the speed of a vehicle and the miles per gallon.

9a. $y = -648.5x + 74{,}447.5$ **9b.** 61,478 **9c.** No; the average attendance will fluctuate with other variables such as how good the team is that year.

11 a. The independent variable is the duration of the eruptions and the dependent variable is the interval of the eruptions. This is because the duration of the eruptions is not affected by the interval.

b. Use (2, 55) and (4, 82)

$m = \frac{y_2 - y_1}{x_2 - x_1}$

$= \frac{82 - 55}{4 - 2}$

$= \frac{27}{2}$

$= 13.5$

So, the slope is 13.5.

$y = 13.5x + b$	$y = 13.5x + 28$
$55 = 13.5(2) + b$	$y = 13.5(7.5) + 28$
$55 = 27 + b$	$y = 101.25 + 28$
$28 = b$	$y = 129.25$ min

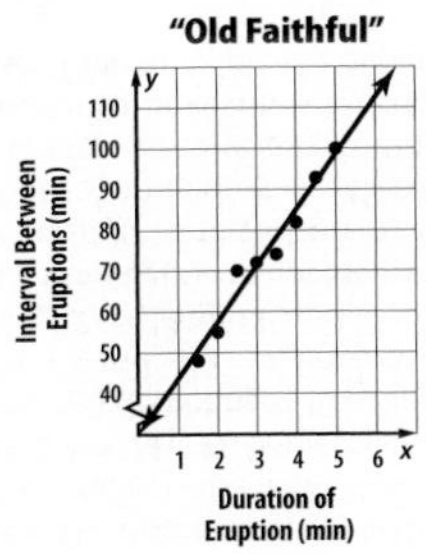

The interval increases as the duration increases, so there is a positive correlation between the independent and dependent variables.

c. Sample answer: The duration of an eruption is not dependent on the previous interval. Only the interval can be predicted by the length of the eruption.

13. Sample answer: The salary of an individual and the years of experience that they have; this would be a positive correlation because the more experience an individual has, the higher the salary would probably be. **15.** Neither; line *g* has the same number of points above the line and below the line. Line *f* is close to 2 of the points; but for the rest of the data, there are 3 points above and 3 points below the line. **17.** Sample answer: You can visualize a line to determine whether the data has a positive or negative correlation. The following graph shows the ages and heights of people. To predict a person's age given his or her height, write a linear equation for the line of fit. Then substitute the person's height and solve for the corresponding age. You can use the pattern in the scatter plot to make decisions.

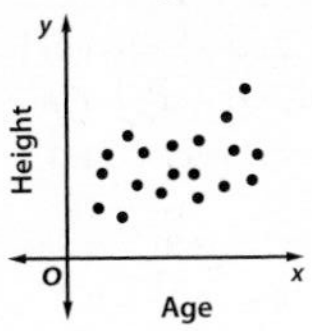

19. F **21.** 22 days
23. neither
25. perpendicular
27. $2x + y = 1$
29. $x - 2y = 12$
31. $2x + 5y = 26$

33.

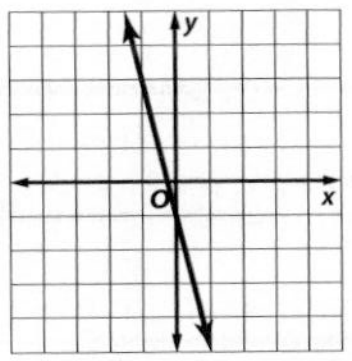

35. $\frac{4}{7}$ **37.** $\frac{3}{5}$
39. 16 **41.** 1.5 h

43.

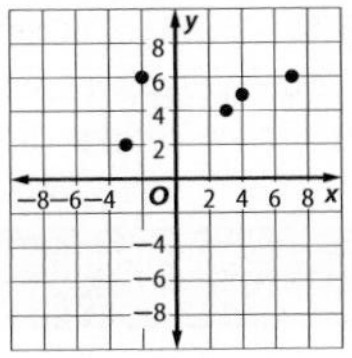

D = {7, 3, 4, −2, −3};
R = {6, 4, 5, 2}

Lesson 4-6

1a. $y = 1.18x + 11$; 0.7181
1b. The residuals appear to be randomly scattered, so the regression line fits the data reasonably well.

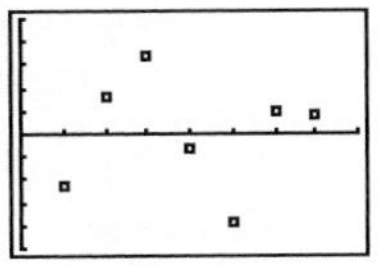

[0, 8] scl: 1.5 by [−5, 5] scl: 1.5

3a. $y = -271.88x + 554.48$
3b. $78.69

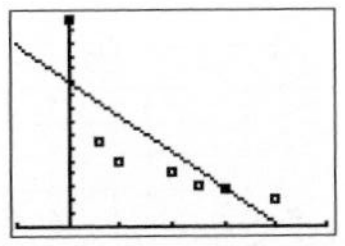

[−0.5, 2.5] scl: 1 by [0, 785] scl: 10

(5) Step 1: Enter the data by pressing STAT and selecting the Edit option. Let the year 2000 be represented by 0. Enter the years since 2000 into List 1 (L1). These will represent the *x*-values. Enter the number of auditions into List 2 (L2). These will represent the *y*-values.
Step 2: Perform the regression by pressing STAT and selecting the CALC option. Scroll down to LinReg(ax + b) and press ENTER.
The equation is $y = 3.54x + 5.54$.
The correlation coefficient is 0.9007.

(7) **a.** Enter the data using 0 for 1975. Use med-med to find $y = 601.44x + 1236.13$.
b. 2003 − 1975 = 28. Substitute 28 into the equation in **a** to get 18,076.45. There were about 18,076 entrants in 2003.

9a. $y = 0.095x - 94.58$

9b.

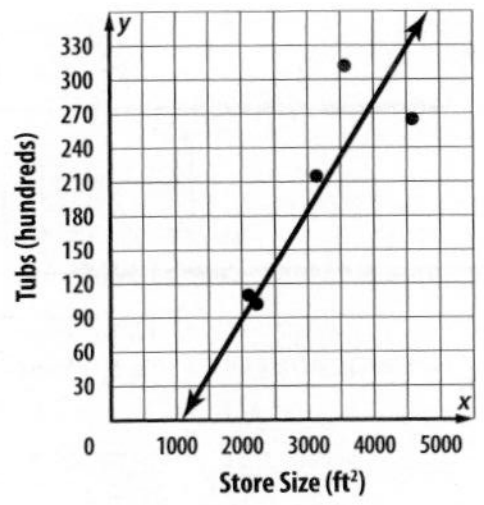

9c. about 48 tubs; about 380 tubs
11a. $y = 0.0326x + 1.598$

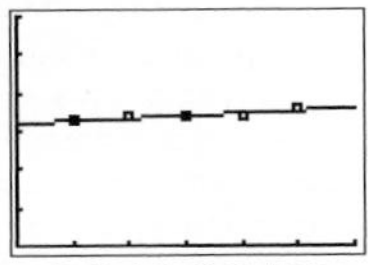

[0, 6] scl: 1 by [0, 3] scl: 0.5

11b. The regression line is a good fit as the residuals appear to almost be on the line.

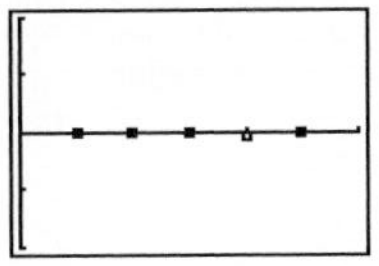

[0, 6] scl: 1 by [−2, 2] scl: 1

11c. about 2.12 million people
13a. $y = 87{,}390.5x + 4{,}018{,}431$ **13b.** about 5,591,460

15.

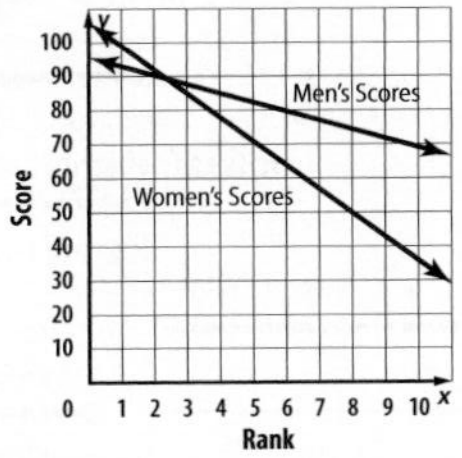

Sample answer: Men: $y = -2.92x + 95.92$; women: $y = -7x + 106$; women's scores have a steeper slope than men's.

19. C **21.** H **23a.** negative correlation **23b.** $3600 **23c.** No; according to the line of fit, the cost would be $0. **25.** $3x - y = 1$ **27.** $2x + y = 8$ **29.** $2x - 3y = -21$ **31.** $\frac{4}{7}$ **33.** $\frac{3}{5}$ **35.** 3 **37.** $a^2 - a + 1$

39.

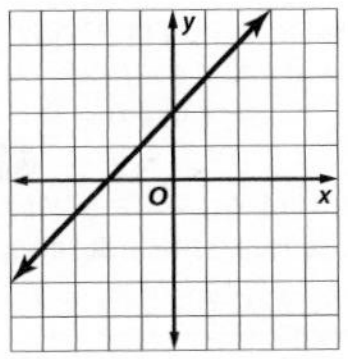

41.

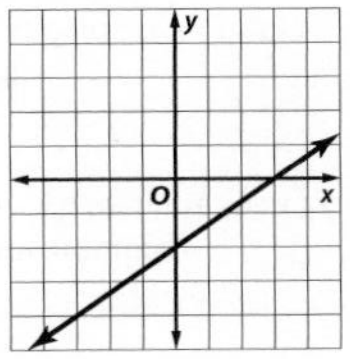

Lesson 4-7

1. {(−15, 4), (−18, −8), (−16.5, −2), (−15.25, 3)}

3.

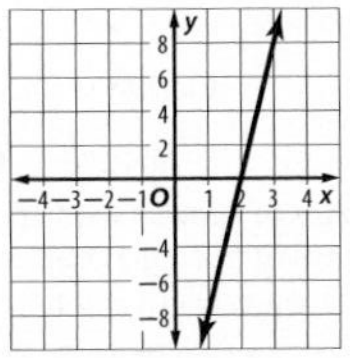

5. $f^{-1}(x) = -\frac{1}{2}x + \frac{7}{2}$ **7a.** $C^{-1}(x) = \frac{1}{70}x - \frac{60}{7}$
7b. *x* is Dwayne's total cost, and $C^{-1}(x)$ is the number of games Dwayne attended. **7c.** 5

(9) Exchange the coordinates of the ordered pairs.
(−4, −49) → (−49, −4) (8, 35) → (35, 8)
(−1, −28) → (−28, −1) (4, 7) → (7, 4)
The inverse is {(−49, −4), (35, 8), (−28, −1), (7, 4)}.

11. {(7.4, −3), (4, −1), (0.6, 1), (−2.8, 3), (−6.2, 5)}

13.

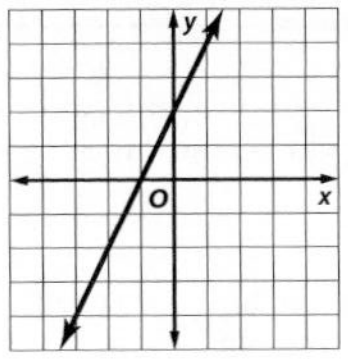

(15)

$f(x) = 17 - \frac{1}{3}x$

$y = 17 - \frac{1}{3}x$

$x = 17 - \frac{1}{3}y$

$x - 17 = -\frac{1}{3}y$

$-3(x - 17) = y$

$-3x + 51 = y$

The inverse of $f(x)$ is $f^{-1}(x) = -3x + 51$.

17. $f^{-1}(x) = -\frac{1}{6}x + 2$ **19.** $f^{-1}(x) = -\frac{3}{4}x - 12$

21a. $C^{-1}(x) = \frac{1}{35}x - \frac{2}{7}$ **21b.** *x* is the total amount collected from the Fosters, and $C^{-1}(x)$ is the number of times Chuck mowed the Fosters' lawn.
21c. 22 **23.** $f^{-1}(x) = 15 - 5x$ **25.** $f^{-1}(x) = \frac{3}{2}x + 12$
27. $f^{-1}(x) = 3x - 3$ **29.** B **31.** A

(33) If the graph of $f(x)$ contains the points (−3, 6) and (6, 12), then the graph of $f^{-1}(x)$ contains the points (6, −3) and (12, 6). Find the slope of the line that passes through these points.

$m = \frac{y_2 - y_1}{x_2 - x_1}$

$= \frac{6 - (-3)}{12 - 6}$

$= \frac{9}{6}$ or $\frac{3}{2}$

Choose (12, 6) and find the *y*-intercept of the line.

$y = mx + b$
$6 = \frac{3}{2}(12) + b$
$6 = 18 + b$
$-12 = b$

The line that passes through (6, −3) and (12, 6) is $y = \frac{3}{2}x - 12$. An equation for $f^{-1}(x)$ is $f^{-1}(x) = \frac{3}{2}x - 12$

35. $f^{-1}(x) = \frac{1}{4}x + \frac{3}{4}$ **37a.** $A(x) = 8(x - 3)$ or $A(x) = 8x - 24$

37b.

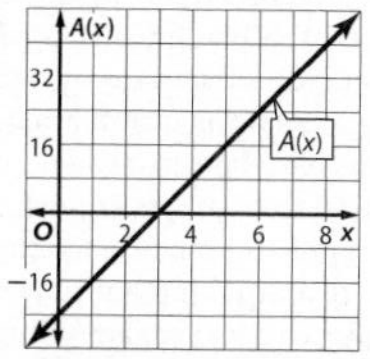

Sample answer: The domain represents possible values of x. The range represents the area of the rectangle and must be positive. This means that the domain of $A(x)$ is all real numbers greater than 3, and the range of $A(x)$ is all positive real numbers. **37c.** $A^{-1}(x) = \frac{1}{8}x + 3$; x is the area of the rectangle and $A^{-1}(x)$ is the value of x in the expression for the length of the side of the rectangle $x - 3$.

37d.

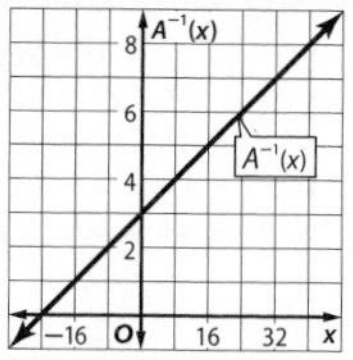

Sample answer: The domain represents the area of the rectangle and must be positive. The range represents possible values for x in the expression $x - 3$. This means that the domain of $A^{-1}(x)$ is all positive real numbers, and the range of $A^{-1}(x)$ is all real numbers greater than 3. **37e.** Sample answer: The domain of $A(x)$ is the range of $A^{-1}(x)$, and the range of $A(x)$ is the domain of $A^{-1}(x)$. **39.** $a = 2$; $b = 14$ **41.** Sometimes; sample answer: $f(x)$ and $g(x)$ do not need to be inverse functions for $f(a) = b$ and $g(b) = a$. For example, if $f(x) = 2x + 10$, then $f(2) = 14$ and if $g(x) = x - 12$, then $g(14) = 2$, but $f(x)$ and $g(x)$ are not inverse functions. However, if $f(x)$ and $g(x)$ are inverse functions, then $f(a) = b$ and $g(b) = a$. **43.** Sample answer: A situation may require substituting values for the dependent variable into a function. By finding the inverse of the function, the dependent variable becomes the independent variable. This makes the substitution an easier process. **45.** F **47.** 4.2 **49.** $y = 8.235x - 17.365$ **51.** $y = 0.325x + 0.89$ **53.** 100 **55.** 11.7 **57.** 171 **59.** −77 **61.** 100

Chapter 4 Study Guide and Review

1. true **3.** true **5.** true **7.** false, inverse function **9.** false, slope-intercept form
11. $y = -2x - 9$ **13.** $y = -\frac{5}{8}x - 2$

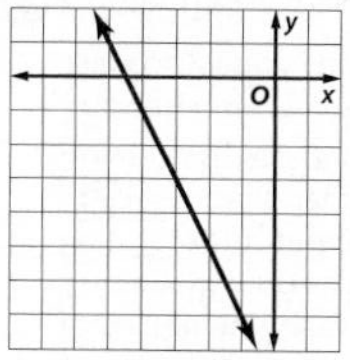

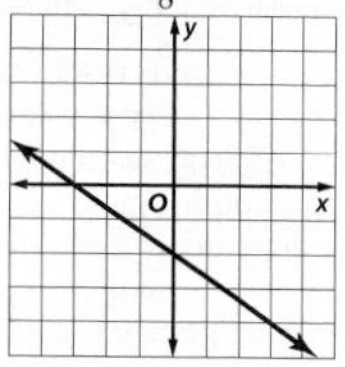

15.

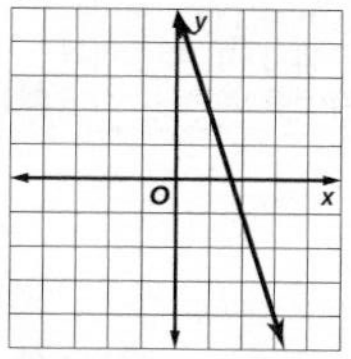

17.

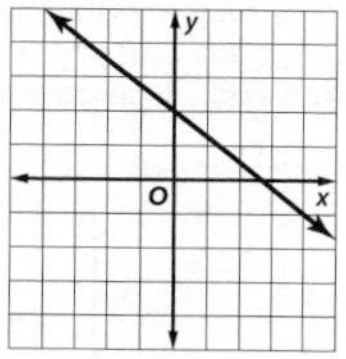

19. $y = 3x - 1$ **21.** $y = \frac{2}{5}x + \frac{1}{5}$ **23.** $y = x - 3$ **25.** $y = \frac{1}{2}x + \frac{7}{2}$ **27.** $y = 60x + 450$ **29.** $y - 1 = -3(x + 2)$ **31.** $5x - y = 7$ **33.** $x - 2y = 11$ **35.** $y = 3x - 13$ **37.** $y = 5x + 2$ **39.** $y = x + 3$ **41.** $y = -2x - 7$ **43.** $y = -\frac{1}{3}x + \frac{14}{3}$ **45.** $y = -3x - 13$ **47.** positive **49.** $y = 5.36x + 11$; 65 **51.** {(3.5, 7), (8, 6.2), (2.7, −4), (1.4, −12)} **53.** {(2.7, −4), (3.8, −1), (4.1, 0), (7.2, 3)} **55.** $f^{-1}(x) = \frac{11}{5}x - 22$ **57.** $f^{-1}(x) = -\frac{1}{4}x - 3$ **59.** $f^{-1}(x) = -\frac{3}{2}x + \frac{3}{8}$

CHAPTER 5 Linear Inequalities

Get Ready

1. −10 **3.** 24.6 **5.** −11 **7.** 21 **9.** 5 **11.** −4 **13.** {−29, 7} **15.** 34%, 30%

Lesson 5-1

1. $\{x \mid x > 10\}$

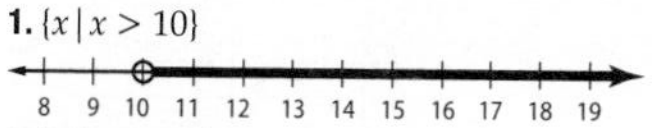

3. $\{g \mid g < -4\}$

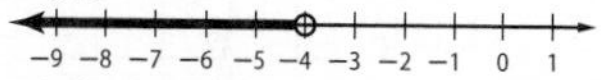

5. $\{n \mid n < 11\}$

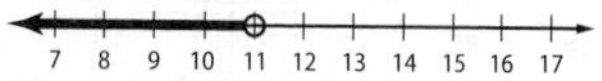

7. $\{r \mid r > 6\}$

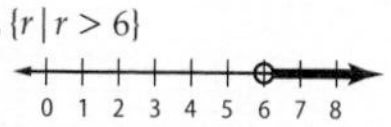

9. Sample answer: Let n = the number, $2n + 4 \geq n + 10$; $\{n \mid n \geq 6\}$. **11.** no more than 92 ft

13
$p - 6 \geq 3$
$p - 6 + 6 \geq 3 + 6$
$p \geq 9$ $\{p \mid p \geq 9\}$

Place a closed circle on 9 and an arrow to the right.

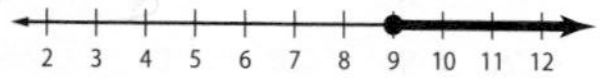

15. $\{t \mid t > -5\}$

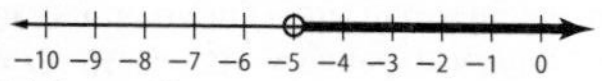

17. $\{r \mid r < -5\}$

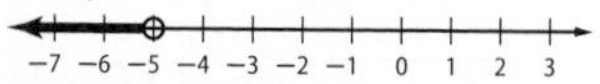

19. $\{q \mid q \leq 7\}$

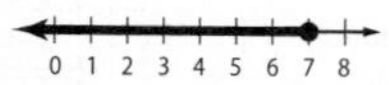

21. $\{h \mid h < 30\}$

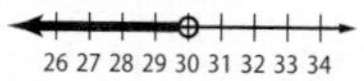

23. $\{c \mid c < -27\}$

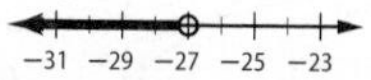

25. $\{z \mid z \leq 4\}$

27. $\{y \mid y \leq -6\}$

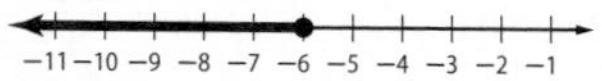

29. $\{a \mid a > -9\}$

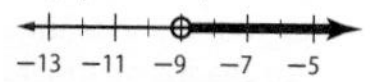

31. Sample answer: Let n = the number, $2n + 5 \leq n - 3$; $\{n \mid n \leq -8\}$. **33.** Sample answer: Let n = the number, $6n - 8 < 5n + 21$; $\{n \mid n < 29\}$. **35.** Sample answer: Let n = the number of online teens that do not use the Internet at school in millions; $n > 21 - 16$; $\{n \mid n > 5\}$, at least 5 million teens use the Internet but not at school. **37.** Sample answer: Let t = the original water temperature; $t + 4 < 81$; $\{t \mid t < 77\}$; the water temperature was originally less than 77°.

39 Let x represent the amount left on the card.
$x + 32 + 26 < 75$
$x + 58 < 75$
$x + 58 - 58 < 75 - 58$
$x < 17$

She will have no more than \$17 left on the card.

41. $\{c \mid c \geq 3.7\}$

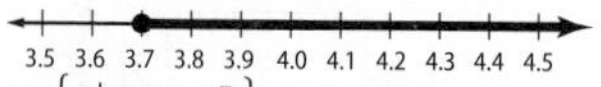

43. $\left\{k \,\middle|\, k > -\frac{5}{12}\right\}$

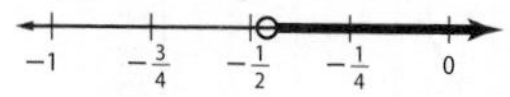

45a.

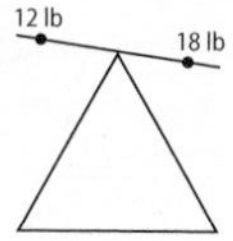

45b. 12 lb < 18 lb

45c.

	12	<	18
$2x$	24	<	36
$3x$	36	<	54
$4x$	48	<	72
$\frac{1}{2}x$	6	<	9
$\frac{1}{3}x$	4	<	6
$\frac{1}{4}x$	3	<	$4\frac{1}{2}$

45d. If a true inequality is multiplied by a positive number, the resulting inequality is also true. If a true inequality is divided by a positive number, the resulting inequality is also true.

47. 10 **49.** 3 **51.** 26 **53.** $c < a < d < b$ **55.** Solving linear inequalities is similar to solving linear equations. You must isolate the variable on one side of the inequality. To graph, if the problem is a less than or a greater than inequality, an open circle is used. Otherwise a dot is used. If the variable is on the left hand side of the inequality, and the inequality sign is less than (or less than or equal to), the graph extends to the left; otherwise it extends to the right. **57.** C **59.** B **61.** $f(x)^{-1} = \frac{1}{7}x + 4$ **63.** $f(x)^{-1} = -3x - 24$ **65.** $y = -x - 2$ **67.** $y = -2x - 1$ **69.** blue **71.** 25 **73.** $y = 7x$; \$210 **75.** −30 **77.** $\frac{1}{10}$ **79.** 16 **81.** $-\frac{1}{9}$

Lesson 5-2

1. Let d = the number of DVDs sold; $15d > 5500$; $d > 366.67$; the band sold at least 367 DVDs.

3. $\{r \mid r \geq 8\}$

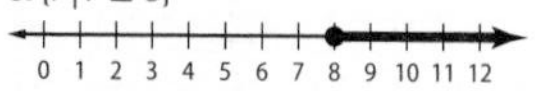

5. $\{h \mid h < -10\}$

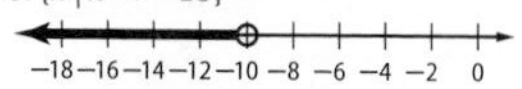

7. $\{v \mid v > -12\}$

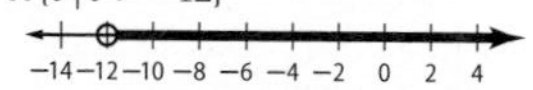

9. $\{z \mid z \geq -8\}$

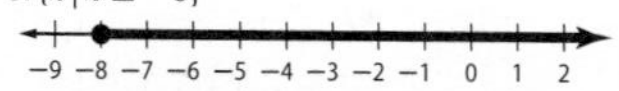

11. Let p = the number of pay periods for which Rodrigo will need to save; $25p \geq 560$; $p \geq 22.4$; Rodrigo will need to save for 23 weeks.

13
$\frac{1}{2}a < 20$
$2\left(\frac{1}{2}a\right) < 2(20)$
$a < 40$ $\{a \mid a < 40\}$

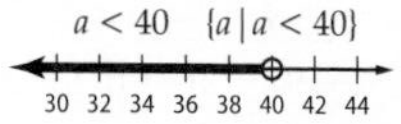

Check by substituting values less than 40.

15. $\{d \mid d \geq 68\}$

17. $\{f \mid f < 432\}$

19. $\{j \mid j \leq -16\}$

21. $\{p \mid p \leq 16\}$

23. $\{y \mid y > -16\}$

25. $\{v \mid v < 12\}$

27. $\left\{b \mid b \leq -\frac{3}{4}\right\}$

29. $\left\{f \mid f < -\frac{5}{7}\right\}$

31. no more than 4 **33.** no more than 32 people

35. b **37.** d

39 $\frac{2}{3}x < 42$

$3\left(\frac{2}{3}x\right) < 3(42)$

$2x < 126$

$x < 63$ fewer than 63 employees

41a.

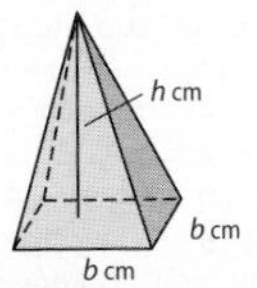

41b. $h = \frac{216}{b^2}$

41c.

b	1	3	6	9	12
h	216	24	6	$\frac{8}{3}$	$\frac{3}{2}$

41d. $b < h$ when $0 < b < 6$; $b > h$ when $h < 6$.

43a. $x > -\frac{5}{a}$ **43b.** $x \geq 8a$ **43c.** $x \leq -\frac{6}{a}$

45. Sometimes; the statement is true when $a > 0$ and $b < 0$. **47.** Sample answer: The same processes are used when solving linear inequalities and equations that involve addition, subtraction, multiplication, or division by a positive number. However, when a linear inequality is multiplied or divided by a negative number, the inequality symbol must change directions so that the inequality remains true. **49.** 10 in. **51.** C

53. $\{y \mid y \geq 21\}$

55. $f^{-1}(x) = -\frac{1}{6}x + 3$ **57.** $f^{-1}(x) = \frac{1}{4}x + \frac{5}{4}$

59. 2 hours **61.** $\{1, 7\}$ **63.** 2 **65.** $\frac{33}{8}$ **67.** 3

Lesson 5-3

1. $4n + 60 \leq 800$; $n \leq 185$; at most 185 lb per person

3 $6h - 10 \geq 32$

$6h - 10 + 10 \geq 32 + 10$

$6h \geq 42$

$h \geq 7$

$\{h \mid h \geq 7\}$

5. $\{x \mid x < -12\}$

7. Sample answer: Let n = the number; $4n - 6 > 8 + 2n$; $\{n \mid n > 7\}$. **9.** $\{v \mid v \geq 0\}$

11. ∅

13 $21 > 15 + 2a$

$21 - 15 > 2a$

$6 > 2a$

$3 > a$ $\{a \mid a < 3\}$

15. $\{w \mid w > 56\}$

17. $\{w \mid w < -3\}$

19. $\left\{p \mid p > -\frac{24}{5}\right\}$

21. $\{h \mid h < -15\}$

23. Sample answer: Let n = the number; $\frac{2}{3}n + 6 \geq 22$; $\{n \mid n \geq 24\}$. **25.** Sample answer: Let n = the number; $8n - 27 \leq -n + 18$; $\{n \mid n \leq 5\}$. **27.** Sample answer: Let n = the number; $3(n + 7) > 5n - 13$; $\{n \mid n < 17\}$

29. $\left\{n \mid n > -\frac{1}{3}\right\}$

31. ∅

33. $\{t \mid t \geq -1\}$

35. Sample answer: Let s = the amount of sales made, $35{,}000 + 0.08s > 65{,}000$; $\{s \mid s > 375{,}000\}$; the sales must be more than $375,000.

37.

$6(m - 3) > 5(2m + 4)$	Original inequality
$6m - 18 > 10m + 20$	Distributive Property
$6m - 18 - 6m > 10m + 20 - 6m$	Subtract $6m$ from each side.
$-18 > 4m + 20$	Simplify.
$-18 - 20 > 4m + 20 - 20$	Subtract 20 from each side.
$-38 > 4m$	Simplify.
$\frac{-38}{4} > \frac{4m}{4}$	Divide each side by 4.
$-9.5 > m$	Simplify.
$\{m \mid m < -9.5\}$	

39a. $5t + 565 \geq 1500$; $t \geq 187$

39b.

41 **a.** Words: temperature can be greater than 104

$t > 104$

b. $F > 104$

$\frac{9}{5}C + 32 > 104$

$\frac{9}{5}C > 72$

$5\left(\frac{9}{5}C > 72\right)$

$9C > 360$

$C > 40$

43. 1, 3, 5, 7; 3, 5, 7, 9; 5, 7, 9, 11; 7, 9, 11, 13

45. $\left\{x \mid x \geq \frac{1}{2}\right\}$ **47.** $\{m \mid m \geq 18\}$ **49.** $\{x \mid x \leq 8\}$

51. $\{x \mid x > -6\}$ **53.** $\{x \mid x \geq 1.5\}$ **55.** Add $3p$ and 2 to each side. The inequality becomes $9 \geq 3p$. Then divide each side by 3 to get $3 \geq p$.

57a. $\left\{x \mid x \geq -\frac{9}{2a}\right\}$ **57b.** $\left\{x \mid x > \frac{2}{1 + a}\right\}$

57c. $\{x \mid x < 6a\}$ **59.** Sample answer: The solution set for an inequality that results in a false statement is the empty set, as in $12 < -15$. The solution set for an inequality in which any value of x results in a true statement is all real numbers, as in $12 \leq 12$.

61. G **63.** D **65.** $\{b \mid b > -4\}$

67. $\{h \mid h < 14\}$

69. $\{m \mid m \geq 1\}$

71. 4

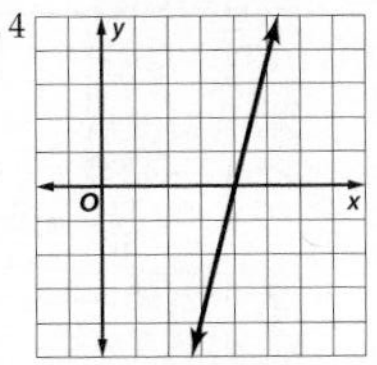

73. about 70.1 million

75. 8 **77.** 12(29.95 + 4) or 12(29.95) + 12(4); $407.40

79.

81.

83.

Lesson 5-4

1. $\{p \mid 12 \leq p \leq 16\}$

3. $\{a \mid a > 5\}$

5. 11 psi $\leq x \leq$ 56 psi

7 $n + 2 \leq -5$ and $n + 6 \geq -6$

$n + 2 - 2 \leq -5 - 2$ and $n + 6 - 6 \geq -6 - 6$

$n \leq -7$ $n \geq -12$

The solution set is $\{n \mid -12 \leq n \leq -7\}$.

9. $\{t \mid t \geq 1$ or $t < -1\}$

11. $\{c \mid -1 \leq c < 2\}$

13. $\{m \mid m$ is a real number.$\}$

15. $\{y \mid y < -3\}$

17. Sample answer: Let x = the smaller of two consecutive odd numbers, then $8 \leq 2x + 2 \leq 24$; $3 \leq x \leq 11$; 3, 5; 5, 7; 7, 9; 9, 11; 11, 13

19 The graph shows $x > -3$ and $x \leq 2$, so the inequality is $-3 < x \leq 2$.

21. $x < -4$ or $x > -3$ **23.** $x \leq -3$ or $x > 0$

25. $\left\{a \mid -3 < a \leq \frac{1}{2}\right\}$

27. $\{n \mid n < -3$ or $n > -3\}$

29. Sample answer: Let n = the number; $5 \le n - 8 \le 14$; $\{n \mid 13 \le n \le 22\}$. **31.** $-5n > 35$ or $-5n < 10$; $\{n \mid n < -7$ or $n > -2\}$ **33.** $t < 75$ or $t > 90$
35. Sample answer: Let t = the temperature; $23 \le t \le 33$.

(37) **a.** Category 3 has wind speeds between 111 and 130: $111 \le x \le 130$
Category 4 has wind speeds between 131 and 155: $131 \le x \le 155$
b. The union is all values between 111 and 155: $111 \le x \le 155$.
The intersection is all values they have in common, which is none. The intersection is the empty set, ∅.

39. Neither; Chloe did not add 5 to 3, and Jonas did not add 5 to 7. **41.** Sample answer: $x \le 2$ or $x \ge 4$ **43.** Sample answer: The speed at which a roller coaster runs while staying on the track could represent a compound inequality that is an intersection. **45.** H **47.** B **49.** at least 22 subscriptions **51.** 5.6 **53.** 3.94 **55.** 3.28 **57.** Yes; for each input there is exactly one output. **59.** No; the domain value −4 is paired with both −1 and 11.

61. $5 + (4 - 2^2)$
$= 5 + (4 - 4)$
$= 5 + 0$
$= 5$

63. $2(4 \cdot 9 - 3) + 5 \cdot \frac{1}{5}$
$= 2(36 - 3) + 5 \cdot \frac{1}{5}$
$= 2(33) + 5 \cdot \frac{1}{5}$
$= 66 + 5 \cdot \frac{1}{5}$
$= 66 + 1$
$= 67$

65. 3 **67.** $12\frac{2}{3}$ **69.** 30 **71.** 10

Lesson 5-5

1. $\{a \mid 2 < a < 8\}$

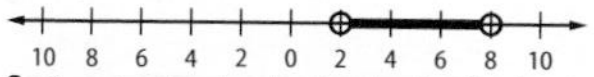

3. ∅

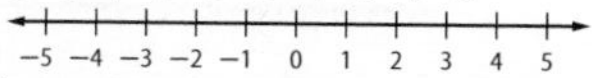

5. $\{n \mid n \le -8$ or $n \ge -2\}$

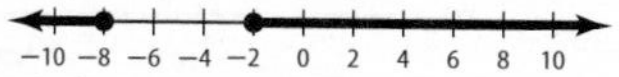

7. $\{m \mid 70.10 \le m \le 71.60\}$

(9) $|r + 1| \le 2$

Case 1:		Case 2:
$r + 1$ is positive.	and	$r + 1$ is negative.
$r + 1 \le 2$	and	$r + 1 \ge -2$
$r \le 1$	and	$r \ge -3$

The solution set is $\{r \mid -3 \le r \le 1\}$.

11. $\{h \mid -3 < h < 5\}$

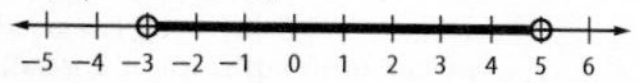

13. ∅

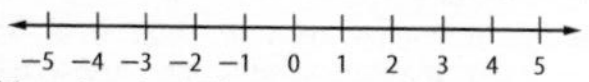

15. $\{k \mid k < 1$ or $k > 7\}$

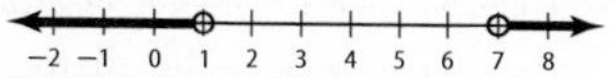

17. $\{p \mid p \le -3$ or $p \ge 2\}$

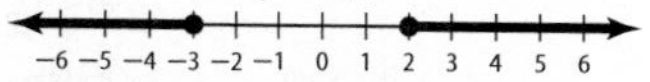

19. $\{c \mid c$ is a real number.$\}$

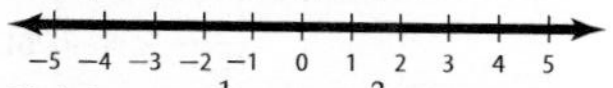

21. $\{n \mid n \le -5\frac{1}{4}$ or $n \ge 3\frac{3}{4}\}$

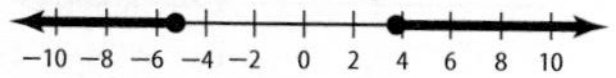

23. $\{h \mid -5\frac{2}{3} < h < 5\}$

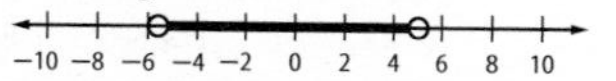

25. ∅

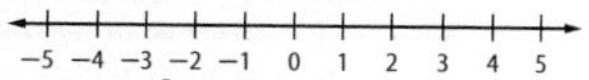

27. $\{r \mid -2 < r < \frac{2}{3}\}$

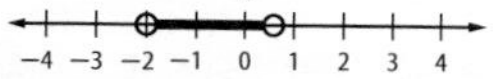

29. $\{h \mid -1.5 < h < 4.5\}$

31a. $\{t \mid t < 32$ or $t > 212\}$
31b.

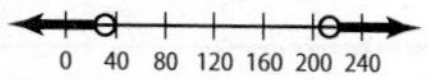

31c. $|t - 122| > 90$ **33.** $|x + 1| \le 4$
35. $|x - 5.5| > 4.5$
(37) $|g - 52| \le 5$

Case 1:		Case 2:
$g - 52$ is positive.	and	$g - 52$ is negative.
$g - 52 \le 5$	and	$g - 52 \ge -5$
$g \le 57$	and	$g \ge 47$

The solution is $\{g \mid 47 \le g \le 57\}$.

39. $|t - 38| \le 1.5$ **41.** $|c - 55| \le 3$ **43.** No; Sample answer: Lucita forgot to change the direction of the inequality sign for the negative case of the absolute value. **45.** Sample answer: If $t = 0$, then the absolute value is equal to 0, not greater than 0.
47. Sample answer: When an absolute value is on the left and the inequality symbol is < or ≤, the compound sentence uses *and*, and if the inequality symbol is > or ≥, the compound sentence used *or*. To solve, if $|x| < n$, then set up and solve the inequalities $x < n$ and $x > -n$, and if $|x| > n$, then set up and solve the inequalities $x > n$ or $x < -n$.
49. J **51.** B **53.** $\{t \mid 5 \le t \le 6\}$

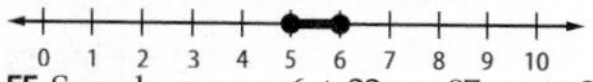

55. Sample answer: $6 + 22w \le 87$; up to 3 withdrawals
57. 18 **59.** −20

61.

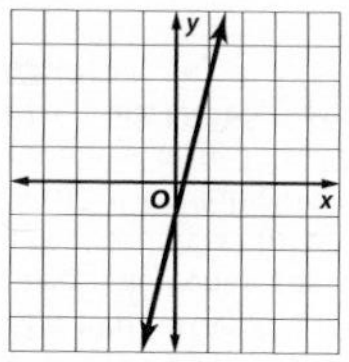

63.

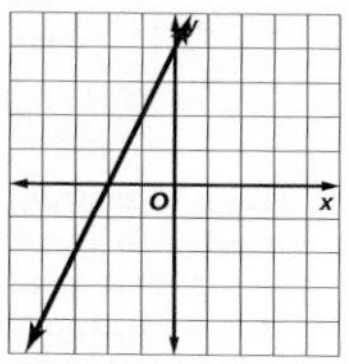

65.

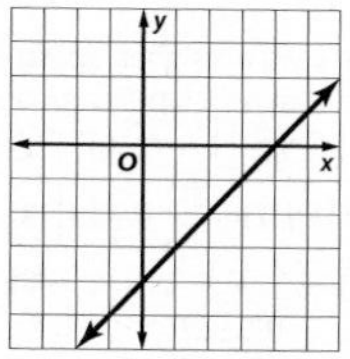

67.

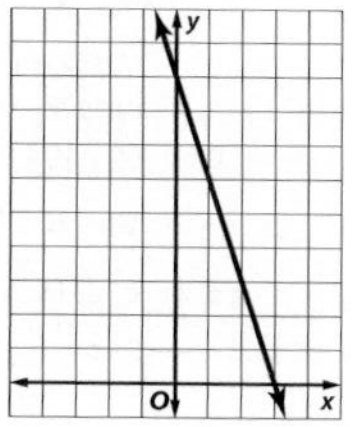

Lesson 5-6

1.

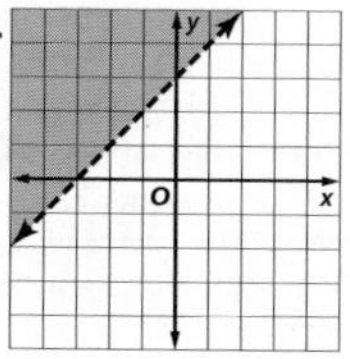

3.

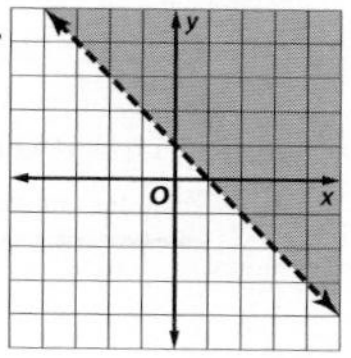

5.

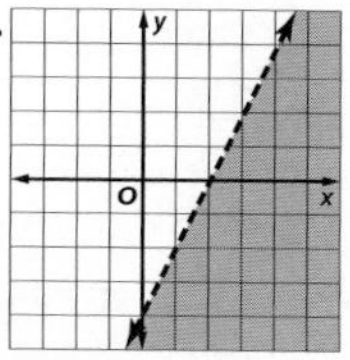

7. $x < 2$

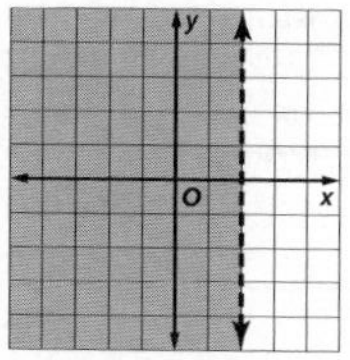

9. $y \le 13$

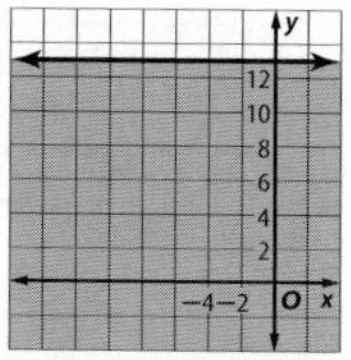

11a. $115x + 685y > 2300$ **11b.** Sample answer: 1 skim board and 4 surfboards

13.

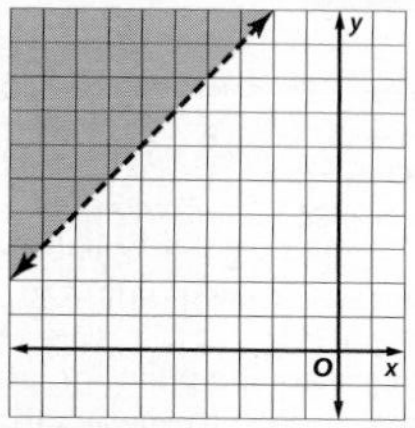

15.

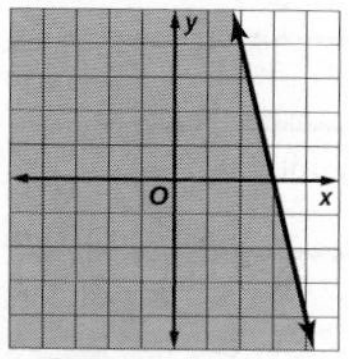

17.

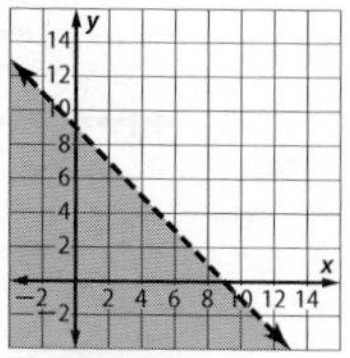

19.

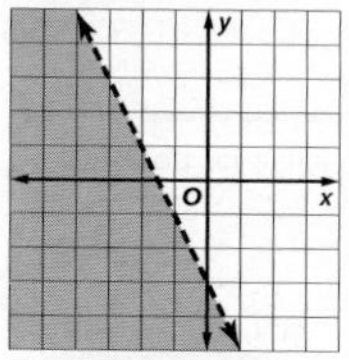

21.

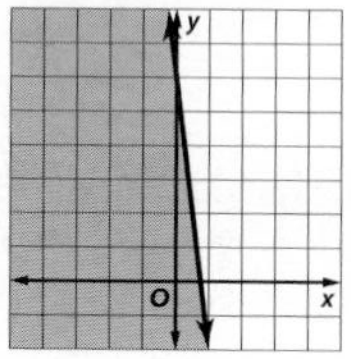

23.

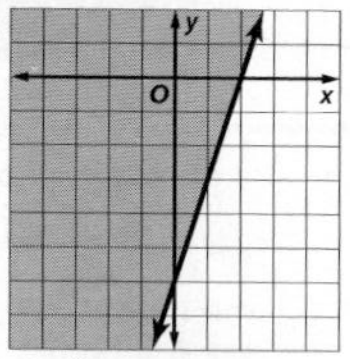

25. $x > 2$

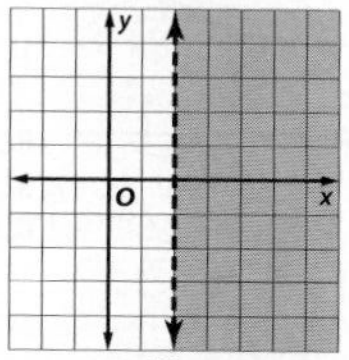

27. $y \le 5$

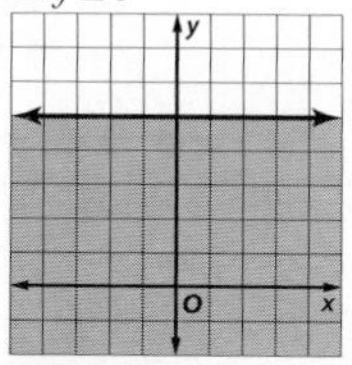

29. $x > -\frac{19}{14}$

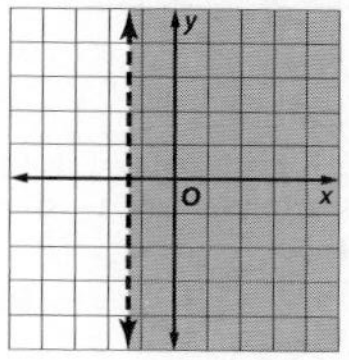

31. $x < -\frac{2}{3}$

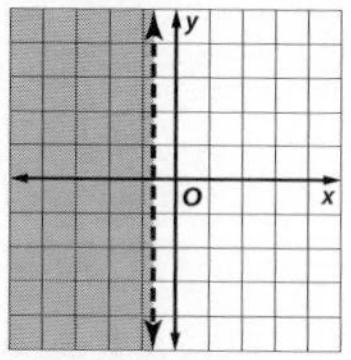

33. $x \le -\frac{2}{3}$

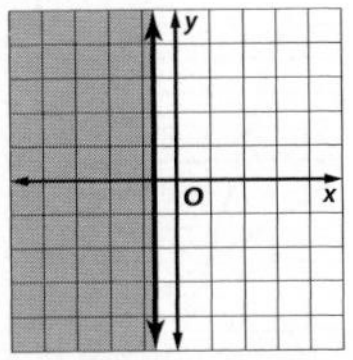

35. $x > \frac{3}{7}$

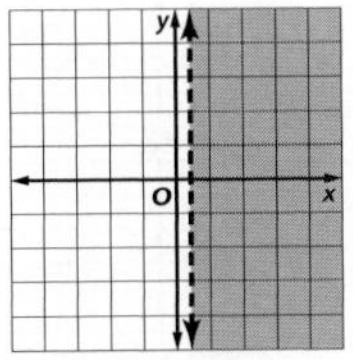

(37) **a.** They need to make more than $2000. Let x represent the number of hot dogs sold and let y represent the number of sodas sold.
$1x + 1.25y \ge 2000$

b. Step 1: First, solve for y in terms of x.
$x + 1.25y \ge 2000$
$1.25y \ge -x + 2000$
$y \ge 0.80x + 2000$
Then, graph $y = 0.80x + 2000$. Because the inequality involves $\ge$, graph the boundary with a solid line.

Step 2: Select a test point in either half-plane. A simple choice is (0, 0).
$x + 1.25y \ge 2000$ Original inequality
$0 + 1.25(0) \overset{?}{\ge} 2000$ Substitution
$0 \not\ge 2000$ false

Step 3: Since this statement is not true, the half-plane containing the origin is not the solution. Shade the other half-plane.

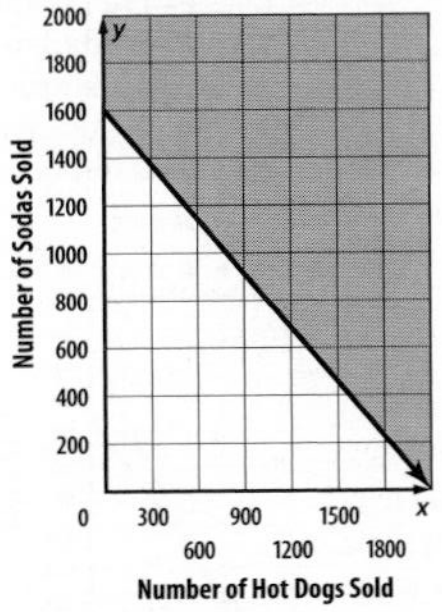

c. Sample answer: (400, 1600), (200, 1500), (300, 1400), (400, 1300), (1000, 1000)

d. Sample points should be in the shaded region of the graph in part **b**.

(39) $x < -4$
Step 1: Graph $x = 4$ with a dotted line since it involves <.
Step 2: Choose a test point in either half-plane. A simple choice is (0, 0).
$0 < -4$
Step 3: Since this statement is not true, the half-plane containing the origin is not the solution. Shade the other half-plane.

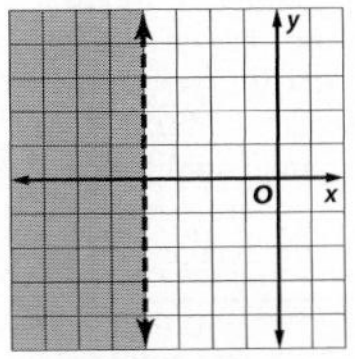

(2, 1): $2 < -4$ no
(−3, 0): $-3 < -4$ no
(0, −3): $0 < -4$ no
(−5, −5): $-5 < -4$ yes
(−4, 2): $4 < -4$ no

41.

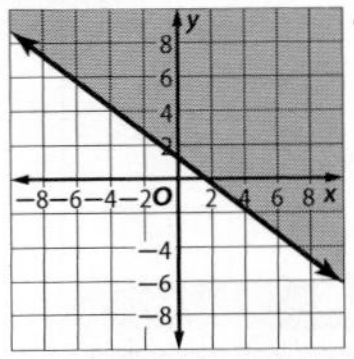

(1, 1), (2, 5), (6, 0)

43.

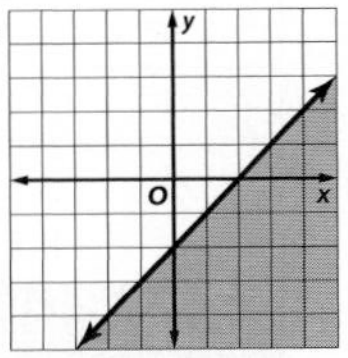

(7, 5), (5, 3), (2, −5)

45a. $y \le 3x - 4$; $y \le -x + 4$

45b.

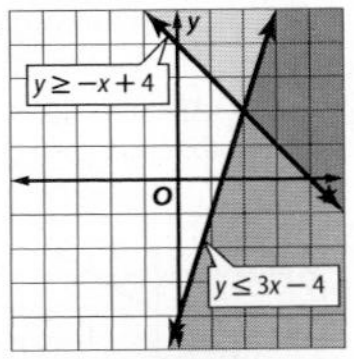

45c. The overlapping region represents the solutions that make both A and B true.

45d.

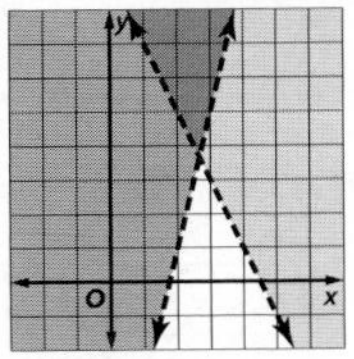

47. Sample answer: $y \le -x + 1$

49. Sample answer: The inequality $y > 10x + 45$ represents the cost of a monthly smartphone data plan with a flat rate of $45 for the first 2 GB of data used, plus $10 per each additional GB of data used. Both the domain and range are nonnegative real numbers because the GB used and the total cost cannot be negative.

51. B **53.** F

55. $\{y \mid y > 6 \text{ or } y < -2\}$ **57.** ∅ **59.** $\{p \mid 4 < p < 10\}$

61. $y = 8x - 11$ **63.** $y = -\frac{3}{2}x - 17$ **65.** $r = \frac{w - sm}{10}$

Chapter 5 Study Guide and Review

1. false; more **3.** false; intersection **5.** true
7. true **9.** true

11. $\{w \mid w > 13\}$

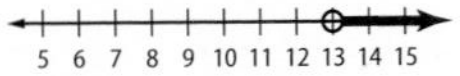

13. $\{h \mid h < -5\}$

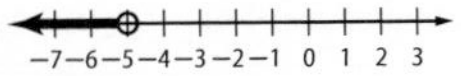

15. $\{p \mid p \le -2\}$

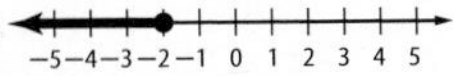

17. no more than 9

19. $\{g \mid g \ge -20\}$

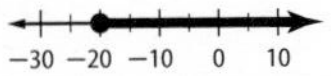

21. $\{w \mid w \le 11\}$

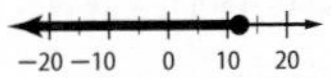

23. $\{t \mid t < -72\}$

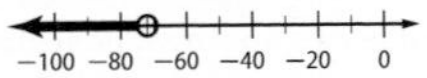

25. $\{h \mid h < 7\}$

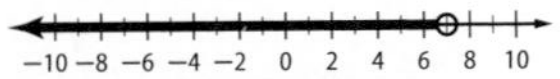

27. $\{x \mid x \le -5\}$

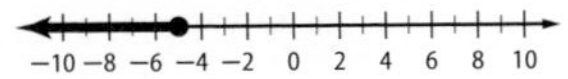

29. Sample answer: Let x = the number; $4x - 6 < -2$; $\{x \mid x < 1\}$.

31. $\{m \mid 2 < m < 9\}$

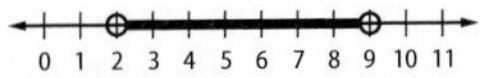

33. $\{x \mid x \le 3 \text{ or } x > 6\}$

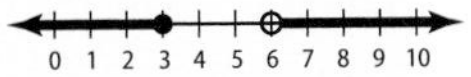

35. $\{x \mid -5 < x < 13\}$

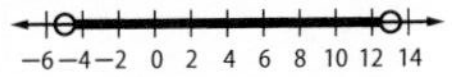

37. $\{c \mid -7 \le c \le 4\}$

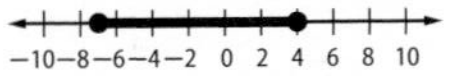

39. $\left\{d \mid -\frac{7}{3} \le d \le 3\right\}$

41. $\{t \mid t < -13 \text{ or } t > 7\}$

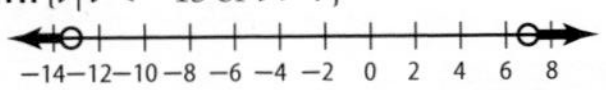

43. $\{m \mid -20 \le m \le -18\}$

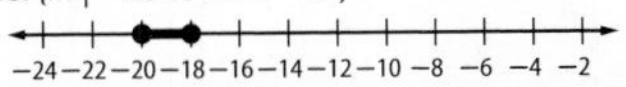

45.

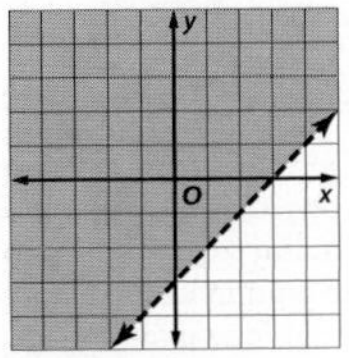

47.

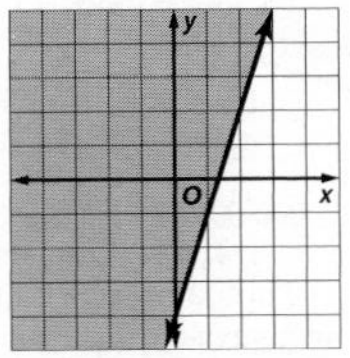

49.

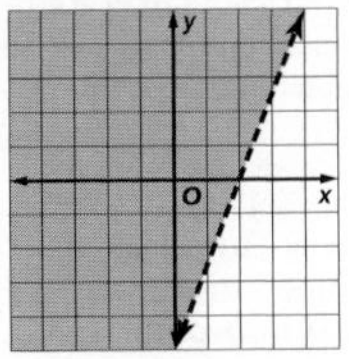

51. (1, 2), (3, −2)

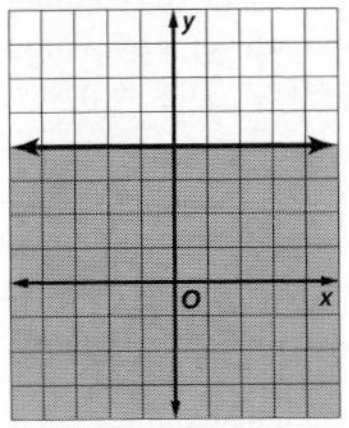

53. $2x + 3y \le 24$

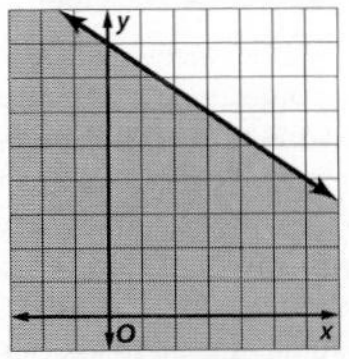

CHAPTER 6
Systems of Linear Equations and Inequalities

Get Ready

1. (4, 0) **3.** (−2, −3) **5.** (−1, −1) **7.** $x = 6 - 2y$
9. $m = 2n + 6$ **11.** $\ell = \frac{P - 2w}{2}$ **13.** $b = \frac{2A}{h}$

Lesson 6-1

1. consistent and independent **3.** inconsistent
5. consistent and independent
7. 1 solution, (−4, 0)

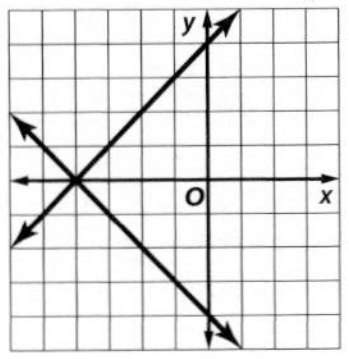

9a. Alberto: $y = 20x + 35$; Ashanti: $y = 10x + 85$

9b.

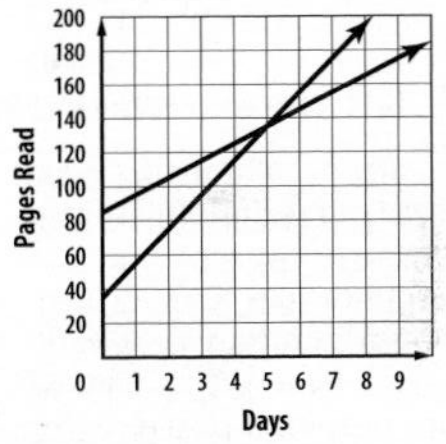

9c. (5, 135); Alberto will have read more after 5 days.

11. consistent and independent

(13) Since these two graphs intersect at one point, there is exactly one solution. Therefore, the system is consistent and independent.

15. consistent and independent

17. 1 solution; $\left(-\frac{5}{6}, -\frac{4}{3}\right)$

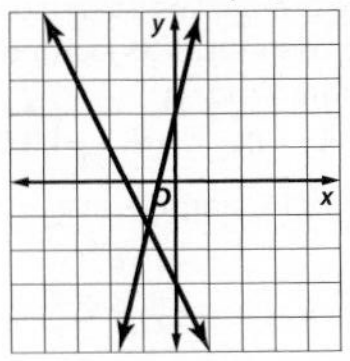

19. infinitely many

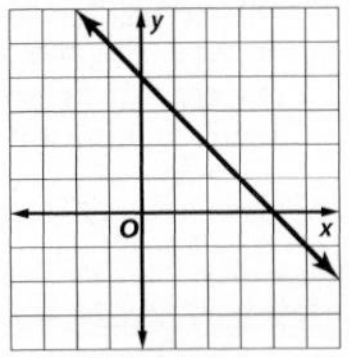

21. 1 solution; (5, −1)

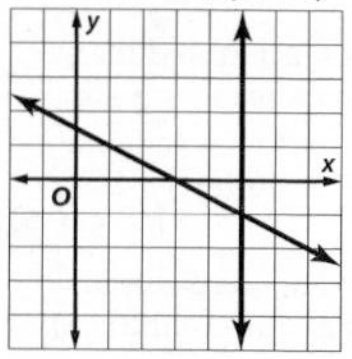

23. no solution

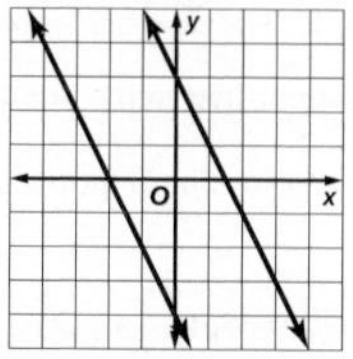

25a. Akira: $y = 30x + 22$; Jen: $y = 20x + 53$

25b.

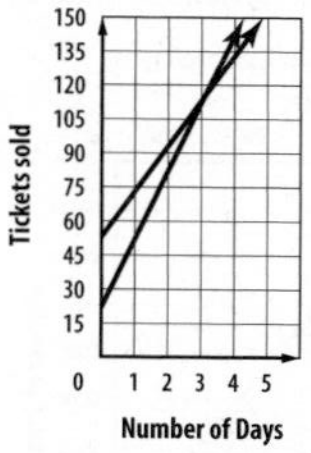

25c. (3.1, 115); After about 3 days Akira will have sold more tickets.

27 Graph the two equations on the same coordinate plane. The graphs appear to intersect at (−4, −2). Check by substituting into the equations.

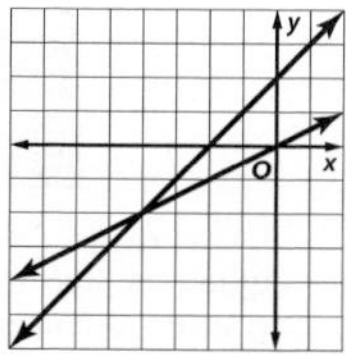

$y = \frac{1}{2}x$

$-2 = \frac{1}{2}(-4)$

$-2 = -2$ Yes

$y = x + 2$

$-2 = -4 + 2$

$-2 = -2$ Yes

So, the solution is (−4, −2).

29. 1 solution, (7, −3)

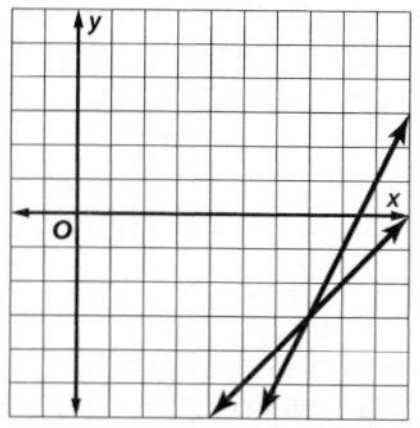

31. 1 solution, (5, 3)

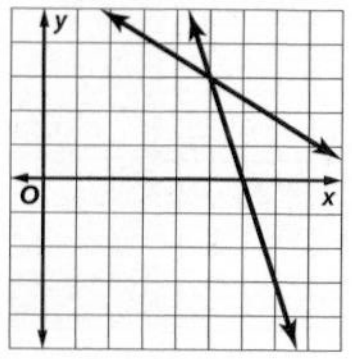

33. infinitely many

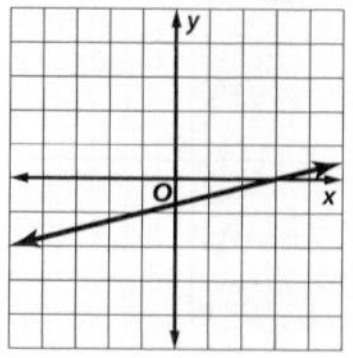

35. no solution

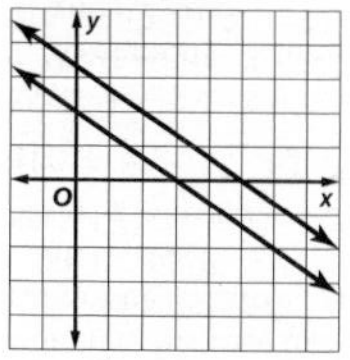

37. no solution

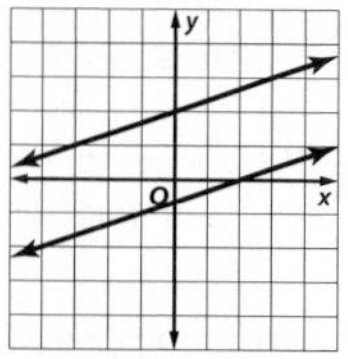

39. no solution

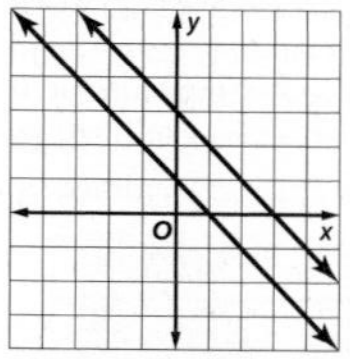

41. 1 solution, (3, −3)

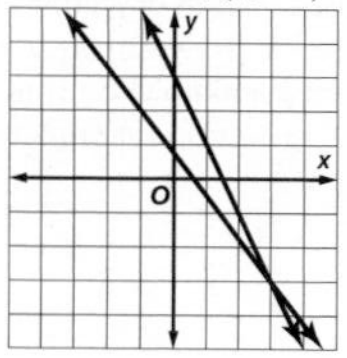

43. no solution

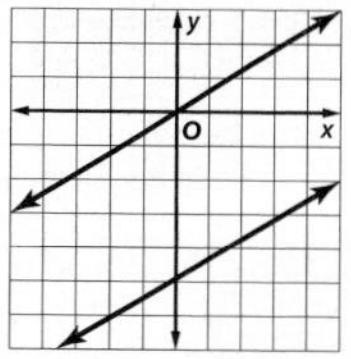

45 **a.** Lookatme:
Words: Started at 2.5 million and rose 13.1 million each year.
Expression: $2.5 + 13.1x$; $y = 13.1x + 2.5$
Buyourstuff:
Words: Started at 59 million and dropped by 2 million each year.
Expression: $59 - 2x$; $y = -2x + 59$

b.

Years Since 2009	Lookatme Vistors (mln)	Buyourstuff Vistors (mln)
0	2.5	59
1	15.6	57
2	28.7	55
3	41.8	53
4	54.9	51

c. Plot each equation on the same coordinate plane.

d. The graphs appear to intersect when $x = 3$, so they are about the same 3 years after 2009, or 2012.

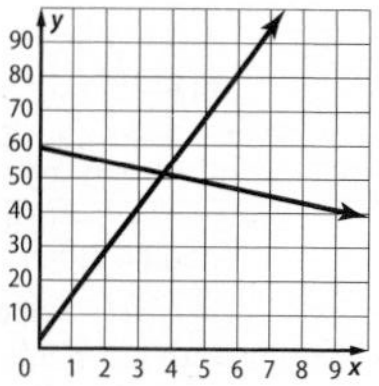

e. The domain, or input values will be all values greater than 0 since negative values do not make sense for years. So, D = $\{x \mid x \geq 0\}$
The range, or output values will be all values greater than 0 since negative values do not make sense for the number of visitors. So, R = $\{y \mid y \geq 0\}$.

47. Francisca; if the item is less than \$100, then \$10 off is better. If the item is more than \$100, then the 10% is better. **49.** If the equations are linear and have more than one common solution, they must be consistent and dependent, which means that they have an infinite number of solutions in common. **51.** Sample answers: $y = 5x + 3$; $y = -5x - 3$; $2y = 10x - 6$ **53.** 14,745,600,000 bacteria **55.** H

57.

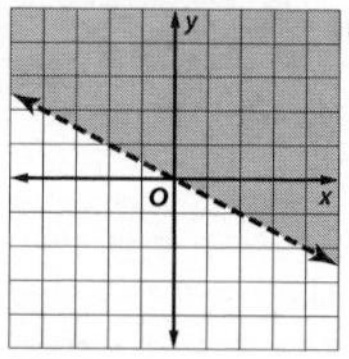

59.

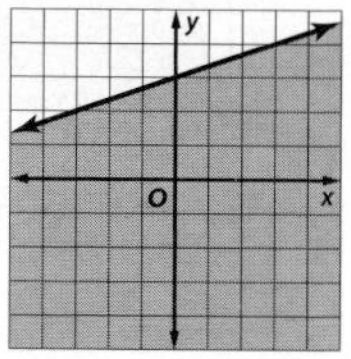

61.

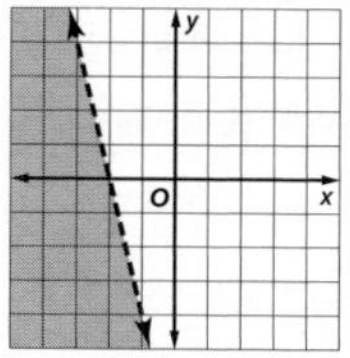

63. 1475 to 1525 books **65.** $y = -3x - 8$
67. $y = \frac{1}{2}x - 3$ **69.** 22 **71.** 92 **73.** −16 **75.** 7

Lesson 6-2

1. (5, 10) **3.** (2, 0) **5.** infinitely many
7a. $x = m\angle X$, $y = m\angle Y$; $x + y = 180$, $x = 24 + y$
7b. $x = 102°$, $y = 78°$

9 Step 1: One equation is already solved for y.
$y = 4x + 5$
$2x + y = 17$
Step 2: Substitute $4x + 5$ for y in the second equation.

$$2x + y = 17$$
$$2x + 4x + 5 = 17$$
$$6x + 5 = 17$$
$$6x = 12$$
$$x = 2$$

Step 3: Substitute 2 for x in either equation to find y.

$y = 4x + 5$
$y = 4(2) + 5$
$y = 8 + 5$
$y = 13$
The solution is (2, 13).

11. (−3, −11) **13.** (−1, 0) **15.** infinitely many
17. (2, 3) **19.** no solution **21.** (2, 0) **23a.** Let x = number of years since 2000, and let y = the number of nurses; supply, $y = 5599.9x + 1{,}890{,}000$; demand, $y = 40{,}520.7x + 2{,}000{,}000$ **23b.** during 1996

25 **a.** Men: 1:51:39 = 60 + 51 = 111, then round up because the number of seconds is greater than 30. So, 1:51:39 rounds to 112.
1:44:51 = 60 + 44 = 104, then round up because the number of seconds is greater than 30. So, 1:44:51 rounds to 105.
Women: 1:54:33 = 60 + 54 = 114, then round up because the number of seconds is greater than 30. So, 1:54:31 rounds to 115.
1:59:14 = 60 + 59 = 119, then round down because the number of seconds is less than 30. So, 1:59:14 rounds to 119.

b. The y-intercept is (0, 112). Find the rate of change.

$m = \frac{112 - 115}{0 - 9}$

$= \frac{7}{9}$

≈ -0.8

So, the equation is $y = -0.8x + 112$.
The y-intercept is (0, 115). Find the rate of change.

$m = \frac{119 - 115}{9 - 0}$

$= \frac{4}{9}$

≈ 0.4

So, the equation is $y = 0.4x + 115$.

c. Never; If you graph the two equations, the graphs do not cross in the positive values of x. Negative values will not make sense in terms of the word problem.

27. Neither; Guillermo substituted incorrectly for b. Cara solved correctly for b but misinterpreted the pounds of apples bought. **29.** Sample answer: The solutions found by each of these methods should be the same. However, it may be necessary to estimate using a graph. So, when a precise solution is needed, you should use substitution.
31. An equation containing a variable with a coefficient of 1 can easily be solved for the variable. That expression can then be substituted into the second equation for the variable.
33. 5/6 **35.** C

37. one solution; (1, –5) **39.** infinitely many solutions

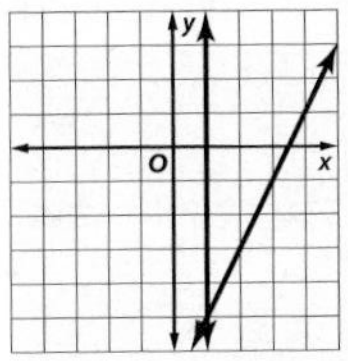
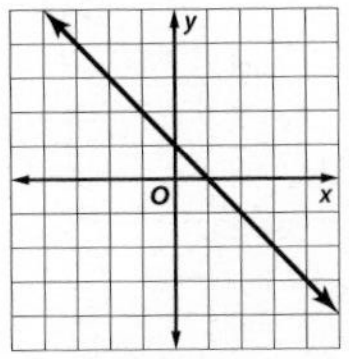

41. $v \geq -2$ **43.** $q \leq -40$ **45.** $t \geq 3$

47. $55b + 15$ **49.** $11h^2 + 12h$

Lesson 6-3

1. (2, 3)

3 Step 1: The like terms are already aligned.
$7f + 3g = -6$
$7f - 2g = -31$
Step 2: Subtract the equations.
$7f + 3g = -6$
$(-)\ 7f - 2g = -31$
$5g = 25$
$g = 5$
Step 3: Substitute 5 for g in either equation to find f.
$7f + 3(5) = -6$
$7f + 15 = -6$
$7f = -21$
$f = -3$
The solution is (–3, 5).

5. 6, 18 **7.** (–3, 4) **9.** (–3, 1) **11.** (4, –2) **13.** (8, –7) **15.** (4, 7) **17.** (4, 1.5) **19.** 5, 17

21 Three times a number minus another number is –3.
$3x - y = -3$
The first number plus the second number is 11.
$x + y = 11$
Steps 1 and 2: Write the equations vertically and add.
$3x - y = -3$
$x + y = 11$
$4x = 8$
$x = 2$
Step 3: Substitute 2 for x in either equation to find y.
$x + y = 11$
$2 + y = 11$
$y = 9$
The numbers are 2 and 9.

23. adult, \$5.95; children, \$3.95 **25.** (2, –1)

27. $\left(-\frac{5}{6}, 3\right)$ **29.** $\left(2\frac{7}{9}, 13\frac{1}{3}\right)$ **31a.** $x + y = 66$; $x = 30 + y$ **31b.** (48, 18) **31c.** There are 48 teams that are not from the U.S. and 18 teams that are from the U.S.

31d.

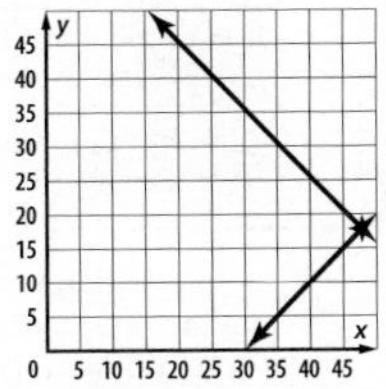

33 **a.** One way to get 15 points is to use 4 pennies and 3 paper clips.
$4(3) + 3 = 12 + 3$
$= 15$

b. The total number of objects is 9.
$p + c = 9$
Pennies are worth 3 points each and paper clips are worth 1 point each for a total of 15 points.
$3p + c = 15$
Solve:
$p + c = 9$
$(-)\ 3p + c = 15$
$-2p = -6$
$p = 3$
Substitute 3 for p in either equation to find c,
$p + c = 9$
$3 + c = 9$
$c = 6$
So, $p = 3$ and $c = 6$.

c.

p	$c = 9 - p$	$3p + c$
0	9	3(0) + 9 = 9
1	8	3(1) + 8 = 11
2	7	3(2) + 7 = 13
3	6	3(3) + 6 = 15
4	5	3(4) + 5 = 17
5	4	3(5) + 4 = 19

d. Yes; since the pennies are 3 points each, 3 of them makes 9 points. Add the 6 points from 6 paper clips and you get 15 points.

35. The result of the statement is false, so there is no solution. **37.** Sample answer: $-x + y = 5$; I used the solution to create another equation with the coefficient of the x-term being the opposite of its corresponding coefficient. **39.** Sample answer: It would be most beneficial when one variable has either the same or opposite coefficients in each of the equations. **41.** A **43.** B **45.** (15, 5) **47.** (3, 11) **49.** (–2, 2) **51.** Yes; each pair of opposite sides have the same or an undefined slope, so they are parallel. **53.** –5 **55.** –20 **57.** $11w^2 - 9w$ **59.** $-2y - 35$

Lesson 6-4

1. (3, 2)

3 Eliminate y:
$(4x + 2y = -14)(-3)$ → $-12x - 6y = 42$
$(5x + 3y = -17)(2)$ → $10x + 6y = -34$
$-2x = 8$
$x = -4$
Now, substitute –4 for x in either equation to find the value of y.
$4x + 2y = -14$
$4(-4) + 2y = -14$
$-16 + 2y = -14$
$2y = 2$
$y = 1$
The solution is (–4, 1).

5. 6 mph **7.** (–1, 3) **9.** (–3, 4) **11.** (–2, 3) **13.** (3, 5) **15.** (1, –5) **17.** (0, 1)

19 Seven times a number plus three times another number equals –1.
$7x + 3y = -1$
The sum of the two numbers is –3.
$x + y = -3$
$7x + 3y = -1$ → $7x + 3y = -1$
$(x + y = -3)(-3)$ → $-3x - 3y = 9$
$4x = 8$
$x = 2$
Now, substitute 2 for x in either equation to find y.
$x + y = -3$
$2 + y = -3$
$y = -5$ The two numbers are 2 and –5.

21. (2.5, 3.25) **23.** $\left(3, \frac{1}{2}\right)$ **25a.** $240n + 360s = 3000$ **25b.** $90n + 120s = 1050$ **25c.** (5, 5); 5 nurses and 5 support staff were placed.

27 **a.** Let x be the cost of a batting token and y be the cost of the miniature golf games.
For the first group, the equation is $16x + 3y = 30$.
For the second group, the equation is $22x + 5y = 43$.
b. Solve.
$(16x + 3y = 30)(5)$ → $80x + 15y = 150$
$(22x + 5y = 43)(-3)$ → $-66x - 15y = -129$
$14x = 21$
$x = 1.5$
Now, substitute 1.5 for x in either equation to find y.
$16x + 3y = 30$
$16(1.5) + 3y = 30$
$24 + 3y = 30$
$3y = 6$
$y = 2$
A batting token costs \$1.50 and a game of miniature golf costs \$2.

29. One of the equations will be a multiple of the other. **31.** Sample answer: $2x + 3y = 6$, $4x + 9y = 5$ **33.** Sample answer: It is more helpful to use substitution when one of the variables has a coefficient of 1 or if a coefficient can be reduced to 1 without turning other coefficients into fractions. Otherwise, elimination is more helpful because it will avoid the use of fractions when solving the system. **35.** G **37.** D **39.** (–1, –1) **41.** (9, 3) **43.** (0, 6)

45. $m \leq 13$ and $m \geq -3$

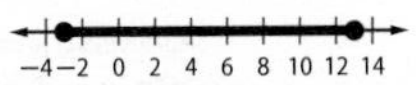

47. $w > 1$ or $w < -10$

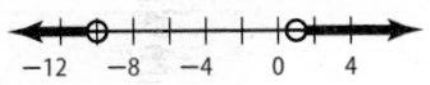

49. $A = \frac{1}{2}bh$ **51.** $V = \ell wh$ **53.** $A = \pi r^2$

Lesson 6-5

1. elim (×); (2, –5) **3.** elim (+); $\left(-\frac{1}{3}, 1\right)$

5a. $4t + 3j = 181$; $t + 2j = 94$ **5b.** substitution **5c.** Each T-shirt cost \$16 and each pair of jeans cost \$39. **7.** subst.; (2, –2) **9.** elim. (–); $\left(1, -\frac{1}{2}\right)$

11 $-5x + 4y = 7$
$-5x - 3y = -14$
Since there are no coefficients of 1, elimination is the best method.
$(-5x + 4y = 7)(-1)$ → $5x - 4y = -7$
$-5x - 3y = -14$ → $-5x - 3y = -14$
$-7y = -21$
$y = 3$
Now substitute 3 for y in either equation to find x,
$-5x + 4y = 7$
$-5x + 4(3) = 7$
$-5x + 12 = 7$
$-5x = -5$
$x = 1$
The solution is (1, 3).

13. $m + t = 40$ and $m = 3t - 4$; 29 movies, 11 television shows **15.** 880 books; If they sell this number, then their income and expenses both equal \$35,200.

17 **a.** Let x be the cost per pound of the aluminum cans and y be the cost per pound of the newspapers.
For Mara, the equation is $9x + 26y = 3.77$.
For Ling, the equation is $9x + 114y = 4.65$.

Selected Answers and Solutions

b. Elimination is the best method for solving these equations.

$(9x + 26y = 3.77)(-1)$ $\quad -9x - 26y = -3.77$
$9x + 114y = 4.65$ $\quad 9x + 114y = 4.65$
$88y = 0.88$
$y = 0.01$

Now substitute 0.01 for y in either equation to find x.

$9x + 26y = 3.77$
$9x + 26(0.01) = 3.77$
$9x + 0.26 = 3.77$
$9x = 3.51$
$x = 0.39$

The aluminum cans are \$0.39 per pound. This solution is reasonable.

19a. \$1.15 **19b.** \$9.15 **21.** Sample answer: $x + y = 12$ and $3x + 2y = 29$, where x represents the cost of a student ticket for the basketball game and y represents the cost of an adult ticket; substitution could be used to solve the system; (5, 7) means the cost of a student ticket is \$5 and the cost of an adult ticket is \$7.

23. Graphing: (2, 5)

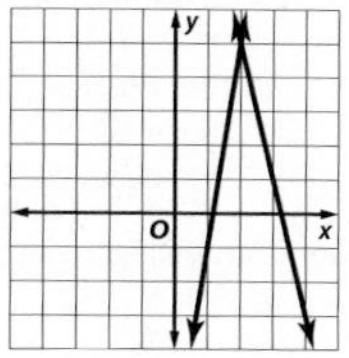

elimination by addition:
$4x + y = 13$
$6x - y = 7$
$10x = 20$
$x = 2$
$4(2) + y = 13$
$y = 5$

substitution:
$y = -4x + 13$
$6x - (-4x + 13) = 7$
$6x + 4x - 13 = 7$
$10x = 20$
$x = 2$
$4(2) + y = 13$
$y = 5$

25. The third system; this system is the only one that is not a system of linear equations. **27.** A **29.** 10 ft **31.** (0, 3) **33.** (2, 1)

35.

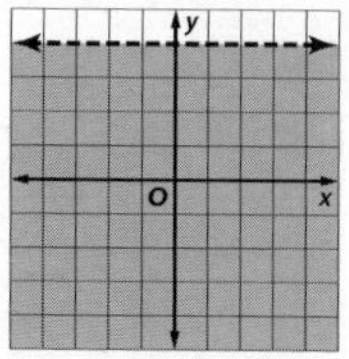

37.

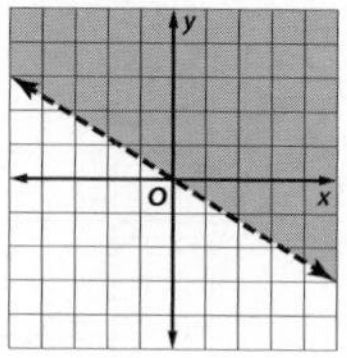

39. −12.31 **41.** 6.6 **43.** −93.19

Lesson 6-6

1.

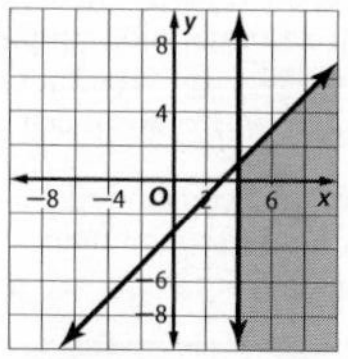

3.

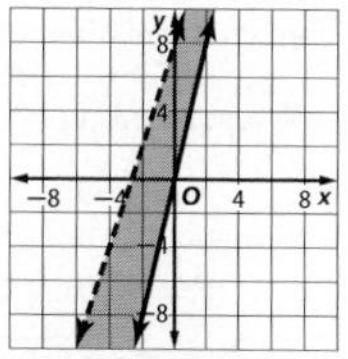

5.

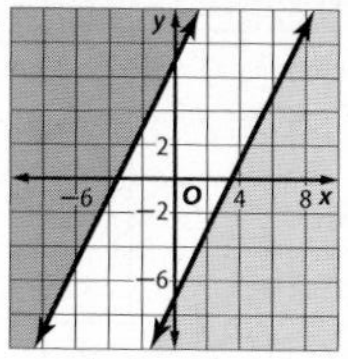

7.

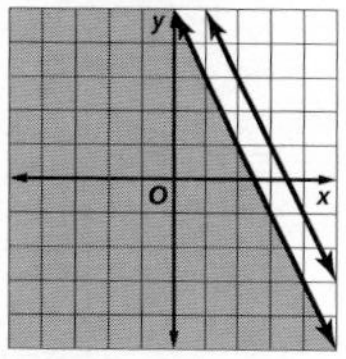

no solution

9a. Let h = the height of the driver in inches and w = the weight of the driver in pounds; $h < 79$ and $w < 295$.

Driving Requirements

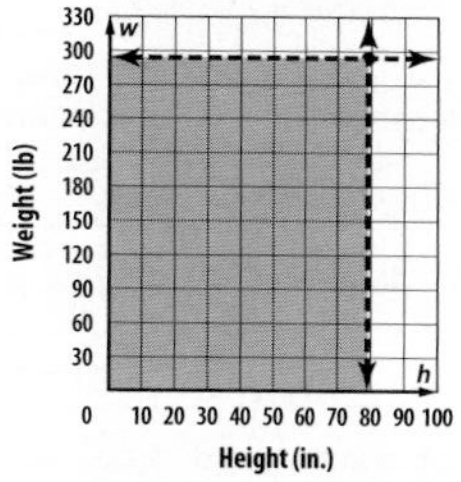

9b. Sample answer: 72 in. and 220 lb **9c.** Yes, the point falls in the overlapping region.

11 Graph both inequalities on the same coordinate plane.
$y \geq 0$ has a solid line.
$y \leq x - 5$ has a solid line.
The solution is the intersection of the shading.

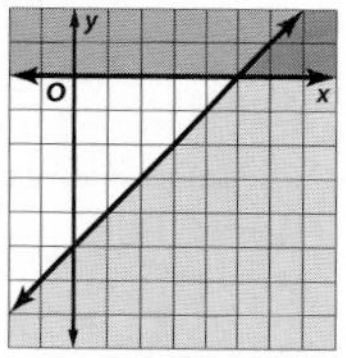

13.

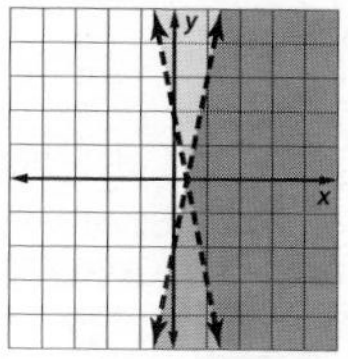

15.

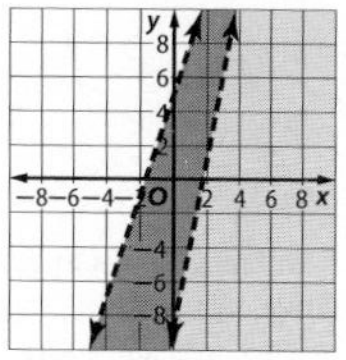

17.

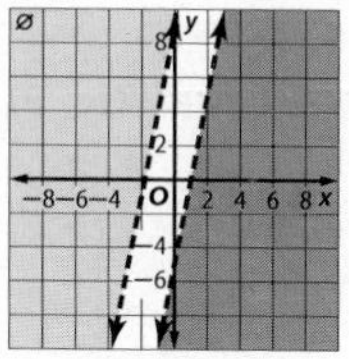

no solution

19.

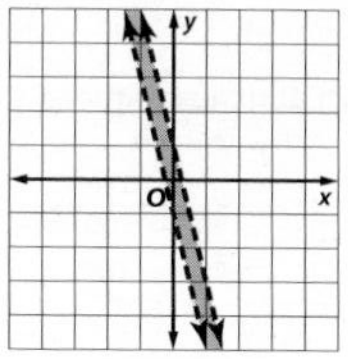

21.

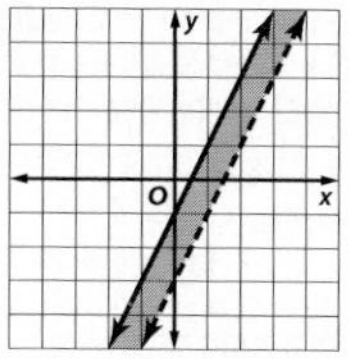

23.

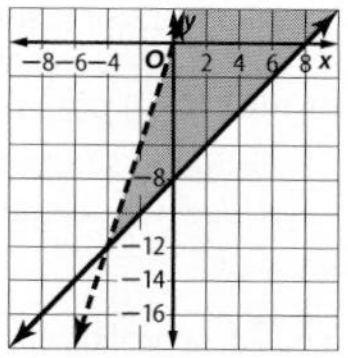

25a. Let f = square footage and let p = price; $1000 \leq f \leq 17{,}000$ and $10{,}000 \leq p \leq 150{,}000$

Ice Rink Resurfacers

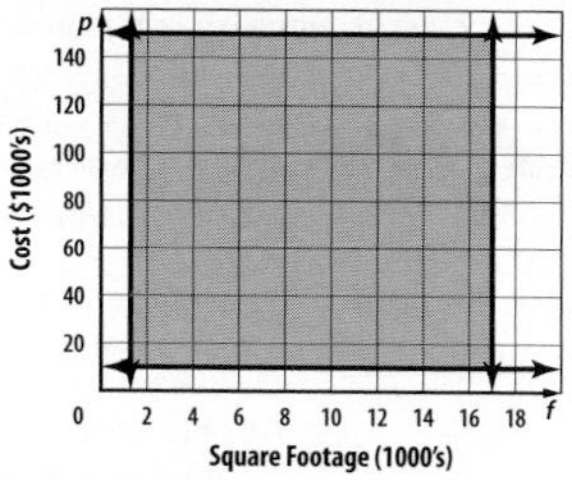

25b. Sample answer: an ice resurfacer for a rink of 5000 ft^2 and a price of \$20,000 **25c.** Yes; the point satisfies each inequality.

27.

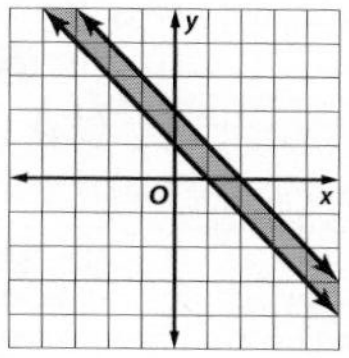

29.

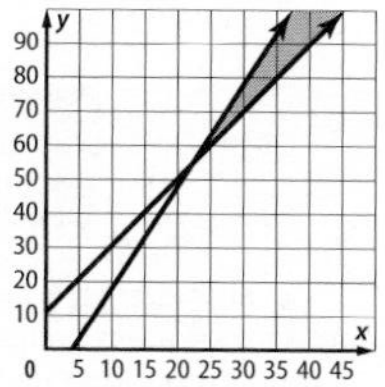

31.

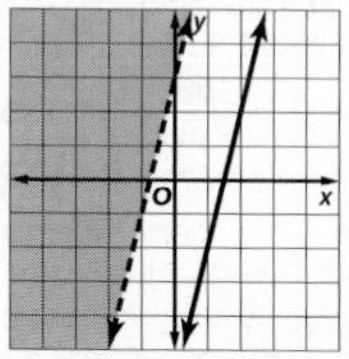

33.

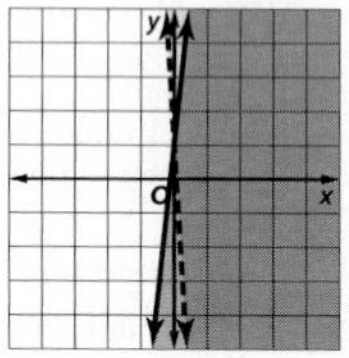

35.

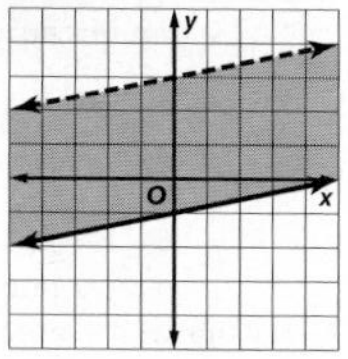

37 **a.** Let x be the number of hours she works for a photographer and y be the number of hours she works coaching.
$x + y \leq 20$
$15x + 10y \geq 90$

b. Graph both inequalities on the same grid. $x + y \leq 20$ and $15x + 10y \geq 90$ have solid lines.
The solution is the intersection of the shading.

Earnings

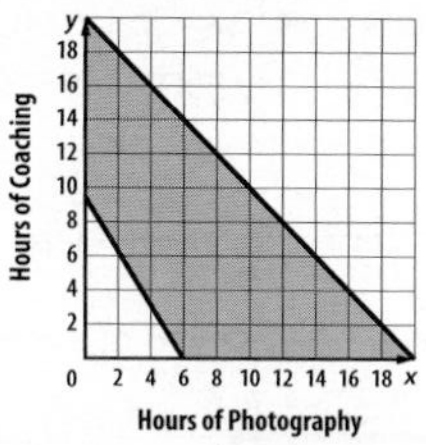

c. Two ordered pairs that are in the shaded area are (6, 10) and (8, 10). This means she could work for the photographer for 6 hours and coach for 10 or work for the photographer for 8 hours and coach for 10.

d. (2, 2) is not a solution because it does not fall in the shaded region. She would not earn enough money.

39. Sometimes; sample answer: $y > 3, y < -3$ will have no solution, but $y > -3, y < 3$ will have solutions. **41.** Sample answer: $3x - y < -4$

43. Sample answer: The yellow region represents the beats per minute below the target heart rate. The blue region represents the beats per minute above the target heart rate. The green region represents the beats per minute within the target heart rate. Shading

in different colors clearly shows the overlapping solution set of the system of inequalities. **45.** D
47. A **49.** (4, 3) **51.** (4, −3)

53.

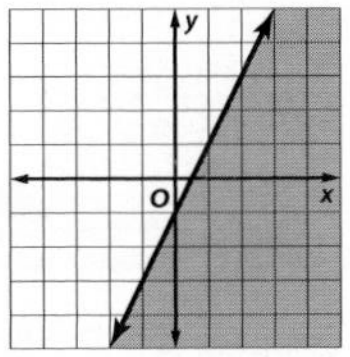

55.

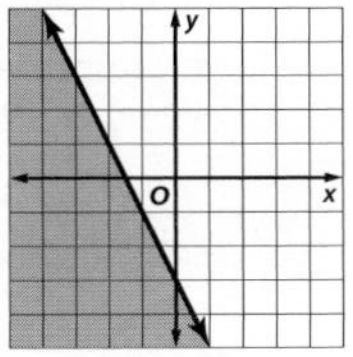

57. 16

Chapter 6 Study Guide and Review

1. true **3.** false; dependent **5.** true **7.** false; system of inequalities

9. one; (3, 2)

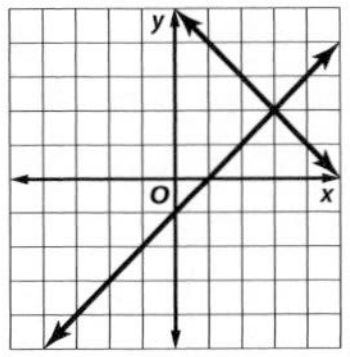

11. one; (0, 2)

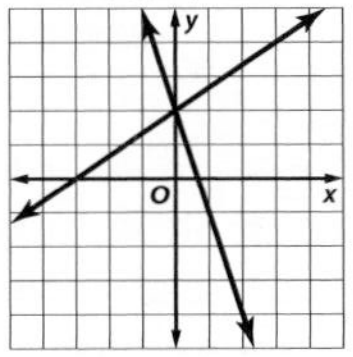

13.

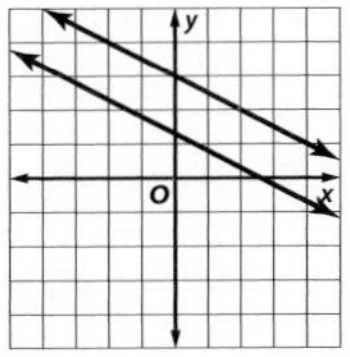

no solution

15. Sample answer: Let x be one number and y the other number; $x + y = 14$; $x - y = 4$; 9 and 5

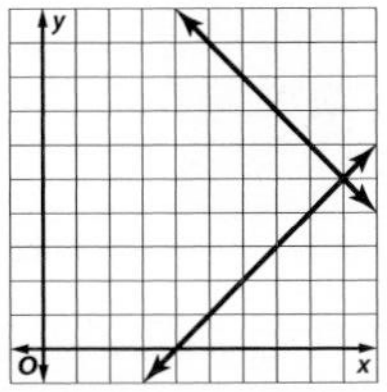

17. (2, −10) **19.** (2, −6) **21.** (−3, 4) **23.** (9, 4) **25.** (4, −2) **27.** $\left(\frac{1}{2}, 6\right)$
29. (−3, 5) **31.** Sample answer: Let f be the first type of card and let c be the second type of card; $f + c = 24$, $f + 3c = 50$; 11 \$1 cards and 13 \$3 cards. **33.** (5, 7) **35.** (2, 5) **37.** (6, −1) **39.** (1, −2) **41.** (2, −6) **43.** (24, −4) **45.** (−2, 1) **47.** (2, 5) **49.** Sample answer: Let d represent the dimes and let q represent the quarters; $d + q = 25$, $0.10d + 0.25q = 4$; 15 dimes, 10 quarters

51.

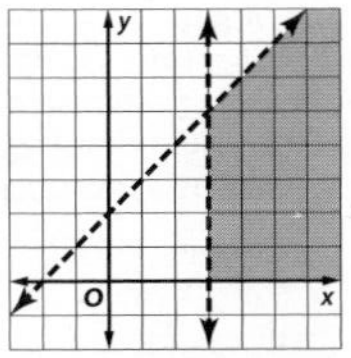

53.

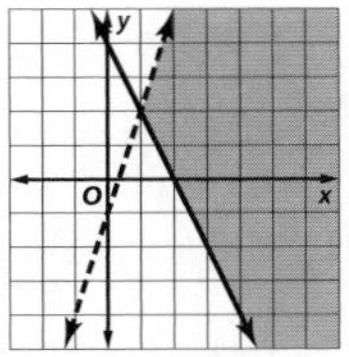

55.

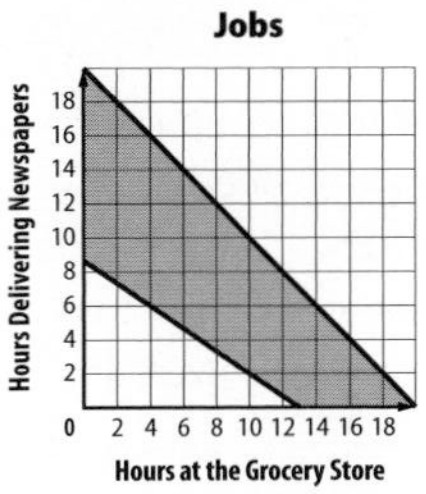

CHAPTER 7
Exponents and Exponential Functions

Get Ready

1. 4^5 **3.** 6^2 **5.** b^6 **7.** $\left(\frac{1}{3}\right)^8$ or $\frac{1}{3^8}$ **9.** 4π m² **11.** 24 in² **13.** 25 **15.** −64 **17.** $\frac{1}{16}$

Lesson 7-1

1. Yes; constants are monomials. **3.** No; there is a variable in the denominator. **5.** Yes; this is a product of a number and variables. **7.** k^4

(9) $2q^2(9q^4) = (2 \cdot 9)(q^2 \cdot q^4)$
$= 18q^{2+4}$
$= 18q^6$

11. 3^8 or 6561 **13.** $16a^8b^{18}c^2$ **15.** $81p^{20}t^{24}$ **17.** $800x^8y^{12}z^4$ **19.** $-18g^7h^3j^{10}$ **21.** Yes; constants are monomials. **23.** No; there is addition and more than one term. **25.** Yes; this can be written as the product of a number and a variable.

(27) $(q^2)(2q^4) = 2(q^2 \cdot q^4)$
$= 2q^{2+4}$
$= 2q^6$

29. $9w^8x^{12}$ **31.** $7b^{14}c^8d^6$ **33.** $j^{20}k^{28}$ **35.** 2^8 or 256 **37.** $4096r^{12}t^6$ **39.** $20c^5d^5$ **41.** $16a^{21}$ **43.** $512g^{27}h^{18}$ **45.** $294p^{27}r^{19}$ **47.** $30a^5b^7c^6$ **49.** $0.25x^6$ **51.** $-\frac{27}{64}c^3$ **53.** $-9x^3y^9$ **55.** $2{,}985{,}984r^{28}w^{32}$ **57a.** $0.12c$ **57b.** \$280 **59.** $15x^7$

(61) a. $V = \pi r^2 h$
$= \pi(2p^3)^2(4p^3)$
$= \pi(22)(p^3)^2(4p^3)$
$= \pi(4)(p^6)(4p^3)$
$= \pi(4 \cdot 4)(p^6 \cdot p^3)$
$= \pi(16)(p^{6+3})$
$= 16\pi p^9$

b.

radius	height	Volume
$4p$	p^7	$16\pi p^9$
$4p^2$	p^5	$16\pi p^9$
$2p^3$	$4p^3$	$16\pi p^9$
$2p^4$	$4p$	$16\pi p^9$
$2p$	$4p^7$	$16\pi p^9$

c. If the height of the container is doubled, the volume of the container is doubled. So, the volume is $32\pi p^9$.

63a.

Power	3^4	3^3	3^3	3^1	3^0	3^{-1}	3^{-3}	3^{-3}	3^{-4}
Value	81	27	9	3	1	$\frac{1}{3}$	$\frac{1}{9}$	$\frac{1}{27}$	$\frac{1}{81}$

63b. 1 and $\frac{1}{5}$ **63c.** $\frac{1}{a^n}$ **63d.** Any nonzero number raised to the zero power is 1.

65a.

Equation	Related Expression	Power of x	Linear or Nonlinear
$y = x$	x	1	linear
$y = x^2$	x^2	2	nonlinear
$y = x^3$	x^3	3	nonlinear

65b.

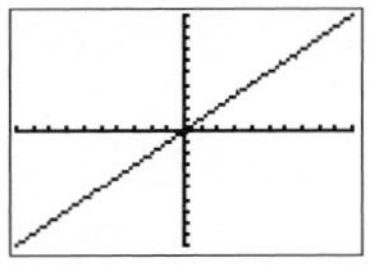

[−10, 10] scl: 1 by [−10, 10] scl: 1

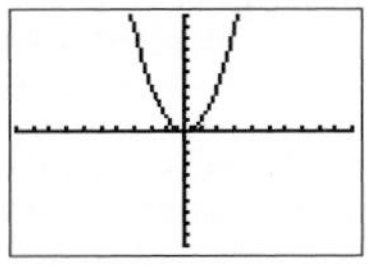

[−10, 10] scl: 1 by [−10, 10] scl: 1

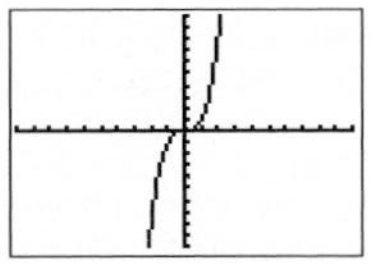

[−10, 10] scl: 1 by [−10, 10] scl: 1

65c. See chart for 65a. **65d.** If the power of x is 1, the equation or its related expression is linear. Otherwise, it is nonlinear. **67.** Sample answer: The area of a circle or $A = \pi r^2$, where r is the radius, can be used to find the area of any circle. The area of a rectangle or $A = w \times \ell$, where w is the width and ℓ is the length, can be used to find the area of any rectangle.
69. F **71.** The x-intercept does not change.

73.

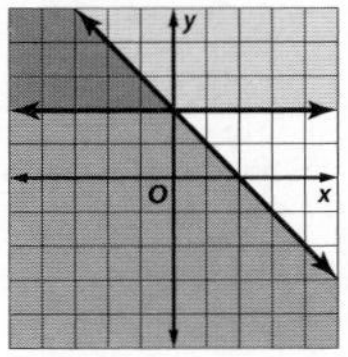

75.

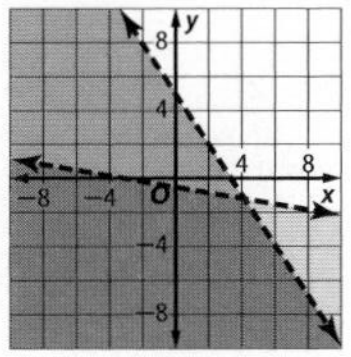

77. $\{p \mid 28 \le p \le 32\}$ **79.** 8 **81.** −7.05 **83.** 13

Lesson 7-2

1. t^3u^3

(3) $\frac{m^6r^5p^3}{m^5r^2p^3} = \left(\frac{m^6}{m^5}\right)\left(\frac{r^5}{r^2}\right)\left(\frac{p^3}{p^3}\right)$
$= m^{6-5}r^{5-2}p^{3-3}$
$= m^1r^3p^0$
$= mr^3$

5. ghm **7.** xyz **9.** $\frac{4a^6b^{10}}{9}$ **11.** $\frac{32c^{15}d^{25}}{3125g^{10}}$ **13.** 1 **15.** $\frac{g^2h^4}{f^3}$ **17.** $\frac{a^5c^{13}}{3b^9}$ **19.** m^2p **21.** $\frac{r^4p^2}{4m^3t^4}$ **23.** $\frac{9x^2y^8}{25z^4}$ **25.** $\frac{p^6t^{21}}{1000}$ **27.** a^2b^7c

(29) $\left(\frac{2r^3t^6}{5u^9}\right)^4 = \frac{2^4(r^3)^4(t^6)^4}{5^4(u^9)^4}$
$= \frac{16r^{12}t^{24}}{625u^{36}}$

31. 1 **33.** $\frac{p^4r^2}{t^3}$ **35.** $\frac{-f}{4}$ **37.** k^2mp^2 **39.** $\frac{3t^7}{u^6v^2}$ **41.** $\frac{r^3}{t^2x^{10}}$ **43.** 10^6; 10^8; about 10^2 or 100 times as many users as hosts **45.** $-\frac{w^9}{3}$ **47.** $1600k^{13}$ **49.** $\frac{5q}{r^6t^3}$ **51.** $\frac{4g^{12}}{h^4}$ **53.** $\frac{4x^8y^4}{z^6}$ **55.** $\frac{16z^2}{y^8}$ **57.** 100

(59) a. the probability is $\frac{1}{6}$ multiplied d times, or $\left(\frac{1}{6}\right)^d$.

b. $\left(\frac{1}{6}\right)^d = (6^{-1})^d$
$= 6^{-d}$

61. Sometimes; sample answer: The equation is true when $x = 0$, $y = 2$, and $z = 3$, but it is false when $x = 1$, $y = 2$, and $z = 3$.
63. $\frac{1}{x^n} = \frac{x^0}{x^n} = x^{0-n} = x^{-n}$ **65.** The Quotient of Powers Property is used when dividing two powers with the same base. The exponents are subtracted. The Power of a Quotient Property is used to find the power of a quotient. You find the power of the numerator and the power of the denominator. **67.** J **69.** B

71.

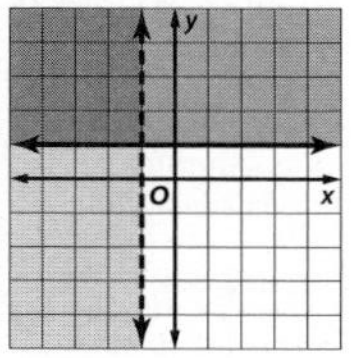

73.

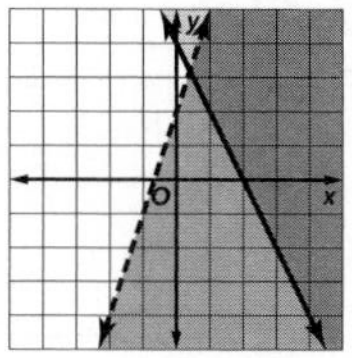

75. $h > 5$ **77.** $u \le 35$ **79.** $n \ge -2$ **81.** 87 **83.** 121 **85.** 10,000 **87.** 125 **89.** 4096

Lesson 7-3

1. $\sqrt{12}$ **3.** $33^{\frac{1}{2}}$ **5.** 8 **7.** 7 **9.** 49

(11) $216^{\frac{4}{3}} = (\sqrt[3]{216})^4 = (\sqrt[3]{6 \cdot 6 \cdot 6})^4 = 6^4$ or 1296

13. 4 **15.** 5.5 **17.** $\sqrt{15}$ **19.** $4\sqrt{k}$ **21.** $26^{\frac{1}{2}}$ **23.** $2(ab)^{\frac{1}{2}}$ **25.** 2 **27.** 6 **29.** 0.1 **31.** 11 **33.** 15 **35.** $\frac{1}{3}$ **37.** 4 **39.** 243 **41.** 625 **43.** $\frac{27}{1000}$ **45.** 5 **47.** $\frac{1}{2}$ **49.** $\frac{3}{2}$ **51.** 8 **53.** 8

(55)
$4^{3x} = 512$ Original equation
$(2^2)^{3x} = 2^9$ Write the expressions with a common base, 2.
$2^{6x} = 2^9$ Power of a Power Property
$6x = 9$ Power Property of Equality
$x = \frac{3}{2}$ Divide each side by 6.

57. 4 ft **59.** $\sqrt[3]{17}$ **61.** $7\sqrt[3]{b}$ **63.** $29^{\frac{1}{3}}$ **65.** $2a^{\frac{1}{3}}$ **67.** 0.3 **69.** a **71.** 16 **73.** $\frac{1}{3}$ **75.** $\frac{1}{27}$ **77.** $\frac{1}{\sqrt{k}}$ **79.** 12 **81.** −5 **83.** $-\frac{3}{2}$ **85a.** 440 Hz
85b. A below middle C, the 37th note

(87)
$r = 0.62V^{\frac{1}{3}}$ Original equation
$3.65 = 0.62V^{\frac{1}{3}}$ $r = \frac{7.3}{2}$ or 3.65
$\frac{3.65}{0.62} \approx V^{\frac{1}{3}}$ Divide each side by 0.62.
$\left(\frac{3.65}{0.62}\right)^{3 \cdot \frac{1}{3}} \approx V^{\frac{1}{3}}$ $\frac{3.65}{0.62} = \left(\frac{3.65}{0.62}\right)^{3 \cdot \frac{1}{3}}$
$\left(\frac{3.65}{0.62}\right)^3 \approx V$ Power Property of Equality
$204.0 \approx V$ Simplify.

$r = 0.62V^{\frac{1}{3}}$ Original equation
$3.8 = 0.62V^{\frac{1}{3}}$ $r = \frac{7.6}{2}$ or 3.8
$\frac{3.8}{0.62} \approx V^{\frac{1}{3}}$ Divide each side by 0.62.
$\left(\frac{3.8}{0.62}\right)^{3 \cdot \frac{1}{3}} \approx V^{\frac{1}{3}}$ $\frac{3.8}{0.62} = \left(\frac{3.8}{0.62}\right)^{3 \cdot \frac{1}{3}}$
$\left(\frac{3.8}{0.62}\right)^3 \approx V$ Power Property of Equality
$230.2 \approx V$ Simplify.
So the volume of a size 3 ball is 204.0 to 230.2 in^3.

$r = 0.62V^{\frac{1}{3}}$ Original equation
$4.0 = 0.62V^{\frac{1}{3}}$ $r = \frac{8.0}{2}$ or 4.0
$\frac{4.0}{0.62} \approx V^{\frac{1}{3}}$ Divide each side by 0.62.
$\left(\frac{4.0}{0.62}\right)^{3 \cdot \frac{1}{3}} \approx V^{\frac{1}{3}}$ $\frac{4.0}{0.62} = \left(\frac{4.0}{0.62}\right)^{3 \cdot \frac{1}{3}}$
$\left(\frac{4.0}{0.62}\right)^3 \approx V$ Power Property of Equality
$268.5 \approx V$ Simplify.

$r = 0.62V^{\frac{1}{3}}$ Original equation
$4.15 = 0.62V^{\frac{1}{3}}$ $r = \frac{8.3}{2}$ or 4.15
$\frac{4.15}{0.62} \approx V^{\frac{1}{3}}$ Divide each side by 0.62.
$\left(\frac{4.15}{0.62}\right)^{3 \cdot \frac{1}{3}} \approx V^{\frac{1}{3}}$ $\frac{4.15}{0.62} = \left(\frac{4.15}{0.62}\right)^{3 \cdot \frac{1}{3}}$
$\left(\frac{4.15}{0.62}\right)^3 \approx V$ Power Property of Equality
$299.9 \approx V$ Simplify.
So the volume of a size 4 ball is 268.5 to 299.9 in^3.

$r = 0.62V^{\frac{1}{3}}$ Original equation
$4.3 = 0.62V^{\frac{1}{3}}$ $r = \frac{8.6}{2}$ or 4.3
$\frac{4.3}{0.62} \approx V^{\frac{1}{3}}$ Divide each side by 0.62.
$\left(\frac{4.3}{0.62}\right)^{3 \cdot \frac{1}{3}} \approx V^{\frac{1}{3}}$ $\frac{4.3}{0.62} = \left(\frac{4.3}{0.62}\right)^{3 \cdot \frac{1}{3}}$
$\left(\frac{4.3}{0.62}\right)^3 \approx V$ Power Property of Equality
$333.6 \approx V$ Simplify.

$r = 0.62V^{\frac{1}{3}}$ Original equation
$4.5 = 0.62V^{\frac{1}{3}}$ $r = \frac{9.0}{2}$ or 4.5
$\frac{4.5}{0.62} \approx V^{\frac{1}{3}}$ Divide each side by 0.62.
$\left(\frac{4.5}{0.62}\right)^{3 \cdot \frac{1}{3}} \approx V^{\frac{1}{3}}$ $\frac{4.5}{0.62} = \left(\frac{4.5}{0.62}\right)^{3 \cdot \frac{1}{3}}$
$\left(\frac{4.5}{0.62}\right)^3 \approx V$ Power Property of Equality
$382.4 \approx V$ Simplify.
So the volume of a size 5 ball is 333.6 to 382.4 in^3.

89. Sample answer: $2^{\frac{1}{2}}$ and $4^{\frac{1}{4}}$ **91.** −1, 0, 1
93. Sample answer: 2 is the principal fourth root of 16 because 2 is positive and $2^4 = 16$. **95.** G **97.** B **99.** c^4d^6 **101.** b^2 **103.** 1 **105.** $y = 3x - 1$ **107.** $y = -2x - 12$ **109.** $y = \frac{2}{3}x + 7$ **111.** 1000 **113.** 0.1

Lesson 7-4

1. 1.85×10^8 **3.** 5.64×10^{-4} **5.** 1.3×10^{10} **7.** 19,800,000 **9.** 0.00000003405 **11.** 1.74×10^{15}; 1,740,000,000,000,000 **13.** 4.7138×10^{-2}; 0.047138 **15.** 4.5×10^3; 4500 **17.** 8.5×10^{-13}; 0.00000000000085 **19a.** 0.01, 0.000001 **19b.** 1×10^{-2}, 1×10^{-6} **19c.** 0.00000000001; 1×10^{-11}

(21) 58,600,000
Step 1: 58,600,000 ⟶ 5.8600000
Step 2: The decimal point moved 7 places to the left, so $n = 7$.
Step 3: $58{,}600{,}000 = 5.8600000 \times 10^7$
Step 4: 5.86×10^7

23. 1.3×10^{-6} **25.** 7.09×10^{-10} **27.** 6.5×10^9 **29.** 94,000,000 **31.** 0.0005 **33.** 0.00000622 **35.** 11,000,000 **37.** 8×10^7; 80,000,000

(39) $(6.5 \times 10^7)(7.2 \times 10^{-2}) = (6.5 \times 7.2)(10^7 \times 10^{-2})$
$= 46.8 \times 10^5$
$= (4.68 \times 10^1) \times 10^5$
$= 4.68 \times 10^6$
$= 4{,}680{,}000$

41. 2.2×10^7; 22,000,000 **43.** 1.96×10^{12}; 1,960,000,000,000 **45.** 6.89×10^5; 689,000 **47.** 9×10^{-4}; 0.0009 **49.** 5×10^{-6}; 0.000005 **51.** 5.184×10^{15}; 5,184,000,000,000,000 **53.** 3.969×10^{-9}; 0.000000003969 **55.** 2.74185×10^5; 274,815 **57.** 6.1×10^{-8}; 0.000000061 **59.** 1.7889×10^{-6}; 0.0000017889 **61.** 4.7008×10^3; 4700.8 **63.** 3×10^5

65.

Time	Kilometers Traveled
1 day	2.592×10^{10}
1 week	1.8144×10^{11}
1 month	7.776×10^{11}
1 year	9.4608×10^{12}

(67) $(6.623 \times 10^9) \div (1.483 \times 10^8)$
$= (6.623 \div 1.483) \times (10^9 \div 10^8)$
$\approx 4.47 \times 10^1$
There are about 44.7 persons per square kilometer.

69a. corn: 9.29×10^7, 92,900,000; soybeans: 6.41×10^7, 64,100,000; cotton: 1.11×10^7, 11,100,000 **69b.** about 1.4493×10^0; 1.4493 **69c.** about 8.3694×10^0; 8.3694 **71.** Pete is correct; Syreeta moved the decimal point in the wrong direction. **73.** Always; if the numbers are $a \times 10^m$ and $b \times 10^n$ in scientific notation, then $1 \le a < 10$ and $1 \le b < 10$. So $1 \le ab < 100$. **75.** Sample answer: Divide the numbers to the left of the × symbols. Then divide the powers of 10. If necessary, rewrite the results in scientific notation. To convert that to standard form, check to see if the exponent is positive or negative. If positive, move the decimal point to the right, and if negative, to the left. The number of places to move the decimal point is the absolute value of the exponent. Fill in with zeros as needed.

77. H **79.** B **81.** 8^3 or 512 **83.** r^6t^5 **85.** $\frac{25d^6g^4}{9h^8}$ **87.** 10^5 **89.** 4 **91.** 0 **93.** −75

Lesson 7-5

1.

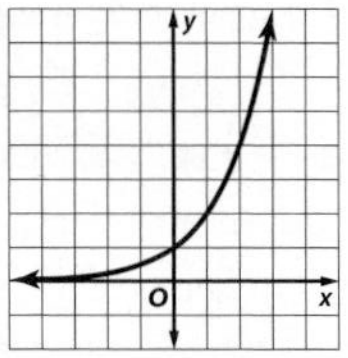

1;
D = {all real numbers};
R = $\{y \mid y > 0\}$

3.

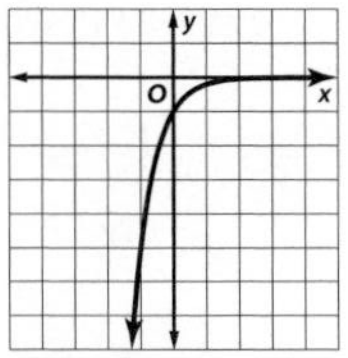

−1;
D = {all real numbers};
R = $\{y \mid y < 0\}$

5.

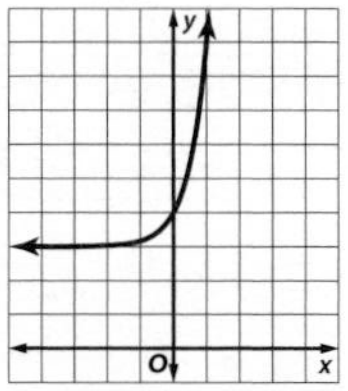

4;
D = {all real numbers};
R = $\{y \mid y > 3\}$

7a. D = $\{d \mid d \ge 0\}$, the number of days is greater than or equal to 0; R = $\{y \mid y \ge 100\}$, the number of fruit flies is greater than or equal to 100. **7b.** about 198 fruit flies **9.** Yes; the domain values are at regular intervals, and the range values have a common factor of 4.

11.

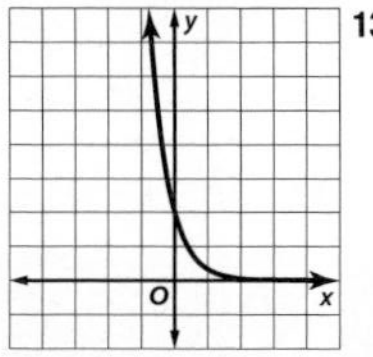

2;
D = {all real numbers};
R = $\{y \mid y > 0\}$

13.

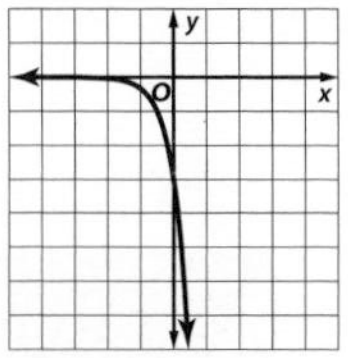

−3;
D = {all real numbers};
R = $\{y \mid y < 0\}$

15.

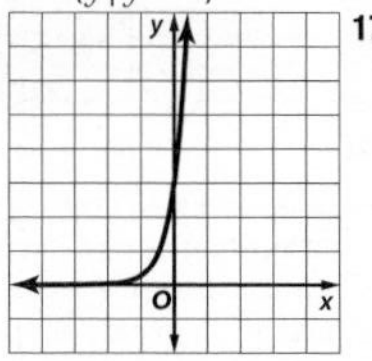

3;
D = {all real numbers};
R = $\{y \mid y > 0\}$

17.

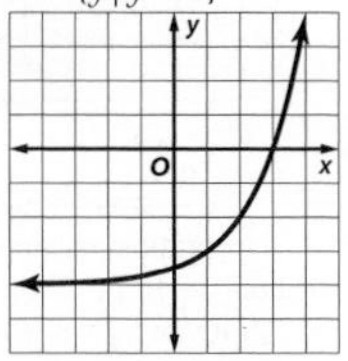

The y-intercept is −3.5;
D = {all real numbers};
R = $\{y \mid y > -4\}$

19. 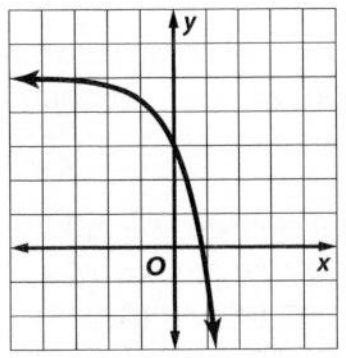

The y-intercept is 3;
D = {all real numbers};
R = $\{y \mid y < 5\}$

(21) No; the domain values are at regular intervals of 4.
$2 \times (-2) = 4$
$-4 \times (-2) = 8$
$8 \times (-2) = -16$
$-16 \times (-2) = 32$
The range values differ by the common factor of −2. The range values do not have a positive common factor.

23. Yes; the domain values are at regular intervals, and the range values have a common factor of 2.

(25) $P = 1.5^x$
$= 1.5^4$
≈ 5.06 or 506%
This enlargement is about 506% bigger than the original.

27. exponential **29.** linear **31.** neither **33.** about 198 students **35.** a vertical stretch by a factor of 3 **37.** a translation down 3 units **39.** a vertical stretch by a factor of 5 and a reflection over the x-axis. **41.** $f(x) = 3(2)^x$ **43.** Sample answer: The number of teams competing in a basketball tournament can be represented by $y = 2^x$, where the number of teams competing is y and the number of rounds is x.

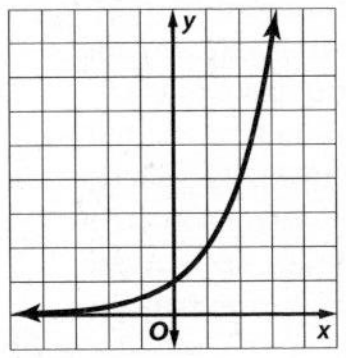

The y-intercept of the graph is 1. The graph increases quickly for $x > 0$. With an exponential model, each team that joins the tournament will play all of the other teams. If the scenario were modeled with a linear function, each team that joined would play a fixed number of teams.

45. Sample answer: First, look for a pattern by making sure that the domain values are at regular intervals and the range values differ by a common factor. **47.** B **49.** A **51.** 2.52×10^2, 252 **53.** 7 **55.** $\frac{1}{2}$ **57.** 7776 **59.** 32 km²/min² **61.** (−5, 20) **63.** 9, 11, 13 **65.** 16.5, 19, 21.5 **67.** $\frac{7}{2}, \frac{17}{4}, 5$

Lesson 7-6

1. about $37,734.73 **3a.** $y = 2200(0.98)^t$ **3b.** about 1624 **5.** about 92,095,349

(7) $A = P\left(1 + \frac{r}{n}\right)^{nt}$
$= 6600\left(1 + \frac{0.045}{12}\right)^{12(4)}$
$= 6600(1.00375)^{48}$
≈ 7898.97 or about $7898.97

9. Sample answer: No; she will have about $199.94 in the account in 4 years.

(11) $y = a(1 + r)^t$
$= 530{,}000(1 - 0.009)^5$
$= 530{,}000(0.991)^5$
$\approx 506{,}575$

13a. $I = 247{,}900(1.014)^t$ **13b.** about $288,864 **15a.** $w(t) = 20{,}500(0.995)^t$ **15b.** $p(t) = 3000t$ **15c.** about 15.2 hr **15d.** $C(t) = 3000t + 20{,}500(0.995)^t$; The function represents the number of gallons of water remaining during the times in which more water is being pumped into the pool. **17.** about 9.2 yr **19.** Sample answer: Exponential models can grow without bound, which is usually not the case of the situation that is being modeled. For instance, a population cannot grow without bound due to space and food constraints. Therefore, when using a model, the situation that is being modeled should be carefully considered when used to make decisions. **21.** C **23.** D

25. 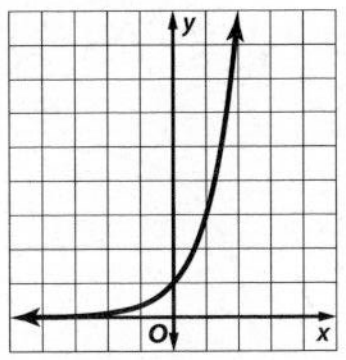

1;
D = {all real numbers},
R = $\{y \mid y > 0\}$

27. 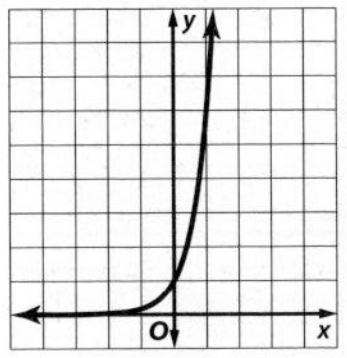

1;
D = {all real numbers},
R = $\{y \mid y > 0\}$ **29.** 3.01×10^{10}; 30,100,000,000 **31.** 1.21×10^{-4}; 0.000121 **33.** 1.9154×10^0; 1.9154 **35.** parallel **37.** neither **39.** $14.77 **41.** $37.45

43. 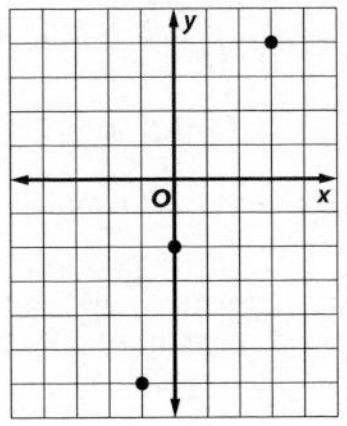

Lesson 7-7

1. Geometric; the common ratio is $\frac{1}{5}$.
3. Arithmetic; the common difference is 3.
5. 160, 320, 640 **7.** $-\frac{1}{16}, -\frac{1}{64}, -\frac{1}{256}$ **9.** $a_n = -6 \cdot (4)^{n-1}$; −1536 **11.** $a_n = 72 \cdot \left(\frac{2}{3}\right)^{n-1}$; $\frac{4096}{2187}$

13. **Experiment**

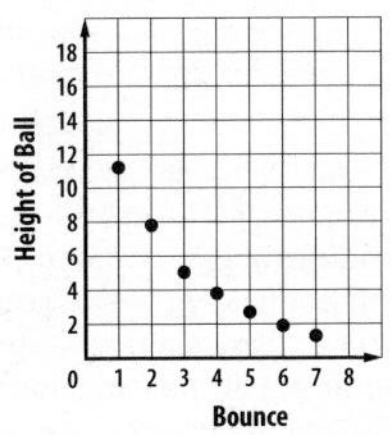

15. Arithmetic; the common difference is 10.
17. Geometric; the common ratio is $\frac{1}{2}$.
19. Neither; there is no common ratio or difference.

(21) Step 1: Find the common ratio.
$36 \times \frac{1}{3} = 12$
$12 \times \frac{1}{3} = 4$
The common ratio is $\frac{1}{3}$.
Step 2: Multiply each term by the common ratio to find the next three terms.
$4\left(\frac{1}{3}\right) = \frac{4}{3}$
$\left(\frac{4}{3}\right)\left(\frac{1}{3}\right) = \frac{4}{9}$
$\left(\frac{4}{9}\right)\left(\frac{1}{3}\right) = \frac{4}{27}$
So, the next three terms are $\frac{4}{3}, \frac{4}{9}$, and $\frac{4}{27}$.

23. $\frac{25}{4}, \frac{25}{16}, \frac{25}{64}$ **25.** $-2, \frac{1}{4}, -\frac{1}{32}$ **27.** 134,217,728 **29.** −1,572,864 **31.** 19,683

(33) a. $1 \times 2 = 2$
$2 \times 2 = 4$
The common ratio is 2, so the second option forms a geometric sequence.

b. first option: She will receive 30(9) = $270
second option: In the 9th week, she will get $a_n = a_1 r^{n-1}$.
$a_n = 1(2)^{9-1}$
$= 1(2)^8$
$= 256$
In the 8th week, she will get $a_n = a_1 r^{n-1}$.
$a_n = 1(2)^{8-1}$
$= 1(2)^7$
$= 128$
Over the nine weeks she will earn: 1 + 2 + 4 + 8 + 16 + 32 + 64 + 128 + 256 or $511.
She should choose the second option.

35. 9; $\frac{1}{3}$

37a.

Richter Number (x)	Increase in Magnitude (y)	Rate of Change (slope)
1	1	—
2	10	9
3	100	90
4	1,000	900
5	10,000	9000

37b. 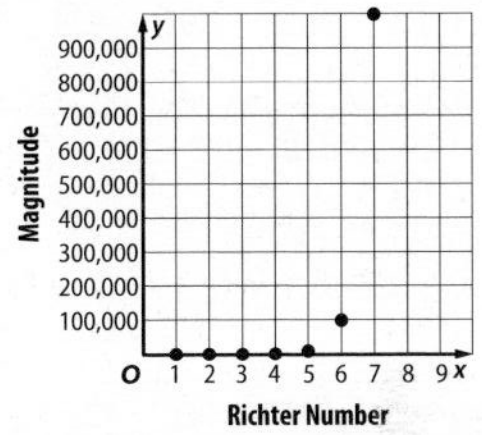

37c. The graph appears to be exponential. The rate of change between any two points does not match any others. **37d.** $1 \cdot (10)^{x-1} = y$ **39.** Neither; Haro calculated the exponent incorrectly. Matthew did not calculate $(-2)^8$ correctly. **41.** Sample answer: When graphed, the terms of a geometric sequence lie on a curve that can be represented by an exponential function. They are different in that the domain of a geometric sequence is the set of natural numbers, while the domain of an exponential function is all real numbers. Thus, geometric sequences are discrete, while exponential functions are continuous. **43.** B **45.** 15 dimes and 20 quarters **47.** 162, 486, 1458 **49.** $\frac{1}{16}, -\frac{1}{32}, \frac{1}{64}$ **51.** 0.1296, 0.07776, 0.046656

53. 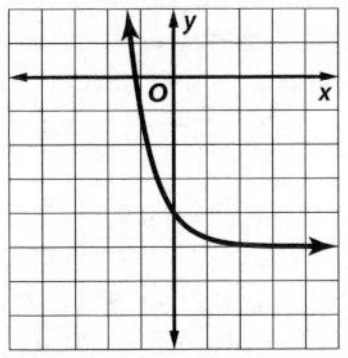

−4;
D = {all real numbers};
R = $\{y \mid y > -5\}$

55. 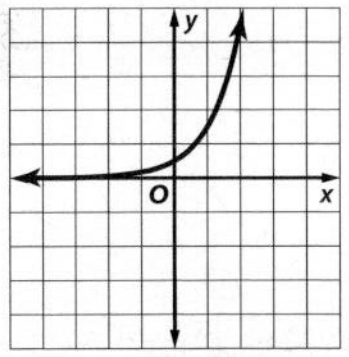

$\frac{1}{2}$;
D = {all real numbers};
R = $\{y \mid y > 0\}$

57. at least $3747 **59.** $y = -3x - \frac{2}{3}$ **61.** $y = \frac{1}{2}x - 9$ **63.** $y = -6x - 7$ **65.** $11a - 2$ **67.** $19w^2 + w$ **69.** $64t - 96$

Lesson 7-8

1. 16, 13, 10, 7, 4 **3.** $a_1 = 1, a_n = a_{n-1} + 5, n \geq 2$
5a. $a_1 = 10, a_n = 0.6a_{n-1}, n \geq 2$

5b. $a_n = 10(0.6)^{n-1}$

7 $a_n = 5n + 8$ is an explicit formula for an arithmetic sequence with $d = 5$ and $a_1 = 5(1) + 8$ or 13. Therefore, $a_1 = 13$, $a_n = a_{n-1} + 5$, $n \geq 2$.
9. $a_n = 22(4)^{n-1}$ **11.** 48, −16, 16, 0, 8 **13.** 12, 15, 24, 51, 132 **15.** $\frac{1}{2}, 2, \frac{7}{2}, 5, \frac{13}{2}$ **17.** $a_1 = 27$, $a_n = a_{n-1} + 14, n \geq 2$ **19.** $a_1 = 100$, $a_n = 0.8a_{n-1}$, $n \geq 2$ **21.** $a_1 = 81$, $a_n = \frac{1}{3}a_{n-1}, n \geq 2$ **23.** $a_1 = 3$, $a_n = 4a_{n-1}, n \geq 2$ **25.** $a_n = 38\left(\frac{1}{2}\right)^{n-1}$

27 **a.** Barbara was the first to receive the message, so the first term is 1. She then forwarded it to 5 of her friends, so the second term is 5. Each of her 5 friends forwarded the message to 5 more friends, so the third term is 5 • 5 or 25. This pattern continues. The fourth term is 25 • 5 or 125, and the fifth term is 125 • 5 or 625. Therefore, the first five terms are 1, 5, 25, 125, 625.
b. There is a common ratio of 5. The sequence is geometric.
$a_n = r \cdot a_{n-1}$
$a_n = 5a_{n-1}$
The first term a_1 is 1, and $n \geq 2$. So, $a_1 = 1$, $a_n = 5a_{n-1}, n \geq 2$.
c. We found that $a_5 = 625$.
$a_6 = 5a_{6-1}$
$= 5a_5$
$= 5(625)$ or 3125
$a_7 = 5a_{7-1}$
$= 5a_6$
$= 5(3125)$ or 15,625
$a_8 = 5a_{8-1}$
$= 5a_7$
$= 5(15{,}625)$ or 78,125

29a. $a_1 = 10$, $a_n = 1.1a_{n-2}, n \geq 2$ **29b.** 16.1 ft
31. Both; sample answer: The sequence can be written as the recursive formula $a_1 = 2$, $a_n = (-1)a_{n-1}, n \geq 2$. The sequence can also be written as the explicit formula $a_n = 2(-1)^{n-1}$.
33. False; sample answer: A recursive formula for the sequence 1, 2, 3, … can be written as $a_1 = 1$, $a_n = a_{n-1} + 1, n \geq 2$ or as $a_1 = 1, a_2 = 2, a_n = a_{n-2} + 2, n \geq 3$. **35.** Sample answer: In an explicit formula, the nth term a_n is given as a function of n. In a recursive formula, the nth term a_n is found by performing operations to one or more of the terms that precede it. **37.** G **39.** F **41.** −54, 81, −121.5 **43.** −64, 32, −16 **45.** 1500; 7500; 37,500 **47.** adults: \$14; children: \$10 **49.** $4x - y = 16$ **51.** $x - 3y = -18$ **53.** $2x + 7y = 26$ **55.** $10x - 64$ **57.** simplified **59.** simplified

Chapter 7 Study Guide and Review

1. monomial **3.** cube root **5.** scientific notation **7.** recursive formula **9.** exponential decay **11.** x^9 **13.** $20a^6b^6$ **15.** $64r^{18}t^6$ **17.** $8x^{15}$ **19.** $45\pi x^4$ **21.** $\frac{27x^3y^9}{8z^3}$ **23.** $\frac{c^6}{a^3}$ **25.** x^6 **27.** $\frac{6}{yx^3}$ **29.** 7 **31.** 5 **33.** 64 **35.** 2401 **37.** 5 **39.** 2.3×10^6 **41.** about 9.1×10^{-2}

43. y-intercept 2; D = {all real numbers}; R = {$y \mid y > 1$}

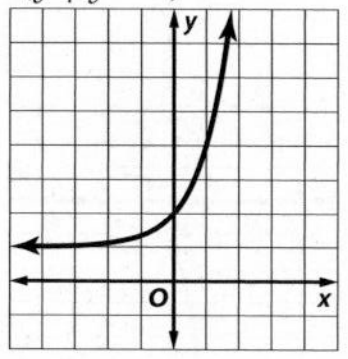

45. y-intercept −2; D = {all real numbers}; R = {$y \mid y > -3$}

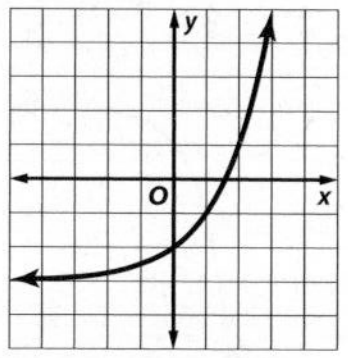

47. \$3053.00 **49.** −1, 1, −1 **51.** 32, 16, 8 **53.** $a_n = 3(3)^{n-1}$

55.

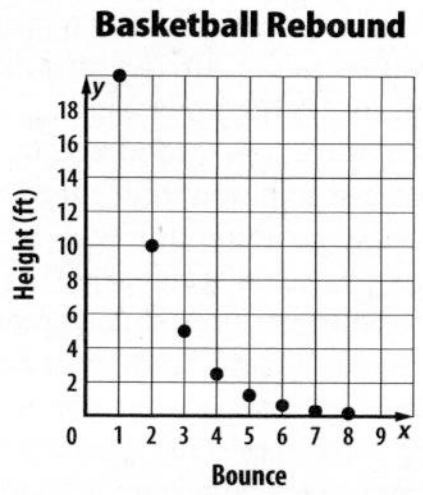

57. 3, 12, 30, 66, 138 **59.** $a_1 = 32$, $a_n = 0.5a_{n-1}, n \geq 2$

CHAPTER 8 Quadratic Expressions and Equations

Chapter 8 Get Ready

1. $a(a) + a(5); a^2 + 5a$ **3.** $n(n) + n(-3n^2) + n(2); n^2 - 3n^3 + 2n$ **5.** 5(9 + 3 + 6); \$90 **7.** $11a - 2$ **9.** $19w^2 + w$ **11.** simplified **13.** $a^2 - 8a + 16$ **15.** $9g^2 - 9g + 2$ **17.** $4n^5$ **19.** $-15z^9$ **21.** $-14a^5c^9$

Lesson 8-1

1. yes; 3; trinomial **3.** yes; 2; monomial **5.** yes; 5; binomial **7.** $2x^5 + 3x - 12$; 2 **9.** $-5z^4 - 2z^2 + 4z$; −5 **11.** $4x^3 + 5$

13 $(4 + 2a^2 - 2a) - (3a^2 - 8a + 7) = (2a^2 - 2a + 4) - (3a^2 - 8a + 7) = (2a^2 - 3a^2) + (-2a - (-8a)) + (4 - 7) = -a^2 + 6a - 3$
15. $-8z^3 - 3z^2 - 2z + 13$ **17.** $4y^2 + 3y + 3$ **19a.** $D(n) = 6n + 14$ **19b.** 116,000 students **19c.** 301,000 students **21.** yes; 0; monomial **23.** No; the exponent is a variable. **25.** yes; 4; binomial **27.** $7y^3 + 8y$; 7 **29.** $-y^3 - 3y^2 + 3y + 2$; −1 **31.** $-r^3 + r + 2$; −1 **33.** $-b^6 - 9b^2 + 10b$; −1

35 $(2x + 3x^2) - (7 - 8x^2) = (2x + 3x^2) + (-7 + 8x^2)$
$= [3x^2 + 8x^2] + 2x + (-7)$
$= 11x^2 + 2x - 7$

37. $2z^2 + z - 11$ **39.** $-2b^2 + 2a + 9$ **41.** $7x^2 - 2xy - 7y$ **43.** $3x^2 - rxt - 8r^2x - 6rx^2$ **45.** quadratic trinomial **47.** quartic binomial **49.** quintic polynomial **51a.** $s = 0.55t^2 - 0.05t + 3.7$ **51b.** 3030 **53a.** the area of the rectangle **53b.** the perimeter of the rectangle **55.** $10a^2 - 8a + 16$ **57.** $7n^3 - 7n^2 - n - 6$

59 **a.** Words: \$15 plus \$0.15 per mile
Expression: $15 + 0.15m$
The expression is $15 + 0.15m$.
b. $15 + 0.15m = 15 + 0.15(145)$
$= 15 + 21.75$
$= 36.75$
The cost is \$36.75.

61. Neither; neither of them found the additive inverse correctly. All terms should have been multiplied by −1. **63.** $6n + 9$ **65.** Sample answer: To add polynomials in a horizontal format, combine like terms. For the vertical format, write the polynomials in standard form, align like terms in columns, and combine like terms. To subtract polynomials in a horizontal format you find the additive inverse of the polynomial you are subtracting, and then combine like terms. For the vertical format, you write the polynomials in standard form, align like terms in columns, and subtract by adding the additive inverse. **67.** $8x + 12$ units **69.** C **71.** Geometric; the common ratio is −4. **73.** Neither; there is no common ratio or difference. **75.** Arithmetic; the common difference is 11. **77.** \$80,000 **79.** no **81.** no **83.** yes; 0.5 **85.** $-2n^8$ **87.** $-40u^5z^9$ **89.** 64 **91.** $288x^8y^{10}z^6$

Lesson 8-2

1. $-15w^3 + 10w^2 - 20w$ **3.** $32k^2m^4 + 8k^3m^3 + 20k^2m^2$

5 $2ab(7a^4b^2 + a^5b - 2a) = 2ab(7a^4b^2) + 2ab(a^5b) + 2ab(-2a)$
$= 14a^5b^3 + 2a^6b^2 + (-4a^2b)$
$= 14a^5b^3 + 2a^6b^2 - 4a^2b$

7. $4t^3 + 15t^2 - 8t + 4$ **9.** $-5d^4c^2 + 8d^2c^2 - 4d^3c + dc^4$ **11.** 20 **13.** $-\frac{20}{9}$ **15.** 20 **17.** 1 **19.** $f^3 + 2f^2 + 25f$ **21.** $10j^5 - 30j^4 + 4j^3 + 4j^2$ **23.** $8t^5u^3 - 40t^4u^5 + 8t^3u$ **25.** $-8a^3 + 20a^2 + 4a - 12$ **27.** $-9g^3 + 21g^2 + 12$ **29.** $8n^4p^2 + 12n^2p^2 + 20n^2 - 8np^3 + 12p^2$

31 $7(t^2 + 5t - 9) + t = t(7t - 2) + 13$
$7t^2 + 35t - 63 + t = 7t^2 - 2t + 13$
$7t^2 + 36t - 63 = 7t^2 - 2t + 13$
$36t - 63 = -2t + 13$
$38t = 76$
$t = 2$

33. $\frac{43}{6}$ **35.** $\frac{30}{43}$ **37.** $20np^4 + 6n^3p^3 - 8np^2$ **39.** $-q^3w^3 - 35q^2w^4 + 8q^2w^2 - 27qw$ **41a.** $53.50 - 0.25h$ **41b.** \$50.50

43 **a.** $A = \ell w$
$= (1.5x + 24)x$
$= 1.5x^2 + 24x$
b. $x(x - 9) = x^2 - 9x$
c. $2(2.5x) = 2(2.5)(36)$
$= 180$ ft
$2(x + 6) = 2(36 + 6)$
$= 2(42)$
$= 84$ ft
Perimeter = 180 + 84 or 264 ft

45. Ted; Pearl used the Distributive Property incorrectly. **47.** $8x^2y^{-2} + 24x^{-10}y^8 - 16x^{-3}$ **49.** Sample answer: $3n$, $4n + 1$; $12n^2 + 3n$ **51.** B **53.** A **55.** $-3x^2 + 1$ **57.** $-9a^2 + 4a + 7$ **59.** $6ab + 2a + 4b$ **61.** $a_1 = 16$, $a_n = a_{n-1} - 14, n \geq 2$ **63.** $a_1 = 27$, $a_n = a_{n-1} + 16, n \geq 2$ **65.** $a_1 = 100$, $a_n = 0.6a_{n-1}, n \geq 2$ **67.** $y - 9{,}500{,}000 = 740{,}000(x - 2003)$; 14,680,000 people **69.** $f(x) = -0.5x$ **71.** $6y^3$ **73.** $15z^7 - 6z^4$ **75.** $-8p^5 + 10p^{10}$

Lesson 8-3

1. $x^2 + 7x + 10$ **3.** $b^2 - 4b - 21$ **5.** $16h^2 - 26h + 3$ **7.** $4x^2 + 72x + 320$ **9.** $16y^4 + 28y^3 - 4y^2 - 21y - 6$ **11.** $10n^4 + 11n^3 - 52n^2 - 12n + 48$ **13.** $2g^2 + 15g - 50$

15 $(4x + 1)(6x + 3) = 4x(6x) + 4x(3) + 1(6x) + 1(3)$
$= 24x^2 + 12x + 6x + 3$
$= 24x^2 + 18x + 3$

17. $24d^2 - 62d + 35$ **19.** $49n^2 - 84n + 36$ **21.** $25r^2 - 49$ **23.** $33z^2 + 7yz - 10y^2$ **25.** $2y^3 - 17y^2 + 37y - 22$ **27.** $m^4 + 2m^3 - 34m^2 + 43m - 12$ **29.** $6b^5 - 3b^4 - 35b^3 - 10b^2 + 43b + 63$ **31.** $2m^3 + 5m^2 - 4$ **33.** $4\pi x^2 + 12\pi x + 9\pi - 3x^2 - 5x - 2$

35 **a.** $A = \ell w$
$= (3y + 4)(6y - 5)$
$= 3y(6y) + 3y(-5) + 4(6y) + 4(-5)$
$= 18y^2 - 15y + 24y - 20$
$= 18y^2 + 9y - 20$
b. $3y + 4 = 31$
$3y = 27$
$y = 9$

So, the width is $6y - 5 = 6(9) - 5$
$= 54 - 5$
$= 49$

$A = \ell w$
$= (31)(49)$
$= 1519 \text{ ft}^2$

37. $a^2 - 4ab + 4b^2$ **39.** $x^2 - 10xy + 25y^2$
41. $125g^3 + 150g^2h + 60gh^2 + 8h^3$ **43a.** $x > 4$; If $x = 4$, the width of the rectangular sandbox would be zero and if $x < 4$ the width of the rectangular sandbox would be negative. **43b.** square **43c.** 4 ft^2
45. Always; by grouping two adjacent terms, a trinomial can be written as a binomial, the sum of two quantities, and apply the FOIL method. For example, $(2x + 3)(x^2 + 5x + 7) = (2x + 3)[x^2 + (5x + 7)] = 2x(x^2) + 2x(5x + 7) + 3(x^2) + 3(5x + 7)$. Then use the Distributive Property and simplify.
47. Sample answer: $x - 1$, $x^2 - x - 1$. $(x - 1)(x^2 - x - 1) = x^3 - 2x^2 + 1$ **49.** The Distributive Property can be used with a vertical or horizontal format by distributing, multiplying, and combining like terms. The FOIL method is used with a horizontal format. You multiply the first, outer, inner, and last terms of the binomials and then combine like terms. A rectangular method can also be used by writing the terms of the polynomials along the top and left side of a rectangle and then multiplying the terms and combining like terms.

51. F **53.** $\frac{3}{2}$ **55.** $4a^2 + 5$ **57.** $3n^3 - 6n^2 + 10$
59. $4b + c + 2$ **61.** $-7m^3 - 3m^2 - m + 17$
63. $-56t^{12}$ **65.** $50y^6 - 27y^9$

Lesson 8-4

1. $x^2 + 10x + 25$

(3) $(2x + 7y)^2 = (2x)^2 + 2(2x)(7y) + (7y)^2$
$= 4x^2 + 28xy + 49y^2$

5. $g^2 - 8gh + 16h^2$ **7a.** $0.5Dy + 0.5y^2$ **7b.** 50%
9. $x^2 - 25$ **11.** $81t^2 - 36$ **13.** $b^2 - 12b + 36$
15. $x^2 + 12x + 36$ **17.** $81 - 36y + 4y^2$ **19.** $25t^2 - 20t + 4$ **21a.** $(T + t)^2 = T^2 + 2Tt + t^2$
21b. *TT*: 25%; *Tt*: 50%; *tt*: 25%

(23) $(b + 7)(b - 7) = b^2 - (7)^2$
$= b^2 - 49$

25. $16 - x^2$ **27.** $9a^4 - 49b^2$ **29.** $64 - 160a + 100a^2$ **31.** $9t^2 - 144$ **33.** $9q^2 - 30qr + 25r^2$
35. $g^2 + 10gh + 25h^2$ **37.** $9a^8 - b^2$ **39.** $64a^4 - 81b^6$
41. $\frac{4}{25}y^2 - \frac{16}{5}y + 16$ **43.** $4m^3 + 16m^2 - 9m - 36$
45. $2x^2 + 2x + 5$ **47.** $6x + 3$ **49.** $c^3 + 3c^2d + 3cd^2 + d^3$ **51.** $f^3 + f^2g - fg^2 - g^3$
53. $n^3 - n^2p - np^2 + p^3$

(55) a. $A = 3.14(r + 9)^2$
$= 3.14(r^2 + 18r + 81)$
$\approx (3.14r^2 + 56.52r + 254.34) \text{ ft}^2$

b. $38^2 - (3.14r^2 + 56.52r + 254.34)$
$= 1444 - 3.14r^2 - 56.52r - 254.34$
$\approx (1189.66 - 3.14r^2 - 56.52r) \text{ ft}^2$

57. Sample answer: $(2c + d)(2c - d)$; The product of these binomials is a difference of two squares and does not have a middle term. The other three do.
59. 81 **61.** Sample answer: To find the square of a sum, apply the FOIL method or apply the pattern. The square of the sum of two quantities is the first quantity squared plus two times the product of the two quantities plus the second quantity squared. The square of the difference of two quantities is the first quantity squared minus two times the product of the two quantities plus the second quantity squared. The product of the sum and difference of two quantities is the square of the first quantity minus the square of the second quantity. **63.** D **65.** C **67.** $2c^2 + 5c - 3$
69. $8h^2 - 34h + 21$ **71.** $40m^2 + 47m + 12$
73. $3c^2 - 2c$ **75.** $-13d^2 - 18d$ **77.** $19p^2 - 18p$
79. (2, 0) **81.** $t < 18$ or $t > 22$ **83.** $y = \frac{1}{5}x + 6$
85. 15 lb **87.** $2p^5 - 5p^4 + p^2 + 12$; 2

Lesson 8-5

1. $3(7b - 5a)$ **3.** $gh(10gh + 9h - g)$

(5) $np + 2n + 8p + 16 = (np + 2n) + (8p + 16)$
$= n(p + 2) + 8(p + 2)$
$= (n + 8)(p + 2)$

7. $(b + 5)(3c - 2)$ **9.** 0, −10 **11.** 0, $\frac{3}{4}$
13a. 0, 2.08125 **13b.** 17.3 ft, 2.6 ft **15.** $8(2t - 5y)$
17. $2k(k + 2)$ **19.** $2ab(2ab + a - 5b)$

(21) $fg - 5g + 4f - 20 = (fg - 5g) + (4f - 20)$
$= g(f - 5) + 4(f - 5)$
$= (g + 4)(f - 5)$

23. $(h + 5)(j - 2)$ **25.** $(9q - 10)(5p - 3)$
27. $(3d - 5)(t - 7)$ **29.** $(3t - 5)(7h - 1)$
31. $(r - 5)(5b + 2)$ **33.** $gf(5f + g + 15)$
35. $3cd(9d - 6cd + 1)$ **37.** $2(8u - 15)(3t + 2)$
39. 0, 3 **41.** $-\frac{1}{2}$, −2 **43.** 0, −3 **45a.** ab
45b. $(a + 6)(b + 6)$ **45c.** $6(a + b + 6)$

47a.

x	y
0	0
1	9
2	12
3	9
4	0

47b.

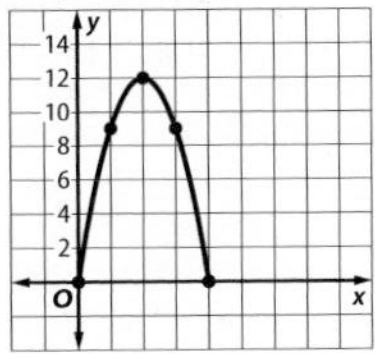

47c. 12 ft

(49) $h = 64t - 16t^2$
$0 = 64t - 16t^2$
$0 = 16t(4 - t)$
$16t = 0$ or $4 - t = 0$
$t = 0$ or $4 = t$
So, the arrow hits the ground after 4 seconds.

51a. 3 and −2

51b.

x^2	$+3x$
$-2x$	-6

51c.

	x	$+3$
x	x^2	$+3x$
-2	$-2x$	-6

$(x + 3)(x - 2)$

51d. Sample answer: Place x^2 in the top left-hand corner and place −40 in the lower right-hand corner. Then determine which two factors have a product of −40 and a sum of −3. Then place these factors in the box. Then find the factor of each row and column. The factors will be listed on the very top and far left of the box. **53.** Since the solutions are $-\frac{b}{a}$ and $\frac{b}{a}$, $a \neq 0$ and b is any real number.
55. Sample answer: $a = 0$ or $a = b$ for any real values of a and b. **57.** D **59.** 350 **61.** $0.5Bb + 0.5b^2$; $\frac{1}{2}$
63. $2b^3 + 2b^2 - 10b$ **65.** $-4x^4 - 4x^3 - 8x^2 + 4x$
67. $-3x^3y - 3x^2y^2 - 6xy^3$ **69.** p^7r^5 **71.** $81x^2y^{14}$
73. 16,777,216 **75.** $\{y \mid y > -11\}$ **77.** $\{k \mid k > -9\}$
79. $\{z \mid z \geq -48\}$

Lesson 8-6

1. $(x + 2)(x + 12)$ **3.** $(n + 7)(n - 3)$ **5.** −3, 7
7. 6, 9 **9.** −8, 9 **11.** 8 in. by 12 in. **13.** $(y - 9)(y - 8)$ **15.** $(n - 7)(n + 5)$ **17.** $(x - 2)(x - 20)$
19. $(m + 6)(m - 7)$

(21) $y^2 + y = 20$
$y^2 + y - 20 = 0$
$(y + 5)(y - 4) = 0$
$y + 5 = 0$ or $y - 4 = 0$
$y = -5$ $y = 4$

23. −2, −9 **25.** 2, 16 **27.** −4, −14 **29.** 4, 12
31. $(x - 6)$ ft **33.** $(q + 2r)(q + 9r)$ **35.** $(x - y)(x - 5y)$

(37) a. Sample answer: Let w represent the width of the swimming pool. So, the length of the pool is $w + 20$.
$A = \ell w$
$= (w + 20)w$
$525 = (w + 20)w$

b. $525 = (w + 20)w$
$525 = w^2 + 20w$
$0 = w^2 + 20w - 525$
$0 = (w + 35)(w - 15)$
$w + 35 = 0$ or $w - 15 = 0$
$w = -35$ $w = 15$

c. The solution of 15 means that the width is 15 feet and the length is 35 feet. The solution −35 does not make sense because length cannot be negative.

39. $4x - 26$ **41.** Charles; Jerome's answer once multiplied is $x^2 - 6x - 16$. The middle term should be positive. **43.** −15, −9, 9, 15 **45.** 4, 6
47. Sample answer: $x^2 + 19x - 20$; $(x - 1)(x + 20)$

49. Sample answer: Find factors m and n such that $m + n = b$ and $mn = c$. If b and c are positive, then m and n are positive. If b is negative and c is positive, then m and n are negative. When c is negative, m and n have different signs and the factor with the greater absolute value has the same sign as b. **51.** 204 **53.** A **55.** $11x(1 + 4xy)$
57. $(2x + b)(a + 3c)$ **59.** $(x - y)(x - y)$
61. (4, 13) **63.** (3, 6) **65.** about 6 ft
67. $(3x - 4)(a - 2b)$

Lesson 8-7

1. $(3x + 2)(x + 5)$ **3.** prime **5.** $-\frac{3}{2}$, −3 **7.** $\frac{4}{3}$, 2
9a. 5 ft **9b.** 2.5 seconds

(11) $2x^2 + 19x + 24$

factors of 48	sum of 19
3, 16	19

$2x^2 + 3x + 16x + 24 = (2x^2 + 3x) + (16x + 24)$
$= x(2x + 3) + 8(2x + 3)$
$= (x + 8)(2x + 3)$

13. $2(2x + 5)(x + 7)$ **15.** $(4x - 5)(x - 2)$ **17.** prime
19. prime **21.** prime **23.** $\frac{3}{2}$, −6 **25.** $\frac{2}{3}$, 8
27. $-\frac{1}{3}$, 2 **29a.** $10 = -16t^2 + 20t + 6$ **29b.** 1 sec
29c. Less; sample answer: It starts closer to the ground so the shot will not have as far to fall.

(31) Words: 6 times the square of a number plus 11 times the number equals 2
Equation: $6 \cdot x^2 + 11 \cdot x = 2$
$6x^2 + 11x = 2$
$6x^2 + 11x - 2 = 0$

factors of −12	sum of 11
−1, 12	11

$6x^2 + 11x - 2 = 0$
$6x^2 - 1x + 12x - 2 = 0$
$(6x^2 - 1x) + (12x - 2) = 0$
$x(6x - 1) + 2(6x - 1) = 0$
$(x + 2)(6x - 1) = 0$
$x + 2 = 0$ or $6x - 1 = 0$
$x = -2$ $6x = 1$
$x = \frac{1}{6}$

The numbers are −2 and $\frac{1}{6}$.

33. $-(x + 2)(4x + 7)$ **35.** $-(2x - 7)(3x - 5)$
37. $-(3x - 4)(4x + 5)$ **39a.** a^2 and b^2 **39b.** $a^2 - b^2$
39c. width: $a - b$, length: $a + b$ **39d.** $(a - b)(a + b)$
39e. $(a - b)(a + b)$; the figure with area $a^2 - b^2$ and the rectangle with area $(a - b)(a + b)$ have the same area, so $a^2 - b^2 = (a - b)(a + b)$. **41.** $(12x + 20y)$ in.; The area of the square equals $(3x + 5y)(3x + 5y)$ in^2, so the length of one side is $(3x + 5y)$ in. The perimeter is $4(3x + 5y)$ or $(12x + 20y)$ in.
43. Sample answer: A quadratic equation may have zero, one, or two solutions. If there are two solutions, you must consider the context of the

situation to determine whether one or both solutions answer the given question. **45.** 6 **47.** J
49. $(x-2)(x-7)$ **51.** $(x+3)(x-8)$
53. $(r+8)(r-5)$ **55.** 0, 9 **57.** 0, 2 **59.** 0, 4

61.

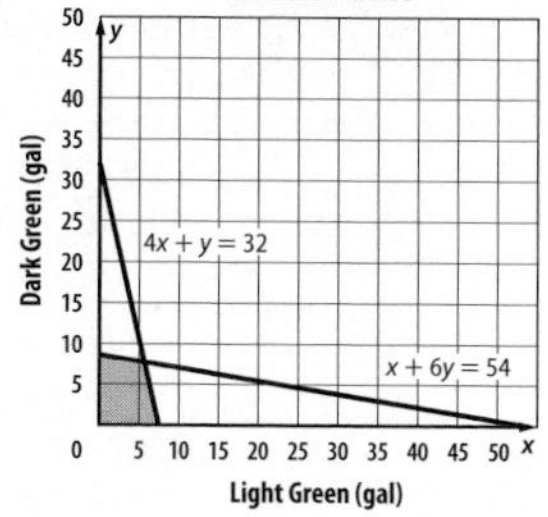

Sample answers: 2 light, 8 dark; 6 light, 8 dark; 7 light, 4 dark

63. $\{d \mid d \le 5 \text{ or } d > 7\}$

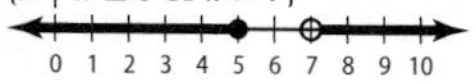

65. ∅

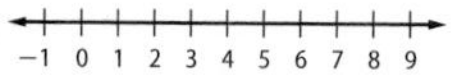

67. $\{y \mid 3 < y < 6\}$

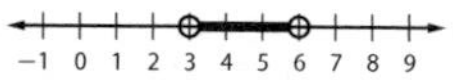

69. 4 **71.** 8 **73.** 11

Lesson 8-8

1. $(x+3)(x-3)$ **3.** $9(m+4)(m-4)$
5. $(u^2+9)(u+3)(u-3)$

(7) $20r^4 - 45n^4 = 5(4r^4 - 9n^4)$
$= 5\left((2r^2)^2 - (3n^2)^2\right)$
$= 5(2r^2 + 3n^2)(2r^2 - 3n^2)$

9. $(c+1)(c-1)(2c+3)$ **11.** $(t+4)(t-4)(3t+2)$
13. 36 mph **15.** $(q+11)(q-11)$
17. $6(n^2+1)(n+1)(n-1)$ **19.** $(r+3t)(r-3t)$
21. $h(h+10)(h-10)$ **23.** $(x+9)(x-9)(2x-1)$
25. $7(h^2+p^2)(h+p)(h-p)$
27. $6k^2(h^2+3k)(h^2-3k)$ **29.** $(f+8)(f-8)(f+2)$
31. $10q(q+11)(q-11)$
33. $p^3r(r+1)(r-1)(r^2+1)$
35. $(r+10)(r-10)(r-5)$ **37.** $(a+7)(a-7)$
39. $3(m^4+81)$ **41.** $2(a+4)(a-4)(6a+1)$
43. $3(m+5)(m-5)(5m+4)$ **45a.** $-0.5x(x-9)$
45b. 9 ft **45c.** 10.125 ft

(47) a. $S = -25m^2 + 125m$
$0 = -25m^2 + 125m$
$0 = -25m(m-5)$
$0 = -25m$ or $0 = m - 5$
$0 = m$ $\quad 5 = m$
So, they will stop selling in month 5.
b. The peak will occur halfway between 0 and 5, or 2.5.
c. The peak amount is $S = -25(2.5)^2 + 125(2.5)$
$= -156.25 + 312.5$
$= 156.25$
The peak is 156,250 copies.

(49) $100 = 25x^2$
$0 = 25x^2 - 100$
$0 = 25(x^2 - 4)$
$0 = 25(x+2)(x-2)$
$x + 2 = 0$ or $x - 2 = 0$
$x = -2$ $\quad x = 2$

51. $\frac{3}{8}, -\frac{3}{8}$ **53.** −45, 45 **55.** $\frac{3}{16}, -\frac{3}{16}$
57. Lorenzo; sample answer: Checking Elizabeth's answer gives us $16x^2 - 25y^2$. The exponent on x in the final product should be 4. **59.** $(x^4-3)(x^4+3) \cdot (x^8+9)$ **61.** false; $a^2 + b^2$ **63.** When the difference of squares pattern is multiplied together using the FOIL method, the outer and inner terms are opposites of each other. When these terms are added together, the sum is zero. **65.** G **67a.** Car A, because it is traveling at 65 mph, and Car B is traveling at 60 mph. **67b.** $5t - 10$ **67c.** 2.5 mi
69. prime **71.** {3, 6} **73.** {6, 16}
75. $\{t \mid t \ge 4\}$

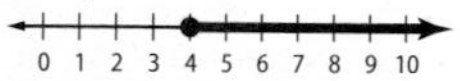

77. $\{k \mid k > 4\}$

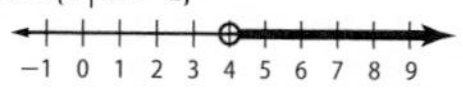

79. $\{m \mid m \ge 3\}$

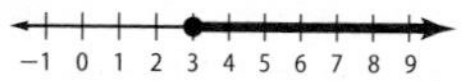

81. the seventh week **83.** $x^2 - 4x + 4$
85. $4x^2 - 20x + 25$ **87.** $16x^2 + 40x + 25$

Lesson 8-9

1. yes; $(5x+6)^2$ **3.** $(x-4)(2x+7)$ **5.** $4(x^2+16)$
7. ±3 **9.** $\frac{3}{8}$ **11.** 0.6 second **13.** yes; $(4x-7)^2$
(15) Since the last term is not a perfect square, the trinomial is not a perfect square trinomial
17. prime **19.** $8(y-5z)(y+5z)$
21. $2m(2m-7)(3m+5)$ **23.** $3(2x-7)^2$
25. $3p(2p+1)(2p-1)$ **27.** $2t(t+6)(2t-7)$
29. $2a(a-b)(b+1)(b-1)$ **31.** $3k(k-4)(k-4)$
33. prime
(35) $(y-4)^2 = 7$
$y - 4 = \pm\sqrt{7}$
$y = 4 \pm \sqrt{7}$
37. $\frac{3}{4}$ **39.** 6 **41.** $\frac{1}{3}$ **43.** $8 \pm \sqrt{6}$ **45.** 20 ft
47. $|4x+5|$
(49) a. 42 in. = 3.5 ft., width = w, length = $w + 5$, height = 3.5
Area of the surface = $\ell \cdot w$ or $(w+5)(w)$
$V = \ell \cdot w \cdot h$
$1750 = (w+5)(w)(3.5)$
$500 = (w+5)(w)$
Area of the surface is 500 ft²
b. $500 = (w+5)(w)$
$= w^2 + 5w$
$0 = w^2 + 5w - 500$
$= (w+25)(w-20)$
$0 = w + 25$ or $0 = w - 20$
$-25 = w$ $\quad 20 = w$
The dimensions are 20 ft by 25 ft by 42 in.
c. Because the volume is doubled, we can double any one of the dimensions. 40 ft by 25 ft by 42 in., 20 ft by 50 ft by 42 in., or 20 ft by 25 ft by 84 in.
d. Because 2 of the dimensions are doubled the volume is increased by a factor of 4.
The ratio is 1:4
51. 6 ft wide by 2 ft long by 15 ft high
53. Adriano; sample answer: Debbie did not factor the expression completely. **55.** Sample answer: $x^2 - 3x + \frac{9}{4} = 0; \left\{\frac{3}{2}\right\}$ **57.** First look for a GCF in all the terms and factor the GCF out of all the terms. Then, if the polynomial has two terms, check if the terms are the differences of squares and factor if so. If the polynomial has three terms, check if the trinomial will factor into two binomial factors or if it is a perfect square trinomial and factor if so. If the polynomial has four or more terms, factor by grouping. If the polynomial does not have a GCF and cannot be factored, the polynomial is a prime polynomial. **59.** Sample answer: $x^4 - 1$; 1, −1
61. B **63.** H
65. $(x-4)(x+4)$ **67.** $(1-10p)(1+10p)$
69. $(5n-1)(5n+1)$ **71.** {−2, 4} **73.** {−2, 1}
75. {2, 3} **77.** 10^1 or 10 **79.** $\frac{1}{10{,}000}$ **81.** $-\frac{2}{3}$
83. $\frac{3}{8}$ **85.** undefined

Chapter 8 Study Guide and Review

1. false; sample answer: $x^2 + 5x + 7$ **3.** true
5. true **7.** true **9.** false; difference of squares
11. $3x^2 + x + 2$ **13.** $x^2 + 3x + 2$ **15.** $-2x^3 - 3$
17. $-x^2 - x + 6$ **19.** 0 **21.** 1 **23.** $x^2 + 4x - 21$
25. $6r^2 + rt - 35t^2$ **27.** $10x^2 + 7x - 12$
29. $9x^2 - 12x + 4$ **31.** $4x^2 - 9$ **33.** $9m^2 - 4$
35. $12(x + 2y)$ **37.** $2y(4x - 8x^3 + 5)$
39. $(2x - 3z)(x - y)$ **41.** 0, 2 **43.** 0, 3
45. $x^2 - 2x + 5$ **47.** $(x+5)(x+4)$
49. $(x+6)(x-3)$ **51.** 2, 4 **53.** −6, 8 **55.** 14 in.
57. prime **59.** $(2a-3)(a+8)$ **61.** $4, -\frac{5}{2}$ **63.** $\frac{5}{3}, -\frac{1}{2}$
65. $(y+9)(y-9)$ **67.** prime **69.** 5, −5 **71.** −9, 9
73. 2 seconds **75.** prime **77.** $(2-7a)^2$
79. $x^2(x+4)(x-4)$ **81.** 1, −2 **83.** $-2, -\frac{1}{2}$

CHAPTER 9
Quadratic Functions and Equations

Chapter 9 Get Ready

1.

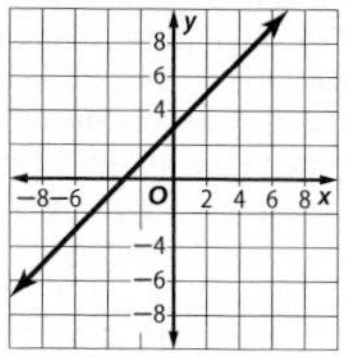

3.

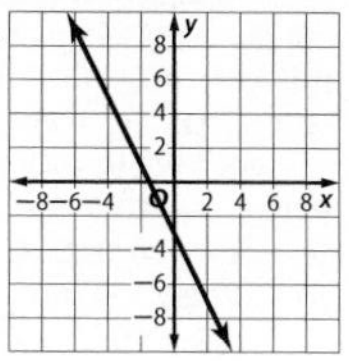

5.

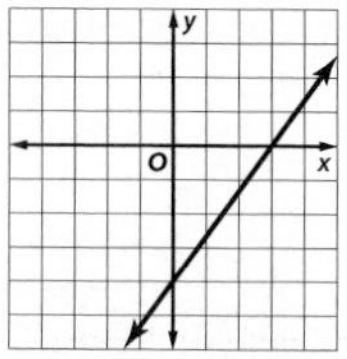

7.

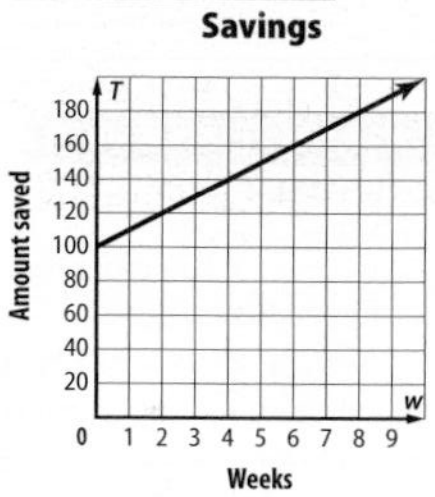

9. no **11.** yes; $(x+10)^2$ **13.** yes; $(k-8)^2$ **15.** no
17. 3 **19.** $2\frac{1}{2}$
21. 4 **23.** −2.5

Lesson 9-1

1.

x	y
−3	0
−2	−6
−1	−8
0	−6
1	0
2	10

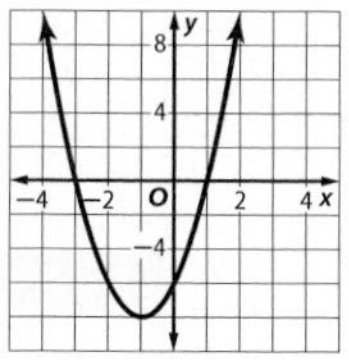

D = {all real numbers}; R = $\{y \mid y \ge -8\}$

3.

x	y
−1	4
0	−3
1	−8
2	−11
3	−12
4	−11
5	−8
6	−3
7	4

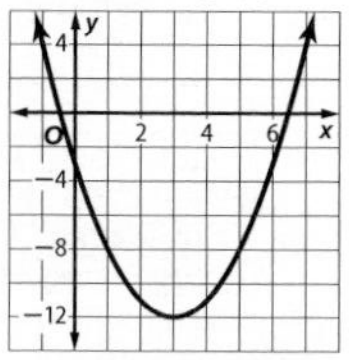

D = {all real numbers};
R = $\{y \mid y \ge -12\}$

5. vertex (−1, 5), axis of symmetry $x = -1$, y-intercept 3 **7.** vertex (−2, −12), axis of symmetry $x = -2$, y-intercept −4 **9.** vertex (1, 2), axis of symmetry $x = 1$, y-intercept −1 **11.** vertex (2, 1), axis of symmetry $x = 2$, y-intercept 5

13 a. Since the a value is −1, the graph opens downward and has a maximum.

b. In this equation $a = -1$, $b = 4$, and $c = -3$.

$x = \frac{-b}{2a}$
$= \frac{-4}{2(-1)}$
$= 2$

To find the vertex, use the value you found for the x-coordinate of the vertex. To find the y-coordinate, substitute the value for x in the original equation.

$y = -x^2 + 4x - 3$
$= -(2)^2 + 4(2) - 3$
$= -4 + 8 - 3$
$= 1$

The maximum is at (2, 1).

c. The domain of the function is D = {x | x is all real numbers}. The range is R = {y | $y \leq 1$}.

15a. maximum **15b.** 6 **15c.** D = {all real numbers}; R = {y | $y \leq 6$}

17.

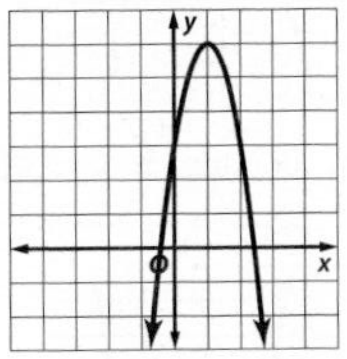

19.

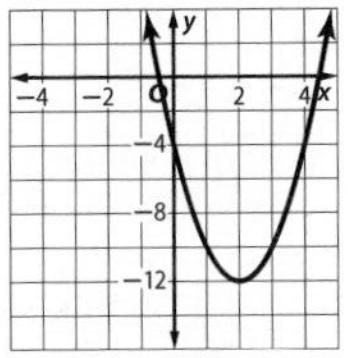

21a.

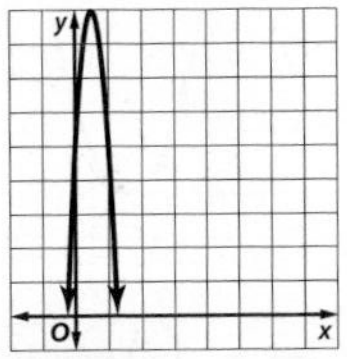

21b. 5 ft **21c.** 9 ft

23.

x	y
−3	13
−2	7
−1	5
0	7
1	13

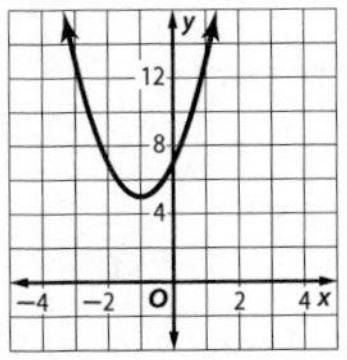

D = {all real numbers}; R = {y | $y \geq 5$}

25.

x	y
0	5
−1	−4
−2	−7
−3	−4
−4	5

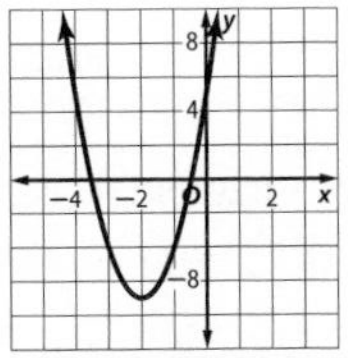

D = {all real numbers}; R = {y | $y \geq -7$}

27.

x	y
3	2
2	−1
1	−2
0	−1
−1	2

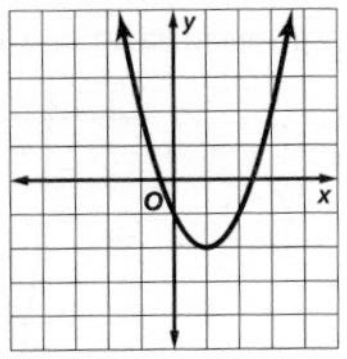

D = {all real numbers}; R = {y | $y \geq -2$}

29. vertex (0, 1), axis of symmetry $x = 0$, y-intercept 1 **31.** vertex (1, 1), axis of symmetry $x = 1$, y-intercept 4 **33.** vertex (0, 0), axis of symmetry $x = 0$, y-intercept 0

35 In this equation $a = 2$, $b = 12$, and $c = 10$.

$x = \frac{-b}{2a}$ $= \frac{-12}{2(2)}$

The equation for the axis of symmetry is $x = -3$.

To find the vertex, use the value you found for the axis of symmetry as the x-coordinate of the vertex. To find the y-coordinate, substitute the value for x in the original equation.

$y = 2x^2 + 12x + 10$
$= 2(-3)^2 + 12(-3) + 10$
$= -8$

The vertex is at (−3, −8).

The y-intercept occurs at (0, c). So, in this case, the y-intercept is 10.

37. vertex (−3, 4), axis of symmetry $x = -3$, y-intercept −5 **39.** vertex (2, −14), axis of symmetry $x = 2$, y-intercept 14 **41.** vertex (1, −15), axis of symmetry $x = 1$, y-intercept −18 **43a.** maximum **43b.** 9 **43c.** D = {all real numbers}, R = {y | $y \leq 9$} **45a.** minimum **45b.** −48 **45c.** D = {all real numbers}, R = {y | $y \geq -48$} **47a.** maximum **47b.** 33 **47c.** D = {all real numbers}, R = {y | $y \leq 33$} **49a.** maximum **49b.** 4 **49c.** D = {all real numbers}, R = {y | $y \leq 4$} **51a.** maximum **51b.** 3 **51c.** D = {all real numbers}, R = {y | $y \leq 3$}

53.

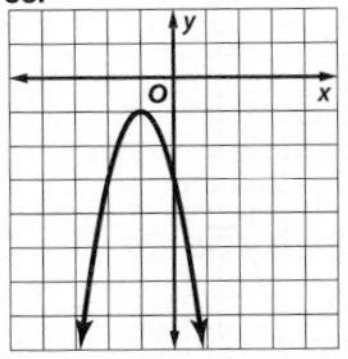

55.

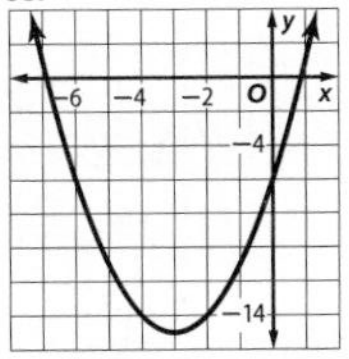

57.

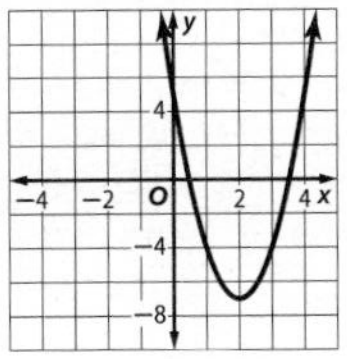

59.

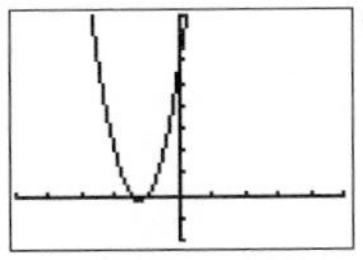

[−5, 5] scl:1 by [−5, 5] scl:1

(−1.25, −0.25)

61.

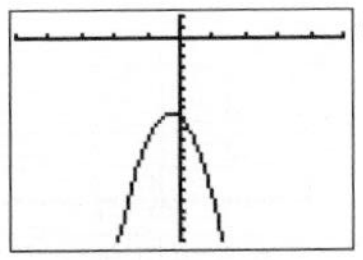

[−5, 5] scl: 1 by [−20, 2] scl: 2

(−0.3, −7.55)

63a.

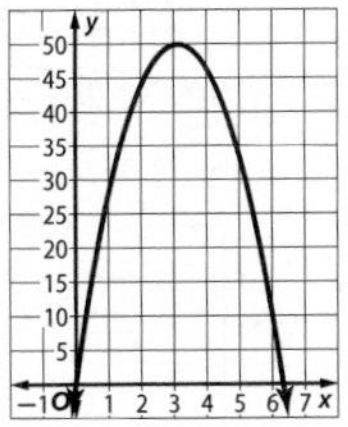

Where $h > 0$, the ball is above the ground. The height of the ball decreases as more time passes.

63b. 0 m **63c.** ≈50.0 m **63d.** ≈6.4 seconds **63e.** D = {x | $0 \leq x \leq 6.4$}; R = {y | $0 \leq y \leq 50.0$}

65 a. $h = -16t^2 + 90t$
$= -16(1)^2 + 90(1)$
$= 74$ ft

b. $126 = -16t^2 - 90t$
$0 = -16t^2 - 90t - 126$
$0 = (t - 3)(-16t + 42)$
$t = 3$ and $t = 2.625$

c. $h = -16t^2 + 90t$
$0 = -16t^2 + 90t$
$0 = -16t(t - 5)$
$t = 0$ and $t = 5.625$

These represent the time that the ball leaves the ground initially and the time it returns to the ground.

67 a.

Equation	Related Function	Zeros	y-Values
$x^2 - x = 12$	$y = x^2 - x - 12$	−3, 4	−3: 8, −6; 4: −6, 8
$x^2 + 8x = 9$	$y = x^2 + 8x - 9$	−9, 1	−9: 11, −9; 1: −9, 11
$x^2 = 14x - 24$	$y = x^2 - 14x + 24$	2, 12	2: 11, −9; 12: −9, 11
$x^2 + 16x = -28$	$y = x^2 + 16x + 28$	−14, −2	−14: 13, −11; −2: −11, 13

b. Use a graphing calculator to graph.

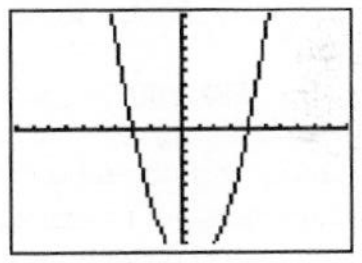

$y = x^2 - x - 12$

[−10, 10] scl: 1 by [−10, 10] scl: 1

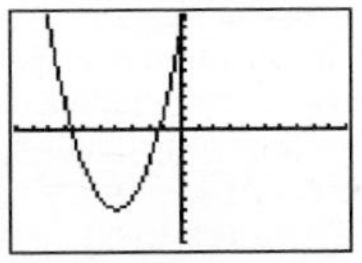

$y = x^2 + 8x - 9$

[−15, 15] scl: 2 by [−30, 30] scl: 5

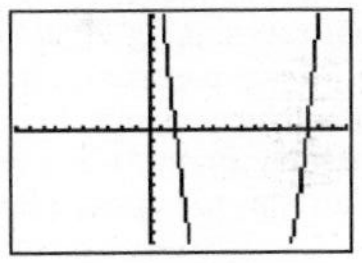

$y = x^2 - 14x + 24$

[−10, 15] scl: 1 by [−10, 10] scl: 1

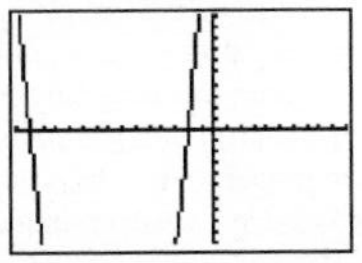

$y = x^2 + 16x + 28$

[−15, 10] scl: 1 by [−10, 10] scl: 1

c. Use the table function on the calculator to identify the zeros. The zeros are the values where y is 0. Also list the y-values that are to the left and right of the zeros.

d. The function values have opposite signs just before and just after the zeros.

69. Chase; the lines of symmetry are $x = 2$ and $x = 1.5$. **75.** C **77.** D **79.** yes; $(2x + 1)^2$ **81.** no

83. prime **85.** $b^2 - 4b - 21$ **87.** $2x^2 + 17x - 9$
89. (2, 1) **91.** (4, 2) **93.** 10 **95.** −6

Lesson 9-2

1. 2, −5

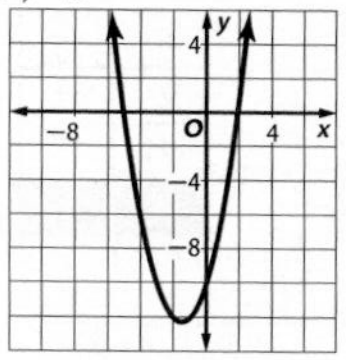

3. −2

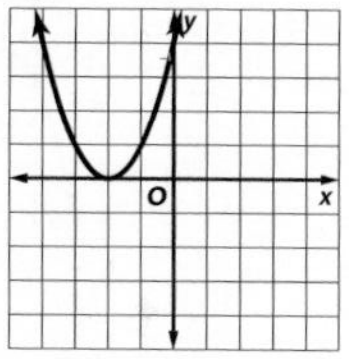

5. −5.2, 0.2

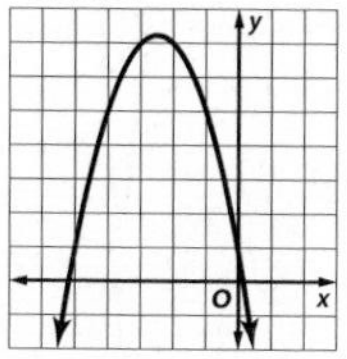

7. 5, −5

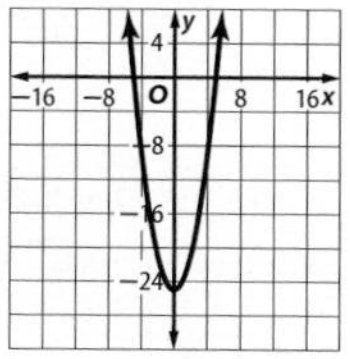

9. about 8.4 seconds

11 Step 1: Graph the related function of $f(x) = x^2 + 2x - 24 = 0$

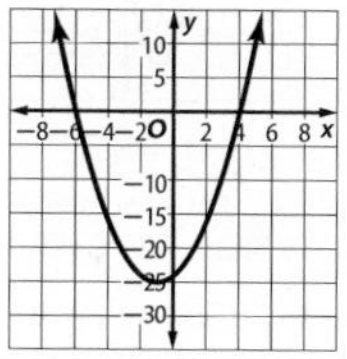

Step 2: The x-intercepts appear to be at −6 and 4, so the solutions are −6 and 4.

13. ∅

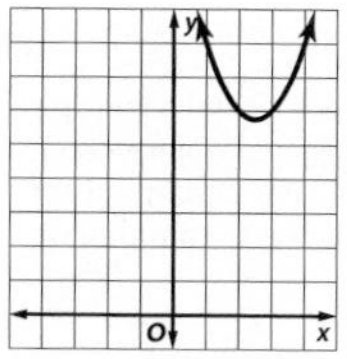

15. 1

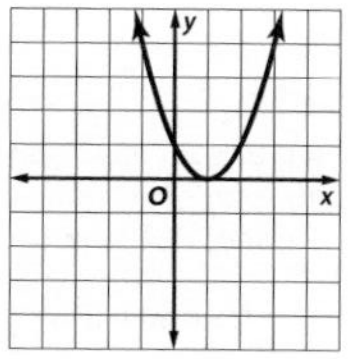

17. ∅

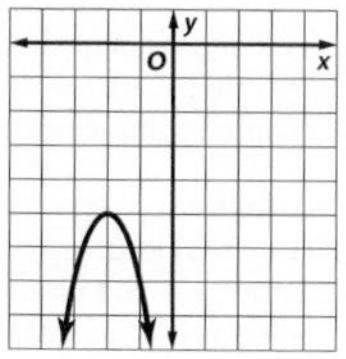

19. −6

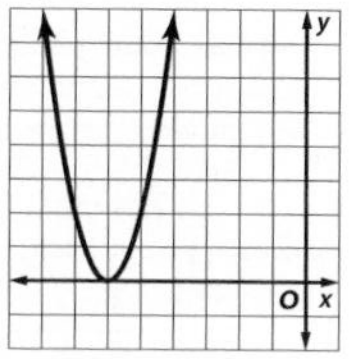

21. 8, −10

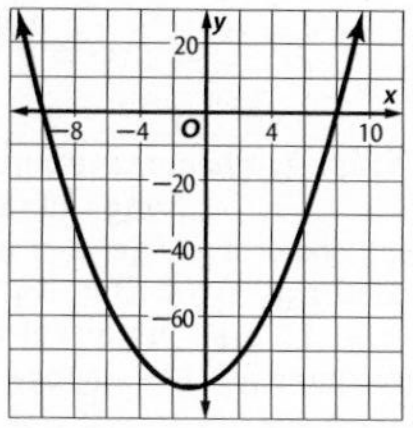

23. 6.9, −2.9

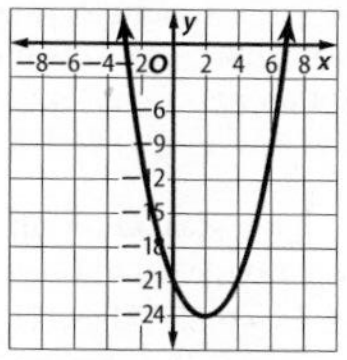

25. 3.3, 1.2

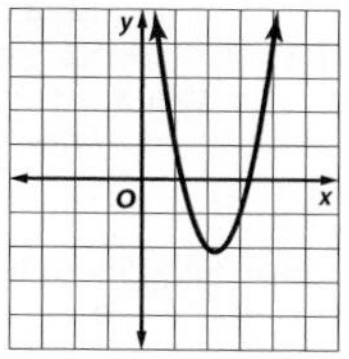

27. 3.1, −8.1

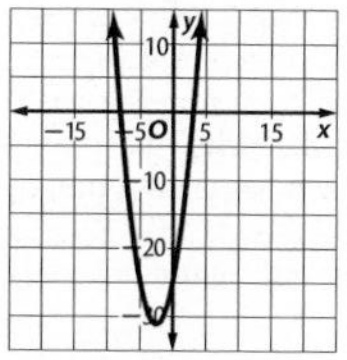

29. about 7.6 seconds **31.** 1; −2
33. 2; −4, −8 **35.** −3, 4

37 **a.** $h = -16t^2 + 30t + 10$
$0 = -16t^2 + 30t + 10$
Graph the equation and find the x-intercepts.

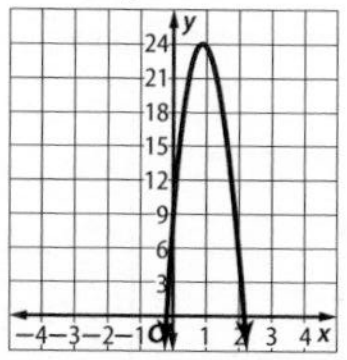

The positive x-intercept appears to be at 2.2, so she is in the air 2.2 seconds.

b. From the graph, she appears to hit a height of 15 feet at 0.2 seconds and 1.7 seconds.

c. $x = \frac{-b}{2a}$
$= \frac{-30}{2(-16)}$
$h = (-16)(0.9375)^2 + 30(0.9375) + 10$
≈ 24 feet
Her maximum height is about 24 feet, so she gets the bonus points.

39. $(x + 2)(x - 1)(x - 4)$ **41.** Iku; sample answer: The zeros of a quadratic function are the x-intercepts of the graph. Since the graph does not cross the x-axis, there are no x-intercepts and no real zeros. **43.** Sometimes; for (1, 3), the y-value is greater than 2, but for (1, −1), it is less than 2.
45. 1.5 and −1.5; Sample answer: Make a table of values for x from −2.0 to 2.0. Use increments of 0.1.
47. A

49. about 21.4 mi

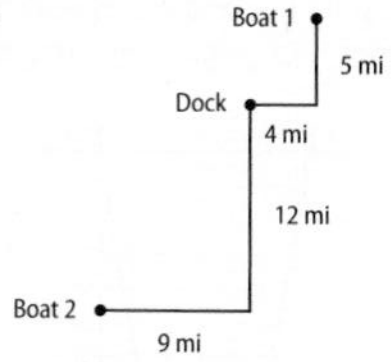

51. $x = 0$; (0, 0); min

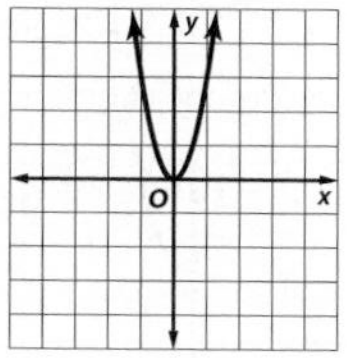

53. $x = 2$; (2, −3); max

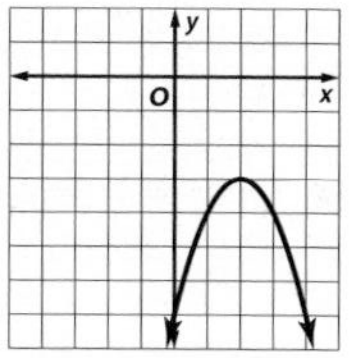

55. $x = -\frac{1}{3}$; $\left(-\frac{1}{3}, \frac{2}{3}\right)$; min

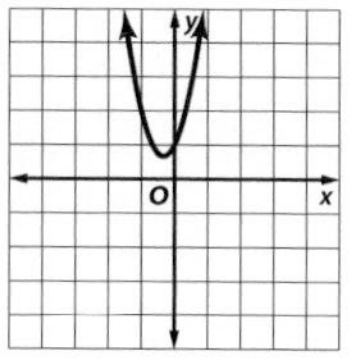

57. −4, 4 **59.** $-\frac{3}{2}, \frac{5}{2}$ **61.** $-3 \pm \sqrt{5}$ **63.** $7n^2 + 1$
65. $-3b^4 + 2b^3 - 9b^2 + 13$ **67.** $x + y = 180$; $x = y + 24$; 102°, 78° **69.** $y - 6 = -7(x + 3)$

71.

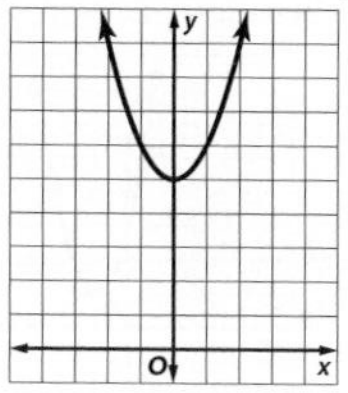

73.

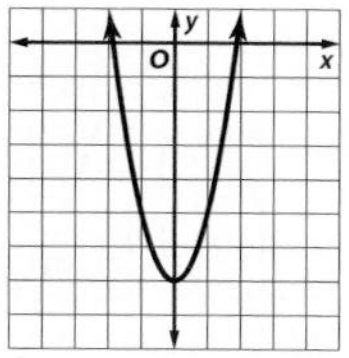

75.

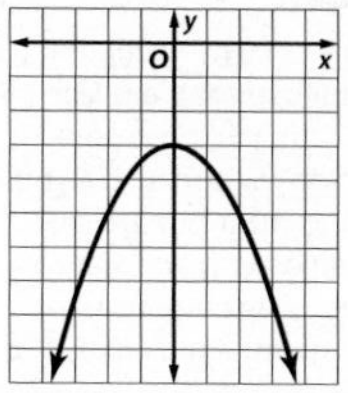

Lesson 9-3

1. translated down **3.** reflected across the x-axis, translated up **5.** reflected across the x-axis, translated left and stretched vertically **7.** C

9 The function can be written as $f(x) = ax^2 + c$ where $a = -1$ and $c = -7$. Since $-7 < 0$ and $-1 < 0$ the graph of $y = -x^2 - 7$ translates the graph of $y = x^2$ down 7 units and reflects it across the x-axis.

11. compressed vertically, translated up
13. stretched vertically, translated up **15.** translated left and up and stretched vertically **17.** stretched vertically, translated down **19.** A **21.** F **23.** E
25. $g(x), h(x)$ **27.** $h(x), g(x), f(x)$

29 **a.** The two equations are $h = -16t^2 + 300$ and $h = -16t^2 + 700$.
b. $0 = -16t^2 + 300$, $t \approx 4.3$; $0 = -16t^2 + 700$, $t \approx 6.6$; $6.6 - 4.3 \approx 2.3$ seconds.

31a. The graph of $g(x)$ is the graph of $f(x)$ translated 200 yards right, compressed vertically, reflected in the x-axis, and translated up 20 yards.
31b. $h(x) = 0.0005(x - 230)^2 + 20$ **33.** Translate the graph of $f(x)$ up 11 units and to the right 5 units.
35a. 20 h **35b.** $h(t) = 40t$ **35c.** $T(t) = -t^2 + 50t + 200$; the fuel in the tank after t hours with refueling
35d. Yes; after about 53 hours 43 minutes.
37. $y = x^2 - 1$ **39.** Sample answer: $f(x) = -\frac{1}{2}x^2$
41. $C = 55 + 30h$ **43.** J

45. ∅

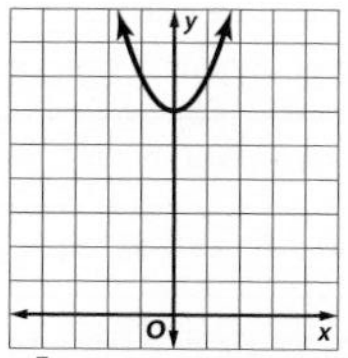

47. 4, −1

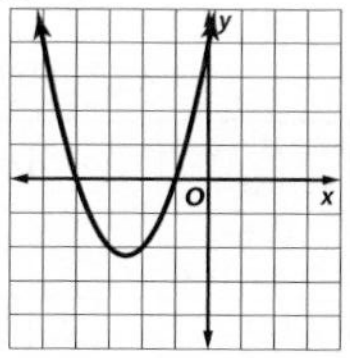

49. $-\frac{5}{2}, 3$

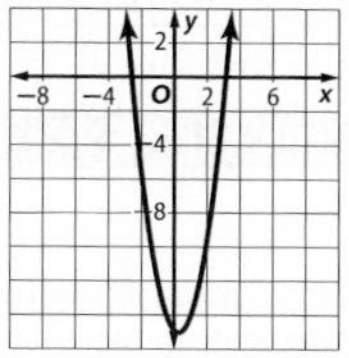

x	$\frac{1}{3}\lvert x\rvert + 4$	$g(x)$
−6	$\frac{1}{3}\lvert -6\rvert + 4$	6
−3	$\frac{1}{3}\lvert -3\rvert + 4$	5
0	$\frac{1}{3}\lvert 0\rvert + 4$	4
3	$\frac{1}{3}\lvert 3\rvert + 4$	5
6	$\frac{1}{3}\lvert 6\rvert + 4$	6

Plot on a coordinate grid.

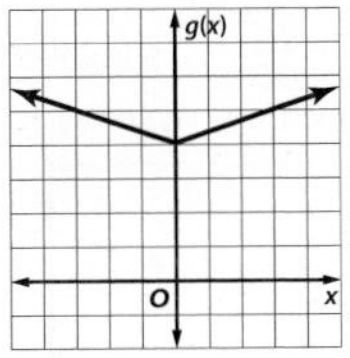

51.

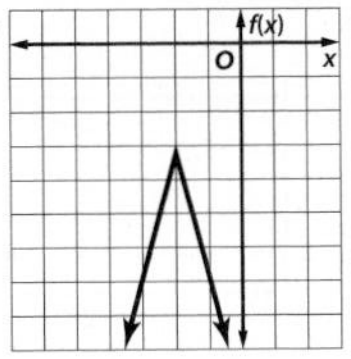

53.

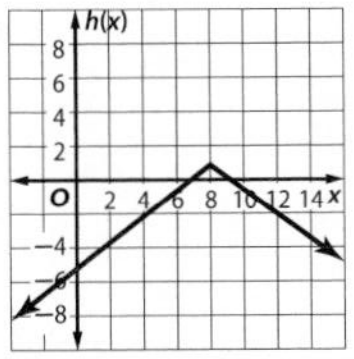

55. No; the pieces of the graph overlap vertically, so the graph fails the vertical line test.

57. $f(x) = \begin{cases} \frac{1}{2}x - 3 & \text{if } x > 6 \\ -\frac{1}{2}x - 1 & \text{if } x \leq 6 \end{cases}$

59. Sample answer: The domain of absolute value, step, quadratic, and exponential functions is all real numbers, while some piecewise functions may not be defined for all real numbers. The range of absolute value, step, quadratic, and exponential functions is limited to a portion of the real numbers, but the range of a piecewise-defined function can be all real numbers. The graphs of absolute value and quadratic functions have either one maximum and no minima or one minimum and no maxima, and both have symmetry with respect to a vertical line through the point where this maximum or minimum occurs. The graphs of absolute value, quadratic, and exponential functions have no breaks or jumps, while graphs of step functions always do and graphs of piecewise-defined functions sometimes do. **61.** C **63.** B **65.** linear **67.** exponential **69.** Positive; it means the more you study, the better your test score. **71.** −4.4 **73.** 1.2 **75.** 3.46 **77.** 12 **79.** 0.24

Chapter 9 Study Guide and Review

1. true **3.** false; parabola **5.** false; two **7.** true **9.** true **11a.** minimum **11b.** 0 **11c.** D = all real numbers; R = $y \mid y \geq 0\}$ **13a.** minimum **13b.** −4 **13c.** D = all real numbers; R = $\{y \mid y \geq -4\}$ **15a.** maximum **15b.** 16 **15c.** D = $\{t \mid 0 \leq t \leq 2\}$; R = $\{h \mid 0 \leq h \leq 16\}$ **17.** 3 **19.** −4.6, 0.6 **21.** −0.8, 3 **23.** shifted up 8 units **25.** vertical stretch **27.** vertical compression **29.** $y = 2x^2 - 3$ **31.** 1, −7 **33.** 10, −2 **35.** −0.7, 7.7 **37.** −8, 6 **39.** −0.7, 0.5 **41.** −5, 1.5 **43.** −2.5, 1.5 **45.** quadratic; $y = 3x^2$ **47.** quadratic; $y = -x^2$

49. D = all real numbers; R = all integers

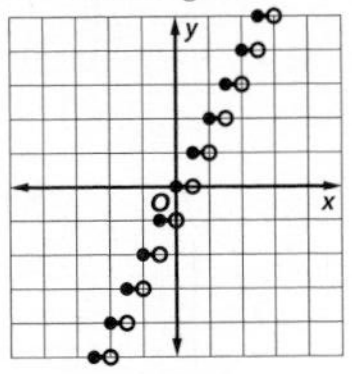

51. D = all real numbers; R = $f(x) \geq 0$

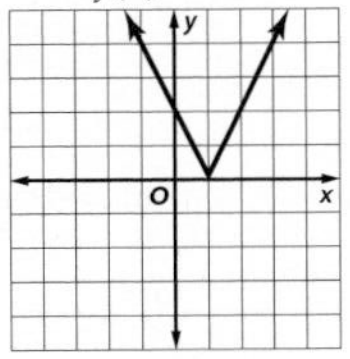

53. D = all real numbers; R = $f(x) \leq -1$ or $f(x) > 3$

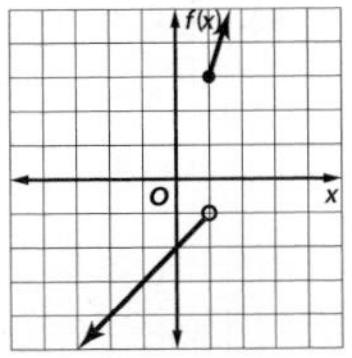

CHAPTER 10
Radical Functions and Geometry

Get Ready

1. 9.06 **3.** 3.87 **5.** 10 ft **7.** $13x - 3y$ **9.** $3m + 3n + 10$ **11.** 0, 2 **13.** 2, 5 **15.** 10

Lesson 10-1

1.

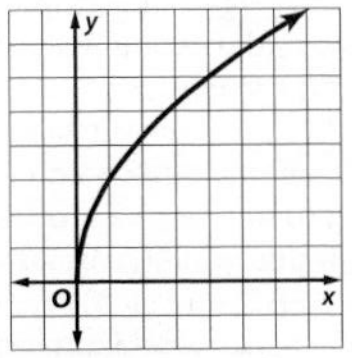

vertical stretch of $y = \sqrt{x}$;
D = $\{x \mid x \geq 0\}$,
R = $\{y \mid y \geq 0\}$

3.

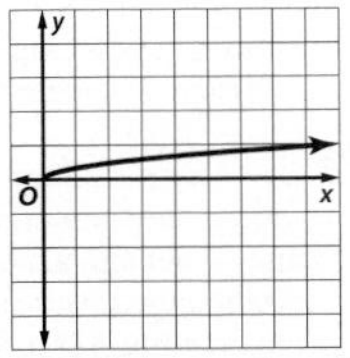

vertical compression of $y = \sqrt{x}$;
D = $\{x \mid x \geq 0\}$,
R = $\{y \mid y \geq 0\}$

5.

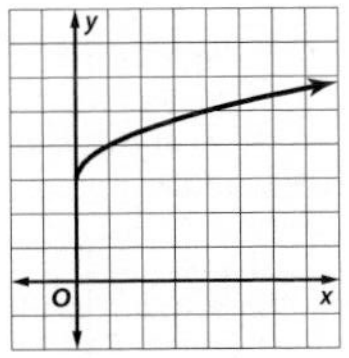

translated up 3;
D = $\{x \mid x \geq 0\}$,
R = $\{y \mid y \geq 3\}$

7.

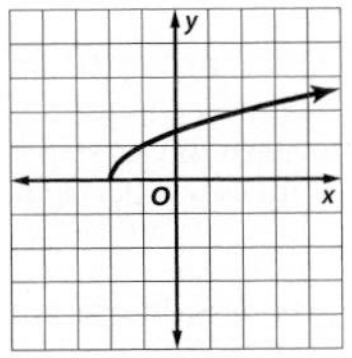

translated left 2;
D = $\{x \mid x \geq -2\}$,
R = $\{y \mid y \geq 0\}$

9.

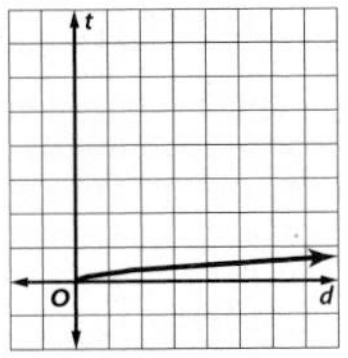

D = $\{d \mid d \geq 0\}$,
R = $\{t \mid t \geq 0\}$

11.

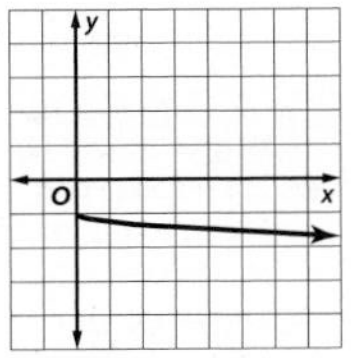

vertical compression of $\sqrt{x}$, reflected across the x-axis and translated down 1;
D = $\{x \mid x \geq 0\}$,
R = $\{y \mid y \leq -1\}$

13.

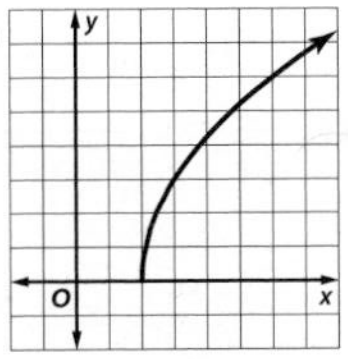

translated right 2 and vertical stretch of $\sqrt{x}$;
D = $\{x \mid x \geq 2\}$,
R = $\{y \mid y \geq 0\}$

15 Step 1: Make a table. Choose nonnegative values for x.

x	y
0	0
0.5	≈0.35
1	0.5
2	0.71
3	0.87
4	1

Step 2: Plot the points and draw a smooth curve.

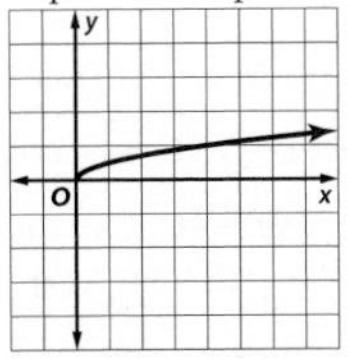

The graph is a vertical compression of $\sqrt{x}$.

The domain is $\{x \mid x \geq 0\}$. The range is $\{y \mid y \geq 0\}$.

17.

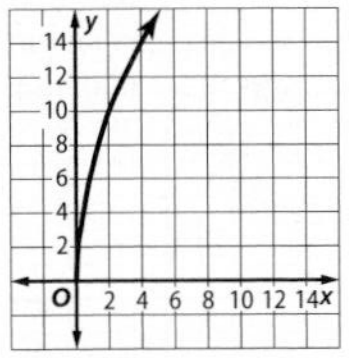

vertical stretch of $\sqrt{x}$;
D = $\{x \mid x \geq 0\}$,
R = $\{y \mid y \geq 0\}$

19.

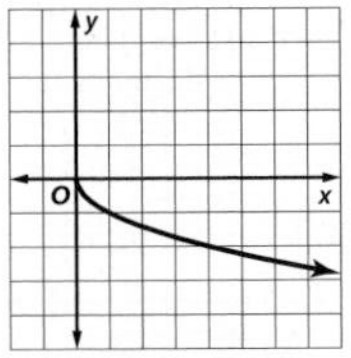

reflected across the x-axis;
D = $\{x \mid x \geq 0\}$,
R = $\{y \mid y \leq 0\}$

21.

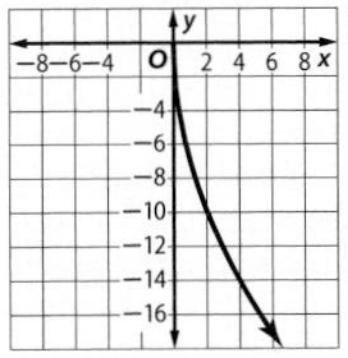

vertical stretch of $\sqrt{x}$ and reflected across the x-axis;
D = $\{x \mid x \geq 0\}$,
R = $\{y \mid y \leq 0\}$

23.

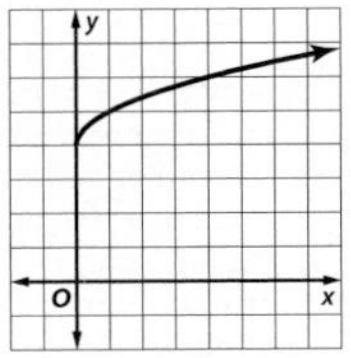

translated up 4;
D = $\{x \mid x \geq 0\}$,
R = $\{y \mid y \geq 4\}$

25.

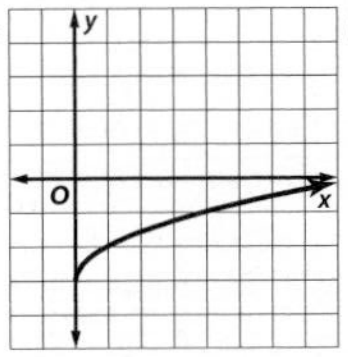

translated down 3;
D = $\{x \mid x \geq 0\}$,
R = $\{y \mid y \geq -3\}$

27.

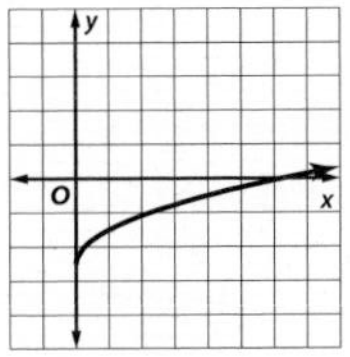

translated down 2.5;
D = $\{x \mid x \geq 0\}$,
R = $\{y \mid y \geq -2.5\}$

29.

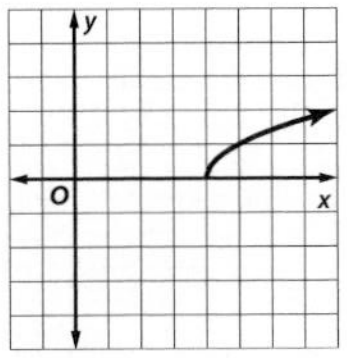

translated right 4;
D = $\{x \mid x \geq 4\}$,
R = $\{y \mid y \geq 0\}$

31.

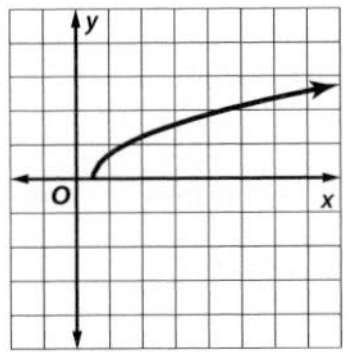

translated right 0.5;
D = $\{x \mid x \geq 0.5\}$,
R = $\{y \mid y \geq 0\}$

33. 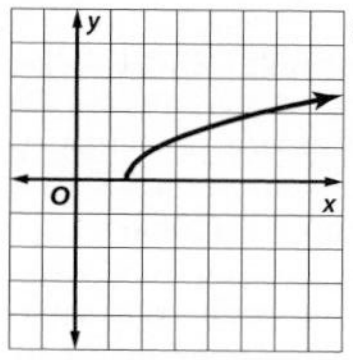
translated right 1.5; D = {x | x ≥ 1.5}, R = {y | y ≥ 0}

35. 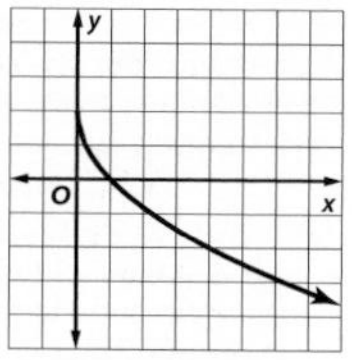
vertical stretch of $y = \sqrt{x}$, reflected across the x-axis, and translated up 2; D = {x | x ≥ 0}, R = {y | y ≤ 2}

37. 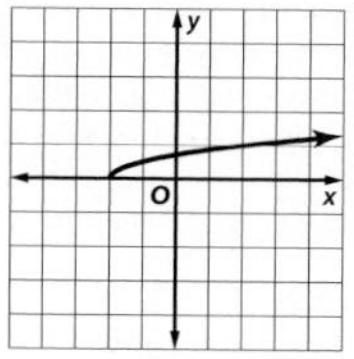
vertical compression of $y = \sqrt{x}$ and translated left 2; D = {x | x ≥ −2}, R = {y | y ≥ 0}

39. 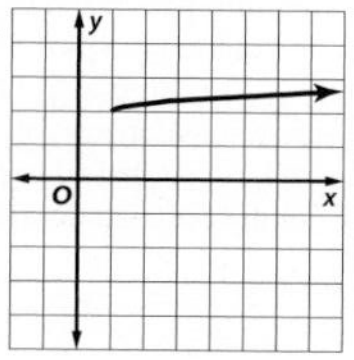
vertical compression of $y = \sqrt{x}$ and translated up 2 and right 1; D = {x | x ≥ 1}, R = {y | y ≥ 2}

41. 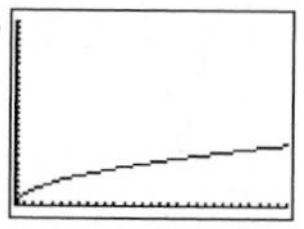
[0, 28] scl: 1 by [0, 28] scl: 1

43 **a.** Use a graphing calculator to graph the equation.

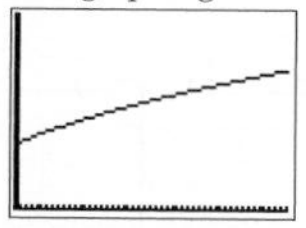
[0, 1000] scl: 20 by [0, 1000] scl: 10

b. $c = 331.5\sqrt{1 + \frac{t}{273.15}}$
$= 331.5\sqrt{1 + \frac{55}{273.15}}$
$= 331.5\sqrt{1.201}$
≈ 363.3 m/s

c. When $t = 65°C$:
$c = 331.5\sqrt{1 + \frac{t}{273.15}}$
$= 331.5\sqrt{1 + \frac{65}{273.15}}$
$= 331.5\sqrt{1.238}$
≈ 368.8 m/s

So, this increase of 10°C increases the speed by about 5.5 m/s.

45. False; sample answer: The domain of $y = \sqrt{x + 3}$ includes −1, −2, and −3.

47. Sample answer: The domain is limited because square roots of negative numbers are imaginary; therefore the radicand must be nonnegative. Since the principal square root of a nonnegative number is a nonnegative number, the range will be nonnegative.

49. $y = \sqrt{x} + 3$; it is a translation of $y = \sqrt{x}$; the other equations represent vertical stretches or compressions. **51.** The value of a is negative. For the function to have negative y-values, the value of a must be negative.

53. A **55.** D

57. 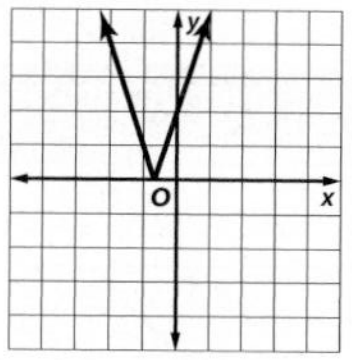

59. 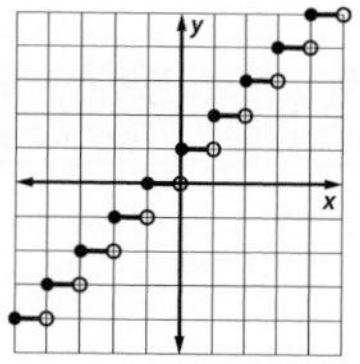

61. 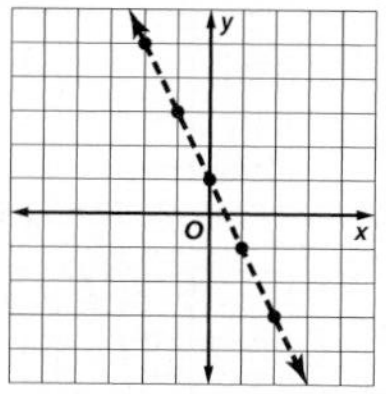
linear

63. 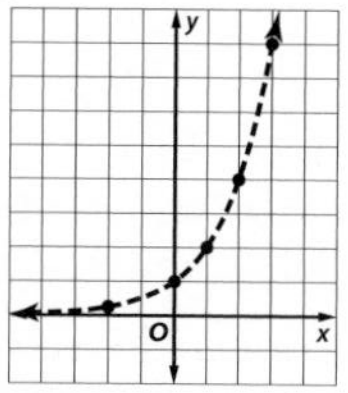
exponential

65a. 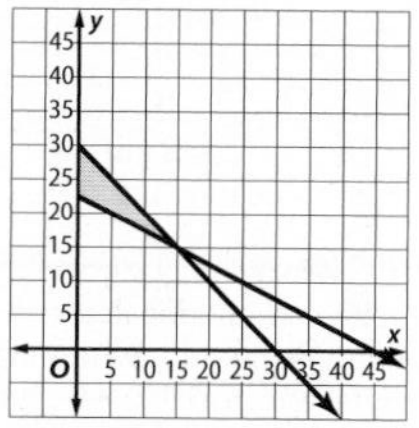

65b. Sample answer: walk: 15 min, jog: 15 min; walk: 10 min, jog: 20 min; walk: 5 min, jog: 25 min
67. $2 \cdot 2 \cdot 7 \cdot n \cdot n \cdot n$ **69.** $2 \cdot 3 \cdot 5 \cdot 5 \cdot r \cdot t$
71. $3 \cdot 3 \cdot 5 \cdot 5 \cdot a \cdot a \cdot a \cdot b \cdot b \cdot c$

Lesson 10-2

1. $2\sqrt{6}$ **3.** 10 **5.** $3\sqrt{6}$ **7.** $2x^2y^3\sqrt{15y}$
9. $3b^2|c|\sqrt{11ab}$ **11.** $\frac{9 - 3\sqrt{5}}{4}$ **13.** $\frac{2 + 2\sqrt{10}}{-9}$
15. $\frac{24 + 4\sqrt{7}}{29}$ **17.** $2\sqrt{13}$ **19.** $6\sqrt{2}$ **21.** $9\sqrt{3}$
23. $5\sqrt{2}$ **25.** $12\sqrt{14}$ **27.** $15|t|$ **29.** $2|a|b\sqrt{7b}$
31. $21m\sqrt{7mp}$ **33.** $2a^3b\sqrt{5b}$

35 **a.** $v = \sqrt{64h}$
$= \sqrt{8 \cdot 8h}$
$= \sqrt{8^2} \cdot \sqrt{h}$
$= 8\sqrt{h}$

b. $v = 8\sqrt{h}$
$= 8\sqrt{134}$
≈ 92.6 ft/s

37 $\sqrt{\frac{32}{t^4}} = \frac{\sqrt{32}}{\sqrt{t^4}}$
$= \frac{\sqrt{16 \cdot 2}}{t^2}$
$= \frac{\sqrt{16} \cdot \sqrt{2}}{t^2}$
$= \frac{4\sqrt{2}}{t^2}$

39. $\frac{2c\sqrt{51ac}}{9a}$ **41.** $\frac{3\sqrt{15}}{20}$ **43.** $\frac{35 - 7\sqrt{3}}{22}$
45. $\frac{6\sqrt{3} + 9\sqrt{2}}{2}$ **47.** $\frac{5\sqrt{6} - 5\sqrt{3}}{3}$ **49a.** $I = \frac{\sqrt{PR}}{R}$
49b. 3.9 amps

51.

Distance	3	6	9	12	15
Height	6	24	4	96	150

53. $\pm\frac{\sqrt{3}}{3}$ **55.** Sample answer: $1 + \sqrt{2}$ and $1 - \sqrt{2}$; $(1 + \sqrt{2})(1 - \sqrt{2}) = 1 - 2 = -1$ **57.** No radicals can appear in the denominator of a fraction. So, rationalize the denominator to get rid of the radicand in the denominator. Then check if any of the radicands have perfect square factors other than 1. If so, simplify. **59.** H **61.** 507.50

63. 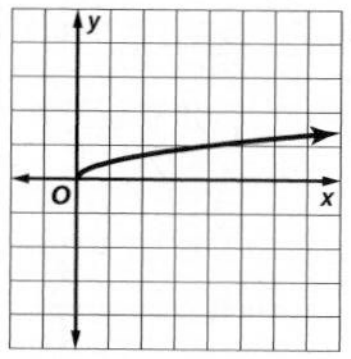
vertical compression of $y = \sqrt{x}$; D = {x | x ≥ 0}, R = {y | y ≥ 0}

65. 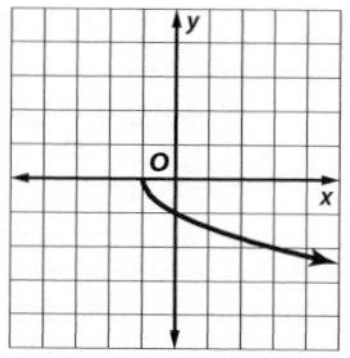
reflected across the x-axis and translated left 1 unit; D = {x | x ≥ −1}, R = {y | y ≤ 0}

67. 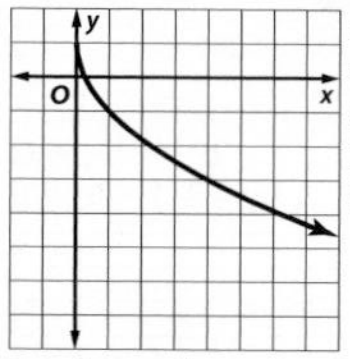
stretched vertically, reflected across the x-axis, and translated up 1 unit; D = {x | x ≥ 0}, R = {y | y ≤ 1}

69. D = {all real numbers}; R = {y | y is an integer}
71. −5, 5 **73.** 5 **75.** −0.1, 1.5 **77.** $(n - 9)(n + 9)$
79. $2x^3(x + 7)(x - 7)$ **81.** prime **83.** about 2,172,453
85. $2^3 \cdot 3$ **87.** $2^2 \cdot 3^2 \cdot 5$ **89.** $2^2 \cdot 3 \cdot 5$

Lesson 10-3

1 $3\sqrt{5} + 6\sqrt{5} = (3 + 6)\sqrt{5}$
$= 9\sqrt{5}$

3. $-5\sqrt{7}$ **5.** $8\sqrt{5}$ **7.** $5\sqrt{2} + 2\sqrt{3}$ **9.** $72\sqrt{3}$
11. $\sqrt{21} + 3\sqrt{6}$ **13.** $14.5 + 3\sqrt{15}$ **15.** $11\sqrt{6}$
17. $3\sqrt{2}$ **19.** $5\sqrt{10}$ **21.** $60 + 32\sqrt{10}$ **23.** $3\sqrt{5} + 6 - \sqrt{30} - 2\sqrt{6}$ **25.** $5\sqrt{5} + 5\sqrt{2}$ **27.** $-\frac{4\sqrt{5}}{5}$
29. $\sqrt{2}$ **31.** $14 - 6\sqrt{5}$

33 **a.** $v_0 = \sqrt{v^2 - 64h}$
$= \sqrt{(120)^2 - 64(225)}$
$= \sqrt{0}$
$= 0$ ft/s

b. Sample answer: In the formula, we are taking the square root of the difference, not the square root of each term.

35. $\sqrt{170}$; about 13 amps **37.** Irrational; irrational; no rational number could be added to or multiplied by an irrational number so that the result is rational. **39.** Sample answer: You can use the FOIL method. You multiply the first terms within the parentheses. Then you multiply the outer terms within the parentheses. Then you would multiply the inner terms within the parentheses. And, then you would multiply the last terms within each parentheses. Combine any like terms and simplify any radicals. Sample answer: $(\sqrt{2} + \sqrt{3})(\sqrt{5} + \sqrt{7}) = \sqrt{10} + \sqrt{14} + \sqrt{15} + \sqrt{21}$. **41.** C **43.** C **45.** $2\sqrt{6}$
47. $5ab^2\sqrt{2ab}$ **49.** $3cd^2f^2\sqrt{7cf}$

51. 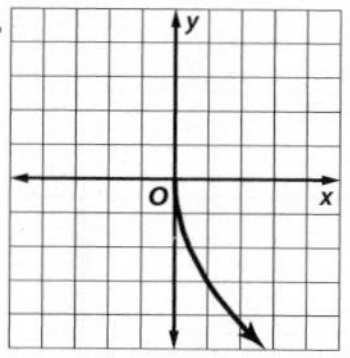
stretched vertically and reflected across the x-axis; D = {x | x ≥ 0}, R = {y | y ≤ 0}

53. 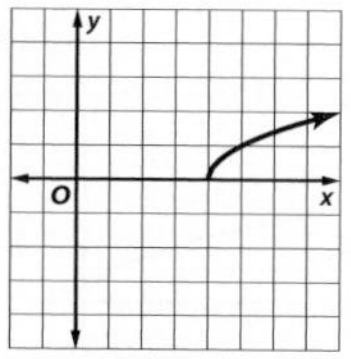
translated right 4 units; D = {x | x ≥ 4}, R = {y | y ≥ 0}

55. 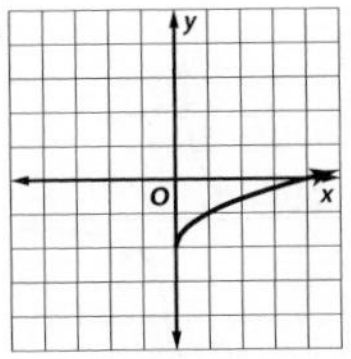

translated down 2 units; D = {x | $x \geq 0$}, R = {y | $y \geq -2$}

57. $(y + 10)(y + 3)$ **59.** $(x - 1)(x + 7)$ **61.** $(w + 12)(w - 6)$ **63.** -0.5 **65.** 18.7 **67.** 24

Lesson 10-4

1. $r = \frac{\sqrt{\pi x}}{2\pi}$ **3.** 2 **5.** 10 **7.** 6

(9)
$$\sqrt{a} + 11 = 21$$
$$\sqrt{a} = 10$$
$$(\sqrt{a})^2 = (10)^2$$
$$a = 100$$

11. 39 **13.** 17 **15.** 3 **17.** 6 **19.** 7 **21a.** 52 ft **21b.** Increases; sample answer: If the length is longer, the quotient and square root will be a greater number than before. **23.** no solution **25.** 235.2 **27.** 3

(29) a. 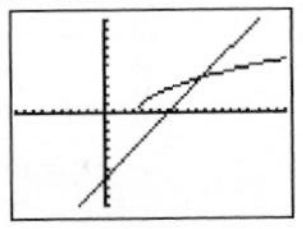

[−10, 20] scl: 1 by [−10, 10] scl: 1

c. 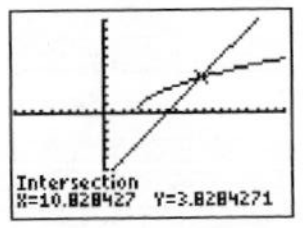

[−10, 20] scl: 1 by [−10, 10] scl: 1

d.
$$\sqrt{2x-7} = x - 7$$
$$(\sqrt{2x-7})^2 = (x-7)^2$$
$$2x - 7 = x^2 - 14x + 49$$
$$0 = x^2 - 16x + 56$$
$$x = \frac{-b \pm \sqrt{b^2 - 4ac}}{2a}$$
$$= \frac{16 \pm \sqrt{(16)^2 - 4(1)(56)}}{2(1)}$$
$$= \frac{16 \pm \sqrt{32}}{2}$$
$$\approx 10.83 \text{ and } 5.17$$

When checking, 5.17 does not work, so the answer is about 10.83 which is the same as we got using the calculator.

31. Jada; Fina had the wrong sign for $2b$ in the fourth step. **33.** Sample answer: In the first equation, you have to isolate the radical first by subtracting 1 from each side. Then square each side to find the value of x. In the second equation, the radical is already isolated, so square each side to start. Then subtract 1 from each side to solve for x. **35.** Sometimes; the equation is true for $x \geq 2$, but false for $x < 2$. **37.** Sample answer: Use addition/subtraction to isolate the term containing the radical on one side. Multiply/divide to change the coefficient of the radical to ±1. Square each side of the equation to eliminate the radical. Solve the resulting equation using the most appropriate method. Check the answers for any extraneous solutions. **39.** C **41.** D **43.** $4\sqrt{3}$ **45.** $42\sqrt{2}$

47. $\frac{c^2\sqrt{5cd}}{2|d^3|}$ **49.** about 1.3 s and 4.7 s **51.** $(2p + 3)(3p - 2)$ **53.** Sample answer: Triangles can be used to represent objects or situations with a triangular shape, and trigonometry or the Pythagorean Theorem can be used to find unknown values. **55.** $(2a + 3)(a - 6)$ **57.** Yes; $4x^3$ is the product of a number and three variables. **59.** No; $4n + 5p$ shows addition, not multiplication alone of numbers and variables. **61.** Yes; $\frac{1}{5}abc^{14}$ is the product of a number, $\frac{1}{5}$, and several variables. **63.** 1,000,000 **65.** $64v^2$ **67.** $1000y^6$

Lesson 10-5

1. 5 **3.** 18.03 **5a.** about 127 ft **5b.** about 117 ft **5c.** about 46 ft **7.** yes **9.** no

(11)
$$a^2 + b^2 = c^2$$
$$(2)^2 + b^2 = 12^2$$
$$4 + b^2 = 144$$
$$b^2 = 140$$
$$b \approx 11.83$$

13. 29.66 **15.** 5.29 **17.** 7.21

(19)
$$a^2 + b^2 = c^2$$
$$(30)^2 + (36)^2 = c^2$$
$$900 + 1296 = c^2$$
$$2196 = c^2$$
$$46.9 \approx c$$

The diagonal of the TV stand is about 46.9 inches which is larger than 42 inches, so the TV will fit.

21. no; no **23.** no; no **25.** no, no **27.** yes; yes **29a.** about 20.20 units **29b.** 111.1 units^2 **31.** a 30-ft ladder **33.** 8.06 **35.** $5\sqrt{3}$ in. or about 8.66 in. **37.** about 6.7 ft

(39)
$$a^2 + b^2 = c^2$$
$$(8)^2 + x^2 = (x + 2)^2$$
$$64 + x^2 = x^2 + 4x + 4$$
$$64 = 4x + 4$$
$$60 = 4x$$
$$15 = x$$

So, $b = 15$ and $c = 15 + 2$, or 17

41. $a = 65; b = 72$ **43.** $a = 9; b = 40; c = 41$ **45a.** 5 units, 8 units; $\left(\frac{5}{2}, 2\right)$, (4, 5)

45b. $|x_2 - x_1|$ units, $|y_2 - y_1|$ units; $\left(\frac{x_1 + x_2}{2}, y\right)$, $\left(x, \frac{y_1 + y_2}{2}\right)$ **45c.** $\left(\frac{x_1 + x_2}{2}, \frac{y_1 + y_2}{2}\right)$ **45d.** $\sqrt{(x_2 - x_1)^2 + (y_2 - y_1)^2}$ units **47.** $8\sqrt{2}$

49. Sample answer: 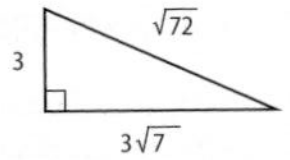

51. C **53.** \$88 **55.** 256 **57.** 10 **59.** 3 **61.** $7\sqrt{3}$ **63.** $10\sqrt{7}$ **65.** $12\sqrt{5} - 5\sqrt{3}$ **67.** translated down 8 **69.** reflected across the x-axis, translated up 5 **71.** reflected across the x-axis, stretched vertically **73.** 3 seconds **75.** $x^2 - 13x + 36$ **77.** $p^2 - 8p - 20$ **79.** $40d^2 + 31d + 6$ **81.** 20 **83.** 8

Lesson 10-6

1. $\sin A = \frac{24}{25}$; $\cos A = \frac{7}{25}$; $\tan A = \frac{24}{7}$

(3)
$$\sin A = \frac{\text{opposite}}{\text{hypotenuse}} = \frac{5}{13}$$
$$\cos A = \frac{\text{adjacent}}{\text{hypotenuse}} = \frac{12}{13}$$
$$\tan A = \frac{\text{opposite}}{\text{adjacent}} = \frac{5}{12}$$

5. 0.6018 **7.** 0.2493 **9.** $m\angle X \approx 51°$; $XY \approx 4.4$; $YZ \approx 5.4$ **11.** $m\angle Q \approx 60°$; $RQ \approx 2.9$; $PQ \approx 5.8$ **13.** about 11,326.2 ft **15.** 66° **17.** 33° **19.** $\sin B = \frac{5}{13}$, $\cos B = \frac{12}{13}$, $\tan B = \frac{5}{12}$ **21.** 0.0349 **23.** 0.7193 **25.** 0.9563 **27.** 0.5

(29) Step 1: Find the measure of $\angle Y$.
$$180° - (90° + 47°) = 43°$$
Step 2: Find $\overline{XY}$ or z. Since you are given the measure of the side opposite $\angle X$, and are finding the measure of the hypotenuse, use the sine ratio.
$$\sin 47° = \frac{16}{z}$$
$$z \sin 47° = 16$$
$$z = \frac{16}{\sin 47°}$$
$$z \approx 21.9 \text{ or } XY \approx 21.9$$
Step 3: Find $\overline{XZ}$ or y. Since you are given the measure of the side opposite $\angle X$, and are finding the measure of the side adjacent to $\angle X$, use the tangent ratio.
$$\tan 47° = \frac{16}{y}$$
$$y \tan 47° = 16$$
$$y = \frac{16}{\tan 47°}$$
$$y \approx 14.9 \text{ or } XZ \approx 14.9$$

31. $m\angle R = 76°$; $QR \approx 7.2$; $PR \approx 1.7$ **33.** $m\angle Y = 39°$; $WU \approx 11.3$; $UY \approx 18.0$ **35.** about 53 ft **37.** 62° **39.** 31° **41.** 50°

(43)
$$\tan 8° = \frac{5000}{x}$$
$$x \tan 8° = 5000$$
$$x = \frac{5000}{\tan 8°}$$
$$x \approx 35{,}577 \text{ ft}$$

45. $\sin A = \frac{\sqrt{7}}{4}$; $\tan A = \frac{\sqrt{7}}{3}$ **47.** $\cos A = \frac{\sqrt{15}}{4}$; $\tan A = \frac{\sqrt{15}}{15}$ **49.** about 0.5 mi **51.** $a = 5$; $c = 7.3$ **53.** Sample answer: Triangles can be used to represent objects or situations with a triangular shape, and trigonometry or the Pythagorean Theorem can be used to find unknown values. **55.** Use the acute angle given and the measure of the known side to set up one of the trigonometric ratios. The sine ratio uses the opposite side and hypotenuse of the triangle. The cosine ratio uses the adjacent side and hypotenuse of the triangle. The tangent ratio uses the opposite and adjacent sides of the triangle. Set up the ratio and solve for the unknown measure. **57.** F **59a.** increase **59b.** Sample answer: The sum of their squares is 16^2 or 256. **59c.** about 15.7 ft **61.** 11 **63.** 6.71 **65.** 5.20 **67.** The amount of sales must be more than \$260,000. **69.** 8 **71.** 4.62

Chapter 10 Study Guide and Review

1. false; Sample answer: 3, 4, and 5 **3.** true **5.** false; longest **7.** false; {x | $x \geq 0$} **9.** true

11. 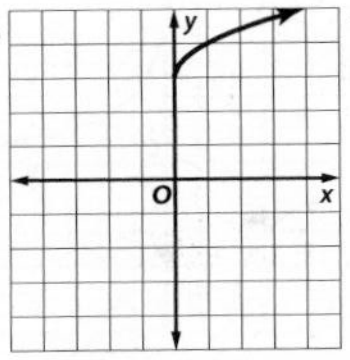

translated up 3 units; D = {x | $x \geq 0$}, R = {y | $y \geq 3$}

13. 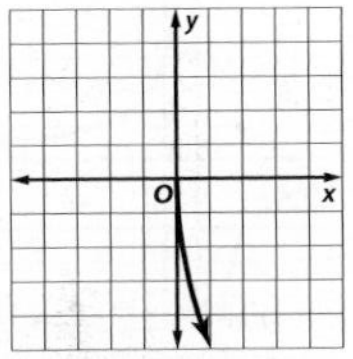

stretched vertically and reflected across the x-axis; D = {x | $x \geq 0$}, R = {y | $y \leq 0$}

15. 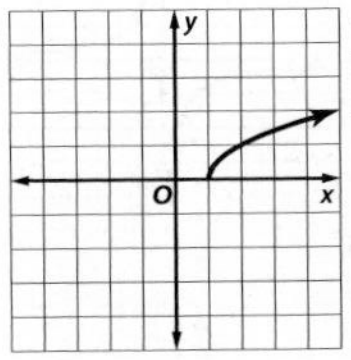

translated right 1 unit; D = {x | $x \geq 1$}, R = {y | $y \geq 0$}

17. 9.5 in. **19.** $2|b|\sqrt{5ab}$ **21.** 36 **23.** $2\sqrt{2} + 3$ **25.** $\frac{\sqrt{30}}{10}$ **27.** $\frac{5\sqrt{7} - 30}{-29}$ **29.** $-2\sqrt{6} + 11\sqrt{3}$ **31.** $4\sqrt{3x}$ **33.** $5\sqrt{2} + 3\sqrt{6}$ **35.** $24\sqrt{10} + 8\sqrt{2} + 6\sqrt{15} + 2\sqrt{3}$

37. no solution **39.** 32 **41.** 12 **43.** 1600 ft **45.** yes **47.** no **49.** yes **51.** no **53.** $\cos A = \frac{5}{13}, \sin A = \frac{12}{13}, \tan A = \frac{12}{5}$ **55.** 6 ft

CHAPTER 11
Rational Functions and Equations

Chapter 11 Get Ready

1. $\frac{8}{3}$ **3.** $\frac{21}{2}$ **5.** $\frac{10}{3}$ or $3\frac{1}{3}$ inches **7.** $2x(x-2)$ **9.** $2c^2d(1-2d)$ **11.** $(m-12)(m+11)$ **13.** $(3x-4)(2x+1)$

Lesson 11-1

1. Direct; the data in the table can be represented by the equation $y = 2x$. **3.** Inverse; $xy = 4$.

5.

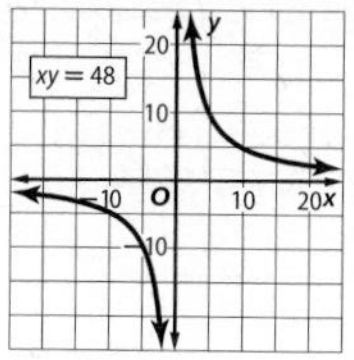

7.

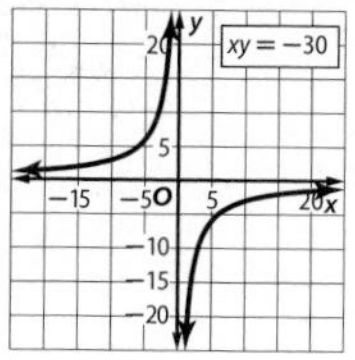

9 $x_1y_1 = x_2y_2$
$(4)(8) = x_2(2)$
$32 = 2x_2$
$16 = x_2$

11. −7.5

13a.

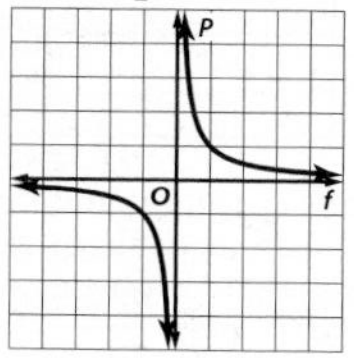

13b. 5 to −2.5 diopters **15.** Direct; $y = -3x$ **17.** Inverse; $xy = -40$ **19.** Inverse; $xy = \frac{1}{4}$ **21.** Direct; $y = 9x$

23. $xy = 72$

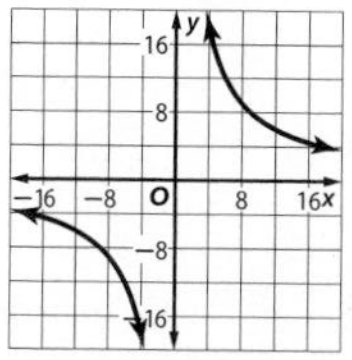

25. $xy = 12$

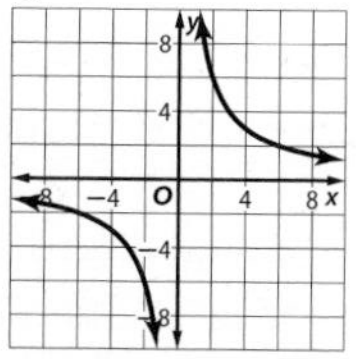

27.

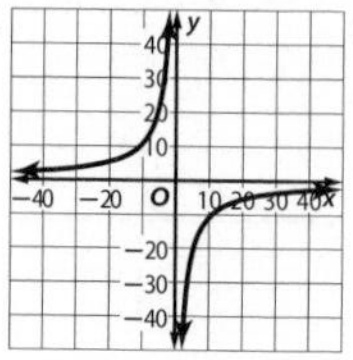

$xy = -108$

29. 15 **31.** −3 **33.** 9.6

35 $x_1y_1 = x_2y_2$
$(420)(523) = (707)y_2$
$219{,}660 = 707y_2$
$311 \approx y_2$
approximately 311 cycles per second

37. Direct; the number of lemonades times the cost per lemonade equals the total cost. So the ratio $\frac{\text{total cost}}{\text{number of lemonades}}$ is a constant \$1.50. **39.** Inverse; the number of friends times the number of tokens per person equals the constant 30. **41.** Inverse; $xy = 21$ **43.** Direct; $y = \frac{1}{2}x$

45 $x_1y_1 = x_2y_2$
$(6)(9.2) = x_2(3)$
$55.2 = 3x_2$
$18.4 = x_2$

47. 2.5 **49.** \$4

51a.

Hours per Week h	Number of Weeks w
1	40
2	20
4	10
5	8
8	5
10	4

51b. The number of weeks decreases.

51c. $hw = 40$ or $w = \frac{40}{h}$

Driving

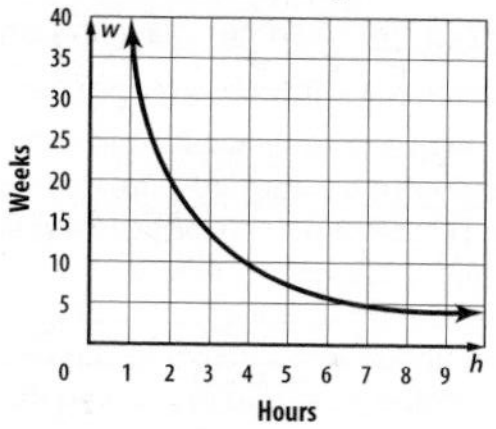

53. direct variation **55.** Sample answer: Newton's Law of Gravitational Force is an example of an inverse variation that models real-world situations. The gravitational force exerted on two objects is inversely proportional to the square of the distances between the two objects. The force exerted on the two objects, times the square of the distance between the two objects, is equal to the gravitational constant times the masses of the two objects. **57.** B **59.** C **61.** $\sin A = 0.7241, \cos A = 0.6897, \tan A = 1.05$ **63.** $\sin A = 0.8182, \cos A = 0.5750, \tan A = 1.4230$ **65.** $\frac{9}{10}$ **67.** 1 **69.** no solution **71.** 7^2 or 49 **73.** $\frac{q^4}{2p^5}$ **75.** $\frac{4a^4b^2}{c^6}$ **77.** $\frac{1}{mn}$

Lesson 11-2

1. $x = 0$ **3.** $x = 1$

5.

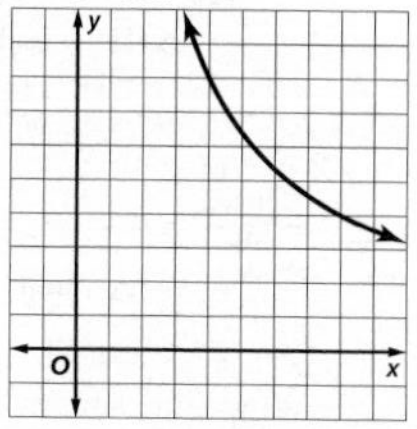

7. $x = 0; y = -1$

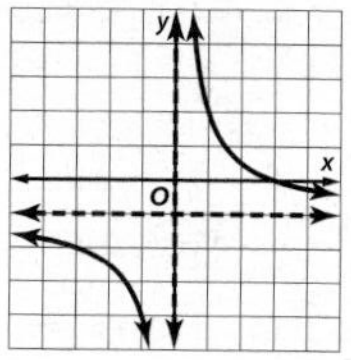

9. $x = -2; y = 0$

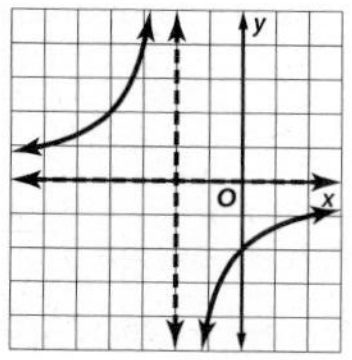

11. $x = -1; y = -5$

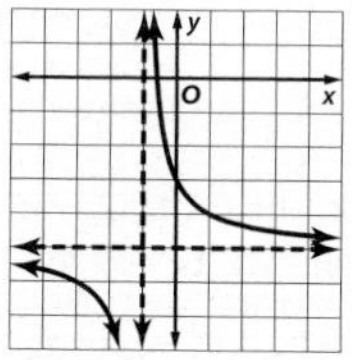

13. $x = 8$ **15.** $x = -6$ **17.** $x = -5$ **19.** $x = -7$

21.

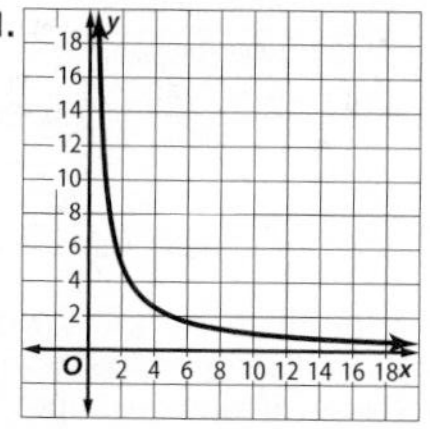

23 Step 1: Identify and graph the asymptotes using dashed lines.
vertical asymptote: $x = 0$
horizontal asymptote: $y = 0$

Step 2: Make a table of values and plot the points. Then connect them.

x	−2	−1	1	2
y	$\frac{3}{2}$	3	−3	$-\frac{3}{2}$

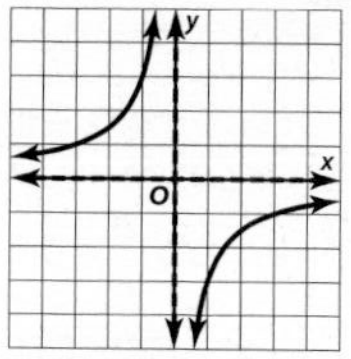

25. $x = 0; y = -2$

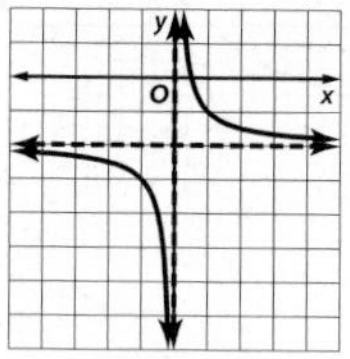

27. $x = 2; y = 0$

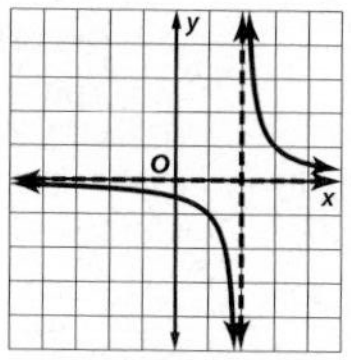

29. $x = 1; y = 0$

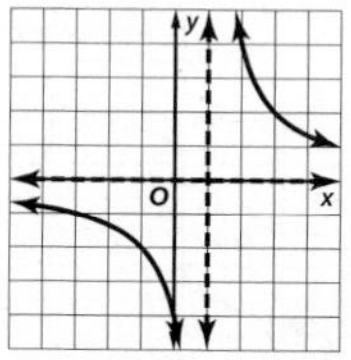

31. $x = 1; y = -2$

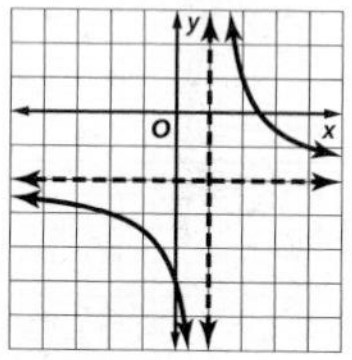

33. $x = -4; y = 3$

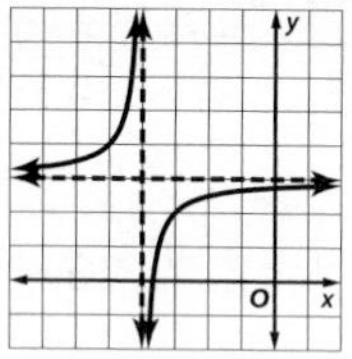

35a. $x = 3$ and $y = 2$ **35b.** $y = \frac{1}{x-3} + 2$
37a. Sample answer: The total cost of the trip equals the cost of a ticket plus the cost of the star-naming package divided by the number of people. **37b.** $y = \frac{95}{p} + 8.50$

37c.

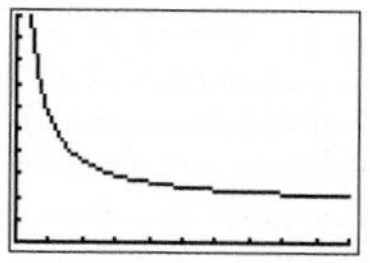

[0, 50] scl: 5 by [0, 50] scl: 5

Sample answer: The end behavior indicates that as the number of people increases, the cost per person approaches 0. Since there is no x-intercept, cost per person will never be 0.

37d. Sample answer: 15 people

39. 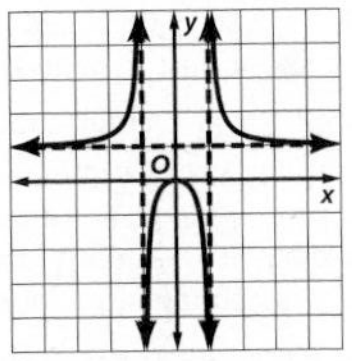

$x = -1, x = 1; y = 1$

41 a. The domain will be positive values since negative values do not make sense for the base of a trapezoid.
The range must also be positive values since negative values do not make sense for the height.
D = {all positive real numbers}
R = {all positive real numbers}

b. Step 1: Identify and graph the asymptotes using dashed lines.
vertical asymptote: $b_1 = -8$
horizontal asymptote: $h = 0$
Step 2: Make a table of values and plot the points. Then connect them.

b_1	2	4	6	8
h	12.8	10.7	9.1	8

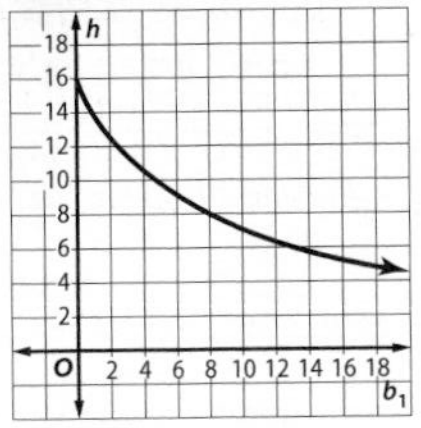

c. When $b_1 = 10$, h will be about 7 units.

43. The graph of $y = \frac{1}{x+5} - 2$ is the graph of $y = \frac{1}{x}$ translated 5 units to the left and 2 units down. **45.** False; sample answer: The graph of $y = \frac{1}{x}$ has no x- or y-intercepts. **47.** Sample answer: Vertical asymptotes occur at values that make the denominator 0; horizontal asymptotes occur at $y = c$ for any rational function of the form $y = \frac{a}{x-b} + c$. **49.** 45 seconds **51.** D **53.** 78° **55.** 40° **57.** 60° **59.** 61.85 **61.** 10.54 **63.** 9.22 **65.** $\sqrt{465}$ or about 21.56 mi **67.** $(w + 16)(w - 3)$ **69.** $(3 + a)(24 + a)$ **71.** $(d - 2)(d - 5)$ **73.** $(n + 9)(n - 6)$ **75.** $(4b - 3)(6b + 1)$ **77.** $2(x - 3)(3x + 2)$

Lesson 11-3

1. 4, −4 **3.** 16.9 units of force

5 $\frac{(-3r)(10r^4)}{6r^5} = \frac{-30r^5}{6r^5}$
$= -5r^0$
$= -5$

The excluded value is when $6r^5 = 0$, or when $r = 0$.

7. $x + 7; -4$ **9.** $-\frac{3}{9+y}; -9, 9$ **11.** 3 **13.** 1, −1 **15.** 3, −8 **17.** $\frac{2\pi(5t)}{\pi(5t)^2} = \frac{2}{5t}; 0$ **19.** $\frac{16}{n^2}; n \neq 0, p \neq 0$ **21.** $-2c; 0$ **23.** $\frac{a}{a-6}; 6, -3$ **25.** $x - 4; -8$ **27.** $\frac{2p}{p+7}; 7, -7$ **29.** $\frac{-(8+c)}{c+1}; 8, -1$

31 $f(x) = \frac{x^2 + 3x - 4}{x^2 + 9x + 20}$

$0 = \frac{x^2 + 3x - 4}{x^2 + 9x + 20}$ $f(x) = 0$

$0 = \frac{(x+4)(x-1)}{(x+4)(x+5)}$ Factor

$0 = \frac{\cancel{(x+4)}(x-1)}{\cancel{(x+4)}(x+5)}$ Divide out common factors

$0 = \frac{x-1}{x+5}$ Simplify.

When $x = 1$, the numerator becomes 0, which makes $f(x) = 0$. Therefore, the zero of the function is 1.

33. 2, 4 **35.** 0, 6 **37a.** $\frac{250\pi}{t}$ **37b.** about 157 ft/min **39.** $\frac{4x^4 - 5y^2}{y^3}; x, y \neq 0$

41 a. Surface area: $2(2x^2) + 2(x^2) + 2(2x^2)$
$= 4x^2 + 2x^2 + 4x^2$
$= 10x^2$
Volume: $2x(x)(x) = 2x^3$
So, the ratio is $\frac{10x^2}{2x^3} = \frac{5}{x}$.
The excluded value is when $2x^3 = 0$, or when $x = 0$.

b. Surface area: $2\pi a^2 + 2\pi ab$
Volume: $\pi a^2 b$
So, the ratio is $\frac{2\pi a^2 + 2\pi ab}{\pi a^2 b} = \frac{2\pi a^2}{\pi a^2 b} + \frac{2\pi ab}{\pi a^2 b}$
$= \frac{2a + 2b}{ab}$
The excluded value is when $\pi a^2 b = 0$, or when $a = 0$ or $b = 0$.

43. No; Colleen did not show the simplified expression, and Sanson used the simplified expression to find the excluded value. **45.** Every polynomial P can be written as $\frac{P}{1}$, where the numerator and denominator are polynomials; hence every polynomial is also a rational expression. **47.** No; the numerator and denominator have $x - 2$ as a common factor. **49.** C **51.** G **53.** 0 **55.** 3 **57.** 20 **59.** 5 **61.** 8.4 in. **63.** $3\sqrt{2}$ **65.** $8\sqrt{2}$ **67.** $2|a|\sqrt{10}$ **69.** $\frac{\sqrt{6}}{3}$ **71.** $2x$ **73.** 1 **75.** $9qt$

Lesson 11-4

1. $4x$ **3.** $\frac{t}{6(t-5)}$ **5.** 6.16 ft/min **7.** $\frac{2}{3x}$ **9.** $\frac{1}{6}$

11 $\frac{10n^2}{4} \cdot \frac{2}{n} = \frac{5n}{1} \cdot \frac{1}{1}$
$= 5n$

13. $9x^4z$ **15.** $3(t + 2)$ **17.** $k + 6$ **19.** $4n$ **21a.** about \$24.66 **21b.** about \$26.09 **23.** x^4y **25.** $\frac{9b^3}{2}$ **27.** $\frac{b-2}{(b+5)(2b+3)}$ **29.** $\frac{x}{2(x-4)}$ **31.** $\frac{(r+2)^2}{4}$ **33.** 15 mi/h **35a.** $\frac{1250 \text{ km}}{1} \cdot \frac{1 \text{ mi}}{1.609 \text{ km}} \cdot \frac{1 \text{ hr}}{540 \text{ mi}}$ **35b.** 1.4 h **37.** 7,744,000 yd²/mo **39.** about 31.4 mi/h **41.** 6.1 c/min **43.** $\frac{1 \text{ cup}}{1 \text{ beat}} \cdot \frac{70 \text{ beats}}{1 \text{ minute}} \cdot \frac{1 \text{ gallon}}{16 \text{ cups}} \cdot \frac{60 \text{ minutes}}{1 \text{ hour}} = 262.5$ gal/h

45 $\frac{\$9.80}{1 \text{ hour}} \cdot \frac{15 \text{ hours}}{\text{week}} \cdot \frac{52 \text{ weeks}}{\text{year}} = \frac{\$7644}{\text{year}}$
This answer represents earning per year.

47. about 71.6 mi/h; converting 32 meters per second to miles per hour **49.** about 52,506.7 ft/s

51 a. $\frac{27 \text{ rotations}}{1 \text{ minute}} \cdot \frac{1 \text{ minute}}{60 \text{ seconds}} \cdot \frac{2\pi(3.1) \text{ meters}}{\text{rotation}}$

b. $\frac{27 \text{ rotations}}{1 \text{ minute}} \cdot \frac{1 \text{ minute}}{60 \text{ seconds}} \cdot \frac{2\pi(3.1) \text{ meters}}{\text{rotation}}$
$\approx \frac{8.8 \text{ meters}}{\text{second}}$
This means that the room moves about 8.8 meters per second.

53. Neither; Tamika did not multiply by the reciprocal, and Mei incorrectly factored out the 2 in $2x + 6$. **55.** $\frac{x-3}{x+7}$ **57.** Sample answer: The height of a cylinder when you know an expression for the volume and radius; $\frac{V}{\pi r^2} = h$; $V = \pi(x^3 - 6x^2 + 9x)$, $r = (x - 3)$. **59.** Sample answer: Write ratios comparing the number of days in one year and the number of hours in one day. Then multiply the ratios: $\frac{365 \text{ days}}{1 \text{ year}} \cdot \frac{24 \text{ hours}}{1 \text{ day}}$; 8760 hours.

61. F **63.** A **65.** $\frac{g^2}{3h}; g \neq 0, h \neq 0$ **67.** $y + 8; -2$ **69.** $\frac{z+2}{z-2}; 2, 1$ **71.** $x = 0, y = 5$ **73.** $x = -3, y = 0$ **75.** $x = 8, y = -3$ **77.** 0 **79.** 2 **81.** 3 **83.** $\{p \mid 28 \leq p \leq 32\}$ **85.** $(x - 2)(x - 3)$ **87.** $(x + 4)(3x - 5)$ **89.** $4(x + 2)(2x - 5)$

Lesson 11-5

1 $(8a^2 + 20a) \div 4a = \frac{8a^2}{4a} + \frac{20a}{4a}$
$= 2a + 5$

3. $2n^2 - n + \frac{5}{2n}$ **5.** $x - 4$ **7.** $3 + \frac{250}{x+50}$ **9.** $4y + \frac{3}{y+2}$ **11.** $3n^2 + n - 4 + \frac{4}{3n-1}$ **13.** $a^2 + 4a - 18$ **15.** $2n - 4 + \frac{1}{n}$ **17.** $\frac{3}{2}m + \frac{5}{6}$ **19.** $x - 8$

21 $(k^2 - 5k - 24) \div (k - 8) = \frac{(k^2 - 5k - 24)}{(k-8)}$
$= \frac{(k-8)(k+3)}{k-8}$
$= k + 3$

23. a^2 **25.** $2t - 1$ **27.** $2h^2 - 3$ **29.** $-n + 18 + \frac{850}{n}$ **31.** $a + 5 + \frac{8}{a-1}$ **33.** $4n + 5 + \frac{16}{n-2}$ **35.** $t^2 - 4t + 14 - \frac{60}{t+4}$ **37.** $2c^2 + c + 2 - \frac{1}{4c-2}$ **39.** $x + 3$ **41.** $x^2 - 2x + 15 - \frac{16}{x+2}$

43a. 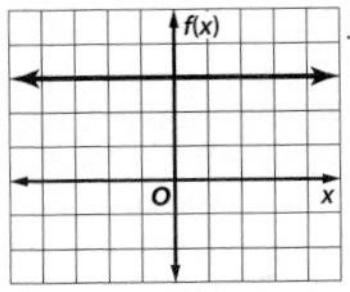

$f(x) = 3 + \frac{7}{x-1}$

43b. 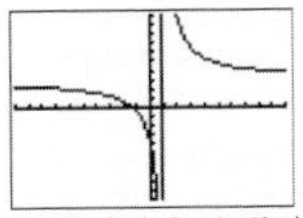
[−10, 10] scl: 1 by [−10, 10] scl:1

43c. The graph of the quotient ignoring the remainder is an asymptote of the graph of the function. **43d.** As x approaches 1 from the left, y approaches negative infinity. As x approaches 1 from the right, y approaches positive infinity.

45 a. Words: 212° decreases by 0.9 for every 500 feet above sea level.
Equation: $T = 212 - 0.9\left(\frac{x}{500}\right)$

b. $212 - 0.9\left(\frac{x}{500}\right) = 212 - 0.9\left(\frac{14{,}494}{500}\right)$
$= 212 - 26.1$
$= 185.9°$ F

47. Andrea; Alvin did not take into account the missing term. **49.** Sample answer: $(a^2 + 4a - 22) \div (a - 3)$; The polynomial $a^2 + 4a - 22$ is prime, so the problem can be solved by using long division. **51.** A **53.** G **55.** $6x$ **57.** $\frac{t}{6(t+4)}$ **59.** −2 **61.** no zero **63.** 81 **65.** 9 **67.** −10, −2 **69.** −0.8, 1 **71.** −0.4, 3.9 **73a.** 6 ft

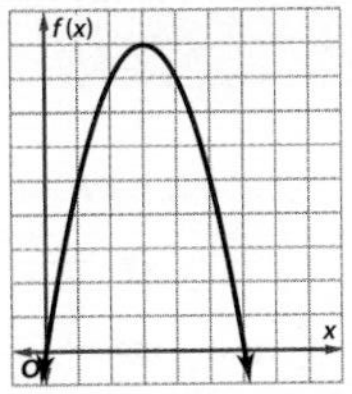

73b. 9 ft **75.** $-2cd + d^2$

Selected Answers and Solutions

Lesson 11-6

1. $\frac{5}{7n}$ **3.** $\frac{16r}{9-r}$ **5.** $24t^2$ **7.** $(x-7)(x-1)(x+2)$
9. $\frac{15y+8x}{20xy}$ **11.** $\frac{16d+5c}{6cd}$ **13.** $\frac{x^2-x+9}{x^2-x-6}$

(15) $\frac{a}{4}+\frac{3a}{4}=\frac{a+3a}{4}$
$=\frac{4a}{4}$
$=a$

17. $\frac{2y}{3}$ **19.** $\frac{8b+3a}{ab}$ **21.** $\frac{c-8}{2c-1}$ **23.** $\frac{1}{2}$ **25.** $\frac{-w+5}{8w}$
27. x^3y^2 **29.** $(3r-1)(r+2)$ **31.** $(x+6)(x+3)$
33. $\frac{27}{20x}$ **35.** $\frac{15b+2a}{10ab}$ **37.** $\frac{7-4k}{4(k+2)}$ **39.** $\frac{-2t+28r}{7rt}$
41. $\frac{d^2+6d+35}{(d+5)(d-1)}$ **43.** $\frac{18-10t}{15t^2}$ **45.** $\frac{w^2-4w-3}{(w+4)(w-5)}$
47. $\frac{-x^2-4x-9}{(x+3)(x+5)}$ **49a.** $\frac{2}{w}+\frac{2}{2.5w}$; $\frac{7}{2.5w}$ **49b.** 48 min
51. $\frac{a+9}{2a+18}$ or $\frac{1}{2}$

(53) $\frac{x+5}{x^2-4}-\frac{3}{x^2-4}=\frac{x+5-3}{x^2-4}$
$=\frac{x+2}{(x+2)(x-2)}$
$=\frac{1}{x-2}$

55. $k+5$ **57.** $\frac{1}{x-1}$ **59.** $\frac{a-6}{3}$ **61.** $\frac{2x^3-16x+1}{x^4}$
63. $\frac{15x^2-11x-7}{9x^3+51x^2-80x+28}$ **65a.** $\frac{9200}{3x}$ **65b.** about 76 min 40 seconds **67.** 8

(69) **a.** $t=D/r$
Day 1: $t=\frac{9+x}{10}$
Day 2: $t=\frac{5+3x}{10}$
So, the total for the 2 days was
$\frac{9+x}{10}+\frac{5+3x}{10}=\frac{9+x+5+3x}{10}$
$=\frac{14+4x}{10}$
$=\frac{7+2x}{5}$

b. $\frac{7+2x}{5}=\frac{7+2(2)}{5}$
$=\frac{7+4}{5}$
$=\frac{11}{5}$ or 2.2 Marina rode her bike 2.2 hours on those 2 days.

71. $\frac{4-7y}{21y-6}$ **73.** always; $\frac{a}{x}+\frac{b}{y}=\frac{a}{x}\cdot\frac{y}{y}+\frac{b}{y}\cdot\frac{x}{x}=\frac{ay}{xy}+\frac{bx}{yx}=\frac{ay+bx}{xy}$, $x, y \neq 0$ **75.** First, factor −1 out of one of the denominators so that it is like the other. Then rewrite the denominator without parentheses. Finally, add or subtract the numerators and write the result over the like denominator. **77.** C **79.** C **81.** $5y^2+\frac{14}{3}$
83. about 15.7 mi/h **85.** 5 **87.** 11.62 **89.** 1.23×10^4
91. 1.255×10^6 **93.** $\frac{2}{3x}$ **95.** $\frac{4}{y+1}$

Lesson 11-7

1. $\frac{2+4n}{n}$ **3.** $\frac{6t+11}{t+1}$ **5a.** $\frac{2\frac{1}{2}\text{ mi}}{\frac{1}{3}\text{ h}}$ **5b.** $\frac{15}{2}$ or $7\frac{1}{2}$ mi/h
7. $\frac{3}{25}$ **9.** $\frac{2y^2}{x}$ **11.** $\frac{1}{(x+y)(r+s)}$ **13.** $\frac{p+3}{p^2-p-2}$

(15) $\frac{p-7}{2p}=\frac{p(2p)}{2p}-\frac{7}{2p}$
$=\frac{2p^2}{2p}-\frac{7}{2p}$
$=\frac{2p^2-7}{2p}$

17. $\frac{3h^2+h+1}{h}$ **19.** $\frac{n^3+4n^2+n-1}{n+4}$
21. $\frac{d^2-12d+43}{d-7}$ **23.** $\frac{3}{4}$ page/min **25.** $\frac{2}{3}$ **27.** $\frac{h}{g^3}$
29. $\frac{2a+12}{a}$ **31.** $\frac{(j-4)(j+4)}{15(j+2)}$ **33.** about 140

(35) $D=\frac{m}{V}$; $V=\frac{4}{3}\pi r^3$
$D=\frac{m}{\frac{4}{3}\pi r^3}$
$D=\frac{3m}{4\pi r^3}$
a. $D=\frac{3(15.6)}{4\pi(0.0748)^3}\approx 8898.794862$ or 8900
The metal is copper.
b. $D=\frac{3(285.3)}{4\pi(0.1819)^3}\approx 11{,}316.57654$ or 11,300
The metal is lead.

37. $\frac{58x+145}{5x+10}$ **39.** $\frac{c-3}{c+7}$ **41.** $\frac{(x-8)(x-1)}{x+2}$
43. Find the lowest common denominator for the fractions in the numerator and simplify to $\frac{y^2-x^2}{xy}$.
45. $\frac{2t^3}{(t-1)(t^2-1)}$ **47.** Sample answer: Time equals distance divided by rate or $\frac{d}{r}$. When the distance or the rate is given as a fraction or mixed number, the expression $\frac{d}{r}$ becomes a complex fraction. Example: Someone walks $\frac{3}{4}$ mile in $10\frac{1}{2}$ minutes; the time in miles per minute is $\frac{\frac{3}{4}}{10\frac{1}{2}}$, which simplifies to $\frac{1}{14}$ mi/min. **49.** 12 days **51.** B
53. $\frac{-d+4}{d-1}$ **55.** $\frac{6m^2-1}{15m^3}$ **57.** $\frac{b^2+4b+18}{(b+3)(b-2)}$
59. $a+7-\frac{1}{a-3}$ **61.** $3y^2+2y-3-\frac{1}{y+2}$
63. $3h^2+2h+3-\frac{2}{3h-2}$

65.
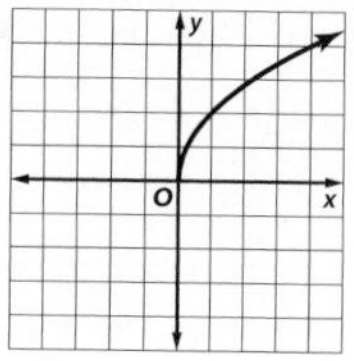

D = {x | x ≥ 0};
R = {y | y ≥ 0}

67.
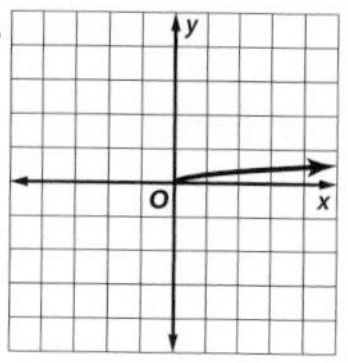

D = {x | x ≥ 0};
R = {y | y ≥ 0}

69. $(a-11)(a+11)$ **71.** $(2y-5)(2y+5)$
73. $4(t-1)(t+1)(t^2+1)$ **75.** 4 **77.** 7 **79.** −11.5

Lesson 11-8

1. −2 **3.** $-\frac{4}{5}$ **5.** −3 **7.** $\frac{15}{38}$ hour or about 0.4 hour

(9) $\frac{8}{n}=\frac{3}{n-5}$
$8(n-5)=3n$
$8n-40=3n$
$-40=-5n$
$8=n$

11. $\frac{2}{3}$ **13.** −13 **15.** 0 **17.** −2, 3 **19.** no solution; extraneous: 1 **21.** $\frac{15}{8}$ hours or $1\frac{7}{8}$ hours
23. 26.2 hours **25a.** line **25b.** $f(x)=\frac{(x+5)(x-6)}{x-6}=x+5$ **25c.** −5 **27a.** parabola **27b.** $f(x)=x^2+6x+12$ **27c.** no real zeros **29a.** $s=r-w$; $s=r+w$ **29b.** $d=t(r-w)$, $d=t(r+w)$; $t=\frac{d}{r-w}$, $t=\frac{d}{r+w}$

(31) **a.** $h=\frac{kp}{c}$
b. $8=\frac{k(100)}{5}$
$8=20k$
$\frac{2}{5}=k$
$h=\frac{\frac{2}{5}p}{c}$
$=\frac{\frac{2}{5}(100)}{10}$
$=4$ hours

33. 0, −4; extraneous: 1 **35.** $\frac{50}{11}$
37. The extraneous solution of a rational equation is the excluded value of one of the expressions in the equation. **39.** Sample answer: $\frac{x}{x-8}=0$ **41.** D
43. D **45.** $\frac{d}{c}$ **47.** $\frac{b-3}{2b}$ **49.** $4h^2$ **51.** $(x-4)(x+2)$
53. linear **55.** quadratic **57.** $0.5Bb+0.5b^2$; $\frac{1}{2}$
59. $\{r \mid r > 49\}$ **61.** 0.3 **63.** 0.75

Chapter 11 Study Guide and Review

1. false; x^2-25 **3.** true **5.** true **7.** false; complex fraction **9.** false; inverse variation **11.** $\frac{1}{3}$
13. $-\frac{9}{16}$ **15.** 3 **17.** 2

19.
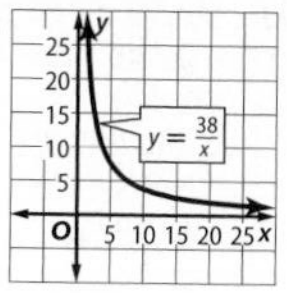

The vertical asymptote is at $x=0$ and the horizontal asymptote is at $y=0$.

21. $\frac{1}{x+8}$ **23.** $\frac{y-5}{y-2}$ **25.** $\frac{1}{2y(y+2)}$ **27.** $-\frac{3}{2}, \frac{1}{3}$
29. $\frac{3}{x^2-3x}$ **31.** $\frac{3}{(b+4)(b-2)}$ **33.** xy **35.** x^2+4x-2 **37.** $4y+1+\frac{8}{12y-1}$ **39.** $\frac{3a}{b}$ **41.** $\frac{-y^2+2y-9}{(y+1)(y-3)}$
43. 4 ft **45.** $\frac{x^2+8x-65}{x^2+8x+12}$ **47.** $\frac{y^2+11y+10}{y^2+6y+8}$ **49.** $\frac{2}{5}$, extraneous: 2 **51.** 24 **53.** −2, 4

CHAPTER 12
Statistics and Probability

Chapter 12 Get Ready

1. $\frac{3}{7}$ **3.** $\frac{4}{7}$ **5.** $\frac{1}{6}$ **7.** $\frac{5}{6}$ **9.** $\frac{7}{256}$ **11.** $\frac{84}{625}$ **13.** 82.4%
15. 85.6% **17.** 35%

Lesson 12-1

1. Sample: the guests who receive the stickered plates; population: all of the guests; simple: all of the guests have an equal chance of receiving a stickered plate. **3.** Unbiased; sample answer: The sample is random, and does not favor one outcome over another. **5.** Survey; sample answer: The data is obtained from opinions given by people that return the questionnaire.

(7) Sample answer: The survey question does not encourage any particular answer, does not cause a strong reaction, does not address more than one issue, and is not confusing. Therefore, the question is unbiased.

9. Biased; sample answer: The survey question encourages the members of the sample to choose Suzanne as class president. **11.** Biased; sample answer: The normal advertising strategy was used in states that have a cooler climate than the states where the new advertising strategy was used.
13. Sample: the cards that Greg selects; population: all of Greg's baseball cards; stratified: Greg divides the cards by teams before the sample is selected.
15. Sample: the five students who win the raffle; population: all of the students at the meeting; simple: each student has an equal chance of winning. **17.** Biased; sample answer: The sample is too small and doesn't represent the population.
19. Unbiased; sample answer: The participants are randomly selected. The fact that the sample is selected at a gas station has no bearing on the conclusion because many different kinds of people enter gasoline stations. **21.** Survey; sample answer: The data is obtained from opinions given by guests that return the paper.

23 This situation describes an experiment. Sample answer: The control group is the team in short sleeves, while the experimental group is wearing long sleeves. The different affects of the clothes worn by each team in the heat are analyzed. It is not an observational study because the members of the teams *are* being affected by the study. It is not a survey since the team members are *not* being asked for responses.

25. unbiased **27.** Biased; sample answer: The question addresses more than one issue.
29. Unbiased; sample answer: The only difference between the two groups is the recreation room.
31. unbiased **33.** Experiment; sample answer: The new color will be tested on a sample group. These members will be affected by the study, so it is an experiment. **35.** Survey; sample answer: Data are collected from responses given by members of a population, so it is a survey.

37 Both; both Amy's and Esteban's methods can result in a more accurate survey. By increasing the number of people in the population to be included, Amy's survey will more closely approximate the entire population. By using more random samples, Esteban's survey will also more closely approximate the entire population.

39. Sample answer: The survey of 150 people at the concert would most likely represent the population. While each survey may have regional bias, more people were surveyed at the concert. The larger the sample size, the more likely it will reflect the population. **41.** Sample answer: They need accurate surveys to make decisions about how to market and sell products that will earn the company the most profit. They also make decisions about marketing and advertising and how to reach their target audience. Finally, they make decisions about the types of products they will develop or continue to sell. **43.** C **45.** B

47. 6 **49.** 2 **51.** $\frac{9}{2}$ **53.** 0 **55a.** $P = \frac{2559.7075}{\pi r^3}$
55b. 4.67 in.

57.

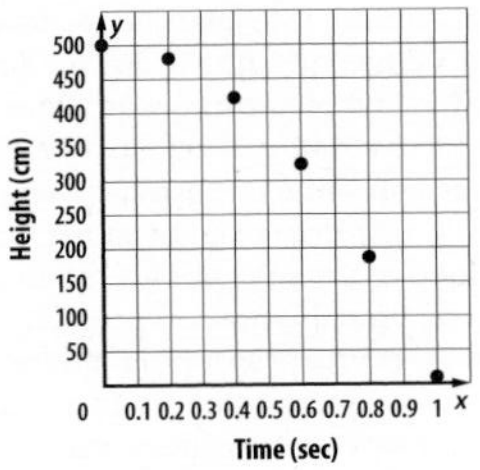

Lesson 12-2

1. sample: 1000 college students; population: all college students in the United States; sample statistic: mean of the money spent on books in a year by the sample; population parameter: mean of money spent on books by all college students in the United States

3 Find the mean.

$\bar{x} = \frac{10 + 12 + 0 + 6 + 9 + 15 + 12 + 10 + 11 + 20}{10}$

or 10.5

Find the sum of the square of the differences, $(\bar{x} - x_n)^2$.

$(10 - 10.5)^2 = 0.25$
$(12 - 10.5)^2 = 2.25$
$(0 - 10.5)^2 = 110.25$
$(6 - 10.5)^2 = 20.25$
$(9 - 10.5)^2 = 2.25$
$(15 - 10.5)^2 = 20.25$
$(12 - 10.5)^2 = 2.25$
$(10 - 10.5)^2 = 0.25$
$(11 - 10.5)^2 = 0.25$
$+ (20 - 10.5)^2 = 90.25$
$= 248.50$

Find the variance.

$\sigma^2 = \frac{(\bar{x} - x_1)^2 + (\bar{x} - x_2)^2 + \ldots + (\bar{x} - x_n)^2}{n}$

$= \frac{248.50}{10}$ or 24.85

Find the standard deviation.

$\sigma = \sqrt{\sigma^2}$

$= \sqrt{24.85}$ or about 4.98

Sample answer: The mean is 10.5 and the standard deviation is about 4.98. The standard deviation is relatively high due to outliers 0 and 20.

5. sample: 1003 voters in Mercy County; population: all voters in Mercy County; sample statistic: the number of people in the sample who would vote for the incumbent candidate; population parameter: the number of people in the county who would vote for the incumbent candidate **7.** sample: stratified random sample of 2500; population: high school students in the country; sample statistic: how much money the 2500 students spent each month; population parameter: how much money all the students in the country spent each month **9.** 14; Sample answer: On average, each day's attendance is 14 people from the mean of 94 people. The mean absolute deviation is affected by outliers 45 and 166. **11.** 2.1; Sample answer: With a mean of 77.875, the standard deviation of about 2.1 suggests that there is very little deviation to the data. Therefore, you can conclude that Carla's archery scores are pretty consistent.

13 **a.** Movie A:

Find the mean.

$\bar{x} = \frac{7+8+7+6+8+6+7+8+6+8+8+6+7+7+8+8}{16}$

or about 7.2

Find the sum of the square of the differences, $(\bar{x} - x_n)^2$.

$(7 - 7.2)^2 = 0.04$
$(8 - 7.2)^2 = 0.64$
$(7 - 7.2)^2 = 0.04$
$(6 - 7.2)^2 = 1.44$
$(8 - 7.2)^2 = 0.64$
$(6 - 7.2)^2 = 1.44$
$(7 - 7.2)^2 = 0.04$
$(8 - 7.2)^2 = 0.64$
$(6 - 7.2)^2 = 1.44$
$(8 - 7.2)^2 = 0.64$
$(8 - 7.2)^2 = 0.64$
$(6 - 7.2)^2 = 1.44$
$(7 - 7.2)^2 = 0.04$
$(7 - 7.2)^2 = 0.04$
$(8 - 7.2)^2 = 0.64$
$+ (8 - 7.2)^2 = 0.64$
$= 10.44$

Find the variance.

$\sigma^2 = \frac{(\bar{x} - x_1)^2 + (\bar{x} - x_2)^2 + \ldots + (\bar{x} - x_n)^2}{n}$

$= \frac{10.44}{16}$ or 0.6525

Find the standard deviation.

$\sigma = \sqrt{\sigma^2}$

$= \sqrt{0.6525}$ or about 0.81

Movie B:

Find the mean.

$\bar{x} = \frac{9+3+8+2+5+10+3+8+10+9+9+10+6+4+9+3}{16}$

or about 6.8

Find the sum of the square of the differences, $(\bar{x} - x_n)^2$.

$(9 - 6.8)^2 = 4.84$
$(3 - 6.8)^2 = 14.44$
$(8 - 6.8)^2 = 1.44$
$(2 - 6.8)^2 = 23.04$
$(5 - 6.8)^2 = 3.24$
$(10 - 6.8)^2 = 10.24$
$(3 - 6.8)^2 = 14.44$
$(8 - 6.8)^2 = 1.44$
$(10 - 6.8)^2 = 10.24$
$(9 - 6.8)^2 = 4.84$
$(9 - 6.8)^2 = 4.84$
$(10 - 6.8)^2 = 10.24$
$(6 - 6.8)^2 = 0.64$
$(4 - 6.8)^2 = 7.84$
$(9 - 6.8)^2 = 4.84$
$+ (3 - 6.8)^2 = 14.44$
$= 131.04$

Find the variance.

$\sigma^2 = \frac{(\bar{x} - x_1)^2 + (\bar{x} - x_2)^2 + \ldots + (\bar{x} - x_n)^2}{n}$

$= \frac{131.04}{16}$ or 8.19

Find the standard deviation.

$\sigma = \sqrt{\sigma^2}$

$= \sqrt{8.19}$ or about 2.86

Sample answer: Movie A had a mean of about 7.2 with a standard deviation of about 0.81. Movie B had a mean of about 6.8 with a standard deviation of about 2.86. While both movies had a mean rating of close to 7, the ratings for Movie B had more variability. In other words, some people really liked it while others didn't like it at all. The ratings for Movie A were much more consistent.

b. Movie A: Sample answer: The reviews are consistent and all are between 6 and 8. You would prefer this movie if you want to see a movie that, while it isn't anyone's favorite, you can assume that it will be decent.
Movie B: Sample answer: While some people didn't like the movie at all, others loved it. You would prefer this movie if you hope to be one of the people that love it.

15 **a.** Step 1: To find the mean, add the numbers and then divide by how many numbers are in the data set.

$\bar{x} = (956 + 966 + 971 + 981 + 986 + 994 + 1001 + 1014 + 1020 + 1023 + 1034 + 1066 + 1076 + 1077 + 1083)/15$

$= \frac{15248}{15}$

= 1016.5 seconds or 16.9 minutes

Step 2: To find the mean absolute deviation, first find the sum of the absolute values of the differences between each value in the set of data and the mean.

$|956 - 1016.5| + |966 - 1016.5| + |971 - 1016.5| + |981 - 1016.5| + |986 - 1016.5| + |994 - 1016.5| + |1001 - 1016.5| + |1014 - 1016.5| + |1020 - 1016.5| + |1023 - 1016.5| + |1034 - 1016.5| + |1066 - 1016.5| + |1076 - 1016.5| + |1077 - 1016.5| + |1083 - 1016.5| = 499.5$

Step 3: Then divide the sum by the number of values in the data set.

$\frac{499.5}{15} \approx 33.3$ seconds

b. The sample is the top 15 runners. The population is all the people who ran.

c. The data is quantitative. No, since the sample is the top 15 runners in the race, it is not random. So, it would not be accurate to apply the mean and standard deviation of the running times to the population.

Selected Answers and Solutions

17. Sometimes; if the samples are truly random, they would rarely contain identical elements and the mean and standard deviation would differ. If the sample produces identical elements, the mean and standard deviation would be the same. **19.** Sample answer: Any set of data with identical terms. For example: 5, 5, 5, 5, 5, 5, 5. **21.** Both are calculated statistical values that show how each data value deviates from the mean of the data set. The mean absolute deviation is calculated by taking the mean of the absolute values of the differences between each number and the mean of the data set. To find the standard deviation, you square each difference and then take the square root of the mean of the squares. **23.** 125 **25.** C **27.** Biased; because they are at a rock concert, they are more likely to select a rock music station. **29.** $\frac{x+3}{x-2}$ **31a.** $y = 880(1.06)^t$ **31b.** about 1576 members **33.** 31; 21; 15; 36 **35.** 11; 21; 18; 25 **37.** 10; 11; 9.5; 13

Lesson 12-3

1.

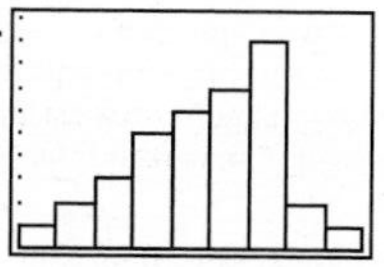

[56, 92] scl: 4 by [0, 10] scl: 1

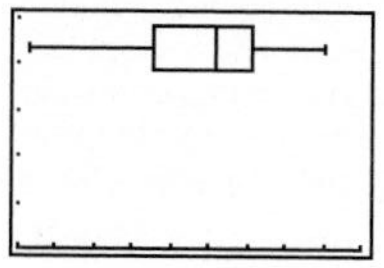

[56, 92] scl: 4 by [0, 5] scl: 1

negatively skewed

3. Sample answer: The distribution is skewed, so use the five-number summary. The range is 92 − 52 or 40. The median is 65, and half of the data are between 59.5 and 74.

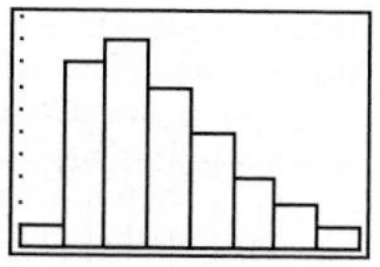

[48, 96] scl: 6 by [0, 10] scl: 1

5.

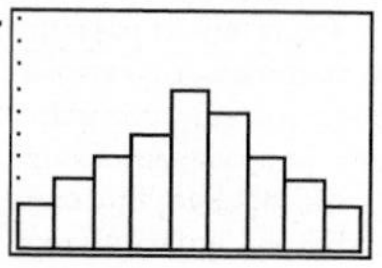

[24, 78] scl: 6 by [0, 10] scl: 1

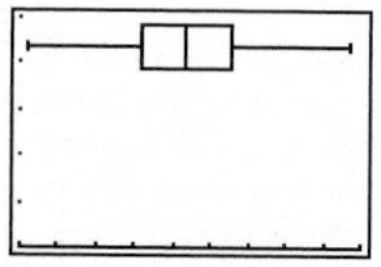

[24, 78] scl: 6 by [0, 5] scl: 1

symmetric

7 Use a graphing calculator to enter the data into L1 and create a histogram. Adjust the window to the dimensions shown. The graph is high on the right. Therefore, the distribution is negatively skewed.

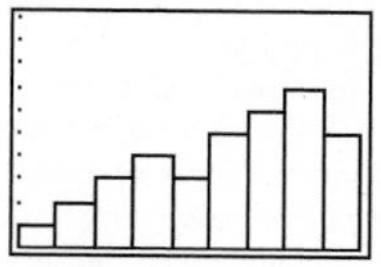

[10, 55] scl: 5 by [0, 10] scl: 1

The distribution is negatively skewed, so use the five-number summary.

```
1-Var Stats
↑n=36
 minX=12
 Q1=28
 Med=39.5
 Q3=48
 maxX=53
```

The range is 53 − 12 or 41. The median of the numbers is 39.5, and half the numbers are between 28 and 48.

9. Sample answer: The distribution is symmetric, so use the mean and standard deviation to describe the center and spread. The mean temperature is 52.8° with standard deviation of about 4.22°.

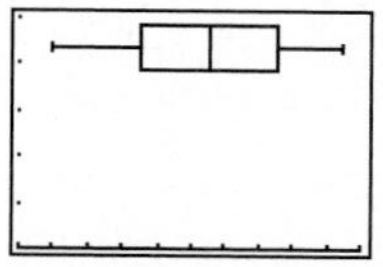

[42, 62] scl: 2 by [0, 5] scl: 1

11 **a.** Enter the list of prices as L1 and create a box-and-whisker plot. Adjust the window to the dimensions shown. The right whisker is longer than the left. The median is closer to the shorter whisker. Thus, the distribution is positively skewed.

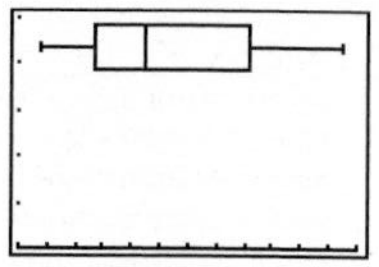

[7, 19] scl: 1 by [0, 5] scl: 1

The distribution is positively skewed, so use the five-number summary.

```
1-Var Stats
↑n=20
 minX=7.75
 Q1=9.625
 Med=11.5
 Q3=15.125
 maxX=18.5
```

The range of prices is \$18.50 − \$7.75 or \$10.75. The median price is \$11.50, and half of the prices are between \$9.625 and \$15.125.

b. Delete all the entries in L1 that are greater than \$15 and create another box-and-whisker plot. The lengths of the whiskers are approximately equal, and the median is in the middle of the data. Thus, the distribution is symmetric.

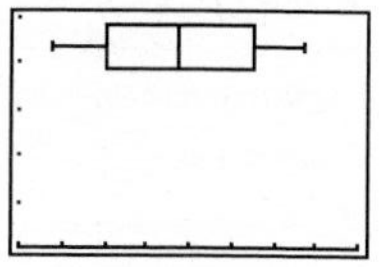

[7, 15] scl: 1 by [0, 5] scl: 1

The distribution is symmetric, so use the mean and standard deviation to describe the center and the spread of the new data.

```
1-Var Stats
 x̄=10.66666667
 Σx=160
 Σx²=1757.625
 Sx=1.907847204
 σx=1.843155507
↓n=15
```

The mean is about \$10.67 with standard deviation of about \$1.84.

13. i **15.** Sample answer: A bimodal distribution is a distribution of data that is characterized by having data divided into two clusters, thus producing two modes, and having two peaks. The distribution can be described by summarizing the center and spread of each cluster of data. **17.** Sample answer: In a symmetrical distribution, the majority of the data is located near the center of the distribution. The mean of the distribution is also located near the center of the distribution. Therefore, the mean and standard deviation should be used to describe the data. In a skewed distribution, the majority of the data lies either on the right or left side of the distribution. Since the distribution has a tail or may have outliers, the mean is pulled away from the majority of the data. The median is less affected. Therefore, the five-number summary should be used to describe the data. **19.** F **21a.** $3w = 2\ell + 3$; $4\ell = 12 + P$ **21b.** 21 in., 15 in. **21c.** 315 in^2 **23.** sample: random sample of 100 seniors; population: all seniors at North Boyton High School; sample statistic: the mean amount of money the sample spent on prom; population parameter: the mean amount of money seniors at North Boyton High School spent on prom **25.** unbiased **27.** $\frac{11a+7}{a+1}$ **29.** $f^{-1}(x) = -\frac{1}{5}x + \frac{17}{5}$ **31.** $f^{-1}(x) = -7x - 7$ **33.** $f^{-1}(x) = -\frac{5}{3}x + 20$ **35.** $\frac{4}{11}$ **37.** $\frac{7}{11}$ **39.** $\frac{1}{2}$

Lesson 12-4

1. 3.5, 3.5, 1, 8, 2.4

3 Find the mean, median, mode, range, and standard deviation of the original set.
Mean: 5.75
Median: 5.5
Mode: 3
Range: 10
Standard Deviation: 3.14
Multiply the mean, median, mode, range, and standard deviation by 3.
Mean: $3 \times 5.75 \approx 17.3$
Median: $3 \times 5.5 = 16.5$
Mode: $3 \times 3 = 9$
Range: $3 \times 10 = 30$
Standard Deviation: $3 \times 3.14 \approx 9.4$

5a. Kyle's Distances

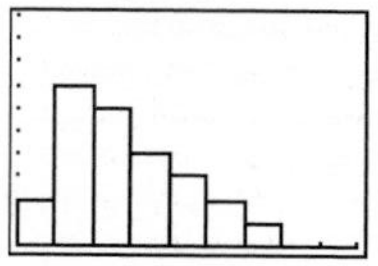

[17, 19.25] scl: 0.25 by [0, 10] scl: 1

Mark's Distances

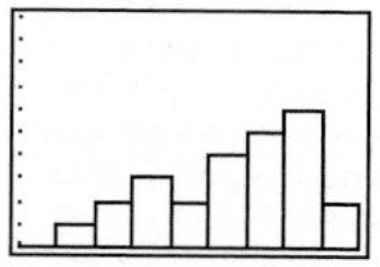

[17, 19.25] scl: 0.25 by [0, 10] scl: 1

Kyle, positively skewed; Mark, negatively skewed **5b.** Sample answer: The distributions are skewed, so use the five-number summaries. Kyle's upper quartile is 17.98, while Mark's lower quartile is 18.065. This means that 75% of Mark's distances are greater than 75% of Kyle's distances. Therefore, we can conclude that overall, Mark's distances are higher than Kyle's distances. **7.** 60.9, 60, 60, 14, 4.7 **9.** 22.5, 21.5, no mode, 24, 7.4 **11.** 36.8, 38, 12, 56, 20.0 **13.** 26.8, 27.2, 29.6, 10.4, 3.5

15a.

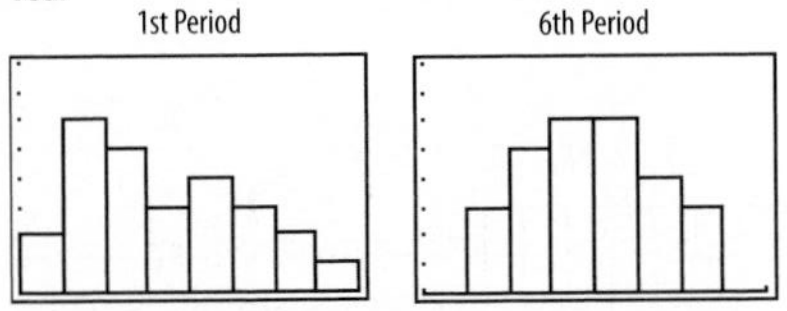

[200, 600] scl: 50 by [0, 8] scl: 1 [200, 600] scl: 50 by [0, 8] scl: 1

1st period, positively skewed; 6th period, symmetric **15b.** Sample answer: One distribution is symmetric and the other is skewed, so use the five-number summaries. The lower quartile for 1st period is 291 pages, while the minimum for 6th period is 294 pages. This means that the lower 25% of data for 1st period is lower than any data from 6th period. The range for 1st period is 578 − 206 or 372 pages. The range for 6th period is 506 − 294 or 212 pages. The median for 1st period is about 351 pages, while the median for 6th period is 392 pages. This means, that while the median for 6th period is greater, 1st period's pages have a greater range and include greater values than 1st period.

(17) **a.** Enter Leon's times as L1 and Cassie's times as L2. Then use STAT PLOT to create a histogram for each list.

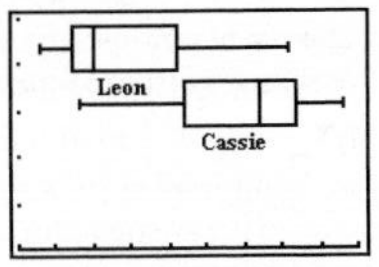

[1.5, 6] scl: 0.5 by [0, 5] scl: 1

For Leon's times, the right whisker is longer than the left, and the median is closer to the left whisker. The distribution is positively skewed. For Cassie's times, the left whisker is longer than the right and the median is closer to the right whisker. The distribution is negatively skewed.

b. One distribution is positively skewed and the other is negatively skewed, so use the five-number summaries to compare the data.

Leon's Times

```
1-Var Stats
↑n=16
 minX=1.8
 Q1=2.2
 Med=2.5
 Q3=3.6
 maxX=5.1
```

Cassie's Times

```
1-Var Stats
↑n=16
 minX=2.3
 Q1=3.7
 Med=4.7
 Q3=5.2
 maxX=5.8
```

The lower quartile for Leon's times is 2.2 minutes, while the minimum for Cassie's times is 2.3 minutes. This means that 25% of Leon's times are less than all of Cassie's times. The upper quartile for Leon's times is 3.6 minutes, while the lower quartile for Cassie's times is 3.7 minutes. This means that 75% of Leon's times are less than 75% of Cassie's time. Overall, we can conclude that Leon completed the brainteasers faster than Cassie.

19a. 52.96, 53, 53, 19, 6.07 **19b.** 47.96, 48, 48, 19, 6.07

(21) Find the total cost of all 20 SUVs and luxury cars.

20 × \$39,250 = \$785,000

Next subtract the price reduction of the 15 SUVs.

\$785,000 − (15 × 2000) = \$755,000

Finally, divide this new total by the 20 cars.

\$755,000 ÷ 20 = \$37,750

The new average price for all the vehicles is \$37,750.

23. Sample answer: Histograms show the frequency of values occurring within set intervals. This makes the shape of the distribution easy to recognize. However, no specific values of the data set can be identified from looking at a histogram, and the overall spread of the data can be difficult to determine. The box-and-whisker plots show the data divided into four sections. This aids when comparing the spread of one set of data to another. However, the box-and-whisker plots are limited because they cannot display the data any more specifically than showing it divided into four sections. **25.** Sample answer: When two distributions are symmetric, the first thing to determine is how close the averages are and how spread out each set of data is. The mean and standard deviation are the best values to use for this comparison. When distributions are skewed, we also want to determine the direction and the degree to which it is skewed. The mean and standard deviation cannot provide any information in this regard, but we can get this information by comparing the range, quartiles, and medians found in the five-number summaries. So, if one or both sets of data are skewed, it is best to compare their five-number summaries. **27.** $m\angle A = 36°$, $c \approx 9.9$, $a \approx 5.8$ **29.** D **31.** 5.58; Sample answer: The standard deviation is relatively high compared to the mean of 6.4 due to the outlier 23. If this outlier were removed, the new mean of the data would be about 5.2 with a standard deviation of about 3.51. **33.** 4 **35.** $(x + 3)(x - 7)$ **37.** $(x - 8)(x - 4)$ **39.** $(x + 10)(x + 2)$ **41.** $4w^3 + 14w^2 + 10w$ **43.** 4 **45.** 0 **47.** 1

Lesson 12-5

(1) We are asked to find the probability of selecting a customer who is older than 12 but younger than 46. Therefore, we need to consider selecting someone who is age 13–17, 18–23, 24–31, and 32–45.

P(older than 12 but younger than 46)

$= \dfrac{\text{sum of customers 13–45}}{\text{total number of customers}}$

$= \dfrac{48 + 42 + 27 + 40}{13 + 28 + 48 + 42 + 27 + 40 + 33 + 23}$

$= \dfrac{157}{254}$

The probability of selecting a customer older than 12 but younger than 46 is $\frac{157}{254}$. The correct answer is B.

(3) **a.** $P(\text{heart}) = \dfrac{\text{frequency of hearts}}{\text{total of frequencies}}$

$= \dfrac{5}{7 + 4 + 5 + 9}$

$= \dfrac{5}{25}$ or $\dfrac{1}{5}$

The experimental probability of drawing a heart is $\frac{1}{5}$ or 20%.

b. We are asked to find the probability of drawing a black card. Therefore, we need to consider drawing a club and drawing a spade.

$P(\text{black}) = \dfrac{\text{sum of clubs and spades}}{\text{sum of all the frequencies}}$

$= \dfrac{7 + 9}{7 + 4 + 5 + 9}$

$= \dfrac{16}{25}$

The experimental probability of drawing a black card is $\frac{16}{25}$ or 64%.

c. Combine the frequencies for each suit for the first and second test.

Suit	clubs	diamonds	hearts	spades
Frequency	12	12	11	15

$P(\text{spade}) = \dfrac{\text{number of spades drawn}}{\text{total number of cards drawn}}$

$= \dfrac{15}{12 + 12 + 11 + 15}$

$= \dfrac{15}{50}$ or $\dfrac{3}{10}$

The experimental probability of drawing a spade for both tests is $\frac{3}{10}$ or 30%.

5a. Sample answer: The theoretical probability that the player gets a hit is 30%, and the theoretical probability that he does not get a hit is 70%. Use a random number generator to generate integers 1 through 10. The integers 1–3 will represent a hit, and the integers 4–10 will represent the player not getting a hit. The simulation will consist of 50 trials. **5b.** Sample answer: P(hit) = 28%, P(not a hit) = 72%

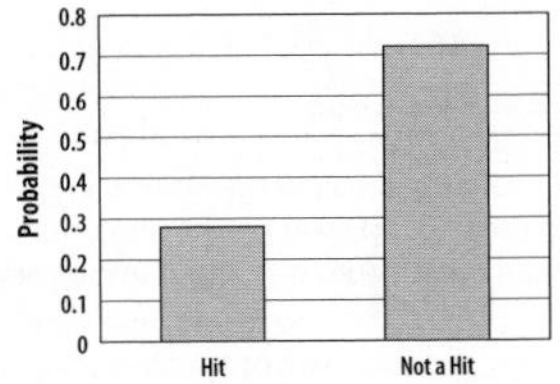

7a. Sample answer: The theoretical probability that a spin results in each prize is 20%. Use a random number generator to generate integers 1 through 5. The integer 1 will represent a hot pretzel, the integer 2 will represent a burger, the integer 3 will represent a large drink, the integer 4 will represent nachos, and the integer 5 will represent a small popcorn. The simulation will consist of 50 trials.
7b. P(hot pretzel) = 20%, P(burger) = 20%, P(large drink) = 28%, P(nachos) = 14%, P(small popcorn) = 18%

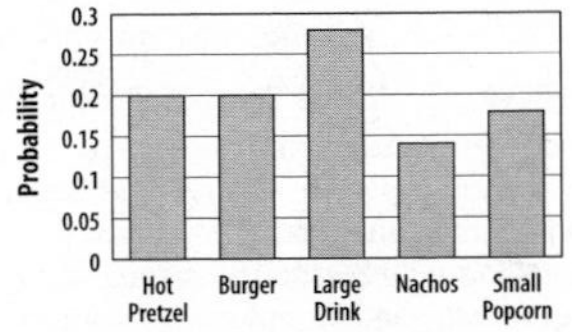

(9) **a.** We are asked to find the experimental probability that a participant was a winner in the second group.

$P = \dfrac{\text{number of winners in second group}}{\text{number of participants in second group}}$

$= \dfrac{15}{50}$ or $\dfrac{3}{10}$

The probability of a participant in the second group being a winner is $\frac{3}{10}$ or 30%.

b. We are asked to find the experimental probability that a participant in any of the three groups was a winner.

$P = \dfrac{\text{sum of winners in all three groups}}{\text{sum of participants in all three groups}}$

$= \dfrac{13 + 15 + 19}{50 + 50 + 50}$

$= \dfrac{47}{150}$

The experimental probability of winning for all three groups is $\frac{47}{150}$ or about 31.3%.

c. Yes; sample answer: In total, there were 150 participants with a success rate of about 31%. This is lower than the 33% success rate required by the owners.

11a. $\frac{1}{6}$ **11b.** Sample answer: The theoretical probability that a 1 is rolled is $\frac{1}{6}$ or about 17%, and the theoretical probability that a 1 is not rolled is $\frac{5}{6}$ or about 83%. Use a random number generator to generate integers 1 through 6. The integer 1 will represent a 1. The integers 2–6 will represent the other numbers on the die.
11c. Sample answer:

Rolling a 1		
Trials	Frequency	Experimental Probability
20	2	$\frac{1}{10}$ or 10%
50	11	$\frac{11}{50}$ or 22%
100	19	$\frac{19}{100}$ or 19%
200	37	$\frac{37}{200}$ or 18.5%

11d. Sample answer: The experimental probability of rolling a 1 is getting closer to the theoretical probability of $\frac{1}{6}$ or 17%. **11e.** Sample answer: As the number of trials increases, the experimental probability should approach the theoretical probability of $\frac{1}{6}$ or 17%. **13.** Sample answer: A simulation can be designed to estimate the probability that a basketball player will make her next free throw if she made 70% of her free throws the previous season. The theoretical probability that she makes her next free throw is 70%, and the theoretical probability that she misses is 30%. Use a random number generator to generate integers 1 through 10. The integers 1–7 will represent a made free throw, and the integers 8–10 will represent a miss. The simulation will consist of 30 trials.
15. Sample answer: Jeremy's concern about the fairness of the coin should be dependent on the number of times he tossed it. If he only completed 4, or even 20 trials, then the sample size is not large enough to warrant concern. However, if he completed 100 or more trials, then he should be concerned since, due to the Law of Large Numbers, the experimental probability should be closer to the theoretical probability of $\frac{1}{2}$ or 50%.
17. A **19.** G **21.** 13.9, 13.5, 9, 12, 3.8 **23.** 7.9, 7, 5, 12, 4.0 **25.** 60 **27.** $xy = 12.4$; −20 **29.** 7.1 ft **31.** 44% **33.** 75% **35.** 27%

Lesson 12-6

1. 720 **3.** combination **5.** 42
(7) Use the combination formula with $n = 6$ and $r = 4$.

$C(n, r) = \frac{n!}{(n-r)!r!}$

$C(6, 4) = \frac{6!}{(6-4)!4!}$
$= \frac{6!}{2!4!}$
$= \frac{6 \cdot 5 \cdot \cancel{4} \cdot \cancel{3} \cdot \cancel{2} \cdot \cancel{1}}{2 \cdot 1 \cdot \cancel{4} \cdot \cancel{3} \cdot \cancel{2} \cdot \cancel{1}}$
$= \frac{30}{2}$ or 15

9. 3003 **11.** 40,320 **13.** 5 **15.** 210 **17.** 10 **19.** 1 **21.** permutation **23.** combination **25.** 1320
(27) First find the total number of outcomes. Since order is not important, this is a combination. Find the number of combinations of 18 songs chosen 8 at a time.

$C(n, r) = \frac{n!}{(n-r)!r!}$
$C(18, 8) = \frac{18!}{(18-8)!8!}$
$= \frac{18!}{10!8!}$ or 43,758

There are 43,758 possible outcomes.
Next, find the number of successes. Of the 43,758 combinations of 8 songs, only one can be all country songs since there are only 8 country songs from which to choose.
Last, find the probability.

$P = \frac{\text{number of successes}}{\text{number of possible outcomes}}$ or $\frac{1}{43{,}758}$

The probability that the first 8 songs played on Kenneth's playlist are country songs is $\frac{1}{43{,}758}$.
29. 281,887,200 **31.** 455 **33.** 40.320
(35) a. Find the total number of pairings. Since order is not important, this is a combination. Find the number of combinations of 32 bowlers chosen 2 at a time.

$C(32, 2) = \frac{32!}{(32-2)!2!}$
$= \frac{32!}{30!2!}$ or 496

Since order is not important, only one pair could be Chris and Kelly. Therefore, the probability that Chris and Kelly bowl against each other in any lane is $\frac{1}{496}$.

b. There are to be 2 bowlers per lane. This will require 16 lanes since 32 bowlers will divide into 16 pairs. The probability of being assigned to the last lane is $\frac{1}{16}$. The probability of Chris and Kelly being selected to bowl against each other in the last lane is the probability of being paired together times the probability of being assigned to the last lane.
$P(\text{Chris vs Kelly and last lane}) = \frac{1}{496} \times \frac{1}{16}$ or $\frac{1}{7936}$

37a. 1,352,078 **37b.** about 99.97% **37c.** Sample answer: A random number generator can be used with 1–4 representing freshmen, 5–9 representing sophomores, 10–15 representing juniors, and 16–23 representing seniors. **37d.** Sample answer: Assume the first number generated is a 3 and the first selection is a freshman. The random number generator can be reconfigured to 1–3 representing freshmen, 4–8 representing sophomores, 9–14 representing juniors, and 15–22 representing seniors. An easier method would be to use the original number generator and ignore any repeats of the number 3. Follow this process for each remaining selection. **39.** Ming; since order is not important, combinations should have been used.
41. Determining class rank in a senior class; this is the only situation in which order matters.
43. Sample answer: choosing 3 clubs out of 8 to join
45. G **47.** $\frac{3}{20}$ **49.** 64.8% **51.** 2 bags **53.** $\frac{2}{n}$
55. $\frac{n-4}{n+4}$ **57.** $\frac{12ag}{5b}$ **59.** $\frac{6}{23}$ **61.** $\frac{8}{23}$ **63.** $\frac{17}{23}$

Lesson 12-7

1. dependent; $\frac{28}{253}$ or about 11% **3.** independent; $\frac{4}{9}$ or about 44% **5.** mutually exclusive; $\frac{2}{13}$ or about 15% **7.** not mutually exclusive; $\frac{4}{13}$ or about 31%
9. independent; $\frac{1}{16}$ or about 6%
(11) These events are dependent because the chocolate is not being replaced.
First, milk chocolate: $P = \frac{10}{24}$
Second, white chocolate: $P = \frac{6}{23}$

$P(\text{milk, then white}) = \left(\frac{10}{24}\right)\left(\frac{6}{23}\right)$
$= \frac{60}{552}$
$= \frac{5}{46}$ or about 11%

13. independent; $\frac{100}{361}$ or about 28% **15.** mutually exclusive; $\frac{3}{4}$ or 75% **17.** not mutually exclusive; $\frac{739}{750}$ or about 98.5% **19.** $\frac{8}{87}$ or about 9%
21. $\frac{42}{145}$ or about 29%
(23) choose white sock: $P = \frac{14}{24}$
choose white sock: $P = \frac{13}{23}$

$P(\text{white, then white}) = \left(\frac{14}{24}\right)\left(\frac{13}{23}\right)$
$= \frac{182}{552}$
$= \frac{91}{276}$ or about 33%

25. $\frac{1}{2}$ or 50% **27.** $\frac{4}{13}$ or about 31% **29.** $\frac{7}{13}$ or about 54% **31a.** 345 **31b.** 159 **31c.** $\frac{227}{345}$ or about 66% **31d.** $\frac{2}{23}$ or about 9%

(33) a.

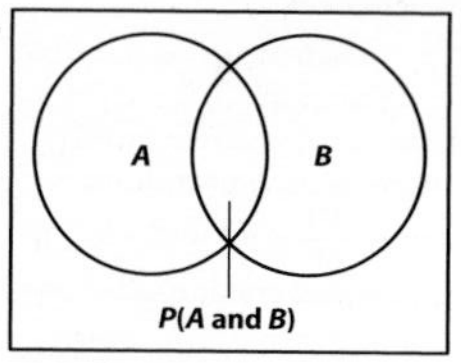

b. Divide the overlap of the two circles by the $P(A)$ circle
c. $P(\text{red}) = \frac{8}{12} = \frac{2}{3}$
$P(\text{red, green}) = \left(\frac{2}{3}\right)\left(\frac{4}{11}\right)$
$= \frac{8}{33}$
d. $P(\text{green} \mid \text{red}) = \frac{\frac{8}{33}}{\frac{2}{3}} = \frac{8}{33} \cdot \frac{3}{2}$ or $\frac{4}{11}$
e. $P(B \mid A) = \frac{P(A \text{ and } B)}{P(A)}$
f. $P(B \mid A) = \frac{P(A \text{ and } B)}{P(A)} = \frac{0.20}{0.80} = 0.25$ or 25%
35. 21 **37.** Sample answer: Choosing a CD to listen to, putting it back, and then choosing another CD to listen to would represent independent events since the CD was placed back before the second CD was chosen. Choosing a pair of jeans to wear would represent dependent events if I did not like the first pair chosen, and I did not put them back.
39. C **41.** 2 ft **43a.** combination **43b.** 220
43c. $\frac{210}{1320}$ or 16% **45.** 8 **47.** $-\frac{3}{2}$ **49.** about 57 pieces
51. −12 **53.** −16 **55.** −63

Lesson 12-8

1a. 4.7% **1b.** 57.4%
3a.

X	$P(X)$
$1000	0.0125
$5000	0.005
$25,000	0.001
$100,000	0.0001
$0	0.9814

3b. $72.50 **3c.** Sample answer: The game show producers expect to lose about $72.50 each time a certain game is played.
(5) a. We are to find the probability of the chosen product having been donated on the 4th day. There were 45 packages donated on the 4th day.

$P(\text{soup}) = \frac{\text{number of donated packages on day 4}}{\text{total number of packages}}$
$= \frac{45}{36 + 22 + 12 + 45}$
$= \frac{45}{115}$ or $\frac{9}{23}$

The probability of a randomly chosen product being donated on the 4th day is $\frac{9}{23}$ or about 39.1%.

b. To find the probability of the chosen product being donated on the 1st or 2nd day, first find the sum of the 1st and 2nd day donations.

P(1st or 2nd day)

$= \frac{\text{sum of donations on 1st and 2nd days}}{\text{total number of packages}}$

$= \frac{36 + 22}{115}$

$= \frac{58}{115}$

The probability of a randomly chosen product being donated on the 1st or 2nd day is $\frac{58}{115}$ or about 50.4%.

7a. All of the values are between 0 and 1; $0.29 + 0.43 + 0.17 + 0.11 + 0 = 1$. **7b.** 71%

7c.

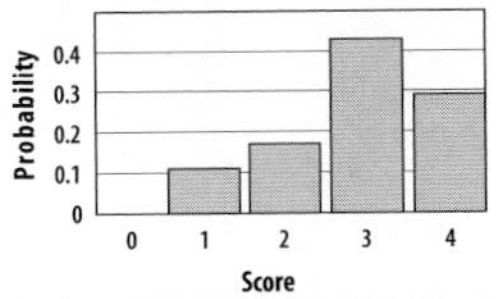

9 **a.** Find the probability associated with each prize. Find the probability of winning \$0 by subtracting the winning something from 1.

X	$P(X)$
\$200	0.002
\$1000	0.0002
\$5000	0.00004
\$25,000	0.00001
\$0	0.99775

b. Calculate the expected value.

$E(X) = [X_1 \cdot P(X_1)] + [X_2 \cdot P(X_2)] + \ldots + [X_n \cdot P(X_n)]$

$= 200(0.002) + 1000(0.0002) + 5000(0.00004) + 25{,}000(0.00001) + 0(0.99775)$

$= 0.4 + 0.2 + 0.2 + 0.25 + 0$

$= 1.05$

The expected value is 1.05 or \$1.05.

c. Sample answer: The makers of the contest expect to lose \$1.05 for each ticket valued at \$1.00. Therefore, they can expect to lose money by doing this contest.

11 **a.** We are to find the probability of the driver having an accident. This will be the sum of the probabilities for all the variables.

$P(\text{accident}) = P(\text{driving record}) + P(\text{vehicle type}) + P(\text{age}) + P(\text{gender}) + P(\text{residence})$

$= \frac{1}{50} + \frac{1}{500} + \frac{1}{250} + \frac{1}{200} + \frac{1}{1000}$

$= \frac{4}{125}$

The probability of the driver having an accident is $\frac{4}{125}$ or 3.2%.

b. The expected payout can be found by calculating the expected value. Each value of X_n will be \$10,000.

$E(X) = [X_1 \cdot P(X_1)] + [X_2 \cdot P(X_2)] + \ldots + [X_n \cdot P(X_n)]$

$= 10{,}000(0.02) + 10{,}000(0.002) + 10{,}000(0.004) + 10{,}000(0.005) + 10{,}000(0.001)$

$= 200 + 20 + 40 + 50 + 10$

$= 320$

The expected payout for this driver would be \$320.

c. Sample answer: The company should charge at least \$320 to cover their expected costs. However, in order to cover other costs such as paying employees and other business expenses and still earn a profit, the company should charge around \$600 for the policy.

13a.

X = Sum	2	3	4	5	6	7	8	9	10	11	12
Frequency	2	3	4	6	7	8	6	5	4	2	1
Probability	$\frac{1}{24}$	$\frac{1}{16}$	$\frac{1}{12}$	$\frac{1}{8}$	$\frac{7}{48}$	$\frac{1}{6}$	$\frac{1}{8}$	$\frac{5}{48}$	$\frac{1}{12}$	$\frac{1}{24}$	$\frac{1}{48}$

13b.

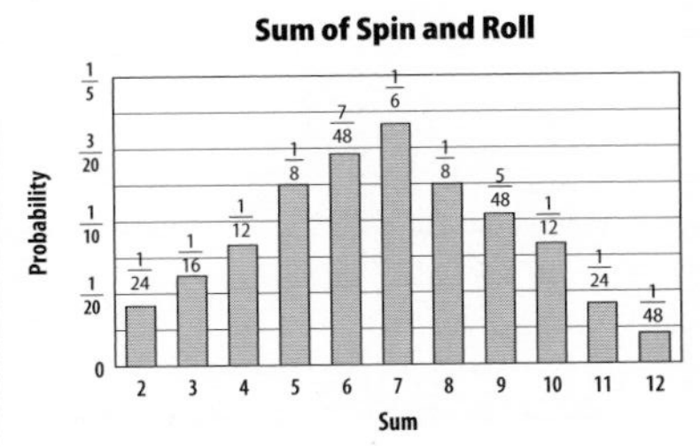

13c. 6.75 **13d.** Sample answer: Use values 1–48 in a random number generator. Set up the following representations. This way, the exact probabilities of each sum are accurately represented.

X = Sum	2	3	4	5	6	7	8	9	10	11	12
Range	1–2	3–5	6–9	10–15	16–22	23–30	31–36	37–41	42–45	46–47	48
Tally	2	3	4	2	7	12	8	7	3	2	0

13e.

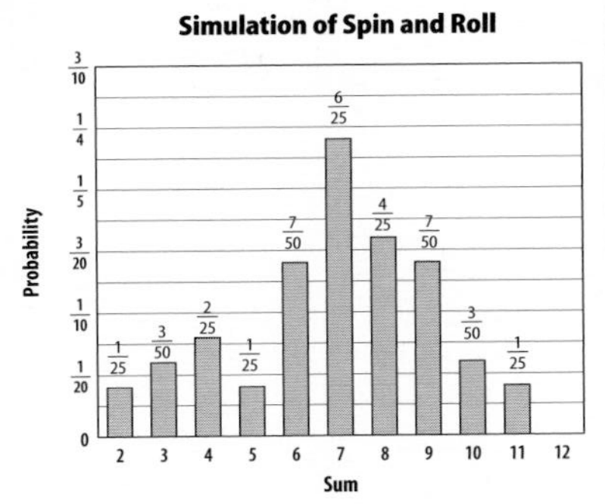

Sample answer: The graph in part b is the theoretical probability, while the graph in part f is the experimental probability. The graphs will be similar in shape, but the experimental probability graph will vary and more than likely will never completely mirror the theoretical probability graph.

15. The sum 7 is most likely to happen.

X = Sum of Dice	2	3	4	5	6	7	8	9	10	11	12
Probability	$\frac{1}{36}$	$\frac{1}{18}$	$\frac{1}{12}$	$\frac{1}{9}$	$\frac{5}{36}$	$\frac{1}{6}$	$\frac{5}{36}$	$\frac{1}{9}$	$\frac{1}{12}$	$\frac{1}{18}$	$\frac{1}{36}$

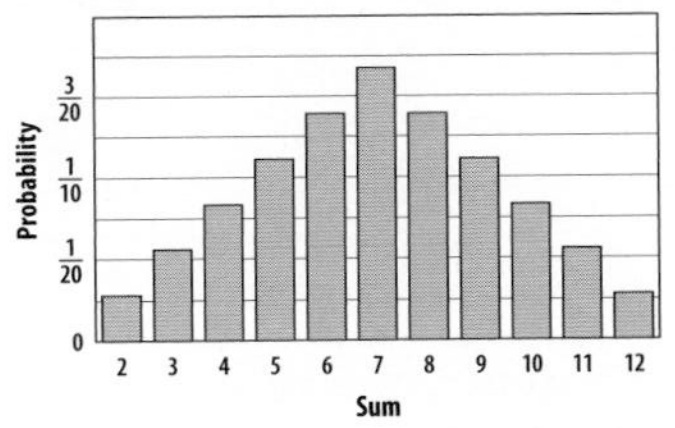

17. True; sample answer: While a discrete random variable is a countable variable, it can still take on an infinite number of values. For example, the number of hits a Web site receives is countable, but can be infinite. **19.** False; sample answer: The expected value of a random variable is the weighted average of the variable. The expected values of a random variable does not even have to be a possible value. For example, the expected value of rolling a die is 3.5, which is not possible.

21. A **23.** H **25.** $\frac{10}{253}$ or about 4% **27.** $\frac{6a + 4}{a^2}$

29. $\frac{9d + 10}{(d + 6)(d + 5)}$ **31.** $\frac{9h(h - 2)}{(h + 6)(h - 3)}$

33. $\sin A = \frac{4}{5}$; $\cos A = \frac{3}{5}$; $\tan A = \frac{4}{3}$ **35.** $\sin A = \frac{4}{5}$; $\cos A = \frac{3}{5}$; $\tan A = \frac{4}{3}$ **37.** $\frac{t\sqrt{t}}{3\sqrt{2}}$ **39.** $\frac{9 + 3\sqrt{5}}{2}$

41. $2 + \sqrt{3}$

Chapter 12 Study Guide and Review

1. permutation **3.** population **5.** random variable **7.** Survey; sample answer: The data are obtained from opinions given by the girls that return the questionnaire. **9.** 0.88; Sample answer: On average, the number of sidewalks that Ben shovels each day is 0.88 away from the mean of 3.4. **11.** The day customers had a mean of about 9.6 times per month with a standard deviation of about 3.5. The night customers had a mean of about 11.7 times per month with a standard deviation of about 2.5. The night customers had a higher average and their data values were more consistent.

13.

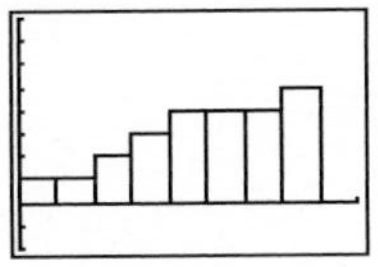

[0, 90] scl: 10 by [−2, 8] scl: 1

negatively skewed

15. 22.5, 21.5, no mode, 24, 7.4

17a. Ms. Miller:

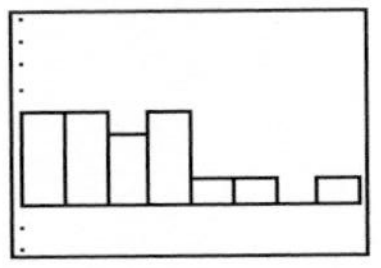

[9, 17] scl: 1 by [−2, 8] scl: 1

Selected Answers and Solutions

Ms. Anderson:

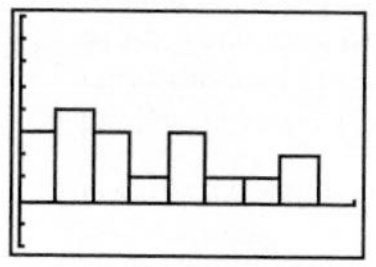

[0, 9] scl: 1 by [−2, 8] scl: 1

both positively skewed

17b. Sample answer: Use the five-number summaries. The range for Ms. Miller is 7. The median is 11. Half of the data are between 10 and 12. The range for Ms. Anderson is 7. The median is 2. Half of the data are between 1 and 4. All of the data in Ms. Anderson's distribution are less than all of the data in Ms. Miller's distribution. Therefore, Ms. Miller will more than likely hand out more disciplinary actions than Ms. Anderson. **19a.** Sample answer: The theoretical probability that the bus is late is 60%, and the theoretical probability that the bus is not late is 40%. Use a random number generator to generate integers 1 through 5. The integers 1–3 will represent the bus being late, and the integers 4–5 will represent the bus not being late. The simulation will consist of 50 trials. **19b.** Sample answer: $P(\text{late}) = 58\%$

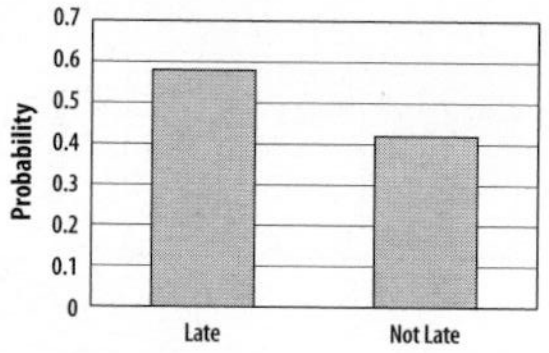

21. permutation **23.** permutation **25.** $\frac{2}{35}$ **27.** $\frac{1}{204}$ **29.** $\frac{22}{325}$ **31.** $\frac{1}{2}$ **33.** For each X, the probability is greater than or equal to 0 and less than or equal to 1, $0.18 + 0.36 + 0.34 + 0.08 + 0.04 = 1$, so the sum of the probabilities is 1.

Glossary/Glosario

MultilingualeGlossary

Go to connectED.mcgraw-hill.com for a glossary of terms in these additional languages:

Arabic	Chinese	Hmong	Spanish	Vietnamese
Bengali	English	Korean	Tagalog	
Brazilian Portugese	Haitian Creole	Russian	Urdu	

English / Español

A

absolute value (p. P11) The distance a number is from zero on the number line.

valor aboluto Es la distancia que dista de cero en una recta numerica.

absolute value function (p. 599) A function written as $f(x) = |x|$, in which $f(x) \geq 0$ for all values of x.

función del valor absoluto Una función que se escribe $f(x) = |x|$, donde $f(x) \geq 0$, para todos los valores de x.

additive identity (p. 16) For any number a, $a + 0 = 0 + a = a$.

identidad de la adición Para cualquier número a, $a + 0 = 0 + a = a$.

additive inverse (p. P11) Two integers, x and $-x$, are called additive inverses. The sum of any number and its additive inverse is zero.

inverso aditivo Dos enteros x y $-x$ reciben el nobre de inversos aditivos. La suma de cualquier número y su inverso aditivo es cero.

algebraic expression (p. 5) An expression consisting of one or more numbers and variables along with one or more arithmetic operations.

expresión algebraica Una expresión que consiste en uno o más números y variables, junto con una o más operaciones aritméticas.

area (p. P26) The measure of the surface enclosed by a geometric figure.

área La medida de la superficie incluida por una figura geométrica.

arithmetic sequence (p. 189) A numerical pattern that increases or decreases at a constant rate or value. The difference between successive terms of the sequence is constant.

sucesión aritmética Un patrón numérico que aumenta o disminuye a una tasa o valor constante. La diferencia entre términos consecutivos de la sucesión es siempre la misma.

asymptote (p. 685) A line that a graph approaches.

asíntota Una línea a que un gráfico acerca.

augmented matrix (p. 370) A coefficient matrix with an extra column containing the constant terms.

matriz aumentada una matriz del coeficiente con una columna adicional que contiene los términos de la constante.

axis of symmetry (p. 543) The vertical line containing the vertex of a parabola.

eje de simetría La recta vertical que pasa por el vértice de una parábola.

connectED.mcgraw-hill.com
R97
Glossary/Glosario

B

bar graph (p. P41) A graphic form using bars to make comparisons of statistics.

base (p. 5) In an expression of the form x^n, the base is x.

best-fit line (p. 255) The line that most closely approximates the data in a scatter plot.

bias (p. 748) An error that results in a misrepresentation of members of a population.

binomial (p. 465) The sum of two monomials.

bivariate data (p. 247) Data with two variables.

boundary (p. 317) A line or curve that separates the coordinate plane into regions.

box-and-whisker plot (p. P43) A diagram that divides a set of data into four parts using the median and quartiles. A box is drawn around the quartile values and whiskers extend from each quartile to the extreme data points.

gráfico de barra Forma gráfica usando barras para comparar estadísticas.

base En una expresión de la forma x^n, la base es x.

recta de ajuste óptimo La recta que mejor aproxima los datos de una gráfica de dispersión.

sesgo Error que resulta en la representación errónea de los miembros de una población.

binomio La suma de dos monomios.

datos bivariate Datos con dos variables.

frontera Recta o curva que divide el plano de coordenadas en regiones.

diagrama de caja y patillas Diagram que divide un conjunto de datos en cuatro partes usando la mediana y los cuartiles. Se dibuja una caja alrededor de los cuartiles y se extienden patillas de cada uno de ellos a los valores extremos.

C

center (p. P24) The given point from which all points on the circle are the same distance.

circle (p. P24) The set of all points in a plane that are the same distance from a given point called the center.

circle graph (p. P42) A type of statistical graph used to compare parts of a whole.

circumference (p. P24) The distance around a circle.

closed (p. 634) A set is closed under an operation if for any numbers in the set, the result of the operation is also in the set.

closed half-plane (p. 317) The solution of a linear inequality that includes the boundary line.

coefficient (p. 28) The numerical factor of a term.

combination (p. 787) An arrangement or listing in which order is not important.

common difference (p. 189) The difference between the terms in an arithmetic sequence.

common ratio (p. 438) The ratio of successive terms of a geometric sequence.

centro Punto dado del cual equidistan todos los puntos de un circulo.

círculo Conjunto de todos los puntos del plano que están a la misma distancia de un punto dado del plano llamado centro.

gráfico del círculo Tipo de gráfica estadística que se usa para comparar las partes de un todo.

circunferencia Longitud del contorno de un círculo.

cerrado Un conjunto es cerrado bajo una operación si para cualquier número en el conjunto, el resultado de la operación es también en el conjunto.

mitad-plano cerrado La solución de una desigualdad linear que incluye la línea de límite.

coeficiente Factor numérico de un término.

combinación Arreglo o lista en que el orden no es importante.

diferencia común Diferencia entre términos consecutivos de una sucesión aritmética.

razón común El razón de términos sucesivos de una secuencia geométrica.

complements (p. P33) One of two parts of a probability making a whole.

completing the square (p. 574) To add a constant term to a binomial of the form $x^2 + bx$ so that the resulting trinomial is a perfect square.

complex fraction (p. 720) A fraction that has one or more fractions in the numerator or denominator.

compound event (p. 793) Two or more simple events.

compound inequality (p. 306) Two or more inequalities that are connected by the words *and* or *or*.

compound interest (p. 433) A special application of exponential growth.

conditional probability (p. 799) The probability of an event under the condition that some preceding event has occurred.

conjugates (p. 630) Binomials of the form $a\sqrt{b} + c\sqrt{d}$ and $a\sqrt{b} - c\sqrt{d}$.

consecutive integers (p. 92) Integers in counting order.

consistent (p. 335) A system of equations that has at least one ordered pair that satisfies both equations.

constant (pp. 155, 391) A monomial that is a real number.

constant function (p. 217) A linear function of the form $y = b$.

constant of variation (p. 182) The number k in equations of the form $y = kx$.

continuous function (p. 48) A function that can be graphed with a line or a smooth curve.

convenience sample (p. 747) A sample that includes members of a population that are easily accessed.

converse (p. 649) The statement formed by exchanging the phrases after *if* and *then* of an if-then statement.

coordinate (p. P8) The number that corresponds to a point on a number line.

coordinate plane (p. 40) The plane containing the x- and y-axes.

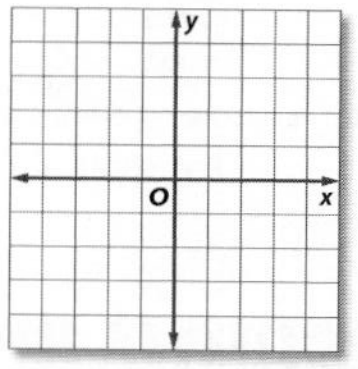

complementos Una de dos partes de una probabilidad que forma un todo.

completar el cuadrado Adición de un término constante a un binomio de la forma $x^2 + bx$, para que el trinomio resultante sea un cuadrado perfecto.

fracción compleja Fracción con una o más fracciones en el numerador o denominador.

evento compuesto Dos o más eventos simples.

desigualdad compuesta Dos o más desigualdades que están unidas por las palabras *y* u *o*.

interés compuesto Aplicación especial de crecimiento exponencial.

probabilidad condicional La probabilidad de un acontecimiento bajo condición que ha ocurrido un cierto acontecimiento precedente.

conjugados Binomios de la forma $a\sqrt{b} + c\sqrt{d}$ and $a\sqrt{b} - c\sqrt{d}$.

enteros consecutivos Enteros en el orden de contar.

consistente Sistema de ecuaciones para el cual existe al menos un par ordenado que satisface ambas ecuaciones.

constante Monomio que es un número real.

función constante Función lineal de la forma $f(x) = b$.

constante de variación El número k en ecuaciones de la forma $y = kx$.

función continua Función cuya gráfica puedes ser una recta o una curva suave.

muestra de conveniencia Muestra que incluye miembros de una población fácilmente accesibles.

recíproco Enunciado que se obtiene al inter cambiar la hipótesis y la conclusión de un enucnciado condicional dado.

coordenada Número que corresponde a un punto en una recta numérica.

plano de coordenadas Plano que contiene los ejes *x* y *y*.

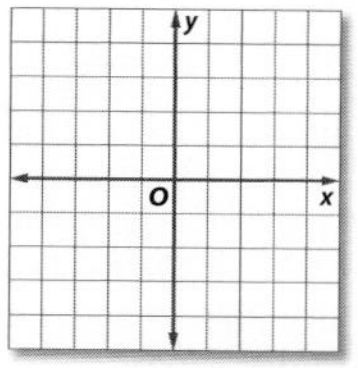

coordinate system (p. 40) The grid formed by the intersection of two number lines, the horizontal axis and the vertical axis.

sistema de coordenadas Cuadriculado formado por la intersección de dos rectas numéricas: los ejes x y y.

correlation coefficient (p. 255) A value that shows how close data points are to a line.

coeficiente de correlación Un valor que demostraciones cómo los puntos de referencias cercanos están a una línea.

cosine (p. 656) For an acute angle of a right triangle, the ratio of the measure of the leg adjacent to the acute angle to the measure of the hypotenuse.

coseno Para un ángulo agudo de un triángulo derecho, el razón de la medida de la pierna adyacente al ángulo agudo de la medida de la hipotenusa.

counterexample (p. 201) A specific case in which a statement is false.

contraejemplo Ejemplo específico de la falsedad de un enunciado.

cube root (p. 407) If $a^3 = b$, then a is the cube root of b.

raíz cúbica Si $a^3 = b$, entonces a es la raíz cúbica de b.

D

deductive reasoning (p. 196) The process of using facts, rules, definitions, or properties to reach a valid conclusion.

razonamiento deductivo Proceso de usar hechos, reglas, definiciones o propiedades para sacar conclusiones válidas.

decreasing (p. 57) The graph of a function goes down on a portion of its domain when viewed from left to right.

decreciente El gráfico de una función va abajo en una porción de su dominio cuando está visto de izquierda a derecha.

defining a variable (p. P5) Choosing a variable to represent one of the unspecified numbers in a problem and using it to write expressions for the other unspecified numbers in the problem.

definir una variable Consiste en escoger una variable para representar uno de los números desconocidos en un problema y luego usarla para escribir expresiones para otros números desconocidos en el problema.

degree of a monomial (p. 465) The sum of the exponents of all its variables.

grado de un monomio Suma de los exponentes de todas sus variables.

degree of a polynomial (p. 465) The greatest degree of any term in the polynomial.

grado de un polinomio El grado mayor de cualquier término del polinomio.

dependent (p. 335) A system of equations that has an infinite number of solutions.

dependiente Sistema de ecuaciones que posee un número infinito de soluciones.

dependent events (p. 794) Two or more events in which the outcome of one event affects the outcome of the other events.

eventos dependientes Dos o más eventos en que el resultado de un evento afecta el resultado de los otros eventos.

dependent variable (p. 42) The variable in a relation with a value that depends on the value of the independent variable.

variable dependiente La variable de una relación cuyo valor depende del valor de la variable independiente.

diameter (p. P24) The distance across a circle through its center.

diámetro La distancia a través de un círculo a través de su centro.

difference of two squares (p. 516) Two perfect squares separated by a subtraction sign.
$a^2 - b^2 = (a + b)(a - b)$ or
$a^2 - b^2 = (a - b)(a + b)$.

diferencia de cuadrados Dos cuadrados perfectos separados por el signo de sustracción.
$a^2 - b^2 = (a + b)(a - b)$ or
$a^2 - b^2 = (a - b)(a + b)$.

dilation (p. 566) A transformation that alters the size of a figure but not its shape.

homotecia Transformacióñ que altera el tamaño de una figure, pero no su forma.

dimension (p. 370) The number of rows, m, and the number of columns, n, of a matrix written as $m \times n$.

dimension El número de filas, de m, y del número de la columna, n, de una matriz escrita como $m \times n$.

dimensional analysis (p. 128) The process of carrying units throughout a computation.

análisis dimensional Proceso de tomar en cuenta las unidades de medida al hacer cálculos.

direct variation (p. 182) An equation of the form $y = kx$, where $k \neq 0$.

variación directa Una ecuación de la forma $y = kx$, donde $k \neq 0$.

discrete function (p. 48) A function of points that are not connected.

función discreta Función de puntos desconectados.

discrete random variable (p. 803) A variable with a value that is a finite number of possible outcomes.

variable aleatoria discreta Variable cuyo valor es un número finito de posibles resultados.

discriminant (p. 586) In the Quadratic Formula, the expression under the radical sign, $b^2 - 4ac$.

discriminante En la fórmula cuadrática, la expresión debajo del signo radical, $b^2 - 4ac$.

Distance Formula (p. 654) The distance d between any two points with coordinates (x_1, y_1) and (x_2, y_2) is given by the formula

$$d = \sqrt{(x_2 - x_1)^2 + (y_2 - y_1)^2}.$$

Fórmula de la distancia La distancia d entre cualquier par de puntos con coordenadas (x_1, y_1) y (x_2, y_2) viene dada por la fórmula

$$d = \sqrt{(x_2 - x_1)^2 + (y_2 - y_1)^2}.$$

distribution (p. 764) A graph or table that shows the theoretical frequency of each possible data value.

distrubución Un gráfico o una tabla que muestra la frecuencia teórica de cada valor de datos posible.

domain (p. 40) The set of the first numbers of the ordered pairs in a relation.

dominio Conjunto de los primeros números de los pares ordenados de una relación.

double root (p. 556) The roots of a quadratic function that are the same number.

raíces dobles Las raíces de una función cuadrática que son el mismo número.

E

element (p. 370) Each entry in a matrix.

elemento Cada entrada de una matriz.

elimination (p. 350) The use of addition or subtraction to eliminate one variable and solve a system of equations.

eliminación El uso de la adición o la sustracción para eliminar una variable y resolver así un sistema de ecuaciones.

end behavior (p. 57) Describes how the values of a function behave at each end of the graph.

comportamiento extremo Describe como los valores de una función se comportan en el cada fin del gráfico.

equally likely (p. P33) The outcomes of an experiment are equally likely if there are n outcomes and the probability of each is $\frac{1}{n}$.

igualmente probablemente Los resultados de un experimento son igualmente probables si hay resultados de n y la probabilidad de cada uno es $\frac{1}{n}$.

equation (p. 33) A mathematical sentence that contains an equals sign, =.

ecuación Enunciado matemático que contiene el signo de igualdad, =.

equivalent equations (p. 83) Equations that have the same solution.

ecuaciones equivalentes Ecuaciones que poseen la misma solución.

equivalent expressions (p. 16) Expressions that denote the same value for all values of the variable(s).

expresiones equivalentes Expresiones que denotan el mismo valor para todos los valores de la(s) variable(s).

evaluate (p. 10) To find the value of an expression.

excluded values (p. 684) Any values of a variable that result in a denominator of 0 must be excluded from the domain of that variable.

expected value (p. 805) The weighted average of all outcomes.

experiment (p. 749) Data are recorded from outcomes involving characteristics of a sample.

experimental probability (p. 780) What actually occurs when conducting a probability experiment, or the ratio of relative frequency to the total number of events or trials.

exponent (p. 5) In an expression of the form x^n, the exponent is n. It indicates the number of times x is used as a factor.

exponential decay (p. 424) When an initial amount decreases by the same percent over a given period of time.

exponential equation (p. 409) An equation in which the variables occur as exponents.

exponential function (p. 424) A function that can be described by an equation of the form $y = a^x$, where $a > 0$ and $a \neq 1$.

exponential growth (p. 424) When an initial amount increases by the same percent over a given period of time.

extraneous solutions (pp. 643, 727) Results that are not solutions to the original equation.

extremes (p. 112) In the ratio $\frac{a}{b} = \frac{c}{d}$, a and d are the extremes.

F

factorial (p. 786) The expression $n!$, read n factorial, where n is greater than zero, is the product of all positive integers beginning with n and counting backward to 1.

factoring (p. 494) To express a polynomial as the product of monomials and polynomials.

factoring by grouping (p. 495) The use of the Distributive Property to factor some polynomials having four or more terms.

factors (p. 5) In an algebraic expression, the quantities being multiplied are called factors.

evaluar Calcular el valor de una expresión.

valores excluidos Cualquier valor de una variable cuyo resultado sea un denominador igual a cero, debe excluirse del dominio de dicha variable.

valor previsto El promédio cargado de todos los resultados.

experimento Los datos se registran de los resultados que implican características de una muestra.

probabilidad experimental Lo que realmente sucede cuando se realiza un experimento probabilístico o la razón de la frecuencia relativa al número total de eventos o pruebas.

exponente En una expresión de la forma x^n, el exponente es n. Éste indica cuántas veces se usa x como factor.

desintegración exponencial La cantidad inicial disminuye según el mismo porcentaje a lo largo de un período de tiempo dado.

ecuación exponencial Ecuación en que las variables aparecen en los exponentes.

función exponencial Función que puede describirse mediante una ecuación de la forma $y = a^x$, donde $a > 0$ y $a \neq 1$.

crecimiento exponencial La cantidad inicial aumenta según el mismo porcentaje a lo largo de un período de tiempo dado.

soluciones extrañas Resultados que no son soluciones de la ecuación original.

extremos En la razón $\frac{a}{b} = \frac{c}{d}$, a y d son los extremos.

factorial La expresión $n!$, que se lee n factorial, donde n que es mayor que cero, es el producto de todos los números naturales, comenzando con n y contando hacia atrás hasta llegar al 1.

factorización La escritura de un polinomio como producto de monomios y polinomios.

factorización por agrupamiento Uso de la Propiedad distributiva para factorizar polinomios que poseen cuatro o más términos.

factores En una expresión algebraica, los factores son las cantidades que se multiplican.

family of graphs (p. 163) Graphs and equations of graphs that have at least one characteristic in common.

FOIL method (p. 481) To multiply two binomials, find the sum of the products of the First terms, the Outer terms, the Inner terms, and the Last terms.

formula (p. 76) An equation that states a rule for the relationship between certain quantities.

four-step problem-solving plan (p. P5)
Step 1 Explore the problem.
Step 2 Plan the solution.
Step 3 Solve the problem.
Step 4 Check the solution.

frequency table (p. P41) A chart that indicates the number of values in each interval.

function (p. 47) A relation in which each element of the domain is paired with exactly one element of the range.

function notation (p. 50) A way to name a function that is defined by an equation. In function notation, the equation $y = 3x - 8$ is written as $f(x) = 3x - 8$.

Fundamental Counting Principle (p. P34) If an event M can occur in m ways and is followed by an event N that can occur in n ways, then the event M followed by the event N can occur in $m \times n$ ways.

G

general equation for exponential decay (p. 433) $y = C(1 - r)^t$, where y is the final amount, C is the initial amount, r is the rate of decay expressed as a decimal, and t is time.

general equation for exponential growth (p. 432) $y = C(1 + r)^t$, where y is the final amount, C is the initial amount, r is the rate of change expressed as a decimal, and t is time.

geometric sequence (p. 438) A sequence in which each term after the first is found by multiplying the previous term by a constant r, called the common ratio.

graph (p. P8) To draw, or plot, the points named by certain numbers or ordered pairs on a number line or coordinate plane.

greatest integer function (p. 598) A step function, written as $f(x) = [\![x]\!]$, where $f(x)$ is the greatest integer less than or equal to x.

familia de gráficas Gráficas y ecuaciones de gráficas que tienen al menos una característica común.

método FOIL Para multiplicar dos binomios, busca la suma de los productos de los primeros (First) términos, los términos exteriores (Outer), los términos interiores (Inner) y los últimos términos (Last).

fórmula Ecuación que establece una relación entre ciertas cantidades.

plan de cuatro pasos para resolver problemas
Paso 1 Explora el problema.
Paso 2 Planifica la solución.
Paso 3 Resuelve el problema.
Paso 4 Examina la solución.

Tabla de frecuencias Tabla que indica el número de valores en cada intervalo.

función Una relación en que a cada elemento del dominio le corresponde un único elemento del rango.

notación funcional Una manera de nombrar una función definida por una ecuación. En notación funcional, la ecuación $y = 3x - 8$ se escribe $f(x) = 3x - 8$.

Principio fundamental de contar Si un evento M puede ocurrir de m maneras y lo sigue un evento N que puede ocurrir de n maneras, entonces el evento M seguido del evento N puede ocurrir de $m \times n$ maneras.

ecuación general de desintegración exponencial $y = C(1 - r)^t$, donde y es la cantidad final, C es la cantidad inicial, r es la tasa de desintegración escrita como decimal y t es el tiempo.

ecuación general de crecimiento exponencial $y = C(1 + r)^t$, donde y es la cantidad final, C es la cantidad inicial, r es la tasa de cambio del crecimiento escrita como decimal y t es el tiempo.

secuencia geométrica Una secuencia en la cual cada término después de que la primera sea encontrada multiplicando el término anterior por un r constante, llamado el razón común.

graficar Marcar los puntos que denotan ciertos números en una recta numérica o ciertos pares ordenados en un plano de coordenadas.

La función más grande del número entero Una función del paso, escrita como $f(x) = [\![x]\!]$, donde está el número entero $f(x)$ es el número más grande menos que o igual a x.

H

half-plane (p. 317) The region of the graph of an inequality on one side of a boundary.

histogram (p. P41) A graphical display that uses bars to display numerical data that have been organized into equal intervals.

hypotenuse (p. 648) The side opposite the right angle in a right triangle.

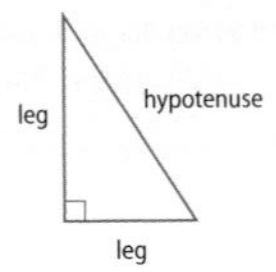

semiplano Región de la gráfica de una desigualdad en un lado de la frontera.

histograma Una exhibición gráfica que utiliza barras para exhibir los datos numéricos que se han organizado en intervalos iguales.

hipotenusa Lado opuesto al ángulo recto en un triángulo rectángulo.

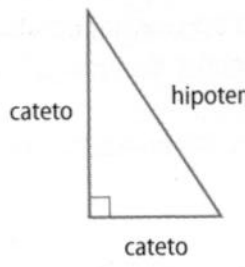

I

identity (pp. 35, 98) An equation that is true for every value of the variable.

identity function (p. 224) The function $y = x$.

identity matrix (p. 371) A square matrix that, when multiplied by another matrix, equals that same matrix. If A is any $n \times n$ matrix and I is the $n \times n$ identity matrix, then $A \cdot I = A$ and $I \cdot A = A$.

inconsistent (p. 335) A system of equations with no ordered pair that satisfy both equations.

increasing (p. 57) The graph of a function goes up on a portion of its domain when viewed from left to right.

independent (p. 335) A system of equations with exactly one solution.

independent events (p. 793) Two or more events in which the outcome of one event does not affect the outcome of the other events.

independent variable (p. 42) The variable in a function with a value that is subject to choice.

inductive reasoning (p. 196) A conclusion based on a pattern of examples.

inequality (p. 285) An open sentence that contains the symbol $<$, $\leq$, $>$, or $\geq$.

integers (p. P7) The set $\{\ldots, -2, -1, 0, 1, 2, \ldots\}$.

identidad Ecuación que es verdad para cada valor de la variable.

unción identidad La función $y = x$.

matriz de la identidad Una matriz cuadrada que, cuando es multiplicada por otra matriz, iguala que la misma matriz. Si A es alguna de la matriz $n \times n$ e I es la matriz de la identidad de $n \times n$, entonces $A \cdot I = A$ e $I \cdot A = A$.

inconsistente Un sistema de ecuaciones para el cual no existe par ordenado alguno que satisfaga ambas ecuaciones.

creciente El gráfico de una función va arriba en una porción de su dominio cuando está visto de izquierda a derecha.

independiente Un sistema de ecuaciones que posee una única solución.

eventos independientes El resultado de un evento no afecta el resultado del otro evento.

variable independiente La variable de una función sujeta a elección.

razonamiento inductivo Conclusión basada en un patrón de ejemplos.

desigualdad Enunciado abierto que contiene uno o más de los símbolos $<$, $\leq$, $>$, o $\geq$.

enteros El conjunto $\{\ldots, -2, -1, 0, 1, 2, \ldots\}$.

interquartile range (p. P38) The range of the middle half of a set of data. It is the difference between the upper quartile and the lower quartile.

intersection (p. 306) The graph of a compound inequality containing *and*; the solution is the set of elements common to both inequalities.

inverse cosine (p. 658) If $\angle A$ is an acute angle and the cosine of A is x, then the inverse cosine of x is the measure of $\angle A$.

inverse sine (p. 658) If $\angle A$ is an acute angle and the sine of A is x, then the inverse sine of x is the measure of $\angle A$.

inverse tangent (p. 658) If $\angle A$ is an acute angle and the tangent of A is x, then the inverse tangent of x is the measure of $\angle A$.

inverse variation (p. 676) An equation of the form $xy = k$, where $k \neq 0$.

irrational numbers (p. P7) Numbers that cannot be expressed as terminating or repeating decimals.

amplitud intercuartílica Amplitude de la mitad central de un conjunto de datos. Es la diferenccia entre el cuartil superior y el inferior.

intersección Gráfica de una desigualdad compuesta que contiene la palabra y; la solución es el conjunto de soluciones de ambas desigualdades.

cosino inverso Si el $\angle A$ es un ángulo agudo y el coseno de A es x, entonces el coseno inverso de x es la medida de $\angle A$.

seno inverso Si $\angle A$ es un ángulo agudo y el seno de A es x, entonces el seno inverso de x es la medida de $\angle A$.

tangente inverso Si el $\angle A$ es un ángulo agudo y la tangente de A es x, entonces la tangente inversa de x es la medida de $\angle A$.

variación inversa Ecuación de la forma $xy = k$, donde $k \neq 0$.

números irracionales Números que no pueden escribirse como decimales terminales o periódicos.

L

leading coefficient (p. 466) The coefficient of the term with the highest degree in a polynomial.

least common denominator (LCD) (p. 714) The least common multiple of the denominators of two or more fractions.

least common multiple (LCM) (p. 713) The least number that is a common multiple of two or more numbers.

legs (p. 648) The sides of a right triangle that form the right angle.

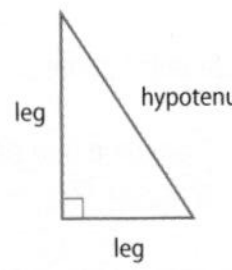

like terms (p. 27) Terms that contain the same variables, with corresponding variables having the same exponent.

linear equation (p. 155) An equation in the form $Ax + By = C$, with a graph that is a straight line.

linear extrapolation (p. 228) The use of a linear equation to predict values that are outside the range of data.

linear function (p. 163) A function with ordered pairs that satisfy a linear equation.

coeficiente inicial El coeficiente del término con el grado más alto (el primer coeficiente inicial) en un polinomio.

mínimo denominador común (mcd) El mínimo común múltiplo de los denominadores de dos o más fracciones.

mínimo común múltiplo (mcm) El número menor que es múltiplo común de dos o más números.

catetos Lados de un triángulo rectángulo que forman el ángulo recto del mismo.

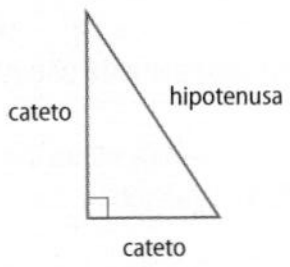

términos semejantes Expresiones que tienen las mismas variables, con las variables correspondientes elevadas a los mismos exponentes.

ecuación lineal Ecuación de la forma $Ax + By = C$, cuya gráfica es una recta.

extrapolación lineal Uso de una ecuación lineal para predecir valores fuera de la amplitud de los datos.

función lineal Función cuyos pares ordenados satisfacen una ecuación lineal.

Glossary/Glosario

linear interpolation (p. 249) The use of a linear equation to predict values that are inside of the data range.

linear regression (p. 255) An algorithm to find a precise line of fit for a set of data.

linear transformation (p. 771) One or more operations performed on a set of data that can be written as a linear function.

line of fit (p. 248) A line that describes the trend of the data in a scatter plot.

literal equation (p. 127) A formula or equation with several variables.

lower quartile (p. P38) Divides the lower half of the data into two equal parts.

M

mapping (p. 40) Illustrates how each element of the domain is paired with an element in the range.

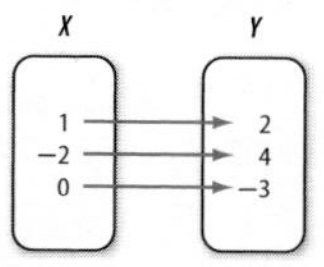

matrix (p. 370) Any rectangular arrangement of numbers in rows and columns.

maximum (p. 58) The highest point on the graph of a curve.

mean (p. P37) The sum of numbers in a set of data divided by the number of items in the data set.

mean absolute deviation (p. 758) The average of the absolute values of differences between the mean and each value in a data set. It is used to predict errors and to judge equality.

means (p. 112) The middle terms of the proportion.

measures of central tendency (p. P37) Numbers or pieces of data that can represent the whole set of data.

measures of position (p. P38) Measures that compare the position of a value relative to other values in a set.

measures of variation (p. P38) Used to describe the distribution of statistical data.

median (p. P37) The middle number in a set of data when the data are arranged in numerical order. If the data set has an even number, the median is the mean of the two middle numbers.

interpolación lineal Uso de una ecuación lineal para predecir valores dentro de la amplitud de los datos.

regresión linear Un algoritmo para encontrar una línea exacta del ajuste para un sistema de datos.

transformación lineal Una o más operaciones que se hacen en un conjunto de datos y que se pueden escribir como una función lineal.

recta de ajuste Recta que describe la tendencia de los datos en una gráfica de dispersión.

ecuación literal Un fórmula o ecuación con varias variables.

cuartil inferior Éste divide en dos partes iguales la mitad inferior de un conjunto de datos.

aplicaciones Ilustra la correspondencia entre cada elemento del dominio con un elemento del rango.

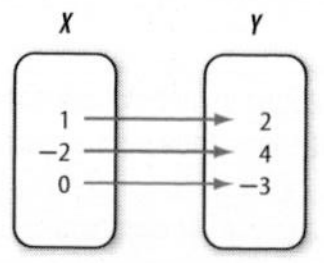

matriz Disposición rectangular de numeros colocados en filas y columnas.

máximo El punto más alto en la gráfica de una curva.

media La suma de los números de un conjunto de datos dividida entre el numero total de artículos.

desviación absoluta media El promedio de los valores absolutos de diferencias entre el medio y cada valor de un conjunto de datos. Ha usado para predecir errores y para juzgar igualdad.

medios Los términos centrales de una proporción.

medidas de tendencia central Números o fragmentos que pueden representar el conjunto de datos total de datos.

medidas de la posición Las medidas que comparar la posición de un valor relativo a otros valores de un conjunto.

medidas de variación Números que se usan para describir la distribución o separación de un conjunto de datos.

mediana El número central de conjunto de datos, una vezque los datos han sido ordenados numéricamente. Si hay un número par de datos, la mediana es el promedio de los datos centrales.

median fit line (p. 258) A type of best-fit line that is calculated using the medians of the coordinates of the data points.

metric (p. 118) A rule for assigning a number to some characteristic or attribute.

midpoint (p. 654) The point halfway between the endpoints of a segment.

minimum (p. 58) The lowest point on the graph of a curve.

mixed expression (p. 720) An expression that contains the sum of a monomial and a rational expression.

mixture problems (p. 132) Problems in which two or more parts are combined into a whole.

mode (p. P37) The number(s) that appear most often in a set of data.

monomial (p. 391) A number, a variable, or a product of a number and one or more variables.

multiplicative identity (p. 17) For any number a, $a \cdot 1 = 1 \cdot a = a$.

multiplicative inverses (pp. P18, 17) Two numbers with a product of 1.

multi-step equation (p. 91) Equations with more than one operation.

mutually exclusive events (p. 795) Events that cannot occur at the same time.

N

nth root (p. 640) If $a^n = b$ for a positive integer n, then a is an nth root of b.

natural numbers (p. P7) The set $\{1, 2, 3, \ldots\}$.

negative (p. 57) A function is negative on a portion of its domain where its graph lies below the x-axis.

negative correlation (p. 247) In a scatter plot, as x increases, y decreases.

negative exponent (p. 400) For any real number $a \neq 0$ and any integer n, $a^{-n} = \frac{1}{a^n}$ and $\frac{1}{a^{-n}} = a^n$.

negative number (p. P7) Any value less than zero.

nonlinear function (p. 50) A function with a graph that is not a straight line.

línea apta del punto medio Tipo de mejor-cupo la línea se calcula que usando los puntos medios de los coordenadas de los puntos de referencias.

métrico Una regla para asignar un número a alguna característica o atribuye.

punto medio Punto que divide a un segmento separándolo en dos segmentos congruentes.

mínimo El punto más bajo en la gráfica de una curva.

expresión mixta Expresión que contiene la suma de un monomio y una expresión racional.

problemas de mezclas Problemas en que dos o más partes se combinan en un todo.

moda El número(s) que aparece más frecuencia en un conjunto de datos.

monomio Número, variable o producto de un número por una o más variables.

identidad de la multiplicación Para cualquier número $a \cdot 1 = 1 \cdot a = a$.

inversos multiplicativos Dos números cuyo producto es igual a 1.

ecuaciones de varios pasos Ecuaciones con más de una operación.

mutuamente exclusivos Eventos que no pueden ocurrir simultáneamente.

raíz enésima Si $a^n = b$ para cualquier entero positive n, entonces a se llama una raíz enésima de b.

números naturales El conjunto $\{1, 2, 3, \ldots\}$.

negativo Una función es negativa en una porción de su dominio donde su gráfico está debajo del eje-x.

correlación negativa En una gráfica de dispersión, a medida que x aumenta, y disminuye.

exponiente negativo Para números reales, si $a \neq 0$, y cualquier número entero n, entonces $a^{-n} = \frac{1}{a^n}$ and $\frac{1}{a^{-n}} = a^n$.

número negativo Cualquier valor menor que cero.

función no lineal Una función con un gráfica que no es una línea recta.

Glossary/Glosario

number theory (p. 92) The study of numbers and the relationships between them.

O

observational study (p. 749) Members of a sample are measured or observed without being affected by the study.

odds (p. P35) The ratio of the probability of the success of an event to the probability of its complement.

open half-plane (p. 317) The solution of a linear inequality that does not include the boundary line.

open sentence (p. 33) A mathematical statement with one or more variables.

opposites (p. P11) Two numbers with the same absolute value but different signs.

ordered pair (p. 40) A set of numbers or coordinates used to locate any point on a coordinate plane, written in the form (x, y).

order of magnitude (p. 401) The order of magnitude of a quantity is the number rounded to the nearest power of 10.

order of operations (p. 10)

1. Evaluate expressions inside grouping symbols.
2. Evaluate all powers.
3. Do all multiplications and/or divisions from left to right.
4. Do all additions and/or subtractions from left to right.

origin (p. 40) The point where the two axes intersect at their zero points.

outliers (p. P39) Data that are more than 1.5 times the interquartile range beyond the quartiles.

P

parabola (p. 543) The graph of a quadratic function.

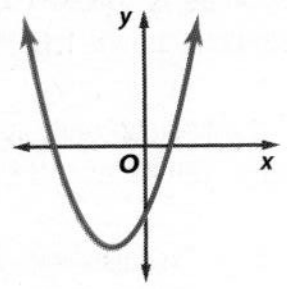

teoría del número El estudio de números y de las relaciones entre ellas.

estudio de observación Los miembros de una muestra son medidos o son observados sin ser afectado por el estudio.

probabilidades El cociente de la probabilidad del éxito de un acontecimiento a la probabilidad de su complemento.

abra el mitad-plano La solución de una desigualdad linear que no incluya la línea de límite.

enunciado abierto Un enunciado matemático que contiene una o más variables.

opuestos Dos números que tienen el mismo valor absolute, pero que tienen distintos signos.

par ordenado Un par de números que se usa para ubicar cualquier punto de un plano de coordenadas y que se escribe en la forma (x, y).

orden de magnitud de una cantidad Un número redondeado a la potencia más cercana de 10.

orden de las operaciones

1. Evalúa las expresiones dentro de los símbolos de agrupamiento.
2. Evalúa todas las potencias.
3. Multiplica o divide de izquierda a derecha.
4. Suma o resta de izquierda a derecha.

origen Punto donde se intersecan los dos ejes en sus puntos cero.

valores atípicos Datos que distan de los cuartiles más de 1.5 veces la amplitude intercuartílica.

parábola La gráfica de una función cuadrática.

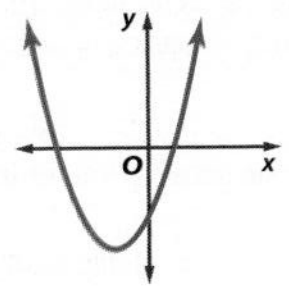

parallel lines (p. 239) Lines in the same plane that do not intersect and either have the same slope or are vertical lines.

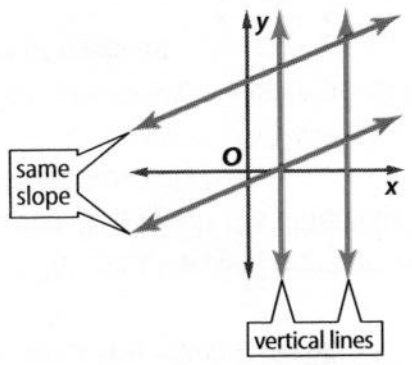

parameter (p. 757) A measure that describes a characteristic of the population as a whole.

parent function (p. 163) The simplest of functions in a family.

parent graph (p. 163) The simplest of the graphs in a family of graphs.

percent (p. P20) A ratio that compares a number to 100.

percent of change (p. 119) When an increase or decrease is expressed as a percent.

percent of decrease (p. 119) The ratio of an amount of decrease to the previous amount, expressed as a percent.

percent of increase (p. 119) The ratio of an amount of increase to the previous amount, expressed as a percent.

percent proportion (p. P20)
$\frac{\text{part}}{\text{whole}} = \frac{\text{percent}}{100}$ or $\frac{a}{b} = \frac{p}{100}$

perimeter (p. P23) The distance around a geometric figure.

perfect square (p. P7) A number with a square root that is a rational number.

perfect square trinomial (p. 522) A trinomial that is the square of a binomial.
$(a + b)^2 = (a + b)(a + b) = a^2 + 2ab + b^2$ or
$(a - b)^2 = (a - b)(a - b) = a^2 - 2ab + b^2$

permutation (p. 786) An arrangement or listing in which order is important.

perpendicular lines (p. 240) Lines that intersect to form a right angle.

rectas paralelas Rectas en el mismo plano que no se intersecan y que tienen pendientes iguales, o las mismas rectas verticales.

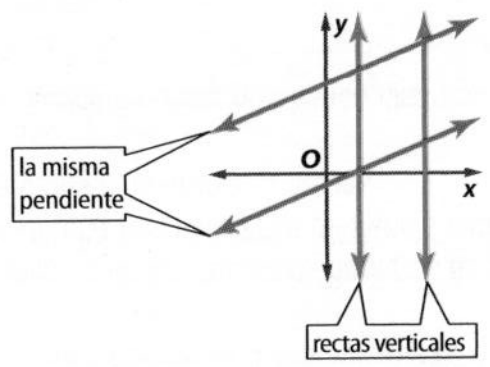

parámetro Una medida que se describe característica de la población en su totalidad.

función basíca La función más fundamental de un familia de funciones.

gráfica madre La gráfica más sencilla en una familia de gráficas.

porcentaje Razón que compara un numero con 100.

porcentaje de cambio Cuando un aumento o disminución se escribe como un tanto por ciento.

porcentaje de disminución Razón de la cantidad de disminución a la cantidad original, escrita como un tanto por ciento.

porcentaje de aumento Razón de la cantidad de aumento a la cantidad original, escrita como un tanto por ciento.

proporción porcentual
$\frac{\text{parte}}{\text{todo}} = \frac{\text{por ciento}}{100}$ or $\frac{a}{b} = \frac{p}{100}$

perímetro Longitud alrededor una figura geométrica.

cuadrado perfecto Número cuya raíz cuadrada es un número racional.

trinomio cuadrado perfecto Un trinomio que es el cuadrado de un binomio.
$(a + b)^2 = (a + b)(a + b) = a^2 + 2ab + b^2$ or
$(a - b)^2 = (a - b)(a - b) = a^2 - 2ab + b^2$

permutación Arreglo o lista en que el orden es importante.

recta perpendicular Recta que se intersecta formando un ángulo recto

piecewise-linear function (p. 598) A function written using two or more linear expressions.

función lineal por partes Función que se escribe usando dos o más expresiones lineal.

piecewise-defined function (p. 599) A function that is written using two or more expressions.

función definida por partes Función que se escribe usando dos o más expresiones.

point-slope form (p. 233) An equation of the form $y - y_1 = m(x - x_1)$, where m is the slope and (x_1, y_1) is a given point on a nonvertical line.

forma punto-pendiente Ecuación de la forma $y - y_1 = m(x - x_1)$, donde m es la pendiente y (x_1, y_1) es un punto dado de una recta no vertical.

polynomial (p. 465) A monomial or sum of monomials.

polinomio Un monomio o la suma de monomios.

population (p. 747) A large group of data usually represented by a sample.

población Grupo grande de datos, representado por lo general por una muestra.

positive (p. 57) A function is positive on a portion of its domain where its graph lies above the *x*-axis.

positiva Una función es positiva en una porción de su dominio donde su gráfico está encima del eje-*x*.

positive correlation (p. 247) In a scatter plot, as *x* increases, *y* increases.

correlación positiva En una gráfica de dispersión, a medida que *x* aumenta, *y* aumenta.

positive number (p. P7) Any value that is greater than zero.

número positivos Cualquier valor mayor que cero.

power (p. 5) An expression of the form x^n, read *x to the nth power.*

potencia Una expresión de la forma x^n, se lee *x a la enésima potencia.*

prime polynomial (p. 512) A polynomial that cannot be written as a product of two polynomials with integral coefficients.

polinomio primo Polinomio que no puede escribirse como producto de dos polinomios con coeficientes enteros.

principal square root (p. P7) The nonnegative square root of a number.

raíz cuadrada principal La raíz cuadrada no negativa de un número.

probability (p. P33) The ratio of the number of favorable equally likely outcomes to the number of possible equally likely outcomes.

probabilidad La razón del número de maneras en que puede ocurrir el evento al numero de resultados posibles.

probability distribution (p. 804) The probability of every possible value of the random variable *x*.

distribución de probabilidad Probabilidad de cada valor posible de una variable aleatoria *x*.

probability graph (p. 804) A way to give the probability distribution for a random variable and obtain other data.

gráfico probabilístico Una manera de exhibir la distribución de probabilidad de una variable aleatoria y obtener otros datos.

probability model (p. 781) A mathematical model used to represent the outcomes of an experiment.

modelo de probabilidad Modelo matemático que se usa para representar los resultados de un experimento.

product (p. 5) In an algebraic expression, the result of quantities being multiplied is called the product.

producto En una expresión algebraica, se llama producto al resultado de las cantidades que se multiplican.

product rule (p. 677) If (x_1, y_1) and (x_2, y_2) are solutions to an inverse variation, then $y_1x_1 = y_2x_2$.

regla del producto Si (x_1, y_1) y (x_2, y_2) son soluciones de una variación inversa, entonces $y_1x_1 = y_2x_2$.

proportion (p. 111) An equation of the form $\frac{a}{b} = \frac{c}{d}$, where $b, d \neq 0$, stating that two ratios are equivalent.

proporción Ecuación de la forma $\frac{a}{b} = \frac{c}{d}$, donde $b, d \neq 0$, que afirma la equivalencia de dos razones.

Pythagorean Theorem (p. 648) If *a* and *b* are the measures of the legs of a right triangle and *c* is the measure of the hypotenuse, then $c^2 = a^2 + b^2$.

Teorema de Pitágoras Si *a* y *b* son las longitudes de los catetos de un triángulo rectángulo y si *c* es la longitud de la hipotenusa, entonces $c^2 = a^2 + b^2$.

Pythagorean triple (p. 649) Counting numbers that satisfy the Pythagorean Theorem.

Triple pitagórico Números de contar que satisfacen el Teorema de Pitágoras.

Q

quadratic equation (pp. 506, 555) An equation of the form $ax^2 + bx + c = 0$, where $a \neq 0$.

ecuación cuadrática Ecuación de la forma $ax^2 + bx + c = 0$, donde $a \neq 0$.

quadratic expression (p. 481) An expression in one variable with a degree of 2 written in the form $ax^2 + bx + c$.

expression cuadratica Una expresión en una variable con un grado de 2, escritos en la forma $ax^2 + bx + c$.

Quadratic Formula (p. 583) The solutions of a quadratic equation in the form $ax^2 + bx + c = 0$, where $a \neq 0$, are given by the formula

$$x = \frac{-b \pm \sqrt{b^2 - 4ac}}{2a}.$$

Fórmula cuadrática Las soluciones de una ecuación cuadrática de la forma $ax^2 + bx + c = 0$, donde $a \neq 0$, vienen dadas por la fórmula

$$x = \frac{-b \pm \sqrt{b^2 - 4ac}}{2a}.$$

quadratic function (p. 543) An equation of the form $y = ax^2 + bx + c$, where $a \neq 0$.

función cuadrática Función de la forma $y = ax^2 + bx + c$, donde $a \neq 0$.

quartile (p. P38) The values that divide a set of data into four equal parts.

cuartile Valores que dividen en conjunto de datos en cuarto partes iguales.

R

radical equations (p. 642) Equations that contain radicals with variables in the radicand.

ecuaciones radicales Ecuaciones que contienen radicales con variables en el radicando.

radical expression (p. 628) An expression that contains a square root.

expresión radical Expresión que contiene una raíz cuadrada.

radical function (p. 621) A function that contains radicals with variables in the radicand.

ecuaciones radicales Ecuaciones que contienen radicales con variables en el radicando.

radicand (p. 621) The expression that is under the radical sign.

radicando La expresión debajo del signo radical.

radius (p. P24) Distance from the center to any point on the circle.

radio Distancia del centro cualquier punto de un círculo.

random variable (p. 803) A variable with a value that is the numerical outcome of a random event.

variable aleatoria Una variable cuyos valores son los resultados numéricos de un evento aleatorio.

range **1.** (p. 40) The set of second numbers of the ordered pairs in a relation. **2.** (p. P38) The difference between the greatest and least data values.

rango **1.** Conjunto de los segundos números de los pares ordenados de una relación. **2.** La diferencia entre los valores de datos más grande o menos.

rate (p. 113) The ratio of two measurements having different units of measure.

tasa Razón de dos medidas que tienen distintas unidades de medida.

rate of change (p. 172) How a quantity is changing with respect to a change in another quantity.

tasa de cambio Cómo cambia una cantidad con respecto a un cambio en otra cantidad.

rate problems (pp. 134, 729) Problems in which an object moves at a certain speed, or rate.

ratio (p. 111) A comparison of two numbers by division.

rational equations (p. 726) Equations that contain rational expressions.

rational exponent (p. 406) For any positive real number b and any integers m and $n > 1$, $b^{\frac{m}{n}} = \left(\sqrt[n]{b}\right)^m$ or $\sqrt[n]{b^m}$. $\frac{m}{n}$ is a rational exponent.

rational expression (p. 690) An algebraic fraction with a numerator and denominator that are polynomials.

rational function (p. 684) An equation of the form $f(x) = \frac{p(x)}{q(x)}$, where $p(x)$ and $q(x)$ are polynomial functions, and $q(x) \neq 0$.

rationalizing the denominator (p. 630) A method used to eliminate radicals from the denominator of a fraction.

rational numbers (p. P7) The set of numbers expressed in the form of a fraction $\frac{a}{b}$, where a and b are integers and $b \neq 0$.

real numbers (p. P7) The set of rational numbers and the set of irrational numbers together.

reciprocal (pp. P18, 17) The multiplicative inverse of a number.

recursive formula (p. 445) Each term is formulated from one or more previous terms.

reflection (p. 566) A transformation where a figure, line, or curve, is flipped across a line.

relation (p. 40) A set of ordered pairs.

relative frequency (p. 802) The number of times an outcome occurred in a probability experiment.

replacement set (p. 33) A set of numbers from which replacements for a variable may be chosen.

residual (p. 256) The difference between an observed y-value and its predicted y-value on a regression line.

root (p. 163) The solutions of a quadratic equation.

row reduction (p. 371) The process of performing elementary row operations on an augmented matrix to solve a system.

problemas de tasas Problemas en el que un objeto se mueue a una velocidad o tasa determinada.

razón Comparación de dos números mediante división.

ecuaciones racionales Ecuaciones que contienen expresiones racionales.

exponent racional Para cualquier número real no nulo b y cualquier entero m y $n > 1$, $b^{\frac{m}{n}} = \left(\sqrt[n]{b}\right)^m$ or $\sqrt[n]{b^m}$. $\frac{m}{n}$ es un exponent racional.

expresión racional Fracción algebraica cuyo numerador y denominador son polinomios.

función racional Ecuación de la forma $f(x) = \frac{p(x)}{q(x)}$, donde $p(x)$ y $q(x)$ son funciones polinomiales y $q(x) \neq 0$.

racionalizar el denominador Método que se usa para eliminar radicales del denominador de una fracción.

números racionales Conjunto de los números que pueden escribirse en forma de fracción $\frac{a}{b}$, donde a y b son enteros y $b \neq 0$.

números reales El conjunto de los números racionales junto con el conjunto de los números irracionales.

recíproco Inverso multiplicativo de un número.

fórmula recursiva Cada tórmino proviene de uno o más terminos anteriores.

reflexión Transformación en que cadapunto de una figura se aplica a través de una recta de simetría a su imagen correspondiente.

relación Conjunto de pares ordenados.

frecuencia relativa Número de veces que aparece un resultado en un experimento probabilístico.

conjunto de sustitución Conjunto de números del cual se pueden escoger sustituciones para una variable.

residual Diferencia entre el valor observado de y y el valor redicho de y en la recta de regression.

raíces Las soluciones de una ecuación cuadrática

reducción de la fila El proceso de realizar operaciones elementales de la fila en una matriz aumentada para solucionar un sistema.

S

sample (p. 747) Some portion of a larger group selected to represent that group.

sample space (p. P33) The list of all possible outcomes.

scale (p. 114) The relationship between the measurements on a drawing or model and the measurements of the real object.

scale model (p. 114) A model used to represent an object that is too large or too small to be built at actual size.

scatter plot (p. 247) A scatter plot shows the relationship between a set of data with two variables, graphed as ordered pairs on a coordinate plane.

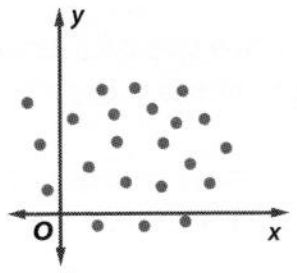

scientific notation (p. 414) A number in scientific notation is expressed as $a \times 10^n$, where $1 \leq a < 10$ and n is an integer.

self-selected sample (p. 747) Members volunteer to be included in the sample.

sequence (p. 189) A set of numbers in a specific order.

set-builder notation (p. 286) A concise way of writing a solution set. For example, $\{t \mid t < 17\}$ represents the set of all numbers t such that t is less than 17.

simple random sample (p. 747) A sample that is as likely to be chosen as any other from the population.

simplest form (p. 27) An expression is in simplest form when it is replaced by an equivalent expression having no like terms or parentheses.

simulation (p. 781) Using an object to act out an event that would be difficult or impractical to perform.

sine (p. 656) For an acute angle of a right triangle, the ratio of the measure of the leg opposite the acute angle to the measure of the hypotenuse.

muestra Porción de un grupo más grande que se escoge para representarlo.

espacio muestral Lista de todos los resultados posibles.

escala Relación entre las medidas de un dibujo o modelo y las medidas de la figura verdadera.

modelo a escala Modelo que se usa para representar un figura que es demasiado grande o pequeña como para ser construida de tamaño natural.

gráfica de dispersión Es un diagrama que muestra la relación entre un conjunto de datos con dos variables, graficados como pares ordenados en un plano coordenadas.

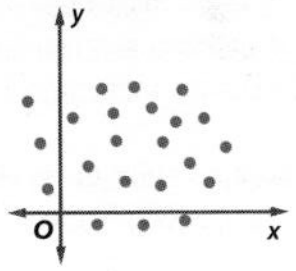

notación científica Un numero en notación científica se escribe con $a \times 10^n$, donde $1 \leq a < 10$ y n es un número entero.

muestra auto-seleccionados Los miembros se ofrecen voluntariamente para ser incluidos en la muestra.

sucesión Conjunto de números en un orden específico.

notación de construcción de conjuntos Manera concisa de escribir un conjunto solución. Por ejemplo, $\{t \mid t < 17\}$ representa el conjunto de todos los números t que son menores o iguales que 17.

muestra aleatoria simple Muestra de una población que tiene la misma probabilidad de escogerse que cualquier otra.

forma reducida Una expresión está reducida cuando se puede sustituir por una expresión equivalente que no tiene ni términos semejantes ni paréntesis.

simulación Uso de un objeto para representar un evento que pudiera ser difícil o poco práctico de ejecutar.

seno La razón entre la medida del cateto opuesto al ángulo agudo y la medida de la hipotenusa de un triángulo rectángulo.

slope (p. 174) The ratio of the change in the y-coordinates (rise) to the corresponding change in the x-coordinates (run) as you move from one point to another along a line.

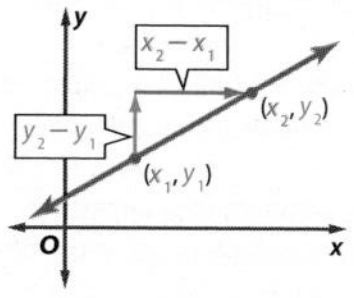

slope-intercept form (p. 216) An equation of the form $y = mx + b$, where m is the slope and b is the y-intercept.

solution (p. 33) A replacement value for the variable in an open sentence.

solution set (p. 33) The set of elements from the replacement set that make an open sentence true.

solve an equation (p. 83) The process of finding all values of the variable that make the equation a true statement.

solving an open sentence (p. 33) Finding a replacement value for the variable that results in a true sentence or an ordered pair that results in a true statement when substituted into the equation.

solving a triangle (p. 657) Finding the measures of all of the angles and sides of a triangle.

square root (p. P7) One of two equal factors of a number.

square root function (p. 621) Function that contains the square root of a variable.

standard deviation (p. 759) The square root of the variance.

standard form (p. 155) The standard form of a linear equation is $Ax + By = C$, where $A \geq 0$, A and B are not both zero, and A, B, and C are integers with a greatest common factor of 1.

standard form of a polynomial (p. 466) A polynomial that is written with the terms in order from greatest degree to least degree.

statistic (p. 757) A quantity calculated from a sample.

statistical inference (p. 757) The statistics of a sample are used to draw conclusions about the population.

pendiente Razón del cambio en la coordenada y (elevación) al cambio correspondiente en la coordenada x (desplazamiento) a medida que uno se mueve de un punto a otro en una recta.

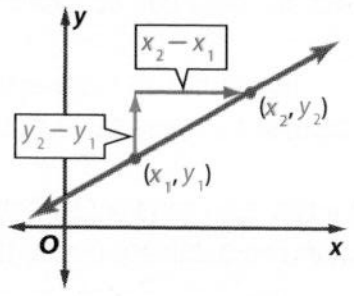

forma pendiente-intersección Ecuación de la forma $y = mx + b$, donde m es la pendiente y b es la intersección y.

solución Valor de sustitución de la variable en un enunciado abierto.

conjunto solución Conjunto de elementos del conjunto de sustitución que hacen verdadero un enunciado abierto.

resolver una ecuación Proceso en que se hallan todos los valores de la variable que hacen verdadera la ecuación.

resolver un enunciado abierto Hallar un valor de sustitución de la variable que resulte en un enunciado verdadero o un par ordenado que resulte en una proposición verdadera cuando se lo sustituye en la ecuación.

resolver un triángulo Hallar las medidas de todos los lados y todos los ángulos de un triángulo.

raíz cuadrada Uno de dos factores iguales de un número.

función radical Función que contiene la raíz cuadrada de una variable.

desviación tipica Calculada como la raíz cuadrada de la varianza.

forma estándar La forma estándar de una ecuación lineal es $Ax + By = C$, donde $A \geq 0$, ni A ni B son ambos cero, y A, B, y C son enteros cuyo máximo común divisor es 1.

forma de estándar de un polinomio Un polinomio que se escribe con los términos en orden del grado más grande a menos grado.

estadística Una cantidad calculaba de una muestra.

inferencia estadística La estadística de una muestra se utiliza para dibujar conclusiones sobre la población.

stratified sample (p. 747) A sample in which the population is first divided into similar, nonoverlapping groups; a simple random sample is then selected from each group.

stem-and-leaf plot (p. P42) A system used to condense a set of data where the greatest place value of the data forms the stem and the next greatest place value forms the leaves.

step function (p. 598) A function with a graph that is a series of horizontal line segments.

substitution (p. 344) Use algebraic methods to find an exact solution of a system of equations.

surface area (p. P31) The sum of the areas of all the surfaces of a three-dimensional figure.

survey (p. 749) Data are from responses given by a sample of the population.

symmetry (p. 57) A geometric property of figures that can be folded and each half matches the other exactly.

system of equations (p. 335) A set of equations with the same variables.

system of inequalities (p. 372) A set of two or more inequalities with the same variables.

systematic sample (p. 747) A sample in which the items in the sample are selected according to a specified time or item interval.

muestra aleatoria estratificada Muestra en que la población se divide en grupos similares que no se sobreponen; luego se selecciona una muestra aleatoria simple, de cada grupo.

diagrama de tallo y hojas Sistema que se usa para condensar un conjunto de datos, en que el valor de posición máximo de los datos forma el tallo y el segundo valor de posiciós máximo forma las hojas. El valor de posición máximo de los datos forma eld tallo y el segundo valor de posición máximo forma las hojas.

funcion escalonada Función cuya gráfica es una serie de segmentos de recto.

sustitución Usa métodos algebraicos para hallar una solución exacta a un sistema de ecuaciones.

área de superficie Suma de las áreas de todas las superficies (caras) de una figura tridimensional.

encuesta Datos son de las respuestas dadas por una muestra de la población.

simetría Propiedad geométrica de figuras que pueden plegarse de modo que cada mitad corresponde exactamente a la otra.

sistema de ecuaciones Conjunto de ecuaciones con las mismas variables.

sistema de desigualdades Conjunto de dos o más desigualdades con las mismas variables.

muestra aleatoria sistemática Muestra en que los elementos de la muestra se escogen según un intervalo de tiempo o elemento específico.

T

tangent (p. 656) For an acute angle of a right triangle, the ratio of the measure of the leg opposite the acute angle to the measure of the leg adjacent to the acute angle.

term (p. 5) A number, a variable, or a product or quotient of numbers and variables.

terms of a sequence (p. 189) The numbers in a sequence.

theoretical probability (p. 780) What should occur in a probability experiment.

transformation (p. 564) A movement of a geometric figure.

translation (p. 564) A transformation where a figure is slid from one position to another without being turned.

tangente La razón entre la medida del cateto opuesto al ángulo agudo y la medida del cateto adyacente al ángulo agudo de un triángulo rectángulo.

término Número, variable o producto, o cociente de números y variables.

términos Los números de una sucesión.

probabilidad teórica Lo que debería ocurrir en un experimento probabilístico.

transformación Desplazamiento de una figura geométrica.

translación Transformación en que una figura se desliza sin girar, de una posición a otra.

tree diagram (p. P34) A diagram used to show the total number of possible outcomes.

diagrama de árbol Diagrama que se usa para mostrar el número total de resultados posibles.

trigonometric ratio (p. 656) A ratio of the lengths of sides of a right triangle.

razón trigonométrica Razón entre las longitudes de dos lados de un triángulo rectángulo.

trigonometry (p. 656) The study of the properties of triangles and trigonometric functions and their applications.

trigonométria Estudio de las relaciones entre los lados y ángulos de un triángulo rectángulo.

trinomials (p. 465) The sum of three monomials.

trinomios Suma de tres monomios.

U

uniform motion problems (p. 134) Problems in which an object moves at a certain speed, or rate.

problemas de movimiento uniforme Problemas en que el cuerpo se mueve a cierta velocidad o tasa.

union (p. 307) The graph of a compound inequality containing or; the solution is a solution of either inequality, not necessarily both.

unión Gráfica de una desigualdad compuesta que contiene la palabra o; la solución es el conjunto de soluciones de por lo menos una de las desigualdades, no necesariamente ambas.

unit analysis (p. 128) The process of including units of measurement when computing.

análisis de la unidad Proceso de incluir unidades de medida al computar.

unit rate (p. 113) A ratio of two quantities, the second of which is one unit.

tasa unitaria Tasa reducida que tiene denominador igual a 1.

univariate data (p. P37) Data with one variable.

datos univariate Datos con una variable.

upper quartile (p. P38) The median of the upper half of a set of data.

cuartil superior Mediana de la mitad superior de un conjunto de datos.

V

variable **1.** (p. 5) Symbols used to represent unspecified numbers or values. **2.** (p. P37) a characteristic of a group of people or objects that can assume different values

variable **1.** Símbolos que se usan para representar números o valores no especificados. **2.** una característica de un grupo de personas u objetos que pueden asumir valores diferentes

variance (p. 759) The mean of the squares of the deviations from the arithmetic mean.

varianza Media de los cuadrados de las desviaciones de la media aritmética.

vertex (p. 543) The maximum or minimum point of a parabola.

vértice Punto máximo o mínimo de una parábola.

vertex form (p. 568) A quadratic function in the form $f(x) = a(x - h)^2 + k$.

forma de vértice Una función cuadrática de la forma $f(x) = a(x - h)^2 + k$.

vertical line test (p. 49) If any vertical line passes through no more than one point of the graph of a relation, then the relation is a function.

prueba de la recta vertical Si cualquier recta vertical pasa por un sólo punto de la gráfica de una relación, entonces la relación es una función.

volume (p. P29) The measure of space occupied by a solid region.

volumen Medida del espacio que ocupa un solido.

W

weighted average (p. 132) The sum of the product of the number of units and the value per unit divided by the sum of the number of units, represented by *M*.

promedio ponderado Suma del producto del número de unidades por el valor unitario dividida entre la suma del número de unidades y la cual se denota por *M*.

whole numbers (p. P7) The set {0, 1, 2, 3, …}.

números enteros El conjunto {0, 1, 2, 3, …}.

work problems (p. 728) Rational equations are used to solve problems involving work rates.

problemas de trabajo Las ecuaciones racionales se usan para resolver problemas de tasas de trabajo.

X

x-axis (p. 40) The horizontal number line on a coordinate plane.

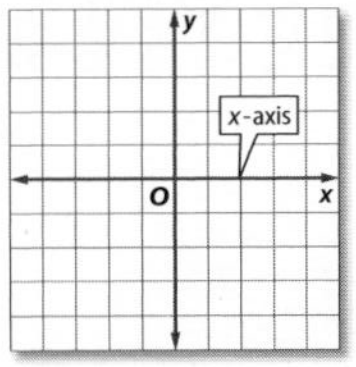

eje *x* Recta numérica horizontal que forma parte de un plano de coordenadas.

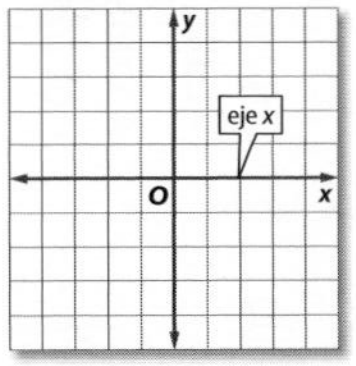

x-coordinate (p. 40) The first number in an ordered pair.

coordenada *x* El primer número de un par ordenado.

x-intercept (p. 56) The *x*-coordinate of a point where a graph crosses the *x*-axis.

intersección *x* La coordenada *x* de un punto donde la gráfica corte al eje de *x*.

Y

y-axis (p. 40) The vertical number line on a coordinate plane.

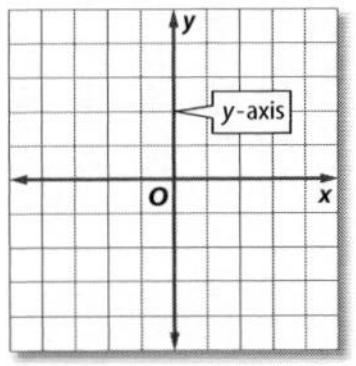

eje *y* Recta numérica vertical que forma parte de un plano de coordenadas.

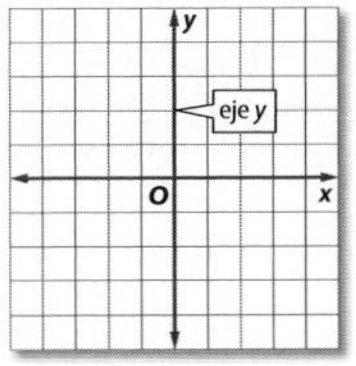

y-coordinate (p. 40) The second number in an ordered pair.

coordenada *y* El segundo número de un par ordenado.

y-intercept (p. 56) The *y*-coordinate of a point where a graph crosses the *y*-axis.

intersección *y* La coordenada *y* de un punto donde la grafica corta al eje de *y*.

Z

zero (p. 163) The *x*-intercepts of the graph of a function; the values of *x* for which $f(x) = 0$.

cero Las intersecciones *x* de la grafica de una función; los puntos *x* para los que $f(x) = 0$.

zero exponent (p. 399) For any nonzero number a, $a^0 = 1$. Any nonzero number raised to the zero power is equal to 1.

exponente cero Para cualquier número distinto a cero a, $a^0 = 1$. Cualquier número distinto a cero levantado al potente cero es igual a 1.

Index

Index

B

Index

D

E

Index

F

Index

Index

H

I

J

K

Index

L

Index

Index

Index

Q

R

Index

Index

Index

Index

T

Index

Index

Symbols

$\neq$	is not equal to	AB	measure of $\overline{AB}$
$\approx$	is approximately equal to	$\angle$	angle
$\sim$	is similar to	$\triangle$	triangle
$>, \geq$	is greater than, is greater than or equal to	$^\circ$	degree
$<, \leq$	is less than, is less than or equal to	π	pi
$-a$	opposite or additive inverse of a	$\sin x$	sine of x
$\|a\|$	absolute value of a	$\cos x$	cosine of x
$\sqrt{a}$	principal square root of a	$\tan x$	tangent of x
$a:b$	ratio of a to b	$!$	factorial
(x, y)	ordered pair	$P(a)$	probability of a
$f(x)$	f of x, the value of f at x	$P(n, r)$	permutation of n objects taken r at a time
$\overline{AB}$	line segment AB	$C(n, r)$	combination of n objects taken r at a time

Algebraic Properties and Key Concepts

Identity	For any number a, $a + 0 = 0 + a = a$ and $a \cdot 1 = 1 \cdot a = a$.
Substitution (=)	If $a = b$, then a may be replaced by b.
Reflexive (=)	$a = a$
Symmetric (=)	If $a = b$, then $b = a$.
Transitive (=)	If $a = b$ and $b = c$, then $a = c$.
Commutative	For any numbers a and b, $a + b = b + a$ and $a \cdot b = b \cdot a$.
Associative	For any numbers a, b, and c, $(a + b) + c = a + (b + c)$ and $(a \cdot b) \cdot c = a \cdot (b \cdot c)$.
Distributive	For any numbers a, b, and c, $a(b + c) = ab + ac$ and $a(b - c) = ab - ac$.
Additive Inverse	For any number a, there is exactly one number $-a$ such that $a + (-a) = 0$.
Multiplicative Inverse	For any number $\frac{a}{b}$, where $a, b \neq 0$, there is exactly one number $\frac{b}{a}$ such that $\frac{a}{b} \cdot \frac{b}{a} = 1$.
Multiplicative (0)	For any number a, $a \cdot 0 = 0 \cdot a = 0$.
Addition (=)	For any numbers a, b, and c, if $a = b$, then $a + c = b + c$.
Subtraction (=)	For any numbers a, b, and c, if $a = b$, then $a - c = b - c$.
Multiplication and Division (=)	For any numbers a, b, and c, with $c \neq 0$, if $a = b$, then $ac = bc$ and $\frac{a}{c} = \frac{b}{c}$.
Addition (>)*	For any numbers a, b, and c, if $a > b$, then $a + c > b + c$.
Subtraction (>)*	For any numbers a, b, and c, if $a > b$, then $a - c > b - c$.
Multiplication and Division (>)*	For any numbers a, b, and c, 1. if $a > b$ and $c > 0$, then $ac > bc$ and $\frac{a}{c} > \frac{b}{c}$. 2. if $a > b$ and $c < 0$, then $ac < bc$ and $\frac{a}{c} < \frac{b}{c}$.
Zero Product	For any real numbers a and b, if $ab = 0$, then $a = 0$, $b = 0$, or both a and b equal 0.
Square of a Sum	$(a + b)^2 = (a + b)(a + b) = a^2 + 2ab + b^2$
Square of a Difference	$(a - b)^2 = (a - b)(a - b) = a^2 - 2ab + b^2$
Product of a Sum and a Difference	$(a + b)(a - b) = (a - b)(a + b) = a^2 - b^2$

** These properties are also true for $<$, $\geq$, and $\leq$.*

Formulas

Slope	$m = \frac{y_2 - y_1}{x_2 - x_1}$
Distance on a coordinate plane	$d = \sqrt{(x_2 - x_1)^2 + (y_2 - y_1)^2}$
Midpoint on a coordinate plane	$M = \left(\frac{x_1 + x_2}{2}, \frac{y_1 + y_2}{2}\right)$
Pythagorean Theorem	$a^2 + b^2 = c^2$
Quadratic Formula	$x = \frac{-b \pm \sqrt{b^2 - 4ac}}{2a}$
Perimeter of a rectangle	$P = 2\ell + 2w$ or $P = 2(\ell + w)$
Circumference of a circle	$C = 2\pi r$ or $C = \pi d$

Area

rectangle	$A = \ell w$	**trapezoid**	$A = \frac{1}{2}h(b_1 + b_2)$
parallelogram	$A = bh$	**circle**	$A = \pi r^2$
triangle	$A = \frac{1}{2}bh$		

Surface Area

cube	$S = 6s^2$	**regular pyramid**	$S = \frac{1}{2}P\ell + B$
prism	$S = Ph + 2B$	**cone**	$S = \pi r\ell + \pi r^2$
cylinder	$S = 2\pi rh + 2\pi r^2$		

Volume

cube	$V = s^3$	**regular pyramid**	$V = \frac{1}{3}Bh$
prism	$V = Bh$	**cone**	$V = \frac{1}{3}\pi r^2 h$
cylinder	$V = \pi r^2 h$		

Measures

Metric	Customary
Length	
1 kilometer (km) = 1000 meters (m)	1 mile (mi) = 1760 yards (yd)
1 meter = 100 centimeters (cm)	1 mile = 5280 feet (ft)
1 centimeter = 10 millimeters (mm)	1 yard = 3 feet
	1 foot = 12 inches (in.)
	1 yard = 36 inches
Volume and Capacity	
1 liter (L) = 1000 milliliters (mL)	1 gallon (gal) = 4 quarts (qt)
1 kiloliter (kL) = 1000 liters	1 gallon = 128 fluid ounces (fl oz)
	1 quart = 2 pints (pt)
	1 pint = 2 cups (c)
	1 cup = 8 fluid ounces
Weight and Mass	
1 kilogram (kg) = 1000 grams (g)	1 ton (T) = 2000 pounds (lb)
1 gram = 1000 milligrams (mg)	1 pound = 16 ounces (oz)
1 metric ton (t) = 1000 kilograms	